Now Barr & Stroud put miniaturised thermal imaging within your grasp.

Electronic module.

Scanning module.

Auxiliary telescope module.

IR18 thermal imager – a breakthrough in infra-red technology.

Barr & Stroud give you the tactical advantages of thermal imaging with a compact, miniaturised scanner, no more than the size of your hand, that cuts size and weight to a minimum without sacrificing performance.

A significant breakthrough in infra-red technology, the IR18 measures only 130 x 220 x 400mm overall and weighs less than 10kg.

The result of Barr & Stroud's fifteen years research and development experience in this field, the IR18 is the first wholly passive, high performance, thermal imaging scanner designed on a modular basis and providing a standard TV picture.

An outstandingly robust and reliable system for armoured fighting vehicles, surface ships, helicopters, fixed wing aircraft and submarines. And just one aspect of our systems and equipment capability.

Whatever your defence requirements, Barr & Stroud have the scientific skills and experience, and the precision mechanical engineering expertise to help improve your watchfulness.

Barr & Stroud

Enquiries to
Barr & Stroud Limited, Melrose House, 4-6 Savile Row, London W1X 1AF
Registered Office & Works
Caxton Street, Anniesland, Glasgow, G13 1HZ

PILKINGTON GROUP

The Canadair Challenger   The British Aerospace 146

How to make flight pay.

☐ With less time on the ground ☐ Short-field takeoff ☐ Fanjet cruising speeds ☐ Quiet, dependable operation.

Nobody likes to wait. Anxious vacationers or busy executives. The Avco Lycoming ALF 502 engines on the British Aerospace 146 and the Canadair Challenger perform as you need them, when you need them.

The ALF 502 requires less ground time. Modular design simplifies maintenance, cuts down tool investment, and keeps you flying. Accessibility and maintainability are built in. And the reliable core engine has been proven during more than 3,000,000 hours of service.

The ALF 502 allows short turboprop takeoffs and fast fanjet cruising speeds. Low noise levels and emissions make the ALF 502 kind to the environment and the neighboring population.

The ALF 502 on the BAe 146 or Canadair Challenger, offers clean, quiet, dependable performance. With simplified maintenance and low fuel consumption. All of which mean time and money savings.

The Avco Lycoming ALF 502 is a practical way to make flight pay. Write Avco Lycoming, Stratford, CT 06497.

⧸⧸AVCO LYCOMING DIVISION

JANE'S
ALL THE WORLD'S AIRCRAFT
1980-81

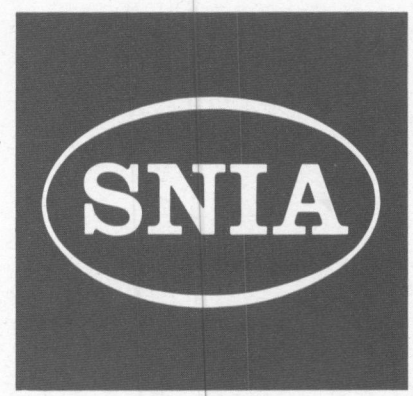

DEFENCE AND SPACE DIVISION

00187 ROME, ITALY – VIA SICILIA, 162 – TEL. (06) 4680 – TLX. 610114

CONVENTIONAL AMMUNITION

■ COMPLETE ROUNDS AND COMPONENTS FOR ARTILLERY AND MORTARS ■ PROPELLING POWDERS AND BURSTING EXPLOSIVES

ROCKETS AND PROPELLANTS

■ AIR TO GROUND AND SURFACE TO SURFACE ROCKETS ■ ECM AND ILLUMINATING ROCKETS ■ ROCKET AND MISSILE WARHEADS ■ ROCKET AND MISSILE SOLID PROPELLANT MOTORS ■ DOUBLE BASE AND COMPOSITE PROPELLANTS

UNGUIDED WEAPON SYSTEMS

■ AIR TO GROUND SYSTEMS FOR USE FROM AIRCRAFT AND HELICOPTERS ■ FIELD SATURATION SYSTEMS ■ INFANTRY SUPPORT SYSTEMS

SPACE ACTIVITIES

■ APOGEE MOTORS ■ STAGE SEPARATION MOTORS ■ ORBITAL TRANSFER SYSTEMS ■ SPACE LAUNCH VEHICLE MOTORS

RESEARCH AND DEVELOPMENT

■ ANALYSIS AND DEVELOPMENT OF DEFENCE SYSTEMS ■ DEVELOPMENT OF NEW WEAPON SYSTEMS AND OF THEIR COMPONENTS

TECHNOLOGIES AND KNOW-HOW

■ ASSISTANCE FOR MANUFACTURE OF MILITARY AND SPACE PRODUCTS AND FOR PLANT INSTALLATION ■ "TURN KEY" PLANT OPERATION

[2]

How can a fighter pilot look outside while monitoring the onboard systems?

THOMSON-CSF's VE 110 CRT head-up display permits head-up navigation and air-to-air and air-to-ground firings.

Its compactness enables the VE 110 to be selected for retrofitting any type of aircraft.

Alphabetical list of advertisers

Under
the curtain

TORNADO   *NATO'S Nº1 in all weathers*

Tornado's unique combination of swing-wing configuration, 2-man crew, advanced avionics and unsurpassed handling characteristics enables it to strike powerfully and precisely beneath the curtain of radar and missile defences – in any terrain and any weather, by day or by night. Its navigation and weapon-aiming systems have the high precision needed to ensure accurate attacks against heavily defended moving or static targets, on land or at sea, in any weather conditions and in the most hostile ECM environment.

Bell Helicopter **TEXTRON**

Whatever your transportation requirements are in administering construction, resource development, or health and rescue programs, there's a Bell helicopter to meet your needs.

Bell is the acknowledged leader in development and production of helicopters. In fact, there are more Bells at work around the world today than all other makes combined. Bell helicopters are noted for their dependability and performance. And professionals everywhere know that Bell's unequalled global service and logistics network keeps them working.

For more information on Bell helicopters serving in civil government operations, contact the Bell representative in your area, or write: Vice President, International Marketing, Dept. 583, Box 482, Ft. Worth, Texas 76101 U.S.A.

Would you like to see what one can do for you?

Classified list of advertisers

AC Motors
Aviaexport
Garrett Corporation
Lucas Aerospace
Thomson CSF

Accelerometers
Aeritalia
Aviaexport
SFENA

Accessories
Aviaexport
Garrett Corporation
SFENA

Accumulators—Cadmium Nickel
Aviaexport
SAFT

Actuators—Electric
Aviaexport
Garrett Corporation
Lucas Aerospace
Meteor
SFENA

Aerials—Aircraft
Aeritalia
Dornier
Siai Marchetti
Thomson CSF

Aerials Survey Instrument
SFENA
Thomson CSF

Aero-Auxiliary Equipment
Garrett Corporation
Lucas Aerospace
Messerschmitt-Bölkow-Blohm
Siai Marchetti

Aero-Engine Test Plant
Avco Lycoming
John Curran
FIAT
Siai Marchetti
SNECMA

Aero-Engines
Avco Lycoming
Aviaexport
FIAT
Garrett Corporation
Lucas Aerospace
MTU
Omnipol
Rinaldo Piaggio
SNECMA
Turbo-Union

Aeronautical Engineers and Consultants
Aviaexport
Boeing Commercial Airplane Co
SFENA
Siai Marchetti

Aerosystems
Boeing Commercial Airplane Co
Meteor
Thomson CSF

Agricultural Aircraft Spray and Dust Systems and Components
Aviaexport
Dornier
Siai Marchetti

Air Compressors
CIT Alcatel
Garrett Corporation

Air Compressors (Cabin) + (Engine Starting)
Garrett Corporation

Air Compressors for Engine Starting
Lucas Aerospace
Meteor

Air-Conditioning Equipment
Aviaexport
Bestobell
Garrett Corporation
ML Aviation

Air-Conditioning Systems
Aviaexport
Garrett Corporation

Air Control Equipment for Cabins
Aviaexport
Bestobell
Garrett Corporation
Lucas Aerospace

Air Cycle Refrigeration Packages
Aviaexport
Garrett Corporation

Air Data Computer Systems
Aviaexport
Bofors
Garrett Corporation

Air Data Computer—Test Set
AAI Corporation

Air Traffic Control Equipment
Aeritalia
Italtel

Airborne Surveillance Drone Systems—Recoverable—Unmanned
Canadair

Aircraft—Agricultural (Dusters & Sprayers)
Aviaexport
Dornier
Siai Marchetti

Aircraft—Ambulance
Aérospatiale
Aviaexport
British Aerospace Aircraft Group
Dornier
Fokker VFW
Israel Aircraft Industries
Rinaldo Piaggio
Siai Marchetti

Aircraft—Commercial
Aeritalia
Boeing Commercial Airplane Co
British Aerospace Aircraft Group
Canadair
Dornier
Fokker VFW
Israel Aircraft Industries
Messerschmitt-Bölkow-Blohm
Rinaldo Piaggio
Saab-Scania
Siai Marchetti

Aircraft—Executive
Aeronautica Macchi
Aviaexport
Boeing Commercial Airplane Co
British Aerospace Aircraft Group
Canadair
Dornier
Fokker VFW
Garrett Corporation
Israel Aircraft Industries
Messerschmitt-Bölkow-Blohm
Rinaldo Piaggio

Aircraft—Integrated Data Systems
Thomson CSF

Aircraft—Military
Aeritalia
Aeronautica Macchi
Aérospatiale
Boeing Commercial Airplane Co
British Aerospace Aircraft Group
Dornier
Fokker VFW
GIAT
Messerschmitt-Bölkow-Blohm
Panavia
Rinaldo Piaggio
Saab-Scania
Siai Marchetti

Aircraft—Naval
Aeritalia
Boeing Commercial Airplane Co
British Aerospace Aircraft Group
Rinaldo Piaggio

Aircraft—Private
Aeronautica Macchi
Aérospatiale
British Aerospace Aircraft Group
Dornier
Messerschmitt-Bölkow-Blohm
Omnipol
Rinaldo Piaggio
Siai Marchetti

Aircraft—Radio Controlled
Flight Refuelling
Meteor

Aircraft—Supersonic
Aeritalia
Aérospatiale
British Aerospace Aircraft Group
Panavia
Saab-Scania

Aircraft—Training
Aeritalia
Aeronautica Macchi
Aérospatiale
Boeing Commercial Airplane Co
British Aerospace Aircraft Group
Dornier
Fokker VFW
Messerschmitt-Bölkow-Blohm
Omnipol
Rinaldo Piaggio
Saab-Scania
Siai Marchetti

Aircraft—Transport
Aeritalia
Aérospatiale
Boeing Commercial Airplane Co
Dornier
Fokker VFW
Israel Aircraft Industries
Messerschmitt-Bölkow-Blohm

BOFORS

Turn night into day

with the SUPER LEPUS
the 7 000 000 candela aircraft parachute flare with
supersonic capability.

Approved for AJ 37 Viggen, Jaguar, F-4, Harrier and
many other aircraft.

CLASSIFIED LIST OF ADVERTISERS

Aircraft V/STOL
Aviaexport
Boeing Commercial Airplane Co
British Aerospace Aircraft Group
Dornier
Fokker VFW
Messerschmitt-Bölkow-Blohm
Omnipol
Siai Marchetti

Aircraft Canopies
Aeritalia
Aeronautica Macchi
Goodyear Tyre & Rubber Co
Lucas Aerospace

Aircraft Development
Aeritalia
Aérospatiale
Boeing Commercial Airplane Co
Canadair
Messerschmitt-Bölkow-Blohm
Rinaldo Piaggio

Aircraft Escape Systems
Garrett Corporation

Aircraft Field Operations & Support
Boeing Commercial Airplane Co

Aircraft Floats
Dornier
Garrett Corporation

Aircraft Freight Handling Equipment
Aviaexport
Boyd Airport Equipment
Dornier
Fokker VFW
Messerschmitt-Bölkow-Blohm

Aircraft Integrated Data Systems
Garrett Corporation

Aircraft Mechanical Handlers
Aviaexport
Dornier
ML Aviation

Aircraft Modifications
Aérospatiale
Boeing Commercial Airplane Co
Messerschmitt-Bölkow-Blohm

Aircraft Product Support
Aérospatiale
Messerschmitt-Bölkow-Blohm
SFENA

Aircraft Propellers
Aviaexport
Snia Viscosa

Aircraft Propeller Governors
Rinaldo Piaggio

Aircraft Wire & Cable
Standard Wire & Cable
Thomson CSF

Airfield Lighting
Aviaexport
Omnipol
Standard Wire & Cable Co

Airline Technical Assistance
Boeing Commercial Airplane Co
Messerschmitt-Bölkow-Blohm
SFENA

Airports—Planning
Messerschmitt-Bölkow-Blohm

Airports—New Passenger Transport Systems
Messerschmitt-Bölkow-Blohm

Airport Maintenance Equipment
Aeronautica Macchi
Israel Aircraft Industries
ML Aviation

Airspeed Indicators
Aeritalia
Aviaexport
Dornier

Alternators
Aviaexport
Garrett Corporation
Lucas Aerospace

Altimeters Encoding
Aeritalia
Gould Inc

Altitude Control Systems
Aviaexport
Eltro

Ammunition Boosters
Meteor
Snia Viscosa

Amplifiers
Racal Acoustics

Antennas
Gould Inc
Messerschmitt-Bölkow-Blohm
Meteor
Thomson CSF

Anti-Skid Systems
Aviaexport
Goodyear Tyre & Rubber Co
SNECMA
Thomson CSF

Armaments for Aircraft
Bofors
Oerlikon-Bührle
GIAT
Messerschmitt-Bölkow-Blohm
ML Aviation
SAMM
Snia Viscosa

Automatic Checkout Systems
AAI Corporation
Aviaexport
Selenia
Thomson CSF

Automatic Parachute Openers
Aviaexport

Automatic Pilots
Aviaexport
Meteor
SFENA

Automatic Voltage and Current Regulators
Aviaexport
EAS Electronique Aérospatiale
Lucas Aerospace

Auxiliary Power Plant
Aviaexport
Garrett Corporation
Lucas Aerospace

Bars—Stainless Steel & Heat Resisting Steel
Aviaexport

Batteries
Aviaexport
Meteor
SAFT

Batteries—Aviation
Aviaexport
SAFT

Battery Chargers
Aviaexport
EAS Electronique Aérospatiale
Lucas Aerospace
SAFT

Battery Testing Equipment
SAFT

Belts—Safety
Aviaexport

Binoculars
Aeritalia
Barr & Stroud

Blades—Gas Turbine
Avco Lycoming
Aviaexport
FIAT
SNECMA

Bomb Carriers
ML Aviation

Bombsights
Thomson CSF

Bonding Jumpers Bus Bars
Standard Wire & Cable Co

Brake Linings
Goodyear Tyre & Rubber Co

Brakes for Aircraft
Aviaexport
Goodyear Tyre & Rubber Co
Israel Aircraft Industries
SNECMA

Cabin Cooling (Tropical Airfield Equipment)
Aviaexport
Garrett Corporation

Cabin Pressure Control System
Aviaexport
Garrett Corporation

Cabin Pressurising Test Equipment
Aviaexport
Garrett Corporation

Cables—Electric
ML Aviation
Standard Wire & Cable

Cables—RF
Standard Wire & Cable
Thomson CSF

Central Air Data Computers
Garrett Corporation

Coatings—Erosion Resistant
Goodyear Tyre & Rubber Co
Israel Aircraft Industries
Lucas Aerospace

[11]

Combustion Systems (Gas Turbine)
Lucas Aerospace

Communications Control Systems
EAS Electronique Aérospatiale
Gould Inc
Racal Acoustics
Thomson CSF

Components
Aviaexport
Bestobell
CIT Alcatel
Dornier
Flight Refuelling
Fokker VFW
Garrett Corporation
Israel Aircraft Industries
Thomson CSF

Computers
Dornier
Hollandse Signaalapparaten
SFENA
Thomson CSF

Computers—Aerodynamic Analogue and Digital
Dornier
Garrett Corporation
Israel Aircraft Industries
SFENA
Thomson CSF

Connectors/Connector Accessories
Aviaexport
Garrett Corporation
ML Aviation
Thomson CSF

Constant Speed Alternator Drive Units
Garrett Corporation
Lucas Aerospace

Control Equipment for Aircraft
Aviaexport
Dornier
Garrett Corporation
Lucas Aerospace
SFENA
SNECMA
Thomson CSF

Controls—Cockpit
Aviaexport

Controls—Main Engine Fuel
Aviaexport
Lucas Aerospace
SNECMA
Thomson CSF

Convoluted Sleeves/Bellows
Bestobell

Cooling Compressors
Aviaexport
Garrett Corporation

Cooling Turbines
Garrett Corporation

Cryogenic Turbines
Garrett Corporation

Data Processing Equipment
CIT Alcatel
Dornier
Garrett Corporation
Selenia
Thomson CSF

Data Processing Equipment for ATC
Dornier
Selenia
Thomson CSF

Data Transmission Equipment
Dornier
Elmer Montedel
Gould Inc.
Selenia
Thomson CSF

DC Generators
Lucas Aerospace

DC Motors
Aviaexport
Garrett Corporation
Lucas Aerospace
Thomson CSF

De-Icing Equipment
Bestobell
EAS Electronique Aérospatiale
Flight Refuelling
Garrett Corporation
Goodyear Tyre & Rubber Co
Lucas Aerospace

Direction Finding Equipment (Triangulation)
Aviaexport
Selenia
Thomson CSF

Drogue Guns
ML Aviation

Drones
Aeronautica Macchi
Dornier
Meteor

Ejection Seats
Aeronautica Macchi
SNECMA

Ejector Release Units
ML Aviation

Electric Auxiliaries
Aviaexport
Garrett Corporation

Electric Tractors
ML Aviation

Electrical Equipment
Aviaexport
EAS Electronique Aérospatiale
Garrett Corporation
Gould Inc.
Lucas Aerospace
ML Aviation

Electrical Plugs and Sockets (waterproof)
Thomson CSF

Electrical Wiring Assemblies
Aviaexport
Fokker VFW
ML Aviation
Standard Wire & Cable

Electrical Wire Cable Cord of all types
Standard Wire & Cable

Electro-Optical Systems
Barr & Stroud
Eltro
Saab-Scania
Selenia
SFENA
Thomson CSF

Electronic Equipment
Aeritalia
Aviaexport
Boeing Commercial Airplane Co
CIT Alcatel
EAS Electronique Aérospatiale
Garrett Corporation
Israel Aircraft Industries
ML Aviation
Saab-Scania
Selenia
SFENA
SNECMA
Thomson CSF

Electronic Fuel Control Systems
Lucas Aerospace
Thomson CSF

Electronics & Guidance
Gould Inc.
Israel Aircraft Industries
Messerschmitt-Bölkow-Blohm
Selenia
SFENA
Thomson CSF

Engine/Bulkhead Fireseals
Bestobell

Engine Compressor Cleaning Rigs
John Curran

Engine Handling Equipment
John Curran

Engine Parts Fabrication
Avco Lycoming
FIAT

Engine Starting Equipment
Lucas Aerospace

Engine Testing Equipment
Avco Lycoming
Aviaexport
John Curran
Garrett Corporation

Engines—Aircraft
Avco Lycoming
Aviaexport
FIAT
Garrett Corporation
MTU
Rinaldo Piaggio
SNECMA

Engines—Auxiliary
Avco Lycoming
Aviaexport
Lucas Aerospace
MTU

Engines—V/STOL
Aviaexport
Garrett Corporation

Environmental Control Systems
Garrett Corporation
Lucas Aerospace
Messerschmitt-Bölkow-Blohm
Selenia

Executive Transport—Twin Fan Jet
Aérospatiale
Canadair

Feel Simulator Controls
Garrett Corporation
Lucas Aerospace

INTERNATIONAL – AN EMPTY WORD? MBB GIVES IT MEANING. EVERY DAY.

MBB shares development and production as partner of multi-national advanced technology programmes with some of the world's major companies.

Helicopters: MBB builds multipurpose helicopters for offshore, rescue, executive, police and military operations. For instance, the BO 105 with its high reputation worldwide. Or the new BK 117.

Defence: MBB develops, manufactures and maintains weapon systems for defence against tank, aircraft or seaborne attack.

Astronautics: MBB cooperates at international level in the development and construction of research and operations satellites for a wide variety of purposes.

Civil aircraft: MBB has joined with partner firms in Europe to build the world's most economical and environmentally acceptable large capacity jetliner, the Airbus A300 – and, for the nineteeneighties, the A310.

Military Aircraft: MBB is the German partner in developing and manufacturing the European combat aircraft "Tornado". Apart from its work on this weapons system at national level, MBB supplies technical and logistic support for Starfighters and Phantom of the Armed Forces of the Federal Republic of Germany and other NATO countries, cooperates internationally on the development of future high-performance aircraft (TKF).

Transportation: MBB has joined forces with other companies to tackle existing transportation problems. The result: such pioneer activities as the "Transrapid" magnetic levitation system, vehicle control and monitoring systems and the Cabintaxi. And in lightweight rail vehicle construction, MBB is busy developing many years of know-how still further. With its multiple unit vehicles for urban rapid transit, and developed versions of the Munich metro trains.

Further activities: environmental control, energy technology, system studies, EDP service and consultation, planning, simulation, communal services technologies, medical engineering, construction of plants.

Partner in international programs

Messerschmitt-Bölkow-Blohm GmbH
Postfach 80 11 09
D-8000 München 80/Germany

ZI-60/80E

CLASSIFIED LIST OF ADVERTISERS

Fibre Optics
Barr & Stroud
ML Aviation
Thomson CSF

Filters—Air
Aviaexport

Filters—Electronic
Aviaexport
Barr & Stroud
CIT Alcatel
EAS Electronique Aérospatiale
Racal Acoustics
Selenia
Thomson CSF

Filters—Fuel & Oil
Aviaexport
Flight Refuelling

Fire Resistant Hose
Bestobell

Fire Suppression Systems
Eltro

Flexible Sleeves, Connectors
Bestobell

Flight Instrument Test Sets
EAS Electronique Aérospatiale
Garrett Corporation
Gould Inc.
Israel Aircraft Industries
SFENA
Thomson CSF

Flotation Gear
Garrett Corporation

Flow Gauges
Aviaexport

Forgings—Steel
SNECMA

Fuel Flow Proportioners
Flight Refuelling
Garrett Corporation
Lucas Aerospace

Fuel Pumps
Aviaexport
Garrett Corporation
Lucas Aerospace

Fuel Systems Protection
PRB

Fuel Systems & Refuelling Equipment
Aviaexport
Flight Refuelling
Israel Aircraft Industries

Fuel Tank Pressurisation Equipment
Flight Refuelling
Garrett Corporation
Israel Aircraft Industries

Furnishings & Aircraft Cabins
Aviaexport
Garrett Corporation
Rinaldo Piaggio

Gas Turbine Starting Systems
Lucas Aerospace

Gas Turbines
Avco Lycoming
Aviaexport
FIAT
Garrett Corporation
MTU
Rinaldo Piaggio
SNECMA

Gas Turbines—Equipment & Accessories
Avco Lycoming
Aviaexport
Bestobell
Garrett Corporation

Gauges
Aviaexport

Generators
Aviaexport
Garrett Corporation
Lucas Aerospace

Ground Refuelling Equipment
Flight Refuelling
Goodyear Tyre & Rubber Co

Ground Support Equipment
Canadair
Thomson CSF

Ground Workshop & Hangar Equipment
Israel Aircraft Industries

Guidance Control Test Set
AAI Corporation
Thomson CSF

Guided Missile Ground Handling Equipment
AAI Corporation
Aeronautica Macchi
Eltro
Garrett Corporation
ML Aviation
Selenia

Guided Missiles
Aérospatiale
Dornier
Messerschmitt-Bölkow-Blohm
Saab-Scania
Selenia
Thomson CSF

Gunnery Training Apparatus
Oerlikon-Bührle
Saab-Scania
SFENA
Thomson CSF

Hand Sets
Racal Acoustics

Hangar Test Stands
Boyd Airport Equipment

Headphones
Racal Acoustics

Heat Exchangers
Lucas Aerospace

Heat Transfer Systems
Garrett Corporation

Heated Windows
Barr & Stroud
Lucas Aerospace

Heated Windscreen Controllers
Lucas Aerospace

Helicopter Deck Restraint Systems
ML Aviation

Helicopter Winches
Lucas Aerospace

Helicopter Parts & Components
Agusta
Aviaexport
Bell Helicopter
Bestobell
Dornier
Israel Aircraft Industries
Messerschmitt-Bölkow-Blohm

Helicopter Searchlights
Garrett Corporation

Helicopter Training & Support
Bell Helicopter

Helicopters—Ambulance
Aérospatiale
Agusta
Bell Helicopter

Helicopters—Commercial-Executive
Aérospatiale
Agusta
Aviaexport
Bell Helicopter
Boeing Commercial Airplane Co
Dornier
Messerschmitt-Bölkow-Blohm

Helicopters—Military-Naval
Aérospatiale
Agusta
Bell Helicopter
Boeing Commercial Airplane Co
Messerschmitt-Bölkow-Blohm

High Pressure Couplings
Flight Refuelling

Hose Clips
Bestobell

Hydraulic Equipment
ML Aviation
SAMM
SNECMA

Hydraulic Pressure Pumps
Lucas Aerospace
SAMM

Hydraulic Test Units—Mobile & Static
Aeronautica Macchi
ML Aviation
SAMM

Inertial Navigation Systems
SFENA

Inflatable Structures
Garrett Corporation

Infra-Red Linescan
Eltro

Infra-Red Materials
Barr & Stroud
Selenia

IAI HAS THE KEY TO AIR DEFENSE

By dealing with IAI – a single dependable source for all your Air Force requirements, you eliminate a lot of problems.

Problems of supply, of on-time delivery, of equipment integration, infrastructure, training, cost.

IAI are pioneers in Conversion in Lieu of Procurement (CILOP). We can upgrade your present aircraft with the latest electronic systems: communications, navigation and weapon delivery. Computers, both on-board and ground-based. Airborne radar. As well as other advanced airborne systems.

Aircraft like Kfir C-2 multimission combat plane, Arava STOL transport, Westwind VIP jet, Sea Scan long range logistic aircraft. Security and surveillance systems. Complete anti-aircraft systems. And a total EW/ECM environment capability.

Whatever your mission. Turn to IAI for Air Force upgrading.

We understand your needs. You know our reputation.

We learned the hard way. Combat. Our combat experience has taught us one thing above all else: to build, through integrated total systems packages, an Air Force that is up-to-date and effective. Combat-effective. Mission-effective. Cost-effective.

Israel Aircraft Industries Ltd.
Ben Gurion International Airport, Israel.
Tel: 973111. Telex: ISRAVIA 031114.
Cables: ISRAELAVIA.
New York: Israel Aircraft Industries International Inc.,
50 West 23rd Street, N. Y. 10010.
Tel: (212) 6204400. Telex: ISRAIR 125180.
Brussels: c/o Embassy of Israel, 50 Ave. des Arts.
Tel: 5131455. Telex: 62718 ISRAVIb.

IAI ISRAEL AIRCRAFT INDUSTRIES LTD
Aircraft and Airborne Systems Marketing

[15]

CLASSIFIED LIST OF ADVERTISERS

Infra-Red Systems
Barr & Stroud
Eltro
Garrett Corporation
Meteor
Selenia
Thomson CSF

Instrument Components (mechanical)
Thomson CSF

Instruments—Aircraft
Aeritalia
EAS Electronique Aérospatiale
Gould Inc.
Israel Aircraft Industries

Instruments—Electronic
Aeritalia
EAS Electronique Aérospatiale
Gould Inc.
Israel Aircraft Industries
SFENA
SNECMA
Thomson CSF

Instruments—Navigation
Aeritalia
Aviaexport
EAS Electronique Aérospatiale
Gould Inc.
SFENA

Instruments—Precision
Barr & Stroud
Gould Inc.
Israel Aircraft Industries

Instruments—Test Equipment
AAI Corporation
Aeritalia
Aviaexport
EAS Electronique Aérospatiale
Garrett Corporation
Gould Inc.
Israel Aircraft Industries
SFENA

Integrated Total Pneumatic Systems
Garrett Corporation

Intercommunication Equipment
Elmer Montedel
Racal Acoustics

Jet Engine Parts
FIAT
Garrett Corporation
MTU
Rinaldo Piaggio
SNECMA

Jet Engine Test Plant
John Curran
FIAT
Garrett Corporation
SNECMA

Jet Fuel Starters
Garrett Corporation
Lucas Aerospace

Jet Propulsion Engines
Avco Lycoming
FIAT
Garrett Corporation
Lucas Aerospace
SNECMA

Jet Trainer—Military
Aérospatiale
Embraer

Jointing Compound
Bestobell
Goodyear Tyre & Rubber Co

Lamps—Cockpit
Aviaexport
Lucas Aerospace

Landing Lamps
Aviaexport

Lasers
Barr & Stroud
Eltro
Garrett Corporation
Messerschmitt-Bölkow-Blohm
Selenia
SFENA

Laser Rangefinder
Barr & Stroud
Eltro
Selenia
Thomson CSF

Life Saving Equipment
Burndept
Garrett Corporation
Saab-Scania

Light Aircraft
Embraer

Lightweight Hose
Bestobell

Lights—Aircraft
Aviaexport

Lights—Landing
Aviaexport

Lights—Navigation
Aviaexport
Lucas Aerospace

Linear Actuators
Garrett Corporation
Lucas Aerospace
SAMM

Linings—Brakes
Goodyear Tyre & Rubber Company

Mach Number Transducers
Garrett Corporation

Machine Tools
CIT Alcatel
SNECMA

Marine Engines
FIAT
Garrett Corporation

Market Intelligence Reports
DMS
Frost & Sullivan

Materials Technology
Boeing Commercial Airplane Company
Thomson CSF

Metal Ducting
Bestobell

Metal Duct Connectors
Bestobell

Metal Fittings
Aviaexport
Bestobell

Microphones
Aviaexport
Racal Acoustics

Missile Optics
Barr & Stroud
Messerschmitt-Bölkow-Blohm
Thomson CSF

Missiles—Guided
Aérospatiale
Dornier
Messerschmitt-Bölkow-Blohm
Saab-Scania
Selenia
Thomson CSF

Motor Generators
Aviaexport
Garrett Corporation
Lucas Aerospace

Motors—Electric
Aviaexport
Garrett Corporation
Lucas Aerospace
Thomson CSF

Motors—Hydraulic
Aviaexport
CIT Alcatel
Garrett Corporation
Lucas Aerospace
SAMM

Navigation Beacons
Gould Inc.

Night Vision Equipment
Barr & Stroud
Eltro
Selenia
Thomson CSF

Non-Destructive Inspect Equipment
Fokker VFW

Oil Valves
Flight Refuelling
Garrett Corporation
SAMM

Optical Equipment
Barr & Stroud
Bofors

Optical Gun Sights
Barr & Stroud
Saab-Scania
Selenia
Thomson CSF

Overhaul & Modification Kits
Dornier
Garret Corporation
Siai Marchetti

Oxygen Apparatus
Aviaexport

Oxygen Breathing Apparatus
Garrett Corporation

Parachute Flares
Bofors
Oerlikon-Bührle

Parachutes
Aviaexport
Meteor

Parachutes—Special Purpose
Aviaexport

Makers of world aerospace history

Today, it's the Challenger — the third-generation business jet — that's keeping us growing. And the world-famous CL-215 — the only aircraft specifically designed to fight forest fires. And the CL-89 Surveillance Drone System — among the very first such systems in operation around the world. And major airframe component subcontracts, including the Boeing 767 aft fuselage.

Yesterday, it was the 24-hour-patrol Argus, the pioneering 'swingtail', and over 3,200 jets including 580 supersonics.

Tomorrow, it promises to be everything from the state-of-the-art, medium-range CL-289 and CL-227 surveillance systems, to the down-to-earth, linear induction-propelled transit system.

Come and talk to us. Our people are not only uniquely versatile, but long experienced in applied aerospace technology.

CANADAIR LIMITED • P.O. BOX 6087, STATION A, MONTREAL, QUÉBEC, CANADA • H3C 3G9 • (514) 744-1511

Der Antrieb
kommt von

mtu la force
motrice

means power
and propulsion

Motoren- und Turbinen-Union München GmbH / W.-Germany

CLASSIFIED LIST OF ADVERTISERS

Seat Belts
Aviaexport

Servo Actuators
Garrett Corporation
Meteor
SAMM
Thomson CSF

Sheet Metal Work
Fokker VFW
Israel Aircraft Industries

Sheet Metal Working Machines
Fokker VFW

Silicone Rubber Components
Bestobell

Simulators
AAI Corporation
Dornier
Messerschmitt-Bölkow-Blohm
Selenia
Siai Marchetti
Thomson CSF

Solenoid Valves
Flight Refuelling
Lucas Aerospace

Space Hardware Recovery
Dornier

Space Satellites
Aeritalia
Aérospatiale
Dornier
Fokker VFW
Messerschmitt-Bölkow-Blohm
Selenia

Space Systems
Aeritalia
Boeing Commercial Airplane Co
Dornier
Fokker VFW
Messerschmitt-Bölkow-Blohm
Saab-Scania
Selenia
Snia Viscosa
Thomson CSF

Spacecraft
Aeritalia
Dornier
Messerschmitt-Bölkow-Blohm
Selenia

Spare Parts for US Built Aircraft
Bestobell
Goodyear Tyre & Rubber Co
Siai Marchetti

Stability Augmentation System
Dornier
Messerschmitt-Bölkow-Blohm
SFENA

Stall Warning Systems
Fokker VFW

Starter Pods—Airborne
Garrett Corporation

Starting Systems—Airborne
Garrett Corporation
Lucas Aerospace

Static Inverters
EAS Electronique Aérospatiale
Lucas Aerospace
SFENA

Station Boxes
Racal Acoustics

Surveillance Systems
Barr & Stroud
Canadair
Garrett Corporation
Messerschmitt-Bölkow-Blohm
Meteor
Selenia

Survival Equipment
Burndept

Switches
Lucas Aerospace
SAMM

Switches—Miniature Electrical
SAMM

Switchgear
Aviaexport
Lucas Aerospace

Synthetic Rubber Mouldings—Extensions
Bestobell

Tachometers
Aviaexport

Target Release & Exchanger Mechanisms
Meteor

Target Towing Winches
Flight Refuelling
Garrett Corporation
Meteor

Technical Publications
Dornier
Flight Refuelling
Fokker VFW
Israel Aircraft Industries
Rinaldo Piaggio
Siai Marchetti

Technical Publications—Special Studies
Dornier

Temperature Control Equipment
EAS Electronique Aérospatiale
Garrett Corporation
Lucas Aerospace

Test Equipment
AAI Corporation
Aeronautica Macchi
Aviaexport
John Curran
EAS Electronique Aérospatiale
Eltro
Garrett Corporation
Gould Inc.
Israel Aircraft Industries
ML Aviation
SFENA
Thomson CSF

Test Equipment—Radar, Air Data Computer, Fire Control System, Avionics etc
AAI Corporation
Aérospatiale
Gould Inc.
SFENA
Thomson CSF

Test Equipment—Airfield Radio
EAS Electronique Aérospatiale
Gould Inc.
Thomson CSF

Test Equipment—Metal Bonding
Aviaexport
Fokker VFW
Siai Marchetti

Thermal/Acoustic Insulation
Bestobell

Thermal Imaging Systems
Barr & Stroud
Eltro
Thomson CSF

Thermo Couple Cables
Israel Aircraft Industries
Standard Wire & Cable Co

Tone Generators
Racal Acoustics

Tractors—Electric
ML Aviation

Training Devices
AAI Corporation
Messerschmitt-Bölkow-Blohm
Oerlikon-Bührle
Thomson CSF

Transformer Rectifier Units
EAS Electronique Aérospatiale
Israel Aircraft Industries
Lucas Aerospace
Thomson CSF

Tubes—Stainless Steel
Aviaexport

Turbines—Ram Air
Garrett Corporation

Turbofan Engines
FIAT
Garrett Corporation
General Electric
MTU
SNECMA

Tyres for Aircraft
Goodyear Tyre & Rubber Co

Undercarriage Equipment
SNECMA

Undercarriage Gear—Retractable
SNECMA

Valves
Flight Refuelling
Garrett Corporation
Israel Aircraft Industries
Siai Marchetti
Thomson CSF

air defence
All weather low and very low altitude
Missile weapon systems

Ground-to-air Crotale system

Ground-to-air Sica system (Shahine version)

Surface-to-air Crotale naval system

 THOMSON-CSF
DIVISION SYSTÈMES ÉLECTRONIQUES
1, RUE DES MATHURINS / B.P. 10 / 92222 BAGNEUX
FRANCE / TÉL. : (1) 657 13 65

3862

CLASSIFIED LIST OF ADVERTISERS

Valves & Miniature Relays
Thomson CSF

Valves—Control Hydraulic
Garrett Corporation
Goodyear Tyre & Rubber Co
Israel Aircraft Industries
Siai Marchetti

Valves—Electronic
Garrett Corporation
Thomson CSF

Valves—Non-Return Fuel
Flight Refuelling
Garrett Corporation

Valves—Non-Return Hydraulic
Flight Refuelling
Garrett Corporation
SAMM

Valves—Relief Hydraulic
Garrett Corporation

Valves & Miniature Relays
Garrett Corporation

'V' Band Clamps
Bestobell

Vertical Take-off Aircraft
British Aerospace Aircraft Group
Dornier
Messerschmitt-Bölkow-Blohm

Visibility Measuring Equipment
SNECMA

Voltage & Current Regulators
EAS Electronique Aérospatiale
Garrett Corporation
Lucas Aerospace

Water Separators
Flight Refuelling
Garrett Corporation

Wheels for Aircraft
Goodyear Tyre & Rubber Co
SNECMA

Wind Tunnel Testing Plant
Aeronautica Macchi
Boeing Commercial Airplane Co
British Aerospace Aircraft Group
John Curran
Dornier

Wire & Cables All Types
Standard Wire & Cable Co

MRCS 403/RAT-31S DEPLOYED ON AUSTRIAN SITE

MRCS-403/RAT-31S
Mobile Reporting and Control System

The Selenia MRCS-403 is a transportable and flexible Air Defence System, which consists of a 3D radar and an associated Operations Shelter and is basically capable of producing an air situation for the control of weapons and transmitting the air situation to superior command centres via narrow band data link.

This is performed with the aid of functions such as automatic initiation, automatic tracking, identification, automatic height measurement, automatic track reporting, interceptors control and/or SAM allocation.

SELENIA

INDUSTRIE ELETTRONICHE ASSOCIATE S.p.A.
RADAR AND MISSILE SYSTEMS DIVISION
Via Tiburtina Km 12.400 - 00131 ROME, ITALY
Phone 43601 / Telex 613690 SELROM I
P.O. Box 7083, 00100 ROME, ITALY

SELENIA IS EXPERIENCE IN AIR DEFENCE SYSTEMS

[23]

Dornier 128/228
The Utility & Commuter Aircraft

More than 1000 Dornier utility aircraft have been sold. 250 Dornier Skyservants are in operation worldwide.
On the basis of this market success, Dornier — one of the most respected names in aviation — introduces a complete family of utility/commuter aircraft.

The Dornier 128/228 Family meets the specific and demanding requirements of utility and commuter operators in the 1980's.

The Dornier 128-2 — Based upon the successful Dornier Skyservant design, it offers more equipment, higher payload and better performance.

The Dornier 128-6 — If you need turboprop power, this version has two Pratt & Whitney PT6A-110 engines.

The Dornier 228-100 — This new turboprop 15-passenger utility/commuter aircraft setting new standards of economy and performance to its class, features Dornier's New Technology Wing.

The Dornier 228-200 — A 19-passenger airplane, stretched version of the Dornier 228-100. The Dornier New Technology Wing saves up to 30 % fuel compared with other aircraft in this class.

Family

The sign of extra power

SAFT delta plus

The exceptional qualities of the new top-level SAFT Delta Plus® batteries will satisfy the most demanding users.

Increased performance at electricity level:
At – 30 °C, the electrical power is double that of standard batteries, ensuring perfect engine starts in very cold conditions. In average-to-warm temperatures, the gain is approximately 15 %.

Faster starts:
Higher voltage shortens start-up time and substantially reduces temperature in the hotter parts of the engine.

Reliability:
The increase in reserve power considerably increases the number of engine starts, and guarantees reliability of emergency equipment.

Maintenance economy:
Such technical advantages ensure better security and provide significant savings in maintenance costs for engines as well as batteries. They are extremely reliable and their lifetime is practically twice as long as standard batteries.

Compliance with existing standards:
SAFT Delta Plus® batteries consist of 20 cells and are in total conformity with current dimensional standards.
The Delta Plus® line is additional demonstration of SAFT's advanced technology.

SAFT STORAGE BATTERY DIVISION
156, avenue de Metz 93230 Romainville – France
Tél. (1) 843.93.61 – Télex 220100

SUBSIDIARIES:

BELGIUM SAFTA, 43, rue du Village, B 1070 Brussels. Tél. (32) 21.79.29.
CANADA SAFT Batteries Limited, 143, Bermondsey Road, Toronto 16 (Ontario M4A 1 x 3). Tél. (416) 752.30.30. Télex 696 3628.
ENGLAND SAFT (United Kingdom) Ltd, Castle Works - Station Road, Hampton, Middlessex. Tél. (1) 979.7755. Télex 23 572.
GERMANY SAFT Akkumulatoren und Batterien GmbH, Kaiserleistrasse 44, 6050 Offenbach/Main. Tél. (611) 88.90.61. Télex 415 28 47.
SOUTH AFRICA SAFT (South Africa) (Pty) Ltd, P.O. Box 39001, Bramley, Transvaal 2018. Tél. 40.6651/2. Télex 84 906.
SPAIN SAFT Iberica S.A., Artapadura 11, Vitoria. Tél. (45) 25.99.00. Télex 35.531.
U.S.A. SAFT America Inc., 711 Industrial Boulevard, Valdosta, Georgia 31601. Tél. (912) 247.2331. Télex 547 620. TWX 810.786.5866.

[27]

Optimum range

Commercial transport aircraft currently in production and
development by British Aerospace, either independently
or in partnership with other European companies, are helping
to meet worldwide requirements ranging from supersonic to
subsonic travel, from feeder lines to intercontinental services,
from executive transport to cargo carriage.

1. *CONCORDE* supersonic airliner†
2. *BAC ONE-ELEVEN* short/medium-range jet family
3. *HS125* executive jet family
4. *HS748* turboprop transport aircraft
5. *AIRBUS A300* and *A310* wide-body airliners*
6. *JETSTREAM* turboprop feeder-liner and VIP transport
7. *BRITISH AEROSPACE 146* wide-body fanjet feederliner

†in partnership with Aerospatiale, France. *as a full partner in Airbus Industrie

BRITISH AEROSPACE
unequalled in its range of aerospace programmes

Defence in depth

The range of military aircraft currently in production and development by British Aerospace meets every permutation of defence requirements from ab initio pilot training to airborne early warning, from low-level strike to high-altitude interception, from VSTOL capability to Mach 2-plus speeds, from tactical close support to long-range ocean patrol.

1. **TORNADO** all-weather combat aircraft †
2. **SEA HARRIER** V/STOL combat aircraft
3. **HAWK** ground attack trainer
4. **JAGUAR** tactical strike aircraft*
5. **COASTGUARDER** maritime patrol aircraft
6. **AEW NIMROD** airborne early warning system
7. **STRIKEMASTER** ground attack/trainer
8. **BUCCANEER** strike/reconnaissance aircraft
9. **BULLDOG** primary trainer

† in partnership with MBB, Germany, and Aeritalia, Italy
* in partnership with Dassault/Breguet, France

AIRCRAFT GROUP

Kingston-upon-Thames, England

RADARS IN PROGRESS RADARS IN PROGRESS
RADARS IN PROGRESS RADARS IN PROGRESS
IN PROGRESS RADARS IN PR
SMA
IN PROGRESS RADA
RADARS IN PROGRESS
PROGRESS RADARS IN
RADARS IN PROGRESS
ROGRESS RADARS

IL-86 WIDE-BODIED AIRLINER

Equipped with modern automatic flight control and navigation systems permitting flights to be performed with high regularity as well as all-weather approaches and landings at all times.

Max passenger accommodation	350 seats
Max payload	42,000 kg
Max take-off weight	206,000 kg
Cruising speed	900 km/h
Range with 40,000 kg payload	3,600 km
Engines: Four turbofans, thrust 13,000 kg each	

More information available from:

V/O "AVIAEXPORT", USSR, MOSCOW

32/34, Smolenskaya-Sennaya Sq.
121200 Moscow, USSR.
Tel. 244-26-86
Telex 411257, 411335
Cable: Aviaexport Moscow

Fully equipped, state-of-the-
art flight deck is designed
for crew efficiency.

The new

The new Fokker F28.
The short-haul jet that's best in the long run.

The only modern fanjet of its size specifically designed to expand your system profitably in the 80's.

No jet matches the new Fokker F28 for economical and efficient operation over short-haul networks where flights average 30-45 minutes and require quick turn-around times. Over a stage length of 250 nautical miles, the F28's two fuel-efficient Rolls-Royce RB183 engines burn 35% less fuel than the nearest competitor in operation. With fuel costs increasing steadily, this is an important economic advantage. Combined with lower costs in maintenance, crew, landing, and navigation charges, the total operating costs of the F28 are nearly 40% less.

The right size. The F28 is the only jet aircraft which combines short-haul capability with an 85-passenger configuration for profitable, low-overhead operation. It's ideal for low-density routes, which would be unprofitable for larger aircraft.

Proven performance. The F28, with its durable metal-to-metal bonded construction, has proven its ability to stand up to the rigors of high-cycle operations of 10 or more take-offs and landings a day. Even its engines are designed for high-cycle use. Unique speed-brakes allow the F28 to descend rapidly, contributing to its high block speeds.

Worldwide support.* With many years of experience supporting its aircraft, Fokker has the international expertise to provide all F28s— even those in remote areas—with the highest level of support, including 24-hour-a-day AOG service.

Bring the new Fokker F28 into your plans for the future. It's the one aircraft you can count on to run up your profits.

In the USA, E-Systems, Inc., of Dallas maintains an on-shore spares stock center in support of Fokker aircraft.

Fokker B.V., P.O. Box 7600,
1117 ZJ Schiphol, Netherlands;
Phone #31 20 5449111; Telex: 11526

Fokker Aircraft (USA) Inc., 2361 Jefferson
Davis Highway, Arlington, Virginia 22202;
Phone (703) 979-6400; Telex: 899462.

The way to grow.
Fokker F28

The best form
of defence is collaboration.

The TURBO-UNION RB 199, powerful, compact and economical, will be familiar to you as the engine of the Tornado.

Less widely recognised, perhaps, are the advantages of its triple nationality.

Its very development was made possible only by the combined defence allocations of the Federal Republic of Germany, the United Kingdom and Italy.

Without the pooled factory capacity and manpower skills of the three nations there would have been difficulty in meeting the initial orders for 2000.

And the amalgamation of their aero-engine know-how provided a short answer to competition.

In Rolls-Royce, MTU and Fiat Aviazioné – the British, German and Italian member companies of the TURBO-UNION consortium formed in 1969 – the partnership was one that had already collaborated for more than a decade.

And from the sharing of their design and engineering experience, their production resources, their management and manufacturing skills, was born the most advanced military gas turbine in the world.

All this – the RB 199 itself, the knowledge, the very partnership – is now at the service of every Allied power.

TURBO-UNION RB 199
There's really no alternative.

AD 5/80 E

Turbo-Union Ltd., **Head-Office:** P. O. Box 3, Filton, Bristol BS 12 7QE, England, **Munich-Office:** Arabellastraße 4, D-8000 München 81, West Germany

A 109   A 109 TOW   A 129   AB 206   AB 206 L 1   AB 205   AB 212

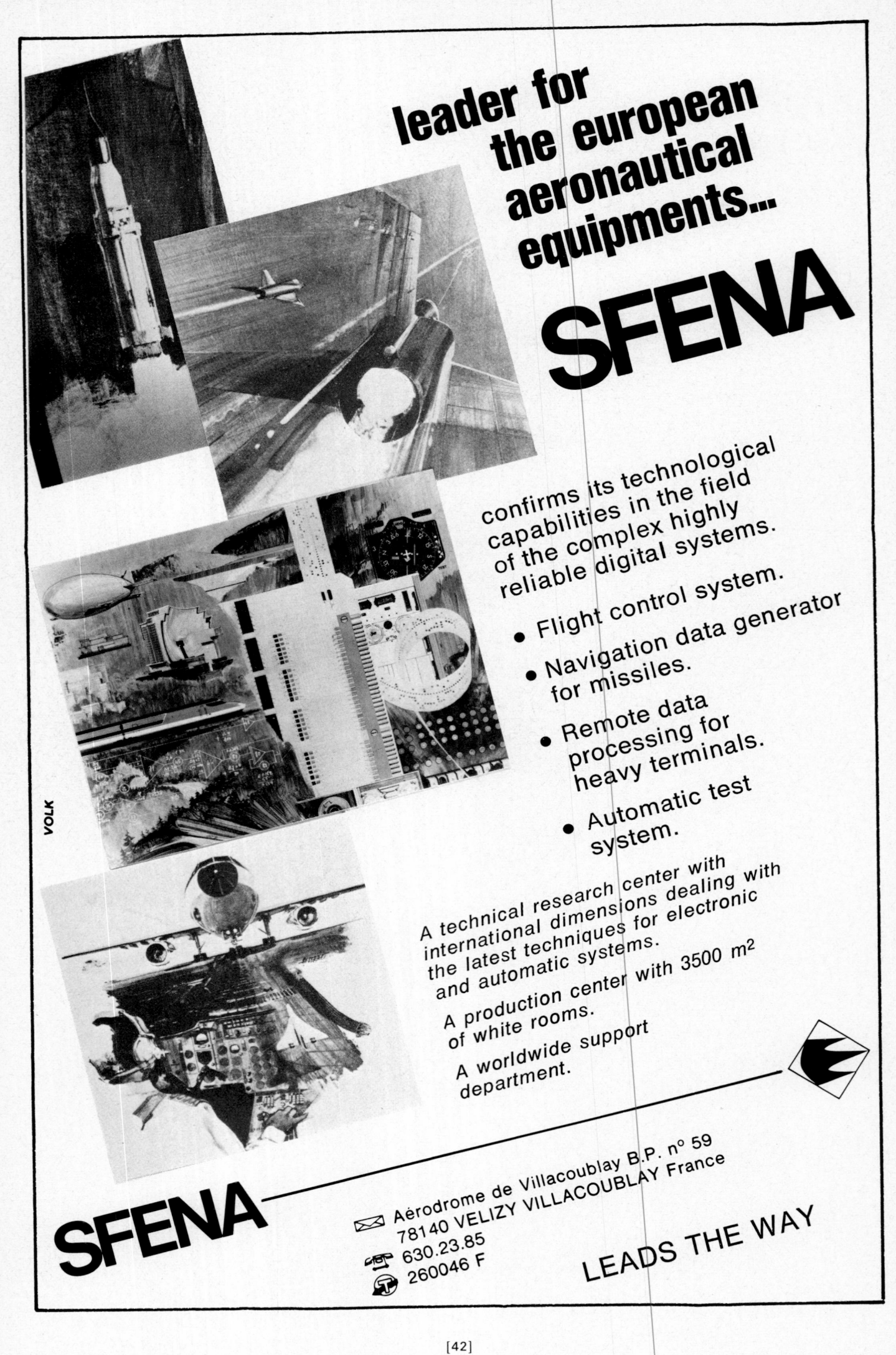
[42]

ELTRO
optronic
know how

Helicopter in thermal image

Development · Manufacture · Maintenance

- ● Laser rangefinders/target illuminators/trackers

- ● Low-level light intensifiers-reconnaissance/aiming devices

- ● Optronic fire suppression systems

- ● Runway visual range measuring systems

- ● Thermal imaging systems

- ● Landmine detectors

- ● IR missile guidance

Eltro GmbH, Gesellschaft für Strahlungstechnik
Postfach 102120 · 6900 Heidelberg 1, W.-Germany

The Bandeirante. Successful today because it's built for tomorrow.

The air transportation market is changing rapidly.

As fuel prices climb higher and higher more people are going by air even on short trips.

Air cargo traffic is increasing, too. Therefore, it's important for commuter operators to select now the equipment that will meet the needs of tomorrow's booming commuter business.

They must look for maximum economy, reliability and flexibility.

And that's why, after exhaustive comparison with other aircraft, they choose the twin turboprop Bandeirante.

Today, more than 280 Bandeirante are in successful operation in 17 countries on 5 continents.

If you're looking for the best combination of versatile performance vs low purchase and operational costs, you'll find it in the Bandeirante.

Because it's built for tomorrow.

←EMBRAER
CEILING UNLIMITED

For more information: Embraer - International Sales Division, 12200, São José dos Campos (SP)
Brazil, Telex (391) 1133589 EBAE BR.

Visit us in Farnborough'80 - South Hall Stand no. 80.

RB 199
A "multi-rôle" engine
for a "multi-rôle" aircraft

Our expertise in this field has
not been achieved overnight; for joint
production (with Rolls Royce and MTU)
of the RB 199 is only the latest in a
series of engine development
activities over the past seventy years.

The RB 199 is a "third generation" engine
with low fuel consumption at cruising speeds,
and outstanding supersonic acceleration:
two requisites needed by the most impressive
military aircraft of our time - the Tornado.

And a sign of the steady advance from
production under licence (through Italian
and European joint ventures) to prestigious
"Atlantic" cooperation agreements.

Research and technology make
our products fit to comply
with the demands
of the new world of aeronautics.

FIAT AVIAZIONE
the history of aviation.

HIGH PERFORMANCE!

Assured through AAI's advanced state-of-the-arts test technology.

High-performance aircraft depend on sophisticated systems operating at peak efficiency for constant readiness. Air installations throughout the free world depend on AAI, a leader in test technology, for fast, accurate, and reliable testing at organizational, intermediate, and depot levels.

Our test and maintenance management expertise includes general purpose radar testers up to computerized units for special applications.

Shown here are the latest in a broad line of test systems developed and produced by AAI.

A Subsidiary of United Industrial Corporation

P.O. Box 6767/Baltimore, Maryland USA 21204
Telephone: (301) 666-1400
TWX: 710-232-1800/Telex: 8-7849
CABLE AAICKYLV Baltimore, Md.

AAI CORPORATION

Depot and Intermediate Level ATE.   Series 5565

A series of modular, ATLAS programmed ATE for support of advanced avionics systems and components. Includes microwave, analog, digital, and fully integrated test systems. Full logistics support and test programming services are provided.

Air Data Computer Test Set, AN/ASM-442

Operates on flight line or in field shop. Provides fully automatic testing of air data computers and associated indicators. Features dynamic air-speed/altitude profiles.

General Purpose X Band Radar Test Set, AN/UPM-145

Provides complete X-Band signal generation and measurement with internal CW, Pulse, and FM modulation. Lightweight, fuly ruggedized and completely solid state. Provides direct digital readout in operating units of measurement. Independent precise control of all signal parameters.

Guidance Control Test Set, TS-3621/DSQ-29 for AIM-9 Sidewinder Missile.

Features automatic testing of mission-essential guidance and control signals. Provides dynamic testing of Tracking and fin torque performance. Readiness of this microprocessor-controlled test set is assured by automatic self test.

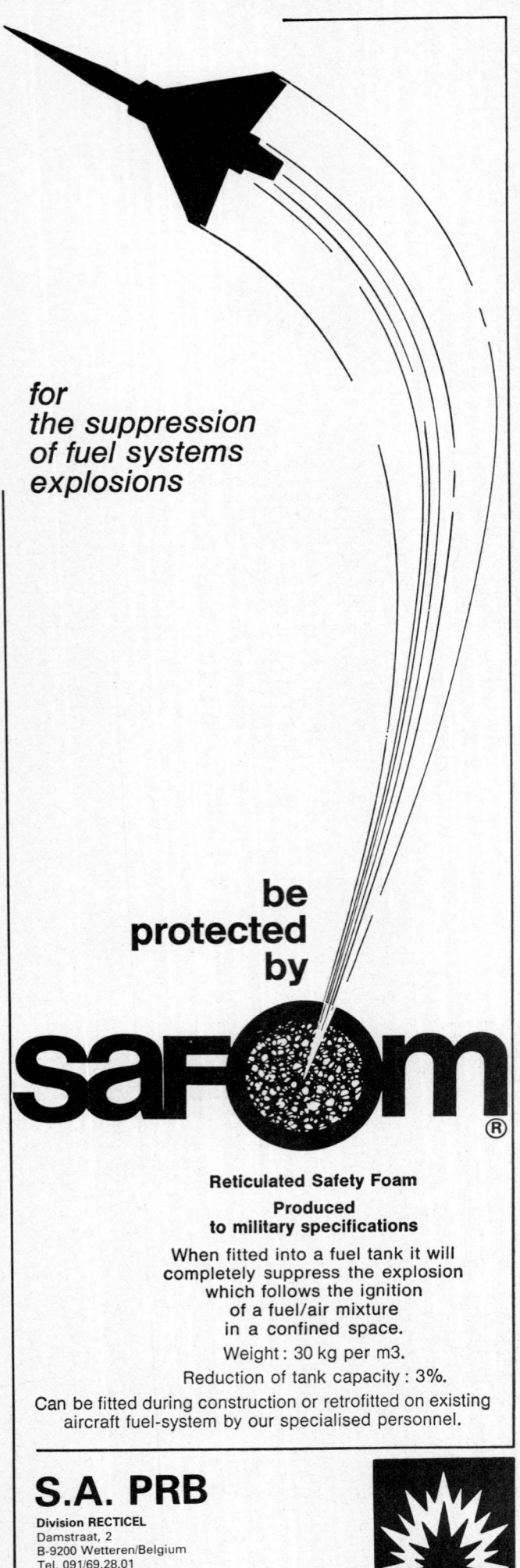

AEROSYSTEM
ELECTRONIC
AEROSYSTEM
ELECTRONIC
AEROSYSTEM
ELECTRONIC
AEROSYSTEM
ELECTRONIC
AEROSYSTEM
ELECTRONIC
AEROSYSTEM
ELECTRONIC

⟶ ANDROMEDA

METEOR
METEOR
METEOR
METEOR
METEOR
METEOR
METEOR
METEOR

MULTIROLE
REMOTELY
PILOTED
OR AUTOMATIC
AIRCRAFT
SYSTEM

AEROSYSTEM
ELECTRONIC A.G.
International Division
Am Balsberg, 30
8302 KLOTEN ZURICH (SWITZERLAND)
Phone: (01) 8141117
Telex: 55660 AERSY CH

METEOR S.p.A.
Via Nomentana, 146
00162 ROMA (ITALY)
Phone: (06) 8380232 8392145
Telex: 68136 METEOROM

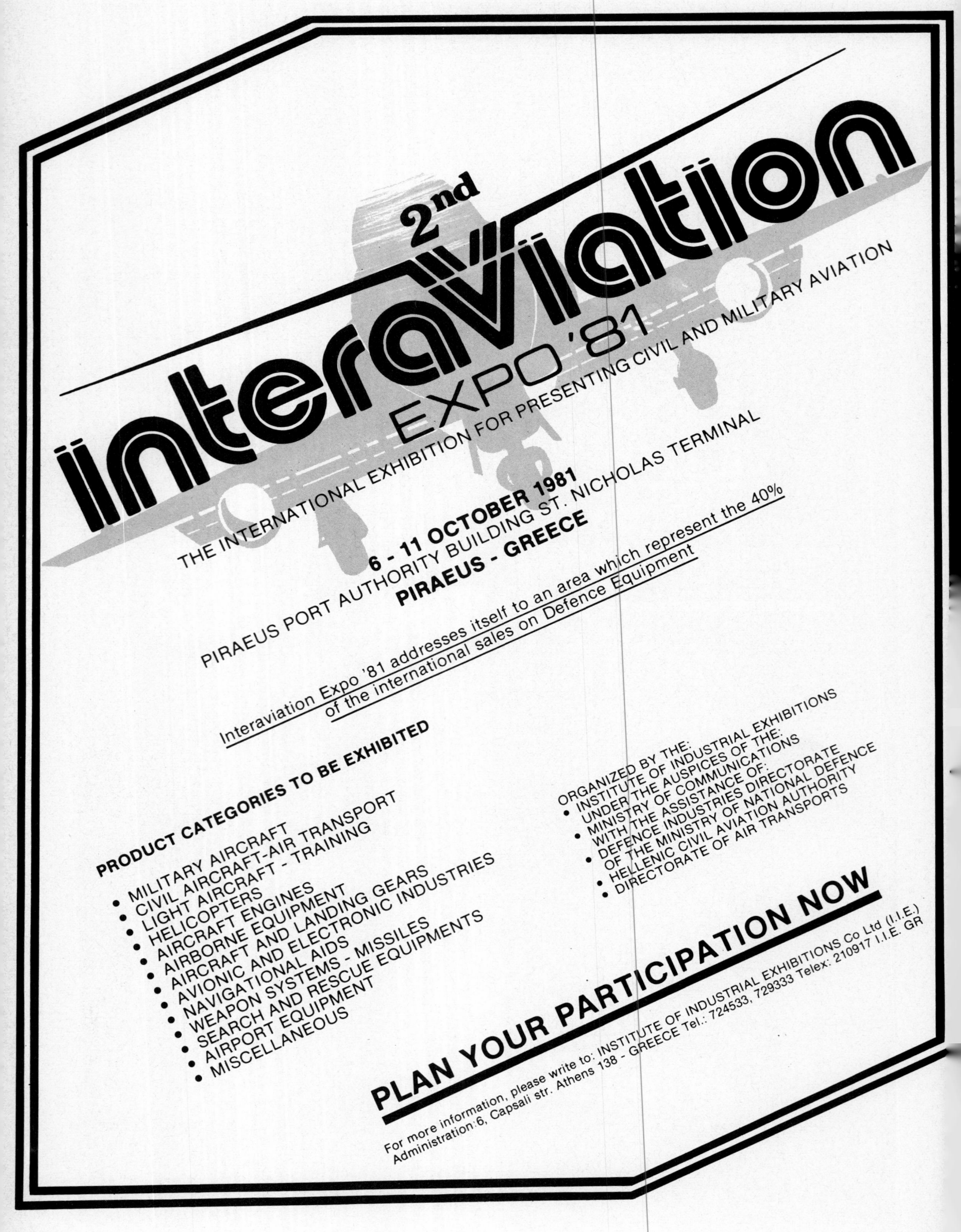

THE TRAINING MATE

When you talk about training, you talk about Aermacchi.
In twenty years, 13 operators all over the world
ordered and re-ordered eight hundred and sixty
MB-326 jet trainers: a tangibile acknowledgement of Aermacchi
unsurpassed experience in the training art.
Now – for the pilots of the eighties – Aermacchi is mass-producing
the cost-effective MB-339, the best promising
new generation trainer with multimission capability.

Everything is in clear view if seen from above.

publei

Aeritalia, a member of the IRI-Finmeccanica Group, and Italy's largest aerospace manufacturer, is playing a significant role in technological progress.

It is engaged in the research, design, development and production of military aircraft: the multi-national Tornado, F-104S, G 91 Y, of transports: G 222, and of assemblies for airliners: DC-9, DC-10, B 727 and B 747. It is participating in the design, development and production of the B 767 advanced commercial aircraft.

It is involved in major space programmes: Spacelab, Ariane, Sirio, OTS, ECS, Marecs, the ESA-NASA space telescope, the Utex telescope, as well as in the design and integration of complete avionics systems and in applied electronics. In addition, it designs and produces aircraft instruments, automatic and inertial navigation systems for civil and military applications, and military optical systems.

Aeritalia has over 10,000 people in its six industrial centres at Naples, Turin and Milan. This human and industrial potential is ready to meet the needs of tomorrow.

AERITALIA
società aerospaziale italiana
80125 NAPOLI Piazzale Tecchio 51
Tel. 619.522 Telex 710370 AERIT I

for ground defence
against aircraft

From the GIAT a diversified range
of anti-aircraft systems
to meet General Staff requirements
in many nations.

Cerbère

Tarasque

Centaure

**confidence
through
ELMER
radiocommunication
systems**

The most
comprehensive range
of multi-purpose
radiocommunication
equipment
integrated in
very advanced
radiocommunication
systems

THE INSIDE STORY ON THE BOEING FAMILY.

Choices. Choices. Choices. No other manufacturer in the world offers everything from 100 to 500 seats.

Five hundred miles, 1,000 miles, 3,500 miles, 6,000 miles. Boeing jetliners have the range flexibility to give airlines all sorts of opportunities to lower operating costs per seat mile.

Thin traffic. High frequency. Nonstop city pairs. High density, long-range markets. High density, short-range markets. Boeing jetliners do it all.

Single aisles. Twin aisles. Wide bodies. Six abreast. Seven abreast.

737   727   757

Eight abreast. Nine abreast. Ten abreast. Eleven abreast. Boeing has the options.

All-freight. Combis. Side cargo door loading. Main deck. Lower lobes. Pallets 88″ × 108″. Containers 40′ long. Virtually anything goes in Boeing jetliners.

The lineup runs like this: the intercontinental 707; 737, The Little Giant; 727, the world's most popular trijet; 747, The Queen of the Sky. And now a new generation—the 757 and 767. That's the basic family. But there are all types of choices within the product line. Gross weight. Engines. Seating. Cargo. Galley. You name it, we can do it. Or, if we haven't done it, we're probably thinking about doing it.

Everything we do has one purpose in mind—to give you the right airplane for the right market.

Our goal: to provide our customers with airplanes that perform with superior operating efficiency and have the flexibility to meet the multiple changing marketing opportunities of the '80s. And beyond.

THE BOEING FAMILY
Getting people together.

767

747

SAAB SH37 Viggen Supersonic STOL all-weather sea surveillance and attack aircraft in service with the Swedish Air Force

JANE'S ALL THE WORLD'S AIRCRAFT

FOUNDED IN 1909 BY FRED T. JANE

COMPILED AND EDITED BY
JOHN W R TAYLOR FRAeS, FRHistS, FSLAET
ASSISTANT EDITOR
KENNETH MUNSON, Associate RAeS, ARthistS

1980-81

JANE'S
LONDON • NEW YORK • SYDNEY
"Jane's" is a registered trade mark

Published in the United Kingdom by
Jane's Publishing Company Limited, 238 City Road, London EC1V 2PU

ISBN 0 7106-0705-9

Published in the United States of America by
Jane's Publishing Incorporated, 730 Fifth Avenue, New York, NY 10019

ISBN 0 531-03953-6

30 mm Aircraft Gun, Type KCA

More than just complementary...

...to guided missiles. The Oerlikon 30 mm high-power revolver gun is equally well suited to air-to-air and air-to-ground engagements against armoured and unarmoured targets.

This gas-operated gun combines a rapid rate of fire with high muzzle velocity. Other main features are: four cartridge chambers, electric firing, belt feed, pyrotechnical or pneumatic recocking.

Technical data:
- Rate of fire: 1350 rounds/min
- Muzzle velocity v_0:   1030 m/s
- Weight of gun: 130 kg

The KCA can be installed in the aircraft fuselage or in pods to obtain optimum weapons system integration.

The KCA gun fires the most effective 30 mm caliber ammunition available today.

TP

HEI

SAPHEI

OERLIKON MILITARY PRODUCTS

OERLIKON

Machine Tool Works Oerlikon-Bührle Ltd.,
Birchstrasse 155, CH-8050 Zurich

Zurich · Geneva · Milan · Grantham

030-340

CONTENTS

The Editor has been assisted in the compilation of this edition as follows:

Kenneth Munson   AIRCRAFT SECTION: ARGENTINA TO FINLAND, GREECE TO TURKEY, UNITED KINGDOM (pp 238-258); RPVs; SAILPLANES

David Mondey   AIRCRAFT SECTION: WEST GERMANY, UNITED KINGDOM (pp 222-238), UNITED STATES OF AMERICA; BALLOONS; INDEX

Bill Gunston   GLOSSARY; AERO-ENGINES

Michael Taylor   HOMEBUILTS; METRIC CONVERSIONS

Maurice Allward   SPACEFLIGHT

The Lord Ventry   AIRSHIPS

LUCAS.
The largest range of aircraft systems and equipment from any single source - world-wide.

Lucas Aerospace systems are in use on over 100 different aircraft types. Major airlines, air forces and operators around the globe, flying thousands of individual aircraft and millions of flying hours each year, depend on Lucas expertise, experience and the world-wide product support they provide.

Rolls Royce, Boeing, Lockheed, McDonnell Douglas, Sikorsky, British Aerospace, Airbus Industrie, Aerospatiale, Panavia, de Havilland Aircraft of Canada, Westland, Fokker and many others gain the benefit of design innovation and engineering skills through close partnership with Lucas Aerospace.

The Lucas Aerospace product range includes: engine management systems; electric, pneumatic and gas-turbine starting systems; ignition and combustion systems; hot and cold thrust reversers; hydraulic, pneumatic, electrical and mechanical actuation systems; ballscrews; small gas turbines; air control valves; electrical power generation and distribution systems; auxiliary power systems; de-icing systems; and transparencies.

Lucas serves the international aerospace industry and combines advanced technology with high reliability. Lucas also supplies the largest range of aircraft systems and equipment from any single source, world-wide.

Lucas Aerospace

Lucas Aerospace Limited, Shirley, Solihull, West Midlands, B90 2JJ, UK. Tel: 021-744 8522. Telex: 336749.
Lucas Industries Inc., Aerospace Division, 30 Van Nostrand Avenue, Englewood, NJ 07631. USA. Tel: (201) 567 6400. Telex: 135374.
and 1320 West Walnut Street, Compton, CA 90224. USA. Tel: (213) 635 3128.
Lucas Industries Canada Limited, Aerospace Division, 5595 Royalmount Avenue, Montreal, Quebec, H4P 1J9.
Tel: 514-735-1536. Telex: 055-61115.
Also at Sydney, Australia: Paris, France: Neuss, W Germany.

FOREWORD

As this Foreword is being written, a pall of black smoke hangs over the Middle East. Beneath it, oil that took millions of years to form, and which represents one of the most precious, dwindling resources of our world, is lost for ever as refineries burn. A man who surveyed Planet Earth from space might well ponder that the fires are raging so very near the plain of Armageddon. There, one of the great books written in the Middle East predicted, the final desperate battle of Earth will be fought as all history draws to its close.

Jane's All the World's Aircraft is concerned with aerospace, not politics or prediction, but it can never ignore developments of this kind. It could not exist in its present form without the friendship and collaboration of professional colleagues and correspondents in every nation of the world where aircraft are built. It has continued to record the products and achievements of the aerospace industry during the past 35 years because a small proportion of those products have maintained a military deterrent policy of peace through fear. It is not an ideal policy in a world where millions starve; but at least it keeps hundreds of millions alive.

Politicians, and others, who suggest that many might survive an all-out nuclear war in the nations primarily involved, are more to be feared than the weapons themselves. Yet, during the past year, there has been increasing talk of techniques for survival, and of limiting the destructiveness of such a war by the restricted, selective use of available weapons. This is delusion, and we can only repeat the warning contained in the Foreword to our 1977-78 edition, that "there would be no victor in such a holocaust. Survivors would never be quite certain that the next mouthful of food was fit to eat, or the next lungful of air safe to breathe. Their first post-war tasks would include disposal of the sixty million dead which computers predict coldly for a nation like the United States, on print-out pages headed Calculated Risk".

Virtual abandonment of the East/West SALT 2 strategic arms limitation agreement might suggest that we have simply drifted three years closer to Armageddon since those words were written; but this is not necessarily so. SALT 2 was good in principle, but dangerously wrong in its detailed content. For example, since that same period of 1977-78, *Jane's* has insisted that the Soviet 'Backfire' bomber needs to be counted as a potent intercontinental weapon, and that America needs urgently a modern aircraft like the B-1 to match it in strategic balance. Those who drafted SALT 2 disagreed with such views.

A spokesman for the US President went on record in stating that the Editor of *Jane's* was wrong. But the latest Annual Report of the US Department of Defense states what US Air Force leaders have known for years, that the 'Backfire' bomber "undoubtedly has some intercontinental capability in the sense that it can (for example) surely reach the United States from Soviet home bases on a one-way, high-altitude, subsonic, unrefuelled flight with recovery in the Caribbean area. With Arctic staging, refuelling, and certain high-altitude cruise flight profiles, it can probably execute a two-way mission to much of the United States".

Almost identical words have appeared in *Jane's* since 1976, one year before President Carter cancelled production of the B-1.

In 1980, the US Congress has debated America's urgent need to replace the vintage B-52, and one of the three options considered was the B-1 in a degraded subsonic form. Such facts are not recorded to suggest that *Jane's* is more clever than Presidential spokespersons, but to re-emphasise the continuing importance of the manned bomber, in the most advanced technological form possible. Those who draft peacekeeping treaties, and have responsibility for peacekeeping military forces, should bear in mind the wise counsel of the late King Abdul Aziz of Saudi Arabia that: "Your friend is he who tells you the truth, not he who keeps telling you you're right".

By comparison, intercontinental ballistic missiles, submarine-launched missiles, and even cruise missiles, lack flexibility. The threat posed by a handful of airborne 'Backfires' or B-1s, heading for a small number of key targets, could well be sufficient to bring sense to political minds and avert a war at the eleventh hour. The value of nuclear missiles in terms of defence, in the true meaning of the word, was summed up by the commander of one of the Royal Navy's Polaris submarines, who said: "If my missiles were ever fired, my home and family would already have ceased to exist".

* * * * * *

One of the alternatives to the B-1 as the USAF's new manned penetrator is the so-called Stealth bomber. Official revelation of the programme in Presidential election year produced all kinds of accusations and outcry in the States. The President's office was said to have leaked the programme to show that Mr Carter had, all the time, been doing the right things to keep America strong. Honest journalists were hauled in front of investigating committees to explain how and why they obtained and published news detrimental to the nation's security. A US aviation journal was said to have sparked off the affair with a story in August 1980. Our old friend the President's spokesman remembered that *Jane's All the World's Aircraft* had carried a reference to such an aeroplane for the past two years. In fact, a first reference to America's Stealth aircraft appeared in *Jane's* in 1977, and was no threat to any nation's security as the programme was unclassified at the time the piece was written.

Three years earlier, during a visit to Teledyne Ryan at San Diego, the Editor had studied a fascinating little reconnaissance RPV prototype. The body shell, made of glassfibre, had no straight edges. Every part of its form curved in a manner more reminiscent of a young bride's first experiment in cooking than of the kind of structure that highly professional designers conceive at their drawing boards. This, explained the guide, was a structure virtually undetectable by radar. A few hundred miles to the north, a day or two later, discussion on the flight deck of the curvacious B-1 mockup had a similar theme. This impressive bomber was, it seemed, intended to have a radar signature equivalent in size to a very small bird, if the defences were sufficiently competent to detect it at high subsonic speed a few hundred feet above the terrain.

Any reader of the aviation press, on either side of the East/West frontier, will know about other technological devices and techniques that became increasingly significant as the war in Viet-Nam dragged on. To reduce the toll of SAM-7 shoulder-fired infra-red missiles, helicopters had their exhaust nozzles tilted upward; other aircraft began to add shielding around their 'hot spots'. Formations of attack aircraft were accompanied by strange variants of familiar types festooned with antennae and bulges. Odd scraps of information suggested the use of avionics that would jam or confuse enemy radars, making the attackers seem more numerous, or far less numerous, than they were; or miles away from their true location; or something different from what they really were. Experiments, as old as military flying, continued trying to paint aircraft so that they would be less conspicuous against a background of high-altitude sky or zero-altitude terrain.

Add together all these well-publicised features, plus a few rumours about exotic paints that absorb, deaden or deflect probing radar signals, and the result is the so-called Stealth aircraft, as far as anyone has yet described it. The real secrets lie in the specifications of the 'invisible paint' if it exists, the frequencies of the ECM/ECCM equipment, and shapes that would be revealed only by sharp, detailed photographs of the actual aircraft, which are said to be based at a secluded test site in Nevada.

The Editor of America's *Armed Forces Journal,* who has published the most balanced report on the Stealth programme yet to appear in print, claims that the US has been test flying several versions of these 'virtually invisible new aeroplanes', in both manned and unmanned versions, since early 1978. A senior Pentagon official has expressed the opinion that within ten years about 10 per cent of all US military aircraft might be Stealth systems.

A lady on the staff of *Armed Forces Journal* asked her Editor if the Russians had such aircraft, and was told "I doubt it". After a moment's reflection, she added "But how would we know, if they can't be seen?"

* * * * * *

The signal-sorters

Integrating given combinations of VHF, UHF, HF, VOR, ADF and other receiver signals into a single interface obviously requires flexibility on the part of an aircraft's Communication Control System equipment.

Flexibility in CCS

And flexibility is exactly what the Racal Six-Ninety Series CCS offers.

These small, highly sophisticated units provide for the selection, control and interface of audio signals from onboard equipment and intercom.

Modular principle

Already in use in military and civil aircraft all over the world, the Series is based on a modular principle which allows equipment to be custom engineered to fit any aircraft from Chinook to Hawk.

Complete range

The station boxes shown above are just two from the complete range, which includes equipment suitable for almost any application.

For full details of the Six-Ninety Series, contact the address below.

RACAL ACOUSTICS for sound communications

Racal Acoustics Limited, Beresford Avenue, Wembley, Middlesex HAO 1RU, England. Telephone: 01-903 1444. Telex: 926288. Telegrams & Cables: Acoustics Wembley. **RACAL**

What we *have* seen of the Soviet military forces during the past year has caused steadily mounting concern among those who believe that the best guarantee of continued peace lies in a strict balance of East/West military might, which can then be diminished progressively and equally to everyone's advantage. In the big league, we have reached the time when America's Minuteman force is vulnerable to Soviet ICBM attack, making development and deployment of the MX missile system utterly essential.

Equally important, for economic survival, is that the anachronistically independent member nations of NATO should think more practically in terms of a single integrated military force. The stupidity of Britain's spending £5,000 million on Trident missile submarines would then be apparent, and emphasis would be placed on providing the kind of conventional weapons that offer the best assurance of stability in Europe.

Outside top military circles, few people have much idea of the form that a Warsaw Pact offensive would take. Chemical and tactical nuclear weapons are regarded as normal elements of any land battle. Even if they were not used, a single sortie by each aircraft of the 16th Air Army in East Germany—including new 'A-10 type' ground attack Shturmoviks—would have the same effect as 360 field guns firing for an hour to soften the defences. NATO AWACS aircraft and anti-tank helicopters would be eliminated before the thousands of Soviet tanks began to roll forward on an 18 km (11 mile) front. Overhead, large formations drawn from 6,000 available Mi-8 ('Hip') helicopters would airlift assault troops and equipment to carefully chosen positions behind the NATO lines, their path cleared by Mi-24 ('Hind') gunships, using their heavy armament to dispose of surface-to-air missile defences, opposing tanks and helicopters with equal facility.

The superior all-weather capability of the Warsaw Pact air forces has been emphasised repeatedly in *Jane's,* as NATO has invested more and more of its resources in aircraft, and missiles like TV Maverick, that lack the ability to operate in conditions experienced all too frequently in Europe. This represents only one way in which the one-time Western lead in quality, which offset Eastern quantitative advantages, has been eroded. Far more worrying is the poor state of readiness of some elements of NATO air forces.

Official statistics released by US Defense Secretary Harold Brown revealed that in Fiscal Year 1979 an average 42 per cent of US Air Force tactical aircraft were 'not mission capable' at any particular time. The relatively unsophisticated A-10 Thunderbolt II came out best, with only 32·6 per cent of the 243-strong force grounded on average through the year. At the other extreme, 65·6 per cent of the 86 F-111Ds were normally not mission capable. Nor was the US Navy in a much healthier state, with an average 47·1 per cent of its 292 F-14A Tomcats unavailable throughout the year, and unimpressive availability of its other five major combat types.

Taking such figures in isolation, with no combat readiness figures for other air forces against which to compare them, is probably unfair to air forces with a great record of achievement. The intention is not to criticise, but to explain how illusory might be any belief in continued Western superiority.

Growing interest in the proposed adverse weather version of the A-10 is good news. So is the fact that the US Congress has refused to let effort on the AV-8B die, despite Department of Defense coldness for the programme. The unique V/STOL capability pioneered by the basic Harrier is one of the major assets retained by the West, and it is time to end the 'shall we/shan't we?' talk that has gone on for too long, on both sides of the Atlantic. If the US Marine Corps is to get the versatile 'bomb truck' that it wants, and the US Navy is to get a fighter that can be flown irrespective of narrow seas, wind direction and other factors that affect shipboard operations, the only answer in sight is the AV-8B. It is a good aeroplane for both US services, but the RAF wants the 'Big Wing' Harrier for a different job and should never be denied the tools that it considers essential. In particular, the Harrier's potential as a helicopter destroyer, resulting from its unique capability of thrust vectoring in forward flight, should not be overlooked.

* * * * * *

It was the late Premier Krushchev who commented that the Soviet Union did not need to attack the West militarily, being able to bury it economically. To those of us who find the ways of economic experts difficult to comprehend, the past year has given new meaning to that boast. In the Spring came a warning that the Belgian Air Force would virtually cease operations from 1 September until the end of 1980 unless it received additional funding for fuel. In July, Britain's Secretary of State for Defence announced that the number of RAF Buccaneer squadrons allocated to NATO was likely to be reduced permanently, because Her Majesty's government could not afford to repair the fatigue cracks in almost half the force.

In April, the German Defence Minister succeeded, quite rightly, in proving that the current 'systems cost figure' of DM 67 million for a Tornado was much the same as the May 1970 estimated cost of DM 28 million, in real terms, and, in any case, compared well with the cost of comparable American combat aircraft, whatever they might be.

The fact is that the RAF and Luftwaffe would cease to exist as effective components of NATO without the Tornado, which really has no counterpart on this side of the Iron Curtain. And the international manufacturers *have* done a good job, both technologically and economically.

It costs money to stay alive in a world full of armies, navies and air forces. So the manufacturers of combat aircraft are always assured of work, if not profits. Manufacturers of commercial aircraft have no such assurance, and 1980 has been a year of problems for manufacturers and operators alike. Ever-lower fares are popular with the public, and help to fill aeroplanes, but do little for profitability. Deregulation, as practised in the USA, can be even worse, leading to the bankruptcy of good operators who face competition from short-term speculators flying cheaply-acquired geriatric jets. ICAO statistics show that world scheduled airline load factors in 1979 reached their highest levels in 20 years, but that operating profits fell from 5 per cent in 1977 and 1978 to only 1 per cent in 1979. Ultimately, correct fare levels for travelling in the best available aircraft, maintained to the highest professional standards, are in everyone's interest.

Even Boeing is feeling the effects of the recession, we are told, and will have to cut back production from the originally-announced 28½ airliners per month. Its domination of the market is emphasised by its competitors' 1979 full-year export delivery figures of 14 TriStars, 39 DC-9s and 35 DC-10s. Only Airbus Industrie seems to be having any major impact on Boeing's market, and has continued to make impressive progress during 1980.

It would be pleasing to see in the development of programmes like Airbus and Tornado the seeds of increasingly successful European collaboration in the aerospace business, but the largest of the industries involved continues to face problems that threaten its stability. The UK's present government is determined to return British Aerospace to partial private ownership. If the Tory Party should be defeated in the next general election, in 1984, the Labour opposition has suggested that it will not only return the lot to state ownership but will withdraw Britain's membership of the European Economic Community. It would take a brave man to predict with confidence the long-term effect of all this on one of the world's great industries, which earned nearly £1,000 million from exports in the first seven months of 1980.

Its only real failure to date has resulted from efforts to resurrect a light aircraft industry in Britain. In the decade since Beagle Aircraft went out of business, there have been numerous attempts. Last year, *Jane's* reported that Shorts intended to build Piper Tomahawks under licence at a rate of ten a month. This did not materialise, but Learavia is now hoping to manufacture Lear Fan Model 2100s at Aldergrove, in Northern Ireland. With two turboshaft engines and accommodation for eight to ten persons, the Lear Fan is hardly a lightplane; but it could give the UK a toehold in a sector of the industry that has eluded it for far too long.

* * * * * *

The past year has been a tough one for the lightplane business worldwide. In the USA, Bellanca encountered financial problems that brought to an end manufacture of the Viking, Citabria, Decathlon and Scout series. Rockwell ended production of the Alpine and Gran Turismo Commanders, and the Commander 700 twin that it built in partnership with Fuji of Japan. Cessna dropped the 'push-and-pull' Model 337 Skymaster, and on 16 April announced that it had laid off about 1,300 employees at its single-engine facilities and 1,200 at its multi-engine division, with 1,500 more temporarily furloughed during an inventory reduction programme. Piper closed three of its four manufacturing divisions completely for a two-week period in April and reduced its work force by 2,350 persons.

THE BK 117. BULK TRANSPORTATION IS ITS SPECIALITY. SIMPLE MAINTENANCE IS ITS STRENGTH. AMPLE POWER IS ITS MOST STRIKING FEATURE.

When two international industrial leaders invest their immense know-how and engineering power in a joint project, the result is something very special – the BK 117, the helicopter for the Eighties, the offshore, rescue, executive, police and multipurpose helicopter the market has been waiting for.

Compact external dimensions and exceptionally ample space inside – this is the BK 117. Big doors make loading easier. With its two powerful engines, the BK 117 gains altitude quickly. Performance on one engine only meets the most critical operating standards. And the BK 117 reaches a ceiling that puts it in a class by itself.

As if that were not enough: the BK 117 is exceptionally easy to maintain, economical to run and available at an unbeatable price for this class of machine. Everything points to it becoming one of the most sought-after helicopters of the Eighties. Maidenflight: 13 June, 1979.

general utility missions

offshore operations

personnel transport

law enforcement

medical operations

search and rescue operations

The Multipurpose Helicopter. The Twin-engined BK 117.

MBB KAWASAKI

Messerschmitt-Bölkow-Blohm GmbH
Helicopter and Transport Systems Division
Postfach 80 11 40, D-8000 München 80
Germany

Kawasaki Heavy Industries, Ltd.
Tokyo Office, World Trade Center Bldg.
4-1, 2-Chome, Hamamatsu-Cho
Minato-Ku, Tokyo, Japan

In an effort to promote sales, the newly-appointed agents for Mitsubishi in Britain offered two free £6,500 Colt Sapporo motor cars to anyone who bought a Diamond I twin-turbofan business aircraft. Significantly, however, the only sector of the market that continued to experience thriving business was at the opposite extreme in terms of sophistication and cost.

The new category of private aircraft that has followed in the post-war wake of ballooning and hang gliding has grown at such a pace that its worldwide pilot-owners have not yet had time to agree a generic name for their primitive-looking, modestly-powered machines. Ultralights, Microlights, Minimum Aircraft and Featherweights are among the more printable possibilities from the USA, UK and Australia. The fact that some are manufactured commercially and sold only as completed aircraft, while others are marketed in kit form as homebuilts, and yet others are described by their makers as powered hang gliders, has caused their dispersion in three different sections of this edition of *Jane's*. Clearly, they will have to be gathered together in a single new section of the 1981-82 book, provided there is agreement on what it should be called.

The aircraft themselves vary tremendously. Some are, literally, powered types using a standard hang glider Rogallo wing. Others are fairly conventional powered aeroplanes in the tradition of the English Electric Wren and its contemporaries of 1923, which could cover up to 76 nm (141 km; 87·5 miles) on one Imp gallon (4·5 litres) of fuel. Their purpose is similar—to travel as far as possible as economically as possible; but the good folk of 1923 could hardly have imagined what that single gallon of petrol would cost in 1980.

The regulations concerning the operation of these modern types vary from one country to another. Even if they were foot-launched, the American FAA insisted on certification as experimental homebuilts prior to 13 May 1977. Before one could be flown, the owner had to obtain a US identification number (free of charge); register the aircraft ($5·00 charge); have the wings and rudders inspected by an FAA inspector (free of charge) before covering them with fabric; and have the completed aircraft inspected by an FAA inspector, who could issue an Airworthiness Certificate (free of charge) provided that the constructional standards met with his approval.

Since the aircraft was certificated, the pilot next had to obtain a third-class medical certificate, costing about $15·00, with which he got a student pilot's licence. After learning how to handle the aircraft while 'taxying' along the ground on his two feet, the pilot was able to fly it under the observation of a certificated flying instructor. When satisfied, the latter could endorse the pilot's licence to indicate that the individual was competent to solo his powered ultralight. This endorsement had to be renewed every 90 days.

From 13 May 1977, powered foot-launched aircraft have been deregulated by the FAA, and can be flown without Experimental Certification, FAA inspections or the need for a pilot's licence. As long as foot-launch capability is retained, the aircraft remains deregulated even if a landing gear is installed. The pilot simply has to adhere to the flight rules of conventional aircraft, as outlined in FAA Regulation Pt 91, Sub-Pt B.

With this new category of flying gaining popularity so rapidly, and likely to require increasing attention in *Jane's*, it was felt worthwhile to outline the history of the basic aircraft type, and the rules for its operation, so far as the major operating and manufacturing nation is concerned. Little is yet sorted out internationally. At the moment, for example, Australian regulations limit flying to heights below 300 ft (91 m), but require no pilot's licence, submission of drawings or inspection of workmanship. In the words of Henry Millicer, designer of the Airtrainer and lecturer in aeronautical engineering at the Royal Melbourne Institute of Technology, "You are free to break your neck if you like". Despite which, he predicts an explosion in the numbers and performance of ultralights over the next 25 years.

* * * * * *

Fuel is, thus, the dominating theme of the aerospace business at the start of the 'eighties. It is at the heart of the latest war in the Middle East; has wrecked the one-time profitability of airlines; is threatening to bring to an eventual close the era of cheap mass air travel; has led to the birth of the new ultralight flying movement; is causing the mainstream manufacturers to devote ever-increasing effort to devising techniques for fuel economy; and is beginning to make everyone think more seriously about alternative fuels of the future.

Lockheed is very much in the forefront of manufacturers in applying thought to the problems and their solution. During 1980, it has demonstrated that fuel consumption of its C-130 Hercules transport can be reduced more than 3 per cent by the simple expedient of adding two ventral fins. It is studying the viability of an 'all-electric' medium transport, without hydraulic or pneumatic systems, which is estimated to cost about £50 million less to build, operate and maintain over its lifetime than a conventional aircraft. And it is continuing its detailed evaluation of various categories of aircraft fuelled by liquid hydrogen.

Generally, however, the world industry is tending to veer away from such exotic fuels to a belief that flying will continue to rely on hydrocarbons well into next century, using coal as one of the primary sources until synthetic fuels are available in quantity.

In no way does the present view of world aviation development seem to offer a place for supersonic airline flying after Concorde. Yet it is inconceivable that, having sampled the benefits of Mach 2 cruising in the pioneer of a new age, man will be content for ever to fly at less than half that speed. One day a new fuel like liquid hydrogen may make it routine to fly at Mach 6 when travelling long distances. Meanwhile, 1980 has produced a fact about the greatest-yet international aviation product that should not go unrecorded.

In a talk to the British Business Association, British Airways Concorde Captain John Hutchinson told his listeners that, on a 3¾ hour flight from Singapore to Bahrain, Concorde covers 20 miles to the gallon (7 km/litre) of kerosene per passenger with 90 passengers on board. With only 60 seats filled, the fuel consumption is still 13½ miles per gallon (4·8 km/litre) per passenger. "When you compare that with an American car, I think you will agree that it does not sound quite as horrendously uneconomic as people would have you believe," added Captain Hutchinson.

It had been suggested that Concorde really needed more fuel than it could carry on the Singapore-Bahrain run. Two days before this particular pilot gave his talk, he took on board 87 tons of fuel at Singapore, and could have carried another 7 tons had it been needed. Sadly, as part of British Airways' latest economy cuts, the Concorde service between Singapore and Bahrain will have been discontinued by the time this book is published.

* * * * * *

When surveying the headlines of a year of aerospace activities, it is difficult to avoid focusing primarily on the East/West military balance, and the international airline scene, because on these depend the wellbeing and commerce of our modern world, even its continued survival in civilised form. But aviation is truly international, and no book reflects this better than *Jane's*.

Aero Boero of Argentina is a small company, but one of its directors told a mutual friend how delighted he is to see his aeroplanes listed first of all in *Jane's,* year after year. Long may this continue, for a hungry world needs all the agricultural aeroplanes it can get from manufacturers like Aero Boero, Agricopteros of Colombia, AAMSA and Anahuac of Mexico, and Aerospace of New Zealand, as well as from the major manufacturers of Brazil, India, Poland, Switzerland and the USA.

More and more of the newer manufacturers are learning their trade through licence production of established products. Nurtanio of Indonesia began with the CASA Aviocar and BO 105 helicopter, and has progressed to joint development of a larger transport with CASA. KAL of Korea has started with Hughes helicopters, Libya with SIAI-Marchetti SF.260 trainers, NAM of the Philippines with BO 105s and Pilatus Britten-Norman Islanders.

Political necessity has built up proud industries in countries like Israel, South Africa and Taiwan. IAI's Kfir-C2 may embody a great deal of French airframe expertise and American engine technology, but it also reflects Israeli capability, as does the Arava. The new Lavi fighter will be awaited with particular interest, as will Sweden's JAS and the Italian/Brazilian AM-X. The traditional combat aircraft builders can often learn much from the way such aircraft are conceived and produced on limited budgets.

It is good to know that SAAB is being given an opportunity to justify a Swedish follow-on to the Draken and Viggen. It has much too good a design record to be condemned to producing someone else's aeroplanes. EMBRAER of Brazil is achieving a comparable reputation, with growing sales of its commuter transports in the US market to prove the quality of its products.

Of particular pleasure to the Editorial team of *Jane's* this year has been the renewal of old and valuable links with the industry of Romania. This was the only manufacturing country in the world

that had failed to provide information in recent years, despite having a range of good powered aircraft and sailplanes to publicise and market.

The Chinese section is another that gains in interest with the passing years. With typical honesty, the Chinese admit that they still have much to learn; but few industries have progressed so far in a short time, and it is a pity that photographs received to date from Peking fail to do justice to the quality of construction and surface finish that is apparent on aircraft like the F-6s delivered to Egypt.

Only the Soviet Union has been less co-operative than usual in the past year, possibly as a result of political tensions. This is disappointing. *Jane's* has always had to rely on its own resources to analyse news and photographs of Soviet military aircraft, with entirely satisfactory results; but it is sad that the supply of *Tass* photographs has been reduced from a steady flow to a trickle, and that requests for news of commercial transports like the Tu-144 and Yak-42 have produced no response. Perhaps the 1981 Paris Air Show will restore the normally happy and productive relationship.

*　　*　　*　　*　　*　　*

If this survey has failed to say much about the manufacturers and products of countries like Canada, France, Italy and Japan, it is because the pages devoted to those products say all that is necessary. The quality of aircraft like the DHC STOL transports, Aérospatiale helicopters, Dassault fighters, and the types built by Aeritalia, Aermacchi, Agusta, Fuji, Kawasaki, Mitsubishi and Shin Meiwa, is acknowledged throughout the world and needs no added eulogy from *Jane's* or anyone else.

Nonetheless, we record gratefully the immense debt we owe to the representatives of these, and all other manufacturers throughout the world, for the unique co-operation we receive from them annually when seeking information and photographs to update our yearbook. The trust they often show us, in providing information long in advance of general publication, enables us to produce a book that could not be more up-to-date and comprehensive despite the long period that is required, inevitably, to cope with one and a half million words and some 1,500 illustrations.

Equally pleasing is to have an opportunity to thank so many old and good friends who have provided additional material and help, often for as many years as the Editor has been associated with *Jane's*. Their names will be familiar to all who read the Foreword to the end annually, but the Editor makes no apology for saying once more "Thank you" to colleagues on the editorial staffs of *Air Force Magazine* (Washington) and *Flug Revue* (West Germany); to Delden Badcock (Australia); Pierre Sparaco (Belgium); Ronaldo S. Olive and Roberto Pereira de Andrade (Brazil); Vico Rosaspina (Italy); Eiichiro Sekigawa (Japan); Antonio Camarasa and Javier Taibo (Spain); Roland Eichenberger and Dr Ulrich Haller (Switzerland); Norman Polmar and Tom DeFrank (USA); Wolfgang Wagner (West Germany); Dipl Ing Andrzej Glass and other friends at the Instytut Lotnictwa in Poland; William Green and Gordon Swanborough of *Air International,* David Dorrell of *Air Pictorial,* and Alan Hall of *Aviation News* (UK); and the editorial staffs of *Flight International* and *Aeroplane Monthly* (UK); *Air et Cosmos* and *Aviation Magazine* (France); *Aerophile* (USA); *FLYGvapenNYTT* (Sweden); and *de Vliegende Hollander* (Netherlands). Photographs have again come from many sources; but the book would be infinitely less attractive without the special contributions of Howard Levy, Gordon S. Williams, Peter M. Bowers, Neil Macdougall, Austin Brown, Brian M. Service and J. M. G. Gradidge. The arduous task of drawing our three-views was again undertaken with great skill by Dennis Punnett of Pilot Press and Michael A. Badrocke.

This leaves only the members of my small editorial team to thank sincerely for another year of loyalty and dedication—Assistant Editor Kenneth Munson; Assistant Compilers Maurice Allward, Bill Gunston, David Mondey, Michael Taylor and the Lord Ventry; and my wife Doris, whose name has never before appeared in *Jane's* but whose countless and normally thankless behind-the-scenes help in a hundred ways has made my part of the job possible for more than twenty years.

October 1980   JWRT

Société Nationale Industrielle
aerospatiale

Europe's number one aerospace manufacturer through
- research, development and production capabilities,
- mastery of advanced technologies,
- leadership of large multinational cooperation programs.

A300/A310 Airbus, Concorde, Ariane launcher, Meteosat weather satellite,
Tactical missiles, helicopters.

Société Nationale Industrielle
aerospatiale
37, bd de Montmorency - 75781 Paris Cedex 16 - France

GLOSSARY

AAM Air-to-air missile.
AC Alternating current.
ACLS (1) Automatic carrier landing system; (2) Air cushion landing system.
ADAC Avion de décollage et attérrissage court (STOL).
ADAV Avion de décollage et attérrissage vertical (VTOL).
ADC (1) US Air Force Aerospace Defense Command (no longer active); (2) air data computer.
ADF Automatic direction finding (equipment).
ADG Accessory-drive generator.
ADI Attitude/director indicator.
aeroplane (N America, airplane) Heavier-than-air aircraft with propulsion and a wing that does not rotate in order to generate lift.
AEW Airborne early warning.
AFB Air Force Base (USA).
AFCS Automatic flight control system.
afterburning Temporarily augmenting the thrust of a turbofan or turbojet by burning additional fuel in the jetpipe.
AGREE Advisory Group on Reliability in Electronic Equipment.
Ah Ampère-hours.
AHRS Attitude/heading reference system.
AIDS Airborne integrated data system.
aircraft All man-made vehicles for off-surface navigation within the atmosphere, including helicopters and balloons.
airstair Retractable stairway built into aircraft.
AM Amplitude modulation.
anhedral Downward slope of wing seen from front, in direction from root to tip.
AP Ammonium perchlorate.
APFD Autopilot flight director.
aphelion The point in a solar (Sun-centred) orbit furthest from the Sun.
apogee The point in an Earth-centred orbit furthest from the Earth.
approach noise Measured 1 nm from downwind end of runway with aircraft passing overhead at 112·6 m (370 ft).
APS Aircraft prepared for service; a fully equipped weight.
APU Auxiliary power unit (part of aircraft).
ARINC Aeronautical Radio Inc, US company whose electronic box sizes (racking sizes) are the international standard.
ASE Automatic stabilisation equipment.
ASI Airspeed indicator.
ASIR Airspeed indicator reading.
ASM Air-to-surface missile.
aspect ratio Measure of wing (or other aerofoil) slenderness seen in plan view, usually defined as the square of the span divided by area.
ASV (1) Air-to-surface-vessel; (2) Anti-surface-vessel.
ASW Anti-submarine warfare.
ATC Air traffic control.
ATR Airline transport radio, series of ARINC standard box sizes.
attack, angle of Angle at which airstream meets aerofoil (angle between mean chord and free-stream direction). Not to be confused with angle of incidence (which see).
augmented Boosted by afterburning.
autogyro Rotary-wing aircraft propelled by a propeller (or other thrusting device) and lifted by a freely running autorotating rotor.
AUW All-up weight (term meaning total weight of aircraft under defined conditions, or at specific time during flight). Not to be confused with MTOGW (which see).
avionics Aviation electronics, such as communications radio, radars, navigation systems and computers.
AWACS Airborne warning and control system (aircraft).

bar Non-SI unit of pressure adopted by this yearbook pending wider acceptance of Pa. 1 bar = 10^5 Pa, and ISA pressure at S/L is 1,013·2 mb, or just over 1 bar.
bare weight Undefined term meaning unequipped empty weight.
basic operating weight MTOGW minus payload (thus, including crew, fuel and oil, bar stocks, cutlery etc).
BCAR British Civil Airworthiness Requirements.
Beta mode Propeller operating regime in which pilot has direct control of pitch.
BFO Beat-frequency oscillator.
BITE Built-in test equipment.
bladder tank Fuel (or other fluid) tank of flexible material.
bleed air Hot high-pressure air extracted from gas-turbine engine compressor or combustor and taken through valves and pipes to perform useful work such as driving machinery or anti-icing by heating surfaces.
blown flap Flap across which bleed air is discharged at high (often supersonic) speed to prevent flow-breakaway.
BOW Basic operating weight.
BPR Bypass ratio.

BTU Non-SI unit of energy (British Thermal Unit) = 0·9478 J.
bus Busbar, main terminal in electrical system to which battery or generator power is supplied.
bypass ratio Airflow through fan duct (not passing through core) divided by airflow through core.

CAA Civil Aviation Administration (UK).
CAB Civil Aeronautics Board (USA).
CAB Pt 298 Sets the commercial standards for non-certificated carriers, mainly commuter airlines.
cabin altitude Height above S/L at which ambient pressure is same as inside cabin.
CAM Cockpit-angle measure (crew field of view).
canards Foreplanes, fixed or controllable aerodynamic surfaces ahead of CG.
CAR Civil Airworthiness Regulations.
CAS Calibrated airspeed, unusual measure in certain supersonic aircraft equipped with ASI calibrated to allow for air compressibility according to ISA S/L.
CBR California bearing ratio, measure of ability of airfield surface (paved or not) to support aircraft.
CCV Control configured vehicle.
CEAM Centre d'Expériences Aériennes Militaires.
CEAT Centre d'Essais Aéronautiques de Toulouse.
CEP Circular error probability (50/50 chance of hit being inside or outside) in bombing, missile attack or gunnery.
CEV Centre d'Essais en Vol.
CFRP Carbonfibre-reinforced plastics.
CG Centre of gravity.
chaff Thin slivers of radar-reflective material cut to length appropriate to wavelengths of hostile radars and scattered in clouds to protect friendly aircraft.
chord Distance from leading-edge to trailing-edge measured parallel to longitudinal axis.
clean In flight configuration with landing gear, flaps, slats etc retracted.
'clean' Without any optional external stores.
c/n Construction (or constructor's) number.
composite material Made of two constituents, such as filaments or short whiskers plus adhesive.
CONUS Continental USA (ie, excluding Hawaii, etc).
core Gas generator portion of turbofan comprising compressor(s), combustion chamber and turbine(s).
CRT Cathode-ray tube.
CSAS Command and stability augmentation system (part of AFCS).
CSD Constant-speed drive (output shaft speed held steady, no matter how input may vary).

daN Decanewtons (Newtons force × 10).
dB Decibel.
DC Direct current.
derated Engine restricted to power less than potential maximum (usually such engine is flat rated).
design weight Different authorities have different definitions; weight chosen as typical of mission but usually much less than MTOGW.
DF Direction finder, or direction finding.
dibber bomb Designed to cause maximum damage to concrete runways.
dihedral Upward slope of wing seen from front, in direction from root to tip.
DINS Digital inertial navigation system.
disposable load Sum of masses that can be loaded or unloaded, including payload, crew, usable fuel etc; MTOGW minus OWE.
DME Distance-measuring equipment; gives slant distance to a beacon directly ahead.
dog-tooth A step in the leading-edge of a plane resulting from an increase in chord. (See also saw-tooth.)
Doppler Short for Doppler radar—radar using fact that received frequency is a function of relative velocity between transmitter or reflecting surface and receiver.
double-slotted flap One having an auxiliary aerofoil ahead of main surface to increase maximum lift.
dP Maximum design differential pressure between pressurised cabin and ambient (outside atmosphere).
drone Pilotless aircraft, usually winged, following preset programme of manoeuvres.

EAA Experimental Aircraft Association (divided into local branches called Chapters).
EAS Equivalent airspeed, RAS minus correction for compressibility.
ECCM Electronic counter-countermeasures.
ECM Electronic countermeasures.
ehp Equivalent horsepower, measure of propulsive power of turboprop made up of shp plus addition due to residual thrust from jet.
ekW Equivalent kilowatts, SI measure of propulsive power of turboprop (see ehp).
elevon Wing trailing-edge control surface combining functions of aileron and elevator.
ELT Emergency locator transmitter, to help rescuers home on to a disabled or crashed aircraft.

EPA Environmental Protection Agency.
EPNdB Effective perceived noise decibel, SI unit of EPNL.
EPNL Effective perceived noise level, measure of noise effect on humans which takes account of sound intensity, frequency, character and duration, and response of human ear.
EPU Emergency power unit (part of aircraft, not used for propulsion).
ERP Effective radiated power.
ESA European Space Agency.
ESM (1) Electronic surveillance (or support) measures; (2) Electronic signal monitoring.
EVA Extra-vehicular activity, ie outside spacecraft.

FAA Federal Aviation Administration.
factored Multiplied by an agreed number to take account of extreme adverse conditions, errors, design deficiencies or other inaccuracies.
FAI Fédération Aéronautique Internationale.
fail-operational System which continues to function after any single fault has occurred.
fail-safe Structure or system which survives failure (in case of system, may no longer function normally).
FAR Federal Aviation Regulations.
FAR Pt 23 Defines the airworthiness of private and air-taxi aeroplanes of 5,670 kg (12,500 lb) MTOGW and below.
FAR Pt 25 Defines the airworthiness of public transport aeroplanes exceeding 5,670 kg (12,500 lb) MTOGW.
FBW Fly by wire (which see).
FDS Flight director system.
feathering Setting propeller or similar blades at pitch aligned with slipstream, to give resultant torque (not tending to turn shaft) and thus minimum drag.
FEBA Forward edge of battle area.
fence A chordwise projection on the surface of a wing, used to modify the distribution of pressure.
fenestron Helicopter tail rotor with many slender blades rotating in short duct.
ferry range Extreme safe range with zero payload.
FFAR Folding-fin (or free-flight) aircraft rocket.
FFVV Fédération Française de Vol à Voile (French gliding authority).
field length Measure of distance needed to land and/or take off; many different measures for particular purposes, each precisely defined.
flaperon Wing trailing-edge surface combining functions of flap and aileron.
flat-four Engine having four horizontally opposed cylinders; thus, flat-twin, flat-six etc.
flat rated Propulsion engine capable of giving full thrust or power for take-off up to high airfield height and/or high ambient temperature (thus, probably derated at S/L).
FLIR Forward-looking infra-red.
fly by wire Flight control system with electrical signalling (ie, without mechanical interconnection between cockpit flying controls and control surfaces).
FM Frequency modulation.
footprint A precisely delineated boundary on the surface, inside which the perceived noise of an aircraft exceeds a specified level during take-off and/or landing.
Fowler flap Moves initially aft to increase wing area and then also deflects down to increase drag.
free turbine Turbine mechanically independent of engine upstream, other than being connected by rotating bearings and the gas stream, and thus able to run at its own speed.
Frise aileron Most common manual aileron, with leading-edge that projects below wing to increase drag when aileron is raised.
FY Fiscal year (1 July to 30 June in US government affairs).

g Acceleration due to mean Earth gravity, ie of a body in free fall.
gallons Non-SI measure; 1 Imp gal (UK) = 4·546 litres, 1 US gal = 3·785 litres.
GCI Ground-controlled interception.
geostationary Of an Earth satellite, rotating with the Earth and thus always overhead the same point. Corresponds to altitude above Earth's surface of about 35,800 km (22,245 miles).
geostationary orbit An Earth-centred orbit at a height above the Earth's surface of about 35,800 km (22,245 miles) and lying approximately in the plane of the equator. A satellite in such an orbit travelling eastwards will remain over the same point, rotating precisely with the Earth.
geosynchronous See geostationary.
GfK Glassfibre-reinforced plastics (German).
glide ratio Of a sailplane, distance travelled along track divided by height lost in still air.
glove In a swing-wing aeroplane with pivots well out from the centreline it is geometrically impossible to have one-piece pivoted wings because at zero sweep the inner ends would overlap; the answer is fixed inner leading portions called gloves.

THE E-2C. IT BRINGS 3 MILLION CUBIC MILES OF HIDING SPACE INTO FOCUS.

Imagine the congested air corridor between the great cities of the world. Hundreds of aircraft. Scores of ships. An army of vehicles. And such false target reflections as stationary land return, noise and clutter. Add electronic countermeasures and you have a routine surveillance environment for the E-2C Hawkeye.

Because of its new APS-125 Advanced Radar Processing System, the E-2C can automatically track hundreds of targets against any background, land or sea. Its detection range of up to 250 miles and from the surface to 100,000 feet extends warning and reaction time to 30 minutes. Time for the E-2C to direct many fighters simultaneously to the most efficient intercept postion.

The E-2C can also monitor ships at sea down to patrol boat size and vehicles on the ground. And with its passive detection system, the E-2C can spot and identify enemy radar emitters to the maximum line-of-sight ranges. Clearly, with the E-2C, there is no place to hide.

Grumman Aerospace Corp., Bethpage, Long Island, N.Y. 11714.

IT TAKES THE BEST TO STAY THE BEST. GRUMMAN

GPU Ground power unit (not part of aircraft).
GPWS Ground-proximity warning system.
green aircraft Aircraft flyable but lacking furnishing and customer's choice of avionics.
gross wing area See wing area.
GRP Glassfibre-reinforced plastics.
GS Glideslope, of ILS.
GSE Ground-support equipment (such as special test gear, steps and servicing platforms).
GTS Gas-turbine starter (ie starter is miniature gas turbine).
gunship Helicopter designed for battlefield attack, normally with slim body carrying pilot and weapon operator only.

h Hour(s).
hardened Protected as far as possible against nuclear explosion.
hardpoint Reinforced part of aircraft to which external load can be attached, eg weapon or tank pylon.
helicopter Rotary-wing aircraft both lifted and propelled by one or more power-driven rotors turning about substantially vertical axes.
HF High frequency.
'hot and high' Adverse combination of airfield height and high ambient temperature, which lengthens required TOD.
hovering ceiling Ceiling of helicopter (corresponding to air density at which maximum rate of climb is zero), either IGE or OGE.
HP High pressure.
hp Horsepower.
HSI Horizontal situation indicator.
HUD Head-up display (bright numbers and symbols projected on pilot's windscreen and focussed on infinity so that pilot can simultaneously read display and look ahead).
HVAR High-velocity aircraft rocket.

IAS Indicated airspeed, ASIR corrected for instrument error.
IATA International Air Transport Association.
ICAO International Civil Aviation Organization.
IFF Identification friend or foe.
IFR Instrument flight rules (ie, not VFR).
IGE In ground effect: helicopter performance with theoretical flat horizontal surface just below the wheels.
ILS Instrument landing system.
IMC Instrument meteorological conditions, basically IFR.
IMK Increased manoeuvrability kit.
INAS Integrated nav/attack system.
incidence Strictly, the angle at which the wing is set in relation to the fore/aft axis. Wrongly used to mean angle of attack (which see).
inertial navigation Measuring all accelerations imparted to a vehicle and, by integrating these with respect to time, calculating speed at every instant (in all three planes) and by integrating a second time calculating total change of position in relation to starting point.
INS Inertial navigation system.
integral construction Machined from solid instead of assembled from separate parts.
integral tank Fuel or other liquid tank formed by sealing part of structure.
intercom Wired telephone system for communication within aircraft.
inverter Electric or electronic device for inverting (reversing polarity of) alternate waves in AC power to produce DC.
IP Intermediate pressure.
IR Infra-red.
IRAN Inspect and repair as necessary.
IRLS Infra-red linescan (builds TV-type picture showing cool regions as dark and hot regions as light).
ISA International Standard Atmosphere.
ISIS (1 Boeing Vertol) Integral spar inspection system; (2 Ferranti) integrated strike and interception sight.
ITE Involute throat and exit (rocket nozzle).

J Joules, SI unit of energy.
JASDF Japan Air Self-Defence Force.
JATO Jet-assisted take-off (actually means rocket-assisted).
JCAB Japan Civil Airworthiness Board.
JDA Japan Defence Agency.
JGSDF Japan Ground Self-Defence Force.
JMSDF Japan Maritime Self-Defence Force.

Kevlar A filament-wound high-strength composite material.
km/h Kilometres per hour.
kN Kilonewtons (the Newton is the SI unit of force; 1 lbf = 4·448 N).
knot 1 nm per hour.
Krüger flap Hinges down and then forward from below the leading edge.
Küchemann tip Wing tip of curving planform intended to minimise drag at high subsonic speed.
kVA Kilovolt-ampères.

kW Kilowatt, SI measure of all forms of power (not just electrical).

LABS Low-altitude bombing system.
LARC Low-altitude ride control.
LBA Luftfahrtbundesamt (Federal German civil aviation authority).
lbf Pounds of thrust.
LCN Load classification number, measure of 'flotation' of aircraft landing gear linking aircraft weight, weight distribution, tyre numbers, pressures and disposition.
LED Light-emitting diode.
LITVC Liquid-injection thrust vector control.
LLTV Low-light TV (thus, LLLTV, low-light-level).
Load factor (1) percentage of max payload; (2) stress limit.
LOC Localiser.
localiser Element giving steering guidance in ILS.
loiter Flight for maximum endurance, such as supersonic fighter on patrol.
longerons Principal fore-and-aft structural members (eg, in fuselage).
Loran (Long Range Navigation) Family of hyperbolic navaids based on ground radio emissions.
lox Liquid oxygen.
LP Low pressure.
LRMTS Laser ranger and marked-target seeker.

m Metre(s), SI unit of length.
M or Mach number· The ratio of the speed of a body to the speed of sound (1,116 ft; 340 m/s in air at 15°C) under the same ambient conditions.
MAC US Air Force Military Airlift Command.
MAD Magnetic anomaly detector.
Madar Maintenance analysis, detection and recording.
Madge Microwave aircraft digital guidance equipment.
marker, marker beacon Ground beacon giving position guidance in ILS.
MASTACS Manoeuvrability augmentation system for tactical air combat simulation.
mb Millibars, bar × 10⁻³.
MBR Marker beacon receiver.
MEPU Monofuel emergency power unit.
MF Medium frequency.
mg Milligrammes, grammes × 10⁻³.
MLS Microwave landing system.
MLW Maximum landing weight.
mm Millimetres, metres × 10⁻³.
MMH Monomethyl hydrazine.
MMO Maximum permitted operating Mach number.
MNPS Minimum navigation performance specification.
monocoque Structure with strength in outer shell, devoid of internal bracing.
MPA Man-powered aircraft.
mph Miles per hour.
MRW Maximum ramp weight.
MTBF Mean time between failures.
MTOGW Maximum take-off gross weight (MRW minus taxi/run-up fuel).
MZFW Maximum zero-fuel weight.

NACA US National Advisory Committee for Aeronautics (now NASA).
Nadge NATO air defence ground environment.
NASA National Aeronautics and Space Administration.
NASC US Naval Air Systems Command (also several other aerospace meanings).
NATC US Naval Air Training Command or Test Center (also several other aerospace meanings).
NBAA US National Business Aircraft Association.
NH₄ClO₄ Ammonium perchlorate.
nm Nautical mile, 1·8532 km, 1·15152 miles.
NOAA US National Oceanic and Atmospheric Administration.
NOE Nap-of-the-Earth (low flying in military aircraft, using natural cover of hills, trees, etc).
NOGS Night observation gunship.
NOS Night observation surveillance.
Ns Newton-second (1 N thrust applied for 1 second).

OBS Omni-bearing selector.
OCU Operational Conversion Unit.
OGE Out of ground effect: helicopter hovering far above nearest surface.
Omega Long-range hyperbolic navaid.
OMI Omni-bearing magnetic indicator.
omni Generalised word meaning equal in all directions (as in omni-range, omni-flash beacon).
OTPI On-top position indicator (indicates overhead of submarine in ASW).
OUV Oskar-Ursinus-Vereinigung (West German chapter of EAA).
OWE Operating weight empty, MTOGW minus payload, usable fuel and oil and other consumables.

PA system Public-address.
pallet (1) for freight, rigid platform for handling by fork-lift or conveyor; (2) for missile, mounting and electronics box outside aircraft.

payload Disposable load generating revenue (passengers, cargo, mail and other paid items); in military aircraft loosely used to mean total load carried of weapons, cargo or other mission equipment.
PD radar Pulse-Doppler.
penaids Penetration aids, such as jammers, chaff or decoys to help aircraft fly safely through hostile airspace.
perigee The point in an Earth-centred orbit nearest to the Earth.
perihelion The point in a solar (Sun-centred) orbit closest to the Sun.
PFA Popular Flying Association (UK).
PHI Position and heading (or homing) indicator.
plane A lifting surface (eg, wing, tailplane).
pneumatic de-icing Covered with flexible surfaces alternately pumped up and deflated to throw off ice.
port Left side, looking forward.
power loading Aircraft weight (usually MTOGW) divided by total propulsive power or thrust at T-O.
pressure fuelling Fuelling via a leakproof connection through which fuel passes at high rate under pressure.
pressure ratio In gas-turbine engine, compressor delivery pressure divided by ambient pressure (in supersonic aircraft, divided by ram pressure downstream of inlet).
primary flight controls Those used to control trajectory of aircraft (thus, not trimmers, tabs, flaps, slats, airbrakes or lift dumpers etc).
pulse-Doppler Radar sending out pulses and measuring frequency-shift of returns from target(s).
pylon Structure linking aircraft to external load (engine nacelle, drop-tank, bomb etc). Also used in conventional sense in pylon racing.

radius In terms of performance, the distance an aircraft can fly from base and return without intermediate landing.
RAE Royal Aircraft Establishment.
RAI Registro Aeronautico Italiano.
ram pressure Increased pressure in forward-facing aircraft inlet, generated by converting (relative) kinetic energy to pressure.
ramp weight Maximum weight at start of flight (MTOGW plus taxi/run-up fuel).
range Too many definitions to list, but essentially the distance an aircraft can fly (or is permitted to fly) with specified load and usually whilst making allowance for specified additional manoeuvres (diversions, stand-off, go-around etc).
RAS Rectified airspeed, IAS corrected for position error.
RATT Radio teletype.
redundant Provided with spare capacity or data channels and thus made to survive failures.
refanned Gas-turbine engine fitted with new fan of higher BPR.
rigid rotor Helicopter rotor without articulating hinges (eg, flapping hinge, drag hinge) but with pitch variation.
RLD Rijksluchtvaartdienst, Netherlands civil aviation department.
RMI Radio magnetic indicator (compass).
R/Nav Area navigation, navaid covering whole of local area instead of just crowded airways.
Rotor-kite Rotary-wing aircraft with no internal power, lifted by a freely running autorotating rotor and towed by an external vehicle.
roving Multiple strands of fibre, as in a rope (but usually not twisted).
RPV Remotely piloted vehicle (pilot in other aircraft or on ground).
RSA Réseau du Sport de l'Air.
RVR Runway visual range.

s Second(s).
SAC US Air Force Strategic Air Command.
safe-life A term denoting that a component has proved by testing that it can be expected to continue to function safely for a precisely defined period before replacement.
salmon (French saumon) Streamlined fairings, usually at wingtip of sailplane, serving same function as endplate and acting also as tip-skid.
SAR Search and rescue.
SATS (1) Small airfield for tactical support; (2) Small Arms Target System.
saw-tooth Same as dog-tooth.
second-source Production of identical item by second factory or company.
semi-active Homing on to radiation reflected from target illuminated by radar or laser energy beamed from elsewhere.
service ceiling Usually height equivalent to air density at which maximum attainable rate of climb is 100 ft/min.
servo A device which acts as a relay, usually augmenting the pilot's efforts to move a control surface or the like.
sfc Specific fuel consumption.
SGAC Secrétariat Général à l'Aviation Civile.
shaft Connection between gas turbine and compressor or other driven unit. Two-shaft engine has second shaft, rotating at different speed, surrounding the first (thus, HP surrounds inner LP or fan shaft).
Shoran Short range navigation (radio).

Range of Activity in electronic defence field:

IFF System and equipment
Interrogator
Transponder
Decoder

Encryption System
Secure Voice Equipment
Secure Telegraph Equipment
Secure Data Equipment

Microwave Tubes
Magnetron
Klystron

Travelling wave tube

UHF Emergency transceiver

SP 889/I01

ITALTEL
SOCIETA' ITALIANA TELECOMUNICAZIONI
20149 Milan (Italy) - 12, Piazzale Zavattari - phone (+ 39.2) 4388.1

shp Shaft horsepower, measure of power transmitted via rotating shaft.

sideline noise EPNdB measure of aircraft landing and taking off, at point 0·25 nm (2- or 3-engined) or 0·35 nm (4-engined) from runway centreline.

SIF Selective identification facility.

signature Characteristic 'fingerprint' of all electromagnetic radiation (radar, IR etc).

single-shaft Gas turbine in which all compressors and turbines are on common shaft rotating together.

S/L Sea level.

SLAR Side-looking airborne radar.

snap-down Air-to-air interception of low-flying aircraft by AAM fired from fighter at a higher altitude.

soft target Not armoured or hardened.

specific fuel consumption Rate at which fuel is consumed divided by power or thrust developed, and thus a measure of engine efficiency. For jet engines (air-breathing, ie not rockets) unit is mg/Ns, milligrams per Newton-second; for shaft engines unit is μg/J, micrograms (millionths of a gram) per Joule (SI unit of work or energy).

specific impulse Measure of rocket engine efficiency; thrust divided by rate of fuel/oxidant consumption per second, the units for mass and force being the same so that the answer is expressed in seconds.

spool One complete axial compressor rotor; thus a two-shaft engine may have a fan plus an LP spool.

SSB Single-sideband (radio).

SSR Secondary surveillance radar.

st Static thrust.

stabiliser Fin (thus, horizontal stabiliser = tailplane).

stall strips Sharp-edged strips on wing leading-edge to induce stall at that point.

stalling speed TAS at which aircraft stalls at 1g, ie wing lift suddenly collapses.

standard day ISA temperature and pressure.

starboard Right side, looking forward.

static inverter Solid-state electronic inverter (ie, not rotary machine).

stick-pusher Stall-protection device that forces pilot's control column forward as stalling angle of attack is neared.

stick-shaker Stall-warning device that noisily shakes pilot's control column as stalling angle of attack is neared.

STOL Short take-off and landing. (Several definitions, stipulating allowable horizontal distance to clear screen height of 35 or 50 ft or various SI measures).

store Object carried as part of payload on external attachment (eg bomb, drop-tank).

strobe light High-intensity flashing beacon.

substrate The underlying layer on which something (such as a solar cell or integrated circuit) is made.

supercritical wing Wing of relatively deep, flat-topped profile generating lift right across upper surface instead of concentrated close behind leading edge.

synchronous See geostationary.

synchronous satellite Geostationary.

t Tonne, 1 Megagram, 1,000 kg.

tabbed flap Fitted with narrow-chord tab along entire trailing-edge which deflects to greater angle than main surface.

tabs Small auxiliary surfaces hinged to trailing-edge of control surfaces for purposes of trimming, reducing hinge moment (force needed to operate main surface) or in other way assisting pilot.

TAC US Air Force Tactical Air Command.

Tacan Tactical air navigation, simple military navaid using ground beacons.

taileron Left and right tailplanes used as primary control surfaces in both pitch and roll.

tailplane Main horizontal tail surface, originally fixed and carrying hinged elevator(s) but today often a single 'slab' serving as control surface.

TANS Tactical air navigation system (Doppler-based computer, control and display unit).

TAS True airspeed, EAS corrected for density (often very large factor) appropriate to aircraft height.

TBO Time between overhauls.

TFR Terrain-following radar (for low-level attack).

T-O Take-off.

T-O noise EPNdB measure of aircraft taking off, at point directly under flight path 3·5 nm from brakes-release (regardless of altitude).

TOD Take-off distance.

TOGW Take-off gross weight (not necessarily MTOGW).

ton Imperial (long).ton = 1·016 t (Mg), US (short) ton = 0·9072 t.

track Distance between centres of contact areas of main landing wheels measured left/right across aircraft (with bogies, distance between centres of contact areas of each bogie).

transceiver Radio transmitter/receiver.

transfer orbit Orbit, or part of an orbit, linking two others at different heights around the same planetary body.

transponder Radio transmitter triggered automatically by a particular received signal.

TRU Transformer/rectifier unit.

TSO Technical Standard Order (FAA).

turbofan Gas turbine jet engine generating most thrust by a large-diameter cowled fan, with small part added by jet from core.

turbojet Simplest form of gas turbine comprising compressor, combustion chamber, turbine and propulsive nozzle.

turboprop Gas turbine in which as much energy as possible is taken from gas jet and used to drive reduction gearbox and propeller.

turboshaft Gas turbine in which as much energy as possible is taken from gas jet and used to drive high-speed shaft (which in turn drives external load such as helicopter gearbox).

TVC Thrust vector control (rocket).

TWT Travelling-wave tube.

tyre sizes In simplest form, first figure is rim diameter (in or mm) and second is rim width (in or mm). In more correct three-unit form, first figure is outside diameter, second is max width and third is wheel diameter.

UHF Ultra-high frequency.

unfactored Performance level expected of average pilot, in average aircraft, without additional safety factors.

usable fuel Total mass of fuel consumable in flight, usually 95-98 per cent of system capacity.

variable-geometry Capable of grossly changing shape in flight, especially by varying sweep of wings.

VD Maximum permitted diving speed

vernier Small thruster, usually a rocket, for final precise adjustment of a vehicle's trajectory and velocity.

VFR Visual flight rules.

VHF Very high frequency.

VLF Very low frequency.

VMO Maximum permitted operating flight speed (IAS, EAS or CAS must be specified).

VNE Never-exceed speed (aerodynamic or structural limit).

VOR VHF omni-directional range, ground navaid usable only when flying along predetermined airways.

VTOL Vertical take-off and landing.

washout Inbuilt wing twist reducing angle of incidence towards the tip.

wheelbase Minimum distance from nosewheel or tailwheel (centre of contact area) to line joining main wheels (centres of contact areas).

wing area Total projected area of clean wing (no flaps, slats etc) including all control surfaces and area of fuselage bounded by leading- and trailing-edges projected to centreline (inapplicable to slender-delta aircraft with extremely large leading-edge sweep angle). Sometimes called gross wing area; net area excludes projected areas of fuselage, nacelles, etc.

wing loading Aircraft weight (usually MTOGW) divided by wing area.

winglet Small auxiliary aerofoil, usually sharply upturned and often swept back, at tip of wing.

wire guidance Guidance of missile or RPV by signals transmitted through fine wire(s) linking it with operator.

zero-fuel weight MTOGW minus usable fuel and other consumables, in most aircraft imposing severest stress on wing.

zero/zero seat Ejection seat designed for use even at zero speed on ground.

ZFW Zero-fuel weight.

μg Microgrammes, grammes × 10^{-6}.

Jane's Aerospace Dictionary by Bill Gunston (Jane's Publishing Company, £15) provides a complete listing of current aerospace expressions with definitions.

FIRST FLIGHTS

Some first flights made during the period 1 June 1979 to 1 September 1980

June 1979

3   PZL Swidnik Kania (SP-PSA) (Poland)
12   Rutan Long-EZ (N79RA) (USA)
13   MBB/Kawasaki BK 117 (D-HBKA) (International)
13   Tô Solar One solar-powered sailplane (UK)
14   Dornier TNT testbed (D-IFNT) (Germany, Federal Republic)
15   Raisbeck (Rockwell) Sabreliner 80A Mark Five (USA)
22   British Aerospace HS 748 Srs 2B (G-BGJV) (UK)
28   Akaflieg Darmstadt D-39 sailplane (Germany, Federal Republic)

July 1979

4   Ohmert Bristol F.2B replica (N29HC) (USA)
6   Delemontez-Cauchy DC-1 (France)
9   Sheppard S-2 (N39S) (USA)
10   Panavia Tornado GR.Mk 1 (ZA319), first UK production (International)
14   Canadair CL-600 Challenger (C-GCGT-X), third pre-production (Canada)
17   Taylor Bird (N303TB) (USA)
20   Chagnes Microstar (F-PYFP) (France)
21   Bell Model 214ST (USA)
23   PZL Mielec M-20 Mewa (SP-DKC) (Poland)
24   Bell XV-15 (N703NA), first conversion to aeroplane mode (USA)
24   NASA/Boeing KC-135A with winglets (55-3129) (USA)
27   Panavia Tornado (43 + 01), first German production (International)
27   Pottier P.50TR Bouvreuil (HB-YBF) (France/Switzerland)
27   Rockwell/NASA/USAF HiMAT RPV, first free flight (USA)

August 1979

2   Schweizer SGS 1-36 sailplane (USA)
10   MBB/Kawasaki BK 117 (JQ0003), first Japanese prototype (International)
13   Cessna Model 335, first production (USA)
20   BGA Supermunk (G-BBNA) (UK)
21   Van's RV-4 (N14RV) (USA)
22   MBB HFB 320 Hansa Jet ECM (D-CANO), first of new batch of four (Germany, Federal Republic)

September 1979

10   SZD-45A Ogar prototype motor glider (SP-0001), after fitting winglets (Poland)
14   Cases Libel-Lula sailplane (Spain)
17   EFF Prometheus 12 motor glider (Switzerland)
21   Canadair CL-600 Challenger, first production (Canada)
26   Aérospatiale Fouga 90 (F-WZJB), re-engined with Astafan IVGs (France)
26   Westland Sea King HC.Mk 4 (ZA290) (UK)
27   Aérospatiale AS 355E Ecureuil 2/Twinstar (F-WZLA) (France)

October 1979

4   Slingsby T.61F Venture T.Mk 3 motor glider, first production (UK)
14   Turner TSW (G-BEBO) (UK)
18   McDonnell Douglas DC-9 Super 80 (N980DC) (USA)

19   Simůnek/Kamarýt SK-1 Trempík (OK-006) (Czechoslovakia)
21   Sawano S25X II Tandem Smoothie (Japan)
25   Gulfstream American GAC 159-C Commuter (N5400C) (USA)
27   Panavia Tornado F.Mk 2 (ZA254) (International)
31   PZL-104 Wilga 35H floatplane (SP-WBK) (Poland)
31   Hughes YAH-64, first Phase 2 prototype (fourth YAH-64, third to fly) (USA)

November 1979

8   CASA C-101 Aviojet, first production (Spain)
14   Aérospatiale AS 355E Ecureuil 2/Twinstar, second prototype (France)
15   Gates Learjet 55 (N552GL), second prototype (USA)
16   PZL Swidnik W-3 Sokól (Poland)
16   Lockheed L-1011-500, first production TriStar with extended wings, active ailerons, etc (USA)
25   Nippi-Pilatus B4-PC11AF sailplane, first Japanese-built (Japan)
27   Boeing 707-700 (N707QT), CFM56 engine testbed (USA)
28   FVA Aachen FVA-20 sailplane (D-6020) (Germany, Federal Republic)

December 1979

2   Gulfstream American Gulfstream III (N300GA) (USA)
3   Lockheed Hercules C.Mk 3 (XV223) (USA)
6   McDonnell Douglas DC-9 Super 80 (N1002G), second aircraft (USA)
12   General Dynamics F-16B (301), first for Norway, Fokker-built (USA/Netherlands)
12   Sikorsky SH-60B Seahawk (161169) (USA)
12   Sunderland MOBA-2C sailplane (Australia)
14   Edgley EA-7 Optica (G-BGMW) (UK)
17   General Avia Pegaso (I-GEAA), first production (Italy)
18   General Dynamics F-16B, first for Denmark, SABCA-built (USA/Belgium)
18   Slingsby T.65C Sport Vega sailplane (UK)
21   NASA/Ames AD-1 (N805NA) (USA)
22   Aérospatiale TB 30 Epsilon (F-WZVO) (France)
24   Beechcraft King Air A90, RB.318 engine testbed (Italy/USA)
24   Gulfstream American Gulfstream III (N901GA), second prototype (USA)
29   Valmet L-70 Vinka (VN-1), first production (Finland)

February 1980

11   Sikorsky SH-60B Seahawk (161170), second prototype (USA)
29   McDonnell Douglas DC-9 Super 80 (N1002W), third aircraft (USA)

March 1980

2   Piel C.P.751 Beryl (F-PYHM) (France)
3   Canadair/Dornier AN/USD-502 (CL-289) surveillance drone (International)
4   Dornier Do 128-6 Turbo-Skyservant, first flight with PT6A-110 engines (Germany, Federal Republic)
4   British Aerospace HS 748, first with Dart hush kit (UK)

4   Vought TA-7H Corsair II (161218) (USA)
11   Aérospatiale AS 355E Ecureuil 2/Twinstar, first production (France)
14   Panavia Tornado, first production strike aircraft (ie, without dual controls) (International)
14   Grob G-109 motor glider (D-KBGF) (Germany, Federal Republic)
16   Hughes YAH-64, third Phase 2 prototype (USA)
23   Boeing Vertol Chinook HC.Mk 1 (ZA670), first for RAF (USA)
28   British Aerospace Jetstream 31 (G-JSSD), development aircraft (UK)
28   Rolladen-Schneider LS4 sailplane (D-6680) (Germany, Federal Republic)

April 1980

6   Glaser-Dirks DG-200/17C sailplane (Germany, Federal Republic)
9   Akaflieg Braunschweig SB-12 sailplane (D-1125) (Germany, Federal Republic)
30   Dassault Mystère-Falcon 20H (F-WZAH) (France)
30   Glaser-Dirks DG-202 sailplane (D-3796) (Germany, Federal Republic)

May 1980

2   Cessna Citation III, second prototype (USA)
3   Schempp-Hirth Ventus b sailplane (D-3551) (Germany, Federal Republic)
10   Glasflügel 304 sailplane (D-9304) (Germany, Federal Republic)
12   Dassault Mirage 2000, fourth prototype (France)
13   Aeritalia G222T, first with Tyne engines (Italy)
30   Aermacchi M.B.339K Veltro 2 (I-BITE) (Italy)

June 1980

4   McDonnell Douglas F-15J, first (US-built) aircraft for Japan (USA)
6   Aérospatiale C.22 target drone (France)
20   Beechcraft Commuter C99 (N4199C) (USA)
23   Mudry CAP 21 (F-WZCH) (France)
24   Microturbo Microjet 200 (F-WZJF) (France)
24   Grumman EA-6B Prowler, ICAP-2 version (USA)

July 1980

12   Aérospatiale Epsilon, second prototype (France)
12   McDonnell Douglas KC-10 Extender (79-0433) (USA)
16   British Aerospace Nimrod AEW.Mk 3 (XZ286) (UK)
16   Wallis WA-122/R-R (G-BGGW) (UK)
18   Panavia Tornado F.Mk 2 (ZA267), second prototype (International)
23   Aérospatiale HH-65A Dolphin (AS 366G) (France)

August 1980

2   Pilatus Britten-Norman BN-2T Turbine Islander (G-BPBN) (UK)
11   Gates Learjet 50 series, first production (USA)
14   Fournier RF-6B (89·5 kW; 120 hp Avco Lycoming O-235-L2A engine) (France)
16   EMBRAER EMB-312/YT-27 (1300) (Brazil)
19   Boeing Vertol Model 234 Commercial Chinook (USA)

British Aerospace Jetstream 31 development aircraft, which made its first flight on 28 March 1980

[79]

OFFICIAL RECORDS
Corrected to September 1980

ABSOLUTE WORLD RECORDS

Seven records are classed as Absolute World Records for aeroplanes by the Fédération Aéronautique Internationale, as follows:

Distance in a straight line (USA)
Major Clyde P. Evely, USAF, in a Boeing B-52H Stratofortress, on 10-11 January 1962, from Okinawa to Madrid, Spain. 10,890·27 nm (20,168·78 km; 12,532·3 miles).

Distance in a closed circuit (USA)
Captain William M. Stevenson, USAF, in a Boeing B-52H Stratofortress, on 6-7 June 1962. Seymour Johnson AFB-Bermuda-Sondrestrom (Greenland)-Anchorage (Alaska)-March AFB-Key West-Seymour Johnson AFB. 9,851·54 nm (18,245·05 km; 11,337 miles).

Height (USSR)
Alexander Fedotov in an E-266M (MiG-25) on 31 August 1977. 37,650 m (123,523 ft).

Height in sustained horizontal flight (USA)
Captain Robert C. Helt and Major Larry A. Elliott (USAF) in a Lockheed SR-71A on 28 July 1976 at Beale AFB, California. 25,929·031 m (85,069 ft).

Height, after launch from a 'mother-plane' (USA)
Major R. White, USAF, in the North American X-15A-3 on 17 July 1962, at Edwards AFB, California. 95,935·99 m (314,750 ft).

Speed in a straight line (USA)
Captain Eldon W. Joersz and Major George T. Morgan Jr (USAF) in a Lockheed SR-71A on 28 July 1976 over a 15/25 km course at Beale AFB, California. 1,905·81 knots (3,529·56 km/h; 2,193·17 mph).

Speed in a closed circuit (USA)
Major Adolphus H. Bledsoe Jr and Major John T. Fuller (USAF) in a Lockheed SR-71A on 27 July 1976, over a 1,000 km closed circuit from Beale AFB, California. 1,818·154 knots (3,367·221 km/h; 2,092·294 mph).

Seven records are classed as Absolute World Records for manned spacecraft by the Fédération Aéronautique Internationale, as follows:

Endurance in Earth orbit (USSR)
Vladimir Lyakhov and Valery Ryumin on board Soyuz 32/Salyut 6/Soyuz 34, from 25 February to 19 August 1979. 175 days 0 h 35 min 36 s.
Awaiting confirmation is a subsequent record of 185 days set by Soyuz 35/Salyut 6/Soyuz 37 cosmonauts Leonid Popov and Valery Ryumin.

Altitude (USA)
F. Borman, J. A. Lovell and W. Anders in Apollo 8, on 21-27 December 1968. 203,925 nm (377,668·9 km; 234,673 miles).

Greatest mass lifted to altitude (USA)
F. Borman, J. A. Lovell and W. Anders in Apollo 8, on 21-27 December 1968. 127,980 kg (282,147 lb).

Distance in Earth orbit (USSR)
Vladimir Lyakhov and Valery Ryumin on board Soyuz 32/Salyut 6/Soyuz 34, from 25 February to 19 August 1979. 62,857,205 nm (116,411,557 km; 72,334,783 miles).
Awaiting confirmation is the greater distance covered by Soyuz 35/Salyut 6/ Soyuz 37 cosmonauts Leonid Popov and Valery Ryumin.

Extravehicular duration (USA)
Eugene A. Cernan, from the Apollo 17 lunar module *Challenger*, on 12, 13 and 14 December 1972, during mission of 7-19 December 1972. 21 h 31 min 44 s.

Number of astronauts remaining simultaneously outside spacecraft (USA)
A. Eliseiev and E. Khrounov, from Soyuz 4 and 5, for 37 min on 14-18 January 1969. Two astronauts.

Accumulated time in spaceflight (USSR)
Valery Ryumin, on board Soyuz 25, Soyuz 32, Salyut 6 and Soyuz 34. 177 days 1 h 20 min 21 s.
Ryumin has since added a further 185 days to this total with his Soyuz 35/Salyut 6/Soyuz 37 flight (awaiting confirmation).

WORLD CLASS RECORDS

Following are details of some of the more important world class records confirmed by the FAI:

CLASS C, GROUP I (Aeroplanes with piston engines)
Distance in a straight line (USA)
Cdr Thomas D. Davies, USN, and crew of three in a Lockheed P2V-1 Neptune, on 29 September-1 October 1946, from Perth, Western Australia, to Columbus, Ohio, USA. 9,763·49 nm (18,081·99 km; 11,235·6 miles).

Distance in a closed circuit (USA)
James R. Bede in the Bede BD-2, on 7-10 November 1969, between Columbus, Ohio, and Toledo, Ohio, USA. 7,797·66 nm (14,441·26 km; 8,973·38 miles).

The Red Baron modified P-51D Mustang, with Griffon engine and contraprops, in which Steve Hinton set the new world speed record for piston-engined aircraft. It was destroyed in a non-fatal accident during the 1979 US National Air Races at Reno, where this photograph was taken (*Dustin W. Carter*)

Height (Italy)
Mario Pezzi, in a Caproni Ca 161*bis*, on 22 October 1938. 17,083 m (56,046 ft).

Speed in a straight line (USA)
Steve Hinton in a modified North American P-51D Mustang, with 2,834 kW (3,800 hp) Rolls-Royce Griffon engine, on 14 August 1979, over 3 km course at Tonopah, Nevada. 433·660 knots (803·138 km/h; 499·047 mph).

CLASS C, GROUP II (Aeroplanes with turboprop engines)
Distance in a straight line (USA)
Lt Col E. L. Allison and crew in a Lockheed HC-130H Hercules, on 20 February 1972. 7,587·99 nm (14,052·95 km; 8,732·098 miles).

Distance in a closed circuit (USA)
Cdr Philip R. Hite and crew in a Lockheed RP-3D Orion, on 4 November 1972. 5,455·46 nm (10,103·51 km; 6,278·03 miles).

Height (USA)
Donald R. Wilson in an LTV Electrosystems L450F, on 27 March 1972, at Majors Field, Greenville, Texas. 15,549 m (51,014 ft).

Speed in a straight line (USA)
Cdr Donald H. Lilienthal and crew in a Lockheed P-3C Orion, over 15/25 km course on 27 January 1971. 435·26 knots (806·10 km/h; 500·89 mph).

Speed in a closed circuit (USSR)
Ivan Sukhomlin and crew in a Tupolev Tu-114, on 9 April 1960, carrying a 25,000 kg payload over a 5,000 km circuit. 473·66 knots (877·212 km/h; 545·07 mph).

CLASS C, GROUP III (Aeroplanes with jet engines)
Distance in a straight line, distance in a closed circuit, height, speed in straight line and speed in 1,000 km closed circuit
See Absolute World Records.

Speed over a 3 km course at restricted altitude (USA)
Darryl Greenamyer in the modified Red Baron F-104RB Starfighter, on 24 October 1977, at Mud Lake, Tonopah, Nevada. 858·77 knots (1,590·45 km/h; 988·26 mph).

Speed in a 100 km closed circuit (USSR)
Alexander Fedotov in a Mikoyan E-266 (MiG-25), on 8 April 1973. 1,406·641 knots (2,605·1 km/h; 1,618·734 mph).

Speed in a 500 km closed circuit (USSR)
M. Komarov in a Mikoyan E-266 (MiG-25), on 5 October 1967, near Moscow. 1,609·88 knots (2,981·5 km/h; 1,852·62 mph).

Speed around the World (USA)
Walter J. Mullikin and crew of four, in a Boeing 747SP of Pan American, on 1-3 May 1976, from New York City, via Delhi and Tokyo, back to New York, in 1 day 22 h 0 min 50 s. 436·95 knots (809·24 km/h; 502·84 mph).

Greatest mass lifted to a height of 2,000 m (USA)
William J. Allsopp and crew in a Boeing 747-236B with Rolls-Royce RB.211 engines, at Le Moore NAS, California, on 1 November 1976. 381,108·25 kg (840,200 lb).

CLASS C.2, ALL GROUPS (Seaplanes)
Distance in a straight line (UK)
Capt D. C. T. Bennett and First Officer I. Harvey, in the Short-Mayo *Mercury*, on 6-8 October 1938, from Dundee, Scotland, to the Orange River, South Africa. 5,211·66 nm (9,652 km; 5,997·5 miles).

Height (USSR)
Georgi Buryanov and crew of two in a Beriev M-10, on 9 September 1961, over the Sea of Azov. 14,962 m (49,088 ft).

Speed in a straight line (USSR)
Nikolai Andrievsky and crew of two in a Beriev M-10, on 7 August 1961, at Joukovski-Petrovskœ, over a 15/25 km course. 492·44 knots (912 km/h; 566·69 mph).

CLASS D, GROUP I (Single-seat sailplanes)
Distance in a straight line (Germany, Federal Republic)
Hans W. Grosse in a Schleicher ASW 12, on 25 April 1972. 788·77 nm (1,460·8 km; 907·70 miles).

Height (USA)
Paul F. Bickle, in a Schweizer SGS 1-23E, on 25 February 1961, at Mojave-Lancaster, California. 14,102 m (46,266 ft).

CLASS D, GROUP II (Two-seat sailplanes)
Distance in a straight line (Australia)
Ingo Renner and Hilmer Geissler in a Caproni Vizzola Calif A-21, on 27 January 1975, from Bendigo Aerodrome to Langley Station, Australia. 523·97 nm (970·4 km; 602·98 miles).

Height (USA)
L. E. Edgar and H. E. Klieforth in a Pratt-Read sailplane, on 19 March 1952, at Bishop, California. 13,489 m (44,256 ft).

CLASS E.1 (Helicopters)
Distance in a straight line (USA)
R. G. Ferry in a Hughes OH-6A, on 6-7 April 1966, 1,923·08 nm (3,561·55 km; 2,213 miles).

Height (France)
Jean Boulet in an Aérospatiale SA 315B Lama on 21 June 1972. 12,442 m (40,820 ft).

Speed in a straight line (USSR)
Gourguen Karapetyan in a Mil A-10 (Mi-24), on 21 September 1978, over a 15/25 km course near Moscow. 198·9 knots (368·4 km/h; 228·9 mph).

Speed in a 100 km closed circuit (USSR)
Boris Galitsky and crew of five in a Mil Mi-6, on 26 August 1964, near Moscow. 183·67 knots (340·15 km/h; 211·36 mph).

CLASS E.2 (Convertiplanes)
Height (USSR)
D. Efremov and crew of two, in the Kamov Ka-22 Vintokryl, on 24 November 1961 at Bykovo. 2,588 m (8,491 ft).

Speed in a straight line (USSR)
D. Efremov and crew of five, in the Kamov Ka-22 Vintokryl, on 7 October 1961, at Joukovski-Petrovskœ, over a 15/25 km course. 192·39 knots (356·3 km/h; 221·4 mph).

Speed in a 100 km closed circuit (New Zealand)
Sqd Ldr W. R. Gellatly and J. G. P. Morton, in the Fairey Rotodyne, on 5 January 1959, White Waltham-Wickham-Radley Bottom-Kintbury-White Waltham. 165·89 knots (307·22 km/h; 190·90 mph).

CLASS E.3 (Autogyros)
Height (UK)
Wing Cdr K. H. Wallis, in a Wallis WA-116/Mc, on 11 May 1968. 4,639 m (15,220 ft).

Distance in a straight line (UK)
Wing Cdr K. H. Wallis, in a Wallis WA-116/F, from Lydd Airport, Kent, to Wick, Scotland, on 28 September 1975. 472·092 nm (874·315 km; 543·274 miles).

Distance in a closed circuit (UK)
Wing Cdr K. H. Wallis, in a Wallis WA-116/F on 13 July 1974. 361·91 nm (670·26 km; 416·48 miles).

Speed in a straight line (UK)
Wing Cdr K. H. Wallis, in a Wallis WA-116/Mc, over a 3 km course, on 12 May 1969. 96·589 knots (179 km/h; 111·225 mph).

Subscription Manager
Jane's Defence Review
238 City Road
London EC1V 2PU
England

AIRCRAFT

ARGENTINA

AERO BOERO
AERO BOERO SRL

HEAD OFFICE: Hipólito Irigoyen 505, 2421 Morteros, Córdoba

Telephone: Morteros 409 and 2121

DIRECTORS: Cesar E. Boero and Hector C. Boero

This company is producing and developing the Aero Boero 150 and 180 series of light aircraft.

AERO BOERO 180 RV and RVR

The original three-seat Aero Boero 180 (1972-73 *Jane's*) was followed by the Aero Boero 180 RV (standard version) and 180 RVR (glider-towing version), the first of which flew for the first time in October 1972. These current versions, to which the description applies, have extended-span all-metal wings, increased fuel capacity, a recontoured fuselage and sweptback vertical tail surfaces. A total of 45 AB 180 RV/RVRs had been built and seven more had been ordered by the Spring of 1978.

TYPE: Three-seat light aircraft.

WINGS: Strut-braced high-wing monoplane. Streamline-section V bracing strut each side. Wing section NACA 23012. Dihedral 1° 45'. Incidence 3° at root, 1° at tip. Light alloy structure, including skins. Ailerons and flaps of aluminium alloy construction.

FUSELAGE: Welded steel tube structure (SAE 4130), covered with Ceconite.

TAIL UNIT: Wire-braced welded steel tube structure, covered with Ceconite. Sweptback vertical surfaces. Ground-adjustable tab on rudder.

LANDING GEAR: Non-retractable tailwheel type, with shock-absorption by helicoidal springs inside fuselage. Main wheels carried on faired-in V struts and half-axles. Main wheels and tyres size 6·00-6, pressure 1·65 bars (24 lb/sq in). Hydraulic disc brakes on main units. Tailwheel steerable and fully castoring.

POWER PLANT: One 134 kW (180 hp) Avco Lycoming O-360-A1A flat-four engine, driving (according to customer's choice) either a Hartzell constant-speed or McCauley 1A200 or Sensenich 76EM8 two-blade fixed-pitch propeller. Three wing fuel tanks, total capacity 201 litres (44 Imp gallons).

ACCOMMODATION: Normal accommodation for pilot and two passengers in enclosed cabin. Baggage compartment on port side, aft of cabin. Transparent roof panel in 180 RVR.

AVIONICS AND EQUIPMENT: One 40A alternator and one 12V battery. VHF radio standard. Provision for night or blind-flying instrumentation at customer's option. Towing hook in 180 RVR.

DIMENSIONS, EXTERNAL:
Wing span	10·72 m (35 ft 2 in)
Wing chord (constant)	1·61 m (5 ft 3½ in)
Wing aspect ratio	7·05
Length overall	7·273 m (23 ft 10¼ in)
Height overall	2·10 m (6 ft 10½ in)
Wheel track	2·05 m (6 ft 8¾ in)
Wheelbase	5·10 m (16 ft 8¾ in)

AREAS:
Wings, gross	16·47 m² (177·3 sq ft)
Ailerons (total)	1·84 m² (19·81 sq ft)
Flaps (total)	1·94 m² (20·88 sq ft)
Fin	0·93 m² (10·01 sq ft)
Rudder, incl tab	0·41 m² (4·41 sq ft)
Tailplane	1·40 m² (15·07 sq ft)
Elevators	0·97 m² (10·44 sq ft)

AB 180 SP biplane version of the Aero Boero 180

WEIGHTS AND LOADINGS:
Weight empty, equipped	550 kg (1,212 lb)
Max T-O weight	844 kg (1,860 lb)
Max wing loading	52·0 kg/m² (10·7 lb/sq ft)
Max power loading	6·30 kg/kW (10·36 lb/hp)

PERFORMANCE (at max T-O weight, except where indicated):
Never-exceed speed	134 knots (249 km/h; 155 mph)
Max level speed at S/L:	
RV	132 knots (245 km/h; 152 mph)
RVR	122 knots (225 km/h; 140 mph)
Max cruising speed at S/L	
	114 knots (211 km/h; 131 mph)
Stalling speed, flaps down	
	41·5 knots (77 km/h; 48 mph)
Max rate of climb at S/L	360 m (1,180 ft)/min
Time to 600 m (1,970 ft), 75% power, with Blanik two-seat sailplane	3 min 10 s
Service ceiling	6,700 m (22,000 ft)
T-O run	100 m (330 ft)
T-O to 15 m (50 ft), two persons	188 m (615 ft)
Landing from 15 m (50 ft)	160 m (525 ft)
Landing run	60 m (195 ft)
Range with max fuel	636 nm (1,180 km; 733 miles)

AERO BOERO 180 Ag

This version of the Aero Boero 180 is certificated in the Restricted category for use as an agricultural aircraft. Ten had been built and six more had been ordered by the Spring of 1978.

The description of the Aero Boero 180 RV and RVR applies also to the 180 Ag, except as follows:

WINGS: Incidence 3° 30' at root, 2° at tip.

ACCOMMODATION: Normal accommodation for pilot only in agricultural role. As AB 180 RV/RVR for non-agricultural use.

EQUIPMENT: Flush-fitting underfuselage pod containing agricultural chemical. Spraybars fitted along rear bar of V strut and horizontally below wings. Electrically-operated rotary atomisers (two each side) fitted to rear bar of V strut.

PERFORMANCE (at max T-O weight):
Never-exceed speed	117 knots (217 km/h; 135 mph)
Max level speed at S/L	
	109 knots (201 km/h; 125 mph)
Max cruising speed at S/L	
	100 knots (185 km/h; 115 mph)
Econ cruising speed at S/L	
	96 knots (177 km/h; 110 mph)
Stalling speed, flaps down	
	48 knots (89 km/h; 55 mph)
Max rate of climb at S/L	107 m (350 ft)/min
T-O run	213 m (700 ft)
T-O to 15 m (50 ft)	335 m (1,100 ft)
Landing from 15 m (50 ft)	229 m (750 ft)
Landing run	152 m (500 ft)
Range with max fuel	434 nm (804 km; 500 miles)

AERO BOERO 180 SP

By adding short-span lower wings (approx 6 m; 19 ft 8¼ in) to the basic AB 180 Ag, Aero Boero produced this biplane version of the aircraft, with improved take-off and landing performance, wider speed range, and greater payload/range capability. Agricultural chemical tankage of approx 330 litres (72·5 Imp gallons) is provided in the lower wings, in place of the underfuselage pack of the AB 180 Ag.

PERFORMANCE:
Max level speed	117 knots (217 km/h; 135 mph)
Max cruising speed	100 knots (185 km/h; 115 mph)
Stalling speed	30·5 knots (56·5 km/h; 35 mph)
Service ceiling with max payload	3,500 m (11,480 ft)
T-O run with max payload	200 m (656 ft)
T-O run without payload	65 m (213 ft)
Landing run without payload	70 m (230 ft)
Range at 75% power	448 nm (830 km; 516 miles)
Endurance at 75% power	4 h 30 min

AERO BOERO 150 RV

Essentially a lower-powered version of the AB 180 RV, the Aero Boero 150 RV is certificated in the Normal category. Four had been built and five more had been ordered by the Spring of 1978.

The description of the Aero Boero 180 RV and RVR applies also to the 150 RV except as follows:

POWER PLANT: One 112 kW (150 hp) Avco Lycoming O-320-A2B flat-four engine, driving a Sensenich 74-DM6-0-54 fixed-pitch propeller. Two wing fuel tanks, total capacity 134 litres (29·5 Imp gallons).

PERFORMANCE (at max T-O weight):
Never-exceed speed	132 knots (245 km/h; 152 mph)
Max cruising speed	114 knots (211 km/h; 131 mph)
Stalling speed, flaps down	42 knots (77 km/h; 48 mph)
Max rate of climb at S/L	270 m (885 ft)/min
T-O run	100 m (328 ft)
T-O to 15 m (50 ft)	220 m (722 ft)

AERO BOERO 150 Ag

This version of the Aero Boero 150 is certificated in the Restricted category for use as an agricultural aircraft. The description of the Aero Boero 180 Ag applies also to the 150 Ag except as follows:

Aero Boero 180 Ag, with ventral chemical pod and underwing spraybars

POWER PLANT: As Aero Boero 150 RV.
EQUIPMENT: Glassfibre non-corrosive underfuselage tank, with capacity of 270 litres (59·4 Imp gallons; 71·3 US gallons) of liquid chemical.
PERFORMANCE (at max T-O weight):
Never-exceed speed   123 knots (228 km/h; 141 mph)
Max level speed   119 knots (220 km/h; 137 mph)
Econ cruising speed   82 knots (152 km/h; 94·5 mph)

AERO BOERO 260 Ag

Aero Boero began the design of this single-seat agricultural monoplane in mid-1971, at which time it was known as the AG.235/260. Construction of a prototype began in October 1971, and this aircraft flew for the first time on 23 December 1972.

A description and illustration of the prototype can be found in the 1979-80 *Jane's*, together with a three-view drawing of the proposed production version. No information regarding the status of this aircraft has been received for several years.

Aero Boero 150 Ag agricultural aircraft (Avco Lycoming O-320 engine)

AMC
AREA DE MATERIAL CÓRDOBA, FUERZA AÉREA ARGENTINA
(Fábrica Militar de Aviones)

Avenida Fuerza Aérea Argentina Km 5½, 5103 Guarnicion Aérea Córdoba
Telephone: 45011/15
Telex: 51965 AMCOR AR
DIRECTOR: Brigadier Jorge Aníbal Martínez Castro
CHIEF OF FABRICATION GROUP: Comodoro Oscar José Julia
CHIEF OF ENGINEERING DEPARTMENT: Vice-Comodoro Ricardo José Angel Valenzuela

The original Fábrica Militar de Aviones (Military Aircraft Factory) was founded in 1927 as a central organisation for aeronautical research and production in Argentina. Its name was changed to Instituto Aerotécnico in 1943 and then to Industrias Aeronáuticas y Mecánicas del Estado (IAME) in 1952. In 1957 it became a State enterprise under the title of Dirección Nacional de Fabricaciones e Investigaciónes Aeronáuticas (DINFIA), but reverted to its original title in 1968. It is now a component of the Area de Material Córdoba division of the Argentinian Air Force.

FMA comprises two large divisions. The Instituto de Investigaciónes Aeronáuticas y Espacial (IIAE) is responsible for the design, manufacture and testing of rockets, sounding equipment and other equipment. The Fábrica Militar de Aviones itself controls the aircraft manufacturing facilities (Grupo Fabricación) situated in Córdoba, as well as the Centro de Ensayos en Vuelo (Flight Test Centre), to which all aircraft produced in Argentina are sent for certification tests. The laboratories, factories and other aeronautical division buildings occupy a total covered area of 261,970 m² (2,819,845 sq ft); the Area de Material Córdoba employs 3,500 persons, of whom about 1,500 are in the Grupo Fabricación.

In current production is the IA 58 Pucará, a nationally designed counter-insurgency aircraft.

The IA 58B Bravo version of this aircraft is currently under development, and the IA 63, a primary and advanced jet trainer, is in the preliminary design stage.

The Grupo Fabricación also produces Cessna single-engined aircraft under licence, under agreements announced in October 1965 and subsequently. These aircraft are repurchased by Cessna for sale through its distributors and dealers in Latin America or sold directly by FMA to Argentinian government agencies. Forty Cessna Model 150s were ordered by the Comando de Regiones

IA 58A Pucará combat aircraft of the Argentinian Air Force

Aéreas for use as trainers by Argentinian flying clubs. The first A182J (Argentinian 182) was completed in August 1966 and delivered to its owner on 2 September 1966. A renewed and extended agreement, announced in April 1971, provided for continued production of the Cessna 182 and, in addition, for the range to be extended to include the Model 150 trainer and the AGwagon agricultural aircraft.

By 1 March 1980, the Fabrication Group had completed 148 Cessna Model A182s, 39 Model A150 trainers, 9 Model A-A150 Aerobats and 33 Model A188 AGwagons. Production of four more Model A182s was scheduled during 1980.

IA 58A PUCARÁ

Design of this twin-turboprop counter-insurgency aircraft, to meet an Argentinian Air Force requirement, began in August 1966. Known originally as the Delfin (Dolphin), it was later renamed Pucará after a type of stone fortress built by the early South American Indians. An unpowered aerodynamic prototype, which first flew on 26 December 1967, was described in the 1968-69 *Jane's*. The first powered prototype, designated A-X2, flew for the first time on 20 August 1969 with 674 kW (904 ehp) AiResearch TPE 331-U-303 turboprop engines, and was described in the 1971-72 *Jane's*. It was later redesignated AX-01.

A second prototype, designated AX-02, flew for the first time on 6 September 1970, powered by 761 kW (1,022 ehp) Turboméca Astazou XVI G turboprops. This

power plant was adopted as standard for the production version, for which the prototype was the similarly-powered AX-03, first flown in mid-1973; the AX-01 also was re-engined with Astazou XVI Gs.

An initial order for 30 IA 58A Pucarás, subsequently increased to 60, was placed by the Argentinian Air Force, and the first of these (A-501) flew for the first time on 8 November 1974. Forty Pucarás had been delivered by 1 March 1980; these are in service with Argentinian Air Force units, including the II Escuadron de Exploración y Ataque at Reconquista air base, with which the Pucará was deployed operationally in late 1976 against terrorist groups in north-western Argentina.

To establish a second source of power plants for the Pucará, a prototype has been re-engined with Garrett-AiResearch TPE331-11-601W turboprop engines, each driving a Dowty R316/4-82F/G propeller. Flight tests in this form were scheduled to start before the end of 1980.

An **IA 58B Pucará Bravo** version, currently under development, is planned to enter production in early 1981. This version is described separately.

The following description applies to the basic IA 58A, production of which was at the rate of approx two per month in early 1980:

TYPE: Twin-turboprop counter-insurgency aircraft.

WINGS: Cantilever low-wing monoplane. Wing section NACA 64$_2$A215 at root, NACA 64$_1$A212 at tip. Dihedral 7° on outer panels. Incidence 2°. No sweepback. Conventional semi-monocoque fail-safe structure of duralumin. Frise-type fabric-covered duralumin ailerons, and all-dural slotted trailing-edge flaps, actuated by pushrods. No slats. Balance tab in starboard aileron, electrically-operated trim tab in port aileron.

FUSELAGE: Conventional semi-monocoque fail-safe structure of duralumin frames and stringers.

TAIL UNIT: Cantilever semi-monocoque structure of duralumin. Fixed-incidence tailplane and elevators mounted near top of fin. Rudder and elevators actuated by pushrods, and each fitted with inset trim tab.

LANDING GEAR: Retractable tricycle type. All units retract forward hydraulically, steerable nose unit into fuselage, main units into engine nacelles. Shock-absorbers of Kronprinz Ring-Feder type. Single wheel on nose unit, twin wheels on main units, all with Dunlop tubeless Type III tyres size 7·50-10. Tyre pressures: 2·82 bars (41 lb/sq in) on main units, 2·41 bars (35 lb/sq in) on nose unit. Dunlop hydraulic disc brakes on main units. No anti-skid units.

POWER PLANT: Two 761 kW (1,022 ehp) Turboméca Astazou XVI G turboprop engines, each driving a Hamilton Standard 23LF/1015-0 three-blade metal propeller with spinner. Fuel in two fuselage tanks (total 800 litres; 176 Imp gallons) and one 230 litre (50·5 Imp gallon) self-sealing tank in each wing, giving overall internal capacity of 1,260 litres (277 Imp gallons). Refuelling point on top of fuselage aft of cockpit. Fuel

FMA IA 58A Pucará twin-turboprop counter-insurgency aircraft (*Pilot Press*)

system includes provision for up to 30 s of inverted flight. A long-range auxiliary tank, capacity 1,200 litres (264 Imp gallons), can be attached to the fuselage centreline pylon, and a 330 litre (72·5 Imp gallon) auxiliary tank on each underwing pylon. Max internal and external fuel capacity 3,120 litres (686 Imp gallons). Oil capacity 11·75 litres (2·6 Imp gallons).

ACCOMMODATION: Pilot and co-pilot in tandem on Martin-Baker Mk AP06A zero-zero ejection seats beneath transparent moulded canopy which is hinged at rear and opens upward. Rear seat elevated 25 cm (9·8 in) above front seat. Bulletproof windscreen, with wiper. Dual controls standard.

SYSTEMS: Hydraulic system, pressure 207 bars (3,000 lb/sq in), supplied by two engine-driven pumps, actuates landing gear, flaps and wheel brakes. Electrical system includes two 28V 300A starter/generators for DC power and three 500/750VA static inverters for 115/200V AC power. One 24V 36Ah SAFT Voltabloc 4006 battery. No APU. Liquid oxygen bottle.

AVIONICS AND EQUIPMENT: Blind-flying instrumentation standard. Avionics include Bendix DFA-73A-1 ADF, Bendix RTA-42A VHF com, Bendix RNA-2bc VHF nav, Northern N-420 HF/SSB com, amplifier and audio-selector system with AS-A-31 panel. Optional avionics include weather radar, IFF, and VHF/FM tactical communications system. Landing/taxying light in leading-edge of each underwing pylon.

ARMAMENT AND OPERATIONAL EQUIPMENT: Two 20 mm Hispano HS-2804 cannon, each with 270 rds, in underside of forward fuselage; and four 7·62 mm FN-Browning machine-guns, each with 900 rds, in sides of fuselage abreast of cockpit. Aero 7A-1 pylon on centreline beneath fuselage, capacity 1,000 kg (2,205 lb). Aero 20A-1 pylon, capacity 500 kg (1,102 lb), beneath each wing outboard of engine nacelle. Total external stores load 1,620 kg (3,571 lb), including gun and rocket pods, bombs, or auxiliary fuel tanks. Matra 83-4-3 reflector gunsight and AN/AWE-1 programmer.

DIMENSIONS, EXTERNAL:
Wing span	14·50 m (47 ft 6¾ in)
Wing chord at root	2·24 m (7 ft 4¼ in)
Wing chord at tip	1·60 m (5 ft 3 in)
Wing aspect ratio	6·95
Length overall	14·25 m (46 ft 9 in)
Length of fuselage	13·32 m (43 ft 8½ in)
Fuselage: Max width	1·24 m (4 ft 0¾ in)
Height overall	5·36 m (17 ft 7 in)
Tailplane span	4·70 m (15 ft 5 in)
Wheel track (c/l of shock-absorbers)	4·20 m (13 ft 9¼ in)
Wheelbase	3·48 m (11 ft 5 in)
Propeller diameter	2·59 m (8 ft 6 in)

DIMENSIONS, INTERNAL:
Cabin: Length	2·85 m (9 ft 4¼ in)
Max width	0·81 m (2 ft 8 in)
Max height	1·25 m (4 ft 1¼ in)
Floor area	2·90 m² (31·2 sq ft)
Volume	2·74 m³ (96·8 cu ft)

AREAS:
Wings, gross	30·30 m² (326·1 sq ft)
Ailerons (total)	3·29 m² (35·41 sq ft)
Trailing-edge flaps (total)	3·58 m² (38·53 sq ft)
Fin	3·465 m² (37·30 sq ft)
Rudder, incl tab	1·565 m² (16·84 sq ft)
Tailplane	4·60 m² (49·51 sq ft)
Elevators, incl tabs	2·612 m² (28·11 sq ft)

WEIGHTS AND LOADINGS:
Weight empty, equipped	4,037 kg (8,900 lb)
Max T-O weight	6,800 kg (14,991 lb)
Max landing weight	5,806 kg (12,800 lb)
Max wing loading	224·4 kg/m² (46 lb/sq ft)
Max power loading	4·46 kg/kW (7·3 lb/ehp)

PERFORMANCE (at max T-O weight except where indicated):
Never-exceed speed	404 knots (750 km/h; 466 mph)
Max level speed at 3,000 m (9,845 ft)	270 knots (500 km/h; 310 mph)
Max cruising speed at 6,000 m (19,685 ft)	259 knots (480 km/h; 298 mph)
Econ cruising speed	232 knots (430 km/h; 267 mph)
Stalling speed, flaps and landing gear up	68 knots (125 km/h; 78 mph)
Stalling speed, flaps and landing gear down, at 4,790 kg (10,560 lb) gross weight	77·5 knots (142·5 km/h; 89 mph)
Max rate of climb at S/L	1,080 m (3,543 ft)/min
Service ceiling	10,000 m (32,810 ft)
Service ceiling, one engine out	6,000 m (19,685 ft)
T-O run	300 m (985 ft)
T-O to 15 m (50 ft)	705 m (2,313 ft)
Landing from 15 m (50 ft) at 5,100 kg (11,243 lb) weight	603 m (1,978 ft)
Landing run at 5,100 kg (11,243 lb) gross weight	200 m (656 ft)
Range with max fuel at 5,000 m (16,400 ft)	1,641 nm (3,042 km; 1,890 miles)
g limits	+6; −3

IA 58B Pucará Bravo, under development for production in 1981

The deepened front fuselage of the IA 58B is shown clearly in this close-up

IA 58B PUCARÁ BRAVO

Design of this improved version of the Pucará started in September 1977, and construction of a prototype began 12 months later. This aircraft (AX-05) flew for the first time on 15 May 1979, and made its public debut at the Paris Air Show in May/June of that year. A total of 40 production Bravos had been ordered by early 1980, and manufacture of these is scheduled to begin in early 1981.

The airframe and power plant remain essentially the same as for the IA 58A, except for deepening of the forward fuselage to accommodate a heavier nose armament. Other improvements include a new avionics installation.

TYPE, WINGS, FUSELAGE, TAIL UNIT AND LANDING GEAR: As for IA 58A, except that forward fuselage is deeper and tyre pressure (all units) is increased to 3·10 bars (45 lb/sq in).

POWER PLANT: As for IA 58A. Internal fuel tank capacity differs slightly (782 litres; 172 Imp gallons in fuselage tanks, 478 litres; 105 Imp gallons in wing tanks), but overall internal capacity of 1,260 litres (277 Imp gallons) remains the same. Provision for one underfuselage and two underwing drop-tanks, as in IA 58A.

ACCOMMODATION: As for IA 58A.

SYSTEMS: Hydraulic system and liquid oxygen bottle as in IA 58A. No APU, pneumatic or wing/tail de-icing systems. Electrical system includes two 28V 175A starter/generators for DC power; two 250VA static inverters for 115/26V AC power, and one giving 1,000/200V AC for windscreen demisting/de-icing. One 24V 36Ah SAFT Voltabloc battery.

AVIONICS AND EQUIPMENT: Standard avionics include Collins 718US HF/AM and dual Bendix VHF/AM radio; dual Bendix VOR/ILS, dual ADF, DME, ATC and IFF/SSB. Optional avionics include Bendix VHF/FM with homing, Omega, and weather radar. Blind-flying instrumentation standard.

ARMAMENT: Two 30 mm DEFA 553 cannon, each with 140 rds, in underside of forward fuselage; and four 7·62 mm FN-Browning machine-guns, each with 900 rds, in fuselage sides abreast of cockpit. One underfuselage and two underwing hardpoints for up to twelve 125 kg bombs; one Dassault 30 mm gun pod, plus four Alkan 530 rocket launchers or two drop-tanks; or six Alkan 530 launchers; or three drop-tanks.

DIMENSIONS, EXTERNAL AND INTERNAL: As IA 58A except:
Length of fuselage	13·68 m (44 ft 10½ in)
Fuselage: Max depth	2·10 m (6 ft 10¾ in)

AREAS: As IA 58A

WEIGHTS AND LOADINGS:
Weight empty, equipped	4,030 kg (8,884 lb)
Max external stores load	1,686 kg (3,717 lb)
Max fuel load: internal	1,005 kg (2,215 lb)
external	1,250 kg (2,755 lb)
Max T-O weight	6,800 kg (14,991 lb)
Max zero-fuel weight	4,546 kg (10,022 lb)
Max landing weight	5,600 kg (12,345 lb)
Max wing loading	224·4 kg/m² (46 lb/sq ft)
Max power loading	4·46 kg/kW (7·3 lb/ehp)

PERFORMANCE (at max T-O weight except where indicated):
Never-exceed speed	404 knots (750 km/h; 466 mph)
Max level speed at 1,000 m (3,280 ft)	252 knots (467 km/h; 290 mph)
Max cruising speed at 1,000 m (3,280 ft)	237 knots (440 km/h; 273 mph)
Stalling speed, flaps up	107 knots (198 km/h; 123 mph)
Stalling speed, flaps down, power reduced	86 knots (159 km/h; 99 mph)
Max rate of climb at S/L	660 m (2,165 ft)/min
Climbing speed at S/L, one engine out	182 knots (338 km/h; 210 mph)
Service ceiling	7,400 m (24,275 ft)
Service ceiling, one engine out	2,300 m (7,550 ft)
T-O run	710 m (2,330 ft)
T-O to 15 m (50 ft)	1,040 m (3,412 ft)
T-O to 15 m (50 ft) at 5,800 kg (12,787 lb) gross weight	750 m (2,460 ft)
Landing from 15 m (50 ft) at max landing weight	605 m (1,985 ft)
Landing run at max landing weight	470 m (1,542 ft)
Range with max internal fuel	728 nm (1,350 km; 839 miles)
Range with max internal and external fuel	1,620 nm (3,000 km; 1,865 miles)

CHINCUL
CHINCUL S.A.C.A.I.F.I.

HEAD OFFICE: 25 de Mayo 489, 6° Piso, Buenos Aires
Telephone: 32 5671/5
Telex: 012 2706
WORKS: Calle Mendoza entre 6 y 7 (Casilla de Correo 80), San Juan
PRESIDENT: Juan José Beraza
VICE-PRESIDENT: José María Beraza
EXECUTIVE DIRECTOR: Aquiles Luis Uriarte
WORKS DIRECTOR: Héctor Carlos Delgado
CHIEF OF ENGINEERING DEPT: Fernando Leon Reisin
CHIEF OF PRODUCTION DEPT: Conrado Risso Patrón
CHIEF OF QUALITY CONTROL AND FLIGHT TEST DEPT:
  Roberto Lucio

This company, a wholly-owned subsidiary of La Macarena SA, Piper's Argentinian distributor, concluded an agreement with Piper Aircraft Corporation in November 1971 for manufacture of a range of Piper products in Argentina. The plan called for a progression through manufacturing phases of increasing complexity, and some Chincul products (such as the Pawnee) are now more than 60% manufactured in Argentina.

Piper aircraft are built at the plant at San Juan, which has a covered area of 14,500 m² (156,075 sq ft) and a work force of 320 people; an additional facility of 2,000 m² (21,530 sq ft) is planned as a maintenance and overhaul workshop.

Chincul's production programme includes the PA-23-250 Aztec and Turbo Aztec; the PA-25-235 Pawnee D; various Cherokees (PA-28-140, -180, -181 and -200R, and PA-32-300 and -300R); Navajos (PA-31-310 and -325 Turbo Navajo, PA-31P Pressurised Navajo and PA-31-350 Chieftain); and the PA-34-200T Seneca. The PA-36 Brave and PA-38 Tomahawk were introduced during 1978, and the PA-31T Cheyenne in January 1979. More than 200 aircraft had been completed by January 1979, and many of these are now operating in various South American countries.

All Piper kits now being delivered to Chincul are for Phase 3 completion, involving the assembly and riveting of wings and control surfaces, manufacture of interiors, upholstery, electrical harness, and other systems installation. Batteries, upholstery, fabrics, tyres, engine instruments, fire extinguishers and glassfibre components are of Argentinian manufacture. Chincul also has an agreement with Narco Avionics under which it assembles Escort 110, Com 11, Com 120, Nav 121 and 122, ADF 31, 140 and 141, OGR 2A2-5, and Nav 11/12 sets.

The company is developing a fully-aerobatic two-seat military trainer based on the Piper Cherokee Arrow.

CHINCUL (PIPER) CHEROKEE ARROW TRAINER

In January 1978 Chincul was flight testing the prototype (LV-X67) of a military training aircraft which it had developed from the Piper Cherokee Arrow four-seat light aircraft. The principal modifications from the standard Arrow are a more powerful engine, a two-seat cockpit with new canopy, revised internal equipment, and provision for a built-in machine-gun and underwing weapons for armament training. Although the basic airframe of the Arrow is retained, it has been entirely restressed to permit certification in the fully-aerobatic category. Production was planned to begin in mid-1979.

TYPE: Two-seat military trainer.
WINGS, FUSELAGE, TAIL UNIT AND LANDING GEAR: Generally similar to those of Piper Arrow (see US section), but with fuselage modified in cabin area. Entire airframe restressed for aerobatic flying.
POWER PLANT: One 194 kW (260 hp) Avco Lycoming AEIO-540 series flat-six engine, driving a two-blade propeller with spinner. Fuel tank in each wing leading-edge, combined capacity 272 litres (71·8 US gallons). Oil capacity 11·5 litres (3 US gallons).
ACCOMMODATION: Seats for instructor and pupil side by side under rearward-sliding framed canopy. Dual controls standard.
AVIONICS AND EQUIPMENT: Two VHF and one HF com; two VOR; one ILS; one DME; two ADF; audio selector panel; oxygen system.
ARMAMENT: Provision for one 7·62 mm machine-gun in lower front fuselage; underwing pylons for bombs and rockets.

DIMENSIONS, EXTERNAL:
Wing span	10·67 m (35 ft 0 in)
Wing chord (constant portion inboard of ailerons)	
	1·60 m (5 ft 3 in)
Wing chord at tip	1·07 m (3 ft 6¼ in)
Length overall	7·25 m (23 ft 9½ in)
Height overall	2·23 m (7 ft 3½ in)
Tailplane span	3·92 m (12 ft 10½ in)
Wheel track	3·05 m (10 ft 0 in)
Wheelbase	2·40 m (7 ft 10½ in)
Propeller diameter	2·03 m (6 ft 8 in)

AREA:
Wings, gross	15·79 m² (170·0 sq ft)

WEIGHTS AND LOADINGS:
Weight empty	785 kg (1,730 lb)
Max T-O weight	1,315 kg (2,900 lb)
Max wing loading	83·25 kg/m² (17·06 lb/sq ft)
Max power loading	6·78 kg/kW (11·15 lb/hp)

PERFORMANCE (at max T-O weight):
Max level speed	169 knots (314 km/h; 195 mph)
Max cruising speed (75% power)	
	156 knots (290 km/h; 180 mph)
Speed for optimum climb 87 knots (161 km/h; 100 mph)	
Stalling speed, flaps and landing gear down	
	54 knots (100 km/h; 62 mph)
Max rate of climb at S/L	238 m (780 ft)/min
Service ceiling	3,962 m (13,000 ft)
T-O run	302 m (990 ft)
Landing run	227 m (744 ft)
Range (75% power, optimum mixture, at optimum altitude)	729 nm (1,352 km; 840 miles)

Prototype Chincul military trainer developed from the Piper Arrow

---

CICARÉ
CICARÉ AERONÁUTICA SC

Ave Ibañez Frocham s/n, Casilla Correo 24, 7260 Saladillo, Provincia de Buenos Aires

ENQUIRIES TO: Comodoro Antonio R. Mantel, Santa Fé 1256, Buenos Aires
Telephone: Buenos Aires 41 5260
This company was formed in 1972 to develop and build small aero-engines and light helicopters. Brief details of the experimental Cicaré I and Cicaré II appeared in the 1970-71, 1973-74 and 1974-75 *Jane's*. The later C.K.1 was described and illustrated in the 1979-80 edition.

RACA
REPRESENTACIONES AERO COMERCIALES ARGENTINAS SA

HEAD OFFICE: Lavalle 715, 5° Piso, 1047 Buenos Aires
Telephone: 393 7334 and 392 9488
Telex: 22844 RACA AR
WORKS: Aeródromo San Fernando, Provincia de Buenos Aires
PRESIDENT: J. R. Fernández Racca

This company is the representative or dealer in Argentina for the Canadair CL-215 and CASA C-212 Aviocar aircraft, and the MBB BO 105 and Hughes helicopters. Under a licence agreement concluded in December 1972 RACA is undertaking, with Argentinian government approval (granted in mid-1973), the progressive local manufacture of a minimum of 120 Hughes Model 500 helicopters (see US section) from knock-down components. These are known locally as RACA-Hughes 500s, and are identical to the Hughes-built version described in the US section.

The programme is covering, in three phases, a period of eight years, to supply military and civil customers in

Hughes Model 500 helicopters under construction by RACA

Argentina and neighbouring countries. In anticipation of this programme, RACA expanded its workshop facilities at San Fernando aerodrome to a covered area of 4,600 m² (49,514 sq ft).

RRA
RONCHETTI, RAZZETTI AVIACIÓN SA

Aeropuerto Internacional Rosario, Casilla Correo 7, 2132 Funes, Provincia de Santa Fé
Telephone: Rosario 58251 or Funes 93276
PRESIDENT: Julio E. Razzetti
HEAD OF DESIGN AND DEVELOPMENT GROUP (RRAFAGA): Ing Norberto S. Cobelo
HEAD OF PRODUCTION: Julio Di Giuseppe

RRAFAGA J-1 MARTIN FIERRO

The J-1 Martin Fierro single-seat agricultural aircraft was designed in Argentina by a team led by Ing Norberto S. Cobelo. Design began in September 1972, and the first of two prototypes made its first flight on 18 December 1975.

Five more J-1s were under construction during 1978, including one for structural testing. Certification by the Argentinian Air Force was anticipated during that year, and plans were then being made for series production. No later news than this has been received.

TYPE: Single-seat agricultural aircraft.
WINGS: Cantilever low-wing monoplane. Thickness/chord ratio 15%. Dihedral 7°. Incidence 2° at root. All-metal single box-spar structure, with detachable leading-edges. All-metal Frise-type ailerons and semi-Fowler trailing-edge flaps. No tabs.
FUSELAGE: Welded tube structure with detachable metal skin.
TAIL UNIT: Cantilever all-metal two-spar structure. Fixed-incidence tailplane. Trim tab in each elevator.
LANDING GEAR: Non-retractable tailwheel type, with spring steel shock-absorption. Cleveland wheels and main-wheel brakes. Goodyear tyres, size 8·50-10 (8 ply) on main units, 2·80-8 (4 ply) on tail unit.
POWER PLANT: One 224 kW (300 hp) Avco Lycoming IO-540-K1JG flat-six engine, driving a Hartzell two-blade variable-pitch constant-speed propeller with spinner. Fuel in two wing-root tanks, total capacity 162 litres (35·6 Imp gallons). Refuelling point on top of each tank. Oil capacity 12 litres (2·64 Imp gallons).

RRA J-1 Martin Fierro agricultural aircraft (Avco Lycoming IO-540-K1JG engine)

Rudder	0·96 m² (10·33 sq ft)
Tailplane	2·64 m² (28·42 sq ft)
Elevators (total, incl tabs)	1·76 m² (18·94 sq ft)

WEIGHTS AND LOADINGS:
Basic operating weight with spray equipment
920 kg (2,028 lb)
Max payload 850 kg (1,874 lb)
Max T-O and landing weight (Restricted category)
2,000 kg (4,409 lb)
Max wing loading 96·14 kg/m² (19·69 lb/sq ft)
Max power loading 8·93 kg/kW (14·70 lb/hp)
PERFORMANCE (at max FAR Pt 23 Aerobatic T-O weight):
Never-exceed speed 188 knots (349 km/h; 217 mph)
Max level speed at S/L, 'clean'
130 knots (241 km/h; 150 mph)
Econ cruising speed at S/L, 'clean'
114 knots (211 km/h; 131 mph)
Stalling speed, flaps up
55 knots (102 km/h; 63 mph)
Stalling speed, flaps down
43 knots (79 km/h; 49 mph)
Max rate of climb at S/L 290 m (950 ft)/min
Service ceiling 3,660 m (12,000 ft)
T-O run 168 m (550 ft)
T-O to 15 m (50 ft) 251 m (824 ft)
Landing from 15 m (50 ft) 244 m (800 ft)
Landing run 85 m (280 ft)
Max range, 45 min reserves
265 nm (490 km; 305 miles)

ACCOMMODATION: Single seat in heated and ventilated framed cockpit. Downward-opening window/door on each side.
SYSTEMS AND EQUIPMENT: 12V 60A Prestolite generator and 12V 30Ah Prestolite battery. Single hopper, forward of cockpit, of 850 litres (187 Imp gallons) capacity. Can be fitted with dusting or spraying systems, for dry or liquid chemicals.
DIMENSIONS, EXTERNAL:
Wing span 13·00 m (42 ft 7¾ in)
Wing chord (constant) 1·60 m (5 ft 3 in)

Wing aspect ratio	8·12
Length overall	7·00 m (22 ft 11¾ in)
Height overall	4·00 m (13 ft 1½ in)
Wheelbase	2·40 m (7 ft 10½ in)
Propeller diameter	2·13 m (7 ft 0 in)
Propeller ground clearance	0·50 m (1 ft 7¾ in)
AREAS:	
Wings, gross	20·80 m² (223·9 sq ft)
Ailerons (total)	2·76 m² (29·71 sq ft)
Trailing-edge flaps (total)	2·76 m² (29·71 sq ft)
Fin	1·44 m² (15·50 sq ft)

TENSA
TENSA SA
Paséo Colon 275, Buenos Aires
Telephone: 122322
On 14 September 1979, Cessna announced that it had signed a long-term manufacturing and distribution agree-

ment with TENSA, a manufacturing and aircraft marketing organisation in Argentina. Initially, TENSA was to assemble three single-engined and two multi-engined Cessna types for the Argentinian market. Later plans call for production of additional single-engined models and three further piston- and turboprop-powered multi-engined aircraft. Cessna estimated that 420 aircraft would

be produced in Argentina during 1979-84. It also planned to introduce its Cessna Pilot Center flight training programme into that country.
Under an earlier agreement, Cessna single-engined aircraft, including the Model 150, 150 Aerobat, Skylane and AGwagon, were assembled by the FMA at Córdoba from 1966 to 1976.

AUSTRALIA

CAC
COMMONWEALTH AIRCRAFT CORPORATION LIMITED
HEAD OFFICE AND WORKS: 304 Lorimer Street, Port Melbourne, Victoria 3207
Telephone: 64 0771
Telex: 30721
CHAIRMAN OF DIRECTORS: N. F. Stevens
GENERAL MANAGER: D. J. Dalziel
MANAGER (ENGINEERING): J. A. C. Kentwell
SECRETARY: E. W. Stodden

Commonwealth Aircraft Corporation Pty Ltd was formed in 1936. On 18 August 1975 it became a public company, changing its name to Commonwealth Aircraft Corporation Limited.
CAC is a major supplier of equipment and services to the Royal Australian Air Force, and holds Dept of Transport approval for civil aviation activities. The company maintains a capability for initial design and in support of manufacturing and overhaul activities.
Major current programmes include life-of-type extension for RAAF Aermacchi M.B. 326H aircraft; modification of RAAF Lockheed P-3C aircraft to

Australian long-range maritime patrol (LRMP) requirements; repair and overhaul, including life-of-type extension, of RAAF Mirage major airframe components; repair and overhaul of RAAF Atar 9C, Viper and Avon engines; manufacture of components and assemblies for GAF Nomad airframes; design and manufacture of in-flight catering equipment for Australian airlines; manufacture of passenger doors for the Lockheed L-1011 TriStar and escape slides for the McDonnell Douglas DC-10.
Ground support equipment is supplied through Static General Engineering Pty Ltd, a CAC subsidiary.

GAF
GOVERNMENT AIRCRAFT FACTORIES
HEADQUARTERS: Fishermen's Bend, Private Bag No. 4, Post Office, Port Melbourne, Victoria 3207
Telephone: 64 0661
Telex: AA 34397
WORKS: Avalon Airfield, Beach Road, Lara, Victoria 3212
Telephone: Lara 82 1202
GENERAL MANAGER: M. C. Morrison
MARKETING MANAGER: E. A. Morris
PUBLIC RELATIONS OFFICER: C. Collinson

The Government Aircraft Factories are units of the Defence Production facilities owned by the Australian government and operated by the Department of Productivity. They have a work force of approximately 2,500 persons. Their functions include the design, development, manufacture, assembly, maintenance and modification of aircraft, target drones and guided weapons. At Avalon airfield, subassembly of components, final assembly, modification, repair and test-flying of jet and other aircraft are undertaken.
Current activity includes development and production of the Nomad twin-turboprop STOL aircraft, the Ikara anti-submarine missile, and the Jindivik target drone.
The GAF are producing elevators for the Boeing 727 and wing flaps for the Fokker F28 Fellowship.

GOVERNMENT AIRCRAFT FACTORIES NOMAD
The N2 prototype of the Nomad twin-turboprop light utility aircraft was flown for the first time on 23 July 1971, and received an Australian Department of Transport type certificate in August 1972. Type certificates for the N22 and N24 initial production versions, described in previous editions of *Jane's*, were issued in May 1975 and October 1977 respectively.

The N22B and N24A current versions were type certificated in August 1975 and May 1978 respectively, and in December 1978 both of these versions were awarded certification under US FAR Pt 135 Appendix A (Transport category). Type certificates have also been issued in various European, Asian, South American and Pacific countries.
Current versions are as follows:
N22B. Short-fuselage civil version, intended primarily as a STOL utility aircraft for short/medium-range transportation of up to 13 passengers and/or cargo. Also used

for aerial ambulance, geophysical and geographical survey duties, particularly in areas with minimal maintenance and landing field facilities. Transparent acrylic flight deck roof panels, as in Mission Master, are available optionally.
N22F. Flight trials were concluded in Minneapolis, USA, in late 1978 of a Nomad equipped with twin Wipline 9812 floats manufactured by Wipaire Inc of Minnesota. These trials showed exceptionally good surface and in-flight stability. FAA certification for the N22F floatplane was awarded in September 1979. Flight trials of an amphibious version began in late 1979, and certification

Twin-float N22F version of the GAF Nomad, certificated by the FAA in 1979

Government Aircraft Factories N22B Nomad, with additional side view (bottom) of N24A and scrap view of forward fuselage of Search Master L *(Pilot Press)*

Wipline 9500 amphibious gear on an N22 Nomad
(Howard Levy)

N24A long-fuselage version of the GAF Nomad, seating up to 17 passengers

was expected in early 1980. The Wipline 9500 amphibious gear uses the same large floats as on the N22F, which are of all-aluminium construction with bonded chines, keels and gunwales, and have a double afterbody which gives the aircraft an additional 3½° of nose-up attitude before the rear of the float enters the water during rotation. The amphibious version has a single size 6·00-6 Cessna wheel and tyre at the front of each float, and twin size 8·00-6 Cessna wheels and tyres at the rear. All wheels are retractable.

Mission Master. Short-fuselage military version, in service in Australia, Papua New Guinea, the Philippines and Indonesia for maritime surveillance, forward area support and surveillance, and as a light military transport for personnel and equipment. Four underwing pylons, load-bearing drop doors in the cabin floor, self-sealing fuel cells, transparent acrylic flight deck roof panels, military avionics, and special equipment according to role.

N24A. Civil version with lengthened fuselage, offering seating for up to 17 passengers and a considerably improved payload capability. Design includes the insertion of a 1·14 m (3 ft 9 in) plug in the cabin, and increased forward baggage capacity. The basic aircraft includes a full commuter interior and IFR avionics.

Search Master B. Basic coastal patrol version, equipped with Bendix RDR 1400 search radar, with 46 cm (18 in) forward-looking flat-plate scanner in nose radome. In service with Indonesian Navy (12) and Papua New Guinea Defence Force.

Search Master L. More sophisticated coastal patrol version, ordered by Indonesian Navy (six) and Australian Customs and Transport Departments (ten). Litton APS-504(V)2 search radar and a 100 cm (40 in) flat-plate phased array scanner rotating 360° in undernose 'guppy' radome. Search capacity significantly increased; choice of Doppler, Omega or INS long-range navigation system also ground-stabilises radar display. Both B and L versions provide a spacious cabin and excellent view for the crew, and may include optional long-range fuel tanks, floor hatch, bubble windows, underwing pylons, radar and navigation consoles.

By the beginning of 1980 about 100 Nomads of all versions had been sold, customers including the Philippine Air Force (12), Indonesian Navy (18), Australian Army (11) and Aeromedical Services (8).

The following description applies generally to all versions, except where a specific model is indicated:

TYPE: Twin-turboprop STOL utility aircraft.

WINGS: Braced high-wing monoplane. Basic NACA 23018 wing section, modified to incorporate increased nose radius and camber. Dihedral 1° from roots. Incidence 2°. No sweepback. Two-spar fail-safe torsion-box structure of riveted light alloy. Full-span double-slotted trailing-edge flaps. All-metal ailerons, which droop with the flaps and transfer their motion progressively to slot-lip ailerons as the flaps extend, resulting in full-span flap. Controls actuated manually by cables and push-rods. Pneumatic de-icing of leading-edges optional. Small stub wings at cabin floor level support the main landing gear fairings from which a single strut on each side braces the main wing.

FUSELAGE: Conventional semi-monocoque riveted light alloy structure of stringers and frames.

TAIL UNIT: Cantilever all-metal structure. One-piece all-moving tailplane, with inset trim and anti-balance tab. Tailplane and rudder actuated manually by cables. Trim tab in rudder. Pneumatic de-icing of leading-edges optional. Ventral fin on N22F.

LANDING GEAR: Retractable tricycle type, with electrical retraction by means of single actuator in the fuselage. GAF oleo-pneumatic shock-absorbers. Single rearward-retracting steerable nosewheel, tyre size 8·00-6, pressure 3·17 bars (46 lb/sq in) on N22B, 3·03 bars (44 lb/sq in) on N24A. Twin wheels on each main unit, tyre size 8·00-6, pressure 2·34 bars (34 lb/sq in) on N22B, 2·69 bars (39 lb/sq in) on N24A. Main wheels retract forward into streamline fairings at outer ends of stub wings. Dual hydraulically-operated single-disc brakes on main units. No anti-skid units. Wipaire Wipline 9812 twin-float gear on N22F. Amphibious Wipline 9500 gear also available.

POWER PLANT: Two 298 kW (400 shp) Allison 250-B17B turboprop engines, each driving a Hartzell three-blade constant-speed fully-feathering reversible-pitch metal propeller. Standard fuel capacity 1,018 litres (224 Imp gallons) plus 20 litres (4·4 Imp gallons) unusable in flexible bag tanks. Provision for internal auxiliary tanks for ferry purposes. An additional fuel capacity of 335 litres (73·7 Imp gallons) is provided by two optional integral tanks, one in each wingtip. Gravity refuelling

via overwing point above each pair of tanks. Oil capacity 8·5 litres (1·9 Imp gallons) per engine.

ACCOMMODATION (N22B): Designed for single-pilot operation, but can accommodate crew of two on side-by-side seats. Access to flight deck by forward-opening door on each side. Main cabin has individual seats for up to 13 passengers, at 74 cm (29 in) pitch, with continuous seat tracks and readily-removable seats which allow rapid rearrangement of the cabin to suit alternative loads. Access to main cabin via double doors on port side, with single emergency exit on starboard side. Baggage compartments in nose (with door on each side) and optionally in rear of fuselage (with internal and external access). Whole interior, including flight deck, is heated and ventilated.

ACCOMMODATION (N24A): Flight deck accommodation and access as for N22B. Lengthened main cabin, with similar internal provision to N22B for up to 17 passengers, and access via double port-side doors as in N22B. Enlarged nose baggage compartment. Rear baggage compartment of same capacity as N22B. Ventilation and heating system with individual adjustable outlets.

SYSTEMS: No air-conditioning, hydraulic or pneumatic systems normally, but air-conditioning and pneumatic airframe de-icing are available optionally. Electrical system comprises a 28V 150A DC starter/generator on each engine, and a 22Ah battery with AC inverters. Other optional systems include oxygen demand system for crew and continuous-flow system for passengers; electrical de-icing for propellers, cabin floor hatch and underwing pylon racks.

AVIONICS AND EQUIPMENT: Provision is made for a wide range of nav/com equipment to meet specific customer requirements. Other optional items include full IFR instrumentation and a lightweight weather radar.

ARMAMENT AND OPERATIONAL EQUIPMENT (Mission Master/Search Master): The military variants have provision for four underwing hardpoints capable of accepting up to 227 kg (500 lb) loads, including gun and rocket pods. The nose bay can be utilised to accommodate surveillance and night vision aid equipment. Removable seat armour and self-sealing fuel tanks can be fitted for added protection. Other equipment as detailed under model listings.

DIMENSIONS, EXTERNAL:

Wing span	16·52 m (54 ft 2·3 in)
Wing chord (constant)	1·81 m (5 ft 11¼ in)
Wing aspect ratio	9·11
Length overall: N22B	12·56 m (41 ft 2·4 in)
N24A	14·36 m (47 ft 1¼ in)
Fuselage (max depth)	1·85 m (6 ft 1 in)
Height overall	5·52 m (18 ft 1½ in)
Tailplane span	5·39 m (17 ft 8·4 in)
Wheel track	3·23 m (10 ft 7 in)
Wheelbase: N22B	3·65 m (11 ft 11·6 in)
N24A	4·37 m (14 ft 4 in)
Length of floats: N22F	8·15 m (26 ft 9 in)
Distance between c/l of floats:	
N22F	3·28 m (10 ft 9 in)
Propeller diameter	2·29 m (7 ft 6 in)
Propeller ground clearance	1·22 m (4 ft 0 in)
Distance between propeller centres	
	4·36 m (14 ft 3·6 in)
Crew doors (each): Height	0·86 m (2 ft 10 in)
Width	0·69 m (2 ft 3 in)
Passenger double doors (port):	
Height	1·32 m (4 ft 4 in)
Width	1·22 m (4 ft 0 in)
Height to sill	0·89 m (2 ft 11 in)
Emergency exit (stbd): Height	0·58 m (1 ft 11 in)
Width	0·63 m (2 ft 1 in)

DIMENSIONS, INTERNAL:

Cabin, excl flight deck and rear baggage compartment:	
Length: N22B	5·18 m (17 ft 0 in)
N24A	6·27 m (20 ft 7 in)
Max width	1·30 m (4 ft 3 in)
Max height	1·58 m (5 ft 2·4 in)
Floor area: N22B	6·53 m² (70·25 sq ft)
N24A	8·08 m² (87·0 sq ft)
Volume: N22B	10·19 m³ (360·0 cu ft)
N24A	11·61 m³ (410·0 cu ft)

Baggage compartment volume (nose):

N22B	0·76 m³ (27·0 cu ft)
N24A	1·13 m³ (40·0 cu ft)

Baggage compartment volume (optional, rear):

N22B, N24A	0·79 m³ (28·0 cu ft)

AREAS:

Wings, gross	30·10 m² (324·0 sq ft)
Ailerons (total net)	2·55 m² (27·4 sq ft)
Trailing-edge flaps (total net)	9·81 m² (105·6 sq ft)
Fin	3·63 m² (39·1 sq ft)
Rudder, incl tab	2·89 m² (31·1 sq ft)
Tailplane, incl tabs	7·25 m² (78·0 sq ft)

WEIGHTS AND LOADINGS:

Manufacturer's basic weight empty:

N22B	2,092 kg (4,613 lb)
N24A	2,377 kg (5,241 lb)

Typical operating weight empty:

N22B	2,150 kg (4,741 lb)
N24A	2,377 kg (5,241 lb)

Max fuel load (usable), N22B and N24A:

standard	803 kg (1,770 lb)
extended range	1,066 kg (2,350 lb)

Max T-O and landing weight:

N22B	3,855 kg (8,500 lb)
N24A	4,263 kg (9,400 lb)

Max wing loading: N22B	127·9 kg/m² (26·2 lb/sq ft)
N24A	141·5 kg/m² (29·0 lb/sq ft)

Max power loading:

N22B	6·47 kg/kW (10·625 lb/shp)
N24A	7·12 kg/kW (11·70 lb/shp)

WEIGHTS (floatplane/amphibious versions):

Weight empty, approx: F	2,358 kg (5,200 lb)
A	2,630 kg (5,800 lb)
Max T-O weight: F	3,855 kg (8,500 lb)
A	3,764 kg (8,300 lb)

PERFORMANCE (at max T-O weight, ISA at S/L, except where indicated otherwise):

Normal cruising speed:

N22B, N24A	168 knots (311 km/h; 193 mph)

Stalling speed, power off, flaps up, at AUW of 3,402 kg (7,500 lb):

N22B, N24A	65 knots (121 km/h; 75 mph)

Stalling speed, power off, flaps down, at AUW of 3,402 kg (7,500 lb):

N22B, N24A	47 knots (88 km/h; 54·5 mph)

Max rate of climb at S/L, both engines, T-O rating for 5 min: N22B

N22B	445 m (1,460 ft)/min
N24A	390 m (1,280 ft)/min
N22B (ISA+20°C)	396 m (1,300 ft)/min
N24A (ISA+20°C)	325 m (1,066 ft)/min

Rate of climb at S/L, one engine out, max continuous rating: N22B

N22B	73 m (240 ft)/min
N24A	67 m (220 ft)/min

GAF Nomad Search Master L, with undernose radome

N22B (ISA+20°C)	52 m (170 ft)/min
N24A (ISA+20°C)	49 m (160 ft)/min

Service ceiling, both engines, climbing at 30·5 m (100 ft)/min, max cruise rating:

N22B at 3,630 kg (8,000 lb) AUW	
	6,400 m (21,000 ft)
N24A at 4,082 kg (9,000 lb) AUW	
	6,100 m (20,000 ft)

Min ground turning radius:

N22B, N24A	11·66 m (38 ft 3 in)

Runway LCN at max T-O weight:

N22B	2·3
N24A	2·5

T-O run:

N22B (FAR 23)	223 m (730 ft)
N24A (FAR 23)	296 m (970 ft)
N22B (STOL)	183 m (600 ft)
N22B (FAR 23), ISA+20°C	296 m (970 ft)
N24A (FAR 23), ISA+20°C	366 m (1,200 ft)
N22B (STOL), ISA+20°C	213 m (700 ft)

T-O to 15 m (50 ft):

N22B (FAR 23)	360 m (1,180 ft)
N24A (FAR 23)	521 m (1,710 ft)
N22B (STOL)	320 m (1,050 ft)
N22B (FAR 23), ISA+20°C	463 m (1,520 ft)
N24A (FAR 23), ISA+20°C	610 m (2,000 ft)

Landing from 15 m (50 ft), AUW of 3,630 kg (8,000 lb):

N22B (FAR 23)	338 m (1,110 ft)

N22B (STOL)	216 m (710 ft)
N22B (FAR 23), ISA+20°C	353 m (1,160 ft)

Landing from 15 m (50 ft), AUW of 4,082 kg (9,000 lb):

N24A (FAR 23)	420 m (1,380 ft)
N24A (FAR 23), ISA+20°C	439 m (1,440 ft)

Landing run, AUW of 3,630 kg (8,000 lb):

N22B (FAR 23)	212 m (695 ft)
N22B (STOL)	76 m (250 ft)
N22B (FAR 23), ISA+20°C	226 m (740 ft)

Landing run, AUW of 4,082 kg (9,000 lb):

N24A (FAR 23)	241 m (790 ft)
N24A (FAR 23), ISA+20°C	256 m (840 ft)

Max range at 90% power, standard fuel, reserves for 45 min hold:

N22B, N24A at S/L	580 nm (1,074 km; 668 miles)
N22B, N24A at 3,050 m (10,000 ft)	
	730 nm (1,352 km; 840 miles)

PERFORMANCE (floatplane/amphibious versions):

Max cruising speed at 1,525 m (5,000 ft)

F	150 knots (278 km/h; 173 mph)
A	147 knots (272 km/h; 169 mph)

Climbing speed, one engine out:

F, A	87 knots (161 km/h; 100 mph)
Min control speed: F, A	63 knots (117 km/h; 73 mph)
Stalling speed: F, A	53 knots (99 km/h; 61·5 mph)

T-O to 15 m (50 ft), FAR 135 standard

	442 m (1,450 ft)

Accelerate/stop distance, FAR 135 standard

	580 m (1,900 ft)

HAWKER DE HAVILLAND
HAWKER DE HAVILLAND AUSTRALIA PTY LTD (Member Company of Hawker Siddeley Group)

HEAD OFFICE: PO Box 30, Bankstown, NSW 2200
Telephone: 772 8111
Telex: 20719
CHAIRMAN OF DIRECTORS: R. Kingsford-Smith

MANAGING DIRECTOR: B. S. Price

Hawker de Havilland is primarily a manufacturing, maintenance and overhaul organisation, concentrating on the defence, aviation and marine fields in Australia and overseas, with centres at Bankstown, Sydney, and Guildford, Perth.

Major activities include the manufacture of components for the GAF Nomad aircraft, and sole source production of selected airframe and engine components for Boeing, Boeing Vertol, Lockheed, McDonnell Douglas, Pratt & Whitney, and Westland. Other aerospace products have included infra-red target mini-RPVs (see RPVs and Targets section). Hawker de Havilland's main activity continues to be the provision of overhaul, modification and repair services to the Australian defence forces and a wide variety of other Australian and regional customers.

MINTY
E. R. MINTY
29 Benning Avenue, Turramurra, Sydney, NSW 2074

MINTY SKYHOOK

Mr Ted Minty began preliminary design of this single-seat lightweight autogyro in 1975, and construction of the prototype was started in early 1978. The completed aircraft was exhibited for the first time at the Schofields Air Show, in October 1978. Mr Minty's selection of a twin tail unit for this autogyro, which he has named Skyhook, was influenced by Mr Martin Hollmann in the USA. (Details of the Hollmann HA-2M Sportster appear on pages 522-523, and this aircraft has a tail unit of similar configuration.) The use of twin tails, which are mounted within the wash of the pusher propeller, provides good directional stability and power-off manoeuvrability. Furthermore, the tails are connected at their base by a horizontal stabiliser which is intended to counteract the pitching moment or 'porpoising' experienced with some autogyro designs. The power plant installation includes ultra-lightweight glassfibre cylinder head cooling cowls, designed by Mr Minty, which allow air to be drawn through inlet ducts and over the cylinder heads, the airflow being induced by the rotation of the pusher propeller. Following some slight modifications, it is Mr Minty's intention to put the Skyhook into production.

TYPE: Single-seat lightweight autogyro.

ROTOR SYSTEM: Two-blade rotor of Haller Rotor-Hawk design, with light alloy blades attached directly to a fully-adjustable hub bar. Rotor mast attached to engine mounting frame, and reinforced by two stainless steel

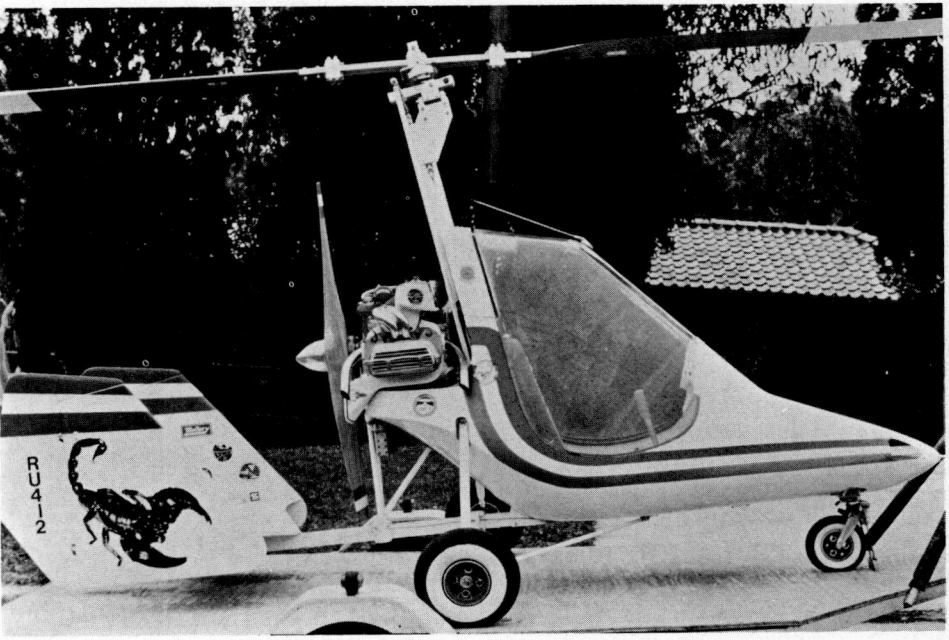

Minty Skyhook single-seat autogyro, intended for commercial production

cables which are attached to the rotor head so that, in the event of a failure of the mast structure, the rotor blades, mast and head cannot be lost.

FUSELAGE: Single keel to which are attached the landing gear, fuselage structure, seat, engine mounting frame and rotor mast, and tail unit. The majority of structural attachments are clamped, rather than bolted or riveted, to reduce to a minimum the number of potential fracture locations in the airframe. Glassfibre fuselage shell weighs only 5·4 kg (12 lb). During the Summer months the aircraft can be flown if desired without the removable Plexiglas windscreen enclosure.

TAIL UNIT: Twin fins and rudders, the base of the fins united by a horizontal stabiliser attached to the keel. The upper ends of the fins are braced by double V

triangular frames of light alloy and chrome molybdenum tube. Fins and rudders each constructed with an Airrx foam core, covered by two layers of continuous woven glassfibre.

LANDING GEAR: Non-retractable tricycle type with single wheel on each unit. Single small tailwheel at aft end of keel. Fully sprung steerable nosewheel. Main wheels are 5 in go-kart wheels, each with a 5·00-5 tyre. Provision for disc brakes.

POWER PLANT: One modified Volkswagen motorcar engine of 1,835 cc capacity, mounted on triangular frame structures supported from the keel, and driving a handmade two-blade silver ash pusher propeller. Fuel tank, incorporated in the base of the pilot's seat, has a capacity of 40·5 litres (8·9 Imp gallons).

ACCOMMODATION: Pilot only, in enclosed cockpit. Aircraft can be flown without Plexiglas windscreen enclosure if desired. Adjustable vents in fuselage nose provide ventilation when the aircraft is flown with the cockpit enclosed.
EQUIPMENT: Standard equipment includes cylinder head high temperature and low fuel warning lights.
DIMENSION, EXTERNAL:
Propeller diameter   1·32 m (4 ft 4 in)
WEIGHTS:
Weight empty   161 kg (354 lb)
Max T-O weight   271 kg (597 lb)
PERFORMANCE:
Max level speed
            more than 87 knots (161 km/h; 100 mph)
Range with max fuel   121 nm (225 km; 140 miles)

SKYCRAFT
SKYCRAFT PTY LTD
138 Bellevue Parade, Carlton, NSW 2218
Telephone: Sydney 546 2501
DIRECTOR: R. G. Wheeler

SKYCRAFT SCOUT
Designed by Mr R. G. Wheeler, and first built and flown in May 1974, the Scout is described as a 'minimum aircraft' which can be quickly dismantled and carried on the roof rack of a motor car. It has been in continuous production since August 1976, when the Australian Department of Transport issued Air Navigation Order 95-10 permitting its operation subject to certain exemptions and limitations. A total of 260 had been ordered and built by early 1979.

The Scout has a wire-braced airframe of aluminium alloy tube, with Dacron-covered (single surface) wings and tail surfaces. The wings have a leading-edge spar, set at a dihedral which raises the tips 0·51 m (20 in) above the centreline, and are set at a mean incidence of 4°. There are no ailerons or wing warping. Tail surfaces are all-moving, comprising a rudder and elevators only, operated by the control column. There is no rudder bar. A non-retractable steel-leaf main landing gear is fitted, forward of the CG, below the A-frame which supports the pilot's glassfibre seat, and has size 12 in × 2·5 in wheels. A small alloy tailwheel is attached to the base of the rudder post.

The Scout is equipped with a 153 cc Aero Pixi piston engine, and a fuel tank of 2·3 litres (0·5 Imp gallon) capacity. It can also be flown power off, as a glider.
DIMENSIONS, EXTERNAL:
Wing span (nominal)   8·69 m (28 ft 6 in)
Wing chord at root   1·75 m (5 ft 9 in)

Skycraft Scout minimum aeroplane (153 cc Aero Pixi engine)

Wing chord at tip	0·41 m (1 ft 4 in)
Wing aspect ratio	6·3
Length overall	5·03 m (16 ft 6 in)
Height overall	1·57 m (5 ft 2 in)
Elevator span	3·00 m (9 ft 10 in)
AREAS:	
Wings (total)	11·71 m² (126·0 sq ft)
Rudder	0·77 m² (8·25 sq ft)
Elevators (total)	1·58 m² (17·00 sq ft)
WEIGHTS AND LOADING:	
Weight empty, equipped	51 kg (112 lb)
Max T-O weight	129 kg (285 lb)
Max wing loading	10·25 kg/m² (2·1 lb/sq ft)

PERFORMANCE (powered):
Max level speed	41 knots (76 km/h; 47 mph)
T-O and landing speed	24 knots (44·5 km/h; 28 mph)
Stalling speed	19-21 knots (35·5-39 km/h; 22-24·5 mph)
Rate of climb	42·5-55 m (140-180 ft)/min
T-O run	64 m (210 ft)
Landing run	28 m (90 ft)
Range	24 nm (44·5 km; 28 miles)
Endurance	40 min

PERFORMANCE (unpowered):
Best glide ratio	24

TRANSAVIA
TRANSAVIA DIVISION, TRANSFIELD (NSW) PTY LTD
73 Station Road, Seven Hills, NSW 2147
Telephone: 624 4244
Telex: 21396 and 70300
CHAIRMAN: F. Belgiorno-Nettis, CBE
DIRECTOR: C. Salteri
GENERAL MANAGER: J. Corby

Transavia, formed in 1964, is a division of Transfield (NSW) Pty Ltd, one of Australia's largest construction companies.

TRANSAVIA PL-12 AIRTRUK
The Airtruk, designed by Mr Luigi Pellarini, was originally type-certificated on 10 February 1966, for spreading fertiliser and for seeding. Swath width is up to 32 m (35 yd) and of unusual uniformity. A liquid-spraying conversion, developed in 1968, is capable of covering a 30·2 m (33 yd) swath. This version has an engine-driven spraypump and a liquid chemical capacity of 818 litres (180 Imp gallons). The PL-12's unconventional layout keeps the tails clear of chemicals, and also permits rapid loading by a vehicle which approaches the aircraft between the tails.

The three-seat prototype Airtruk flew for the first time on 22 April 1965. Delivery of production Airtruks began in December 1966, and 112 had been built by January 1980, for customers in Australia, Europe, Asia and Africa.

Production, mainly of the PL-12 and T-300 Skyfarmer (which see), was continuing in 1980, together with manufacture of the **PL-12-U**, a military-purpose cargo/passenger/ambulance/aerial survey version of which a prototype flew for the first time in December 1970. Certification of this version was granted in February 1971, by which time two production aircraft had been completed; deliveries began later in that year.

Ten Airtruks are assembled by Flight Engineers Ltd in New Zealand (which see).

The following description applies to both the PL-12 and PL-12-U, except where a particular version is indicated:
TYPE: Single-engined agricultural (PL-12) or multipurpose (PL-12-U) aircraft.
WINGS: Strut-braced sesquiplane. Wing section NACA 23012. Dihedral 1° 30′ on upper wings. Incidence

(upper wings) 3° 30′, stub-wings 4°. Conventional all-metal structure, covered with Alclad sheet. All-metal trailing-edge flaps and ailerons, covered with ribbed Alclad sheet, and operated manually. Upper-wing fence on each side of each tailboom to ensure full aileron control, even below stalling speeds. Small stub-wings below fuselage, braced to cabin by a single strut and to upper wings by a V strut on each side.
FUSELAGE: Pod-shaped structure, of 4130 welded steel tube construction with 2024 Alclad covering and glassfibre tailcone.
TAIL UNIT: Twin units, each comprising a fin, rudder and separate T tailplane and elevator, and each carried on a cantilever tubular Alclad boom extending from the upper wings. Small bumper fairing underneath each fin. Manually-operated control surfaces. Adjustable tab in each elevator. Fixed tab on starboard rudder.
LANDING GEAR: Non-retractable tricycle type, each of the three wheels being carried on a pivoted trailing leg. Oleo-pneumatic shock-absorbers on all units. All wheels and tyres same size, 8·00-6. Nosewheel tyre pressure 1·38 bars (20 lb/sq in); main-wheel tyre pressure 2·21 bars (32 lb/sq in). Cleveland hydraulic disc brakes with parking lock.
POWER PLANT: One 224 kW (300 hp) Rolls-Royce Continental IO-520-D flat-six engine, driving a McCauley D2A34C58/90AT-2 two-blade constant-speed metal propeller with spinner. Two upper-wing fuel tanks, total capacity 189 litres (41·5 Imp gallons). Optional long-range installation of second tank in each upper mainplane, increasing total capacity to 379 litres (83·4 Imp gallons). Refuelling point above each upper wing. Oil capacity 11·4 litres (2·5 Imp gallons).
ACCOMMODATION (PL-12): Single-seat cockpit, with door on starboard side. Two-seat cabin aft of chemical hopper/tank for carriage of ground crew, with door at rear of lower deck. Accommodation heated and ventilated.
ACCOMMODATION (PL-12-U): Single-seat cockpit as in PL-12. By removing the central hopper or tank, passenger cabin is enlarged to seat one passenger on upper deck (back to back with pilot's seat) and four more passengers on lower deck. Doors on upper deck (starboard side) and lower deck (port side). Lower-deck cabin is heated.
SYSTEM: 12V electrical system standard.

AVIONICS AND EQUIPMENT: Optional avionics for PL-12-U include VHF (available optionally for PL-12), HF, ADF, artificial horizon and directional gyro. Standard 907 kg (2,000 lb) capacity hopper aft of cockpit, with twin nozzles for dry chemical dispersal and seeding. Optional Powermist spray system (up to 454 litres; 120 US gallons; 100 Imp gallons/min) for liquid chemical (max capacity 816 litres; 216 US gallons; 180 Imp gallons). Hopper can be filled in 15-20 s and contents jettisoned in 3·2-4·5 s. Other optional equipment includes spray nozzles; additional wing fuel tanks; radio; lighting system, including iodine quartz lamps, for night spraying; windscreen demister.
DIMENSIONS, EXTERNAL:
Upper wing span	11·98 m (39 ft 3½ in)
Upper wing chord (constant portion)	1·76 m (5 ft 9¼ in)
Upper wing chord at tip	1·27 m (4 ft 2 in)
Stub-wing span	4·93 m (16 ft 2 in)
Length overall	6·35 m (20 ft 10 in)
Length of fuselage	4·19 m (13 ft 9 in)
Height overall	2·79 m (9 ft 2 in)
Fuselage: Max width	0·97 m (3 ft 2 in)
Tailplane span (each)	2·13 m (7 ft 0 in)
Distance between tailplanes	3·48 m (11 ft 5 in)
Wheel track	2·44 m (8 ft 0 in)
Wheelbase	1·64 m (5 ft 4½ in)
Propeller diameter	2·23 m (7 ft 4 in)
Min propeller ground clearance	0·30 m (1 ft 0 in)
Passenger door (PL-12, rear):	
Height	0·97 m (3 ft 2 in)
Passenger doors (PL-12-U, stbd upper and port lower, each): Height	0·91 m (3 ft 0 in)

DIMENSIONS, INTERNAL (PL-12):
Rear passenger cabin: Length	1·83 m (6 ft 0 in)
Max width	0·97 m (3 ft 2 in)
Max height	2·03 m (6 ft 8 in)
Floor area	0·37 m² (4 sq ft)
Volume: Passenger cabin	0·85 m³ (30 cu ft)
Chemical hopper	1·02 m³ (36 cu ft)

DIMENSIONS, INTERNAL (PL-12-U):
Passenger cabin: Length	2·74 m (9 ft 0 in)
Max width	0·97 m (3 ft 2 in)
Max height	2·11 m (6 ft 11 in)
Floor area	1·67 m² (18 sq ft)
Volume	2·10 m³ (74 cu ft)

AREAS:
Wings, gross 23·78 m² (256·0 sq ft)
Ailerons, total 1·67 m² (18·0 sq ft)
Trailing-edge flaps, total 1·67 m² (18·0 sq ft)
Fins, total 1·30 m² (14·0 sq ft)
Rudders, total 0·56 m² (6·0 sq ft)
Tailplanes, total 2·60 m² (28·0 sq ft)
Elevators, total, incl tabs 1·30 m² (14·0 sq ft)

WEIGHTS AND LOADINGS:
Weight empty: PL-12 839 kg (1,850 lb)
PL-12-U 830 kg (1,830 lb)
Max T-O weight:
PL-12 (agricultural category) 1,855 kg (4,090 lb)
PL-12-U (normal category) 1,723 kg (3,800 lb)
Max landing weight (both) 1,723 kg (3,800 lb)
Max wing loading: PL-12 79 kg/m² (16·2 lb/sq ft)
PL-12-U 73 kg/m² (15·0 lb/sq ft)
Max power loading: PL-12 8·28 kg/kW (13·7 lb/hp)
PL-12-U 7·69 kg/kW (12·7 lb/hp)

PERFORMANCE (at max T-O weight except where indicated):
Never-exceed speed:
PL-12, PL-12-U 155 knots (286 km/h; 178 mph)
Max level speed at S/L, ISA:
PL-12 103 knots (192 km/h; 119 mph)
PL-12-U 112 knots (208 km/h; 129 mph)
Max cruising speed (75% power) at S/L, ISA:
PL-12 95 knots (175 km/h; 109 mph)
PL-12-U 102 knots (188 km/h; 117 mph)
Stalling speed, flaps up:
PL-12 55 knots (103 km/h; 64 mph)
PL-12-U 52 knots (97 km/h; 60 mph)
Stalling speed, flaps down:
PL-12 52 knots (97 km/h; 60 mph)
PL-12-U 50 knots (94 km/h; 58 mph)
Max rate of climb at S/L: PL-12 183 m (600 ft)/min
PL-12-U 244 m (800 ft)/min
Service ceiling (both versions) 3,200 m (10,500 ft)
*T-O run: PL-12 334 m (1,095 ft)
PL-12-U 274 m (900 ft)
*T-O to 15 m (50 ft): PL-12 564 m (1,850 ft)
PL-12-U 457 m (1,500 ft)
Landing run (both versions, at max landing weight)
183 m (600 ft)
Normal range with standard fuel
286 nm (531 km; 330 miles)
Ferry range, standard fuel
330 nm (611 km; 380 miles)
*DCA Australia technique

TRANSAVIA T-300 SKYFARMER

A prototype of the Skyfarmer was flown for the first time in July 1978. This aircraft is a development of the

Transavia T-300 Skyfarmer, showing separated-tails configuration and upper-wing fences

PL-12, the significant difference being that it is powered by a 224 kW (300 hp) Avco Lycoming IO-540-K1A5 flat-six engine, driving a 2·13 m (7 ft 0 in) diameter Hartzell HC-C3YR-1RF/F8468-2R three-blade constant-speed propeller. It also incorporates some of the improved features of the T-320 (1979-80 *Jane's*).

The description of the PL-12 Airtruk applies also to the Skyfarmer, except for the power plant and the following details:

WEIGHTS AND LOADINGS:
Weight empty 907 kg (2,000 lb)
Max T-O weight (agricultural category)
1,855 kg (4,090 lb)
Max landing weight 1,723 kg (3,800 lb)
Max wing loading 78·6 kg/m² (16·1 lb/sq ft)
Max power loading 8·28 kg/kW (13·6 lb/hp)
PERFORMANCE (at max T-O weight, ISA at S/L, except where indicated):
Never-exceed speed 155 knots (286 km/h; 178 mph)
Max level speed 111 knots (206 km/h; 128 mph)
Max cruising speed (75% power)
106 knots (196 km/h; 122 mph)

*Max light-weight cruising speed
116 knots (214 km/h; 133 mph)
Stalling speed, flaps up
55 knots (102 km/h; 63·5 mph)
Stalling speed, flaps down
52 knots (96·5 km/h; 60 mph)
*Light-weight stalling speed, flaps up, power off
45 knots (83·5 km/h; 52 mph)
*Light-weight stalling speed, flaps down, power off
42 knots (78 km/h; 48·5 mph)
Max rate of climb at S/L 198 m (650 ft)/min
*Max light-weight rate of climb at S/L
538 m (1,765 ft)/min
Service ceiling 3,810 m (12,500 ft)
*Light-weight service ceiling 6,890 m (22,600 ft)
T-O run 275 m (902 ft)
*Light-weight T-O run 77 m (252 ft)
T-O to 15 m (50 ft) 475 m (1,558 ft)
*Light-weight landing run 82 m (270 ft)

*Weight of empty aircraft plus pilot and 50% standard fuel

BELGIUM

SABCA
SOCIÉTÉ ANONYME BELGE DE CONSTRUCTIONS AÉRONAUTIQUES

HEAD OFFICE: Chaussée de La Hulpe 185, B-1170 Brussels

Telephone: Brussels (02) 660 00 64
WORKS:
Haren-Brussels, Chaussée de Haecht 1470, B-1130 Brussels

Telephone: Brussels (02) 216 80 10
Telex: SABUSH 21 237
Aéroport de Gosselies-Charleroi, B-6200 Gosselies

Telephone: Charleroi (071) 35 01 70
Telex: SABGO 51 251
CHAIRMAN: B. C. Vallières
DIRECTOR, GENERAL MANAGER: P. G. Willekens

Founded in 1920, SABCA is the oldest aerospace company in Belgium. Before the second World War, it pro-

duced more than 600 military and civil aircraft of 19 different types, some of its own design and some manufactured under licence. Already, at that time, SABCA had participated in various European aircraft programmes.

SABCA's current activities are carried out at two manufacturing plants: Haren-Brussels, where 70% of its activities are concentrated, and Gosselies-Charleroi.

At Haren, the company is working on servo controls, components and equipment for the General Dynamics F-16; Dassault-Breguet/Dornier Alpha Jet; Dassault Mirage F1, Mirage III and Mirage 5; Fokker F27 and F28; and Aérospatiale SA 330 Puma. SABCA manufactures hydraulic components and tanks for F-104G and TF-104G aircraft in European service. It participates in space projects, developing the servo motors for the Ariane space launcher and being involved also in the Spacelab programme.

At Gosselies, SABCA is assembling and testing the 33 Alpha Jets for the Belgian Air Force and the 174 General Dynamics F-16s for Belgium and Denmark. Deliveries of

both types have been made regularly since the handover of the first Alpha Jet in December 1978. SABCA is also continuing to maintain and overhaul Mirage 5 and F-104G aircraft for the Belgian Air Force, and is engaged in overhaul and repair of other military aeroplanes and helicopters for the Belgian and foreign armed forces.

SABCA's Electronic Division is manufacturing IFF, SATT and Doppler equipment, and a variety of aircraft electronic ground equipment. It undertakes work on electronic equipment under F-104G overhaul contracts, and is currently integrating ECM equipment in Mirage 5 aircraft. This division produces a laser tank fire control system for the Belgian, Canadian and Australian Armies and other armed forces, for new and updated main battle tanks.

SABCA is a member of various European industrial consortia; Dassault-Breguet and Fokker have parity holdings in the company.

In 1980 the Haren and Gosselies works occupied a total area of approx 72,000 m² (775,000 sq ft) and between them employed 2,175 people.

SONACA
SOCIÉTÉ NATIONALE DE CONSTRUCTION AÉROSPATIALE

HEAD OFFICE, WORKS AND AIRPORT: Parc Industriel, Route Nationale Cinq, B-6200 Gosselies
Telephone: Charleroi (071) 35 01 90
Telex: 51241

DIRECTORS:
M. Claisse (Managing)
J. Lodewijckx (Financial and Personnel)

P. Wacquez (Manufacturing)
R. Bouniton (Commercial)
E. Barthelemy (Research and Development)
J. Maitre (Quality Control)

SONACA SA, formerly Fairey SA, was formed in April 1978 with an initial capital of BF 95 million, of which 50% is funded by the Belgian government.

Based at Gosselies, SONACA participates in civil and military aviation manufacturing programmes, co-producing the General Dynamics F-16 light fighter and components for the Airbus A310. It also supplies parts for

the Dassault-Breguet Atlantic, Mirage III and Mirage F1, and the Dassault-Breguet/Dornier Alpha Jet, as well as carrying out repairs and maintenance in the civil and military fields.

Recently, SONACA acquired a licence to manufacture and sell the world's lightest passenger seat. It also designed and sells aircraft galley polycarbonate standard units.

The company's present work force is 1,550 persons. In 1980 the plant was undergoing considerable enlargement, involving an investment of BF 500 million, to facilitate the application of the industry's most advanced technology.

BRAZIL

AEROTEC
AEROTEC S/A INDUSTRIA AERONÁUTICA

HEAD OFFICE AND WORKS: Caixa Postal 286, 12200 São
José dos Campos, São Paulo State
Telephone: (0123) 21 8011 and 21 8877
GENERAL AND INDUSTRIAL DIRECTOR: Eng Carlos
Gonçalves
COMMERCIAL AND ADMINISTRATIVE DIRECTOR: Almir
Medeiros

This company was formed in 1962. It designed and built
the Uirapuru light aircraft, which, under the military
designation T-23, was ordered by the Brazilian, Bolivian
and Paraguayan air forces and for civil flying clubs.

Aerotec builds wings for the EMBRAER Ipanema
agricultural aircraft (which see). The company is also participating in EMBRAER's general aviation aircraft construction programme, by building fuselages for the
EMB-720C/D Minuano, EMB-721C/D Sertanejo and
EMB-810C Seneca II.

In 1979 Aerotec employed 110 persons and its premises
occupied approx 7,000 m² (75,350 sq ft) of covered space.

AEROTEC A-122 UIRAPURU
Brazilian Air Force designation: T-23

The Uirapuru prototype (PP-ZTF), with an 80·5 kW
(108 hp) Avco Lycoming O-235-C1 engine, flew for the
first time on 2 June 1965 and was described and illustrated
in the 1966-67 *Jane's*. It was followed by a second prototype and two military pre-production models.

Aerotec then built 126 military **A-122A** Uirapurus (100
for the Brazilian Air Force, 18 for Bolivia and eight for
Paraguay), plus approx 25 of the **A-122B** civil model, with
different cockpit canopy.

A total of 155 Uirapurus, including prototype and pre-
production aircraft, had been built by early 1977, when
production was suspended. Meanwhile, 46 Brazilian Air
Force T-23s are being fitted with new engine cowlings, fuel
tanks and canopies (as designed for the Uirapuru II) during IRAN work, to improve performance.

A full description of the A-122A military version can be
found in the 1978-79 *Jane's*.
TYPE: Two-seat primary trainer.
POWER PLANT: One 119 kW (160 hp) Avco Lycoming
O-320-B2B flat-four engine, driving a Sensenich
M-74-DM-6-060 two-blade fixed-pitch metal propeller. Variable-pitch propeller optional. Two integral fuel
tanks in wing leading-edges, with total capacity of 140
litres (31 Imp gallons). Optional 40 litre (8·8 Imp gallon) wingtip tanks.

Model of the civil version of the Aerotec A-132 Uirapuru II two-seat aerobatic trainer *(Ronaldo S. Olive)*

DIMENSIONS, EXTERNAL:
Wing span	8·50 m (27 ft 10¾ in)
Wing area, gross	13·50 m² (145·3 sq ft)
Length overall	6·60 m (21 ft 8 in)
Height overall	2·70 m (8 ft 10 in)

WEIGHTS:
Weight empty	540 kg (1,191 lb)
Max T-O weight	840 kg (1,852 lb)

PERFORMANCE (at max T-O weight, S/L, ISA. A-122A in
original form before new IRAN update):
Max level speed	122 knots (227 km/h; 141 mph)
Max cruising speed (75% power)	100 knots (185 km/h; 115 mph)
Econ cruising speed (65% power)	89 knots (164 km/h; 102 mph)
Max rate of climb at S/L	255 m (836 ft)/min
Service ceiling	4,500 m (14,760 ft)
Max range	429 nm (800 km; 497 miles)

AEROTEC A-132 UIRAPURU II

Aerotec began the development of a higher-powered,
fully aerobatic trainer for the Brazilian Air Force, based
on the A-122A but with modified wings and tail and
improved cockpit layout and avionics. This has the designation A-132 Uirapuru II; it is intended to replace existing
T-23s of the Brazilian Air Force, which is expected to
order 100 initially, with deliveries to begin in the first half
of 1981.

Principal changes include a flat-sided fuselage, slightly
increased wing span, enlarged vertical tail, and improved canopy design.

Two prototypes are being built, the first of which was
scheduled to fly in October 1980. The other is for static
testing.
POWER PLANT: One 149 kW (200 hp) Avco Lycoming
IO-360-C1C6 flat-four engine, driving a two-blade
constant-speed variable-pitch propeller.

DIMENSIONS, EXTERNAL:
Wing span	9·00 m (29 ft 6¼ in)
Wing dihedral	7°
Length overall	7·20 m (23 ft 7½ in)
Height overall	2·70 m (8 ft 10 in)

WEIGHTS:
Weight empty	600 kg (1,322 lb)
Baggage weight	50 kg (110 lb)
Max T-O weight	920 kg (2,028 lb)

PERFORMANCE (estimated, at max T-O weight, ISA):
Max level speed	141 knots (262 km/h; 163 mph)
Cruising speed (75% power)	116 knots (215 km/h; 133 mph)
Econ cruising speed (60% power)	104 knots (192 km/h; 119 mph)
Max rate of climb at S/L	305 m (1,000 ft)/min
Endurance	4 h

CTA
CENTRO TÉCNICO AEROESPACIAL

HEADQUARTERS: São José dos Campos, São Paulo State

The Centro Técnico Aeroespacial (Aerospace Technical Centre) is a Ministry of Aeronautics establishment for
training aeronautical and aerospace personnel and for
conducting aeronautical and aerospace research and
development. It is composed of four institutes: the
Instituto Tecnológico de Aeronáutica (ITA); the Instituto
de Pesquisas e Desenvolvimento (IPD); the Instituto de
Atividades Espaciais (IAE); and the Instituto de Fomento
e Coordenação Industrial (IFI).

The **ITA** is a college of engineering for aeronautical and
aerospace personnel. The **IPD** conducts aeronautical
research and development. The **IAE** conducts space
research and development. The **IFI** is responsible for the
fostering and co-ordination of the Brazilian aerospace
industry, and for the certification of civil aircraft and
approval of other aeronautical products.

EMBRAER
EMPRESA BRASILEIRA DE AERONÁUTICA SA

HEAD OFFICE AND WORKS: Av Brig Faria Lima No. 2170,
Caixa Postal 343, 12200 São José dos Campos, São
Paulo State
Telephone: (0123) 21 5400
Telex: (391) 1122445 EBAE BR or (391) 1125105
EBAE BR
RIO OFFICE: Aeroporto Santos Dumont, Sobreloja, Salão
de Embarque No. 2, Rio de Janeiro, RJ
Telephone: (021) 222 8981
PRESIDENT AND SUPERINTENDENT DIRECTOR: Ozires Silva
COMMERCIAL DIRECTOR: Ozilio Carlos da Silva
TECHNICAL DIRECTOR: Guido Fontegalante Pessotti
PRODUCTION DIRECTOR: Antonio Garcia da Silveira
FINANCIAL DIRECTOR: Alberto Franco Faria Marcondes
INDUSTRIAL RELATIONS DIRECTOR: Renato José da Silva
PUBLIC RELATIONS: Mário Leme Galvão
PRESS RELATIONS: Fernando Laux

EMBRAER was created on 19 August 1969, and came
into operation on 2 January 1970 to promote the
development of the Brazilian aircraft industry. It now has
an authorised capital of Cr $2,000 million (about US $68
million), of which Cr $1,285 million (US $44 million) had
been subscribed by mid-1979. The Brazilian government
owns 51% of the voting shares, 90% of the subscribed
capital being held by private shareholders. EMBRAER
had a work force in May 1980 of 5,046 persons and a
factory area of 124,700 m² (1,342,260 sq ft). By the end of
1979 EMBRAER had built a total of 2,053 aircraft, of
which 1,222 were of Piper design. The 2,000th aircraft, an
EMB-110P1 Bandeirante, was delivered to Aeromech, an
American commuter airline, on 26 February 1980.

Since August 1974, EMBRAER has had a comprehen-

EMBRAER EMB-110P1 Bandeirante, with side views (right, top to bottom) of B1, S1, K1 and P1 *(Pilot Press)*

sive co-operative agreement with Piper Aircraft Corporation involving the assembly and later manufacture in
Brazil of the Seneca II and Navajo Chieftain twin-engined
aircraft and worldwide distribution of the products of both
companies. At the beginning of 1975, this agreement was
extended to include the single-engined Cherokee series.

In consequence, with the co-operation of other Brazilian companies (Neiva, Aerotec, Aeromot and Motortec), EMBRAER now produces and markets these aircraft in Brazil.

Since 1976, EMBRAER has manufactured in Brazil components for the Northrop F-5E Tiger II combat aircraft.

EMBRAER has in current production the EMB-110 Bandeirante, the EMB-111 maritime reconnaissance version of the Bandeirante, the pressurised EMB-121 Xingu twin-turboprop transport aircraft, the EMB-326GB Xavante licence-built version of the Italian Aermacchi M.B.326GC jet trainer and ground attack aircraft, the EMB-201A Ipanema agricultural aircraft, and various EMBRAER-built versions of Piper single- and twin-engined light aircraft. Types under development include the EMB-120 Brasilia commuter transport and the EMB-312 basic trainer.

On 10 March 1980, EMBRAER purchased the entire stockholding in Neiva (which see), which thus became a wholly-owned subsidiary. It is planned to transfer production of the Ipanema and Piper types to Neiva, in order to devote more EMBRAER factory space and manpower to Bandeirante, Brasilia, Xingu and EMB-312 production.

EMBRAER EMB-110 BANDEIRANTE (PIONEER)

Brazilian Air Force designations: C-95, EC-95 and R-95

The Bandeirante twin-turboprop light transport was developed to a Brazilian Ministry of Aeronautics specification calling for a general-purpose aircraft capable of carrying out missions such as transport, navigation training and aeromedical evacuation.

The first YC-95 prototype (2130) flew for the first time on 26 October 1968, followed by the second (2131) on 19 October 1969, and the basically similar third aircraft (PP-ZCN) on 26 June 1970. These prototypes, designated EMB-100, were described in the 1970-71 *Jane's*.

The first production EMB-110 Bandeirante (C-95/2133) flew for the first time on 9 August 1972, and was test-flown until December 1972 as part of the certification programme. Following the completion of testing to FAR Pt 23, the aircraft was certificated by the Aerospace Technical Centre of the Ministry of Aeronautics, and the first three Bandeirantes were delivered to the Brazilian Air Force on 9 February 1973.

By 1 January 1980 a total of 252 Bandeirantes of various models had been sold, to some 60 operators. The 200th Bandeirante was delivered on 18 December 1978; the production rate was increased to six per month in 1979, and deliveries totalled 241 by the Spring of 1980. A total of 59 Bandeirantes was scheduled to be delivered during 1980.

The Bandeirante is available in the following versions:

EMB-110. Basic 12-seat aircraft; 60 operated by Brazilian Air Force as **C-95**.

EMB-110A. Navaid checking and calibration version. Four operated by Brazilian Air Force as **EC-95**.

EMB-110B. Aerial photogrammetric version, with electrically-operated ventral sliding door, size 0·84 m (2 ft 9 in) × 1·86 m (6 ft 1¼ in), permitting the use of aerial cameras (Zeiss RMK A8·5/23, RMK A15/23, RMK A30/23 and Wild RC-10), a Zeiss IRU regulator, and Zeiss NT-1 navigation visors. Other equipment includes Decca 72 Doppler navigation system. Crew includes three equipment operators. Six operated by Brazilian Air Force as **R-95**. TerraFoto, a Brazilian enterprise, has an **EMB-110B1**, with quick-change aerial photogrammetric/nine-passenger executive interior. One B1 also ordered by Uruguayan Air Force, with convertible aerial photogrammetric/14-passenger feederliner interior.

EMB-110C. Standard 15-passenger commercial transport version. Entered commercial service with Transbrasil on 16 April 1973. Acquired also by Chilean Navy (three) as **R-95**. and Uruguayan Air Force (five).

EMB-110C(N) and Uruguayan Air Force (five).

EMB-110E(J). Executive transport version with accommodation for seven passengers, four in individual seats and three on a sideways-facing sofa. Other features

include a galley, wardrobe, and stereo AM/FM and tape deck.

EMB-110K1. All-cargo military version, lengthened by insertion of a 0·85 m (2 ft 9½ in) plug between the flight deck and the centre-fuselage, and with upward-opening 1·80 m × 1·42 m (5 ft 10½ in × 4 ft 8 in) cargo door on port side of rear fuselage. Ventral fin. Two 559 kW (750 shp) PT6A-34 engines. Twenty ordered initially by Brazilian Air Force as **C-95A**; 20 more ordered in 1979. Described separately.

EMB-110P. Commercial third-level commuter version for 18 passengers, developed from EMB-110C. Described separately.

EMB-110P1. Quick-change version of EMB-110P2, for passenger and cargo operations. Total of 46 built by December 1979, for operators in Australia, Finland, Guam, Mexico, New Zealand, Saudi Arabia, the UK and the USA. Three ordered by Gabon Air Force for 1980 delivery.

EMB-110P2. Third-level commuter transport version, carrying up to 21 passengers. First flown on 3 May 1977. Total of 25 delivered by 1 January 1980 to operators in Australia, Fiji, France, Upper Volta, Papua New Guinea, the UK and the USA. Detailed description applies to this version.

EMB-110P3. Pressurised transport version, seating up to 19 passengers; powered by 875 kW (1,173 shp) PT6A-65 turboprop engines. Described separately.

EMB-110S1. Geophysical survey version, with 559 kW (750 shp) PT6A-34 engines, increased internal fuel (1,914 litres; 421 Imp gallons), and provision for two 318 litre (70 Imp gallon) wingtip tanks. Proton magnetometer in extended tailboom, gamma ray spectrometers, Doppler navigation system and data recording system.

EMB-111. Maritime patrol version, described separately.

The following description, except where noted, applies to the standard production EMB-110P2:

TYPE: Twin-turboprop general-purpose transport.

WINGS: Cantilever low-wing monoplane. Wing section NACA 23016 (modified) at root, NACA 23012 (modified) at tip. Sweepback 19′ 48″ at quarter-chord. Dihedral 7° at 28% chord. Incidence 3°. All-metal two-spar structure, of 2024-T3 and -T4 aluminium alloy, with detachable glassfibre wingtips. Glassfibre wing/fuselage fairing. All-metal statically-balanced Frise-type ailerons and double-slotted flaps. Trim tab in port aileron. De-icing system optional.

FUSELAGE: All-metal semi-monocoque structure of 2024-T3 aluminium alloy. Two upward-hinged doors, one on each side of nose, provide access to avionics.

TAIL UNIT: Cantilever all-metal structure, with sweptback vertical surfaces. Glassfibre dorsal fin. Ventral fin (K1, P1 and P2 only). Trim tabs in rudder and port elevator. Tab in starboard elevator linked to flaps, to offset pitching moment during flap extension. De-icing system optional.

LANDING GEAR: Hydraulically-retractable tricycle type, with single wheel and ERAM oleo-pneumatic (nitrogen) shock-absorber on each unit. Main-wheel tyre size 670 × 270-12 (10 ply rating), pressure 5·86-6·20 bars (85-90 lb/sq in). Steerable, forward-retracting nosewheel unit has tyre size 6·50-8, pressure 4·27-4·69 bars (62-68 lb/sq in).

POWER PLANT: Two 559 kW (750 shp) Pratt & Whitney Aircraft of Canada PT6A-34 turboprop engines, each driving a Hartzell HC-B3TN-3C/T10178H-8R constant-speed three-blade metal propeller with autofeathering and full reverse-pitch capability. Four integral fuel tanks in wings, with total capacity of 1,720 litres (378 Imp gallons). Oil capacity 8·7 litres (1·9 Imp gallons). Gravity refuelling point on top of each wing. Optional de-icing system for engine air inlets and propellers.

ACCOMMODATION: Pilot and co-pilot side by side on flight deck. Seats for up to 21 passengers in main cabin, at 74 cm (29 in) pitch. Crew/passenger door at front and passenger/baggage door at rear, both on port side; emergency exit over wing on each side, and opposite crew/passenger door on starboard side. Crew/passenger door can also be used as emergency exit. Cabin floor stressed for uniformly distributed loads of up to 488 kg/m² (100 lb/sq ft). Baggage compartment at rear of cabin, with total capacity of 2·0 m³ (70·6 cu ft). Flush-type toilet in compartment at rear of cabin. Toilet/lavatory standard. Windscreen de-icing optional.

SYSTEMS: Air-cycle-type air-conditioning system with cooling capacity of 25,000 BTU/h and engine bleed heating. Hydraulic system, pressure 207 bars (3,000 lb/sq in), for landing gear actuation, dual independent braking systems, nosewheel steering and parking brake. Electrical system utilises two starter/generators, giving 200A continuously or 300A for one minute, and one 24V 34Ah nickel-cadmium battery with two 250VA static inverters to supply 115/26V 400Hz AC power. External power receptacle on port side of forward fuselage. Oxygen system for crew and passengers, using oxygen cylinder in rear of fuselage with capacity of 3·3 m³ (115 cu ft) at 128 bars (1,850 lb/sq in) pressure.

AVIONICS AND EQUIPMENT: Avionics available in one of three standard packages. No. 1 package includes two Collins 618M-3 360-channel VHF transceivers, two Collins VIR-30A VOR/ILS/marker beacon receivers, two Collins DF-206 ADF receivers, and one or two Collins PN-101 gyromagnetic compass systems. No. 2 package includes one Collins 51Z-6 marker beacon receiver, two Bendix DFA-73A ADF systems, one Collins 618M-2B VHF1 system and one Whinner TC-609 VHF2 system, one Sunair ASB-100A HF system, one Collins 51R-7A/51V-5 VOR/ILS receiver, and one or two Collins PN-101 gyromagnetic compass systems. No. 3 package includes one or two King KC 55A gyromagnetic compass systems, two King KX 175BE VHF nav/com, two King KN 75 glideslope receivers, two King KR 21 marker beacon receivers, and two King

R-95 (EMB-110B) photogrammetric version of the EMBRAER Bandeirante

The 21-seat EMB-110P2 third-level commuter transport version of the Bandeirante, in the insignia of Air Volta

KR 85 ADF receivers. Optional avionics include one Sunair ASB-100A HF/AM/SSB transceiver, one RCA AVQ-47 or Bendix RDR-1200 weather radar, Bendix M4-C or M4-D autopilot, one Collins DME-40 or two King KN 65A DME systems, one Collins TDR-90 or two King KT 76A ATC transponders, one Garrett Rescu/88L emergency locator transmitter, one Collins AVR-101 voice recorder, one Collins ALT-50 or King KRA 405 radio altimeter, entertainment radio, tape deck and PA system. Standard equipment includes engine fire detection system, propeller synchroniser, eight-day clock, annunciator panel, dual heated pitot heads, heated static port, external power socket, dual landing lights, taxi light, rotating beacons, dual map lights, instrument lighting system, soundproofing, low-profile glareshield and towbar. Optional equipment includes three-light strobe system, complete de-icing and anti-icing systems, toilet, a variety of cabinets and a range of galley equipment.

DIMENSIONS, EXTERNAL:

Wing span	15·32 m (50 ft 3¼ in)
Wing chord at root	2·45 m (8 ft 0½ in)
Wing chord at tip	1·35 m (4 ft 5 in)
Wing aspect ratio	8·10
Length overall	15·10 m (49 ft 6½ in)
Length of fuselage	14·59 m (47 ft 10½ in)
Height overall	4·92 m (16 ft 1¾ in)
Fuselage: Max width	1·72 m (5 ft 7¾ in)
Tailplane span	7·54 m (24 ft 9 in)
Propeller diameter	2·36 m (7 ft 9 in)
Distance between propeller centres	
	4·80 m (15 ft 9 in)
Propeller ground clearance	0·276 m (10¾ in)
Wheel track	4·94 m (16 ft 2½ in)
Wheelbase	5·01 m (16 ft 5¼ in)
Passenger door (rear, port):	
Height	1·35 m (4 ft 5¼ in)
Width	0·85 m (2 ft 9½ in)
Crew/passenger door (fwd, port):	
Height	1·42 m (4 ft 8 in)
Width	0·63 m (2 ft 1 in)
Passenger emergency exits (two, each):	
Height	0·80 m (2 ft 7½ in)
Width	0·63 m (2 ft 1 in)
Crew emergency exit: Height	0·80 m (2 ft 7½ in)
Width	0·55 m (1 ft 9¾ in)

DIMENSIONS, INTERNAL:

Cabin: Max length	9·53 m (31 ft 3¼ in)
Width	1·60 m (5 ft 3 in)
Height	1·60 m (5 ft 3 in)
Floor area	12·00 m² (129·2 sq ft)
Volume	20·4 m³ (720·4 cu ft)

AREAS:

Wings, gross	29·10 m² (313·23 sq ft)
Ailerons (total)	2·16 m² (23·25 sq ft)
Flaps (total)	4·90 m² (52·74 sq ft)
Fin, excl dorsal fin	3·81 m² (41·01 sq ft)
Dorsal fin	0·82 m² (8·83 sq ft)
Ventral fin (K1, P1 and P2)	0·80 m² (8·61 sq ft)
Rudder, incl tab	1·69 m² (18·19 sq ft)
Tailplane	5·51 m² (59·31 sq ft)
Elevators, incl tabs	4·31 m² (46·39 sq ft)

WEIGHTS AND LOADINGS:

Weight empty, equipped	3,516 kg (7,751 lb)
Max payload	1,681 kg (3,706 lb)
Max T-O weight	5,670 kg (12,500 lb)
Max landing and max zero-fuel weight	
	5,450 kg (12,015 lb)
Max wing loading	195·52 kg/m² (40·04 lb/sq ft)
Max power loading	5·07 kg/kW (8·33 lb/shp)

PERFORMANCE (EMB-110P2 at max T-O weight, ISA, except where indicated):

Max level speed at 2,440 m (8,000 ft)	
	248 knots (460 km/h; 286 mph)
Max cruising speed at 3,050 m (10,000 ft)	
	225 knots (417 km/h; 259 mph)
Econ cruising speed at 3,050 m (10,000 ft)	
	176 knots (326 km/h; 203 mph)
Stalling speed at max landing weight	
	71 knots (132 km/h; 82 mph) CAS
Max rate of climb at S/L	545 m (1,788 ft)/min
Rate of climb at S/L, one engine out	
	136 m (446 ft)/min
Time to 3,050 m (10,000 ft)	6 min
Time to 4,575 m (15,000 ft)	10 min
Service ceiling at AUW of 5,300 kg (11,684 lb)	
	7,350 m (24,100 ft)
Service ceiling, one engine out, at AUW of 5,300 kg	
(11,684 lb)	3,780 m (12,400 ft)
T-O run	430 m (1,410 ft)
T-O to 15 m (50 ft)	675 m (2,215 ft)
Landing from 15 m (50 ft)	850 m (2,790 ft)
Landing run	565 m (1,854 ft)
Range at 3,050 m (10,000 ft), 45 min reserves:	
with max fuel	1,025 nm (1,900 km; 1,180 miles)
with 1,440 kg (3,175 lb) standard payload	
	268 nm (497 km; 309 miles)

Brazilian Air Force C-95A Bandeirante (EMB-110K1), with a typical cargo load

EMBRAER EMB-110K1 and P1 BANDEIRANTE
Brazilian Air Force designation of EMB-110K1: C-95A

The following description applies to the K1 and P1, both of which are in current production:

WINGS: As EMB-110P2, but with optional inflatable de-icing boots on leading-edges.

FUSELAGE: As EMB-110P2, but with enlarged rear door for cargo loading.

TAIL UNIT, LANDING GEAR AND POWER PLANT: As EMB-110P2, including ventral fin.

ACCOMMODATION (EMB-110K1): Pilot and co-pilot side by side on flight deck. Crew door forward on port side; emergency exit forward of wing on starboard side. Cabin equipped for cargo only, with enlarged cargo door on port side at rear. Flush-type toilet behind co-pilot's seat.

ACCOMMODATION (EMB-110P1): As K1, but with quick-change cabin seating up to 18 persons. Overwing emergency exit on each side, making three in all.

SYSTEMS: Air-conditioning, hydraulic and electrical systems as for EMB-110P2. Oxygen system optional.

AVIONICS AND EQUIPMENT: Standard and optional avionics and equipment as for EMB-110P2.

DIMENSIONS, EXTERNAL: As EMB-110P2 plus:

Cargo door (rear, port):		
Height		1·42 m (4 ft 8 in)
Width		1·80 m (5 ft 11 in)

DIMENSIONS, INTERNAL: As EMB-110P2

AREAS: As EMB-110P2

WEIGHTS AND LOADINGS: As EMB-110P2 except:

Max payload:		
K1		1,804 kg (3,977 lb)
P1 (passenger configuration)		1,633 kg (3,600 lb)

PERFORMANCE (at max T-O weight, ISA): As EMB-110P2 except:

Range at 3,050 m (10,000 ft), 45 min reserves:	
K1 with 1,750 kg (3,856 lb) standard payload	
	165 nm (306 km; 190 miles)
P1 with 1,440 kg (3,175 lb) standard payload	
	225 nm (417 km; 259 miles)

EMBRAER EMB-110P BANDEIRANTE

WINGS, FUSELAGE, TAIL UNIT AND LANDING GEAR: As EMB-110P2, except for shorter fuselage, fewer doors and emergency exits (see 'Accommodation' paragraph), and no ventral fin.

POWER PLANT: Two 507 kW (680 shp) Pratt & Whitney Aircraft of Canada PT6A-27 turboprop engines; otherwise as EMB-110P2.

ACCOMMODATION: Pilot and co-pilot side by side on flight deck, which is separated from main cabin by door. Cabin seats up to 18 passengers. Downward-hinged door on port side, aft of wing, with built-in airstairs. Cabin floor stressed for loads of up to 450 kg/m² (92 lb/sq ft). Emergency exit over wing on each side. Baggage compartment at rear of cabin, with total capacity of 2·0 m³ (70·6 cu ft). Toilet/lavatory standard.

SYSTEMS: As EMB-110P2.

AVIONICS AND EQUIPMENT: Standard avionics include two Collins 618M-2B 360-channel VHF transceivers, one

Sunair ASB-100A HF/AM/SSB transceiver, one Collins 51R-7A VOR/ILS receiver, two Bendix DFA-73A1 ADF receivers, one Collins 51Z-6 marker beacon receiver, and one Collins 51V-5 glideslope receiver. Optional avionics include RCA AVQ-47 or Bendix RDR-1200 weather radar, Bendix M4-C or M4-D autopilot, single or dual Sperry STARS IVB or IVC flight directors, entertainment radio, tape deck, PA system, and complete de-icing and anti-icing system. Standard and optional equipment as listed for EMB-110P2.

DIMENSIONS, EXTERNAL: As EMB-110P2 except:

Length overall	14·23 m (46 ft 8¼ in)
Length of fuselage	13·74 m (45 ft 1 in)
Wheelbase	4·56 m (14 ft 11½ in)
Crew/passenger door (fwd, port)	None
Emergency exits	Two only

DIMENSIONS, INTERNAL: As EMB-110P2 except:

Cabin: Max length	8·65 m (28 ft 4½ in)
Floor area (incl flight deck)	10·9 m² (117·3 sq ft)
Volume	18·4 m³ (649·8 cu ft)

AREAS: As EMB-110P2 (except no ventral fin)

WEIGHTS AND LOADINGS:

Weight empty, equipped	3,403 kg (7,502 lb)
Max payload	1,645 kg (3,626 lb)
Max T-O weight	5,600 kg (12,345 lb)
Max landing and max zero-fuel weight	
	5,300 kg (11,684 lb)
Max wing loading	193·10 kg/m² (39·55 lb/sq ft)
Max power loading	5·52 kg/kW (9·08 lb/shp)

PERFORMANCE (at max T-O weight, ISA, except where indicated):

Max level speed at 2,285 m (7,500 ft)	
	244 knots (452 km/h; 280 mph)
Max cruising speed at 3,050 m (10,000 ft)	
	232 knots (430 km/h; 267 mph)
Econ cruising speed at 3,050 m (10,000 ft)	
	184 knots (341 km/h; 212 mph)
Stalling speed at max landing weight	
	71 knots (132 km/h; 82 mph) CAS
Max rate of climb at S/L	442 m (1,450 ft)/min
Rate of climb at S/L, one engine out	137 m (450 ft)/min
Time to 3,050 m (10,000 ft)	8 min
Time to 4,575 m (15,000 ft)	13 min
Service ceiling at AUW of 5,300 kg (11,684 lb)	
	7,700 m (25,300 ft)
Service ceiling, one engine out, at AUW of 5,300 kg	
(11,684 lb)	3,750 m (12,300 ft)
T-O run	452 m (1,480 ft)
T-O to, and landing from, 15 m (50 ft)	
	695 m (2,280 ft)
Landing run	372 m (1,220 ft)
Range at 3,050 m (10,000 ft), 45 min reserves:	
with max fuel	1,100 nm (2,038 km; 1,266 miles)
with standard payload	320 nm (593 km; 368 miles)

EMBRAER EMB-110P3 BANDEIRANTE

A T-tail characterises this 19-passenger pressurised version of the Bandeirante, which also has redesigned landing gear and is powered by two 875 kW (1,173 shp) PT6A-65 turboprop engines. First flight is scheduled for early 1982, with deliveries beginning about a year later.

LANDING GEAR: Redesigned compared with earlier Bandeirante models, with twin wheels on each unit.

ACCOMMODATION: Cabin seating 19 passengers. Additional airstair door on starboard side, serving both for access to baggage compartment and as second emergency exit.

SYSTEM: Cabin max differential of 0·17 bars (2·5 lb/sq in)

WEIGHTS:

Baggage compartment load	260 kg (573 lb)
Max T-O weight	7,000 kg (15,432 lb)

PERFORMANCE (estimated, at max T-O weight):

Cruising speed	265 knots (491 km/h; 305 mph)

Range with max payload, normal fuel reserves
more than 600 nm (1,112 km; 691 miles)

Artist's impression of the T-tailed pressurised EMB-110P3 Bandeirante

EMBRAER EMB-111

Brazilian Air Force designation: P-95

This land-based maritime reconnaissance aircraft, based on the EMB-110 Bandeirante, was designed to meet specifications issued by the Comando Costeiro, the Brazilian Air Force's Coastal Command, which has ordered 12. The main external differences in this version are the large nose radome, housing search radar, and the addition of wingtip fuel tanks.

The first EMB-111 (2262) flew for the first time on 15 August 1977; Brazilian Air Force aircraft, the first three of which were delivered on 11 April 1978, serve with the 1° Esquadrão of the 7° Grupo de Aviação, located at Salvador AFB, Bahia.

Six have been delivered to the Chilean Navy. These aircraft have some mission equipment changes, including full de-icing system, and passive ECM antennae under the nose and at the tail. One EMB-111 has been ordered by the Gabon Air Force, for 1981 delivery.

TYPE: Twin-turboprop maritime reconnaissance aircraft.

WINGS: As EMB-110P2, but with reinforced leading-edges and fitted with tip-tanks.

FUSELAGE: Similar to EMB-110P2, but with large nose radome.

TAIL UNIT AND LANDING GEAR: As EMB-110P2.

POWER PLANT: Two 559 kW (750 shp) Pratt & Whitney Aircraft of Canada PT6A-34 turboprop engines, each driving a Hartzell three-blade reversible-pitch propeller with spinner. Four integral fuel tanks in wings (total capacity 1,914 litres; 421 Imp gallons), and two permanent wingtip tanks (total capacity 636 litres; 140 Imp gallons). Overall total fuel capacity 2,550 litres (561 Imp gallons), of which 2,454 litres (540 Imp gallons) are usable. Oil capacity 8·7 litres (1·9 Imp gallons).

ACCOMMODATION: Pilot and co-pilot side by side on flight deck. Main cabin can accommodate search radar/radio operator, ECM operator, one or two observers, and a second radar or ECM operator. Port-side door at rear, for crew and cargo, opens inwards and can be used for airdrop of paratroops and survival equipment. Galley and toilet in main cabin.

AVIONICS AND EQUIPMENT: One Collins 618T-3B or 718U-5 AM/SSB/CW transceiver, two Collins 618M-3 VHF transceivers, one Collins AN/ARC-159 UHF transceiver, Collins Audio interphone, two Sperry C-14 gyromagnetic compasses, two Bendix DFA-74A or Collins DF-206 ADF receivers, two Collins VIR-30A or VIR-31A VOR/ILS/marker beacon receivers, one Collins AN/APX-92 IFF transponder, one Collins DF-301E VHF/DF or one Collins DME-40 DME, one Bendix ALA-51 or Collins ALT-50 radio altimeter, one Litton LN-33 inertial navigation system, Thomson-CSF passive ECM, and one AIL AN/APS-128 (SPAR-1) sea patrol radar. Optional avionics include Bendix M4-D autopilot and ONS-25 Omega, single or dual Sperry STARS IVB or IVC flight directors, entertainment radio, tape deck, PA systems and complete de-icing and anti-icing system.

ARMAMENT AND OPERATIONAL EQUIPMENT: Four underwing pylons for eight 5 in HVAR air-to-surface rockets (two per pylon), or four launchers each with seven 2·75 in FFAR rockets; or three stores pylons, plus a leading-edge-mounted 50 million candlepower searchlight on the starboard wing. For target marking, six Brazilian-built MK-6 smoke grenades are carried, as well as a Motorola SST-121 transponder. Flares of 200,000 candlepower also available for illumination of targets at night. Ventral chute for smoke marker buoys, high-intensity flares or chaff dispensing. Provision for 1·4 kW loud-hailer system.

EMB-111 patrol version of the Bandeirante, developed by EMBRAER *(Pilot Press)*

DIMENSIONS, EXTERNAL:

Wing span over tip-tanks	15·95 m (52 ft 4 in)
Wing mean chord (aerodynamic)	1·95 m (6 ft 4¾ in)
Wing area, gross	29·10 m² (313·2 sq ft)
Wing aspect ratio	8·07
Length overall	14·91 m (48 ft 11 in)
Length of fuselage	14·38 m (47 ft 2¼ in)
Height overall	4·91 m (16 ft 1¼ in)
Wheel track	4·94 m (16 ft 2½ in)
Wheelbase	4·26 m (13 ft 11¾ in)
Propeller diameter	2·36 m (7 ft 9 in)
Propeller ground clearance	0·28 m (11 in)

Main door (rear, port):

Height	1·35 m (4 ft 5¼ in)
Width	0·80 m (2 ft 7½ in)
Height to sill	1·26 m (4 ft 1½ in)

Emergency exit (overwing, stbd):

Height	0·80 m (2 ft 7½ in)
Width	0·63 m (2 ft 0¾ in)

DIMENSIONS, INTERNAL:

Cabin: Max length	8·65 m (28 ft 4½ in)
Width	1·60 m (5 ft 3 in)
Height	1·60 m (5 ft 3 in)
Floor area	11·60 m² (124·9 sq ft)

AREAS: As EMB-110P2

WEIGHTS AND LOADINGS:

Weight empty, equipped	3,760 kg (8,289 lb)
Max T-O weight	7,000 kg (15,432 lb)
Max ramp weight	7,030 kg (15,498 lb)
Max zero-fuel weight	5,150 kg (11,354 lb)
Max landing weight	5,450 kg (12,015 lb)
Max wing loading	241·38 kg/m² (49·44 lb/sq ft)
Max power loading	6·26 kg/kW (10·29 lb/shp)

PERFORMANCE (at max T-O weight, ISA+15°C, except where indicated):

Max cruising speed at 3,050 m (10,000 ft)
208 knots (385 km/h; 239 mph)

Econ cruising speed at 3,050 m (10,000 ft)
190 knots (352 km/h; 218 mph)

Stalling speed at max landing weight
71 knots (132 km/h; 82 mph) CAS

Max rate of climb at S/L	362 m (1,190 ft)/min
Time to 3,050 m (10,000 ft)	13 min
Time to 4,575 m (15,000 ft)	28 min

Service ceiling, at AUW of 5,300 kg (11,684 lb)
7,770 m (25,500 ft)

Service ceiling, one engine out, at AUW of 5,300 kg (11,684 lb)
4,025 m (13,200 ft)

T-O run	940 m (3,084 ft)
T-O to 15 m (50 ft)	1,590 m (5,217 ft)
Landing from 15 m (50 ft)	725 m (2,379 ft)
Landing run	405 m (1,329 ft)
Min ground turning radius	12·80 m (42 ft 0 in)

Range at 3,050 m (10,000 ft), max fuel, 45 min reserves
1,590 nm (2,945 km; 1,830 miles)

EMBRAER EMB-120 BRASILIA

The EMB-120 Brasilia is a twin-turboprop passenger and cargo transport, design of which was started in September 1979. Certification, scheduled for 1984, will be to FAR Pt 25. A mockup of the passenger version was displayed for the first time in Rio de Janeiro on 25 April 1980; general appearance can be seen in the accompanying illustration. Options on approx 40 Brasilias were held in Spring 1980 by several of the country's regional operators.

Military versions, including maritime patrol and ECM models, are expected to be developed.

TYPE: Twin-turboprop general-purpose transport.

WINGS: Cantilever low-wing monoplane. Wing section NACA 23016 (modified) at root, NACA 23012 (modified) at tip. Dihedral 6° from roots. Incidence 2°. Sweepback 0° at 66% chord. Three-spar fail-safe structure between engine nacelles (across fuselage), two-spar on outer panels, forming a continuous tip-to-tip torsion box. Machined and bonded extrusions of 2024 aluminium alloy on spar caps. Chemically milled skin. Double-slotted semi-Fowler all-metal trailing-edge flaps, supported on twin, fully fail-safe tracks. All-metal Frise-type ailerons, each with inset trim tab. Pneumatic-boot de-icing of leading-edges.

FUSELAGE: Conventional metal semi-monocoque fail-safe structure, of circular cross-section. Machined windscreen frames and wing attachment fittings. Chemically milled skin. Structure pressurised, except for nosecone and tailcone.

EMBRAER EMB-111 maritime reconnaissance aircraft, with searchlight and underwing rockets

TAIL UNIT: Cantilever T tail, of three-spar all-metal construction with chemically milled skin. Fixed-incidence swept tailplane, with horn-balanced elevators. Swept-back fin and double-hinged rudder. Pneumatic booster on rudder (for single-engined operation only); trim and anti-servo tabs in elevators. Pneumatic-boot de-icing of leading-edges.

LANDING GEAR: Retractable tricycle type, with twin wheels and oleo-pneumatic shock-absorber on each unit. Hydraulic actuation; all units retract forward (main units into engine nacelles). Tyre sizes 560 × 200 mm (main), 460 × 140 mm (nose); tyre pressure 5·17 bars (75 lb/sq in) on main units, 5·86 bars (85 lb/sq in) on nose unit. Multiple-disc brakes, actuated hydraulically by means of a proportional anti-skid system.

POWER PLANT: Two Pratt & Whitney Aircraft of Canada PT7A-1 turboprop engines, each flat rated to 1,118·5 kW (1,500 shp) and driving a Hamilton Standard 14RF-1 four-blade constant-speed reversible-pitch double-actuated propeller. Fuel in one 1,610 litre (354 Imp gallon) integral tank in each wing; total capacity 3,220 litres (708 Imp gallons). Single-point pressure refuelling, plus overwing gravity point in upper surface of each wing. Oil capacity 16 litres (3·5 Imp gallons).

ACCOMMODATION: Pilot and co-pilot on flight deck; cabin attendant in passenger version. Main cabin accommodates 30 passengers in three-abreast seating, with overhead lockable baggage racks, in pressurised and air-conditioned environment. Baggage compartment aft of passenger cabin. Provisions for wardrobe, galley and toilet. Main passenger door, with airstairs, forward of wing on port side. Service door in starboard side at rear, also with airstairs. Overwing emergency exit on each side. Optional large cargo/service door at rear on port side.

SYSTEMS: Hamilton Standard air-conditioning and pressurisation system (max differential 0·48 bars; 7 lb/sq in), with dual packs of recirculating equipment. Single main hydraulic system (pressure 207 bars; 3,000 lb/sq in), powered by dual pumps (one on each engine), plus emergency standby system for landing gear extension. Rudder booster actuated pneumatically by engine bleed air. Main electrical power supplied by two 24 kW 28V DC starter/generators; two 5 kW 28V DC auxiliary generators and 24V 40Ah battery for secondary power. Single high-pressure oxygen cylinder for crew; individual chemical system for passengers. Pneumatic de-icing for wing and tail leading-edges; electrical heaters to de-ice windscreens, engine air intakes, propellers and pitot tubes. The starboard engine, with propeller stopped, will serve as an APU to provide bleed air for air-conditioning and electrical power on the ground.

AVIONICS AND EQUIPMENT: Blind-flying instrumentation standard. Provisions for full Category II operation, depending upon avionics and equipment selection by individual customers. Special navigation systems (INS, Omega, satellite) also available optionally.

DIMENSIONS, EXTERNAL:

Wing span	19·77 m (64 ft 10¼ in)
Wing chord at root	2·50 m (8 ft 2½ in)
Wing chord at tip	1·40 m (4 ft 7 in)
Wing aspect ratio	10
Length overall	19·63 m (64 ft 4¾ in)
Length of fuselage	18·38 m (60 ft 3½ in)
Fuselage: Max diameter	2·29 m (7 ft 6 in)
Height overall	6·05 m (19 ft 10¼ in)
Tailplane span	6·58 m (21 ft 7 in)
Wheel track (c/l of shock-struts)	5·90 m (19 ft 4¼ in)
Wheelbase	6·67 m (21 ft 10½ in)
Propeller diameter	3·20 m (10 ft 6 in)
Propeller ground clearance (min)	0·35 m (1 ft 1¾ in)

Passenger door (fwd, port):

Height	1·60 m (5 ft 3 in)
Width	0·70 m (2 ft 3½ in)
Height to sill	1·60 m (5 ft 3 in)

Service door (rear, stbd):

Height	1·40 m (4 ft 7 in)
Width	0·70 m (2 ft 3½ in)
Height to sill	1·60 m (5 ft 3 in)

EMBRAER EMB-120 Brasilia twin-turboprop transport *(Pilot Press)*

Cargo door (rear, port, optional):

Height	1·60 m (5 ft 3 in)
Width	2·00 m (6 ft 6¾ in)
Height to sill	1·60 m (5 ft 3 in)

Emergency exits (overwing, each):

Height	0·92 m (3 ft 0¼ in)
Width	0·51 m (1 ft 8 in)

Emergency exits (flight deck side windows, each):

Max height	0·48 m (1 ft 7 in)
Max width	0·51 m (1 ft 8 in)

DIMENSIONS, INTERNAL:
Cabin, excl flight deck and baggage compartment:

Length	9·11 m (29 ft 10¾ in)
Max width	2·16 m (7 ft 1 in)
Max height	1·75 m (5 ft 9 in)
Floor area	14·00 m² (150·69 sq ft)

Rear baggage compartment:

Length	2·55 m (8 ft 4½ in)
Floor area	3·50 m² (37·67 sq ft)
Volume	6·80 m³ (240 cu ft)

Cabin, incl flight deck and baggage compartment:

Total volume	approx 33·0 m³ (1,165 cu ft)

AREAS:

Wings, gross	38·03 m² (409·35 sq ft)
Ailerons (total)	3·18 m² (34·23 sq ft)
Trailing-edge flaps (total)	6·50 m² (69·97 sq ft)
Fin	6·90 m² (74·27 sq ft)
Rudder	2·20 m² (23·68 sq ft)
Tailplane	8·86 m² (95·37 sq ft)
Elevators, incl tabs	3·45 m² (37·14 sq ft)

WEIGHTS AND LOADINGS:

Basic operating weight empty	5,270 kg (11,618 lb)
Max payload	3,130 kg (6,900 lb)
Max fuel	2,280 kg (5,026 lb)
Max T-O weight	9,072 kg (20,000 lb)
Max ramp weight	9,155 kg (20,183 lb)
Max zero-fuel weight	8,400 kg (18,518 lb)
Max landing weight	8,872 kg (19,560 lb)
Max wing loading	239 kg/m² (49 lb/sq ft)
Max power loading	4·05 kg/kW (6·66 lb/shp)

PERFORMANCE (estimated, at max T-O weight, ISA):
Never-exceed speed
270 knots (500 km/h; 310 mph) EAS
Max level and max cruising speed at 7,315 m (24,000 ft)
294 knots (545 km/h; 338 mph)
Econ cruising speed 250 knots (463 km/h; 288 mph)
Stalling speed, flaps up, power off
105 knots (195 km/h; 121 mph) EAS

Stalling speed, flaps down, power off
81 knots (150 km/h; 94 mph) EAS
Max rate of climb at S/L 884 m (2,900 ft)/min
Rate of climb at S/L, one engine out
244 m (800 ft)/min
Service ceiling 10,210 m (33,500 ft)
Service ceiling, one engine out 5,485 m (18,000 ft)
Balanced T-O field length at S/L, and 0·6 weighted landing field length at S/L 1,200 m (3,937 ft)
Min ground turning radius 15·50 m (50 ft 10¼ in)
Range with 30 passengers, no optional fittings, reserves for 100 nm (185 km; 115 miles) alternate plus 45 min
350 nm (648 km; 403 miles)
Range with max fuel, reserves as above
1,400 nm (2,594 km; 1,612 miles)

EMBRAER EMB-121 XINGU
Brazilian Air Force designation: VU-9

The prototype Xingu (PP-ZXI) flew for the first time on 10 October 1976. A second airframe was built for static testing, and a third is being used for fatigue testing. First production Xingu (PP-ZCT) was flown on 20 May 1977, and Brazilian CTA certification was awarded in May 1979. British CAA certification was granted in July of the same year. Nineteen production Xingus had been completed by January 1980, and production was scheduled to reach a rate of four per month by the end of 1980. Six VU-9s have been delivered to the Grupo de Transporte Especial (Special Transport Group) of the Brazilian Air Force and are in service with the 6° Esquadrão de Transporte Aéreo (6th Air Transport Squadron) at Brasilia. Other customers include CSE in the UK (one), the Belgian CAA (five), Sabena (five), the French Air Force (35), Saudi Arabia (one on lease), and Brazilian civil operators (six).

TYPE: Twin-turboprop general-purpose transport.
WINGS: Cantilever low-wing monoplane. Utilises same wing as EMB-110P2 (which see), but with reduced span and modified tips. Leading-edge pneumatic de-icing boots optional.

FUSELAGE: All-metal semi-monocoque fail-safe structure of aluminium alloy, with circular cross-section, designed for a max operating pressure differential of 0·414 bars (6·0 lb/sq in).

TAIL UNIT: Cantilever metal T tail, with glassfibre dorsal fin. Pneumatic de-icing boots optional for fin and tailplane leading-edges. Trim and balance tabs in rudder and each elevator. Ventral fin.

LANDING GEAR: Hydraulically-retractable tricycle type, with oleo-pneumatic shock-absorber on each unit. Single main wheels, with tyres size 670 × 210-12 (10 ply rating), pressure 5·52-5·86 bars (80-85 lb/sq in). Steerable, forward-retracting twin nosewheels, with tyres size 16 × 44 (six ply rating), pressure 5·52-5·86 bars (80-85 lb/sq in).

POWER PLANT: Two 507 kW (680 shp) Pratt & Whitney Aircraft of Canada PT6A-28 turboprop engines, each driving a Hartzell HC-B3TN-3D/T10178HB-8R three-blade constant-speed metal propeller with autofeathering and full reverse-pitch capability. Four integral fuel tanks in wings, with total capacity of 1,666 litres (366 Imp gallons). Gravity refuelling point on top of each wing. Oil capacity 8·3 litres (1·8 Imp gallons).

ACCOMMODATION: Two seats side by side on flight deck. Cabin seats up to nine passengers. Downward-hinged door on port side, aft of wing, with built-in airstairs. Emergency exit over wing on starboard side. Baggage compartments in nose (with external access) and at rear of cabin (with internal access). Toilet/lavatory and galley standard.

First production EMBRAER EMB-121 Xingu (two PT6A-28 turboprop engines)

SYSTEMS: Air-cycle type air-conditioning system, max capacity 20,000 BTU/h for cooling and 40,000 BTU/h for heating. Pressurisation system (max differential 0·41 bars; 6 lb/sq in) maintains S/L cabin environment up to 4,270 m (14,000 ft) and 2,440 m (8,000 ft) environment up to 8,335 m (27,350 ft). Primary electrical system is 28V DC, supplied by two 9 kW starter/generators and a 40Ah alkaline battery with a temperature sensor. Two 125VA or 600VA static inverters provide 115/26V single-phase AC power at 400Hz. Electrical anti-icing of windscreen, engine air intakes and propellers; pneumatic-boot de-icing of wing and tail unit leading-edges.

AVIONICS: Standard avionics include dual RCA AVC-110A VHF com transceivers, dual RCA AVN-220A VOR/ILS/marker beacon receivers, dual Collins ADF-60A ADF, one VOR/ILS OBS indicator (co-pilot), dual RCA AVA-310 audio panels, one Sperry C-14 gyromagnetic compass with dual Sperry RD-44 course indicator (pilot), one AIM-200 DC FM directional gyro (co-pilot), one Sperry GH-14-330 gyro horizon (pilot), one AIM-500 DC FM gyro horizon (co-pilot), one Collins TDR-90 transponder with Smiths 01-200-105 encoding altimeter, one Collins DME-40 DME, two Telex TEL-66C microphones, two pairs of Telex A1210 earphones, dual Flite-Tronics PC-15 BC(D) static converters, and one Sunair ASB-100A HF transceiver. Optional avionics are available in three standard packages, with dual Collins DF-206 ADF, Sunair ASB-100A HF/AM/SSB, dual RCA AVA-310 and Sperry SPZ-200 autopilot common to all three. In addition, package No. 1 offers dual RCA AVC-110A VHF com, one RCA AVN-220A VHF nav and one Sperry C-14 gyromagnetic compass; package No. 2 offers dual RCA AVC-110A VHF com, dual RCA AVN-220A VHF nav, dual Sperry C-14 gyromagnetic compasses, and Garrett Rescu/88L ELT; package No. 3 offers dual Collins VHF-20A VHF com, dual Collins VIR-30A VHF nav, dual Sperry C-14 gyromagnetic compasses, Garrett Rescu/88L ELT, Collins ALT-50 radio altimeter, and dual Sperry STARS IVC flight directors for pilot and co-pilot. Bendix RDR-1200 or RCA Primus 40 weather radar, cabin music and PA systems are optional extras on all three packages; Collins TDR-90 transponder on packages 2 and 3; Collins DME-40 on package 3; and pilot's Sperry STARS IVB or IVC on package 2.

EQUIPMENT: Standard equipment comprises maximum permissible airspeed indicator, eight-day clock, chronometer, cabin rate of climb indicator, cabin altitude and differential pressure indicator, annunciator panel, heated stall warning system, dual heated pitot tubes and heated static ports, external power sockets, wing ice light, dual landing lights, dual taxi lights, dual anti-collision strobe lights, dual map lights, cabin dome lights, instrument lighting system, low profile glareshield, and hand-type cabin fire extinguishers. Optional equipment includes three-light strobe system, fire extinguishing system, de-icing and anti-icing system, toilet, and a range of galley equipment.

DIMENSIONS, EXTERNAL:

Wing span	14·45 m (47 ft 5 in)
Wing chord at root	2·33 m (7 ft 7¾ in)
Wing chord at structural tip	1·49 m (4 ft 10¾ in)
Wing chord at fuselage c/l	2·47 m (8 ft 1¼ in)
Wing aspect ratio	7·18
Length overall	12·25 m (40 ft 2¼ in)
Length of fuselage	11·16 m (36 ft 7½ in)
Fuselage max width	1·86 m (6 ft 1¼ in)
Height overall	4·74 m (15 ft 6½ in)
Tailplane span	5·58 m (18 ft 3¾ in)
Wheel track	5·24 m (17 ft 2¼ in)
Wheelbase	2·88 m (9 ft 5½ in)
Propeller diameter	2·36 m (7 ft 9 in)
Distance between propeller centres	5·10 m (16 ft 8¾ in)

Passenger door (rear, port):

Height	1·32 m (4 ft 4 in)
Width	0·63 m (2 ft 0¾ in)

Emergency exit (one, overwing):

Height	0·96 m (3 ft 1¾ in)
Width	0·51 m (1 ft 8 in)

DIMENSIONS, INTERNAL:
Cabin, incl flight deck:

Max length	5·18 m (17 ft 0 in)
Max width	1·74 m (5 ft 8½ in)
Max height	1·52 m (4 ft 11¾ in)

Baggage compartment volume:

nose	0·30 m³ (10·6 cu ft)
rear	0·71 m³ (25·1 cu ft)

AREAS:

Wings, gross	27·50 m² (296·0 sq ft)
Ailerons (total)	1·84 m² (19·81 sq ft)
Trailing-edge flaps (total)	4·90 m² (52·74 sq ft)
Vertical tail surfaces (total, excl dorsal fin)	4·00 m² (43·06 sq ft)
Rudder, incl tab	1·30 m² (13·99 sq ft)
Dorsal fin	0·54 m² (5·81 sq ft)
Ventral fin	0·94 m² (10·12 sq ft)
Horizontal tail surfaces (total)	5·84 m² (62·86 sq ft)
Elevator, incl tabs	2·17 m² (23·36 sq ft)

WEIGHTS AND LOADINGS:

Weight empty, equipped	3,500 kg (7,716 lb)
Max payload	1,477 kg (3,256 lb)
Max T-O weight	5,670 kg (12,500 lb)
Max zero-fuel weight	4,660 kg (10,273 lb)
Max landing weight	5,340 kg (11,772 lb)
Max cabin floor loading	488 kg/m² (100 lb/sq ft)
Max wing loading	206·2 kg/m² (42·2 lb/sq ft)
Max power loading	5·59 kg/kW (9·19 lb/shp)

PERFORMANCE (at max T-O weight, ISA, except where indicated):

Max cruising speed at 3,350 m (11,000 ft)	243 knots (450 km/h; 280 mph)
Econ cruising speed at 6,100 m (20,000 ft)	203 knots (376 km/h; 234 mph)
Stalling speed at max T-O weight, flaps up	96 knots (178 km/h; 111 mph)
Stalling speed at max landing weight, flaps down	74 knots (137·5 km/h; 85·5 mph)
Max rate of climb at S/L	426 m (1,400 ft)/min
Service ceiling	7,925 m (26,000 ft)
Service ceiling, one engine out	3,960 m (13,000 ft)
T-O to 15 m (50 ft)	865 m (2,840 ft)
Landing from 15 m (50 ft) at max landing weight	850 m (2,790 ft)
Range with 900 kg (1,985 lb) payload at 6,100 m (20,000 ft), 45 min reserves	900 nm (1,666 km; 1,035 miles)
Range with max fuel and 610 kg (1,345 lb) payload at 6,100 m (20,000 ft), ISA, 45 min reserves	1,270 nm (2,352 km; 1,461 miles)

EMBRAER EMB-121B XINGU II

From the 49th aircraft onward, EMBRAER plans to switch production of the Xingu to the slightly larger Xingu II, with more powerful PT6A-42 engines and a lengthened cabin. Design of this version began in January 1979, and construction of a prototype started in June of that year. This aircraft was due to make its first flight in May 1980; first deliveries of production aircraft are due in 1981.

WINGS: Similar to those of EMB-121, but with increased span. Safe-life construction. Vortex generators on upper surfaces, forward of ailerons. Trim tab in port aileron, balance tab in starboard aileron. Pneumatic-boot de-icing of leading-edges.

FUSELAGE: Generally similar to that of EMB-121, but cabin lengthened by 0·84 m (2 ft 9 in). Fail-safe structure except for wing carry-through members, which are safe-life. Chemically milled skin. Pressurised, except for non-pressurised nosecone and tailcone.

TAIL UNIT: Generally similar to EMB-121, but with larger-area fin and tailplane, and smaller elevators.

LANDING GEAR: Similar to that of EMB-121, but with size 40 × 110 mm nosewheel tyres and ERAM multiple-disc brakes.

POWER PLANT: Two 634 kW (850 shp) Pratt & Whitney Aircraft of Canada PT6A-42 turboprop engines, each driving a Dowty R314 constant-speed reversible-pitch propeller. Fuel tank in each wing, combined usable capacity 2,170 litres (477 Imp gallons). Gravity refuelling point in upper surface of each wing. Pitot-type engine intakes, with inertial separator to prevent solid particle ingestion. Electrical de-icing of engine air intakes; NACA flush-type intakes for oil coolers.

ACCOMMODATION: Normal flight crew of two; to be certificated also for single-pilot operation. Basic layout for eight or nine passengers, with seats at 79 cm (31 in) pitch, plus toilet. Alternative club layout with seven seats, two folding tables, galley and toilet. Baggage compartments in nose (unpressurised) and at rear of cabin (pressurised). Passenger door aft of wing on port side; overwing emergency exit on starboard side. Nose baggage compartment has door on each side. Entire accommodation pressurised and air-conditioned.

SYSTEMS: Hamilton Standard air-conditioning system; pressurisation system max differential 0·41 bars (6 lb/sq

in). Single hydraulic system (pressure 207 bars; 3,000 lb/sq in) for landing gear extension/retraction, brakes (incl parking brake) and nosewheel steering. Emergency gear extension by manual pump, brake actuation by pressure accumulators. Primary electrical system is 28V DC, supplied by two 9 kW starter/generators and a 40Ah nickel-cadmium battery, for flap actuation, propeller and engine intake anti-icing, autopilot and trim servos, and windscreen anti-icing. Pneumatic-boot de-icing of wing and tail unit leading-edges. High-pressure oxygen bottle for crew, individual chemical system for passengers.

AVIONICS AND EQUIPMENT: Basic single King Silver Crown II avionics system, plus Bendix RDR-1200 weather. radar and Sperry SPZ-200 autopilot. Blind-flying instrumentation standard.

DIMENSIONS, EXTERNAL: As for EMB-121 except:

Wing span	14·83 m (48 ft 7¾ in)
Wing aspect ratio (geometric)	7·88
Length overall	13·44 m (44 ft 1¼ in)
Length of fuselage	12·05 m (39 ft 6½ in)
Tailplane span	6·05 m (19 ft 10¼ in)
Wheelbase	3·19 m (10 ft 5½ in)

Passenger door (rear, port):

Height	1·32 m (4 ft 4 in)
Width	0·63 m (2 ft 0¾ in)
Height to sill	1·20 m (3 ft 11¼ in)

Baggage doors (fwd, port and stbd) and service door (rear, stbd):

Height	0·47 m (1 ft 6½ in)
Width	0·90 m (2 ft 11½ in)
Height to sill	1·50 m (4 ft 11 in)

Emergency exit (overwing, stbd):

Height	0·96 m (3 ft 1¾ in)
Width	0·51 m (1 ft 8 in)

DIMENSIONS, INTERNAL:
Cabin, excl flight deck:

Length	4·50 m (14 ft 9¼ in)
Max width	1·70 m (5 ft 7 in)
Max height	1·52 m (5 ft 0 in)
Floor area	5·30 m² (57·05 sq ft)
Volume	9·00 m³ (317·8 cu ft)

Baggage compartment volume:

nose	0·34 m³ (12·00 cu ft)
rear of cabin	0·80 m³ (28·25 cu ft)

AREAS: As EMB-121 except:

Wings, gross	27·90 m² (300·3 sq ft)
Fin (incl dorsal and ventral fins)	5·48 m² (58·99 sq ft)
Tailplane	6·90 m² (74·27 sq ft)
Elevators, incl tab	1·83 m² (19·70 sq ft)

WEIGHTS AND LOADINGS:

Basic operating weight empty	3,850 kg (8,487 lb)
Max payload	950 kg (2,094 lb)
Max fuel	1,690 kg (3,725 lb)
Max T-O weight	5,670 kg (12,500 lb)
Max ramp weight	5,700 kg (12,566 lb)
Max zero-fuel weight	4,800 kg (10,582 lb)
Max landing weight	5,450 kg (12,015 lb)
Max wing loading	203 kg/m² (41·60 lb/sq ft)
Max power loading	4·48 kg/kW (7·36 lb/shp)

PERFORMANCE (estimated, at max T-O weight, ISA):

Never-exceed speed	253 knots (468 km/h; 291 mph) EAS
Max cruising speed	272 knots (504 km/h; 313 mph)
Econ cruising speed	232 knots (430 km/h; 267 mph)
Stalling speed, flaps up, power off	96 knots (178 km/h; 111 mph) EAS
Stalling speed, flaps down, power off	76 knots (141 km/h; 88 mph) EAS
Max rate of climb at S/L	731 m (2,400 ft)/min
Rate of climb at S/L, one engine out	176 m (580 ft)/min
Service ceiling	8,840 m (29,000 ft)
Service ceiling, one engine out	4,360 m (14,300 ft)
T-O run	450 m (1,477 ft)
T-O to 15 m (50 ft)	715 m (2,346 ft)

EMB-121B Xingu II nine-passenger twin-turboprop transport (*Pilot Press*)

Landing from 15 m (50 ft)	860 m (2,822 ft)
Landing run	540 m (1,772 ft)
Min ground turning radius	11·20 m (36 ft 9 in)

Range, cruising at 7,620 m (25,000 ft), 45 min reserves:
with 900 kg (1,984 lb) payload
650 nm (1,205 km; 748 miles)
with max fuel   1,580 nm (2,928 km; 1,820 miles)

EMBRAER (AERMACCHI) EMB-326GB XAVANTE

Brazilian Air Force designation: AT-26

Under an agreement signed in May 1970, EMBRAER is assembling under licence the Aermacchi M.B.326GB jet trainer/ground attack aircraft for the Brazilian Air Force, by whom the type is known as the AT-26 Xavante, the name of a Brazilian Indian tribe.

The initial order called for the manufacture of 112 aircraft, at a rate of two per month. Further orders were placed for 40 in December 1975, three during 1976, 20 in 1979 and nine in 1980, making an overall total of 184. The first Brazilian-assembled Xavante made its first flight on 3 September 1971, and the first two aircraft were handed over to the Brazilian Air Force a few days later. The three Xavantes ordered in 1976 were for the Togolese Air Force, which now has six; the nine ordered and delivered in 1980 were for the Paraguayan Air Force.

By 31 March 1980 a total of 163 Xavantes had been delivered. Those of the Brazilian Air Force are in service with the 3° Esquadrão Misto de Reconhecimento e Ataque (3rd Mixed Reconnaissance and Attack Squadron) at Santa Cruz AFB, Rio de Janeiro; the 4° Esquadrão Misto de Reconhecimento e Ataque at Santa Maria AFB, Rio Grande do Sul State; the 4° Grupo de Aviação (4th Aviation Group) at Fortaleza, Ceará State; the CATRE (Centro de Aplicações Táticas e Recompletamento de Equipagens: Tactical and Aircrew Training Centre) at Natal, Rio Grande do Norte State; the 10° Grupo de Aviação at Cumbica AFB, São Paulo State; and other units.

A description of the standard M.B. 326GB appears in the Italian section of this edition; the version for the Brazilian Air Force is basically similar, except in the following respects:

AVIONICS AND EQUIPMENT: Two Collins Type 618M-2B 360-channel VHF transceivers, Collins CIA-102A interphone system, Bendix DFA 73A-1 ADF, and a complete VOR/ILS system using a Collins 51RV-1 VOR/LOC/glideslope receiver, Collins 51Z-4 marker beacon receiver and AN/APX-72. Provision for IFF transponder.

ARMAMENT: Six underwing points for bombs, gun pods or other stores. Typical loads include six 250 lb bombs; two 500 lb bombs and two twin 7·62 mm gun pods; four 250 lb bombs and two twin 7·62 mm gun pods; two twin 7·62 mm gun pods and two underwing drop-tanks; two twin 7·62 mm gun pods and four LM-70/7 rocket pods (each with seven SBAT 70 mm folding-fin air-to-ground projectiles); two twin 7·62 mm gun pods and two LM-37/36 rocket pods (each with thirty-six SBAT 37 mm air-to-ground rockets); six LM-70/7 rocket pods; or two LM-70/19 rocket pods (each with nineteen SBAT 70 mm air-to-ground rockets); or photographic reconnaissance pods. All armament loads are designed and manufactured in Brazil.

EMBRAER EMB-312

Brazilian Air Force designation: T-27

Design of the EMB-312, by a team under the leadership of Ing Joseph Kovacs, began in January 1978 as part of a programme to develop a new basic trainer for the Brazilian Air Force. On 6 December that year a contract was awarded to EMBRAER by the Departamento de Pesquisas e Desenvolvimento (Department of Research and Development) of the Brazilian Ministry of Aeronautics, calling for the completion of two flying prototypes plus additional airframes for static and fatigue testing.

During the past year the EMB-312 design has undergone a number of design changes from the configuration described in the 1979-80 Jane's. These include slightly greater wing and tailplane span, a reduction in overall length, non-swept instead of sweptback vertical tail surfaces, a wider wheel track and longer wheelbase. A radio controlled model was used to investigate some of the flying characteristics, including spinning.

Design characteristics of the EMB-312 include high manoeuvrability, short take-off and landing, the ability to operate from unprepared runways, and a high degree of stability. Intended to meet the requirements of FAR Pt 23 Appendix A, its construction embodies such modern techniques as integral machining by numerical control machinery, chemical milling, and metal-to-metal bonding.

The EMB-312 has been allocated the Brazilian Air Force designation T-27, and 168 have been ordered. These are scheduled to begin entering service in late 1982 or early 1983, initially to replace the Cessna T-37C. The first prototype made its initial flight on 16 August 1980. Production may be undertaken by EMBRAER's subsidiary, Neiva.

TYPE: Tandem two-seat basic trainer.

WINGS: Cantilever low-wing monoplane. Wing section NACA 63₂A-415 at root, NACA 63A-212 at tip.

EMBRAER AT-26 Xavante (Aermacchi M.B.326GB) of the Brazilian Air Force

Dihedral 5° 30′ at 30% chord. Incidence 1° 25′. Geometric twist 2° 12′. Sweepback 0° 43′ 26″ at quarter-chord. Aluminium alloy two-spar torsion-box structure of 2024T-3511 extrusions and 2024T-3 sheet. Single-slotted trailing-edge flaps of 2024T-3, supported on 4130 steel tracks. Frise-type constant-chord balanced ailerons. Mechanically actuated spring tab in each aileron.

FUSELAGE: Conventional semi-monocoque structure of 2024T-3 aluminium alloy.

TAIL UNIT: Cantilever all-metal structure, of similar construction to wings. Non-swept fin and horn-balanced rudder. Non-swept fixed-incidence tailplane and balanced elevators. Trim tab in port elevator.

LANDING GEAR: Hydraulically retractable tricycle type, with single wheel and Piper oleo-pneumatic shock-absorber on each unit. Shimmy damper on nose unit. Rearward-retracting nose unit; main units retract inward into wings. Cleveland 40-130 main wheels, 40-76B nosewheel. Tyre sizes 508 × 165 mm on main wheels, 305 × 152 mm on nosewheel. Cleveland 30-95A brakes.

POWER PLANT: One 559 kW (750 shp) Pratt & Whitney Aircraft of Canada PT6A-25C turboprop engine, flat rated to 432·5 kW (580 shp) and driving a Hartzell HC-B3TN-3C/T10178H-8R three-blade constant-speed propeller with spinner. Two integral fuel tanks in each wing, total capacity 1,400 litres (308 Imp gallons). Gravity refuelling point in each wing upper surface. Fuel system allows for up to 35 s of inverted flight.

ACCOMMODATION: Instructor and pupil in tandem, on Martin-Baker Mk 04B ejection seats, in air-conditioned cockpit. One-piece fully-transparent moulded canopy, opening sideways to starboard. Rear seat elevated. Dual controls standard. Baggage compartment in rear fuselage, with access via door on port side.

SYSTEMS: Freon cycle air-conditioning system, with engine-driven compressor. Single hydraulic system, pressure 131 bars (1,900 lb/sq in), for landing gear extension and retraction. No pneumatic system. 28V DC electrical power provided by a 6 kW starter/generator, 22Ah battery and, for AC power at 115V 400Hz, a 250VA inverter. Oxygen system for occupants conforms to MIL-C-5887 and is supplied by six MS 21227 D2 type cylinders (total capacity approx 1,200 litres; 264 Imp gallons) at a pressure of 31 bars (450 lb/sq in).

AVIONICS AND EQUIPMENT: Standard avionics include two Collins VHF-20A VHF transceivers; two Collins 387C-4 audio systems; one EMBRAER radio transferring system; one Collins VIR-31A VOR/ILS/marker beacon receiver; one Collins TRD-90 ATC transponder; one Collins DME-40 DME; one Collins PN-101 gyromagnetic compass; and one Collins ADF-60A ADF. Landing/taxying light in each wing leading-edge.

ARMAMENT: Two hardpoints under each wing, each stressed for a max load of 150 kg (330 lb). Max external stores load 560 kg (1,234 lb). Typical loads, on Aermacchi MA-4A pylons, include two 7·62 mm MS10-21/22-10A machine-gun pods, each with 350 rds; four 25 lb Mk 76 practice bombs; four 250 lb Mk 81 general-purpose bombs; or four LM-37/7A or LM-70/7 launchers, each with seven rockets (Avibras SBAT-37 and SBAT-70 respectively). D.F. Vasconcelos RFR-01 fixed reflex-type gunsight for use with machine-gun pods.

DIMENSIONS, EXTERNAL:

Wing span	11·14 m (36 ft 6½ in)
Wing chord at root	2·30 m (7 ft 6½ in)
Wing chord at tip	1·07 m (3 ft 6¼ in)
Wing aspect ratio	6·4
Length overall	9·94 m (32 ft 7¼ in)
Length of fuselage (excl rudder)	8·53 m (27 ft 11¾ in)
Fuselage: Max width	1·00 m (3 ft 3¼ in)
Max depth	1·55 m (5 ft 1 in)
Height overall (static)	3·15 m (10 ft 4 in)
Tailplane span	4·66 m (15 ft 3½ in)
Wheel track	3·76 m (12 ft 4 in)
Wheelbase	3·16 m (10 ft 4½ in)
Propeller diameter	2·36 m (7 ft 9 in)
Propeller ground clearance (static)	0·25 m (9¾ in)

Baggage compartment door:

Height	0·60 m (1 ft 11½ in)
Width	0·54 m (1 ft 9¼ in)
Height to sill	1·25 m (4 ft 1¼ in)

DIMENSIONS, INTERNAL:

Cockpits: Combined length	2·90 m (9 ft 6¼ in)
Max height	1·43 m (4 ft 8¼ in)
Max width	0·85 m (2 ft 9½ in)
Baggage compartment volume	0·20 m³ (7·1 cu ft)

EMBRAER EMB-312 tandem two-seat trainer

AREAS:

Wings, gross	19·40 m² (208·82 sq ft)
Ailerons (total)	1·97 m² (21·20 sq ft)
Trailing-edge flaps (total)	2·58 m² (27·77 sq ft)
Fin	2·08 m² (22·39 sq ft)
Rudder	1·46 m² (15·72 sq ft)
Tailplane	4·57 m² (49·19 sq ft)
Elevators, incl tab	2·00 m² (21·53 sq ft)

WEIGHTS AND LOADINGS:

Basic weight empty	1,582 kg (3,487 lb)
Max fuel load (usable)	587 kg (1,294 lb)
Max T-O and landing weight	2,350 kg (5,180 lb)
Max ramp weight	2,368 kg (5,220 lb)
Max zero-fuel weight	1,900 kg (4,188 lb)
Max wing loading	121 kg/m² (24·8 lb/sq ft)
Max power loading	4·2 kg/kW (6·9 lb/shp)

PERFORMANCE (estimated, at max T-O weight):

Never-exceed speed
292 knots (541 km/h; 336 mph) EAS
Max level speed at 4,115 m (13,500 ft)
247 knots (458 km/h; 284 mph)
Max cruising speed at 4,570 m (15,000 ft)
236 knots (437 km/h; 272 mph)
Econ cruising speed at 3,050 m (10,000 ft)
185 knots (343 km/h; 213 mph)
Stalling speed, flaps up, power off
73 knots (135·5 km/h; 84·5 mph) EAS
Stalling speed, flaps down, power off
68 knots (126 km/h; 78·5 mph) EAS

Max rate of climb at S/L	649 m (2,130 ft)/min
Service ceiling	9,935 m (32,600 ft)
T-O run	290 m (951 ft)
T-O to 15 m (50 ft)	510 m (1,673 ft)
Landing from 15 m (50 ft)	505 m (1,657 ft)
Landing run	240 m (787 ft)

Range with max fuel, 30 min reserves
1,140 nm (2,112 km; 1,313 miles)

Endurance with max fuel	4 h
g limits (Aerobatic)	+6·0; −3·0

EMBRAER EMB-201A IPANEMA

The original version of this agricultural aircraft was designed and developed to specifications laid down by the Brazilian Ministry of Agriculture. Design was started in May 1969, and the EMB-200 prototype (PP-ZIP) made its first flight on 30 July 1970. A type certificate was granted on 14 December 1971. Ipanema is the name of a famous beach in Rio, and also of a farm which is the headquarters of the Agricultural Air School of the Ministry of Agriculture, where the EMB-200 was flight tested.

The following versions of the Ipanema have been or are being produced:

EMB-200 and EMB-200A. Initial versions. Production of 73 aircraft, completed in mid-1974. Described in 1973-74 *Jane's.*

EMB-201. Developed version, produced between mid-1974 and March 1977; total of 200 built. Described in 1976-77 *Jane's.*

EMB-201A. Current production version, first flown 10 March 1977. Incorporates several modifications requested by operators as a result of field experience, including new wing profile, wingtips and other aerodynamic improvements, improved systems, and revised cockpit layout. Detailed description applies to this version, of which approx 125 had been built by July 1980.

EMB-201R. Glider towing version of EMB-201. Three built for Brazilian Air Force (designation **U-19**). Described and illustrated in 1977-78 *Jane's.*

EMBRAER is conducting studies for a version of the Ipanema powered by a Pratt & Whitney Aircraft of Canada PT6 turboprop engine.

The following description applies to the standard production EMB-201A:

TYPE: Single-seat agricultural aircraft.

WINGS: Cantilever low-wing monoplane. Wing section NACA 23015 (modified), with cambered leading-edges. Dihedral 7° from roots. Incidence 3°. All-metal single-spar structure of 2024 aluminium alloy with all-metal Frise-type ailerons outboard and all-metal slotted flaps on trailing-edge, and all-detachable cambered leading-edges. No tabs. Cambered wingtips standard.

FUSELAGE: Rectangular-section all-metal safe-life structure, of welded 4130 steel tube with removable skin panels of 2024 aluminium alloy. Structure is specially treated against chemical corrosion.

TAIL UNIT: Cantilever two-spar all-metal structure of 2024 aluminium alloy. Slight sweepback on fin and rudder. Fixed-incidence tailplane. Trim tab in starboard elevator.

LANDING GEAR: Non-retractable main and tail wheels, with oleo shock-absorbers on main units. Tailwheel has tapered spring shock-absorber. Main wheels and tyres size 8·50-10. Tailwheel diameter 250 mm (10 in). Tyre pressures: main, 2·07-2·41 bars (30-35 lb/sq in); tailwheel, 3·79 bars (55 lb/sq in). Hydraulic disc brakes on main wheels.

POWER PLANT: One 224 kW (300 hp) Avco Lycoming IO-540-K1J5D flat-six engine, driving a Hartzell two-blade constant-speed metal propeller with spinner. Integral fuel tanks in each wing leading-edge, with total capacity of 292 litres (64·2 Imp gallons). Refuelling

EMBRAER EMB-201A Ipanema single-seat agricultural aircraft (*Pilot Press*)

point on top of each tank. Oil capacity 12 litres (2·6 Imp gallons).

ACCOMMODATION: Single horizontally/vertically-adjustable seat in fully-enclosed cabin with bottom-hinged window/door on each side. Ventilation system in cabin. Inertial type shoulder harness standard.

SYSTEM: 28V DC electrical system supplied by a 24Ah BB639/U battery and a Bosch K.1 28V 35A alternator. Power receptacle for external battery (AN-2552-3A type) on port side of forward fuselage.

AVIONICS AND EQUIPMENT: Standard VFR avionics include 360-channel Bendix RT-241A VHF transceiver and Bendix T-12C ADF transceiver. Hopper for agricultural chemicals has capacity of 680 litres (149·5 Imp gallons) liquid or 750 kg (1,653 lb) dry. Dusting system below centre of fuselage. Spraybooms and Micronair atomisers aft of and above wing trailing-edges.

DIMENSIONS, EXTERNAL:

Wing span	11·69 m (38 ft 4¼ in)
Wing chord (constant)	1·71 m (5 ft 7½ in)
Wing aspect ratio	6·85
Length overall (tail up)	7·43 m (24 ft 4½ in)
Height overall (tail down)	2·22 m (7 ft 3½ in)
Fuselage: Max width	0·93 m (3 ft 0½ in)
Tailplane span	3·66 m (12 ft 0 in)
Wheel track	2·20 m (7 ft 2½ in)
Wheelbase	5·20 m (17 ft 7¼ in)
Propeller diameter	2·13 m (7 ft 0 in)

DIMENSIONS, INTERNAL:

Cockpit: Max length	1·20 m (3 ft 11¼ in)
Max width	0·85 m (2 ft 9½ in)
Max height	1·34 m (4 ft 4¾ in)

AREAS:

Wings, gross	19·94 m² (214·63 sq ft)
Ailerons (total)	1·60 m² (17·22 sq ft)
Trailing-edge flaps (total)	2·30 m² (24·76 sq ft)
Fin	0·58 m² (6·24 sq ft)
Rudder	0·63 m² (6·78 sq ft)
Tailplane	3·17 m² (34·12 sq ft)

WEIGHTS AND LOADINGS (N: Normal; R: Restricted category):

Max payload: N, R	750 kg (1,653 lb)
Max T-O and landing weight: N	1,550 kg (3,417 lb)
R	1,800 kg (3,968 lb)
Max wing loading: N	77·75 kg/m² (15·92 lb/sq ft)
R	90·29 kg/m² (18·49 lb/sq ft)
Max power loading: N	6·92 kg/kW (11·39 lb/hp)
R	8·03 kg/kW (13·23 lb/hp)

PERFORMANCE (at max T-O weight, 'clean' configuration, ISA):

Never-exceed speed:

N	165 knots (305 km/h; 190 mph)
R	104 knots (193 km/h; 120 mph)

Max level speed at S/L:

N	124 knots (230 km/h; 143 mph)
R	121 knots (225 km/h; 140 mph)

Max cruising speed (75% power) at 1,830 m (6,000 ft):

N	115 knots (212 km/h; 132 mph)
R	110 knots (204 km/h; 127 mph)

Stalling speed, power off (N):

flaps up	56 knots (103 km/h; 64 mph)
8° flap	54 knots (100 km/h; 62 mph)
30° flap	49·5 knots (92 km/h; 57 mph)

Stalling speed, power off (R):

flaps up	59·5 knots (109·5 km/h; 68 mph)
8° flap	57·5 knots (106·5 km/h; 66 mph)
30° flap	53 knots (98·5 km/h; 61 mph)

Max rate of climb at S/L, 8° flap:

N	283 m (930 ft)/min
R	201 m (660 ft)/min

Service ceiling, 8° flap: R   3,470 m (11,385 ft)

T-O run at S/L, 8° flap, asphalt runway:

N	282 m (925 ft)
R	368 m (1,208 ft)

T-O to 15 m (50 ft), conditions as above:

N	438 m (1,437 ft)
R	707 m (2,320 ft)

Landing from 15 m (50 ft) at S/L, 30° flap, asphalt runway: N   489 m (1,605 ft)
R   507 m (1,664 ft)

Landing run, conditions as above: N 150 m (492 ft)
R   168 m (551 ft)

Range at 1,830 m (6,000 ft), no reserves:

N	506 nm (938 km; 583 miles)
R	474 nm (878 km; 545 miles)

EMBRAER-PIPER LIGHT AIRCRAFT PROGRAMME

Detailed descriptions of the Piper aircraft built by EMBRAER (see introductory copy) can be found in the US section, except for the .EMB-710 Carioca. EMBRAER names and designations are as follows:

EMB-710C Carioca. Piper PA-28-235 Cherokee Pathfinder; named after inhabitants of Rio de Janeiro. Total of 264 licence-built by EMBRAER, which continued production in Brazil after manufacture by Piper had ended. Brazilian production ended in 1979. Last described in 1979-80 *Jane's.* It was planned to replace the Carioca from September 1980 by a PA-28-236 version designated **EMB-710D.**

EMB-711C Corisco (Spark). Piper PA-28R-200 Cherokee Arrow II. Total of 250 sold by January 1980. Production being transferred to **EMB-711T** (PA-28RT-201) and, from April 1980, to **EMB-711ST** turbocharged version (PA-28RT-201T).

EMB-201A Ipanema (Avco Lycoming IO-540-K1J5D engine) in agricultural service, fitted with spraygear

EMB-712 Tupi. Piper PA-28-181 Cherokee Archer II; named after a Brazilian Indian nation. Production, under subcontract by Neiva, began in October 1979. Total of 25 sold by January 1980.

EMB-720C Minuano. Piper PA-32-300 Cherokee SIX; named after a wind of southern Brazil. Total of 107 sold by January 1980. Production being transferred to

EMB-720D version (PA-32-300) with tapered wings by June 1980.

EMB-721C Sertanejo. Piper PA-32R-300 Cherokee Lance; named after a farming people of the Brazilian interior. Total of 141 sold by January 1980. Production being transferred to **EMB-721D** version (PA-32R-300) by June 1980.

EMB-810C Seneca II. Piper PA-34-200T Seneca II. Total of 308 sold by January 1980, including 10 for the Brazilian Air Force, by which they are designated **U-7**.

EMB-820C Navajo. Piper PA-31-350 Navajo Chieftain. First flight of Brazilian-built example 31 December 1975. Total of 109 sold by January 1980.

HELIBRAS
HELICÓPTEROS DO BRASIL SA

HEADQUARTERS: Rua Alcides Faria 68, Salas 401/402, Caixa Postal 184, 37500 Itajubá, Provincia de Minas Gerais

Telephone: (035) 622 2440 and 622 2455

WORKS: Distrito Industrial de Itajubá, Caixa Postal 184, 37500 Itajubá, Provincia de Minas Gerais

SUPERINTENDENT DIRECTOR: Nivaldo Alves da Silva
COMMERCIAL DIRECTOR: Sylvio Carlos Diniz Borges
PRODUCTION DIRECTOR: Alain Adrien Royer

Formation of this company was announced in October 1977. Owned jointly by Aérospatiale of France and the State of Minas Gerais (45% each) and Aerofoto (10%), it is engaged in a 10-year programme involving the assembly (graduating to local manufacture) of 30 Aérospatiale SA 315B Lama and 200 AS 350B Ecureuil helicopters, in a new factory at Itajubá in Minas Gerais State. The first

assembly hall to be completed, which is 5,500 m² (59,200 sq ft) in area, was officially inaugurated on 28 March 1980. The complete facility extends over an area of nearly 210,000 m² (2,260,420 sq ft). The first Lamas were assembled in Brazil during the second half of 1979; the first Brazilian-assembled Ecureuils were also delivered in 1979. Brazilian names of the two helicopters are **Gavião** and **Esquilo** respectively. By June 1980, Helibras had sold six Esquilos to the Brazilian Navy, and had four Gaviãos under assembly.

Left: Helibras Gavião (Aérospatiale Lama) with agricultural spraygear; right: Helibras Esquilo (Aérospatiale Ecureuil) of the Brazilian Navy *(both Ronaldo S. Olive)*

NEIVA
INDÚSTRIA AERONÁUTICA NEIVA S/A (subsidiary of EMBRAER)

HEAD OFFICE AND WORKS: Estrada Velha Rio-São Paulo 2176, São José dos Campos, SP, Caixa Postal 247, Código 12200

Telephone: (0123) 21 6333
Telex: 011 33673 SOAN BR
OTHER WORKS: Av Brigadeiro Faria Lima s/n, São José dos Campos, SP, Código 12200
Rua Nossa Senhora de Fátima 360, Botucatu, SP, Caixa Postal 10, Código 18600

DIRECTORS:
José Carlos de Barros Neiva (President)
Breno A. B. Junqueira

In early 1980 Neiva was negotiating further orders for the N-621 (T-25) Universal basic trainer, and was continuing to develop the N-622 Universal II. It has a work force of approx 400 people.

The company participates in EMBRAER's general aviation aircraft production programme, partially manufacturing and assembling the EMB-711 Corisco, EMB-712 Tupi and EMB-721 Sertanejo, and building components for the EMB-720 Minuano. Neiva also participates in EMBRAER's agricultural aircraft production programme, building at Botucatu the fuselage structure of the EMB-201A Ipanema.

Neiva became a wholly-owned subsidiary of EMBRAER on 10 March 1980, as a result of which Ipanema and Piper production is expected to be transferred entirely to Neiva factories.

NEIVA N-621 UNIVERSAL
Brazilian Air Force designation: T-25 and T-25A

The Universal was designed by Eng Joseph Kovacs to meet a Brazilian Air Force requirement. Initial design started in January 1963, and the prototype (PP-ZTW) flew for the first time on 29 April 1966.

The first production T-25 was flown on 7 April 1971, and 132 were delivered to the Brazilian Air Force between Autumn 1971 and early 1975. Delivery of a further eight to the same customer was completed in late 1979; additional orders were being negotiated in early 1980. Ten T-25s were supplied to the Chilean Army; these were transferred subsequently to the Chilean Air Force.

The T-25 is in service, as an advanced trainer, with the Academia da Força Aérea (Air Force Academy) at Pirassununga, São Paulo State; and, as the T-25A, with the Brazilian Air Force's EMRAs (Reconnaissance and Attack Squadrons).

TYPE: Two/three-seat basic trainer.
WINGS: Cantilever low-wing monoplane. Wing section NACA 63₂A315 at root, NACA 63₁212 at tip. Dihedral 6°. Incidence 2°. Single-spar structure of riveted aluminium alloy. All-metal dynamically-balanced slotted ailerons. All-metal split flaps. Ground-adjustable tab on each aileron.

FUSELAGE: Welded steel tube centre fuselage with aluminium skin panels. Semi-monocoque tailcone of riveted aluminium alloy.
TAIL UNIT: Cantilever all-metal structure, with electrically-actuated tab in port elevator.
LANDING GEAR: Retractable tricycle type. Hydraulic retraction, main units inward, nosewheel rearward. ERAM oleo shock-absorbers. Main wheels fitted with Goodyear tyres size 6·50-8 and Goodyear or OLDI disc brakes. Nosewheel steerable and fitted with Goodyear tyre size 6·00-6. Tyre pressure 2·28 bars (33 lb/sq in) on main units, 1·79 bars (26 lb/sq in) on nose unit.
POWER PLANT: One 224 kW (300 hp) Avco Lycoming IO-540-K1D5 flat-six engine, driving a Hartzell HC-C2YK-4/C8475-A2 non-feathering two-blade constant-speed metal propeller. Six aluminium fuel tanks in wings, total capacity 332 litres (73 Imp gallons). Refuelling points above wings. Oil capacity 11·5 litres (2·5 Imp gallons).
ACCOMMODATION: Two seats side by side, with full dual controls, and optional third seat at rear. Large rearward-sliding transparent canopy. Baggage compartment aft of rear seat.
SYSTEMS: Electrically-actuated hydraulic system, pressure 103 bars (1,500 lb/sq in), for flaps and landing gear. Manual emergency pump. 28V electrical system.
AVIONICS AND EQUIPMENT: 140-channel Brazilian-made VHF radio, ADF and VOR/LOC. Complete IFR instrumentation.
ARMAMENT: Two underwing hardpoints for 7·62 mm machine-gun pods.
DIMENSIONS, EXTERNAL:

Wing span	11·00 m (36 ft 1 in)
Wing chord at root	2·00 m (6 ft 6½ in)
Wing chord at tip	1·08 m (3 ft 6½ in)
Wing aspect ratio	7·1

Length overall	8·60 m (28 ft 2½ in)
Height overall	3·00 m (9 ft 9¾ in)
Tailplane span	3·95 m (12 ft 11½ in)
Wheel track	2·65 m (8 ft 8¼ in)
Wheelbase	2·33 m (7 ft 7¾ in)
Propeller diameter	2·13 m (7 ft 0 in)
Propeller ground clearance	0·37 m (1 ft 2½ in)

DIMENSIONS, INTERNAL:

Cabin: Length	2·20 m (7 ft 2½ in)
Max width	1·25 m (4 ft 1 in)
Max height	1·25 m (4 ft 1 in)
Floor area	3·0 m² (32 sq ft)
Volume	4·00 m³ (141 cu ft)
Baggage compartment volume	0·35 m³ (12·5 cu ft)

AREAS:

Wings, gross	17·20 m² (185·14 sq ft)
Ailerons (total)	1·47 m² (15·82 sq ft)
Trailing-edge flaps (total)	1·34 m² (14·42 sq ft)
Fin	0·82 m² (8·83 sq ft)
Rudder	0·90 m² (9·69 sq ft)
Tailplane	2·20 m² (23·68 sq ft)
Elevators, incl tab	1·35 m² (14·53 sq ft)

WEIGHTS AND LOADINGS (A: Aerobatic; U: Utility):

Weight empty, equipped: A, U		1,150 kg (2,535 lb)
Max T-O weight: A		1,500 kg (3,306 lb)
U		1,700 kg (3,747 lb)
Max wing loading: A		88·2 kg/m² (18·1 lb/sq ft)
U		100·0 kg/m² (20·5 lb/sq ft)
Max power loading: A		6·70 kg/kW (11·02 lb/hp)
U		7·59 kg/kW (12·49 lb/hp)

PERFORMANCE (at max T-O weight. A: Aerobatic; U: Utility):
Never-exceed speed:
A, U   269 knots (500 km/h; 310 mph)

Neiva T-25 Universal two/three-seat basic training aircraft of the Brazilian Air Force

Max level speed at S/L:
A   162 knots (300 km/h; 186 mph)
U   160 knots (296 km/h; 184 mph)
Max cruising speed (75% power) at S/L:
A   153 knots (285 km/h; 177 mph)
U   151 knots (280 km/h; 174 mph)
Stalling speed, flaps up:
A   63·5 knots (117 km/h; 73 mph)
U   66 knots (122 km/h; 76 mph)
Stalling speed, flaps down:
A   56·5 knots (104 km/h; 65 mph)
U   59·5 knots (110 km/h; 68·5 mph)
Max rate of climb at S/L: A   400 m (1,312 ft)/min
U   320 m (1,050 ft)/min
Service ceiling: A   6,100 m (20,000 ft)
U   5,000 m (16,400 ft)
T-O run at S/L: A   350 m (1,148 ft)
U   455 m (1,493 ft)
T-O to 15 m (50 ft) at S/L: A   510 m (1,673 ft)
U   650 m (2,133 ft)
Landing from 15 m (50 ft) at S/L:
A   600 m (1,970 ft)
U   760 m (2,493 ft)
Range (75% power) at 2,000 m (6,560 ft), 10%
reserves: A   539 nm (1,000 km; 621 miles)
U   809 nm (1,500 km; 932 miles)

Neiva YT-25B Universal II basic training aircraft developed from the N-621 *(Pilot Press)*

NEIVA N-622 UNIVERSAL II
Brazilian Air Force designation: YT-25B

The N-622 is a more powerful version of the N-621 Universal, with a strengthened airframe and an Avco Lycoming IO-720 flat-eight engine in place of the IO-540 flat-six used in the T-25.

A YT-25B prototype of the Universal II was ordered by the Brazilian Air Force. This aircraft, converted from the first production T-25 (Brazilian Air Force serial number 1831), made its first flight on 22 October 1978, and in early 1980 was nearing the end of a preliminary evaluation by the CTA. At that time it had completed nearly 100 hours' flying.

WINGS: As T-25.

FUSELAGE, TAIL UNIT AND LANDING GEAR: As T-25, except for lengthened nose and enlarged tail surfaces.

POWER PLANT: One 298 kW (400 hp) Avco Lycoming IO-720-D1B flat-eight engine, driving a Hartzell HC-C3YR-4F/FC8475 three-blade constant-speed propeller with spinner.

ACCOMMODATION, SYSTEMS, AVIONICS AND EQUIPMENT: As T-25.

ARMAMENT: Six underwing hardpoints standard on basic version.

DIMENSIONS, EXTERNAL: As T-25 except:
Length overall   8·78 m (28 ft 9¾ in)
Height overall   3·40 m (11 ft 2 in)
AREAS: As T-25 except:
Fin   0·85 m² (9·15 sq ft)
Rudder   0·96 m² (10·33 sq ft)
Tailplane   2·36 m² (25·40 sq ft)
Elevators, incl tab   1·43 m² (15·39 sq ft)
WEIGHTS:
Max T-O weight: Aerobatic   1,650 kg (3,637 lb)
Utility   1,900 kg (4,189 lb)
Max landing weight   1,820 kg (4,012 lb)

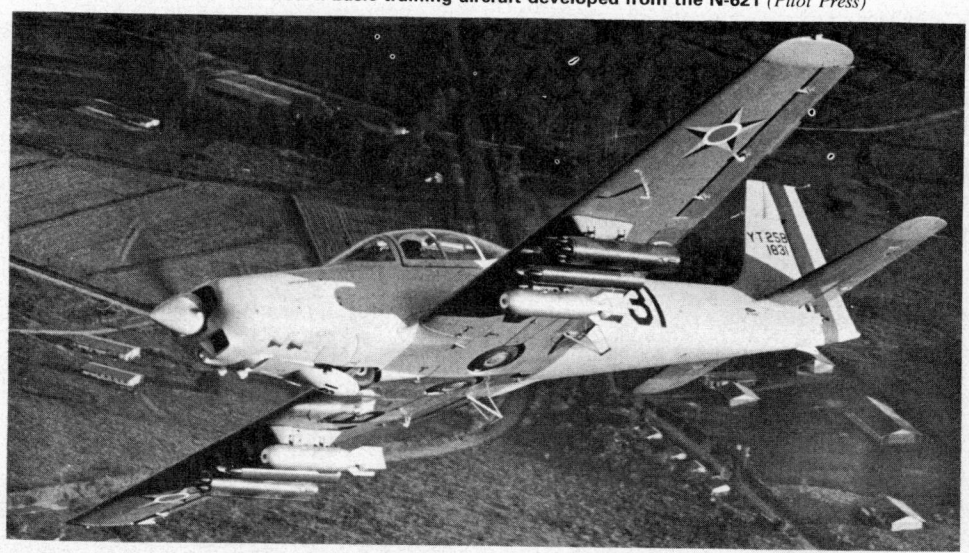

YT-25B prototype of the Neiva N-622 Universal II with two practice bombs, two rocket launchers and two large rockets underwing

PERFORMANCE (estimated, at AUW of 1,800 kg; 3,968 lb, 'clean'):
Never-exceed speed   269 knots (500 km/h; 310 mph)
Max level speed   173 knots (320 km/h; 199 mph)
Cruising speed at 3,000 m (9,845 ft)
         163 knots (302 km/h; 188 mph)
Stalling speed, flaps down
         57 knots (105 km/h; 66 mph)

Max rate of climb at S/L   540 m (1,770 ft)/min
Service ceiling   5,000 m (16,400 ft)
T-O to 15 m (50 ft)   600 m (1,970 ft)
Landing from 15 m (50 ft)   500 m (1,640 ft)
Range (75% power at 1,500 m; 5,000 ft, standard fuel)   277 nm (515 km; 320 miles)

SÃO CARLOS
SÃO CARLOS ENGINEERING SCHOOL, UNIVERSITY OF SÃO PAULO
São Carlos, São Paulo State
DIRECTORS:
Dr Eng Romeu Corsini
Eng Sylvio de Oliveira

Under the direction of Dr Corsini, formerly of the IPT, the São Carlos Engineering School provides facilities for training aircraft engineers, developing new aircraft and carrying out associated test programmes. It is adjacent to a 3,000 m (9,840 ft) paved runway, hangarage and other airport facilities, and a large dam from which waterborne aircraft can operate. Its two most recent ventures are the IPAI-26 Tuca and the IPAI-28 Super Surubim light aircraft.

IPAI-26 TUCA

The Tuca light aircraft was designed by Prof Dawilson Lucato, and built in two-seat prototype form by a group of students of the São Carlos Engineering School. Some features are similar to those of the SP-18 Onça built by Dr Eng Romeu Corsini in the mid-1960s, which is still flown in São Carlos as a flying testbed. Flight testing of the Tuca began in 1979.

TYPE: Two-seat fully-aerobatic light aircraft.

WINGS: Strut-braced high-wing monoplane. Wing section NACA 23012.

FUSELAGE: Welded steel tube structure, with easily-removable metal and glassfibre skin panels.

TAIL UNIT: Cantilever T tail, with sweptback vertical surfaces.

IPAI-26 Tuca light cabin monoplane

São Carlos IPAI-28 Super Surubim tandem two-seat light aircraft in uncompleted state
(José Fernandez)

LANDING GEAR: Non-retractable tricycle type, with single wheel on each unit. Rubber-sprung nose unit; cantilever main-wheel legs of flexible reinforced glassfibre.
POWER PLANT: One 80·5/86 kW (108/115 hp) Avco Lycoming O-235-C1 flat-four engine, driving a two-blade propeller with spinner. Other engines expected to be tested during trials programme: structure is capable of accepting engines of up to 134 kW (180 hp) without modification, in which form the Tuca could be used as a utility four-seater, with fuel for up to four hours' endurance.
ACCOMMODATION (prototype): Seats for two persons side by side in fully enclosed, extensively glazed and reinforced cabin. Dual controls standard.

DIMENSIONS, EXTERNAL:
Wing span   11·00 m (36 ft 1 in)
Wing mean aerodynamic chord   1·58 m (5 ft 2¼ in)
Wing area, gross   16·99 m² (182·88 sq ft)
Wing aspect ratio   7·12
Length overall   6·82 m (22 ft 4½ in)
WEIGHT AND LOADING (prototype):
Max T-O weight   700 kg (1,543 lb)
Max wing loading   40·61 kg/m² (8·32 lb/sq ft)
PERFORMANCE (Normal category):
Max level speed at S/L 102 knots (190 km/h; 118 mph)
Cruising speed at S/L 100 knots (185 km/h; 115 mph)

Stalling speed at S/L 41·5 knots (76 km/h; 47·5 mph)
Service ceiling   3,600 m (11,810 ft)
T-O and landing run at S/L   250 m (820 ft)
Endurance   1 h 30 min

IPAI-28 SUPER SURUBIM

Due to fly in early 1980, the Super Surubim was designed by Eng Sylvio de Oliveira and completed at São Carlos City Flying Club. Design parameters were calculated with the assistance of the São Carlos Engineering School; assistance was also provided by EMBRAER, the Oldi aircraft instruments factory, the Conal aircraft maintenance company, Neiva, and several aero club pilots. Certification was expected during 1980.
TYPE: Tandem two-seat aerobatic trainer; g limits ±8·0.
WINGS: Cantilever low-wing monoplane, with highly tapered wings. Wing section NACA 23016·7 at root, NACA 23012 at tip. Dihedral from roots. All-metal two-spar structure, with rear auxiliary spar, with skins of 2024-T3 Alclad aluminium alloy, chemically treated against corrosion. Wings built in one piece and attached to underside of fuselage by bolts. Trailing-edge split flaps between ailerons and fuselage; ailerons have 100% balancing. No tabs. 'Letterbox' fixed slots near outer leading-edges, forward of ailerons.

FUSELAGE: Conventional all-metal semi-monocoque structure of frames and longerons.
TAIL UNIT: Cantilever metal structure, of similar construction to wings. Trim tab in rudder and starboard elevator. Rudder and elevators have 100% balancing.
LANDING GEAR: Non-retractable type, with single main wheels and tailwheel. Main units have strut bracing, leg and wheel fairings, 190 mm diameter wheels from a Neiva T-25 Universal, and are fitted with Oldi brakes. Main-wheel tyre size 7·00-6, pressure 2·76 bars (40 lb/sq in). Small tailwheel, carried on leaf spring.
POWER PLANT: One 146 kW (196 hp) Ranger 6-440-C4 six-cylinder inverted in-line aircooled engine, driving a two-blade propeller with spinner. Fuel in two wing tanks, combined capacity 140 litres (30·75 Imp gallons).
ACCOMMODATION: Seats for two persons in tandem. Rearward-sliding framed canopy, jettisonable in flight.

DIMENSIONS, EXTERNAL:
Wing span   9·10 m (29 ft 10¼ in)
Wing area, gross   10·12 m² (108·9 sq ft)
Wing aspect ratio   8·18
Length overall   8·10 m (26 ft 7 in)
Height overall   2·12 m (6 ft 11½ in)
Wheel track   2·40 m (7 ft 10½ in)
Propeller diameter   2·20 m (7 ft 2½ in)
WEIGHTS AND LOADINGS:
Weight empty   650 kg (1,433 lb)
Max T-O weight   950 kg (2,094 lb)
Max wing loading   93·8 kg/m² (19·21 lb/sq ft)
Max power loading   6·5 kg/kW (10·68 lb/hp)
PERFORMANCE (estimated, at max T-O weight):
Never-exceed speed 215·5 knots (400 km/h; 248 mph)
Max level speed   146 knots (270 km/h; 168 mph)
Max cruising speed   129 knots (240 km/h; 149 mph)
Stalling speed, flaps up 59·5 knots (110 km/h; 68·5 mph)
Stalling speed, flaps down
  54·5 knots (100 km/h; 62·5 mph)
Max rate of climb at S/L   320 m (1,050 ft)/min

IPAI-30

This new and improved version of the IPAI-26 Tuca was under development by Prof Lucato at the beginning of 1980. No details were known at the time of closing for press.

CANADA

BOEING
BOEING OF CANADA LTD (Vertol Division)
Arnprior Airport, Box 338, Arnprior, Ontario
Telephone: (613) 233 7414 and 623 4215

BOEING VERTOL/CAF SARCUP PROGRAMME
CAF designations: CH-113 Labrador and CH-113A Voyageur

In March 1980 the Canadian government awarded a $20 million contract jointly to Boeing Vertol (see US section) and Boeing of Canada Ltd for the second phase of the Canadian Armed Forces' programme known as SARCUP (Search And Rescue Capability Upgrade Project).

The programme involves the upgrading of six CH-113 and five CH-113A helicopters to a single, improved maritime search and rescue standard by mid-1984. The first phase, started in 1978, involved improvements to the communications and navigation avionics, and the installation of high-powered searchlights. In the second phase each aircraft's flight deck will be modified, as far as possible, to achieve a common configuration. An APU, weather radar and external rescue system will be added to the CH-113s; the CH-113As will be upgraded by adding two 1,893 litre (500 US gallon) auxiliary fuel tanks, a water dam, external rescue system and weather radar.

These improvements will extend the aircraft's range,

One of the CH-113 helicopters being modified by Boeing of Canada in the SARCUP programme

and enable them to fly search and rescue missions in adverse weather conditions by day and by night. Production of the improvement kits, aircraft modification and

flight testing will be undertaken by Boeing of Canada; Boeing Vertol in Philadelphia will provide engineering, training and other support for the SARCUP programme.

CANADAIR
CANADAIR LIMITED
HEAD OFFICE AND WORKS: Cartierville Airport, 1800 Laurentien Boulevard, St Laurent H4R 1K2, Quebec
POSTAL ADDRESS: PO Box 6087, Station 'A', Montreal, Quebec H3C 3G9
Telephone: (514) 744 1511
Telex: 05-826747

CHAIRMAN OF THE BOARD: Léo Lavoie
PRESIDENT AND CHIEF EXECUTIVE OFFICER: Frederick R. Kearns
EXECUTIVE VICE-PRESIDENT: Harry Halton
VICE-PRESIDENTS:
Peter J. Aird (Finance)
Justin Battle (Public Relations)
Leonard B. Box (Canadair Services)
Frank M. Francis (Development Programmes)
James R. Humphreys (Engineering)

Ronald D. Neal (Challenger)
Jacques Ouellet (Resources)
Jacques A. Sincennes (Technical Support)
James B. Taylor (Marketing)
Roger G. Tetreault (Materiel)
Andreas Throner (Manufacturing)
Harvie D. Walford (Corporate Planning)
Robert A. Wohl (Legal and Admin)
DIRECTOR, PRODUCT ENGINEERING: Dr Roy Swanson
Canadair Inc, 274 Riverside Avenue, Westport, Connecticut 06880, USA (US sales subsidiary)
Telephone: (203) 226 1581
Telex: 0096-4282
PRESIDENT: James B. Taylor

Canadair Limited, formerly the Canadian subsidiary of General Dynamics Corporation and owned since 1976 by the Canadian government, has been engaged in the development and manufacture of military and commercial aircraft since 1944. It has also been employed in the

research, design, development and production of missile components, pilotless surveillance systems and a variety of non-aerospace products. Canadair has 232,257 m² (2·5 million sq ft) of covered floor space and a work force of nearly 5,600. Work on a new 27,870 m² (300,000 sq ft) assembly plant at Dorval International Airport, Montreal, began in late 1979.

The CL-600 Challenger twin-turbofan executive transport entered production during 1978; manufacture of the fourth series of CL-215 tanker/utility amphibians (aircraft No. 66 onwards) was due to begin in 1980; production of the CL-89 and development of the CL-289 surveillance systems (see RPVs and Targets section) continue. Major subcontracts concern structural components for the US Navy's P-3C Orion and the CP-140 Aurora Canadian version of this aircraft (see under Lockheed in US section), various components for the McDonnell Douglas F-15, and aft fuselage sections for the Boeing 747SP and 767. Production of aircraft spares, and the modification,

Second pre-production Canadair CL-600 Challenger business transport (two Avco Lycoming ALF 502L turbofan engines)

repair and overhaul of aircraft, are also included in the current work programme.

CANADAIR CL-600 CHALLENGER

In April 1976, Canadair acquired from the late Mr William P. Lear Sr the worldwide exclusive rights to design, manufacture, market and support the latter's LearStar 600; this concept envisaged an aircraft using an advanced-technology wing and two high bypass ratio turbofan engines. With 53 firm orders supported by deposits in hand on 29 October 1976, the programme was launched. In March 1977, major design changes were announced and the aircraft became known as the Canadair Challenger.

Construction of three pre-production Challengers to be used in the flight test programme began in April 1977. The first of these (C-GCGR-X) made its first flight on 8 November 1978. The second aircraft (C-GCGS-X) flew on 17 March 1979, and the third (C-GCGT-X) on 14 July 1979. First flight by a production Challenger was made on 21 September 1979. The first prototype was lost in an accident on 3 April 1980, but by 16 July 1980 more than 1,270 hours' flying had been accumulated by the first four Challengers in 706 flights. The fifth Challenger was at that time being fitted out as the company's demonstration aircraft.

In early June 1979 the second pre-production Challenger flew nonstop from Cartierville to Le Bourget in 7 h 20 min, to take part in the Paris Air Show. Canadian type approval was granted on 11 August 1980; FAA certification was expected to follow shortly thereafter.

Firm orders for the Challenger had reached 128 by August 1980; five were then ready for delivery. Later production Challengers will be offered with 38·48 kN (8,650 lb st) General Electric CF34-1A turbofans as an alternative power plant. The latter engines are standard in the CL-610 Challenger E, which is described separately.

The following description applies to the basic CL-600 passenger version:

TYPE: Twin-turbofan business, cargo and commuter transport.

WINGS: Cantilever low-wing monoplane, built in one piece. Advanced-technology wing section. Thickness/chord ratio 14% at root, 12% at leading-edge sweep break and 10% at tip. Dihedral 2° 20'. Incidence 3° at root. Sweepback at quarter-chord 25°. Two-spar structure, primarily of aluminium alloy, with skin-stringer panels to form rigid torsion box. Two-section double-slotted trailing-edge flaps. Hydraulically-powered aluminium plain ailerons. Inboard spoilers for descent control and ground lift dumping. No tabs. Thermal anti-icing of leading-edges by engine bleed air.

FUSELAGE: Aluminium alloy damage-tolerant semi-monocoque pressurised structure of circular cross-section, with clad frames, stringers, and chemically-milled skins.

TAIL UNIT: Cantilever multi-spar aluminium alloy T tail, with swept vertical and horizontal surfaces. All control surfaces powered. Tailplane incidence adjusted by electric trim motor. No tabs.

LANDING GEAR: Hydraulically-retractable tricycle type, with twin wheels and Dowty Rotol oleo-pneumatic shock-absorbers on each unit. Main wheels retract inward into wing centre-section, nose unit forward. Nose unit steerable and self-centering. Main wheels have Goodyear 26 × 6·65 tyres, pressure 11·38 bars (165 lb/sq in); nosewheels have Goodyear 18 × 4·4 tyres, pressure 8·27 bars (120 lb/sq in). Goodyear hydraulically-operated multiple-disc carbon brakes with fully-modulated anti-skid system.

POWER PLANT: Two 33·36 kN (7,500 lb st) Avco Lycoming ALF 502L turbofan engines, one pylon-mounted on each side of rear fuselage, fitted with cascade-type fan-air thrust reversers. Integral fuel tank in centre-section

(capacity 2,839 litres; 624 Imp gallons; 750 US gallons) and one in each wing (each 2,744 litres; 604 Imp gallons; 725 US gallons). Total fuel capacity 8,327 litres (1,832 Imp gallons; 2,200 US gallons). Pressure and gravity fuelling and defuelling. Oil capacity 13·6 litres (3 Imp gallons).

ACCOMMODATION: Pilot and co-pilot side by side on flight deck with dual controls. Blind-flying instrumentation standard. Typical accommodation includes three pairs of facing seats at front of cabin, with tables between; a further three pairs at rear, with inward-facing three-place settee on each side (total 18 seats). Wardrobe at front on port side. Provision for crew locker, buffet, bar, storage cabinet(s) or second wardrobe, depending on number and layout of seats. Toilet and/or baggage area aft of cabin. Upward-opening door on port side, forward of wing. (Downward-opening door to be fitted from c/n 24 onwards.) Overwing emergency exit on starboard side. Entire accommodation heated, ventilated and air-conditioned.

SYSTEMS: Sundstrand pressurisation and Garrett-AiResearch air-conditioning systems, max pressure differential 0·64 bars (9·3 lb/sq in). Three independent hydraulic systems, each of 207 bars (3,000 lb/sq in). No. 1 system powers flight controls (via servo-actuators positioned by cables and pushrods); No. 2 system for flight controls and brakes; No. 3 system for flight controls, landing gear extension/retraction, brakes and nosewheel steering. Nos. 1 and 2 systems each powered by an engine-driven pump, supplemented by an AC electrical pump; No. 3 system by two AC pumps. Two 300kVA engine-driven generators supply primary three-phase AC electrical power at 115/200V 400Hz. Three transformer-rectifiers to convert AC power to 28V DC; one nickel-cadmium battery. Alternative primary power provided by APU and an air-driven generator, the latter being deployed automatically if the engine-driven generators and APU are inoperative. Stall warning system, with stick shakers and stick pusher. Garrett-AiResearch gas turbine APU (to be certificated for in-flight operation) for engine start, ground air-conditioning and other services. Electrical anti-icing of windscreen, flight deck side windows and pitot heads; Sundstrand bleed air anti-icing of wings, tailplane, engine intake cowls and guide vanes. Gaseous oxygen system, pressure 124 bars (1,800 lb/sq in). Continuous-element fire detectors in each engine nacelle and APU; two-shot extinguishing system for engines, single-shot system for APU.

AVIONICS: Standard avionics include dual Collins VHF-20A com, dual Collins VIR-30A VOR/ILS/marker beacon receiver, dual SPZ 600 flight directors, SPZ 600 autopilot with dual servos, dual TDR-90 transponders, dual DME (with HSI display), one ALT-55B radio altimeter, dual C-14 compasses, standby compass, one ADF-60 ADF, dual intercom system, comparator warning system, RCA Primus 400 weather radar, HF and other antennae. Provision, at customer's option, for HF com, third VHF com, second ADF, VLF nav, INS, GPWS, ELT, flight data recorder and cockpit voice recorder.

DIMENSIONS, EXTERNAL:
Wing span	18·85 m (61 ft 10 in)
Wing chord at root	4·89 m (16 ft 0½ in)
Wing chord at tip	1·27 m (4 ft 1·9 in)
Wing area (basic)	41·81 m² (450 sq ft)
Wing aspect ratio	8·5
Length overall	20·85 m (68 ft 5 in)
Fuselage: Max diameter	2·69 m (8 ft 10 in)
Height overall	6·30 m (20 ft 8 in)
Tailplane span	6·20 m (20 ft 4 in)
Wheel track (c/l of shock-struts)	3·18 m (10 ft 5 in)
Wheelbase	7·99 m (26 ft 2½ in)

Passenger door (port, fwd): Height	1·78 m (5 ft 10 in)
Width	0·91 m (3 ft 0 in)
Height to sill	1·61 m (5 ft 3½ in)
Baggage door (port, aft): Height	0·84 m (2 ft 9 in)
Width	0·71 m (2 ft 4 in)
Height to sill	1·61 m (5 ft 3½ in)
Overwing emergency exit (stbd):	
Height	0·91 m (3 ft 0 in)
Width	0·51 m (1 ft 8 in)

DIMENSIONS, INTERNAL:
Cabin: Length, incl galley, toilet and baggage area, excl flight deck	8·61 m (28 ft 3 in)
Max width	2·49 m (8 ft 2 in)
Width at floor level	2·18 m (7 ft 2 in)
Max height	1·85 m (6 ft 1 in)
Floor area, incl galley, toilet and baggage area, excl flight deck	18·81 m² (202 sq ft)
Volume	32·6 m³ (1,150 cu ft)

WEIGHTS:
Manufacturer's weight empty	7,711 kg (17,000 lb)
Typical operating weight empty	9,208 kg (20,300 lb)
Max fuel	6,785 kg (14,960 lb)
Max payload	3,400 kg (7,500 lb)
Payload with max fuel	426 kg (940 lb)
Max T-O weight	16,329 kg (36,000 lb)
Max ramp weight	16,556 kg (36,500 lb)
Max landing weight	14,969 kg (33,000 lb)
Max zero-fuel weight	11,703 kg (25,800 lb)

PERFORMANCE (estimated, at max T-O weight):
Max level speed	Mach 0·85 (488 knots; 904 km/h; 562 mph)
Long-range cruising speed	Mach 0·75 (430 knots; 797 km/h; 495 mph)
Time to 14,935 m (49,000 ft)	17 min
Max certificated operating altitude	14,935 m (49,000 ft)
Service ceiling, one engine out	7,620 m (25,000 ft)
Balanced T-O field length (ISA at S/L)	1,372 m (4,500 ft)
Landing distance	1,219 m (4,000 ft)
Min ground turning radius	14·63 m (48 ft 0 in)
Range with NBAA IFR reserves (200 nm; 370 km; 230 mile alternate):	
with standard fuel	3,300 nm (6,115 km; 3,800 miles)
with additional fuel	3,600 nm (6,671 km; 4,145 miles)
Design g limit	+2·7

OPERATIONAL NOISE LEVELS (FAR Pt 36, estimated):
T-O	81·6
Sideline	89·3
Approach	91·2

CANADAIR CL-610 CHALLENGER E

The E (for Extended) version of the Challenger, announced on 3 July 1979 and scheduled for delivery from early 1983 has a lengthened fuselage, new power plant, increased fuel capacity and payload, and greater range. Programme go-ahead was given on 14 March 1980. First flight is scheduled for early 1982.

Main differences from the basic CL-600 (which see) are as follows:

WINGS: Modified to include leading-edge high-lift devices, changes to trailing-edge flaps, and larger fuel tanks.

FUSELAGE: Lengthened by insertion of 1·72 m (5 ft 8 in) section forward of wings and 0·94 m (3 ft 1 in) section aft of wings. Second overwing emergency exit, on port side.

POWER PLANT: Two 38·48 kN (8,650 lb st) General Electric CF34-1A turbofan engines, with pneumatically-controlled fan air thrust reversers. Fuel capacity increased to 13,044 litres (2,869 Imp gallons; 3,446 US gallons).

ACCOMMODATION: Room for separate cabin between main cabin and rear toilet/baggage area for, typically, two seats and inward-facing three-place settee; or private bedroom. Max seating capacity: 24 passengers.

SYSTEMS: Similar to CL-600 except for cabin max pressure differential of 0·62 bars (8·98 lb/sq in).

AVIONICS: Similar to CL-600, but with three VHF transceivers, cockpit voice recorder and two ADF as standard; and options which include provisions for HF com, ELT, flight data recorder, GPWS, INS, and VLF nav.

DIMENSIONS, EXTERNAL: As CL-600 except:

Wing span	19·99 m (65 ft 7 in)
Wing chord at root	5·26 m (17 ft 3 in)
Wing area (net)	45·52 m² (490 sq ft)
Wing aspect ratio	8·77
Length overall	23·52 m (77 ft 2 in)
Wheelbase	9·89 m (32 ft 5½ in)

DIMENSIONS, INTERNAL: As CL-600 except:

Cabin: Length, incl toilet, galley and baggage area, excl flight deck	11·28 m (37 ft 0 in)
Floor area	24·62 m² (265 sq ft)
Volume	42·6 m³ (1,505 cu ft)

WEIGHTS:

Manufacturer's weight empty	9,072 kg (20,000 lb)
Typical operating weight empty	11,226 kg (24,750 lb)
Max fuel	10,568 kg (23,300 lb)
Max payload	2,154 kg (4,750 lb)
Payload with max fuel	544 kg (1,200 lb)
Max T-O weight	22,226 kg (49,000 lb)
Max ramp weight	22,339 kg (49,250 lb)
Max landing weight	15,875 kg (35,000 lb)
Max zero-fuel weight	13,381 kg (29,500 lb)

PERFORMANCE (estimated, at max T-O weight):

Max cruising speed	Mach 0·83 (476 knots; 882 km/h; 548 mph)
Long-range cruising speed	Mach 0·78 (448 knots; 830 km/h; 516 mph)
Max certificated operating altitude	13,715 m (45,000 ft)
Balanced T-O field length (ISA at S/L)	2,042 m (6,700 ft)
Landing distance	1,097 m (3,600 ft)
Min ground turning radius	12·34 m (40 ft 6 in)
Range with NBAA IFR reserves (200 nm; 370 km; 230 mile alternate)·	4,400 nm (8,154 km; 5,066 miles)
Design g limit at 22,226 kg (49,000 lb) gross weight	+2·5

OPERATIONAL NOISE LEVELS (FAR Pt 36, estimated):

T-O	88
Sideline	90
Approach	92

CANADAIR CL-215

The Canadair CL-215 is a twin-engined amphibian, intended primarily for firefighting but adaptable to a wide variety of other duties. It is designed for simplicity of operation and maintenance, and can operate from small airstrips, lakes, ocean bays etc.

The CL-215 made its first flight on 23 October 1967, and its first water take-off on 2 May 1968.

The Securité Civile of France has operated CL-215s since June 1969. Following an initial purchase of 10 aircraft, it took delivery of a further five. The French aircraft have seen considerable action fighting forest fires in southern France, Corsica, the Federal Republic of Germany and Italy.

The Province of Quebec operates 15 aircraft, mainly in a firefighting role.

The Spanish government, which has operated two aircraft since February 1971, took delivery of eight more in 1974. The latter aircraft, although equipped for search and rescue, are capable of firefighting and other roles. Seven more were ordered subsequently by Spain. Tailplanes for these last 15 aircraft are built by CASA.

The Greek government took delivery of two CL-215s in 1974; three more were delivered in 1976. Three further orders in 1977-79 raised the Greek total to 11.

The Province of Manitoba took delivery of one CL-215 in 1977, and the Royal Thai Navy has two equipped for coastal patrol, transport and firefighting. In February 1979 the Venezuelan operator CVG Ferrominera Orinoco CA took delivery of two dual-purpose firefighting/passenger transport versions.

Production of the third series of aircraft (Nos. 51-65) has been completed; weight and performance figures for the first and second series can be found in the 1977-78 *Jane's,* and for the third series in the 1979-80 edition.

The go-ahead for continued production of further aircraft was given in May 1979. Five more had been sold by April 1980, and deliveries from this batch, which will include four for the Yugoslav government, are scheduled to begin in the last quarter of 1981. A production rate of 1½ per month is planned.

The CL-215 firefighting installation consists of two internal tanks, two retractable probes and two drop doors, plus the associated operating systems. It attacks fires in the following ways:

(a) with water or chemical retardants ground-loaded at airports; or

(b) with fresh or salt water scooped from a suitable body of water as the aircraft skims across the surface.

The aircraft carries a maximum water or retardant load of 5,455 litres (1,200 Imp gallons). The tanks can be ground-filled in 90 s, or scoop-filled in 10 s while the aircraft planes at 60 knots (111 km/h; 69 mph). Pickup distance in still air, from 15 m (50 ft) above the surface during landing to 15 m (50 ft) above the surface during climb-out, is 1,220 m (4,000 ft).

On a number of occasions single CL-215s have made over 100 drops totalling more than 545,520 litres (120,000 Imp gallons) in one day. Full loads have been scooped from the Mediterranean in wave heights of up to 2 m (6 ft). In June 1978 a Manitoba government CL-215 made 160 drops (totalling 872,824 litres; 192,000 Imp gallons) on fires in one day.

An integrated liquid spray system is being developed. This system, consisting of underwing booms, a compact pump installed permanently in one of the water tanks, and associated equipment, was due to be flight-tested in 1980. This system is suitable for use in the diverse tasks of insecticide application and oil slick dispersal.

Tests conducted at Canadair have shown that the CL-215 can be used to extinguish oil fires by airdropping a suitable foaming agent.

TYPE: Twin-engined multi-purpose amphibian.

WINGS: Cantilever high-wing monoplane. No dihedral. All-metal one-piece fail-safe structure, with front and rear spars at 16% and 49% chord. Spars of conventional construction, with extruded caps and webs stiffened by vertical members. Aluminium alloy skin, with riveted spanwise extruded stringers, is supported at 762 mm (30 in) pitch by interspar ribs. Leading-edge consists of aluminium alloy skin attached to pressed nose-ribs and spanwise stringers. Hydraulically-operated all-metal single-slotted flaps, supported by four external hinges on interspar ribs on each wing. Trim tab and geared tab in port aileron, rudder/aileron interconnect tab in starboard aileron. Detachable glassfibre wingtips.

FUSELAGE: All-metal single-step flying-boat hull of conventional fail-safe construction.

TAIL UNIT: Cantilever all-metal fail-safe structure with horizontal surfaces mounted midway up fin. Structure of aluminium alloy sheet, honeycomb panels, extrusions and fittings. Elevators and rudder fitted with dynamic balance, trim tab (port elevator only) and spring tabs and geared tabs. Provision for de-icing of leading-edges.

LANDING GEAR: Hydraulically-retractable tricycle type. Fully-castoring, self-centering twin-wheel nose unit retracts rearward into hull and is fully enclosed by

Canadair CL-610 Challenger E 'stretched' twin-turbofan executive transport, with additional side elevation (centre) of basic short-fuselage CL-600 *(Pilot Press)*

Canadair CL-215 utility amphibian (two Pratt & Whitney R-2800 radial engines) operated by the Spanish Ministry of Agriculture

Search and rescue version of the Canadair CL-215 twin-engined amphibian, with nose radome (*Pilot Press*)

Forward door: Height	1·37 m	(4 ft 6 in)
Width	1·03 m	(3 ft 4 in)
Rear door: Height	1·12 m	(3 ft 8 in)
Width	1·03 m	(3 ft 4 in)
Water-drop door: Length	1·60 m	(5 ft 3 in)
Width	0·81 m	(2 ft 8 in)
Emergency exit: Height	0·91 m	(3 ft 0 in)
Width	0·51 m	(1 ft 8 in)

DIMENSIONS, INTERNAL:

Cabin, excl flight deck: Length	9·38 m	(30 ft 9½ in)
Max width	2·39 m	(7 ft 10 in)
Max height	1·90 m	(6 ft 3 in)
Floor area	19·69 m²	(212 sq ft)
Volume	35·03 m³	(1,237 cu ft)

AREAS:

Wings, gross	100·33 m²	(1,080 sq ft)
Ailerons (total)	8·05 m²	(86·6 sq ft)
Flaps (total)	22·39 m²	(241 sq ft)
Vertical tail surfaces (total)	17·23 m²	(185·5 sq ft)
Rudder, incl tabs	6·02 m²	(64·75 sq ft)
Horizontal tail surfaces (total)	28·43 m²	(306 sq ft)
Elevators, incl tabs	7·88 m²	(84·8 sq ft)

WEIGHTS AND LOADINGS:

Manufacturer's weight empty	12,160 kg	(26,810 lb)
Typical operating weight empty	12,672 kg	(27,938 lb)
Max payload: Water bomber	5,443 kg	(12,000 lb)
Utility version	3,838 kg	(8,462 lb)
Max T-O weight (land)	19,731 kg	(43,500 lb)
Max T-O weight (water)	17,100 kg	(37,700 lb)
Max zero-fuel weight	19,275 kg	(42,500 lb)
Max landing weight: on land	15,603 kg	(34,400 lb)
on water	16,780 kg	(37,000 lb)
Cabin floor loading	732 kg/m²	(150 lb/sq ft)
Max wing loading	196·66 kg/m²	(40·3 lb/sq ft)
Max power loading	6·23 kg/kW	(10·36 lb/hp)

PERFORMANCE:

Cruising speed (max recommended power) at AUW of 18,595 kg (41,000 lb) at 3,050 m (10,000 ft)
157 knots (291 km/h; 181 mph)
Stalling speed, 15° flap, AUW of 19,731 kg (43,500 lb)
78·5 knots (145 km/h; 90 mph)
Stalling speed, 25° flap, AUW of 15,603 kg (34,400 lb), power off
66 knots (123 km/h; 76 mph)
Max rate of climb at S/L at AUW of 19,731 kg (43,500 lb) at max continuous power 305 m (1,000 ft)/min
Rate of climb at S/L, one engine out, at AUW of 17,100 kg (37,700 lb) at T-O power 75 m (245 ft)/min
T-O to 15 m (50 ft):
from land at AUW of 19,731 kg (43,500 lb)
811 m (2,660 ft)
from water at AUW of 17,100 kg (37,700 lb)
800 m (2,620 ft)
Landing from 15 m (50 ft):
on land at AUW of 15,603 kg (34,400 lb)
732 m (2,400 ft)
on water at AUW of 16,780 kg (37,000 lb)
835 m (2,740 ft)
Range with 1,587 kg (3,500 lb) payload:
at max cruise power
925 nm (1,714 km; 1,065 miles)
at long-range cruise power
1,130 nm (2,094 km; 1,301 miles)

doors. Main gear support structures retract into wells in sides of hull. A plate mounted on each main gear assembly encloses bottom of wheel well. Main-wheel tyre pressure 5·31 bars (77 lb/sq in); nosewheel tyre pressure 6·55 bars (95 lb/sq in). Hydraulic disc brakes. Non-retractable stabilising floats are each carried on a pylon cantilevered from wing box structure, with breakaway provision.

POWER PLANT: Two 1,566 kW (2,100 hp) Pratt & Whitney R-2800-CA3 eighteen-cylinder radial engines, each driving a Hamilton Standard Hydromatic constant-speed fully-feathering three-blade propeller, with 43E60 hub and type 6903 blades. Two fuel tanks, each of eight flexible cells, in wing spar box, with total usable capacity of 5,910 litres (1,300 Imp gallons). Gravity refuelling through two points above each tank. Oil in two tanks, with total capacity of 272·75 litres (60 Imp gallons), aft of engine firewalls.

ACCOMMODATION (water bomber version): Crew of two side by side on flight deck. Dual controls standard. Two 2,673 litre (588 Imp gallon) water tanks in main fuselage compartment, with retractable pickup probe in each side of hull bottom. Water-drop door in each side of hull bottom. Flush-type doors on port side of fuselage forward and aft of wings. Emergency exit on starboard side aft of wing trailing-edge. Emergency hatch above starboard cockpit. Mooring hatch on top of hull nose below flight deck windows. Side-facing canvas folding seats for eight people are located in the forward cabin area.

ACCOMMODATION (other roles): When configured for patrol and search and rescue missions, the aircraft has additional stations for a flight engineer, navigator and two observers. The navigator's station, located immediately behind the flight deck, includes a search and radar display. The observers' stations are located in the rear fuselage, and have sliding seats which can be positioned alongside blister windows. A toilet is provided in the rear of the cabin and a galley is installed.

Additional seats and/or stretchers are available. In the passenger transport configuration, up to 26 forward-facing seats can be fitted in a fully-furnished interior with toilet and galley. Utility passenger interiors provide foldup side-facing canvas seats. Cargo tiedown fittings are provided for the carriage of loads up to 3,630 kg (8,000 lb). Provision exists for the installation of extra cabin windows, to a maximum of 14.

SYSTEMS: Hydraulic system, pressure 207 bars (3,000 lb/sq in), utilises two engine-driven pumps to actuate landing gear, flaps, water-drop doors and pickup probes, and wheel brakes. Electric pump in system provides power for emergency actuation of landing gear and brakes and closure of water doors. Electrical system includes two 250VA 115V 400Hz single-phase inverters, two 28V 200A DC generators, one 34Ah lead-acid battery and one aircooled petrol-engine-driven 28V 200A generator GPU. In the SAR version, two 800VA inverters are installed.

AVIONICS AND EQUIPMENT: Standard installation includes dual VHF and VHF/FM com, dual VOR/ILS receivers, ADF, marker beacon receiver and ATC transponder. Optional avionics include HF, DME, radio altimeter, second ADF, and ELT. The SAR version includes a search radar, DME and radio altimeter as standard.

DIMENSIONS, EXTERNAL:

Wing span	28·60 m	(93 ft 10 in)
Wing chord (constant)	3·54 m	(11 ft 7½ in)
Wing aspect ratio	8·15	
Length overall	19·82 m	(65 ft 0½ in)
Beam	2·59 m	(8 ft 6 in)
Length/beam ratio	7·5	
Height overall (on land)	8·92 m	(29 ft 3 in)
Tailplane span	10·97 m	(36 ft 0 in)
Wheel track	5·28 m	(17 ft 4 in)
Wheelbase	7·23 m	(23 ft 8½ in)
Propeller diameter	4·34 m	(14 ft 3 in)

COX
COX AIR RESOURCES LTD

Hangar No. 3, Municipal Airport, Edmonton, Alberta T5G 2Z3
PRESIDENT: Ray S. Cox
CHIEF DESIGNER: Aimo Pitkanen

COX (DHC-3-T) TURBO OTTER

This company produced a prototype conversion to turboprop power of the de Havilland DHC-3 Otter, substituting a Pratt & Whitney Aircraft of Canada PT6A-27 engine for the original 447 kW (600 hp) Pratt & Whitney R-1340 Wasp nine-cylinder radial piston engine.

Modification began in mid-1976, and was completed in April 1978; the prototype made its first flight on 26 September 1978.

No recent news has been received from the company. A description and illustration of the prototype conversion appeared in the 1979-80 *Jane's*.

DE HAVILLAND CANADA
THE DE HAVILLAND AIRCRAFT OF CANADA LTD

HEAD OFFICE AND WORKS: Garrett Boulevard, Downsview, Ontario M3K 1Y5
Telephone: (416) 633 7310
Telex: 06-22128
CHAIRMAN: D. N. Kendall
PRESIDENT: John W. Sandford
VICE-PRESIDENTS:
D. B. Annan (Senior Vice-President)
M. C. W. Davy (Engineering)
W. J. Easdale (Personnel and Industrial Relations)
W. T. Heaslip (Special Projects)
F. A. Johnson (Customer Support)
S. B. Kerr (Finance)
R. G. McCall (Operations)
J. A. Timmins (Marketing and Sales)
DIRECTOR, PRODUCT ENGINEERING: John Thompson
MANAGER, PUBLIC RELATIONS: Scott Langdon

The de Havilland Aircraft of Canada Ltd was established in early 1928 as a subsidiary of The de Havilland Aircraft Co Ltd, and became subsequently a member of the Hawker Siddeley Group. On 26 June 1974 ownership was transferred to the Canadian government, which plan-

ned to operate the company only until responsible Canadian investors were found to purchase and operate de Havilland.

In January 1980 facilities covered a total area of 113,246 m² (1,218,980 sq ft), comprising a 77,023 m² (829,070 sq ft) main plant on the southern border of Downsview airport, 30,455 m² (327,815 sq ft) of leased space on the northern boundary of the airport, and an additional 4,988 m² (53,690 sq ft) of leased storage and warehousing space. A further 780 m² (8,400 sq ft) of office space for the Marketing and Sales Engineering departments is also included. To handle the increased production rates, an expansion programme at the main plant was begun in 1979. This consists of a 3,326 m² (35,800 sq ft) extension for small parts manufacturing, plus a 7,153 m² (77,000 sq ft) high-bay aircraft assembly and preparation area.

DHC-5D BUFFALO

The Buffalo, first flown on 9 April 1964, is a developed version of the DHC-4 Caribou with an enlarged fuselage and two General Electric T64 turboprop engines. Development costs were shared equally by the US Army, the Canadian government and de Havilland Canada.

Details have appeared in earlier editions of *Jane's* of the DHC-5 (four for US Army evaluation, now designated

C-8A), DHC-5A (15 for the Canadian Armed Forces, designated CC-115), and DHC-5A/C-115 (24 for the Brazilian Air Force and 16 for the Peruvian Air Force). The DHC-5B and C were versions proposed in 1974 with CT64-P4C and Rolls-Royce Dart RDa.12 engines respectively.

The current production version is the DHC-5D, with a higher gross weight and improved performance. The first production DHC-5D set up, in February 1976, the following time-to-height records, subsequently confirmed by the FAI: 2 min 12·75 s to 3,000 m; 4 min 27·5 s to 6,000 m and 8 min 3·5 s to 9,000 m. These times qualify both in the C1 class for turboprop-powered aircraft of unlimited weight category, and Class C1h for those in the 12,000-16,000 kg weight category.

Deliveries of the DHC-5D began in early 1976 and a total of 41 had been sold by January 1980. Part of these orders will be fulfilled from a new batch of 24 aircraft, and production was continuing at the rate of one per month during 1980. Customers for the DHC-5D include the air forces of Ecuador (two), Kenya (six), Mauritania (two), Mexico (one, plus one for Mexican Navy), Togo (two), Zaïre (three), Zambia (seven), Oman (one), Sudan (four), Tanzania (four) and the United Arab Emirates (four).

A civil version of the Buffalo, known as the **DHC-5E Transporter,** is also available; this is described separately.

de Havilland Canada DHC-5D Buffalo STOL aircraft (two General Electric CT64-820-4 turboprop engines)

The following description applies to the military DHC-5D:

TYPE: Twin-turboprop STOL utility transport.

WINGS: Cantilever high-wing monoplane. Wing section NACA 64₃A417·5 (mod) at root, NACA 63₂A615 (mod) at tip. Dihedral 0° inboard of nacelles, 5° outboard. Incidence 2° 30′. Sweepback at quarter-chord 1° 40′. Conventional fail-safe two-spar box structure of high-strength aluminium alloys. Full-span double-slotted aluminium alloy flaps, outboard sections functioning as ailerons. Aluminium alloy slot-lip spoilers, forward of inboard flaps, are actuated by Jarry Hydraulics unit. Spoilers coupled to manually-operated ailerons for lateral control, uncoupled for symmetrical ground operation. Electrically-actuated trim tab in starboard aileron. Geared tab in each aileron. Rudder/aileron interconnect tab in port aileron. Outer wing leading-edges fitted with electrically-controlled flush pneumatic rubber de-icing boots.

FUSELAGE: Fail-safe non-pressurised structure of high-strength aluminium alloy. Longitudinal keel members support cargo floor.

TAIL UNIT: Cantilever structure of high-strength aluminium alloy, with fixed-incidence T-tailplane. Elevator aerodynamically and mass balanced. Fore and trailing serially-hinged rudders are powered by tandem jacks operated by two independent hydraulic systems manufactured by Jarry Hydraulics. Trim tab in port half of elevator, spring tab in starboard half. Electrically-controlled flush pneumatic rubber de-icing boot on tailplane leading-edge.

LANDING GEAR: Retractable tricycle type, with twin wheels on each unit. Hydraulic actuation, nose unit retracting aft, main units forward. Jarry Hydraulics oleo-pneumatic shock-absorbers. Goodrich main wheels and tyres, size 37 × 15-12, pressure 3·10 bars (45 lb/sq in) for STOL assault role, 4·14 bars (60 lb/sq in) as STOL transport. Goodrich nosewheels and tyres, size 8·9 × 12·5, pressure 3·17 bars (46 lb/sq in). Goodrich multi-disc anti-skid brakes.

POWER PLANT: Two General Electric CT64-820-4 turboprop engines, each rated at 2,336 kW (3,133 shp) and driving a Hamilton Standard 63E60-25 three-blade constant-speed reversible-pitch fully-feathering metal propeller with Beta control. Propellers have integral hydraulic systems and electrical de-icing of spinners, cuffs and blades. Fuel in one integral tank in each inner wing, capacity 4,841 litres (1,065 Imp gallons; 1,279 US gallons), and ten interconnected rubber bag tanks in each outer wing, capacity 3,137 litres (690 Imp gallons; 829 US gallons). Total fuel capacity 7,978 litres (1,755 Imp gallons; 2,108 US gallons). Refuelling points above wings and in starboard side of fuselage for pressure refuelling. Total oil capacity 45·5 litres (10 Imp gallons; 12 US gallons).

ACCOMMODATION: Crew of three, comprising pilot, co-pilot and crew chief. Main cabin can accommodate roll-up troop seats or folding forward-facing seats for 41 troops or 35 paratroops, or 24 stretchers and six seats. Provision for toilet in forward part of cabin. Door on each side at rear of cabin. Loading height with rear cargo loading door up and ramp down 2·90 m (9 ft 6 in). 508 mm (20 in) grid of tiedown points, with additional tiedowns at sides of cabin.

SYSTEMS: AiResearch bleed air cabin heating and cooling system. Two independent hydraulic systems, each of 207 bars (3,000 lb/sq in), actuate landing gear, flaps, spoilers, rudders, brakes, nosewheel steering, winch and APU starting. 3·45 bar (50 lb/sq in) pneumatic system

for engine starting, de-icing and environmental control. Two Lucas Aerospace engine-driven variable-frequency 3-phase 20kVA AC generators with 28V DC and 400Hz conversion subsystems. Solar T-62T-40-5 gas turbine APU in port engine nacelle provides electric (10kVA generator), hydraulic and pneumatic power for environmental control, hydraulic operation of cargo winch, electrical systems, and other utility functions.

AVIONICS AND EQUIPMENT: Full IFR instrumentation and weather radar standard, as are 34 troop seats, cargo buffer rail, cargo winch, roller conveyors, parachute anchor cables and retrieval system, pendulum release system, Brooks and Perkins palletised loading system with integral side rail restraint, tiedown straps and chains, and crew oxygen system. Optional items include seven forward-facing troop seats, airframe de-icing, toilet, cabin oxygen system, and self-sealing fuel cells.

DIMENSIONS, EXTERNAL:

Wing span	29·26 m (96 ft 0 in)
Wing chord at root	3·59 m (11 ft 9¼ in)
Wing chord at tip	1·19 m (5 ft 11 in)
Wing aspect ratio	9·75
Length overall	24·08 m (79 ft 0 in)
*Height overall	8·73 m (28 ft 8 in)
Tailplane span	9·75 m (32 ft 0 in)
Wheel track	9·29 m (30 ft 6 in)
Wheelbase	8·48 m (27 ft 10 in)
Propeller diameter	4·42 m (14 ft 6 in)
Propeller/fuselage clearance	0·97 m (3 ft 2½ in)
Propeller ground clearance	0·97 m (3 ft 2½ in)
Cabin doors (each side):	
Height	1·68 m (5 ft 6 in)
Width	0·84 m (2 ft 9 in)
*Height to sill	1·17 m (3 ft 10 in)
Emergency exits (each side, below wing leading-edge):	
Height	1·02 m (3 ft 4 in)
Width	0·66 m (2 ft 2 in)
*Height to sill	approx 1·52 m (5 ft 0 in)
Rear cargo loading door and ramp:	
Height	6·33 m (20 ft 9 in)
Width	2·34 m (7 ft 8 in)
*Height to ramp hinge	1·17 m (3 ft 10 in)

*will vary with aircraft configuration and loading conditions

DIMENSIONS, INTERNAL:

Cabin, excl flight deck:	
Length, cargo floor	9·58 m (31 ft 5 in)
Width at floor	2·36 m (7 ft 9 in)
Max width	2·67 m (8 ft 9 in)
Max height (aft of wings)	2·08 m (6 ft 10 in)
Height forward of rear spar	1·98 m (6 ft 6 in)
Floor area	22·48 m² (242 sq ft)
Volume (rectangular)	44·74 m³ (1,580 cu ft)

AREAS:

Wings, gross	87·8 m² (945 sq ft)
Ailerons (total)	3·62 m² (39 sq ft)
Trailing-edge flaps (total, incl ailerons)	
	26·01 m² (280 sq ft)
Spoilers (total)	2·34 m² (25·2 sq ft)
Fin	8·55 m² (92 sq ft)
Rudder	5·57 m² (60 sq ft)
Tailplane	14·07 m² (151·5 sq ft)
Elevator, incl tabs	7·57 m² (81·5 sq ft)

WEIGHTS AND LOADINGS (A: STOL assault mission from unprepared airfield; B: STOL transport mission, firm smooth airfield surface):

Operational weight empty (incl 3 crew and 680 kg; 1,500 lb allowance for options and electronics):	
A, B	11,412 kg (25,160 lb)

Max payload:	A	5,370 kg (11,840 lb)
	B	8,164 kg (18,000 lb)
Max normal fuel:	A, B	6,212 kg (13,696 lb)
Max unit load for air drop:		
	A, B	2,721 kg (6,000 lb)
Manoeuvring limit load factor:	A	3·0
	B	2·5
Max T-O weight:	A	18,597 kg (41,000 lb)
	B	22,316 kg (49,200 lb)
Max landing weight:	A	17,735 kg (39,100 lb)
	B	21,273 kg (46,900 lb)
Max zero-fuel weight:	A	16,782 kg (37,000 lb)
	B	19,731 kg (43,500 lb)
Max wing loading:	A	211·8 kg/m² (43·4 lb/sq ft)
	B	254·4 kg/m² (52·1 lb/sq ft)
Max uniform cabin floor loading:		
	A, B	976 kg/m² (200 lb/sq ft)
Max power loading:	A	3·98 kg/kW (6·54 lb/shp)
	B	4·78 kg/kW (7·85 lb/shp)

PERFORMANCE (at max T-O weight except where indicated. A: STOL assault mission from unprepared airfield; B: STOL transport mission from firm smooth airfield surface):

Max cruising speed at 3,050 m (10,000 ft):		
***A		252 knots (467 km/h; 290 mph)
*B		227 knots (420 km/h; 261 mph)
Stalling speed, 40° flap:		
A at 17,690 kg (39,000 lb) AUW		
		67 knots (124 km/h; 77 mph)
B at 21,273 kg (46,900 lb) AUW		
		73 knots (135 km/h; 84 mph)
Max rate of climb at S/L, normal rated power:		
A		710 m (2,330 ft)/min
B		555 m (1,820 ft)/min
Rate of climb at S/L, one engine out:		
A, max power		205 m (675 ft)/min
B, military power		116 m (380 ft)/min
†Service ceiling, normal rated power:		
A		9,450 m (31,000 ft)
B		8,380 m (27,500 ft)
Service ceiling, one engine out:		
A, military power		5,575 m (18,300 ft)
*B, max power		3,810 m (12,500 ft)
STOL T-O run:		
**A		289 m (950 ft)
B		701 m (2,300 ft)
STOL T-O to 15 m (50 ft), mid-CG:		
**A		381 m (1,250 ft)
B		876 m (2,875 ft)
STOL landing from 15 m (50 ft):		
**A		346 m (1,135 ft)
B		613 m (2,010 ft)
STOL landing run:		
**A		168 m (550 ft)
B		259 m (850 ft)
Range at 3,050 m (10,000 ft):		
A, max payload		225 nm (416 km; 259 miles)
B, max payload		600 nm (1,112 km; 691 miles)
A, B, zero payload		
		1,770 nm (3,280 km; 2,038 miles)

† Recommended max operating altitude of 7,620 m (25,000 ft)
* at 21,200 kg (46,737 lb) AUW
** with 5,443 kg (12,000 lb) payload
***at 17,667 kg (38,950 lb) AUW

DHC-5E Transporter civil passenger/cargo version of the DHC-5D Buffalo

DHC-5 BUFFALO AUGMENTOR WING JET STOL RESEARCH AIRCRAFT

A full description of this NASA-owned modified C-8A Buffalo appeared under the NASA heading in the US section of the 1978-79 *Jane's*; further details appeared in the DHC entry in the 1979-80 edition.

By the end of 1979 the aircraft had accumulated 635 hours' flying in 669 flights. More than 2,400 STOL landings had been accomplished, many of them in the fully-automatic mode. In 7½ years of operation, the Spey turbofan engines have accumulated 790 hours' running time without a single in-flight shutdown.

The NASA/DITC flight research programme at Ames was due to end in the Spring of 1980. Plans were then being made to return the aircraft to Canada in order to continue research and development of the augmentor wing system.

DHC-5 BUFFALO QUIET SHORT-HAUL RESEARCH AIRCRAFT (QSRA)

The QSRA is a C-8A acquired by NASA for evaluation of the USB (upper surface blowing) powered lift system. It has a new wing, four Avco Lycoming YF102 turbofan engines, and a modified tail assembly furnished by NASA. The prototype was converted under NASA contract by Boeing. Further details can be found under the NASA heading in the US section.

DHC-5E TRANSPORTER

The Transporter is a civil version of the DHC-5D Buffalo which will be certificated to CAR 4b and SR 442b standards for commercial operation. A demonstration aircraft (C-GTLW) was exhibited at the Paris Air Show in June 1979. Airframe, engines, propellers and APU are the same as those of the DHC-5D; some systems are modified, and military installations are replaced by a civil passenger interior which can be transformed quickly for freight-carrying.

The Transporter is available with a 44-seat utility interior as standard, with seats folding into the side walls to convert for freight loading. Optional configurations include a VIP/executive version, seating up to 19 persons in two cabins; and a de luxe 'hard wall' interior with increased soundproofing and air ventilation system.

Initial certification is to be at a max T-O weight of 18,597 kg (41,000 lb). Operated to civil regulations, the Transporter will require a 1,106 m (3,630 ft) field length; but it retains the capability to operate from 457 m (1,500 ft) strips, provided a clear stopway is available at each end.

By June 1981, civil certification is to be achieved at a max T-O weight of 22,316 kg (49,200 lb), permitting carriage of a max payload of 8,165 kg (18,000 lb). At this higher weight the Transporter would require a 1,463 m (4,800 ft) field length, but would retain the capability to operate from 876 m (2,875 ft) strips.

TYPE: Twin-turboprop general-purpose transport aircraft.
WINGS, FUSELAGE, TAIL UNIT, LANDING GEAR: As for DHC-5D Buffalo.
POWER PLANT: As for DHC-5D Buffalo. Fuel in one integral tank in each inner wing, capacity 4,841 litres (1,065 Imp gallons; 1,279 US gallons), and one tank in each outer wing, capacity 3,134 litres (689 Imp gallons; 828 US gallons). Total fuel capacity 15,950 litres (3,508 Imp gallons; 4,214 US gallons). Oil capacity as for DHC-5D.
ACCOMMODATION: Pilot and co-pilot on flight deck; cabin attendant. Standard utility layout for 44 passengers in four-abreast seating at 76 cm (30 in) pitch. Alternative VIP/executive and quick-change cargo/passenger layouts available optionally. Toilet and baggage compartment optional. Access to passenger cabin via airstair door at rear on port side, and side-hinged door at rear on starboard side. Push-out emergency door beneath wing on each side; crew escape hatch in flight deck roof.

Entire accommodation heated, ventilated and air-conditioned.
SYSTEMS: Nose-mounted refrigeration unit supplies cooled bleed air at 11·3 m³ (400 cu ft)/min. Two independent hydraulic systems, as in DHC-5D. Additional, entirely independent system for rudder power control. Emergency hydraulic system powered by handpump. Pneumatic system confined to use of compressed air cylinders for emergency lowering of nose gear and emergency operation of main-wheel brakes. Electrical power supplied by two AC generators, each with separate distribution system. DC system has 28V nickel-cadmium battery for APU starting, and to power fuel system, engine controls, and fire detection/extinguishing systems. 110V AC available for propeller and spinner de-icing, windscreen and miscellaneous heating, fuel booster pump and landing lamps. All AC, 400Hz and DC systems are duplicated for safety. Fixed-diluter oxygen systems: demand type for flight crew, portable equipment with mask and eye protection for occupants of main cabin. De-icing available for propellers, spinners, air intakes, windscreen, and windscreen wipers/washers. Anti-icing of wings and tailplane available optionally. Solar T-62T-40-5 gas turbine APU provides electric and hydraulic power for ground operation, bleed air for flight deck and passenger cabin heating and cooling, and main engine starting.
AVIONICS AND EQUIPMENT: Four-position audio system, comprising two VHF-20B VHF com; one 718U-5 HF com; one TDR-90 transponder; and one C-3000 emergency locator transmitter. Other avionics include Primus 40 radar; TCN-40 Tacan; and dual VIR-30AGM VHF nav, ADF-60 ADF, and C-14 compasses.
DIMENSIONS, EXTERNAL: As DHC-5D Buffalo
DIMENSIONS, INTERNAL: As DHC-5D Buffalo except:
Cabin, excl flight deck: Volume 43·6 m³ (1,540 cu ft)
Freight hold (rear cargo-loading door and ramp):
Volume   7·7 m³ (272 cu ft)

AREAS: As DHC-5D Buffalo
WEIGHTS AND LOADINGS:
Operating weight empty   11,430 kg (25,200 lb)
Useful load (fuel and payload) 6,713 kg (14,800 lb)
Max fuel load   6,212 kg (13,696 lb)
Max T-O weight   18,597 kg (41,000 lb)
Max zero-fuel and landing weight 18,144 kg (40,000 lb)
Max wing loading   211·8 kg/m² (43·4 lb/sq ft)
Max power loading   3·98 kg/kW (6·54 lb/shp)
PERFORMANCE (estimated, at max T-O weight):
Max cruising speed at 3,050 m (10,000 ft)
                                250 knots (463 km/h; 287 mph)
Econ cruising speed at 3,050 m (10,000 ft)
                                183 knots (339 km/h; 210 mph)
Stalling speed, 35° flap 71 knots (132 km/h; 82 mph)
Max rate of climb at S/L   710 m (2,330 ft)/min
Rate of climb at S/L, one engine out 183 m (600 ft)/min
Recommended operating altitude 7,620 m (25,000 ft)
Service ceiling   9,450 m (31,000 ft)
Service ceiling, one engine out 4,875 m (16,000 ft)
Runway LCN (10 in pavement)   7·5
STOL T-O run   290 m (950 ft)
STOL T-O to 15 m (50 ft)   381 m (1,250 ft)
T-O field length (SR 422B)   930 m (3,050 ft)
Landing field length (SR 422B) 1,107 m (3,630 ft)
STOL landing from 15 m (50 ft) 346 m (1,135 ft)
STOL landing run   168 m (550 ft)
Range with max fuel, long-range cruising speed at 3,050 m (10,000 ft), 45 min VFR reserves at 1,525 m (5,000 ft)   1,720 nm (3,185 km; 1,980 miles)
Range with 6,713 kg (14,800 lb) fuel and payload, ISA, at econ cruising speed with anti-icing off
                                100 nm (185 km; 115 miles)

DHC-6 TWIN OTTER SERIES 300
CAF designation: CC-138
US Army designation: UV-18A
USAF designation: UV-18B

First announced in 1964, the Twin Otter is a STOL transport powered by two Pratt & Whitney Aircraft of Canada PT6A series turboprop engines. Design began in

de Havilland Canada DHC-5E Transporter twin-turboprop STOL utility transport (*Michael A. Badrocke*)

Twin Otter 300 for the People's Republic of China, equipped for geophysical survey

January 1964, and construction of five aircraft began in November of the same year. The first of these (CF-DHC-X), powered by two 432 kW (579 ehp) PT6A-6 engines, flew on 20 May 1965.

The fourth and subsequent aircraft of the initial Series 100 version were fitted with PT6A-20 engines, and the first delivery of a production aircraft, to the Ontario Department of Lands and Forests, was made in July 1966, shortly after the Twin Otter received FAA Type Approval. All Series are certificated to FAR 23 Pt 135.

By 1 February 1980, a total of 721 Twin Otters had been sold in more than 80 countries, and operating hours totalled more than 5 million. The 650th DHC-6 was delivered in November 1979, and production in early 1980 had been increased to six aircraft per month. The 700th aircraft was earmarked for delivery to Widerøe's Flyveselskap Air Service of Norway, bringing that operator's total fleet of DHC-6s to 18.

Military operators of Twin Otters include the Argentinian Air Force (six) and Army (two); Chilean Air Force (five); Ecuadorean Air Force (three); Ethiopian Army Air Corps (three); Jamaica Defence Force (one); Royal Norwegian Air Force (four); Peruvian Air Force (twelve); the Canadian Armed Forces (eight CC-138 for SAR and utility duties); the US Army (two); and the US Air Force Academy (two).

The Twin Otter is available as a maritime surveillance aircraft. One has been modified for Greenlandair Charter for use on ice patrol/maritime surveillance duties. Changes include operation at a higher MTOGW (6,350 kg; 14,000 lb), provision of a Litton LASR-2 search radar in a chin radome, paradrop doors, four observers' stations with bubble windows, additional fuel tanks in the cabin with a max capacity of 567 kg (1,250 lb) each, a VLF navigation system, and provision for photographic equipment.

The Twin Otter is used as a photo survey aircraft in Switzerland and the Sudan. Three such aircraft have also been delivered to the People's Republic of China. A fourth aircraft, especially modified for geophysical surveying, was delivered in April 1979.

Four production versions of the Twin Otter have so far been announced, of which the Series 100 (115 built), Series 200 (115 built) and Series 300S (six built) were described in the 1967-68, 1970-71 and 1976-77 *Jane's* respectively. The current production version is:

Series 300. Deliveries began in the Spring of 1969 with the 231st Twin Otter off the line. Available, with short nose, as floatplane. Ten of the 12 aircraft supplied to Peru were fitted with floats, for operation by Grupo Aéreo No. 42 of the Peruvian Air Force, based at Iquitos.

TYPE: Twin-turboprop STOL transport.

WINGS: Strut-braced high-wing monoplane. Wing section NACA 6A series mean line; NACA 0016 (modified) thickness distribution. Dihedral 3°. No sweepback. All-metal safe-life structure, each wing being attached to the fuselage by two bolts at the front and rear spar fitting and braced by a single streamline section strut on each side. Light alloy riveted construction is used throughout except for the upper skin panels, which have spanwise corrugated stiffeners bonded to them. All-metal double-slotted full-span trailing-edge flaps.

Spoilers fitted to Series 300S aircraft only. All-metal ailerons which also droop for use as flaps. Electrically-actuated tab in port aileron; geared trim tabs in both port and starboard ailerons. Optional pneumatic-boot de-icing equipment.

FUSELAGE: Conventional semi-monocoque safe-life structure, built in three sections. Primary structure of frames, stringers and skin of aluminium alloy. Windscreen and cabin windows of acrylic plastics. Cabin floor is of low-density aluminium-faced sandwich construction and is designed to accommodate distributed loads of up to 976 kg/m² (200 lb/sq ft).

TAIL UNIT: Cantilever all-metal structure of high-strength aluminium alloys. Fin and fixed-incidence tailplane are bolted to rear fuselage. Manually-operated trim tabs in rudder and elevators. A geared tab is fitted to the rudder to lighten control forces, and a tab fitted to the starboard elevator is linked to the flaps to control longitudinal trim during flap retraction and extension. Optional pneumatic-boot de-icing of tailplane leading-edge.

LANDING GEAR: Non-retractable tricycle type, with single wheel on each unit. Fully-steerable nosewheel. Urethane compression-block shock-absorption on main units. Oleo-pneumatic nosewheel shock-absorber. Goodyear main-wheel tyres size 11·00-12, pressure 2·62 bars (38 lb/sq in). Goodyear nosewheel tyre size 8·90-12·50, pressure 2·28 bars (33 lb/sq in). Goodrich independent, hydraulically-operated disc brakes on main wheels. Anti-skid braking system in Series 300S. Alternatively, high-flotation wheels and tyres, for operation in soft-field conditions, are available at customer's option, size 15·0-12·0 for nosewheel and

main wheels. Provision for alternative wheel/ski landing gear. Twin-float gear available for short-nose Srs 300, with added wing fences and small auxiliary fins.

POWER PLANT: Two 486 kW (652 ehp) Pratt & Whitney Aircraft of Canada PT6A-27 turboprop engines, each driving a Hartzell HC-B3TN-3DY three-blade reversible-pitch fully-feathering metal propeller with Beta control. Two underfloor fuel tanks (eight cells), total capacity of 1,446 litres (318 Imp gallons). Refuelling point for each tank on port side of fuselage. Oil capacity 9·1 litres (2 Imp gallons) per engine. Optional electrical de-icing system for propellers and air intakes.

ACCOMMODATION: Side-by-side seats for one or two pilots on flight deck, access to which is by a forward-opening car-type door on each side or via the passenger cabin. Dual controls standard. Windscreen demisting and defrosting standard. Cabin divided by bulkhead into main passenger or freight compartment and baggage compartment. Seats for up to 20 passengers in main cabin. Standard interior is 20-seat commuter layout, with Douglas track, carpets, double windows, individual air vents and reading lights, and airstair door. Optional layouts include 18- or 19-seat commuter versions, 13/20-passenger utility version with foldaway seats and double cargo doors with ladder, and 11-passenger layout in Series 300S. Access to cabin by door on each side of rear fuselage; airstair door on the port side. Optional double door for cargo on port side instead of airstair door. Compartments in nose and aft of main cabin, each with upward-hinged door on port side, for 136 kg (300 lb) and 227 kg (500 lb) of baggage respectively; rear baggage hold accessible from cabin in emergency. Emergency exits near front of cabin on each side. Heating of flight deck and passenger cabin by engine bleed air; ventilation via a ram-air intake on the port side of the fuselage nose. Oxygen system for crew and passengers optional. Executive, survey or ambulance interiors can be fitted at customer's option. Tiedown cargo rings are installed as standard for the freighter role.

SYSTEMS: Hydraulic system, pressure 103 bars (1,500 lb/sq in), for flaps, brakes, nosewheel steering and (where fitted) ski retraction mechanism. A handpump in the crew compartment provides emergency pressure for standby or ground operation if the electric pump is inoperative. Accumulators smooth the system pressure pulses and provide pressure for parking and emergency braking. Optional low-pressure pneumatic system (1·24 bars; 18 lb/sq in) for operation of autopilot or wing and tail de-icing boots, if fitted. Primary electrical system is 28V DC, with one 200A starter/generator on each engine. One 40Ah 20-cell nickel-cadmium battery (optionally a 36Ah lead-acid battery) for emergency power and engine starting. Separate 3·6Ah battery supplies independent power for engine starting relays and ignition. 250VA main and standby static inverters provide 400Hz AC power for instruments and avionics. External DC receptacle aft of port side cabin door permits operation of complete system on the ground.

AVIONICS AND EQUIPMENT: Navigation and communications equipment, including weather radar, to customer's specification. Blind-flying instrumentation standard.

DIMENSIONS, EXTERNAL:

Wing span	19·81 m (65 ft 0 in)
Wing chord (constant)	1·98 m (6 ft 6 in)
Wing aspect ratio	10
Length overall: landplane	15·77 m (51 ft 9 in)
seaplane	15·09 m (49 ft 6 in)
*Height overall: landplane	5·94 m (19 ft 6 in)
seaplane	6·04 m (19 ft 10 in)
Tailplane span	6·30 m (20 ft 8 in)
Wheel track (landplane)	3·71 m (12 ft 2 in)
Wheelbase (landplane)	4·53 m (14 ft 10½ in)

de Havilland Canada DHC-6 Twin Otter Series 300 STOL utility transport *(Pilot Press)*

Seaplane track (c/l of floats)	4·06 m (13 ft 4 in)
Propeller diameter	2·59 m (8 ft 6 in)
Passenger door (port side): Height	1·27 m (4 ft 2 in)
Width	0·76 m (2 ft 6 in)
*Height to sill	1·32 m (4 ft 4 in)
Passenger door (starboard side):	
Height	1·15 m (3 ft 9½ in)
Width	0·77 m (2 ft 6¼ in)
*Height to sill	1·32 m (4 ft 4 in)
Baggage compartment door (nose):	
Mean height	0·69 m (2 ft 3¼ in)
Width	0·76 m (2 ft 5¾ in)
*Height to sill	1·32 m (4 ft 4 in)
Baggage compartment door (port, rear):	
Max height	0·97 m (3 ft 2 in)
Width	0·65 m (2 ft 1½ in)
Cargo double door (port, rear):	
Height	1·27 m (4 ft 2 in)
Width	1·42 m (4 ft 8 in)
*Height to sill	1·32 m (4 ft 4 in)

will vary with aircraft configuration and loading conditions

DIMENSIONS, INTERNAL:
Cabin, excl flight deck, galley and baggage compartment: Length	5·64 m (18 ft 6 in)
Max width	1·61 m (5 ft 3¼ in)
Max height	1·50 m (4 ft 11 in)
Floor area	7·45 m² (80·2 sq ft)
Volume	10·87 m³ (384 cu ft)
Baggage compartment (nose):	
Volume	1·08 m³ (38 cu ft)
Baggage compartment (rear):	
Length	1·88 m (6 ft 2 in)
Volume	2·49 m³ (88 cu ft)

AREAS:
Wings, gross	39·02 m² (420 sq ft)
Ailerons (total)	3·08 m² (33·2 sq ft)
Trailing-edge flaps (total)	10·42 m² (112·2 sq ft)
Fin	4·46 m² (48·0 sq ft)
Rudder, incl tabs	3·16 m² (34·0 sq ft)
Tailplane	9·29 m² (100·0 sq ft)
Elevator, incl tabs	3·25 m² (35·0 sq ft)

WEIGHTS:
Typical operating weight (20-seat commuter, incl 2 crew and 59 kg; 130 lb of electronics)	3,363 kg (7,415 lb)
Max payload for 100 nm (185 km; 115 miles)	1,941 kg (4,280 lb)
Max T-O weight	5,670 kg (12,500 lb)
Max landing weight:	
wheels and skis	5,579 kg (12,300 lb)
floats	5,670 kg (12,500 lb)

PERFORMANCE (at max T-O weight, ISA):
Max cruising speed at 3,050 m (10,000 ft)	182 knots (338 km/h; 210 mph)
Stalling speed, flaps up	74 knots (137·5 km/h; 85·5 mph) EAS
Stalling speed, flaps down	58 knots (108 km/h; 67 mph) EAS
Max rate of climb at S/L	488 m (1,600 ft)/min
Rate of climb at S/L, one engine out	104 m (340 ft)/min
Service ceiling	8,140 m (26,700 ft)
Service ceiling, one engine out	3,530 m (11,600 ft)
T-O run: STOL	213 m (700 ft)
CAR Pt 3	262 m (860 ft)
T-O to 15 m (50 ft): STOL	366 m (1,200 ft)
CAR Pt 3	457 m (1,500 ft)
Landing from 15 m (50 ft): STOL	320 m (1,050 ft)
CAR Pt 3	591 m (1,940 ft)
Landing run: STOL	157 m (515 ft)
CAR Pt 3	290 m (950 ft)
Range at long-range cruising speed with 1,134 kg (2,500 lb) payload	700 nm (1,297 km; 806 miles)
Range at long-range cruising speed with 862 kg (1,900 lb) payload and wing tanks	920 nm (1,704 km; 1,059 miles)

DHC-7 DASH 7
CAF designation: CC-132

The Dash 7 'quiet STOL' airliner project was begun by de Havilland Canada in late 1972, following a worldwide market survey of short-haul transport requirements.

Two pre-production aircraft were built, the first of these (C-GNBX-X) flying on 27 March 1975 and the second (C-GNCA-X) on 26 June 1975. A third airframe was built for structural testing and a fourth for fatigue testing. The first production Dash 7 (C-GQIW, aircraft No. 3), flew on 30 May 1977 and, together with the two pre-production aircraft, participated in the flight test programme.

Certification by the Canadian Department of Transport to FAR 25 was received on 2 May 1977; STOL performance is approved under conventional FAR 25 and FAR 121 regulations. In addition, certification has been given for 7° 30′ glideslope and 10·7 m (35 ft) landing reference height adopted by the FAA for STOL aircraft.

The first Dash 7 to enter service was aircraft No. 4, with Rocky Mountain Airways (USA), on 3 February 1978. By February 1980 a total of 18 Dash 7s were in service with

Standard DHC-6 Twin Otter Series 300 in the insignia of Brymon Airways of the UK

de Havilland Canada DHC-7 Dash 7 four-turboprop STOL transport *(Pilot Press)*

Spantax (Spain), the Canadian Armed Forces, Air Wisconsin (USA), Ransome (USA) and Air Pacific (USA). The all-cargo **DHC-7 Series 101** was then in service with Emirates Air Service (Abu Dhabi), Gronlandsfly (Greenland), the Canadian Armed Forces (replacing the Convair CC-109 Cosmopolitan transports based in West Germany), and Alyemda (South Yemen).

Orders and options for the Dash 7 by March 1980 had reached a total of 83, of which 83 per cent were for export Most recent customers were Widerøe (Norway), Golden West (USA), Time Air (Canada), Brymon (UK), Ansha (Honduras), Henson (USA), Yemen Airways, Tyrolean (Europe), Hawaiian Airlines, Rio Airways (USA), Ethiopian Airlines, Loganair (UK), and CIS (USA). The Dash 7 production rate was to remain at two per month throughout 1980.

A maritime reconnaissance variant, the **DHC-7R Ranger**, is described separately. The following description applies to the standard production DHC-7:

TYPE: Four-engined short/medium-range quiet STOL transport.

WINGS: Cantilever high-wing monoplane, with 4° 30′ dihedral from centre-section. Wing section NACA 63A418 (modified) at root, NACA 63A415 (modified) at tip. Incidence 3° at root. Conventional all-metal two-spar bonded skin/stringer structure. Double-slotted flaps, extending over approx 80% of trailing-edge, are actuated mechanically for take-off, by irreversible screwjacks, and hydraulically for landing. Two inboard ground spoilers/lift dumpers and two outboard air spoilers in each upper surface, forward of flaps, also actuated hydraulically. Outboard sections can be operated symmetrically, or differentially in combination with the cable-operated ailerons. Trim tab in starboard aileron; servo-tab in each aileron. Pneumatic-boot de-icing of leading-edges outboard of the inner nacelles.

FUSELAGE: Conventional all-metal stressed-skin pressurised structure, of bonded skin/stringer construction. Basically circular cross-section, with flattened profile under floor level.

TAIL UNIT: Cantilever all-metal T-tail, with large dorsal fin. Fixed-incidence tailplane, and one-piece cable-operated horn-balanced elevator with trim tabs. Two-piece vertically-split rudder, actuated hydraulically. Pneumatic-boot de-icing of leading-edges of tailplane and of elevator horns.

LANDING GEAR: Menasco retractable tricycle type, with twin wheels on all units. Oleo-pneumatic shock-absorbers. Hydraulic retraction, main units forward into inboard engine nacelles, steerable nose unit rearward

into fuselage. Main-wheel tyres size 30 × 9·00-15, pressure 7·38 bars (107 lb/sq in); nosewheel tyres size 6·50-10, pressure 5·31 bars (77 lb/sq in). Larger, low-pressure tyres optional, with pressures of 4·83 bars (70 lb/sq in) on main units, 4·76 bars (69 lb/sq in) on nose unit. Anti-skid hydraulic braking system for all units. Small retractable tailskid under rear fuselage.

POWER PLANT: Four 835 kW (1,120 shp) Pratt & Whitney Aircraft of Canada PT6A-50 turboprop engines, each driving a Hamilton Standard 24PF-305 constant-speed fully-feathering reversible-pitch four-blade glassfibre propeller, with Beta control, of slow-turning type (1,210 rpm) to reduce noise level. Fuel in two integral tanks in each wing, total capacity 5,602 litres (1,480 US gallons; 1,232 Imp gallons). Single pressure refuelling/defuelling point on underside of rear fuselage, aft of pressure dome. Pneumatic de-icing of engine air intakes; electrical de-icing for propellers. Oil capacity 23 litres (6 US gallons; 5 Imp gallons).

ACCOMMODATION: Flight crew of two, plus one or two cabin attendants. Seats for 50 passengers at 81 cm (32 in) pitch, in pairs on each side of centre aisle, with generous provision for underseat carry-on baggage. Outward-opening airstair door at rear on port side. Emergency exits on each side at front of cabin and on starboard side at rear. Baggage compartment in rear fuselage (capacity 998 kg; 2,200 lb), with external access on starboard side and internal access from cabin. Galley, coat rack and toilet at rear of cabin. Optional arrangements include movable bulkhead for mixed freight/passenger loads with large forward freight door on port side. Up to five standard pallets can be accommodated in an all-cargo role. Quick-change cargo handling system available optionally. Entire accommodation pressurised and air-conditioned.

SYSTEMS: Cabin pressure differential 0·294 bars (4·26 lb/sq in). Two air-cycle systems, driven by engine bleed air, for cabin air-conditioning. Two independent hydraulic systems, each of 207 bars (3,000 lb/sq in). No. 1 system actuates flaps, rudder, wing spoilers and main-wheel brakes; No. 2 system actuates landing gear, nosewheel and backup main-wheel brakes, parking brakes, nosewheel steering, rudder and outboard wing spoilers. Primary DC power provided by four Phoenix 28V 250A 7·5kW starter/generators. 115/200V three-phase AC power at 400Hz from four 10kVA Lucas brushless generators for propeller and windscreen de-icing and standby fuel pumps. Lucas static inverters supply constant-frequency 400Hz loads, including engine instrumentation and navigational systems.

DHC-7 Dash 7 four-turboprop quiet STOL transport, in the insignia of Air Wisconsin of the USA

Nickel-cadmium batteries for engine starting. APU, for cabin air-conditioning and electrics, and engine starting, available optionally.

AVIONICS AND EQUIPMENT: Standard avionics include crew interphone system; cabin PA system; flight data recorder; flight compartment voice recorder; emergency locator transmitter; two independent VHF communications systems; two independent VHF (VOR/ILS) radio navigation systems; one LF (ADF) radio navigation system; one ATC transponder; one DME; one RCA Primus 40 weather radar; one marker beacon; Sperry Flight Systems SPZ-700 autopilot/flight director system, incorporating Z-500 flight computer and ADC-200 central air data computer; Sperry STARS ADI and HSI; Sperry AA-215 radio altimeter; and two Sperry C-14 slaved gyro compasses and VG-14 vertical gyros. Provision for variety of optional avionics to customer's requirements. Standard options include Collins 618M-3 communications transceiver, Collins 51RV-4D navigation receiver, Collins 51Z-4 glideslope/marker receiver, and Collins 621A-6 transponder.

DIMENSIONS, EXTERNAL:

Wing span	28·35 m (93 ft 0 in)
Wing chord at root	3·81 m (12 ft 6 in)
Wing chord at tip	1·68 m (5 ft 6 in)
Wing mean aerodynamic chord	2·99 m (9 ft 9¾ in)
Wing aspect ratio	10
Length overall	24·58 m (80 ft 7·7 in)
*Height overall	7·98 m (26 ft 2 in)
Tailplane span	9·45 m (31 ft 0 in)
Fuselage: Max diameter	2·79 m (9 ft 2 in)
Wheel track	7·16 m (23 ft 6 in)
Wheelbase	8·38 m (27 ft 6 in)
Propeller diameter	3·43 m (11 ft 3 in)
*Propeller ground clearance (inboard engines)	1·60 m (5 ft 3 in)
Min propeller/fuselage clearance 0·75 m (2 ft 5·4 in)	
Passenger door (rear, port):	
Height	1·75 m (5 ft 9 in)
Width	0·76 m (2 ft 6 in)
*Height to sill	1·09 m (3 ft 7 in)
Emergency exit door (rear, stbd):	
Height	1·35 m (4 ft 5 in)
Width	0·61 m (2 ft 0 in)
*Height to sill	1·09 m (3 ft 7 in)
Emergency exit doors (fwd, each):	
Height	0·91 m (3 ft 0 in)
Width	0·51 m (1 ft 8 in)
*Height to sill	1·55 m (5 ft 1 in)
Baggage hold door (rear, stbd):	
Height	1·02 m (3 ft 4 in)
Width	0·84 m (2 ft 9 in)
*Height to sill	1·47 m (4 ft 10 in)
Cargo door (fwd, port, optional):	
Height	1·78 m (5 ft 10 in)
Width	2·31 m (7 ft 7 in)
*Height to sill	approx 1·22 m (4 ft 0 in)

will vary with aircraft configuration and loading conditions

DIMENSIONS, INTERNAL:

Cabin, excl flight deck: Length	12·04 m (39 ft 6 in)
Max width	2·59 m (8 ft 6 in)
Floor width	2·13 m (7 ft 0 in)
Max height	1·94 m (6 ft 4½ in)
Height under wing	1·85 m (6 ft 1 in)
Volume	54·1 m³ (1,910 cu ft)
Baggage compartment (rear fuselage):	
Max length	2·30 m (7 ft 6½ in)
Volume	6·8 m³ (240 cu ft)

AREAS:

Wings, gross	79·90 m² (860·0 sq ft)
Ailerons (total)	2·16 m² (23·22 sq ft)
Trailing-edge flaps (total)	27·33 m² (294·20 sq ft)
Spoilers (total)	3·63 m² (39·04 sq ft)
Vertical tail surfaces (total, excl dorsal fin)	
	15·79 m² (170·0 sq ft)
Horizontal tail surfaces (total) 20·16 m² (217·0 sq ft)	

WEIGHTS AND LOADINGS:

Basic weight empty (standard 50-passenger layout)	
	12,247 kg (27,000 lb)
Operating weight empty	12,542 kg (27,650 lb)
Max payload (50 passengers or cargo)	
	5,148 kg (11,350 lb)
Max fuel (standard tanks)	4,563 kg (10,060 lb)
Max T-O weight	19,958 kg (44,000 lb)
Max zero-fuel weight	17,690 kg (39,000 lb)
Max landing weight	19,050 kg (42,000 lb)
Max cabin floor loading	366·2 kg/m² (75 lb/sq ft)
Max wing loading	249·8 kg/m² (51·17 lb/sq ft)
Max power loading	5·98 kg/kW (9·82 lb/shp)

PERFORMANCE (at max T-O weight, FAR Pt 25, at S/L, ISA, except where indicated):

Max cruising speed at 2,440 m (8,000 ft) at AUW of 18,597 kg (41,000 lb)
231 knots (428 km/h; 266 mph)

Max cruising speed at 4,570 m (15,000 ft) at AUW of 18,597 kg (41,000 lb)
227 knots (420 km/h; 261 mph)

En-route rate of climb, flaps and landing gear up:
4 engines, max climb power   372 m (1,220 ft)/min
3 engines, max continuous power 220 m (720 ft)/min

Service ceiling at AUW of 18,597 kg (41,000 lb):
4 engines, max climb power   6,400 m (21,000 ft)
3 engines, max continuous power
3,855 m (12,650 ft)

T-O field length, 25° flap   689 m (2,260 ft)

T-O field length at 3,050 m (10,000 ft), 15° flap
1,829 m (6,000 ft)

Landing field length at max landing weight, 45° flap
594 m (1,950 ft)

Landing field length at 3,050 m (10,000 ft) at 18,915 kg (41,700 lb) landing weight, 45° flap
823 m (2,700 ft)

Min ground turning radius   8·84 m (29 ft 0 in)

Runway LCN with 32 × 11·50-15 low-pressure tyres, rigid, 30 in relative stiffness   16·2

Range at 3,960 m (13,000 ft) with 50 passengers and baggage, at long-range cruising speed, IFR reserves
730 nm (1,352 km; 840 miles)

Max range at 4,570 m (15,000 ft) with standard fuel and 3,040 kg (6,700 lb) payload, long-range cruising speed   1,160 nm (2,148 km; 1,335 miles)

OPERATIONAL NOISE CHARACTERISTICS (FAR Pt 36 at S/L, ISA + 10°C, confirmed):

T-O noise level	80·5 EPNdB
Approach noise level on 3° glideslope	91·4 EPNdB
Sideline noise level	82·8 EPNdB

DHC-7R RANGER

First details of this maritime reconnaissance version of the Dash 7 were given on 5 September 1976, at the Farnborough International air show in the UK.

Principal differences from the standard Dash 7 airliner are increased fuel tankage, to provide approx 10-12 h endurance at normal patrol speeds; two observers' stations in the fuselage, with bubble windows; a nose-mounted Texas Instruments search radar; and onboard avionics and equipment for a range of maritime surveillance duties including day and night photography. The Ranger can be converted easily to a standard 50-passenger transport configuration, and retains the capacity to carry up to 26 passengers without removal of the reconnaissance installation.

In addition, the advantages inherent in the basic DHC-7 design include multi-engine safety; low fuel consumption; quiet operation, with low interior vibration and noise levels; and the ability to use short, semi-prepared airstrips close to the reconnaissance area.

TYPE: Four-turboprop maritime reconnaissance aircraft.

WINGS: As for DHC-7.

FUSELAGE: Generally as for DHC-7, except for enlarged nose radome and bubble cabin windows for observers.

TAIL UNIT AND LANDING GEAR: As for DHC-7.

POWER PLANT: Four 835 kW (1,120 shp) Pratt & Whitney Aircraft of Canada PT6A-50 turboprop engines, as in DHC-7, each driving a Hamilton Standard 24PF series constant-speed fully-feathering reversible-pitch slow-turning (1,210 rpm) propeller with four glassfibre blades. Fuel load increased from 4,563 kg (10,060 lb) in DHC-7 to 8,165 kg (18,000 lb) in DHC-7R, equivalent to increase in total tank capacity from 5,602 litres (1,232 Imp gallons; 1,480 US gallons) to 9,350 litres (2,056 Imp gallons; 2,470 US gallons).

ACCOMMODATION: Pilot and co-pilot on flight deck. Work stations in forward part of cabin for two observers (one each side), with swivelling seats and 180° bubble windows, and for navigator/tactical co-ordinator aft of starboard observer's station. Fully-equipped galley and toilet/washroom at rear of cabin. All reconnaissance installations are of modular design, permitting quick

Artist's impression of the DHC-7R Ranger four-turboprop maritime patrol aircraft

and easy removal to make entire interior available for use in transport role. Alternatives to primary reconnaissance layout include 50-passenger transport, with reconnaissance installation removed; seating for up to 26 passengers in rear of cabin without removal of reconnaissance installation at front; or mixed passenger/cargo layout with reconnaissance installation removed, freight loading door and movable cabin bulkhead added (typical load, three standard freight pallets and 18 passengers). With all of these layouts, toilet and buffet provisions at rear of cabin, and 6·8 m³ (240 cu ft) of baggage space, are standard.

SYSTEMS: Generally as described for DHC-7, including cabin pressurisation at 0·294 bars (4·26 lb/sq in); dual hydraulic systems, each of 207 bars (3,000 lb/sq in); and 115/200V AC and 28V DC electrical systems. Adequate electrical power is provided to allow mission to be completed in event of an engine shutdown.

AVIONICS: Standard avionics comprise VHF/FM (maritime), dual VHF and HF/SSB communications; Litton LTN-72 INS; Canadian Marconi CMA-734 Omega VLF navigation system; dual VHF nav with glideslope; marker beacon; DME; ATC transponder; ADF with remote magnetic indicator; radar altimeter; gyro magnetic compass system; autopilot; dual flight director system; two air data computers; flight data recorder; flight compartment voice recorder; integrated audio system; and emergency locator beacon. Optional avionics include UHF com; UHF/DF receiver; and Doppler navigation system.

OPERATIONAL EQUIPMENT: Avionics racks on port side near front of cabin, just aft of observer's station, with flare stowage and flare launcher (for night photography) to rear of these racks. Vinten reconnaissance camera mounted in fuselage. Photo annotation system records on the film the appropriate position data obtained from the aircraft's navigation system. Main camera can be supplemented by hand-held cameras at the two observers' stations. Six-man life raft at front of cabin, adjacent to starboard observer's station. Nose-mounted weather radar is optional. A range of specialised sensing equipment can be installed, to customer's requirements, for resource surveillance.

DIMENSIONS, EXTERNAL AND INTERNAL:
As for DHC-7
WEIGHTS AND LOADINGS (estimated):
Basic weight empty (standard) 12,633 kg (27,850 lb)
Operating weight empty (standard)
13,172 kg (29,040 lb)
Max payload 4,518 kg (9,060 lb)
Max fuel (standard tanks) 8,165 kg (18,000 lb)
Max T-O weight 20,865 kg (46,000 lb)
Max zero-fuel weight 17,690 kg (39,000 lb)
Max landing weight 19,050 kg (42,000 lb)
Max wing loading 255·4 kg/m² (52·3 lb/sq ft)
Max power loading 6·25 kg/kW (10·27 lb/shp)
PERFORMANCE (estimated, at max T-O weight except where indicated):
Max cruising speed at 2,440 m (8,000 ft), AUW of 19,500 kg (43,000 lb):
ISA 230 knots (426 km/h; 265 mph)
ISA +15°C 221 knots (409 km/h; 254 mph)
Rate of climb at S/L, AUW of 20,865 kg (46,000 lb), flaps up:
4 engines, max climb power:
ISA 335 m (1,100 ft)/min
ISA + 15°C 268 m (880 ft)/min
3 engines, max continuous power:
ISA 183 m (600 ft)/min
ISA + 15°C 171 m (560 ft)/min
Service ceiling (30·5 m; 100 ft/min rate of climb):
ISA 6,555 m (21,500 ft)
ISA + 15°C 5,790 m (19,000 ft)
Service ceiling, one engine out (FAR Pt 25):
ISA 4,085 m (13,400 ft)
ISA + 15°C 3,320 m (10,900 ft)

T-O to 15 m (50 ft) at S/L:
ISA 688 m (2,257 ft)
ISA + 20°C 778 m (2,554 ft)
Landing run at S/L at max landing weight:
ISA 355 m (1,164 ft)
ISA + 20°C 376 m (1,235 ft)
Typical mission profile, incl radar search at 1,525 m (5,000 ft) and 30 min inspection at 305 m (1,000 ft), at 800 nm (1,480 km; 920 miles) from base, reserves for 100 nm (185 km; 115 mile) diversion at 3,355 m (11,000 ft) and 45 min hold at 1,525 m (5,000 ft):
time on search, out and back at 3,050 m (10,000 ft)
1 h 41 min
time on search, out and back at 6,100 m (20,000 ft)
2 h 45 min
total mission time, out and back at 3,050 m (10,000 ft)
10 h 10 min
total mission time, out and back at 6,100 m (20,000 ft)
10 h 56 min
Typical patrol endurance, at long-range cruising speed at 4,570 m (15,000 ft), reserves as above:
total mission time 12 h
Range with max fuel, at long-range cruising speed at 6,100 m (20,000 ft), reserves as above:
2,480 nm (4,595 km; 2,855 miles)

DHC-8 DASH 8

The DHC-8 is being developed by de Havilland Canada to fill the growing demand for a quiet, fuel-efficient short-haul transport in the 30/40-seat category, and is scheduled to make its first flight in early 1983.
Sized to accommodate 32 to 36 passengers, the Dash 8 fits in between the company's 19-passenger Twin Otter and 50-passenger Dash 7, and is designed to meet the requirements of FAR Pt 25. Worldwide applications include scheduled airline service on routes of up to 485 nm (805 km; 500 miles); convertible passenger/cargo operations in developing countries overseas; or comparable corporate and military transport roles. The PT7A power plant is an advanced technology turboprop engine, currently being developed by Pratt & Whitney Aircraft of Canada to provide major improvements in fuel efficiency.
The following brief details of the Dash 8 were released on 2 April 1980, concurrently with the news that norOntair, the air service sector of the Ontario Northland Transportation Commission, had ordered two of these aircraft.

de Havilland Canada Dash 8 quiet short-haul transport aircraft (Michael A. Badrocke)

By 27 June 1980, de Havilland Canada had received letters of intent to purchase 73 Dash 8s, including 51 for US customers and 13 for Canadian operators. The first DHC-8 for norOntair is due for delivery in July 1984, and to enter service later that year.
TYPE: Twin-turboprop quiet short-range transport.
WINGS: Cantilever high-wing monoplane, with constant-chord centre-section and tapered outer panels. Fowler-type flaps inboard and outboard of engine nacelles. Two-section spoilers forward of each outer flap segment. Balanced ailerons.
FUSELAGE: Conventional semi-monocoque pressurised structure, of circular cross-section.
TAIL UNIT: Cantilever T tailplane, with full-span balanced elevator. Sweptback fin, with large dorsal fin, and two-segment serially-hinged rudder.
LANDING GEAR: Retractable tricycle type, with twin wheels on each unit.
POWER PLANT: Two 1,342 kW (1,800 shp) Pratt & Whitney Aircraft of Canada PT7A-2R turboprop engines, each driving a large-diameter four-blade propeller (1,200 rpm at T-O for low noise level).
ACCOMMODATION: Crew of two on flight deck, plus one attendant in cabin. Standard layout provides seating in main cabin for 32 passengers at 81 cm (32 in) pitch, plus buffet, toilet and large forward baggage compartment. Alternative 36-passenger layout available at customer's option. Passenger door on port side at rear; large portside door forward of wing for cargo loading. Emergency exit each side, just aft of wing trailing-edge. Entire accommodation pressurised and air-conditioned.
DIMENSIONS, EXTERNAL:
Wing span 25·60 m (84 ft 0 in)
Length overall 23·01 m (75 ft 6 in)
Height overall 7·62 m (25 ft 0 in)
Wheel track (c/l of shock-struts) 7·92 m (26 ft 0 in)
WEIGHTS:
No details available
PERFORMANCE (estimated, at max T-O weight):
Max cruising speed 260 knots (482 km/h; 300 mph)
Max operating altitude, standard aircraft
7,620 m (25,000 ft)
FAR Pt 25 T-O and landing field length at S/L
915 m (3,000 ft)
Range with IFR reserves:
normal 600 nm (1,112 km; 691 miles)
max 1,100 nm (2,038 km; 1,266 miles)

HAWKER SIDDELEY
HAWKER SIDDELEY CANADA INC (Member Company of Hawker Siddeley Group)
HEAD OFFICE: 7 King Street East, Toronto, Ontario M5C 1A3
Telephone: (416) 362 2941
Telex: 06 217711

CHAIRMAN: Sir Arnold Hall, FRS
VICE-CHAIRMEN:
J. F. Howard, QC
F. H. Wood
PRESIDENT AND CHIEF EXECUTIVE OFFICER: E. J. White
DIRECTOR OF CORPORATE AFFAIRS: J. F. A. Painter

Known as A. V. Roe Canada Ltd until 1962, and Hawker Siddeley Canada Ltd until 1 July 1980, this company controls operating units and subsidiaries in Canada, the UK and the USA employing about 7,600 people.
The company's chief aviation unit is Orenda Division (see Aero-engines section).

McKINNON
McKINNON-VIKING ENTERPRISES
HEAD OFFICE AND WORKS: Hangar No. 2, Victoria International Airport (PO Box 2004), Sidney, British Columbia V8L 3S3
Telephone: (604) 656 7227
PRESIDENT, OWNER AND MANAGER: N. Christensen
McKinnon-Viking, formed in 1978, supersedes the former McKinnon Enterprises Inc, included previously in

the US section. McKinnon (formerly McKinnon-Hickman Company) entered the aircraft conversion field in 1953 when it began to undertake the conversion of Grumman Widgeon twin-engined light amphibians into executive aircraft. The success of this programme led to development and manufacture of a four-engined conversion of the larger Grumman Goose amphibian, known as the McKinnon G-21 Goose, details of which can be found in the 1966-67 Jane's. It was superseded by the turboprop-

powered G-21C and D Turbo-Goose, described in the 1976-77 Jane's.
Details of more recent conversions are as follows:

McKINNON G-21G TURBO-GOOSE
This version of the Turbo-Goose is an 8/12-seat conversion of the standard Grumman G-21A. Modifications to the airframe include a 0·38 m (15 in) nose extension to accommodate radar, metallising treatment of the wings

McKinnon G-21G Turbo-Goose, an 8/12-seat turboprop-powered conversion of the Grumman G-21A

and provision of a wraparound windscreen, retractable wingtip floats, rotating beacon on top of the fin, a small dorsal fin and hull vents. Optional improvements include provision of picture windows for the cabin, a centre main fuel tank of increased capacity, dual landing lights in wing leading-edges, electrically-operated retraction of landing gear and enlargement of the cabin by removing the bulkhead at station 26. McKinnon has received FAA approval for this conversion.

TYPE: Twin-turboprop light amphibian.

WINGS: Cantilever high-wing monoplane. Wing section NACA 23000. Dihedral 2° 30′. All-metal structure with metal covering. Fabric-covered metal ailerons.

FUSELAGE: All-metal semi-monocoque flying-boat hull with two steps.

TAIL UNIT: Braced all-metal structure.

LANDING GEAR: Retractable tailwheel type. All wheels retract electrically into hull, with manual extension. Bendix oleo-pneumatic shock-absorbers. Goodyear wheels and double-disc brakes. Retractable wingtip stabilising floats.

POWER PLANT: Two 507 kW (680 shp) Pratt & Whitney Aircraft of Canada PT6A-27 turboprop engines, driving Hartzell three-blade constant-speed reversible-pitch and fully-feathering propellers. Fuel tanks in wings, total capacity 2,218 litres (586 US gallons).

ACCOMMODATION: Pilot and up to 11 passengers in standard version. Bow-loading entrance and baggage space in nose. Main cabin, forward of the standard rear door, seats seven people, with four more in a cabin aft of the door. Baggage compartment, capacity 136 kg (300 lb).

DIMENSIONS, EXTERNAL:

Wing span	15·49 m (50 ft 10 in)
Wing chord at root	3·05 m (10 ft 0 in)
Wing chord at tip	1·52 m (5 ft 0 in)
Wing aspect ratio	6·84
Length overall	12·07 m (39 ft 7 in)
Width of hull	1·52 m (5 ft 0 in)
Tailplane span	6·02 m (19 ft 9 in)
Wheel track	2·29 m (7 ft 6 in)
Wheelbase	5·23 m (17 ft 2 in)

AREAS:

Wings, gross	35·08 m² (377·64 sq ft)
Ailerons (total)	2·75 m² (29·64 sq ft)
Fin	1·97 m² (21·20 sq ft)
Rudder	2·49 m² (26·80 sq ft)
Tailplane	3·67 m² (39·48 sq ft)
Elevators	3·99 m² (42·92 sq ft)
Elevator tab	0·195 m² (2·10 sq ft)

WEIGHTS:

Weight empty, equipped (approx)	3,039 kg (6,700 lb)
Max T-O weight	5,670 kg (12,500 lb)

PERFORMANCE (at max T-O weight):

Max operating speed	211 knots (391 km/h; 243 mph)
Service ceiling	6,100 m (20,000 ft)
Service ceiling, one engine out	3,660 m (12,000 ft)
Range with 2,218 litres (586 US gallons) fuel	1,390 nm (2,575 km; 1,600 miles)

McKINNON TURBOPROP GOOSE CONVERSION

For owners of Goose amphibians who do not require a full conversion of their aircraft to G-21G standard, McKinnon offers a simple conversion which involves only replacement of the original R-985 piston engines with two 507 kW (680 shp) Pratt & Whitney Aircraft of Canada PT6A-27 turboprop engines driving three-blade constant-speed reversible-pitch propellers.

Any of the other modifications incorporated on the G-21G can be made during this conversion. Speed and take-off performance are comparable with those of the G-21G. Range is also comparable after fitment of the optional auxiliary tanks to provide a total fuel capacity of 2,218 litres (586 US gallons).

WEIGHTS (minimum conversion):

Weight empty, equipped	3,009 kg (6,635 lb)
Max T-O weight	5,670 kg (12,500 lb)
Max landing weight, on land or water	5,445 kg (12,000 lb)

McKINNON SUPER WIDGEON

The Super Widgeon is an executive conversion of the Grumman Widgeon light amphibian, with the two original 149 kW (200 hp) Ranger six-cylinder in-line inverted engines replaced by two 201 kW (270 hp) Avco Lycoming GO-480-B1D flat-six engines driving Hartzell three-blade fully-feathering propellers. Modifications to the hull and landing gear permit an increase in loaded weight. Extra tanks are provided in the outer wings to increase the fuel capacity from 408 to 582 litres (108 to 154 US gallons). Other new features include picture windows, a modern IFR instrument panel, improved soundproofing and the provision of an emergency escape hatch. Approval to install retractable floats was obtained in 1960.

The cabin is arranged to accommodate a pilot, co-pilot and three or four passengers.

Well over 70 Widgeons have been converted to Super Widgeon standard by McKinnon, and several retractable float installations have been completed.

DIMENSIONS, EXTERNAL:

Wing span	12·19 m (40 ft 0 in)
Length overall	9·47 m (31 ft 1 in)
Height overall	3·48 m (11 ft 5 in)

WEIGHT:

Max T-O weight	2,500 kg (5,500 lb)

PERFORMANCE (at max T-O weight):

Max level speed at S/L	165 knots (306 km/h; 190 mph)
Cruising speed at 3,050 m (10,000 ft) (62½% power)	156 knots (290 km/h; 180 mph)
Cruising speed at S/L (70% power)	152 knots (282 km/h; 175 mph)
Landing speed	54 knots (100 km/h; 62 mph)
Max rate of climb at S/L	534 m (1,750 ft)/min
Service ceiling	5,490 m (18,000 ft)
Service ceiling, one engine out	1,525 m (5,000 ft)
T-O run on land	183 m (600 ft)
T-O from smooth water	10 s
Range with max fuel, 30 min reserves	868 nm (1,600 km; 1,000 miles)

McKinnon Super Widgeon with retractable wingtip floats

NWI

NORTHWEST INDUSTRIES LIMITED (A subsidiary of CAE Industries Ltd)

Edmonton Municipal and International Airports, PO Box 517, Edmonton, Alberta T5J 2K5

Telephone: (403) 455 3161

Telex: 037 2681

DIRECTOR, INDUSTRIAL RELATIONS AND FACILITIES: T. Luykenaar

Employing some 500 people, NWI is one of Canada's largest and most experienced aircraft maintenance, repair, overhaul and modification centres for military and commercial aircraft, including the Lockheed C-130 Hercules, Dassault Falcon, Lockheed T-33 and Canadair CL-41 jet trainers, and the CF-104 Starfighter. It operates western Canada's largest airframe manufacturing facility, and is currently producing major airframe components and air-conditioning ducting for the Lockheed L-1011 TriStar.

The company also maintains an environmentally-controlled instruments and electronics laboratory for the repair and overhaul of aircraft instruments and avionics, and for the design and installation of airborne avionics packages.

NWI has been awarded a Canadian government contract valued at more than $17 million to extend the useful service life of CF-104 ground strike support aircraft of the

One of the Canadian Armed Forces Lockheed CF-104s to undergo refurbishment by NWI

Canadian Armed Forces. The programme, which will extend over a three-year period and employs more than 200 of NWI's 500 personnel, will ensure the continued active role of the CF-104 in its NATO and Canadian defence assignments until replaced by the McDonnell Douglas Hornets chosen by the Canadian government to fulfil the CAF's New Fighter Aircraft (NFA) requirement.

European-based CF-104s are being airlifted, two aircraft per trip, from Federal Germany to Edmonton in a Lockheed L 100-30 Commercial Hercules transport aircraft of Pacific Western Airlines, operated under subcontract to NWI.

This CF-104 service life extension programme involves the embodiment of extensive fuselage repairs and non-destructive testing, as well as in-depth visual inspections.

ROBIN
AVIONS ROBIN CANADA
Lachute, Quebec

SALES MANAGER: Jacques Lacrivain

This company was established by Avions Pierre Robin of France (which see) to assemble in Canada and market certain models of the current Robin range. The government of Quebec has a 48 per cent holding in the company, and the Canadian government contributed 25 per cent of the cost of the buildings and machinery.

The three models chosen for initial production in Canada are the Robin R 1180, R 2112 and R 2160. Assembly is from French-built subassemblies and components, with US engines, propellers, tyres, instruments and radios being added on the Canadian production line.

First example of the R 2160, which has Canadian DoT type approval, was scheduled to fly in January 1980, with deliveries planned to begin within a few months. It was hoped to begin delivering the R 2112 later in the same year.

TRIDENT
TRIDENT AIRCRAFT LIMITED
PO Box 2428, Sidney, British Columbia V8L 3Y4
Telephone: (604) 656 7294
Telex: 049 7194
PRESIDENT: D. A. Hazlewood, PEng
CHIEF EXECUTIVE OFFICER: J. C. Vaverek

TRIDENT TR-1 TRIGULL
Design of the Trigull six-seat light amphibian started in Canada in July 1971. The first prototype (C-FTRI-X) flew for the first time on 5 August 1973. A second prototype made its first flight on 2 July 1976, and a third airframe was completed for static tests. Certification from the Canadian Dept of Transport and the FAA was received on 28 October and 16 December 1976 respectively.

Production of the Trigull is awaiting suitable funding, but the company expected to be able to begin deliveries during 1981.

A **Turbo Trigull** version, with 253·5 kW (340 hp) Avco Lycoming TIO-540-J2BD turbocharged engine, is also being offered. On 5 December 1979 an aircraft of this type (C-GATE) was flown to a height of 9,601 m (31,500 ft), an unofficial world record for single-engine amphibians.
TYPE: Six-seat light amphibian.
WINGS: Cantilever high-wing monoplane. Wing section NACA 23015R-4 (modified). Dihedral 2° from roots. Incidence 2° 15'. No sweepback. Two-spar aluminium (2024-T3) stressed-skin fail-safe structure, of constant chord, with drooped leading-edges. Electrically-operated single-slotted aluminium Fowler flap and Frise-type aileron on each trailing-edge. Ground-adjustable tab on port aileron.
FUSELAGE: Flying-boat type, with single-step hull and rear boom to support tail unit. Conventional semi-monocoque structure. Cabin, above the boat hull and forward of the engine pylon, is of glassfibre/foam sandwich. Engine cowling panels and doors are of glassfibre, wingtip float bottoms and other fairings of ABS plastics.
TAIL UNIT: Cantilever type, of 2024-T3 aluminium stressed-skin construction, with single sweptback fin and rudder. Variable-incidence tailplane, actuated by screwjack, with electrical trim. Balanced elevator, with tips of ABS plastics. Trim tab on rudder.
LANDING GEAR: Fuselage hull and independently retractable wing floats. Manually retractable water rudder, extending from air rudder. Retractable tricycle-type gear for operation on land, with single wheel on each unit. Electrical retraction of floats, hydraulic retraction of wheeled gear. Main wheels retract outward into wings, nosewheel (which is steerable) upward to lie semi-recessed in nose to act as bumper. Oleo-pneumatic shock-absorbers. Cleveland hydraulic disc brakes and parking brake. Main wheels and tube-type tyres size 7·00-6, nosewheel tyre size 6·00-6. Tyre pressure 2·41 bars (35 lb/sq in).
POWER PLANT: One 223·5 kW (300 hp) Avco Lycoming IO-540-M1A5D flat-six fuel-injection engine, driving a Hartzell three-blade constant-speed reversible-pitch metal pusher propeller. Fuel in single bag-type tank in lower hull, capacity 378 litres (100 US gallons). Refuelling point in hull. Oil capacity 11·4 litres (3 US gallons).
ACCOMMODATION: Seating for pilot and up to five passengers, in three pairs, in enclosed, heated, ventilated and soundproofed cabin. Access via large forward-hinged door on each side and centre-hinged bow door on starboard side. Space for 68 kg (150 lb) of baggage aft of cabin in compartment with restraint net, tiedown points and exterior lockable door. Dual controls optional. Alternative layouts available, for use as ambulance (one stretcher and one medical attendant in addition to pilot) or freighter.
SYSTEMS: Hydraulic system for landing gear actuation; manually operated standby pump. Electrical system includes 28V 50A alternator, 24V battery and 28V voltage regulator.
AVIONICS AND EQUIPMENT: Basic VFR and IFR instrumentation standard. Radio and other avionics to customer's specification. Standard equipment includes cabin speaker, electric clock, magnetic compass, instrument panel glareshield, sensitive altimeter, outside air temperature gauge, rate of climb indicator, audible stall warning indicator, turn co-ordinator, flap position indicator, landing gear position indicator lights and audible

Trident TR-1 Trigull prototype (Avco Lycoming IO-540 engine)

warning indicator, aileron and elevator control locks, instrument post lights, cabin carpeting, pilot's storm window, windscreen defroster, overhead dome light, map pockets, inertia-reel shoulder harness for crew, front and rear adjustable cabin ventilators, tiedown and docking rings, landing/strobe/navigation lights, and towbar. Optional equipment includes anchor light, cabin cargo floor, courtesy lights, ELT, engine winterisation kit, fire extinguisher, first aid kit, two floor baggage containers, passenger headrests, microphone and headset, portable oxygen system, propeller spinner, quick-drain oil valve, rear bench seat with lap belts, seaplane operating kit, and tinted windows.

DIMENSIONS, EXTERNAL:

Wing span: floats up	12·73 m (41 ft 9 in)
floats down	11·84 m (38 ft 10 in)
Wing chord, constant	1·83 m (6 ft 0 in)
Wing aspect ratio: floats up	7·11
floats down	6·55
Length overall, wheels down	8·94 m (29 ft 4 in)
Height overall	3·81 m (12 ft 6 in)
Hull: Max width	1·22 m (4 ft 0 in)
Elevator span	4·70 m (15 ft 5 in)
Wheel track	3·66 m (12 ft 0 in)
Wheelbase	3·68 m (12 ft 1 in)
Propeller diameter	2·08 m (6 ft 10 in)
Passenger doors (each): Height	1·04 m (3 ft 5 in)
Width	1·036 m (3 ft 4·8 in)
Bow door (stbd): Height	0·99 m (3 ft 3 in)
Width	0·70 m (2 ft 3·4 in)
Baggage compartment door:	
Height	0·39 m (1 ft 3·4 in)
Width	0·50 m (1 ft 7·7 in)

DIMENSIONS, INTERNAL:

Cabin: Max length	2·46 m (8 ft 0·8 in)
Max width	1·19 m (3 ft 11 in)
Max height	1·275 m (4 ft 2·2 in)
Volume (cargo)	3·03 m³ (107 cu ft)
Aft baggage compartment volume	
	0·36 m³ (12·9 cu ft)

AREAS:

Wings, gross: floats up	22·78 m² (245·2 sq ft)
floats down	21·39 m² (230·2 sq ft)
Ailerons (total)	0·89 m² (9·6 sq ft)
Trailing-edge flaps (total)	4·11 m² (44·2 sq ft)
Fin	2·91 m² (31·3 sq ft)
Rudder	0·91 m² (9·8 sq ft)
Tailplane	2·75 m² (29·6 sq ft)
Elevators (total)	2·44 m² (26·3 sq ft)

WEIGHTS AND LOADINGS:

Basic operating weight, empty	1,134 kg (2,500 lb)
Max T-O weight: Trigull	1,723 kg (3,800 lb)
Turbo Trigull	1,791 kg (3,950 lb)
Max wing loading (Trigull):	
floats up	75·64 kg/m² (15·50 lb/sq ft)
floats down	80·57 kg/m² (16·51 lb/sq ft)
Max power loading (Trigull) 7·70 kg/kW (12·67 lb/hp)	

PERFORMANCE (at max T-O weight; A: Trigull; B: estimated for Turbo Trigull):
Never-exceed speed 183 knots (339 km/h; 211 mph)
Max level speed:

A at S/L	148 knots (274 km/h; 170 mph)
B at 4,875 m (16,000 ft)	
	165 knots (306 km/h; 190 mph)

Max cruising speed (75% power):

A at 1,830 m (6,000 ft)	
	140 knots (259 km/h; 161 mph)
B at 3,050 m (10,000 ft)	
	150 knots (278 km/h; 173 mph)

Cruising speed (A) at 3,050 m (10,000 ft):

65% power	136 knots (252 km/h; 157 mph)
60% power	131 knots (243 km/h; 151 mph)
45% power	107 knots (198 km/h; 123 mph)

Stalling speed, gear or floats down, power off:
A, B 50 knots (93 km/h; 58 mph) CAS
Stalling speed, gear and floats up, power off:
A 56 knots (104 km/h; 64·5 mph) CAS
Max rate of climb at S/L: A 326 m (1,070 ft)/min
B 350 m (1,150 ft)/min
Max rate of climb at 3,050 m (10,000 ft):
A 168 m (550 ft)/min
Service ceiling: A 5,490 m (18,000 ft)
T-O run at S/L, ISA: A from land 275 m (900 ft)
A from water 408 m (1,340 ft)
T-O to 15 m (50 ft) at S/L, ISA:

A from land	503 m (1,650 ft)
A from water	615 m (2,015 ft)
B from water	549 m (1,800 ft)

Landing from 15 m (50 ft) at S/L, ISA:

A on land	485 m (1,590 ft)
A on water	415 m (1,360 ft)

Landing run at S/L, ISA: A on land 265 m (870 ft)
A on water 238 m (780 ft)
Range (A) with max usable fuel and 317·5 kg (700 lb) payload, incl pilot and allowances for T-O, climb, cruise, descent and landing, plus 45 min reserves:
75% power at 1,830 m (6,000 ft)
760 nm (1,408 km; 875 miles)
65% power at 3,050 m (10,000 ft)
825 nm (1,529 km; 950 miles)
60% power at 3,050 m (10,000 ft)
868 nm (1,609 km; 1,000 miles)
45% power at 3,050 m (10,000 ft)
977 nm (1,810 km; 1,125 miles)
Range (A) with max payload, allowances as above:
109 nm (201 km; 125 miles)
Range (B) with pilot, 5 passengers and 68 kg (150 lb) baggage, 45 min reserves 100 nm (185 km; 115 miles)
Range (B) with pilot, 3 passengers and 68 kg (150 lb) baggage, 45 min reserves
595 nm (1,103 km; 685 miles)
Range (B) with max fuel, no reserves
868 nm (1,609 km; 1,000 miles)
Max endurance (B) 6 h 6 min

ZENAIR
ZENAIR LTD

HEAD OFFICE: 236 Richmond Street, Richmond Hill, Ontario L4C 3Y8
Telephone: (416) 884 9044
WORKS: 25 King Road, Nobleton, Ontario
Telephone: (416) 859 4556
PRESIDENT AND DESIGNER: Christophe Heintz

This company was formed by M Christophe Heintz, formerly designer with Avions Pierre Robin of France, to market plans, materials, parts and complete kits of his single-seat, two-seat and three-seat Zénith light aircraft (see Homebuilt Aircraft section).

Additionally, Zenair is building prototypes of the four-seat Zénith-CH 400, intended for eventual factory production.

HEINTZ ZÉNITH-CH 400

Design began in 1976 of a new four-seat version of the Zénith which retains the basic configuration of the earlier aircraft but in scaled-up form. Construction of three prototypes at Zenair's plant began in September 1977, and the first of these was expected to fly for the first time in late 1980. The CH 400 is expected to become available in 1981 as a factory-built aircraft.

TYPE: Four-seat light aircraft.
WINGS: Cantilever low-wing monoplane. Wing section NACA 33015. Dihedral 6° 30' on tapered outer panels. Incidence 3° 30'. Single-spar aluminium alloy structure. Frise-type ailerons and slotted flaps of aluminium alloy. No tabs.
FUSELAGE: Conventional aluminium alloy stressed-skin structure of basically rectangular section, with rounded top-decking.
TAIL UNIT: Cantilever one-piece all-moving tailplane, with automatic and controllable anti-servo trim tab, and one-piece all-moving rudder (no fin). Single-spar structures, with ribs and skins of aluminium.
LANDING GEAR: Non-retractable tricycle type, with steel spring main-gear legs. All three wheels and tyres size 6·00-6, pressure 2·21 bars (32 lb/sq in). Hydraulically-actuated disc brakes on main gear. Steerable nosewheel. Wheel fairings optional.
POWER PLANT: One 134 kW (180 hp) Avco Lycoming O-360A flat-four engine, driving a Sensenich M76EMM-2-66 metal fixed-pitch propeller. Fuel tanks in wings, standard capacity 210 litres (46 Imp gallons). Refuelling points in top of wings. Fuselage tank of 80 litres (17·5 Imp gallons) capacity optional. Oil capacity 9 litres (2 Imp gallons).

ACCOMMODATION: Pilot and passenger on individual front seats, with rear bench seat for two further passengers. Forward-sliding Plexiglas canopy. Baggage compartment, with two separate doors, capacity 60 kg (132 lb).
SYSTEM: 12V alternator for electrical system.
AVIONICS: As required. Full IFR potential.

DIMENSIONS, EXTERNAL:
Wing span	9·20 m (30 ft 2¼ in)
Wing chord at root	1·82 m (5 ft 11¾ in)
Wing chord at tip	1·38 m (4 ft 6¼ in)
Wing aspect ratio	5·6
Length overall	7·80 m (25 ft 7 in)
Fuselage: Max width	1·12 m (3 ft 8 in)
Height overall	2·70 m (8 ft 10¼ in)
Tailplane span	3·00 m (9 ft 10 in)
Wheel track	3·00 m (9 ft 10 in)
Wheelbase	1·60 m (5 ft 3 in)
Propeller diameter	1·88 m (6 ft 2 in)
Propeller ground clearance	0·27 m (10¾ in)

AREAS:
Wings, gross	15·20 m² (163·6 sq ft)
Ailerons (total)	0·94 m² (10·12 sq ft)
Flaps (total)	1·62 m² (17·44 sq ft)
Rudder	1·15 m² (12·38 sq ft)
Tailplane (incl tabs)	2·70 m² (29·06 sq ft)

WEIGHTS AND LOADINGS:
Weight empty, equipped	638 kg (1,406 lb)
Max T-O weight	1,170 kg (2,580 lb)
Max wing loading	77 kg/m² (15·77 lb/sq ft)
Max power loading	8·73 kg/kW (14·33 lb/hp)

PERFORMANCE (estimated):
Never-exceed speed	188 knots (350 km/h; 217 mph)
Max level speed	146 knots (270 km/h; 168 mph)
Max cruising speed	135 knots (250 km/h; 155 mph)
Econ cruising speed	124 knots (230 km/h; 143 mph)
Stalling speed, flaps up	56 knots (103 km/h; 64 mph)
Stalling speed, flaps down	48·5 knots (90 km/h; 56 mph)
Max rate of climb at S/L	274 m (900 ft)/min
Service ceiling	4,875 m (16,000 ft)
T-O and landing run	244 m (800 ft)
T-O to, and landing from, 15 m (50 ft)	457 m (1,500 ft)
Range with standard fuel and max payload	647 nm (1,200 km; 745 miles)
Range with max fuel	863 nm (1,600 km; 994 miles)
Endurance with standard fuel and max payload	4 h 45 min
Endurance with max fuel	6 h 30 min

Heintz Zénith-CH 400 four-seat light aircraft (Avco Lycoming O-360 engine) *(Michael A. Badrocke)*

CHINA
(PEOPLE'S REPUBLIC)

STATE AIRCRAFT FACTORIES

WORKS: Shenyang, Liaoning Province; Sian, Shensi Province; Harbin, Heilungkiang Province; Shanghai, Chekiang Province; Beijing (Peking), Hopei Province; Nanchang, Kiangsi Province; and elsewhere

Longest-established of the Chinese national aircraft factories is the works at Shenyang, which had its origin in the Mukden plant of the Manshu Aeroplane Manufacturing Company, one of several aircraft and aero-engine manufacturing facilities established in Manchukuo (Manchuria) by the Japanese invaders in 1938. After the Communist regime became responsible for the whole of mainland China in 1949 the Manchurian factories were re-established and re-equipped with Soviet assistance. Today Shenyang (formerly Mukden) and Harbin (also known as Pinkiang) are the main centres of Chinese aircraft and aero-engine production, under the jurisdiction of the Third Ministry of Machine Building. There are design and development centres at Shenyang, Peking (now known as Beijing), Harbin and elsewhere.

In the middle and late 1950s the Shenyang factory produced in large numbers under licence several aircraft types, the first of these being the Yak-18, for which a licence agreement was signed in November 1952. In October 1954 this was followed by a licence for the Antonov An-2 biplane*, the Mil Mi-4 helicopter, and their ASh-62 and ASh-82 engines.

*CAAC airline timetables refer to the An-2 by the Chinese designation Yun-5 (Y-5), and other transports have appeared in Chinese publications with Y prefixes which have been reported in the Western press. On other occasions, the Chinese have used a prefix C when referring to the same aircraft. This is, perhaps, more logical, being consistent with use of the Westernised F, B and T for fighters, bombers and trainers respectively.

Chinese two-seat training versions of the MiG-17F/F-4

First jet aircraft to be built in China were the single-seat MiG-15bis and two-seat MiG-15UTI, both of which have the Chinese name Sinshi-lyan Chaen-to Chi (Type 2 Fighting Aeroplane) and designation F-2. These were followed by the MiG-17F (Sinshi-si Chaen-to Chi: Type 4 Fighting Aeroplane, designation F-4) and MiG-17PF (Sinshi-wu Chaen-to Chi: Type 5 Fighting Aeroplane, designation F-5). The MiG fighters and their Klimov VK-1 engines were produced at Shenyang, deliveries of both the MiG-15UTI and MiG-17F beginning in late 1956; by mid-1959 these were almost totally of Chinese manufacture. A 'UTI' tandem two-seat conversion of the MiG-17F/F-4 was also produced by the Chinese: this, too, has the designation F-4, and is a standard advanced trainer type. Several hundred MiG-15s (mostly UTIs) remain in service, and over 1,000 F-4s and F-5s still equip more than 20 air regiments in air-to-air and fighter-bomber roles. A small

number of F-4s also continues in service with the Aviation of the People's Navy. F-4s were exported to Albania (30), Kampuchea and North Viet-Nam. These types were followed by Chinese versions of the MiG-19 (F-6), licence production of the Yak-18A (BT-5), and design and manufacture of the BT-6 trainer.

Aircraft built at the Sian works include the Soviet Tupolev Tu-16 bomber (Chinese designation B-6), Chinese versions of the MiG-21 (F-7), and the Yin-an No. 1 utility aircraft. Harbin's products have included the Czechoslovak Super Aero 45 two/three-passenger twin-engined utility aircraft, the Heilungkiang No. 1 agricultural/utility aircraft resembling the Soviet Yak-12 and, currently, the Soviet Ilyushin Il-28 jet bomber (Chinese B-5), Mil Mi-4 helicopter (Chinese H-5), and the C-11 agricultural/utility light twin. Another Yak-12 development, known as the Red Banner No. 1, was produced at Peking, together with two light piston-engined transports known as the Capital No. 1 and Peking No. 1. Most of the older types were illustrated in *Jane's* between 1959 and 1964.

The present capability of China's aircraft industry was first revealed openly by study of the F-6 single-seat day fighters supplied to Pakistan, generally similar to the Soviet MiG-19SF. An assessment of the F-6 by a western observer described the general standard of workmanship of the airframe as very good. At low altitudes this fighter was said to outmanoeuvre any type of combat aircraft then in service in Asia except the F-86, and to outclimb the MiG-21 and F-104 Starfighter. The potential of the Pakistani F-6s was much enhanced by supplementing their standard cannon armament with two Sidewinder missiles.

The indications are that output of older fighters is now diminishing, with increasing emphasis being placed on the development of new aircraft making use of China's increasing technological capability. The A-5/F-6bis 'Fantan' twin-jet fighter-bomber is in production and service, and prototypes have been built of an all-weather interceptor and of a four-jet transport aircraft, both of indigenous design.

The Chairman of the US Joint Chiefs of Staff, in his FY 1979 Military Posture statement, reported that the Chinese Air Force of the People's Liberation Army then had an operational home defence fighter force of about 4,000 MiG-15s, -17s, -19s and -21s, and a tactical air force of more than 1,000 MiG-15s, Tupolev Tu-2s, Ilyushin Il-28s and 'Fantan-As'. The Chinese Air Force currently deploys a medium bomber force of about 90 Tu-16s, which are nuclear-capable. More than 90 MRBMs and IRBMs are also deployed in a mobile strategic role, supplemented by a few limited-range ICBMs.

SHENYANG (MIKOYAN) F-6

**Chinese name: Sinshi-liyu Chaen-to Chi
(Type 6 Fighting Aeroplane)**

**NATO reporting names: Farmer-C (MiG-19SF) and
Farmer-D (MiG-19PF)**

The F-6 is basically a MiG-19 fighter built under licence in China. Its original design was initiated by the Mikoyan bureau in the USSR, where the I-350 prototype flew for the first time in September 1953.

The initial production MiG-19 day fighter began to enter service with the Soviet air defence force in early 1955. Before long an all-moving tailplane replaced the former, ineffective, elevators. This new version, which also had three 30 mm guns (instead of the original armament of one 37 mm and two 23 mm cannon) and introduced an attachment under each wing for a bomb or air-to-surface rocket, was known as the MiG-19S (for Stabilisator).

With the adoption in 1957 of the Tumansky (Mikulin) R-9 axial-flow turbojet as the standard power plant, the aircraft's designation was again changed, to MiG-19SF (Forsirovanny; increased power). At the same time, another version with limited all-weather capability was put into production as the MiG-19PF (Perekhvatchik; interceptor), with a small Izumrud (Emerald) radar scanner inside its engine air intake and a ranging unit in the intake top lip. The later MiG-19PM (Modifikatsirovanny; modified) differed from the PF in having four first-generation radar-homing missiles (NATO 'Alkali') instead of guns.

In the Soviet Union the MiG-19 was phased out of production by the end of the 'fifties, but a licence agreement for its manufacture in China was signed in January 1958. Many MiG-19s had been delivered to China in knocked-down form before the deterioration of Moscow-Peking relations. The designation F-6 was given to the Chinese version of the MiG-19S fighter, which first flew in December 1961 and from mid-1962 became stan-

dard equipment in the Chinese Air Force of the People's Liberation Army.

Production of the F-6 was stepped up from about 1966, and several thousand have been built to date, including counterparts of the Soviet MiG-19PF and MiG-19SF versions. China has developed a number of variants of its own design. One of these is a tactical reconnaissance model, with a camera pack in the lower forward fuselage. The F-6 from Sinkiang air base in Fukien Province, whose pilot defected to Taiwan in July 1977, was one of the original Soviet-supplied aircraft converted to this configuration. It was equipped with a vertical/oblique camera installation in the lower forward fuselage, from which the underfuselage 30 mm cannon had been deleted. This aircraft was reported to belong to the 1st Reconnaissance Air Unit; the two wing-root cannon showed no traces of having been fired. Some of the limited all-weather models have a different centrebody radar housing of longer, slim-conical form. Another variant in service is the **TF-6**, a trainer version with a tandem two-seat cockpit installation (see accompanying illustration) similar to that of the MiG-19UTI. The 'Fantan-A' strike fighter, derived from the F-6, is described separately.

Immediately after the Indo-Pakistan war of September 1965, China offered F-6s to Pakistan. Forty were supplied initially and the first PAF squadron was operational within a year. Subsequent deliveries brought to 150 the total of F-6s acquired by Pakistan, and by early 1978 these equipped seven PAF ground-attack squadrons. By the Spring of 1974 the Air Wing of the Tanzanian People's Defence Force had received sufficient F-6s for a single squadron; 40 have been delivered to Egypt, including some two-seat TF-6s, and others to Bangladesh.

In the Chinese Air Force of the PLA, the F-6 equips more than 40 air regiments, each regiment having three or four squadrons. Roles for which the aircraft are employed include air-to-air interception, battlefield interdiction, close support, counter air and tactical reconnaissance. The F-6 also serves in small numbers with the Aviation of the People's Navy.

In early 1980, US aerospace industry visitors to China were told that Shenyang had the capacity to build 30 F-6s per month; but it appeared to be involved primarily on overhaul programmes at that time.

The following description is based on known details of the basic MiG-19SF, modified where possible to apply specifically to the Chinese F-6:

TYPE: Single-seat day fighter, attack and tactical reconnaissance aircraft.

WINGS: Cantilever all-metal mid-wing monoplane. Wing section TsAGI S-12S at root, SR-7S at tip. Thickness/chord ratio (mean) 8·24%. Anhedral 4° 30'. Sweepback at quarter-chord 55°. Entire trailing-edge of each wing formed by aileron (outboard) and large Fowler-type flap, both hydraulically powered. Compressed-air emergency extension system for flaps. Trim tab in port aileron. Large full-chord boundary layer fence above each wing at mid-span to enhance aileron effectiveness. Spoiler forward of each aileron.

FUSELAGE: Conventional all-metal semi-monocoque structure of circular section, with divided air intake in nose and side-by-side twin orifices at rear. Top and bottom 'pen-nib' fairings aft of nozzles. Entire rear fuselage detaches at wing trailing-edge for engine servicing. Forward-hinged door-type airbrake, operated hydraulically, on each side of fuselage aft of wing trailing-edge. Forward-hinged perforated door-type airbrake under centre of fuselage. Shallow ventral strake under rear of fuselage. Upward-hinged pitot boom mounted on lower lip of nose intake.

TAIL UNIT: Conventional all-metal structure. Hydraulically-actuated one-piece horizontal surfaces, with electrical emergency actuation in the event of hydraulic failure. Anti-flutter weight projecting forward from each tailplane tip. Stick-to-tailplane gearing, via electro-mechanical linkage, reduces required stick forces during high-g manoeuvres. Sweepback on vertical surfaces 57° 37'. Electrically-actuated trim tab in rudder. Large dorsal fin between fin and dorsal spine enclosing actuating rods for tail control surfaces.

F-6 single-seat day fighter supplied by China to the Egyptian Air Force *(Denis Hughes)*

A TF-6 two-seat fighter trainer of the Egyptian Air Force *(Denis Hughes)*

Chinese-built MiG-19PF (F-6) all-weather fighter

Note the unusual slim pointed radome fitted to the F-6 (MiG-19PF) at rear

Shenyang F-6 (Chinese-built MiG-19SF) single-seat day fighter *(Pilot Press)*

LANDING GEAR: Wide-track retractable tricycle type, with single wheel on each unit. Hydraulic actuation, nose-wheel forward, main units inward into wing roots. Pneumatic emergency extension system. All units of levered-suspension type, with oleo-pneumatic shock-absorbers. Main-wheel tyres size 660 × 220 mm; max pressure 8·83 bars (128 lb/sq in). Nosewheel tyre size 500 × 180; pressure 5·88 bars (85·3 lb/sq in). Pneumatically-operated brakes on main wheels, with pneumatic emergency backup. Pneumatically-deployed brake parachute housed in bottom of rear fuselage above ventral strake. Small tail bumper.

POWER PLANT: Two Shenyang-built WP-6 developments of Tumansky (Mikulin bureau) R-9BF turbojet, each rated at 25·5 kN (5,730 lb st) dry and 32·4 kN (7,277 lb st) with afterburning. Hydraulically-actuated nozzles. Two main fuel tanks in tandem between cockpit and engines, and two smaller tanks under forward end of engine tailpipes, total capacity 2,155 litres (474 Imp gallons). Provision for two 800 litre (176 Imp gallon) underwing drop-tanks, raising max total fuel capacity to 3,755 litres (826 Imp gallons).

ACCOMMODATION: Pilot only, on ejection seat (Martin-Baker PKD Mk 10 automatic zero-zero rocket-assisted type in Pakistani aircraft), under rearward-sliding blister canopy. In emergency canopy is jettisoned by an explosive charge at the lock, after which it is carried away by the slipstream. Fluid anti-icing system for windscreen. Cockpit pressurised, heated and air-conditioned.

SYSTEMS: Cockpit pressurised by air-conditioning system mounted in top of fuselage aft of cockpit, using compressor bleed air. Constant temperature maintained by adjustable electric thermostat. Two independent hydraulic systems. Main system, powered by pump on starboard engine, actuates landing gear retraction and extension, flaps, airbrakes and afterburner nozzle mechanism. System for tailplane and aileron boosters is powered by a pump on the port engine, and can also be supplied by the main system should the booster system fail. Electrical system powered by two DC starter/generators, supplemented by a battery, providing 27V DC, and 115V 400Hz and 36V 400Hz AC.

AVIONICS AND EQUIPMENT: Standard avionics include VHF radio, blind-flying equipment, radio compass, radio altimeter, tail-warning system, navigation lights, taxying light on nosewheel leg and landing light in bottom of front fuselage.

ARMAMENT: Installed armament of two or three 30 mm NR-30 cannon, one in each wing root and (not on MiG-19PF) one under starboard side of nose. Aircraft supplied to Pakistan have an attachment under each wing for a Sidewinder air-to-air missile, outboard of drop-tank. Alternatively, an attachment inboard of each tank for a bomb weighing up to 250 kg (or 500 lb), a rocket of up to 212 mm calibre, or a pack of eight air-to-air rockets. Optical gunsight. Gun camera in top lip of air intake of MiG-19SF; Izumrud airborne interception radar in centre of nose intake of MiG-19PF, with ranging unit in top lip of intake.

DIMENSIONS, EXTERNAL:
Wing span	9·20 m (30 ft 2¼ in)
Wing chord, mean	3·02 m (9 ft 10¾ in)
Wing aspect ratio	3·24
Length overall (MiG-19SF):	
incl nose probe	14·90 m (48 ft 10½ in)
excl nose probe	12·60 m (41 ft 4 in)
Length of fuselage	11·82 m (38 ft 9½ in)
Height overall	3·88 m (12 ft 8¾ in)
Tailplane span	5·00 m (16 ft 4¾ in)
Wheel track	4·15 m (13 ft 7½ in)

AREAS:
Wings, gross	25·00 m² (269 sq ft)
Ailerons (total)	1·56 m² (16·79 sq ft)
Trailing-edge flaps (total)	3·44 m² (37·03 sq ft)
Airbrakes (three, total)	1·50 m² (16·15 sq ft)
Ventral strake	0·614 m² (6·61 sq ft)
Vertical tail surfaces (total)	4·62 m² (49·73 sq ft)
Rudder	1·90 m² (20·45 sq ft)
Horizontal tail surfaces (total)	4·62 m² (49·73 sq ft)

WEIGHTS AND LOADINGS:
Weight empty, nominal	5,760 kg (12,700 lb)
Normal T-O weight	7,600 kg (16,755 lb)
Max T-O weight	8,700 kg (19,180 lb)
Max wing loading	348 kg/m² (71·28 lb/sq ft)
Max power loading	136·4 kg/kN (1·34 lb/lb st)

PERFORMANCE:
Max level speed at 10,000 m (32,800 ft)	
	783 knots (1,452 km/h; 902 mph)
Cruising speed	512 knots (950 km/h; 590 mph)
Stalling speed, flaps up	
	189 knots (350 km/h; 218 mph)
Landing speed	127 knots (235 km/h; 146 mph)
Max rate of climb at S/L	6,900 m (22,635 ft)/min
Time to service ceiling	8 min 12 s
Service ceiling	17,900 m (58,725 ft)
Absolute ceiling	19,870 m (65,190 ft)
T-O run, with afterburning	515 m (1,690 ft)
T-O run, with underwing tanks, no afterburning	
	900 m (2,953 ft)
T-O to 25 m (82 ft), with afterburning	
	1,525 m (5,000 ft)
T-O to 25 m (82 ft), with underwing tanks, no afterburning	
	1,880 m (6,170 ft)
Landing from 25 m (82 ft), with brake-chute	
	1,700 m (5,580 ft)
Landing from 25 m (82 ft), without brake-chute	
	1,980 m (6,495 ft)
Landing run, with brake-chute	600 m (1,970 ft)
Landing run, without brake-chute	890 m (2,920 ft)
Combat radius with external tanks	
	370 nm (685 km; 426 miles)
Normal range at 14,000 m (46,000 ft)	
	750 nm (1,390 km; 863 miles)
Max range with external tanks	
	1,187 nm (2,200 km; 1,366 miles)
Max endurance at 14,000 m (46,000 ft)	2 h 38 min

NANCHANG A-5/F-6bis
Chinese name: Sinshi-wu Kiang Chi
(Type 5 Attack Aeroplane)
NATO reporting name: Fantan-A

This twin-engined fighter-bomber, derived from the F-6/MiG-19 produced in China, was thought formerly to have the Chinese designation F-9. Its correct designation was later stated to be F-6bis, but the designation A-5 was used by Chinese officials in 1980 when discussing the aircraft with visiting members of the US aerospace industry. This may indicate a separate attack role for the aircraft, and does not necessarily invalidate the F-6bis designation. According to Chinese spokesmen, the design was then "about ten years old".

The airframe is based substantially upon that of the F-6, with overall dimensions increased by about 10% to give a longer fuselage, higher aspect ratio wings and taller vertical tail surfaces. The wings retain the four external attachment points and large boundary layer fences of the F-6. The principal change of configuration occurs in the forward fuselage, which is longer than that of the F-6 and terminates in a 'solid' conical nose radome. Introduction of this radome has necessitated the provision of lateral air intakes for the twin engines, abreast of the single-seat cockpit, and the shape of these increases the area-rule 'waisting' of the central portion of the fuselage. The cockpit canopy differs from that on the F-6 in being hinged at the rear to open upwards. The centre and rear fuselage sections retain the various louvres and external airscoops of the F-6, supporting the belief that the latter's power plant of two side-by-side Shenyang-built Tumansky (Mikulin bureau) R-9BF turbojet engines (Chinese designation WP-6) remains basically unchanged. One report has suggested that the engines in the A-5/F-6bis are of the R-9B-811 type, having a rating of 25·5 kN (5,730 lb st) dry and 36·8 kN (8,267 lb st) with afterburning. The taller main fin has a smaller dorsal fin than the F-6, and the strake fairing below the tail is shorter. Horizontal tail surfaces, including anti-flutter weights at their tips, appear to be the same as those of the F-6. As on the F-6, the nosewheel retracts forward, the main units inward into the wings, and there is a brake parachute housed in the tail-cone.

Camera windows identify the tactical reconnaissance F-6

This view of the underside of the A-5/F-6bis shows the fuselage weapon bay and external stores racks *(Camera Press)*

The A-5/F-6bis retains the two wing-mounted 30 mm cannon of the F-6, these now occupying the revised wing-root position outboard of the engine air intake trunks. The third (nose-mounted) gun carried by most versions of the F-6 appears to be omitted. Underwing weapon load is thought to be in the order of 1,000 kg (2,205 lb), typical combinations including two 500 kg or four 250 kg bombs, two 250 kg bombs and two drop-tanks, two 'Atoll' type air-to-air missiles, or four pods each with eight 57 mm air-to-surface rockets (S-5 type or similar). Drop-tanks, usually carried on the outboard pylon beneath each wing, appear to be of the same size as the 800 litre (176 Imp gallon) tanks carried in this position by the F-6. There is also an internal fuselage weapons bay, capable of housing about 1,500 kg (3,300 lb) of stores, aft of the airbrake. Small external stores racks can be mounted to each side of this bay.

Details of the A5/F-6bis avionics are necessarily speculative, but one report has suggested that the nose radar may be similar to the Soviet R2L (NATO 'Spin Scan B'); and that other equipment includes items based on, or similar to, the SRO-2 IFF (NATO 'Odd Rods'), ARK-5 radio compass, RV-UM low-altitude radio altimeter, MRP-48P marker beacon receiver, and RSIU-4 VHF com radio. Such details should, however, be regarded as highly provisional.

According to one report, "at least 210" 'Fantan-As' were in service with the Chinese Air Force in 1979, serving with tactical strike fighter squadrons of the People's Liberation Army. A 1980 report claimed that the aircraft had been built in "relatively large numbers". It is known to serve also in an air defence role with the Aviation of the People's Navy.

DIMENSIONS, EXTERNAL (estimated):
Wing span	10·20 m (33 ft 5 in)
Length overall	15·25 m (50 ft 0 in)

WEIGHTS (estimated):
Weight empty	6,200 kg (13,670 lb)
Max T-O weight	10,700 kg (23,590 lb)
Max landing weight	9,200 kg (20,280 lb)

PERFORMANCE (estimated):
Max level speed at high altitude	close to Mach 2
	(1,145 knots; 2,125 km/h; 1,320 mph)
Max level speed at low altitude	
Mach 1·56	(1,032 knots; 1,913 km/h; 1,188 mph)
Service ceiling	16,000 m (52,500 ft)
T-O run	620 m (2,035 ft)
T-O to 15 m (50 ft)	920 m (3,020 ft)
Landing run	900 m (2,950 ft)
Combat radius	up to 430 nm (800 km; 500 miles)

SIAN F-7 (MIKOYAN MiG-21)
Chinese name: Sinshi-tsi Chaen-to Chi (Type 7 Fighting Aeroplane)
NATO reporting name: Fishbed

Design of this Chinese copy of the Mikoyan MiG-21 fighter was based initially on that of a number of Soviet-built MiG-21Fs ('Fishbed-Cs') delivered to China prior to the political break in 1960. The difficult task of copying the airframe, the R-11 afterburning turbojet (built at Shenyang) and equipment was completed so quickly that the F-7 made its first flight in December 1964 and began to enter service with the Chinese Air Force of the PLA in 1965. The design was later updated by reference to Soviet-built MiG-21PFs ('Fishbed-D') when examples of the latter were staged through China en route to North Viet-Nam.

In early 1975 General George S. Brown, USAF, told the Senate Armed Services Committee that China "has produced a number of MiG-21s, but for reasons which are not yet fully clear . . . production was suspended and only a

A-5/F-6bis 'Fantan' tactical strike aircraft, in service with the Chinese Air Force

A-5/F-6bis 'Fantan-A' single-seat twin-jet combat aircraft *(Pilot Press)*

small number of PRC (People's Republic of China) produced MiG-21s are operational with the PRC Air Force. The balance of the operational MiG-21s were Soviet-provided some years ago".

Chinese production of the MiG-21 was thought to have ended in 1966 after between 60 and 80 had been completed, but is reported to have been resumed more recently, perhaps with engine, cockpit and avionics changes. A reconnaissance version is also said to have been developed. The MiG-21/F-7 is currently believed to equip two air regiments of the People's Liberation Army; it was reported in 1980 that deliveries to Egypt were expected to begin before the end of that year.

SHENYANG F-8

A delegation from the US Department of Defense, headed by Under-Secretary for Research and Engineering William J. Perry, is reported to have examined the prototype of a fighter designated F-8 during a visit to the Shenyang works in September 1980. It is described as a Mach 2 delta-wing aircraft, powered by a Chinese-built Tumansky R-11 turbojet and with an air intake similar to that of the MiG 21. Equally reliable reports have suggested, on the other hand, that the F-8 is a Chinese-designed fighter owing much to technology gleaned from the Soviet MiG-23 variable-geometry combat aircraft, one or more examples of which were offered to China by Egypt in 1976. The power plant is described as being less efficient than that of the MiG-23. Production has started.

F-12

Agency reports originating in Hong Kong in late 1977 referred to this new fighter, which is under development in China. Subsequent reports of this aircraft, which should be regarded as very provisional, suggest that it is intended to have a maximum speed of up to Mach 2·4 and to be able to operate from 600 m (1,970 ft) airstrips. Gross weight is thought to be in the order of 20,000 kg (44,100 lb), the power plant probably being a pair of Sian-built Rolls-Royce RB.168-25R Spey Mk 202M afterburning turbo-fan engines (each 54·5 kN; 12,250 lb st dry, 91·25 kN; 20,515 lb st with afterburning). The first Chinese-built Spey engine completed a 150 h acceptance test at Rolls-Royce Derby in the Spring of 1980.

HARBIN (ILYUSHIN) B-5
Chinese name: Sinshi-wu Houng-chai Chi (Type 5 Bombing Aeroplane)
NATO reporting names: Beagle and Mascot

Believed to equip about a dozen air regiments of the People's Liberation Army, with about 100 more in service with the Aviation of the People's Navy, the B-5 is the Chinese-built equivalent of the Soviet Ilyushin Il-28 three-seat tactical light bomber.

According to the US FY 1979 Military Posture statement, Chinese planners "still appear to consider it an important weapon system. Four hundred Il-28s are now

F-7 Chinese-built counterpart of the MiG-21F ('Fishbed-C')

Ilyushin Il-28 twin-jet light bomber (built in China as the B-5) in the insignia of the Egyptian Air Force (*Denis Hughes*)

operational (in China); the number, if any, configured for nuclear weapons delivery is unknown''. To this, the Military Posture statement for FY 1981 added that ''China's capability to conduct strategic air operations is limited by obsolescent aircraft and inadequate crew training. The force consists primarily of Tu-16 'Badger' intermediate range bombers. In addition, a few Il-28 'Beagle' medium-range bombers may be configured for nuclear weapon delivery. Both the 'Badger' and the 'Beagle' are still in production. The limited range of the 'Beagle' makes it only marginally suitable for long-range operations''. The latter statement is the first recent official indication that production of the Il-28 is still undertaken in China.

Designed in the USSR by the Ilyushin bureau, the Il-28 was developed to meet a 1946 requirement for which prototypes were also built by the Sukhoi and Tupolev design teams. Sukhoi's Su-10, powered by four 14·7 kN (3,306 lb st) Lyulka TR-1A turbojet engines, was abandoned in early 1948 when the prototype was almost completed; a series of Tupolev prototypes led eventually to the Tu-14 twin-jet light bomber which was built in comparatively small numbers for Soviet Naval Aviation. The clear leader among the three competing designs was the Il-28, which was given a high development priority following a personal order from the Soviet leader, Josef Stalin, in the Spring of 1947.

Three Il-28 prototypes were completed, the first of these making its initial flight on 8 August 1948, flown by the veteran test pilot Vladimir K. Kokkinaki. Powered at first by two 22·3 kN (5,004 lb st) RD-45 centrifugal-flow turbojet engines, a Soviet derivative of the Rolls-Royce Nene, the prototype Il-28 registered a maximum speed of 493 knots (913 km/h; 567 mph) during early test flying. This was before armament and full military equipment had been installed; after these had been added, a max level speed of 449 knots (833 km/h; 518 mph) at 5,000 m (16,400 ft) was recorded.

State acceptance trials were completed in the Spring of 1949, and, again under direct order from Stalin, a total of 25 Il-28s was available in time to take part in the 1950 May Day flypast, led by Lt Col A. A. Anpilov. Most or all of these are believed to have been pre-production aircraft, possibly powered by RD-45FA engines, an improved version of the RD-45 rated at 26·9 kN (6,040 lb st).

The first V-VS (Soviet tactical aviation) units to be equipped with the Il-28 began working up in the late Summer of 1950, although major deliveries did not begin until the following year. From then until about 1960, several thousand Il-28s were built, in a number of Soviet factories and also for a time in Czechoslovakia, where the aircraft was known by the Czechoslovak designation B-228. Production aircraft have VK-1A engines, an improved development of the RD-45 produced by the Klimov design bureau.

About 500 Il-28s were supplied to other Communist and Socialist states, including Afghanistan, Algeria, Bulgaria, Cuba, Czechoslovakia, Egypt, Finland, Germany (Democratic Republic), Hungary, Indonesia, Korea (People's Republic), Nigeria, Poland, Romania and Viet-Nam (People's Republic). A similar number was supplied to the People's Republic of China, where the Il-28 entered licence production after the political break with the Soviet Union. A dual-control version is also produced in China.

Five main versions of the Il-28 received Soviet type designations, as follows:

Il-28. Standard three-seat tactical light bomber. Detailed description applies to this version except where indicated.

Il-28U (Uchebny: instruction). Two-seat operational and pilot training version, which appeared in 1951. NATO reporting name 'Mascot'. Armament and ventral ground-mapping radar fairing deleted; 'solid' nose; second, 'stepped' cockpit (with full dual controls) ahead of and below pilot's cockpit. Two or three supplied to each operational Il-28 unit.

Il-20. 'Demilitarised' version, with armament and some military equipment deleted. Several were acquired by Aeroflot, the Soviet state airline, in the mid-1950s. This 'squadron', based at Vnukovo Airport, was used for the high-speed transportation of newspaper matrices to such major cities as Sverdlovsk and Novosibirsk, to ensure publication simultaneously with that of Moscow editions. Cargo was loaded via the navigator's hatch in the forward fuselage.

Il-28R (Razvedchik: reconnaissance). Three-seat tactical reconnaissance version. Wingtip auxiliary fuel tanks standard; weapons bay occupied by alternative packs containing cameras or electronic sensors. Some examples fitted with second radome under centre of fuselage.

Il-28T (Torpedonosets: torpedo carrier). Three-seat torpedo-bomber version for AV-MF (Soviet Naval Aviation), contemporary with Il-28R. Modified avionics; one large or two smaller torpedoes, or mines or depth charges, in weapons bay.

In addition to the above, many Il-28s when obsolescent in their original roles were converted for target towing (with hook attachment under tailcone), meteorological reconnaissance, and other second-line duties.

The description which follows applies primarily to the standard Il-28 bomber, but is modified where possible to apply to other models, including the Chinese-built B-5:

TYPE: Three-seat tactical light bomber.
WINGS: Cantilever shoulder-wing monoplane, with non-swept leading-edges and tapered trailing-edges. TsAGI SR-5S wing section, with max thickness/chord ratio of 12%. Incidence 0° 38'. Dihedral 3° from roots. Two-spar torsion-box structure, comprising integral centre-section (carrying straight through fuselage) and outer panels; built in upper and lower halves and riveted together. Construction mainly of D16-T duralumin, with skins varying from 2 to 4 mm in thickness. Hydraulically-actuated trailing-edge slotted flaps, inboard and outboard of each engine nacelle, with settings of 0°, 20° and 50°. Plain ailerons, which deflect 15° up and 20° down. Trim tab in each aileron. Hot-air de-icing of leading-edges.
FUSELAGE: Conventional all-metal semi-monocoque structure, of circular cross-section. Construction mainly of D16-T duralumin, with flush-riveted skins varying in thickness from 0·8 to 2·0 mm. Glazed nose, with optically-flat bomb-aiming panel. 'Solid' fairing aft of pilot's cockpit is of ATIM-X and ANZM magnesium alloys and incorporates a dielectric panel. Single ventral radome standard, forward of weapons bay; some aircraft have two such radomes, others none. Compartment in rear of fuselage for radio, batteries, air-conditioning and other equipment.
TAIL UNIT: All-swept cruciform structure, of similar construction to wings. Fin, on root platform built integrally with fuselage, has leading-edge sweep of 45°. Fixed-incidence tailplane has 33° sweepback on leading-edges and 7° dihedral. Trim tabs in rudder and each elevator. Hot-air de-icing of fin and tailplane leading-edges; de-icing air vents in fin and tailplane tips.
LANDING GEAR: Hydraulically-actuated retractable tricycle type, with pneumatic emergency extension. Oleo-pneumatic shock-absorber on each unit. Twin-wheel nose unit, with shimmy damper, retracts rearward into fuselage. Single-wheel main units retract forward and upward into engine nacelles, the legs rotating through 90° during retraction to enable the wheels to lie flat behind doors which form a bulge under the nacelle. Main-wheel tyres size 1,150 × 355 mm, pressure 6·86 bars (99·5 lb/sq in); nosewheel tyres size 600 × 180 mm, pressure 4·41 bars (64 lb/sq in).
POWER PLANT: Two Klimov VK-1A non-afterburning turbojet engines, each rated at 26·5 kN (5,952 lb st) and mounted in an underwing pod. Fuel in five flexible fuselage tanks (three forward and two aft of weapons bay), integral wing tanks, and (standard on Il-28R, optional on other models) wingtip auxiliary tanks. Total

fuel capacity, including tip-tanks, 7,908 litres (1,740 Imp gallons). Refuelling points in fuselage (four), wings and each tip-tank. Bifurcated intakes, each with central 'bullet' fairing to facilitate distribution of airflow. Provision for assisted take-off using JATO rocket under fuselage on each side.
ACCOMMODATION: Flight crew of three (instructor and pupil only in Il-28U), all in pressurised and air-conditioned accommodation. Pilot on ejection seat in single 'fighter' type cockpit, under jettisonable canopy which opens sideways to starboard. Navigator/bomb-aimer, also on ejection seat, occupies a position forward, below and to starboard of pilot, access to which is via an upward-opening jettisonable hatch above the nose and offset to starboard. (In Il-28U, roof hatch of forward cockpit hinges sideways to starboard.) Access to radio operator/rear gunner's position is via a power-operated downward-opening hatch in underside of rear fuselage, which also serves as escape hatch for this member of the crew. Dual controls in Il-28U.
SYSTEMS: Pressurisation system (max differential 0·4 bars; 5·8 lb/sq in) maintains accommodation at a 2,500 m (8,200 ft) environment at altitudes up to 5,000 m (16,400 ft) and at 4,250 m (13,940 ft) up to 12,000 m (39,370 ft). MWP hydraulic system, pressure 110 bars (1,595 lb/sq in), actuates flaps and landing gear via an AK-150 engine-driven compressor. Pneumatic system, max pressure 150 bars (2,175 lb/sq in), with operating pressures of 55 bars (800 lb/sq in) and 25 bars (362 lb/sq in), for emergency landing gear extension, sealing of weapons bay doors and crew hatches, and gun charging. Electrical system incorporates a 9 kW GSR-9000 starter/generator and two 28V 30Ah 12-A-30 batteries. PSR-1500-15 APU, rated at 14·7 kN (3,306 lb st) for 15 s, provides power for engine start via ST-2-48 starter motor in each air intake.
AVIONICS AND EQUIPMENT: HF and UHF radio (HF antenna on fairing aft of pilot's cockpit); radio compass; radio altimeter; IFF; PSB-N ground-mapping radar in underfuselage fairing forward of weapons bay; tail warning radar in fairing beneath tailcone; landing light in nosewheel leg door.
ARMAMENT AND OPERATIONAL EQUIPMENT: Two fixed, forward-firing Nudelman-Richter 23 mm NR-23 cannon (each with 100 rds) in lower forward fuselage, one each side of nosewheel bay; associated gyro gunsight in pilot's cockpit. Two similar guns, each with 225 rds, on Il-K6 ball-type movable mounting in tail turret. Internal weapons bay in mid-fuselage, with normal and max capacities of 1,000 kg (2,205 lb) and 3,000 kg (6,614 lb) respectively. Typical loads may include four 500 kg or eight 250 kg bombs or (Il-28T) one large or two smaller torpedoes, mines or depth charges. Some B-5s may be configured for nuclear weapon delivery. FAB-3000 primary bombsight is a modification of the US Norden M-9 of the second World War. Provision in standard Il-28 for single AFA 33/20, 33/75-50 or 33/100 vertical camera, installed beneath rearmost forward-fuselage fuel tank. Il-28R can carry from three to five cameras in the weapons bay, plus 12 to 18 flares or photoflash bombs.
DIMENSIONS, EXTERNAL:

Wing span (excl tip-tanks)	21·45 m (70 ft 4½ in)
Wing chord, mean	2·955 m (9 ft 8½ in)
Wing area, gross	60·80 m² (654·45 sq ft)
Wing aspect ratio	7·55
Length of fuselage (excl tail guns)	17·65 m (57 ft 11 in)
Fuselage: Max diameter	1·80 m (5 ft 10¾ in)
Distance between c/l of engine nacelles	6·80 m (22 ft 3¾ in)
Height overall	6·70 m (21 ft 11¾ in)
Tailplane span	7·10 m (23 ft 3½ in)
Wheel track	7·40 m (24 ft 3½ in)
Wheelbase	approx 8·10 m (26 ft 7 in)

WEIGHTS AND LOADINGS:

Weight empty, equipped	12,890 kg (28,417 lb)
Fuel load: normal	3,800 kg (8,377 lb)
max (incl 200 kg; 441 lb in tip tanks)	6,600 kg (14,550 lb)
Internal weapon load: normal	1,000 kg (2,205 lb)
max	3,000 kg (6,614 lb)
Normal T-O weight	18,400 kg (40,565 lb)
Max T-O weight	21,200 kg (46,738 lb)
Wing loading: at normal T-O weight	approx 303 kg/m² (62 lb/sq ft)
at max T-O weight	approx 349 kg/m² (71·5 lb/sq ft)
Power loading: at normal T-O weight	approx 347·5 kg/kN (3·4 lb/lb st)
at max T-O weight	approx 400 kg/kN (3·9 lb/lb st)

PERFORMANCE (at normal T-O weight except where indicated):

Max level speed:	
at S/L	432 knots (800 km/h; 497 mph)
at 1,750 m (5,740 ft)	473 knots (876 km/h; 544 mph)
at 4,500 m (14,760 ft)	487 knots (902 km/h; 560 mph)
at 8,000 m (26,250 ft)	473 knots (876 km/h; 544 mph)

```
            at 10,000 m (32,800 ft)
                     461 knots (855 km/h; 531 mph)
            at 12,000 m (39,370 ft)
                     434 knots (805 km/h; 500 mph)
  Typical cruising speed
                     415 knots (770 km/h; 478 mph)
  Unstick speed:
    at normal T-O weight 119 knots (220 km/h; 137 mph)
    at max T-O weight  126 knots (234 km/h; 145 mph)
  Touchdown speed    100 knots (185 km/h; 115 mph)
  Rate of climb:
    max, at S/L              900 m (2,952 ft)/min
    at 5,000 m (16,400 ft)   630 m (2,067 ft)/min
    at 8,000 m (26,250 ft)   420 m (1,378 ft)/min
    at 12,000 m (39,370 ft)   72 m (236 ft)/min
  Time to 5,000 m (16,400 ft)        6 min 30 s
  Time to 10,000 m (32,800 ft)      18 min 0 s
  Service ceiling         12,300 m (40,350 ft)
  T-O run: at normal T-O weight  875 m (2,870 ft)
    at max T-O weight        1,150 m (3,773 ft)
  Landing run at landing weight of 14,690 kg (32,385 lb)
                           1,170 m (3,838 ft)
  Range with max fuel, at max T-O weight:
    at 410 knots (760 km/h; 472 mph) at 1,000 m (3,280
      ft)             612 nm (1,135 km; 705 miles)
    at 415 knots (770 km/h; 478 mph) at 10,000 m
      (32,800 ft)   1,176 nm (2,180 km; 1,355 miles)
    at 232 knots (430 km/h; 267 mph) at 10,000 m
      (32,800 ft)   1,295 nm (2,400 km; 1,490 miles)
```

SIAN (TUPOLEV) B-6
Chinese name: Sinshi-liyu Houng-chai Chi
(Type 6 Bombing Aeroplane)
NATO reporting name: Badger

First steps to assemble the Tupolev Tu-16 bomber under licence in China were taken in 1958, but work was suspended in 1960 after the political break with the USSR. A production programme was reinstated some two years later, and the formidable task was undertaken of copying the design without Soviet assistance. Deliveries of the Chinese-built B-6 version did not begin until about 1968. Six of the 12 nuclear devices tested at Lop Nor up to 1971 were air-dropped from Tu-16/B-6s, but production of this aircraft has been relatively slow. By the early 1970s, about 60 had been completed.

The FY 1979 Military Posture statement by General George S. Brown, USAF, Chairman of the US Joint Chiefs of Staff, suggested that "More than 80 of these Soviet-designed bombers are now operational. Although no radical changes to the 'Badger' basic design are expected, limited production of ECM, reconnaissance or tanker variants could be initiated at any time. An air-to-surface missile carrier still remains a possibility in the future."

HARBIN (MIL) H-5
Chinese name: Sinshi-wu Chiou-sung Chi
(Type 5 Vertical-flight Aeroplane)
NATO reporting name: Hound

The H-5 is the Chinese-built military version of the Mil Mi-4 general-purpose helicopter, some 300-350 of which are estimated to be in service with the Air Force of the People's Liberation Army. A further 50 or so serve with the Aviation of the People's Navy for anti-submarine and search and rescue duties.

A civil version of the Mi-4/H-5 has the Chinese name **Syuan Fen** (Whirlwind). Combined military and civil production is believed to total about 1,000.

At least two other types of helicopter have been developed in China; one of these is an Mi-4/H-5 converted to utilise a Pratt & Whitney Aircraft of Canada PT6T-6 Turbo Twin Pac turboshaft power plant and first flown in 1979 (see accompanying illustration). Approximately 600 Mi-4/H-5s, in military and civil use, are available for similar conversion.

H-6
At Shanghai in early 1980 the Chinese displayed a component said to belong to a helicopter having the Chinese designation H-6. Positive identification of this type was still awaited at the time of closing for press.

Two views of B-6 strategic bombers, based on the Tupolev Tu-16

PRC (AÉROSPATIALE) SA 365N DAUPHIN 2
A licence agreement was signed on 2 July 1980 between Aérospatiale of France and the Chinese government for the former's Dauphin 2 twin-turboshaft helicopter (which see) to be manufactured in China. The agreement is for an initial batch of 50, most of which will be used for offshore oil exploration work.

PRC (BELL) MODELS 212 and 412
Eight Bell Model 212 helicopters were purchased by China in 1979, and photographs of these being assembled after arrival at Tianjin (Tientsin) Airport appeared in the Western press in early 1980. In the Spring of 1980, negotiations were under way with a view to a four-year programme in which the Harbin factory would assemble, and eventually manufacture, a further 50 Bell helicopters. Plans envisaged the assembly of 20 Model 212s from knocked-down components, after which Bell would provide assistance at Harbin during the manufacture of 30 Model 412s. Similar negotiations with Pratt & Whitney Aircraft of Canada, for China to produce the helicopters' PT6 turboshaft engines, were in hand at the same time.

SHENYANG (YAKOVLEV) BT-5
Chinese name: Sinshi-wu Kao Chi Chao Lien
(Type 5 Basic Trainer)
NATO reporting name: Max
A Sino-Soviet agreement of November 1952 provided

for the licence manufacture in China of the Yakovlev Yak-18 (Chinese name: Sinshi-san Tso Chi Chao Lien: Type 3 Primary Trainer) and its 119 kW (160 hp) M-11FR engine. The first example was flown in July 1954; Chinese-built engines were introduced in 1956.

The original Yak-18 was superseded by the Yak-18A, following a subsequent agreement in January 1958 for this version to be built in China, where it has the designation BT-5. Ivchenko AI-14R engines for the BT-5 were also manufactured in China as the Hou-sai-5. The BT-5 was superseded in production and service by the BT-6 (which see).

SHENYANG BT-6
Chinese name: Sinshi-liyu Kao Chi Chao Lien
(Type 6 Basic Trainer)
Despite a close similarity to the Yak-18A/BT-5 (see previous entry), the BT-6 is regarded as an essentially indigenous design of the Chinese aerospace industry, and was the first such design to enter large-scale production.

Evolved to replace the BT-5 in the basic training role, the two-seat BT-6 is powered by a 213 kW (285 hp) Hou-sai-6 nine-cylinder aircooled radial engine, based on the Ivchenko AI-14RF and driving a two-blade propeller. It is reported to have been in production since 1961, with more than 2,000 delivered, including exports to Bangladesh, Korea, Viet-Nam and Zambia. As shown in the accompanying illustrations, features include a tricycle landing gear and large, square-cut vertical tail surfaces.

Nose of Harbin-built H-5 helicopter, re-engined with PT6T-6 Turbo Twin Pac power plant

Shenyang BT-6 basic trainer (Chinese-built Hou-sai-6 engine)

DIMENSIONS, EXTERNAL:
Wing span	10·70 m (35 ft 1¼ in)
Length overall	8·40 m (27 ft 6¾ in)
Height overall	3·30 m (10 ft 10 in)

WEIGHTS:
Weight empty	1,095 kg (2,415 lb)
Max fuel	110 kg (243 lb)
Max T-O weight	1,400 kg (3,088 lb)

PERFORMANCE:
Max level speed	155 knots (286 km/h; 178 mph)
Cruising speed	124 knots (230 km/h; 143 mph)
Landing speed	62 knots (115 km/h; 71·5 mph)
Max rate of climb at S/L	380 m (1,248 ft)/min
Service ceiling	5,080 m (16,680 ft)
T-O run	280 m (920 ft)
Landing run	350 m (1,150 ft)
Endurance	3 h 36 min

Shenyang BT-6 tandem two-seat basic training aircraft *(Pilot Press)*

HARBIN (ANTONOV) C-5 (Y-5)
Chinese name: Sinshi-wu Yuong-shu Chi
(Type 5 Transport Aeroplane)
NATO reporting name: Colt

The Antonov An-2 general-purpose biplane was supplied to, and built under licence in, China in considerable
numbers (more than 1,000). It has been used extensively
in a civil capacity for agricultural and general transport
work, and several hundred still serve with the Chinese Air
Force.

Chinese-produced examples have included a number of
variants differing from the standard Soviet- or Polish-built
production models, and some of them have reportedly
been fitted with turboprop power plants.

SHANGHAI C-10 (Y-10)

The first jet airliner of Chinese design and manufacture
was quoted as "being readied for flight test" in mid-1980.
This prototype is the second aircraft, the No.1 airframe
having been used at Sian for structural testing.

Although of similar configuration to the Boeing 707, the
C-10 is a smaller aircraft, seating 120 passengers in a
five-abreast layout. Initial design began in about 1970,
some two years before the first 707s were delivered to
China, and was undertaken to demonstrate the Chinese
industry's capability to develop an aircraft of this type. The
prototype is powered by four Pratt & Whitney JT3D-7
turbojet engines, already available in the country as 707
spares. The engine pods, which incorporate thrust
reversers, and the underwing pylons, are of Chinese
design; some parts of the aircraft are said to be of British
origin.

Other details of the C-10, according to US aerospace
industry representatives who visited China in early 1980,
include a wing span of 42·98 m (141 ft), payload of 17,000
kg (37,500 lb), max T-O weight of 110,000 kg (242,500
lb), cruising speed of Mach 0·88, and range of nearly 4,340
nm (8,045 km; 5,000 miles).

C-11 utility aircraft under construction at Harbin

C-11 (Y-11) twin-engined general-purpose aircraft, designed and built in China

Harbin C-11 (Y-11) twin-engined agricultural and utility aircraft *(Pilot Press)*

HARBIN C-11 (Y-11)
Chinese name: Sinshi-shi Yuong-shu Chi
(Type 11 Transport Aeroplane)

First details of this new Chinese twin-engined utility
aircraft were given on 26 August 1977, in the
French/Chinese publication *Chine Nouvelle,* which stated
that it had been designed and developed by the Chinese
aerospace industry and was in production as a replacement
for the Antonov An-2, which has the Chinese designation
C-5 or Y-5. First flight is believed to have taken place in
1975, and production takes place at the Harbin Aircraft
Works.

The C-11 is intended for use primarily in agricultural
and forestry applications, and was described as "a new
contribution towards speeding up the modernisation of
agriculture" in China. In June/July 1977, it underwent
operational trials for crop-dusting and spraying missions.

In overall size and general configuration the C-11
resembles the Australian GAF Nomad, in which the
Chinese government reportedly expressed an interest in
1976-77. Its engines are fitted with louvred intakes to
control cooling, and may be related to the Soviet
Vedeneev-developed Ivchenko AI-14RF. It was reported
in mid-1980 that China was negotiating for licence manufacture of Pratt & Whitney Aircraft of Canada PT6A-
110 turboprop engines to power a new version of the
C-11.

TYPE: Twin-engined agricultural and general-purpose aircraft.

WINGS: Braced high-wing all-metal monoplane, with constant chord from root to tip. No dihedral. Drooping
ailerons and two-section slotted flaps along full span of
trailing-edges. Leading-edge slats from nacelle to tip of
each wing, with smaller inboard flap or slat on each side
between nacelle and fuselage. Small stub-wings at cabin
floor level support the main landing gear units; bracing
strut from each stub-wing out to approx mid-span.

FUSELAGE: Conventional semi-monocoque all-metal
structure of basically rectangular cross-section, swept
upward at rear.

TAIL UNIT: Cantilever non-swept metal structure, with
low-set tailplane and small dorsal fin. Horn-balanced
rudder and elevators. Inset tab in rudder and port
elevator.

LANDING GEAR: Non-retractable tricycle type, with oleo-pneumatic shock-absorber in each unit. Twin-wheel main units, attached to underside of stub-wings. Single steerable nosewheel. Small bumper under tailcone.

POWER PLANT: Two 213 kW (285 hp) Hou-sai-6 nine-cylinder radial aircooled engines, each driving a two-blade variable-pitch propeller, underslung from wings and fitted with louvred intakes in front of cylinders to control cooling.

ACCOMMODATION: Crew of two on flight deck, with separate forward-opening door(s) for access. Dual controls. Cabin accommodates six to eight passengers or equivalent cargo. Cargo/passenger double door on port side of fuselage, in line with wing trailing-edge. Underside of

rear fuselage, aft of this door, probably lets down to act as a loading ramp for bulky cargo.

AVIONICS AND EQUIPMENT: Radio; operational equipment according to mission. Agricultural version has hopper with capacity of 855 kg (1,885 lb) or 975 litres (214 Imp gallons), and six rotary atomisers for spraying.

DIMENSIONS, EXTERNAL:
Wing span	17·00 m (55 ft 9¼ in)
Wing aspect ratio	8·5
Length overall	12·017 m (39 ft 5⅛ in)
Height overall	4·64 m (15 ft 2¾ in)
Wheel track (c/l of shock-absorbers)	
	approx 3·00 m (9 ft 10 in)
Wheelbase	approx 3·70 m (12 ft 1¾ in)

DIMENSIONS, INTERNAL:
Cabin: Length	3·58 m (11 ft 9 in)
Width	1·27 m (4 ft 2 in)
Height	1·48 m (4 ft 10¼ in)

AREA:
Wings, gross	34·00 m² (365·97 sq ft)

WEIGHTS:
Weight empty	2,050 kg (4,519 lb)
Fuel load	210 kg (463 lb)
Max T-O weight	3,500 kg (7,715 lb)

PERFORMANCE:
Max level speed	119 knots (220 km/h; 137 mph)
Cruising speed, 57% power	
	89 knots (165 km/h; 102 mph)
Service ceiling	4,000 m (13,125 ft)
T-O and landing run	140 m (460 ft)

COLOMBIA

AGRICOPTEROS
AGRICOPTEROS LTDA
Apartado Aéreo 1789, Cali
PRESIDENT: Eng Maximo Tedesco

This company, which undertakes crop-spraying operations in Colombia, is assembling kits of a modified agricultural version of the Aerosport Scamp (see under USA in the Homebuilt Aircraft section).

AGRICOPTEROS (AEROSPORT) SCAMP MODEL B

Following a visit to the USA in 1976 the President of Agricopteros Ltda ordered two kits of the Aerosport Scamp homebuilt biplane, with a view to the possible adaptation of this aircraft for agricultural duties. In collaboration with Aerosport, he introduced a number of modifications into the new Scamp B version, and the first example made its initial flight on 27 May 1977.

This was the basic aircraft, in which the major changes included a slight increase in wing span, the provision of ailerons on the lower as well as the upper wings, and a different power plant. No agricultural equipment was installed at that time; this was designed subsequently by Sr Tedesco, and consists primarily of an underfuselage glassfibre chemical tank, wind-driven pressure pump, spraybars, and nozzles. The entire installation weighs only 17 kg (38 lb). A T-type hydraulic valve system forces the ultra-low-volume liquid chemical into the spraybars at a pressure of 5·52 bars (80 lb/sq in), and it is discharged through the nozzles at 4·14 bars (60 lb/sq in). The tank is fitted with a quick-release trapdoor, and the entire chemical load can be jettisoned in 2 s in an emergency. If the aircraft is required for cross-country journeys, the tank can be used to carry auxiliary fuel instead of chemical.

The Scamp B is now being produced by Agricopteros by the assembly of kits supplied by Aerosport.

TYPE: Single-seat Restricted category (export) agricultural light aircraft.

WINGS: Braced biplane structure, with V-type interplane strut each side. Flying and landing wires of streamline section. Single 5 × 12·5 cm (2 × 5 in) extruded section of 6063-T3 light alloy tubing forms a pylon to support the centre-section of the upper wing. Wing section NACA 23012. Dihedral 3° on lower wings only. All-metal light alloy tubular front and main spars. Light alloy plain ailerons, with piano hinge at upper surface, on upper and lower wings. Lower ailerons actuated by slaved push/pull tube connected to upper pair. No flaps or tabs.

FUSELAGE: All-metal light alloy semi-monocoque structure.

TAIL UNIT: Braced T-tail of light alloy construction. Single bracing strut each side. Fixed-incidence tailplane. Ground-adjustable trim tab on rudder.

LANDING GEAR: Non-retractable tricycle type. Cantilever spring main-gear struts of light alloy. Wheel fairing optional for each unit.

POWER PLANT: One 74·5 kW (100 hp) Revmaster 2,100 cc modified Volkswagen engine, driving an Aerial 56-38 two-blade fixed-pitch wooden propeller. Fuel tank in fuselage nose, aft of firewall, capacity 30·5 litres (6·7 Imp gallons). Refuelling point on fuselage upper surface, forward of windscreen.

ACCOMMODATION: Single seat in open cockpit.

EQUIPMENT: Underfuselage tank for ultra-low-volume

Agricopteros-built Aerosport Scamp B, with belly tank and spraybars

chemical or auxiliary fuel, capacity 60 litres (13·2 Imp gallons).

DIMENSIONS, EXTERNAL:
Wing span	5·94 m (19 ft 6 in)
Wing chord, constant	0·91 m (3 ft 0 in)
Wing area, gross	10·82 m² (116·5 sq ft)
Length overall	4·37 m (14 ft 4 in)
Height overall	1·73 m (5 ft 8 in)
Tailplane span	1·98 m (6 ft 6 in)
Wheel track	1·52 m (5 ft 0 in)
Wheelbase	1·22 m (4 ft 0 in)
Propeller diameter	1·42 m (4 ft 8 in)

WEIGHTS:
Weight empty	259 kg (572 lb)
Normal T-O weight	360 kg (795 lb)
Max T-O weight with chemical	428 kg (945 lb)

PERFORMANCE:
Never-exceed speed	100 knots (185 km/h; 115 mph)
Max level speed	82 knots (153 km/h; 95 mph)
Cruising speed	76 knots (140 km/h; 87 mph)
Max manoeuvring speed	72 knots (134 km/h; 83 mph)
Stalling speed	43·5 knots (81 km/h; 50 mph)
Service ceiling: tested	2,590 m (8,500 ft)
estimated	3,810 m (12,500 ft)
T-O run	122 m (400 ft)
Landing run	152 m (500 ft)
Range at cruising speed	130 nm (241 km; 150 miles)
Max range with auxiliary fuel in underfuselage tank	
	477 nm (885 km; 550 miles)
Max endurance with auxiliary fuel in underfuselage tank	6 h 45 min
Swath width	8·5 m (28 ft)

AVIONES DE COLOMBIA
AVIONES DE COLOMBIA SA
HEAD OFFICE: Calle 26 No. 4A-45 Piso 8, Bogotá
Telephone: (282) 9648, 9668 and 9728
Telex: 45 220
WORKS: Aeropuerto Guaymaral, Apartado Aéreo 6876, Bogotá
Telephone: (254) 1515 and 8831
SALES MANAGER: Rafael Urdaneta

This company, established in the 1950s and known formerly as Urdaneta y Galvez Ltda, has been a South

American distributor for Cessna aircraft since 1961. In 1969 it also began assembling and partly building selected Cessna types under licence. Sixty-five aircraft were so produced in 1973, and a further 93 in 1974, some 40% of these being Cessna Model A188B AGwagons (see US section). Production in 1974 was limited to wings, tail units and seats for the Cessna range, but welding and other techniques were learnt, and the company has since become qualified to manufacture complete airframes. Facilities include 464·5 m² (5,000 sq ft) of office space in Bogotá, and 13,935 m² (150,000 sq ft) at Guaymaral, the general aviation airport for Bogotá. Service facilities

include complete engine, propeller and avionics workshops. A new 1,350 m² (14,530 sq ft) paint shop was being added in 1980.

By 31 January 1980 the company had a work force of 250 persons, and had assembled a total of 668 Cessna aircraft including 50 Model 150s, 48 Model 172s, six Model 177RGs and 70 Model 182s. Of the types continuing in production, Aviones de Colombia had completed at that date 19 Model 152s, 31 Model 172XPs, four Model 182RGs, 24 Model 185s, 241 Model 188s, 117 Model 206s, 30 Model 210s, seven Model 310s, nine Model 337s, five Model 340s and seven Model 402s. About 20 per cent of total production is exported to Bolivia, Ecuador and Peru.

AVIONES DE COLOMBIA/CESSNA AGTRAINER

Illustrated in an accompanying photograph, the AgTrainer is modified by Aviones de Colombia from the Cessna Model 188 AGtruck. The cabin has been widened to accommodate two persons side by side, increasing the empty weight by approx 91 kg (200 lb). Flight characteristics remain unchanged. Two prototypes have flown (the first of them on 16 September 1976), and by 1 January 1979 these two aircraft had accumulated nearly 2,000 flying hours. The first prototype has been operated by Aeroandes, a local crop-spraying flying school.

It was hoped that production of the AgTrainer would be able to begin in mid-1980.

First prototype of the Aviones de Colombia/Cessna AgTrainer, a modified Cessna 188 AGtruck

CZECHOSLOVAKIA

Central direction of the Czechoslovak aircraft industry is by a body known as the GeneřIní Reditelstvi Aero—Ceskoslovenské Letecke Podniky; Trust Aero—Czechoslovak Aeronautical Works, Prague-Letnany, whose General Manager is Josef Skarohlid.

About 29,000 people are employed by the Czecho-slovak aircraft industry. Principal factories concerned with aircraft manufacture are the Aero Vodochody National Corporation, Let National Corporation and Zlin Aircraft-Moravan National Corporation, whose current products appear under the appropriate headings in this section. Other Czechoslovak factories engaged in the pro-duction of aero-engines and sailplanes are listed in the relevant sections of this edition.

Sales of all aircraft products outside Czechoslovakia are handled by the Omnipol Foreign Trade Corporation, whose address is given below.

OMNIPOL
FOREIGN TRADE CORPORATION
Nekázanka 11, 112 21 Prague 1
Telephone: 268261/8

Telex: 121299
GENERAL MANAGER: Ing Tomás Marecek, GE
SALES MANAGER: Ing Ludvik Skocdopole
PUBLICITY MANAGER: Jirí Matula

This concern handles the sales of products of the Czechoslovak aircraft industry outside Czechoslovakia and furnishes all information requested by customers with regard to export goods.

AERO
AERO VODOCHODY NÁRODNÍ PODNIK (Aero Vodochody National Corporation)
Vodochody, p. Odelená Voda, near Prague
MANAGING DIRECTOR: Jirí Chmelícek
VICE-DIRECTORS:
  Ing Josef Sedlácek (Technical)
  Jan Spára (Production)
  Ing Otakar Stella (Sales)
  Ing Václav Klouda (Works Economy)
CHIEF DESIGNER: Dipl Ing Jan Vlcek
PROJECT ENGINEER, L-39: Ing Vlastimil Havelka
CHIEF PILOT: Antonin Saller

This factory perpetuates the name of one of the three founder companies of the Czechoslovak aircraft industry, which began activities shortly after the first World War with the manufacture of Austrian Phönix fighters. Subsequent well-known products included the A 11 military general-purpose biplane and its derivatives, and licence manufacture of the French Bloch 200 twin-engined bomber. The present works was established on 1 July 1953, since when it has seven times received the Red Banner award of the Ministry of Engineering and UVOS, as well as many other awards including those of Exemplary Exporting Corporation and the Order of Labour.

Aero's major product from 1963-74 was the L-29 Delfin jet basic and advanced trainer, of which approx 3,600 were built. A full description of this can be found in the 1974-75 edition of *Jane's*. It has now been superseded in production by the L-39, a description of which follows:

AERO L-39 ALBATROS

The L-39 basic and advanced jet trainer was developed in the Aero works at Vodochody by a team led by the chief designer, Dipl Ing Jan Vlcek, working in close co-operation with the USSR. Two prototype airframes were built initially, of which the first was used for structural testing. The first flight, on 4 November 1968, was made by the second aircraft. By the end of 1970, five flying prototypes and two for ground testing had been completed. Slightly larger and longer air intake trunks were fitted after preliminary flight tests.

A pre-production batch of ten aircraft began to join the flight test programme in 1971, and series production started in late 1972, following official selection of the L-39 to succeed the L-29 Delfin (1974-75 *Jane's*) as the standard jet trainer for the air forces of the Soviet Union, Czechoslovakia and the German Democratic Republic. Service acceptance trials, in Czechoslovakia and the USSR, took place in 1973, and by the Spring of 1974 the L-39 had begun to enter service with the Czechoslovak Air Force.

The L-39 forms part of a comprehensive training system which includes a specially designed pilot training flight simulator (TL-39), a pilot ejection ground training simulator (NK-TL-29/39), and vehicle-mounted mobile automatic test equipment (AKZ-KL-39). The aircraft is capable of operation from grass strips (with a bearing strength of 6 kg/cm^2; 85 lb/sq in) at up to 4,600 kg (10,141 lb) T-O weight, or from unprepared runways.

By May 1977, when the L-39 made its first appearance in the West, at the Paris Air Show, approximately 1,000 had been ordered. Of these, some 400-500 were then in service with several air forces. It is expected that the L-39 will be built in numbers comparable to those of the L-29 Delfin. Like the L-29, the Albatros is used in Czechoslovakia for all pilot training, including that of helicopter pilots. On average, pupils solo after approx 12 hours' dual instruction on the L-39.

Official Czechoslovak designations for the different L-39 versions are as follows:

L-39C (C for Cvicný: training). Basic and advanced flying training version, to which the detailed description chiefly applies. In service with the air forces of Afghanistan, Czechoslovakia, Germany (Democratic Republic) and USSR.

L-39Z0 (Z for Zbrojní: armed). Jet trainer with four underwing weapon stations and reinforced wings. Export customers include the air forces of Iraq and Libya.

L-39Z (Z for Zbrojní: armed). Weapon system training version, with underfuselage gun and four underwing weapon stations; reinforced wings and landing gear. Can also be used as light attack aircraft. Production was expected to begin in late 1979 or early 1980.

The following description applies to the current production L-39C trainer version, except where indicated:

TYPE: Two-seat basic and advanced jet trainer (L-39C, L-39Z0 and L-39Z); L-39Z also has light attack capability.

WINGS: Cantilever low-wing monoplane, with 2° 30′ dihedral from roots. Wing section NACA 64A012 mod. 5. Incidence 2°. Sweepback 6° 26′ on leading-edges, 1° 45′ at quarter-chord. One-piece all-metal stressed-skin structure, with main spar and auxiliary spar; four-point attachment to fuselage. All-metal double-slotted trailing-edge flaps, operated by push/pull rods actuated by a single hydraulic jack. Flaps retract automatically when airspeed reaches 167 knots (310 km/h; 193 mph). Small fence above and below each trailing-edge between flap and aileron. Electrically-operated servo tab in each aileron; port tab, used also for trim, is operated by electromechanical actuator. Flaps deflect 25° for take-off, 44° for landing; ailerons deflect 16° up or down; airbrakes deflect 55° downward. Non-jettisonable wing-tip fuel tanks, incorporating landing/taxying lights.

FUSELAGE: Metal semi-monocoque structure, built in two portions. Front portion consists of three sections, the first of which is a laminated glassfibre nosecone housing avionics, antennae, battery, compressed air and oxygen bottles and the nose landing gear. Next comes the pressurised compartment for the crew. The third section incorporates the fuel tanks, air intakes and the engine bay. The rear fuselage, carrying the tail unit, can be removed quickly to provide access for engine installation and removal. Two airbrakes side by side under fuselage, just forward of wing leading-edge, actuated by single hydraulic jack; these are lowered automatically as airspeed nears a maximum of Mach 0·8.

TAIL UNIT: Conventional all-metal cantilever structure, with sweepback on vertical surfaces. Variable-incidence tailplane. Control surfaces actuated by pushrods. Electrically-operated trim tab in each elevator; servo tab in rudder. Elevators deflect 30° up, 20° down; rudder 30° to right and left.

LANDING GEAR: Retractable tricycle type, with single wheel and oleo-pneumatic shock-absorber on each unit. Gear is designed for a touchdown sink rate of 3·4 m (11·15 ft)/s at AUW of 4,600 kg (10,141 lb). Retraction/extension is operated hydraulically, with electrical control. All wheel-well doors close automatically after wheels are lowered, to prevent ingress of dirt and debris. Main wheels retract inward into wings (with automatic

Aero L-39C Albatros two-seat basic and advanced jet trainer *(Pilot Press)*

braking during retraction), nosewheel forward into fuselage. K24 main wheels, fitted with Barum tubeless tyres size 610 × 215 mm (610 × 185 mm on early production aircraft), pressure 5·88 bars (85·34 lb/sq in). K25 castoring and self-centering nosewheel fitted with Barum tubeless tyre size 450 × 165 mm (430 × 150 mm on early production aircraft), pressure 3·92 bars (56·89 lb/sq in). Hydraulic disc brakes and anti-skid units on main wheels; shimmy damper on nosewheel leg. Landing gear of L-39Z reinforced to cater for higher operating weights.

POWER PLANT: One 16·87 kN (3,792 lb st) Ivchenko AI-25 TL turbofan engine mounted in rear fuselage, with semi-circular lateral air intake, fitted with splitter plate, on each side of fuselage above wing centre-section. Fuel in five rubber bag-type main tanks aft of cockpit, with combined capacity of 1,055 litres (232 Imp gallons), and two 100 litre (22 Imp gallon) non-jettisonable wingtip tanks. Total internal fuel capacity 1,255 litres (276 Imp gallons). Gravity refuelling points on top of fuselage and on each tip-tank. Provision for two 150 or 350 litre (33 or 77 Imp gallon) underwing drop-tanks on inboard underwing pylons, increasing total overall fuel capacity to a maximum of 1,955 litres (430 Imp gallons). Fuel system permits up to 20 s of inverted flight.

ACCOMMODATION: Crew of two in tandem, on VS-1-BRI rocket-assisted ejection seats, operable at zero height and at speeds down to 81 knots (150 km/h; 94 mph), beneath individual transparent canopies which hinge sideways to starboard and are jettisonable. One-piece windscreen hinges forward to provide access to front instrument panel. Internal transparency between front and rear cockpits. Dual controls standard.

SYSTEMS: Cabin pressurised (max differential 0·23 bars; 3·34 lb/sq in) and air-conditioned. Air-conditioning system provides automatic temperature control from 10° to 25°C at ambient air temperatures from −55°C to +45°C. Main and standby interconnected hydraulic systems, the main system having a variable-flow pump with an operating pressure of 147 bars (2,133 lb/sq in) for actuation of landing gear, flaps, airbrakes, ram-air turbine and wheel brakes. Emergency system incorporates three accumulators. Pneumatic canopy seals supplied by one 2 litre compressed air bottle in nose (pressure 147 bars; 2,133 lb/sq in). Electrical system (28·5V DC) is powered by a 9kW VG 7500 Ja engine-driven generator. If primary generator fails, a V 910 ram-air turbine is extended automatically into the airstream and generates up to 3kW of emergency power for essential services. 12V 28Ah SAM 28 lead-acid battery for standby power and for APU starting. Two 800VA static inverters (the first for radio equipment, ice warning lights, engine vibration measurement and air-conditioning, the second for navigation and landing systems, IFF and air-to-air missiles) provide 115V single-phase AC power at 400Hz. A second circuit incorporates a 500VA rotary inverter and 40VA static inverter to provide 36V three-phase AC power, also at 400Hz. Saphir 5 compressed air generator and SV-25 turbine for engine starting. Air intakes and windscreen anti-iced by engine bleed air; normally, anti-icing is sensor-activated automatically, but a manual standby system is also provided. Six-bottle oxygen system for crew.

AVIONICS AND EQUIPMENT: Standard avionics include R-832 M two-band radio (VHF 118-140MHz, UHF 220-389MHz); SPU-9 crew intercom; RKL-41 ADF (150-1,800kHz); RV-5 radio altimeter; MRP-56 P/S marker beacon receiver; SRO-2 IFF; and RSBN-5S navigation and landing system. VOR/ILS system available at customer's option. Landing and taxying light in forward end of each tip-tank.

ARMAMENT (L-39Z): Four underwing hardpoints, the inboard pair each stressed for loads of up to 500 kg (1,102 lb) and the outer pair for loads of up to 250 kg (551 lb) each; max external underwing stores load 1,100 kg (2,425 lb). Non-jettisonable pylons, each comprising a D3-57D stores rack. Typical underwing stores can include various combinations of bombs up to 500 kg in size; four UB-16-57 M pods each containing sixteen S-5 57 mm air-to-surface rockets; infra-red air-to-air missiles (outer pylons only); a five-camera day reconnaissance pod (port inboard pylon only); or (on inboard stations only) two 150 or 350 litre (33 or 77 Imp gallon) drop-tanks. Underfuselage pod, below front cockpit, housing a single 23 mm Soviet GSh-23 two-barrelled cannon; ammunition for this gun (max 150 rds) is housed in fuselage, above gun pod. Gun/rocket firing and weapon release controls, including electrically-controlled ASP-3 NMU-39 Z gyroscopic gunsight and FKP-2-2 gun camera, in front cockpit only.

DIMENSIONS, EXTERNAL:
Wing span	9·46 m (31 ft 0½ in)
Wing chord (mean)	2·15 m (7 ft 0½ in)
Wing aspect ratio (geometric)	4·4
Length overall	12·13 m (39 ft 9½ in)
Height overall	4·77 m (15 ft 7¾ in)
Tailplane span	4·40 m (14 ft 5 in)
Wheel track	2·44 m (8 ft 0 in)
Wheelbase	4·39 m (14 ft 4¾ in)

Aero L-39Z0 version of the Albatros, in the insignia of the Iraqi Air Force

AREAS:
Wings, gross	18·80 m² (202·36 sq ft)
Ailerons (total)	1·23 m² (13·26 sq ft)
Trailing-edge flaps (total)	2·68 m² (28·89 sq ft)
Airbrakes (total)	0·50 m² (5·38 sq ft)
Vertical tail surfaces (total)	3·51 m² (37·78 sq ft)
Tailplane	3·93 m² (42·30 sq ft)
Elevators, incl tabs	1·14 m² (12·27 sq ft)

WEIGHTS AND LOADINGS (A1: two-seat, aircraft 'clean'; A2: two-seat, gun only; F1: single-seat, gun plus one camera pod and one 350 litre drop-tank; G1: single-seat, gun only; G2: single-seat, gun plus two 150 litre drop-tanks; G3: single-seat, gun plus two 350 litre drop-tanks; P1: single-seat, gun plus four 250 kg bombs; P2: single-seat, gun plus two 500 kg bombs; P3: single-seat, gun plus six 100 kg bombs; P4: single-seat, gun plus four 100 kg bombs; P5: single-seat, gun plus eight 50 kg bombs; P6: single-seat, gun plus two 250 kg bombs and two 150 litre drop-tanks; P7: single-seat, gun plus two 100 kg bombs and two 350 litre drop-tanks; PR1: single-seat, gun plus two rocket launchers and two 250 kg bombs; R1: single-seat, gun plus four rocket launchers; R2: single-seat, gun plus two rocket launchers and two 150 litre drop-tanks; R3: single-seat, gun plus two rocket launchers and two 350 litre drop-tanks; R4: single-seat, gun plus two missiles and two 350 litre drop-tanks; T1: two-seat, gun plus two 100 kg bombs; T2: two-seat, gun plus two rocket launchers; T3: two-seat, gun plus two missiles):

Weight empty: single-seat	3,490 kg (7,694 lb)
two-seat	3,565 kg (7,859 lb)
Crew: single-seat	80 kg (176 lb)
two-seat	160 kg (352 lb)
Fuel load: A1, A2, P1, P2	824 kg (1,816 lb)
F1	1,252 kg (2,760 lb)
G1, P3, P4, P5, PR1, R1, T1, T2, T3	980 kg (2,160 lb)
G2, P6, R2	1,214 kg (2,676 lb)
G3, P7, R3, R4	1,524 kg (3,360 lb)
Max underwing stores load	1,100 kg (2,425 lb)
Mission T-O weight: A1	4,549 kg (10,028 lb)
A2	4,682 kg (10,322 lb)
F1	5,138 kg (11,327 lb)
G1	4,720 kg (10,405 lb)
G2	5,063 kg (11,162 lb)
G3	5,396 kg (11,896 lb)
P1, P3	5,602 kg (12,350 lb)
P2	5,596 kg (12,337 lb)
P4	5,306 kg (11,697 lb)
P5	5,458 kg (12,032 lb)
P6	5,539 kg (12,211 lb)
P7	5,646 kg (12,447 lb)
PR1	5,510 kg (12,147 lb)
R1	5,262 kg (11,600 lb)
R2	5,291 kg (11,664 lb)
R3	5,624 kg (12,398 lb)
R4	5,588 kg (12,319 lb)
T1	5,131 kg (11,312 lb)
T2	5,109 kg (11,263 lb)
T3	5,029 kg (11,087 lb)
Max landing weight: L-39C	4,300 kg (9,480 lb)
L-39Z	4,600 kg (10,141 lb)
Wing loading 'clean'	243 kg/m² (49·77 lb/sq ft)
Power loading 'clean'	270·9 kg/kN (2·65 lb/lb st)

GENERAL PERFORMANCE (A: at 'clean' AUW of 4,570 kg; 10,075 lb with tip-tanks empty; B: at AUW of 5,270 kg; 11,618 lb with full internal fuel and four underwing rocket pods; C: at AUW of 4,300 kg; 9,480 lb, except where indicated):

Max limiting Mach number (VNE) above 1,300 m (4,265 ft)	0·85
Max permitted diving speed (VD)	491 knots (910 km/h; 565 mph)
Max level speed at S/L:	
C	378 knots (700 km/h; 435 mph)
Max level speed at altitude:	
A at 6,000 m (19,685 ft)	421 knots (780 km/h; 485 mph)
B at 6,000 m (19,685 ft)	340 knots (630 km/h; 391 mph)

Close-up of underfuselage gun installation on Aero L-39Z

C at 5,000 m (16,400 ft)	405 knots (750 km/h; 466 mph)
Cruising speed at 5,000 m (16,400 ft):	
C	367 knots (680 km/h; 423 mph)
Stalling speed:	
C, flaps up	97 knots (180 km/h; 112 mph)
C, 25° flap	90 knots (165 km/h; 103 mph)
C, 44° flap	84 knots (155 km/h; 97 mph)
Touchdown speed:	
A at 4,500 kg (9,920 lb) AUW	94·5 knots (175 km/h; 109 mph)
B at 4,600 kg (10,141 lb) AUW	98 knots (182 km/h; 113 mph)
Max rate of climb at S/L: A	1,320 m (4,330 ft)/min
B	960 m (3,150 ft)/min
Optimum climbing speed:	
C	210 knots (390 km/h; 242 mph)
Service ceiling: A	11,500 m (37,730 ft)
B	9,000 m (29,525 ft)
T-O run, 25° flap, ISA:	
at 4,300 kg (9,480 lb) AUW, concrete	480 m (1,575 ft)
at 4,300 kg (9,480 lb) AUW, grass	630 m (2,067 ft)
at 4,570 kg (10,075 lb) AUW	500 m (1,640 ft)
at 5,270 kg (11,618 lb) AUW	800 m (2,625 ft)
T-O to 25 m (82 ft):	
at 4,300 kg (9,480 lb) AUW	630 m (2,067 ft)
Landing from 25 m (82 ft):	
at 4,300 kg (9,480 lb) AUW	1,120 m (3,675 ft)
Landing run, 44° flap, ISA:	
at 4,100 kg (9,039 lb) AUW	620 m (2,034 ft)
at 4,300 kg (9,480 lb) AUW	690 m (2,264 ft)
g limits:	
at 4,200 kg (9,259 lb) AUW	+8; −4
at 4,400 kg (9,700 lb) AUW	+7·5; −3·75
at 4,600 kg (10,141 lb) AUW	+7; −3·5
at 5,500 kg (12,125 lb) AUW	+5·2; −2·6

TYPICAL MISSION PERFORMANCE (at mission weights as defined under 'Weights and Loadings' heading):
Max permissible Mach No: A1, A2	0·80
G3, P7, R1	0·75
Max level speed at S/L:	
A1	378 knots (700 km/h; 435 mph)
A2	375 knots (695 km/h; 432 mph)
G3	351 knots (650 km/h; 404 mph)
P7	329 knots (610 km/h; 379 mph)
R1	318 knots (590 km/h; 366 mph)
Max level speed at 3,000 m (9,845 ft):	
A1	399 knots (740 km/h; 460 mph)
A2	396 knots (735 km/h; 457 mph)
G3	372 knots (690 km/h; 429 mph)
P7	340 knots (630 km/h; 391 mph)
R1	332 knots (615 km/h; 382 mph)
Max level speed at 5,000 m (16,400 ft):	
A1	405 knots (750 km/h; 466 mph)
A2	402 knots (745 km/h; 463 mph)
G3	372 knots (690 km/h; 429 mph)
P7	340 knots (630 km/h; 391 mph)
R1	326 knots (605 km/h; 376 mph)

Max rate of climb at S/L:

A1	1,230 m (4,035 ft)/min	A2	13 min 18 s	P7	270 nm (500 km; 310 miles)
A2	1,140 m (3,740 ft)/min	G3	20 min 0 s	R1	148 nm (275 km; 170 miles)

Service ceiling: A1 11,000 m (36,100 ft)

Radius of action, hi-lo-hi at 5,000/500/5,000 m (16,400/1,640/16,400 ft), conditions as above:

Max rate of climb at S/L:
A1   1,230 m (4,035 ft)/min
A2   1,140 m (3,740 ft)/min
G3   960 m (3,150 ft)/min
P7   780 m (2,560 ft)/min
R1   870 m (2,854 ft)/min

Max rate of climb at 5,000 m (16,400 ft):
A1   690 m (2,264 ft)/min
A2   600 m (1,968 ft)/min
G3   450 m (1,476 ft)/min
P7   270 m (886 ft)/min
R1   360 m (1,181 ft)/min

Time to 5,000 m (16,400 ft):
A1   5 min 30 s
A2   6 min 12 s
G3   8 min 30 s
P7   11 min 0 s
R1   9 min 30 s

Time to 8,000 m (26,250 ft):
A1   11 min 0 s

A2   13 min 18 s
G3   20 min 0 s

Service ceiling: A1   11,000 m (36,100 ft)
A2   10,200 m (33,460 ft)
G3   9,000 m (29,525 ft)
P7   7,500 m (24,600 ft)
R1   8,400 m (27,560 ft)

T-O run (concrete):
A1   530 m (1,739 ft)
A2   660 m (2,165 ft)
G3   950 m (3,117 ft)
P7   1,050 m (3,445 ft)
R1   880 m (2,887 ft)

Landing run (concrete):
A1, A2   660 m (2,165 ft)
P7, R1   750 m (2,460 ft)

Radius of action, lo-lo-lo at 500 m (1,640 ft), last 27 nm (50 km; 31 miles) at max rpm for 3 min, 5% reserves:
G3   286 nm (530 km; 329 miles)

P7   270 nm (500 km; 310 miles)
R1   148 nm (275 km; 170 miles)

Radius of action, hi-lo-hi at 5,000/500/5,000 m (16,400/1,640/16,400 ft), conditions as above:
G3   410 nm (760 km; 472 miles)
P7   323 nm (600 km; 373 miles)
R1   167 nm (310 km; 192 miles)

Max range, 5% reserves:
A1   593 nm (1,100 km; 683 miles)
A2   566 nm (1,050 km; 652 miles)
G3   944 nm (1,750 km; 1,087 miles)
P7   658 nm (1,220 km; 758 miles)
R1   453 nm (840 km; 522 miles)

Max endurance at econ speed, 5% reserves:
A1, R1   2 h 0 min
A2   1 h 54 min
G3   3 h 36 min
P7   3 h 0 min

L-410UVP current production model of the Turbolet general-purpose transport aircraft

LET
LET NÁRODNÍ PODNIK (Let National Corporation)

Uherské Hradiste-Kunovice
Telephone: Uherské Hradiste 5121
Telex: 060180 and 060181
MANAGING DIRECTOR: Ing Stanislav Boura
CHIEF DESIGNER: Ing Ladislav Smrcek
CHIEF PILOT: Frantisek Srnec

The Let plant at Kunovice was established in 1950, its early activities including licence production of the Soviet Yak-11 piston-engined trainer under the Czechoslovak designation C-11. It contributed to the production of the Aero 45, was responsible for the L 200 Morava twin-engined air taxi and Z-37 Cmelák agricultural aircraft, and the L 13 Blanik sailplane; it is currently responsible for development and manufacture of the L-410 twin-turboprop light transport aircraft.

The factory also produces apparatus and equipment for radar and computer technology.

LET L-410 TURBOLET

Design of the L-410 twin-turboprop light transport was started in 1966, by a team led by Ing Ladislav Smrcek. The first prototype (OK-YKE), powered by Pratt & Whitney Aircraft of Canada PT6A-27 turboprop engines, flew for the first time on 16 April 1969. Three additional PT6A-engined prototypes were completed subsequently; the second of these was later test-flown with Hartzell four-blade propellers in a successful demonstration of reduced aircraft vibration and cabin noise levels.

The following versions of the L-410 have been announced:

L-410A. Initial passenger/cargo production version, powered by 533 kW (715 ehp) Pratt & Whitney Aircraft of Canada PT6A-27 engines. Entered service with Czechoslovak domestic operator Slov-Air in late 1971. Total of 31 built by 31 January 1979, including prototypes. Described in 1978-79 and earlier editions of *Jane's*.

L-410AF. Aerial photography/survey version, generally similar to L-410A but with larger, wider and extensively glazed nose compartment. One built, which was exported to Hungary in 1974. Other details in 1978-79 and earlier editions of *Jane's*.

L-410M. Similar to L-410A, but with Motorlet M 601 A engines and seats for up to 17 passengers. First flown 1973; first production example delivered 1976. Total of 110 built, including prototype. Described in 1978-79 *Jane's*, with amended weight and performance data in 1979-80 edition. Superseded in 1979 by L-410UVP.

L-410UVP. Standard production version from beginning of 1979; first of three prototypes flown on 1

November 1977. Changes include increased wing span and area; fuselage lengthened by 0·47 m (1 ft 6½ in) compared with L-410M; enlarged vertical tail surfaces; dihedral tailplane; improved cockpit systems and additions to standard instrumentation; introduction of spoilers, automatic bank control flaps, automatic propeller feathering, and anti-skid system for main landing gear units; fabric-covered elevators and rudder; and later-model M 601 engines and V 508 propellers. Basic version is for passenger transportation, but cabin can be converted easily to all-cargo, aeromedical, parachutist or firefighting configuration; aircraft can also be equipped for aerial photography or calibration of ground navigation aids. The L-410UVP can operate from grass, sand and gravel strips as well as from paved runways, and in snow and ice conditions. It is being manufactured in large numbers, and will become standard Aeroflot equipment on Soviet internal feederline services, in company with the PZL Mielec (Antonov) An-28. Stringent Aeroflot requirements included the ability to operate in temperatures ranging from −50°C to +45°C; systems were required to be survivable in temperatures as low as −60°C.

Production of the L-410UVP is planned to reach about 100 a year, most of them for Aeroflot. By 20 January 1980, three prototypes and 45 production L-410UVPs had been completed.

The following description applies to the L-410UVP:

TYPE: Twin-turboprop general-purpose light transport.

WINGS: Cantilever high-wing monoplane. Wing section NACA 63A418 at root, NACA 63A412 at tip. Dihedral 1° 45'. Incidence 2° at root, −0° 30' at tip. No

sweepback at front spar. Conventional all-metal two-spar torsion-box structure, attached to fuselage by four-point mountings. Chemically machined skin with longitudinal reinforcement. Hydraulically actuated double-slotted metal flaps, with both slots variable. Spoiler forward of each flap. All-metal ailerons, forward of which are 'pop-up' bank control surfaces that come into operation automatically during single-engine operation and decrease the lift on the side of the running engine. Kléber-Colombes pneumatic de-icing of leading-edges.

FUSELAGE: Conventional all-metal semi-monocoque spot welded and riveted structure, built in three main portions.

TAIL UNIT: Conventional cantilever structure, of all-metal construction except for elevators and rudder, which are fabric-covered. Vertical tail surfaces swept back 35°; shallow dorsal fin and deeper ventral fin. One-piece tailplane, with 7° dihedral from roots, mounted partway up fin. Balance tab in rudder and each elevator. Kléber-Colombes pneumatic de-icing of leading-edges.

LANDING GEAR: Retractable tricycle type, with single wheel on each unit. Hydraulic retraction, nosewheel forward, main wheels inward to lie flat in fairing on each side of fuselage. Technometra Radotin oleo-pneumatic shock-absorbers. Non-braking nosewheel, with servo-assisted steering, fitted with 548 × 221 mm (9·00-6) tubeless tyre, pressure 2·74 bars (39·8 lb/sq in). Nosewheel is also steerable by rudder pedals. Main wheels fitted with 718 × 306 mm (12·50-10) tubeless tyres, pressure 3·14 bars (45·5 lb/sq in). All wheels manufactured by Moravan Otrokovice, tyres by Rudy Rijen, Gottwaldow. Moravan Otrokovice hydraulic disc brakes, parking brake and anti-skid units on main wheels. Metal ski landing gear, with plastics undersurface, optional.

POWER PLANT: Two 544 kW (730 ehp) Walter M 601 B turboprop engines, each driving an Avia V 508 B three-blade reversible-pitch fully-feathering metal propeller. At higher ambient temperatures, engine power can be increased to 590 kW (790 ehp) for short periods by water injection into compressor. De-icing for propeller blades (electrical) and lower intakes; anti-icing flaps inside each nacelle. Eight bag-type fuel tanks in wings, total capacity 1,290 litres (284 Imp gallons). Total oil capacity (incl oil in cooler) 22 litres (4·8 Imp gallons). Water tank capacity (for injection into compressor) 11 litres (2·4 Imp gallons).

ACCOMMODATION: Crew of one or two on flight deck. Dual controls standard. Standard accommodation in main cabin for 15 passengers, with pairs of adjustable seats on starboard side of aisle and single seats opposite, all at 76 cm (30 in) pitch. Baggage compartment (at rear, accessible from cabin), toilet and wardrobe standard in this version. Cabin heated by engine bleed air. Alternative layouts include all-cargo; ambulance, accommodating

Let L-410UVP Turbolet twin-turboprop 15-passenger light transport *(Pilot Press)*

six stretchers, five sitting patients and a medical attendant; accommodation for 14 parachutists and a despatcher/instructor; firefighting configuration, carrying 12 firefighters and a pilot/observer. All-cargo version has protective floor covering, crash nets on each side of cabin, and tiedown provisions; floor is at truck-bed height. Aircraft can also be equipped for aerial photography or for calibration of ground navigation aids. Double upward-opening doors aft on port side, with stowable steps; right hand door serves as passenger entrance and exit. Both doors open for cargo loading, and can be removed for paratroop training missions. Rearward-opening door, forward on starboard side, serves as emergency exit.

SYSTEMS: No APU, air-conditioning or pressurisation systems. Duplicated hydraulic systems, No. 1 system actuating landing gear, flaps, spoilers, automatic pitch trim surfaces, main-wheel brakes, nosewheel steering and windscreen wipers. No. 2 system for emergency landing gear extension, flap actuation and parking brake. Electrical system includes AC power from three three-phase 36V 400Hz rotary inverters and two single-phase 115V 400Hz inverters, guaranteeing against a loss of power for essential instruments; DC power from two 5·6kW generators and two 25Ah batteries.

AVIONICS AND EQUIPMENT: Standard instrumentation provides for flight in IMC conditions, with all basic instruments duplicated and three artificial horizons. Communications include two VHF with a range of 65 nm (120 km; 75 miles) at 1,000 m (3,280 ft) altitude, and crew intercom. Standard navigation instruments include artificial horizons (three); barometric altimeters, airspeed indicators, rate of climb indicators, turn indicators, RMIs, gyro-compasses, ILS, and ARK-15M ADF with range of 97 nm (180 km; 112 miles) at 1,000 m (3,280 ft) altitude (two of each); and radio altimeter with ground proximity warning, ASI with stall warning, magnetic compass, GMK-1GE VOR, and ILS with marker beacon receiver (one of each). Cockpit, instrument and passenger cabin lights, navigation lights, three landing lights in nose (each with two levels of light intensity), crew and cabin fire extinguishers, windscreen wipers, and alcohol spray for windscreen and wiper de-icing, are also standard.

DIMENSIONS, EXTERNAL:

Wing span	19·478 m (63 ft 10¾ in)
Wing chord at root	2·534 m (8 ft 3¾ in)
Length overall	14·467 m (47 ft 5½ in)
Height overall	5·829 m (19 ft 1½ in)
Tailplane span	6·736 m (22 ft 1¼ in)
Wheel track	3·65 m (11 ft 11½ in)
Wheelbase	3·666 m (12 ft 0¼ in)
Propeller diameter	2·50 m (8 ft 2½ in)
Distance between propeller centres	4·816 m (15 ft 9½ in)

Passenger/cargo door (port, aft):

Height	1·46 m (4 ft 9½ in)
Width overall	1·25 m (4 ft 1¼ in)
Width (passenger door only)	0·75 m (2 ft 5½ in)
Height to sill	0·80 m (2 ft 7½ in)

Emergency exit door (stbd, fwd):

Height	0·97 m (3 ft 2¼ in)
Width	0·66 m (2 ft 2 in)
Height to sill	0·80 m (2 ft 7½ in)

DIMENSIONS, INTERNAL:

Cabin, exl flight deck: Length	6·34 m (20 ft 9½ in)
Max width	1·95 m (6 ft 4¾ in)
Max height	1·658 m (5 ft 5¼ in)
Aisle width at 0·4 m (1 ft 3¾ in) above cabin floor	0·34 m (1 ft 1½ in)
Floor area	9·69 m² (104·3 sq ft)
Volume	17·86 m³ (630·7 cu ft)
Baggage compartment volume (rear)	0·77 m³ (27·2 cu ft)

AREAS:

Wings, gross	35·18 m² (378·67 sq ft)
Ailerons (total)	2·89 m² (31·11 sq ft)
Automatic bank control flaps (total)	0·49 m² (5·27 sq ft)
Trailing-edge flaps (total)	5·92 m² (63·72 sq ft)
Spoilers (total)	0·87 m² (9·36 sq ft)
Fin	4·49 m² (48·33 sq ft)
Rudder, incl tab	2·81 m² (30·25 sq ft)
Tailplane	6·41 m² (69·00 sq ft)
Elevators, incl tabs	3·15 m² (33·91 sq ft)

WEIGHTS:

Basic empty weight	3,725 kg (8,212 lb)
Max fuel	965 kg (2,127 lb)
Max payload	1,310 kg (2,888 lb)
Max T-O weight	5,700 kg (12,566 lb)
Max landing weight	5,500 kg (12,125 lb)

PERFORMANCE (at max T-O weight, ISA, except where indicated):

Never-exceed speed	194 knots (360 km/h; 224 mph) EAS
Max cruising speed at 3,000 m (9,850 ft)	169 knots (313 km/h; 194 mph) EAS
Econ cruising speed at 3,000 m (9,850 ft)	194 knots (360 km/h; 224 mph) TAS
Stalling speed, flaps up	78 knots (144 km/h; 90 mph) EAS
Stalling speed, flaps down, at max landing weight	61 knots (112 km/h; 70 mph) EAS
Max rate of climb at S/L	468 m (1,535 ft)/min
Rate of climb at S/L, one engine out	90 m (295 ft)/min
Service ceiling	8,950 m (29,360 ft)
Service ceiling, one engine out	2,850 m (9,350 ft)
T-O run	400 m (1,312 ft)
T-O to 10·5 m (35 ft)	710 m (2,330 ft)
Landing from 9 m (30 ft) at max landing weight	862 m (2,828 ft)
Landing run at max landing weight	328 m (1,000 ft)
Range with max fuel and 850 kg (1,874 lb) payload, 30 min reserves	561 nm (1,040 km; 646 miles)
Range with max payload and 505 kg (1,113 lb) fuel, 30 min reserves	248 nm (460 km; 285 miles)

VZLU
VYZKUMNY A ZKUSEBNÍ LETECKY USTAV (Aeronautical Research and Test Institute)

Beranovych 130, Prague 9-Letnany 19905
Telephone: Prague 827041 and 826541

Telex: Prague 1493

MANAGING DIRECTOR: Ing J. Havlicek

This Institute, whose title is self-explanatory, was founded in 1922 and undertakes a range of activities corresponding broadly to those carried out by the RAE in Britain. Details of its principal facilities appeared in the 1970-71 and 1972-73 *Jane's*. It is a member of the Czechoslovak aircraft manufacturing group, under the general management of Aero (which see).

ZLIN
MORAVAN NÁRODNÍ PODNIK (Zlin Aircraft Moravan National Corporation)

Otrokovice 76581
Telephone: Gottwaldov 92 2041-44
Telex: Gottwaldov 067 334

MANAGING DIRECTOR: Frantisek Klapil
VICE-DIRECTORS:
Ing Stanislav Machálka (Technical)
Jan Munclinger (Production)
Frantisek Muzny (Sales)
Ing Adolf Dolezal (Works Economy)
CHIEF DESIGNER: Ing Jirí Navrátil
CHIEF PILOT: Zdenek Polásek

The Moravan works, responsible for production of the famous range of Zlin aerobatic and light touring aircraft, was formed originally on 8 July 1935 as Zlinská Letecká Akciová Spolecnost (Zlin Aviation Joint Stock Co) in Zlin, although manufacture of Zlin aircraft was actually started two years earlier by the Masarykova Letecká Liga (Masaryk League of Aviation). The factory was renamed Moravan after the second World War. At present, in addition to production of the Zlin 42 M and Zlin 50 L, and development of the Zlin 142, Moravan is building items of aircraft equipment.

ZLIN 42 M
The prototype Zlin 42 was first flown on 17 October 1967, and in 1969 began undergoing flight trials prior to certification on 7 September 1970. Standard power plant of the initial version, which entered production in 1971 and was described in the 1973-74 *Jane's*, was the 134 kW (180 hp) M 137 A engine, with which the Z 42 conforms to FAR Pt 23 airworthiness specifications in the Aerobatic category and is suitable for service in climates with temperatures between +40° and −20°C. The principal customer for this version was the German Democratic Republic, which acquired several dozen for military liaison duties.

The following description applies to the subsequent **Zlin 42 M** production version, of which a prototype was first flown in November 1972, certification under FAR Pt 23 in the Aerobatic (+6g to −3·5g) and Normal categories being obtained on 30 November 1973. This differs from the initial version in having a constant-speed propeller and a tail fin identical to that of the Z43 (see 1977-78 *Jane's*).

At the request of a number of operators of the initial production version, their aircraft have during overhaul been fitted retrospectively with Avia V 503 A two-blade metal propellers of the type fitted to the current production Z 42 M. The aircraft so modified are then redesignated **Zlin 42 MU.**

Production of the Zlin 42 M began in 1974, and is continuing. By early 1979, total Zlin 42 production (all versions) was in excess of 170.

TYPE: Two-seat light training and touring aircraft.

WINGS: Cantilever low-wing monoplane. Wing section NACA 63₂416·5. Dihedral 6° from roots. Sweepforward 4° 20' at quarter-chord. All-metal structure with single main spar and auxiliary spar. All-metal slotted ailerons and flaps all have same dimensions. Mass-balanced flaps and ailerons, operated mechanically by control rods. Ground-adjustable tab in each aileron.

FUSELAGE: Engine cowlings of sheet metal. Centre fuselage of welded steel tube construction, covered with laminated glassfibre panels. Rear fuselage is all-metal semi-monocoque structure.

TAIL UNIT: Cantilever all-metal structure. Control surfaces have partial mass and aerodynamic balance. Trim tabs on elevator and rudder. Rudder actuated by control cables, elevator by control rods.

LANDING GEAR: Non-retractable tricycle type, with nosewheel offset to port. Oleo-pneumatic nosewheel shock-absorber. Main wheels carried on flat spring steel legs. Nosewheel steering by means of rudder pedals. Single wheel on each unit. Main wheels and Barum tyres size 420 × 150, pressure 1·86 bars (27 lb/sq in); nosewheel and Barum tyre size 350 × 135, pressure 2·45 bars (35·6 lb/sq in). Hydraulic disc brakes on main wheels can be operated from either seat. Parking brake standard. Wheel fairings and skis optional.

POWER PLANT: One 134 kW (180 hp) Avia M 137 AZ inverted six-cylinder aircooled in-line engine, with low-pressure injection pump, driving a two-blade Avia V 503 A fully-automatic constant-speed metal propeller. Fuel tanks in each wing leading-edge, with total capacity of 130 litres (28·5 Imp gallons). Fuel and oil systems permit aerobatic and inverted flying. Oil capacity 12 litres (2·64 Imp gallons).

ACCOMMODATION: Individual side-by-side seats for two persons, the pilot's seat being to port. Both are adjustable for height and permit the use of back-type parachutes. Space for up to 20 kg (44 lb) of baggage aft of seats (except in Aerobatic category). Cabin and windscreen heating and ventilation. Forward-opening jettisonable door on each side of cabin. Dual controls standard.

SYSTEMS: Electrical system includes a 600W 24V engine-driven generator and 24V 25Ah Teledyne battery. External power source can be used for starting the engine.

Zlin 42 M two-seat light training and touring aircraft (Avia M 137 AZ engine)

AVIONICS AND EQUIPMENT: VHF radio and IFR instrumentation optional. Towing gear, for gliders of up to 500 kg (1,102 lb) weight, optional.

DIMENSIONS, EXTERNAL:

Wing span	9·11 m (29 ft 10¾ in)
Wing chord (constant)	1·42 m (4 ft 8 in)
Length overall	7·07 m (23 ft 2½ in)
Height overall	2·69 m (8 ft 10 in)
Elevator span	2·90 m (9 ft 6 in)
Wheel track	2·33 m (7 ft 7¾ in)
Wheelbase	1·66 m (5 ft 5¼ in)
Propeller diameter	2·00 m (6 ft 6¾ in)

DIMENSIONS, INTERNAL:

Cabin: Length	1·80 m (5 ft 10¾ in)
Width	1·12 m (3 ft 8 in)
Height	1·20 m (3 ft 11¼ in)
Baggage space	0·2 m³ (7·1 cu ft)

AREAS:

Wings, gross	13·15 m² (141·5 sq ft)
Ailerons (total)	1·408 m² (15·16 sq ft)
Trailing-edge flaps (total)	1·408 m² (15·16 sq ft)
Fin	0·54 m² (5·81 sq ft)
Rudder, incl tab	0·81 m² (8·72 sq ft)
Tailplane	1·23 m² (13·24 sq ft)
Elevator, incl tab	1·36 m² (14·64 sq ft)

WEIGHTS AND LOADINGS:

Basic weight empty	645 kg (1,422 lb)
Max T-O weight: Aerobatic	920 kg (2,028 lb)
Normal	970 kg (2,138 lb)
Max wing loading: Aerobatic	70 kg/m² (14·3 lb/sq ft)
Normal	74 kg/m² (15·2 lb/sq ft)
Max power loading:	
Aerobatic	6·87 kg/kW (11·27 lb/hp)
Normal	7·24 kg/kW (11·88 lb/hp)

PERFORMANCE (at max T-O weight, ISA. A: Aerobatic; N: Normal category):

Max level speed at S/L:	
A	122 knots (226 km/h; 140 mph)
N	120 knots (223 km/h; 138 mph)
Cruising speed:	
A at 600 m (1,975 ft)	
	116 knots (215 km/h; 134 mph)
N at S/L	114 knots (211 km/h; 131 mph)
Stalling speed, flaps up, power off:	
A	54 knots (100 km/h; 62·5 mph) CAS
N	55 knots (102 km/h; 63·5 mph) CAS
Stalling speed, flaps down, power off:	
A	49 knots (89 km/h; 56 mph) CAS
N	50 knots (91 km/h; 57 mph) CAS

Zlin 142 two-seat light aircraft, developed from the Z 42 M *(Pilot Press)*

Max rate of climb at S/L:	
A	312 m (1,025 ft)/min
N	288 m (945 ft)/min
Service ceiling: A	4,250 m (13,950 ft)
N	3,800 m (12,470 ft)
T-O run: A	185 m (607 ft)
T-O to 15 m (50 ft): A	380 m (1,245 ft)
N	410 m (1,345 ft)
Landing from 15 m (50 ft): A	410 m (1,345 ft)
N	420 m (1,378 ft)
Landing run: A	135 m (443 ft)
Range with max standard fuel:	
A	286 nm (530 km; 329 miles)
g limits: Aerobatic	+6·0; −3·5
Normal	+3·8; −1·5

ZLIN 142

A prototype of the Zlin 142 (OK-078) was flown for the first time on 29 December 1978, and began certification trials in early 1979.

Essentially, the Z 142 is a slightly enlarged and more powerful version of the Z 42 M, and is being certificated in the Aerobatic, Normal and Utility categories.

Principal differences from the Z 42 M are as follows:

WINGS: Sweepforward 4° 31′ at quarter-chord.

POWER PLANT: One 156·5 kW (210 hp) Avia M 337 AK inverted six-cylinder aircooled in-line engine, driving a two-blade Avia V 500 A constant-speed metal propeller with spinner. Fuel and oil capacities as for Z 42 M.

SYSTEMS: 28V 600W generator; battery as for Z 42 M.

DIMENSIONS, EXTERNAL: As Z 42 M except:

Wing span	9·16 m (30 ft 0½ in)
Wing area, gross	13·30 m² (143·16 sq ft)
Wing aspect ratio	6·3
Length overall	7·33 m (24 ft 0½ in)
Height overall	2·75 m (9 ft 0¼ in)

WEIGHTS AND LOADINGS:

Basic weight empty (all versions)	730 kg (1,609 lb)
Max T-O weight:	
Aerobatic	970 kg (2,138 lb)
Utility	1,020 kg (2,248 lb)
Normal	1,090 kg (2,403 lb)
Max wing loading:	
Aerobatic	72·93 kg/m² (14·94 lb/sq ft)
Utility	76·69 kg/m² (15·71 lb/sq ft)
Normal	81·95 kg/m² (16·78 lb/sq ft)
Max power loading:	
Aerobatic	6·26 kg/kW (10·28 lb/hp)
Utility	6·58 kg/kW (10·81 lb/hp)
Normal	7·03 kg/kW (11·55 lb/hp)

PERFORMANCE (at max Aerobatic T-O weight except where indicated):

Max level speed at S/L, ISA	
	124 knots (230 km/h; 143 mph)
Cruising speed at 210 m (690 ft)	
	116 knots (215 km/h; 134 mph)
Stalling speed, flaps up	61 knots (113 km/h; 70·5 mph)
Stalling speed, flaps down	
	55 knots (102 km/h; 63·5 mph)
Max rate of climb at S/L, ISA	330 m (1,082 ft)/min
Service ceiling	5,000 m (16,400 ft)
T-O to 15 m (50 ft)	430 m (1,410 ft)
Landing from 15 m (50 ft)	395 m (1,296 ft)
Range with max fuel at Normal category max T-O weight	507 nm (940 km; 584 miles)
g limits: Aerobatic	+6·0; −3·5
Normal	+5·0; −3·0

Zlin Z 50 L light aircraft (Avco Lycoming AEIO-540-D4B5 engine)

ZLIN Z 50 L

The Z 50 L is a fully-aerobatic single-seat competition light aircraft, the design of which began in 1973. Construction of a prototype was started in 1975, and this aircraft flew for the first time on 18 July 1975. Two additional prototypes and 18 production aircraft had been completed by 1 January 1979.

Five Z 50 Ls took part in the 1976 World Aerobatic Championships at Kiev, USSR, gaining 2nd place in the team event and 3rd place in the men's individual competitions. Thirteen took part in the 1978 Championships at Hosin, Czechoslovakia, gaining 1st and 3rd places in the men's individual competitions and 1st place in the team event.

TYPE: Single-seat aerobatic aircraft.

WINGS: Cantilever low-wing monoplane. Wing section NACA 0018 at root, NACA 0012 at tip. Dihedral 1° 7′ 24″. All-metal structure, with single continuous main spar, rear auxiliary spar, and aluminium-clad duralumin skin. All-metal mass-balanced ailerons, actuated by pushrods, occupy most of each trailing-edge. Ground-adjustable tab on port outer aileron; automatic trim tab on each inboard aileron. No flaps. Provision for fitting wingtip fuel tanks for cross-country flights.

FUSELAGE: All-metal semi-monocoque stressed-skin structure, with duralumin skin.

TAIL UNIT: Conventional metal structure. Braced tailplane and fin duralumin-covered, balanced elevators and rudder fabric-covered. One mechanically-adjustable tab and one automatic trim tab on elevators; automatic trim tab on rudder. Elevators actuated by pushrods, rudder by cables.

Zlin Z 50 L single-seat aerobatic aircraft *(Pilot Press)*

LANDING GEAR: Non-retractable tailwheel type. Main wheels carried on flat-spring titanium cantilever legs. Mechanical main-wheel brakes actuated by rudder pedals. Fully-castoring tailwheel, with flat-spring shock-absorption, has automatic locking device to maintain aircraft on a straight track during taxying, take-off, and landing. Main wheels size 350 × 135 mm, pressure 2·5 bars (36 lb/sq in); tailwheel size 200 × 80 mm, pressure 1·0 bar (14·5 lb/sq in). Main-wheel fairings optional.

POWER PLANT: One 194 kW (260 hp) Avco Lycoming AEIO-540-D4B5 flat-six engine, without reduction gear, driving a Hoffmann HO-V123K-F/200AH three-blade constant-speed variable-pitch wooden propeller with spinner. Single main fuel tank in fuselage, aft of firewall, capacity 60 litres (13·2 Imp gallons). Auxiliary 50 litre (11 Imp gallon) tank can be attached to each wingtip for cross-country flights only. Fuel and oil systems designed for full aerobatic manoeuvres, including inverted flight. Oil capacity 12 litres (2·64 Imp gallons).

ACCOMMODATION: Single seat under fully-transparent sideways-opening (to starboard) bubble canopy, which can be jettisoned in an emergency. Seat and backrest are adjustable, and permit the use of a back-type parachute. Cockpit ventilated by sliding panel in canopy.

SYSTEM: Electrical system includes an alternator as main power source and a Varley battery. External power socket in fuselage side for engine starting.

AVIONICS AND EQUIPMENT: VHF radio optional.

DIMENSIONS, EXTERNAL:

Wing span	8·58 m (28 ft 1¾ in)
Wing span over tip-tanks	9·03 m (29 ft 7½ in)
Wing chord at root	1·73 m (5 ft 8¼ in)
Wing chord at tip	1·21 m (3 ft 11¾ in)
Wing mean aerodynamic chord	1·4853 m (4 ft 10½ in)
Wing aspect ratio	5·88
Length overall (tail up)	6·62 m (21 ft 8¾ in)
Height over tail (static)	1·985 m (6 ft 6¼ in)
Elevator span	3·44 m (11 ft 3½ in)
Wheel track	1·90 m (6 ft 2¾ in)
Wheelbase	5·05 m (16 ft 7 in)
Propeller diameter	2·00 m (6 ft 6¾ in)
Propeller ground clearance (tail up)	0·31 m (1 ft 0¼ in)

AREAS:

Wings, gross	12·50 m² (134·55 sq ft)
Ailerons (total)	2·80 m² (30·14 sq ft)
Fin	0·59 m² (6·35 sq ft)
Rudder, incl tab	0·81 m² (8·72 sq ft)
Tailplane	1·66 m² (17·87 sq ft)
Elevators (total, incl tabs)	1·20 m² (12·92 sq ft)

WEIGHTS AND LOADINGS (Aerobatic category):

Weight empty, equipped	570 kg (1,256 lb)
Max T-O weight	720 kg (1,587 lb)
Max wing loading	57·6 kg/m² (11·80 lb/sq ft)
Max power loading	3·72 kg/kW (6·11 lb/hp)

PERFORMANCE (at max Aerobatic T-O weight):

Never-exceed speed	181·5 knots (337 km/h; 209 mph) CAS
Max level speed at S/L, ISA	156 knots (290 km/h; 180 mph)
Max cruising speed at 1,000 m (3,280 ft), ISA	147 knots (273 km/h; 169 mph)
Econ cruising speed at 1,000 m (3,280 ft), ISA	134 knots (248 km/h; 154 mph)
Stalling speed	53 knots (98 km/h; 61 mph) CAS
Max rate of climb at S/L	720 m (2,360 ft)/min
Service ceiling	7,000 m (2,300 ft)
T-O run	170 m (558 ft)
T-O to 15 m (50 ft)	290 m (952 ft)
Landing from 15 m (50 ft)	530 m (1,740 ft)
Landing run	250 m (820 ft)
Range with max fuel (incl wingtip tanks)	345 nm (640 km; 397 miles)
g limits: Aerobatic	+9; −6

EGYPT

ABHC
ARAB BRITISH HELICOPTER COMPANY
PO Box 73, Helwan
Telephone: Cairo 823377 and 932822
Telex: 93789 ABH UN
PARTICIPATING COMPANIES:
Arab Organisation for Industrialisation (AOI)
Westland Helicopters Ltd
CHAIRMAN: K. H. El Shishini, BSc (Aeronautics Engineering), MSc
VICE-CHAIRMAN: A. V. N. Reed, BSc (Tech), CEng, FRAeS, AMBIM
MANAGING DIRECTOR: B. Baxter, BEng, CEng, MIMechE, MIProdE
DEPUTY MANAGING DIRECTOR: A. Abdin BSc, MSc
COMMERCIAL DIRECTOR: F. P. Stanton
BOARD MEMBERS:
Gen K. A. Elazayem (Egypt)
Lt Col Fadel Saeed (United Arab Emirates)

Capt Hamad Fand (Qatar)
Capt Eng M. A. R. Katouaa

The Arab Organisation for Industrialisation (AOI), funded jointly by Saudi Arabia, Qatar, the United Arab Emirates and Egypt, embarked upon a major programme to re-establish an aircraft and aero-engine industry in Egypt, to meet the needs of the participating states.

The first step in this programme was the signing of a contract, on 27 February 1978, between the AOI and Westland Helicopters and Rolls-Royce of the UK to produce the Westland/Aérospatiale Lynx helicopter and its Gem engines in Egypt. The ABHC, and a corresponding engine company (ABEC), were set up to manage the programme; ABHC has an initial capital of $30 million, with Westland having a 30% shareholding.

Also in the Spring of 1978, the AOI signed a similar agreement, concerning the Dassault-Breguet/Dornier Alpha Jet, with the French government.

In May 1979, the non-Egyptian members of AOI stated that they intended to withdraw from the organisation.

ABHC/WESTLAND LYNX
Under an initial £55 million contract, Westland is to supply 20 British-built Lynx helicopters to Egypt, followed by components for a further 30 which will be assembled by ABHC in manufacturing facilities to be developed adjacent to the existing Egyptian aircraft factory (formerly Factory 36) at Helwan, 29 km (18 miles) south of Cairo. Subsequently, with technical and management training assistance from Westland, Egyptian personnel are to progress towards complete manufacture. The announced plans were for up to 230 Lynx to be so produced, for the armed forces of Egypt, Saudi Arabia, Qatar and the United Arab Emirates; similarly, ABEC, with Rolls-Royce assistance, was to produce up to 750 Gem turboshaft engines for the programme, which was expected to extend over about seven years. Lynx assembly in Egypt began in February 1979.

FINLAND

VALMET
VALMET OY KUOREVEDEN TEHDAS
OFFICE AND WORKS: 35600 Halli
Telephone: 942 82810 Exchange
Telex: 28269 Valku SF
MANAGER: Heikki Mäntylä
GENERAL MANAGER, KUOREVESI WORKS: Juhani Mäkinen
PROJECT MANAGER: L-70: Pekka Kaipio

Valmet Oy Kuoreveden Tehdas (Kuorevesi Works) is affiliated to Valmet Oy, a State-owned company consisting of several metal-working factories. It continues the traditions of Ilmailuvoimien Lentokonetehdas, established in 1921, and was formerly a part of the Valmet Oy Tampere factory group, from which it was separated in 1974. It is now an independent factory directly responsible to Valmet's Head Office in Helsinki, and is currently the largest aircraft industry establishment in Finland. Since 1922, Valmet Oy Kuoreveden Tehdas and its predecessors have built 30 different types of aircraft, of which 18 have been of Finnish design. Valmet Oy was responsible for assembly of the 12 Saab 35XS Drakens ordered by Finland in 1970.

Current activities of Valmet Oy Kuoreveden Tehdas include the overhaul and repair of military and civil aircraft, piston engines and instruments. The factory has a covered area of approximately 14,000 m² (150,695 sq ft). Valmet Oy Linnavuoren Tehdas, at Siuro, is concerned primarily with the overhaul and repair of aircraft jet engines.

The Kuorevesi and Linnavuori Works are also participating in the manufacture and assembly of 46 of the 50 BAe Hawk Mk 51 jet trainers and their Adour Mk 851 jet engines, purchased by the Finnish Air Force from the UK in early 1978. Deliveries of these aircraft are to take place in 1981-85.

The latest aircraft of Finnish design to be built by Valmet is the L-70 Miltrainer piston-engined trainer. It was designed by Ilmailuteollisuuden Kehitysosasto (IKO), which was formed on 15 September 1970.

VALMET L-70 MILTRAINER
Finnish Air Force name: Vinka (Blast)
In late 1970 an aeronautical research and development group was established in Finland, its first major task being to study a Finnish Air Force requirement for a basic training aircraft to replace the Saab 91 Safir. It was decided to produce an entirely Finnish design to fulfil this need, and a development contract was placed with Valmet by the Finnish Air Force on 23 March 1973. The aircraft, which was originally designated Leko-70, an abbreviation of 'Lentokone', the Finnish word for 'aeroplane', is named Vinka by the Finnish Air Force.

The prototype made its first flight at Kuorevesi on 1 July 1975. A second prototype was used for static and fatigue testing; a full-size cockpit mockup and components for a third aircraft were also completed.

The Finnish Air Force ordered 30 Vinkas on 28 January 1977. Manufacture of these began on 15 January 1977,

and the first production Vinka made its initial flight on 29 December 1979. Deliveries began in February 1980.

The Miltrainer is designed for aerobatic flying as a two-seater. In civil use, in Normal or Utility category, it is capable of seating up to four persons, depending upon the amount of baggage carried.
TYPE: Two-seat training or two/four-seat touring aircraft.
WINGS: Cantilever low-wing monoplane. Wing section NACA 63₂A615 (modified). Dihedral 6° from roots. Incidence 2°. Fail-safe structure of main spar, auxiliary spar, ribs and stringers, of constant chord except for forward-swept wing-root leading-edges, and attached to fuselage by steel fittings. Riveted aluminium alloy skin. Electrically-operated slotted flaps, and mass-balanced slotted ailerons, on trailing-edges, all of aluminium alloy riveted construction. Ailerons actuated by stainless steel control cables. Flaps and ailerons have fluted skins. Adjustable geared tab in each aileron.

First production example of the Valmet L-70 Vinka two-seat trainer for the Finnish Air Force

Valmet L-70 Miltrainer two/four-seat training and touring aircraft *(Pilot Press)*

FUSELAGE: Conventional aluminium alloy semi-monocoque fail-safe structure of frames and longerons, with riveted skin. Welded steel tube engine mount and wing carry-through structure; stainless steel firewall. Cockpit floor panels of bonded sandwich.

TAIL UNIT: Cantilever aluminium alloy structure, with fluted and riveted skin. Slight sweepback on vertical surfaces; shallow dorsal fin. Elevators and rudder aerodynamically and mass balanced, and actuated by stainless steel control cables. Geared trim tabs in rudder and each elevator.

LANDING GEAR: Non-retractable tricycle type. Cantilever main legs. Automotive Products oleo-pneumatic shock-absorbers on all units. Cleveland P410 main wheels, with 17·5 × 6·30-6 tyres, pressure 1·86 bars (27 lb/sq in); Goodyear 5·00-5 nosewheel, with 14·2 × 4·95-5 tyre, pressure 2·07 bars (30 lb/sq in). Cleveland 30-52K disc brakes. Provision for fitting Finncraft skis.

POWER PLANT: One 149 kW (200 hp) Avco Lycoming AEIO-360-A1B6 flat-four engine, driving a Hartzell HC-C2YK-4F/FC 7666A-2 two-blade constant-speed propeller with spinner. Christen-801 inverted fuel and oil systems. Semi-integral bonded sandwich fuel tank in each wing root ahead of main spar; total capacity 176 litres (38·7 Imp gallons). Overwing fuelling point above each tank. Oil capacity 7·6 litres (1·7 Imp gallons).

ACCOMMODATION: Side-by-side seats for instructor and pupil in trainer version, with integral longitudinal central console which serves also to reinforce fuselage floor. Dual controls standard, but instructor's or pupil's control column can be removed if desired. Windscreen and one-piece rearward-sliding fully-transparent jettisonable canopy, with steel tube turnover frame. Canopy can be locked in partially open position if required. Provision for two more seats at rear, which can be removed to make room for additional baggage. Up to 280 kg (617 lb) of baggage or freight can be carried internally, or externally if flown as a single-seater. As ambulance, can accommodate one stretcher patient and medical attendant in addition to pilot. Cockpit heated and ventilated.

SYSTEM: 24V 70A DC electrical system, with brushless generator and 25Ah nickel-cadmium battery.

AVIONICS AND EQUIPMENT: Two VHF, one ADF, one VOR/ILS, one ATC transponder, two RMI, and one gyromagnetic compass. Blind-flying instrumentation standard. Landing/taxying lights in starboard wing leading-edge. Equipment for secondary roles may include glider or target towing hook; one long-focus or four short-focus vertical cameras (provision for 35 × 40 cm; 13·8 × 15·75 in aperture, with hinged doors, in floor of rear cockpit); four underwing pylons (total capacity

300 kg; 661 lb) for external freight or supplies; and dispersal equipment for agricultural missions.

DIMENSIONS, EXTERNAL:
Wing span	9·85 m (32 ft 3¾ in)
Wing chord (constant over most of span)	1·53 m (5 ft 0¼ in)
Wing aspect ratio	6
Length overall	7·50 m (24 ft 7¼ in)
Height overall	3·31 m (10 ft 10¼ in)
Tailplane span	3·60 m (11 ft 9¾ in)
Wheel track	2·30 m (7 ft 6½ in)
Wheelbase	1·61 m (5 ft 3½ in)
Propeller diameter	1·88 m (6 ft 2 in)
Propeller ground clearance	0·25 m (9¾ in)

AREAS:
Wings, gross	14·00 m² (150·70 sq ft)
Ailerons (total)	1·41 m² (15·18 sq ft)
Trailing-edge flaps (total)	1·90 m² (20·45 sq ft)
Fin	0·87 m² (9·36 sq ft)
Rudder, incl tab	0·79 m² (8·50 sq ft)
Tailplane	2·01 m² (21·64 sq ft)
Elevators, incl tabs	1·01 m² (10·87 sq ft)

WEIGHTS AND LOADINGS:
Operating weight empty, equipped	767 kg (1,691 lb)
Max payload with full fuel	380 kg (838 lb)
Max T-O weight: Aerobatic	1,040 kg (2,293 lb)
Normal	1,250 kg (2,756 lb)
Max wing loading	89·3 kg/m² (18·53 lb/sq ft)
Max power loading	8·38 kg/kW (13·78 lb/hp)

PERFORMANCE (at max Aerobatic T-O weight):
Never-exceed speed	193 knots (360 km/h; 223 mph)
Max level speed at S/L	129 knots (240 km/h; 149 mph)
Cruising speed (75% power) at 1,525 m (5,000 ft)	120 knots (222 km/h; 138 mph)
Stalling speed, flaps up, power off	53 knots (98 km/h; 61 mph)
Stalling speed, flaps down, power off	46 knots (85 km/h; 53 mph)
Max rate of climb at S/L	342 m (1,120 ft)/min
Service ceiling	5,000 m (16,400 ft)
T-O run	180 m (590 ft)
T-O to 15 m (50 ft)	260 m (855 ft)
Landing from 15 m (50 ft)	300 m (985 ft)
Landing run	150 m (490 ft)
Min ground turning radius	8·00 m (26 ft 3 in)
Range with max fuel	547 nm (1,015 km; 630 miles)
Range with max payload, no reserves	464 nm (860 km; 534 miles)
Endurance at S/L (65% power)	4 h 48 min
g limits: Aerobatic	+6·00; −3·00
Utility	+4·40; −2·02
Normal	+3·80; −1·80

FRANCE

AÉROSPATIALE
SOCIÉTÉ NATIONALE INDUSTRIELLE AÉROSPATIALE

HEAD OFFICE: 37 boulevard de Montmorency, 75781 Paris Cédex 16
Telephone: 524 43 21
Telex: AISPA X 620059 F

BOARD OF DIRECTORS
CHAIRMAN: Jacques Mitterrand, Général d'Armée Aérienne (CPN)
REPRESENTATIVES OF THE SHAREHOLDERS:
René Ravaud, Ingénieur Général de l'Armement (President and Director General of SNECMA)
Roger Martin (President of the Saint-Gobain company, Pont à Mousson)
Banque Nationale de Paris, represented by René Thomas (Deputy Director General)
REPRESENTATIVES OF THE STATE:
Jean-Pierre Barbery, Ingénieur Général de l'Armement (representing the Ministry of Defence)
Claude Abraham (Director General of Civil Aviation, representing the Secretary of State for Transport)
REPRESENTATIVES OF THE EMPLOYEES:
Paul Bienfait (representing executives)
Jean Masse and Vincent Valente (representing workmen, office staff, technicians and supervisors)

GENERAL MANAGEMENT
PRESIDENT AND DIRECTOR GENERAL: Jacques Mitterrand
DIRECTOR GENERAL DELEGATE: Roger Chevalier
DEPUTY GENERAL MANAGER, ECONOMICS AND FINANCE: Yves Barbé
DEPUTY GENERAL MANAGER, INDUSTRIAL AND TECHNICAL MATTERS: Joseph Millara
GENERAL SECRETARY: Roger Courot
DIRECTOR OF THE PRESIDENT'S OFFICE: Jean-Charles Poggi
INSPECTOR GENERAL: Jean Soissons
PRESS AND INFORMATION ADVISER TO THE PRESIDENT: Jean E. Lagrange

DIRECTOR OF PUBLIC RELATIONS: Claude Loiseau
INDUSTRIAL DIRECTOR: Roger Berthier
CENTRAL FINANCIAL DIRECTOR: Michel Euvrard
CENTRAL TECHNICAL DIRECTOR: Jacques Balazard
DIRECTOR (INDUSTRIAL RELATIONS): André Escoulin
DIRECTOR (QUALITY ASSURANCE): Georges Sertour
DEPUTY DIRECTOR OF INDUSTRIAL RELATIONS (DIRECTOR HEADQUARTERS ESTABLISHMENT): Didier Godechot

AIRCRAFT DIVISION
MANAGING DIRECTOR: André Etesse
ASSISTANT MANAGING DIRECTOR: René Dor
ASSISTANT MANAGING DIRECTOR, PROGRAMMES: Georges Roche
MILITARY ADVISER: Gen (ret) Pierre Delachenal
TECHNICAL DIRECTOR: Pierre Lecomte
FINANCIAL DIRECTOR: Joseph Carpentier
COMMERCIAL DIRECTOR: Henri Puel
FLIGHT TEST DIRECTOR: Henri Perrier
DIRECTOR, SUPPORT SERVICES: Pierre Magnani
DIRECTOR (QUALITY ASSURANCE): André Despeyroux
WORKS AND FACILITIES:
Toulouse. DIRECTOR: Jean Pierson
Nantes-Bouguenais. DIRECTOR: Jean-Louis Fache
Saint-Nazaire. DIRECTOR: Jean Renon
Méaulte. DIRECTOR: Jean-Paul Chandez

HELICOPTER DIVISION
MANAGING DIRECTOR: François Legrand
TECHNICAL DIRECTOR: Georges Petit
DIRECTOR OF ENGINEERING: René Mouille
DIRECTOR OF COMMERCIAL PROGRAMME: André Renaud
SALES DIRECTOR: Jean-Claude Rebuffel
DIRECTOR (PRODUCT SUPPORT): Marc Fourcade
FLIGHT TEST DIRECTOR: Jean-Marie Besse
DIRECTOR (QUALITY ASSURANCE): André Breton
WORKS AND FACILITIES:
Marignane. DIRECTOR: Fernand Carayon
La Courneuve. DIRECTOR: Lucien Fournier

TACTICAL MISSILES DIVISION
MANAGING DIRECTOR: Michel Allier
ASSISTANT MANAGING DIRECTOR: Philippe Girard
SALES DIRECTOR: Pierre Frojet
TECHNICAL DIRECTOR: Jean Guillot
DIRECTOR OF DESIGN: Yves de Rougemont
DIRECTOR OF ECONOMIC AFFAIRS: Jacques Pottier
WORKS AND FACILITIES:
Châtillon. DIRECTOR: Jean-Claude Renaut
Bourges. DIRECTOR: Georges Barroy

SPACE AND BALLISTIC SYSTEMS DIVISION
MANAGING DIRECTOR: Pierre Usunier
ASSISTANT MANAGING DIRECTOR—DIRECTOR OF SYSTEMS SUBDIVISION: Gérard Payelle
INTERNATIONAL AND COMMERCIAL AFFAIRS (SPACE): Alexandre Dauguet
WORKS AND FACILITIES:
Aquitaine. DIRECTOR: Jean-Rémy Hugues
Les Mureaux. DIRECTOR: Séverin Golbert
Cannes. DIRECTOR: Gérard Chauvallon

SUBSIDIARIES
Société Girondine d'Entretien et de Réparation de Matériel Aéronautique (SOGERMA)
Société de Construction d'Avions de Tourisme et d'Affaires (Socata)
Société d'Exploitation et de Constructions Aéronautiques (SECA)
Electronique Aérospatiale (EAS)
Société Charentaise d'Equipements Aéronautiques (SOCEA)
Aérospatiale Helicopter Corporation (USA)
European Aerospace Corporation (USA)

The Société Nationale Industrielle Aérospatiale was formed on 1 January 1970, by decision of the French government, as a result of the merger of the former Sud-Aviation, Nord-Aviation and SEREB companies. It is the biggest aerospace company in the Common Market countries on the Continent of Europe, with a registered capital of 447,400,000 francs, facilities extending over a total area of 9,790,000 m² (105,380,000 sq ft), of which 1,778,000 m² (19,138,000 sq ft) are covered, and a staff (including subsidiary companies) of 38,173 persons at the beginning of 1980.

In the aircraft field, major products include the short/medium-range large-capacity A300/A310 European Airbus, in co-operation with Deutsche Airbus GmbH, British Aerospace, VFW, Fokker and CASA; and the Transall heavy multi-purpose transport, in co-operation with MBB and VFW.

Aérospatiale produces a range of light piston-engined aircraft through its subsidiary, Socata (which see). It is also a major manufacturer of helicopters, guided missiles, spacecraft and research rockets.

Helicopter activities, concentrated at Marignane, involve the development and production of a wide range of turbine-powered types, described under this entry. Agreements concluded with Westland in the UK covered joint development and production of the Puma and Gazelle, and the Westland-designed Lynx, after all three types had been chosen to equip the French and British armed forces.

By the beginning of 1980, the Helicopter Division had sold a total of 5,950 production helicopters to 497 customers in 94 countries. Orders for 511 helicopters were received in 1979, about 94 per cent for export.

AÉROSPATIALE/BAe CONCORDE

Details of the Concorde programme can be found in the International section of this edition.

AÉROSPATIALE FOUGA 90A

The Fouga 90A was intended as a successor to the CM 170 Magister trainer and light tactical support aircraft, of which 929 were built between 1953 and 1969. When designing it, Aérospatiale retained the aerodynamics of the wing and tail unit of the Magister. The centre-fuselage was redesigned and deepened, to accommodate pilot and instructor in the now-preferred stepped positions, to give the occupant of the rear seat an optimum forward view. More modern electronics and systems were installed; and the original Marboré turbojets were replaced by turbofans, offering much reduced specific fuel consumption and improved noise characteristics.

A prototype, designated Fouga 90, flew for the first time on 20 August 1978, powered by Astafan IIG turbofans. These engines were replaced subsequently with Astafan IVGs, and the prototype was redesignated Fouga 90A. First flight with the new engines was made on 26 September 1979. In mid-1980, the decision was taken to terminate the Fouga 90A programme in favour of a completely new transition trainer to meet future French Air Force requirements.

A structural description of the Fouga 90A can be found in the 1979-80 *Jane's*. The following data have been revised:

TYPE: Light twin-turbofan basic and transition trainer, with tactical support capability.

POWER PLANT: Two Turboméca Astafan IVG turbofan engines, each rated at 7·75 kN (1,740 lb st). Fuel in two fuselage tanks and wing leading-edge tanks, with total capacity of 1,440 litres (317 Imp gallons).

WEIGHTS AND LOADINGS:

Weight empty, equipped	2,550 kg (5,622 lb)
Max T-O weight, 'clean'	3,800 kg (8,380 lb)
Max T-O weight, with armament	4,500 kg (9,920 lb)
Max wing loading	244·8 kg/m² (50·15 lb/sq ft)
Max power loading	290·3 kg/kN (2·85 lb/lb st)

PERFORMANCE (at AUW of 3,200 kg; 7,055 lb):

Never-exceed speed	Mach 0·8
Max level speed at 9,145 m (30,000 ft)	378 knots (700 km/h; 435 mph)
Max level speed at S/L	355 knots (657 km/h; 408 mph)
Max rate of climb at S/L	1,446 m (4,745 ft)/min
Service ceiling	13,100 m (43,000 ft)

Aérospatiale Fouga 90A tandem two-seat transition trainer prototype

T-O to 10·7 m (35 ft)	380 m (1,247 ft)
Landing from 15 m (50 ft)	670 m (2,200 ft)
Range with max fuel	1,394 nm (2,582 km; 1,604 miles)
Endurance with max fuel, no reserves	4 h

AÉROSPATIALE SA 315B LAMA
Indian Army name: Cheetah

Design of the SA 315B Lama began in late 1968, initially to meet a requirement of the Indian armed forces, and a prototype was flown for the first time on 17 March 1969. French certification was granted on 30 September 1970 and FAA Type Approval on 25 February 1972.

The Lama combines features of the Alouette II and III, having the airframe (with some reinforcement) of the former and the dynamic components, including the Artouste power plant and rotor system, of the SA 316 Alouette III.

During demonstration flights in the Himalayas in 1969 a Lama, carrying a crew of two and 140 kg (308 lb) of fuel, made the highest landings and take-offs ever recorded, at a height of 7,500 m (24,600 ft).

On 21 June 1972, a Lama set a helicopter absolute height record of 12,442 m (40,820 ft). The pilot was Jean Boulet, holder of the previous record in an SE 3150 Alouette.

The production Lama is capable of transporting an external load of 1,135 kg (2,500 lb) at an altitude of more than 2,500 m (8,200 ft). In an agricultural role, it can be fitted with spraybars and an underbelly tank of 1,135 litres (300 US gallons) capacity, developed jointly by Aérospatiale Helicopter Corporation and Simplex Manufacturing Company. The tank is equipped with an electrical emergency dump system.

An alternative agricultural installation, using two side-mounted glassfibre tanks of Simplex manufacture, was shown for the first time at the 1976 US National Agriculture Aviation Association convention. Up to 1,000 kg (2,200 lb) of liquid chemicals can be carried in these tanks, which weigh 132 kg (290 lb) empty. A high-performance electric pump dispenses up to 455 litres (120 US gallons)/min at 2·10 kg/cm² (30 lb/sq in) boom pressure.

A total of 312 Lamas had been sold by 1 March 1980. In addition to manufacture by Aérospatiale, the SA 315B is produced under licence by HAL for the Indian Army under the name Cheetah.

TYPE: Turbine-driven general-purpose helicopter.

ROTOR SYSTEM: Three-blade main and anti-torque rotors. All-metal main rotor blades, of constant chord, are on articulated hinges, with hydraulic drag-hinge dampers. Rotor brake standard.

ROTOR DRIVE: Main rotor driven through planetary gearbox, with freewheel for autorotation. Take-off drive for tail rotor at lower end of main gearbox, from where a torque shaft runs to a small gearbox which supports the tail rotor and houses the pitch-change mechanism. Cyclic and collective pitch controls are powered.

FUSELAGE: Glazed cabin has light metal frame. Centre and rear of fuselage have a triangulated steel tube framework.

LANDING GEAR: Skid type, with removable wheels for ground manoeuvring. Pneumatic floats for normal operation from water, and emergency flotation gear, inflatable in the air, are available.

POWER PLANT: One 649 kW (870 shp) Turboméca Artouste IIIB turboshaft engine, derated to 410 kW (550 shp). Fuel tank in fuselage centre-section, with capacity of 575 litres (126·5 Imp gallons), of which 573 litres (126 Imp gallons) are usable.

ACCOMMODATION: Glazed cabin seats pilot and passenger side by side in front and three passengers behind. Provision for external sling for loads of up to 1,135 kg (2,500 lb). Can be equipped for rescue (hoist capacity 160 kg; 352 lb), liaison, observation, training, agricultural, photographic and other duties. As an ambulance, can accommodate two stretchers and a medical attendant.

DIMENSIONS, EXTERNAL:

Main rotor diameter	11·02 m (36 ft 1¾ in)
Tail rotor diameter	1·91 m (6 ft 3¼ in)
Main rotor blade chord (constant)	0·35 m (13·8 in)
Length overall, both rotors turning	12·92 m (42 ft 4¾ in)
Length of fuselage	10·26 m (33 ft 8 in)
Height overall	3·09 m (10 ft 1¾ in)
Skid track	2·38 m (7 ft 9¾ in)

WEIGHTS:

Weight empty	1,021 kg (2,251 lb)
Normal max T-O weight	1,950 kg (4,300 lb)
Max T-O weight with externally-slung cargo	2,300 kg (5,070 lb)

PERFORMANCE (at AUW of 2,300 kg; 5,070 lb, with slung load):

Max cruising speed	65 knots (120 km/h; 75 mph)
Max rate of climb at S/L	234 m (768 ft)/min
Service ceiling	3,000 m (9,840 ft)
Hovering ceiling IGE	2,950 m (9,675 ft)
Hovering ceiling OGE	1,550 m (5,085 ft)

AÉROSPATIALE SA 316B ALOUETTE III

The Alouette III helicopter was evolved from the Alouette II, with larger cabin, greater power, improved equipment and higher performance. The prototype flew for the first time on 28 February 1959, and a total of 1,423 Alouette IIIs had been sold by 1 March 1980.

Those delivered up to the end of 1969 were designated **SE 3160**. The subsequent Artouste-engined **SA 316B** has strengthened main and rear rotor transmissions, higher AUW and increased payload. It flew for the first time on 27 June 1968; first deliveries were made in 1970, and this version received FAA Type Approval on 25 March 1971. The **SA 319B**, with Astazou engine, is described separately, but is included in the total sales figures above.

The sale of Alouette IIIs to India, Romania and Switzerland included a licence agreement for manufacture of the aircraft in those countries. Quantities involved were 250 in India, 180 in Romania and 60 in Switzerland.

In 1977, an SA 316B operated by Trans North Turbo Air for the Canadian Park Service evacuated a mountain climber, suffering from pulmonary edema and frostbite, from a point at the 4,235 m (13,900 ft) level on the east ridge of Mount Logan. This is thought to be the greatest height at which a hoist rescue has been effected.

TYPE: Turbine-driven general-purpose helicopter.

ROTOR SYSTEM: Three-blade main and anti-torque rotors. All-metal main rotor blades, on articulated hinges, with hydraulic drag-hinge dampers. Rotor brake standard.

ROTOR DRIVE: Main rotor driven through planetary gearbox, with freewheel for autorotation. Take-off drive for tail rotor at lower end of main gearbox, from where a torque shaft runs to a small gearbox which supports the tail rotor and houses the pitch-change mechanism. Cyclic and collective pitch controls are powered.

Aérospatiale SA 315B Lama (Turboméca Artouste IIIB turboshaft engine)

FUSELAGE: Welded steel tube centre-section, carrying the cabin at the front and a semi-monocoque tailboom.

TAIL UNIT: Cantilever all-metal fixed tailplane, with twin endplate fins, mounted on tailboom.

LANDING GEAR: Non-retractable tricycle type, manufactured by Messier-Hispano-Bugatti. Nosewheel is fully-castoring. Provision for pontoon landing gear.

POWER PLANT: One 649 kW (870 shp) Turboméca Artouste IIIB turboshaft engine, derated to 425 kW (570 shp). Fuel in single tank in fuselage centre-section, with capacity of 575 litres (126·5 Imp gallons), of which 573 litres (126 Imp gallons) are usable.

ACCOMMODATION: Normal accommodation for pilot and six persons, with three seats in front and a four-person folding seat at the rear of the cabin. Two baggage holds in centre-section, on each side of the welded structure and enclosed by the centre-section fairings. Provision for carrying two stretchers athwartships at rear of cabin, and two other persons, in addition to pilot. All passenger seats removable to enable aircraft to be used for freight-carrying. Provision for external sling for loads of up to 750 kg (1,650 lb). One forward-opening door on each side, immediately in front of two rearward-sliding doors. Dual controls and cabin heating optional.

OPERATIONAL EQUIPMENT (military version): In the assault role, the Alouette III can be equipped with a wide range of weapons. A 7·62 mm AA52 machine-gun (with 1,000 rds) can be mounted athwartships on a tripod behind the pilot's seat, firing to starboard, either through a small window in the sliding door or through the open doorway with the door locked open. The rear seat is removed to allow the gun mounting to be installed. In this configuration, max accommodation is for pilot, co-pilot, gunner and one passenger, although normally only the pilot and gunner would be carried. Alternatively, a 20 mm MG 151/20 cannon (with 480 rds) can be carried on an open turret-type mounting on the port side of the cabin. For this installation all seats except that of the pilot are removed, as is the port side cabin door, and the crew consists of pilot and gunner. Instead of these guns, the Alouette III can be equipped with four AS.11 or two AS.12 wire-guided missiles on external jettisonable launching rails, with an APX-Bézu 260 gyro-stabilised sight, or 68 mm rocket pods.

DIMENSIONS, EXTERNAL:
Diameter of main rotor	11·02 m (36 ft 1¾ in)
Main rotor blade chord (each)	0·35 m (13·8 in)
Diameter of tail rotor	1·91 m (6 ft 3¼ in)
Length overall, rotors turning	12·84 m (42 ft 1½ in)
Length overall, blades folded	10·03 m (32 ft 10¾ in)
Width overall, blades folded	2·60 m (8 ft 6¼ in)
Height to top of rotor head	3·00 m (9 ft 10 in)
Wheel track	2·60 m (8 ft 6¼ in)

WEIGHTS:
Weight empty	1,143 kg (2,520 lb)
Max T-O weight	2,200 kg (4,850 lb)

PERFORMANCE (standard version, at max T-O weight):
Max level speed at S/L	113 knots (210 km/h; 130 mph)
Max cruising speed at S/L	100 knots (185 km/h; 115 mph)
Max rate of climb at S/L	260 m (850 ft)/min
Service ceiling	3,200 m (10,500 ft)
Hovering ceiling IGE	2,880 m (9,450 ft)
Hovering ceiling OGE	1,520 m (5,000 ft)
Range with max fuel at S/L	258 nm (480 km; 298 miles)

Aérospatiale SA 319B Alouette III Astazou operated by the French Gendarmerie

Range at optimum altitude
290 nm (540 km; 335 miles)

AÉROSPATIALE SA 319B ALOUETTE III ASTAZOU
Indian military name: Chetak

The SA 319B Alouette III Astazou is a direct development of the SA 316B, from which it differs principally in having an Astazou XIV turboshaft engine (649 kW; 870 shp, derated to 447 kW; 600 shp) with increased thermal efficiency and a 25 per cent reduction in fuel consumption.

A prototype SA 319 was completed in 1967. The production total is included in the figures given under the SA 316B entry.

OPERATIONAL EQUIPMENT (naval version): The Alouette III can fulfil a variety of shipborne roles; features common to all naval configurations include a quick-mooring harpoon to ensure instant and automatic mooring on landing and before take-off, a nosewheel locking device, and folding main rotor blades. For detecting and destroying small surface craft such as torpedo-boats, it can be equipped with a SFENA three-axis stabilisation system, OMERA ORB 31 radar, APX-Bézu 260 gyro-stabilised sight and two AS.12 wire-guided missiles. For the ASW role, it can carry two Mk 44 homing torpedoes beneath the fuselage, or one torpedo and MAD (magnetic anomaly detection) gear in a streamlined container which is towed behind the helicopter on a 50 m (150 ft) cable. The aircraft can be used for air/sea rescue when the cabin floor is protected by an anti-corrosion covering to prevent sea water from reaching vital components. Rescue hoist (capacity 225 kg; 500 lb) mounted on port side of fuselage.

WEIGHTS:
Weight empty	1,146 kg (2,527 lb)
Max T-O weight	2,250 kg (4,960 lb)

PERFORMANCE (at max T-O weight):
Max level speed at S/L	118 knots (220 km/h; 136 mph)
Max cruising speed at S/L	106 knots (197 km/h; 122 mph)
Max rate of climb at S/L	270 m (885 ft)/min
Hovering ceiling IGE	3,100 m (10,170 ft)
Hovering ceiling OGE	1,700 m (5,575 ft)

Range with 6 passengers (80 kg; 176 lb each), T-O at S/L
325 nm (605 km; 375 miles)

AÉROSPATIALE SA 321 SUPER FRELON

The Super Frelon is a three-engined multi-purpose helicopter derived from the smaller SA 3200 Frelon (see 1961-62 *Jane's*).

Under a technical co-operation contract, Sikorsky Aircraft, USA, provided assistance in the development of the Super Frelon, in particular with the detail specifications, design, construction and testing of the main and tail rotor systems. Under a further agreement, the main gearcase and transmission box are produced in Italy by Fiat.

The first prototype of the Super Frelon (originally designated SA 3210-01) flew on 7 December 1962, powered by three 985 kW (1,320 shp) Turmo IIIC$_2$ engines, and represented the troop transport version. In July 1963 this aircraft set up several international helicopter records, including a speed of 184 knots (341 km/h; 212 mph) over a 3 km course, and a speed of 189·115 knots (350·47 km/h; 217·77 mph) over a 15/25 km course.

The second prototype, flown on 28 May 1963, was representative of the naval version, with stabilising floats on the main landing gear supports. Four pre-production aircraft followed, and the French government ordered an initial production series of 17, designated SA 321G, in October 1965. By 1 March 1980, a total of 99 Super Frelons had been sold.

Passenger and utility versions of the Super Frelon are available, and the main differences between the current versions are summarised as follows:

SA 321F. Commercial airliner, designed to carry 34-37 passengers in a standard of comfort comparable to that of fixed-wing airliners, over 94 nm (175 km; 108 mile) stage lengths at a cruising speed of 124 knots (230 km/h; 143 mph), with 20 min reserve fuel. The prototype was designed in accordance with US FAR 29 regulations and flew for the first time on 7 April 1967. Type certification was granted by the SGAC on 27 June 1968 and by the FAA on 29 August 1968.

SA 321G. Anti-submarine helicopter. First version of the SA 321 to enter production. The first SA 321G flew on 30 November 1965 and deliveries began in early 1966. Twenty-four built. In service with Flottille 32F of Aéronavale, which was commissioned at Lanvéoc-Poulmic on 5 May 1970. Duties of this squadron include

Aérospatiale SA 321G Super Frelon of Aéronavale, equipped for development launches of Exocet anti-ship missiles

patrols in support of *Redoutable* class nuclear submarines entering and leaving their base on the Île Longue. The SA 321G can also be operated from the French helicopter carrier *Jeanne d'Arc*. Under a contract placed in late 1979, the original ORB 31 Héraclès I radar fitted to these aircraft is being replaced with ORB 32 Héraclès II of doubled performance in terms of power (80 kW) and scan (360°).

SA 321H. Version for air force and army service, without stabilising floats or external fairings on each side of lower fuselage. Turmo IIIE₆ engines instead of Turmo IIIC₆ in other versions. No de-icing equipment fitted.

SA 321Ja. Utility and public transport version, intended to fulfil the main roles of personnel and cargo transport. Designed to carry a maximum of 27 passengers. External loads of up to 5,000 kg (11,023 lb) can be suspended from the cargo sling and carried 27 nm (50 km; 31 miles), the aircraft returning to base without load. An internal payload of 4,000 kg (8,818 lb) can be carried over 100 nm (185 km; 115 miles) at 124 knots (230 km/h; 143 mph) with 20 min fuel reserves. The SA 321J prototype flew for the first time on 6 July 1967. A French certificate of airworthiness was granted in December 1971.

The following description applies generally to current production models of the Super Frelon, except where specific variants are indicated:

TYPE: Three-engined heavy-duty helicopter.

ROTOR SYSTEM: Six-blade main rotor and five-blade anti-torque tail rotor. Main rotor head consists basically of two six-armed star-plates carrying the drag and flapping hinges for each blade. The root of each blade carries a fitting for pitch control and each blade has an individual hydraulic damper to govern movement in the drag plane. Each main blade is 8·60 m (28 ft 2½ in) long, with constant chord and NACA 0012 section. All-metal construction, with D-section main spar forming leading-edge. Tail rotor of similar construction to main rotor, with blades 1·60 m (5 ft 3 in) long. Rearward folding of all six main rotor blades of SA 321G is accomplished automatically by hydraulic jacks, simultaneously with automatic folding of the tail rotor pylon.

ROTOR DRIVE: The driveshaft from the rear engine is geared directly to the shaft from the port forward engine. The two forward engines have a common reduction gear from which an output shaft drives the main rotor shaft through helical gearing. There are two reduction gear stages on the main rotor shaft. The tail rotor shaft is driven by gearing from the shaft linking the rear and port forward engines and incorporates two-stage reduction. The rotor can be stopped within 40 s by a boosted disc-type rotor brake fitted to this shaft. Main rotor rpm 207 and 212. Tail rotor rpm 990.

FUSELAGE: Boat-hull fuselage of conventional metal semi-monocoque construction, with watertight compartments inside planing bottom. On the SA 321G, there is a small stabilising float attached to the rear landing gear support structure on each side. The tail section of the SA 321G folds for stowage. Small fixed stabiliser on starboard side of tail rotor pylon on all versions. The SA 321F does not have stabilising floats, but large external fairings on each side of the centre fuselage serve a similar purpose and also act as baggage containers.

LANDING GEAR: Non-retractable tricycle type, by Messier-Hispano-Bugatti. Twin wheels on each unit. Oleo-pneumatic shock-absorbers can be shortened on the SA 321G to reduce height of aircraft for stowage. Magnesium alloy wheels, all of same size. Tyre pressure 6·9 bars (100 lb/sq in). Optionally, low-pressure (3·45 bars; 50 lb/sq in) tyres may be fitted. Hydraulic disc brakes on main wheels. Nosewheel unit is steerable and self-centering.

POWER PLANT: Three 1,156 kW (1,550 shp) Turboméca Turmo IIIC₆ turboshaft engines (IIIE₆ in SA 321H); two mounted side by side forward of main rotor shaft and one aft of rotor shaft. Fuel in flexible tanks under floor of centre fuselage, with total standard capacity of 3,975 litres (874 Imp gallons) in SA 321G/H and 3,900 litres (858 Imp gallons) in SA 321Ja. Optional auxiliary fuel tankage comprises two 500 litre (110 Imp gallon) external tanks on all models, two 500 litre (110 Imp gallon) internal tanks in the SA 321G, and three 666 litre (146·5 Imp gallon) internal tanks in the SA 321H/Ja.

ACCOMMODATION (military versions): Crew of two on flight deck, with dual controls and advanced all-weather equipment. Equipment in the SA 321G, which carries a flight crew of five, includes a tactical table and a variety of devices for anti-submarine detection and attack, towing, minesweeping and other duties. This version also has provision for carrying 27 passengers. SA 321H transport accommodates 27-30 troops, 5,000 kg (11,023 lb) of internal or external cargo, or 15 stretchers and two medical attendants. Rescue hoist of 275 kg (606 lb) capacity. Main cabin is ventilated and sound-proofed. Sliding door on starboard side of front fuselage. Rear loading ramp is actuated hydraulically and can be opened in flight.

ACCOMMODATION (SA 321F): Airliner seats for up to 37 passengers (34 if toilets are installed) in three-abreast rows with centre aisle. Alternative layouts for 8, 14 or 23 passengers, with toilets, or 11, 17 or 26 passengers

without toilets, the remainder of the cabin space being blanked off by movable partitions and used for the carriage of freight; with these configurations, unused seats are folded against the cabin wall. All seats and interior furnishings are designed for quick removal when the helicopter is to be used for all-freight services. To cater for operations over marshland or water, the hull and lateral cargo compartments are sealed sufficiently to permit an occasional landing on water.

ACCOMMODATION (SA 321Ja): Seating for up to 27 passengers in the personnel transport role. As a cargo transport, external loads of up to 5,000 kg (11,023 lb) can be suspended from the cargo sling. Loading of internal cargo (up to 5,000 kg; 11,023 lb) is effected via the rear ramp-doors, with the assistance of a Tirefor hand winch.

OPERATIONAL EQUIPMENT: The ASW SA 321G operates normally in tactical formations of three or four aircraft, each helicopter carrying the full range of detection, tracking and attack equipment, including a self-contained navigation system associated with a Doppler radar, a 360° radar with transponder and display console, and dipping sonar. Four homing torpedoes can be carried in pairs on each side of the main cabin. Both the SA 321G and H can be fitted with an anti-surface vessel weapon system, consisting of two Exocet missiles and launch installation, associated with an Omera-Segid Héraclès ORB 31D or ORB 32 radar for target designation.

DIMENSIONS, EXTERNAL:

Diameter of main rotor	18·90 m (62 ft 0 in)
Main rotor blade chord (each)	0·54 m (1 ft 9¼ in)
Diameter of tail rotor	4·00 m (13 ft 1½ in)
Tail rotor blade chord (each)	0·30 m (11¾ in)
Length overall, rotors turning	23·03 m (75 ft 6⅝ in)
Length of fuselage, incl tail rotor	20·08 m (65 ft 10¾ in)
Length of fuselage	19·40 m (63 ft 7¾ in)
Length overall:	
SA 321G, blades and tail folded	17·07 m (56 ft 0 in)
Width overall:	
SA 321G, blades and tail folded	5·20 m (17 ft 0¾ in)
SA 321F, incl baggage containers	5·04 m (16 ft 6⅜ in)
Width of fuselage	2·24 m (7 ft 4¼ in)
Height at tail rotor (normal)	6·66 m (21 ft 10¼ in)
Height overall:	
SA 321G, blades and tail folded	4·94 m (16 ft 2½ in)
Wheel track	4·30 m (14 ft 1 in)
Wheelbase	6·56 m (21 ft 6¼ in)
Cabin door: Height	1·55 m (5 ft 1 in)
Width	1·20 m (3 ft 11¼ in)
Rear loading ramp: Length	1·90 m (6 ft 2¾ in)
Width	1·90 m (6 ft 2¾ in)

DIMENSIONS, INTERNAL:

Cabin: Length: SA 321F	9·67 m (31 ft 9 in)
SA 321G and Ja	7·00 m (22 ft 11½ in)
Width: SA 321F	1·96 m (6 ft 5 in)
SA 321G and Ja, at floor	1·90 m (6 ft 2¾ in)
Height: SA 321F	1·80 m (5 ft 11 in)
SA 321G and Ja	1·83 m (6 ft 0 in)
Usable volume:	
SA 321G and Ja	25·3 m³ (893 cu ft)

WEIGHTS:

Weight empty, standard aircraft:	
SA 321G	6,863 kg (15,130 lb)
SA 321H	6,702 kg (14,775 lb)
SA 321Ja	6,868 kg (15,141 lb)
Max T-O weight	13,000 kg (28,660 lb)

PERFORMANCE (at max T-O weight):

Never-exceed speed at S/L	148 knots (275 km/h; 171 mph)
Cruising speed at S/L	135 knots (250 km/h; 155 mph)
Cruising speed at S/L, one engine out	113 knots (210 km/h; 130 mph)
Max rate of climb at S/L	400 m (1,312 ft)/min
Rate of climb at S/L, one engine out	146 m (479 ft)/min

Service ceiling	3,150 m (10,325 ft)
Service ceiling, one engine out	1,200 m (3,940 ft)
Hovering ceiling IGE	2,170 m (7,120 ft)
Normal range at S/L	442 nm (820 km; 509 miles)
Normal range at S/L, one engine out	496 nm (920 km; 572 miles)
Range at S/L with 3,500 kg (7,716 lb) payload	549 nm (1,020 km; 633 miles)
Endurance in ASW role	4 h

AÉROSPATIALE SA 330 PUMA

The twin-engined SA 330 Puma was developed initially to meet a French Army requirement for a medium-sized *hélicoptère de manoeuvre*, able to operate by day or night in all weathers and all climates. In 1967, the SA 330 was selected for the RAF Tactical Transport Programme, and was included in the joint production agreement between Aérospatiale and Westland in the UK.

The first of two SA 330 prototypes flew on 15 April 1965, and the last of six pre-production models on 30 July 1968, followed in September 1968 by the first production aircraft.

Details of six early versions of the Puma can be found in the 1976-77 *Jane's*. Current production versions are as follows:

SA 330J/L. Civil (J) and military (L) versions introduced in 1976 with main rotor blades of composite materials. Increased max T-O weight.

On 25 April 1978, the SA 330J became the first helicopter outside the Soviet Union to be certificated for all-weather operations, including flight in icing conditions. Equipment for this comprises thermal de-icing of the main rotor blades; thermal anti-icing of the tail rotor blades; special lengthened air intakes to ensure normal air supply into engines regardless of ambient conditions, including protection against sand and sea spray; and installation of weather radar.

A total of 652 Pumas and Super Pumas (described separately) had been sold by 1 March 1980. Nurtanio of Indonesia is to begin production of Pumas in the early 1980s.

TYPE: Medium-sized transport helicopter.

ROTOR SYSTEM: Four-blade main rotor, with a fully-articulated hub and integral rotor brake. The blade cuffs, equipped with horns, are connected by link-rods to the swashplate, which is actuated by three hydraulic twin-cylinder servo-control units. Each of the moulded blades is made up of a glassfibre roving spar, a composite glass and carbon fibre fabric skin, with Moltoprene/honeycomb filler. The leading-edge is covered with a stainless steel protective section. Attachment of the blades to their sleeve by means of two pins enables them to be folded back quickly by manual methods. The five-blade tail rotor has flapping hinges only, and is located on the starboard side of the tailboom.

ROTOR DRIVE: Mechanical shaft and gear drive. Main gearbox, mounted on top of cabin behind engines, has two separate inputs from the engines and five reduction stages. The first stage drives, from each engine, an intermediate shaft directly driving the alternator and the ventilation fan, and indirectly driving the two hydraulic pumps. At the second stage the action of the two units becomes synchronised on a single main driveshaft by means of freewheeling spur gears. If one or both engines are stopped, this enables the drive gears to be rotated by the remaining turbine or autorotating rotor, thus maintaining drive to the ancillary systems when the engines are stopped. Drive to the tail rotor is via shafting and an intermediate angle gearbox, terminating at a right-angle tail rotor gearbox. Turbine output 23,000 rpm, main rotor shaft 265 rpm. Tail rotor shaft 1,278 rpm. The hydraulically-controlled rotor brake, installed on the main gearbox, permits stopping of the rotor 15 s after engine shutdown.

FUSELAGE: Conventional all-metal semi-monocoque structure. Local use of titanium alloy under engine installation, which is outside the main fuselage shell. Monocoque tailboom supports the tail rotor on the starboard side and a horizontal stabiliser on the port side.

Aérospatiale SA 330J Puma (two Turboméca Turmo IVC turboshaft engines)

Aérospatiale SA 330 Puma transport helicopter *(Pilot Press)*

Height overall	5·14 m (16 ft 10½ in)
Height to top of rotor hub	4·38 m (14 ft 4½ in)
Width over wheel fairings	3·00 m (9 ft 10 in)
Wheel track	2·38 m (7 ft 10¾ in)
Wheelbase	4·045 m (13 ft 3 in)
Passenger cabin doors, each:	
Height	1·35 m (4 ft 5 in)
Width	1·35 m (4 ft 5 in)
Height to sill	1·00 m (3 ft 3¼ in)
Floor hatch, rear of cabin:	
Length	0·98 m (3 ft 2¾ in)
Width	0·70 m (2 ft 3½ in)
DIMENSIONS, INTERNAL:	
Cabin: Length	6·05 m (19 ft 10 in)
Max width	1·80 m (5 ft 10¾ in)
Max height	1·55 m (5 ft 1 in)
Floor area	7·80 m² (84 sq ft)
Usable volume	11·40 m³ (403 cu ft)
AREAS:	
Main rotor blades (each)	4·00 m² (43 sq ft)
Tail rotor blades (each)	0·28 m² (3·01 sq ft)
Main rotor disc	177·0 m² (1,905 sq ft)
Tail rotor disc	7·30 m² (78·6 sq ft)
Horizontal stabiliser	1·34 m² (14·4 sq ft)
WEIGHTS:	
Weight empty, standard aircraft:	
SA 330J	3,766 kg (8,303 lb)
SA 330L	3,615 kg (7,970 lb)
Max T-O and landing weight	7,400 kg (16,315 lb)*

*Certification for T-O weight of 7,500 kg (16,535 lb), *for cargo-sling mission only,* is anticipated

PERFORMANCE (SA 330J/L: A at 6,000 kg; 13,230 lb AUW, B at 7,400 kg; 16,315 lb AUW):

Never-exceed speed:	
A	158 knots (294 km/h; 182 mph)
B	142 knots (263 km/h; 163 mph)
Max cruising speed:	
A	146 knots (271 km/h; 168 mph)
B	139 knots (258 km/h; 160 mph)
Max rate of climb at S/L:	
A	552 m (1,810 ft)/min
B	366 m (1,200 ft)/min
Service ceiling (30 m; 100 ft/min rate of climb):	
A	6,000 m (19,680 ft)
B	4,800 m (15,750 ft)
Hovering ceiling IGE:	
A, ISA	4,400 m (14,435 ft)
A, ISA +20°C	3,700 m (12,135 ft)
B, ISA	2,300 m (7,545 ft)
B, ISA +20°C	1,600 m (5,250 ft)
Hovering ceiling OGE:	
A, ISA	4,250 m (13,940 ft)
A, ISA +20°C	3,600 m (11,810 ft)
B, ISA	1,700 m (5,575 ft)
B, ISA +20°C	1,050 m (3,445 ft)
Max range at normal cruising speed, no reserves:	
A	309 nm (572 km; 355 miles)
B	297 nm (550 km; 341 miles)

LANDING GEAR: Messier-Hispano-Bugatti semi-retractable tricycle type, with twin wheels on each unit. Main units retract upward hydraulically into fairings on sides of fuselage; self-centering nose unit retracts rearward. When landing gear is down, the nosewheel jack is extended and the main-wheel jacks are telescoped. Dual-chamber oleo-pneumatic shock-absorbers. All tyres same size (7·00-6), of Dunlop or Kléber-Colombes tubeless type, pressure 6·0 bars (85 lb/sq in) on all units. Hydraulic differential disc brakes, controlled by foot pedals. Lever-operated parking brake. Emergency pop-out flotation units can be mounted on rear landing gear fairings and forward fuselage.

POWER PLANT: Two Turboméca Turmo IVC turboshaft engines, each with max rating of 1,175 kW (1,575 shp) and fitted with intake anti-icing. Engines are mounted side by side above cabin forward of the main rotor assembly and separated by a firewall. They are coupled to the main rotor transmission box, with shaft drive to tail rotor, and form a completely independent system from the fuel tanks up to the main gearbox inputs. Fuel in four flexible tanks and one auxiliary tank beneath cargo compartment floor, with total capacity of 1,544 litres (339·5 Imp gallons). Provision for additional 1,900 litres (418 Imp gallons) in four auxiliary ferry tanks installed in cabin. External auxiliary tanks (two, each 350 litres; 77 Imp gallons capacity) are available. For long-range missions (mainly offshore) one or two special internal tanks (each 215 litres; 47·25 Imp gallons) can be fitted in the cabin. Each engine is supplied normally by a pair of interconnected primary tanks, the lower halves of which have self-sealing walls for protection against small-calibre projectiles. Refuelling point on starboard side of main cabin. Oil capacity 22 litres (4·8 Imp gallons) for engines, 25·5 litres (5·6 Imp gallons) for transmission.

ACCOMMODATION: Crew of one or two side by side on anti-crash seats on flight deck, with jump-seat for third crew member if required. Door on each side of flight deck on current versions. Internal doorway connects flight deck to cabin, with folding seat in doorway for an extra crew member or cargo supervisor. Dual controls standard. Accommodation in main cabin for 16 individually-equipped troops, six stretchers and six seated patients, or equivalent freight. The number of troops can be increased to 20 in the high-density version. Strengthened floor for cargo-carrying, with lashing points. Jettisonable sliding door on each side of main cabin; or port-side door with built-in steps and starboard-side double door in VIP or airline configurations. Removable panel on underside of fuselage, at rear of main cabin, permits longer loads to be accommodated and also serves as emergency exit on SA 330L version. Removable door with integral steps for access to baggage racks on SA 330J version. A hatch in the floor below the centreline of the main rotor is provided for carrying loads of up to 3,200 kg (7,055 lb) on an internally-mounted cargo sling. A fixed or retractable rescue hoist (capacity 275 kg; 606 lb) can be mounted externally on the starboard side of the fuselage. The cabin can be equipped in 8/9/12-seat VIP, 17-seat commuter or 20-seat high-density layouts, with baggage compartment and/or toilet facilities in rear of cabin. Cabin and flight deck are heated, ventilated and soundproofed. Demisting, de-icing, washers and wipers for pilots' windscreens.

SYSTEMS: Two independent hydraulic systems, each 172 bars (2,500 lb/sq in), supplied by self-regulating pumps driven by the main gearbox. Each system supplies one set of servo unit chambers, the left-hand system supplying in addition the autopilot, landing gear, rotor brake and wheel brakes. Freewheels in main gearbox ensure that both systems remain in operation, for supplying the servo-controls, if the engines are stopped in flight. Other hydraulically-actuated systems can be operated on the ground from the main gearbox, or by external power through the ground power receptacle. There is also an independent auxiliary system, fed through a handpump, which can be used in an emergency to lower the landing gear and pressurise the accumulator for the parking brake on the ground. Three-phase 200V AC electrical power supplied by two 15kVA 400Hz alternators, driven by the port side intermediate shaft from the main gearbox and available on the ground under the same conditions as the hydraulic ancillary systems. 28·5V 10kW DC power provided from the AC system by two transformer-rectifiers. Main aircraft battery used for self-starting and emergency power in flight. For the latter purpose, an emergency 400VA inverter can supply the essential navigation equipment from the battery, permitting at least 20 min continued flight in the event of a main power failure. De-icing of engines and engine air intakes by warm air bled from compressor. Anti-snow shield for Winter operations.

ELECTRONICS AND EQUIPMENT: Optional communications equipment includes VHF, UHF, tactical HF and HF/SSB radio installations and intercom system. Navigational equipment includes radio compass, radio altimeter, VLF Omega, Decca navigator and flight log, Doppler, and VOR/ILS with glidepath. Autopilot, with provision for coupling to self-contained navigation and microwave landing systems. Full IFR instrumentation available optionally. The search and rescue version has nose-mounted Bendix RDR 1400 or RCA Primus 40 or 50 search radar, Doppler, and Decca self-contained navigation system, including navigation computer, polar indicator, roller-map display, hover indicator, route mileage indicator and ground speed and drift indicator.

ARMAMENT (optional): A wide range of armament can be carried, including side-firing 20 mm cannon, axial-firing 7·62 mm machine-guns, missiles and rockets.

DIMENSIONS, EXTERNAL:

Diameter of main rotor	15·00 m (49 ft 2½ in)
Diameter of tail rotor	3·04 m (9 ft 11½ in)
Distance between rotor centres	9·20 m (30 ft 2¾ in)
Blade chord, main rotor	0·60 m (1 ft 11½ in)
Ground clearance of tail rotor	2·00 m (6 ft 6¾ in)
Length overall	18·15 m (59 ft 6½ in)
Length of fuselage	14·06 m (46 ft 1½ in)
Length, blades folded	14·80 m (48 ft 6¾ in)
Width, blades folded	3·50 m (11 ft 5¾ in)

AÉROSPATIALE AS 332 SUPER PUMA

Design of this derivative of the SA 330 Puma was started in 1974, and the programme received a formal 'go-ahead' from the French government in June 1975. As a first stage, Aérospatiale retrofitted a Puma airframe with two Turboméca Makila turboshaft engines and an uprated transmission. This experimental helicopter, designated AS 331, flew for the first time on 5 September 1977. It was followed, on 13 September 1978, by the first flight of the prototype AS 332 Super Puma, embodying more extensive changes to provide increased payload and performance, simplified maintenance, reduced cabin noise level, reduced vulnerability to hostile fire in combat areas, and

Aérospatiale AS 332B/C Super Puma (two Turboméca Makila turboshaft engines) *(Pilot Press)*

better crew survivability in a crash. Original plans to fit a 'fenestron' ducted tail rotor were dropped after evaluation of a 'fenestron' on the SA 330Z testbed (see 1976-77 *Jane's*, page 812) indicated no worthwhile performance gains.

Externally evident airframe changes compared with the SA 330 Puma include a lengthened nose; increased wheelbase and wheel track; a new landing gear with a single wheel on each of the main units, which offer an optional 'kneeling' capability to reduce overall dimensions for shipboard stowage; and an added ventral fin. The main and tail rotor blades have a new and more efficient profile.

There are four versions of the Super Puma:

AS 332B. Military version. Standard fuselage, seating 20 troops.

AS 332C. Civil version. Standard fuselage, seating 17 passengers.

AS 332L. As 332C, but with cabin lengthened by 0·76 m (2 ft 6 in) to provide four more seats and two additional windows. Fourth production Super Puma, to this standard, was scheduled to fly in September 1980.

AS 332M. As 332B, but with cabin lengthened by 0·76 m (2 ft 6 in) to provide four more seats and two additional windows.

All variants will offer all-weather flight capability, including operation in forecast icing conditions.

DGAC and FAA certification of the Super Puma was planned for late 1980, with deliveries beginning in 1981 (AS 332B/C) or 1982 (AS 332L/M). To facilitate integration of the aircraft into existing fleets of Pumas (notably in French Army service), Aérospatiale hopes to launch a programme under which SA 330 Pumas will be retrofitted with the engines, some dynamic components and the composite-blade tail rotor of the Super Puma.

TYPE: Twin-turbine multi-role helicopter.

ROTOR SYSTEM: Four-blade main rotor, with a fully-articulated hub and integral rotor brake. Each drag hinge is fitted with an elastomeric frequency adaptor. The blade cuffs, equipped with horns, are connected by link-rods to the swashplate, which is actuated by three hydraulic twin-cylinder servo-control units. Each of the moulded blades is made up of a glassfibre roving spar and a composite glass and carbon fibre fabric skin, with Moltoprene filler. The leading-edge is covered with a titanium protective section. Attachment of the blades to their sleeve by means of two pins enables them to be folded back quickly by manual methods. The five-blade tail rotor has flapping hinges only, and is located on the starboard side of the tailboom. The rotors may be equipped with a de-icing system similar to that certificated for the Puma.

ROTOR DRIVE: Mechanical shaft and gear drive. Modular main gearbox is fitted with two torquemeters and has two separate lubrication circuits. It is mounted on top of the cabin behind the engines, has two separate inputs from the engines and five reduction stages. The first stage drives, from each engine, an intermediate shaft directly driving the alternator and indirectly driving the two hydraulic pumps, with a further shaft drive to the ventilation fan. At the second stage the action of the two units becomes synchronised on a single main driveshaft by means of freewheeling spur gears. If one or both engines are stopped, this enables the drive gears to be rotated by the remaining turbine or the autorotating rotor, thus maintaining drive to the ancillary systems when the engines are stopped. Drive to the tail rotor is via shafting and an intermediate angle gearbox, terminating at a right-angle tail rotor gearbox. Turbine output 23,840 rpm, main rotor shaft 265 rpm. Tail rotor shaft 1,278 rpm. The hydraulically-controlled rotor brake, installed on the main gearbox, permits stopping of the rotor 15 s after engine shutdown.

FUSELAGE: Conventional all-metal semi-monocoque structure, embodying anti-crash features. Local use of titanium alloy under engine installation, which is outside the main fuselage shell. Monocoque tailboom supports the tail rotor on the starboard side and a horizontal stabiliser with fixed leading-edge slat on the port side. Optional folding tailboom for aircraft that will serve on ships such as frigates.

LANDING GEAR: Retractable tricycle type, of Messier-Hispano-Bugatti high energy-absorbing design. All units retract rearward hydraulically, main wheels into fairings on sides of fuselage. Dual-chamber oleo-pneumatic shock-absorbers. Optional 'kneeling' capability for main units. Twin-wheel self-centering nose unit, tyre size 466 × 176, pressure 6.0 bars (85 lb/sq in). Single wheel on each main unit with tyre size 615 × 225-10, pressure 6.0 bars (85 lb/sq in). Hydraulic differential disc brakes, controlled by foot pedals. Lever-operated parking brake. Emergency pop-out flotation units can be mounted on main landing gear fairings and forward fuselage.

POWER PLANT: Two Turboméca Makila IA turboshaft engines, each with max rating of 1,309 kW (1,755 shp). Air intakes protected by a grille against ingestion of ice, snow and foreign objects; but multi-purpose intake is necessary for flight into sandy areas. Standard versions have five flexible fuel tanks under cabin floor, with total capacity of 1,544 litres (339·5 Imp gallons). Stretched versions have a basic fuel system of six flexible tanks

with total capacity of 2,044 litres (450 Imp gallons). Provision for additional 1,900 litres (418 Imp gallons) in four auxiliary ferry tanks installed in cabin. Two external auxiliary tanks are available, with total capacity of 700 litres (154 Imp gallons). For long-range missions (mainly offshore), a special internal tank, capacity 600 litres (132 Imp gallons), and an auxiliary tank, capacity 330 litres (72·5 Imp gallons) are available; latter fits in cargo-sling well beneath cabin floor and is quickly removable to permit use of sling. Refuelling point on starboard side of cabin. Fuel system is designed to avoid fuel leakage following a crash, with flexible fuel lines and interconnections between tanks, self-sealing valves and automatic fuel pump shutdown in a crash. Options include a fuel dumping system, pressure refuelling, and crash-resistant tanks.

ACCOMMODATION: One pilot (VFR) or two pilots side by side (IFR) on flight deck, with jump-seat for third crew member or paratroop dispatcher. Door on each side of flight deck and internal doorway connecting flight deck to cabin. Dual controls, co-pilot instrumentation and anti-crash flight deck floor. AS 332B/C accommodate in main cabin up to 20 troops in normal seating, 16 troops in anti-crash seats, six stretchers and six seated casualties/attendants, 17 civilian passengers, or eight, nine or twelve VIP passengers in special interiors with toilet and galley. AS 332L/M accommodate in main cabin up to 24 troops in normal seating, 18 troops in anti-crash seats, nine stretchers and three seated casualties/attendants, 21 civilian passengers, or nine, ten or 15 VIP passengers with toilet and galley. Strengthened floor for cargo carrying, with lashing points. Jettisonable sliding door on each side of main cabin; or port side door with built-in steps and starboard-side double door in VIP or airline configurations. Removable panel on underside of fuselage, at rear of main cabin, permits longer loads to be accommodated, and also serves as emergency exit. Removable door with integral steps for access to baggage racks optional. A hatch in the floor below the centreline of the main rotor is provided for carrying loads of up to 4,000 kg (8,818 lb) on an internally-mounted cargo sling. A fixed or retractable rescue hoist (capacity 275 kg; 606 lb) can be mounted externally on the starboard side of the fuselage. Cabin and flight deck are heated, ventilated and soundproofed. Demisting, de-icing, washers and wipers for pilots' windscreens.

SYSTEMS: Two independent hydraulic systems, supplied by self-regulating pumps driven by the main gearbox. Each system supplies one set of servo unit chambers, the left-hand system supplying in addition the autopilot, landing gear, rotor brake and wheel brakes. Freewheels in main gearbox ensure that both systems remain in operation, for supplying the servo-controls, if the engines are stopped in flight. Other hydraulically-actuated systems can be operated on the ground from the main gearbox (when a special disconnect system is installed to permit running of port engine with rotors stationary), or by external power through the ground power receptacle. There is also an independent auxiliary system, fed through a hand pump, which can be used in an emergency to lower the landing gear. Three-phase 200V AC electrical power supplied by two 20kVA 400Hz alternators, driven by the port side intermediate shaft from the main gearbox and available on the ground under the same conditions as the hydraulic ancillary systems. 28·5V DC power provided from the AC system by two transformer-rectifiers. Main aircraft battery used for self-starting and emergency power in flight.

AVIONICS AND EQUIPMENT: Optional communications equipment includes VHF, UHF, tactical HF and HF/SSB radio installations and intercom system. Navigational equipment includes radio compass, radio altimeter, VLF Omega, Decca navigator and flight log, Doppler, and VOR/ILS with glidepath. Autopilot, with provision for coupling to self-contained navigation and microwave landing systems. Full IFR instrumentation

Aérospatiale AS 332C Super Puma twin-turbine multi-role helicopter

available optionally. The search and rescue version has nose-mounted Bendix RDR 1400 or RCA Primus 40 or 50 search radar, Doppler, and Crouzet Nadir or Decca self-contained navigation system, including navigation computer, polar indicator, roller-map display, hover indicator, route mileage indicator and ground speed and drift indicator. For naval ASW and ASV missions, aircraft can be fitted with nose-mounted OMERA type ORB 32 ASD 360° radar, linked to a tactical table.

ARMAMENT AND OPERATIONAL EQUIPMENT (optional): Typical alternatives for army/air force missions are one 20 mm gun, two 7·62 mm machine-guns, or two pods each containing twenty-two 68 mm rockets or nineteen 2·75 in rockets. Armament for naval missions includes two Exocet missiles, or two torpedoes and sonar, or MAD and sonobuoys.

DIMENSIONS, EXTERNAL:

Diameter of main rotor	15·00 m (49 ft 2½ in)
Diameter of tail rotor	3·04 m (9 ft 11½ in)
Blade chord, main rotor	0·60 m (1 ft 11½ in)
Length overall: standard	18·46 m (60 ft 6¾ in)
Length of fuselage: standard	14·76 m (48 ft 5 in)
stretched	15·52 m (50 ft 11 in)
Length, blades folded: standard	15·60 m (51 ft 2 in)
stretched	16·36 m (53 ft 8 in)
Length, blades and tail pylon folded:	
standard	12·64 m (41 ft 5½ in)
stretched	13·40 m (43 ft 11½ in)
Width, blades folded	3·90 m (12 ft 9½ in)
Height overall	4·92 m (16 ft 1¾ in)
Height to top of rotor hub	4·48 m (14 ft 8½ in)
Width over wheel fairings	3·90 m (12 ft 9½ in)
Wheel track	3·00 m (9 ft 10 in)
Wheelbase	4·49 m (14 ft 8¾ in)
Passenger cabin doors, each:	
Height	1·35 m (4 ft 5 in)
Width	1·35 m (4 ft 5 in)
Floor hatch, rear of cabin:	
Length	0·98 m (3 ft 2¾ in)
Width	0·70 m (2 ft 3½ in)

DIMENSIONS, INTERNAL:

Cabin: Length: standard	6·05 m (19 ft 10½ in)
stretched	6·81 m (22 ft 4 in)
Max width	1·80 m (5 ft 11 in)
Max height	1·55 m (5 ft 1 in)
Floor area: standard	7·80 m² (84 sq ft)
Usable volume: standard	11·40 m³ (403 cu ft)
stretched	13·30 m³ (469·5 cu ft)

WEIGHTS:

Weight empty:	
AS 332B	3,850 kg (8,488 lb)
AS 332C	3,920 kg (8,642 lb)
AS 332L	4,010 kg (8,840 lb)
AS 332M	3,940 kg (8,686 lb)
Max T-O weight	7,800 kg (17,196 lb)

PERFORMANCE (Basic version, at max T-O weight):

Max cruising speed at S/L	157 knots (291 km/h; 181 mph)
Econ cruising speed at S/L	140 knots (260 km/h; 161 mph)
Max rate of climb at S/L	582 m (1,910 ft)/min
Service ceiling, one engine out	2,300 m (7,550 ft)
Hovering ceiling OGE: ISA	2,300 m (7,550 ft)
ISA + 20° C	1,600 m (5,250 ft)

Range at S/L, no reserves:

standard tanks	337 nm (625 km; 388 miles)
with external (2 × 350 litre) and auxiliary (330 litre) tanks	566 nm (1,050 km; 652 miles)
with external, auxiliary and cabin (600 litre) tanks	712 nm (1,320 km; 820 miles)
with external and four ferry tanks	928 nm (1,720 km; 1,068 miles)

Max endurance at S/L, no reserves:

standard tanks	3 h 20 min
with external and auxiliary tanks	5 h 35 min
with external, auxiliary and 600 litre cabin tanks	6 h 55 min

AÉROSPATIALE SA 341/342 GAZELLE

The first prototype of this five-seat lightweight helicopter (designated SA 340) made its first flight on 7 April 1967, powered by an Astazou III engine. It was followed by a second prototype on 12 April 1968 and then by four pre-production SA 341 Gazelles.

The first production SA 341 Gazelle flew for the first time on 6 August 1971, with a longer cabin than its predecessors, enlarged tail unit, additional door on the starboard side at rear (optional on production aircraft) and uprated Astazou IIIA engine.

Details of early versions of the Gazelle can be found in the 1979-80 *Jane's*. Versions being marketed by Aérospatiale in 1980 were as follows:

SA 341G. Civil version, with Astazou IIIA engine. Certificated by SGAC on 7 June 1972 and by the FAA on 18 September 1972. In January 1975, it was announced that the SA 341G had become the first helicopter in the world authorised to be flown by a single pilot under IFR Cat I conditions. It is now certificated for IFR Cat II operation, with a ceiling of 30 m (100 ft) and 365 m (1,200 ft) forward visibility. Equipment fitted to the aircraft which qualified for this FAA certification comprised a Sperry flight director coupled to SFENA servo-dampers. A variant, known as the **Stretched Gazelle**, has the rear portion of the cabin modified to provide an additional 20 cm (8 in) of legroom for the rear-seat passengers.

SA 342J. Similar to SA 342L, for commercial operators. Higher max T-O weight. Improved 'fenestron' tail rotor. Certificated by DGAC on 27 April 1976. Deliveries began in 1977.

SA 342L. Military counterpart of SA 342J, with improved 'fenestron' tail rotor.

SA 342M. For ALAT (French Army Light Aviation Corps). Differs from SA 342L in having an ALAT instrument panel and 640 kW (859 shp) Astazou XIVM turboshaft with automatic startup and high-energy ignition. Optional equipment specified by ALAT includes SFIM PA 85G autopilot, Crouzet Nadir self-contained navigation system, Decca 80 Doppler, infra-red homing, exhaust deflector, and night flying equipment. Order for first increment of planned total of about 120 announced in December 1978, each armed with four Hot missiles and gyro-stabilised sight for anti-tank warfare. Delivery to ALAT began on 9 June 1980.

A two-stretcher ambulance configuration has received FAA Standard Type Certification. No major modification is necessary to convert the aircraft to carry two patients longitudinally on the port side of the cabin, one above the other, leaving room for the pilot and a medical attendant in tandem on the starboard side. The dual spine board arrangement weighs 27 kg (60 lb) and stows into the baggage compartment when not in use.

Under an Anglo-French agreement signed in 1967, Gazelles are produced jointly with Westland Helicopters Ltd, and are also built under licence in Yugoslavia. A total of 846 had been sold by 1 March 1980.

Three Class E1c records were set by the SA 341-01 at Istres on 13 and 14 May 1971. These were: 167·28 knots (310·00 km/h; 192·62 mph) in a straight line over a 3 km course; 168·36 knots (312·00 km/h; 193·87 mph) in a straight line over a 15/25 km course; and 159·72 knots (296·00 km/h; 183·93 mph) over a 100 km closed circuit.

The following details apply to the SA 341, except where indicated:

TYPE: Five-seat light utility helicopter.

Aérospatiale SA 342M Gazelle, armed with four Hot missile launchers

ROTOR SYSTEM: Three-blade semi-articulated main rotor and 13-blade shrouded-fan anti-torque tail rotor (known as a 'fenestron' or 'fan-in-fin'). Rotor head and rotor mast form a single unit. The main rotor blades are of NACA 0012 section, attached to NAT hub by flapping hinges. There are no drag hinges. Each blade has a single leading-edge spar of plastics material reinforced with glassfibre, a laminated glass-fabric skin and honeycomb filler. Tail rotor blades are of die-forged light alloy, with articulation for pitch change only. Main rotor blades can be folded manually for stowage. Rotor brake standard.

ROTOR DRIVE: Main reduction gearbox forward of engine, which is mounted above the rear part of the cabin. Intermediate gearbox beneath engine, rear gearbox supporting the tail rotor. Main rotor/engine rpm ratio 378·3 : 6,179. Tail rotor/engine rpm ratio 5,774 : 6,179.

FUSELAGE: Cockpit structure is based on a welded light alloy frame which carries the windows and doors. This is mounted on a conventional semi-monocoque lower structure consisting of two longitudinal box sections connected by frames and bulkheads. Central section, which encloses the baggage hold and fuel tank and supports the main reduction gearbox, is constructed of light alloy honeycomb sandwich panels. Rear section, which supports the engine and tailboom, is of similar construction. Honeycomb sandwich panels are also used for the cabin floors and transmission platform. Tailboom is of conventional sheet metal construction, as are the horizontal tail surfaces and the tail fin.

TAIL UNIT: Small horizontal stabiliser on tailboom, ahead of tail rotor fin.

LANDING GEAR: Steel tube skid type. Wheel can be fitted at rear of each skid for ground handling. Provision for alternative float or ski landing gear.

POWER PLANT: One Turboméca Astazou IIIA turboshaft, installed above fuselage aft of cabin and delivering 440 kW (590 shp) for take-off (max continuous rating also 440 kW; 590 shp). Main fuel tank in fuselage, usable capacity 445 litres (98 Imp gallons). Provision for 90 litre (19·8 Imp gallon) auxiliary tank beneath baggage compartment and/or 200 litre (44 Imp gallon) ferry tank inside rear cabin. Total possible usable fuel capacity 735 litres (161 Imp gallons). Refuelling point on starboard side of cabin. Oil capacity 13 litres (2·8 Imp gallons) for engine, 3·5 litres (0·77 Imp gallons) for gearbox.

ACCOMMODATION: Crew of one or two on side-by-side seats in front of cabin, with bench seat to the rear for a further three persons. The bench seat can be folded into floor wells to leave a completely flat cargo floor. Access to baggage compartment via rear cabin bulkhead, or via optional door on starboard side. Cargo tiedown points in cabin floor. Forward-opening car-type door on each side of cabin, immediately behind are rearward-opening auxiliary cargo loading doors. Baggage compartment at rear of cabin. Ventilation standard. Dual controls optional.

SYSTEMS: Hydraulic system, pressure 40 bars (570 lb/sq in), serves three pitch change jacks for main rotor head and one for tail rotor. 28V DC electrical system supplied by 4kW engine-driven generator and 40Ah battery. Optional 26V AC system, supplied by 0·5kVA alternator at 115/200V 400Hz.

ELECTRONICS AND EQUIPMENT: Optional communications equipment includes UHF, VHF, HF, intercom systems and homing aids. Optional navigation equipment includes radio compass, radio altimeter and VOR. Blind-flying instrumentation optional. A variety of operational equipment can be fitted, according to role, including a 700 kg (1,540 lb) cargo sling, 135 kg (300 lb) rescue hoist, one or two stretchers (internally), or photographic and survey equipment.

ARMAMENT (SA 342): Military loads can include two pods of Matra or Brandt 2·75 in or 68 mm rockets, four AS.11 or two AS.12 wire-guided missiles with APX-Bézu 334 gyro-stabilised sight, four or six Hot wire-guided missiles with APX 397 gyro-stabilised sight, two forward-firing 7·62 mm machine-guns, reconnaissance flares or smoke markers.

DIMENSIONS, EXTERNAL:

Diameter of main rotor	10·50 m (34 ft 5½ in)
Diameter of tail rotor	0·695 m (2 ft 3⅜ in)
Distance between rotor centres	5·85 m (19 ft 2¼ in)
Main rotor blade chord (constant)	0·30 m (11·8 in)
Length overall	11·97 m (39 ft 3⁵/₁₆ in)
Length of fuselage	9·53 m (31 ft 3³/₁₆ in)
Width, rotors folded	2·015 m (6 ft 7⁵/₁₆ in)
Height to top of rotor hub	2·72 m (8 ft 11⅛ in)
Height overall	3·15 m (10 ft 2⅝ in)
Skid track	2·015 m (6 ft 7⁵/₁₆ in)
Main cabin doors, each:	
Height	1·05 m (3 ft 4⁹/₁₆ in)
Width	1·00 m (3 ft 3¼ in)
Height to sill	0·63 m (2 ft 0¾ in)
Auxiliary cabin doors, each:	
Height	1·05 m (3 ft 4⁹/₁₆ in)
Width	0·48 m (1 ft 6¾ in)
Height to sill	0·63 m (2 ft 0¾ in)

Aérospatiale SA 341 Gazelle five-seat light utility helicopter *(Pilot Press)*

DIMENSIONS, INTERNAL:

Cabin: Length	2·20 m (7 ft 2⁹⁄₁₆ in)
Max width	1·32 m (4 ft 4 in)
Max height	1·21 m (3 ft 11⅝ in)
Floor area	1·50 m² (16·1 sq ft)
Volume	1·80 m³ (63·7 cu ft)
Baggage hold volume	0·45 m³ (15·9 cu ft)

AREAS:

Main rotor blades, each	1·57 m² (16·9 sq ft)
Tail rotor blades, each	0·007 m² (0·075 sq ft)
Main rotor disc	86·5 m² (931 sq ft)
Tail rotor disc	0·37 m² (3·98 sq ft)
Fin	0·45 m² (4·84 sq ft)
Tailplane	1·80 m² (19·4 sq ft)

WEIGHTS AND LOADING:

Weight empty:	
341G	917 kg (2,022 lb)
342	955 kg (2,105 lb)
Max T-O and landing weight:	
341G	1,800 kg (3,970 lb)
342J	1,900 kg (4,190 lb)
Max disc loading:	
341G	19·5 kg/m² (4 lb/sq ft)

PERFORMANCE (at max T-O weight):

Never-exceed speed at S/L:	
SA 341, 342	167 knots (310 km/h; 193 mph)
Max cruising speed at S/L:	
SA 341, 342	142 knots (264 km/h; 164 mph)
Econ cruising speed at S/L:	
SA 341	126 knots (233 km/h; 144 mph)
SA 342	128 knots (238 km/h; 148 mph)
Max rate of climb at S/L:	
SA 341	540 m (1,770 ft)/min
SA 342	612 m (2,010 ft)/min
Service ceiling:	
SA 341	5,000 m (16,400 ft)
SA 342	4,300 m (14,100 ft)
Hovering ceiling IGE:	
SA 341	2,850 m (9,350 ft)
SA 342	3,650 m (11,970 ft)
Hovering ceiling OGE:	
SA 341	2,000 m (6,560 ft)
SA 342	2,875 m (9,430 ft)
Range at S/L with max fuel:	
SA 341	361 nm (670 km; 416 miles)
Range with max fuel, econ cruising speed, no reserves:	
SA 342	407 nm (755 km; 469 miles)
Range with pilot and 500 kg (1,102 lb) payload:	
SA 341	193·5 nm (360 km; 223 miles)

AÉROSPATIALE AS 350 ECUREUIL/ASTAR

Intended as a successor to the Alouette, the AS 350 Ecureuil (Squirrel) was designed with an emphasis on low operating and maintenance costs, and low noise and vibration levels. It embodies Aérospatiale's Starflex type of main rotor hub, made of glassfibre, with elastomeric spherical stops and oleo-elastic frequency matchers.

The decision to build prototypes of the Ecureuil was taken in April 1973. The first of these (F-WVKH) flew on 27 June 1974, powered by an Avco Lycoming LTS 101 turboshaft engine. It was followed on 14 February 1975 by a second prototype (F-WVKI) with a Turboméca Arriel turboshaft.

The Avco Lycoming-powered version is marketed only in North America, as the **Astar**, and the Arriel-powered **AS 350B Ecureuil** throughout the rest of the world. French certification of the AS 350B was obtained on 27 October 1977 and deliveries began in March 1978. FAA certification of the original **AS 350C** Astar was obtained on 21 December 1977 and the first production delivery was made in April 1978. The AS 350C was superseded in 1978 by the **AS 350D** with a more powerful version of the Avco Lycoming engine. By 1 March 1980 a total of 562 Ecureuils and Astars had been sold. Production was intended to build up to 7 Ecureuils and 16 Astars per month by February 1980.

TYPE: Six-seat light general-purpose helicopter.

ROTOR SYSTEM: Three-blade main rotor, with Starflex glassfibre hub in which the three conventional hinges for each blade are replaced by a single ball-joint of rubber/steel sandwich construction, requiring no maintenance. Glassfibre blades, with stainless steel leading-edge sheath, produced by an entirely mechanised process. Symmetrical blade section. Two-blade tail rotor; each blade comprises a sheet metal skin around a glassfibre spar, the flexibility of which obviates the need for hinges.

ROTOR DRIVE: Simplified transmission, with single epicyclic main gear train. By comparison with Alouette II, number of gear wheels is reduced from 22 to 9 and number of bearings from 23 to 9. Tail rotor drive-shaft coupling on engine.

FUSELAGE: Basic structure of light alloy pressings, with skin mainly of thermoformed plastics, including baggage compartment doors.

TAIL UNIT: Horizontal stabiliser, of inverted aerofoil section, mid-mounted on tailboom. Sweptback fin, in two sections above and below tailboom.

LANDING GEAR: Steel tube skid type. Emergency flotation gear optional.

POWER PLANT: One 478 kW (641 shp) Turboméca Arriel (AS 350B) or 459 kW (616 shp) Avco Lycoming LTS 101-600A.2 (AS 350D) turboshaft engine, mounted above fuselage to rear of cabin. Plastics fuel tanks with total capacity of 530 litres (116·5 Imp gallons).

ACCOMMODATION: Two individual bucket seats at front of cabin and two two-place bench seats are standard. In the alternative layout the two benches are replaced by three armchair seats. Large forward-hinged door on each side. Optional sliding door at rear of cabin on port side. Baggage compartment aft of cabin, with full-width upward-hinged door on starboard side. Top of baggage compartment reinforced to provide platform on each side for inspecting and servicing rotor head.

SYSTEMS: Hydraulic system includes four single-body servo units, operating at 40 bars (570 lb/sq in) pressure, and accumulators to protect against a hydraulic power supply failure. Electrical system includes a 4·5kW engine-driven starter/generator, a 16Ah 24V nickel-cadmium battery and a ground power receptacle connected to the bus bar which distributes power to the electrical equipment. Cabin air-conditioning system optional.

AVIONICS AND EQUIPMENT: Optional com/nav radio equipment includes VHF/AM, ICS, VOR/LOC/glideslope, marker beacon indicator, radio compass, HF/SSB, transponder and DME. IFR instrumentation optional. Available equipment includes a SFIM PA 85E autopilot, 750 kg (1,650 lb) cargo sling, a 900 kg (1,984 lb) sling associated with a max T-O weight of 2,100 kg (4,630 lb), and a 135 kg (297 lb) electrical hoist.

DIMENSIONS, EXTERNAL:

Diameter of main rotor	10·69 m (35 ft 0¾ in)
Main rotor blade chord	300 mm (11·8 in)
Diameter of tail rotor	1·86 m (6 ft 1¼ in)
Length overall	13·00 m (42 ft 8 in)
Length of fuselage	10·91 m (35 ft 9½ in)
Width of fuselage	1·80 m (5 ft 10¾ in)
Height overall	3·08 m (10 ft 1¼ in)
Wheel track	2·10 m (6 ft 10¾ in)
Cabin doors (standard, each):	
Height	1·15 m (3 ft 9¼ in)
Width	1·10 m (3 ft 7¼ in)

DIMENSIONS, INTERNAL:

Cabin: Length	2·42 m (7 ft 11¼ in)
Width at rear	1·65 m (5 ft 5 in)
Height	1·35 m (4 ft 5 in)
Baggage compartment volume	1·00 m³ (35·31 cu ft)

WEIGHTS:

Weight empty: AS 350B	1,045 kg (2,304 lb)
AS 350D	1,070 kg (2,359 lb)
Max T-O weight: normal	1,950 kg (4,300 lb)
with max slung load	2,100 kg (4,630 lb)

PERFORMANCE (at T-O weight of 1,950 kg; 4,300 lb):

Never-exceed speed below 500 m (1,640 ft):	
Both versions	147 knots (272 km/h; 169 mph)
Max cruising speed:	
AS 350B	125 knots (232 km/h; 144 mph)
AS 350D	124 knots (230 km/h; 143 mph)
Max rate of climb at S/L:	
Both versions	492 m (1,615 ft)/min
Service ceiling:	
AS 350B	4,875 m (16,000 ft)
AS 350D	4,575 m (15,000 ft)
Hovering ceiling IGE:	
AS 350B	3,000 m (9,840 ft)
AS 350D	2,500 m (8,200 ft)
Hovering ceiling OGE:	
AS 350B	2,250 m (7,380 ft)
AS 350D	1,800 m (5,900 ft)
Range with max fuel at S/L, no reserves:	
AS 350B	383 nm (710 km; 441 miles)
AS 350D	410 nm (760 km; 472 miles)

AÉROSPATIALE AS 355 ECUREUIL 2/TWINSTAR

The AS 355 represents a twin-engined addition to the AS 350 Ecureuil/Astar family. Many components, such as the main rotor mast and head, tail rotor hub, servo units, cabin and landing gear, are identical to those of the AS 350. Major changes apply to the main rotor blades, power plant, transmission, fuel system and fuselage structure.

Development of the basic **AS 355E** began in mid-1978. Construction of the first of two prototypes (F-WZLA) started at the beginning of 1979, and this aircraft flew for the first time on 27 September 1979, followed by the second prototype on 14 November. Each was fitted with rotor blades identical to those of the AS 350, and the helicopter entered production in this form. The first production AS 355E flew on 11 March 1980. It was planned to progress to an **AS 355F** version after delivery of about 250 aircraft, to introduce improved main rotor blades of increased chord and OA 209 section, twin-body servo-command units, and two electrical generators. In fact, the AS 355F will now be the standard production model from the start, permitting an increase in max T-O weight and payload. DGAC certification for IFR operation is

Aérospatiale AS 350B Ecureuil (Turboméca Arriel turboshaft engine)

Aérospatiale AS 350 Ecureuil six-seat light helicopter (*Pilot Press*)

Twin-engined Aérospatiale AS 355E Ecureuil 2/Twinstar *(Pilot Press)*

Aérospatiale AS 355E Ecureuil 2/Twinstar twin-turbine five/six-seat light helicopter

expected during 1981. DGAC certification for VFR operation was expected by October 1980, followed by FAA certification two months later. This helicopter is intended primarily for the civil market, in particular for use by companies working in the oil industry. By 1 March 1980, sales totalled 217. The version for the North American market is known as the **Twinstar**; aircraft marketed elsewhere are named **Ecureuil 2**.

TYPE: Twin-turbine light general-purpose helicopter.

ROTOR SYSTEM: As for AS 350B, except that main rotor blades of AS 355F have increased chord and OA 209 section.

ROTOR DRIVE: Single main gearbox, made up of three modules (coupling gearbox with freewheel, angle gearing with spiral-bevel gears, and epicyclic gear train including five oscillating planetary gears). Power take-offs for the accessories and tail rotor.

FUSELAGE: Light alloy centre-fuselage structure, with deep-drawn sheet-metal forms of simple geometric design. Cabin skin of thermoformed plastics. Tapered tailboom of light alloy sheet wrapped and riveted around deep-drawn sheet metal cylindrical frames.

TAIL UNIT AND LANDING GEAR: As for AS 350B.

POWER PLANT: Two Allison 250-C20F turboshaft engines, each rated at 313 kW (420 shp) for take-off, mounted above fuselage to rear of cabin. Two structural fuel tanks, with total usable capacity of 720 litres (158 Imp gallons), in body structure.

ACCOMMODATION: As for AS 350B, except sliding doors are optional on both sides, and there are three baggage holds with external doors.

SYSTEMS, AVIONICS AND EQUIPMENT: As for AS 350B, except that twin-body servo-command units and a second electrical generator are standard on AS 355F. Options include a second VHF/AM, radio altimeter, autopilot and casualty installations.

DIMENSIONS, EXTERNAL AND INTERNAL:
As for AS 350B, except:
Main rotor blade chord: AS 355F 350 mm (13·8 in)

WEIGHTS:
Weight empty: AS 355E   1,230 kg (2,712 lb)
Max T-O weight: AS 355E   2,100 kg (4,630 lb)
  AS 355F   2,300 kg (5,070 lb)

PERFORMANCE (at max T-O weight, ISA):
Never-exceed speed (structural limitation):
  AS 355E/F   147 knots (272 km/h; 169 mph)
Max cruising speed at S/L:
  AS 355E   129 knots (240 km/h; 149 mph)
  AS 355F   124 knots (230 km/h; 143 mph)
Econ cruising speed at S/L:
  AS 355E/F   119 knots (220 km/h; 137 mph)

Cruising speed at max power, one engine out:
  AS 355E   97 knots (180 km/h; 112 mph)
  AS 355F   94 knots (175 km/h; 108 mph)
Max rate of climb at S/L:
  AS 355E   522 m (1,710 ft)/min
Service ceiling: AS 355E   4,000 m (13,125 ft)
  AS 355F   3,100 m (10,170 ft)
Service ceiling, one engine out:
  AS 355E   2,450 m (8,030 ft)
Hovering ceiling IGE: AS 355E 2,200 m (7,215 ft)
Hovering ceiling OGE: AS 355E 1,500 m (4,920 ft)
Range with max fuel at S/L, no reserves:
  AS 355E   459 nm (850 km; 528 miles)
  AS 355F   453 nm (840 km; 522 miles)
Range with six occupants, each 80 kg (176 lb):
  AS 355E   200 nm (370 km; 230 miles)

AÉROSPATIALE SA 360C DAUPHIN

The SA 360 Dauphin was developed, with the twin-engined SA 365 variant (described separately), as a replacement for the Alouette III. The first of two SA 360 prototypes (F-WSQL) flew for the first time on 2 June

1972, powered by a 730 kW (980 shp) Turboméca Astazou XVI turboshaft engine. After 180 flights, it was re-engined with an Astazou XVIIIA turboshaft and modified in certain respects, including the addition of small weights to the rotor blades, to eliminate ground resonance and reduce vibration to an unprecedented level, even at high speed. The aircraft flew for the first time in its modified form on 4 May 1973, having been joined by the second prototype (F-WSQX) on 29 January 1973.

DGAC certification of the basic SA 360C was awarded on 18 December 1975, followed by FAA certification on 31 March 1976. By 1 March 1980, Aérospatiale had received orders for a total of 124 SA 360C and SA 365 helicopters, including a first increment of 23 AS 365Ns, out of 90 required by the US Coast Guard.

Three helicopter speed records in Class E1d (1,750 to 3,000 kg weight) were set at Istres by the first prototype of the SA 360 on 15, 16 and 17 May 1973, piloted by Roland Coffignot. Carrying a payload equivalent to eight persons and fuel for one hour's flying, the SA 360 achieved, successively, 161·4 knots (299 km/h; 185·8 mph) over a 100 km closed circuit; 168·4 knots (312 km/h; 193·9 mph) over a 3 km course; and 163·5 knots (303 km/h; 188·3 mph) over a 15 km course.

TYPE: Turbine-powered general-purpose helicopter.

ROTOR SYSTEM: Four-blade semi-articulated main rotor and 13-blade shrouded-fan anti-torque tail rotor (known as a 'fenestron' or 'fan-in-fin'). Main rotor blades are of symmetrical NACA 0012 section, with a theoretical twist of 8° and constant chord, and are attached to the NAT hub via flapping hinges. There are no drag hinges. Each blade has a single leading-edge spar of polyester plastics, extending back to about 30% chord at top and bottom. The outer skin is of glassfibre, with an inner skin of carbon fibre, and the entire blade is filled with Nomex honeycomb. The leading-edge is formed by a layer of Vulkollan plastics with an outer protective shield of thin-gauge stainless steel. Tail rotor blades are of die-forged light alloy, with articulation for pitch change only. Main rotor blades can be folded manually for stowage. Rotor brake and main rotor blade de-icing optional.

ROTOR DRIVE: Main reduction gearbox forward of engine, which is mounted above the fuselage to the rear of the cabin. Output shaft enters main transmission box above the driveshaft to the tail rotor. Self-lubricating bearings. Main rotor rpm: 348 normal; 393 in autorotation. Tail rotor rpm: 4,700.

FUSELAGE: Conventional all-metal assembly of cabin and semi-monocoque tailboom. Cabin built on a strong box structure embodying two transverse frames and the cabin floor.

TAIL UNIT: Horizontal stabiliser mid-set on tailboom, forward of shrouded tail rotor, with endplate fins. Tailboom terminates in large fin of unsymmetrical section, housing the tail rotor. The section of this fin is such that in cruising flight it counters the torque of the main rotor; the tail rotor is thus required to provide only yaw control, with minimal variation of pitch, requiring only small power intake.

LANDING GEAR: Steel tube skid type, or ERAM non-retractable tailwheel-type landing gear, with single wheel on each unit. Main legs of wheel gear embody hydraulic shock-absorbers. Tailwheel carried on anti-shimmy leg which can be locked manually in central position. Dunlop main-wheel tyres size 355 × 150-4, pressure 5 bars (73 lb/sq in). Dunlop tailwheel tyre size 260 × 80-4, pressure 5 bars (73 lb/sq in). Disc brakes on main wheels. Wheel fairings standard. Provision for emergency flotation gear, and skis.

Aérospatiale SA 360C Dauphin 10-seat general-purpose helicopter

Aérospatiale SA 360C Dauphin (Turboméca Astazou XVIIIA turboshaft engine) with wheel-type landing gear
(Pilot Press)

POWER PLANT: One Turboméca Astazou XVIIIA turboshaft engine, delivering 783 kW (1,050 shp) for takeoff. Four Kléber-Colombes bag-type fuel tanks under cabin floor, total normal capacity 640 litres (141 Imp gallons). Provision for ferry tank of 475 litres (104 Imp gallons) capacity on the cabin floor and one auxiliary tank of 215 litres (47 Imp gallons) capacity at the back of the cabin.

ACCOMMODATION: Standard 10-seat version has seats for pilot (to starboard) and co-pilot or passenger in front, and two rows of four seats to the rear. Interior of the cabin is clear except for a vertical duct, housing the flying control rods, positioned centrally aft of the centre row of seats. Two large forward-hinged doors on each side. Optional rearward-sliding doors. Compartment for hand baggage or coats aft of rear row of seats. Separate main baggage compartment aft of cabin, with door on starboard side. Alternative 14-seat layout has an extra row of four seats attached to the cabin rear wall, and no space for hand baggage or coats. Ambulance version carries four stretcher patients, a medical attendant and two crew. Mixed-traffic version carries six persons at front of cabin, with 2·50 m³ (88·3 cu ft) of cargo space to the rear. The floor in this area will support a loading of 610 daN/m² (125 lb/sq ft). Executive versions are available with VIP interiors for four or six passengers. Cabin is heated and ventilated.

SYSTEMS: Two sets of three single-body servo controls mounted in series on the flight control channel, each supplied by an independent hydraulic system: one main set at the main rotor head, one auxiliary set capable of integrating an autopilot, and one tail rotor servo unit. Electrical system includes a 4·5kW engine-driven starter/generator, a 0·5kVA 115/200V 400Hz generator, a 23Ah nickel-cadmium battery and a ground power receptacle.

AVIONICS AND EQUIPMENT: Optional equipment includes IFR instrumentation, autopilot, 1,300 kg (2,865 lb) capacity cargo sling, 272 kg (600 lb) capacity rescue hoist, air-conditioning system, VHF/AM, ICS, VOR/LOC/glideslope, marker beacon indicator, HF/SSB, transponder and DME.

DIMENSIONS, EXTERNAL:
Diameter of main rotor	11·50 m (37 ft 8¾ in)
Main rotor blade chord (constant)	0·35 m (1 ft 1¾ in)
Diameter of tail rotor	0·90 m (2 ft 11⁷⁄₁₆ in)
Length overall	13·20 m (43 ft 3½ in)
Length of fuselage	10·98 m (36 ft 0 in)
Height overall	3·50 m (11 ft 6 in)
Stabiliser span	3·15 m (10 ft 4 in)
Wheel track	1·95 m (6 ft 4¾ in)
Wheelbase	7·23 m (23 ft 8¾ in)
Cabin doors (fwd, each): Height	1·16 m (3 ft 9½ in)
Width	1·14 m (3 ft 9 in)
Cabin doors (aft, each): Height	1·16 m (3 ft 9½ in)
Width	0·87 m (2 ft 10¼ in)
Freight compartment door: Height	0·56 m (1 ft 10 in)
Width	0·75 m (2 ft 5½ in)

DIMENSIONS, INTERNAL:
Cabin: Usable length	2·30 m (7 ft 6½ in)
Height at front	1·40 m (4 ft 7 in)
Height at rear	1·06 m (3 ft 5¾ in)
Width at front	1·92 m (6 ft 3½ in)
Width at rear	1·60 m (5 ft 3 in)
Floor area	4·20 m² (45·20 sq ft)
Volume	5·0 m³ (176 cu ft)
Baggage compartment volume	1·00 m³ (35·31 cu ft)

WEIGHTS:
Basic operating weight	1,637 kg (3,609 lb)
Max payload: internal	1,363 kg (3,005 lb)
slung	1,300 kg (2,865 lb)
Max T-O weight	3,000 kg (6,614 lb)

PERFORMANCE (at AUW of 2,600 kg; 5,732 lb):
Never-exceed speed at S/L	170 knots (315 km/h; 196 mph)
Cruising speed at S/L	148 knots (275 km/h; 171 mph)
Max rate of climb at S/L	540 m (1,770 ft)/min
Hovering ceiling IGE	3,850 m (12,630 ft)
Range at S/L with max fuel	367 nm (680 km; 423 miles)
Endurance at S/L	4 h

AÉROSPATIALE SA 365C DAUPHIN 2

Announced in early 1973, the SA 365C is a twin-engined version of the SA 360, powered by Turboméca Arriel turboshaft engines. The prototype (F-WVKE) flew for the first time on 24 January 1975. DGAC certification for VFR flight was received in July 1978, and for IFR flight in December 1978. FAA and CAA certification was achieved by the Autumn of the same year and delivery of production SA 365Cs began in December 1978, initially to Offshore Helicopters Inc of the USA. A total of 37 had been delivered by 1 January 1980.

The SA 365C is designed for single-pilot IFR flight. It differs from the SA 360C in the following details:

ROTOR SYSTEM: Main rotor blades are attached to Starflex glassfibre hub, as described under entry for AS 350 Ecureuil.

ROTOR DRIVE: The installation of free-turbine engines has eliminated the need for a clutch in the output drive from each engine into the main gearbox.

FUSELAGE: The profile of the firewall between the two turboshaft engines is extended rearward in the form of a curved fairing which blends into the dorsal spine fairing over the tail rotor driveshaft.

TAIL UNIT: Horizontal stabiliser has inverted-camber aerofoil section, and the fixed vertical tail fins are offset to produce a lateral component which enhances the anti-torque function of the unsymmetrical surfaces. These features increase the efficiency of the 'fenestron' tail rotor, notably during hover.

POWER PLANT: Two Turboméca Arriel free-turbine turboshaft engines, each rated at 507 kW (680 shp), mounted side by side above the fuselage, aft of the main rotor driveshaft. Four separate bag-type fuel tanks, filling full width of fuselage under cabin floor. Two refuelling points aft of rear cabin door on port side.

DIMENSIONS, EXTERNAL:
Diameter of main rotor	11·68 m (38 ft 4 in)
Length overall	13·32 m (43 ft 8½ in)

WEIGHTS:
Weight empty	1,876 kg (4,136 lb)
Max T-O weight	3,400 kg (7,495 lb)

PERFORMANCE (at AUW of 3,000 kg; 6,613 lb):
Never-exceed speed	170 knots (315 km/h; 196 mph)
Cruising speed	137 knots (255 km/h; 158 mph)
Max rate of climb at S/L	600 m (1,970 ft)/min
Service ceiling (60 m; 200 ft/min climb)	6,000 m (19,680 ft)
Hovering ceiling IGE	3,570 m (11,710 ft)
Hovering ceiling OGE	2,840 m (9,315 ft)
Max range at econ cruising speed, no reserves	251 nm (465 km; 289 miles)

OPERATING LIMITS:
Max pressure altitude	4,570 m (15,000 ft)
Max temperature	+40°C
Min temperature	−40°C

AÉROSPATIALE AS 365N DAUPHIN 2

This version of the Dauphin 2 was first stated to be under development in mid-1977, but few details were released until June 1979, when the prototype (F-WZJD) was exhibited at the Paris Air Show. First flown on 31 March 1979, it introduced more refined external lines, a fully-retractable landing gear, uprated engines and a considerably increased range, making this version particularly suitable for offshore commercial and naval applications.

The first production AS 365N (F-WZJJ) introduced a number of changes to the rotor mast fairings, engine cowlings, crew doors, transmission and main rotor blades, as well as larger tail surfaces. On 6 February 1980, it established a record for the round trip between Issy-les-Moulineaux, Paris, and Battersea Heliport, London, at an average speed of 158·89 knots (294·26 km/h; 182·84 mph). Its T-O weight of 3,800 kg (8,377 lb) included ten occupants and 30 min fuel reserves. The Paris-London leg was covered in 1 h 7 min 48 s, the return journey in 1 h 11 min 8 s. No landing at Battersea was necessary, as the total distance of 367 nm (680 km; 422 miles) was within the aircraft's range with full normal payload.

Two days later, the same aircraft, carrying six persons, set new records between Issy and Battersea, with a landing in London. Time for the Paris-London flight was 1 h 3 min 30 s, at an average speed of 173·82 knots (321·91 km/h; 200·03 mph); the return flight took 1 h 12 min 9 s, at an average speed of 151·75 knots (281·05 km/h; 174·64 mph).

It was hoped to obtain civil certification for VFR operation by December 1980, and for single/two-pilot IFR operation by early 1981. Deliveries of the AS 365N are expected to begin in the first quarter of 1981. The AS 366, with different power plant, is described separately.

TYPE: Twin-turbine military and commercial general-purpose helicopter.

ROTOR SYSTEM: Four-blade main rotor, with blades of glassfibre and carbonfibre, attached to Starflex glassfibre rotor head with quick-disconnect pins. Blades fold for stowage and a rotor brake is standard. Thirteen-blade 'fenestron' type of metal ducted-fan anti-torque tail rotor.

FUSELAGE: Conventional light alloy semi-monocoque structure.

TAIL UNIT: Horizontal stabiliser mid-set on tailboom, forward of 'fenestron', with endplate fins of different form to those on SA 365C.

LANDING GEAR: Retractable tricycle type, with twin-wheel self-centering nose unit and single wheel on each rearward-retracting main unit. Oleo-pneumatic shock-absorbers. Tyre pressure 7 bars (101 lb/sq in) for main wheels, 4 bars (58 lb/sq in) for nosewheels. Disc brakes.

POWER PLANT: Two Turboméca Arriel IC free-turbine turboshaft engines, each rated at 522 kW (700 shp). Five fuel tanks divided in two groups under cabin floor, with total capacity of 1,140 litres (250 Imp gallons). Refuelling point on port side. Oil capacity 14 litres (3 Imp gallons).

ACCOMMODATION: Standard accommodation for one pilot and nine passengers in VFR configuration. Crew of two

Aérospatiale SA 365C Dauphin 2 with twin Turboméca Arriel turboshaft engines

for IFR operation. High-density seating for one pilot and 13 passengers. VIP configurations for four to six persons in addition to pilot. Three forward-opening doors on each side. Freight hold aft of cabin rear bulkhead. Cabin heated and ventilated.

SYSTEMS: SEMCA air-conditioning system optional. Duplicated hydraulic system. Electrical system includes two 4·5 kW starter/generators, one 17Ah 24V battery and two 250VA 115V 400Hz inverters. Provision for de-icing system.

AVIONICS AND EQUIPMENT: Optional avionics include VHF and HF com/nav, VOR, ILS, ADF, transponder, DME, radar and self-contained nav system. Optional equipment includes a SFIM 155 duplex autopilot, a 1,500 kg (3,300 lb) capacity cargo sling, and 275 kg (605 lb) capacity hoist with 80 m (260 ft) cable length.

ARMAMENT AND OPERATIONAL EQUIPMENT: Provision for complete ASW and ASV weapon system, including omnidirectional radar with target designation capability.

DIMENSIONS, EXTERNAL:
Diameter of main rotor	11·68 m (38 ft 4 in)
Diameter of tail rotor	0·90 m (2 ft 11⁷/₁₆ in)
Blade chord, main rotor	0·385 m (1 ft 3¼ in)
Length overall	13·34 m (43 ft 9 in)
Length overall, rotor blades folded	
	11·38 m (37 ft 4 in)
Width, rotor blades folded	3·21 m (10 ft 6½ in)
Height to top of rotor hub	3·40 m (11 ft 1¾ in)
Height overall	3·77 m (12 ft 4½ in)
Wheel track	2·03 m (6 ft 8 in)
Wheelbase	3·61 m (11 ft 10¼ in)
Main cabin door (fwd, each side):	
Height	1·16 m (3 ft 9½ in)
Width	1·14 m (3 ft 9 in)
Main cabin door (rear, each side):	
Height	1·16 m (3 ft 9½ in)
Width	0·87 m (2 ft 10¼ in)
Baggage compartment door (stbd):	
Height	0·51 m (1 ft 8 in)
Width	0·73 m (2 ft 4¾ in)

DIMENSIONS, INTERNAL:
Cabin: Length	2·30 m (7 ft 6½ in)
Max width	1·92 m (6 ft 3½ in)
Max height	1·40 m (4 ft 7 in)
Floor area	4·20 m² (45·20 sq ft)
Volume	5·00 m³ (176 cu ft)
Baggage compartment volume	2·20 m³ (77·7 cu ft)

WEIGHTS:
Weight empty, standard aircraft	1,940 kg (4,277 lb)
Max T-O weight	3,800 kg (8,377 lb)

First production Aérospatiale AS 365N Dauphin 2 twin-turbine helicopter

PERFORMANCE (at max T-O weight):
Never-exceed speed at S/L	
	175 knots (324 km/h; 201 mph)
Max cruising speed at S/L	
	155 knots (287 km/h; 178 mph)
Econ cruising speed at S/L	
	130 knots (240 km/h; 149 mph)
Max rate of climb at S/L	462 m (1,515 ft)/min
Hovering ceiling IGE	1,600 m (5,250 ft)
Hovering ceiling OGE	950 m (3,115 ft)
Range with max fuel, no reserves	
	496 nm (920 km; 571 miles)

AÉROSPATIALE AS 366 DAUPHIN 2
US Coast Guard designation: HH-65A Dolphin

At the 1979 Paris Air Show, Aérospatiale announced that it had won with this aircraft the competition for a helicopter to perform SRR (Short Range Recovery) duties with the US Coast Guard. The initial requirement is for 90 **AS 366Gs**, basically similar to the AS 365N but with engines and equipment of US manufacture accounting for about 60 per cent of the total cost of each aircraft. The first order, for 23, was received in 1979.

The AS 366G will be powered by two Avco Lycoming LTS 101-750 turboshafts, each rated at 507 kW (680 shp). Rockwell Collins is prime contractor for the advanced communications, navigation and all-weather search equipment. Flight testing was expected to begin in August 1980, to permit civil certification in October 1981 and

deliveries to the Coast Guard between the early months of 1982 and 1986.

A civil counterpart, the **AS 366N**, is planned for the North American market. To meet French military requirements, notably for Aéronavale, a version is projected with two Turboméca Arriel turboshaft engines, strengthened landing gear, deck-landing harpoon, radar, hoist and other special equipment.

DIMENSIONS, EXTERNAL (AS 366G):
Diameter of main rotor	11·68 m (38 ft 4 in)
Length overall	13·35 m (43 ft 9½ in)
Length overall, rotor blades folded	
	11·40 m (37 ft 4¾ in)
Width, rotor blades folded	3·20 m (10 ft 6 in)
Height overall	3·81 m (12 ft 6 in)

WEIGHTS (AS 366G):
Weight empty, incl mission equipment	
	2,530 kg (5,577 lb)
Max T-O weight	3,810 kg (8,400 lb)

PERFORMANCE (AS 366G, estimated at max T-O weight):
Max level speed	133 knots (246 km/h; 153 mph)
SRR range	166 nm (307 km; 191 miles)
Range with max passenger load	
	216 nm (400 km; 248 miles)
Max range, one engine out	
	327 nm (605 km; 376 miles)
Range with max fuel	420 nm (778 km; 483 miles)
Endurance with max fuel	4 h 11 min

C.A.A.R.P. — *See 'Mudry'*

DASSAULT-BREGUET
AVIONS MARCEL DASSAULT/BREGUET AVIATION

HEAD OFFICE: 27 rue du Professeur Victor Pauchet, 92420 Vaucresson
POSTAL ADDRESS: BP 32, 92420 Vaucresson
Telephone: 741 79 21
Telex: 60755 Brevau
PRESS INFORMATION OFFICE: 46 avenue Kléber, 75116 Paris
Telephone: 727 61 19

WORKS: 92210 Saint-Cloud, 77000 Melun-Villaroche, 95100 Argenteuil, 92100 Boulogne/Seine, 78140 Vélizy-Villacoublay, 33610 Martignas, 33700 Bordeaux-Mérignac, 33400 Talence, 33630 Cazaux, 31770 Toulouse-Colomiers, 64600 Biarritz Anglet, 64200 Biarritz-Parme, 13800 Istres, 74370 Argonay, 59113 Lille-Seclin, 86000 Poitiers
FOUNDER: Marcel Dassault
PRESIDENT AND CHIEF EXECUTIVE: B. C. Vallières

GENERAL MANAGER, INTERNATIONAL AFFAIRS: H. de l'Estoile
DEPUTY GENERAL MANAGER: X. D'Iribarne
DEPUTY GENERAL MANAGER: J. Estebe
SECRETARY GENERAL: C. Edelstenne
GENERAL TECHNICAL MANAGER: J. Cabrière
TECHNICAL ADVISER: H. Deplante
EXPORT TECHNICAL MANAGER: Y. Thiriet
MILITARY AIRCRAFT SALES MANAGER: F. Serralta
MILITARY AIRCRAFT SALES MANAGER: P. E. Jaillard
CIVIL AIRCRAFT MANAGER: B. Latreille
PRODUCTION MANAGER: J. C. Veber
FLIGHT TEST MANAGER: J. F. Cazaubiel
PRESS INFORMATION MANAGER: A. Segura

Avions Marcel Dassault/Breguet Aviation resulted from the merger on 14 December 1971 of the Avions Marcel Dassault and Breguet Aviation companies. On 1 January 1979, it announced that, in accordance with an option taken in 1976, it had transferred 21 per cent of its stock to the French government.

Dassault-Breguet is engaged in the development and production of military and civil aircraft, guided missiles

and servo control equipment. Series production of its aircraft is undertaken under a widespread subcontracting programme, with final assembly and flight testing handled by the company. Its 16 separate works and facilities covered 620,800 m² (6,682,300 sq ft), with a total of 15,553 employees, including 2,259 engineers, at the beginning of 1980.

Dassault-Breguet has established close links with the industries of other countries. The original programme for the Atlantic maritime patrol aircraft (now undergoing major new development) associated manufacturers in Belgium, France, West Germany, Italy and the Netherlands under the overall responsibility of their respective governments. In the same way the British and French governments are associated in the SEPECAT concern, formed to control the Dassault-Breguet/BAe Jaguar programme; and the West German and French governments are associated in the Dassault-Breguet/Dornier Alpha Jet programme.

Purchase of Mirage fighters by Belgium and Spain led to Belgian and Spanish participation in Mirage III/5 and Mirage F1 production. Sales in 1979 totalled 216 aircraft, including 39 Falcon 10/20/50 jet transports.

DASSAULT MIRAGE III

The Mirage III was designed initially as a Mach 2 high-altitude all-weather interceptor, capable of performing ground support missions and requiring only small airstrips. Developed versions include a two-seat trainer, long-range fighter-bomber and reconnaissance aircraft, and a total of more than 1,380 Mirage III/5/50s of all types had been ordered by 1 February 1980, including licence production abroad. Current contracts will maintain production until at least the end of 1982.

The experimental prototype flew for the first time on 17 November 1956, powered by a SNECMA Atar 101G turbojet with afterburner (44·1 kN; 9,900 lb st). Versions currently available include the following:

Mirage III-D. Two-seat version, built initially in Australia for the RAAF. Similar, French-built models ordered by 12 countries, including six more for Australia.

Dassault Mirage III-EBR fighter-bomber/intruder of the Brazilian Air Force

Dassault Mirage III-E single-seat combat aircraft in French Air Force configuration *(Pilot Press)*

Tandem seating under one-piece canopy; radar deleted, but fitted with radio beacon equipment. Intended primarily as a trainer, but suitable for strike sorties, carrying air-to-surface armament. Total of 180 Mirage III-B/III-D/5 two-seaters sold to 20 countries.

Mirage III-D2Z. For South Africa. Generally similar to III-D but with SNECMA Atar 9K-50 turbojet. Delivered 1974-75.

Mirage III-E. Long-range fighter-bomber/intruder version, of which 523 have been built for 13 air forces. First of three prototypes flew on 5 April 1961, and the first delivery of a production III-E was made in January 1964. Thirty III-Es of the 4e Escadre of the French Air Force, equipping two squadrons at Luxeuil, are carriers of the 15 kT AN 52 tactical nuclear weapon.

Mirage III-R. Reconnaissance version of III-E. Set of five OMERA type 31 cameras, in place of radar in nose, can be focused in four different arrangements for very low altitude, medium altitude, high altitude and night reconnaissance missions. Self-contained navigation system. Provision for air-to-surface armament. Two prototypes, of which the first flew in November 1961. Total of 159 production models ordered, including Mirage 5-Rs, for nine air forces.

Mirage III-R2Z. For South Africa. Generally similar to III-R but with SNECMA Atar 9K-50 turbojet. Delivered 1974-75.

Mirage III-RD. Similar to III-R but with improved Doppler navigation system in fairing under front fuselage, gyro gunsight and automatic cameras. Provision for carrying SAT Cyclope infra-red tracking equipment in ventral fairing, and two 1,700 litre (374 Imp gallon) underwing auxiliary fuel tanks. Twenty built for French Air Force.

The following description refers to the Mirage III-E, but is generally applicable to all versions.

TYPE: Single-seat fighter-bomber/intruder aircraft.

WINGS: Cantilever low-wing monoplane of delta planform, with conical camber. Thickness/chord ratio 4·5% to 3·5%. Anhedral 1°. No incidence. Sweepback on leading-edge 60° 34'. All-metal torsion-box structure; stressed skin of machined panels with integral stiffeners. Elevons hydraulically powered by Dassault twin-cylinder actuators with artificial feel. Airbrakes, comprising small panels hinged to upper and lower wing surfaces, near leading-edge.

FUSELAGE: All-metal structure, 'waisted' in accordance with the area rule.

TAIL UNIT: Cantilever fin and hydraulically-actuated powered rudder only. Dassault twin-cylinder actuators with artificial feel.

LANDING GEAR: Retractable tricycle type, with single wheel on each unit. Hydraulic retraction, nosewheel rearward, main units inward. Messier-Hispano-Bugatti shock-absorbers and disc brakes. Main-wheel tyre pressure 5·9-9·8 bars (85·5-142 lb/sq in). Braking parachute.

POWER PLANT: One SNECMA Atar 9C turbojet engine (60·8 kN; 13,670 lb st with afterburning), fitted with an overspeed system which is engaged automatically from Mach 1·4 and permits a thrust increase of approx 8 per cent in the high supersonic speed range. Optional and jettisonable SEPR 844 single-chamber rocket motor (14·7 kN; 3,300 lb st) or interchangeable fuel tank. Movable half-cone centrebody in each air intake. Total internal fuel capacity 3,330 litres (733 Imp gallons) when rocket motor is not fitted. Provision for this to be augmented by two 625, 1,100, 1,300 or 1,700 litre (137, 242, 285 or 374 Imp gallon) underwing drop-tanks; 500 litre (110 Imp gallon) non-jettisonable auxiliary tanks; JL-100 jettisonable tanks each housing both 280 litres (61 Imp gallons) fuel and air-to-surface rockets; Bidon Cyclope jettisonable tanks each housing 1,100

litres (242 Imp gallons) fuel and electronic equipment; or Bidon Homing jettisonable tanks housing 850 litres (187 Imp gallons) fuel and electronic equipment.

ACCOMMODATION: Single seat under rearward-hinged canopy. Hispano-built Martin-Baker Type RM.4 zero-altitude ejection seat.

SYSTEMS: Two separate air-conditioning systems for cockpit and avionics. Two independent hydraulic systems, pressure 207 bars (3,000 lb/sq in), for flying controls, landing gear and brakes. Power for DC electrical system from 24V 40Ah batteries and a 26·5V 9kW generator. AC electrical system power provided by one 200V 400Hz transformer and one 200V 400Hz 9kVA alternator.

AVIONICS AND EQUIPMENT: Duplicated UHF, Tacan, Doppler, CSF Cyrano II fire-control radar in nose, navigation computer, bombing computer, automatic gunsight.

The Mirage III-E has a normal magnetic detector mounted in the fin, and a central gyro and other avionics to provide accurate and stabilised heading information. The pilot's equipment determines at any instant the geographical co-ordinates of the aircraft and compares them with the co-ordinates of the target, the differences between the two being presented to the pilot as a 'course to steer' and 'distance to run'. Associated with this facility is a rotative magazine in the cockpit in which it is possible to insert up to twelve plastics punch-cards. Each card represents the co-ordinates of a geographical position. Therefore it is possible before take-off at point A to select point B on the rotating magazine. During take-off, ie after reaching 150 knots (278 km/h; 173 mph), the computer will switch on and the heading and distance to point B will be presented to the pilot. When overhead point B (assuming a pure navigational sortie) he can either select point A or the next turning point, or if required this sequence can continue until a maximum of twelve pre-set turning points have been used. Another facility available in the computer is known as the 'additional base'. Assuming that between points A and B the pilot receives instructions by radio to go to point C (and that there is no punch-card in the magazine for point C) the pilot can, by means of setting knobs, wind on the bearing and distance of point C from point B; then, when he selects the switch 'additional base', the heading to steer and distance to run to point C will be indicated.

Marconi Doppler equipment provides the ground speed and drift information for the above, while Tacan is presented as a 'bearing and distance' on the navigation indicator located on the starboard side of the instrument panel.

The Cyrano II installation in the aircraft's nose provides orthodox air-to-air interception radar, and has the additional mode available of control from the ground.

In the latter case the pilot simply obeys his gunsight instructions, and radio silence is maintained. Cyrano II also functions in an air-to-ground role for high-level navigation, presenting a radar picture of the ground; for low-level navigation, presenting the obstacles above a preselected altitude; for blind descent, presenting obstacles that intercept the descent path; for anti-collision, presenting the obstacles that can be avoided by applying a 0·1g pull-up; and for distance measuring, by presenting in the sight the oblique aircraft-to-ground distance.

Allied to the Cyrano II installation is the CSF 97 sighting system, of illuminated points, dots, bars and figures, giving air-to-air facility for cannon and missiles, air-to-ground facility for dive-bombing or LABS, and navigation facility for horizon and heading.

ARMAMENT: Ground attack armament consists normally of two 30 mm DEFA cannon in fuselage, each with 125 rounds of ammunition, and two 1,000 lb bombs, or an AS.30 air-to-surface missile under the fuselage and 1,000 lb bombs under the wings. Alternative underwing stores include JL-100 pods, each with 18 rockets, and jettisonable underwing fuel tanks. For interception duties, one Matra R.530 air-to-air missile can be carried under fuselage, with optional guns and two Sidewinder missiles.

DIMENSIONS, EXTERNAL:

Wing span	8·22 m (26 ft 11½ in)
Wing aspect ratio	1·94
Length overall: III-E	15·03 m (49 ft 3½ in)
III-R	15·50 m (50 ft 10¼ in)
Height overall	4·50 m (14 ft 9 in)
Wheel track	3·15 m (10 ft 4 in)
Wheelbase: III-E	4·87 m (15 ft 11¾ in)

AREAS:

Wings, gross	34·85 m² (375 sq ft)
Vertical tail surfaces (total)	4·5 m² (48·4 sq ft)

WEIGHTS AND LOADING:

Weight empty: III-E	7,050 kg (15,540 lb)
III-R	6,600 kg (14,550 lb)
T-O weight 'clean': III-E	9,600 kg (21,165 lb)
Max T-O weight: III-E, R	13,700 kg (30,200 lb)
Max wing loading: III-E, R	393·1 kg/m² (80·53 lb/sq ft)

PERFORMANCE (Mirage III-E, in 'clean' condition with guns installed, except where indicated):

Max level speed at 12,000 m (39,375 ft)	Mach 2·2 (1,268 knots; 2,350 km/h; 1,460 mph)
Max level speed at S/L	750 knots (1,390 km/h; 863 mph)
Cruising speed at 11,000 m (36,000 ft)	Mach 0·9
Approach speed	183 knots (340 km/h; 211 mph)
Landing speed	157 knots (290 km/h; 180 mph)
Time to 11,000 m (36,000 ft), Mach 0·9	3 min
Time to 15,000 m (49,200 ft), Mach 1·8	6 min 50 s
Service ceiling at Mach 1·8	17,000 m (55,775 ft)
Ceiling, using rocket motor	23,000 m (75,450 ft)
T-O run, according to mission (up to max T-O weight)	700-1,600 m (2,295-5,250 ft)
Landing run, using brake parachute	700 m (2,295 ft)
Combat radius, ground attack	647 nm (1,200 km; 745 miles)

DASSAULT MIRAGE 5

The Mirage 5 is a ground attack aircraft using the same airframe and engine as the Mirage III-E. The basic VFR version has simplified avionics, 500 litres (110 Imp gallons) greater fuel capacity than III-E and considerably extended stores carrying capability. It combines the full Mach 2+ capability of the Mirage III, and its ability to operate from semi-prepared airfields, with simpler maintenance. In ground attack configuration, up to 4,000 kg (8,820 lb) of weapons and 1,000 litres (220 Imp gallons) of fuel can be carried externally on seven wing and fuselage attachment points. The Mirage 5 can also be flown as an interceptor, with two Sidewinder air-to-air missiles and 4,700 litres (1,034 Imp gallons) of external fuel. At customer's option, any degree of IFR/all-weather operation can be provided for, with reduced fuel or weapons load. The Mirage 5 was flown for the first time on 19 May 1967.

Up to 1 February 1980, a total of 480 Mirage 5s had been ordered for eleven air forces, including Mirage 5-R reconnaissance variants and two-seat Mirage 5-Ds.

Dassault Mirage III-RD reconnaissance aircraft of the Pakistan Air Force

Dassault Mirage 5 single-seat ground attack aircraft *(Pilot Press)*

Dassault Mirage 5-DM two-seat trainer/combat aircraft supplied to Zaire

The structural description of the Mirage III-E is generally applicable to the Mirage 5, with the following exceptions:

ARMAMENT: Seven attachment points for external loads, with multiple launchers permitting a max load of more than 4 tons. Ground attack armament consists normally of two 30 mm DEFA cannon in fuselage, each with 125 rounds of ammunition, and two 1,000 lb bombs or an AS.30 air-to-surface missile under the fuselage and 1,000 lb bombs under the wings. Alternative underwing stores include tank/bomb carriers, each with 500 litres (110 Imp gallons) of fuel and four 500 lb or two 1,000 lb bombs, and JL-100 pods, each with eighteen 68 mm rockets and 250 litres (55 Imp gallons) of fuel. For interception duties, two Sidewinder missiles can be carried under the wings.

EQUIPMENT: Can have Aïda II radar rangefinder in nose.

DIMENSIONS, EXTERNAL: As III-E, except:
Length overall   15·55 m (51 ft 0¼ in)

WEIGHTS AND LOADING: As III-E, except:
Weight empty   6,600 kg (14,550 lb)

PERFORMANCE (in 'clean' condition, with guns installed, except where indicated): As III-E, plus:
Combat radius with 907 kg (2,000 lb) bomb load:
hi-lo-hi   700 nm (1,300 km; 808 miles)
lo-lo-lo   350 nm (650 km; 404 miles)
Ferry range with three external tanks
      2,158 nm (4,000 km; 2,485 miles)

DASSAULT MIRAGE 50

First displayed in representative form at the 1975 Paris Air Show, the Mirage 50 retains the basic airframe of the Mirage III/5 series, but is powered by the higher-rated SNECMA Atar 9K50 turbojet, as fitted in the Mirage F1-Cs of the French Air Force and Mirage III-R2Zs of the South African Air Force. This gives 70·6 kN (15,873 lb st) with afterburning, representing a 16 per cent thrust increase compared with standard Mirage III/5s.

The prototype Mirage 50 flew for the first time on 15 May 1979. First customer is the Air Force of Chile.

The Mirage 50 is a multi-mission fighter, suitable for air superiority duties with guns and dogfight missiles, air patrol and supersonic interception, and ground attack combined with self-defence capability. It can carry the full range of operational stores, armament and equipment developed for the Mirage III/5 series, plus Agave or Cyrano IVM multi-function radar, with Matra Magic or 530 air-to-air missiles respectively, an inertial or Doppler nav/attack system, and head-up display. It is available in reconnaissance configuration. A two-seat training version is also projected. Improvements compared with other delta-wing Mirages include better take-off performance, higher rate of climb, faster acceleration and better manoeuvrability. Maximum internal fuel capacity is 3,475 litres (764 Imp gallons). Underwing and underfuselage tanks can increase total capacity to 4,700 litres (1,034 Imp gallons).

DIMENSIONS, EXTERNAL:
Wing span   8·22 m (27 ft 0 in)

Length overall	15·56 m (51 ft 0½ in)
Height overall	4·50 m (14 ft 9 in)

AREA:
Wings, gross	35·00 m² (376·7 sq ft)

WEIGHTS:
Weight empty, equipped	7,150 kg (15,765 lb)
T-O weight, 'clean'	9,900 kg (21,825 lb)
Max T-O weight	13,700 kg (30,200 lb)

PERFORMANCE:
Max level speed at altitude	Mach 2·2
	(750 knots; 1,390 km/h; 863 mph IAS)
Max rate of climb at S/L	11,100 m (36,400 ft)/min
Time to 12,200 m (40,000 ft): 'clean'	4 min 24 s
with 2 Magic missiles	5 min 24 s
Service ceiling at Mach 2	18,000 m (59,055 ft)
T-O run with 2 Magic missiles	915 m (3,000 ft)
T-O run at max T-O weight	1,830 m (6,000 ft)
Combat radius at low altitude with two 400 kg bombs	
	340 nm (630 km; 391 miles)

DASSAULT MIRAGE F1

Details of the early history of the Mirage F1 can be found in the 1977-78 *Jane's*. The prototype flew for the first time on 23 December 1966 and was followed by three pre-series aircraft.

The primary role of the Mirage F1 is that of all-weather interception at any altitude, and the **F1-C** production version, to which the detailed description applies, utilises weapon systems similar to those of the same Mirage III-E. It is equally suitable for attack missions, carrying a variety of external loads beneath the wings and fuselage. A ground attack version designated **F1-A** is also in production, with much of the more costly avionic equipment deleted and the space so vacated occupied by an additional fuel tank. Further versions include the **F1-B** two-seat trainer, the first of which made its first flight on 26 May 1976; the **F1-E**, similar to the F1-C but with more comprehensive nav/attack system; and the **F1-R** reconnaissance variant.

Twenty-five F1-Cs of the French Air Force have been modified to **F1-C-200** standard by permanent installation of a flight refuelling probe for long-range reinforcement capability. Four of these aircraft, which serve with the 5e Escadre at Orange, made a six-hour non-stop flight from Solenzarra (Corsica) to Djibouti on 29 January 1980. In-flight refuelling was provided by a C-135F tanker. Point-to-point distance flown was about 2,700 nm (5,000 km; 3,100 miles).

By January 1980, a total of 610 Mirage F1s had been ordered, comprising 230 for the French Air Force and 380 for service with the air forces of Ecuador (F1-A and E), Greece (F1-C), Iraq (F1-C), Jordan (F1-E), Kuwait (F1-C and B), Libya (F1-A, B and E), Morocco (F1-C and E), South Africa (F1-A and C) and Spain (F1-B and C). The first production F1 flew on 15 February 1973 and was delivered officially to the French Air Force on 14 March 1973. The first unit to receive the F1 was the 30e Escadre at Reims, which became operational in early 1974. It was followed by the 5e Escadre at Orange and the 12e Escadre at Cambrai. Each Escadre comprised two interceptor squadrons in early 1980, but creation of a third squadron at Cambrai is planned for 1981. A squadron of 15 two-seat F1-Bs entered service with the French Air Force in 1980; each aircraft is equipped with the same Cyrano IV radar, weapon system and air-to-air missiles as the F1-C.

In February 1979, it was announced that the French Air Force had decided to purchase about 30 F1-Rs, to replace Mirage III-R/RD aircraft equipping two squadrons of the 33e Escadre de Reconnaissance, at Strasbourg. These aircraft will carry an OMERA 40 panoramic camera and an OMERA 35 camera internally, together with an infra-red sensor and an OMERA 360 sight recorder. Further electromagnetic or optical sensors will be carried in an underbelly pod. Other new equipment will include a SAGEM Uliss 47 inertial navigation system and EMD navigation radar. The first F1-R squadron is expected to become operational in 1983.

By the beginning of 1980 a total of 336 Mirage F1s had been completed, with production continuing at the rate of six per month. Current orders will sustain production until at least the end of 1983.

The Mirage F1 is produced by Dassault-Breguet in co-operation with the Belgian companies SABCA, in

Dassault Mirage 50 fighter (SNECMA Atar 9K50 turbojet engine)

Dassault Mirage F1 single-seat multi-mission fighter and attack aircraft *(Pilot Press)*

Dassault Mirage F1 in advanced ground attack configuration

Dassault Mirage F1-B two-seat combat trainer

which Dassault-Breguet has a parity interest, and Sonaca, which is building rear fuselage sections for all Mirage F1s ordered. Dassault-Breguet also has a technical and industrial co-operation agreement with the Armaments Development and Production Corporation of South Africa Ltd, whereby the latter company has rights to build the Mirage F1 under licence.

The following description applies to the F1-C production version for the French Air Force:

TYPE: Single-seat multi-mission fighter and attack aircraft.
WINGS: Cantilever shoulder-wing monoplane. Anhedral from roots. Sweepback 47° 30' on leading-edges, with extended chord on approximately the outer two-thirds of each wing. All-metal two-spar torsion-box structure, making extensive use of mechanically or chemically milled components. Trailing-edge control surfaces of honeycomb sandwich construction. Entire leading-edge can be drooped hydraulically (manually for T-O and landing, automatic in combat). Two differentially-operating double-slotted flaps and one aileron on each trailing-edge, actuated hydraulically by servo controls. Ailerons are compensated by trim devices incorporated in linkage. Two spoilers on each wing, ahead of flaps.
FUSELAGE: Conventional all-metal semi-monocoque structure. Primary frames are milled mechanically, secondary frames and fuel tank panels chemically. Electrical spot-welding for secondary stringers and sealed panels, remainder titanium flush-riveted or bolted and sealed. Titanium alloy also used for landing gear trunnions, engine firewall and certain other major structures. High-tensile steel wing attachment points. Nosecone over radar, and antennae fairings on fin, are of plastics. Large hydraulically-actuated door-type airbrake in forward underside of each intake trunk.
TAIL UNIT: Cantilever all-metal two-spar structure, with sweepback on all surfaces. All-moving tailplane mid-set on fuselage, and actuated hydraulically by electrical or manual control. Tailplane trailing-edge panels are of honeycomb sandwich construction. Auxiliary fin beneath each side of rear fuselage.
LANDING GEAR: Retractable tricycle type, by Messier-Hispano-Bugatti. Hydraulic retraction, nose unit rearward, main units upward into rear of intake trunk fairings. Twin wheels on each unit. Nose unit steerable and self-centering. Oleo-pneumatic shock-absorbers. Main-wheel tyre pressure 9-11 bars (130-160 lb/sq in), permitting operation from semi-prepared airfields. Messier-Hispano-Bugatti brakes and anti-skid units. Brake parachute in bullet fairing at base of rudder.
POWER PLANT: One SNECMA Atar 9K50 turbojet engine, rated at 70·6 kN (15,873 lb st) with afterburning. Movable semi-conical centrebody in each intake. Fuel in integral tanks in wings and fuselage, on each side of intake trunks, able to be pressure-refuelled completely in about 6 min. Provision for three jettisonable auxiliary fuel tanks (each 1,200 litres; 264 Imp gallons) to be carried under fuselage and on inboard wing pylons. Non-retractable flight refuelling probe on starboard side of nose optional.
ACCOMMODATION: Single SEMMB (Martin-Baker Mk 4) ejection seat for pilot, under rearward-hinged canopy. Cockpit is air-conditioned, and is heated by warm air

bled from engine which also heats the radar compartment and certain equipment compartments. Intertechnique liquid oxygen system for pilot.
SYSTEMS: Two independent hydraulic systems, for landing gear retraction, flaps and flying controls, supplied by pumps similar to those fitted in Mirage III. Electrical system includes two Auxilec 15kVA variable-speed alternators, either of which can supply all functional and operational requirements. Emergency and standby power provided by SAFT Voltabloc 40Ah nickel-cadmium battery and EMD static converter. DC power provided by transformer-rectifiers operating in conjunction with battery. Liquid oxygen system standard.
AVIONICS AND EQUIPMENT: Thomson-CSF Cyrano IV fire-control radar in nose. This permits all-sector interception at any altitude and incorporates a system to eliminate 'fixed' echoes when following low-flying aircraft. Two UHF transceivers (one UHF/VHF), Socrat 6200 VOR/ILS with Socrat 5600 marker, LMT Tacan, LMT NR-AI-4-A IFF, remote-setting interception system, three-axis generator, central air data computer, Bézu Sphere with ILS indicator, Crouzet Type 63 navigation indicator and SFENA 505 autopilot. CSF head-up display, with magnifying lens, provides all necessary data for flying and fire control. SAGEM Uliss 47 inertial navigation system optional. Equipment for attack role can include Doppler radar and bombing computer, navigation computer, position indicator, laser rangefinder and terrain-avoidance radar.
ARMAMENT AND OPERATIONAL EQUIPMENT: Standard fixed armament of two 30 mm DEFA 553 cannon, with 125 rds/gun, mounted in lower front fuselage. Two Alkan universal stores attachment pylons under each wing and one under centre-fuselage, plus provision for carrying one air-to-air missile at each wingtip. Max external combat load 4,000 kg (8,820 lb). Externally-mounted weapons for interception role include Matra R.530 or Super 530 radar homing or infra-red homing air-to-air missiles on underfuselage and inboard wing pylons, and/or a Sidewinder or Matra 550 Magic infra-red homing air-to-air missile at each wingtip station. For ground

attack duties, typical loads may include one AS.37 Martel anti-radar missile or AS.30 air-to-surface missile, eight 450 kg bombs, four launchers each containing 18 air-to-ground rockets, or six 600 litre (132 Imp gallon) napalm tanks. Other possible external loads include three 1,200 litre (264 Imp gallon) auxiliary fuel tanks, or two photoflash containers and a reconnaissance pod incorporating an SAT Cyclope infra-red system and EMI side-looking radar.

DIMENSIONS, EXTERNAL:
Wing span	8·40 m (27 ft 6¾ in)
Length overall	15·00 m (49 ft 2½ in)
Height overall	4·50 m (14 ft 9 in)
Wheel track	2·50 m (8 ft 2½ in)
Wheelbase	5·00 m (16 ft 4¾ in)

AREA:
Wings, gross	25·00 m² (269·1 sq ft)

WEIGHTS AND LOADING:
Weight empty	7,400 kg (16,314 lb)
T-O weight, 'clean'	10,900 kg (24,030 lb)
Max T-O weight	15,200 kg (33,510 lb)
Max wing loading	608 kg/m² (124·5 lb/sq ft)

PERFORMANCE:
Max level speed (high altitude)	Mach 2·2
Max level speed (low altitude)	Mach 1·2
Approach speed	141 knots (260 km/h; 162 mph)
Landing speed	124 knots (230 km/h; 143 mph)
Max rate of climb at S/L (with afterburning)	
	12,780 m (41,930 ft)/min
Max rate of climb at high altitude (with afterburning)	
	14,580 m (47,835 ft)/min
Service ceiling	20,000 m (65,600 ft)
Stabilised supersonic ceiling	18,500 m (60,700 ft)
T-O run (AUW of 11,500 kg; 25,355 lb)	
	450 m (1,475 ft)
T-O run (typical interception mission)	
	640 m (2,100 ft)
Landing run (AUW of 8,500 kg; 18,740 lb)	
	500 m (1,640 ft)
Landing run (typical interception mission)	
	610 m (2,000 ft)
Endurance	3 h 45 min

DASSAULT MIRAGE 2000

Following cancellation of the ACF (Avion de Combat Futur) programme, described briefly in the 1975-76 *Jane's*, the Mirage 2000 was selected on 18 December 1975 as the primary combat aircraft of the French Air Force from the mid-eighties. Under French government contract, it is being developed initially as an interceptor and air superiority fighter, powered by a single SNECMA M53 turbofan engine. The Mirage 2000 will be equally suitable for reconnaissance, close support, and low-altitude attack missions in areas to the rear of a battlefield.

Reversion to a Mirage III/5 type of delta-wing design, without horizontal tail surfaces, caused some surprise after Dassault's choice of a tailed sweptwing configuration for the later Mirage F1 and ACF. It resulted from considerable study of the requirements of a smaller and less ambitious aircraft than the ACF. Research left no doubt that a delta wing embodying the latest aerodynamic concepts offers an excellent compromise between structural simplicity, light weight, high speed characteristics and the demands of rapid acceleration, high rate of climb and manoeuvrability for an aeroplane of relatively modest size and installed power. In particular, a delta layout offers low drag over a wide range of angles of attack in flight, while providing the largest practicable wing area, with attendant benefits in terms of tight turning capability and high service ceiling.

Former shortcomings, such as higher landing speed than a comparable sweptwing type, are overcome by the addition of automatic leading-edge flaps which, used in conjunction with the elevons, constitute a variable-camber wing. At the same time, the adoption of fly-by-wire control for the wing surfaces and rudder, with artificial stability ensured by a central computer, permits acceptance of a far-aft centre of gravity. This makes possible a much reduced landing speed for the Mirage 2000, and improves its manoeuvrability in combat.

Dassault Mirage F1-C-200 of the French Air Force, carrying two Matra 550 Magic air-to-air missiles on wingtip launchers and an underbelly R.530 missile. This uprated version, operated exclusively by the 5e Escadre de Chasse, is equipped with a flight refuelling probe

Having tested successfully a carbonfibre rudder on a Mirage III, and boron horizontal tail surfaces on a Mirage F1 throughout the flight regime to Mach 2·2, Dassault decided to utilise both materials in the Mirage 2000, achieving weight saving of 15-20 per cent in the components so constructed.

Wing area of the Mirage 2000 is some 15 per cent greater than that of the Mirage III/5, enabling it to carry more internal fuel. The combined effect of all the technological advances was summarised by Général Maurice Saint-Cricq, Chief of Staff of the French Air Force, in the Spring of 1977. He said that the Mirage 2000 is intended to fly at Mach 2·2 at a height of 18,000 m (59,000 ft); to offer low-speed characteristics at least as good as those of the Mirage F1; a rate of climb twice that of the Mirage III, enabling it to attack a Mach 3 aircraft penetrating at high altitude approximately five minutes from brake release; and a 30 per cent better range than that of the Mirage III, after take-off from a 1,200 m (3,940 ft) strip, enabling it to maintain coverage of a combat area for three times as long.

Five prototypes have been built, of which four were funded by the French Air Force and one by the manufacturers. The first of these made its first flight, at Istres, on 10 March 1978, only 27 months after programme launch in December 1975. The second flew on 18 September 1978, the third on 26 April 1979 and the fourth on 12 May 1980. The fifth, a two-seat trainer version, was also scheduled to fly during 1980. Delivery of production Mirage 2000s is expected to begin in 1983. The manufacturers' prototype will be used to develop equipment and other changes proposed for future variants and for export models of the Mirage 2000. Further airframes have been built for static and fatigue testing.

Initial production contracts, in 1979-82, were expected to finance 127 single-seat and two-seat Mirage 2000s in 'air defence' configuration, with an eventual requirement for 200 aircraft in this role; the first four were ordered in the 1979 budget and 22 were requested in 1980. Dassault believes that a further 200 Mirage 2000s will be required for reconnaissance and strike duties. A single basic type would then make up a high proportion of the French Air Force's planned first-line strength of 450 combat aircraft by the second half of the 1980s.

Because of development delays, the first production Mirage 2000s will have RDM multi-mission radar (as offered to export customers) instead of the RDI pulse-Doppler interception radar specified by the French Air Force. RDI systems will be fitted from 1985.

Two prototypes of the two-seat low-altitude penetration version of the Mirage 2000 are expected to fly in 1983. Production deliveries of this model, with Antilope radar and provision for carrying ASMP nuclear missiles, are scheduled to start in 1986.

The following description applies to the single-seat air defence version of the Mirage 2000.

TYPE: Single-seat interceptor and air superiority fighter.

WINGS: Cantilever multi-spar low-wing monoplane of delta planform, with cambered profile. Leading-edge sweepback 58°. Large-radius root fairings. Full-span automatic leading-edge flaps operate in conjunction with two-section elevons which form entire trailing-edge of each wing, to provide variable camber in combat and during landing approach. Leading-edge flaps are retracted during all phases of acceleration and low-altitude cruise, to reduce drag. Fly-by-wire control system for elevons and flaps, with surfaces actuated by hydraulic servo-units. No tabs. Retractable airbrakes above and below each wing.

FUSELAGE: Conventional all-metal semi-monocoque structure, 'waisted' in accordance with area rule. Small fixed strake, with marked dihedral, near leading-edge of each air intake trunk.

TAIL UNIT: Cantilever fin and inset rudder only; latter actuated by fly-by-wire control system via hydraulic servo-units. Much of fin skin and all rudder skin of

Third prototype Dassault Mirage 2000 (SNECMA M53-5 afterburning turbofan engine)

Dassault Mirage 2000 (one SNECMA M53 afterburning turbofan engine) *(Pilot Press)*

boron/epoxy/carbon composites. Sweepback on fin leading-edge 45°. No tab.

LANDING GEAR: Retractable tricycle type by Messier-Hispano-Bugatti, with twin nosewheels, and single wheel on each main unit. Hydraulic retraction, nosewheels rearward, main units inward. Oleo-pneumatic shock-absorbers. Electro-hydraulic nosewheel steering, through 45° to each side. Manual disconnect permits nosewheel unit to castor through 360° for ground towing. Light alloy wheels and tubeless tyres, size 360 × 135-6 on nosewheels, 750 × 230-15 on main wheels. Messier-Hispano-Bugatti hydraulically-actuated graphite composite disc brakes on main wheels, with anti-skid units. Runway arrester gear standard. Brake-chute in canister above jet nozzle.

POWER PLANT: One '10,000 kg class' SNECMA M53 afterburning turbofan engine. The 83·4 kN (18,740 lb st) M53-2 fitted for early prototype testing was replaced in 1980 by the 88·3 kN (19,840 lb st) M53-5, which will also power initial production aircraft. Under development for eventual use is the M53-P2, rated at 95·1 kN (21,385 lb st). Movable half-cone centrebody in each air intake. Internal fuel capacity 3,800 litres (835 Imp gal-

lons). Provision for a jettisonable fuel tank under each wing. Flight refuelling probe forward of cockpit on starboard side.

ACCOMMODATION: Pilot only, under transparent canopy, in air-conditioned and pressurised cockpit.

SYSTEMS: Two independent hydraulic systems, pressure 280 bars (4,000 lb/sq in), to actuate flying control servo-units, landing gear and brakes. Electrical system includes two Auxilec 20110 aircooled 20kVA 400Hz constant-frequency alternators, two Bronzavia DC transformers, a SAFT 40Ah battery and ATEI static inverter.

AVIONICS AND EQUIPMENT: Pulse-Doppler RDI radar, developed and produced by Thomson-CSF in collaboration with Electronique Marcel Dassault, with operating range of 54 nm (100 km; 62 miles), capability of detecting targets at all altitudes, and good ECCM characteristics (interchangeable with Thomson-CSF RDM multi-role radar. Strike version will have EMD/Thomson-CSF Antilope 5 ground-scan radar). SAGEM Uliss 52 inertial platform. EMD central digital computer. Thomson-CSF VE-130 head-up and VMC-180 head-down displays. SFENA 605 autopilot. ECM, including passive radar warning, LMT Deltac Tacan and IFF, Socrat VOR/ILS/marker beacon receiver, TRT radio altimeter and UHF and V/UHF com.

ARMAMENT: Two 30 mm DEFA cannon. Nine attachments for external stores, five under fuselage and two under each wing. Typical interception weapons comprise two Matra Super 530 missiles (inboard) and two Matra 550 Magic missiles (outboard) under wings. (Strike version will carry up to 5,800 kg (12,785 lb) of external stores, including nuclear weapons such as the ASMP.)

DIMENSIONS, EXTERNAL (estimated):
Wing span	9·00 m (29 ft 6 in)
Length overall	15·33 m (50 ft 3½ in)
Wheel track	3·40 m (11 ft 1¾ in)
Wheelbase	5·00 m (16 ft 4¾ in)

WEIGHT (estimated):
T-O weight, combat mission	9,000 kg (19,840 lb)

PERFORMANCE:
Max level speed	over Mach 2·3
Max continuous speed	Mach 2·2
Approach speed	140 knots (260 km/h; 162 mph)
Rate of climb at S/L	15,000 m (49,200 ft)/min
Time to 15,250 m (50,000 ft) and Mach 2	4 min
Service ceiling	20,000 m (65,600 ft)

This photograph shows clearly the difference in size between the Mirage 2000 (foreground) and the Super Mirage 4000. The first prototype Mirage 2000, illustrated, now has revised engine air intakes and fairings between the wing trailing-edge and fuselage

Ferry range with external tanks
2,100 nm (3,900 km; 2,420 miles)

DASSAULT SUPER MIRAGE 4000

When the French Air Force abandoned development of the ACF (Avion de Combat Futur) programme, in favour of the single-engined Mirage 2000, M Marcel Dassault announced, in December 1975, that Dassault-Breguet would develop at the French industry's own expense a twin-turbofan scale-up of the Mirage 2000, intended primarily for interception and low-altitude penetration attacks on targets a considerable distance from its base. Potential export customers were assured that the new aircraft would offer overall performance superior to that of any aircraft in its class known to be in production or under development.

A mockup of the new type, now designated Super Mirage 4000 (originally Super Mirage Delta), was unveiled in December 1977. The prototype achieved a speed of Mach 1·2 during its first flight on 9 March 1979, Mach 1·6 on its second flight three days later, and Mach 2·2 during its sixth flight on 11 April, when an initial spin analysis was also made and it was flown at angles of attack up to 25°.

Its general configuration is shown in the accompanying illustrations. Dimensions, weights, performance, and details of armament are generally classified; but installation of two engines of the type fitted in the single-engined Mirage 2000 will give the Super Mirage 4000 a power:weight ratio well above 1:1 in an interceptor role. It was said to have taken off at a loaded weight of about 20,000 kg (44,000 lb) for early flight tests.

The Super Mirage 4000 has computer-derived aerodynamics, with a rearward CG made possible by a fly-by-wire active control system. Other features include foreplanes, a blister-type cockpit canopy giving a 360° field of view, a very large nose radome, and extensive use of boron and carbonfibre composites for structures such as the fin, rudder, elevons, fuselage access panels and foreplanes.

The following details should be regarded as provisional:

TYPE: Single-seat multi-role combat aircraft (two-seat version under study).

WINGS: Cantilever mid-wing monoplane of delta planform, with computer-derived aerodynamics. Large-radius root fairings. Two-section elevons form entire trailing-edge of each wing. Full-span automatic leading-edge flaps provide variable camber in combat. Fly-by-wire active control system for elevons and flaps. No tabs.

FUSELAGE: Conventional semi-monocoque structure, 'waisted' in accordance with area rule. Door-type airbrake in each intake trunk above wing-root leading-edge.

TAIL UNIT AND FOREPLANES: Cantilever fin and inset rudder; latter actuated by fly-by-wire control system. Fin is made of carbon composite and contains fuel tankage. No tab. Variable-incidence swept canard foreplane near lip of each engine air intake duct.

LANDING GEAR: Retractable tricycle type, of Messier-Hispano-Bugatti design, with twin nosewheels and single wheel on each main unit. Hydraulic retraction, nosewheels forward, main units inward. Oleopneumatic shock-absorbers. Electro-hydraulic nose-wheel steering. Aluminium alloy main wheels, with tubeless tyres and steel disc brakes on prototype; graphite composite brakes planned on production aircraft.

POWER PLANT: Two '10,000 kg class' SNECMA M53 afterburning turbofan engines side by side in rear fuselage. Movable half-cone centrebody in each air intake.

Dassault Super Mirage 4000 (two SNECMA M53 afterburning turbofan engines)

Dassault Super Mirage 4000 multi-role combat aircraft (Pilot Press)

Provision for a large jettisonable fuel tank under each wing and under fuselage. Fuel tankage in fin helps to give total capacity about three times that of the Mirage 2000.

ACCOMMODATION: Pilot only, on Martin-Baker Mk 10 zero-zero ejection seat, under sideways-opening (to starboard) transparent canopy; 360° field of view.

SYSTEMS: Messier-Hispano-Bugatti hydraulic system, pressure 280 bars (4,000 lb/sq in), powered by four advanced pumps and using lightweight titanium pipelines. Two Auxilec electrical generators. Turboméca Palouste gas turbine APU, in compartment aft of pilot's seat, for engine starting.

AVIONICS AND EQUIPMENT: Provision for a radar of 90 cm (35·4 in) diameter in nose, to provide search range of up to 65-70 nm (120-130 km; 75-80 miles). Digital autopilot, multi-mode displays, SAGEM Uliss 52 inertial navigation system, Crouzet Type 80 air data computer, Thomson-CSF VE.120 head-up display and digital automated weapon delivery system.

ARMAMENT: Provision for two 30 mm DEFA guns in bottom of air intake trunks and a rail under each outer wing for a Matra 550 Magic air-to-air missile, plus a wide range of air-to-air and air-to-surface weapons. Total of eleven hardpoints for external stores.

DIMENSIONS, EXTERNAL:
Wing span	12·00 m (39 ft 4½ in)
Length overall	18·70 m (61 ft 4¼ in)
Wheel track	4·36 m (14 ft 3½ in)
Wheelbase	6·90 m (22 ft 7½ in)

AREA:
Wings, gross	73·00 m² (786 sq ft)

DASSAULT SUPER ETENDARD

Dassault is producing for the French Navy an updated version of its Etendard IV-M carrier-based fighter which has served with the Navy's operational squadrons since 1962, and was last described in the 1965-66 Jane's. The airframe and equipment of the new version, known as the Super Etendard, were expected to be 90 per cent common with those of the Etendard IV-M, except for the nav/attack system. In fact, the installation of a more powerful turbojet engine and equipment of enhanced capability, together with the adoption of improved aerodynamic features and modern manufacturing techniques, has made the Super Etendard 90 per cent new.

The Super Etendard is a transonic single-seat strike fighter, for low and medium altitude operations from ships in the class of the French Navy's Clémenceau and Foch. Its equipment includes a highly sophisticated and accurate nav/attack integrated avionics system. Inherent long range is increased by flight refuelling capability, and it is able to operate as a tanker for other aircraft.

The Atar 8K-50 turbojet engine is a non-afterburning version of the Atar 9K-50 used in the Mirage F1 multi-mission fighter and attack aircraft. It has a lower specific fuel consumption than the Atar 8 fitted in the Etendard IV-M. The thrust increase of about ten per cent, combined with a new wing leading-edge and redesigned flaps, allows a significant increase in gross weight for catapulting and, hence, permits increased fuel load and armament.

Two prototypes were produced by conversion of standard IV-M airframes. The first of these flew for the first time on 28 October 1974. Its programme included engine development, followed in 1978 by tests of the Super Etendard's external load-carrying capability and firing trials of the Exocet AM39 air-to-surface anti-shipping missile.

Dassault Super Etendard carrier-based fighter landing on the Clémenceau

The second prototype, which flew for the first time on 25 March 1975, was used for tests of the Super Etendard's navigation system and bombing capabilities. Its subsequent tasks included shipboard operation under open-sea conditions in waters other than the Mediterranean, where all early trials took place.

It was intended originally to build 100 production aircraft, but the number was reduced to 71 in order to conform with budget limitations. The first aircraft flew on 24 November 1977. Deliveries began on 28 June 1978, when the third production aircraft was accepted officially by the French Navy, and Dassault had delivered 33 Super Etendards by the end of March 1980, with production continuing at the rate of two aircraft per month.

It was announced in 1980 that the French Navy was studying the possibility of developing a reconnaissance version of the Super Etendard. The first export order, for 14, was placed by the Argentine Navy in 1979.

TYPE: Single-seat transonic carrier-based strike fighter.

WINGS: Cantilever mid-wing monoplane. Thickness/chord ratio varies from 6% at root to 5% at tip. Anhedral 1°. Sweepback at quarter-chord 45°. All-metal two-spar torsion-box structure; stressed skin of machined panels with integral stiffeners. Tips fold upward for carrier stowage. Inset ailerons, hydraulically-powered by Dassault irreversible dual circuits with artificial feel. Spoiler on top surface of each wing, ahead of special double-slotted flap with second slot in form of an integral 'gutter'. Flap travel increased by comparison with Etendard IV-M. Hydraulically-powered drooping leading-edges, with extended chord on outer panels.

FUSELAGE: All-metal semi-monocoque structure, 'waisted' in accordance with area rule. Perforated airbrake under each side of centre-fuselage.

TAIL UNIT: Cantilever all-metal structure, with tailplane mid-set on fin. All surfaces swept. All-moving tailplane (with electrically-powered pitch trim) and rudder are powered in same way as ailerons.

LANDING GEAR: Retractable tricycle type, with single wheel on each unit, manufactured by Messier-Hispano-Bugatti. Nosewheel retracts rearward, main units inward into wings and fuselage. Messier-Hispano-Bugatti oleo-pneumatic shock-absorbers and disc brakes. Main-wheel tyres size 30 × 7.7-16; nosewheel tyre size 490 × 155-9. Brake-chute in fairing at junction of fin and tailplane trailing-edges.

POWER PLANT: One SNECMA Atar 8K-50 non-afterburning turbojet, rated at 49 kN (11,025 lb st). Fuel in integral tanks in wings and rubber tanks in fuselage, with total capacity of 3,200 litres (704 Imp gallons; 845 US gallons). Provision for an external tank of 1,100 litres (242 Imp gallons; 290 US gallons) under each wing, and a 600 litre (132 Imp gallon; 158 US gallon) centreline tank or flight refuelling 'buddy' pack under the fuselage. Retractable flight refuelling probe in front of windscreen.

ACCOMMODATION: Pilot only, on Hispano-built Martin-Baker SEMMB CM4 A lightweight ejection seat in pressurised and air-conditioned cockpit. Extensively armoured.

SYSTEMS: Duplicated hydraulic circuits for flying controls, landing gear, brakes and airbrakes, and wing leading-edge droop.

AVIONICS AND EQUIPMENT: SAGEM-Kearfott ETNA inertial navigation and attack system; Thomson-CSF/EMD Agave lightweight search/track/designation/telemetry/navigation radar; Thomson-CSF VE-120 head-up display; Crouzet Type 97 navigation display, armament control panel and selector box, and Type 66 air data computer; TRT radio altimeter; SFIM three-axis attitude indicator; LMT micro-Tacan and IFF, and SOCRAT VOR.

ARMAMENT: Two DEFA 30 mm guns, each with 125 rds, in bottom of engine air intake trunks. Underfuselage

Dassault Super Etendard naval fighter (SNECMA Atar 8K-50 turbojet engine) *(Pilot Press)*

attachments for two 250 kg bombs. Four underwing attachments for 400 kg bombs, Magic air-to-air missiles or rocket pods. Optionally, one Exocet AM39 air-to-surface missile under starboard wing, and one external fuel tank under port wing.

DIMENSIONS, EXTERNAL:
Wing span	9.60 m (31 ft 6 in)
Width, wings folded	7.80 m (25 ft 7 in)
Wing aspect ratio	3.23
Length overall	14.31 m (46 ft 11½ in)
Height overall	3.86 m (12 ft 8 in)
Wheel track	3.50 m (11 ft 6 in)
Wheelbase	4.80 m (15 ft 9 in)

AREA:
Wings, gross	28.4 m² (305.7 sq ft)

WEIGHTS:
Weight empty	6,450 kg (14,220 lb)
Max fuel, incl two 1,100 litre underwing tanks	4,800 kg (10,580 lb)
Max weapon load, internal fuel only	2,100 kg (4,630 lb)
Max T-O weight	12,000 kg (26,455 lb)

PERFORMANCE:
Max level speed at height	approx Mach 1
Max level speed at low altitude	650 knots (1,204 km/h; 748 mph)
Approach speed for shipboard landing at AUW of 7,800 kg (17,200 lb)	122 knots (226 km/h; 140 mph)
Service ceiling	13,700 m (45,000 ft)
Radius of action, with AM39 missile	390 nm (720 km; 450 miles)

DASSAULT-BREGUET/DORNIER ALPHA JET

Details of the Alpha Jet programme can be found in the International section of this edition.

DASSAULT-BREGUET/BAe JAGUAR

Details of the Jaguar programme can be found under 'SEPECAT' in the International section of this edition.

DASSAULT-BREGUET ATLANTIC ANG

The Atlantic ANG (Atlantic Nouvelle Génération) is a twin-turboprop maritime patrol aircraft derived directly from the earlier Atlantic that was produced in 1964-74 for operation by the armed services of France (40, of which 3 were sold subsequently to Pakistan), West Germany (20, including 5 special-purpose ECM aircraft), Italy (18) and the Netherlands (9). Design definition of the new version was initiated by a French government instruction to proceed in July 1977, with the aim of providing a replacement for the first generation Atlantic and the Neptune during the period from 1985 to 1990. This led to launch of the development phase of the ANG programme in September 1978. Initial requirement is for 42 aircraft for the French Navy.

Two prototypes are being produced by modification of first generation Atlantic airframes. Work started in January 1979, and the prototypes are scheduled to fly in their new form in early 1981 and at the beginning of 1982 respectively. Series production is expected to begin in 1981, to permit delivery of the first production Atlantic ANG in early 1985. The work is likely to be shared by the same European SECBAT (Société d'Etudes et de Construction du Breguet Atlantic) consortium that was responsible for the earlier programme, with possible modification of the work-split to reflect varying national interests in the ANG aircraft. The Tyne engines will be produced by SNECMA of France, Rolls-Royce of the UK, FN of Belgium and MAN of West Germany; and propellers by Ratier of France and British Aerospace.

Structural changes by comparison with the first generation Atlantic will include use of a refined bonding technique, improved anti-corrosion protection, better sealing between skin panels, and design improvements offering longer fatigue life and more economical maintenance. These are intended to ensure increased serviceability, with 75 per cent of squadron aircraft permanently available for operations; readiness to take off within 20 minutes of an order to go; and an aircraft life of more than 25 years, or at least 15,000 flying hours.

The basic mission performance requirements envisaged for the ANG are quite similar to those of the Atlantic now in service: a high cruising speed to the operational area, quick descent from cruising altitude to patrol height, lengthy patrol endurance at low altitude, and a high degree of manoeuvrability at sea level. It will be able to carry a wide variety of weapons and equipment for finding and attacking both submarines and surface targets in all weathers. Like the original Atlantic, the ANG will be able to perform minelaying, logistic support, and passenger and freight transport missions. It could be adapted for advanced AEW and flight refuelling duties, and is suitable for civilian tasks such as air/sea rescue and patrol of offshore fishing and oil interests.

TYPE: Twin-turboprop maritime patrol aircraft.

WINGS: Cantilever mid-wing monoplane, with streamlined avionics pods on tips. Wing section NACA 64 series. Dihedral 6° on outer panels only. Incidence 3°. Tapered planform, with 9° sweepback on leading-edge. All-metal three-spar fail-safe structure, with bonded light alloy honeycomb skin panels on torsion box and on main landing gear doors. Two conventional all-metal ailerons on each wing, actuated by SAMM twin-cylinder jacks. All-metal slotted flaps, with bonded light alloy honeycomb filling, in three segments on each wing, over 75% of span. Three hinged spoilers on upper surface of each outer wing, forward of flaps. Metal airbrake above and below each wing. No trim tabs. Air Equipement/Kléber-Colombes pneumatic de-icing system on leading-edges.

FUSELAGE: All-metal 'double-bubble' fail-safe structure, with bonded honeycomb sandwich skin on pressurised central section of upper lobe, weapons bay doors and nosewheel door.

TAIL UNIT: Cantilever all-metal structure, with bonded honeycomb sandwich skin panels on torsion boxes. Fixed-incidence tailplane, with dihedral. Control surfaces operated through SAMM twin-cylinder jacks. No trim tabs. Air Equipement/Kléber-Colombes pneumatic de-icing system on leading-edges.

LANDING GEAR: Retractable tricycle type, supplied by Messier-Hispano-Bugatti, with twin wheels on each unit. Hydraulic retraction, nosewheels rearward, main units forward into engine nacelles. Kléber-Colombes or Dunlop tyres; size 39 × 13-20 on main wheels, pressure 12 bars (170 lb/sq in), 26 × 8-13 on nosewheels, pressure 6.5 bars (94 lb/sq in). New Messier-Hispano-

Dassault-Breguet Atlantic ANG twin-turboprop maritime patrol aircraft *(Pilot Press)*

Bugatti disc brakes with higher braking energy, and Modistop anti-skid units.

POWER PLANT: Two 4,638 kW (6,220 ehp) Rolls-Royce Tyne RTy.20 Mk 21 turboprop engines, each driving a four-blade Ratier/British Aerospace constant-speed propeller type PD 249/476/3. Six pressure-refuelled integral fuel tanks in wings, with total capacity of 23,000 litres (5,059 Imp gallons). Provision for auxiliary tankage in weapons bay, capacity 4,600 litres (1,012 Imp gallons). Updated gauging system. Oil capacity 100 litres (22 Imp gallons).

ACCOMMODATION: Normal flight crew of 12, comprising observer in nose; pilot, co-pilot and flight engineer on flight deck; a radio-navigator, ESM-ECM-MAD operator, radar-IFF operator, tactical co-ordinator and two acoustic sensor operators at stations on the starboard side of the tactical compartment; and two observers in beam positions at the rear. Provision for carrying relief crew, or 12 other personnel. Rest compartment, with eight seats, in centre-fuselage, forward of crew room with tables and seats, galley, toilet and wardrobe. Primary access via extending airstair door in bottom of rear fuselage. Emergency exits above and below flight deck and on each side of fuselage, above wing trailing-edge.

SYSTEMS: Air-conditioning system by ABG/SEMCA, supplied by two compressors driven by gearboxes. Heat exchangers and bootstrap system for cabin temperature control. Duplicated hydraulic system, to operate flying controls, landing gear, flaps, weapons bay doors and retractable radome. Three basic electrical systems: variable-frequency three-phase 115/208V AC system, with two 60/80kVA generators and modernised control and protection equipment; fixed-frequency three-phase 115/208V 400Hz AC system, with four 20kVA Auxilec generators, two on each engine; 28V DC system, with four 6kW transformer-rectifiers supplied from the variable-frequency AC system, and one 40Ah battery. One 60kVA emergency AC generator, driven at constant speed by APU. Individual oxygen bottles for emergency use. Electrical anti-icing for engine air intake lips, propeller blades and spinners. Astadyne gas turbine APU for engine starting, emergency electrical supply, and air-conditioning on ground.

ARMAMENT AND OPERATIONAL EQUIPMENT: Main weapons bay in unpressurised lower fuselage can accommodate all NATO standard bombs, depth charges, eight homing torpedoes or two air-to-surface missiles (typical load comprises three torpedoes and one AM39 Exocet missile). Four underwing attachments for stores, including rockets, missiles or containers. Up to 78 sonobuoys in compartment aft of weapons bay, where whole of upper and lower fuselage provides storage for sonobuoys and marker flares. Forward-looking infra-red sensor under nose. Thomson-CSF Iguane retractable radar immediately forward of weapons bay, with LMT IFF interrogator and SECRE decoder. Cameras in port side of nose and in bottom of rear fuselage. Crouzet-manufactured MAD in tail sting. Thomson-CSF Arar 13 radar detector for ESM. Other equipment includes HF com, Tacan and DME by LMT, VHF/AM com by Socrat, TRT radio altimeter, Collins MF and V/UHF radio compass, dual SAGEM Uliss 53 inertial navigation systems, SAGEM teleprinters, Crouzet geographical display and air data computer. UHF and VHF/FM suppliers not yet designated. Thomson-CSF Sadang system for processing active and passive acoustic detection data.

DIMENSIONS, EXTERNAL:

Wing span, incl wingtip pods	37·36 m (122 ft 6¾ in)
Wing aspect ratio	10·94
Length overall	31·75 m (104 ft 2 in)
Height overall	11·34 m (37 ft 2½ in)
Fuselage: Max depth	4·00 m (13 ft 1½ in)
Tailplane span	12·31 m (40 ft 4½ in)
Wheel track	9·00 m (29 ft 6¼ in)
Wheelbase	9·45 m (31 ft 0 in)
Propeller diameter	4·88 m (16 ft 0 in)
Distance between propeller centres	
	9·00 m (29 ft 6¼ in)
Main weapons bay: Length	9·00 m (29 ft 6¼ in)
Width	2·10 m (6 ft 10¾ in)

DIMENSIONS, INTERNAL:

Cabin, incl rest compartment, galley, toilet, aft observers' stations: Length	18·50 m (60 ft 8½ in)
Max width	3·60 m (11 ft 9½ in)
Max height	2·00 m (6 ft 6¾ in)
Floor area	155 m² (1,668 sq ft)
Volume	92 m³ (3,250 cu ft)

AREAS:

Wings, gross	120·34 m² (1,295·3 sq ft)
Ailerons (total)	5·26 m² (56·62 sq ft)
Flaps (total)	26·80 m² (288·48 sq ft)
Spoilers (total)	1·66 m² (17·87 sq ft)
Vertical tail surfaces (total)	16·64 m² (179·11 sq ft)
Rudder	5·96 m² (64·15 sq ft)
Horizontal tail surfaces (total)	
	33·00 m² (355·21 sq ft)
Elevators	8·30 m² (89·34 sq ft)

WEIGHTS AND LOADINGS:

Weight empty, equipped, standard mission	
	25,000 kg (55,115 lb)
Military load: ASW mission	2,200 kg (4,850 lb)
ASV mission	3,000 kg (6,610 lb)
Max fuel	18,500 kg (40,785 lb)
Mission T-O weight: ASW	43,900 kg (96,780 lb)
ASV	45,400 kg (100,090 lb)
Max overload T-O weight	46,200 kg (101, 850 lb)
Max zero-fuel weight	29,000 kg (63,935 lb)
Normal design landing weight	36,000 kg (79,365 lb)
Max landing weight, emergency	
	46,000 kg (101,400 lb)
Max wing loading	385 kg/m² (78·96 lb/sq ft)
Max power loading	5·07 kg/kW (8·34 lb/ehp)

PERFORMANCE (estimated, at T-O weight of 45,000 kg; 99,200 lb, except where indicated):

Never-exceed speed	Mach 0·7
Max level speed at optimum height	
	355 knots (657 km/h; 408 mph)
Max level speed at S/L 320 knots (592 km/h; 368 mph)	
Max cruising speed at 7,600 m (25,000 ft)	
	300 knots (555 km/h; 345 mph)
Normal patrol speed, S/L to 1,525 m (5,000 ft)	
	180 knots (333 km/h; 207 mph)
Stalling speed, flaps down 90 knots (167 km/h; 104 mph)	
Max rate of climb at S/L, AUW of 30,000 kg (66,140 lb)	
	884 m (2,900 ft)/min
Max rate of climb at S/L, AUW of 40,000 kg (88,185 lb)	
	610 m (2,000 ft)/min
Rate of climb at S/L, one engine out, AUW of 30,000 kg (66,140 lb)	365 m (1,200 ft)/min
Rate of climb at S/L, one engine out, AUW of 40,000 kg (88,185 lb)	213 m (700 ft)/min
Service ceiling	9,100 m (30,000 ft)
Runway LCN at max T-O weight	60
T-O to 10·5 m (35 ft)	1,620 m (5,315 ft)
T-O to 10·5 m (35 ft), one engine out	2,240 m (7,350 ft)
Landing from 15 m (50 ft)	1,500 m (4,922 ft)
170 knot turning radius at AUW of 40,000 kg (88,185 lb) at:	
30° bank	1,500 m (4,925 ft)
45° bank	600 m (1,970 ft)
60° bank	500 m (1,640 ft)
Ferry range with max fuel	
	4,400 nm (8,150 km; 5,065 miles)
Typical endurance at low altitude:	
600 nm (1,110 km; 690 miles) from base	8 h
1,000 nm (1,850 km; 1,150 miles) from base	5 h
Max endurance	18 h

DASSAULT MYSTÈRE-FALCON 20 SERIES F

Details of the early history of this twin-turbofan light transport can be found in the 1977-78 Jane's.

Dassault builds the wings and Aérospatiale the fuselages and tail units of production aircraft, which are marketed in the USA under the name Falcon and elsewhere as Mystère 20s. The first production aircraft flew on 1 January 1965, and by 1 June 1980 sales of Mystère-Falcon 20s had reached 459, of which 164 were for customers in the areas marketed by Dassault. Of these, 422 had been delivered, including about 260 to the Business Jets Division of Pan American and its successor, Falcon Jet Corporation, formed jointly by Dassault-Breguet and Pan American in 1973. Production is continuing at the rate of two aircraft per month.

Basic current production version is the **Mystère-Falcon 20 Series F**, which introduced high-lift devices to improve T-O and landing performance, more powerful engines than earlier Falcons and increased wing fuel tank capacity. The prototype was displayed at the Paris Air Show in June 1969 and deliveries began in July 1970. During 1970 the Series F became the first aircraft to receive type approval under FAR Pt 36 anti-noise regulations. This approval was subsequently extended to other versions.

The **Mystère-Falcon 20 Series G** and **Series H** are described separately.

All versions of the Mystère-Falcon 20 can be modified as follows for specific duties:

Calibration: Two aircraft ordered by the SGAC, one by the Spanish government and one by the Indonesian government are used for the calibration of radio navigation aids. The equipment includes a removable console, thus retaining the full passenger-carrying capability of the aircraft. The Indonesian aircraft is fitted with an infra-red tracking system supplied by SAT.

Airline crew training: Since 20 September 1966, several Mystère-Falcon 20s have been used by Air France to train pilots for its jet airliners, with up to five aircraft being used simultaneously. Japan Air Lines also bought three of this version.

Cross-country: Similar to basic aircraft, but with low-pressure tyres for soft-field operation at the same take-off and landing weights. Described in 1968-69 Jane's.

Quick-change and cargo: A quick-change kit, consisting of an assembly of nets and supports, keeps the centre aisle free and allows direct access to nine freight compartments. Total usable volume of these compartments is 6·65 m³ (235 cu ft), and transformation from executive configuration to cargo configuration, or vice versa, takes less than one hour. A cargo version of the Falcon is also available and is described separately. For both versions an increase of the maximum zero-fuel weight from 8,900 kg (19,600 lb) to 9,980 kg (22,000 lb) allows an increased payload of up to 3,000 kg (6,615 lb).

Aerial photography: The French Institut Géographique National has a Mystère-Falcon 20 fitted with two cameras (Zeiss RMK 610 mm focal length, and Wild RC8, RC9 or RC10) and an intervalometer. This enables the aircraft to be used for high-altitude photography and photogrammetry duties.

Systems trainer: Two aircraft fitted with Mirage III-E combat radar and navigation systems are in service with the French Air Force for training its Mirage pilots. This version, known as the **Falcon ST**, has been sold also to Libya.

TYPE: Twin-turbofan executive transport.

WINGS: Cantilever low-wing monoplane. Thickness/chord ratio varies from 10·5 to 8%. Dihedral 2°. Incidence 1° 30′. Sweepback at quarter-chord 30°. All-metal (copper-bearing alloys) fail-safe torsion-box structure with machined stressed skin. Ailerons are each operated by Dassault twin-body actuators, from dual hydraulic systems, and have artificial feel. Non-slotted slats inboard of fence, and slotted slats outboard, on each wing. Hydraulically-actuated spoilers forward of the hydraulically-actuated two-section single-slotted flaps. Leading-edges anti-iced by engine bleed air.

FUSELAGE: All-metal semi-monocoque structure of circular cross-section, built on fail-safe principles.

TAIL UNIT: Cantilever all-metal structure, with electrically-controlled variable-incidence tailplane mounted halfway up fin. Elevators and rudder each actuated by twin hydraulic servos. No trim tabs.

LANDING GEAR: Retractable tricycle type, by Messier-Hispano-Bugatti, with twin wheels on all three units. Hydraulic retraction, main units inward, nosewheels forward. Oleo-pneumatic shock-absorbers. Goodyear disc brakes and anti-skid units. Normal tyre pressure 9·15 bars (133 lb/sq in) on all units. Low-pressure gear (4·5 bars; 65 lb/sq in) available optionally. Steerable and self-centering nosewheels. Braking parachute standard.

POWER PLANT: Two General Electric CF700-2D-2 turbofan engines (each 20 kN; 4,500 lb st) mounted in pod on each side of rear fuselage. Fuel in two integral tanks in wings and two auxiliary tanks aft of rear pressure bulkhead in fuselage, with total capacity of 5,200 litres (1,144 Imp gallons; 1,374 US gallons). Separate fuel system for each engine, with provision for cross-feeding. Single-point pressure refuelling. Emergency refuelling by gravity.

ACCOMMODATION: Crew of two on flight deck, with full dual controls and airline-type instrumentation. Normal seating for eight or ten passengers in individual reclining chairs, with tables between forward pairs of seats and a central 'trench' aisle, or 12-14 passengers at reduced pitch without tables. Toilet at rear. Baggage space and wardrobe on starboard side, immediately aft of flight deck opposite door, and at rear of cabin. Buffet with ice-box, food and liquid storage at front of cabin on port side. Downward-opening door has built-in steps.

SYSTEMS: Duplicated air-conditioning and pressurisation system, supplied with air bled from both engines. Pressure differential 0·57 bars (8·3 lb/sq in). Two independent hydraulic systems, pressure 207 bars (3,000 lb/sq

Dassault Mystère-Falcon 20 of the Spanish Air Force, by which it is designated TM.11 (Antonio Camarasa)

in), with twin engine-driven pumps and emergency electric pump, actuate primary flying controls, flaps, landing gear, wheel brakes, spoilers and nosewheel steering. 28V DC electrical system with a 9kW 28V DC starter/generator on each engine, one 1500VA and two 750VA 400Hz 118/208V inverters and two 40Ah batteries. Automatic emergency oxygen system. 9kW Microturbo Saphir II APU optional.

AVIONICS AND EQUIPMENT: Standard equipment includes duplicated VHF and VOR/glideslope, single ADF and DME, marker beacon receiver, ATC transponder, cockpit audio and duplicated blind-flying instrumentation. Optional equipment includes integrated flight instrument system, weather radar, HF communications radio, autopilot, second ADF and DME, and cabin address system.

DIMENSIONS, EXTERNAL:

Wing span	16·30 m (53 ft 6 in)
Wing chord (mean)	2·85 m (9 ft 4 in)
Wing aspect ratio	6·4
Length overall	17·15 m (56 ft 3 in)
Length of fuselage	15·55 m (51 ft 0 in)
Height overall	5·32 m (17 ft 5 in)
Tailplane span	6·74 m (22 ft 1 in)
Wheel track	3·69 m (12 ft 1¼ in)
Wheelbase	5·74 m (18 ft 10 in)
Passenger door: Height	1·52 m (5 ft 0 in)
Width	0·80 m (2 ft 7½ in)
Height to sill	1·09 m (3 ft 7 in)
Emergency exits (each side, over wing):	
Height	0·66 m (2 ft 2 in)
Width	0·48 m (1 ft 7 in)

DIMENSIONS, INTERNAL:

Cabin, incl fwd baggage space and rear toilet:	
Length	7·08 m (23 ft 2¾ in)
Max width	1·87 m (6 ft 1¾ in)
Max height	1·73 m (5 ft 8 in)
Volume	20·0 m³ (700 cu ft)
Baggage compartment (fwd)	0·70 m³ (24·7 cu ft)
Baggage compartment (aft)	0·37 m³ (13·1 cu ft)

AREAS:

Wings, gross	41·00 m² (440 sq ft)
Horizontal tail surfaces (total)	11·30 m² (121·6 sq ft)
Vertical tail surfaces (total)	7·60 m² (81·8 sq ft)

WEIGHTS:

Weight empty, equipped	7,530 kg (16,600 lb)
Max payload	1,180 kg (2,600 lb)
Max T-O and ramp weight	13,000 kg (28,660 lb)
Max zero-fuel weight	8,900 kg (19,600 lb)
Typical landing weight	8,930 kg (19,685 lb)

PERFORMANCE:

Never-exceed speed at S/L
350 knots (650 km/h; 404 mph) IAS
Never-exceed speed at 7,000 m (23,000 ft)
390 knots (725 km/h; 450 mph) IAS
Max cruising speed at 7,620 m (25,000 ft) at AUW of 9,071 kg (20,000 lb)
465 knots (862 km/h; 536 mph)
Econ cruising speed at 12,200 m (40,000 ft)
405 knots (750 km/h; 466 mph)
Stalling speed 82 knots (152 km/h; 95 mph)
Absolute ceiling 12,800 m (42,000 ft)
Service ceiling, one engine out, at AUW of 8,500 kg (18,700 lb)
7,480 m (24,500 ft)
T-O to 10·7 m (35 ft) at AUW of 12,580 kg (27,735 lb) (full tanks, 8 passengers and baggage)
915 m (3,000 ft)
FAR 25 balanced T-O field length, AUW as above
1,450 m (4,750 ft)
FAR 121 landing field length at AUW of 8,550 kg (18,870 lb) (8 passengers, 45 min reserves)
985 m (3,230 ft)
Landing from 15 m (50 ft) 590 m (1,930 ft)
Range with max fuel and 725 kg (1,600 lb) payload at econ cruising speed, with reserves for 45 min cruise 1,808 nm (3,350 km; 2,080 miles)

DASSAULT MYSTÈRE-FALCON 20 SERIES G

US Coast Guard designation: HU-25A Guardian

When Dassault-Breguet released preliminary details of the Garrett-engined version of its Mystère-Falcon 20 twin-turbofan business jet in the late Spring of 1976, it stated that the new power plant, complete with nacelles and thrust reversers, would be offered initially as a retrofit for existing aircraft, with full production of the new model, designated Mystère-Falcon 20G, scheduled for a later date.

A further statement, in the Autumn of 1976, announced that a tender by Falcon Jet Corporation, distributor and support centre for Falcons in the USA, had proved the lowest bid to meet a US Coast Guard requirement for a medium-range surveillance aircraft known by the project designation HX-XX. This was confirmed on 5 January 1977, when William T. Coleman Jr, then US Secretary of Transportation, authorised the Coast Guard to award a contract for 41 aircraft to Falcon Jet Corporation.

A prototype (F-WATF) flew for the first time on 28 November 1977, and was the 362nd Mystère-Falcon 20 to be completed. Production aircraft are expected to have 44 per cent French content and 56 per cent US content.

Dassault Mystère-Falcon Guardian, prototype for the US Coast Guard's HU-25A

The 41 Falcon 20Gs ordered by the US Coast Guard, as **HU-25As**, are to be delivered at the rate of about one a month, from early 1981. In choosing the type to meet its HX-XX requirement, the Coast Guard had expressed a preference for a turbofan-powered aircraft, with a minimum cabin/cockpit volume of 17 m³ (600 cu ft), able to perform the full range of MRS (medium-range surveillance) missions. These were listed as search and rescue (28·5% of total flight hours), marine environmental protection (30·3%), enforcement of laws and treaties (18·9%), marine science activities (10·6%), logistics support (5·4%), engineering support (3·8%), domestic ice-breaking (1·7%) and short-range aids to navigation (0·8%).

The basic airframe of the HU-25A is little changed from that of the Mystère-Falcon 20F. The most significant new features are as follows:

AIRFRAME: Fuselage is modified to embody a drop hatch, and one search window on each side. Four hardpoints under fuselage: two for 500 kg (1,100 lb) loads, two for 200 kg (440 lb) loads. Four underwing hardpoints: two for 660 kg (1,455 lb) loads, two for 230 kg (507 lb) loads.

POWER PLANT: Two Garrett-AiResearch ATF 3-6-2C turbofan engines (each 24·65 kN; 5,538 lb st), meeting current and proposed FAR Pt 36 noise standards. Entire engine open to borescope inspection. Fuel tankage, total capacity 5,770 litres (1,269 Imp gallons; 1,524 US gallons), divided into two identical halves, one for each engine with cross-feed capability. Wing feeder tanks pressurised with bleed air, so that fuel will continue to flow to engines with all pumps turned off. Provision for auxiliary fuel tank in rear of cabin. Single-point refuelling in about nine minutes. Fuel heaters and bacterial protection standard.

ACCOMMODATION: Normal crew of five to seven. Typical complement will comprise two pilots, one surveillance system operator (SSO) at a console on the starboard side at the rear of the cabin, two search crew members at side windows. A three-seat sofa is provided for passengers, on the port side. A drop-hatch for stores, with floor-mounted roller conveyor, is located towards the front of the cabin. Galley and retractable toilet on port side. Provision for carrying four stretchers.

SYSTEMS: Pressurisation and air-conditioning by engine bleed air; max pressure differential 0·585 bars (8·5 lb/sq in). Two independent hydraulic systems, with twin engine-driven pumps; electric standby pump to power primary flight control system in emergency. All primary flight controls utilise dual hydraulic actuators, artificial feel, electric trim and manual backup. Each half of the dual actuator is fed by one of the hydraulic systems; failure of either system will not affect handling, as each actuator has sufficient power for full control deflection. DC electrical system, with two 9kW engine-driven starter/generators, two nickel-cadmium batteries and two 1,000VA static inverters. Ground power receptacle. One 20kVA alternator driven by hydraulic motor, plus one 4kVA alternator driven by APU. Wings and nacelles anti-iced by engine bleed air, permitting flight under maximum icing conditions with one engine out.

AVIONICS: Basic avionics package includes dual HF, VHF-AM, IFF, single VHF-FM and UHF. Nav equipment includes inertial sensor system, Omega, dual VOR/ILS/MBR, DME, ADF, radio altimeters, area navigation system and single Tacan. Sensors include maritime search and weather radar and optional SLAR, infra-red and ultra-violet scanners, FLIR, aerial reconnaissance camera and steerable TV camera with laser illumination invisible to human eyes.

DIMENSIONS, EXTERNAL:

Wing span	16·30 m (53 ft 6 in)
Wing aspect ratio	7·02
Length overall	17·15 m (56 ft 3 in)
Height overall	5·32 m (17 ft 5 in)
Tailplane span	6·74 m (22 ft 1 in)

AREA:

Wings, gross	41·80 m² (450 sq ft)

WEIGHTS:

Weight empty	8,620 kg (19,000 lb)
Operating weight empty, with 5 crew and complete avionics package	9,475 kg (20,890 lb)
Max fuel	4,636 kg (10,220 lb)
Max zero-fuel weight	10,215 kg (22,520 lb)
Max T-O weight	14,515 kg (32,000 lb)
Max landing weight	12,510 kg (27,580 lb)

PERFORMANCE (at max T-O weight, except where indicated):

Max cruising speed at 12,200 m (40,000 ft) Mach 0·8
(461 knots; 855 km/h; 531 mph)
Econ cruising speed at 12,500 m (41,000 ft) Mach 0·72
Min manoeuvring speed at low altitude
150 knots (278 km/h; 173 mph)
Initial cruising height 12,500 m (41,000 ft)
T-O run 1,235 m (4,050 ft)
FAR 25 landing run at typical landing weight
625 m (2,050 ft)
Range with 5 crew, reserves of 5% total fuel plus 30 min at S/L 2,250 nm (4,170 km; 2,590 miles)

Dassault Mystère-Falcon 20 Series H (*Pilot Press*)

DASSAULT MYSTÈRE-FALCON 20 SERIES H and GARDIAN

This new version of the Mystère-Falcon 20 was announced at the 1979 Paris Air Show. As well as representing the latest variant of the executive transport, it is the basic aircraft for maritime surveillance, under the name Gardian/Guardian; five have been ordered by the French Navy, to replace P-2H Neptunes, and others by the Japan Maritime Safety Agency.

The Series H retains almost unchanged the airframe, varied configurations and operational flexibility of the Mystère-Falcon 20 Series F, but is powered by two Garrett-AiResearch turbofans of the type used in the Series G/HU-25A and is fitted with the new rear fuselage structural fuel tank developed for the Mystère-Falcon 50. This combination of engines with improved sfc and increased fuel capacity enables the Series H to offer a 42 per cent longer range than the Series F with eight passengers and 45 min fuel reserves, without any sacrifice of cabin volume.

To hasten development, Dassault flew for the first time on 24 April 1979 an aircraft known as the **Mystère-Falcon 20FH** (F-WZAH), embodying the new fuselage fuel tank and associated system changes, but retaining the General Electric CF700 engines of the Series F. The same aircraft was then re-engined with Garrett turbofans and resumed flying as a fully-representative Series H prototype. Certification of the new model was scheduled for the second half of 1980.

The description of the Mystère-Falcon 20F applies also to the Series H, except as follows:

POWER PLANT: Two Garrett-AiResearch ATF 3-6-2C turbofan engines (each 24·65 kN; 5,538 lb st). Fuel in two integral tanks in wings and large integral tank in rear fuselage, with total capacity of 6,100 litres (1,342 Imp gallons; 1,611 US gallons).

WEIGHTS:
Weight empty	8,070 kg (17,790 lb)
Max fuel	4,900 kg (10,800 lb)
Payload with max fuel	910 kg (2,006 lb)
T-O weight with 2 crew, 8 passengers and max fuel	13,150 kg (28,990 lb)
Max T-O weight	14,060 kg (31,000 lb)
Max zero-fuel weight	10,000 kg (22,050 lb)

PERFORMANCE (estimated):
Max cruising speed at 10,050 m (33,000 ft)
 Mach 0·80 (470 knots; 870 km/h; 540 mph)
Balanced T-O field length with 8 passengers and max fuel 1,520 m (5,000 ft)
Landing field length with 8 passengers and reserves 1,000 m (3,280 ft)
Range with 8 passengers, 45 min reserves 2,520 nm (4,670 km; 2,900 miles)

DASSAULT FALCON CARGO JET

Under contract from Pan American Business Jets, Little Rock Airmotive converted a Falcon 20 into a specialised cargo aircraft. Known as the Falcon Cargo Jet, the prototype flew for the first time on 28 March 1972. By the Summer of the same year, Federal Express Corporation, of Little Rock, had three similar aircraft in service and expanded its fleet subsequently to a total of 32 Falcon D Cargo Jets.

The cargo conversion can be applied to any Mystère-Falcon 20 and is offered on the current Series F aircraft.

Basic feature of the conversion is replacement of the standard cabin door by a hydraulically-actuated cargo

Dassault Mystère-Falcon 10MER radar training aircraft of the French Navy

door 1·88 m wide by 1·44 m high (6 ft 2 in × 4 ft 9 in), forward of the wing on the port side. This door opens upward, with its sill at cabin floor level. The flooring itself is new and offers a completely flat area 7·01 m long by 1·62 m wide (23 ft × 5 ft 4 in). Made of aluminium honeycomb, it can sustain loadings of up to 488 kg/m² (100 lb/sq ft) and affords a vast number of alternative tiedown points for retainer nets and pallets. Floor-mounted rollers are optional.

The Falcon Cargo Jet's Category II solid-state avionics standard includes dual com/nav, dual flight directors, autopilot and weather radar. Specifically, in the case of the Federal Express fleet, the fit comprises RCA com/nav with DME, dual Collins FD-108 flight directors, RCA AVQ-21 radar, Collins AP-105 autopilot, Teledyne angle-of-attack system, Collins ADF and RCA transponder. Also installed on these aircraft is a Fairchild integral electronic weight and balance system, which indicates as a cockpit readout whether or not cargo weight and distribution are within the legal limits. Standard safety provisions include a quick-release cargo restraint system able to withstand 9g.

Dimensions, weights and performance are largely unchanged by this conversion scheme. Nominal empty weight is 6,963 kg (15,350 lb) and max zero-fuel weight is increased to 9,980 kg (22,000 lb). Range varies from 1,215 nm (2,250 km; 1,400 miles) with max payload to 1,736 nm (3,215 km; 2,000 miles) with max fuel and a 2,040 kg (4,500 lb) payload. Usable cabin volume is 14·15 m³ (500 cu ft).

DASSAULT MYSTÈRE-FALCON 10

The Mystère-Falcon 10 is basically a scaled-down version of the Mystère-Falcon 20, with similar wing high-lift devices to those of the Mystère-Falcon 20F and powered by two small turbofans in the 14·6 kN (3,300 lb st) class. It is designed to fail-safe principles and to comply with US FAR 25 transport category requirements.

A prototype (F-WFAL), with General Electric CJ610 turbojets, made its first flight on 1 December 1970. Flight testing was resumed on 7 May 1971 following modifications to the angles of wing incidence and dihedral and an increase in wing sweepback. The modified aircraft set a 1,000 km closed-circuit speed record of 502·05 knots (930·4 km/h; 578·13 mph) in FAI Class C1f on 1 June 1971.

A second prototype (F-WTAL), with Garrett-AiResearch TFE 731-2 engines, flew for the first time on 15 October 1971, followed by a third aircraft on 14

October 1972, with similar engines. This third Mystère-Falcon 10 set a 2,000 km closed-circuit speed record of 494·83 knots (917·02 km/h; 569·809 mph) in Class C1f on 29 May 1973.

The first production Mystère-Falcon 10 with TFE 731-2 engines flew on 30 April 1973. French certification was granted on 11 September 1973, followed by FAA certification nine days later, allowing deliveries of production aircraft to begin on 1 November. A total of 160 had been delivered by 1 June 1980, at which time 194 Mystère-Falcon 10s had been ordered. They include three **Mystère-Falcon 10MER** aircraft for the French Navy, which uses them as intruders for interception training of Super Etendard pilots, as conventional instrument and night flying trainers, for calibration of shipboard radars and for medical evacuation, as well as for communications duties. The Navy has an option on two more.

At the beginning of 1979, rate of production at the Istres assembly plant was two per month. Fuselages are provided by the Potez works at Aire-sur-Adour, which assembles components built by SOGERMA, SOCEA and SOCATA. Wings come from CASA of Spain; tail units and nose assemblies from IAM of Italy; and many other components such as tail fins, doors and emergency exits from Latécoère's Toulouse works.

Like the Mystère-Falcon 20, the Mystère-Falcon 10 can be equipped for liaison, executive transport, navigation/attack system training, aerial photography, radio navigation aid calibration and ambulance duties.

TYPE: Twin-turbofan executive transport.

WINGS: Cantilever low-wing monoplane with increased sweepback on inboard leading-edges. All-metal torsion-box structure, with leading-edge slats and double-slotted trailing-edge flaps and plain ailerons. Two-section spoilers above each wing, forward of flaps.

FUSELAGE: All-metal semi-monocoque structure, designed to fail-safe principles.

TAIL UNIT: Cantilever all-metal structure, similar to that of Falcon 20.

LANDING GEAR: Retractable tricycle type, manufactured by Messier-Hispano-Bugatti, with twin wheels on main gear, single wheel on nose gear. Hydraulic retraction, main units inward, nosewheel forward. Oleo-pneumatic shock-absorbers. Low-pressure tyres for soft-field operation.

POWER PLANT: Two Garrett-AiResearch TFE 731-2 turbofan engines (each 14·4 kN; 3,230 lb st), mounted in pod on each side of rear fuselage. Fuel in two integral tanks in wings and two feeder tanks aft of rear bulkhead, with total capacity of 3,340 litres (735 Imp gallons; 882 US gallons). Separate fuel system for each engine, with provision for cross-feeding. Pressure refuelling system.

ACCOMMODATION: Crew of two on flight deck, with dual controls and airline-type instrumentation. Provision for third crew member on a jump-seat. Normal seating for four passengers (two individual seats and a three-seat sofa) or for seven passengers, with two individual seats added. Each pair of single seats is separated by a table. Coat compartment on starboard side, immediately aft of flight deck opposite door; rear baggage compartment behind sofa. Galley on left of entrance. Optional front toilet compartment. Downward-opening door with built-in steps.

SYSTEMS: Duplicated air-conditioning and pressurisation systems supplied with air bled from both engines. Pressure differential 0·61 bars (8·8 lb/sq in). Two independent hydraulic systems, each of 207 bars (3,000 lb/sq in) pressure and with twin engine-driven pumps and emergency electric pump, to actuate primary flight controls, flaps, landing gear, wheel brakes, spoilers, yaw damper and nosewheel steering. 28V DC electrical system with a 9kW DC starter/generator on each engine, three 750VA 400Hz 115V inverters and two 23Ah batteries. Automatic emergency oxygen system.

AVIONICS AND EQUIPMENT: Standard avionics include duplicated VHF and VOR/glideslope, single ADF, marker beacon receiver, ATC transponder, autopilot, intercom system and duplicated blind-flying instrumentation. Optional avionics include duplicated DME and flight director, second ADF, weather radar and radio altimeter.

Dassault Mystère-Falcon 10 four/seven-passenger executive transport (Pilot Press)

DIMENSIONS, EXTERNAL:

Wing span	13·08 m (42 ft 11 in)
Wing chord (mean)	2·046 m (6 ft 8½ in)
Wing aspect ratio	7·1
Length overall	13·85 m (45 ft 5 in)
Length of fuselage	12·47 m (40 ft 11 in)
Height overall	4·61 m (15 ft 1½ in)
Tailplane span	5·82 m (19 ft 1 in)
Wheel track	2·86 m (9 ft 5 in)
Wheelbase	5·38 m (17 ft 8 in)
Passenger door: Height	1·47 m (4 ft 10 in)
Width	0·80 m (2 ft 7 in)
Height to sill	0·884 m (2 ft 10¾ in)
Emergency exit (stbd side, over wing):	
Height	0·914 m (3 ft 0 in)
Width	0·508 m (1 ft 8 in)

DIMENSIONS, INTERNAL:

Cabin, excl flight deck: Length	5·00 m (16 ft 5 in)
Max width	1·46 m (4 ft 9 in)
Max height	1·50 m (4 ft 11 in)
Volume	7·50 m³ (264·6 cu ft)
Baggage compartment volume:	
front (wardrobe)	0·35 m³ (12·35 cu ft)
rear	0·70 m³ (24·7 cu ft)

AREAS:

Wings, gross	24·1 m² (259 sq ft)
Horizontal tail surfaces (total)	6·75 m² (72·65 sq ft)
Vertical tail surfaces (total)	4·54 m² (48·87 sq ft)

WEIGHTS:

Weight empty, equipped	4,880 kg (10,760 lb)
Max payload	1,060 kg (2,337 lb)
Max T-O weight	8,500 kg (18,740 lb)
Max zero-fuel weight	6,120 kg (13,500 lb)
Max landing weight	8,000 kg (17,640 lb)

PERFORMANCE:

Never-exceed speed at S/L	
	350 knots (648 km/h; 402 mph)
Max operating Mach number	0·87
Max cruising speed	494 knots (915 km/h; 568 mph)
FAR 25 balanced T-O field length with four passengers and fuel for a 1,000 nm (1,850 km; 1,150 mile) stage, 45 min reserves	930 m (3,050 ft)
FAR 25 balanced T-O field length, with four passengers and max fuel	1,250 m (4,100 ft)
FAR 25 landing run, with four passengers and 45 min reserves	630 m (2,070 ft)
Range with four passengers and 45 min reserves	1,918 nm (3,555 km; 2,209 miles)

DASSAULT-BREGUET MYSTÈRE-FALCON 50

The Mystère-Falcon 50 is a three-turbofan executive transport derived from the Mystère-Falcon 20. It has an entirely new wing of supercritical section, adapted to flight at high Mach numbers and embodying efficient high-lift devices, and complies with FAR Pt 36 noise requirements. Standard accommodation is for a crew of two and eight passengers; but in 1980 an ambulance version became available, with the interior laid out for three stretchers (or two stretchers and heavy medical equipment) and two doctors.

The original prototype (F-WAMD) flew for the first time on 7 November 1976, followed by a second prototype (F-WINR) on 16 February 1978 and the third (and sole pre-production) aircraft on 13 June 1978. DGAC certification was received on 27 February 1979, followed by FAA type approval on 8 March. Falcon 50 No. 4, flown on 2 March 1979, was the first built on Dassault-Breguet's Mérignac assembly line and became Falcon Jet's US demonstrator. Orders totalled 123 on 1 June 1980, by which date 13 had been delivered. The first delivery was made in July 1979, when Falcon 50 No. 3 was handed over to a customer who had owned a Falcon 20 for 12 years. In early 1980, the fifth aircraft was delivered to GLAM (Groupe de Liaisons Aériennes Ministérielles) for priority use by the President of the Republic. Another was supplied to the King of Morocco. Production was at the rate of three per month in 1980.

Fuselages for the Mystère-Falcon 50 are produced at Aérospatiale's Saint-Nazaire works, wings at the Colomiers plant of Dassault-Breguet, tail units by Aérospatiale at Méaulte, and cowlings by Hurel-Dubois at Vélizy-Villacoublay.

TYPE: Three-turbofan executive transport.

WINGS: Cantilever low-wing monoplane, with compound leading-edge sweepback and supercritical section. Each wing is attached to the central box structure by multiple bolts and forms an integral fuel tank. Full-span leading-edge slats, of which the outboard sections are slotted. Double-slotted trailing-edge flaps and ailerons. Three-section two-position airbrakes on top surface of each wing.

FUSELAGE: All-metal semi-monocoque structure of circular cross-section, with aft baggage compartment included in pressure-cell.

TAIL UNIT: Cantilever all-metal structure, with horizontal surfaces mounted partway up fin. Tailplane incidence adjustable by screwjack, driven by two electric motors controlled by 'normal' and 'emergency' controls located respectively on the control wheels and pedestal.

LANDING GEAR: Retractable tricycle type by Messier-Hispano-Bugatti, with twin wheels on each unit. Hydraulic retraction, main units inward, nosewheels forward. Four-disc brakes designed for 400 landings with normal-energy braking.

POWER PLANT: Three Garrett-AiResearch TFE 731-3 turbofan engines, each rated at 16·5 kN (3,700 lb st) for take-off. Two engines pod-mounted on sides of rear fuselage, the third attached by two top mounts. Thrust reverser on centre engine. Fuel in wing and fuselage tanks, with total capacity of 5,829 litres (1,540 US gallons). Single-point pressure fuelling.

ACCOMMODATION: Crew of two side by side on flight deck, with full dual controls and airline-type instrumentation. Normal accommodation for eight passengers in individual reclining seats, with first two rows facing each other and separated by stowable tables. Lavatory with water supply and flushing toilet at rear. Wardrobe and galley in forward part of cabin. Downward-opening airstair door. Optional layout provides a five-passenger lounge at the rear and a forward lavatory. An ambulance version is available.

Dassault-Breguet Mystère-Falcon 50 extended-range three-turbofan executive transport *(Pilot Press)*

Dassault Mystère-Falcon 50 No. 5, delivered to GLAM for priority use by the President of the Republic

SYSTEMS: Air-conditioning system utilises bleed air from all three engines. Max pressure differential 0·61 bars (8·8 lb/sq in). Pressurisation maintains a max cabin altitude of 2,440 m (8,000 ft) to a flight altitude of 13,700 m (45,000 ft). Two independent hydraulic systems, pressure 207 bars (3,000 lb/sq in), with three engine-driven pumps and one emergency electric pump, actuate primary flying controls, flaps, slats, landing gear, wheel brakes, airbrakes and nosewheel steering. 28V DC electrical system, with a 9kW 28V DC starter-generator on each engine and two 23Ah batteries. Automatic emergency oxygen system. Optional 9kW Garrett-AiResearch APU.

AVIONICS: Standard items include Omega, inertial navigation system, duplicated VHF and VOR, ADF, DME, ATC and HF, radio altimeter and weather radar. Basic aircraft includes Collins AP-580 autopilot and two FCS-80 flight directors.

DIMENSIONS, EXTERNAL:
Wing span	18·86 m (61 ft 10½ in)
Wing chord (mean)	2·84 m (9 ft 3¾ in)
Wing aspect ratio	7·6

Length overall	18·30 m (60 ft 0½ in)
Length of fuselage	17·66 m (57 ft 11 in)
Height overall	6·90 m (22 ft 7½ in)
Tailplane span	7·74 m (25 ft 4¾ in)
Wheel track	3·98 m (13 ft 0¾ in)
Wheelbase	7·24 m (23 ft 9 in)
Passenger door: Height	1·52 m (4 ft 11¾ in)
Width	0·80 m (2 ft 7½ in)
Height to sill	1·30 m (4 ft 3¼ in)
Emergency exits (each side, over wing):	
Height	0·92 m (3 ft 0¼ in)
Width	0·51 m (1 ft 8 in)

DIMENSIONS, INTERNAL:
Cabin, incl forward baggage space and rear toilet:
Length	7·14 m (23 ft 5 in)
Max width	1·86 m (6 ft 1¼ in)
Max height	1·79 m (5 ft 10½ in)
Volume	18·3 m³ (646·2 cu ft)
Baggage compartment (aft)	2·55 m³ (90 cu ft)

AREAS:
Wings, gross	46·83 m² (504·1 sq ft)
Horizontal tail surfaces (total)	13·35 m² (143·7 sq ft)
Vertical tail surfaces (total)	9·82 m² (105·7 sq ft)

WEIGHTS:
Weight empty, equipped	9,000 kg (19,840 lb)
Max payload	1,370 kg (3,020 lb)
Max T-O and ramp weight	17,600 kg (38,800 lb)
Max zero-fuel weight	10,650 kg (23,480 lb)
Max landing weight	16,200 kg (35,715 lb)

PERFORMANCE:
Max operating Mach No.	Mach 0·86
Max operating speed at S/L	
	350 knots (648 km/h; 402 mph)IAS
Max operating speed at 7,225 m (23,700 ft)	
	370 knots (685 km/h; 425 mph)IAS
Max cruising speed	
	Mach 0·82 or 470 knots (870 km/h; 540 mph)
Service ceiling	13,800 m (45,300 ft)
FAR 25 balanced field length with 8 passengers and fuel for 3,400 nm (6,295 km; 3,910 miles)	
	1,340 m (4,400 ft)
FAR 121 landing distance with 8 passengers and FAR 121 reserves	
	1,050 m (3,450 ft)
Range at Mach 0·75 with 8 passengers and FAR 121 reserves	
	3,510 nm (6,500 km; 4,038 miles)

FOURNIER
FOURNIER AVIATION

OFFICE AND WORKS: Aérodrome d'Athée-Nitray, 37270 Montlouis
Telephone: (47) 50 68 30
Telex: 696 254
MANAGING DIRECTOR: René Caillet

Fournier Aviation was formed in 1978, bringing together the assets and activities of the former Avions Fournier SA and the Fournier Design Office, in close collaboration with M René Fournier. It is continuing to manufacture the RF-6B two-seat light aircraft, of which details follow.

Fournier Aviation has also developed the RF-9 motor glider (see Sailplanes section).

FOURNIER RF-6B

The prototype of this two-seat aerobatic aircraft, designed by M René Fournier, flew for the first time on 12 March 1974; certification was obtained in April 1975.

Production of five pre-series RF-6Bs began during the first half of 1975, and the first of these (F-BVKS) flew for the first time on 4 March 1976. It introduced a longer nose than the prototype and a more powerful engine. By June 1979, a total of 45 RF-6Bs had been produced.

Intended primarily for use as an aerobatic or training aircraft, the RF-6B is stressed to +6g and −3g.

To improve aerobatic performance, the prototype of a new version with a more powerful (88 kW; 118 hp) Avco Lycoming O-235-L2A engine was flown for the first time in the Spring of 1980 and is likely to follow in production the original version, of which details follow. A Christen fuel system for inverted flight will be offered as an option on the new model.

TYPE: Two-seat aerobatic, training and sporting aircraft.
WINGS: Cantilever low-wing monoplane. Wing section NACA 23015 at root, NACA 23013 at tip. Dihedral 3° 30′. Incidence 3°. All-wood single-spar structure with plywood and Dacron covering. Frise-type ailerons of wooden construction, Dacron covered. Plain trailing-edge flaps of wooden construction with Dacron covering.
FUSELAGE: All-wood oval structure, plywood covered.
TAIL UNIT: Cantilever structure of wood with Dacron covering. Fixed-incidence tailplane. Trim tab in port elevator.

Fournier RF-6B (Rolls-Royce Continental O-200-A engine)

LANDING GEAR: Non-retractable tricycle type. Oleo-pneumatic shock-absorber in each unit. Steerable nosewheel. Main-wheel tyres size 380 × 150. Nose-wheel tyre size 300 × 100. Hydraulic disc brakes.
POWER PLANT: One 74·5 kW (100 hp) Rolls-Royce Continental O-200-A flat-four engine, driving a Hoffmann two-blade fixed-pitch wooden propeller with spinner. Fuselage fuel tank, immediately aft of firewall, capacity 80 litres (17·6 Imp gallons). Refuelling point on fuselage upper surface, forward of windscreen. Oil capacity 4 litres (0·88 Imp gallons).
ACCOMMODATION: Two seats side by side under transparent canopy, which swings upward and aft for access to cockpit. Dual controls standard. Cockpit heated and ventilated. Baggage space aft of seats.
SYSTEMS: Hydraulic system for brakes only. Electrical power supplied by 12V 40A engine-driven alternator and 12V battery.
AVIONICS AND EQUIPMENT: Nav and com radios optional. Blind-flying instrumentation optional.
DIMENSIONS, EXTERNAL:
Wing span	10·50 m (34 ft 5½ in)
Wing chord at root	1·53 m (5 ft 0¼ in)
Wing chord at tip	0·83 m (2 ft 8¾ in)
Wing aspect ratio	8·5
Length overall	7·00 m (22 ft 11¾ in)
Height overall	2·52 m (8 ft 3 in)
Tailplane span	3·40 m (11 ft 1¾ in)

Propeller diameter	1·75 m (5 ft 9 in)
Propeller ground clearance	0·28 m (11 in)

AREAS:
Wings, gross	13·00 m² (139·9 sq ft)
Ailerons (total)	1·07 m² (11·52 sq ft)
Trailing-edge flaps (total)	1·52 m² (16·36 sq ft)
Rudder	0·74 m² (7·97 sq ft)
Tailplane	1·65 m² (17·76 sq ft)
Elevators (incl tab)	1·00 m² (10·76 sq ft)

WEIGHTS AND LOADINGS:
Weight empty	500 kg (1,102 lb)
Max T-O weight: Aerobatic	720 kg (1,587 lb)
Utility	750 kg (1,653 lb)
Max wing loading	57·7 kg/m² (11·8 lb/sq ft)
Max power loading	10·07 kg/kW (16·53 lb/hp)

PERFORMANCE (at max T-O weight):
Never-exceed speed	162 knots (300 km/h; 186 mph)
Max level speed at S/L	
	108 knots (200 km/h; 124 mph)
Max cruising speed at S/L	
	97 knots (180 km/h; 112 mph)
Stalling speed	46 knots (85 km/h; 53 mph)
Min sinking speed, engine off	2·0 m (6·6 ft)/s
Max rate of climb at S/L	210 m (690 ft)/min
Service ceiling	4,000 m (13,125 ft)
T-O to 15 m (50 ft)	290 m (950 ft)
Landing from 15 m (50 ft)	250 m (820 ft)
Landing run, no braking	200 m (655 ft)
Range with max fuel	350 nm (650 km; 404 miles)

HELICOP-JET

Héliport de Paris, 4 avenue de la Porte de Sèvres, 75015 Paris
Telephone: 554 69 13
PROPRIETOR: Charles Déchaux

HELICOP-JET

A full-scale mockup of this 'cold-jet' tip-driven light helicopter was first exhibited at the Paris Air Show in June 1969. Construction of a pre-production prototype was started by Établissements Charles Déchaux in 1970, and this aircraft made its first flight in December 1976 at Issy-les-Moulineaux. It logged about 60 flying hours, powered by a 186 kW (250 hp) Turboméca Palouste air generator, with which it could lift only the pilot.

The definitive prototype, with an Astazou engine, was displayed at the Paris Air Show in June 1979, and was expected to fly in October 1979. There has been no news of such a flight, or of further progress with planned production of the Helicop-Jet, of which an illustrated description can be found in the 1979-80 *Jane's*.

ISSOIRE
SOCIÉTÉ ISSOIRE-AVIATION

HEAD OFFICE AND WORKS: Aérodrome d'Issoire-le-Broc, BP No. 7, 63501 Issoire Cédex
Telephone: (73) 89 01 54
Telex: Issavia 990.185F
PRESIDENT AND DIRECTOR GENERAL: X. Laguette

Issoire-Aviation, formed on 1 February 1978, took over the premises at Issoire Aerodrome that had belonged to the former Wassmer company (see 1977-78 *Jane's*), following the liquidation of Wassmer on 16 September 1977. It also acquired the industrial assets of Wassmer, and thus assumed responsibility for the continued airworthiness of aircraft of Wassmer design.

Activities of Issoire-Aviation were intended to be devoted 50 per cent to subcontract work for major French aerospace manufacturers such as Dassault-Breguet, Matra and Aérospatiale, and 50 per cent to general aviation programmes. Currently, work in the latter category includes the maintenance and repair of aircraft, and the production of E 78 and D 77 sailplanes (see Sailplanes section) and IA 80 Piranha light aircraft.

At the beginning of 1980, Issoire-Aviation occupied 4,000 m² (43,050 sq ft) of covered workshop area and 180 m² (1,935 sq ft) of offices at Issoire-le-Broc, and had 55 employees.

ISSOIRE IA 80 PIRANHA

Developed by the former Wassmer company, and first flown in November 1975 as the WA 80 Piranha, this two-seat trainer has a fuselage generally similar to that of the four-seat Wassmer WA 51 Pacific (see 1977-78 *Jane's*) and is therefore unusually roomy. It is certificated in the Utility category, and spinning is permitted.
TYPE: Two-seat light training and general purpose aircraft.
WINGS: Cantilever low-wing monoplane. Wing section NACA 63418. Dihedral 6° 40′ from roots. All-plastics (polyester resin) structure produced by vacuum-forming process to give a very precise smooth surface. Sweptforward wing-root leading-edges, embodying stall strips. No sweep on outer wings at quarter-chord. Slightly-inset ailerons, with foam rubber gap seals, are operated through control rods. Manually-operated four-position flaps.
FUSELAGE: All-plastics (polyester resin) structure. Main shell and integral fin moulded in two halves. Frames and stringers also of plastics.
TAIL UNIT: Conventional cantilever configuration, with sweptback vertical surfaces and small dorsal fin.

Elevators operated through control rods, rudder by cables. All-plastics (polyester resin) construction. Controllable trim tab on port elevator.

LANDING GEAR: Non-retractable tricycle type. Main wheels mounted inside each end of a one-piece laminated polyester resin spring. Nosewheel carried on steerable oleo-pneumatic leg. Disc brakes on main wheels. Small tail bumper.

POWER PLANT: One 74·5 kW (100 hp) Rolls-Royce Continental O-200-A flat-four engine, driving a two-blade fixed-pitch EVRA wooden propeller. Fuel tank in fuselage, aft of cockpit, capacity 90 litres (19·75 Imp gallons).

ACCOMMODATION: Two seats side by side, with stick-type dual controls standard. Adjustable seats. Gull-wing door on each side, port one jettisonable. Baggage compartment aft of seats, over fuel tank.

Issoire IA 80 Piranha (Rolls-Royce Continental O-200-A engine) *(Flight International)*

DIMENSIONS, EXTERNAL:

Wing span	9·40 m (30 ft 10 in)
Wing aspect ratio	7·1
Length overall	7·50 m (4 ft 7¼ in)
Height overall	2·10 m (6 ft 10¾ in)
Wheel track	2·10 m (6 ft 10¾ in)

DIMENSIONS, INTERNAL:

Cabin: Length	2·40 m (7 ft 10½ in)
Max height	1·18 m (3 ft 10½ in)
Baggage space	1·2 m³ (42·3 cu ft)

AREA:

Wings, gross	12·40 m² (133·5 sq ft)

WEIGHTS AND LOADINGS:

Weight empty	500 kg (1,102 lb)
Max T-O weight	800 kg (1,763 lb)
Max wing loading	64·51 kg/m² (13·2 lb/sq ft)
Max power loading	10·74 kg/kW (17·63 lb/hp)

PERFORMANCE (at max T-O weight):

Never-exceed speed	163 knots (302 km/h; 187 mph)
Max speed at S/L	129 knots (240 km/h; 149 mph)
Max cruising speed at S/L	102 knots (190 km/h; 118 mph)
Stalling speed, flaps up	51·5 knots (95 km/h; 59 mph)
Stalling speed, flaps down	43·5 knots (80 km/h; 50 mph)
Rate of climb at S/L	210 m (690 ft)/min
Service ceiling	4,000 m (13,125 ft)
T-O run	200 m (655 ft)
T-O to 15 m (50 ft)	300 m (985 ft)
Landing from 15 m (50 ft)	300 m (985 ft)
Landing run	150 m (495 ft)
Range with max fuel (75% power)	378 nm (700 km; 435 miles)
g limits	+4·4, −2·2

MICROTURBO
MICROTURBO SA

21 avenue Clément Ader, 31770 Colomiers
Telephone: (61) 78 54 44
Telex: MIJET 521804 F
MJ 200 PROGRAMME MANAGER: J. Grangette

MICROTURBO MICROJET 200

To promote utilisation of the small gas turbine engines that it manufactures, Microturbo SA initiated the design and development of an aircraft known as the Microjet 200 (MJ 200), of which a prototype (F-WZJF) was flown for the first time by M Jacques Grangette on 24 June 1980. A full-size mockup had been exhibited previously at the 1979 Paris Air Show, and was illustrated in the 1979-80 *Jane's*. Three more flying prototypes and a structure test airframe will be completed during 1981.

Aim of the programme is to offer economies in military pilot training by use of very small high-performance jet aircraft with comparatively low initial and operating costs.

The Microjet 200 is an all-metal two-seater, of simple configuration, powered by two Microturbo TRS 18-046 turbojets, each rated at 1·08 kN (243 lb st). Mounted in the rear fuselage, the engines are supplied with air via NACA type flush inlets, on each side of the fuselage aft of the cockpit, and exhaust through lateral jetpipes forward of, and below, the V tail (included angle 110°). The unswept wings have a relatively high thickness/chord ratio and are fitted with slotted flaps. The tricycle landing gear is retractable.

Pupil and instructor are seated side by side under the one-piece canopy, with the seats slightly staggered to minimise cockpit width and to enable a single set of panel instruments to serve both pilots. Each has a miniature control stick, mounted on a side console. Avionics and equipment include an EAS ERC741 VHF or TRU750 UHF transceiver, radio or SFIM 130 gyromagnetic compass, SAFT 28V 15Ah battery and oxygen system. Optional items include an LMT 3560J IFF transceiver and LMT 1A microtacan.

DIMENSIONS, EXTERNAL:

Wing span	7·58 m (24 ft 10½ in)
Wing aspect ratio	8
Length overall	6·00 m (19 ft 8¼ in)
Height overall	1·90 m (6 ft 2¾ in)

AREA:

Wings, gross	6·12 m² (65·9 sq ft)

WEIGHTS:

Weight empty, equipped	600 kg (1,323 lb)
Max fuel	296 kg (652 lb)
Max T-O weight: Aerobatic	930 kg (2,050 lb)
Utility	1,050 kg (2,315 lb)

PERFORMANCE (estimated):

Never-exceed speed	300 knots (555 km/h; 345 mph)
Max cruising speed	250 knots (463 km/h; 287 mph)
Stalling speed	64 knots (118 km/h; 74 mph)
Rate of climb at S/L at max T-O weight	660 m (2,165 ft)/min
T-O to 15 m (50 m) at max T-O weight	680 m (2,230 ft)
Service ceiling	above 9,145 m (30,000 ft)
Range with max fuel at 8,225 m (27,000 ft), 30 min reserves	540 nm (1,000 km; 620 miles)
Endurance for aerobatics at 3,050 m (10,000 ft) with 156 kg (344 lb) of fuel	40 min

Microturbo Microjet 200 two-seat lightweight training aircraft with landing gear extended

MOTO-DELTA
JEAN MARC GEISER

95 boulevard Saint-Michel, 75005 Paris
Telephone: 326 50 99

MOTO-DELTA G11

The Moto-Delta G11, as the accompanying photograph shows, is a simple ultralight powered flexwing aircraft. It has been produced as a low-cost, economical to run, easy to fly aircraft and is road-transportable on top of a family car.

The fuselage, landing gear legs and main beam of the wing are built entirely of laminated glassfibre, with some Klégécel and polyurethane foam plastics. The tail unit consists of a fin and rudder only. A 13·5 kW (18 hp) flat-twin two-stroke engine is mounted behind the pilot's seat and drives a pusher propeller.

The first prototype flew originally as the G10 with a completely open pilot's seat, as illustrated in the 1976-77 *Jane's*. The current G11 version, displayed at the 1977 Paris Air Show, has a streamlined cockpit fairing of glassfibre, with a windscreen to protect the pilot.

The delta-shaped flexwing is made of Dacron, mounted on a tubular duralumin frame. An overhead control arm regulates the movement of the wing. Pedals actuate the rudder and nosewheel steering.

Geiser Moto-Delta G11 powered flexwing-type aircraft

DIMENSIONS, EXTERNAL:
Wing span 8·00 m (26 ft 3 in)
Wing area, gross 14·00 m² (151 sq ft)
Length overall 3·40 m (11 ft 2 in)
WEIGHTS:
Weight empty 52 kg (115 lb)
Max T-O weight 140 kg (308 lb)

PERFORMANCE:
Max level speed 49 knots (90 km/h; 56 mph)
Max cruising speed 38 knots (70 km/h; 43·5 mph)
Stalling speed 16 knots (30 km/h; 19 mph)
Max rate of climb at S/L 120 m (395 ft)/min
T-O run 25 m (82 ft)

Landing run 0-15 m (0-49 ft)
Endurance with max fuel 2 h

MOTO-DELTA G20

This two-seat version of the Moto-Delta was under development in 1979. No details are yet available.

MUDRY
AVIONS MUDRY et CIE

Aérodrome de Bernay, BP 47, 27300 Bernay
Telephone: (32) 43 47 34
DIRECTOR: Auguste Mudry

M Auguste Mudry established this company in the works of the former Société Aérienne Normande at Bernay, and operated it in parallel with his other aircraft manufacturing company, C.A.A.R.P. of Beynes (see 1977-78 *Jane's*). All activities of C.A.A.R.P. were subsequently combined with those of Avions A. Mudry, at Bernay, where the CAP 10 B and CAP 20 L aerobatic light aircraft continue in production. Under development is a new single-seat light aircraft designated CAP 21.

MUDRY CAP 10 B

Developed from the Piel Emeraude two-seat light aircraft (see Homebuilts section), via the prototype C.P. 100 aerobatic version built by C.A.A.R.P., the CAP 10 is intended for use as a training, touring or aerobatic aeroplane. The prototype was flown for the first time in August 1968, and certification of the CAP 10 was granted on 4 September 1970. Construction is to French AIR 2052 (CAR 3) Category A standards for aerobatic flying, with load factors of +6g and −4·5g.

A total of 112 CAP 10s had been built by June 1980, including 36 for the French Air Force and six for the French Navy. Some are in service with the Air Force's Equipe de Voltige Aérienne (EVA) at Salon-de-Provence, others with its basic flying training schools at Clermont-Ferrand-Aulnat and Cognac, and the Navy's pilot selection centre at St Raphaël. Fourteen more of the current CAP 10 B version were ordered for the French Air Force in 1979.

TYPE: Two-seat aerobatic light aircraft.
WINGS: Cantilever low-wing monoplane. Wing section NACA 23012. Dihedral 5° from roots. Incidence 0°. No sweepback. All-spruce single-spar torsion-box structure, with trellis ribs, rear auxiliary spar and okoumé plywood covering. Inner section of each wing is rectangular in plan, outer section semi-elliptical. Wooden trailing-edge plain flaps and slotted ailerons.
FUSELAGE: Conventional spruce girder structure, built in two halves and joined by three main frames. Of basically rectangular section with rounded top-decking. Polyester fabric covering. Forward section also has an inner plywood skin for added strength. Engine cowling panels of non-inflammable laminated plastics.
TAIL UNIT: Conventional cantilever structure. All-wood single-spar fin, integral with fuselage, and tailplane. All surfaces plywood-covered except rudder, which is covered with both plywood and polyester fabric. Tailplane incidence adjustable on ground. Trim tab in each elevator. Automatic rudder trim.
LANDING GEAR: Non-retractable tailwheel type. Mainwheel legs of light alloy, with ERAM type 9 270 C oleo-pneumatic shock-absorbers. Single wheel on each main unit, tyre size 380 × 150. Solid tailwheel tyre, size 6 × 200. Tailwheel is steerable by rudder linkage but can be disengaged for ground manoeuvring. Hydraulically-actuated main-wheel disc brakes (controllable from port seat) and parking brake. Streamline fairings on main wheels and legs.
POWER PLANT: One 134 kW (180 hp) Avco Lycoming IO-360-B2F flat-four engine, driving a Hoffmann two-blade fixed-pitch wooden propeller. Standard fuel tank aft of engine fireproof bulkhead, capacity 72 litres (16 Imp gallons). Optional auxiliary tank, capacity 75

CAP 10 B two-seat aerobatic light aircraft of the French Air Force

litres (16·5 Imp gallons), beneath baggage compartment. Fuel and oil systems modified to permit periods of inverted flying.
ACCOMMODATION: Side-by-side adjustable seats for two persons, with provision for back parachutes, under rearward-sliding and jettisonable moulded transparent canopy. Special aerobatic shoulder harness standard. Space for 20 kg (44 lb) of baggage aft of seats in training and touring models.
SYSTEMS: Electrical system includes Delco-Rémy 40A engine-driven alternator and SAFT 12V DC nickel-cadmium battery.
AVIONICS AND EQUIPMENT: CSF 262 12-channel VHF radio and g meter fitted. Optional equipment includes starboard brake pedals; Narco, Jolliet or Badin VHF; Narco VOR; radio compass; IFR instrumentation; navigation and landing lights; and heated pitot.
DIMENSIONS, EXTERNAL:
Wing span 8·06 m (26 ft 5¼ in)
Wing aspect ratio 5·96
Length overall 7·16 m (23 ft 6 in)
Height overall 2·55 m (8 ft 4½ in)
Tailplane span 2·90 m (9 ft 6 in)
Wheel track 2·06 m (6 ft 9 in)
DIMENSION, INTERNAL:
Cabin: Max width 1·054 m (3 ft 5½ in)
AREAS:
Wings, gross 10·85 m² (116·79 sq ft)
Ailerons (total) 0·79 m² (8·50 sq ft)
Vertical tail surfaces (total) 1·32 m² (14·25 sq ft)
Horizontal tail surfaces (total) 1·86 m² (20·0 sq ft)
WEIGHTS (A: Aerobatic, U: Utility):
Weight empty, equipped:
A, U 540 kg (1,190 lb)
Fuel load:
A 54 kg (119 lb)
U 108 kg (238 lb)
Max T-O weight:
A 760 kg (1,675 lb)
U 830 kg (1,829 lb)

PERFORMANCE (at max T-O weight):
Never-exceed speed 183 knots (340 km/h; 211 mph)
Max level speed at S/L
146 knots (270 km/h; 168 mph)
Max cruising speed (75% power)
135 knots (250 km/h; 155 mph)
Stalling speed, flaps up
52 knots (95 km/h; 59·5 mph)
Stalling speed, flaps down
44 knots (80 km/h; 50 mph)
Max rate of climb at S/L over 360 m (1,180 ft)/min
Service ceiling 5,000 m (16,400 ft)
Range with max fuel 647 nm (1,200 km; 745 miles)

MUDRY CAP 20L

First flown on 15 January 1976, the CAP 20L ('léger') is a lightweight development of the earlier CAP 20. It is intended as both a comparatively inexpensive high-performance type for private individuals to fly in competitive aerobatics, and as an aircraft superior to any previous version of the CAP 20 for the Armée de l'Air and for international competition against the best aerobatic types of foreign design.

The prototype (F-WVKY) flew as a **CAP 20L-180**, with 134 kW (180 hp) Avco Lycoming AEIO-360 engine. Standard production model is the **CAP 20LS-200**, with 149 kW (200 hp) Avco Lycoming engine and constant-speed propeller, the first example of which flew for the first time on 6 November 1976. A total of 20 had been delivered by mid-1980, when the decision was taken to terminate production in favour of the new CAP 21.

The 100th aircraft of the CAP 10/20 series, delivered on 4 March 1978, was a CAP 20LS-200. The following data apply to this version:
TYPE: Single-seat aerobatic light aircraft.
WINGS: Cantilever low-wing monoplane. All-wood single-spar wings, similar in construction to those of CAP 10 but with only ailerons on trailing-edge.
FUSELAGE: Conventional all-wood structure, of basically triangular section with rounded top-decking. Wooden covering, except for laminated plastics engine cowling.
TAIL UNIT: Cantilever all-wood structure. Trim tab in rudder and each elevator.
LANDING GEAR: Non-retractable tailwheel type. Oleo-pneumatic shock-absorbers. Streamline fairings on main wheels and legs. Disc brakes.
POWER PLANT: One 149 kW (200 hp) Avco Lycoming AIO-360-B1B flat-four engine, driving a Hartzell two-blade constant-speed metal propeller. Fuel tank aft of cockpit, capacity 80 litres (17·5 Imp gallons), with system modified to permit periods of inverted flight.
ACCOMMODATION: Single seat under transparent moulded canopy which opens sideways to starboard and is jettisonable. Special aerobatic shoulder harness.
DIMENSIONS, EXTERNAL:
Wing span 7·57 m (24 ft 10 in)
Length overall 6·46 m (21 ft 2½ in)
Height overall 1·52 m (5 ft 0 in)
AREA:
Wings, gross 10·47 m² (112·7 sq ft)
WEIGHTS:
Weight empty 500 kg (1,102 lb)
Max T-O weight (Aerobatic) 650 kg (1,433 lb)

Mudry CAP 20LS-200 single-seat aerobatic aircraft

PERFORMANCE:
Max cruising speed (75% power)
     162 knots (300 km/h; 186 mph)
Stalling speed   46 knots (85 km/h; 53 mph)
Max rate of climb at S/L   840 m (2,755 ft)/min
Endurance with max fuel   2 h
g limits   +8; −6

MUDRY CAP 21

The prototype of this new single-seat aerobatic competition aircraft (F-WZCH) was displayed at the 1979 Paris
Air Show. It flew for the first time on 23 June 1980, at
which date five pre-production CAP 21s were under construction. The first delivery, to a customer in Brazil, was
scheduled for November 1980.

The CAP 21 retains the fuselage and tail unit of the
CAP 20LS-200, but has cantilever main landing gear legs
of glassfibre, and an entirely new wing of V16 F section,
with a different planform and built by a new production
method. This wing has improved the rate of roll by comparison with the CAP 20L, and facilitates the execution of
snap manoeuvres. It has a thickness/chord ratio of 16%,
dihedral of 1° 30′ and no twist. Other features of the CAP
21 include a max fuel capacity of 75 litres (16·5 Imp
gallons), a 15 litre (3·3 Imp gallon) gravity tank for
inverted flying, and a glassfibre seat for the pilot. The 149
kW (200 hp) Avco Lycoming AEIO-360-A1B engine of
the prototype drives a two-blade Hartzell variable-pitch
propeller, but a fixed-pitch propeller is available optionally.

Prototype CAP 21 (Avco Lycoming AEIO-360-A1B engine)

DIMENSIONS, EXTERNAL:
Wing span   8·08 m (26 ft 6 in)
Wing aspect ratio   6·95
Length overall   6·46 m (21 ft 2½ in)
Height overall   1·52 m (5 ft 0 in)
AREA:
Wings, gross   9·2 m² (99·0 sq ft)

WEIGHTS:
Weight empty   490 kg (1,080 lb)
Max T-O weight, Aerobatic   600 kg (1,323 lb)
PERFORMANCE:
Max cruising speed 172 knots (320 km/h; 199 mph)
Stalling speed   46 knots (85 km/h; 53 mph)
Endurance with max fuel   2 h

REIMS AVIATION
REIMS AVIATION SA

OFFICE AND WORKS: Reims-Prunay Airport, BP 2745,
  51062 Reims Cédex
Telephone: (26) 06 96 55
Telex: REMAVIA 830754
PARIS OFFICE: 18 quai Alphonse le Gallo, 92100
  Boulogne-Billancourt
Telephone: 604 81 36
CHAIRMAN: Pierre Clostermann
CHIEF OPERATING OFFICER AND PRODUCTION MANAGER:
  Jean Pichon
FINANCIAL DIRECTOR: Jean Luc Varga
ADMINISTRATIVE DIRECTOR: Armand Blang
PUBLIC RELATIONS: Frédéric Amanou
CHIEF PILOT: Franck Bardou

Under an agreement signed on 16 February 1960, the
Cessna Aircraft Company of Wichita, Kansas, USA,
acquired a 49 per cent holding in this company, which was
then known as Société Nouvelle des Avions Max Holste.

Reims Aviation has the right to manufacture under
licence Cessna designs for sale in Europe, Africa and Asia.
By 1 January 1980 it had assembled a total of 1,712
Cessna F 150 and F 152, and 360 FRA 150 and FA 152
two-seat aircraft; 1,950 F 172 and 657 FR 172, 173 F 182
and 45 FR 182 RG four-seat aircraft; and 168 F 337, FT
337P, and STOL FTB 337 six-seat aircraft. Nearly 88 per
cent of all products are exported. A total of 373 aircraft
were delivered in the 1979 calendar year.

Reims Aviation is a subcontractor to Dassault-Breguet
in the Mystère-Falcon 10, 20 and 50, Mirage F1 and Super
Étendard programmes. It had 540 employees on 1
January 1980. Its offices and factory at Reims-Prunay
Airport have an area of 23,000 m² (260,500 sq ft).

REIMS/CESSNA F 152 and FA 152 AÉROBAT

Standard and aerobatic versions of the Cessna 152
assembled under licence by Reims Aviation are designated F 152 and FA 152 Aérobat respectively. The first
FA 152 was flown on 25 April 1977, followed four days
later by the first F 152. Production was at the rate of 160
F 152s and 15 FA 152s a year in early 1980.

Details of the current Cessna 152 series can be found in
the US section.

Reims/Cessna FR 172K Hawk XP II (Continental IO-360-K engine)

REIMS/CESSNA F 172 SKYHAWK/100 and FR 172K HAWK XP

Cessna Skyhawk and Skyhawk II aircraft assembled
under licence by Reims Aviation are designated **F 172
Skyhawk/100** and **Skyhawk/100 II** respectively.

Until 1971, Reims Aviation retained a 145 hp Rolls-
Royce Continental engine in the F 172, of which the first
example was flown on 4 January 1963, with 805 delivered
by the end of 1971. The current F 172 has a 119 kW (160
hp) Avco Lycoming O-320-H2AD. Production in early
1980 was at the rate of 170 aircraft per year.

In early 1967 Reims Aviation flew the prototype of a
more powerful version of the F 172, which it named the
Reims Rocket. Details of this aircraft, which the company
produced exclusively for worldwide sale, can be found in
the 1976-77 *Jane's*. Production ended after 590 Rockets
had been completed, and Reims Aviation is now assembling standard Cessna R172 Hawk XP and Hawk XP/II
aircraft as the **FR 172K Hawk XP** and **Hawk XP/II** respectively. The prototype flew for the first time on 21 September 1976, and current rate of production is 20 per year.

Full details of the current Cessna Skyhawk and Hawk
XP series can be found in the US section.

REIMS/CESSNA F 182 and FR 182 RG

The first Reims-assembled **F 182** flew for the first time
on 2 June 1975. Production was at the rate of 40 aircraft
per year in early 1980.

First example of the retractable-gear version of this type
was flown on 9 December 1977, as the **FR 182 RG**. Reims
began deliveries in 1978. Production was at the rate of 30
per year in January 1980.

Full descriptions of the similar Skylane and Skylane RG
can be found under the Cessna entry in the US section.

REIMS/CESSNA 337 SKYMASTER

In 1969 Reims Aviation began assembly under licence
of the Cessna 337 Skymaster six-seat twin-engined light
aircraft. Primary structures were supplied by Cessna, and
engines by Rolls-Royce; smaller components and equipment were French-built.

Assembly of the standard F 337 and pressurised FT
337P versions ended in 1978, but Reims Aviation continued to produce the FTB 337 G, which it developed in
1974 at the request of various government agencies. This
is described separately.

In mid-1980 it was announced that production of the
Model 337 Skymaster series by Cessna, at Wichita, had
been stopped, but that Reims Aviation would continue to
maintain the manufacture and marketing of the Model
FTB 337 G. The detailed description of the Skymaster
airframe has been left in the US section for this year.

REIMS AVIATION FTB 337 G

The airframe of this five/six-seat push-and-pull light
twin is basically similar to that of the F 337, but embodies
STOL (ADAC) modifications, comprising high-lift
trailing-edge flaps, and is fitted with two 168 kW (225 hp)
Rolls-Royce Continental TSIO-360-D turbocharged
engines. The FTB 337 G is not pressurised but can be
equipped for maritime or overland patrol duties, sea or
land rescue, or other specialised tasks by day and night,
with four underwing pylons for containers of food and
medicine, dinghies and locator beacons, radar, or equipment to detect illegal oil jettison and slicks at sea, or forest
fires, including a SAT Super Cyclope infra-red sensor. The
rear of the cabin can be cleared to carry cargo or two
stretchers. The aircraft can also be equipped for navigation and IFR training.

An FTB 337 G was specially equipped with underwing
containers and a belly pack and searchlight for anti-
pollution operations over the English Channel in 1977.

Reims/Cessna FA 152 Aerobat at Reims-Prunay Airport

By 1 January 1980 Reims Aviation had delivered 61 FTB 337 Gs, and expected to build two or three more during 1980.

DIMENSIONS, EXTERNAL: As Reims/Cessna 337, except:
Wing span	12·10 m (39 ft 8½ in)
Height overall	2·84 m (9 ft 4 in)

AREA:
Wings, gross	18·81 m² (202·5 sq ft)

WEIGHTS AND LOADING:
Weight empty	1,454 kg (3,206 lb)
Max T-O weight	2,100 kg (4,630 lb)
Max wing loading	113 kg/m² (23·2 lb/sq ft)

PERFORMANCE (at max T-O weight):
Max level speed at S/L	
	205 knots (380 km/h; 236 mph)
Cruising speed (75% power):	
at 3,000 m (10,000 ft)	
	186 knots (344 km/h; 214 mph)
at 6,000 m (20,000 ft)	
	200 knots (370 km/h; 230 mph)
Stalling speed, power reduced, wheels and flaps up	
	67 knots (124 km/h; 77 mph)
Max rate of climb at S/L	375 m (1,230 ft)/min
Rate of climb at S/L, one engine out	
	100 m (328 ft)/min
Rate of climb at 3,000 m (10,000 ft)	
	346 m (1,135 ft)/min
Service ceiling	7,300 m (23,950 ft)
Service ceiling, one engine out	6,000 m (20,000 ft)
STOL T-O to 15 m (50 ft)	245 m (804 ft)
STOL landing from 15 m (50 ft)	260 m (853 ft)
Max range, no reserves:	
75% power at 6,000 m (20,000 ft)	
	955 nm (1,770 km; 1,100 miles)
econ power at 3,000 m (10,000 ft)	
	1,085 nm (2,012 km; 1,250 miles)
econ power at 6,000 m (20,000 ft)	
	1,150 nm (2,132 km; 1,325 miles)
Max endurance at 120 knots (222 km/h; 138 mph), no reserves	approx 5 h

Reims/Cessna FR 182 RG (Lycoming O-540-J3C5D engine)

Reims Aviation FTB 337 G, equipped with remote sensing systems in underbelly pack, including Super Cyclope infra-red sensor and Hasselblad electric cameras

ROBIN
AVIONS PIERRE ROBIN

HEAD OFFICE AND WORKS: Aérodrome de Dijon-Darois, 21121 Fontaine-les-Dijon Cédex
COMMERCIAL MANAGEMENT:
Robin SA
Aérodrome de Dijon Val-Suzon Darois, 21121 Fontaine-les-Dijon Cédex
Telephone: (80) 31 61 01
Telex: 350818 Robin F
PRESIDENT DIRECTOR GENERAL, AVIONS PIERRE ROBIN: Pierre Robin
PRESIDENT DIRECTOR GENERAL, ROBIN SA: Thérèse Robin
SALES SUPERVISOR: Jacques Bernardin
PRODUCTION DIRECTOR: Philippe Estassy
TECHNICAL DIRECTOR: Michel Brandt

This company was formed in October 1957 as Centre Est Aéronautique to design, manufacture and sell touring aircraft. In 1969 the name of the company was changed to Avions Pierre Robin. Marketing and after-sales service of its products are the responsibility of Robin SA. Details of its subsidiary, Avions Pierre Robin Inc, can be found in the Canadian section.

Since 1973, Avions Pierre Robin has manufactured the DR 400 series of wooden light aircraft, all of which represent highly-refined developments of the company's earlier Jodel designs and were first flown in prototype form in 1972. They are described in detail, together with the company's current range of all-metal light aircraft, some with retractable landing gear.

Robin is also engaged on extensive subcontracting, including the manufacture of components for the Pilatus Turbo-Porter and Turbo-Trainer, Alpha Jet and Aérospatiale helicopters.

The company's works currently cover an area of about 11,000 m² (118,400 sq ft) and it employs 160 people.

ROBIN DR 400/100 2+2
Production of this two/four-seat light aircraft has ended. Details can be found in the 1979-80 *Jane's*.

ROBIN DR 400/120 DAUPHIN 80
The prototype of this DR 400 series lightplane flew for the first time on 15 May 1972 and received DGAC certification on the 10th of that month, followed by CAA certification in December 1972. The original version had a 93 kW (125 hp) engine and was manufactured as the DR 400/125 Petit Prince. It was superseded in 1975 by the DR 400/120 Petit Prince, with 88 kW (118 hp) engine, as described in the 1979-80 *Jane's*. The current version has a fine-pitch propeller and new instrument panel, and entered production in 1979 as the Dauphin 80, to which the following details apply:

TYPE: Three/four-seat light training and touring aircraft.
WINGS: Cantilever low-wing monoplane. Wing section NACA 23013·5 (modified). Centre-section has constant chord and no dihedral; outer wings have a dihedral of 14°. All-wood one-piece structure, with single box-spar. Leading-edge plywood-covered; Dacron covering overall. Wooden ailerons, covered with Dacron. Aluminium alloy flaps. Ailerons and flaps interchangeable port and starboard. Manually-operated airbrake under spar outboard of landing gear on each side. Picketing ring under each wingtip.
FUSELAGE: Wooden semi-monocoque structure of basic rectangular section, plywood-covered.
TAIL UNIT: Cantilever all-wood structure, covered with Dacron. Sweptback fin and rudder. All-moving one-piece horizontal surface, with tab.
LANDING GEAR: Non-retractable tricycle type, with oleo-pneumatic shock-absorbers and Manu hydraulically-actuated drum brakes. All three wheels and tyres are size 380 × 150, pressure 1·57 bars (22·8 lb/sq in) on

nose unit, 1·77 bars (25·6 lb/sq in) on main units. Nose-wheel steerable via rudder bar. Fairings over all three legs and wheels. Tailskid with damper. Parking brake.
POWER PLANT: One 83·5 kW (112 hp) Avco Lycoming O-235-L2A flat-four engine, driving a Sensenich 72 CKS 6-0-56 two-blade fixed-pitch metal propeller, or Hoffmann two-blade fixed-pitch wooden propeller. Fuel tank in fuselage, usable capacity 100 litres (22 Imp gallons); optional 50 litre (11 Imp gallon) auxiliary tank. Oil capacity 5·7 litres (1·25 Imp gallons).
ACCOMMODATION: Enclosed cabin, with seats for three or four persons, in pairs, up to a max weight of 154 kg (340 lb) on front pair and 136 kg (300 lb), including baggage, at rear. Access via forward-sliding jettisonable transparent canopy. Dual controls standard. Cabin heated and ventilated. Baggage compartment with internal access.
SYSTEMS AND EQUIPMENT: Standard equipment includes a 12V 50A alternator, 12V 32Ah battery, push-button starter, audible stall warning, and windscreen de-icing. Radio, blind-flying equipment, and navigation, landing and anti-collision lights to customer's requirements.

DIMENSIONS, EXTERNAL:
Wing span	8·72 m (28 ft 7¼ in)
Wing chord, centre-section (constant)	
	1·71 m (5 ft 7½ in)
Wing chord at tip	0·90 m (3 ft 0 in)
Wing aspect ratio	5·6
Length overall	6·96 m (22 ft 10 in)
Height overall	2·23 m (7 ft 3¾ in)
Tailplane span	3·20 m (10 ft 6 in)
Wheel track	2·60 m (8 ft 6¼ in)
Wheelbase	5·20 m (17 ft 0¾ in)
Propeller diameter	1·78 m (5 ft 10 in)

DIMENSIONS, INTERNAL:
Cabin: Length	1·62 m (5 ft 3¾ in)
Max width	1·10 m (3 ft 7¼ in)
Max height	1·23 m (4 ft 0½ in)
Baggage space, volume	0·39 m³ (13·75 cu ft)

AREAS:
Wings, gross	13·60 m² (146·39 sq ft)
Ailerons, total	1·15 m² (12·38 sq ft)
Flaps, total	0·70 m² (7·53 sq ft)
Fin	0·61 m² (6·57 sq ft)
Rudder	0·63 m² (6·78 sq ft)
Horizontal tail surfaces, total	2·88 m² (31·00 sq ft)

WEIGHTS AND LOADINGS:
Weight empty, equipped	530 kg (1,169 lb)
Max baggage	40 kg (88 lb)
Max T-O and landing weight	900 kg (1,984 lb)
Max wing loading	66·2 kg/m² (13·56 lb/sq ft)
Max power loading	10·23 kg/kW (16·8 lb/hp)

PERFORMANCE (at max T-O weight):
Never-exceed speed	166 knots (308 km/h; 191 mph)
Max level speed at S/L	
	130 knots (241 km/h; 150 mph)

Robin DR 400/120 Dauphin 80 three/four-seat light aircraft

Max cruising speed at 2,250 m (7,400 ft)
    116 knots (215 km/h; 133 mph)
Econ cruising speed at 3,000 m (9,800 ft)
    105 knots (195 km/h; 121 mph)
Stalling speed, flaps down
    45 knots (82 km/h; 51 mph)
Stalling speed, flaps up
    51 knots (94 km/h; 59 mph)
Max rate of climb at S/L 183 m (600 ft)/min
Service ceiling   3,650 m (12,000 ft)
T-O run   235 m (771 ft)
T-O to 15 m (50 ft)   535 m (1,755 ft)
Landing from 15 m (50 ft) 460 m (1,510 ft)
Range with standard fuel at max cruising speed, no
 reserves   464 nm (860 km; 534 miles)

ROBIN DR 400/160 MAJOR 80

The first DR 400/160 flew on 29 June 1972. It was awarded DGAC certification on 6 September 1972, and CAA certification in December of the same year, and was manufactured as the Chevalier (see 1979-80 *Jane's*). The current version, with wing-root fuel tanks, a baggage hold door, a propeller of finer pitch and a new instrument panel based on experience with the Aiglon, has been in production since 1980 as the Major 80.

TYPE: Four-seat light aircraft.

WINGS, FUSELAGE, TAIL UNIT, LANDING GEAR: Generally as for DR 400/120 but with external baggage door aft of cabin, in top of fuselage on port side.

POWER PLANT: One 119 kW (160 hp) Avco Lycoming O-320-D flat-four engine, driving a Sensenich two-blade metal fixed-pitch propeller. Fuel tank in fuselage, capacity 110 litres (24 Imp gallons), and two tanks in wing-root leading-edges, giving total capacity of 190 litres (41·75 Imp gallons), of which 182 litres (40 Imp gallons) are usable. Provision for auxiliary tank, raising total capacity to 240 litres (52·75 Imp gallons). Oil capacity 7·55 litres (1·66 Imp gallons).

ACCOMMODATION: Seating for four persons, on two side-by-side adjustable front seats (max load 154 kg; 340 lb total) and rear bench seat (max load 154 kg; 340 lb total). Forward-sliding transparent canopy gives access to all seats. Up to 40 kg (88 lb) of baggage can be stowed aft of rear seats when four occupants are carried.

SYSTEMS AND EQUIPMENT: As for DR 400/120.

DIMENSIONS AND AREAS: As for DR 400/120, except:
Propeller diameter   1·83 m (6 ft 0 in)
Baggage door: Height 0·47 m (1 ft 6½ in)
 Width   0·55 m (1 ft 9½ in)
Wing area   14·20 m² (152·8 sq ft)

WEIGHTS AND LOADINGS:
Weight empty, equipped 570 kg (1,257 lb)
Max T-O and landing weight 1,050 kg (2,315 lb)
Max wing loading 74·2 kg/m² (15·20 lb/sq ft)
Max power loading 8·82 kg/kW (14·47 lb/hp)

PERFORMANCE (at max T-O weight):
Never-exceed speed 166 knots (308 km/h; 191 mph)
Max level speed at S/L
   146 knots (271 km/h; 168 mph)
Max cruising speed (75% power) at 2,440 m (8,000
 ft)   132 knots (245 km/h; 152 mph)
Econ cruising speed (65% power) at 3,200 m (10,500
 ft)   130 knots (241 km/h; 150 mph)
Stalling speed, flaps up 56 knots (103 km/h; 64 mph)
Stalling speed, flaps down
   50 knots (93 km/h; 58 mph)
Max rate of climb at S/L 255 m (836 ft)/min
Service ceiling   4,115 m (13,500 ft)
T-O run   300 m (985 ft)
T-O to 15 m (50 ft) 500 m (1,640 ft)
Landing from 15 m (50 ft) 545 m (1,788 ft)
Landing run   250 m (820 ft)
Range with standard fuel at econ cruising speed, 45 min
 reserves 693 nm (1,285 km; 798 miles)

ROBIN DR 400/180 RÉGENT

First flown on 27 March 1972, this most powerful, four/five-seat member of the wooden DR 400 series received DGAC certification on 10 May 1972, and CAA certification in December 1972.

The DR 400/180 is generally similar to the DR 400/160 Major 80, except in the following details:

POWER PLANT: One 134 kW (180 hp) Avco Lycoming O-360-A flat-four engine. Fuel tankage as for DR 400/160.

ACCOMMODATION, SYSTEMS AND EQUIPMENT: Basically as for DR 400/160, but optional seating for three persons on rear bench seat. Baggage capacity 55 kg (121 lb).

DIMENSIONS AND AREAS: As for DR 400/160, except:
Propeller diameter   1·93 m (6 ft 4 in)

WEIGHTS AND LOADINGS:
Weight empty, equipped 600 kg (1,322 lb)
Max T-O and landing weight 1,100 kg (2,425 lb)
Max wing loading 77·7 kg/m² (15·91 lb/sq ft)
Max power loading 8·21 kg/kW (13·47 lb/hp)

PERFORMANCE (at max T-O weight):
Never-exceed speed 166 knots (308 km/h; 191 mph)
Max level speed at S/L
   150 knots (278 km/h; 173 mph)
Max cruising speed (75% power) at 2,440 m (8,000
 ft)   144 knots (267 km/h; 166 mph)

Robin DR 400/180 Régent (Avco Lycoming O-360-A engine)

Robin DR 400/180R Remorqueur glider-towing aircraft

Econ cruising speed (60% power) at 3,650 m (12,000
 ft)   134 knots (249 km/h; 155 mph)
Stalling speed, flaps up
   56·5 knots (105 km/h; 65 mph)
Stalling speed, flaps down
   51·5 knots (95 km/h; 59 mph)
Max rate of climb at S/L 252 m (825 ft)/min
Service ceiling   4,720 m (15,475 ft)
T-O run   315 m (1,035 ft)
T-O to 15 m (50 ft) 610 m (2,000 ft)
Landing from 15 m (50 ft) 530 m (1,740 ft)
Landing run   249 m (817 ft)
Range with standard fuel at 65% power, no reserves
   783 nm (1,450 km; 900 miles)

ROBIN DR 400/180R REMORQUEUR

The DR 400/180R is a member of the DR 400 range designed for use as a glider-towing aircraft, although it can also be flown as a normal four-seat tourer. The prototype first flew on 6 November 1972 and received DGAC certification on the 28th of that month. Details are generally the same as for the DR 400/180 Régent, except for the following items:

FUSELAGE: No external baggage door. The baggage compartment is covered with transparent Plexiglas as an extension of the canopy, allowing optimum rearward vision.

POWER PLANT: One 134 kW (180 hp) Avco Lycoming O-360-A flat-four engine, driving (for glider-towing) a Sensenich 76 EM 8S5 058 or Hoffmann HO-27-HM-180/138 two-blade propeller. For touring operation a Sensenich 76 EM 8S5 064 propeller of the same diameter is fitted. Fuel capacity as for DR 400/120.

DIMENSIONS AND AREAS: As for DR 400/120, except:
Propeller diameter   1·83 m (6 ft 0 in)

WEIGHTS AND LOADINGS:
Weight empty, equipped 560 kg (1,234 lb)
Max T-O and landing weight 1,000 kg (2,205 lb)
Max wing loading 73·5 kg/m² (15·05 lb/sq ft)
Max power loading 7·46 kg/kW (12·25 lb/hp)

PERFORMANCE (glider tug, at max T-O weight):
Never-exceed speed 166 knots (308 km/h; 191 mph)
Max level speed at S/L (70% power)
   124 knots (230 km/h; 143 mph)
Max cruising speed at 2,440 m (8,000 ft)
   124 knots (230 km/h; 143 mph)
Econ cruising speed (56% power) at 3,650 m (12,000
 ft)   122 knots (226 km/h; 140 mph)
Stalling speed, flaps up
   54 knots (99 km/h; 62 mph)
Stalling speed, flaps down
   47 knots (87 km/h; 54 mph)
Max rate of climb at S/L towing Bijave sailplane
   210 m (690 ft)/min
Service ceiling   6,000 m (19,675 ft)
T-O run   205 m (673 ft)
T-O to 15 m (50 ft) 400 m (1,313 ft)
Landing from 15 m (50 ft) 470 m (1,542 ft)
Landing run   220 m (722 ft)
Range at econ cruising speed, max fuel, no reserves
   444 nm (825 km; 512 miles)

ROBIN HR 100/250TR PRESIDENT

Production of this four/five-seat all-metal light aircraft has ended.

ROBIN R 1180 AIGLON

The R 1180 Aiglon is an all-metal four-seat light aircraft of conventional low-wing monoplane layout. It has non-retractable landing gear, and is powered by a 134 kW (180 hp) Avco Lycoming O-360-A3AD engine which

Robin R 1180 Aiglon four-seat light aircraft (Avco Lycoming O-360 engine)

drives a two-blade Sensenich fixed-pitch propeller. Wing section is NACA 23015. The prototype (F-WVKU) flew for the first time in late 1976; the first production Aiglon (F-GBAM), with a larger, tinted canopy and other changes, received DGAC certification on 19 September 1978. Eighteen have been ordered for use at French civil aviation training schools. These introduced a number of refinements, including a redesigned instrument panel, a control column adjustable for height, increased fuel capacity of 258 litres (56·75 Imp gallons) in integral wing tanks, and improved soundproofing.

DIMENSIONS, EXTERNAL:
Wing span	9·08 m (29 ft 9½ in)
Wing aspect ratio	5·46
Length overall	7·26 m (23 ft 9¾ in)
Height overall	2·38 m (7 ft 9¾ in)
Propeller diameter	1·93 m (6 ft 4 in)

DIMENSIONS, INTERNAL:
Cabin: Length	2·00 m (6 ft 6¾ in)
Width	1·12 m (3 ft 8 in)
Height	1·22 m (4 ft 0 in)

AREA:
Wings, gross	15·1 m² (162·5 sq ft)

WEIGHTS:
Weight empty	650 kg (1,433 lb)
Max.T-O weight	1,150 kg (2,535 lb)

PERFORMANCE (at max T-O weight):
Max level speed at S/L	
	135 knots (251 km/h; 156 mph)
Max cruising speed (75% power) at height	
	133 knots (247 km/h; 153 mph)
Cruising speed (65% power) at height	
	127 knots (235 km/h; 146 mph)
Stalling speed, flaps up	
	58 knots (107 km/h; 66·5 mph)
Stalling speed, flaps down	
	50 knots (92 km/h; 57 mph)
Max rate of climb at S/L	258 m (846 ft)/min
Service ceiling	5,030 m (16,500 ft)
T-O to 15 m (50 ft)	970 m (3,185 ft)
Landing from 15 m (50 ft)	460 m (1,510 ft)
Range with max fuel at 65% power, with reserves	
	876 nm (1,624 km; 1,009 miles)

ROBIN R 2000 ALPHA SERIES

First of a new generation of light aircraft designated R for Robin, the R 2160 prototype (F-WZAC) flew for the first time in September 1976 and was announced officially in the following month. Further variants of the R 2000 series have since been developed. Those currently available differ as follows:

R 2112 Alpha. Two-seat aerobatic light aircraft with an 83·5 kW (112 hp) Avco Lycoming engine. Second example built was demonstrated at the 1979 Paris Air Show.

R 2160 Alpha Sport. Generally similar to R 2112, but with a 119 kW (160 hp) Avco Lycoming O-320-D engine.

Robin R 2160 Alpha Sport two-seat aerobatic aircraft (Avco Lycoming O-320-D engine) *(J. M. G. Gradidge)*

Robin R 2112 Alpha, basic current model of the R 2000 series

Prototype of the R 2000 series flew originally in this form. Seventeen ordered by the Service de la Formation Aéronautique in Spring 1978.

The R 2000 series were derived from the Robin HR 200, which they superseded, and embody many components of that aircraft, including the basic fuselage and tail fin. The wing is completely new, of increased chord and different section; the rudder is larger and there is a long, shallow ventral fin to improve spinning characteristics. All R 2000 variants are being certificated in the Aerobatic Category, and are being fully tested for spin recovery, including inverted spin. They will be manufactured in Canada, by Avions Pierre Robin Inc, as well as in France.

The following details refer specifically to the R 2160 Alpha Sport, but are generally applicable to the R 2112:

TYPE: Two-seat aerobatic light aircraft.

WINGS: Cantilever low-wing monoplane. Wing section NACA 23015. Dihedral 6° 20' from roots. Incidence 3°. No sweep. Conventional single-spar aluminium alloy structure. Entire trailing-edge of each wing comprises an inboard slotted flap and a fully balanced slotted aileron, both of aluminium alloy construction.

FUSELAGE: Conventional aluminium alloy semi-monocoque structure.

TAIL UNIT: Cantilever structure of aluminium alloy construction. All-moving single-spar horizontal surfaces, with anti-tab on trailing-edge each side. Rudder is horn-balanced, with no tab.

LANDING GEAR: Non-retractable tricycle type, with oleo-pneumatic shock-absorbers. All three tyres size 380 × 150. Cleveland disc brakes on main wheels. Three wheel and leg fairings standard.

POWER PLANT: One 119 kW (160 hp) Avco Lycoming O-320-D flat-four engine, driving a Sensenich two-blade fixed-pitch propeller. Fuel tank in fuselage, capacity 120 litres (26·5 Imp gallons). Refuelling point at side of fuselage.

ACCOMMODATION: Two seats side by side under large transparent canopy, the front half of which slides forward for access. Seats are adjustable.

SYSTEM: 12V electrical system.

AVIONICS AND EQUIPMENT: Blind-flying instruments, radio, VOR, ADF and ILS available to customer's requirements.

DIMENSIONS, EXTERNAL:
Wing span	8·33 m (27 ft 4 in)
Wing chord (constant)	1·554 m (5 ft 1¼ in)
Wing aspect ratio	5·34
Length overall	7·10 m (23 ft 3½ in)
Height overall	2·135 m (7 ft 0 in)
Tailplane span	3·04 m (9 ft 11¾ in)
Wheel track	2·91 m (9 ft 6½ in)
Wheelbase	1·434 m (4 ft 8½ in)
Propeller diameter	1·88 m (6 ft 2 in)

DIMENSION, INTERNAL:
Cabin: Width	1·06 m (3 ft 5¾ in)

AREA:
Wings, gross	13·00 m² (140 sq ft)

WEIGHTS:
Weight empty: R 2112	535 kg (1,180 lb)
R 2160	550 kg (1,213 lb)
Max T-O weight:	
R 2112 and R 2160	800 kg (1,764 lb)

PERFORMANCE (at max T-O weight):
Never-exceed speed:	
R 2112 and R 2160	
	180 knots (333 km/h; 207 mph)
Max level speed at S/L:	
R 2112	112 knots (208 km/h; 129 mph)
R 2160	138 knots (257 km/h; 160 mph)
Max cruising speed (75% power) at 2,285 m (7,500 ft):	
R 2112	114 knots (212 km/h; 131 mph)
R 2160	130 knots (242 km/h; 150 mph)
Cruising speed (65% power) at 3,350 m (11,000 ft):	
R 2112	94 knots (175 km/h; 108 mph)
R 2160	126 knots (234 km/h; 145 mph)
Stalling speed, flaps down:	
R 2112	45 knots (83 km/h; 52 mph)
R 2160	46 knots (85 km/h; 53 mph)
Max rate of climb at S/L:	
R 2112	222 m (728 ft)/min
R 2160	312 m (1,025 ft)/min
Service ceiling:	
R 2112	3,660 m (12,000 ft)
R 2160	4,575 m (15,000 ft)
Range with max fuel at 65% power:	
R 2112	631 nm (1,170 km; 727 miles)
R 2160	430 nm (796 km; 495 miles)

ROBIN R 3000 SERIES

This new series of all-metal light aircraft was under development in 1980, to replace types in current production. All models will embody common components, and design emphasis has been placed on reduced manufacturing time. Versions currently projected are as follows:

R 3100. Two-seat trainer, powered by an Avco Lycoming O-135-L engine rated at 74·5 kW (100 hp). Non-retractable landing gear.

R 3120. Four-seat light aircraft, with Avco Lycoming O-135 engine rated at 82-85·75 kW (110-115 hp). Endurance of 5 h with pilot, three passengers and no baggage. Non-retractable landing gear.

R 3140. As R 3120, but with 104 kW (140 hp) Avco Lycoming O-320 engine. This will be the first version to fly, with certification and series production scheduled for late 1982.

R 3170. As R 3120, but with 119 kW (160 hp) Avco Lycoming O-360 engine. A version for glider-towing is also projected.

R 3180. Four-seater with 134 kW (180 hp) engine and retractable landing gear. Max T-O weight not to exceed 1,150 kg (2,535 lb).

Robin R 2160 side-by-side two-seat training aircraft *(Pilot Press)*

SOCATA
SOCIÉTÉ DE CONSTRUCTION D'AVIONS DE TOURISME ET D'AFFAIRES (Subsidiary of Aérospatiale)

HEAD OFFICE, WORKS AND AFTER-SALES SERVICE: Aérodrome de Tarbes-Ossun-Lourdes, BP 38, 65001 Tarbes Cédex
Telephone: (62) 93 97 30
Telex: SOCATA 520828 F
SALES: 12 rue Pasteur, 92150 Suresnes
Telephone: (1) 506 37 60
Telex: AIRSPA 620 059 F
FLYING SCHOOL: Aérodrome de Toussus-le-Noble, BP 2, 78530 Buc
Telephone: 956 21 00
Telex: SOCAERO 697836 F
PRESIDENT AND DIRECTOR GENERAL: Pierre Gautier

This company was formed in 1966, as a subsidiary of Aérospatiale (then Sud-Aviation), to be responsible for producing all of the group's piston-engined light aircraft.

Socata also produces components for the A300 Airbus, Super Étendard, Alpha Jet, Mystère-Falcon 10, 20 and 50 business aircraft, and Puma, Dauphin and Ecureuil helicopters. It is responsible for overhaul and repair of MS 760 Paris light jet aircraft.

Socata's works cover an area of 47,672 m² (513,135 sq ft), and employ a total of about 850 people.

SOCATA RALLYE SERIES

The Rallye had its origin in a competition organised by the SFACT in 1958 and was developed originally by the old-established Morane-Saulnier company. The prototype (67 kW; 90 hp MS 880A) Rallye-Club flew on 10 June 1959, and the initial production versions were the MS 880B Rallye-Club and the MS 885 Super Rallye. FAA certification was obtained on 21 November 1961.

The 3,000th Rallye built in France was delivered to the Aéro-Club Renault on 26 May 1977. Versions of the Rallye are also built under licence in Poland, by the PZL-Warszawa organisation (which see).

When Socata launched its 1979 production programme, on 17 May, the seven aircraft constituting the current Rallye series were given names, instead of the former designations, as follows:

Galopin (formerly Rallye 110 ST). This version may be operated either as a two-seater cleared for spinning or as a three/four-seater with spins prohibited. It has an 82 kW (110 hp) Avco Lycoming O-235-L2A engine, driving a two-blade McCauley fixed-pitch propeller.

Garnement (formerly Rallye 160 ST). Similar to Galopin, but with 115 kW (155 hp) Avco Lycoming O-320-D2A engine. Developed as a high-performance aircraft for flying clubs and for use in countries where high temperatures or high altitude might impose limitations on lower-powered aircraft.

Galérien (formerly Rallye 180 T). Specialised glider and banner towing version, developed to meet West German noise regulations. Powered by 134 kW (180 hp) Avco Lycoming O-360-A3A engine, driving a two-blade fixed-pitch propeller. Certificated in September 1977.

Gaillard (formerly Rallye 180 GT). Four-seat version with 134 kW (180 hp) Avco Lycoming O-360-A3A engine, driving a fixed-pitch or constant-speed propeller, strengthened structure to permit increased AUW, larger rudder and ailerons, fillets of increased size between wing trailing-edges and fuselage, longer nosewheel leg to give increased propeller clearance, enlarged dorsal fin, modified cockpit canopy and a baggage compartment. Streamlined wheel fairings optional. Prototype flew for first time on 7 December 1964. French certification received on 27 April 1965; FAA type approval on 23 June 1971. Total of 742 built by 1 January 1979; 100 ordered by the SFACT for duty as glider tugs at French gliding centres. A variant with a TV camera pod mounted under the starboard wing was demonstrated in 1978. Known as ATAL, this equipment allows the aircraft to be used for aerial surveillance of highway traffic, transmitting images to ground stations over a radius of about 27 nm (50 km; 31 miles). The camera is steerable by the pilot, who also sees the images on a cockpit monitor.

Gabier (formerly Rallye 235 GT). High-performance version, with 175 kW (235 hp) Avco Lycoming O-540-B4B5 engine, driving a Hartzell HC-C2YK-1/8468-6 two-blade constant-speed metal propeller, and with accommodation for four persons. Construction of prototype began in January 1975. First flight was made on 1 April 1975. Total of 103 built by 1 January 1979. A variant (formerly Rallye 235 A) is available with dual control columns instead of control wheels. Another variant (formerly Rallye 235 C) has a tailwheel type landing gear instead of the standard tricycle type.

Gaucho (formerly Rallye 235 CA). Agricultural version of Gabier with tailwheel landing gear. Described separately.

Guerrier (formerly Rallye 235 G). Military version. Described separately.

The Gabier and Gaillard are authorised for use as ambulance aircraft carrying a pilot, one stretcher patient and medical attendant. They can also be used for glider towing, and some 400 Rallyes are employed in this role, including more than 250 in France. Agricultural spraygear

can be fitted and tests have been conducted with various models on ski landing gear.

The following details apply to all French-built versions listed:

TYPE: Two/four-seat light monoplane.
WINGS: Cantilever low-wing monoplane. Wing section NACA 63A416 (modified). Dihedral 7°. Incidence 4°. All-metal single-spar structure. Wide-chord slotted ailerons. Full-span automatic slats. Long-span slotted flaps. Ailerons and flaps have corrugated metal skin. Ground-adjustable aileron tabs. No anti-icing equipment.
FUSELAGE: All-metal semi-monocoque structure.
TAIL UNIT: Cantilever all-metal structure with corrugated skin on the mass-balanced control surfaces. Fixed-incidence tailplane. One automatic tab and one controllable tab on elevator. One controllable tab on rudder.
LANDING GEAR: Non-retractable tricycle type on all but Gaucho and non-standard Gabier. Oleo-pneumatic shock-absorbers. Castoring nosewheel. Standard Gabier has Cleveland main wheels with tyres size 6·00-6, pressure 1·8 bars (26·1 lb/sq in); nosewheel tyre size 5·00-4, pressure 1·4 bars (20·3 lb/sq in). Cleveland hydraulic disc brakes. Provision for fitting skis or floats.
POWER PLANT: One flat-four or flat-six engine (details under entries for individual models), driving a two-blade fixed-pitch or constant-speed metal propeller. Fuel in two metal tanks in wings, with total capacity of 105 litres (23 Imp gallons) in Galopin, 184 litres (40·5 Imp gallons) in Garnement and Galérien, 235 litres (52 Imp gallons) in Gaillard, and 282 litres (62 Imp gallons) in Gabier. Refuelling points above wings. Oil capacity 6 litres (1·3 Imp gallons) in Galopin, 8 litres (1·75 Imp gallons) in Garnement, Galérien and Gaillard, 12 litres (2·6 Imp gallons) in Gabier.
ACCOMMODATION: Two seats side by side at front, and rear bench seat for one/two persons in Galopin, under large rearward-sliding canopy. Other versions are full four-seaters. Dual control columns on Galopin, Garnement, Galérien, Gaucho, Guerrier and both non-standard variants of Gabier. Dual control wheels on Gaillard and standard Gabier. Individual adjustable front seats and baggage space aft of rear seats (accessible internally) on the Gaillard, Gabier and Guerrier. Heating and ventilation standard.
SYSTEMS: Electrical system includes 12V 18A battery and 12V 40A alternator in Galopin; 12V 32A battery and 12V 40A alternator in Garnement, Galérien and Gaillard; 12V 32A battery and 12V 55A alternator in Gabier.
AVIONICS AND EQUIPMENT: The instrument panel is fitted with an anti-glare visor, and is designed to take full radio-navigation equipment to customer's requirements.

DIMENSIONS, EXTERNAL (A, Galopin; B, Garnement; C, Galérien; D, Gaillard; E, Gabier):

Wing span	9·74 m (31 ft 11 in)
Wing chord (constant)	1·30 m (4 ft 3 in)
Wing aspect ratio	7·57
Length overall: A, B, C, D	7·24 m (23 ft 9 in)
E	7·25 m (23 ft 9½ in)
Height overall	2·80 m (9 ft 2¼ in)
Tailplane span	3·67 m (12 ft 0½ in)
Wheel track	2·01 m (6 ft 6½ in)
Wheelbase	1·71 m (5 ft 7¼ in)

DIMENSIONS, INTERNAL:

Cabin: Length: A, B, C	1·80 m (5 ft 11 in)
D, E	2·25 m (7 ft 4 in)
Width	1·13 m (3 ft 8½ in)

AREAS:

Wings, gross: A, B, C	12·66 m² (136·3 sq ft)
D, E	12·76 m² (137·3 sq ft)
Trailing-edge flaps (total)	2·40 m² (25·83 sq ft)
Vertical tail surfaces (total)	1·74 m² (18·73 sq ft)
Horizontal tail surfaces (total)	3·48 m² (37·50 sq ft)

WEIGHTS AND LOADINGS:

Weight empty: A	520 kg (1,145 lb)
B	540 kg (1,191 lb)
C	545 kg (1,200 lb)
D	570 kg (1,257 lb)
E	694 kg (1,530 lb)

Max T-O and landing weight: A	770 kg (1,697 lb)
B	870 kg (1,918 lb)
C	950 kg (2,094 lb)
D	1,050 kg (2,315 lb)
Max T-O weight: E	1,200 kg (2,645 lb)
Max landing weight: E	1,140 kg (2,513 lb)
Max wing loading: E	95 kg/m² (19·45 lb/sq ft)
Max power loading: E	6·69 kg/kW (10·98 lb/hp)

PERFORMANCE (at max T-O weight):

Max level speed at S/L:	
A	110 knots (204 km/h; 126 mph)
B	119 knots (220 km/h; 137 mph)
C	122 knots (226 km/h; 140 mph)
D	130 knots (240 km/h; 150 mph)
E	148 knots (275 km/h; 171 mph)
Max cruising speed (75% power):	
A	104 knots (192 km/h; 119 mph)
B	115 knots (213 km/h; 132 mph)
C	113 knots (209 km/h; 130 mph)
D	122 knots (226 km/h; 140 mph)
E	132 knots (245 km/h; 152 mph)
Econ cruising speed (65% power):	
A	95 knots (176 km/h; 109 mph)
B	109 knots (202 km/h; 125 mph)
C	111 knots (205 km/h; 127 mph)
D	115 knots (213 km/h; 132 mph)
E	125 knots (231 km/h; 144 mph)
Stalling speed, flaps down:	
A	41 knots (75 km/h; 47 mph)
B	45 knots (83 km/h; 52 mph)
C	46 knots (85 km/h; 53 mph)
D	50 knots (92 km/h; 57·5 mph)
E	54 knots (100 km/h; 62 mph)
Max rate of climb at S/L: A	192 m (630 ft)/min
B	246 m (805 ft)/min
C	265 m (870 ft)/min
D	231 m (760 ft)/min
E	300 m (984 ft)/min
Service ceiling: A	3,200 m (10,500 ft)
B	3,950 m (12,950 ft)
C	4,500 m (14,750 ft)
D	3,600 m (11,800 ft)
E	4,500 m (14,760 ft)
T-O run: A, B	214 m (700 ft)
C	240 m (790 ft)
D	250 m (820 ft)
E	360 m (1,180 ft)
T-O to 15 m (50 ft): A	418 m (1,370 ft)
B	365 m (1,200 ft)
C	408 m (1,340 ft)
D	445 m (1,460 ft)
E	500 m (1,640 ft)
Landing from 15 m (50 ft): A	268 m (880 ft)
B	335 m (1,100 ft)
C	342 m (1,120 ft)
D	360 m (1,180 ft)
E	397 m (1,300 ft)
Landing run: A	113 m (370 ft)
B	170 m (560 ft)
C	146 m (480 ft)
D	150 m (490 ft)
E	165 m (540 ft)

Range with max fuel (allowances for T-O, climb and descent, 45 min reserves):

A	400 nm (740 km; 460 miles)
B	520 nm (963 km; 598 miles)
C	460 nm (852 km; 529 miles)
D	600 nm (1,110 km; 690 miles)
E	590 nm (1,090 km; 679 miles)

SOCATA RALLYE GUERRIER

This military aircraft (known originally as the Rallye 235 G) is generally similar to the high-performance Gabier four-seat light aircraft, with a 175 kW (235 hp) Avco Lycoming O-540-B4B5 engine, but has four Alkan 663 underwing stores pylons which enable it to be used for a variety of armed and support missions. The pylons are attached under each wing between ribs 8 and 9, and ribs 15 and 16, and are connected to a weapon selection box installed centrally on the radio panel in the cockpit.

Stores that can be carried on these pylons include Matra F2 rocket launchers, each containing six 68 mm rockets;

Aircraft of the basic Rallye series are similar externally. This light Rallye airframe is used for the Galopin, Garnement and Galérien. The more powerful variants have a heavy airframe

Socata Guerrier in ground support configuration, with two F2 rocket packs and two gun pods on underwing attachments

Type AA 52 pods, each containing two 7·62 mm machine-guns with 500 rds/gun, and large enough to retain all spent cartridge cases and links after firing; 50 kg operational or practice bombs; rescue packs for airdropping over water, desert, jungle or polar regions; flares for use during operational or rescue missions by night; a surveillance pack containing a TV camera and transmitter to send images to a ground station. The camera is fitted with a zoom lens, and can scan to 45° on each side of the aircraft, with a vertical scan of 110°. The pilot has a control box (normal and zoom), and a monitor on which to check precisely the images the camera is viewing. All underwing loads can be jettisoned in an emergency.

The cockpit of the Guerrier contains two side-by-side seats, with dual controls, enabling the aircraft to be used for both basic and operational training, as well as combat missions. A rear bench seat can be installed to permit the carriage of two passengers and a quantity of baggage or freight. Structure of the aircraft is basically unchanged, except for some reinforcement, notably to the wings in the vicinity of the weapon pylons.

PERFORMANCE:
Range/endurance:
Armed reconnaissance with 2 gun pods at 70% power, 30 min fuel reserves
5 h or 556 nm (1,030 km; 640 miles)
Armed reconnaissance with 4 rocket launchers at 70% power, 30 min fuel reserves
2 h 40 min or 286 nm (530 km; 329 miles)
Ground support with 2 gun pods at 75% power at 915 m (3,000 ft), 30 min fuel reserves, 10 min over target
243 nm (450 km; 280 miles)
Ground support with 4 rocket launchers at 75% power at 915 m (3,000 ft), 30 min fuel reserves, 10 min over target
130 nm (240 km; 149 miles)
Ground support with 2 rocket launchers and 2 gun pods at 75% power at 915 m (3,000 ft), 15 min fuel reserves, 10 min over target
43 nm (80 km; 50 miles)
Unarmed reconnaissance with TV pod at 70% power, 30 min fuel reserves
545 nm (1,010 km; 627 miles)

SOCATA RALLYE GAUCHO

The high-lift and safety characteristics inherent in the basic Rallye series well suit it for agricultural operations. It has been possible to purchase standard models adapted for spraying/dusting for some years. The Gaucho represents a more specialised development, with a tailwheel-type landing gear instead of the normal tricycle type; a faired-in rear cabin to house a 580 litre (127·5 Imp gallon) chemical tank; reinforced structure, with anti-corrosive treatment on metal surfaces; and a propeller specially designed for heavy duty at low speeds. The airframe is based on that of the Gabier, and a generally similar 175 kW (235 hp) Avco Lycoming O-540-B2B5 engine is fitted.

The cockpit is equipped normally with a single seat, on the port side, with entrance via an upward-opening canopy/door hinged on the centreline. The forward portion of the chemical tank projects into the starboard side of the cockpit, alongside the pilot. If desired, it can be removed, and replaced by a cover plate and second seat. The aircraft can then be used as a dual-control agricultural pilot trainer, with tank capacity reduced to 500 litres (110 Imp gallons).

Between the seasons for agricultural flying, the Gaucho's cockpit canopy, cabin fairing, chemical tank, spraybars and other specialised equipment can be removed and replaced by conventional Gabier seats and sliding canopy, converting the aircraft into a four-seat touring aircraft or light freighter.

A variety of dispersal equipment is available for the Gaucho, including four Micronair units, two above each wing trailing-edge; a Sorensen underfuselage pump with a capacity of 2 to 40 litres/hectare (1 to 22 Imp gallons/acre) and spraybars with 24 or 32 nozzles; or a Transland spreader for solids. Steel wire-cutters are fitted on the front of each main landing gear leg and on the windscreen centreline, with a steel cable from the latter to the tip of the fin.

The Gaucho was certificated in May 1978.
DIMENSIONS: As for Gabier, except:
Length overall	7·26 m (23 ft 10 in)
Height overall	2·31 m (7 ft 7 in)
WEIGHTS:
Weight empty	694 kg (1,530 lb)
Max chemical payload	425 kg (935 lb)
Max T-O weight	1,350 kg (2,980 lb)
PERFORMANCE (at max T-O weight):
Max cruising speed at S/L
119 knots (220 km/h; 137 mph)
Econ cruising speed (65% power)
115 knots (213 km/h; 132 mph)
Stalling speed, flaps down 54 knots (100 km/h; 62 mph)
Spraying speed 70 knots (130 km/h; 80 mph)
Max rate of climb at S/L 300 m (984 ft)/min
T-O run 365 m (1,200 ft)
T-O to 15 m (50 ft) 495 m (1,620 ft)
Landing from 15 m (50 ft) 435 m (1,430 ft)
Landing run 315 m (1,030 ft)
Range, with allowances for T-O, climb and descent, 45 min reserves 485 nm (900 km; 558 miles)

SOCATA RALLYE TAMPICO AND TOBAGO

The prototype for this new series of all-metal light aircraft was the original TB 10 (F-WZJP), of which design was initiated by Socata's Research and Development Department in February 1975, under the direction of Philippe Stuckelberger. Construction of the prototype began in February 1976, and it made a 25 min first flight at

Tarbes on 23 February 1977, powered by a 119 kW (160 hp) Avco Lycoming O-320-D2A engine. It was lost during the final phases of spin testing at the CEV on 15 December 1977.

The second prototype of the TB 10 was fitted with a 134 kW (180 hp) Lycoming engine. A further airframe underwent static tests at the CEA, Toulouse.

Versions announced by mid-1980 are as follows:

TB 9 Tampico. Four-seater, with 119 kW (160 hp) Avco Lycoming O-320-D2A engine, fixed-pitch propeller, and fuel capacity of 155 litres (34 Imp gallons).

TB 10 Tobago. Four/five-seater, with 134 kW (180 hp) engine.

TB 20. Basically similar to TB 10, but with a 186 kW (250 hp) Avco Lycoming engine derated to 175 kW (235 hp), and retractable landing gear. Fuel capacity increased. Scheduled to fly for the first time in late 1980 and to enter production in 1981.

Following certification of the TB 10 by the DGAC, on 26 April 1979, the TB 9 and TB 10 entered production. By 1 April 1980, sales totalled 30 TB 9s and 119 TB 10s, with production at the rate of 15 aircraft per month. The 100th TB 10 was delivered in July 1980.

Manufacture of these aircraft is simplified by comparison with the Rallye, by the elimination of certain features such as wing leading-edge slats. The following description applies to the initial production Tobago:

TYPE: Four/five-seat all-metal light aircraft.

WINGS: Cantilever low-wing monoplane. Wing section RA 163 CW3. Thickness/chord ratio 16%. Dihedral 4° 30' from roots. No incidence at root. No sweep. Conventional light alloy single-spar structure of constant chord. Balanced ailerons and electrically-actuated slotted flaps, of laminated plastics. Ground-adjustable tabs.

FUSELAGE: Conventional light alloy semi-monocoque structure.

TAIL UNIT: Cantilever all-metal type, with sweptback vertical surfaces and constant-chord all-moving horizontal surfaces mounted at extreme tail, aft of rudder. Ground-adjustable tab at top of rudder. Anti-tab in horizontal surfaces.

LANDING GEAR: Non-retractable tricycle type, with steerable nosewheel. Oleo-pneumatic shock-absorbers. Wheel fairings on all three units. Disc brakes. Parking brake.

POWER PLANT: One 134 kW (180 hp) Avco Lycoming O-360-A1AD flat-four engine, driving a Hartzell two-blade constant-speed propeller with spinner. Two fuel tanks, with total capacity of 208 litres (45·75 Imp gallons). Oil capacity 7·5 litres (1·6 Imp gallons).

This view of the Socata Gaucho shows the wing spraybars

Socata Gaucho, with hopper aft of cabin and tailwheel landing gear *(Pilot Press)*

Socata Tobago four/five-seat light aircraft (Avco Lycoming O-360-A1AD engine)

Socata Tobago four/five-seat all-metal light aircraft *(Pilot Press)*

ACCOMMODATION: Four/five seats in enclosed cabin. Sharply-inclined low-drag windscreen. Access via upward-hinged window/doors. Baggage compartment aft of cabin, with external door on port side. Cabin carpeted, soundproofed, heated and ventilated. Windscreen defrosting standard.

SYSTEMS: Electrical system includes 12V 60A alternator and 12V 32A battery, landing and navigation lights, four individual cabin lights and instrument panel lighting. Hydraulic system for wheel brakes only.

AVIONICS AND EQUIPMENT: Avionics to customer's specification. Standard equipment includes seat belts for all seats, armrests, glove box, map pockets, antiglare visors, stall warning indicator, tiedown fittings and towbar.

DIMENSIONS, EXTERNAL (Tampico and Tobago):

Wing span	9·76 m (32 ft 0¼ in)
Wing chord (constant)	1·22 m (4 ft 0 in)
Wing aspect ratio	8
Length overall	7·64 m (25 ft 0¾ in)
Height overall	3·20 m (10 ft 6 in)
Tailplane span	3·20 m (10 ft 6 in)
Wheelbase	1·95 m (6 ft 5 in)
Propeller diameter	1·88 m (6 ft 2 in)
Propeller ground clearance	0·10 m (4 in)
Cabin doors (each): Width	0·89 m (2 ft 11 in)
Height	0·76 m (2 ft 6 in)
Baggage door: Width	0·63 m (2 ft 1 in)
Height	0·43 m (1 ft 5 in)

DIMENSIONS, INTERNAL (Tampico and Tobago):

Cabin: Length, firewall to rear bulkhead	2·54 m (8 ft 4 in)
Length, panel to rear bulkhead	2·00 m (6 ft 6¾ in)
Max width, at rear seats	1·27 m (4 ft 2 in)
Max width, at front seats	1·15 m (3 ft 9¼ in)
Max height, floor to roof	1·12 m (3 ft 8 in)

AREAS:

Wings, gross	11·9 m² (128·1 sq ft)
Ailerons (total)	0·91 m² (9·80 sq ft)
Trailing-edge flaps (total)	3·72 m² (40·04 sq ft)
Horizontal tail surfaces (total)	2·56 m² (27·56 sq ft)

WEIGHTS (A, Tampico; B, Tobago):

Weight empty: A	650 kg (1,433 lb)
B	670 kg (1,477 lb)
Max T-O weight: A	1,060 kg (2,340 lb)
B	1,150 kg (2,530 lb)

PERFORMANCE (at max T-O weight):

Max level speed: A	125 knots (231 km/h; 144 mph)
B	133 knots (246 km/h; 153 mph)
Max cruising speed (75% power):	
A	121 knots (224 km/h; 139 mph)
B	127 knots (235 km/h; 146 mph)
Econ cruising speed (65% power):	
A	115 knots (213 km/h; 132 mph)
B	119 knots (220 km/h; 137 mph)
Stalling speed, flaps up:	
A	59 knots (110 km/h; 68 mph)
B	60 knots (111 km/h; 69 mph)
Stalling speed, flaps down:	
A	50 knots (92 km/h; 57·5 mph)
B	52 knots (97 km/h; 60 mph)
Max rate of climb at S/L: A	214 m (700 ft)/min
B	240 m (790 ft)/min
Service ceiling: A	4,270 m (14,000 ft)
B	3,960 m (13,000 ft)
T-O run: A	380 m (1,250 ft)
B	360 m (1,180 ft)
T-O to 15 m (50 ft): A	570 m (1,870 ft)
B	540 m (1,770 ft)
Landing from 15 m (50 ft): A	380 m (1,250 ft)
B	420 m (1,380 ft)
Landing run: A	183 m (600 ft)
B	190 m (620 ft)

Range with max fuel, allowances for T-O, climb and descent, 45 min reserves:

A	460 nm (852 km; 529 miles)
B	580 nm (1,074 km; 667 miles)

AÉROSPATIALE EPSILON

At the Farnborough Air Show, in September 1978, Aérospatiale released first details of this tandem two-seat primary trainer, then known by the project designation TB 30, which it had proposed to meet the French Air Force's 'Epsilon' requirement for a propeller-driven aircraft for use in the first stages of a more cost-effective future training sequence. In June 1979, at the Paris Air Show, the company was able to announce receipt of an order from the Air Force for two prototypes, which were to adopt the name Epsilon, together with two further airframes for static and fatigue testing.

The first prototype (F-WZVO) flew for the first time on 22 December 1979; the second flew on 12 July 1980.

The Epsilon programme was conceived to reduce costs by curtailment of the formerly-adopted all-through jet sequence. It is claimed that the relatively high performance of the aircraft, and the fact that its cockpit layout resembles closely that of contemporary combat aircraft, will permit more satisfactory grading of pupil pilots after an initial few hours of flying, and again after completion of the basic training curriculum, covering aerobatics, blind and night flying, close formation flying, combat manoeuvres and VFR/IFR navigation, prior to advanced training for combat or transport flying.

Initial development of the Epsilon was undertaken by Aérospatiale's Aircraft Division, which remains prime contractor, but design and production have been subcontracted to Socata at Tarbes. The following description applies to the prototype:

TYPE: Two-seat military primary trainer.

WINGS: Cantilever low-wing monoplane. Wing section RA 1643 at root, RA 1243 at tip. Thickness/chord ratio 16% at root, 12% at tip. Dihedral 5°. Incidence 2°. All-metal light alloy structure, with single main spar and rear auxiliary spar, built in two panels attached directly to sides of fuselage. Press-formed ribs and heavy-gauge skin without stringers. Electrically-actuated single-slotted flaps. Light alloy mass-balanced ailerons, covered with polyester fabric. Controllable trim tab in port aileron.

FUSELAGE: Light alloy semi-monocoque structure of four longerons, frames and heavy-gauge skin, without stringers.

TAIL UNIT: Cantilever single-spar light alloy structure. Fixed surfaces metal-covered; elevators and rudder covered with polyester fabric. Fixed-incidence tailplane mid-set on fin. Balanced elevators and rudder, with controllable trim tabs.

LANDING GEAR: Hydraulically-retractable tricycle type, with single wheel on each unit. Inward-retracting main units and rearward-retracting nosewheel. Independent hydraulic single-disc brake on each main wheel.

POWER PLANT: One 224 kW (300 hp) Avco Lycoming AEIO-540-L1B5D flat-six engine, suitable for inverted flight and driving a Hartzell HC-C2YR-4-F/FC 8475-6 two-blade constant-speed metal propeller, with spinner. Fuel in two wing leading-edge tanks, with total capacity of 211 litres (46·5 Imp gallons). Refuelling points on wing upper surface.

ACCOMMODATION: Two seats in tandem, with rear seat raised by 70 mm (2·7 in). Seats are adjustable, up and down, and rudder pedals are mechanically adjustable fore and aft. Rearward-sliding two-section Plexiglas canopy, with pyrotechnic system for emergency jettison. Baggage compartment aft of cabin.

SYSTEMS: Hydraulic system for actuating landing gear and brakes. 28V electrical system includes engine-driven alternator, battery for engine starting and emergency use, and external power receptacle on port side of fuselage aft of wing. Cabin heated and ventilated. Windscreen demister.

Aérospatiale Epsilon tandem two-seat military primary trainer *(Pilot Press)*

AVIONICS AND EQUIPMENT: Radio com and blind-flying instrumentation standard. Second prototype has VHF, UHF, automatic VOR and a transponder, with Tacan to be added later.

DIMENSIONS, EXTERNAL:

Wing span	7·35 m (24 ft 1½ in)
Wing chord at root	1·46 m (4 ft 9½ in)
Wing chord at tip	0·92 m (3 ft 0¼ in)
Wing aspect ratio	6
Length overall	7·40 m (24 ft 3¼ in)
Height overall	2·50 m (8 ft 2½ in)
Tailplane span	2·75 m (9 ft 0¼ in)
Wheel track	2·30 m (7 ft 6½ in)
Wheelbase	1·80 m (5 ft 10¾ in)
Propeller diameter	1·98 m (6 ft 6 in)
Propeller ground clearance	0·25 m (10 in)

AREAS:

Wings, gross	9·00 m² (96·88 sq ft)
Fin	1·08 m² (11·63 sq ft)
Tailplane	1·74 m² (18·73 sq ft)

WEIGHTS AND LOADINGS:

Weight empty, equipped	828 kg (1,825 lb)
Max T-O and landing weight (aerobatic)	1,150 kg (2,535 lb)
Max wing loading (aerobatic)	128 kg/m² (26·17 lb/sq ft)

Max power loading (aerobatic) 5·13 kg/kW (8·45 lb/hp)

PERFORMANCE (at max aerobatic T-O weight):

Never-exceed speed	281 knots (522 km/h; 324 mph)
Max level speed at S/L	190 knots (352 km/h; 218 mph)
Max cruising speed (75% power) at 1,830 m (6,000 ft)	180 knots (333 km/h; 207 mph)
Stalling speed, flaps down, power off	60 knots (111 km/h; 69 mph)
Max rate of climb at S/L	550 m (1,800 ft)/min
Time to 1,525 m (5,000 ft)	3 min
Service ceiling	6,100 m (20,000 ft)
T-O run	293 m (960 ft)
T-O to 15 m (50 ft)	465 m (1,525 ft)
Landing from 15 m (50 ft)	575 m (1,890 ft)
Landing run	250 m (820 ft)
Endurance (75% power)	3 h
g limits	+7; −3·5

First prototype of the Aérospatiale Epsilon (Avco Lycoming AEIO-540-L1B5D engine)

GERMANY
(FEDERAL REPUBLIC)

AIRCONCEPT
AIRCONCEPT FLUGZEUG UND GERÄTEBAU GmbH und Co KG

Flughafen, an der Niersbrucke, 4050 Mönchengladbach 1
Telephone: 02161 661489
Telex: 08 52 168
DIRECTOR: Alois Neikes

The 1977-78 *Jane's* contained an illustrated entry on an ultra-lightweight single-seat sporting aircraft known as the VoWi 10, designed and built by the late Ing Helmut Wilden. This aircraft (D-EGWI) consisted basically of a wire-braced all-moving wing and V tail unit, linked by a light alloy tube 'backbone', and with an exposed seat for the pilot carried on a tubular structure beneath the wing. It flew for the first time on 16 April 1975, powered by two 6 kW (8 hp) Stihl-Baumsägen single-cylinder two-stroke aircooled engines.

Subsequently, the VoWi 10 was almost completely redesigned to make it suitable for series production, and Airconcept was formed to manufacture and market the aircraft in its developed form.

The VoWi 10 has been given the name Airbuggy, and was to be marketed in kit form from October 1980, for construction by amateurs, and as a completed production aircraft.

Airconcept VoWi 10 Airbuggy two-seat ultralight aircraft (Limbach SL 1700 EA engine)

AIRCONCEPT VoWi 10 AIRBUGGY

In its current form, the VoWi 10 is a two-seater with a fixed strut-braced wing and conventional flat-four engine. The prototype (D-ENWS) made its first flight at Mönchengladbach in the Spring of 1978.

The Airbuggy is claimed to enter a light and distinct 'mush', rather than pitching, when stalled. It shows no tendency to spin unintentionally.

TYPE: Ultra-lightweight two-seat sporting and utility aircraft.

WINGS: Braced high-wing monoplane. Single bracing strut each side, supplemented by wire bracing to front of cabin. Gö 535 (modified) wing section. Constant chord. Dihedral from roots. No sweep. GfK sandwich construction, without ailerons. Lateral control by cable-operated spoilers mounted at 50% chord. No flaps. Wings can be folded back alongside fuselage for storage and transport.

FUSELAGE: Basic structure of aluminium tubing; sheet aluminium cabin fairing and floor, and triangular stabilising surface between rear of cabin and 'backbone'.

TAIL UNIT: Braced V tail, comprising twin fins and horn-balanced rudders of GfK sandwich with aluminium tube leading-edges. Tail surfaces can be folded upward for storage and transport.

LANDING GEAR: Non-retractable tricycle type, with single wheel on each unit. Cantilever main legs of Gfk. Castoring nosewheel. Shoe brakes on main wheels.

POWER PLANT: One 44·5 kW (60 hp) Limbach SL 1700 EA flat-four engine, mounted on end of fuselage 'backbone', forward of cabin, and driving a two-blade fixed-pitch propeller with spinner. Usable fuel capacity 25·4 litres (5·6 Imp gallons).

ACCOMMODATION: Two seats side by side in open-sided cabin. Controls accessible from either seat.

DIMENSIONS, EXTERNAL:

Wing span	11·00 m (36 ft 1 in)
Wing chord (constant)	1·34 m (4 ft 4¾ in)
Length overall	5·89 m (19 ft 4 in)
Height overall	2·22 m (7 ft 3½ in)

AREA:

Wings, gross	13·0 m² (139·9 sq ft)

WEIGHTS AND LOADINGS:

Weight empty	265 kg (584 lb)
Max T-O weight	430 kg (948 lb)
Max wing loading	33·1 kg/m² (6·78 lb/sq ft)
Max power loading	9·66 kg/kW (15·8 lb/hp)

PERFORMANCE (at max T-O weight, A: with pilot only; B: two-seat):

Max cruising speed	59 knots (110 km/h; 68 mph)
Econ cruising speed	49-51 knots (90-95 km/h; 56-59 mph)
Min control speed: A	29 knots (54 km/h; 33·5 mph)
B	31·5 knots (58 km/h; 36 mph)
Max rate of climb at S/L: A	198 m (650 ft)/min
B	120 m (395 ft)/min
T-O run: A	55 m (180 ft)
B	75 m (250 ft)
T-O to 15 m (50 ft): A	140 m (460 ft)
B	160 m (525 ft)
Landing from 15 m (50 ft): A	110 m (361 ft)
B	120 m (394 ft)
Landing run: A	40 m (131 ft)
B	50 m (165 ft)
Endurance, 15 min reserves	2 h

DEUTSCHE AIRBUS
DEUTSCHE AIRBUS GmbH

8000 München 81, Arabellastrasse 30, Postfach 810260
Telephone: (089) 92 63 1

Telex: 5215149
CHAIRMAN OF THE SUPERVISORY BOARD: Dr Franz-Josef Strauss
MANAGEMENT:
Dipl Kfm Rolf Siebert
Dipl-Ing Klaus Hamann

PUBLIC RELATIONS: Jochen H. Eichen
This company is the West German partner in the consortium formed for development and production of the European A300 and A310 high-capacity transport aircraft described under the Airbus heading in the International section.

DORNIER
DORNIER GmbH

HEAD OFFICE: Postfach 1420, 7990 Friedrichshafen/Bodensee
Telephone: Immenstaad (07545) 81+
Telex: 0734372
WORKS:
Research and Development: 7759 Immenstaad/Bodensee (near Friedrichshafen)
Production: Postfach 2160, Trimburgstrasse, 8000 München 66

AIRFIELD AND FLIGHT TEST CENTRE: 8031 Oberpfaffenhofen, near München
BONN OFFICE: Allianzplatz, 5300 Bonn
BOARD OF DIRECTORS:
Prof Dipl-Ing Claudius Dornier Jr (Chairman)
Dr Ing Fritz Mader
Dipl-Ing Dr Bernhard Schmidt
Dipl-Ing Dr jur Karl-Wilhelm Schäfer
Rainer Hainich
Werner Kresin
PUBLIC RELATIONS: Gerhard Patt

Dornier GmbH, formerly Dornier-Metallbauten, was formed in 1922 by the late Professor Claude Dornier as the successor to the 'Do' division of the former Zeppelin Werke, Lindau, GmbH. It has been operated in the form of a Gesellschaft mit beschränkter Haftung since 22 December 1972. Of more than 8,000 employees, approximately 43% are production staff, 32% in research and development, and 25% engaged in technical and logistic support.

Member companies, in addition to Dornier GmbH, include Dornier-Reparaturwerft GmbH, at Oberpfaffenhofen (aircraft servicing and maintenance), Dornier

Dornier Do 128-2 Skyservant equipped with auxiliary fuel tanks on wing pylons

System GmbH of Friedrichshafen (spaceflight, new technologies, electronics, management consultancy and contract research) and Lindauer Dornier GmbH of Lindau, which produces machinery for the textile industry and for the manufacture of plastics foils.

The Skyservant twin-engined STOL transport and utility aircraft continues in production and is now available also in turboprop form as the Turbo-Skyservant. In 1980, improved versions of these two aircraft were allocated new commercial designations, the Do 28 D-2 Skyservant becoming Do 128-2, with the Do 28 D-6 Turbo-Skyservant now identified as Do 128-6. Dornier intends to supplement these types with a larger twin-turboprop transport designated Dornier 228, of which two versions will begin development in prototype form during 1981. These will embody advanced technology features, including the TNT wing being tested on a specially converted Skyservant airframe.

Dornier is also active in development of various types of RPVs and tethered rotor platforms (see RPVs and Targets section).

The company continues in partnership with the Dassault-Breguet group in France to develop and produce the Alpha Jet training/light attack aircraft, described in the International section. Under Federal German government contract, Dornier has designed and constructed a transonic supercritical wing, to explore the aerodynamic and mechanical properties of such a wing for use by subsonic combat aircraft. Following initial wind tunnel tests by Dornier, and in the large wind tunnel by ONERA, in France, it was planned to flight test the wing on an Alpha Jet in the Autumn of 1980.

Dornier is also involved in licence production of components for the McDonnell Douglas Phantom fighter; and is collaborating with Pilatus of Switzerland (which see) in marketing the latter company's Turbo-Trainer, and with Gulfstream American Corporation in marketing the Ag-Cat in Europe, Africa and parts of the Middle East. In another important programme, Dornier is responsible for integrating the operational avionics in the 18 Boeing E-3A Sentry AWACS aircraft being acquired between 1982 and 1985 by NATO for use in Europe.

Dornier is responsible also for the technical and logistic servicing of the Breguet Br 1150 Atlantic aircraft operated by the Dutch and Federal German navies. Under a contract awarded by the German Federal Procurement Agency, Dornier is prime contractor for the modernisation of the Federal German navy's Atlantics. This programme covers the buoy jettison, ESM, navigation, radar, sonar systems, and magnetic tape data recorder.

Dornier is one of the companies within the West German aerospace industry which is carrying out independent studies that will lead to definition and, ultimately, design of the TKF 90 tactical fighter project. This is envisaged as a successor to the Luftwaffe's F-4F Phantom, as well as for service with other European air forces, in the 1990s.

DORNIER Do 28 D-2 SKYSERVANT

Despite its designation, the Skyservant inherited only the basic configuration of the earlier Do 28. The prototype (D-INTL) first flew on 23 February 1966. Type approval for the basic Do 28 D was granted on 24 February 1967, and for the developed Do 28 D-1 on 6 November 1967. FAA certification of the Do 28 D-1 was granted on 19 April 1968. Military type approval of the Do 28 D-1 was granted in January 1970, and of the Do 28 D-2 in late 1971, in accordance with MIL-specification standards. Initial deliveries of the Skyservant were made in the Summer of 1967; by mid-1979 sales totalled 260 aircraft, to more than 25 countries. Of these, 245 had been delivered by June 1979, including 101 Do 28 D-2s to the Federal German Luftwaffe for general duties and 20 to the Marineflieger for support duties. Others are in service with the air forces of Cameroun, Ethiopia, Israel, Nigeria, Somalia, Thailand, Turkey and Zambia.

Under contract to the Federal Ministry of Defence, Dornier has re-engined one of the Luftwaffe's Do 28 D-2s with Avco Lycoming TIGO-540 turbocharged engines. This aircraft, redesignated **Do 28 D-2T**, flew for the first

time in its new form in March 1980. All Do 28 D-2s in service with the Federal German armed forces may be upgraded to this standard.

Details of the Do 28 D-2 can be found in the 1979-80 *Jane's*. It has been superseded in production by the Do 128-2.

DORNIER Do 128-2 SKYSERVANT

Based on the Do 28 D-2, this 10-seat utility aircraft became available in 1980. A version fitted with undernose radar, for maritime patrol duties, was exhibited at the 1980 Hanover Show.

TYPE: Twin-engined STOL transport and utility aircraft.

WINGS: Cantilever high-wing monoplane. Wing section NACA 23018 (modified), with nose slot in the outer half of each wing. Dihedral 1° 30'. Incidence 4°. All-metal box-spar structure. Double-slotted ailerons and flaps have metal structure, partly Eonnex-covered. Balance tabs on ailerons. Pneumatic de-icing optional.

FUSELAGE: Conventional all-metal stressed-skin structure.

TAIL UNIT: Cantilever all-metal structure, with rudder and horizontal surfaces partly Eonnex-covered. All-moving horizontal surface, with combined anti-balance and trim tab. Trim tab in rudder. Pneumatic de-icing optional.

LANDING GEAR: Non-retractable tailwheel type. Dornier oleo-pneumatic shock-absorbers on main units,

glassfibre sprung tailwheel unit. Main-wheel tyres size 8·50-10, pressure 3·38 bars (49 lb/sq in). Twin-contact tailwheel tyre size 5·50-4, pressure 2·76 bars (40 lb/sq in). Double-disc hydraulic brakes. Fairings on main legs and wheels standard.

POWER PLANT: Two 283 kW (380 hp) Avco Lycoming IGSO-540-A1E flat-six engines, mounted on stub-wings and each driving a Hartzell Type HC-B3W30-2B/W10151 B-8R three-blade constant-speed and fully-feathering propeller. Fuel tanks in engine nacelles, with total usable capacity of 893 litres (196·5 Imp gallons). Refuelling points above nacelles. Provision for two underwing auxiliary fuel tanks with combined capacity of 474 litres (104 Imp gallons). Total capacity of separate oil tanks, 33 litres (7·25 Imp gallons).

ACCOMMODATION: Pilot and either co-pilot or passenger side by side on flight deck. Dual controls standard. Main cabin equipped normally to carry eight passengers in pairs, with centre aisle, or five stretchers and five folding seats, all layouts including toilet and/or baggage compartment and/or darkroom for aerial survey missions aft of cabin. Alternatively, cabin can be stripped for cargo-carrying. Door on each side of flight deck. Emergency exit on starboard side of cabin. Combined two-section passenger and freight door on port side of cabin, at rear.

AVIONICS AND EQUIPMENT: Provision for com/nav antennae installation, and avionics, to customer's requirements. Standard equipment includes directional slaved gyro, cabin heating, dual brake system, 100A alternators, and provisions for optional de-icing system.

DIMENSIONS, EXTERNAL:

Wing span	15·55 m (51 ft 0¼ in)
Wing chord (constant)	1·90 m (6 ft 2¾ in)
Wing aspect ratio	8·33
Length overall	11·41 m (37 ft 5¼ in)
Height overall	3·90 m (12 ft 9½ in)
Tailplane span	6·61 m (21 ft 8¼ in)
Wheel track	3·52 m (11 ft 6 in)
Wheelbase	8·63 m (28 ft 3¾ in)
Propeller diameter	2·36 m (7 ft 9 in)
Passenger door (port, rear):	
Height	1·34 m (4 ft 4¾ in)
Width	0·65 m (2 ft 1½ in)
Height to sill	0·60 m (1 ft 11½ in)
Freight door (port, rear):	
Height	1·34 m (4 ft 4¾ in)
Width, incl passenger door	1·28 m (4 ft 2½ in)

Dornier Do 128-2 Skyservant STOL utility light transport aircraft *(Pilot Press)*

Dornier Do 128-2 with undernose radome for maritime surveillance duties *(Brian M. Service)*

DIMENSIONS, INTERNAL:
Cabin, excl flight deck and rear baggage compartment:

Max length	3·97 m (13 ft 0½ in)
Max width	1·37 m (4 ft 6 in)
Max height	1·61 m (5 ft 3½ in)
Floor area	5·30 m² (57·05 sq ft)
Volume	8·00 m³ (282·5 cu ft)

AREAS:

Wings, gross	29·00 m² (312·2 sq ft)
Ailerons (total)	2·64 m² (28·4 sq ft)
Trailing-edge flaps (total)	4·80 m² (51·6 sq ft)
Fin, incl dorsal fin	3·65 m² (39·3 sq ft)
Rudder, incl tab	1·40 m² (15·1 sq ft)
Tailplane, incl tab	7·65 m² (82·3 sq ft)

WEIGHTS AND LOADINGS:

Weight empty, standard	2,346 kg (5,172 lb)
Max payload	805 kg (1,775 lb)
Max T-O weight	3,842 kg (8,470 lb)
Max T-O weight with optional external fuel tanks	4,015 kg (8,852 lb)
Max ramp weight	3,862 kg (8,514 lb)
Max landing weight	3,650 kg (8,050 lb)
Max wing loading	132 kg/m² (27·1 lb/sq ft)
Max power loading	6·79 kg/kW (11·14 lb/hp)

PERFORMANCE (at max T-O weight):

Max level speed at 3,050 m (10,000 ft)	175 knots (325 km/h; 202 mph)
Max cruising speed at 3,050 m (10,000 ft)	164 knots (304 km/h; 189 mph)
Max cruising speed at S/L	147 knots (273 km/h; 170 mph)
Econ cruising speed, 50% power at 3,050 m (10,000 ft)	114 knots (211 km/h; 131 mph)
Stalling speed, power off, flaps down	56·5 knots (104 km/h; 65 mph)
Min control speed, power on, flaps down	35 knots (65 km/h; 40 mph)
Max rate of climb at S/L	312 m (1,025 ft)/min
Rate of climb at S/L, one engine out	24 m (80 ft)/min
Service ceiling	7,680 m (25,200 ft)
Service ceiling, one engine out	2,620 m (8,595 ft)
T-O run	280 m (920 ft)
T-O to 15 m (50 ft)	560 m (1,835 ft)
Landing from 15 m (50 ft)	390 m (1,280 ft)
Landing run	201 m (660 ft)
Range at max cruising speed	346 nm (642 km; 399 miles)
Range with max fuel and payload	615 nm (1,140 km; 708 miles)

DORNIER Do 128-6 TURBO-SKYSERVANT

Dornier flew for the first time on 9 April 1978 the Do 28 D-5X prototype of a turboprop-powered version of the Skyservant (D-IBUF). In this prototype the piston engines of the Do 28 D-2 were replaced by two 447 kW (600 shp) Avco Lycoming LTP 101-600-1A turboprop engines, derated to 298 kW (400 shp) and each driving a three-blade constant-speed metal propeller. Two Pratt & Whitney Aircraft of Canada PT6A-110 free-turbine turboprops, each derated to 298 kW (400 shp), are standard on production Do 128-6 Turbo-Skyservants, each driving a Hartzell Type B3TN-3D T10282B-9·5 three-blade constant-speed metal propeller. The first flight of the prototype with this power plant installation was made on 4 March 1980.

Except for reinforced landing gear, to permit a higher landing weight, the airframe of the Do 128-6 is generally similar to that described for the Do 128-2, and can also be made available in maritime patrol form with a large undernose radome.

Delivery of the Turbo-Skyservant to operators is scheduled to begin in early 1981.

Dornier TNT research aircraft to evaluate the company's new technology wing

WEIGHTS AND LOADINGS (PT6A-110 engines):

Weight empty	2,184 kg (4,815 lb)
Operating weight empty	2,540 kg (5,600 lb)
Max payload	1,273 kg (2,806 lb)
Max T-O weight	4,300 kg (9,480 lb)
Max landing weight	4,100 kg (9,039 lb)
Max wing loading	148 kg/m² (30·4 lb/sq ft)
Max power loading	7·21 kg/kW (11·85 lb/shp)

PERFORMANCE (at max T-O weight except where indicated; PT6A-110 engines):

Max cruising speed at 3,050 m (10,000 ft)	183 knots (340 km/h; 211 mph)
Cruising speed, 75% power at 3,050 m (10,000 ft)	165 knots (305 km/h; 190 mph)
Cruising speed, max range power at 3,050 m (10,000 ft)	140 knots (259 km/h; 161 mph)
Cruising speed, 50% power at 3,050 m (10,000 ft)	138 knots (256 km/h; 159 mph)
Landing speed	67·5 knots (125 km/h; 78 mph)
Max rate of climb at S/L	384 m (1,260 ft)/min
Rate of climb at S/L, one engine out	54 m (177 ft)/min
Service ceiling	8,200 m (26,900 ft)
T-O to 15 m (50 ft)	554 m (1,820 ft)
Landing from 15 m (50 ft)	435 m (1,430 ft)
Range with max fuel at max cruising speed	607 nm (1,125 km; 699 miles)
Range with 805 kg (1,774 lb) payload, no reserves	788 nm (1,460 km; 907 miles)
Range with max fuel at max range power	894 nm (1,658 km; 1,030 miles)

DORNIER NEW TECHNOLOGY WING (TNT) TESTBED AIRCRAFT

The advanced technology wing (*Tragflügel Neuer Technologie: TNT*) has been developed by Dornier with support from the Federal Ministry of Research and Technology. The first phase of the TNT programme, including design, aerodynamic and structural studies, began in mid-1975 and was completed at the end of 1976. Phase II covered engineering, construction of the wing, and its installation on the testbed aircraft, a Do 28 D-2 Skyservant. This was modified by extending the centre-fuselage 1·36 m (4 ft 5½ in) and installing a longer nose; fitting standard Alpha Jet landing gear in a non-retractable form; and fitting two Garrett-AiResearch TPE 331-5-252D turboprop engines, one on each wing. The first flight of this research aircraft (D-IFNT) was made on 14 June 1979, beginning a full year of testing under Phase III of the programme.

By mid-July 1980 the aircraft had made more than 100 test flights, confirming the performance expectations of the new wing. Testing was then under way of seven of the most modern types of Hartzell and Dowty propeller, featuring supercritical and extra-wide-chord blades, and three- or four-blade types with Kevlar blades. Additional propellers, and other advanced technologies, were due to be tested later.

The first production application of the TNT wing is intended to be in the Dornier Do 228 commuter transport (which see).

The description of the Do 128-2 applies also to the TNT testbed aircraft, except as follows:

WINGS: Cantilever high-wing monoplane. Special Dornier wing section. Thickness/chord ratio reduces from 16% over the full centre-section to 13% at the tip. Dihedral 0° on centre-section; 4° on outer panels. Incidence at root 2° 12'. Twist on outer panels −3°. Composite structure, with spars, panels and ribs of torsion box integrally milled from light alloy; leading-edge boxes of conventional sheet metal construction; trailing-edge boxes and sharply-swept wingtips of glassfibre sandwich. Electrically-operated single-slotted Fowler type trailing-edge flaps. Adjustable slotted ailerons, which can be drooped up to 10°, have Flettner tabs to offload control forces, and trim tabs.

FUSELAGE AND TAIL UNIT: Generally similar to Do 128-2, but fuselage extended in length.

LANDING GEAR: Non-retractable tricycle type, consisting of standard production Alpha Jet landing gear units.

POWER PLANT: Two 533 kW (715 shp) Garrett-AiResearch TPE 331-5-252D turboprop engines, each driving a Hartzell type HC-B4TN-5CL/L 10282+4 four-blade constant-speed metal propeller. Integral fuel tanks in wing centre-section, outside fuselage area, with combined capacity of 2,000 kg (4,409 lb).

SYSTEMS: Generally as for Do 128-2, but the electrical system has been modified to meet the requirements of the turboprop engines and their new location.

AVIONICS: Have been selected to satisfy the test assignment and meet IFR requirements.

DIMENSIONS, EXTERNAL:

Wing span	16·97 m (55 ft 8 in)
Wing chord (mean aerodynamic)	2·04 m (6 ft 8¼ in)
Wing aspect ratio	9
Length overall (excl nose probe)	13·35 m (43 ft 9½ in)
Height overall	4·96 m (16 ft 3¼ in)
Wheel track	3·02 m (9 ft 10¾ in)
Wheelbase	4·19 m (13 ft 9 in)
Propeller diameter	2·73 m (8 ft 11½ in)

AREA:

Wings, gross	32·00 m² (344·5 sq ft)

WEIGHTS AND LOADINGS:

Weight empty	3,010 kg (6,636 lb)
Max T-O weight	4,500 kg (9,921 lb)
Max wing loading	140·6 kg/m² (28·80 lb/sq ft)
Max power loading	4·22 kg/kW (6·94 lb/shp)

PERFORMANCE (estimated, at max T-O weight except where indicated):

Never-exceed speed	231 knots (428 km/h; 266 mph)
Cruising speed	185 knots (342 km/h; 213 mph)
Max rate of climb at S/L, AUW of 4,000 kg (8,818 lb)	942 m (3,091 ft)/min
Rate of climb, one engine out, conditions as above	348 m (1,142 ft)/min
T-O to 15 m (50 ft) at AUW of 4,000 kg (8,818 lb)	250 m (820 ft)

DORNIER Do 228

Under this general designation, Dornier is developing two new types of increased-capacity utility and commuter aircraft, as follows:

Dornier Do 228-100. Basic version, with accommodation for 15 passengers in standard airline-type seats at 76 cm (30 in) pitch. Suitable for a wide range of other duties, including freight or mixed cargo/passenger transport, executive travel, air taxi service, maritime surveillance (with undernose search radar), airways calibration, training, ambulance or search and rescue operations, and paramilitary missions. Main fuselage segments, cabin door and cockpit equipment standardised with those of Do 128. Fitted with the Dornier 'new technology (TNT) wing', and Garrett-AiResearch turboprop power plant.

Dornier Do 228-200. Lengthened fuselage, providing accommodation for 19 passengers, but otherwise generally similar to Do 228-100.

The design of these aircraft has been formulated to comply with US certification regulations. One prototype of each version is being built, and is scheduled to fly in Spring 1981. Initial deliveries of production aircraft are planned for late 1981 or the beginning of 1982.

TYPE: Twin-turboprop light transport.

WINGS: Cantilever high-wing monoplane, comprising rectangular centre-section and two tapered outer

Dornier Do 28 D-5X Turbo-Skyservant prototype (two Avco Lycoming LTP 101-600-1A turboprop engines)

Do 128-2 Skyservant testbed for the wing of the Dornier Do 228 transport aircraft *(Pilot Press)*

panels. Dornier Do A-5 supercritical wing section. Dihedral outboard of engines. Wing leading-edge and raked wingtips of glassfibre/Kevlar composites. Fowler-type single-slotted trailing-edge flaps and ailerons of carbonfibre composites. Ailerons can be drooped symmetrically to augment trailing-edge flaps, and are operated differentially to serve as conventional ailerons. Remainder of wing of light alloy construction.

FUSELAGE: Conventional stressed-skin structure of light alloy.

TAIL UNIT: Cantilever all-metal structure, with rudder and horizontal surfaces partly Eonnex-covered. All-moving tailplane, with combined anti-balance and trim tab. Trim tab in rudder.

LANDING GEAR: Retractable tricycle type, with single wheel on each unit. Main units retract forward and inward into fairings built on to the lower fuselage. Nosewheel retracts forward. Low-pressure tyres optional.

POWER PLANT: Two 533 kW (715 shp) Garrett-AiResearch TPE 331-5 turboprop engines, each driving a Hartzell four-blade constant-speed reversible-pitch metal propeller. Alternative engines which may become available at a later date, to meet differing customer requirements, include the Garrett-AiResearch TPE 331-10, and Pratt & Whitney Aircraft of Canada PT6A-41 and PT6A-135.

ACCOMMODATION: Crew of two, and 15 or 19 passengers as described under model listings. Individual seats down each side of the cabin with a central aisle. Combined two-section passenger and freight door, with integral steps, on port side of cabin at rear. Baggage compartment at rear of cabin accessible from cabin. Additional baggage space in fuselage nose. Modular units for rapid changes of role.

DIMENSIONS, EXTERNAL:

Wing span	16·97 m (55 ft 8 in)
Length overall: 228-100	15·03 m (49 ft 3¾ in)
228-200	16·55 m (54 ft 3½ in)
Height overall	4·86 m (15 ft 11½ in)
Wheel track	3·30 m (10 ft 10 in)
Wheelbase: 228-100	5·50 m (18 ft 0½ in)
228-200	6·30 m (20 ft 8 in)
Passenger door (port, rear):	
Height	1·34 m (4 ft 4¾ in)
Width	0·65 m (2 ft 1½ in)

Height to sill	0·60 m (1 ft 11½ in)
Freight door (port, rear):	
Height	1·34 m (4 ft 4¾ in)
Width, incl passenger door	1·28 m (4 ft 2½ in)
DIMENSIONS, INTERNAL:	
Cabin: Length: 228-100	6·30 m (20 ft 8 in)
228-200	7·80 m (25 ft 7 in)
Max width	1·35 m (4 ft 5¼ in)
Max height	1·61 m (5 ft 3½ in)
Floor area: 228-100	8·50 m² (91·49 sq ft)
228-200	10·55 m² (113·56 sq ft)
Volume: 228-100	11·60 m³ (409·6 cu ft)
228-200	13·60 m³ (480·3 cu ft)
Baggage volume: 228-100	1·97 m³ (69·6 cu ft)
228-200	3·17 m³ (111·95 cu ft)
AREA:	
Wings, gross	32·00 m² (344·4 sq ft)
WEIGHTS (estimated):	
Weight empty: 228-100	2,798 kg (6,168 lb)
228-200	2,908 kg (6,411 lb)
Max payload: 228-100	2,207 kg (4,865 lb)
228-200	2,057 kg (4,535 lb)
Max T-O weight (both)	5,700 kg (12,566 lb)
PERFORMANCE (estimated, at max T-O weight):	
Max level speed	233 knots (432 km/h; 268 mph)
Econ cruising speed	179 knots (332 km/h; 206 mph)
Max rate of climb at S/L	624 m (2,050 ft)/min
Rate of climb at S/L, one engine out	162 m (531 ft)/min
Service ceiling	9,020 m (29,600 ft)
T-O run	415 m (1,362 ft)
T-O to 15 m (50 ft)	525 m (1,725 ft)
Range at max cruising speed:	
228-100	933 nm (1,730 km; 1,075 miles)
228-200	555 nm (1,030 km; 640 miles)
Range with max fuel:	
228-100	1,063 nm (1,970 km; 1,224 miles)
228-200	621 nm (1,150 km; 715 miles)

Dornier Do 228-100 light transport, with additional side view (bottom) of Do 228-200 *(Pilot Press)*

EQUATOR
EQUATOR AIRCRAFT GESELLSCHAFT FÜR FLUGZEUGBAU mbH ULM

HEAD OFFICE: Benzstrasse 15, D-7904 Erbach
Telephone: (073) 04 6116 and 05 6116
PRESIDENT: Günther Pöschel

This company was known until 1974 as Pöschel Aircraft GmbH. Its President designed and built the prototype of a five/six-seat light STOL aircraft named the P-300 Equator. This flew for the first time on 8 November 1970, powered by a 216 kW (290 hp) Avco Lycoming IO-540 flat-six engine, and was last described in the 1972-73 *Jane's*. Simultaneously with flight testing the P-300, a turboprop-powered version of the same design was built as the P-400 Turbo-Equator STOL amphibian (see Addenda to 1977-78 *Jane's*). Following an incident caused by engine failure when the P-400 was taking off for its eighth test flight, the configuration has been changed extensively, and a common basic airframe is being developed for a family of different models, as follows:

EQUATOR, TWIN EQUATOR AND TURBO EQUATOR

This series of STOL aircraft utilises a common airframe, related to that of the earlier P-300 and P-400 but with the wing lowered from high-wing to mid-wing position, swept vertical tail surfaces, and a pylon-mounted power plant, above the cabin instead of being carried on the tail unit.

Differences between the six projected models are as follows:

P-300 Equator. Similar to P-350, except for non-retractable tricycle landing gear with streamline wheel and main-leg fairings.

P-350 Equator. Basic retractable-gear version with a 261 kW (350 shp) Avco Lycoming TIO-540-J2BD flat-six engine, driving a three-blade constant-speed and reversible-pitch metal tractor propeller. Prototype under construction in 1979, with fuselage and wings manufactured by the Glasflügel and Glaser-Dirks sailplane companies respectively.

P-400 Equator. Generally similar to P-350, but with a 298 kW (400 hp) Avco Lycoming IO-720-B1BD flat-eight engine and 'pusher' propeller.

P-420 Twin Equator. Generally similar to P-350, but with 'push and pull' tandem pair of 157 kW (210 hp) Avco Lycoming TO-360-C1A6D turbocharged flat-four engines, driving three-blade constant-speed fully-feathering and reversible-pitch propellers.

P-450 Equator. Generally similar to P-350, but with a 336 kW (450 hp) Avco Lycoming TIGO-541-D1B flat-six engine.

P-550 Turbo Equator. Generally similar to P-350, but with a Pratt & Whitney Aircraft of Canada PT6A-27 turboprop engine, flat rated to 410 kW (550 shp) and driving a three-blade constant-speed and reversible-pitch metal 'pusher' propeller.

All of these models are intended normally to be completed as light transports for eight or ten persons, including one or two pilots, and with retractable tricycle landing gear. Non-retractable gear can be fitted to any version.

Equator light transport at 1980 Hanover Air Show *(Brian M. Service)*

Non-STOL versions are available, with simplified flaps; these have increased useful load, fuel capacity and range, but longer T-O and landing runs and higher stalling speeds than those quoted. The fuselage can be adapted for amphibious operation, with a retractable step, water rudder and bilge pump. Other major options include cabin pressurisation, with a loss-of-pressure warning system, emergency oxygen, a cabin altimeter and cabin rate of climb indicator.

The interior can be converted for a wide variety of alternative roles, including freight transport, search and rescue, aerial photography and survey. The following description applies to the basic P-350 STOL version:

TYPE: Eight/ten-seat cabin monoplane.

WINGS: Cantilever mid-wing monoplane. Wing section Wortmann FX-78-P-160/200. Dihedral 6°. Incidence 2°. Forward sweep at quarter-chord 2°. Laminar-flow wing of fail-safe construction, utilising a fibre epoxy honeycomb sandwich structure. Drooping ailerons and double-slotted trailing-edge flaps of similar construction. Electrical de-icing of wing leading-edges optional.

FUSELAGE: Conventional fail-safe semi-monocoque structure, using construction materials similar to those of wing.

TAIL UNIT: Cantilever structure, with all-moving tailplane mounted approximately two-thirds up the fin. Constructed of the same materials as wing and fuselage. Electrically-operated trim tab in elevator and rudder. Electrical de-icing of tailplane and fin leading-edges optional.

LANDING GEAR: Hydraulically-retractable tricycle type, with single wheel on each unit. Main units retract outward. Oleo-pneumatic shock-absorbers. Main-wheel tyres size 6·50-8. Steerable nosewheel with tyre size 6·00-6. Goodyear brakes. Parking brake.

POWER PLANT: One or two engines as detailed in model listings. Fuel capacity 1,000 litres (220 Imp gallons).

ACCOMMODATION: Standard accommodation for a pilot and seven passengers, or pilot and co-pilot with six passengers. Rear baggage and bar compartment may be used optionally to accommodate 9th and 10th seats, or toilet. Door on each side at forward end of cabin. Dual controls standard. Shoulder harness for two front seats standard. Baggage space, with internal and external access, at rear of cabin. Accommodation heated and ventilated.

SYSTEMS: 24V electrical system. Vacuum system for blind-flying instrumentation. Air-conditioning, oxygen system, pressurisation system, and electrical de-icing system with 100A alternator, optional.

AVIONICS AND EQUIPMENT: Standard avionics include dual nav/com with VOR/LOC and VOR/ILS, marker beacon receiver, ADF, transponder, and audio panel. Standard equipment includes blind-flying instrumentation, clock, exhaust gas temperature gauge, outside air temperature gauge, map compartment, sun visors, heated pitot, stall warning device, cabin fresh air vents, dome lights, beacon lights, landing light, navigation lights, taxi light, static wicks and tiedown rings. Optional avionics include autopilot, DME, RNAV, radar altimeter and weather radar. Optional equipment includes cabin altimeter and rate of climb indicator; tinted windows; amphibian conversion with retractable step, water rudder and bilge pump; fixed landing gear, oversize wheels, ski gear; and cargo doors.

DIMENSIONS, EXTERNAL:
Wing span   12·20 m (40 ft 0¼ in)

P-450 Equator eight/ten-seat light transport, with scrap view of the P-420 Twin Equator *(Michael A. Badrocke)*

Length overall	10·00 m (32 ft 9¾ in)	
Height overall	3·80 m (12 ft 5½ in)	

AREA:
Wings, gross	18·00 m² (193·75 sq ft)

WEIGHTS AND LOADING (estimated, A: P-300; B: P-350; C: P-400; D: P-420; E: P-450; F: P-550):
Weight empty: A	1,070 kg (2,359 lb)
B	1,100 kg (2,425 lb)
C	1,123 kg (2,475 lb)
D	1,242 kg (2,738 lb)
E	1,162 kg (2,561 lb)
F	989 kg (2,180 lb)
*Max T-O weight, all versions	2,000 kg (4,410 lb)
Max wing loading, all versions	111 kg/m² (22·7 lb/sq ft)

*Can be increased to 2,520 kg (5,555 lb) subject to conditions of CAR 8, for increased range

PERFORMANCE (estimated, at 2,000 kg (4,410 lb) max T-O weight, ISA):
Max level speed:	
B at 4,570 m (15,000 ft)	220 knots (407 km/h; 253 mph)
D at 3,050 m (10,000 ft)	221 knots (409 km/h; 254 mph)
E at 4,570 m (15,000 ft)	233 knots (431 km/h; 268 mph)
F at 9,145 m (30,000 ft)	285 knots (528 km/h; 328 mph)
Max level speed at S/L:	
B	188 knots (348 km/h; 216 mph)
C	197 knots (365 km/h; 227 mph)
D	200 knots (370 km/h; 230 mph)
E	205 knots (379 km/h; 236 mph)
F	220 knots (407 km/h; 253 mph)
Cruising speed:	
A at 4,500 m (14,760 ft)	178 knots (330 km/h; 205 mph)

B at 4,500 m (14,760 ft)	189 knots (350 km/h; 217 mph)
C at 2,560 m (8,400 ft)	183 knots (340 km/h; 211 mph)
D at 3,000 m (9,840 ft)	189 knots (350 km/h; 217 mph)
E at 4,500 m (14,760 ft)	200 knots (370 km/h; 230 mph)
F at 9,000 m (29,530 ft)	243 knots (450 km/h; 279 mph)
Stalling speed, flaps and wheels down, all STOL versions	54 knots (100 km/h; 63 mph)
Max rate of climb at S/L: A	480 m (1,575 ft)/min
B	570 m (1,870 ft)/min
C	660 m (2,165 ft)/min
D	690 m (2,263 ft)/min
E	720 m (2,362 ft)/min
F	900 m (2,952 ft)/min
Service ceiling: A	9,500 m (31,170 ft)
B	10,700 m (35,100 ft)
C	9,400 m (30,840 ft)
D	11,300 m (37,100 ft)
E	11,800 m (38,700 ft)
F	13,200 m (43,300 ft)
STOL T-O to 15 m (50 ft): A	460 m (1,509 ft)
B	410 m (1,345 ft)
C	360 m (1,181 ft)
D	330 m (1,083 ft)
E	310 m (1,017 ft)
F	280 m (919 ft)
STOL landing from 15 m (50 ft), all versions	300 m (985 ft)
Range with max fuel:	
A	2,590 nm (4,800 km; 2,982 miles)
B	2,428 nm (4,500 km; 2,796 miles)
C, D, E	2,158 nm (4,000 km; 2,485 miles)
F	1,618 nm (3,000 km; 1,864 miles)

FUS
FLUGZEUG-UNION-SÜD GmbH
(subsidiary of MBB)

HEAD OFFICE: PO Box 83 17 20, 8000 München 83
Telephone: (089) 60 00 3107, 60 00 4965
Telex: 5 29 132 fus d
LIGHT AIRCRAFT DEPARTMENT: Otto-Hahn-Strasse 4, 8012 Ottebrunn (Riemerling)
MANAGER: Josef Fuchshuber

MBB FLAMINGO-TRAINER

Flugzeug-Union-Süd, a subsidiary of Messerschmitt-Bölkow-Blohm, is marketing a trainer derived from the MBB 223 Flamingo, last described under the CASA heading in the Spanish section of the 1975-76 *Jane's*. It is available in three versions:

Flamingo-Trainer A1. Standard version, with 149 kW (200 hp) Avco Lycoming IO-360 engine and Hartzell HC-E2YR-1BF/F8467-7R two-blade constant-speed metal propeller.

Flamingo-Trainer K1. Aerobatic version, with 149 kW (200 hp) Avco Lycoming AIO-360 engine, and propeller as above.

Flamingo-Trainer T1. Turbocharged version, with 157 kW (210 hp) Avco Lycoming TO-360-C1A6D turbocharged engine and two-blade propeller as above or, optionally, with a Hoffmann HO-Y123K/180 R+8 three-blade constant-speed composite propeller.

FUS MBB Flamingo-Trainer, a two/three-seat multi-role trainer

A prototype of the Flamingo-Trainer (D-EFWC) flew for the first time on 25 April 1979. By comparison with the original Flamingo, it benefits from the improvements in construction, equipment and materials which have been

developed during the 16 years which separate these aircraft. It is being marketed as a multi-role trainer for both civil and military use. Production of 25-30 was planned by the end of 1980.

TYPE: Two/three-seat light trainer.

WINGS: Cantilever low-wing monoplane. Wing section NACA 64$_2$-A215. Dihedral 3°. Incidence 3°. No sweepback. All-metal constant-chord two-spar structure. Main spars pass through fuselage side walls and are bolted together on aircraft centreline. Rear spars are attached to fuselage sides. Wingtip fairings of GRP are easily removable. Frise-type ailerons of metal construction. Trim tab in starboard aileron. Electrically-actuated trailing-edge plain flaps of similar construction to ailerons.

FUSELAGE: Conventional semi-monocoque structure of light alloy with riveted skins.

TAIL UNIT: Cantilever all-metal structure with fixed-incidence tailplane. Shallow dorsal fin from canopy to fin. Horn-balanced elevators and rudder. Trim tab in rudder, and in port elevator.

LANDING GEAR: Non-retractable tricycle type. Shock-absorption of all units by rubber in compression, assisted by hydraulic dampers. Steerable and self-centering nosewheel. All three wheels have tyres size 6·00-6, pressure 2·15 bars (31 lb/sq in). Hydraulic disc brakes. Parking brake.

POWER PLANT: One Avco Lycoming flat-four engine as detailed in model listings, driving a two-blade, or optional three-blade, propeller with spinner. Integral fuel tank in each wing, combined capacity 100 litres (22 Imp gallons) in Utility version, 170 litres (37·4 Imp gallons) in Normal category version. Refuelling point on upper surface of each wing.

ACCOMMODATION: Two seats side by side, with bench seat aft for additional trainee, beneath aft-sliding transparent canopy. Rear bench seat removable. Removal of starboard front seat permits the carriage of a stretcher or bulky cargo. Canopy is jettisonable, and incorporates a foul-weather window in the port side. Dual controls standard; starboard control column easily removed. Accommodation is air-conditioned.

SYSTEMS: Hydraulic system for brakes only. Electrical system includes a 28V engine-driven generator and two 24V 25Ah storage batteries.

AVIONICS AND EQUIPMENT: Avionics to customer's specific requirements. Standard equipment includes blind-flying instrumentation on port side, heated pitot, stall warning device, instrument lights; anti-collision, landing, navigation and taxi lights; and external power socket. Blind-flying instrumentation for starboard side is optional.

DIMENSIONS, EXTERNAL:
Wing span	8·28 m (27 ft 2 in)
Wing chord, constant	1·40 m (4 ft 7 in)
Wing aspect ratio	5·96
Length overall	7·60 m (24 ft 11¼ in)
Height overall	2·70 m (8 ft 10¼ in)
Wheel track	2·72 m (8 ft 11 in)
Wheelbase	1·60 m (5 ft 3 in)
Propeller diameter: two-blade	1·95 m (6 ft 4¾ in)
optional three-blade	1·88 m (6 ft 2 in)

AREAS:
Wings, gross	11·50 m² (123·8 sq ft)
Ailerons (total)	0·77 m² (8·24 sq ft)
Trailing-edge flaps (total)	0·94 m² (10·12 sq ft)
Horizontal tail surfaces (total)	2·45 m² (26·37 sq ft)
Vertical tail surfaces (total)	1·84 m² (19·81 sq ft)

WEIGHTS AND LOADINGS (T1, A: Normal; B: Utility category):
Weight empty: A, B	700 kg (1,543 lb)
Max fuel weight: A	122·4 kg (270 lb)
B	72 kg (159 lb)
Max payload: A	227·6 kg (502 lb)
B	208 kg (458 lb)
Max T-O weight: A	1,050 kg (2,315 lb)
B	980 kg (2,160 lb)
Max wing loading: A	91·3 kg/m² (18·70 lb/sq ft)
B	85·2 kg/m² (17·45 lb/sq ft)
Max power loading: A	6·69 kg/kW (11·02 lb/hp)
B	6·24 kg/kW (10·29 lb/hp)

PERFORMANCE (T1, at max T-O weight):
Max level speed at 4,570 m (15,000 ft)	
	150 knots (278 km/h; 173 mph)
Max cruising speed, 75% power at 3,050 m (10,000 ft)	
	130 knots (241 km/h; 150 mph)
Stalling speed, flaps up	
	65 knots (120 km/h; 75 mph) IAS
Stalling speed, flaps down	
	56 knots (102 km/h; 64 mph) IAS
Max rate of climb at S/L	323 m (1,060 ft)/min
Certificated ceiling	6,690 m (22,000 ft)
T-O to 15 m (50 ft)	365 m (1,200 ft)
Landing from 15 m (50 ft)	375 m (1,230 ft)
Range with max fuel, 65% power at 4,570 m (15,000 ft)	
	482 nm (893 km; 555 miles)

GYROFLUG
GYROFLUG INGENIEURGESELLSCHAFT mbH
Freihofstrasse 37, 7000 Stuttgart 40
Telephone: (07 11) 802603/609853
Telex: 723268 AFID
MANAGEMENT:
Dipl-Ing Wolfgang Schiller
Jörg Elzenbeck

Gyroflug was formed in July 1978 to manufacture and market, as a ready-to-fly production aircraft, a developed version of the two-seat VariEze lightweight sporting aircraft designed by Burt Rutan for amateur construction (see Rutan entry in US Homebuilt section). The company's executives had earlier built and flown, in April 1977, the first VariEze completed in Europe (D-EEEZ).

Gyroflug's development of the VariEze is known as the Speed-Canard. It was hoped to begin delivery of production aircraft in late 1980.

GYROFLUG SPEED-CANARD
As well as being slightly larger overall than the Rutan VariEze, on which it is based, the Speed-Canard differs in a number of important details. Its 18° swept wing retains the NASA winglets that have proved so successful on the

original design, but utilises a new aerofoil designed by Prof Eppler which is claimed to reduce drag by 30 per cent. Instead of retaining the glassfibre/foam core structure of the VariEze, which is well suited to amateur construction, the Speed-Canard is made of glassfibre and carbonfibre reinforced plastics laid up in female moulds, giving a lighter structure optimised for series production. The forward fuselage embodies a flush canopy similar to that of the latest sailplanes, with the rear seat raised to ensure a good field of view for both occupants.

A more powerful engine is standard, in the form of an 86 kW (115 hp) Avco Lycoming O-235 flat-four engine, driving a Hoffmann HO-V72G/17OU-10 two-blade constant-speed pusher propeller with spinner. Gyroflug is studying the possibility of fitting two Klöckner-Humboldt-Deutz KHD 117 lightweight turbojets in a later version of the Speed-Canard, giving an estimated max level speed of 237 knots (440 km/h; 273 mph).

Construction of the moulds in which to build components of the piston-engined prototype had been completed by the end of 1979, and it was anticipated that the first flight would be made in April 1980.

DIMENSIONS, EXTERNAL:
Wing span	7·00 m (22 ft 11½ in)
Foreplane span	3·61 m (11 ft 10⅛ in)
Foreplane chord (constant)	0·34 m (1 ft 1⅜ in)
Length overall	5·32 m (17 ft 5½ in)
Length of fuselage	4·32 m (14 ft 2 in)
Max width of fuselage	0·74 m (2 ft 5 in)
Height to top of fuselage	1·66 m (5 ft 5½ in)

AREAS:
Wings, gross	5·30 m² (57·05 sq ft)
Foreplane, gross	1·22 m² (13·13 sq ft)

WEIGHTS AND LOADINGS (estimated):
Weight empty	280 kg (617 lb)
Max fuel	130 kg (287 lb)
Max T-O weight	600 kg (1,323 lb)
Max wing loading	92·02 kg/m² (18·85 lb/sq ft)
Max power loading	6·98 kg/kW (11·5 lb/hp)

PERFORMANCE (estimated, at max T-O weight):
Never-exceed speed	215 knots (400 km/h; 248 mph)
Max cruising speed, 75% power	
	191 knots (354 km/h; 220 mph)
Econ cruising speed, 45% power	
	146 knots (270 km/h; 168 mph)
Stalling speed	51 knots (94 km/h; 58·5 mph)
Max rate of climb at S/L	480 m (1,575 ft)min
T-O run	300 m (984 ft)
Max range	1,349 nm (2,500 km; 1,553 miles)

MBB
MESSERSCHMITT-BÖLKOW-BLOHM GmbH
HEAD OFFICE: Ottobrunn bei München, 8000 München 80, Postfach 80 11 09
Telephone: (089) 6000-1
Telex: 5287-0 mbbd
WORKS:
Augsburg, Donauwörth, Hamburg-Finkenwerder, Laupheim, Manching, Munich, Nabern/Teck, Ottobrunn, Schrobenhausen and Stade
PRESIDENT AND GENERAL MANAGER: Prof Dipl-Ing Gero Madelung
EXECUTIVE VICE-PRESIDENT AND DEPUTY GENERAL MANAGER: Sepp Hort
EXECUTIVE VICE-PRESIDENTS:
Dr Johannes Broschwitz
Fritz Killguss
Peter C. Küchler
Ernst-Georg Pantel
VICE-PRESIDENTS, DIVISION MANAGING DIRECTORS:
Ernst-Georg Pantel (Commercial Aircraft Division)
Günther Kuhlo (Dynamics Division)
Johannes Schubert (Space Division)
Kurt Pfleiderer (Helicopter and Transport Systems Division)
Gunter Horstkotte (Ottobrunn Operations Division)
CHAIRMAN OF THE SUPERVISORY BOARD: Max Streibl
PUBLIC RELATIONS: Eduard Roth

In May 1969 the former Messerschmitt-Bölkow GmbH and Hamburger Flugzeugbau GmbH (see 1968-69 *Jane's*) merged to form a new group known as Messerschmitt-Bölkow-Blohm GmbH. Shareholders in this company include the State of Hamburg, which has a 20·25% interest, the State of Bavaria (direct and indirect) (22·65%), the Messerschmitt Foundation (11·50%), Dr-Ing h.c. Ludwig Bölkow (4·14%), the Blohm family (0·75%), Allianz/Bosch (12·15%), Aérospatiale (2·96%) and Fides GmbH (25·59%). MBB is the largest aerospace

First of the new batch of HFB 320 Hansa Jet ECM trainers completed by MBB's Commercial Aircraft Division

company in West Germany, and is affiliated with a number of national and international corporations.

It was the intention of the Federal German government that MBB should be merged with VFW before the end of 1980.

Development work on the Panavia Tornado multi-role combat aircraft, as the German Federal Republic's prime contractor, is MBB's main military aircraft activity. MBB has a 42·5% shareholding in Panavia Aircraft GmbH (which see), together with BAe (42·5%) and Aeritalia (15%). It is supplying PAH-1 anti-tank helicopters to the Federal German Army, and is working with Aérospatiale of France on the second-generation PAH-2 (see International section). MBB is participating in the resumed production of the Transall C-160 military transport aircraft. Its Manching facilities are responsible for overhaul of F-104G Starfighter and F-4 Phantom aircraft flown by the Federal German armed services.

The main civil aircraft programme involves work on the Airbus A300 and A310 for Airbus Industrie (which see). The company is also making major assemblies for the Fokker F28 Fellowship. MBB's BO 105 was the first twin-turbine lightweight utility helicopter to enter series production, and it is now working in partnership with Kawasaki Heavy Industries of Japan on a new helicopter known as the BK 117 (see International section).

MBB is also involved extensively in missile and RPV development and production, and is a prime contractor or system leader in a number of European space programmes. Details of these activities can be found in the appropriate sections of this edition.

In 1980 the company was engaged in study of the TKF 90 project to provide a new generation tactical fighter aircraft for the Luftwaffe and other European air forces in the 1990s, and was devoting much of its market research/design effort towards new-generation European airliners. In addition, the company is engaged in research and development programmes concerned with CCV (control configured vehicle) technology, carbonfibre technology, and the evolution of more simple, more reliable aircraft subsystems.

Since 1966, MBB has been developing a new type of conventional weapon system, designated **MW-1**, which will be carried by the Tornado and can equip other types such as the F-4F Phantom. It consists of a dispenser carried under the aircraft's belly, from which a large number of small munitions can be ejected pyrotechnically. For use against tanks, the munitions may be shaped-charge bombs which detonate on impact or mines that are set off when the tanks run over them. They can be of types designed to destroy airfield runways, splinter mines with fuses triggered by aircraft movements, or a type designed to destroy aircraft inside shelters.

MBB HFB 320 HANSA JET

As a result of the success of the three Hansa Jet ECM trainers already in service, the German Federal Defence Technology and Procurement Office ordered four more of these aircraft for the Luftwaffe in late 1977. The first of these (D-CANO) flew for the first time on 22 August 1979 and, after production flight testing, was ferried to Rome in October to have its special avionics installed by Elettronica SpA. It was scheduled for delivery to the Luftwaffe in early 1980.

Full details of the basic Hansa Jet can be found in the 1973-74 *Jane's*.

MBB BO 105

Design of this light utility helicopter was started in July 1962 and construction of prototypes began in 1964, under Federal German government contract. The first BO 105 prototype was fitted with an existing conventional rotor and two Allison 250-C18 turboshaft engines; subsequent aircraft have had a rotor system based on a rigid titanium hub, with feathering hinges only, and hingeless flexible glassfibre blades. From the Spring of 1970 'droop-snoot' rotor blades of MBB design have been standard.

Details of subsequent prototypes, early production helicopters and special variants can be found in previous editions of *Jane's*. Current models are as follows:

BO 105 CB. Standard production version since 1975, with two Allison 250-C20B engines, operable in air temperatures ranging from −45° to +54°C, and strengthened rotor gearing. LBA certification received in November 1976.

BO 105 CBS. Version with increased seating or cargo capacity in a 0·25 m (10 in) longer fuselage. Available in five-seat executive or six-seat high-density configurations. Similar to the version marketed in the USA as the BO 105 Executaire by MBB's newly-established subsidiary, the MBB Helicopter Corporation (which see). Identified by small additional window aft of rear door on each side.

BO 105 D. Variant as supplied to the UK, with modified equipment. The BO 105 D has been approved since 1973 by the CAA for commercial single-pilot IFR operation, even in controlled airways.

BO 105 LS. Variant due for certification by end of 1981, and which is described separately.

BO 105 M (VBH). Liaison and light observation helicopter for the Federal German Army, with uprated transmission. Production of 227 examples approved by the Federal government, to permit replacement of Alouette IIs. Deliveries under way in mid-1980.

BO 105 P (PAH-1). Anti-tank version, with outriggers able to carry six Euromissile Hot missiles, and with a

MBB BO 105 CBS, the 'stretched' five/six-seat version of the BO 105, here fitted with nose radar (*Brian M. Service*)

BO 105 CB five-seat light helicopter (two Allison 250-C20B turboshaft engines) (*Pilot Press*)

stabilised sight above the co-pilot's position. The German Federal government has given approval for the procurement of 212 examples for the Federal German Army, and deliveries began in September 1979. Uprated transmission, Singer AN/ASN-128 Doppler navigation system. Deliveries under way in mid-1980.

In the Philippines and Indonesia, NAM and Nurtanio respectively (which see) are participating in licence assembly programmes for the BO 105. A contract for 60 BO 105s was signed by the Spanish Ministry of Defence in late June 1979. These aircraft will be assembled in Spain, by CASA, and will be operated by Spanish Army aviation units for communications, observation and anti-tank missions.

Orders for all versions of the BO 105 totalled about 1,000 by the Summer of 1980.

The description which follows applies to the BO 105 CB production version:

TYPE: Five-seat light helicopter.

ROTOR SYSTEM: Four-blade main rotor, comprising rigid titanium hub and GRP blades, with titanium anti-erosion strip forming leading-edge of each blade. MBB-designed 'droop-snoot' blades of NACA 23012 asymmetrical section, having a specially-designed trailing-edge giving improved control in pitching moment. Flexible tension/torsion blade retention, to take up centrifugal forces. Roller bearings for pitch change. Main rotor blade folding optional. Two-blade semi-rigid tail rotor; blades of GRP, with titanium anti-erosion strip on leading-edge. Main rotor rpm 424. Tail rotor rpm 2,220.

ROTOR DRIVE: Main transmission utilises two bevel gear input stages with freewheeling clutches and a spur collector gear stage. Planetary reduction gear; three auxiliary drives for accessories. Main transmission rated for twin-engine input of 257 kW (345 shp) per engine, or a single engine input of 283 kW (380 shp). Tail rotor gearbox on fin. Main rotor/engine rpm ratio 1 : 14·2. Tail rotor/engine rpm ratio 1 : 2·7.

FUSELAGE: Conventional light alloy semi-monocoque structure of pod and boom type. Glassfibre-reinforced cowling over power plant. Titanium sheet engine deck.

TAIL UNIT: Horizontal stabiliser of conventional light alloy construction with small endplate fins.

MBB BO 105 P (PAH-1) fitted with six Hot anti-tank missiles and SFIM stabilised target acquisition and tracking sight (*Brian M. Service*)

LANDING GEAR: Skid type, with cross tubes designed for energy absorption by plastic deformation in the event of a heavy landing. Inflatable emergency floats can be attached to skids.

POWER PLANT: Two 313 kW (420 shp) Allison 250-C20B turboshaft engines, each with a max continuous rating of 298 kW (400 shp). Bladder-type fuel tanks under cabin floor, capacity 580 litres (127·5 Imp gallons), of which 570 litres (125·3 Imp gallons) are usable. Fuelling point on port side of cabin. Provision for fitting auxiliary tanks in freight compartment. Oil capacity: engine 9 litres (1·98 Imp gallons), gearbox 7 kg (15·4 lb).

ACCOMMODATION: Pilot and co-pilot or passenger on individual front seats, with safety belts. Optional dual controls. Bench seat at rear for three persons, removable for cargo and stretcher carrying. Entire rear fuselage aft of seats and under power plant available as freight and baggage space, with access through two clamshell doors at rear. Two standard stretchers can be accommodated in ambulance role. One forward-opening hinged and jettisonable door and one sliding door on each side of cabin. Heating system optional.

SYSTEMS: Tandem fully-redundant hydraulic system for powered main rotor controls. Electrical system powered by two 150A 28V DC starter/generators and a 24V 22Ah nickel-cadmium battery; external power socket.

AVIONICS AND EQUIPMENT: Standard equipment includes clock, outside air temperature gauge, battery overheat warning lights, heated pitot, tiedown rings in cargo compartment, cabin and cargo compartment dome lights, position lights and collision warning lights. A wide range of optional avionics and equipment is available, including Doppler navigation, search radar, pilot and co-pilot adjustable shoulder harness, rear seat assembly, dual controls, heating system, windscreen wiper, rescue winch, landing light, searchlight, externally-mounted loudspeaker, fuel dump valve, external load hook, settling protectors, snow skids, rotor brake, and main rotor blade folding. A completely equipped ambulance version is available.

ARMAMENT (military versions): Provision for a variety of alternative military loads, including six Hot anti-tank missiles and associated stabilised sight.

DIMENSIONS, EXTERNAL:
Diameter of main rotor	9·84 m (32 ft 3·4 in)
Diameter of tail rotor	1·90 m (6 ft 2¾ in)
Main rotor blade chord	0·27 m (10·63 in)

Tail rotor blade chord	0·18 m (7·09 in)
Distance between rotor centres	5·95 m (19 ft 6¼ in)
Length, incl main and tail rotors	11·86 m (38 ft 11 in)
Length, excl main rotor	8·56 m (28 ft 1 in)
Height to top of main rotor head	3·00 m (9 ft 10 in)
Width over skids, unladen	2·53 m (8 ft 3½ in)
Width over skids, laden	2·58 m (8 ft 5½ in)
Rear loading doors: Height	0·64 m (2 ft 1 in)
Width	1·40 m (4 ft 7 in)

DIMENSIONS, INTERNAL:
Cabin, incl cargo compartment:
Length	4·30 m (14 ft 1 in)
Max width	1·40 m (4 ft 7 in)
Max height	1·25 m (4 ft 1 in)
Volume	4·80 m³ (169 cu ft)
Cargo compartment: Length	1·85 m (6 ft 0¾ in)
Max width	1·20 m (3 ft 11¼ in)
Max height	0·57 m (1 ft 10½ in)
Floor area	2·20 m² (23·7 sq ft)
Volume	1·50 m³ (53 cu ft)

WEIGHTS AND LOADINGS:
Weight empty, basic	1,189 kg (2,622 lb)
Weight empty, operating	1,279 kg (2,820 lb)
Standard fuel	460 kg (1,014 lb)
Fuel, incl auxiliary tanks	780 kg (1,720 lb)
Max T-O weight	2,400 kg (5,291 lb)
Normal disc loading	26·5 kg/m² (5·43 lb/sq ft)
Max disc loading	30·5 kg/m² (6·25 lb/sq ft)

PERFORMANCE (at T-O weight of 2,300 kg; 5,070 lb):
Never-exceed speed at S/L
145 knots (270 km/h; 167 mph)
Max cruising speed at S/L
132 knots (245 km/h; 152 mph)
Normal cruising speed
125 knots (232 km/h; 144 mph)
Max rate of climb at S/L	540 m (1,773 ft)/min
Vertical rate of climb at S/L	258 m (847 ft)/min
Max operating height	5,180 m (17,000 ft)
Single-engine service ceiling	1,280 m (4,200 ft)
Hovering ceiling IGE	2,900 m (9,514 ft)
Hovering ceiling OGE	1,980 m (6,500 ft)
Range with standard fuel and max payload, no reserves:
at S/L	310 nm (575 km; 357 miles)
at 1,525 m (5,000 ft)	355 nm (656 km; 408 miles)
Ferry range with auxiliary tanks, no reserves:
at S/L	540 nm (1,000 km; 621 miles)
at 1,525 m (5,000 ft)	600 nm (1,112 km; 691 miles)

MBB BO 105 LS

This version of the BO 105 has more powerful engines and an uprated transmission, permitting operation at a higher gross weight with external load. It was first flown in late March 1979. The description of the BO 105 CB applies also to the BO 105 LS, except as follows:

ROTOR DRIVE: Main transmission, type ZF-FS 112, is rated for a twin-engine input of 294 kW (395 shp) per engine, or a single engine input of 368 kW (493 shp) continuous, or 404 kW (542 shp) for 2·5 min.

POWER PLANT: Two Allison 250-C28C turboshaft engines, each rated at 410 kW (550 shp) for 2·5 min, and with a 5 min take-off or max continuous power rating of 373 kW (500 shp). Fuel system generally as for BO 105 CB, but max standard capacity 380 kg (838 lb).

SYSTEMS: As for BO 105 CB, except 24V battery is of 25Ah capacity.

WEIGHTS:
Weight empty	1,250 kg (2,756 lb)
Max T-O weight, internal load	2,400 kg (5,291 lb)
Max T-O weight, external load	2,500 kg (5,512 lb)

PERFORMANCE (at max T-O weight):
Never-exceed speed at S/L
146 knots (270 km/h; 168 mph)
Max cruising speed at S/L
136 knots (252 km/h; 157 mph)
Max rate of climb at S/L	600 m (1,970 ft)/min
Max operating height	6,100 m (20,000 ft)
Service ceiling, one engine out	2,880 m (9,450 ft)
Hovering ceiling IGE	4,000 m (13,120 ft)
Hovering ceiling OGE	3,440 m (11,290 ft)
Range at S/L, standard fuel, max internal payload, no reserves | 248 nm (460 km; 286 miles) |

MBB/AÉROSPATIALE PAH-2

Details of this second-generation anti-tank helicopter can be found in the International section.

MBB/KAWASAKI BK 117

Following signature of an agreement on 25 February 1977, MBB is developing in conjunction with Kawasaki of Japan an 8/10-seat multi-purpose helicopter known as the BK 117. A description of this aircraft can be found in the International section.

MYLIUS
LEICHTFLUGZEUGE-ENTWICKLUNGEN DIPL ING HERMANN MYLIUS
Kuckucksweg 6, 8011 Brunnthal

In addition to heading the light aircraft technical development activities of MBB, Dipl Ing Hermann Mylius develops and builds sporting aircraft privately.

MYLIUS MY 102 TORNADO, MY 103 MISTRAL and MY 104 PASSAT

In July 1971, Dipl Ing Mylius began privately the development of a single-seat version of the MHK 101, intended for competitive aerobatics. Construction of a prototype (D-EMYS) was started in December 1971, and this flew for the first time on 7 July 1973. Known as the MY 102 Tornado, it has achieved considerable success in competition.

Development of the MY 102 is continuing and a second prototype, embodying a number of modifications, is being completed. Two larger versions are also being developed, to provide a family of three basically similar aircraft:
MY 102 Tornado. Basic single-seat model.
MY 103 Mistral. Generally similar to Tornado, but with accommodation for pilot and one passenger. Three examples under construction.
MY 104 Passat. Four-seat version of the MY 102, expected to fly in 1980.

The following description applies in particular to the MY 102, but specification details of the MY 103 and MY 104 are given also:

TYPE: Single-seat sporting and aerobatic aircraft.

WINGS: Cantilever low-wing monoplane. Wing section NACA 64218 at root, NACA 64212 at tip. Dihedral 2° 30'. Incidence 2°. Sweepback 1° 24' at quarter-chord. Single-spar all-metal structure with glassfibre wingtips. All-metal differentially-operated ailerons. Electrically-operated all-metal plain trailing-edge flaps. By removing three bolts on each side, the wings can be folded back alongside the fuselage to facilitate stowage in a confined space or to permit the aircraft to be towed on ordinary roads behind a car. Control lines to flaps and ailerons disconnect and reconnect automatically during folding and unfolding.

FUSELAGE: Conventional semi-monocoque structure of light alloy, except for glassfibre engine cowlings.

TAIL UNIT: Single all-metal fin and rudder, with sweepback on fin leading-edge and dorsal fairing from base of fin to rear of cockpit canopy. All-moving metal tailplane, with glassfibre tips, mid-mounted on extreme rear of fuselage, with cable-controlled full-span antiservo tab.

LANDING GEAR: Tricycle type, with fixed or optionally rearward-retracting nosewheel and non-retractable main wheels. Nosewheel is steerable by means of the rudder pedals, the controls being disconnected automatically during retraction, which is accomplished electrically. Nosewheel can be locked in the down position during flight, if required. Main-gear legs are cantilever steel struts, inclined outward at 45° from fuselage main bulkhead. Cleveland wheels size 5·00-5; Continental tyres 5·00-5 on nosewheel and 5·50-5 on main wheels. Streamlined fairings on main wheels. Cleveland hydraulically-actuated brakes. Small skid under rear fuselage, which can be fitted with an adapter for transport by road.

POWER PLANT: One 168 kW (225 hp) modified Avco Lycoming AIO-360-B1B flat-four engine, driving a Hoffmann three-blade constant-speed metal propeller with spinner. Fuel in two tanks in wings, each with capacity of 73·4 litres (19·4 US gallons). Total fuel capacity 146·8 litres (38·8 US gallons). Refuelling point in upper surface of each wing.

ACCOMMODATION: Pilot only, beneath rearward-sliding tinted canopy.

SYSTEMS: DC electrical system for flaps, nose gear actuation and engine starting, provided by 40A engine-driven alternator and 12V 33Ah battery. Hydraulic system for brakes only.

AVIONICS: Becker AR400 radio.

DIMENSIONS, EXTERNAL (A: MY 102; B: MY 103; C: MY 104):
Wing span:	A	7·89 m (25 ft 10⅝ in)
	B	8·40 m (27 ft 6¾ in)
	C	10·46 m (34 ft 3¾ in)
Wing aspect ratio:	A	6·6
	B	6·85
	C	8
Length overall:	A, B	6·40 m (21 ft 0 in)
	C	7·60 m (24 ft 11¼ in)
Height overall:	A, B	2·31 m (7 ft 7 in)
	C	2·38 m (7 ft 9¾ in)

Vibration testing a Hoffmann three-blade constant-speed propeller on the MY 102 Tornado prototype

AREAS:
Wings, gross: A	9·40 m² (101·18 sq ft)	
B	10·30 m² (110·87 sq ft)	
C	13·50 m² (145·32 sq ft)	

WEIGHTS AND LOADINGS (B and C estimated):
Weight empty: A	530 kg (1,168 lb)	
B	554 kg (1,221 lb)	
C	680 kg (1,499 lb)	

Max T-O weight (Normal category):
A	820 kg (1,808 lb)
B	920 kg (2,028 lb)
C	1,258 kg (2,773 lb)

Max T-O weight (Aerobatic):
A	650 kg (1,433 lb)
B	780 kg (1,720 lb)

Max wing loading (Normal category):
A	87·23 kg/m² (17·87 lb/sq ft)
B	89·32 kg/m² (18·29 lb/sq ft)
C	93·19 kg/m² (19·08 lb/sq ft)

Max wing loading (Aerobatic):
A	69·15 kg/m² (14·16 lb/sq ft)
B	75·73 kg/m² (15·51 lb/sq ft)

Max power loading: A 4·88 kg/kW (8·04 lb/hp)
B 5·48 kg/kW (9·01 lb/hp)
C 7·49 kg/kW (12·32 lb/hp)

PERFORMANCE (at max Normal T-O weight, B and C estimated):
Never-exceed speed:
A, B, C 216 knots (400 km/h; 249 mph)
Max level speed at S/L:
A	173 knots (320 km/h; 199 mph)
B	167 knots (310 km/h; 193 mph)
C	162 knots (300 km/h; 186 mph)

Cruising speed: A 159 knots (295 km/h; 183 mph)
B 154 knots (285 km/h; 177 mph)
C 148 knots (275 km/h; 171 mph)
Landing speed: A 48·5 knots (90 km/h; 56 mph)
B, C 55 knots (102 km/h; 63 mph)
Max rate of climb at S/L: A 750 m (2,460 ft)/min
B 600 m (1,970 ft)/min
Service ceiling: A 7,500 m (24,610 ft)
B 7,000 m (22,970 ft)
C 5,000 m (16,400 ft)

MY 104 Passat four-seat development of the Mylius MY 102 (*Michael A. Badrocke*)

Range with max fuel, 15 min reserves:
A	485 nm (900 km; 559 miles)		
B	647 nm (1,200 km; 745 miles)		
C	782 nm (1,450 km; 900 miles)		

Endurance, at 65% power: A 3 h 30 min
B 4 h 18 min
C 5 h 30 min
g limits: A ±9
B ±7·5
C ±4·7

RFB
RHEIN-FLUGZEUGBAU GmbH (Subsidiary of VFW GmbH)

HEAD OFFICE AND MAIN WORKS: D-4050 Mönchengladbach 1, Flugplatz, Postfach 408
Telephone: (0 21 61) 662031
Telex: 08/52506
OTHER WORKS: D-5050 Porz-Wahn, Flughafen Köln-Bonn, Halle 6; and D-2401 Lübeck-Blankensee, Flugplatz
EXECUTIVE DIRECTORS:
Dipl-Volkswirt Wolfgang Kutscher
Dipl-Ing Alfred Schneider

This company, founded in 1956, has since 1976 held 100% of the stock of Sportavia-Pützer (which see).

RFB is engaged in the development and manufacture of airframe structural components, with particular reference to wings and fuselages made entirely of glassfibre-reinforced resins. Current programmes include series and individual production of aircraft components and assemblies made of light alloy, steel and glassfibre-reinforced resin, for aircraft in quantity production by other West German companies, as well as spare parts and ground equipment.

Under contract to the Federal German government, RFB is servicing military aircraft, and is providing target-towing flights and other services with special aircraft. It operates a factory-certificated service centre for all types of Piper aircraft and for the Mitsubishi MU-2 utility transport aircraft. General servicing of other types of all-metal aircraft is undertaken.

In the aircraft propulsion field, RFB has been engaged for some years in the development of specialised applications for ducted propellers, leading to the Fantrainer military multi-purpose training aircraft.

RFB FANTRAINER 400

This tandem two-seat training aircraft was first projected in 1970, at which time a model was exhibited at the Hanover Air Show. It utilises a ducted fan propulsion system which, in the original concept, comprised a Dowty variable-pitch fan, integral with the rear fuselage and driven by a 224 kW (300 hp) Wankel four-disc rotary engine.

In March 1975 the Federal German Defence Ministry awarded RFB a contract to develop and build two Fantrainer prototypes, for evaluation as potential replacements for the Piaggio P.149D primary trainers now used by the Luftwaffe. They were designed to conform to US FAR Pt 23 specifications in the Aerobatic and Utility categories, and it is suggested that pupils might be able to make direct transition from the Fantrainer to the Alpha Jet.

The first prototype, designated **AWI-2**, flew for the first time on 27 October 1977, powered by two 112 kW (150 hp) Wankel engines driving a variable-pitch fan through a reduction gearbox, with airbrakes in the fan shroud. The **ATI-2** second prototype (D-EATI) flew for the first time on 31 May 1978 and had one Allison 250-C20B turboshaft engine. It logged 62 flying hours before being lost on 7 September 1978.

In 1978, the first prototype (D-EATJ) was brought up to proposed production configuration for the Luftwaffe, as the **Fantrainer 400**, with Allison 250-C20B turboshaft engine. It had logged 180 flying hours by September 1979, including 55 hours with its original Wankel engines.

An uprated version, with 448 kW (600 shp) Allison 250 or Avco Lycoming LTS 101 turboshaft, has been proposed to the US Air Force by Vought Corporation as a contender in the USAF's T-37 replacement programme. Known as the Vought 538, it is entered as a Vought/RFB team design; if selected, RFB would have a 50 per cent share in its production.

The description which follows applies to the Fantrainer 400:

TYPE: Two-seat basic and IFR training aircraft; g limits +6/−3.
WINGS: Cantilever mid-wing monoplane. Wing section Eppler 502. Thickness/chord ratio 15·7%. Dihedral 2° 30′. No incidence. Sweepforward 6° at quarter-chord. Constructed mainly of glassfibre and plastics tube sandwich. Frise-type ailerons and electrically-actuated Fowler-type trailing-edge flaps. No tabs.
FUSELAGE: The load-carrying fail-safe structure of the forward and centre-fuselage is of light alloy, with non-load-bearing glassfibre skin, sections of which are removable for servicing purposes. Cruciform metal rear fuselage is connected to the centre-fuselage at three points. The integral fan duct is free of structural loads. Large airbrake on each side of fan duct, operation of which causes no lift or stability changes.
TAIL UNIT: All-metal T tail of light alloy, with conventional rudder and elevators. Servo tab in trailing-edge of each elevator. Trim tab in rudder.
LANDING GEAR: Retractable tricycle type, with single wheel on each unit. Electro-hydraulic actuation, with manual emergency extension. All units retract into fuselage, nosewheel rearward, main units inward and upward into wing roots. Leaf-spring legs, of glassfibre-reinforced plastics. Cleveland main wheels size 15 × 6·00-6, tyre pressure 4·7 bars (68 lb/sq in). Goodyear nosewheel size 5·00-5, tyre pressure 3·45 bars (50 lb/sq in). Cleveland wheel brakes.
POWER PLANT: One 313 kW (420 shp) Allison 250-C20B turboshaft engine, driving a Dowty Rotol seven-blade constant-speed ducted fan. Four integral fuel tanks in wings, with combined capacity of 310 litres (68 Imp gallons). Refuelling points at wingtips. Oil capacity 16

RFB Fantrainer 400 two-seat basic and IFR training aircraft (*Pilot Press*)

litres (3·5 Imp gallons). Engine air intakes in wing leading-edges.

ACCOMMODATION: Two seats in tandem cockpit, meeting US MIL specifications in terms of dimensions and layout. Seats and rudder pedals adjustable. Provision for seat and back parachutes. Fighter-type side consoles. Canopy over each seat hinges sideways (to stbd) independently. Accommodation heated and ventilated.

SYSTEMS: Electrical system includes a starter/generator and battery. Electro-hydraulic system for operation of landing gear and airbrakes.

DIMENSIONS, EXTERNAL:

Wing span	9·70 m (31 ft 10 in)
Wing chord at root	1·89 m (6 ft 2½ in)
Wing chord at tip	1·02 m (3 ft 4 in)
Wing aspect ratio	6·6
Length overall, incl nose probe	9·00 m (29 ft 6¼ in)

Height overall	2·90 m (9 ft 6 in)
Tailplane span	3·29 m (10 ft 9½ in)
Wheel track	1·94 m (6 ft 4¼ in)
Wheelbase	3·80 m (12 ft 5½ in)
Fan diameter	1·20 m (3 ft 11¼ in)

AREAS:

Wings, gross	13·9 m² (149·6 sq ft)
Ailerons (total)	1·19 m² (12·81 sq ft)
Trailing-edge flaps (total)	1·40 m² (15·07 sq ft)
Rudder, incl tab	2·20 m² (23·68 sq ft)
Tailplane	2·90 m² (31·22 sq ft)
Elevators, incl tab	0·77 m² (8·29 sq ft)

WEIGHTS AND LOADINGS (A: Aerobatic; B: Utility category):

Weight empty, equipped	925 kg (2,040 lb)
Max T-O weight: A	1,350 kg (2,976 lb)
B	1,580 kg (3,483 lb)

Max wing loading: A	97 kg/m² (19·9 lb/sq ft)
B	114 kg/m² (23·3 lb/sq ft)
Max power loading: A	4·3 kg/kW (7·09 lb/shp)
B	5·05 kg/kW (8·29 lb/shp)

PERFORMANCE (at AUW of 1,350 kg; 2,976 lb):

Max level speed at S/L	195 knots (362 km/h; 225 mph)
Max cruising speed at 3,000 m (9,840 ft)	178 knots (330 km/h; 205 mph)
Max rate of climb at S/L	610 m (2,000 ft)/min
Service ceiling	6,100 m (20,000 ft)
T-O run	230 m (755 ft)
Landing run	250 m (820 ft)
Range with max fuel, optimum cruising speed at 3,000 m (9,840 ft), no reserves	950 nm (1,760 km; 1,093 miles)
Endurance with max fuel at 3,000 m (9,840 ft), no reserves	6 h 18 min

---

SPORTAVIA
SPORTAVIA-PÜTZER GmbH u Co KG

HEAD OFFICE AND WORKS: D-5377 Dahlem-Schmidtheim, Flugplatz Dahlemer Binz
Telephone: (02447) 277/8
Telex: 08 33 602
SALES MANAGER: Alfons Pützer

This company was formed in 1966 by Comte Antoine d'Assche, director of the French company Alpavia SA, and Herr Alfons Pützer, originally to take over from Alpavia manufacture of the Avion-Planeur series of light aircraft designed by M René Fournier.

In 1969, RFB (which see), a subsidiary of VFW GmbH, acquired a 50 per cent holding in Sportavia: the remaining shares were acquired in January 1977, from which date Sportavia became wholly owned by RFB.

In current production is a four-seat lightweight sporting aircraft known as the RS 180 Sportsman.

Sportavia was also responsible for developing the P.68 Observer variant of the Partenavia P.68B Victor twin-engined light aircraft (see Italian section).

SPORTAVIA RS 180 SPORTSMAN

M René Fournier began design of the Sportsman in December 1970. Construction of the first of two prototypes started 14 months later, and this aircraft made its first flight on 1 March 1973, powered by a 93 kW (125 hp) Avco Lycoming O-235-F2A engine.

The second prototype, a completely new four-seat design developed by Sportavia, had the designation RF6C, and this flew for the first time on 28 April 1976. It differed from the first prototype in having a more powerful engine, increased cabin volume, and a GRP outer skin.

The RF6C entered production in late 1976. The change of designation to RS 180 took effect in early 1978, simultaneously with raising of the tailplane from its original position at the top of the fuselage.

TYPE: Four-seat lightweight sporting aircraft.
WINGS: Cantilever low-wing monoplane. Wing section NACA 63-218 at root, NACA 63-215 at tip. Dihedral 5° from roots. Incidence 0°. One-piece single spar of laminated beech, birch plywood and pine ribs, mahogany plywood covering (upper surfaces only), and GRP outer skin. All-metal split flap on each trailing-edge, with electrical actuation. Fabric-covered wooden Frise-type ailerons, actuated by pushrods. No tabs.
FUSELAGE: Conventional wooden structure of frames and longerons, with mahogany plywood covering and GRP outer skin.
TAIL UNIT: Cantilever wooden structure, with GRP-covered fixed surfaces and fabric-covered control surfaces. Fixed-incidence tailplane mounted part-way up

Sportavia RS 180 Sportsman four-seat light aircraft (Avco Lycoming O-360-A3A engine)

fin. Rudder and elevators actuated by pushrods. Flettner tab in port elevator.
LANDING GEAR: Non-retractable tricycle type. Main units have hydraulic shock-absorption. Steerable nosewheel, with oleo-pneumatic shock-absorber. Single wheel on each unit. Hydraulic disc brakes. Streamline fairings over all three wheels.
POWER PLANT: One 134 kW (180 hp) Avco Lycoming O-360-A3A flat-four engine, driving a Hoffmann two-blade wooden fixed-pitch propeller with spinner. Fuel tank in each wing, combined capacity 210 litres (46·2 Imp gallons), of which 206 litres (45·3 Imp gallons) are usable. Overwing refuelling point above each tank. Oil capacity 6·5 litres (1·5 Imp gallons).
ACCOMMODATION: Four seats in side-by-side pairs under rearward-sliding Perspex 'bubble' canopy. Front seats adjustable. 'Solid' canopy roof is optional on production aircraft. Dual controls. Cabin heated and ventilated.
SYSTEMS: Hydraulic system for brakes. Electrical power provided by 12V 60A engine-driven generator.
AVIONICS AND EQUIPMENT: Radio, radio navigation equipment and full blind-flying instrumentation to customer's requirements.
DIMENSIONS, EXTERNAL:

Wing span	10·50 m (34 ft 5½ in)
Wing aspect ratio	7·6
Wing taper ratio	0·65
Length overall	7·15 m (23 ft 5½ in)
Height overall	2·55 m (8 ft 4⅜ in)
Propeller diameter	1·80 m (5 ft 10¾ in)

AREA:

Wings, gross	14·50 m² (156·08 sq ft)

WEIGHTS AND LOADINGS:

Weight empty	640 kg (1,411 lb)
Max T-O weight	1,100 kg (2,425 lb)
Max wing loading	75·86 kg/m² (15·54 lb/sq ft)
Max power loading	8·19 kg/kW (13·47 lb/hp)

PERFORMANCE (at max T-O weight):

Never-exceed speed	172 knots (320 km/h; 198 mph)
Cruising speed, 75% power at 2,590 m (8,500 ft)	122 knots (225 km/h; 140 mph)
Stalling speed, flaps up	59 knots (110 km/h; 68·5 mph)
Stalling speed, flaps down	49 knots (90 km/h; 56 mph)
Max rate of climb at S/L	324 m (1,063 ft)/min
Service ceiling	5,400 m (17,725 ft)
T-O run	234 m (768 ft)
T-O to 15 m (50 ft)	501 m (1,644 ft)
Range with max fuel, no reserves	750 nm (1,390 km; 864 miles)

VFW
VEREINIGTE FLUGTECHNISCHE WERKE GmbH

HEAD OFFICE: Hünefeldstrasse 1-5, 2800 Bremen 1 (Postfach 10 78 45)
Telephone: (0421) 538 2305
Telex: 245 821
WORKS: Bremen, Einswarden, Hoykenkamp, Lemwerder, Speyer and Varel

DIRECTORS:
Dipl Ing Johann Schäffler (Chairman)
Dipl Volkswirt August Ackermann (Finance)
Dipl Ing Hans E. W. Hoffmann (Research and Development)
Bernd Kosegarten (Marketing and Personnel)

PUBLIC RELATIONS MANAGER: Joseph Grendel

Vereinigte Flugtechnische Werke GmbH (VFW) was formed at the end of 1963 by a merger of the two

Bremen-based aircraft companies of Focke-Wulf GmbH and 'Weser' Flugzeugbau GmbH. They were joined in 1964 by Ernst Heinkel Flugzeugbau GmbH. Details of the history and products of these former companies can be found in earlier editions of *Jane's*.

With effect from 1 January 1970, VFW became an equal partner with Fokker of the Netherlands in a company known as Zentralgesellschaft VFW-Fokker mbH, as detailed in the 1979-80 and earlier editions of *Jane's*. The name of the VFW company was changed to VFW-Fokker GmbH as a consequence of the amalgamation, which was ended by mutual agreement on 11 February 1980. In announcing this, the companies stated that current joint programmes would not be affected, and that future co-operation on other programmes was likely.

At present VFW, which had a work force of some 11,000 persons in 1979, is a partner in the Fokker F28 and Transall C-160 transport programmes, and is collaborating also in development and production of the Panavia Tornado multi-role combat aircraft, General Dynamics

F-16 fighter and Airbus A300/A310. VFW was responsible for development of the C4 convertible cargo version of the Airbus A300, and has also converted more than 30 A300B-100s into A300B4-203s with increased max T-O weight and extended range.

Other work includes the overhaul and repair of Transall C-160, JetStar, CH-53G and Sea King aircraft, together with modification work on the F-104G.

In 1968-69, VFW acquired 65 per cent of the shares of RFB (Rhein-Flugzeugbau GmbH, which see) but has since become 100 per cent shareholder and has also a 50 per cent holding in Henschel Flugzeugwerke AG of Kassel.

Through its wholly-owned subsidiary, ERNO Raumfahrttechnik GmbH, VFW is participating in the Spacelab programme as prime contractor, and in the Ariane programme with responsibility for the second stage.

It was the intention of the Federal German government that VFW should be merged with MBB before the end of 1980.

GREECE

HAI
HELLENIC AEROSPACE INDUSTRY

ATHENS OFFICE: 2-4 Mesoghion Avenue, PO Box 3110, Ambelokipi, Athens 610
Telephone: 7799 678/9
Telex: 21-9528 HAI GR
WORKS: PO Box 23, Schimatari, Viotia
Telephone: (0262) 30080/1
Telex: 27-2106 HAI GR
CHAIRMAN OF THE BOARD: J. Stratos
GENERAL MANAGER: H. E. Mack
MARKETING DIRECTOR: R. P. Stone
TECHNICAL DIRECTOR: R. F. Bennett
ADMINISTRATIVE DIRECTOR: D. Georgiou
MANAGEMENT SERVICES DIRECTOR: E. Contogeorgis

The establishment of an aerospace industry in Greece became effective in November 1975. Its main purposes are to provide manufacturing and repair facilities in the country, to execute both civil and military work, and to achieve independence in this field from foreign companies. The Hellenic Aerospace Industry (HAI) venture was formed following the signing of contracts between the Greek government and a group of leading international aerospace and construction firms. The total investment will exceed $300 million. The company is owned by the Greek government and is headed by a Greek nine-member board of directors.

Contracts were signed with the Lockheed, Westinghouse, General Electric and Austin companies to assist in the buildup and initial stages of the operation. Construction began on 4 February 1977, and the HAI facility was opened officially on 18 December 1979 by the Greek Prime Minister, Mr C. Karamanlis. It is the most modern of its type in the Mediterranean area, and represents one of the largest single construction programmes ever undertaken in Greece. The complex consists of an aircraft depot, engine depot, electronics depot and accessory depot, in addition to the usual flight line support, utility and ancillary buildings.

The aircraft depot, with high bay and low bay hangars, covers 27,500 m² (296,007 sq ft) of space. The commercial hangar section has a 22 m (72 ft) clearance for aircraft such as the Boeing 747 and Airbus A300.

The 16,000 m² (172,222 sq ft) engine depot, with overhaul and test shops, has capability for more than 20 types of engine. The computerised engine test facility has a present capacity for engines of up to 133·45 kN (30,000 lb st); it is planned to increase this capacity to cover all types of modern high-power engines. The accessory and shop depot, which covers 15,500 m² (166,840 sq ft) of space, includes 33 shops and facilities, led by the engine and electronic departments. Among these are workshops for sheet-metal fabrication and repair, machine tooling, heat treatment and welding, plastics and woodworking, pneumatics, instruments and electrical work.

The electronics depot covers 9,500 m² (102,257 sq ft) and contains 18 shops for servicing airborne and ground-to-air electronics equipment and instrumentation, accelerometers and inertial guidance platforms.

HAI also offers technical and management training covering a wide variety of aeronautical skills related to military and civil aircraft maintenance. HAI is located in Tanagra, approx 60 km (37 miles) north of Athens; it is served by a 3,660 m (12,000 ft) runway, and is adjacent to main highways and international rail/sea links. More than 2,500 people were employed at the facility in early 1980; within two years it is anticipated that this figure will rise to more than 3,000.

INDIA

HAL
HINDUSTAN AERONAUTICS LIMITED

Indian Express Building, Vidhana Veedhi, PO Box 5150, Bangalore 560 001
Telephone: 76901 (8 lines)
Telex: 845-266 HAL IN

CHAIRMAN: Air Marshal S. J. Dastur (Retd)

DIRECTORS:
A. Chandmal
P. D. Chopra
Air Marshal L. S. Grewal
L. K. Joshi
B. K. Kapur
S. C. Keshu
Dr D. N. Prasad
Raj Mahindra
Dr R. Ramanna
B. M. Menon

EXECUTIVE DIRECTORS:
G. Narasimhan (Corporate Planning)
K. K. Kirtikar (Jaguar Project)

GENERAL MANAGERS:
Bangalore Complex:
K. N. R. Swamy (Aircraft Division)
S. K. Khanna (Engine Division)
Gp Capt Willie Raj (Overhaul Division)
N. Nagaraja Rao (Foundry and Forge Division)
S. K. Ohrie (Helicopter Division)

MiG Complex:
B. S. Balooja (Nasik Division)
C. V. Vijayaraghavan (Koraput Division)

Accessories Complex:
Gp Capt R. S. Sivaswamy (Retd) (Hyderabad Division)
H. K. Singh (Lucknow Division)

CHIEF TEST PILOT: Wg Cdr I. M. Chopra (Retd)
CHIEF OF MARKETING: Air Cdre R. J. M. Upot (Retd)

Hindustan Aeronautics Limited (HAL) was formed on 1 October 1964, amalgamating the former Hindustan Aircraft Ltd (formed 1940) and Aeronautics India Ltd (formed 1963), and has 10 Divisions, five at Bangalore and one each at Nasik, Koraput, Hyderabad, Kanpur and Lucknow, with a total work force of about 40,000 people. The company, whose principal customer is the Indian Air Force, is currently manufacturing and overhauling many types of aircraft, helicopters, and their related aero-engines, avionics, instruments and accessories. It is also manufacturing components for satellites on behalf of the Indian Space Research Organisation (ISRO).

The Bangalore Complex is engaged in the manufacture of military aircraft and aero-engines, both under licence and of indigenous design. This Complex has a large organisation undertaking repair and overhaul of airframes, engines, and allied instruments and accessories. It has also a self-contained foundry and forge.

Kanpur Division has been engaged mainly in the manufacture of different versions of the British Aerospace HS 748 under licence. It is responsible for series production of the Basant agricultural aircraft, designed at the Bangalore design bureau.

Nasik, Koraput and Hyderabad Divisions are manufacturing the airframe, engine and avionics respectively of the Soviet MiG-21 fighter with the collaboration of the USSR.

Lucknow Division, formed in late 1969, is producing aircraft accessories under licence from various manufacturers in the UK, France and the USSR, including wheels and brakes, ejection seats, instruments, fuel accessories, air-conditioning and pressurisation systems. The Division has successfully developed a number of electrical and hydraulic accessories which have entered production. It is planned to begin manufacturing gyros for use in airborne systems.

In addition to its manufacturing programmes, HAL is pursuing design and development activities relating to aircraft, helicopters, avionics and accessories. The design bureau at Bangalore is engaged in the design and development of the HPT-32 piston-engined basic trainer, an armed version of the HJT-16 Kiran, and a trainer version of the Ajeet. As noted in the International section, HAL is to be responsible for assembly and/or licence construction of approximately three-quarters of the 40 SEPECAT Jaguar International combat aircraft ordered by the Indian government. The helicopter design department at Bangalore is designing an Advanced Light Helicopter (ALH) with the assistance of Aérospatiale of France. The avionics design department at Hyderabad is pursuing the design and development of airborne electronic equipment, and the design department at Lucknow is developing aircraft instruments and accessories.

BANGALORE COMPLEX

Bangalore Complex 560 017 (Karnataka State)
Telephone: 53201 and 50773

The Bangalore Complex of HAL consists essentially of the former Hindustan Aircraft Limited, the activities of which, since its formation in 1940, were described in previous editions of *Jane's*. The Complex is subdivided into an Aircraft Division, Helicopter Division, Engine Division, Overhaul Division, and Foundry and Forge Division.

Bangalore Complex is engaged in producing aircraft designed and developed by the HAL design bureau, and also in manufacturing various aircraft and aero-engines under licence. The Engine Division's activities are described in the appropriate section of this edition.

Licence production of Aérospatiale SA 315B Lama and SA 316B Alouette III helicopters, undertaken initially by the Aircraft Division, is undertaken by the Helicopter Division, officially inaugurated on 19 July 1974.

The Overhaul Division of Bangalore Complex repairs and overhauls HAL HF-24 and HT-2 and Hawker Siddeley (de Havilland) Dove/Devon aircraft, DHC-4 Caribou, Fairchild C-119 Packet transports and English Electric Canberra bombers, and various piston engines. Jet engines are overhauled at the Engine Division. The branch factory at Barrackpore near Calcutta continues to concentrate on repair and overhaul of DC-3s of the Indian Air Force and non-scheduled operators.

HAL HJT-16 Mk I KIRAN (RAY OF LIGHT)

In December 1959, the government of India approved the design and development by HAL of a side-by-side two-seat jet basic trainer designated HJT-16 Mk I, powered by a Rolls-Royce Viper 11 turbojet.

Detailed design work on the HJT-16 Mk I began in April 1961 under the leadership of Dr V. M. Ghatage. The first prototype flew for the first time on 4 September 1964.

HAL HJT-16 Mk IA Kiran two-seat jet basic trainer

It was followed by a second aircraft in August 1965.

A total of 24 pre-production HJT-16 Mk Is were delivered to the Indian Air Force, the initial delivery (of six aircraft) being made in March 1968. The HJT-16 Mk I is now in series production. By 1 January 1980 a total of 147 had been produced, to meet the requirements of both the Indian Air Force and Indian Navy. Total IAF/IN requirement is for 190 aircraft.

The Kiran is suitable for use in armament training or light attack roles, and the 119th and subsequent Kirans, designated **Mk IA**, are fitted with a hardpoint beneath each wing capable of carrying weapons or a drop-tank. In addition, HAL is developing a Mk II version of the Kiran for these roles, and this is described separately.

TYPE: Two-seat jet basic trainer.

WINGS: Cantilever low-wing monoplane. Wing section NACA 23015 at root, NACA 23012 at tip. Dihedral 4° from roots. Incidence 0° 30' at root. Conventional all-metal three-spar structure. Frise-type differential ailerons. Hydraulically-actuated trailing-edge split flaps. Two full-chord boundary layer fences on upper surface of each wing.

HAL HJT-16 Mk IA Kiran side-by-side two-seat basic trainer and light attack aircraft *(Pilot Press)*

FUSELAGE: All-metal semi-monocoque structure of light alloy. Hydraulically-actuated door-type airbrake under centre of fuselage.

TAIL UNIT: Cantilever all-metal structure. Electrically-operated variable-incidence tailplane. Ground-adjustable tab on rudder.

LANDING GEAR: Retractable tricycle type, of HAL manufacture. Hydraulic actuation. Main units retract inward into fuselage; self-centering twin-contact non-steerable nosewheel retracts forward. Oleo-pneumatic shock-absorbers. Main-wheel tyres size 19 × 6·25-9, pressure 6·21 bars (90 lb/sq in). Nosewheel tyre size 15·4 × 4-6, pressure 4·83 bars (70 lb/sq in). Hydraulic brakes, without cooling.

POWER PLANT: One 11·12 kN (2,500 lb st) Rolls-Royce Viper 11 turbojet engine. Internal fuel in main saddle tanks in fuselage (two 209 litre; 46 Imp gallon), wing centre-section collector tank (282 litres; 62 Imp gallons) and outboard wing tanks (two 218 litre; 48 Imp gallon), giving total capacity of 1,137 litres (250 Imp gallons). Provision for two underwing tanks with total capacity of 454 litres (100 Imp gallons). System permits 30 s of inverted flight.

ACCOMMODATION: Crew of two side by side in air-conditioned and pressurised cockpit, on Martin-Baker Mk H4 HA zero-altitude fully-automatic ejection seats. Clamshell-type canopy. Dual controls and duplicated blind-flying instruments.

SYSTEMS: Air-conditioning system has max pressure differential of 0·12 bars (1·75 lb/sq in). Dowty hydraulic system for landing gear, flaps and airbrake, pressure 207 bars (3,000 lb/sq in). Accumulator for manual emergency system. Electrical system is of 28V DC single-wire earth return type, with two 24V 25Ah batteries. Normalair pressure-demand oxygen system.

AVIONICS AND EQUIPMENT: STR 9X/M 10-channel VHF transceiver, AX-3 single-channel VHF standby set and Marconi Avionics DFA-73 ADF manufactured by BEL-India. Landing light in nose.

ARMAMENT: Hardpoint beneath each wing of 119th and subsequent aircraft, each capable of carrying a 500 lb bomb, an HAL pod containing two 7·62 mm FN machine-guns, a pod containing seven 68 mm SNEB rockets, or a 227 litre (50 Imp gallon) drop-tank.

DIMENSIONS, EXTERNAL:
Wing span	10·70 m (35 ft 1¼ in)
Wing chord at root	2·35 m (7 ft 8½ in)
Wing chord at tip	1·02 m (3 ft 4 in)
Wing aspect ratio	6
Length overall	10·60 m (34 ft 9 in)
Height overall	3·635 m (11 ft 11 in)
Tailplane span	3·90 m (12 ft 9½ in)
Wheel track	2·42 m (7 ft 11 in)
Wheelbase	3·50 m (11 ft 6 in)

AREAS:
Wings, gross	19·00 m² (204·5 sq ft)
Ailerons (total)	1·55 m² (16·68 sq ft)
Flaps (total)	2·34 m² (25·19 sq ft)
Vertical tail surfaces (total)	2·10 m² (22·60 sq ft)
Rudder, incl tab	0·714 m² (7·69 sq ft)
Horizontal tail surfaces (total)	3·72 m² (40·04 sq ft)
Elevators	1·14 m² (12·27 sq ft)

WEIGHTS AND LOADINGS:
Weight empty	2,560 kg (5,644 lb)
Normal T-O weight	3,600 kg (7,936 lb)
Max T-O weight (with two 50 Imp gallon drop-tanks)	4,100 kg (9,039 lb)
Max wing loading	190 kg/m² (38·9 lb/sq ft)
Thrust/weight ratio	0·315

PERFORMANCE (at normal T-O weight):
Max level speed at S/L	
	375 knots (695 km/h; 432 mph)
Max level speed at 9,150 m (30,000 ft)	
	371 knots (688 km/h; 427 mph)
Max cruising speed	175 knots (324 km/h; 201 mph)
Stalling speed, flaps and landing gear up	
	81 knots (151 km/h; 94 mph)
Stalling speed, flaps and landing gear down	
	71 knots (132 km/h; 82 mph)
Ceiling	9,150 m (30,000 ft)
Time to 9,150 m (30,000 ft)	20 min
Min ground turning radius	5·50 m (18 ft 0½ in)
T-O run	442 m (1,450 ft)
Endurance on internal fuel at 230 knots (426 km/h; 265 mph) at 9,150 m (30,000 ft)	1 h 45 min

HAL KIRAN Mk II

This version of the Kiran, suitable for armament training or counter-insurgency duties, is being developed by the HAL design bureau at Bangalore. Principal differences include improved weapon-carrying capability, a more powerful engine, updated avionics and an improved hydraulic system. The engine is a derated version of the Orpheus 701 turbojet, rated at 15·1 kN (3,400 lb st), which gives the Kiran Mk II improved maximum speed, climb and manoeuvrability. The range, with two underwing drop-tanks fitted as standard, remains the same as for the Mk I. The first prototype made its initial flight on 30 July 1976. A second prototype was flown in February 1979.

ARMAMENT: Two 7·62 mm machine-guns in nose, with 250 rds/gun. Two Ferranti F 195R ISIS gunsights, with common control unit. Two hardpoints beneath each wing, the inboard ones each capable of carrying a 227 litre (50 Imp gallon) drop-tank, a 500 lb high-explosive bomb, a Type 122·1 68 mm rocket pod or a 25 lb practice bomb carrier. Each outboard pylon is capable of carrying a similar weapon load or drop-tank.

HAL AJEET (INVINCIBLE)

The Hawker Siddeley Gnat light fighter and fighter-bomber was built under licence by HAL between 1962 and 1974, as described in the 1974-75 and 1975-76 editions of *Jane's*.

The design bureau completed in 1974 the design of a Mk II version of the Gnat known as the Ajeet, with improved performance characteristics and equipment, including improved communications and navigation systems; more reliable longitudinal control; and increased combat capability. The last-named characteristic is achieved by a redesigned fuel system, dispensing with the underwing drop-tanks in favour of integral wing tanks, so permitting additional underwing armament to be carried.

The last two Gnat Mk I aircraft were converted as prototypes for the Ajeet; the first of these was flown on 5 March 1975, and the second on 5 November 1975.

First flight of a production Ajeet was made on 30 September 1976. By mid-January 1980 a total of 23 Ajeets had been completed, of approximately 80 then on order.

TYPE: Single-seat lightweight interceptor and ground attack aircraft.

WINGS: Cantilever shoulder-wing monoplane. Sweptback wings, of RAE 102 section. Thickness/chord ratio 8%. Anhedral 5°. Sweepback 40° at quarter-chord. One-piece wing of two-spar thick-skin light alloy construction, fitting into recess in top of fuselage and secured by bolts at four points. Inboard ailerons, powered by hydraulic actuators, droop 22° to serve as flaps when the landing gear is lowered.

FUSELAGE: Light alloy semi-monocoque structure of pressed frames and extruded stringers.

TAIL UNIT: Cantilever all-metal structure. Three-spar sweptback fin, integral with fuselage. One-piece three-spar variable-incidence tailplane, operated hydraulically by modified Hobson PFC 1003 actuator. Rear portions of tailplane can be unlocked to perform as elevators; or locked to provide the functions of an all-moving tailplane. Ground-adjustable tab on rudder.

LANDING GEAR: Retractable tricycle type, all units retracting rearward hydraulically into fuselage. Dowty Rotol oleo-pneumatic shock-absorber struts. Wheel well fairings attached to individual landing gear units serve as airbrakes when landing gear is partly lowered, the relative movements of the airbrakes being so adjusted that no change of trim occurs at any speed. Dunlop main-wheel tyres size 20 × 5·25, pressure 9·3 bars (135 lb/sq in); twin nosewheel tyres, size 17 × 3·25, pressure 5·65 bars (82 lb/sq in). Hydraulically operated brakes and Maxaret anti-skid units on main wheels. Braking parachute in fairing at base of fin.

POWER PLANT: One Rolls-Royce Orpheus 701-01 non-afterburning turbojet engine, rated at 20 kN (4,500 lb st). Compressed-air starting. Air intakes in sides of fuselage. Seven crashproof flexible tanks and two metal tanks in fuselage, and two 250 litre (55 Imp gallon) integral wing tanks. Total internal fuel capacity 1,350 litres (297 Imp gallons). Fuel supplied to engine by electrically-driven booster pump in one of the tanks.

First prototype HAL Kiran Mk II armament training and counter-insurgency aircraft

Prototype of the Ajeet lightweight combat aircraft, developed by HAL from the Hawker Siddeley Gnat

Provision for two 150 litre (33 Imp gallon) underwing drop-tanks.

ACCOMMODATION: Pilot only, on Martin-Baker GF-4 zero-height/90 knot (167 km/h; 104 mph) lightweight ejection seat. Pressurised, heated and air-conditioned cockpit, with jettisonable canopy which is hinged at rear and opens upward.

SYSTEMS: Normalair air-conditioning and pressurisation system, max differential of 0·24 bars (3·5 lb/sq in) at 12,800 m (42,000 ft). Oxygen system with demand-type regulator. Dowty hydraulic system of 207 bars (3,000 lb/sq in), with Abex pump, for aileron, landing gear, main-wheel brake and tailplane actuation. 28V DC electrical system, with 3·5 kW Rotax generator and two 12V 25Ah Varley batteries. Oxygen system for pilot.

AVIONICS AND EQUIPMENT: Bendix TA/RA-22 VHF transceiver (initially; V/UHF later) and BEL AX-3 standby VHF set; Bendix DFA-73 ADF; IFF Mk 10 (BAT) transponder.

ARMAMENT: Two 30 mm Aden Mk 4 cannon in air intake fairings, one on each side of fuselage, with 90 rds/gun. Ferranti F 195R/3 ISIS weapons sight. Vinten G90 gun camera. Four underwing hardpoints able to carry two 500 lb bombs (inner pylons), four Arrow Type 122 pods each containing eighteen 68 mm rockets, or two 150 litre (33 Imp gallon) drop-tanks (outer pylons).

DIMENSIONS, EXTERNAL:

Wing span	6·73 m (22 ft 1 in)
Wing chord at c/l	2·58 m (8 ft 5·6 in)
Wing chord at tip	1·17 m (3 ft 10 in)
Wing area, gross	14·65 m² (157·7 sq ft)
Wing aspect ratio	3·575
Length overall	9·04 m (29 ft 8 in)
Height overall	2·46 m (8 ft 1 in)
Tailplane span	2·84 m (9 ft 4 in)
Wheel track	1·55 m (5 ft 1 in)
Wheelbase	2·36 m (7 ft 9 in)

WEIGHTS AND LOADINGS:

Basic weight empty	2,307 kg (5,086 lb)
T-O weight 'clean'	3,539 kg (7,803 lb)
Max T-O weight	4,170 kg (9,195 lb)
Normal landing weight	2,767 kg (6,100 lb)
Max wing loading	284·6 kg/m² (58·3 lb/sq ft)

PERFORMANCE (in configurations indicated; A: ISA; B: ISA + 15°C; C: ISA + 30°C):

Max Mach No. at 12,000 m (39,375 ft) at 'clean' T-O weight: A	0·96
B	0·953
C	0·948
Max level speed at S/L at 'clean' T-O weight:	
A	595 knots (1,102 km/h; 685 mph)
B	612 knots (1,134 km/h; 705 mph)
C	622 knots (1,152 km/h; 716 mph)
Time to 12,000 m (39,375 ft) from brakes off, at 'clean' T-O weight: A	6 min 2 s
B	7 min 43 s
C	9 min 33 s
Service ceiling: A, B, C	13,720 m (45,000 ft)
Turning performance at 450 knots (834 km/h; 518 mph) IAS at S/L: A	5·30g
B	5·28g
C	5·00g
T-O run at S/L, zero wind, at T-O weight of 4,136 kg (9,118 lb) with two Arrow rocket pods and two 33 Imp gallon drop-tanks: A	1,034 m (3,390 ft)
B	1,180 m (3,870 ft)
C	1,376 m (4,515 ft)
Landing run 'clean' at S/L, zero wind, at normal landing weight, no brake 'chute: A	951 m (3,120 ft)
B	997 m (3,270 ft)
C	1,047 m (3,435 ft)
Landing run 'clean' at S/L, zero wind, at normal landing weight, with brake 'chute: A	658 m (2,160 ft)
B	695 m (2,280 ft)
C	725 m (2,379 ft)

First prototype HAL HPT-32 two/three-seat basic training aircraft

HAL HPT-32 two/three-seat basic trainer, as projected with retractable landing gear (Pilot Press)

Combat radius (A, B and C), low level ground attack mission:

with two 500 lb bombs on inboard stations
110 nm (204 km; 127 miles)
with two Arrow rocket pods inboard and two 33 Imp gallon drop-tanks outboard
140 nm (259 km; 161 miles)
with four Arrow rocket pods
104 nm (193 km; 120 miles)

HAL AJEET TRAINER

This tandem two-seat trainer version of the Ajeet, which retains the four underwing hardpoints and full combat capability of the single-seater, is evolved in a similar manner to that in which the T.Mk 1 trainer was evolved from the original Gnat fighter. To accommodate the second cockpit, two of the fuselage fuel tanks are deleted, although this can be offset by deleting the Aden cannon to make room for an additional 273 litres (60 Imp gallons) of fuel internally; in this event, provision is made for carrying a 7·62 mm gun pod on each of the inboard wing pylons. Sections 0·70 m (2 ft 3½ in) long are inserted in the fuselage fore and aft of the wings, increasing the overall length of the Ajeet Trainer to 10·44 m (34 ft 3 in).

The Ajeet Trainer is powered by a single Orpheus 701 turbojet engine, and retains the main hydraulic system and powered flying controls of the single-seater. Normal and emergency operation of the landing gear is also similar,

but with duplicated controls and a mechanical override facility in the rear cockpit. All instruments, including those for blind flying, are duplicated in the rear cockpit, which will be illuminated, air-conditioned and pressurised similarly to the front cockpit. A gunsight is fitted in the front cockpit only. Both occupants are provided with Martin-Baker GF-4 ejection seats. Avionics and equipment include a multi-channel VHF transceiver (to be replaced eventually by a V/UHF set), ADF and IFF Mk 10.

A prototype is under construction, and was expected to undergo evaluation in 1980-81.

HAL HPT-32

Currently under development for the Indian Air Force, the HPT-32 is a fully-aerobatic piston-engined basic trainer, with side-by-side seats for instructor and pupil and a third seat at the rear. A four-seat version is under consideration for the liaison role. The trainer can be used for a wide range of ab initio training, including instrument, navigation, night flying and formation flying; for armed patrol; for observation, liaison or sport flying; or for weapon training, light strike duties, supply dropping, search and rescue, reconnaissance, or glider or target towing. The airframe, which is of all-metal construction, is designed to FAR 23, and is expected to have a fatigue life of 6,500 h.

The first prototype (X2157) made its first flight on 6 January 1977. The second was flown on 12 March 1979; a third was expected to fly in July 1980.

TYPE: Two/three-seat basic trainer or four-seat liaison aircraft.

WINGS: Cantilever low-wing monoplane of all-metal construction. Dihedral 5° from roots. Incidence 2° 30' at root. Ground-adjustable tab on each aileron.

FUSELAGE: All-metal semi-monocoque structure.

TAIL UNIT: Cantilever all-metal structure, with sweptback vertical surfaces. One-piece elevator. Trim tabs in rudder and port half of elevator.

LANDING GEAR: Non-retractable tricycle type on prototype and ab initio version. Main wheels size 6·00-6·5, nosewheel 5·00-5. Dunlop tyres on all wheels, pressure 2·41-2·76 bars (35-40 lb/sq in) on main units, 3·10 bars (45 lb/sq in) on nose unit.

POWER PLANT: Prototype powered by 194 kW (260 hp) Avco Lycoming AEIO-540-D4B5 flat-six engine, driving a Hartzell two-blade constant-speed metal propeller with spinner. Two integral wing fuel tanks, with total capacity of 227 litres (50 Imp gallons); provision for 136·5 litre (30 Imp gallon) tank in place of rear seat. For production aircraft, an indigenous engine of similar power is under development.

ACCOMMODATION: Side-by-side seats for two persons in front, with provision for one or two seats plus baggage space at rear, under rearward-sliding jettisonable

HAL Ajeet lightweight interceptor/ground attack aircraft, with additional side view (bottom) of trainer version
(Pilot Press)

framed canopy. Front two seats adjustable in height by 127 mm (5 in); rear seat(s) not adjustable. Full dual controls, and adjustable rudder pedals, for instructor and pupil.

ARMAMENT AND EQUIPMENT: Four underwing attachments for armament or other stores, up to a total of 255 kg (562 lb). VHF radio.

DIMENSIONS, EXTERNAL:

Wing span	9·50 m (31 ft 2 in)
Wing chord at root	2·24 m (7 ft 4¼ in)
Wing chord at tip	0·92 m (3 ft 0¼ in)
Wing aspect ratio	6·013
Length overall	7·715 m (25 ft 3¾ in)
Height overall	3·27 m (10 ft 8¾ in)
Wheel track	3·45 m (11 ft 4 in)
Wheelbase	2·10 m (6 ft 10¾ in)
Propeller diameter	2·032 m (6 ft 8 in)
Propeller ground clearance (static)	0·241 m (9½ in)

AREAS:

Wings, gross	15·01 m² (161·6 sq ft)
Ailerons (total)	1·04 m² (11·19 sq ft)
Trailing-edge flaps (total)	1·83 m² (19·70 sq ft)
Fin	2·316 m² (24·93 sq ft)
Rudder, incl tab	1·078 m² (11·60 sq ft)
Tailplane	3·02 m² (32·50 sq ft)
Elevator, incl tab	1·35 m² (14·53 sq ft)

WEIGHTS AND LOADINGS:

Weight empty	926 kg (2,041 lb)
Normal T-O weight	1,250 kg (2,756 lb)
Max T-O weight	1,375 kg (3,031 lb)
Max wing loading	91·6 kg/m² (18·76 lb/sq ft)
Max power loading	7·09 kg/kW (11·66 lb/hp)

PERFORMANCE (at Normal T-O weight, ISA):

Max level speed at S/L	117 knots (217 km/h; 135 mph)
Stalling speed, flaps up	59 knots (110 km/h; 68 mph)
Stalling speed, flaps down	55 knots (102 km/h; 63 mph)
Max rate of climb at S/L	335 m (1,100 ft)/min

HAL Cheetah, Indian-assembled version of the Aérospatiale SA 315B Lama helicopter

Service ceiling	4,750 m (15,580 ft)
T-O run	205 m (673 ft)
Range at 1,525 m (5,000 ft) with 50 Imp gallons fuel	378 nm (700 km; 435 miles)
Endurance at 1,525 m (5,000 ft) with 50 Imp gallons fuel	4 h 0 min
g limits	+6·0; −3·0

HAL (AÉROSPATIALE) SA 315B LAMA
Indian name: Cheetah

The Bangalore Complex's Helicopter Division is building the French Aérospatiale SA 315B Lama five-seat general-purpose helicopter (which see) under licence in India, where it is known as the Cheetah.

Initial production was from French-built components. The first Indian-assembled Cheetah was test-flown on 6 October 1972, and a total of 85 had been delivered by 1 January 1980. Production of aircraft manufactured from raw materials began in 1976-77.

HAL-assembled Aérospatiale Alouette III helicopter in Indian military insignia

An agricultural version of the Cheetah is under development. Preliminary spraying trials have been conducted, and further modifications are in progress.

HAL (AÉROSPATIALE) SA 316B ALOUETTE III
Indian name: Chetak

The Bangalore Complex's Helicopter Division is building the French Aérospatiale SA 316B Alouette III under a licence granted in June 1962. The first Indian-assembled Alouette III was flown for the first time on 11 June 1965.

By January 1980 a total of 221 Alouette IIIs had been manufactured by HAL. A few Alouette IIIs were presented to the Royal Nepal Army in 1974. HAL also supplies Indian-built components for French-built Alouette IIIs.

An armed version, known as the Chetak, is being developed by HAL, carrying four air-to-surface missiles on laterally-mounted booms. Target identification and fire control is via a monocular periscopic sight on the cabin roof. Successful firing trials have been carried out.

HAL LIGHT HELICOPTER

The Design Bureau of HAL has under development a high-performance advanced light helicopter (ALH). Two versions are being developed: a standard version for Indian Air Force/Army use, and a variant for the Indian Navy. The former will have a capability for combat missions, communications duties, armed reconnaissance and surveillance, casualty evacuation, crew rescue, external cargo carrying and training. The naval version will be able to perform anti-submarine search and strike, air to surface vessel search and strike, search and rescue, reconnaissance, casualty evacuation, and vertical replenishment duties at sea.

The ALH will be a twin-engined helicopter, for which considerable design work has already been done.

KANPUR DIVISION

Chakeri, Kanpur
Telephone: HAL PABX 62471-4
Telex: HAL KP 243

When the decision was taken to build the Hawker Siddeley (now British Aerospace) 748 twin-turboprop transport in India, as a replacement for the Dakotas of the Indian Air Force, four hangars at Kanpur were taken over, on 23 January 1960, as the IAF Aircraft Manufacturing Depot. The Depot was incorporated in Aeronautics (India) Ltd in June 1964 and subsequently became the Kanpur Division of Hindustan Aeronautics Ltd.

HAL HS 748

The first Indian-built 748 flew on 1 November 1961, followed by the second one on 13 March 1963. The first

four Indian 748s were Srs 1 aircraft, utilising components imported from the UK.

The first Indian-built Srs 2 flew for the first time on 28 January 1964, and 17 were delivered to Indian Airlines between 1967 and 1972. Since then three more have been modified for a photographic survey role and delivered to the Indian Air Force. Three others are being delivered to the Indian Directorate General of Civil Aviation (for a calibration role) and the National Remote Sensing Agency.

HAL has also produced the aircraft in several versions for the Indian Air Force. These include 10 VIP executive transports, 10 as navigation trainers and 18 as trainers for pilots of multi-engined aircraft.

A prototype HS 748(M) military freighter, developed by Kanpur Division, flew for the first time on 16 February

1972 and successfully completed flight trials with the Indian Air Force. An order for 10 more HS 748s was announced in June 1975. These aircraft are built to the military freighter standard. A further 10 HS 748(M)s were ordered in 1978, extending production until 1983.

HAL HA-31 Mk II BASANT (SPRING)

Design of this agricultural aircraft began at the Bangalore design bureau in mid-1968. The prototype, designated HA-31 Mk I, was powered by a 186 kW (250 hp) Rolls-Royce Continental engine, and was described in the 1971-72 *Jane's*. The aircraft was subsequently completely redesigned as the HA-31 Mk II, with a 298 kW (400 hp) engine, and a prototype of this version flew for the first time on 30 March 1972. A second, pre-production prototype flew in September 1972, and certification was obtained in March 1974. A pre-production batch of 20 Basants was built by the design bureau, and the first eight of these were handed over to the Indian Ministry of Food and Agriculture on 21 June 1974. Responsibility for series manufacture of the Basant was then assigned to the Kanpur Division, which is to build 100. A total of 39 had been built by 1 January 1980.

The Basant is intended primarily for aerial application of pesticides and fertilisers. It can also be used for aerial survey, fire/patrol duties and cloud seeding.

TYPE: Single-seat agricultural and utility aircraft.

WINGS: Strut-braced low-wing monoplane. Constant-chord wings, of USA 35B section with rounded tips. Thickness/chord ratio 11·6%. Dihedral 5° from roots. No incidence or sweepback. Spars (two) and ribs of light alloy, with fabric covering. Fowler-type trailing-edge flaps and Frise-type ailerons, of similar construction to wings and operated manually. Tab in port aileron. Single inverted-Vee bracing strut and cross-strut on each side, attached to fuselage forward of cockpit.

FUSELAGE: Conventional structure, of welded chrome-molybdenum steel tube with fabric covering in most areas. Structure forward of cockpit designed to absorb impact in the event of a crash. Cockpit structure, seat

HAL HA-31 Mk II Basant (Avco Lycoming IO-720-C1B engine) *(Pilot Press)*

and attachment, seat belt and shoulder harness all designed to withstand 40*g* loads in the event of a crash.

TAIL UNIT: Conventional alloy structure, with fixed-incidence metal-skinned tailplane. One-piece elevator, with central trim tab. Fabric-covered fin and rudder. Fixed tab in rudder.

LANDING GEAR: Non-retractable tailwheel type, with HAL oleo-pneumatic shock-absorbers on all units. Size 24·7 × 7·5-10 tyres on main wheels, 11·28 × 4-3·5 on tailwheel. Tyre pressure 2·41 bars (35 lb/sq in) on main units, 2·76 bars (40 lb/sq in) on tail unit. Dunlop hydraulic disc brakes on main units.

POWER PLANT: One 298 kW (400 hp) Avco Lycoming IO-720-C1B flat-eight engine, driving a Hartzell three-blade constant-speed metal propeller. Two inboard fuel tanks (each 91 litres; 20 Imp gallons) and two outboard tanks (each 63·5 litres; 14 Imp gallons) in each wing, and 9 litre (2 Imp gallon) collector tank. Total fuel capacity 318 litres (70 Imp gallons). Refuelling point on each tank. Oil capacity (nominal) 19·3 litres (4·25 Imp gallons).

ACCOMMODATION: Single seat in fully-enclosed cockpit. Forward-hinged door on starboard side; emergency door on port side. Cockpit heated and ventilated.

SYSTEMS: Hydraulic motor for crop spraying. Electrical power, from 24V 50A alternator and 24V 25Ah battery, for engine starting, instruments, VHF radio etc.

AVIONICS AND EQUIPMENT: VHF radio optional. Glassfibre hopper, installed between engine firewall and front wall of cockpit enclosure, has 0·93 m³ (33 cu ft) capacity and can carry up to 605 kg (1,333 lb) of pesticide for Normal category operation and up to 907 kg (2,000 lb) in Restricted category.

DIMENSIONS, EXTERNAL:

Wing span	12·00 m (39 ft 4½ in)
Wing chord (constant)	2·00 m (6 ft 6½ in)
Wing aspect ratio	6·17
Length overall	9·00 m (29 ft 6¼ in)

HAL HA-31 Mk II Basant single-seat agricultural and utility aircraft

Height overall	2·55 m (8 ft 4½ in)
Tailplane span	3·86 m (12 ft 8 in)
Wheel track	2·70 m (8 ft 10¼ in)
Wheelbase	6·00 m (19 ft 8¼ in)
Propeller diameter	2·13 m (7 ft 0 in)
Propeller ground clearance	0·25 m (10 in)

AREAS:

Wings, gross	23·34 m² (251·23 sq ft)
Ailerons (total)	2·14 m² (23·03 sq ft)
Trailing-edge flaps (total)	2·618 m² (28·18 sq ft)
Fin	1·06 m² (11·41 sq ft)
Rudder, incl tab	0·86 m² (9·26 sq ft)
Tailplane	2·44 m² (26·26 sq ft)
Elevator, incl tab	1·80 m² (19·37 sq ft)

WEIGHTS AND LOADINGS:

Weight empty	1,200 kg (2,645 lb)
Basic operating weight	1,954 kg (4,300 lb)
Max T-O weight	2,270 kg (5,000 lb)
Max wing loading	97·25 kg/m² (19·92 lb/sq ft)
Max power loading	7·62 kg/kW (12·6 lb/hp)

PERFORMANCE (at basic operating weight):

Never-exceed speed	164 knots (305 km/h; 189 mph)
Max level speed at S/L	121 knots (225 km/h; 140 mph)
Max cruising speed at 2,440 m (8,000 ft)	100 knots (185 km/h; 115 mph)
Econ cruising speed	87 knots (161 km/h; 100 mph)
Stalling speed, flaps up	52 knots (96 km/h; 60 mph)
Stalling speed, flaps down	49 knots (91 km/h; 57 mph)
Max rate of climb at S/L	228 m (750 ft)/min
Service ceiling	3,800 m (12,500 ft)
Min ground turning radius	7·00 m (22 ft 11 in)
T-O run	214 m (700 ft)
T-O to 15 m (50 ft)	365 m (1,200 ft)
Landing from 15 m (50 ft)	305 m (1,000 ft)
Landing run	183 m (600 ft)
Range with max fuel, no payload	348 nm (645 km; 400 miles)
Endurance with max payload, 30 min reserves	1 h

MiG COMPLEX

The MiG Complex was originally formed with the Nasik, Koraput and Hyderabad Divisions of HAL, which, under an agreement concluded in 1962, built respectively the airframes, power plants and avionics equipment of MiG-21 fighters under licence from the USSR.

As a result of the reorganisation of HAL, the Hyderabad Division, with Lucknow Division, now constitutes the Accessories Complex. Nasik had a work force of

approx 8,000 in early 1980, of whom about 800 were technical and management staff.

HAL (MIKOYAN) MiG-21
Indian Air Force designations: Type 66-400, 66-600, 74, 76, 77 and 96
NATO reporting name: Fishbed

Several versions of the MiG-21 have been supplied to or, since 1966, manufactured in, India. These have

HAL-built MiG-21FL single-seat combat aircraft in Indian Air Force insignia

included the MiG-21F (IAF designation Type 74) and MiG-21PF (Type 76) of which details can be found in the 1976-77 *Jane's;* and the MiG-21FL (Type 77) and MiG-21U (Types 66-400 and 66-600), as described in the 1977-78 *Jane's.* Other versions include:

MiG-21M. Current production version since 1972 with R-11F2S-300 engine. First aircraft, assembled from imported components, handed over to IAF on 14 February 1973. Manufacture from locally produced materials began in 1975. IAF designation **Type 96.** Fifty Soviet-built MiG-21PFMAs, to supplement Indian production, were placed in service with Nos. 7 and 108 Squadrons; No. 26 Squadron is among those also reportedly equipped with MiG-21M. Production scheduled to phase out in 1981-82 in favour of MiG21 bis.

MiG-21MF ('Fishbed-J'). Improved production version, having more powerful Tumansky R-13-300 turbojet engine and increased fuel.

MiG-21 bis ('Fishbed-N'). Deliveries of Soviet-built examples of this version, initially for service with No. 21 Squadron of IAF, were reported in 1977. Indian production of the MiG-21 bis, and its Tumansky R-25 engine, were reported to have begun by early 1980, and this will supersede the MiG-21M as the major production version from 1981-82. To reduce cost and engineering problems, modified MiG-21M wings are being used on the Indian MiG-21 bis.

A full description of the MiG-21 appears in the USSR section of this edition.

INDONESIA

LAPAN
LEMBAGA PENERBANGAN DAN ANTARIKSA NASIONAL (National Aeronautics and Space Institute)

HEADQUARTERS: Jalan Pemuda Persil No. 1, PO Box 3048, Jakarta
Telephone: (021) 482802 and 485125
Telex: 45675 LAPAN IA
CHAIRMAN: Air Vice-Marshal Dr Sunaryo
VICE-CHAIRMAN: Prof Wiranto Arismunandar

Pusat Teknologi Dirgantara (Aerospace Technology Center)

Rumpin Airfield, Bogor, West Java
HEAD OF AEROSPACE TECHNOLOGY CENTER: Dr Haryono Djojodihardjo
MANAGER, AEROSPACE TECHNOLOGY DEVELOPMENT: Ir Jaidun Kromodihardjo

Established in 1963 under the original chairmanship of Air Vice-Marshal J. Salatun, LAPAN had 525 personnel at the beginning of 1979, accommodated within four centres: the Aerospace Technology Center at Rumpin Airfield, near Bogor; the Aerospace Study Center and the Space Applications Center, both at Jakarta; and the

Atmospheric and Space Research Center at Bandung. In FY 1977 it began construction of a prototype of the XT-400 eight-seat transport aircraft, and also built and test-flew a mini-RPV, the XTG-01.

LAPAN XT-400

In the same class as the Britten-Norman Islander, the XT-400 differs from that aircraft by having an upswept rear fuselage with clamshell rear-loading doors. Designed by a team under the leadership of Dipl-Ing Suharto, it is of all-metal construction, and is the first Indonesian aircraft of indigenous design able to accommodate more than three people. The initial version will carry one pilot and up to seven passengers; a future version is planned, with seats for 11 passengers. Design is to FAR Pts 23 and 25 (Utility category), and the XT-400 will have STOL capability, including the ability to operate from grass or semi-prepared runways. Applications include those of passenger and cargo transport, aerial survey (equipped with photographic or geographical survey equipment), and ambulance.

The following description applies to the prototype:

TYPE: Twin-engined light STOL transport.

WINGS: All-metal high-wing monoplane, with single

streamline-section bracing strut each side which is attached to a stub-wing at fuselage floor level. Wing section NACA 2415. Dihedral 2°. Inboard half of each semi-span carries a slotted trailing-edge flap (25% of overall chord); aileron on outboard half of each semi-span. No tabs.

FUSELAGE: Conventional all-metal semi-monocoque structure, with riveted skin. Basically rectangular cross-section in main cabin area. Upswept at rear, to facilitate cargo loading.

TAIL UNIT: Cantilever all-metal structure, with slightly-swept vertical surfaces and long dorsal fin extending almost to wing trailing-edge. One-piece fixed-incidence tailplane aft of fin, with wide-span elevator. Trim tab in rudder.

LANDING GEAR: Non-retractable tricycle type, with single wheel and oleo-pneumatic shock-absorber on each unit. Main units attached to tips of stub-wings. Steerable nosewheel. Main-wheel tyres size 7·50-10, pressure 2·55 bars (37 lb/sq in); nosewheel tyre size 6·00-6, pressure 1·65 bars (24 lb/sq in).

POWER PLANT: Two 186·5 kW (250 hp) Avco Lycoming IO-540-C flat-six engines, each driving a Hartzell

LAPAN XT-400 eight-seat STOL utility transport *(Pilot Press)*

Wing aspect ratio	7·8
Length overall	10·20 m (33 ft 5½ in)
Height overall	4·30 m (14 ft 1¼ in)
Tailplane span	5·20 m (17 ft 0¾ in)
Wheel track	2·84 m (9 ft 4 in)
Wheelbase	3·62 m (11 ft 10½ in)
Propeller diameter	2·03 m (6 ft 8 in)

DIMENSIONS, INTERNAL:

Cabin: Length	3·75 m (12 ft 3½ in)
Width	1·08 m (3 ft 6½ in)
Height	1·23 m (4 ft 0½ in)
Floor area	3·90 m² (41·98 sq ft)
Volume	4·25 m³ (150·1 cu ft)

AREAS:

Wings, gross	25·36 m² (272·97 sq ft)
Ailerons (total)	2·16 m² (23·25 sq ft)
Trailing-edge flaps (total)	3·56 m² (38·32 sq ft)
Fin	2·75 m² (29·60 sq ft)
Rudder	1·10 m² (11·84 sq ft)
Tailplane	4·01 m² (43·16 sq ft)
Elevator	2·18 m² (23·46 sq ft)

WEIGHTS AND LOADINGS:

Weight empty, with basic equipment	1,422 kg (3,136 lb)
Max payload (8 persons plus baggage)	762 kg (1,680 lb)
Max T-O weight	2,540 kg (5,600 lb)
Max wing loading	100 kg/m² (20·5 lb/sq ft)
Max power loading	6·8 kg/kW (11·2 lb/hp)

PERFORMANCE (estimated):

Max level speed	148 knots (273 km/h; 170 mph)
Max cruising speed (75% power)	139 knots (257 km/h; 160 mph)
Econ cruising speed (60% power)	126 knots (233 km/h; 145 mph)
Stalling speed	58 knots (106 km/h; 66 mph)
Max rate of climb at S/L	274 m (900 ft)/min
Service ceiling	4,665 m (15,300 ft)
T-O to 15 m (50 ft)	300 m (980 ft)
Landing from 15 m (50 ft)	380 m (1,250 ft)
Range with max fuel	521 nm (965 km; 600 miles)
Range with max payload	260 nm (483 km; 300 miles)
g limits	+3·6; −1·5

constant-speed propeller with spinner. Total fuel capacity 494 litres (130·5 US gallons). Oil capacity 11·4 litres (3 US gallons).

ACCOMMODATION: Passenger version accommodates up to eight persons, including pilot, on four pairs of seats. Pilot's seat adjustable fore and aft. Aeromedical version can accommodate two stretchers and attendants. Two forward-opening car-type doors on port side of main cabin, and one on starboard side. Baggage compartment at rear of cabin, accessible via downward-opening clamshell doors in underside of upswept rear fuselage. These doors also facilitate rear loading and unloading of freight or stretchers in cargo and ambulance versions.

SYSTEMS: Internal/external lighting and other electrical services powered by 24V generator and voltage regulator.

AVIONICS AND EQUIPMENT: Optional items include blind-flying instrumentation.

DIMENSIONS, EXTERNAL:

Wing span	14·59 m (47 ft 10½ in)
Wing chord, constant	1·80 m (5 ft 10¾ in)
Wing area, gross	25·36 m² (273·0 sq ft)

PT NURTANIO
PT INDUSTRI PESAWAT TERBANG NURTANIO (Nurtanio Aircraft Industries Ltd)

Lanuma Husein Sastranegara (Husein Sastranegara Air Force Base), Jalan Pajajaran 154, Bandung
Telephone: Bandung 613662, 613191, 613835 and 613836
Telex: 28295 NUR BD
PRESIDENT DIRECTOR: Prof Dr-Ing B. J. Habibie
SECRETARY TO PRESIDENT DIRECTOR: Tatang Endan
DIRECTORS:
Prof Dr-Ing B. J. Habibie (General Affairs)
Ir Yuwono VI (Production)
Ir Harsono Pusponegoro (Technology)
MANAGERS:
Ir Ermis Burhan (General Workshop Division)
Ir Sutadi Suparlan (Fixed Wing Division)
Ir Ramelan (Rotary Wing Division)
Ir Paramayuda (Aircraft Services Division)
ASST FOR COMMERCIAL AFFAIRS: Ir Paramayuda
ASST FOR FINANCE: Dr Bambang Ekoyono
GENERAL INSPECTOR: Dr S. Parlin Napitupulu
CHIEF OF PUBLIC RELATIONS: Suripto Sugondo

This company was officially inaugurated in August 1976 when, as a result of a government order dated 5 April 1976, the former Lipnur (Lembaga Industri Penerbangan Nurtanio: see 1977-78 *Jane's*) combined its aircraft industry activities with those of the Pertamina oil company. It is named in honour of the late Air Marshal Nurtanio Pring-

Nurtanio-built NC-212 Aviocar commercial transport, in the insignia of Sabang Merauke Air Charter

goadisuryo, who was largely responsible for establishing an aircraft industry in Indonesia.

Construction of a new 36 hectare (89 acre) manufacturing facility at Bandung Airport was under way in the Spring of 1980.

In addition to the programmes listed, PT Nurtanio has rights to manufacture the Aérospatiale Puma in Indonesia, and planned to begin assembly of this helicopter in late 1980, with deliveries beginning in January 1981. The initial batch, ordered under a contract signed on 13 May 1980, will comprise 15 SA 330 Pumas and AS 332 Super Pumas. Customers for these include the Indonesian Air Force and Pelita Air Service.

Nurtanio and CASA (see Spanish section) are developing a 35-seat transport aircraft of their own design.

NURTANIO (CASA) NC-212 AVIOCAR

The C-212 Aviocar twin-turboprop transport aircraft has been manufactured in Indonesia since the first half of 1976, under licence from CASA of Spain (which see); 28 had been completed by the beginning of 1980. These have the Indonesian designation NC-212.

By that time more than 16 Aviocars were in operation throughout Indonesia with Pelita Air Service, Merpati Nusantara Airlines, Bouraq Indonesia Airlines, PT Deraya Air Taxi and the Indonesian Air Force. Two Aviocars equipped for rain-making have been exported to Thailand.

The Indonesian Air Force has ordered one complete squadron of 16 Aviocars; others have been ordered by Dirgantara Air Service (three), Sabang Merauke Air Charter (two), Pelita (12) and Merpati Nusantara (two).

NURTANIO (MBB) NBO 105

The BO 105 helicopter has been manufactured in Indonesia since May 1976, under licence from MBB of the Federal Republic of Germany (which see).

By the beginning of 1980 a total of 42 had been completed, of which 27 had been delivered for operation with the Indonesian Army and Navy, Pelita Air Service, the Gudang Garam Cigarette Co and PT Gunung Madu. These have the Indonesian designation NBO 105.

The Indonesian Air Force has ordered one complete squadron of 16 NBO 105s, and 10 have been ordered by the Royal Malaysian Air Force.

Nurtanio-built NBO 105 multi-purpose helicopter

INTERNATIONAL PROGRAMMES

AIRBUS
AIRBUS INDUSTRIE

HEAD OFFICE: Avenue Lucien Servanty, BP No. 33, 31700 Blagnac, France
Telephone: (61) 71 11 11
Telex: AI TO 530526 F
PARIS OFFICE: 12bis avenue Bosquet, 75007 Paris, France
Telephone: 551 40 95
AIRFRAME PRIME CONTRACTORS:

Aérospatiale, 37 boulevard de Montmorency, 75781 Paris Cédex 16, France

Deutsche Airbus GmbH, 8000 München 81, Arabellastrasse 30, Postfach 810260, Federal Republic of Germany

British Aerospace Aircraft Group, Richmond Road, Kingston upon Thames, Surrey KT2 5QS, England
CHAIRMAN OF SUPERVISORY BOARD: Dr Franz-Josef Strauss
PRESIDENT AND CHIEF EXECUTIVE: Bernard Lathière
EXECUTIVE VICE-PRESIDENT AND GENERAL MANAGER: Roger Béteille
SENIOR VICE-PRESIDENTS:
  J. Roeder (Technical)
  G. Warde (Commercial)
  F. Kracht (Production)
  G. Ville (Finance and Administration)
  B. Ziegler (Flight and Support)
PROGRAMME MANAGERS:
  J. Thomas (A300)
  J. Plénier (A310)
  D. Brown (Future Projects)

Airbus Industrie was set up in December 1970 as a 'Groupement d'Intérêt Economique' to manage the development, manufacture, marketing and support of a twin-engined large-capacity short/medium-range transport aircraft known as the A300. This management now extends to the developed version known as the A310. Airbus Industrie has design leadership and is responsible for the A300/310 activities of the partner companies, as well as for any future aircraft launched within the same co-operative framework. Members are Aérospatiale of France, which has a 37·9% interest in the programme, Deutsche Airbus (MBB and VFW) of West Germany (37·9%), British Aerospace (20%), and CASA of Spain (4·2%). Fokker (Netherlands) is an associate in the A300 and A310 programmes; Belairbus (Belgium) is an associate in the programme for the A310.

AIRBUS A300

The Airbus A300 is a wide-bodied aircraft with underwing pods for two turbofan engines. The early history of the project has appeared in previous editions of *Jane's*.

Construction of the first A300, a B1, began in September 1969. This aircraft (F-WUAB, later F-OCAZ) made its first flight on 28 October 1972, and was followed by the second B1 (F-WUAC) on 5 February 1973. The B1 was described in detail in the 1971-72 *Jane's*. Initial certification covered automatic approach and landing in Category 2 weather conditions. Certification for Category 3A automatic approach and landing was granted on 30 September 1974.

The A300 is offered currently with two General Electric CF6-50C or C2 turbofans, or two Pratt & Whitney JT9D-59As or Bs. CF6-50 engines are available with a weight and fuel saving 'short' nozzle. The first A300 with JT9D engines, a B2 for SAS, made its first flight on 28 April 1979. The CF6-80C1, JT9D-7R4H and Rolls-Royce RB.211-524D4 are also available as customer options.

The following versions are available:

A300B2-100 (formerly A300B2). Initial production version. Third and fourth aircraft are to this configuration,

Airbus A300B4-100 twin-turbofan transport in the insignia of Thai Airways International

flying for the first time on 28 June and 20 November 1973 respectively. Aircraft No. 4 subsequently delivered to Air Inter on 22 January 1977 as F-BUAE. Type certificated by DGAC and LBA on 15 March 1974; entered service, with Air France, between Paris and London on 30 May 1974. Designated **B2-101** with CF6-50C engines.

A300B2-200 (formerly A300B2K). Basically as B2-100 series, but fitted with wing-root leading-edge Krueger flaps developed originally for A300B4. With same wheels and brakes also as B4, is suitable for operation from 'hot and high' airports. First aircraft of this type, No. 32 (ZS-SDA), first flew on 30 July 1976. First delivery, of ZS-SDB to South African Airways, made on 23 November 1976. Designation 'dash' numbers, according to power plant, are **B2-201** (CF6-50C) and **B2-220** (JT9D-59A).

A300B2-300. Basically as B2-200, but increased zero-fuel and landing weights for increased payload and multi-stop flexibility.

A300B2-600. Advanced version of B2-200, currently in definition stage. Described separately.

A300B4-100 (formerly A300B4 Stage I and Stage II). Basic longer-range version. Developed from original A300B2, with same external dimensions and volumetric payload capacity, but with increased design weights and fuel capacity, and Krueger flaps at wing-root leading-edges to improve T-O performance. Aircraft No. 9 (F-WLGA) was the first built to this configuration, and first flew on 26 December 1974. French and West German certification granted on 26 March 1975, and FAA Type Approval on 30 June 1976. First delivery, of D-AMAX to Germanair, made in May 1975; this aircraft entered service on 1 June 1975. Designation 'dash' numbers, according to power plant, are **B4-101** (CF6-50C), **B4-103** (CF6-50C2) and **B4-120** (JT9D-59A).

A300B4-200 (formerly A300B4 Stage III). Announced on 19 January 1978, concurrently with order for three by Air France. Compared with -100 series, has reinforced wings and fuselage, strengthened landing gear, and size 49 × 17-20 main-wheel tyres. This allows certification at higher T-O weight, enabling full payload of passengers and cargo to be carried on stages of up to 1,954 nm (3,621 km; 2,250 miles) with standard airline reserves. Optional additional fuel tank available with this version: installed in

rear cargo hold in place of two LD3 containers, it extends the range with full complement of passengers to 3,100 nm (5,740 km; 3,565 miles). Designation 'dash' numbers, according to power plant, are **B4-201** (CF6-50C), **B4-203** (CF6-50C2), **B4-220** (JT9D-59A), and **B4-221** (JT9D-59B).

A300B4-600. Advanced version of B4-200, currently in definition stage. Described separately.

A300C4 Freighter conversion of B4; described separately.

A310. Developed version, with shorter fuselage and redesigned wings; described separately.

By 1 July 1980, orders and options totalling 278 A300s (including C4s) had been received, as follows:

	Orders	Options
Air Afrique (B4-200)	1	—
Air France (B2-100, B4-100/200)	23	12
Air Inter (France) (B2-100)	7	—
Alitalia (B4-200)	8	3
Cruzeiro do Sul (Brazil) (B4-203)	3	1
Eastern Air Lines (USA) (B2-200, B4-100)	25	9
Egyptair (B4-200)	3	4
Garuda (Indonesia) (B4-220)	6	6
Hapag Lloyd (West Germany) (B4-100, C4-200)	7	—
Iberia (B4-120)	9	5
Indian Airlines (B2-100)	8	3
Iran Air (B2-200)	6	3
Korean Air Lines (B4-100)	8	—
*Laker Airways (UK) (B4-200)	10	—
Lufthansa (West Germany) (B2-100, B4-100)	11	—
Malaysian Airline System (B4-200)	4	—
Olympic Airways (Greece) (B4-100)	8	2
Pakistan International (B4-200)	4	6
Philippine Air Lines (B4-100)	5	—
SAS (Scandinavia) (B2-320)	4	8
Singapore Airlines (B4-200)	6	6
South African Airways (B2-200, B4-100, C4)	6	2
Thai International (B4-100)	10	4
Toa Domestic Airlines (Japan) (B2-200)	9	—
Trans Australia Airlines (B4-100)	4	3
Trans European Airways (Belgium) (B1)	1	—
Tunis Air (B4-200)	1	1
Undisclosed	—	3

*option for last four to be A310s

A total of 104 A300s (37 B2s and 63 B4s) had been delivered by 1 July 1980; the 100th was an Alitalia B4-200.

Aérospatiale is responsible for manufacturing the entire nose section (including the flight deck), lower centre fuselage and engine pylons, and for final assembly. Deutsche Airbus is responsible for manufacturing the forward fuselage, between the flight deck and wing box, the upper centre fuselage, the rear fuselage and the vertical tail surfaces. British Aerospace has design responsibility for the wings, builds the wing fixed structures, and is working in collaboration with Fokker, which is building the wing moving surfaces. CASA manufactures the horizontal tail surfaces, fuselage main doors and landing gear doors.

Airbus A300B4 wide-bodied short/medium-range transport (CF6 engines) *(Pilot Press)*

Cruzeiro do Sul, which has ordered the B4-203 version of the Airbus A300, is the first South American operator of this wide-bodied transport aircraft

Large A300 sections are flown from their places of manufacture in Europe to the final assembly line in Toulouse on board two Super Guppy outsize cargo aircraft, acquired by Airbus Industrie in November 1971 and September 1973 respectively. After assembly, painting in customers' colour scheme is carried out at Toulouse. Aircraft are then flown to Hamburg for installation of interior furnishings and equipment before returning to Toulouse for final customer acceptance.

General Electric engines are assembled under licence by SNECMA; some components are also licence-built by SNECMA (France) and MTU (West Germany). The whole power plant assembly is virtually identical to that of the McDonnell Douglas DC-10-30, and nacelles are supplied by McDonnell Douglas. Nacelles for Pratt & Whitney engines are manufactured by Rohr (West Germany) and are interchangeable with those of JT9D-59-powered DC-10-40 aircraft and JT9D-70-powered Boeing 747s.

In 1979 Airbus Industrie received 133 firm orders and 88 options for the A300/310, including orders from 12 new customers. This was the second largest total sale of any commercial transport aircraft during that year. Production was increased from two to three per month in 1979, will reach four per month in 1981, and is planned to reach 10 per month in 1985.

TYPE: Large-capacity wide-bodied short/medium-range transport.

WINGS: Cantilever mid-wing monoplane. Thickness/chord ratio 10·5%. Sweepback 28° at quarter-chord. Primary two-spar box-type structure, integral with fuselage and incorporating fail-safe principles, built of high-strength aluminium alloy. Third spar across inboard sections. Machined skin with open-sectioned stringers. Each wing has three-section leading-edge slats (no slat cutout over the engine pylon), and three Fowler-type double-slotted flaps on trailing-edge; a Krueger flap on the leading-edge wing root (B2-200/B4); an all-speed aileron between inboard flap and outer pair; and a low-speed aileron outboard of the outer pair of flaps. Lift dump facility by combination of three spoilers (outboard) and two airbrakes (inboard) on each wing, forward of outer pair of flaps, plus two additional airbrakes forward of inboard flap. The flaps extend over 84% of each half-span, and increase the wing chord by 25% when fully extended. The datum of the all-speed aileron is deflected downward by up to 10° with flap operation to maintain trailing-edge continuity with deflected flaps. Drive mechanisms for flaps and slats are similar to one another, each powered by twin motors driving ball screwjacks on each surface with built-in protection against asymmetric operation. Two slat positions for take-off and landing. Pre-selection of the airbrake/lift dump lever allows automatic extension of the lift dumpers on touchdown. All flight controls are powered by triplex hydraulic servo-jacks, with no manual reversion. Anti-icing of wing leading-edges, outboard of engine pods, is by hot air bled from engines.

FUSELAGE: Conventional semi-monocoque structure of circular cross-section, with frames and open Z-section stringers. Built mainly of high-strength aluminium alloy, with steel or titanium for some major components. Skin panels integrally machined in areas of high stress. Honeycomb panels or restricted glassfibre laminates for secondary structures.

TAIL UNIT: Cantilever all-metal structure, with sweepback on all surfaces. Variable-incidence tailplane and separately-controlled elevators. Tailplane powered by two motors driving a fail-safe ball screwjack. No anti-icing of leading-edges.

LANDING GEAR: Hydraulically-retractable tricycle type, of Messier-Hispano-Bugatti design, with Messier-Hispano-Bugatti/Liebherr/Dowty shock-absorbers and wheels standard. Twin-wheel nose unit retracts for-

ward, main units inward into fuselage. Free-fall extension. Each four-wheel main unit comprises two tandem-mounted bogies, interchangeable left with right. Standard bogie size is 927 × 1,397 mm (36½ × 55 in); wider bogie of 978 × 1,397 mm (38½ × 55 in) is available on B4-100/200. Main-wheel tyre sizes and pressures as follows: B2, 46 × 16-20 (standard bogie) at 12·4 bars (180 lb/sq in); B2-200, 49 × 17-20 (standard bogie) at 11·4 bars (165 lb/sq in); B4-100, 46 × 16-20 (standard), 49 × 17-20 (standard) or 49 × 17-20 (wide bogie), with respective pressures of 14·2, 11·9 and 10·6 bars (206, 172 and 154 lb/sq in); B4-200, 49 × 17-20 (standard) or 49 × 17-20 (wide bogie), with respective pressures of 12·4 and 11·1 bars (180 and 161 lb/sq in). Nosewheel tyres size 40 × 14-16 on all these B2/B4 models, with pressures of 8·6 bars (125 lb/sq in) on B2 variants and 9·0 bars (131 lb/sq in) on B4 variants. Steering angles 65°/95°. Messier-Hispano-Bugatti/Liebherr/Dowty hydraulic disc brakes standard on all main wheels. Duplex anti-skid units fitted, with a third standby hydraulic supply for wheel brakes. Bendix or Goodrich wheels and brakes available optionally.

POWER PLANT: Underwing location of the power plant enables the A300 to use any advanced technology turbofan engine in the 222·5 kN (50,000 lb thrust) class. It is currently being offered with the following engines:
Two 227 kN (51,000 lb st) General Electric CF6-50C turbofans (B2-101/201 and B4-101/201);
Two 233·5 kN (52,500 lb st) General Electric CF6-50 C2 (B4-103/203); or
Two 236 kN (53,000 lb st) Pratt & Whitney JT9D-59A (B2-220 and B4-120/220) or -59B (B4-221).
These engines are installed in pods interchangeable with those of the McDonnell Douglas DC-10 Series 30 and 40. For details of other engines available, see introductory copy.

Fuel in two integral tanks in each wing, with total usable capacity of 43,000 litres (9,460 Imp gallons) in B2. Fifth integral tank in wing centre-section of B4, increasing total usable capacity to 59,700 litres (13,133 gallons). For B4-200 series, an optional self-contained fuselage fuel tank is available, capacity 6,000 litres (1,320 Imp gallons). This unit fits into the rear cargo hold, where it takes the place of two standard LD3 containers. Two standard refuelling points beneath each wing, outboard of engine pylons.

ACCOMMODATION (B2 and B4): Crew of three on flight deck, plus two observer's seats. Seating for between 220 and 320 passengers in main cabin in six, seven, eight or nine-abreast layout with 79/86 cm (31/34 in) seat pitch. Typical economy class layout has 269 seats, eight abreast with two aisles, at 86 cm (34 in) seat pitch. This layout includes one galley and one toilet forward, with provision for a second one, and one more galley and four toilets aft. Up to 336 passengers can be carried at 76 cm (30 in) seat pitch in single-class high-density layout. Closed hatracks on each side, forming baggage lockers (max individual capacity 0·062 m³; 2·19 cu ft). Provision for central double-sided rack. Two outward parallel-opening plug-type passenger doors ahead of wing leading-edge on each side, and one on each side at rear. Underfloor baggage/cargo holds fore and aft of wings, with doors on starboard side. The forward hold will accommodate four 2·24 × 3·18 × 1·63 m (88 × 125 × 64 in) pallets or twelve LD3 or IATA A1 containers; the rear hold will accommodate eight LD3 containers each of 4·25 m³ (150 cu ft) capacity. Additional bulk loading of freight provided for in an extreme rear compartment with usable volume of 16·0 m³ (565 cu ft). The latter compartment can be used for the transport of livestock. Entire accommodation is pressurised, including freight, baggage and avionics compartments.

SYSTEMS: Air for air-conditioning system can be provided

from engines, the APU or a high pressure ground source. Supply is controlled by separate and parallel bootstrap-type units, each of which includes a flow limiting unit, cooler unit, water separator and temperature control unit. In addition, air from each engine passes through a pressure control pre-cooler unit. Distribution in flight deck and three cabin areas, with independent regulation. Two independent automatic systems, with manual override, control the cabin altitude, its rate of change and the differential pressure. Cabin pressure differential for normal operations is 0·57 bars (8·25 lb/sq in). Hydraulic system comprises three fully-independent circuits, operating simultaneously. Fluid used is a fire-resistant phosphate-ester type, working at a pressure of 207 bars (3,000 lb/sq in). The three circuits provide triplex power for primary flying controls; if any circuit fails, full control of the aircraft is retained without any necessity for action by the crew. All three circuits supply the all-speed and low-speed ailerons, rudder and elevator; 'blue' circuit additionally supplies tail trim, spoilers, slats and rudder variable-gear unit; 'green' circuit additionally supplies airbrakes, spoilers, slats, elevator artificial feel units, flaps, steering, wheel brakes and normal landing gear requirements; 'yellow' circuit additionally supplies tail trim, airbrakes, lift dumpers, rudder variable-gear unit, elevator artificial feel units, flaps, wheelbrakes and steering. Each circuit normally powered by engine-driven self-regulating pumps, one on each engine for the green circuit and one each for the blue and yellow circuits. Dowty Rotol ram-air turbine-driven pump provides standby hydraulic power should both engines become inoperative. Main electrical power is supplied by two Westinghouse three-phase constant-frequency AC generators mounted on the engines. A third identical generator, driven by the APU, can supply power both in flight, to replace a failed engine-driven generator, and on the ground. Supply frequency is 400Hz and voltage is 115/200V. Any one generator can supply sufficient power to operate all equipment and systems necessary for take-off and landing. A conventional generator CSD system is installed, the two units being mounted on opposite sides of the engine gearbox with the CSD driving an aircooled generator at a constant 8,000 rpm. Each generator is rated at 90kVA, with overload ratings of 135kVA for 5 minutes and 180kVA for 5 seconds. The APU generator is driven at constant speed through a gearbox. Three unregulated transformer-rectifier units (TRUs) supply 28V DC power. Three 24V 25Ah nickel-cadmium batteries are used for APU starting and fuel control, engine starter control, standby lights and, by selection, emergency busbar. This busbar and a 115V 400Hz static inverter provide standby power in flight if normal power is unavailable. This system is separated completely from the main system . Hot air protection for engine intakes and slat sections on the wings outboard of the engine. Garrett-AiResearch TSCP 700-5 or (from c/n 246) GTCP 331-250 APU in tailcone, exhausting upward. The installation incorporates APU noise attenuation. Fire protection system is self-contained, and firewall panels protect main structure from an APU fire. The APU can be operated on the ground, in flight up to 10,675 m (35,000 ft), and in icing conditions. Relights are possible up to 7,620 m (25,000 ft). Aircraft is completely independent of ground power sources, since all major services can be operated by the APU.

AVIONICS AND EQUIPMENT: Standard communications avionics include two VHF sets and one Selcal system, plus interphone and passenger address systems. An accident recorder and voice recorder are also installed. Standard navigation avionics include two VOR, two ILS, two radio altimeters, marker beacon receiver, two

ADF, two DME, two ATC transponders and a weather radar. Sperry digital air data computer standard. Most other avionics available to customer's requirements, only those related to the blind landing system (ILS and radio altimeter) being selected and supplied by the manufacturer. Additional optional avionics include one or two HF, third VHF, second marker beacon receiver, second radar, navigation computer and pictorial display. Both the pilot and co-pilot have an integrated instrument system combining heading and attitude (three SAGEM MGC 10/ARINC 569 are standard in B2, but they can be replaced by MGC 30/ARINC 571 Mk 1 inertial sensors, which are modular with the MGC 10); SFENA autopilot/flight director system; and radio information. The SFENA/Smiths/Bodenseewerk automatic flight control system includes a comprehensive range of en-route facilities such as VOR coupling, heading select, height acquire, turbulence, rate of descent (if required) and control wheel steering, in addition to the normal height, speed, pitch-and-roll attitude and heading locks. An optional speed reference system with built-in windshear protection is available. Dual automatic landing system provides coupled approach and automatic landing facilities suitable for Category 3A operation. The system is designed to allow future extension to Category 3B automatic landing capability. An automatic braking system is available.

DIMENSIONS, EXTERNAL (B2-100/200/300, B4-100/200):
Wing span	44·84 m (147 ft 1 in)
Wing aspect ratio	7·73
Length overall	53·62 m (175 ft 11 in)
Length of fuselage	52·03 m (170 ft 8½ in)
Fuselage max diameter	5·64 m (18 ft 6 in)
Height overall	16·53 m (54 ft 2¾ in)
Tailplane span	16·94 m (55 ft 7 in)
Wheel track	9·60 m (31 ft 6 in)
Wheelbase (c/l of shock-absorbers)	18·60 m (61 ft 0 in)

Passengers doors (each):
Height	1·93 m (6 ft 4 in)
Width	1·07 m (3 ft 6 in)
Height to sill: fwd	4·60 m (15 ft 1 in)
centre	4·80 m (15 ft 9 in)
rear	5·50 m (18 ft 0½ in)
Emergency exits (each): Height	1·60 m (5 ft 3 in)
Width	0·61 m (2 ft 0 in)
Height to sill	4·87 m (15 ft 10 in)

Underfloor cargo door (fwd):
Height	1·71 m (5 ft 7½ in)
Width	2·44 m (8 ft 0 in)
Height to sill	2·56 m (8 ft 4¾ in)

Underfloor cargo door (rear):
Height	1·71 m (5 ft 7½ in)
Width	1·81 m (5 ft 11¼ in)
Height to sill	2·96 m (9 ft 8½ in)

Underfloor cargo door (extreme rear):
Height	0·95 m (3 ft 1 in)
Width	0·95 m (3 ft 1 in)
Height to sill	3·30 m (10 ft 10 in)

DIMENSIONS, INTERNAL (B2-100/200/300, B4-100/200):
Cabin, excl flight deck:
Length	39·15 m (128 ft 6 in)
Max width	5·35 m (17 ft 7 in)
Max height	2·54 m (8 ft 4 in)

Underfloor cargo hold:
Length: fwd	10·60 m (34 ft 9¼ in)
rear	6·89 m (22 ft 7¼ in)
extreme rear	3·10 m (10 ft 2 in)
Max height	1·76 m (5 ft 9 in)
Max width	4·20 m (13 ft 9¼ in)

Underfloor cargo hold volume:
fwd	75·1 m³ (2,652 cu ft)
rear	46·8 m³ (1,652 cu ft)
extreme rear	16·0 m³ (565 cu ft)
Max total volume for bulk loading	140·0 m³ (4,944 cu ft)

AREAS (B2, B4):
Wings, gross	260·0 m² (2,798·6 sq ft)
Vertical tail surfaces (total)	45·2 m² (486·5 sq ft)
Horizontal tail surfaces (total)	69·5 m² (748·1 sq ft)

WEIGHTS AND LOADINGS:
Manufacturer's weight empty:
B2-100/120	77,062 kg (169,892 lb)
B2-200/220	77,427 kg (170,697 lb)
B4-100/120	79,070 kg (174,319 lb)
B4-200/220	79,833 kg (176,000 lb)

Typical operating weight empty:
B2-100/120, B2-200	85,910 kg (189,400 lb)
B2-220	87,500 kg (192,905 lb)
B4-100 (basic)	88,100 kg (194,227 lb)
B4-120 (basic)	89,300 kg (196,873 lb)
B4-200 (optional)	88,500 kg (195,109 lb)
B4-220 (optional)	89,700 kg (197,755 lb)

Max payload (structural):
B2-100/120	34,590 kg (76,258 lb)
B2-200	34,600 kg (76,280 lb)
B2-220	33,000 kg (72,752 lb)
B4-100 (basic)	35,900 kg (79,146 lb)
B4-120 (basic)	34,700 kg (76,500 lb)
B4-200 (optional)	35,200 kg (77,602 lb)
B4-220 (optional)	34,300 kg (75,618 lb)

Max usable fuel:
B2-200/220 (basic)	34,000 kg (74,957 lb)
B4-100/120 (basic)	47,500 kg (104,720 lb)

Max T-O weight:
B2-100	137,000 kg (302,030 lb)
	or 142,000 kg (313,055 lb)
B2-200	142,000 kg (313,055 lb)
B4-100	150,000 kg (330,690 lb)
	or 153,000 kg (337,305 lb)
	or 157,500 kg (347,230 lb)
B4-200	165,000 kg (363,760 lb)

Max ramp weight:
B2-200	142,900 kg (315,040 lb)
B4-200	165,900 kg (365,745 lb)

Max landing weight:
B2-100	127,500-134,000 kg (281,090-295,420 lb)
B2-200	130,000-134,000 kg (286,600-295,420 lb)
B4-100	133,000-136,000 kg (293,215-299,825 lb)
B4-200	134,000 kg (295,420 lb)

Max zero-fuel weight:
B2-100	116,500-124,000 kg (256,835-273,375 lb)
B2-200	120,500 kg (265,655 lb)
	or 124,000 kg (273,375 lb)
B4-100	122,000-126,000 kg (268,960-277,780 lb)
B4-200	124,000 kg (273,375 lb)

Max wing loading:
B2-200	546 kg/m² (111·8 lb/sq ft)
B4-100	606 kg/m² (124·1 lb/sq ft)
B4-200	635 kg/m² (130·0 lb/sq ft)

Max power loading:
B2-201 (CF6-50C)	312·8 kg/kN (3·07 lb/lb st)
B2-220 (JT9D-59A)	300·8 kg/kN (2·95 lb/lb st)
B4-101 (CF6-50C)	346·9 kg/kN (3·40 lb/lb st)
B4-103 (CF6-50C2)	337·3 kg/kN (3·31 lb/lb st)
B4-203 (CF6-50C2)	353·3 kg/kN (3·46 lb/lb st)
B4-220 (JT9D-59A)	349·6 kg/kN (3·43 lb/lb st)
B4-221 (JT9D-59B)	340·2 kg/kN (3·34 lb/lb st)

PERFORMANCE (at max T-O weight except where indicated):
Max operating speed (MMO/VMO):
B2
Mach 0·86 (345 knots; 639 km/h; 397 mph) CAS
B4
Mach 0·82 (345 knots; 639 km/h; 397 mph) CAS
Max cruising speed at 7,620 m (25,000 ft):
B2, B4	492 knots (911 km/h; 567 mph)
Typical high-speed cruise at 9,145 m (30,000 ft):
B2, B4	495 knots (917 km/h; 570 mph)
Typical long-range cruising speed at 9,450 m (31,000 ft): B2, B4 457 knots (847 km/h; 526 mph)
Approach speed at typical weight:
B2	131 knots (243 km/h; 151 mph) CAS
B4	128 knots (237 km/h; 147 mph) CAS
Max operating altitude: B2 10,675 m (35,000 ft)
Min ground turning radius (wingtips)
33·51 m (109 ft 11¼ in)
Runway LCN at max T-O weight (A: flexible pavement of 51 cm; 20 in thickness, B: rigid pavement of 76 cm; 30 in radius of relative stiffness):
B2-100: A	75
B	68
B2-200: A	73
B	67
B4-100 (46 × 16-20 tyres): A	86
B	79
B4-100 (49 × 17-20 tyres): A	78
B	70
B4-100 (49 × 17-20 tyres, wide bogie):	
A	70
B	62
B4-200 (49 × 17-20 tyres): A	85
B	74
B4-200 (49 × 17-20 tyres, wide bogie):	
A	77
B	67

T-O field length (S/L, ISA + 15°C):
B2	1,951 m (6,400 ft)
B4-100/120	2,750 m (9,020 ft)
B4-200/220	3,000 m (9,845 ft)

Landing field length at typical weight:
B2	1,630 m (5,350 ft)
B4-100/120	1,660 m (5,445 ft)

Range with 269 passengers and baggage:
B2-200/220	1,800 nm (3,334 km; 2,074 miles)
B4-100/120	2,600 nm (4,818 km; 2,994 miles)
B4-200/220	2,750 nm (5,095 km; 3,165 miles)

Range with max fuel:
B2-200/220	2,300 nm (4,261 km; 2,648 miles)
B4-100/120	3,200 nm (5,930 km; 3,685 miles)

OPERATIONAL NOISE CHARACTERISTICS (FAR Pt 36):
T-O noise level: B2	90 EPNdB
B4-100/120	92 EPNdB
B4-200/220	94 EPNdB
Approach noise level: B2, B4	101 EPNdB
Sideline noise level: B2, B4	95 EPNdB

AIRBUS A300B2-600 and A300B4-600

These advanced versions of the B2-200 and B4-200 incorporate a number of improvements, including increased passenger and freight capacity. Modifications include use of the A310 rear fuselage, which is shorter but volumetrically more efficient than that of the A300, with an extension of the parallel section of the fuselage to restore tail moment arm. Passenger capacity is thus increased by two seat rows for an increase in overall length equivalent to only one frame pitch.

An extensive weight reduction programme, including simplified systems and the use of composite materials for some secondary structural components, allows greater payload capacity to be offered with very little change in empty weight. Performance improvements, offering better payload/range capability and greater fuel economy, result from a comprehensive 'drag clean-up' programme carried out on an A300 development aircraft (c/n 3). Power plants on offer will be advanced derivatives of current high bypass ratio turbofan engines.

Detailed definition of the -600 models was in progress in mid-1980, aimed at delivery of the first examples in early 1984.

DIMENSIONS, EXTERNAL AND INTERNAL: As for B2-100/200/300 and B4-100/200 except:
Underfloor cargo door (fwd):
Height	1·71 m (5 ft 7½ in)
Width	2·69 m (8 ft 10 in)

Cabin, excl flight deck:
Length	40·21 m (131 ft 11 in)

Underfloor cargo hold length:
rear	7·95 m (26 ft 1 in)
extreme rear	3·40 m (11 ft 2 in)

Underfloor cargo hold volume:
rear	55·0 m³ (1,942 cu ft)
extreme rear	17·3 m³ (611 cu ft)

WEIGHTS AND LOADINGS:
Max T-O weight:
B2-600	142,000 kg (313,055 lb)
B4-600	165,000 kg (363,760 lb)

Max ramp weight:
B2-600	142,900 kg (315,040 lb)
B4-600	165,900 kg (365,745 lb)

Max landing weight:
B2-600	134,000 kg (295,420 lb)
B4-600	138,000 kg (304,240 lb)

Max zero-fuel weight:
B2-600	124,000 kg (273,375 lb)
B4-600	130,000 kg (286,600 lb)

AIRBUS A300C4/F4

The A300C4 is a convertible freighter version of the A300B4, available with the same range of power plant options. Main differences from the B4 are a large upper-deck cargo door, a reinforced cabin floor, a smoke detection system in the main cabin, and an interior trim adaptable to the freighter role. The upper-deck cargo door is on

Airbus A300C4-200 freighter for Hapag Lloyd of West Germany, converted in 1979 by VFW

the opposite side to that of the underfloor holds, enabling loading or unloading to be carried out simultaneously at all positions.

In the freight mode the loading system, consisting of ball mats, roller tracks and electrical drive units, is fitted to the existing seat rails, and permits the carriage of up to thirteen 2·24 × 3·17 m (88 × 125 in) pallets, twelve 2·44 × 3·17 m (96 × 125 in) pallets, or eight of the former plus five of the latter, in basic configurations. Total upper-deck volume thus varies between 173 m³ (6,100 cu ft) and 179 m³ (6,315 cu ft). A 9g barrier net is installed in the front of the cabin. Total cargo-carrying capability of the A300C4 is approx 41,000 kg (90,390 lb). Modification kits covering the forward fuselage section, in which the upper-deck cargo door is installed, are built in Bremen by VFW.

For customers requiring it, the A300C4 has the capability for conversion to passenger or mixed passenger/cargo configuration. Typical options include accommodation (in mainly eight-abreast seating) for up to 315 passengers on the upper deck; or 145 passengers (seven/eight-abreast) plus six 88 × 125 in pallets; or 75 passengers plus nine 88 × 125 in pallets; or fourteen 88 × 125 in or 96 × 125 in pallets; or twenty 86 × 125 in pallets.

The first A300C4 (c/n 83), for Hapag Lloyd of West Germany, made its initial flight in mid-1979; after fitting of the upper-deck cargo door, it was rolled out of VFW's Lemwerder plant on 9 November 1979, and delivered in January 1980.

Airbus Industrie has also defined an **A300F4** freighter version, with a maximum payload of 46,000 kg (101,410 lb). This is similar to the C4, but with all passenger provisions removed completely and the cabin windows replaced by metal blanking plates. It can carry up to twenty 88 × 125 in pallets on the upper deck, or eight 8 ft × 8 ft × 10 ft ISO containers plus five 96 × 125 in pallets. Loadable volume of the upper deck of the A300F4 is 294·5 m³ (10,400 cu ft).

The description of the A300B4 applies generally also to the convertible C4, except as outlined above and detailed below:

DIMENSIONS, EXTERNAL: As A300B4, plus:
Upper-deck cargo door (fwd, port):
Height (projected)   2·56 m (8 ft 4¾ in)
Width   3·58 m (11 ft 9 in)
DIMENSIONS, INTERNAL: As A300B4, except:
Cabin upper deck usable for cargo:
Length   31·78 m (104 ft 3 in)
Min height   2·16 m (7 ft 1 in)
Max height   2·44 m (8 ft 0 in)
Volume   173–179 m³ (6,100–6,315 cu ft)
Max total volume for bulk loading (upper and lower decks)   286 m³ (10,087 cu ft)
WEIGHTS:
Manufacturer's weight empty (basic):
passenger mode   81,000 kg (178,575 lb)
freight mode   81,900 kg (180,560 lb)
pure freighter   78,300 kg (172,620 lb)
Manufacturer's weight empty (optional):
passenger mode   81,300 kg (179,235 lb)
freight mode   82,200 kg (181,220 lb)
pure freighter   78,600 kg (173,285 lb)
Operating weight empty (basic):
*passenger mode   89,000 kg (196,210 lb)
freight mode   82,900 kg (182,765 lb)
pure freighter   79,000 kg (174,165 lb)
Operating weight empty (optional):
*passenger mode   89,200 kg (196,650 lb)
freight mode   83,200 kg (183,425 lb)
pure freighter   79,400 kg (175,045 lb)
Max payload (structural) (basic):
passenger mode   35,000 kg (77,160 lb)

freight mode   41,100 kg (90,610 lb)
pure freighter   45,000 kg (99,210 lb)
Max payload (structural) (optional):
passenger mode   36,800 kg (81,130 lb)
freight mode   42,800 kg (94,360 lb)
pure freighter   46,600 kg (102,735 lb)
Max T-O weight:
basic   157,500 kg (347,230 lb)
optional   165,000 kg (363,765 lb)
Max landing weight:
basic   134,000 kg (295,420 lb)
optional   136,000 kg (299,830 lb)
Max zero-fuel weight:
basic   124,000 kg (273,375 lb)
optional   126,000 kg (277,780 lb)

*incl weight of underfloor cargo hold containers and pallets

PERFORMANCE (estimated):
Range with max (structural) payload, allowances for ground manoeuvring, 30 min hold at 460 m (1,500 ft), no diversion:
basic   2,100 nm (3,890 km; 1,825 miles)
optional   2,500 nm (4,635 km; 2,170 miles)
Range with max fuel, no payload, allowances as above:
passenger mode   3,900 nm (7,230 km; 3,390 miles)
freight mode   4,100 nm (7,600 km; 3,560 miles)
pure freighter   4,200 nm (7,785 km; 3,650 miles)

AIRBUS A310

Known originally as the A300B10, the A310 short-fuselage development of the A300 was launched in July 1978. Compared with the A300, the cabin is shorter by 11 frames and the overall fuselage by 13 frames. The cabin thus normally seats from 210–234 passengers, although the aircraft will be certificated to carry up to 255 persons. The A310 retains the same fuselage cross-section as the A300, thus being able to carry standard LD3 containers two abreast, and/or standard pallets installed crosswise. Capacity is 14 (optionally 15) standard LD3s, or three pallets and six (optionally seven) containers.

The A310 also has new, advanced-technology wings, of reduced span and area, designed by the British Aerospace Aircraft Group; a new and smaller tailplane; new 'multi-role' pylons able to support all types of engine offered; and landing gear modified to cater for these changes in size and weight. The first five wing sets are due to be delivered by BAe in 1981.

Like the A300, the A310 can be powered by General Electric, Pratt & Whitney or Rolls-Royce turbofan engines. The customers so far identified (up to mid-1980) have selected for their aircraft the 213·5 kN (48,000 lb st) General Electric CF6-80A1 or A3; or the 208·6 kN (46,900 lb st) Pratt & Whitney JT9D-7R4D; and the aircraft is to be certificated initially with these two types of engine. Studies to power the A310 with the 222·4 kN (50,000 lb st) Rolls-Royce RB.211-524D4 are under way.

At present, the A310 is offered in one basic version, the A310-200, for short/medium-haul operations, including transcontinental routes. However, it is to be certificated and offered at different weight options, to match different airline needs, and further developments will offer increases in payload/range capability.

First flight of the A310 is scheduled for Spring 1982, and entry into service for early 1983. The following versions have been announced:

A310-200. Basic designation of passenger version. Model designations, according to power plant, include **A310-202** (CF6-80A1), **A310-203** (CF6-80A3), **A310-220** (JT9D-7R4D), **A310-221** (JT9D-7R4D1), **A310-240** (RB.211-524B4) and **A310-241** (RB.211-524D4).
A310C-200. Convertible version.
A310F-200. Freighter version.

By 1 October 1980, orders and options totalling 144 had been received, as follows:

	Orders	Options
Air Afrique	2	—
Air France (A310-202)	5	10
Austrian Airlines (A310-220)	2	2
British Caledonian	3	3
KLM (Netherlands) (A310-200)	10	10
Kuwait Airways (A310-200)	11	—
Lufthansa (West Germany) (A310-200)	25	25
Martinair (Netherlands)	3	1
Sabena (Belgium) (A310-220)	3	3
Swissair (A310-220)	10	10
Undisclosed	2	4

TYPE: Large-capacity wide-bodied short/medium-range transport.
WINGS: Cantilever mid-wing monoplane. Thickness/chord ratio 15·2% at root, 11·8% at 'break' in trailing-edge, and 10·8% at tip. Dihedral at trailing-edge 11° 8' (inboard) and 4° 3' (outboard). Incidence 5° 3' at root. Sweepback 28° at quarter-chord. Three-section leading-edge slats on each wing over almost full span, with no cutout over engine pylon. Simple Fowler-type trailing-edge flap on outboard section of each wing; double-slotted Fowler-type flap inboard. All-speed aileron between flaps. Three roll spoilers/lift dumpers (outboard) and two airbrakes/lift dumpers (inboard) forward of each outer flap. Two further airbrakes/lift dumpers forward of each inboard flap. Construction generally similar to that of A300. In-spar ribs built by Hawker de Havilland Australia.
FUSELAGE: Generally similar to A300, except for reduced length (see introductory copy), resulting in deletion of two passenger doors.
TAIL UNIT: Vertical surfaces as for A300; horizontal surfaces similar to A300, but with slightly reduced dimensions.
LANDING GEAR: Messier-Hispano-Bugatti type, generally similar to that of A300, but modified to cater for new dimensions and weights. Bendix wheels and brakes optional.
POWER PLANT: Currently ordered or available with the following turbofan engines:
Two 213·5 kN (48,000 lb st) General Electric CF6-80A1 (A310-202) or Pratt & Whitney JT9D-7R4D1 (A310-221);
Two 208·6 kN (46,900 lb st) Pratt & Whitney JT9D-7R4D (A310-220);
Two 222·4 kN (50,000 lb st) General Electric CF6-80A3 (A310-203) or Rolls-Royce RB.211-524B4 (A310-240); or

Model of the Airbus A310 developed version of the A300

Airbus A310 short-fuselage short/medium-range transport aircraft (*Pilot Press*)

Two 235·75 kN (53,000 lb st) Rolls-Royce RB.211-524D4 (A310-241).

Usable total fuel capacity approx 55,000 litres (12,098 Imp gallons).

ACCOMMODATION: Crew of two or three in forward-facing crew cockpit (FFCC), in which all crew members face forward at all times. Provision for fourth crew member. Standard cabin arranged for 195-282 seats in six/seven/eight-abreast layout; nine-abreast seating available for high-density configurations. Overhead baggage stowage as for A300, rising to average of 0·07 m³ (2·33 cu ft) per passenger with optional central stowage in 212-seat layout. Four passenger doors only, one forward and one aft on each side. Type I emergency exit over wing on each side. Underfloor baggage/cargo holds fore and aft of wings, each with door on starboard side. Forward hold will accommodate eight LD3 containers or three 2·24 × 3·17 m (88 × 125 in) standard pallets; its door is sized for the latter, but a wider door is optional, enabling 2·44 × 3·17 m (96 × 125 in) pallets to be loaded. Rear hold will accommodate six LD3 containers. Additional compartment aft of rear hold for bulk loading.

SYSTEMS: Sundstrand electric power generation system, utilising two engine-driven integrated drive generators. Garrett-AiResearch GTCP 331-250 APU.

AVIONICS AND EQUIPMENT: Digital AFCS (automatic flight control system) standard, with computer-based flight control, thrust control and stability augmentation, confers capability for Category 2 landings; full provision to upgrade to Category 3 by adding second flight control computer and fail-operational capability. Basic flight management system is digital, with area navigation computer, electronic HSI and ADI, CRT displays and basic AIDS (airborne integrated data system); developed AIDS, with engine monitoring computer and digital data recorder, under evaluation. Head-up displays optional. Push-button selector/indicators replace conventional switches and serve also as warning/failure indicators. Rosemount angle of attack transmitters. Leading-edge slats and trailing-edge flaps controlled by microprocessors developed jointly by Marconi Avionics (UK) and Liebherr-Aerotechnik (West Germany); two digital units per aircraft control the electro-hydraulic motors which actuate these surfaces.

DIMENSIONS, EXTERNAL:

Wing span	43·90 m (144 ft 0¼ in)
Wing chord at root	8·38 m (27 ft 6 in)
Wing chord at tip	2·18 m (7 ft 1¾ in)
Wing aspect ratio	8·8
Length overall	46·67 m (153 ft 1½ in)
Length of fuselage	45·13 m (148 ft 0¾ in)
Fuselage: Max diameter	5·64 m (18 ft 6 in)
Height overall	15·81 m (51 ft 10½ in)
Tailplane span	16·26 m (53 ft 4¼ in)
Wheel track	9·60 m (31 ft 6 in)
Wheelbase (c/l of shock-absorbers)	15·21 m (49 ft 10¾ in)

Passenger door (fwd, port):

Height	1·93 m (6 ft 4 in)
Width	1·07 m (3 ft 6 in)
Height to sill	4·54 m (14 ft 10¾ in)

Passenger door (aft, port):

Height	1·93 m (6 ft 4 in)
Width	1·07 m (3 ft 6 in)
Height to sill	4·85 m (15 ft 11 in)

Servicing doors (fwd and aft, stbd):
  As corresponding passenger doors

Emergency exits (overwing, port and stbd, each):

Height	1·39 m (4 ft 6¾ in)
Width	0·67 m (2 ft 2½ in)

Underfloor cargo door (fwd):

Height	1·71 m (5 ft 7½ in)
Width	2·69 m (8 ft 10 in)
Height to sill	2·611 m (8 ft 6¾ in)

Underfloor cargo door (rear):

Height	1·71 m (5 ft 7½ in)
Width	1·81 m (5 ft 11¼ in)
Height to sill	2·72 m (8 ft 11 in)

DIMENSIONS, INTERNAL:

Cabin. excl flight deck:

Length	33·24 m (109 ft 0¾ in)
Max width	5·29 m (17 ft 4¼ in)
Max height	2·33 m (7 ft 7¾ in)
Fwd cargo hold: Length	7·63 m (25 ft 0½ in)
Max width	4·18 m (13 ft 8½ in)
Height	1·71 m (5 ft 7¼ in)
Volume	50·3 m³ (1,776·3 cu ft)
Aft cargo hold: Length	5·07 m (16 ft 7½ in)
Max width	4·17 m (13 ft 8¼ in)
Height	1·67 m (5 ft 5¾ in)
Volume	34·5 m³ (1,218·4 cu ft)
Aft bulk hold: Volume	17·3 m³ (610·9 cu ft)
Total overall volume	102·1 m³ (3,605·6 cu ft)

AREAS:

Wings, gross	219 m² (2,357·3 sq ft)
Vertical tail surfaces (total)	45·2 m² (486·5 sq ft)
Horizontal tail surfaces (total)	64·0 m² (688·9 sq ft)

WEIGHTS:

Typical operating weight empty:

202	76,616 kg (168,910 lb)
220	76,869 kg (169,467 lb)
221	76,895 kg (169,525 lb)
Max payload: 202	31,884 kg (70,292 lb)
220	31,631 kg (69,734 lb)
221	31,605 kg (69,677 lb)
Max usable fuel	43,000 kg (94,798 lb)
Max T-O weight	132,000 kg (291,010 lb)
Max ramp weight	132,900 kg (292,995 lb)
Max landing weight	118,500 kg (261,250 lb)
Max zero-fuel weight	108,500 kg (239,200 lb)

PERFORMANCE (A310-200, estimated, with 237 passengers except where indicated):

Max operating speed: all versions
  Mach 0·84 (360 knots; 667 km/h; 414 mph CAS)
Typical high-speed cruise at 9,145 m (30,000 ft)
  Mach 0·82 (483 knots; 895 km/h; 556 mph)
Typical long-range cruise at 11,275 m (37,000 ft)
  Mach 0·78 (447 knots; 828 km/h; 515 mph)
Approach speed at max landing weight
  133 knots (246 km/h; 153 mph)
Approach speed at typical landing weight
  125 knots (232 km/h; 144 mph)
T-O field length at max T-O weight, S/L, ISA:

202	1,845 m (6,053 ft)
220	1,960 m (6,430 ft)
221	1,815 m (5,955 ft)

Landing field length (S/L airport):

at max landing weight	1,665 m (5,463 ft)
at typical landing weight	1,475 m (4,840 ft)

Range, with allowances for ground manoeuvring and approach manoeuvring, reserves for overshoot at destination, 5% of stage fuel, 200 nm (370 km; 230 mile) diversion, and 45 min hold at 1,525 m (5,000 ft):

with max passenger payload:

202	2,530 nm	(4,688 km; 2,913 miles)
220	2,500 nm	(4,633 km; 2,878 miles)
221	2,470 nm	(4,577 km; 2,844 miles)

with max structural payload:

202, 220, 221	1,460 nm (2,705 km; 1,681 miles)

with max fuel:

202	3,510 nm	(6,504 km; 4,041 miles)
220, 221	3,490 nm	(6,467 km; 4,018 miles)

A300/A310 FUTURE DEVELOPMENTS

In 1980, Airbus Industrie was studying the following possible future developments of the A300/310 family:

TA9 (formerly A300B9). 'Stretched' version of A300-600, with 310-340 seats typically, 410 maximum, and increased cargo capacity. Optimised for short/medium-range operation. Eight or nine-abreast seating, with twin aisles, in same fuselage cross-section as A300. Advanced flight deck with CRT displays, fully digital systems, flight management computer, electrical signalling for some control surfaces, quieter APU. Extensive use of composites and improved metallic materials. Two variants proposed: TA9-100 short-range version (1,500 nm; 2,780 km; 1,727 mile range with full passenger payload), and TA9-200 medium range version (3,000 nm; 5,560 km; 3,454 mile range with full passenger payload). Powerplants would be high-thrust versions of current CF6-80, JT9D-7R4 and RB.211-524 engines.

TA11 (formerly A300B11). Long-range twin-aisle aircraft, using structural components of A300 and A310. Four underwing turbofan engines in 133·45 kN (30,000 lb st) class.

SA (formerly JET). Completely new single-aisle aircraft, with standard body fuselage, to seat approx 130 (SA1) and 160 passengers (SA2). Similar configuration to A300/A310, with two underwing-mounted engines and fuselage-mounted tailplane. SA1 and SA2 will have same fuselage, wing and tail structures, and same systems and flight deck; SA2 will have longer parallel fuselage section. SA series will utilise such modern technology as composite constructional materials, CRT flight deck displays, electrical signalling for control surfaces, and relaxed stability system.

AIRBUS INDUSTRIE SUPER GUPPY

To cater for the currently increasing A300 production rate, Airbus Industrie is to acquire two more Super Guppy cargo transports in Spring 1982 and Spring 1983 respectively. Conversion of basic Stratocruiser airframes will be undertaken under subcontract to Airbus Industrie by UTA Industries at Le Bourget, France, in conjunction with Aero Spacelines of Santa Barbara, California, from whom Airbus Industrie has now acquired the production rights and technical drawings. Operation of its Super Guppies is subcontracted by Airbus Industrie to Aéromaritime, a charter subsidiary of UTA. A description of the Super Guppy can be found under the Aero Spacelines entry in the US section of the 1973-74 *Jane's*.

Super Guppy outsize cargo aircraft, used to transport major components of the Airbus A300 to the final assembly centre at Toulouse

AIRTECH

PARTICIPATING COMPANIES:

Construcciones Aeronauticas SA, Rey Francisco 4, Apartado 193, Madrid 8, Spain
Telephone: 247 25 00
Telex: 27418

PT Industri Pesawat Turbang Nurtanio, Lanuma, Husein Sastranegara (Husein Sastranegara Air Force Base), Jalan Pajajaran 154, Bandung, Indonesia

Telephone: Bandung 56191 and 56662

Telex: 28295 nur bd

Airtech is a joint company formed by CASA of Spain and PT Nurtanio of Indonesia to develop a 35-passenger twin-turboprop transport aircraft. It is intended for production in both countries.

ALPHA JET

AIRFRAME PRIME CONTRACTORS:

Avions Marcel Dassault/Breguet Aviation, 27 rue du Professeur Pauchet, BP 32, 92420 Vaucresson, France
Telephone: 741 7921
Telex: 0734372

Dornier GmbH, Postfach 1420, 7990 Friedrichshafen, Federal Republic of Germany
Telephone: (07545) 82307
Telex: 0734372

On 22 July 1969 the French and Federal German governments announced a joint requirement for a new subsonic basic/advanced training and light attack aircraft to enter service with their armed forces in the 1970s. Each government had a potential requirement for about 200 such aircraft, to replace Magister, Lockheed T-33A and Mystère IV-A trainers, and Fiat G91 attack aircraft, then in service.

On 24 July 1970, it was announced that the Alpha Jet design had been selected for development to meet the requirement.

DASSAULT-BREGUET/DORNIER ALPHA JET

Dassault-Breguet of France and Dornier of West Germany are jointly producing the Alpha Jet, with Dassault-Breguet as main contractor and Dornier as industrial collaborator, the total work load being shared primarily between the two groups.

The Alpha Jet programme received joint French-West German government approval in late 1972; approval to proceed with the production phase was announced on 26 March 1975.

Four flying prototypes were built, plus two airframes for static and fatigue testing. Structural testing was completed on 18 January 1977.

Flight testing was carried out predominantly in France, by both French and West German pilots. The 01 made its first flight, at Istres, on 26 October 1973; all four had flown by the end of 1974. Details of the prototypes can be found in the 1978-79 and earlier editions of *Jane's*. By the beginning of 1980 the Alpha Jet had accumulated about 10,000 flying hours.

The French and Federal German governments agreed to procure 400 Alpha Jets, 200 each for the Armée de l'Air and the Luftwaffe. Trainers for France are designated **Alpha Jet E** and close-support aircraft for West Germany are known as **Alpha Jet A**s. In addition, Belgium ordered 33 of the E version, which it designates **Alpha Jet 1B**. The Togolese Air Force has ordered five, and the air forces of the Ivory Coast 6, Morocco 24 and Nigeria 12. Six others have been ordered by the Qatar Emiri Air Force.

The 100th Alpha Jet, an E for France, was delivered on 22 February 1980; the 200th was due to be delivered in

November 1980. The first 100 aircraft were delivered as follows: France 33, West Germany 34, Belgium 26 and Morocco 7. The last Belgian Alpha Jet was delivered in April 1980.

Dassault-Breguet and Dornier are teamed with Lockheed-California to enter the Alpha Jet in the US Navy's VTX advanced trainer competition; if selected, it would be built under licence in the USA by Lockheed.

Under a Federal Ministry of Defence contract, Dornier has developed an SKF (Superkritischer Flügel) transonic wing of supercritical section, which was due to begin flight testing on an Alpha Jet in the Autumn of 1980.

The first production Alpha Jet, the E1 for the French Air Force, made its first flight at Istres on 4 November 1977. This replaced the 04 prototype, for service testing by the CEV at Istres and the CEAM at Mont-de-Marsan. Deliveries to the Armée de l'Air started in the Summer of 1978, beginning with the E2 aircraft, and went first to the 314e Groupement École at Tours. This unit is due to receive 65 Alpha Jet Es to replace Lockheed T-33As at present in service. All were due to have been delivered by the end of 1980. During 1980, twelve Alpha Jet Es were being delivered to the French national aerobatic team, the Patrouille de France, and will be followed by 14 to the Centre d'Entraînement au Vol Sans Visibilité in 1981, and 30 in 1982 to the 8e Escadre de Transformation at Cazaux to replace Mystère IV-As in the weapons training role.

The first Alpha Jet 1B for Belgium (AT-01, the fifth production aircraft) first flew on 20 June 1978, and was delivered to the Belgian Air Force during the following month. Like the French aircraft, the Belgian Alpha Jets are being used primarily for advanced flying and weapons training, for which they replace the Magister and T-33A with Nos. 2 and 7 Squadrons.

The second production Alpha Jet to fly, on 12 April 1978, was the A1 first close support model for West Germany. Deliveries of the Alpha Jet A to the Luftwaffe, which is to receive 175 of this version, began in mid-March 1979. It became operational with that service in February 1980 and is to equip three Jagdbombergeschwader (fighter-bomber groups) at Fürstenfeldbrück (JaboG 49), Oldenburg (JaboG 43) and Husum (JaboG 41), replacing the Fiat G91R in the close support and reconnaissance role. The first 32 Alpha Jet As were handed over to JaboG 49 on 20 March 1980. One hundred Alpha Jet As were due to be delivered by the end of 1980.

All production Alpha Jets have identical structure, power plant, landing gear and standard equipment; there are assembly lines in France, West Germany and Belgium. The outer wings, tail unit, rear fuselage, landing gear doors and cold-flow exhaust are manufactured in West Germany; the forward and centre fuselage (with integrated wing centre-section) are manufactured in France. Fuselage nosecones and wing flaps are manufactured in Belgium by SABCA. The power plant prime contractors are

Turboméca and SNECMA in France, and MTU and KHD in West Germany; and, for the landing gear, Messier-Hispano-Bugatti in France and Liebherr Aero Technik in West Germany. A total of 230 Alpha Jets were due for completion by the end of 1980, during which year output was at the rate of 13 per month.

TYPE: Tandem two-seat basic, low-altitude and advanced jet trainer and close support and battlefield reconnaissance aircraft.

WINGS: Cantilever shoulder-wing monoplane, with 6° anhedral from roots. Thickness/chord ratio 10·2% at root, 8·6% at tip. Sweepback 28° at quarter-chord. All-metal numerically- or chemically-milled structure, consisting of two main wing panels bolted to a centre frame. Extended chord on outer wings. Hydraulically actuated Fowler-type slotted flaps on each trailing-edge. Ailerons actuated by double-body irreversible hydraulic servo, with trimmable artificial feel system.

FUSELAGE: All-metal semi-monocoque structure, numerically or chemically milled, of basically oval cross-section. Built in three sections: nose (including cockpit), centre-section (including engine air intake trunks and main landing gear housings) and rear (including engine mounts and tail assembly). Narrow strake on each side of nose of Alpha Jet E and 1B. Pointed nose, with pitot probe, on close support version. Electrically controlled, hydraulically actuated airbrake on each side of rear upper fuselage, of carbonfibre-reinforced epoxy resin.

TAIL UNIT: Cantilever type, of similar construction to wings, with 45° sweepback on fin leading-edge and 30° on tailplane leading-edge. Dorsal spine fairing between cockpit and fin. All-flying tailplane, with trimmable and IAS-controlled artificial feel system. Glassfibre fin tip and tailplane tips. Double-body irreversible hydraulic servo-actuated rudder, with trimmable artificial feel system. Yaw damper on close support version.

LANDING GEAR: Forward-retracting tricycle type, of Messier-Hispano-Bugatti/Liebherr design. All units retract hydraulically, main units into underside of engine air intake trunks. Single wheel and low-pressure tyre (approx 4 bars; 58 lb/sq in at normal T-O weight) on each unit. Tyre sizes 615 × 255-10 on main units, 380 × 150-4 on nose unit. Steel disc brakes and anti-skid units on main gear (Minispad on A version, Mini-stop on E). Emergency braking system. Hydraulic nose-wheel steering and arrester hook on close support version. Nosewheel offset to starboard to permit ground firing from gun pod.

POWER PLANT: Two SNECMA/Turboméca Larzac 04-C5 turbofan engines, each rated at 13·24 kN (2,976 lb st) for production aircraft, mounted on sides of fuselage. Splitter plate in front of each intake. Fuel in two integral tanks in outer wings, one in centre-section and three fuselage tanks. Internal fuel capacity 1,900 litres (418 Imp gallons). Provision for 310 litre (68·2 Imp gallon) capacity drop-tank on each outer wing pylon. Pressure refuelling standard for all tanks, including drop-tanks. Gravity system for fuselage tanks and drop-tanks. Pressure refuelling point near starboard engine air intake. Fuel system incorporates provision for inverted flying.

ACCOMMODATION: Two persons in tandem, in pressurised cockpit under individual upward-opening canopies. Dual controls standard. Rear seat (for instructor in trainer versions) is elevated. French trainer versions fitted with Martin-Baker AJRM-4 ejection seats, operable (including ejection through canopy) at zero height and speeds down to 90 knots (167 km/h; 104 mph). Aircraft for West Germany fitted with licence-built (by RFB) Stencel S-III-S3AJ zero-zero ejection seats; Martin-Baker Mk 10 zero-zero seats in aircraft for Belgium. Baggage compartment in tailcone, with access door on starboard side.

SYSTEMS: Cockpit air-conditioning and demisting system. Cabin pressure differential 0·30 bars (4·3 lb/sq in). Two independent and redundant hydraulic systems, each 207 bars (3,000 lb/sq in), with engine-driven pumps (emergency electric pump on one circuit), for actuating control surfaces, landing gear, brakes, flaps, airbrakes, and (when fitted) nosewheel steering. Pneumatic system, for cockpit pressurisation and air-conditioning, occupants' pressure suits and fuel tank pressurisation, is supplied by compressed air from engines. Main electrical power supplied by two 28V 9kW starter/generators, one on each engine. Circuit includes a 36Ah nickel-cadmium battery for self-starting and two static inverters for supplying 115V AC current at 400Hz to auxiliary systems. External ground DC power receptacle in port engine air intake trunk. Hydraulic and electrical systems can be sustained by either engine in the event of the other engine becoming inoperative. Liquid-film anti-icing system; de-icing by electrical heater mats. Oxygen mask for each occupant, supplied by liquid oxygen converter of 10 litres (2·2 Imp gallons) capacity. Emergency gaseous oxygen bottle for each occupant.

AVIONICS AND EQUIPMENT: Large avionics bay in rear fuselage, containing most of the radio and navigation equipment. Standard avionics, according to version, include VHF and UHF transceivers, IFF/SIF, VOR/ILS/marker, Tacan, gyro platform and intercom.

First French Air Force Alpha Jet E, with underfuselage gun pod and underwing weapons and drop-tanks

Alpha Jet E basic and advanced trainer *(Pilot Press)*

Landing light on starboard mainwheel leg, taxying light on port leg. Trainer version has SFIM 550 gyro platform, Thomson-CSF 920 weapon-aiming computer, LMT Micro-Tacan, EAS Socrat 6200NRAX-7 VOR/ILS/marker beacon receiver, TEAM com radio and intercom, and LMT IFF/SIF. Close support version has Kaiser/VDO KM 808 head-up display, TRT AHV 6-18 radar altimeter, Lear Siegler LSI 6000 E attitude and heading reference system, and Litef LDN Doppler navigation system with LR-1416 navigation computer, Litef ABE control unit and Teledyne Ryan speed sensor, Elettronica (Italy) ECM, SEL Mitac/Setac Tacan with ILS, Siemens STR 700 IFF/SIF, Becker VCS 220 intercom, Rohde und Schwarz XT 3011 com radio, and EAS IMT 565 BDHI.

ARMAMENT AND OPERATIONAL EQUIPMENT: For armament training and close support missions, the Alpha Jet can be equipped with an underfuselage detachable pod containing a 30 mm DEFA or 27 mm Mauser cannon with 150 rds. Provision also for two hardpoints under each wing, with non-jettisonable adaptor pylons. On these can be carried M155 launchers for eighteen 68 mm rockets; HE or retarded bombs of 50, 125, 250 or 400 kg; 625 lb cluster dispensers; 690 or 825 lb special-purpose tanks; combined external multistore adaptor (CEM-1) for six to eighteen rockets and four practice bombs, or one 500 lb bomb, or six penetration bombs, or grenades or other stores; practice launchers for bombs or rockets; Dassault-Breguet CC-420 30 mm gun pods; or two 310 litre (68·2 Imp gallon) drop-tanks (outer pylons only). Provision also for carrying air-to-air or air-to-surface missiles such as Magic or Maverick, target demonstration devices or reconnaissance pod. Total payload for all five stations 2,500 kg (5,510 lb). Fire control system for air-to-air or air-to-ground firing, dive bombing and low-level bombing. Firing by trainee pilot (in front seat) is governed by a safety interlock system controlled by the instructor, which energises the forward station trigger circuit and illuminates a fire clearance indicator in the trainee's cockpit. Thomson-CSF Type 902 sight and gun camera in French version; Kaiser/VDO KM 808 sight, head-up display and gun camera in West German version.

DIMENSIONS, EXTERNAL:
Wing span | 9·11 m (29 ft 10¾ in)
Wing aspect ratio | 4·8
Length overall: trainer | 12·29 m (40 ft 3¾ in)
close support version incl probe | 13·23 m (43 ft 5 in)
Height overall (at normal T-O weight) | 4·19 m (13 ft 9 in)
Tailplane span | 4·33 m (14 ft 2½ in)
Wheel track | 2·71 m (8 ft 10¾ in)
Wheelbase | 4·72 m (15 ft 5¾ in)

AREAS:
Wings, gross | 17·50 m² (188·4 sq ft)
Ailerons (total) | 1·04 m² (11·19 sq ft)
Trailing-edge flaps (total) | 2·86 m² (30·78 sq ft)
Airbrakes (total) | 0·74 m² (7·97 sq ft)
Fin | 2·97 m² (31·97 sq ft)
Rudder | 0·62 m² (6·67 sq ft)
Horizontal tail surfaces (total) | 3·94 m² (42·41 sq ft)

WEIGHTS:
Weight empty, equipped:
trainer | 3,345 kg (7,374 lb)
close support version | 3,515 kg (7,749 lb)
Max fuel load:
internal | 1,415 kg (3,120 lb)
external | 500 kg (1,102 lb)
Max external load | 2,500 kg (5,510 lb)
Normal T-O weight:
trainer, 'clean' | 5,000 kg (11,023 lb)
Max T-O weight:
with external stores | 7,500 kg (16,535 lb)

PERFORMANCE (at normal 'clean' T-O weight, except where indicated):
Max level speed at 10,000 m (32,800 ft) | Mach 0·85
Max level speed at S/L | 540 knots (1,000 km/h; 622 mph)
Max speed for flap and landing gear extension | 200 knots (370 km/h; 230 mph)
Approach speed | 110 knots (204 km/h; 127 mph)
Stalling speed, flaps and landing gear up | 116 knots (216 km/h; 134 mph)
Stalling speed, flaps and landing gear down | 90 knots (167 km/h; 104 mph)
Landing speed at normal landing weight | 92 knots (170 km/h; 106 mph)
Max rate of climb at S/L | 3,420 m (11,220 ft)/min
Rate of climb at S/L, one engine out, at 4,782 kg (10,542 lb) AUW, in landing configuration | 330 m (1,085 ft)/min
Time to 9,145 m (30,000 ft) | less than 7 min
Service ceiling | 14,630 m (48,000 ft)
T-O run | 410 m (1,345 ft)
Landing run | 610 m (2,000 ft)
Low altitude radius of action (trainer):
'clean', max internal fuel 232 nm (430 km; 267 miles)
with external tanks 300 nm (555 km; 345 miles)
High altitude radius of action (trainer), reserves of 15% internal fuel:
'clean', max internal fuel | 593 nm (1,100 km; 683 miles)
with external tanks 739 nm (1,370 km; 851 miles)
Lo-lo-lo mission radius (close support version), incl 5 min combat at max continuous thrust:
with belly gun pod and underwing weapons | 195 nm (362 km; 225 miles)
with belly gun pod, underwing weapons and external tanks 305 nm (565 km; 351 miles)
Hi-lo-hi mission radius (close support version), incl 5 min combat at max continuous thrust, reserves for two GCA landings:
with belly gun pod and underwing weapons | 310 nm (575 km; 357 miles)
with belly gun pod, underwing weapons and external tanks 555 nm (1,028 km; 639 miles)
Ferry range (internal fuel and two 310 litre external tanks) | 1,550 nm (2,872 km; 1,785 miles)
Endurance (internal fuel only):
low altitude | more than 2 h 30 min
high altitude | more than 3 h 30 min
g limits (ultimate) | +12; −6·4

First production Alpha Jet 1B two-seat advanced trainer for the Belgian Air Force

CONCORDE
CONCORDE SUPERSONIC TRANSPORT

AIRFRAME PRIME CONTRACTORS:
British Aerospace Aircraft Group, Richmond Road, Kingston upon Thames, Surrey KT2 5QS, England
Telephone: 01 546 7741
Aérospatiale, 37 boulevard de Montmorency, 75781 Paris Cédex 16, France
Telephone: 524 43 21

CONCORDE

By the beginning of 1980 a total of 20 Concordes had flown, including 16 production models (see accompanying table). In development, production and test flying with the manufacturers more than 3,000 flights had then been made, of which nearly 1,900 involved flight at supersonic speeds. A total of 6,900 h block time had been amassed, including more than 2,550 h supersonic. In addition, by 31 December 1979 airline service had involved 10,500 flights amounting to 34,500 flying hours and 500,000 passengers carried. The schedule for December 1979 amounted to 1,200 commercial hours per month for Air France and British Airways. Both airlines have approval to operate Concorde in Category III weather conditions. Special category certificates of airworthiness were granted in May and June 1975 by the DGAC and CAA, anticipating the full airworthiness certificates which were granted on 9 October and 4 December 1975.

The two prototype and two pre-production Concordes have been fully described in previous editions of *Jane's*. These have since been allocated to the Musée de l'Air at Le Bourget (001), the Fleet Air Arm Museum at RNAS Yeovilton (002), RAF Station Duxford (01) and Orly Airport, Paris (02).

Initially, British Airways ordered five production Concordes, and Air France four. British Airways signed purchase agreements for a sixth Concorde (No. 216) on 15 November 1979, and for a seventh (No. 214) on 17 January 1980. On 21 September 1979 the French government announced the allocation of the three remaining unsold French-assembled Concordes (Nos. 203, 213 and 215) to Air France, for use as and when needed. Following these arrangements, the former preliminary purchase agreements with Iran and China were cancelled.

Air France started a daily service to New York on 22 November 1977 and British Airways on 12 February 1978. Air France continues to operate a daily service, while British Airways operates 12 services a week to New York. Air France extended its Paris-Washington service to Mexico City twice a week from 20 September 1978. A joint service between British Airways and Singapore Airlines opened from Bahrain to Singapore on 9 December 1977; a thrice-weekly service was suspended after only three flights, but Malaysian airspace was then cleared to Concorde, and Singapore services were reopened on 24 January 1979 for a trial period extending until 24 January 1980.

On 10 February 1977, Braniff Airways of the USA announced the signing of interchange agreements with British Airways and Air France. Under the terms of these agreements Braniff operates Concorde arrivals and departures five days a week between Dallas/Fort Worth and Washington Dulles. Air France operates two services a week to Dallas, and British Airways three, all through Washington Dulles. These services were inaugurated on 12 January 1979, three days after the issue of Concorde's FAA Type Certificate.

In 1977-79, BAe flight-tested modifications to the wing and tail control surfaces, and to the engine intakes, designed to reduce drag and fuel consumption. These

Final production Concorde, taking off from Filton for its first flight on 20 April 1979

modifications, detailed in the 1979-80 *Jane's*, have been applied to Concordes in service with British Airways, and will be applied to those of Air France. They extend the operating range by 85 nm (157 km; 98 miles).

A full description of the production Concorde can be found in the 1979-80 *Jane's*.

POWER PLANT: Four Rolls-Royce/SNECMA Olympus 593 Mk 610 turbojet engines, each rated at 169·3 kN (38,050 lb st) with 17% afterburning, and Type 28 thrust reversers. Fuel tanks are of integral construction and are in two groups, with total usable capacity of 119,786 litres (26,350 Imp gallons).

ACCOMMODATION: Pilot and co-pilot side by side on flight deck, with third crew member behind on starboard side. Provision for supernumerary seat behind pilot. Air France and British Airways aircraft operate with single-class layout for 100 passengers at 96·5 cm (38 in) seat pitch. Toilets at front and centre of cabin. Baggage space under forward cabin and aft of cabin. Passenger doors forward of cabin and amidships on port side, with service doors opposite. Baggage door aft of cabin on starboard side. Emergency exits in rear half of cabin on each side. Two galley areas.

DIMENSIONS, EXTERNAL:
Wing span	25·56 m (83 ft 10 in)
Length overall	62·10 m (203 ft 9 in)
Height overall	11·40 m (37 ft 5 in)
Wheel track	7·72 m (25 ft 4 in)
Wheelbase	18·19 m (59 ft 8¼ in)

WEIGHTS:
Operating weight empty	78,700 kg (173,500 lb)
Typical payload	11,340 kg (25,000 lb)
Max payload	12,700 kg (28,000 lb)

Concorde production aircraft

Aircraft No.	Registration	First Flight	Allocation	Remarks
201	F-WTSB	6 Dec 73	Aérospatiale	Development aircraft
202	G-BBDG	13 Feb 74	BAe	Development aircraft
203	F-BTSC	31 Jan 75	Air France	Originally F-WTSC
204	G-N81AC	27 Feb 75	British Airways	Originally F-BVFA
205	N-94FA	25 Oct 75	Air France	Originally G-BOAA
206	G-N94AA	5 Nov 75	British Airways	Originally F-BVFB
207	N-94FB	6 Mar 76	Air France	Originally G-BOAB
208	G-N94AB	18 May 76	British Airways	
209	F-BVFC	9 Jul 76	Air France	
210	G-N94AD	25 Aug 76	British Airways	Originally G-BOAD
211	F-BVFD	10 Feb 77	Air France	
212	G-N94AE	17 Mar 77	British Airways	Originally G-BOAE
213	F-BTSD	26 June 78	Air France	Delivered 9 May 1980
214	G-BFKV	21 Apr 78	British Airways	
215	F-BVFF	26 Dec 78	Air France	
216	G-N94AF	20 Apr 79	British Airways	Originally G-BFKX

Max T-O weight	185,065 kg (408,000 lb)	Service ceiling	approx 18,290 m (60,000 ft)
Max zero-fuel weight	92,080 kg (203,000 lb)	T-O to 10·7 m (35 ft)	3,410 m (11,200 ft)
Max landing weight	111,130 kg (245,000 lb)	Landing from 10·7 m (35 ft)	2,220 m (7,300 ft)

PERFORMANCE (calculated, at max T-O weight):
Max cruising speed at 15,635 m (51,300 ft)
Mach 2·04 or 530 knots CAS, whichever is the lesser, equivalent to TAS of
1,176 knots (2,179 km/h; 1,354 mph)
T-O speed   214 knots (397 km/h; 246 mph)
Landing speed   162 knots (300 km/h; 187 mph)
Rate of climb at S/L   1,525 m (5,000 ft)/min

Range with max fuel, FAR reserves and 8,845 kg (19,500 lb) payload
3,550 nm (6,580 km; 4,090 miles)
Range with max payload, FAR reserves:
at Mach 0·95 at 9,100 m (30,000 ft)
2,760 nm (5,110 km; 3,180 miles)
at Mach 2·02 cruise/climb
3,360 nm (6,230 km; 3,870 miles)

EHI
EH INDUSTRIES

PARTICIPATING COMPANIES:

Costruzioni Aeronautiche Giovanni Agusta SpA, Casella Postale 480, 21017 Cascina Costa, Gallarate, Italy
Telephone: (0331) 220478
Telex: 332569

Westland Helicopters Ltd, Yeovil, Somerset BA20 2YB, England
Telephone: Yeovil (0935) 5222
Telex: 46277

This company was formed in 1980 by Westland and Agusta to undertake the joint development, production and marketing of an SKR (Sea King Replacement) helicopter, for which the Royal Navy and Italian Navy both have a requirement. Such a programme was initiated by Westland in the UK in 1977, leading to the WG 34 helicopter described under that company's heading in the 1979-80 *Jane's*. The design is now being adapted to incorporate specific Italian Navy requirements, and has the new designation EH 101.

Westland and Agusta each have a 50 per cent interest in EHI, which will have its headquarters in London.

EH INDUSTRIES EH 101

Development of this helicopter began, initially under British Ministry of Defence (Navy) contract, as a replacement for the Royal Navy's Sea King HAS. Mk 2 shipboard anti-submarine helicopters.

In the Spring of 1977 the MoD(N) completed a series of feasibility studies to examine how an SKR (Sea King Replacement) would operate, and what sensors and performance standards it would require. These studies demonstrated:

(a) the need for the aircraft to operate at long ranges from its base, and independently of other units;

(b) that this autonomy of operation would best be served by the use of sonobuoys instead of the traditional active dipping sonar;

(c) the need for an automated data handling system to exploit the capability of the acoustic sensors, and to control the variety of supporting sensors required (radar, radar intercept equipment, and magnetic anomaly detector);

(d) that a payload capability greater than that of the present Sea King was needed to carry the required weight of sensors, avionics, weapons, and the fuel load necessary to achieve a useful endurance; and

(e) that a rotating-wing aircraft of similar dimensions to the Sea King would best meet these requirements while remaining compatible with the size of ships which would carry the new aircraft.

Westland's WG 34 design, marginally smaller than the Sea King but with substantially more payload capability,

Artist's impression of the EH Industries EH 101 anti-submarine helicopter

was selected by the MoD (Navy) for development in the late Summer of 1978. The Italian Navy has a requirement broadly similar to that of the Royal Navy, and in 1980 Westland and Agusta decided to join forces to develop a joint design, the EH 101, to meet the requirements of both services.

The following provisional description is based on details of the WG 34 released up to mid 1980, but may be modified to meet the EH 101 specification:

TYPE: Three/four-seat anti-submarine helicopter.

AIRFRAME: For general appearance, see accompanying illustration. Landing gear is fully retractable, main units retracting into fairings on fuselage sides.

POWER PLANT: Under a 1979 contract, General Electric was due to deliver to Westland in 1980 nine examples of its 1,193 kW (1,600 shp) T700-GE-700 turboshaft engine, to power a rotor system ground rig and a three-engined flight dynamics test example of the WG 34.

ACCOMMODATION: Crew of three normally (pilot, observer, and acoustics systems operator); provision for co-pilot if required.

SYSTEMS AND OPERATIONAL EQUIPMENT: Marconi Avionics acoustics processing and display systems, developed from the AQS-901 system now being fitted to the BAe Nimrod MR. Mk 2. Ferranti search radar, developed from the Sea Spray currently fitted in the Royal Navy's Lynx HAS. Mk 2. Decca ESM (electronic support measures) equipment, also developed from that in the Lynx HAS. Mk 2. Decca Doppler or Omega navigation system. ECM-resistant Joint Tactical Information Distribution System (JTIDS) data link equipment. Magnetic anomaly detector (MAD) of the towed 'bird' type, probably the US ASQ-81, stowed internally in rear fuselage when not in use. Secure voice communications. Ferranti automated tactical data handling system for effective management of sensors. Airframe anti-icing system.

ARMAMENT: Fully enclosed weapons bay, capable of accommodating a homing torpedo or other weapons. No details of individual weapons yet available.

DIMENSIONS:
Diameter of main rotor	16·92 m (55 ft 6 in)
Length overall, rotors turning	20·57 m (67 ft 6 in)
Length of fuselage	17·30 m (56 ft 9 in)
Height overall, rotors turning	5·44 m (17 ft 10 in)
Height to top of main rotor head	4·11 m (13 ft 6 in)
Wheel track (c/l of main units)	3·05 m (10 ft 0 in)

WEIGHT:
Max T-O weight	approx 11,340 kg (25,000 lb)

MBB/AÉROSPATIALE

PARTICIPATING COMPANIES:

Messerschmitt-Bölkow-Blohm GmbH, Ottobrunn bei München, 8 München 80, Postfach 801220, Federal Republic of Germany
Telephone: (089) 60001

Aérospatiale, 37 boulevard de Montmorency, 75781 Paris Cédex 16, France
Telephone: 524 43 21

MBB PAH-2/AÉROSPATIALE HAC

MBB and Aérospatiale have been designated by their respective governments to design, develop and produce an anti-tank helicopter that will meet the requirements of the French and Federal German armies for service in the second half of the 1980s. This programme is known in West Germany as the PAH-2 (Panzerabwehr Hubschrauber 2) and in France as the HAC (Hélicoptère

Anti-Char). MBB has leadership of the programme, and is responsible for the rotor system, fuselage centre-section, equipment, controls, hydraulic and fuel systems, engine installation, electrical and automatic flight control systems, and overall design integration. Aérospatiale's responsibilities include the main and tail rotor gearboxes, forward fuselage and cockpit, tailboom, control surfaces, landing gear, integration of avionics and weapon systems.

The programme was in the definition phase in Spring 1980, and the accompanying artist's impression of the PAH-2 should be regarded as provisional. The Federal German Army has a requirement for 212 PAH-2s; the French forces plan to acquire 120. Armament will include eight improved Hot anti-tank missiles.

Artist's impression of the MBB/Aérospatiale PAH-2/HAC anti-tank helicopter

MBB/KAWASAKI

AIRFRAME PRIME CONTRACTORS:

Messerschmitt-Bölkow-Blohm GmbH, Ottobrunn bei München, 8 München 80, Postfach 801220, Federal Republic of Germany
Telephone: (089) 60001

Kawasaki Heavy Industries Ltd, World Trade Center Building, 4-1 Hamamatsu-cho 2-chome, Minato-ku, Tokyo, Japan
Telephone: Tokyo (03) 435 2971

MBB/KAWASAKI BK 117

Following nearly two years of negotiations, an agreement was signed on 25 February 1977 between MBB and Kawasaki to develop jointly an 8/10-seat multi-purpose helicopter known as the BK 117. This superseded two earlier, separate projects known as the MBB BO 107 and the Kawasaki KH-7.

Both civil and military applications are foreseen, and the BK 117 has many components and accessories interchangeable with those of the MBB BO 105. Its rotor head is identical to that of the BO 105, from which aircraft the hydraulic boost system is also adapted. The transmission is based on that developed by Kawasaki for its earlier KH-7 design. The two-blade tail rotor is mounted on the central fin, forward of which is a horizontal stabiliser carrying twin endplate fins.

Development costs of the BK 117 programme are being shared equally between the two companies, with support from the West German and Japanese governments. MBB is responsible for the main and tail rotor systems, tailboom and tail unit, skid landing gear, hydraulic system, cabin floor, engine firewall and cowlings, power-amplified controls and systems integration; Kawasaki is responsible for the fuselage, transmission and electrical systems, and some items of equipment.

Four prototypes have been built, of which the P1 first prototype is being used at Gifu in Japan as a ground test vehicle for endurance trials, and the fourth aircraft (P4) for static and fatigue testing. Initial flight testing has been undertaken by the second and third prototypes, which flew for the first time, in West Germany and Japan respectively, on 13 June 1979 (D-HBKA) and 10 August 1979 (JQ-0003). An S01 pre-production aircraft is being completed in West Germany, and this, together with the third prototype in Japan, will carry out the certification flying programme.

By August 1980 more than 100 BK 117s had been ordered, and initiation of the first 100 production aircraft had been authorised. West German, Japanese and FAA certification for the initial VFR version was expected in early 1981, with IFR certification to follow; certification will be to FAR Pt 29, Categories A and B. There will be two production centres, at Munich and Gifu, and deliveries of production aircraft are expected to begin in late 1981.

TYPE: Twin-turbine multi-purpose helicopter.

ROTOR SYSTEM: Four-blade 'System Bölkow' rigid main rotor; head identical to that of BO 105; main rotor blades similar to those of BO 105, but larger. Two-blade tail rotor. Main rotor has a titanium head, to which are attached hingeless, fail-safe GRP blades of NACA 23012/23010 section with a stainless steel anti-erosion strip on each leading-edge. Rotor brake standard; provision for folding two blades of main rotor. Main rotor rpm: 383. Two-blade semi-rigid (teetering) tail rotor, mounted on port side of vertical fin and rotating clockwise when viewed from that side. Blades are of GRP, with high impact resistance and MBB-S102E performance/noise-optimised section. Tail rotor rpm: 2,169.

ROTOR DRIVE: Each engine has separate drive input into Kawasaki KB 03 main transmission (see 'Power Plant' paragraph for transmission ratings), via single bevel gear and collector. Auxiliary drives for accessories. Dual redundant lubrication system.

FUSELAGE: Of typical pod-shaped configuration, comprising flight deck, cabin, cargo compartment and engine deck. Structure, designed to fulfil requirements of FAR Pt 29, is generally similar to that of BO 105, main components being of semi-monocoque riveted aluminium construction with single-curvature sheets and bonded aluminium sandwich panels. Secondary components are compound-curvature shells with sandwich panels and Kevlar skins. Floor extends throughout cockpit, cabin and cargo compartment at same level. Engine deck forms roof of cargo compartment and, adjacent to engine bays, is of titanium to serve as a firewall.

TAIL UNIT: Semi-monocoque tailboom, of tapered conical section, attached integrally to engine deck at forward end. Rear end, which is detachable, carries main fin/tail rotor support, and horizontal stabiliser with smaller, endplate fins. General design similar to that of BO 105, except for shape of outer fins.

LANDING GEAR: Non-retractable tubular skid type, of aluminium construction, similar to that of BO 105.

Skids are detachable from cross-tubes. Ground handling wheels standard. Emergency flotation gear, settling protectors and snow skids available optionally.

POWER PLANT: Two Avco Lycoming LTS 101-650B-1 turboshaft engines, each rated at 447 kW (600 shp) for 5 min for take-off, 485 kW (650 shp) for 2½ min, and 410 kW (550 shp) for max continuous operation. Transmission rated at 632 kW (848 shp) for twin-engine take-off and max continuous operation; and, for single-engine operation, at 441·5 kW (592 shp) for 2½ min, 405 kW (543 shp) for 30 min, and 368 kW (493 shp) max continuous. Fuel in four flexible bladder-type tanks (forward and aft main tanks, with two supply tanks between), in compartments under cabin floor. Two independent fuel feed systems, each able to supply both engines. Total standard fuel capacity 603 litres (132·5 Imp gallons). Provision for two 200 litre (44 Imp gallon) auxiliary tanks, raising total capacity to 1,003 litres (220·5 Imp gallons).

ACCOMMODATION: Pilot and up to six (executive version) or seven passengers (standard or offshore IFR-equipped versions). High-density layouts available for nine or eleven passengers in addition to pilot. Provision for two-pilot operation. Jettisonable forward-hinged door on each side of flight deck, each with openable window. Jettisonable rearward-sliding passenger door on each side of cabin, lockable in open position. Fold-down steps on port side. Two hinged, clamshell doors at rear of cabin, providing access to cargo compartment. Rear cabin window on each side. Aircraft can be equipped, according to mission, for offshore, medical evacuation (pilot, four stretchers and two attendants), firefighting, search and rescue, law enforcement, cargo transport or other operations. Cabin floor hatch optional.

SYSTEMS: Ram-air and electrical ventilation system. Fully redundant tandem hydraulic boost system (one operating and one standby) for flight controls. Main DC electrical power from two 150A 30V starter/generators (one on each engine) and a 24V 22Ah nickel-cadmium battery. AC power provided by two independent inverters. Emergency busbar provides direct battery power to essential services in event of a double generator failure. External DC power receptacle.

AVIONICS AND EQUIPMENT: Basic aircraft has instrumentation for single-pilot VFR operation, including airspeed indicator, electrically-heated pitot tube, altimeter, rate of climb indicator, 10 cm (4 in) attitude direction indicator with turn and slip indication, directional gyro, RMI, and magnetic compass. Dual controls and dual VFR instrumentation available optionally. Com/nav and other avionics available to customer's requirements, including VHF and HF transceivers; nav, RNav, ADF and VLF/Omega systems; radar altimeter; encoding altimeter; DME; ATC transponder; multi-mode radar; IFR instrumentation packages; and stability augmentation system. Standard basic equipment includes annunciator panel, master caution light, rotor rpm/engine fail warning control unit, fuel quantity indicator and low level sensor, outside air temperature indicator, clock, engine and transmission oil pressure and temperature indicators, dual exhaust temperature indicators, dual torque indicators, instrument panel lights, cockpit/cabin/cargo compartment dome lights, position lights, anti-collision warning lights, retractable landing light, portable flashlight, ground handling wheels, pilot's windscreen wiper, floor covering, interior panelling and sound insulation, ashtrays, map/document case, tiedown rings in cabin and cargo compartment, engine compartment fire warning indicator, engine fire extinguishing system, portable fire extinguisher, engine fire handle, first aid kit, and single colour exterior paint scheme. Optional equipment includes high-density seating arrangement, bleed air heating system, fuel dump valve, two long-range fuel tanks, emergency flotation gear, snow skids, main rotor blade folding kit, non-

MBB/Kawasaki BK 117 twin-turboshaft multi-purpose helicopter *(Pilot Press)*

Second flying prototype of the MBB/Kawasaki BK 117, under test in Japan

Max width	1·23 m (4 ft 0½ in)
Max height	1·23 m (4 ft 0½ in)
Volume	1·34 m³ (47·3 cu ft)
AREAS:	
Main rotor disc	47·52 m² (511·5 sq ft)
Tail rotor disc	1·42 m² (15·3 sq ft)
WEIGHTS:	
Weight empty, equipped	1,520 kg (3,351 lb)
Fuel: standard	480 kg (1,058 lb)
incl auxiliary tanks	800 kg (1,764 lb)
Max T-O weight:	
internal payload	2,800 kg (6,173 lb)
with externally-slung load	3,000 kg (6,614 lb)
PERFORMANCE (at max T-O weight, ISA):	
Never-exceed speed at S/L	
	148 knots (275 km/h; 171 mph)
Max cruising speed at S/L	
	142 knots (264 km/h; 164 mph)
Econ cruising speed at S/L	
	126 knots (234 km/h; 145 mph)
Max forward rate of climb at S/L	600 m (1,968 ft)/min
Max vertical rate of climb at S/L	420 m (1,378 ft)/min
Max operating altitude	5,180 m (17,000 ft)
Hovering ceiling IGE	4,100 m (13,450 ft)
Hovering ceiling OGE	3,150 m (10,335 ft)
Service ceiling, one engine out, 46 m (150 ft)/min climb	
reserve	3,000 m (9,845 ft)
Ferry range at S/L with two 200 litre auxiliary tanks, no	
reserves	491 nm (910 km; 565 miles)
Range at S/L with pilot and 7 passengers, standard fuel,	
no reserves	294 nm (545 km; 338 miles)
Endurance, conditions as above	3 h 0 min

retractable landing light, co-pilot's windscreen wiper, stretcher installation, cargo hook, rescue winch, searchlight, external loudspeaker, and sand filter. Special optional equipment planned to include self-sealing fuel feeder tank, multi-purpose pylon, wheel-type landing gear, and special mission kits for rescue, law enforcement, VIP transport and military roles.

DIMENSIONS, EXTERNAL:

Main rotor diameter	11·00 m (36 ft 1 in)
Tail rotor diameter	1·90 m (6 ft 2¾ in)
Main rotor blade chord	0·31 m (1 ft 0¼ in)
Tail rotor blade chord	0·18 m (7·1 in)
Length overall, main and tail rotors turning	
	13·00 m (42 ft 8 in)
Length of fuselage	9·88 m (32 ft 5 in)
Fuselage: Max width	1·60 m (5 ft 3 in)

Height overall, main and tail rotors turning	
	3·84 m (12 ft 7¼ in)
Height to top of main rotor hub	3·30 m (10 ft 10 in)
Height to top of main fin	3·30 m (10 ft 10 in)
Tailplane span (over endplate fins)	2·57 m (8 ft 5¼ in)
Tail rotor ground clearance	1·93 m (6 ft 4 in)
Width over skids	2·50 m (8 ft 2½ in)
Cabin floor hatch (optional):	
Length	0·50 m (1 ft 7¾ in)
Width	0·40 m (1 ft 3¾ in)
DIMENSIONS, INTERNAL:	
Passenger cabin: Length	2·02 m (6 ft 7½ in)
Max width	1·43 m (4 ft 8¼ in)
Max height	1·29 m (4 ft 2¾ in)
Volume	3·22 m³ (113·7 cu ft)
Cargo compartment: Length	1·10 m (3 ft 7¼ in)

PANAVIA
PANAVIA AIRCRAFT GmbH

HEAD OFFICE: 8 München 86, Postfach 860629, Arabellastrasse 16, Federal Republic of Germany

Telephone: (089) 92171
Telex: 05 29 825

DIRECTORS:

Prof Gero Madelung (MBB) (Chairman)
Sir Frederick Page (BAe) (Deputy Chairman)
Dott R. Bonifacio (Aeritalia) (Deputy Chairman)
A. H. C. Greenwood (BAe)
A. F. Atkin (BAe)
I. R. Yates (BAe)
Dott C. Innocenti (Aeritalia)
G. Sarzotti (Aeritalia)
Dott R. Mautino (Aeritalia)
F. Forster-Steinberg (MBB)
O. Friedrich (MBB)
H. Plückthun (MBB)

MANAGING DIRECTOR: Dr C. P. Fichtmüller
DEPUTY MANAGING DIRECTOR: Dr I. A. M. Hall
FUNCTIONAL DIRECTORS:

J. L. Dell (Flight Operations)
V. von Tein (Systems Engineering, Munich)
Dr I. A. M. Hall (Programme Management)
B. O. Heath (Systems Engineering, Warton)
H. J. Klapperich (Finance and Contracts)
Dott P. Ricci (Systems Engineering, Turin)
Prof Dr-Ing R. Riccius (Marketing)
R. Sanitz (Product Support)
Dott R. Sassi (Production)
J. A. Thornber (Procurement)

PUBLICITY MANAGER: F. Oelwein

Panavia was formed on 26 March 1969 to design, develop and produce a multi-role combat aircraft (MRCA) for service from the late 1970s with the air forces of the United Kingdom, the Federal Republic of Germany and Italy, and the Federal German Navy. The name Tornado for this aircraft was adopted officially in March 1976. This programme is one of the largest European industrial programmes ever undertaken. The three component companies of Panavia are British Aerospace (42·5% participation), MBB (42·5%) and Aeritalia (15%).

The Federal German, British and Italian governments set up a joint organisation known as NAMMO (NATO MRCA Management and production Organisation). This has its executive agency NAMMA (NATO MRCA Management Agency) in the same building as Panavia, in Munich.

On 29 July 1976 the three governments signed a Memorandum of Understanding for the production of 809 Tornadoes (805 new, and four of the pre-production aircraft), enabling the three partner countries to embark upon the production programme.

PANAVIA TORNADO
RAF designation (IDS version): Tornado GR. Mk 1

The Tornado is a twin-engined two-seat supersonic aircraft capable of fulfilling the agreed operational requirements of its three sponsoring countries. The use of a variable-geometry wing gives it the necessary flexibility to achieve this.

The aircraft is intended to fulfil six major requirements, some of which are shared by more than one of the partners. These are:

(a) Close air support/battlefield interdiction
(b) Interdiction/counter air strike
(c) Air superiority
(d) Interception/air defence
(e) Naval strike
(f) Reconnaissance

The 809 aircraft to be produced for the participating nations, which will include four of the six pre-series aircraft brought up to production standard, will comprise 644 of the IDS (Interdictor Strike) version, and 165 examples of the ADV (Air Defence Variant) for the RAF. A total of 671 Tornadoes will be operational aircraft, and 138 will be dual-control trainers with full operational capability.

The RAF is to have 385 Tornadoes, of which 220 will be of the interdictor/strike version and 165 of the air defence variant. These are due to become operational with Strike Command in 1982 and will, in the first instance, replace the Vulcans and Buccaneers of Nos. 9, 12, 15, 16, 35, 44, 50, 101 and 617 Squadrons in the overland strike and reconnaissance roles. Later, the air defence version will succeed the Phantom; and finally the Tornado will replace the Buccaneer for maritime strike tasks. Some two-thirds

of the RAF's front-line aircraft will eventually be Tornadoes.

The Luftwaffe is to receive 212 Tornadoes, to replace the Lockheed F-104G in the battlefield interdiction, counter air and close air support roles. Four wings (Jabos 31, 32, 33 and 34) and one training squadron are to be equipped, starting in 1982. The 112 for Marineflieger-gruppen 1 and 2 of the Federal German Navy will be equipped for strike missions against sea and coastal targets, and for reconnaissance. MFG 1 is due to begin converting to the Tornado in early 1982.

The Italian Air Force will use 54 of its 100 Tornadoes to replace F-104G and G91R aircraft of the 20°, 102°, 154° and 186° Gruppi in the air superiority, ground attack and reconnaissance roles. Of the remainder, 34 will be kept in reserve and 12 will be equipped as dual-control trainers.

Structural design of the Tornado was completed in August 1972. Nine flying prototypes have been built—four in the UK, three in West Germany and two in Italy. Static tests with airframe No. 10 began at Warton in the Spring of 1974.

The 01 first prototype (D-9591), assembled by MBB, made its first flight at Manching, West Germany, on 14 August 1974. The 08 (XX950) flew in the UK on 15 July 1976 (the 470th Tornado flight), and the 09 (X-587) in Italy on 5 February 1977. Details of all nine prototypes can be found in the 1978-79 and earlier editions.

Of the six pre-series Tornadoes which followed, all had flown by 1979: No. 11 in West Germany on 5 February 1977, No. 12 (XZ630) in the UK on 14 March 1977, No. 13 in West Germany on 10 January 1978, No. 14 in Italy on 8 January 1979, No. 15 in the UK on 24 November 1978, and No. 16 in West Germany on 26 March 1979. No. 14 was fitted with production-standard wings; No. 15 with production-standard rear fuselage, tailerons, fin and actuators; and No. 16 with production-standard forward fuselage.

By 1 January 1980, prototype and pre-series Tornadoes had accumulated a total of 3,300 hours' flying in 3,100 flights. During test flights the Tornado has been flown at indicated airspeeds of up to 800 knots (1,480 km/h; 920 mph) at comparatively low levels.

Tornado No. 11, the third (and first West German) dual-control aircraft, has RB.199-34R-03 engines (each

First production Panavia Tornado GR. Mk 1 interdictor/strike aircraft

approx 37·8 kN; 8,500 lb st dry and 66·7 kN; 15,000 lb st with afterburning) and production-standard fin fillet and 'full-length' rudder; No. 12 also has -03 engines; and the similarly-powered No. 13 introduced a kinked leading-edge to the tailplane. The first production-standard -04 engines were fitted to the No. 1 prototype in March 1978.

With the major part (90%) of the flight envelope already cleared, delivery to service test centres began with No. 12 to the Aeroplane and Armament Experimental Establishment at Boscombe Down on 3 February 1978, followed by No. 11 to the Official Test Centre at Manching, West Germany, and No. 14 to Pratica di Mare, Italy.

Three production contracts have so far been placed for the Tornado. The first, for 40 aircraft, will provide 20 Tornado GR. Mk 1 interdictor/strike versions for the RAF; three F. Mk 2 prototypes for the RAF (see separate description); and 17 Tornadoes for the Federal German Luftwaffe and Marineflieger. The second contract, for 110 Tornadoes, will provide 55 aircraft for the RAF, 40 for Germany, and 15 for the Aeronautica Militare Italiana. The third contract, signed on 6 June 1979, was for 164 aircraft (68 each for the UK and West Germany and 28 for Italy), bringing the total then on firm order to 314. The fourth contract, covering a further 162 aircraft, was expected to be signed before the end of 1980. The first production batch is under way: the first example to be completed was BT 001 (British Trainer 001), which made its initial flight on 10 July 1979. The first production West German Tornado (GT 001) flew for the first time on 27 July 1979. The third production aircraft made its first flight at Warton on 14 December 1979. The fourth production Tornado, which flew for the first time at Warton on 14 March 1980, was the first production strike aircraft (BS 001), the previous three all having been dual-control trainers. The second West German production aircraft flew at Manching on 31 March 1980. In November 1979, Tornado BT 001 and pre-series aircraft No. 15 were delivered to RAF Boscombe Down; pre-series aircraft No. 11 was delivered to the West German official test centre at Manching in 1979, followed by GT 001 in early 1980. It is planned to reach a peak output of nine Tornadoes per month by 1982-83.

A Tri-national Tornado Training Establishment (TTTE) has been set up at RAF Cottesmore, to which the first two Tornadoes (BT 002 and BS 002) were delivered on 1 July 1980. When training reaches its peak, there will be nearly 50 Tornadoes based at Cottesmore. Anglo-German weapons training will be performed from RAF Honington. Initial production aircraft have RB.199-34R-04 Mk 101 engines, which are expected to deliver approx 40·0 kN (9,000 lb st) dry and 71·2 kN (16,000 lb st) with afterburning.

Nominal max weapons load of the IDS (interdictor/strike) Tornado is 8,165 kg (18,000 lb) on three twin hardpoints in tandem under the fuselage, two inboard points in tandem underwing, and two single outboard points underwing. A new missile known as Sea Eagle, a turbojet-powered active-radar sea-skimming development of the BAe/Matra Martel, is to be developed for the RAF's GR. Mk 1, which is also expected to have the capability to carry Pave Spike pods for laser weapons guidance. Primary armament of the Federal German Navy Tornadoes will be four MBB Kormoran anti-shipping missiles. Italy's Tornadoes are expected to be equipped with the Selenia Aspide 1A air-to-air missile.

In partnership with Grumman Aerospace Corporation, Panavia in 1979 submitted the Tornado to the US Air Force as a candidate in the latter's ETF (Enhanced Tactical Fighter) programme.

The following details apply to the basic IDS production version:

TYPE: Twin-engined multi-purpose military aircraft.

WINGS: Cantilever shoulder-wing monoplane. All-metal wings, of variable geometry, having a leading-edge sweep of 25° in the fully forward position and 68° when fully swept. Wing carry-through box is of electron-beam-welded titanium alloy; majority of remaining wing structure is of aluminium alloy, with integrally stiffened skin. There is a Krueger flap on the leading-edge of each wing glove box. The wings each pivot hydraulically, on Teflon-plated bearings, from a point in the centre-section just outboard of the fuselage. The root of the outer wing mates with the pivot pin through attachment members made of titanium alloy and fixed to the upper and lower light alloy panels of the outer wing box, and a so-called 'round rib', also of titanium alloy, transmitting the normal aerodynamic load. Sweep actuators are of the ballscrew type, with hydraulic motor drive. In the event of wing sweep failure, the aircraft can land safely with the wings fully swept. High-lift devices on the outer wings include full-span leading-edge slats (three sections on each side), full-span double-slotted fixed-vane trailing-edge flaps (four sections each side), and spoilers (two on upper surface on each side). Spoilers give augmented roll control at unswept and intermediate wing positions at low speed, and also act as lift dumpers after touchdown. All flying control surfaces actuated by electrically-controlled tandem hydraulic jacks. No ailerons. Entire outer wings, including control surfaces, are Italian-built, Aeritalia

Panavia Tornado IDS multi-role combat aircraft (*Pilot Press*)

having prime responsibility for final assembly and production, assisted by Aermacchi, Aeronavali Venezia, Piaggio, Saca and SIAI-Marchetti as subcontractors. Microtecnica (Italy) is prime subcontractor for the wing sweep system.

FUSELAGE: Conventional all-metal semi-monocoque structure, mainly of aluminium alloy, built in three main sections. MBB in West Germany is prime contractor for the centre fuselage section, including the engine air intake trunks and wing centre-section box and pivot mechanism. This task includes responsibility for the surface interface between the movable wing and the fixed portion, to ensure both a smooth and slender external contour and proper sealing against aerodynamic pressure over a range of wing sweep positions. The present design uses fibre-reinforced plastics in these areas, and an elastic seal between the outer wings and the fuselage sides. Responsibility for the front fuselage, including both cockpits, and for the rear fuselage, including the engine installation, is undertaken by BAe (Warton). Radar-transparent nose-cone by AEG-Telefunken, assisted by Aeritalia and BAe, hinges sideways to starboard. Door-type airbrake on each side at top of rear fuselage.

TAIL UNIT: Cantilever all-metal structure, consisting of single sweptback two-spar fin and rudder, and low-set all-moving horizontal surfaces ('tailerons') which operate together for pitch control and differentially for roll control, assisted by use of the wing spoilers when the wings are not fully swept. Rudder and tailerons actuated by electrically-controlled tandem hydraulic jacks. Passive ECM antenna fairing near top of fin. Ram-air intake for heat exchanger at base of fin. Entire tail unit is the responsibility of BAe.

LANDING GEAR: Hydraulically-retractable tricycle type, with forward-retracting twin-wheel steerable nose unit. Single-wheel main units retract forward and upward into centre section of fuselage. Development and manufacture of the complete landing gear and associated hydraulics is headed by Dowty Rotol (UK). Dunlop aluminium alloy wheels, brakes and low-pressure tyres (to permit operation from soft, semi-prepared surfaces) and Goodyear anti-skid units. Main-wheel tyres size 30 × 11·50-14·5, Type VIII (20 ply); nosewheel tyres size 18 × 5·5, Type VIII (12 ply). Runway arrester hook beneath rear of fuselage.

POWER PLANT: Two Turbo-Union RB.199-34R-04 turbofan engines, each rated at approx 40·0 kN (9,000 lb st) dry and 71·2 kN (16,000 lb st) with afterburning, fitted with bucket-type thrust reversers and installed in rear fuselage with downward-opening doors for servicing and engine change. Four large 'blow-out' doors in top of each trunk, above the double-wedge variable-ramp intake. Dowty Boulton Paul air intake ramp actuators and afterburner control system. All integral fuel in multi-cell Uniroyal self-sealing integral fuselage tanks and/or wing box tanks, all fitted with press-in fuel sampling and water drain plugs, and all refuelled from a single-point NATO connector. Detachable and retractable in-flight refuelling probe can be mounted on starboard side of fuselage, adjacent to cockpit. System also designed to accept a buddy-to-buddy refuelling pack. Provision for drop-tanks of various sizes up to 1,500 litres (330 Imp gallons) to be carried beneath outer wings. Dowty Fuel Systems/Lucas/Microtecnica afterburning fuel control system. AEG-Telefunken intake de-icing system.

ACCOMMODATION: Crew of two on tandem Martin-Baker Mk 10A zero-zero ejection seats under Kopperschmidt/AIT one-piece canopy, which is hinged at rear and opens upward. Flat centre windscreen panel and curved side panels, built by Lucas Aerospace, incorporate Sierracote electrically-conductive heating film for de-icing and internal demisting. Seats provide safe escape at zero altitude and at speeds from zero up to 630 knots (1,166 km/h; 725 mph) IAS.

SYSTEMS: Nordmicro/BAe/Microtecnica air intake control system, and Dowty Boulton Paul/Liebherr Aerotechnik engine intake ramp control actuators. Two separate independent hydraulic systems, one driven by each engine, provide fully duplicated power for wing sweep, flaps, slats, spoilers, airbrakes, landing gear, tailerons and rudder. Main system includes Vickers pump, Dowty accumulators and Teves power pack. Fairey Hydraulics system for actuation of spoilers, rudder and taileron control. Provision for reversion to single-engine drive of both systems, via a mechanical cross-connection between the two engine auxiliary gearboxes, in the event of a single engine failure. In the event of a double engine flameout, an emergency pump in No. 1 system has sufficient duration for re-entry into the engine cold relight boundary. Flying control circuits are protected from loss of fluid due to leaks in other circuits by isolating valves which shut off the utility circuits if the reservoir contents drop below a predetermined safety limit level. Duplicated AC and DC electrical power is provided by two alternators, each driven by its respective engine auxiliary gearbox, to two separate main AC busbars and one essential AC busbar, and through two fan-cooled transformer-rectifier units (TRUs) to two main DC busbars. Lucas/Siemens 40/60kVA 200V 400Hz three-phase constant-frequency AC generating system. Either generator can cope with the full demand of the electrical systems in the event of a single generator failure. If both TRUs fail, an on-board Varta battery supplies the essential DC busbar. In the event of a total loss of power the battery also drives an electro-hydraulic pump which provides power for the primary flying controls. Under normal conditions the battery drives the KHD/Microtecnica/Lucas T312 APU for engine starting, but a DC ground supply is provided to assist starting if required. Plessey emergency power unit (EPU) and power systems controller. Normalair-Garrett precooler and cold-air unit, Marston Excelsior intercooler and Teddington temperature control system. Normalair-Garrett/Draegerwerk/OMI demand-type oxygen system, using a lox converter. KHD accessory drive gearboxes and Rotax/Lucas/Siemens integrated drive generator. Marconi flow-metering system. Eichweber fuel gauging system and Flight Refuelling flexible couplings. Graviner fire detection and extinguishing systems. Rotax contactors. Smiths engine speed and temperature indicators.

AVIONICS AND EQUIPMENT: Communications equipment includes Plessey PTR 1721 (UK and Italy) or Rohde und Schwarz (West Germany) UHF/VHF transceiver; AEG-Telefunken UHF/DF (UK and West Germany only); Chelton UHF homer aerial; SIT/Siemens emergency UHF with Rohde und Schwarz switch; BAe HF/SSB aerial tuning unit; Rohde und Schwarz (UK and West Germany) or Montedel (Italy) HF/SSB radio; Ultra communications control system; Marconi Avionics central suppression unit; Epsylon voice recorder; and Chelton communications and landing system aerials.

Primary self-contained nav/attack system includes Texas Instruments multi-mode forward-looking radar; Ferranti FIN 1010 three-axis digital inertial navigation system (DINS) and combined radar display; Decca Type 72 Doppler radar system; Microtecnica air data computer; Litef Spirit 3 16-bit central digital computer; Aeritalia radio/radar altimeter; Smiths/Teldix/OMI electronic head-up display with Davall camera; Ferranti nose-mounted laser ranger and marked target receiver; Marconi Avionics TV tabular display produced in partnership with AEG and Selenia; Astronautics (USA) bearing distance heading indicator and contour map display. Defensive equipment includes Siemens (West Germany) or Cossor SSR-3100 (UK) IFF transponder; Elettronica warning radar; and MSDS/Plessey/Decca Sky Shadow passive ECM system.

Flight control system includes a Marconi Avionics/Bodenseewerk triplex command stability augmentation system (CSAS), incorporating fly-by-wire and auto-stabilisation; Marconi Avionics/Aeritalia autopilot and flight director (APFD), using two self-monitoring digital computers; Marconi Avionics triplex transducer unit (TTU), with analogue computing and sensor channels; Marconi Avionics terrain-following E-scope (TFE), produced in partnership with Selenia; Fairey/Marconi Avionics quadruplex electro-hydraulic actuator; and Microtecnica air data set. The APFD provides pre-selected attitude, heading or barometric height hold, heading and track acquisition, and Mach number or airspeed hold with autothrottle. Flight director operates in parallel with, and can be used as backup for, the autopilot. Automatic approach, terrain-following and radio height-holding modes are also available. Other instrumentation includes Smiths horizontal situation indicator, vertical speed indicator and standby altimeter; AEG-Telefunken ADF; Lital standby attitude and heading reference system; SEL (with Setac) or (in UK aircraft) Marconi Avionics AD2770 (without Setac) Tacan; Cossor CILS 75 ILS; Bodenseewerk attitude direction indicator; Marconi Avionics central suppression unit (CSU); and Dornier System flight data recorder.

Overall responsibility for the avionics rests with Panavia, with EASAMS (UK) as the avionics prime contractor, and ESG (Germany) and SIA (Italy) as subcontractors. The avionics systems, while standardised as far as possible, retain the flexibility necessary to perform the various roles required. They provide accurate low- and high-level navigation; precision visual attack on ground targets in blind and poor weather conditions; air-to-ground and air-to-air attack with a wide variety of weapons; manually controlled and automatic attack; and comprehensive onboard check-out and mission data recording; with minimisation of ground support facilities at bases and the front line.

ARMAMENT: Fixed armament comprises two 27 mm IWKA-Mauser cannon, one in each side of the lower forward fuselage. Other armament varies according to version, with emphasis on the ability to carry a wide range of advanced non-nuclear weapons on three underfuselage attachments and up to four swivelling hardpoints beneath the outer wings. A Marconi Avionics/Selenia stores management system is fitted, and Sandall Mace 355 and 762 mm (14 and 30 in) ejector release units are standard. Initial weapon systems evaluation included trials of a modified Raytheon Sparrow missile, fitted with a British warhead and fuse. The battlefield interdiction version is capable of carrying defensive 'streuwaffen' (scatter weapons) such as the MBB MW-1 munitions dispenser, and of carrying weapons to suit 'hard' or 'soft' targets. The naval and interdictor strike versions have provision for carrying additional, externally-mounted fuel tanks. The air superiority version can carry a wide range of guided and semi-active homing air-to-air weapons. Among the weapons already specified for, or suitable for carriage by, the IDS Tornado are the Sidewinder air-to-air missile; AS.30, Martel, Sea Eagle and Kormoran air-to-surface missiles; napalm; BL-755 600 lb cluster bombs; MW-1 munitions dispenser; Mk 83 or other 1,000 lb bombs; 'smart' or retarded bombs; Lepus flare bombs; LR-25 rocket launchers; active or passive ECM pods.

DIMENSIONS, EXTERNAL:

Wing span: fully spread	13·90 m (45 ft 7¼ in)
fully swept	8·60 m (28 ft 2½ in)
Length overall	16·70 m (54 ft 9½ in)
Height overall	5·70 m (18 ft 8½ in)
Tailplane span	6·80 m (22 ft 3½ in)
Wheel track	3·10 m (10 ft 2 in)
Wheelbase	6·20 m (20 ft 4 in)

WEIGHTS (prototype/pre-series aircraft up to mid-1980, with development engines):

Weight empty, equipped	9,980–10,430 kg (22,000–23,000 lb)
Max weapon load carried	7,257 kg (16,000 lb)
Max T-O weight:	
'clean', full internal fuel	20,411 kg (45,000 lb)
with external stores	26,490 kg (58,400 lb)

Panavia Tornado F. Mk 2, armed with Sky Flash and Sidewinder missiles *(Pilot Press)*

PERFORMANCE (prototype/pre-series aircraft up to mid-1980, with development engines):

Max level speed at altitude, 'clean'	Mach 2·2
(1,261 knots; 2,337 km/h; 1,452 mph)	
Max level speed with external stores	
Mach 0·92 (600 knots; 1,112 km/h; 691 mph)	
Max level speed at low altitude	
above 800 knots (1,480 km/h; 920 mph) IAS	
Landing speed approx 115 knots (213 km/h; 132 mph)	
Time to 9,145 m (30,000 ft) from brakes off	
less than 2 min	
Terrain following	down to 61 m (200 ft)
T-O and landing run	approx 366 m (1,200 ft)
Max normal acceleration	7·5g
Max 360° rapid-roll clearance with full lateral control	
	4·0g
Radius of action with heavy weapons load, hi-lo-lo-hi	
	750 nm (1,390 km; 863 miles)
Ferry range approx 2,100 nm (3,890 km; 2,420 miles)	
g limit	+7·5

PANAVIA TORNADO ADV

RAF designation: Tornado F. Mk 2

Full-scale development of the Tornado ADV (air defence variant) was authorised by the British government on 4 March 1976. This version is being developed specifically for the RAF, which will include 165 of this long-range interceptor model, designated F. Mk 2, in its total procurement of 385 Tornadoes, to re-equip two Lightning squadrons and seven squadrons of Phantoms.

Most of the 165 ADV Tornadoes will be based in the United Kingdom, both for the air defence of the UK and to protect the northern and western approaches of NATO. The F. Mk 2 will also fulfil the RAF's commitments to provide long-range air defence of Britain's maritime forces, over a wide UK defence region extending from the Atlantic approaches to the Baltic and from Iceland to the English Channel; and to contribute towards air defence in the Central Region of Europe. It will be able to loiter on patrol for several hours, using in-flight refuelling when necessary, and to detect, identify and destroy enemy aircraft approaching at supersonic speeds at high-medium or low altitudes, using its snap-up or snap-down missiles. Its fire control system will be able to engage multiple targets in rapid succession; its weapon systems will be highly resistant to enemy ECM; and it will be able to operate from damaged airfields by virtue of its good short-field performance. Supersonic acceleration is better than that of the IDS version. A genuine long-range autonomous capability will enable it to operate more than 350 nm (645 km; 400 miles) from its base at night, in bad weather, in heavy ECM conditions, against multiple targets at low level.

Armament of the Tornado F. Mk 2 consists of a single 27 mm built-in IWKA-Mauser cannon in the starboard side of the lower forward fuselage, four British Aerospace (Dynamics Group) Sky Flash medium-range air-to-air missiles semi-recessed under the centre-fuselage, and two NWC AIM-9L Sidewinder short-range infra-red air-to-air missiles on the inboard wing stations.

These weapons will be operated in conjunction with a new, all-British track-while-scan pulse-Doppler airborne interception radar named Foxhunter, designed and developed by Marconi Avionics, with Ferranti as subcontractor for the transmitter and aerial scanning mechanism. Foxhunter will enable the Tornado F. Mk 2 to detect targets more than 100 nm (185 km; 115 miles) away, and to track several targets simultaneously; the Sky Flash missiles, each fitted with an MSDS monopulse seeker head, will be able to engage targets at high altitude or at levels below 75 m (250 ft), in the face of heavy ECM, and at stand-off ranges of more than 22 nm (40 km; 25 miles). A new release system, designed specially for Sky Flash, permits the missile to be fired over the Tornado's full flight envelope. Furthermore, the missile is highly capable of tracking targets in a ground clutter environment, and of discriminating between closely-spaced targets. An EMI Electronics active fusing system allows these benefits to be realised fully in snap-down attacks against targets flying at very low level. The first phase of Sky Flash air trials was completed by early 1978.

The Tornado F. Mk 2 carries a two-man crew, the rear (navigator's) cockpit being equipped with a Ferranti FH 31A AC-driven 3 in horizon gyro which, in addition to providing an attitude display for the navigator, feeds pitch and roll signals to other avionics systems in the aircraft in certain modes. A pilot's head-up display, ESM (electronic surveillance measures) and ECCM are also standard, as are an extremely advanced modular radar homing and warning receiver being developed by Marconi Space and Defence Systems, and a low light level TV visual augmentation system, developed by Marconi Avionics, for identifying enemy aircraft. Other avionics include an IFF interrogator, and an ECM-resistant data link system which is interoperable with all other NATO systems. Its comprehensive avionics enable the Tornado ADV to contribute significantly to the transfer of vital information over the entire tactical area; it can, if necessary, partially fulfil the roles of both AEW and ground-based radar.

Although possessing some 80% commonality with the IDS (interdictor/strike) version, the Tornado F. Mk 2 differs in several important respects, and the initial production contract for 40 Tornadoes included provision for three prototypes of the fighter version. The first of these (ZA254) made its first flight on 27 October 1979. By the end of the year it had logged 26½ hours and flown at Mach 1·8; 41¼ hours had been logged by the end of January 1980. This aircraft, not fitted with the Foxhunter radar at the time of its first flight, is acting as the aerodynamic and missile release test aircraft. The second prototype (ZA 267) flew on 18 July 1980, and a third was due to fly before the end of 1980. The first two aircraft are being used for avionics and weapon system testing and integration. The third prototype will be concerned primarily with evaluating the AI radar. By early August 1980 the A 01 first prototype had extended the flight envelope clearance to an IAS of 800 knots (1,480 km/h; 920 mph), a milestone passed by the IDS Tornado in 1979.

The contract for the first production batch of F. Mk 2s was due to be signed in 1980. Deliveries to the RAF will begin during the first half of the 1980s, with IOC (initial operational capability) scheduled to be achieved by late 1984. The production F. Mk 2 will be powered by an uprated version of the RB.199-34R-04 engine at present standard for the IDS Tornado.

Two main airframe modifications distinguish the ADV Tornado from the IDS version. The principal one is a 1·36 m (4 ft 5½ in) increase in fuselage length, created by the longer nose radome and the need for a small 'stretch' aft of the cockpit to allow the four Sky Flash missiles to be

First prototype Tornado F. Mk 2 air defence variant for the RAF, with four underfuselage Sky Flash missiles

carried in two tandem pairs. The other external difference is that the fixed inboard portions of the wings are extended forward at the leading-edges, to give additional chord. Extension of the fuselage provides additional space for avionics and for an extra 909 litres (200 Imp gallons) of internal fuel. A fully-retractable flight refuelling probe is mounted in the nose, and drop-tanks can be carried on the

inner underwing stations.

DIMENSIONS, EXTERNAL: As for the IDS version, except:
Length overall   18·06 m (59 ft 3 in)
PERFORMANCE (estimated):
Normal touchdown speed
                    115 knots (213 km/h; 132 mph)

T-O run with normal weapon and fuel load
                    762 m (2,500 ft)
Landing run, with thrust reversal   366 m (1,200 ft)
Radius of action (combat air patrol), loiter for more than 2 h, with sufficient fuel for interception including 10 min combat
                    300-400 nm (555-742 km; 345-461 miles)

SAAB/FAIRCHILD

AIRFRAME PRIME CONTRACTORS:
Saab-Scania Aktiebolag, S-581 88 Linköping, Sweden
Telephone: Int. +46 13 12 90 20
Telex: 50040 SAABLGS
Fairchild Industries Inc, 20301 Century Boulevard, Germantown, Maryland 20767, USA
Telephone: (301) 428 6000
CHIEF EXECUTIVE (MARKETING): Alan R. Buley

Saab-Scania and Fairchild Industries announced in January 1980 that the two companies had signed an agreement jointly to develop, produce and market a new commuter transport aircraft. A jointly-owned Swedish company, with an office in Paris, will be responsible for marketing the aircraft in all parts of the world except North America.

SAAB-FAIRCHILD MODEL 340 COMMUTER

This new transport aircraft, the first collaborative venture of its kind between members of the European and US aerospace industries, is being developed jointly by Saab-Scania and Fairchild Republic for entry into service in 1984. First flight is scheduled to take place in late 1982 or early 1983.

Design emphasis is being placed on simplicity of systems, operation and maintenance, with quick turnarounds made possible by a number of built-in features which will make the aircraft independent of ground handling equipment. The airliner is designed specially for short-haul, low-density routes and will have two new-generation turboprop engines offering low fuel consumption, low operating costs and low operating noise levels. It is also expected to appeal to corporate aviation and other non-airline markets.

Joint technical and market studies by the two companies began in mid-1979. Final assembly of the aircraft will take place in Sweden.
TYPE: Twin-turboprop commuter transport aircraft.
WINGS: Cantilever low-wing monoplane, with dihedral from roots. Tapered, non-swept wings embodying fail-safe and safe-life design principles. Single-slotted trailing-edge flaps. Tab in each aileron.
FUSELAGE: Conventional fail-safe/safe-life semi-monocoque pressurised structure, of circular cross-section.
TAIL UNIT: Cantilever cruciform structure, with swept-back vertical and non-swept horizontal surfaces. Construction similar to that of wings. Tab in rudder and each elevator.
LANDING GEAR: Retractable tricycle type, with twin wheels on each unit. All units retract forward, main units into engine nacelles. Steerable nosewheels.
POWER PLANT: Two General Electric CT7 turboprop engines, each rated at more than 1,230 kW (1,650 shp). Fuel in two integral tanks in wings, combined capacity 3,331 litres (733 Imp gallons; 880 US gallons). Single

Saab-Fairchild 340 commuter airliner, for service in 1984 *(Michael A. Badrocke)*

pressure refuelling point, permitting complete refuelling of empty tanks in 12 min.
ACCOMMODATION: Crew of two on flight deck; seat for attendant at front of passenger cabin on stbd side. Main cabin accommodates up to 34 passengers, in 10 rows of three, with aisle, and a final row of four. Seat pitch 76 cm (30 in). Movable bulkhead aft of last row of seats. Toilet (starboard) and wardrobe (port) at forward end of cabin; provision for optional galley installation. An 8/14-seat corporate/executive version is planned. Passenger door at front of cabin on port side. Opposite this on starboard side, and on each side aft of wing trailing-edge, is a service door. Baggage space under each passenger seat. Main baggage/cargo compartment aft of passenger cabin, with large access door on port side.
SYSTEM: Pressurisation system (max differential 0·48 bars; 7 lb/sq in) maintains a S/L cabin environment up to an altitude of 3,660 m (12,000 ft).
DIMENSIONS, EXTERNAL:
Wing span   21·44 m (70 ft 4 in)
Length overall   19·43 m (63 ft 9 in)
Height overall   6·61 m (21 ft 8¼ in)
Wheel track   6·71 m (22 ft 0 in)
Wheelbase   7·10 m (23 ft 3½ in)

DIMENSIONS, INTERNAL:
Cabin: Length   10·26 m (33 ft 8 in)
       Width   2·16 m (7 ft 1 in)
       Height   1·83 m (6 ft 0 in)
Baggage/cargo compartment volume
                            6·4 m³ (225·0 cu ft)

WEIGHTS (typical, for multi-stop operations of four 108 nm; 200 km; 124 mile stage lengths):
Operating weight empty   6,600 kg (14,550 lb)
Payload   3,400 kg (7,495 lb)
Fuel   1,350 kg (2,975 lb)
T-O weight   11,350 kg (25,020 lb)
Zero-fuel weight   10,000 kg (22,045 lb)
Landing weight   11,110 kg (24,495 lb)

PERFORMANCE (ISA, estimated):
Max cruising speed   260 knots (481 km/h; 300 mph)
Max rate of climb at S/L   610 m (2,000 ft)/min
Rate of climb at S/L, one engine out
                            228 m (750 ft)/min
Balanced field length   less than 1,200 m (3,940 ft)
Range, with IFR reserves:
   34 passengers   800 nm (1,480 km; 920 miles)
   23 passengers   1,570 nm (2,900 km; 1,805 miles)

SEPECAT
SOCIÉTÉ EUROPÉENNE DE PRODUCTION DE L'AVION E.C.A.T.

AIRFRAME COMPANIES:
British Aerospace Aircraft Group, Richmond Road, Kingston upon Thames, Surrey KT2 5QS, England
Telephone: 01 546 7741
Avions Marcel Dassault/Breguet Aviation, BP 32, 92420 Vaucresson, France
Telephone: 970 38 50
DIRECTORS:
I. R. Yates (alternate Chairman)
P. E. Jaillard (alternate Chairman)
Sir Frederick Page
J. Bonnet
C. Edelstenne
M. Berjon
R. H. Evans
A. Constantine
PUBLIC RELATIONS:
G. B. Hill (BAe)
C. P. Raffin (Dassault-Breguet)

This Anglo-French company was formed in May 1966 by Breguet Aviation and British Aircraft Corporation, to design and produce the Jaguar supersonic strike fighter/trainer. The Jaguar project was initiated by the Defence Ministries of Britain and France on 17 May 1965. The governments of the two countries appointed an official Jaguar Management Committee to look after their interests. SEPECAT is the complementary industrial organisation.

SEPECAT JAGUAR

The Jaguar, which has evolved from the Breguet Br121 project, was designed by Breguet and BAe to meet a common requirement of the French and British air forces laid down in early 1965. This requirement called for a dual-role aircraft, to be used as an advanced and operational trainer and a tactical support aircraft of light weight and high performance, to enter French service in 1972 and with the RAF in 1973. The Jaguar M French naval version (1972-73 *Jane's*) was abandoned in 1973.

The following versions of the Jaguar have been built:
Jaguar A. French single-seat tactical support version. Prototypes (A-03 and A-04) first flown on 23 March and 27 May 1969. Total of 160 ordered, of which 139 had been delivered by 31 March 1980. France's final 30 Jaguar As are fitted with a laser guidance system and can carry two AS.30 air-to-surface missiles, as detailed under the appropriate 'Avionics and Operational Equipment' paragraph.

The first operational Armée de l'Air Jaguar unit (Esc. 1/7 'Provence') was formed at St Dizier in eastern France on 19 June 1973. The French Air Force has nine Jaguar A squadrons: three each with the 7th and 11th Escadres at St Dizier and Toul-Rosières, one with the 3rd Escadre at Nancy, and two with the 92nd Escadre. In December 1977 and May 1978, Jaguars of the Armée de l'Air were the first of their type to enter combat, when they were used to attack guerrilla forces in Mauritania. A Martin Marietta/Thomson-CSF target TV acquisition and laser designation pod, named ATLIS, is carried by some French Jaguars.

Jaguar B (RAF designation: Jaguar T.Mk 2). British two-seat operational training version. Prototype B-08 (XW566) first flown on 30 August 1971. Total of 37 built initially; one more on order in 1980. First T.Mk 2 delivered to RAF was XX137.
Jaguar E. French two-seat advanced training version. Prototypes (E-01 and E-02) first flown on 8 September 1968 and 11 February 1969. Total of 40 built. First production Jaguar, designated E-1, flew for the first time on 2 November 1971, and deliveries to the CEAM at Air Base 118, Mont de Marsan, began in May 1972. The first unit to equip with this version was Esc. 1/7 at St Dizier.
Jaguar S (RAF designation: Jaguar GR. Mk 1). British single-seat tactical support version, basically similar to A but with an advanced inertial navigation and weapon-aiming system (NAVWASS) controlled by a digital computer. Prototypes first flown on 12 October 1969 and 12 June 1970. Total of 165 built. The first production GR. Mk 1 (XX108) flew on 11 October 1972, and this version now equips eight RAF front-line squadrons: Nos. 2 (AC), 14, 17, 20 and 31 with the Second Allied Tactical Air Force in West Germany and Nos. 6, 41 and 54 at Coltishall in the UK. Nos. 2 (AC) and 41 Squadrons are reconnaissance units. Since 1978, RAF Jaguars have been refitted with uprated Adour Mk 104 engines, equivalent to the Mk 804 which powers the Jaguar International (see following paragraph). This programme was nearing completion in the Spring of 1980.
Jaguar International. Export version, first flown (G27-266) on 19 August 1976. Differs little from Jaguar S or B except in having more powerful Adour turbofan

French Air Force Jaguar As and Es formating on a C-135F flight refuelling tanker. The Jaguar A second from left has an undernose Omera 40 panoramic camera installation

engines (initially the Adour Mk 804, rated at 23·40 kN; 5,260 lb st dry and 38·25 kN; 8,600 lb st with afterburning), which give improved combat performance with substantially enhanced manoeuvrability and acceleration in the low-level speed range. The next standard of engine, the Mk 811, is now available, and uprating to this standard is possible during overhaul of the Mk 804 engines. The Mk 811 increases the thrust still further to +15% on take-off, and +40% under combat conditions, compared with the original Adour Mk 102. Dry thrust is also significantly improved. Flight trials with the Mk 811 began on 14 August 1978; in 1978 and 1979 the aircraft was demonstrated at the Farnborough and Paris Air Shows, the demonstration on both occasions including take-offs and landings on grass strips.

Other customer options include overwing pylons compatible with Matra R.550 Magic or similar dogfight missiles; a multi-purpose radar such as the Thomson-CSF Agave, with which flight trials were completed in March 1977; up to four anti-shipping weapons such as Harpoon, Exocet and Kormoran on the underwing and underfuselage hardpoints; and night sensors such as low light level TV.

Initial orders were placed by the Sultan of Oman's Air Force (12) and Ecuadorean Air Force (12), each order including two two-seaters. Deliveries to Ecuador were made in January-November 1977, and to Oman between March 1977 and July 1978. SOAF aircraft are fitted with a Marconi Avionics 920ATC NAVWASS computer and have provision for carrying overwing Magic missiles. A further 12 Jaguar Internationals, powered by Adour Mk 811 engines, were ordered by Oman in 1980.

Under a 1979 agreement, an initial batch of 40 Jaguar Internationals is being purchased from Britain by the Indian government; the agreement provides for a further 45 to be assembled subsequently in India from British-built components, leading eventually to full manufacture under licence by Hindustan Aeronautics Ltd, Bangalore. About three-quarters of the total will be assembled and/or built by HAL. Meanwhile, the Indian Air Force is receiving on loan 18 RAF Jaguars, the first two of which were handed over on 19 July 1979. Two more arrived in that country on 14 October 1979, and the Indian Air Force's first Jaguar squadron (No. 14) had become operational by the Summer of 1980.

The Jaguar International is also available in a maritime strike version, similarly powered by Adour Mk 804 (current standard) or Mk 811 (optional) turbofan engines. This also would have the Agave nose radar, and ability to carry Harpoon, Exocet or Kormoran missiles. The capacity to carry overwing Magic missiles is retained.

A total of 202 Jaguars have been built for the RAF and 200 are being built for the French air force. The first formal production contract, placed in the Autumn of 1969, covered 50 Jaguars for France; the second was for 30 for the RAF. Subsequent contracts brought total Anglo-French orders to 402 by early 1976; one additional Jaguar B was ordered later. Of this total of 403, SEPECAT had delivered 377 by 1 March 1980.

Dassault-Breguet factories at Toulouse and Biarritz are responsible for the front and centre fuselage. BAe has responsibility for the rear fuselage, air intakes, wings and tail unit. There are final assembly lines for complete aircraft in both Britain and France.

The Jaguar is fully power-controlled in all three axes and is automatically stabilised as a weapons platform by gyros which sense disturbances and feed appropriate correcting data through a computer to the power control assemblies, in addition to the human pilot manoeuvre demands. The power controls are all of duplex tandem arrangement, with both mechanical and electrical servovalves of the established Fairey platen design. Air-to-air combat capability can be enhanced by the inclusion of roll/yaw dampers, to increase lateral stability, and by increasing the slat and flap angles.

Training versions can operate from conventional runways only 2,000 m (6,560 ft) long, with full provision for safety in the event of an engine failure at the critical point of take-off.

TYPE: Single-seat tactical support aircraft (Jaguar A, S and International) and two-seat operational or advanced trainer (Jaguar B and E).

WINGS: Cantilever shoulder-wing monoplane. Anhedral 3°. Sweepback 40° at quarter-chord. All-metal two-spar torsion-box structure, the skin of which is machined from solid aluminium alloy, with integral stiffeners. Entire wing unit is British-built. Main portion built as single unit, with three-point attachment to each side of fuselage. Outer panels fitted with slat which also gives effect of extended-chord leading-edge. No conventional ailerons. Lateral control by two-section spoilers, forward of outer flap on each wing, in association (at low speeds) with differential tailplane. Hydraulically-operated (by screwjack) full-span double-slotted trailing-edge flaps. Fairey Hydraulics powered flying controls. Leading-edge slats can be used in combat.

FUSELAGE: All-metal structure, mainly aluminium, built in three main units and making use of sandwich panels and, around the cockpit(s), honeycomb panels. Local use of titanium alloy in engine bay area. The forward and centre fuselage, up to and including the main undercarriage bays, and including cockpit(s), main systems installations, forward fuel tanks and landing gear, are of French construction. The air intakes, and entire fuselage aft of the main-wheel bays, including engine installation, rear fuel tanks and complete tail assembly, are British-built. Two door-type airbrakes under rear fuselage, immediately aft of each main-wheel well. Structure and systems, aft of cockpit(s), are identical for single-seat and two-seat versions.

TAIL UNIT: Cantilever all-metal two-spar structure, covered with aluminium alloy sandwich panels. Rudder and outer panels and trailing-edge of tailplane have honeycomb core. Sweepback at quarter-chord 40° on horizontal, 43° on vertical surfaces. All-moving slab-type tailplane, with 10° of anhedral, the two halves of which can operate differentially to supplement the spoilers. No separate elevators. Fairey Hydraulics powered flying controls. Ventral fins beneath the rear fuselage. Entire tail unit is British-built.

LANDING GEAR: Messier-Hispano-Bugatti retractable tricycle type, all units having Dunlop wheels and low-pressure tyres for rough-field operation. Hydraulic retraction, with oleo-pneumatic shock-absorbers. Forward-retracting main units each have twin wheels,

tyre size 615 × 225-10, tyre pressure 5·8 bars (84 lb/sq in). Wheels pivot during retraction to stow horizontally in bottom of fuselage. Single rearward-retracting nose-wheel, with tyre size 550 × 250-6 and pressure of 3·9 bars (57 lb/sq in). Twin landing/taxiing lights in nose-wheel door. Dunlop hydraulic brakes. Anti-skid units and arrester hook standard. Irvin brake parachute of 5·5 m (18 ft 0½ in) diameter housed in fuselage tailcone.

POWER PLANT: Two Rolls-Royce Turboméca Adour Mk 102 turbofan engines initially (each rated at 22·75 kN; 5,115 lb st dry and 32·5 kN; 7,305 lb st with afterburning). French Jaguars still have this power plant. RAF Jaguars now nearly all have Adour Mk 104, rated at 23·7 kN (5,320 lb st) dry and 35·75 kN (8,040 lb st) with afterburning. Jaguar International offered initially with Adour Mk 804 (same ratings as Mk 104); now available with Adour Mk 811, rated at 24·6 kN (5,520 lb st) dry and 37·4 kN (8,400 lb st) with afterburning. Lateral-type fixed-geometry air intake on each side of fuselage aft of cockpit. Fuel in six tanks, one in each wing and four in fuselage. Total internal fuel capacity 4,200 litres (924 Imp gallons). Armour protection is provided for critical fuel system components. In the basic tactical sortie the loss of fuel from one tank at the halfway point would not prevent the aircraft from regaining its base. Provision for carrying three auxiliary drop-tanks, each of 1,200 litres (264 Imp gallons) capacity, on fuselage and inboard wing pylons. Jaguar A and S equipped for in-flight refuelling, with a retractable probe forward of the cockpit on the starboard side.

ACCOMMODATION (Jaguar B and E): Crew of two in tandem on Martin-Baker Mk 9 zero-zero ejection seats (Jaguar B) or Mk 4 seats (Jaguar E) giving zero-altitude ejection at speeds down to 90 knots (167 km/h; 104 mph). Individual rearward-hinged canopies. Rear seat is 38 cm (15 in) higher than front seat. Windscreen bullet-proof against 7·5 mm rifle fire.

ACCOMMODATION (Jaguar A and S): Enclosed cockpit for pilot, with rearward-hinged canopy and Martin-Baker Mk 9 (Jaguar S) or Mk 4 (Jaguar A) ejection seat as in two-seaters. Bulletproof windscreen, as in two-seat versions.

SYSTEMS: Air-conditioning and pressurisation systems maintain automatically, throughout the flight envelope, comfortable operating conditions for the crew, and also control the temperature in certain equipment bays. Two independent hydraulic systems, powered by two Vickers engine-driven pumps. Hydraulic pressure 207 bars (3,000 lb/sq in). First system (port engine) supplies one channel of each actuator for the flying controls, the hydraulic motors which actuate the flaps and slats, the landing gear retraction and extension system, the brakes and anti-skid units. The second system supplies the other half of each flying control actuator, two further hydraulic motors actuating the slats and flaps, the air-brake and landing gear emergency extension jacks, nosewheel steering system and the wheel brakes. In addition to the duplicated hydraulic power systems, there is an emergency hydraulic power transfer unit. Electrical power provided by two 15kVA AC generators, either of which can sustain functional and operational equipment without load-shedding. DC power provided by two 4kW transformer-rectifiers. Emergency power for essential instruments provided by 15Ah battery and static inverter. De-icing, rain clearance and demisting standard. Liquid oxygen system installed, which also pressurises the pilot's anti-g suit.

AVIONICS AND OPERATIONAL EQUIPMENT (French versions): Avionics in Jaguar E include VHF/UHF radio, VOR/ILS and IFF; Tacan with Crouzet Type 90 navigation indicator; SFIM 153-6 twin-gyro inertial platform with two SFIM 810 all-attitude roll and pitch spherical indicators; SFIM 511 directional compass; Jaeger ELDIA air data system with Jaeger altitude indicator; CSF RL 50Pj incidence probe with angle of attack indicator; CSF 121 fire control sighting unit with weapon selector and adaptor for sighting head camera. Except for the use of a SFIM 250-1 twin-gyro platform, and the addition of a vector adder to the navigation indicator, this equipment is repeated in the Jaguar A, which has in addition an EMD Decca RDN 72 Doppler radar, Crouzet Type 90 navigation computer with target selector, CFTH passive radar warning (ECM) detector, CSF 31 weapon aiming computer, a Dassault fire control computer for Martel anti-radar missiles and a CSF laser rangefinder. Provision for the addition to these basic installations of such other items as terrain-following radar or sighting equipment for low light level targets.

JI004, the fourth (and second single-seat) Jaguar International delivered to the Indian Air Force

About six Jaguar As in each French squadron have an Omera 40 panoramic camera installed under the nosecone to give 180° horizon-to-horizon coverage. The final 30 Jaguar As for France carry an ATLIS (Automatic Tracking Laser Illumination System) pod, developed by Martin Marietta and Thomson-CSF, on the centreline pylon. The pod contains a laser designator, and a wide-angle TV camera with its field of view centred along the line of the laser beam. The second part of the system is a modular laser guidance unit known as Ariel, which is implanted in the nosecone of the aircraft's rockets, missiles or bombs. The system is such that one aircraft can illuminate a target with its ATLIS pod while another releases its laser-guided weapons. The missile chosen by the French Air Force to operate with the ATLIS system is the Aérospatiale AS.30; Ariel can also be fitted to the Thomson-Brandt 100 mm rocket. A development of Ariel, known as TMV 630 Eblis, can be fitted to free-fall laser-guided bombs, and can be adapted to fit other 250, 400 or 1,000 kg bombs.

AVIONICS AND OPERATIONAL EQUIPMENT (British versions): Basic avionics of both the Jaguar B and S are similar. They include a Smiths-built Honeywell radio altimeter, slip indicator, E2B standby compass and autostabilising system, Plessey PTR 377 VHF/UHF radio and Marconi Avionics HF radio; Cossor CILS 75 ILS (being extended in 1979 to full VOR/ILS capability); IFF; Tacan; Marconi Avionics digital/inertial navigation and weapon aiming subsystem (NAVWASS) with MCS 920M digital computer, E3R three-gyro inertial platform, inertial velocity sensor, navigation control unit and projected-map display; Marconi Avionics air data computer; Smiths electronic head-up display; Smiths FS6 horizontal situation indicator; Sperry C2J gyro amplifier master unit, compass controller and magnetic detector; Plessey weapon control system. Jaguar S fitted with Ferranti Type 105 laser rangefinder and Type 106 marked target seeker in modified nose. Ferranti FIN 1064 digital inertial navigation and weapon aiming equipment selected to replace major elements of NAVWASS equipment in RAF Jaguars. The BAe-designed flush-fitting reconnaissance pod for RAF Jaguars, carried on the fuselage centreline, has optical cameras for horizon-to-horizon coverage and BAe Dynamics (HS) 401 infra-red linescan (IRLS) for additional daylight, poor weather and night capability. Cameras are installed in two rotatable drums within the pod, the forward drum (for low/medium altitude missions) containing two Vinten F95 Mk 10 oblique and one F95 Mk 7 forward-looking cameras. The rear drum can carry alternative modules: two F95 Mk 10 cameras for low-level sorties, or a single F126 for medium altitude reconnaissance. The IRLS package is installed in the rear end of the pod, adjacent to a data conversion unit linked to the onboard NAVWASS digital computer.

AVIONICS AND OPERATIONAL EQUIPMENT (Jaguar International): Differ according to individual customer requirements; details of these are not releasable.

ARMAMENT (Jaguar A, S and International): Two 30 mm cannon (DEFA 553 in Jaguar A, Aden in Jaguar S) in lower fuselage aft of cockpit. One stores attachment point on fuselage centreline and two under each wing. Centreline and inboard wing points can each carry up to 1,134 kg (2,500 lb) of weapons, and the outboard underwing points up to 567 kg (1,250 lb) each. Maximum external stores load, including overwing loads on Jaguar International, is 4,763 kg (10,500 lb). Jaguar As in service can carry the AN 52 tactical nuclear weapon. Typical alternative loads include one Martel AS.37 anti-radar missile and two 1,200 litre (264 Imp gallon) drop-tanks; eight 1,000 lb bombs; various combinations of free-fall and retarded bombs, Hunting BL755 or

Beluga cluster bombs, Matra R.550 Magic missiles and air-to-surface rockets, including the 68 mm SNEB rocket; a reconnaissance-camera pack; or two drop-tanks. Jaguar International has full weapon capability of Jaguar S, plus the ability to carry up to four Matra Magic air-to-air missiles on overwing pylons.

ARMAMENT (Jaguar B and E): Two 30 mm DEFA 553 cannon in Jaguar E; Jaguar B has single 30 mm Aden cannon on port side. The two-seat versions have similar weapons capability to the tactical models, and can be employed for operational missions as required.

DIMENSIONS, EXTERNAL:
Wing span	8·69 m (28 ft 6 in)
Wing chord at root	3·58 m (11 ft 9 in)
Wing chord at tip	1·13 m (3 ft 8½ in)
Wing aspect ratio	3·12
Length overall, incl probe:	
A and S	16·83 m (55 ft 2½ in)
B and E	17·53 m (57 ft 6¼ in)
Length overall, excl probe:	
A and S	15·52 m (50 ft 11 in)
B and E	16·42 m (53 ft 10½ in)
Height overall	4·89 m (16 ft 0½ in)
Tailplane span	4·53 m (14 ft 10¼ in)
Wheel track	2·41 m (7 ft 11 in)
Wheelbase	5·69 m (18 ft 8 in)

AREAS:
Wings, gross	24·18 m² (260·27 sq ft)
Leading-edge slats (total)	1·05 m² (11·30 sq ft)
Trailing-edge flaps (total)	4·12 m² (44·35 sq ft)
Spoilers (total)	0·90 m² (9·67 sq ft)
Vertical tail surfaces (total)	3·90 m² (42·00 sq ft)
Horizontal tail surfaces (total)	7·80 m² (83·96 sq ft)

WEIGHTS AND LOADINGS:
Typical weight empty	7,000 kg (15,432 lb)
Normal T-O weight (single-seater, with full internal fuel and ammunition for built-in cannon)	10,954 kg (24,149 lb)
Max T-O weight, with external stores	15,700 kg (34,612 lb)
Max wing loading	649·3 kg/m² (133 lb/sq ft)
Max power loading:	
Adour Mk 102	241·5 kg/kN (2·37 lb/lb st)
Adour Mks 104, 804	219·6 kg/kN (2·15 lb/lb st)
Adour Mk 811	209·9 kg/kN (2·06 lb/lb st)

PERFORMANCE:
Max level speed at S/L	
Mach 1·1	(729 knots; 1,350 km/h; 840 mph)
Max level speed at 11,000 m (36,000 ft)	
Mach 1·6	(917 knots; 1,699 km/h; 1,056 mph)
Landing speed	115 knots (213 km/h; 132 mph)
T-O run with typical tactical load	580 m (1,900 ft)
T-O to 15 m (50 ft) with typical tactical load	940 m (3,085 ft)
Landing from 15 m (50 ft) with typical tactical load	785 m (2,575 ft)
Landing run with typical tactical load	470 m (1,545 ft)
Typical attack radius, internal fuel only:	
hi-lo-hi	440 nm (815 km; 507 miles)
lo-lo-lo	310 nm (575 km; 357 miles)
Typical attack radius with external fuel:	
hi-lo-hi	760 nm (1,408 km; 875 miles)
lo-lo-lo	490 nm (908 km; 564 miles)
Ferry range with external fuel	1,902 nm (3,524 km; 2,190 miles)
g limits	+8·6; +12 (ultimate)

SEPECAT JAGUAR DEVELOPMENT

In addition to earlier developments listed in the previous entry, BAe is considering other means of developing the power plant and Jaguar airframe for possible future versions.

The Adour engine is capable of considerable further growth, the greatest potential being represented currently by the 'Dash 63', which has 38 per cent more T-O thrust with afterburning than the Mk 102, and 65 per cent more in the combat regime. Various Adour models, with dash numbers between 58 (now the Adour Mk 811) and 63, are being studied.

BAe is also studying designs for a new wing which could either be fitted to a new aircraft with the minimum of design change, or be retrofitted to existing Jaguars.

Development contracts have already been placed for an advanced fly-by-wire installation, and for a carbon-fibre wing, for the Jaguar. The Marconi Avionics/Dowty quadruplex FBW flight control system, which has all-electric signalling and no manual backup, is being installed by BAe in an RAF Jaguar GR. Mk 1, and was due to be test-flown in 1980. BAe is also studying a version of the Jaguar with a new, larger wing with inboard extensions of the leading-edges.

SEPECAT Jaguar International single-seat strike aircraft, with additional side view (top) of Jaguar B two-seat operational training version and scrap view of version with Agave nose radar (Pilot Press)

SOKO/CNIAR

PARTICIPANTS:
SOKO, Mostar, Yugoslavia
Centrul National al Industriei Aeronautice Române, Bucharest, Romania

SOKO/CNIAR ORAO (EAGLE)/IAR-93

This twin-jet ground attack fighter is under development to meet a joint requirement of the air forces of Romania and Yugoslavia. In the latter country it is known

as the Orao (Eagle); its Romanian designation is IAR-93. The joint programme is known as 'Yurom' (from Yugoslavia-Romania).

The Orao/IAR-93 was designed jointly by Yugoslav engineers from the Vazduhoplovno Tehnicki Institut in Zarkovo, near Belgrade, and by Romanian engineers from the Institutul de Mecanica Fluidelor si Constructii Aerospatiale in Bucharest. Manufacture of single-seat prototypes began simultaneously in the two countries, and a first flight in each country was made on 31 October 1974. On 15 April 1975 the Yugoslav prototype, bearing serial number 25001, was demonstrated publicly during the Victory Day parade at Batajnica military airfield near Belgrade. A tandem two-seat dual-control prototype was then built and flown in each country, after which Yugoslavia and Romania each completed a number of pre-production aircraft. A formation of three IAR-93s was flown publicly on 23 August 1979, during the Liberation Day celebrations in Bucharest.

More than 33 factories in Yugoslavia are involved in the Orao manufacturing programme, led by SOKO, which has prime responsibility for final assembly and flight testing. In Romania, CNIAR is co-ordinating the factories involved and is responsible for delivering completed aircraft to the Ministry of National Defence.

Prototype of the Orao/IAR-93 single-seat tactical fighter (two Rolls-Royce Viper turbojet engines)

Orao/IAR-93 single-seat tactical fighter, developed jointly by Romania and Yugoslavia *(Pilot Press)*

It is anticipated that 200 or more of these aircraft will be built for each country, including a proportion of two-seat dual-control operational trainers. The initial production batch is estimated to be nearly 40, including two-seaters; one unconfirmed report has suggested that the Yugoslav Air Force has already ordered 150 single-seaters and 50 two-seaters.

TYPE: Single-seat close support aircraft and interceptor.

WINGS: Cantilever shoulder-wing monoplane, of low aspect ratio. Anhedral 3° 30′ from roots. Sweepback approx 43° on leading-edges. Leading-edge slats. Two small boundary layer fences on upper surface of each wing. Wide-chord semi-Fowler-type trailing-edge flaps. Trim tab in starboard aileron. Ailerons controlled by Dowty servo-actuators with autostabiliser system.

FUSELAGE: All-metal semi-monocoque structure. Door-type perforated airbrake under each side of fuselage, forward of main-wheel bays. Dorsal spine fairing houses systems circuits and flight control rods. 'Pen-nib' fairing above exhaust nozzles. Rear fuselage detachable to facilitate access to engines. Space provision in nose for ranging radar.

TAIL UNIT: Cantilever metal structure, with sweepback on all surfaces. Low-set all-moving tailplane. Small dorsal fin. Tailplane and rudder controlled by Dowty servo-actuators with autostabiliser system. Auxiliary ventral fin on each side beneath rear fuselage.

LANDING GEAR: Retractable tricycle type, with single-wheel steerable nose unit and twin-wheel main units. Manufactured by PPT factories (for Yugoslav aircraft) and CNIAR factories (Romanian aircraft). All units have two-stage oleo-pneumatic shock-absorbers. Hydraulic actuation, all units retracting forward into fuselage. Braking parachute in bullet fairing at base of rudder.

POWER PLANT: Two 17·8 kN (4,000 lb st) Rolls-Royce Viper Mk 632-41 non-afterburning turbojet engines, mounted side by side in rear fuselage, with lateral air intakes. Internal fuel capacity approx 3,200 litres (704 Imp gallons). Production aircraft will be fitted with Rolls-Royce-developed afterburners, increasing power of each engine to approx 22·3 kN (5,008 lb st); afterburners will be produced under licence in Yugoslavia and Romania.

ACCOMMODATION: Pilot only, on ejection seat beneath rear-hinged, upward-opening canopy; or crew of two in tandem under elongated canopy in operational training version. Dual controls in training version.

SYSTEMS AND EQUIPMENT: Autostabiliser system for control surface servo-actuators. Standard equipment varies according to operator and mission/performance requirements. Landing lights under nose, forward of nosewheel bay, and on nosewheel leg. Ram-air scoop aft of cockpit on each side; additional airscoops on top of fuselage, aft of canopy and at front of dorsal fin, and below rear fuselage.

ARMAMENT: Two 23 mm cannon in lower front fuselage, aft of nosewheel bay; one underfuselage and four underwing stations for external stores. Max external load approx 2,500 kg (5,510 lb).

DIMENSIONS, EXTERNAL:
Wing span	9·63 m	(31 ft 7⅛ in)
Wing area, gross	26·00 m²	(279·86 sq ft)
Wing aspect ratio	3·57	
Length overall:		
incl probe	14·88 m	(48 ft 9⅞ in)
excl probe	13·99 m	(45 ft 10¾ in)
Height overall	4·45 m	(14 ft 7¼ in)
Wheel track (c/l of shock-struts)		
	2·50 m	(8 ft 2½ in)
Wheelbase	5·35 m	(17 ft 6⅝ in)

WEIGHTS AND LOADINGS (A: prototypes, B: production version):
Weight empty, equipped: A	6,100 kg	(13,448 lb)
B	5,700 kg	(12,566 lb)
Internal fuel load: A	2,600 kg	(5,732 lb)
B	2,700 kg	(5,952 lb)
T-O weight 'clean': A	8,880 kg	(19,577 lb)
B	8,600 kg	(18,959 lb)
Max T-O weight with external stores:		
A, B	10,500 kg	(23,148 lb)
Wing loading:		
A at T-O weight 'clean'	341 kg/m²	(69·8 lb/sq ft)
B at T-O weight 'clean'	330 kg/m²	(67·6 lb/sq ft)
A and B at max T-O weight		
	404 kg/m²	(82·7 lb/sq ft)
Power loading:		
A at T-O weight 'clean'	250 kg/kN	(2·45 lb/lb st)
A at max T-O weight	295 kg/kN	(2·89 lb/lb st)
B at T-O weight 'clean'	192 kg/kN	(1·88 lb/lb st)
B at max T-O weight	235 kg/kN	(2·30 lb/lb st)

PERFORMANCE (A: without afterburning; B: production version with afterburning):
Max level speed at low level:		
A	556 knots	(1,030 km/h; 640 mph)
B	610 knots	(1,130 km/h; 702 mph)
Max level speed at high altitude:		
A	529 knots	(980 km/h; 609 mph)
B	577 knots	(1,070 km/h; 665 mph)
Landing speed:		
A, B	130 knots	(240 km/h; 149 mph)
Max rate of climb at S/L at 'clean' T-O weight:		
A	2,310 m	(7,578 ft)/min
B	4,536 m	(14,882 ft)/min
Time to 12,000 m (39,370 ft): A		10 min 15 s
Time to 13,000 m (42,650 ft): B		5 min 30 s
Service ceiling: A	12,000 m	(39,370 ft)
B	13,000 m	(42,650 ft)
T-O run:		
A at 8,500 kg (18,740 lb) AUW	925 m	(3,035 ft)
B at max T-O weight	1,000 m	(3,280 ft)
Landing run:		
A at 8,500 kg (18,740 lb) AUW	900 m	(2,953 ft)
B at max T-O weight	1,100 m	(3,609 ft)
Combat radius (A and B) with 2,000 kg (4,410 lb) external stores:		
lo-lo-lo	162 nm	(300 km; 186 miles)
hi-lo-hi	194 nm	(360 km; 224 miles)
g limits: A, B		+7·0

Two-seat version of the Orao/IAR-93 (nearest camera) with single-seater

TRANSALL
ARBEITSGEMEINSCHAFT TRANSALL

AIRFRAME COMPANIES:

Aérospatiale, 37 boulevard de Montmorency, 75781 Paris Cédex 16, France
Telephone: 524 43 21
Telex: 620059 F

MBB, PO Box 950109, 2103 Hamburg 95, Federal Republic of Germany
Telephone: (040) 747 5164
Telex: 217684

VFW, Hünefeldstrasse 1-5, 28 Bremen 1, Federal Republic of Germany
Telephone: (0421) 5381
Télex: 245821b

The Transall (Transporter Allianz) group was formed in January 1959 by MBB, Aérospatiale and VFW, to undertake joint development and production of the C-160 twin-turboprop military transport for the French and German air forces. Others were built for the air forces of South Africa and Turkey. Initial production, of the C-160 D (90), C-160 F (50), C-160 T (20) and C-160 Z (9), was shared between the three participating companies and ended in 1972, as described in earlier editions of *Jane's*. Production was reinstated in 1977 to meet an additional French order and requests from other countries.

TRANSALL C-160 (Second Series)

The Transall C-160 was developed originally to meet the specific requirements of the Federal German and French governments for a military transport aircraft capable of carrying troops, casualties, freight, supplies and

vehicles, and of operating from semi-prepared surfaces.

An industrial agreement was signed on 29 October 1976, sharing the work on new production between Aérospatiale (50%) and the two German companies (50%), with a single final assembly line at Toulouse. Aérospatiale builds the wings, wing/fuselage fairings, fuselage doors, emergency exits and engine nacelles. The centre-fuselage, main landing gear fairings and all main tail surfaces are built by VFW. Manufacture of the nosecone, front and rear fuselage sections (including the rear-loading ramp/door) and dorsal fin is undertaken by MBB. The engines, as before, are manufactured jointly by Rolls-Royce, SNECMA, MTU and FN-Herstal. Components are airlifted to Toulouse by Super Guppy transport for final assembly and flight testing.

The main improvements in this second production series are updated avionics, and extended range resulting from a reinforced wing with an optional additional fuel tank in the centre-section. Provision is made for in-flight refuelling and, as a part of the programme, the CEV in France was in 1979-80 evaluating various types of refuelling boom, using an existing C-160 F.

One of the original-production Transall C-160 Fs in service with the French Air Force

In July 1977 the French government gave its approval to the launching of the second production series, primarily to satisfy a requirement of the French Air Force for additional aircraft. The current programme calls for 75 aircraft, of which 25 will be delivered to the French Air Force, joining the 48 remaining original C-160 Fs operated by COTAM (Commandement du Transport Aérien Militaire) and based with the 64th Escadre de Transport at Evreux. Ten of these 25 new aircraft will be fitted at the outset with inflight refuelling equipment (hose reel and drogue) in the port main landing gear fairing; five others will incorporate provisions for this equipment, and be capable of rapid adaptation to the tanker role if needed. All 25 will have a 4 m (13·12 ft) boom receiver mounted above and behind the flight deck.

In addition to the French order, three second-series Transalls have been ordered by the Indonesian government. By mid-1980, eight aircraft were under construction in France and eight in West Germany. First flight is scheduled for March 1981. Deliveries to the French Air Force are due to begin in October 1981, and to Indonesia in 1982.

The following details refer to the new French Air Force/export C-160:

TYPE: Twin-engined turboprop transport.

WINGS: Cantilever high-wing monoplane. Dihedral on outer wings 3° 26′. All-metal two-spar structure designed on fail-safe principles. Wing in three sections, comprising a centre-section, which carries the engines, and two outer panels. All-metal ailerons and hydraulically-operated double-slotted flaps. Hydraulically-operated airbrakes (inboard, above and below wings) and spoilers (outboard) forward of flaps on each wing. Electrical de-icing of leading-edges.

FUSELAGE: Aluminium alloy (2024-T3) semi-monocoque structure of circular basic section, flattened at the bottom, and designed on fail-safe principles. Underside of upswept rear fuselage lowers to form loading ramp for vehicles.

TAIL UNIT: Cantilever aluminium alloy (2024-T3) structure. Large dorsal fin.

LANDING GEAR: Retractable tricycle type, built by Messier-Hispano-Bugatti and Liebherr-Aerotechnik. Hydraulic retraction and hydraulic/pneumatic shock-absorption. Each main unit comprises two pairs of wheels in tandem and is mounted inside a fairing on the side of the fuselage. Wheels can be raised to lower the fuselage for loading. Steerable twin-wheel nose unit. Main-wheel tyres size 15·00 × 16; nosewheel tyres size 12·5 × 16. Tyre pressure 3·79 bars (55 lb/sq in) on main units, 3·14 bars (45·5 lb/sq in) on nose unit. Messier-Hispano-Bugatti brakes.

POWER PLANT: Two 4,549 kW (6,100 ehp) Rolls-Royce Tyne RTy.20 Mk 22 turboprop engines, each driving a Ratier Forest-built BAe Dynamics 4/8000/6 four-blade constant-speed fully-feathering reversible-pitch propeller. Single-point pressure refuelling; gravity refuelling available optionally. Fuel in four integral wing tanks with total capacity of 19,050 litres (4,190 Imp gallons). Additional wing centre-section tank optional, capacity 9,000 litres (1,980 Imp gallons). Provision for in-flight refuelling. Water-methanol usable capacity 318·5 litres (70 Imp gallons). Oil capacity (total) 68·4 litres (15 Imp gallons).

ACCOMMODATION: Pressurised accommodation for crew of three, comprising pilot, co-pilot, and flight engineer. Typical payloads include 93 troops or 61-88 fully-equipped paratroops; 62 stretchers and four attendants; armoured vehicles, tanks and tractors not exceeding 17,000 kg (37,478 lb) total weight. Flight deck and cargo compartment air-conditioned and pressurised in flight and on the ground. Power-assisted controls. Paratroop door on each side immediately aft of the landing gear fairings; hydraulically-operated rear loading ramp. The floor and all doors are at truckbed height. The floor is provided with lashing points of 5,000 kg (11,023 lb) capacity, arranged in a 51 cm (20 in) grid, and 12,000 kg (26,455 lb) capacity on the sidewalls, and is stressed to carry large military vehicles. Loads which cannot be driven in can be taken on board rapidly by an automatic translation and stowing system. Individual loads of up to 8,000 kg (17,637 lb) can be air-dropped, including drops at low altitude (3-9 m; 10-30 ft) or during touch-and-go.

SYSTEMS: Normalair pressurisation and air-conditioning

Transall C-160 twin-turboprop general-purpose transport aircraft *(Pilot Press)*

system, differential 0·302-0·322 bars (4·38-4·67 lb/sq in). Two separate primary hydraulic systems, pressure 175 bars (2,500 lb/sq in), for flying controls, loading ramp, landing gear, wheel brakes, flaps, spoilers, airbrakes, nosewheel steering and other auxiliaries. Two more systems, pressure 175 bars (2,538 lb/sq in), for emergency and ground services, as well as a hand-pump driven emergency system. AC electrical system includes two 60kVA 380-580Hz generators, one 60kVA 400Hz generator and two 9kVA 400Hz generators. 28V DC system and 40Ah batteries. Garrett-AiResearch GTCP-85-160A APU in forward part of port main undercarriage fairing.

AVIONICS AND EQUIPMENT: Socrat TRAP-138 VHF; TRT TRAP-139 UHF; LMT 3527C or Collins 628T-1 HF; TEAM AS-1227B PA system; TEAM TF-AP 14 intercom; EAS RNA-720 VOR/ILS; Collins NRAN-19 or DF 206 ADF; LMT DM-820 or Collins 860E-5 (without Micro-Tacan) DME; LMT-3560 or Collins 621A-6A ATC transponder; Omera ORB-37 weather radar; TRT AHV-6 radio altimeter; EAS RM-671 or Collins 51Z-4 marker beacon; Jaeger 60571 or Jaeger 64111 encoding altimeter; SFIM CADV automatic flight control system, incorporating two vertical gyros, two gyro-compasses, PA-51 autopilot and DV-86 flight director; and EMD RDN-72 Doppler navigation radar. Export version available with LMT Micro-Tacan; Collins DF-301E UHF/DF (with UHF com system); Sercel Crouzet type Equinox Omega; and TRT APS-500 GPWS.

DIMENSIONS, EXTERNAL:

Wing span	40·00 m (131 ft 3 in)
Wing chord at root	4·84 m (15 ft 10½ in)
Wing chord at tip	2·428 m (7 ft 11½ in)
Wing chord (mean)	4·176 m (13 ft 8½ in)
Wing aspect ratio	10
Length overall	32·40 m (106 ft 3½ in)
Fuselage: Max diameter	4·30 m (14 ft 1¼ in)
Height overall	11·65 m (38 ft 2¾ in)
Tailplane span	14·50 m (47 ft 7 in)
Wheel track	5·10 m (16 ft 9 in)
Wheelbase	10·48 m (34 ft 4½ in)
Propeller diameter	6·50 m (21 ft 4 in)
Distance between propeller centres	
	10·90 m (35 ft 9¼ in)
Crew door (fwd, port): Height	1·22 m (4 ft 0 in)
Width	0·62 m (2 ft 0½ in)
Paratroop door (each side):	
Height	1·90 m (6 ft 2½ in)
Width	0·90 m (3 ft 0 in)
Rear loading ramp: Length	3·70 m (12 ft 1½ in)
Width	3·15 m (10 ft 3½ in)
Emergency exits:	
Main hold, fwd, stbd side (one):	
Height	0·88 m (2 ft 10½ in)
Width	0·54 m (1 ft 9¼ in)
Flight deck roof (one); roof of main hold, fwd (one); and two in roof of main hold at rear (one each side of dorsal fin): Height	0·54 m (1 ft 9¼ in)
Width	0·64 m (2 ft 1¼ in)

DIMENSIONS, INTERNAL:

Cabin, excl flight deck and ramp:	
Length	13·51 m (44 ft 4 in)
Max width	3·15 m (10 ft 3½ in)
Max height	2·98 m (9 ft 8½ in)
Floor area	42·6 m² (458·5 sq ft)
Volume	115·0 m³ (4,061 cu ft)
Cabin, incl ramp: Length	17·21 m (56 ft 6 in)
Floor area	54·25 m² (584 sq ft)
Volume	139·9 m³ (4,940 cu ft)

AREAS:

Wings, gross	160·00 m² (1,722 sq ft)
Ailerons (total)	6·88 m² (74·06 sq ft)
Trailing-edge flaps (total, extended)	
	34·54 m² (371·8 sq ft)
Spoilers (total)	0·80 m² (8·61 sq ft)
Fin: excl dorsal fin	29·50 m² (317·5 sq ft)
incl dorsal fin	36·00 m² (387·5 sq ft)
Rudder	10·20 m² (109·8 sq ft)
Tailplane	43·80 m² (471·5 sq ft)
Elevators	10·30 m² (110·9 sq ft)

WEIGHTS AND LOADINGS:

Min operating weight empty	28,000 kg (61,729 lb)
Typical operating weight empty	
	29,000 kg (63,934 lb)
Max payload	16,000 kg (35,274 lb)
Max T-O weight	51,000 kg (112,435 lb)
Max zero-fuel weight	45,000 kg (99,208 lb)
Max landing weight	47,000 kg (103,617 lb)
Max wing loading	319 kg/m² (65·34 lb/sq ft)
Max power loading	5·61 kg/kW (9·22 lb/ehp)

PERFORMANCE (at max T-O weight except where indicated):

Never-exceed speed:	
at 4,875-9,145 m (16,000-30,000 ft)	Mach 0·64
below 4,875 m (16,000 ft)	
	320 knots (593 km/h; 368 mph)
Max level speed at 4,875 m (16,000 ft)	
	277 knots (513 km/h; 319 mph)
Stalling speed, flaps down	
	95 knots (177 km/h; 110 mph)
Max rate of climb at S/L	396 m (1,300 ft)/min
Rate of climb at S/L, one engine out	
	91 m (300 ft)/min
Service ceiling at 45,000 kg (99,208 lb) AUW	
	8,535 m (28,000 ft)
Service ceiling, one engine out at 45,000 kg (99,208 lb) AUW	
	3,050 m (10,000 ft)
T-O run, 20° flap	730 m (2,395 ft)
T-O to 10·5 m (35 ft), 20° flap	990 m (3,248 ft)
Landing from 15 m (50 ft), 40° flap, at max landing weight without propeller reversal	869 m (2,850 ft)
Landing run, normal	550 m (1,800 ft)
Min ground turning radius	28·60 m (93 ft 10 in)
Range, reserve of 5% initial fuel, allowance for 30 min hold at S/L, OWE of 29,000 kg (63,934 lb):	
with 8,000 kg (17,640 lb) payload	
	2,750 nm (5,095 km; 3,166 miles)
with 16,000 kg (35,275 lb) payload	
	1,000 nm (1,852 km; 1,151 miles)
Max ferry range with centre-section wing tank	
	4,780 nm (8,858 km; 5,504 miles)

ISRAEL

IAI
ISRAEL AIRCRAFT INDUSTRIES LTD
HEAD OFFICE AND WORKS: Ben Gurion International Airport, Lydda (Lod)
Telephone: 03 973111
Telex: Isravia 31114

PRESIDENT: G. Gidor
EXECUTIVE VICE-PRESIDENT: A. Ostrinski
VICE-PRESIDENTS:
M. Keret (Aircraft and Airborne Systems Marketing)
N. Rosen (Naval Systems and Missiles Marketing)
A. Ezroni (General Manager, Bedek Aviation Division)

M. Blumkin (General Manager, Engineering Division)
Y. Ben-Bassat (General Manager, Manufacturing Division)
Y. Giladi (General Manager, Combined Technologies Division)
M. Na'aman (General Manager, Electronics Division)
M. Dvir (Research and Development)

D. Mozes (Finance)
Mrs. H. Ron (General Counsel)
Y. Zinger (Comptroller)
COMMERCIAL DIRECTOR, ARAVA: H. Pearlman
COMMERCIAL DIRECTOR, WESTWIND: S. Samach

This company was established in 1953 as Bedek Aircraft Company. The change of name, to Israel Aircraft Industries, was made on 1 April 1967.

IAI employs more than 22,000 people in all its facilities, which occupy á total covered floor area of 300,000 m² (3,229,170 sq ft). It is licensed by, among others, the Israel Civil Aviation Administration, US Federal Aviation Administration, British Civil Aviation Authority and the Israeli Air Force as an approved repair station and maintenance organisation.

Israel Aircraft Industries Ltd is composed of several divisions, plants and subsidiary companies. These underwent a major reorganisation in the latter part of 1977, and are now disposed in five divisions, as follows:

Bedek Aviation, now incorporating Turbochrome, is an internationally approved multi-faceted single-site civil and military aircraft service centre. Present programmes include the turnaround inspection, overhaul, repair, retrofitting, outfitting and testing of 30 types of aircraft, including the Boeing 707/720 and McDonnell Douglas DC-8; 28 types of civil and military engines, including the 244·7 kN (55,000 lb st) Pratt & Whitney JT9D; and 8,000 types of components, accessories and systems. Offshore workload includes the supply of total technical support to several international operators. The division holds warranty and/or approved service centre approvals from many of the world's leading component manufacturers. Bedek has refurbished and resold numerous Boeing 707/720s, often after conversion from passenger to cargo configuration. The procedure for the structural modification was developed jointly by Boeing and Bedek Aviation.

Bedek Aviation has a total floor area of some 74,322 m² (800,000 sq ft) and in 1978 employed a staff of about 3,500.

The **Manufacturing Division** produces the Kfir fighter, the IAI-designed Arava STOL transport, and the turbofan-powered Westwind business aircraft. In addition, it is engaged in the manufacture of a vast variety of spares and assemblies for aircraft and jet engines, to meet Israeli Air Force requirements. As a subcontractor to many US and European aircraft manufacturers, the Division produces major aircraft structures, flight control surfaces, cargo loading systems and spares. It had a work force of about 5,500 in 1978.

The **Engineering Division** is responsible for engineering research, design, development and testing of aerospace systems. It provides engineering support in system analysis, aerodynamics, materials and processing, landing and control systems, and in structural, flight and environmental testing. The Division performed modification and production support for the manufacture of the Magister jet trainer for the IAF; and major structural conversions of the Boeing Model 377, for military applications such as swing-tail freighter and hose-refuelling tanker. The Division designed and developed the Arava STOL transport aircraft and developed both the 1123 and 1124 Westwind.

In 1979 the Engineering Division, which then employed about 1,800 people, was engaged in a variety of programmes which included the development of a supercritical wing for the Westwind, a fly-by-wire system for flight testing in the Kfir, and research into materials, structures and electronic countermeasures. It is now developing a new single-seat strike fighter known as the Lavi (Lion), intended to replace eventually the Israeli Air Force's A-4 Skyhawks and F-4 Phantoms.

The **Electronics Division** incorporates the company's former electronics subsidiary, Elta, the MBT Weapon Systems subsidiary, Tamam Precision Instruments, and MLM Systems Engineering and Integration. It specialises in the design, development and production of sophisticated electronic equipment such as airborne, ground and shipborne communications and radars, transceivers and navigational

aids, general communications equipment, automatic test systems, and such electronic medical devices as cardiac resuscitation instruments. MBT participated in the development of the Gabriel shipborne surface-to-surface missile system, among others, as well as of an electronic warning fence and an audible bomb release altimeter. Tamam manufactures and assembles high-precision electromechanical components and servo-systems for such mechanisms as aerosystems, torque motors and gyroscopes.

The SHL (Servo-Hydraulics Lod), PML, Ramta, MATA Helicopters and Golan Industries subsidiaries now make up the **Combined Technologies Division.** This designs, develops and manufactures hydraulic and fuel system components, hydraulic flight control servo-systems, landing gears and brake systems; produces air-actuated chucks, miniature gears, clutches and brakes; is a custom-moulder of reinforced plastics, producing parts for aircraft, cabs and trucks, concrete casting moulds and sheet products; manufactures ground support equipment, stainless steel tanks, the Dabur patrol boat and the RBY armoured vehicle; manufactures high precision metal products for the aircraft and military industries; and produces electronic assemblies and subassemblies for aircraft.

IAI NESHER (EAGLE)

A total of 26 Nesher fighters (see 1977-78 *Jane's*) were sold to the Argentinian Air Force in 1978-79, to equip two squadrons, according to reports in the Israeli press. Known as Daggers in Argentina, the aircraft are operated by No. VI Brigada Aérea, from Tandil, near Buenos Aires.

IAI LAVI (YOUNG LION)

Israeli government approval has been given for IAI to develop a new, single-engined single-seat strike fighter for the Israeli Air Force. No other details were known at the time of closing for press. Unconfirmed reports suggest that US government approval is being sought for licence manufacture in Israel of General Electric F404 low bypass turbofans for this programme.

IAI KFIR (LION CUB)

Following manufacture of the Nesher fighter, powered by an Atar turbojet, IAI developed a more extensively modified and further improved version of the same airframe, powered by a General Electric J79 afterburning turbojet engine. One of these engines was installed in a much-modified Israeli Air Force Mirage III-B, with which it was first test-flown in September 1971, and production of the J79-engined Mirage began in 1972. A prototype of the Kfir was flown in 1973, before the outbreak of the October 'Yom Kippur' war, and details of this further-modified version were made public officially for the first time on 14 April 1975, when two of the new aircraft were displayed at Ben Gurion Airport.

The Kfir utilises a basic airframe similar to that of the Dassault Mirage 5, the main changes being a shorter but larger-diameter rear fuselage, to accommodate the J79 engine; an enlarged and flattened undersurface to the forward portion of the fuselage; introduction of four small fuselage airscoops, plus a larger dorsal airscoop in place of the triangular dorsal fin, to provide cooling air for the afterburner; and a strengthened landing gear, with longer-stroke oleos. Several internal changes have also been made, including a redesigned cockpit layout, addition of a considerable amount of Israeli-built avionics equipment, and revised internal fuel tankage compared with the Mirage 5. Intended for both air defence and ground attack roles, the Kfir retains the standard Mirage fixed armament of two 30 mm DEFA cannon, and can carry a variety of external weapons including the Rafael Shafrir 2 air-to-air and Luz-1 air-to-surface missiles. It has demonstrated stall-free gun firing throughout the flight envelope. Two squadrons of the Israeli Air Force were equipped with this initial Kfir-C1 version.

On 20 July 1976, at the Israeli Air Force base at Hatzerim, in the Negev, the first public demonstration took

Kfir-C2, showing bulged main-wheel doors
(Israeli Government Press Office)

place of a modified version known as the **Kfir-C2**, which by that time was already in Israeli Air Force service, having entered production in 1974. The Kfir-C2 has a number of changes from the C1, the most significant of which is the addition of non-retractable, sweptback canard surfaces just aft of the engine air intakes; a small strake on each side of the extreme nose; and an extended wing leading-edge, created by increasing the chord on approximately the outer 40% of each half-span. The canard surfaces can be detached for missions not requiring high manoeuvrability.

The Kfir-C2 is the principal production version, both for the Israeli Air Force and for export. The modifications, which are reportedly being retrofitted to existing Kfirs, were designed to improve the aircraft's dogfighting manoeuvrability at the lower end of the speed range and to enhance take-off and landing performance. It is claimed that, in particular, they give a better sustained turning performance, with improved lateral, longitudinal and directional control; contribute to a very low gust response at all operational altitudes, especially at very low level; offer improved handling qualities at all angles of attack, high g loadings, and low speeds; reduce take-off and landing distances, and landing speeds; and permit a more stable (and, if required, a steeper) approach, with a flatter angle of approach and touchdown. Later versions of the C2 have Elta EL/M-2001B nose radar in an extended nose, increasing the overall length by 0·80 m (2 ft 7½ in).

A two-seat trainer version of the Kfir-C2 is reported to be under development. Overall dimensions, power plant and performance are expected to be similar to those of the single-seat version.

Approximately 150 Kfirs and Kfir-C2s were believed to have been built by the Spring of 1979, with production then continuing at an approximate rate of two to three C2s per month.

The following description applies to the Kfir-C2:

TYPE: Single-seat interceptor, long range patrol fighter and ground attack aircraft.

WINGS: Cantilever low-wing monoplane of delta planform, with conical camber. Thickness/chord ratio 4·5% to 3·5%. Anhedral 1°. Incidence 1°. Sweepback on leading-edges 60° 35'. All-metal torsion-box structure, with stressed skin of machined panels with integral stiffeners. Two-section elevons on each trailing-edge, with smaller elevator/trim flap inboard of inner elevon. Elevons powered by hydraulic jacks; trim flaps are servo-assisted. Small, hinged plate-type airbrake above and below each wing, near leading-edge. Extended chord on outer leading-edges. Small leading-edge fence on some aircraft, at approx one-third span.

IAI Kfir-C2 single-seat interceptor, long range patrol fighter and ground attack aircraft *(Israeli Defence Force)*

IAI Kfir-C2 (General Electric J79-J1E afterburning turbojet engine) *(Pilot Press)*

CANARDS: Detachable sweptback canard surface above and forward of each wing, near top lip of engine air intake.

FUSELAGE: All-metal semi-monocoque structure, 'waisted' in accordance with area rule. Cross-section of forward fuselage has a wider and flatter undersurface than that of Mirage 5. Nosecone built of locally-developed composite materials, with a small horizontal strake or 'body fence' on each side near the tip. UHF antenna under front of fuselage, forward of nosewheel door. Enlarged-diameter rear fuselage, compared with Mirage 5, with approx 0·61 m (2 ft) shorter tailpipe. Ventral fairing under rear fuselage.

TAIL UNIT: Cantilever all-metal fin; rudder powered by hydraulic jack, with servo-assisted trim. UHF antenna in tip of fin. Triangular-section dorsal airscoop forward of fin, to provide cold air for afterburner cooling. No horizontal tail surfaces.

LANDING GEAR: Retractable tricycle type, with single SHL wheel on each unit. Electrically operated hydraulic actuation, nose unit retracting rearward, main units inward into fuselage. Longer-stroke oleos than on Mirage 5, and all units strengthened to permit higher operating weights. Low-pressure tubeless tyres on all units. Main-gear leg fairings shorter than on Mirage; inner portion of each main-leg door is integral with fuselage-mounted wheel door. Steerable nosewheel, with anti-shimmy damper. Oleo-pneumatic shock-absorbers, SHL hydraulic disc brakes and anti-skid units. Braking parachute in bullet fairing below rudder.

POWER PLANT: One General Electric J79-J1E turbojet engine (modified GE-17), with variable-area nozzle, rated at 52·9 kN (11,890 lb st) dry and 79·62 kN (17,900 lb st) with afterburning. Air intakes enlarged, compared with Mirage 5, to allow for higher mass flow. Adjustable half-cone centrebody in each air intake. Internal fuel in five fuselage and four integral wing tanks. Total internal capacity 3,243 litres (713 Imp gallons). There is a refuelling point on top of the fuselage, above the forward upper tank. In addition, there are wet-points for the carriage of one or two drop-tanks beneath each wing, and one under the fuselage; these tanks may be of 500, 600, 1,300 or 1,700 litres (110, 132, 286 or 374 Imp gallons) capacity. Max external fuel load 3,900 litres (858 Imp gallons).

ACCOMMODATION: Pilot only, on Martin-Baker IL10P zero-zero ejection seat, under rearward-hinged upward-opening canopy. Cockpit pressurised, heated and air-conditioned. A two-seat version is under development.

SYSTEMS: Two separate environmental control systems (ECS), one (using engine bleed air) for cockpit heating, pressurisation and air-conditioning, and one for avionics compartments. Two independent hydraulic systems, probably of 207 bars (3,000 lb/sq in) pressure. No. 1 system actuates flying control surfaces and landing gear; No. 2 actuates flying controls, airbrakes, landing gear, wheel brakes and utilities. Fully redundant primary AC electrical system, with two 1.5kVA (115V 400Hz) alternators, each driven by a CSD (constant-speed drive) unit, and a 750VA Oram static inverter connected for split-bus non-synchronised operation. DC system includes two Elta 200A 28V transformer-rectifiers and a 24V 40Ah nickel-cadmium battery. External AC and DC power receptacles. Oxygen system for pilot.

AVIONICS AND EQUIPMENT: MBT twin-computer flight control system (ASW-41 control augmentation and ASW-42 stability augmentation systems), with Elta integrated memory unit (IMU), Tamam two-axis gyro and standby compass, autopilot, MBT radar altimeter, angle of attack transmitter and indicator, and accelerometer indicator. Elbit S-8600 multi-mode navigation

(Singer-Kearfott licence) and Rafael Mahat weapon delivery system or IAI WDNS-141 weapon delivery and navigation system, Tamam central air data computer, Tacan, Elta EL/M-2001B or EL/M-2021 X-band air-to-air and air-to-surface pulse-Doppler target acquisition and tracking radar, IFF/SIF and fire control, Israel Electro-optics head-up display and automatic gunsight. Two Elta AN/ARC-51 UHF transceivers. Twin landing lights on nosewheel leg; anti-collision light in fin leading-edge.

ARMAMENT: Fixed armament of one IAI-built 30 mm DEFA 552 cannon in underside of each engine air intake (140 rds/gun). Seven hardpoints (three under fuselage and two under each wing) for up to 4,295 kg (9,468 lb) of external stores. For interception duties, one Rafael Shafrir 2 infra-red homing air-to-air missile can be carried under each outer wing. Ground attack version can carry two 1,000 lb bombs, four 500 lb bombs, or a Rafael Luz-1 or similar air-to-surface missile under the fuselage, and two 1,000 lb or six 500 lb bombs (conventional or 'concrete dibber' type) under the wings. Alternative external stores may include IMI rocket pods; napalm; Shrike, Maverick or Hobos air-to-surface missiles; ECM pods; or drop-tanks.

DIMENSIONS, EXTERNAL:
Wing span	8·22 m (26 ft 11½ in)
Wing chord at root	8·04 m (26 ft 4½ in)
Wing aspect ratio	1·94
Canard span	3·73 m (12 ft 3 in)
Length overall, incl probe	15·65 m (51 ft 4¼ in)
Height overall	4·55 m (14 ft 11¼ in)
Wheel track	3·20 m (10 ft 6 in)
Wheelbase	4·87 m (15 ft 11¾ in)

AREAS:
Wings, gross	34·8 m² (374·6 sq ft)
Canards (total)	1·66 m² (17·87 sq ft)

WEIGHTS AND LOADINGS:
Weight empty (interceptor, estimated)	7,285 kg (16,060 lb)
Max internal fuel	2,572 kg (5,670 lb)
Max external fuel	3,075 kg (6,780 lb)

Typical combat weight:
interceptor, 50% internal fuel, two Shafrir missiles	9,390 kg (20,700 lb)
interceptor, two 500 litre drop-tanks, two Shafrir missiles	11,603 kg (25,580 lb)
combat air patrol, three 1,300 litre drop-tanks, two Shafrir missiles	14,270 kg (31,460 lb)
ground attack, two 1,300 litre drop-tanks, seven 500 lb bombs, two Shafrir missiles	14,670 kg (32,340 lb)
Max combat T-O weight	14,700 kg (32,408 lb)
Wing loading at 9,390 kg (20,700 lb) combat weight	270 kg/m² (55·3 lb/sq ft)
Thrust/weight ratio at 9,390 kg (20,700 lb) combat weight	0·87

PERFORMANCE:
Max speed above 11,000 m (36,100 ft) over Mach 2·3 (1,317 knots; 2,440 km/h; 1,516 mph)	
Max sustained level speed at height, 'clean'	Mach 2·0
Max level speed at S/L, 'clean'	750 knots (1,389 km/h; 863 mph)
Max rate of climb at S/L	14,000 m (45,950 ft)/min
Time to 15,250 m (50,000 ft), full internal fuel, two Shafrir missiles	5 min 10 s
Height attainable in zoom climb	22,860 m (75,000 ft)
Stabilised ceiling (combat configuration)	17,680 m (58,000 ft)
T-O run at max T-O weight	1,450 m (4,750 ft)
Landing from 15 m (50 ft) at 11,566 kg (25,500 lb) landing weight	1,555 m (5,100 ft)
Landing run at 11,566 kg (25,500 lb) landing weight	1,280 m (4,200 ft)

Combat radius, 20 min fuel reserves:
interceptor, two 500 litre drop-tanks, two Shafrir missiles	187 nm (346 km; 215 miles)
combat air patrol, three 1,300 litre drop-tanks, two Shafrir missiles	377 nm (699 km; 434 miles)
ground attack, hi-lo-hi, seven 500 lb bombs, two Shafrir missiles, two 1,300 litre drop-tanks	415 nm (768 km; 477 miles)
g limit	+7

IAI 101, 102 and 201 ARAVA

Design of the Arava light STOL transport started in 1966, and construction of a prototype began towards the end of that year. This airframe was used for structural testing; it was followed by a flying prototype (4X-IAI), which first flew on 27 November 1969. A second Arava (4X-IAA) began flight trials on 8 May 1971.

The following versions have been announced:

IAI 101. Civil transport version, certificated by FAA in April 1972.

IAI 102. Civil transport version, based on original IAI 101, certificated by Israel Civil Aviation Administration in April 1976. This version can accommodate 20 passengers in airline-standard four-abreast configuration, with toilet. It is available also in a VIP configuration for up to 12 passengers, as an all-cargo transport, as a medical clinic for flying doctor services, and in versions for mapping, mining research, rainmaking and bridge construction, as flying laboratories for agriculture and health ministries, and for supplying oil prospecting units.

IAI 201. Military transport version, based upon the original IAI 101. A prototype (4X-IAB) began its flight tests on 7 March 1972, and this version is now in production. The standard equipment available for the IAI 201 enables a wide variety of missions to be undertaken, and in 1977 IAI announced a version suitable for maritime surveillance duties, fitted with either an AD-9 modification to extend the range and detection capability of the standard search/weather radar, or a more advanced detection system.

IAI 202. Modified version, described in 1979-80 and earlier editions of *Jane's*. Differs from other versions principally in being longer, and in having a fully 'wet' wing with endplate surfaces ('winglets') at the tips, and a boundary layer fence just inboard of each tip. Other features

IAI 201 Arava twin-turboprop STOL light military transport *(Pilot Press)*

IAI 201 Arava twin-turboprop military transport for the Salvadorean Air Force

include 559 kW (750 shp) Pratt & Whitney Aircraft of Canada PT6A-36 turboprop engines, and a single-point pressure refuelling system. The winglet modification (but not the increased fuel capacity) is available as a retrofit modification of existing Aravas.

Prior to the October 1973 war 15 military Aravas had been ordered, 14 of them for export. During that conflict three Aravas were lease-operated by the Israeli Air Force.

Sales of the Arava have reached more than 80, of which more than 60 had been delivered by the beginning of 1979. Customers include the Israeli Air Force (14), Bolivian Air Force (6), Colombian Air Force (3), Ecuadorean Army (6) and Navy (3), Guatemalan Air Force (10), Honduran Air Force (3), Mexican Air Force (more than 10), Nicaraguan Air Force (2) and Salvadorean Air Force (5). Six civil Arava 102s have been sold to customers in Argentina and two in Africa.

The following description applies to the IAI 201, except where indicated otherwise:

TYPE: Twin-turboprop STOL light military transport.

WINGS: Braced high-wing monoplane, with single streamline-section strut each side. Wing section NACA 63(215)A 417. Dihedral 1° 30′. Incidence 0° 27′. No sweepback. Light alloy two-spar torsion-box structure. Frise-type light alloy ailerons. Electrically-operated double-slotted light alloy flaps. Scoop-type light alloy spoilers, for lateral control, above wing at 71% chord. Electrically-actuated trim tab in port aileron.

FUSELAGE: Conventional semi-monocoque light alloy structure of stringers, frames and single-skin panels.

TAIL UNIT: Cantilever light alloy structure, with twin fins and rudders, carried on twin booms extending rearward from engine nacelles. Fixed-incidence tailplane. Geared tab and electrically-actuated trim tab in elevator and geared trim tab in each rudder. Tailbooms are built by IAI Combined Technologies Division.

LANDING GEAR: Non-retractable tricycle type, of Servo-Hydraulics Lod manufacture, with single main wheels and steerable nosewheel. Main wheels carried on twin struts, incorporating oleo-pneumatic shock-absorbers. Main wheels size 11·00-12, tyre pressure 3·31 bars (48 lb/sq in); nosewheel size 9·00-6, tyre pressure 2·90 bars (42 lb/sq in). Disc brakes on main units. Float landing gear reportedly under development.

POWER PLANT: Two 559 kW (750 shp) Pratt & Whitney Aircraft of Canada PT6A-34 turboprop engines, each driving a Hartzell HC-B3TN three-blade hydraulically-actuated fully-feathering reversible-pitch metal propeller. Electrical de-icing of propellers optional. Two integral fuel tanks in each wing, with total usable capacity of 1,663 litres (366 Imp gallons). Four overwing refuelling points. Optional pressure refuelling point in fuselage/strut fairing. Two cabin-mounted tanks, each of 1,022 litres (225 Imp gallons), are available optionally for self-ferry flights.

ACCOMMODATION: Crew of one or two on flight deck, with door on starboard side. Main cabin of IAI 101 has folding inward-facing metal-framed fabric seats along each side, and can accommodate 20 civilian passengers. IAI 201 has similar seating for 24 fully-equipped troops or 17 paratroops and a dispatcher. IAI 102 has airline-type seating for up to 20 passengers, plus toilet. Outward-opening door at rear of cabin, opposite which, at floor level, is an emergency exit door/cargo door on the starboard side. Rear doors are built by IAI Combined Technologies Division. Aft section of fuselage is hinged to swing sideways through more than 90° to provide unrestricted access to main cabin. Alternative interior configurations available for ambulance role (12 stretchers and two sitting patients or medical attendants); as all-freight transport carrying (typically) a Jeep-mounted recoil-less rifle and its four-man crew; or as a maritime patrol aircraft fitted with search radar and other special equipment.

SYSTEMS: Hydraulic system (pressure 172 bars; 2,500 lb/sq in) for brakes and nosewheel steering only. Electrical

system includes two 28V 170A DC engine-driven starter/generators, a 28V 40Ah nickel-cadmium battery, and two 250VA 115/26V 400Hz static inverters.

AVIONICS AND EQUIPMENT: Blind-flying instrumentation standard. Optional avionics include VHF, VOR/ILS, ADF, marker beacon receiver and PA system.

ARMAMENT: Optional 0·50 in Browning machine-gun pack on each side of fuselage, above a pylon for a pod containing six 82 mm rockets. Provision for aft-firing machine-gun. Librascope gunsight.

DIMENSIONS, EXTERNAL (IAI 201):

Wing span	20·96 m (68 ft 9 in)
Wing chord (constant)	2·09 m (6 ft 10½ in)
Wing aspect ratio	10
Length overall	13·03 m (42 ft 9 in)
Length of fuselage pod	9·33 m (30 ft 7 in)
Diameter of fuselage	2·50 m (8 ft 2 in)
Height overall	5·21 m (17 ft 1 in)
Tailplane span (c/l of tailbooms)	5·21 m (17 ft 1 in)
Wheel track	4·01 m (13 ft 2 in)
Wheelbase	4·62 m (15 ft 2 in)
Propeller diameter	2·59 m (8 ft 6 in)
Propeller ground clearance	1·75 m (5 ft 9 in)
Crew door (fwd, stbd): Height	0·93 m (3 ft 0½ in)
Width	0·48 m (1 ft 7 in)
Passenger door (rear, port):	
Height	1·57 m (5 ft 2 in)
Width	0·62 m (2 ft 0½ in)
Cargo drop door (rear, port):	
Height	1·75 m (5 ft 9 in)
Width	2·33 m (7 ft 8 in)
Emergency/baggage door (rear, stbd):	
Height	1·12 m (3 ft 8 in)
Width	0·61 m (2 ft 0 in)
Emergency window exits (each):	
Height	0·66 m (2 ft 2 in)
Width	0·48 m (1 ft 7 in)

DIMENSIONS, INTERNAL:

Cabin, excl flight deck and hinged tailcone:	
Length	3·87 m (12 ft 8 in)
Max width	2·33 m (7 ft 8 in)
Max height	1·75 m (5 ft 9 in)
Floor area	7·16 m² (77 sq ft)
Volume	12·7 m³ (449·2 cu ft)
Baggage compartment volume	2·60 m³ (91·8 cu ft)
Cargo door volume	3·20 m³ (113 cu ft)

AREAS (IAI 201):

Wings, gross	43·68 m² (470·2 sq ft)
Ailerons (total)	1·75 m² (18·84 sq ft)
Trailing-edge flaps (total)	8·80 m² (94·72 sq ft)
Spoilers (total)	0·85 m² (9·2 sq ft)
Fins (total)	4·86 m² (52·31 sq ft)
Rudders (total incl tabs)	3·44 m² (37·03 sq ft)
Tailplane	9·36 m² (100·75 sq ft)
Elevator, incl tabs	2·79 m² (30·03 sq ft)

WEIGHTS AND LOADINGS (IAI 201):

Basic operating weight	3,999 kg (8,816 lb)
Max payload	2,351 kg (5,184 lb)
Max T-O and landing weight	6,803 kg (15,000 lb)
Max zero-fuel weight	6,350 kg (14,000 lb)
Max wing loading	153·5 kg/m² (31·44 lb/sq ft)
Max power loading	6·08 kg/kW (10·00 lb/hp)

PERFORMANCE (IAI 201, at max T-O weight):

Never-exceed speed	215 knots (397 km/h; 247 mph)
Max level speed at 3,050 m (10,000 ft)	176 knots (326 km/h; 203 mph)
Max cruising speed at 3,050 m (10,000 ft)	172 knots (319 km/h; 198 mph)
Econ cruising speed at 3,050 m (10,000 ft)	168 knots (311 km/h; 193 mph)
Stalling speed, 0° flap	75 knots (140 km/h; 87 mph)
Stalling speed, 54° flap	62 knots (115 km/h; 71·5 mph)
Max rate of climb at S/L	393 m (1,290 ft)/min
Rate of climb at S/L, one engine out	55 m (180 ft)/min
Service ceiling	7,620 m (25,000 ft)
Service ceiling, one engine out	2,375 m (7,800 ft)
STOL T-O run	293 m (960 ft)
STOL T-O to 15 m (50 ft)	463 m (1,520 ft)
STOL landing from 15 m (50 ft)	469 m (1,540 ft)
STOL landing run	250 m (820 ft)
Range with max payload, 45 min reserves	151 nm (280 km; 174 miles)
Range with max fuel, 45 min reserves	705 nm (1,306 km; 812 miles)

IAI 1124/WESTWIND I
Israeli Navy designation: 1124 Sea Scan

A total of 186 early-model Jet Commander/Commodore Jet executive aircraft were sold by Aero Commander and IAI, and have been described in previous editions of *Jane's*. Aircraft from c/n 187 onwards have Garrett/AiResearch TFE 731 turbofan engines and are named Westwind. The IAI 1124 longer-range version of the Westwind was certificated by the FAA in the Spring of 1976. Two 1123 Westwinds (see 1976-77 *Jane's*) had been modified as flight test aircraft and the first of these made its first flight on 21 July 1975. A total of 100 Model 1124s had been sold by September 1979; in early 1980 production was being increased to a rate of four per month. Recent orders include four for use as high-speed target tugs for the West German Marineflieger.

Aircraft from c/n 240 onwards are designated **Westwind I**. Major changes in the Westwind I from the original 1124 are a 317 kg (700 lb) increase in fuel load, installed in a removable tank in one of the two baggage compartments; and an increase of approx 5% in cabin useful volume by relocation of some avionics and by lowering the floor in the toilet/lavatory compartment. Environmental and fuel systems have been improved, and standard avionics include an RCA Primus 400 colour radar.

An advanced version, the **Westwind 2**, is described separately.

The following maritime reconnaissance version is available:

1124 Sea Scan. The first operational Sea Scan was delivered in the last quarter of 1978. Several versions are available, equipped for specific operational requirements. Sea Scan is provided with thrust reversers, single-point pressure refuelling, anti-corrosion protection, external stores pylons, bubble windows, Litton APS-504(V)2 360° search radar, VLF/Omega navigation, complete VHF/UHF communications system, operators' consoles to individual customer's requirements, lavatory and refreshment centre. Additional sensor equipment for multi-mission capability can readily be accommodated, including IFF, MAD and low light level TV. A low-altitude search range of 1,379 nm (2,555 km; 1,588 miles), and search endurance of more than 6 h 30 min, enables the Sea Scan to cover a search area of 82,740 nm² (268,056 km²; 103,496 sq miles) along a 60 nm (111 km; 69 mile) search band at a height of 915 m (3,000 ft). Increased search range and endurance to 2,500 nm (4,633 km; 2,878 miles) and over 8 h can be attained at altitudes up to 13,720 m (45,000 ft).

IAI 1124 Westwind I (two Garrett-AiResearch TFE 731-3-1G turbofan engines)

IAI 1124 Sea Scan maritime reconnaissance version of the Westwind

IAI 1124 Westwind twin-turbofan light executive transport *(Pilot Press)*

The description which follows applies to the standard civil Westwind I, which continues in current production:

TYPE: Twin-turbofan business transport.

WINGS: Cantilever mid-wing monoplane. Wing section NACA 64A212. Dihedral 2°. Incidence 1° at root, −1° at tip. Sweepback 4° 37′ at quarter-chord. All-metal flush-riveted two-spar fail-safe structure. Manually-operated all-metal ailerons. Electrically-operated all-metal double-slotted trailing-edge Fowler-type flaps and drooped and cambered leading-edges. Electrically-operated trim tab in port aileron. Hydraulically-actuated speed brake and two lift dumpers above each wing, forward of flap. All skins chemically milled and fully sealed. All primary control surfaces, including tabs, are fully mass-balanced. Pneumatic anti-icing boots standard.

FUSELAGE: All-metal semi-monocoque flush-riveted structure with pressurised fail-safe cabin and baggage compartment. Built in two main sections and joined at aft pressure bulkhead. Forward section, except for nosecone, is fully pressurised.

TAIL UNIT: Cantilever all-metal structure, with 28° sweepback at quarter-chord. Variable-incidence tailplane, actuated electrically. Manually-operated statically-balanced elevators and rudder. Trim tab in rudder. Pneumatic anti-icing boots standard.

LANDING GEAR: Hydraulically-retractable tricycle type, main wheels retracting outward into wings, twin nose-wheels rearward. Oleo-pneumatic shock-absorbers. Single wheels on main units, pressure 10·69 bars (155 lb/sq in). Nose unit steerable and self-centering. Nose-wheel tyre pressure 3·45 bars (50 lb/sq in). Multiple-disc brakes, with fully-modulated anti-skid system having automatic computer/sensor to prevent wheel lock and maintain brake effectiveness. Parking brake fitted.

POWER PLANT: Two 16·46 kN (3,700 lb st) Garrett-AiResearch TFE 731-3-1G turbofan engines, with Grumman thrust reversers, mounted in pod on each side of rear fuselage. 85 % of wing area forms an integral fuel tank, and additional fuel is carried separately in wingtip tanks and rear fuselage tanks. Total usable capacity 4,920 litres (1,082 Imp gallons), including wingtip tanks. Increased weight option permits additional 317 kg (700 lb) of fuel to be carried in a removable tank in one of the two baggage compartments. Single-point pressure refuelling.

ACCOMMODATION: Standard seating for two pilots and up to 10 passengers in pressurised cabin. Interior layout to customer's requirements, with galley and toilet standard. Two separate heated compartments for up to 476 kg (1,050 lb) of baggage. Passenger door at front on port side; emergency exit on each side, forward of wing. Entire accommodation heated, ventilated and air-conditioned.

SYSTEMS: Primary hydraulic system, pressure 138 bars (2,000 lb/sq in), operates through two engine-driven pumps to actuate landing gear, wheel brakes, nosewheel steering, speed brakes and lift dumpers. Electrically-operated emergency system, pressure 69 bars (1,000 lb/sq in), for brakes only. DC electrical system with two 350A 28V engine-driven starter/generators and two 37Ah long-life nickel-cadmium batteries. One main bus for each generator, connected to the central battery bus. A 400Hz 115V AC system is installed, and is powered by two solid-state static inverters, each of 1,000VA capacity, with power fed from the main DC buses. Each inverter is independently capable of supplying the entire AC load if required. Pneumatic system for anti-icing of wing and tail leading-edges only. Warm air bled from engines to prevent icing of air intakes. Windscreen is heated electrically. Garrett-AiResearch cabin environmental control system. Cabin pressure differential 0·61 bars (8·8 lb/sq in).

AVIONICS AND EQUIPMENT: Full dual IFR instrumentation standard. Radio and other avionics include Collins NCS-31A R/Nav and control system (Global Navigation NS-500A VLF on Sea Scan), RCA Primus 40 weather radar, Collins FD-109Z flight director and AP-105 autopilot. Canadian Marconi CMA-734 Omega navigation system approved for use in US and North Atlantic airspace.

DIMENSIONS, EXTERNAL:

Wing span	13·16 m (43 ft 2 in)
Wing span over tip-tanks	13·65 m (44 ft 9½ in)
Wing chord at root	3·20 m (10 ft 6 in)
Wing chord at tip	1·07 m (3 ft 6 in)
Wing aspect ratio	6·51
Length overall	15·93 m (52 ft 3 in)
Fuselage: Max width	1·57 m (5 ft 2 in)
Max depth	1·83 m (6 ft 0 in)
Height overall	4·81 m (15 ft 9½ in)
Tailplane span	6·40 m (21 ft 0 in)
Wheel track	3·35 m (11 ft 0 in)
Wheelbase	7·79 m (25 ft 6¾ in)
Passenger door: Height	1·37 m (4 ft 6 in)
Width	0·61 m (2 ft 0 in)
Height to sill	0·51 m (1 ft 8 in)

DIMENSIONS, INTERNAL:

Cabin, excl flight deck: Length	4·72 m (15 ft 6 in)
Max width	1·45 m (4 ft 9 in)
Max height	1·50 m (4 ft 11 in)
Volume	9·83 m³ (347 cu ft)
Baggage compartments (3), total volume	1·78 m³ (63 cu ft)

AREAS:

Wings, gross	28·64 m² (308·26 sq ft)
Ailerons (total)	1·43 m² (15·39 sq ft)
Trailing-edge flaps (total)	3·86 m² (41·58 sq ft)
Fin	4·51 m² (48·60 sq ft)
Rudder, incl tab	0·99 m² (10·66 sq ft)
Tailplane	4·87 m² (52·42 sq ft)
Elevators	1·64 m² (17·66 sq ft)

WEIGHTS AND LOADINGS:

Weight empty, equipped	5,578 kg (12,300 lb)
Typical basic operating weight (incl two pilots and service load)	5,760 kg (12,700 lb)
Max payload	1,496 kg (3,300 lb)
	or 1,542 kg (3,400 lb)
Max T-O weight	10,364 kg (22,850 lb)
	or 10,659 kg (23,500 lb)
Max ramp weight	10,432 kg (23,000 lb)
	or 10,727 kg (23,650 lb)
Max landing weight	8,618 kg (19,000 lb)
Max zero-fuel weight	7,257 kg (16,000 lb)
	or 7,484 kg (16,500 lb)
Max cabin floor loading	976 kg/m² (200 lb/sq ft)
Max wing loading	361·9 kg/m² (74·13 lb/sq ft)
	or 372·2 kg/m².(76·23 lb/sq ft)
Max power loading	314 kg/kN (3·09 lb/lb st)
	or 324 kg/kN (3·18 lb/lb st)

PERFORMANCE (at max T-O weight of 10,364 kg; 22,850 lb, except where stated):

Max level speed, S/L to 5,900 m (19,400 ft)	471 knots (872 km/h; 542 mph)
Max operating speed, S/L to 5,900 m (19,400 ft)	360 knots (666 km/h; 414 mph) IAS
Max operating Mach No. from 5,900 m (19,400 ft) to 13,725 m (45,000 ft)	Mach 0·765
Econ cruising speed at 12,500 m (41,000 ft)	400 knots (741 km/h; 460 mph)
Stalling speed, flaps and landing gear down, at max landing weight	99 knots (183 km/h; 114 mph) CAS
Max rate of climb at S/L	1,524 m (5,000 ft)/min
Max operating height	13,725 m (45,000 ft)
FAA T-O balanced field length	1,495 m (4,900 ft)
T-O balanced field length at 8,165 kg (18,000 lb) AUW	945 m (3,100 ft)
Landing distance from 15 m (50 ft) at max landing weight, with thrust reversal	625 m (2,050 ft)
Landing distance from 15 m (50 ft) at 6,350 kg (14,000 lb) AUW, with thrust reversal	518 m (1,700 ft)
Range with 7 passengers and baggage, IFR reserves	more than 2,150 nm (3,983 km; 2,475 miles)
Max range with 2 passengers and baggage, 45 min reserves	more than 2,600 nm (4,815 km; 2,993 miles)
Range with long-range fuel tank, 5 passengers and baggage, IFR reserves, at T-O weight of 10,659 kg; 23,500 lb	2,400 nm (4,446 km; 2,763 miles)
Range with long-range fuel tank, 2 passengers and baggage, 45 min reserves, at T-O weight of 10,659 kg; 23,500 lb	2,900 nm (5,373 km; 3,339 miles)

OPERATIONAL NOISE CHARACTERISTICS (FAR 36 at max T-O weight):

T-O noise level	84·2 EPNdB
Approach noise level	93·0 EPNdB
Sideline noise level	88·4 EPNdB

IAI 1124A/WESTWIND 2

At the US National Business Aircraft Association Convention, in September 1979, Israel Aircraft Industries displayed the prototype of the Westwind 2 (4X-CMK), which had made its first flight on 24 April 1979 and will supplement the Westwind I in production. The Westwind 2 was awarded FAA certification on 17 April 1980, and the prototype was delivered to Helicol of Colombia on 16 May 1980. Orders for 18 Westwind 2s had been received by the Summer of that year, and production deliveries were expected to begin in September 1980.

The Westwind 2 has IAI's new 'Sigma' wing of NACA 64A-212 modified supercritical section and fitted with winglets above the tip-tanks. The elliptical cabin section increases seated headroom and allows a flat rather than 'trenched' cabin floor, an airline-type flushing toilet, and improved placing of the overhead passenger service units. Standard features and equipment include thrust reversers, a lift-dump system, fully-modulated anti-skid brakes, wide-profile tyres, single-point pressure refuelling, strobe lights, dual batteries, digital weather radar, radio altimeter, Collins APS-80 autopilot and a full range of Collins Pro-Line solid-state avionics.

Standard seating is for a crew of two and 10 passengers.

The Garrett-AiResearch TFE 731 turbofans of the Westwind I are retained on the Westwind 2.

DIMENSIONS, EXTERNAL: As Westwind I

DIMENSIONS, INTERNAL:

Cabin:	
Length excl flight deck	4·74 m (15 ft 6½ in)
Length incl flight deck and toilet	6·08 m (19 ft 11¼ in)
Max width	1·37 m (4 ft 6 in)
Max height	1·50 m (4 ft 11 in)
Floor area, excl flight deck	6·52 m² (70·2 sq ft)
Volume, excl flight deck	9·83 m³ (347 cu ft)
Baggage compartments:	
fwd (main)	1·13 m³ (40 cu ft)
rear	0·40 m³ (14 cu ft)
cabin	0·25 m³ (9 cu ft)

AREAS: As Westwind I except:
Ailerons (total)   1·43 m² (15·40 sq ft)
Trailing-edge flaps (total)
                                    3·85 m² (41·40 sq ft)
Speed brakes/lift dumpers (total)
                                    1·37 m² (14·80 sq ft)
Fin   3·02 m² (35·52 sq ft)
Rudder, incl tab   1·02 m² (11·00 sq ft)
Tailplane   4·86 m² (52·28 sq ft)
WEIGHTS AND LOADINGS:
Weight empty, equipped   6,010 kg (13,250 lb)
Max payload   1,474 kg (3,250 lb)
Max fuel load   4,286 kg (9,450 lb)
Max T-O weight   10,660 kg (23,500 lb)
Max ramp weight   10,725 kg (23,650 lb)
Max zero-fuel weight   7,485 kg (16,500 lb)
Max landing weight   8,620 kg (19,000 lb)
Max wing loading   372·0 kg/m² (76·23 lb/sq ft)
Max power loading   332·6 kg/kN (3·26 lb/lb st)
PERFORMANCE (at max T-O weight except where indi-
cated):
Never-exceed speed at 8,840 m (29,000 ft)
                463 knots (858 km/h; 533 mph)
Max level and max cruising speed at 8,840 m (29,000 ft)
                463 knots (858 km/h; 533 mph)
Econ cruising speed at 11,890-12,500 m (39,000-
41,000 ft)   390 knots (723 km/h; 449 mph)
Stalling speed at max landing weight, flaps down,
engines idling 99 knots (184 km/h; 114 mph)

New 'Sigma' wings and winglets identify IAI's Westwind 2

Max rate of climb at S/L   1,524 m (5,000 ft)/min
T-O balanced field length   1,600 m (5,250 ft)
Landing from 15 m (50 ft) at max landing weight
                                747 m (2,450 ft)

Range, NBAA VFR reserves:
4 passengers   2,905 nm (5,383 km; 3,345 miles)
10 passengers   2,390 nm (4,429 km; 2,752 miles)

ITALY

AERITALIA
AERITALIA—SOCIETÀ AEROSPAZIALE ITALIANA p.a.
HEAD OFFICE: Piazzale Vincenzo Tecchio 51 (Casella Postale 3065), 80125 Naples
Telephone: (081) 619522, 619721, 619845, 619149, 619703
Telex: N. 710370 (AERIT)
OFFICE OF THE CHAIRMAN, AND BRANCH OFFICE (COMMERCIAL): Via Panama 52, 00198 Rome
Telephone: (06) 841441
Telex: N. 611395 (AERIT)
HONORARY PRESIDENT: Dott Egidio Ortona
PRESIDENT AND CHAIRMAN OF THE BOARD: Ing Renato Bonifacio
VICE-PRESIDENT: Ing Luigi D'Agostino
GENERAL MANAGER: Ing Fausto Cereti
JOINT GENERAL MANAGER: Ing Giovanni Sarzotti
BOARD OF DIRECTORS:
    Ing Fausto Cereti
    Ing Giulio Ciampolini
    Ing Corrado Innocenti
    Ing Francesco La Via
    Dott Giorgio Massone
    Dott Francesco Palma
    Ing Amilcare Porro
    Ing Beppe Sacchi
    Ing Franco Schepis
EXECUTIVE DIRECTORS:
    Ing Stefano Abbà (Space and Alternative Energy Group)
    Ing Roberto Mannu (Commercial)
    Ing Riccardo Mautino (Strategic Development)
    Dott Massimo Rizzo (General Secretary and External Relations)
PUBLIC RELATIONS AND PRESS DIRECTOR: Cesare Falessi
    Aeritalia is a joint stock company which was formed on 12 November 1969 by an equal shareholding of Fiat and IRI-Finmeccanica, to combine Fiat's aerospace activities (except those which concerned aero-engines) with those of Aerfer and Salmoiraghi of the Finmeccanica group. The

company became fully operational under the new title on 1 January 1972. On 28 September 1976 IRI-Finmeccanica purchased the Aeritalia stock owned by Fiat, thus acquiring complete control of the company's stock capital. Aeritalia has a total work force of approx 12,000.
    Aeritalia's organisation is based upon a centralised general management and four operational groups: Combat Aircraft Group, Transport Aircraft Group, Equipment Group, and Space and Alternative Energy Group. The production centres are located in Turin (Corso Marche, Caselle Nord and Caselle Sud), Milan (Nerviano) and Naples (Pomigliano d'Arco, Casoria and Capodichino).
    Following an inter-company agreement on 2 June 1978, Aeritalia and Aeronautica Macchi (which see) are continuing the definition phase of the AMX strike fighter, under an Italian Defence Ministry contract. In August 1978 Aeritalia and Boeing of the USA signed a formal agreement under which Aeritalia is responsible for designing and manufacturing about 15% of the Boeing 767 transport aircraft, including wing control surfaces, trailing-edge flaps, leading-edge slats, wingtips, elevator, fin, rudder and radome. The first of these items were being delivered during 1980 to Boeing for final assembly.

COMBAT AIRCRAFT GROUP
HEADQUARTERS AND TURIN WORKS: Corso Marche 41, 10146 Turin
Telephone: (011) 33321
Telex: N. 221076 (AERITOR)
CASELLE WORKS: Turin Airport CP, 10100 Turin
Telephone: (011) 991362
Telex: 210086
    The Turin area factories are engaged in the manufacture, assembly and flight testing of the F-104S combat aircraft; in the design and manufacture of structural components, final assembly and flight testing of the Panavia Tornado (see International section); design, manufacture, assembly and flight test of standard and special versions of the Aeritalia G222; and repair, overhaul and maintenance of test equipment. Other activities include the repair, overhaul and maintenance of F-104G, F-104S and TF-104G aircraft.

TRANSPORT AIRCRAFT GROUP
HEADQUARTERS AND NAPLES AREA WORKS: 80038 Pomigliano d'Arco, Naples
Telephone: (081) 8841544
Telex: N. 710082 and 710522 (AERITPOM)
CAPODICHINO WORKS: Via del Riposo alla Doganella, Aeroporto di Capodichino, 80144 Naples
Telephone: (081) 444166
Telex: N. 710356
    Aeritalia's principal activities in the Naples area comprise construction of the complete series of fuselage structural panels for the McDonnell Douglas DC-9; fuselage upper panels and the vertical tail surfaces for the DC-10 commercial airliner; engine support pylons for the Boeing 747; outboard ailerons, trailing-edge flaps, spoilers and vertical tail surfaces and manufacture, assembly and flight testing of the Aeritalia G222. Other activities include the repair, overhaul and modification of aircraft of various nations, including Italy and the United States, and the repair and maintenance of Breguet 1150 Atlantic, and G91R, G91T and G91Y aircraft.

EQUIPMENT GROUP
CASELLE WORKS: CAP 10072 Caselle-Turin
Telephone: (011) 991362
Telex: N. 210411 and 210095
    Since its creation within the Fiat Aircraft Division, the activities of this Sector have been extended to include research and experimentation with equipment installed in new prototypes, and the series production of electronic equipment and systems, both of original design and under licence. The Sector has also taken an important part in Italian and ESRO/NASA international space programmes. Avionics include complex electronics systems and specific equipment for aerospace applications. Design work includes both aerospace systems and new systems for other civil purposes. Activities include the manufacture, repair and overhaul of sophisticated electronics and space equipment, for both aircraft and space components of Aeritalia's own production and for the international market.
NERVIANO WORKS: Viale Europa, 20014 Nerviano, Milan
Telephone: (0331) 587330
Telex: 330675
    The Nerviano works manufactures a wide range of avionics equipment and instrumentation, including systems and instruments for aeronautical, missile and space applications.

SPACE AND ALTERNATIVE ENERGY GROUP
    See Spaceflight section.

AERITALIA AM-X
    This subsonic single-seat and single-engined combat aircraft is under development to meet the requirements of the Italian Air Force. Aermacchi is an associate contractor in the programme.
    In the Italian Air Force the AM-X is intended to take over duties performed currently by four types of aircraft: the G91, which will be phased out of its close air support role by 1985/86; the G91Y interdictor, also due for phase-out by 1985/86; and the F-104G and F-104S versions of the Starfighter, scheduled for replacement in the strike role by 1986/87 and 1990 respectively.

Artist's impression of AM-X; three-view in Addenda

Aeritalia G222 twin-turboprop general-purpose military transport aircraft *(Pilot Press)*

The close air support and interdiction tasks will be undertaken fully by the AM-X; counter-air duties will be shared with the longer-range Tornado. A total of 187 aircraft is needed to meet these re-equipment plans, with deliveries beginning ideally in 1986, to ensure initial operational capability by the Spring of 1987.

Work on the AM-X project was started by Aeritalia in 1977. By early 1979 the definition phase, due to last for 18 months, had been initiated under Italian Air Force contract. Major programme milestones include a first flight scheduled to take place in 1983. Six prototypes have been ordered by the Italian Air Force.

Basic design features include a max take-off weight of some 12,000 kg (26,455 lb), very good field performance, good gust response and high manoeuvrability rather than extreme subsonic speeds at low level. This implies use of advanced high-lift devices of a purely aerodynamic type, with valuable crossfeed from Aeritalia's current Tornado work, but not a 'swing-wing'.

Primary roles of the AM-X were laid down as close interdiction over a combat radius of 180 nm (333 km; 205 miles), anti-ship operations, reconnaissance and close air support. Secondary roles are foreseen as counter-air missions, notably against enemy forward airfields, and air defence against low-level intruders. Emphasis is being placed on the ability to carry a wide variety of external weapons, on four underwing pylons, and flexibility in the avionics package; a typical combat load would comprise 1,360 kg (3,000 lb) of external ordnance, two wingtip-mounted infra-red air-to-air missiles for self-defence, one internally-mounted 20 mm rotary-barrel gun, and internal ECM equipment. The possibility of developing an advanced training version as a G91T replacement is being borne in mind.

In October 1978 the Italian Air Force officially selected as the AM-X power plant a non-afterburning version of the Rolls-Royce Spey Mk 807 turbofan engine, currently rated at approx 49·1 kN (11,030 lb st). This engine is undergoing detail definition for completion by the end of 1981.

At the Farnborough Air Show, in September 1980, it was announced that EMBRAER of Brazil was to join Aeritalia and Aermacchi as a partner in the AM-X programme, in order to meet a Brazilian Air Force requirement for about 100 generally similar aircraft. Differences in the Brazilian version will be restricted mainly to the avionics and weapon delivery systems.

DIMENSIONS, EXTERNAL:
Wing span (excl wingtip missile rails)

	8·88 m (29 ft 1½ in)
Length overall	13·44 m (44 ft 1¼ in)
Length of fuselage	12·55 m (41 ft 2 in)
Height overall	4·17 m (13 ft 8¼ in)
Wheel track	2·15 m (7 ft 0¾ in)
Wheelbase	5·02 m (16 ft 5¾ in)

AERITALIA G222

The G222 was originally conceived in four separate configurations, three of which were halted at the research project stage. Two prototypes were built of the military transport version, originally designated G222 TCM; the first of these (MM582) flew for the first time on 18 July 1970 and the second (MM583) on 22 July 1971. The first prototype was handed over to the Italian Air Force on 21 December 1971 for operational evaluation. One airframe was completed for static and fatigue testing.

The Italian Air Force has ordered 44 production G222s, the first of which flew on 23 December 1975. Deliveries began in late 1976, and 30 had been delivered by the beginning of 1980. These are in service with the 46th Brigade at Pisa, and are operated in the primary roles of troop, paratroop or cargo transport, or for aeromedical duties. The G222 can operate from semi-prepared airstrips and in all weathers.

The Argentinian Army has three G222s, and in November 1976 one was delivered to the Dubai government, which has an option on a second. The Somali Air Force ordered four, for 1980 delivery.

Several major Italian airframe companies share in the construction programme, including Aermacchi (outer wings); Piaggio (wing centre-section); SIAI-Marchetti (tail unit); CIRSEA (landing gear); and IAM (miscellaneous airframe components). Fuselages are built by Aeritalia's Transport Aircraft Group, in the Pomigliano d'Arco Works near Naples; final assembly takes place at Capodichino Airport, Naples.

Design of the G222 makes it suitable for adaptation to such other roles as maritime patrol, anti-submarine warfare, navigation training, electronic warfare, and for such civil applications as firefighting, crop-spraying, aerial photogrammetry, and radio calibration. Firefighting tests with the second prototype (I-MAXB), designated **G222 SAMA** (Sistema Aeronautico Modulare Antincendio) and equipped with a dispersal system designed by Food Machinery Corporation, were completed successfully in 1976. Electronic warfare, navaid calibration and maritime surveillance versions are described separately.

Aeritalia is developing the **G222T** with 3,624 kW (4,860 shp) Rolls-Royce Tyne RTy.20 turboprop engines. This version, which flew for the first time on 13 May 1980, has an operating weight empty of 18,000 kg (39,683 lb), max payload of 9,000 kg (19,841 lb), max T-O weight of 29,000 kg (63,935 lb) and max landing weight of 27,200 kg (59,965 lb). The Libyan Air Force is reported to have ordered 20 of this version.

In 1979 Aeritalia qualified a new variant of the GE-powered aircraft, known as the **G222-28**, with the T64-P4D engines uprated to 3,057 kW (4,100 shp), an additional 1,200 kg (2,645 lb) of centre-section fuel, accommodation for 53 troops or 42 parachute troops, and max T-O weight of 28,000 kg (61,730 lb).

The following description applies to the standard G222 military transport version currently in production, except where indicated:

TYPE: Twin-turboprop general-purpose transport aircraft.

WINGS: Cantilever high-wing monoplane, with thickness/chord ratio of 15%. Dihedral 2° 30′ on outer panels. Aluminium alloy three-spar fail-safe box structure, built in three portions. One-piece constant-chord centre-section fits into recess in top of fuselage and is secured by bolts at six main points. Outer panels tapered on leading- and trailing-edges. Upper-surface skins are of 7075-T6 alloy, lower-surface skins of 2024-T3 alloy. All control surfaces have bonded metal skins with metal honeycomb core. Double-slotted flaps extend over 60% of trailing-edge. Two-section spoilers ahead of each outboard flap segment, used also as lift dumpers on landing. Spoilers and flaps fully powered by tandem hydraulic actuators. Manually-operated ailerons, each with inset servo tab. Pneumatically-inflated de-icing boots on leading-edges, using engine bleed air.

FUSELAGE: Pressurised fail-safe structure of aluminium alloy stressed-skin construction and circular cross-section. Easily removable stiffened floor panels.

TAIL UNIT: Cantilever safe-life structure of aluminium alloy, with sweptback three-spar fin and non-swept two-spar variable-incidence tailplane. Pneumatically-inflated de-icing boots on fin and tailplane leading-edges, using engine bleed air. Rudder and elevators of metal honeycomb construction. Two tabs in each elevator; no rudder tabs. Rudder fully powered by tandem hydraulic actuators; elevators operated manually.

LANDING GEAR: Hydraulically-retractable tricycle type, suitable for use from prepared runways or grass fields. Messier-Hispano-Bugatti design, built under licence by CIRSEA (Nardi-Magnaghi). Steerable twin-wheel nose unit retracts forward. Main units, each consisting of two single wheels in tandem, retract into fairings on sides of fuselage. Oleo-pneumatic shock-absorbers. Gear can be lowered by gravity in emergency, the nose unit being aided by aerodynamic action and the main units by the shock-absorbers, which remain compressed in the retracted position. Oleo pressure in shock-absorbers is adjustable to permit variation in height and attitude of the cabin floor from the ground. Low-

pressure tubeless tyres on all units, size 37·91 × 12·35 in (Type III) on main wheels, 27·56 × 10·51 in (Type III) on nosewheels. Tyre pressures 4·41 bars (64 lb/sq in) on main units, 3·92 bars (56·88 lb/sq in) on nose unit. Hydraulic multi-disc brakes. No anti-skid units.

POWER PLANT: Two 2,535 kW (3,400 shp) Fiat-built General Electric T64-GE-P4D turboprop engines, each driving a Hamilton Standard 63E60 three-blade variable-pitch propeller with spinner. Provision in fuselage for eight Aerojet General JATO rockets with total additional thrust of 35·3 kN (7,937 lb), for T-O with extra-heavy loads. Fuel in integral tanks: two in the outer wings, combined capacity 6,800 litres (1,495 Imp gallons), and two centre-section tanks, combined capacity 5,200 litres (1,143 Imp gallons), with cross-feed provision to either engine. Total overall fuel capacity 12,000 litres (2,638 Imp gallons). Single pressure refuelling point on starboard side of fuselage. Overwing gravity refuelling point above each tank. Electrical de-icing of spinners and propeller leading-edges. Engine intakes anti-iced by electrical/hot air system.

ACCOMMODATION: Normal crew of three (two pilots and radio operator/flight engineer) on flight deck. Provision for fourth crew member or jumpmaster when required. Standard troop transport version has 32 foldaway sidewall seats and 12 stowable seats for 44 fully-equipped troops, and carries also two 20-man life rafts stowed in the wing/fuselage fairing and a single 9-man life raft in the cargo compartment. Paratroop transport version can carry up to 32 fully-equipped paratroops, and is fitted with the 32 sidewall seats and life rafts as in the troop transport version, plus door jump platforms and static lines. Cargo transport version can accept standard pallets of up to 2·24 m (7 ft 4 in) wide, and can carry up to 9,000 kg (19,841 lb) of freight. Provision is made for 135 cargo tiedown points and a 1,500 kg (3,306 lb) capacity cargo hoist. Typical Italian military equipment loads can include two CL-52 light trucks; one CL-52 with a 105 mm L4 howitzer or one-ton trailer; Fiat AR-59 Campagnola reconnaissance vehicle with 106 mm recoilless gun or 250 kg (550 lb) trailer; or five standard A-22 freight containers. In the aeromedical role the G222 can accommodate 36 stretchers, two sitting patients and four medical attendants. A second toilet can be installed, and provision can be made to increase the water supply and to install supplementary electrical points and hooks for medical treatment bottles. In this version, the cabin oxygen system is available to all stretcher positions. Crew access door is forward of cabin on port side. Passenger doors, at front and rear of main cabin on starboard side and at rear on port side, can be used also as emergency exits. Two emergency hatches in cabin roof, forward and aft of wing carry-through structure. Hydraulically operated rear loading ramp and upward-opening door in underside of upswept rear fuselage, which can be opened in flight for air-drop operations. In cargo version, five loads of up to 1,000 kg (2,205 lb) each can be air-dropped from rear opening, or a single load of up to 5,000 kg (11,023 lb). Paratroop jumps can be made either from this opening or from the rear side doors. Windscreens and quarter-light panels are de-iced and demisted electrically. Wipers and screen wash for both windscreens. Entire accommodation pressurised and air-conditioned.

SYSTEMS: Pressurisation system maintains a cabin differential of 0·41 bars (5·97 lb/sq in), giving a 1,200 m (3,940 ft) environment at altitudes up to 6,000 m (19,685 ft). Air-conditioning system uses engine bleed air during flight; on ground, it is fed by compressor bleed air from APU to provide cabin heating to a minimum of 18°C. Two independent hydraulic systems, each of 207 bars (3,000 lb/sq in) pressure. No. 1 system actuates flaps, spoilers, rudder and wheel brakes; No. 2 system actuates flaps, spoilers, rudder, wheel brakes, nosewheel steering, landing gear extension and retraction, rear ramp/door and windscreen wipers. Auxiliary hydraulic system, fed by APU-powered pump, can take over from No. 2 system in flight, if both main systems fail, to operate essential services. In addition, a standby hand pump is provided for emergency use to lower the landing gear and, on the ground, to operate the ramp/door and parking brakes. Three 45kVA alternators, one driven by each engine through constant-speed drive units and one by the APU, provide 115/200V three-phase AC electrical power at 400Hz. 28V DC power is supplied from the main AC buses via two transformer-rectifiers, with 24V 34Ah nickel-cadmium battery and static inverter for standby and emergency power. External AC power socket. Garrett-AiResearch 113·3 kW (152 hp) APU, installed in starboard main landing gear fairing, provides power for engine starting, hydraulic pump and alternator actuation, air-conditioning on ground, and all hydraulic and electrical systems necessary for loading and unloading on ground. Liquid oxygen system for crew and passengers (with cabin wall outlets); this system can be replaced by a gaseous oxygen system if required. Emergency oxygen system available for all occupants in the event of a pressurisation failure.

Aeritalia G222 twin-turboprop military transport aircraft in the insignia of the Italian Air Force

AVIONICS AND EQUIPMENT: Standard communications equipment includes 3,500-channel UHF/AM, 1,630-channel emergency VHF/AM, 930-channel VHF/AM, VHF/FM, 28,000-channel HF/SSB/CW, crew intercom and PA system. Navigation equipment includes Omega dead-reckoning system, with projected-map display, Doppler radar, two-axis gyro platform, PHI and TAS computer; and an integrated ground-based system incorporating Collins autopilot, flight director, two compasses, two vertical gyros, two VOR, marker beacon, two ILS, ADF, two Tacan, and horizontal situation indicator. Other avionics include Meteo weather radar, with secondary terrain-mapping mode; radar altimeter; and IFF/ATC transponder including altitude reporting. Provision for head-up display. Landing light on nosewheel leg.

EQUIPMENT (G222 SAMA): Modular palletised firefighting pack can be installed in under two hours without any modification to the basic transport aircraft. The module consists of a 6,300 litre (1,385 Imp gallon) tank and four pressurised air containers to activate the pneumatic actuators and discharge the retardant/fertiliser through two nozzles. Length of area covered averages 300 m (985 ft).

DIMENSIONS, EXTERNAL:

Wing span	28·70 m (94 ft 2 in)
Wing chord at root	3·40 m (11 ft 1¾ in)
Wing chord at tip	1·685 m (5 ft 6¼ in)
Wing aspect ratio	9·15
Length overall	22·70 m (74 ft 5½ in)
Height overall	9·80 m (32 ft 1¾ in)
Fuselage: Max diameter	3·55 m (11 ft 7¾ in)
Tailplane span	12·40 m (40 ft 8¼ in)
Wheel track	3·668 m (12 ft 0½ in)
Wheelbase (to c/l of main units)	6·23 m (20 ft 5¼ in)
Propeller diameter	4·42 m (14 ft 6 in)
Distance between propeller centres	9·50 m (31 ft 2 in)

Rear-loading ramp/door:

Width	2·45 m (8 ft 0½ in)
Height	2·25 m (7 ft 4½ in)

DIMENSIONS, INTERNAL:

Main cabin:

Length	8·58 m (28 ft 1¾ in)
Width	2·45 m (8 ft 0½ in)
Height	2·25 m (7 ft 4½ in)
Volume	58·0 m³ (2,048 cu ft)

AREAS:

Wings, gross	82·00 m² (882·6 sq ft)
Ailerons (total)	3·65 m² (39·29 sq ft)
Trailing-edge flaps (total)	18·40 m² (198·06 sq ft)
Spoilers (total)	1·65 m² (17·76 sq ft)
Fin (incl dorsal fin)	12·19 m² (131·21 sq ft)
Rudder	7·02 m² (75·56 sq ft)
Tailplane	19·09 m² (205·48 sq ft)
Elevators (total)	4·61 m² (49·62 sq ft)

WEIGHTS AND LOADINGS (standard transport):

Weight empty	14,590 kg (32,165 lb)
Weight empty, equipped	15,400 kg (33,950 lb)
Operating weight empty	15,700 kg (34,612 lb)
Max payload	9,000 kg (19,841 lb)
Max fuel load	9,400 kg (20,723 lb)
Normal T-O weight	24,500 kg (54,013 lb)
Max T-O weight	28,000 kg (61,730 lb)
Max landing weight	26,500 kg (58,422 lb)
Max zero-fuel weight	24,400 kg (53,792 lb)
Max cargo floor loading	750 kg/m² (155 lb/sq ft)
Max wing loading	341·5 kg/m² (69·9 lb/sq ft)
Max power loading	5·52 kg/kW (9·1 lb/shp)

WEIGHTS (G222 SAMA):

Operating weight empty	15,700 kg (34,614 lb)

SAMA equipment module	2,200 kg (4,850 lb)
Retardant	6,800 kg (14,990 lb)
Fuel	1,800 kg (3,968 lb)
Max T-O weight	26,500 kg (58,422 lb)

PERFORMANCE (standard G222 transport, at max T-O weight except where indicated):

Max level speed at 4,575 m (15,000 ft)	
	291 knots (540 km/h; 336 mph)
Econ cruising speed at 6,000 m (19,685 ft)	
	237 knots (439 km/h; 273 mph)
Air-drop speed (paratroops or cargo)	
110-140 knots (204-259 km/h; 127-161 mph) IAS	
Stalling speed, flaps and landing gear down	
	84 knots (155 km/h; 96·5 mph)
Time to 4,500 m (14,750 ft)	8 min 35 s
Max rate of climb at S/L	520 m (1,705 ft)/min
Rate of climb at S/L, one engine out	
	125 m (410 ft)/min
Service ceiling	7,620 m (25,000 ft)
Service ceiling, one engine out	5,000 m (16,400 ft)
T-O run	662 m (2,172 ft)
T-O to 15 m (50 ft)	1,000 m (3,280 ft)
Landing from 15 m (50 ft)	775 m (2,543 ft)
Landing run at max landing weight	545 m (1,788 ft)
Accelerate/stop distance	1,200 m (3,937 ft)
Min ground turning radius	20·80 m (68 ft 3 in)

Range with max payload, optimum cruising speed at 6,000 m (19,685 ft)   378 nm (700 km; 435 miles)
Range with 44 troops 1,198 nm (2,220 km; 1,380 miles)
Range with 36 stretchers and 4 medical attendants
1,349 nm (2,500 km; 1,553 miles)
Ferry range with max fuel
2,670 nm (4,950 km; 3,075 miles)

g limit	+2·5

PERFORMANCE (G222 SAMA at max T-O weight): As standard transport except:

Max cruising speed	250 knots (463 km/h; 287 mph)
Drop speed (T-O configuration)	
	120 knots (222 km/h; 138 mph)
Optimum height above ground during drop	
	50-100 m (165-330 ft)
Range with max retardant load	
	172 nm (320 km: 200 miles)

AERITALIA G222 (ELECTRONIC WARFARE, NAVAID CALIBRATION AND MARITIME SURVEILLANCE VERSIONS)

Aeritalia has developed an electronic warfare version of the G222 and is developing flight inspection (radio/radar calibration) and maritime patrol, search and rescue versions. Dimensions, weights and performance of all three are similar to those of the standard troop transport.

Carrying a pilot, co-pilot and up to 10 systems operators, the electronic warfare version has a modified cabin fitted with racks and consoles for detection, signal processing and data recording equipment, and an electrical system providing up to 40kW of power for its operation. Externally, it is distinguishable by a small 'thimble' radome beneath the nose and a larger 'doughnut' radome on top of the tail-fin. A prototype, designated G222VS, was flown for the first time on 9 March 1978.

The flight inspection version is externally similar to the standard troop transport. Known as the G222RM, it is equipped for flights below 3,050 m (10,000 ft) to calibrate airport flight paths and radio assistance, enabling it to check VOR, ILS, DME, Tacan, PAR, NDB, marker beacon receivers, and air traffic control systems, in addition to VHF and UHF radio transmissions. Onboard equipment includes separate receivers and displays, a central computer to collect inertial navigation data (updated continually by DME), and data on the state of the radio aid(s) being calibrated. Only one equipment operator is necessary, in addition to the two-man flight crew, and ample space remains in the rear of the hold to carry a Jeep-type vehicle for ground-based operations. This version has an optional secondary capability to perform survey missions, at altitudes between 6,100 and 7,620 m (20,000 and 25,000 ft), for multiple control of flight path assistance, using SAFI screened flight path equipment.

AERITALIA (LOCKHEED) F-104S

The first of two Lockheed-built F-104S prototypes flew during December 1966. Aeritalia is building 205 under licence for the Italian Air Force, the first of which was flown on 30 December 1968. Deliveries began in the Spring of 1969, and the 200th F-104S was flown in May 1976. These aircraft are in service with the 4°, 5°, 6°, 9°, 36°, 51° and 53° Wings of the Italian Air Force. Forty were delivered to the Turkish Air Force between December 1974 and mid-1976. Production for the Italian Air Force was continuing in 1980.

Details of Lockheed production of earlier models of the F-104 Starfighter can be found in the 1972-73 and earlier editions of *Jane's*. The following description applies to the Aeritalia-built F-104S:

TYPE: Single-seat multi-purpose combat aircraft.

WINGS: Cantilever mid-wing monoplane. Bi-convex supersonic wing section with a thickness/chord ratio of 3·36%. Anhedral 10°. No incidence. Sweepback 18° 6' at quarter-chord. All-metal structure with two main spars and top and bottom one-piece skin panels. Each half-wing is a separate structure cantilevered from five forged frames in fuselage. Full-span electrically-actuated drooping leading-edge. Entire trailing-edge hinged, with inboard sections serving as landing flaps and outboard sections as ailerons. Ailerons are of aluminium, each powered by a servo control system which is irreversible and hydraulically powered, and each actuated by ten small hydraulic cylinders. Trim

Aeritalia-built Lockheed F-104S combat aircraft in the insignia of the Italian Air Force

control is applied to position the aileron relative to the servo control position. An electric actuator positions the aileron trim. Flaps are of aluminium, actuated electrically. Above each flap is the air delivery tube of a boundary layer control system, which ejects air bled from the engine compressor over the entire flap span when the flaps are lowered to the landing position.

FUSELAGE: All-metal monocoque structure. Hydraulically-operated aluminium airbrake on each side of rear fuselage.

TAIL UNIT: T-type cantilever unit with 'all-flying' one-piece horizontal tail surface hinged at mid-chord point at top of the vertical fin and powered by a hydraulic servo. Tailplane has similar profile to wing and is all-metal. Rudder is fully powered by a hydraulic servo. Trim control is applied to position the tailplane relative to the servo control position, by means of an electric actuator. Rudder trim is operated by an electric actuator located in the fin. The rudder itself is trimmed in the same way as the tailplane. Narrow-chord ventral fin on centreline and two smaller lateral fins under fuselage to improve stability.

LANDING GEAR: Retractable tricycle type with Dowty patent liquid-spring shock-absorbers on main units, oleo-pneumatic shock-absorbers on nose unit. Hydraulic actuation. Main wheels raised in and forward. Steerable nosewheel retracts forward into fuselage. Main-wheel legs are hinged on oblique axes so that the wheels lie flush within the fuselage when retracted. Main wheels size 26 × 8·0, with Goodrich tyres size 26 × 8·0 type VIII (18-ply rating), pressure 11·93 bars (173 lb/sq in). Nosewheel tyre size 18 × 5·5 type VII (14-ply rating). Bendix hydraulic disc brakes with Goodyear anti-skid units. Arrester hook under rear of fuselage. Braking parachute in rear fuselage.

POWER PLANT: One General Electric J79-GE-19 turbojet engine, rated at 52·8 kN (11,870 lb st) dry and 79·62 kN (17,900 lb st) with afterburning. Electrical de-icing elements fitted to air intakes. Most of the aircraft's hydraulic equipment mounted inside large engine bay door under fuselage to facilitate servicing. Internal fuel in five bag-type fuselage tanks with total usable capacity of 3,392 litres (896 US gallons). Provision for external fuel in two 740 litre (195 US gallon) pylon tanks and two 645 litre (170 US gallon) wingtip tanks. Pressure refuelling of all internal and external tanks through single point on upper port fuselage just forward of air intake duct. Gravity fuelling point for internal tanks aft of pressure refuelling point, with individual gravity fuelling of external tanks. In-flight refuelling can be provided through Lockheed-designed probe-drogue system. Probe, mounted below port sill of cockpit, is removable but when installed is non-retractable. Oil capacity 15 litres (4 US gallons).

ACCOMMODATION: Pressurised and air-conditioned cockpit well forward of wings. Canopy hinged to starboard for

access. Martin-Baker IQ-7A zero-zero ejection seat.

SYSTEMS: Air-conditioning package by Garrett-AiResearch, using engine bleed air. Pressure differential 0·34 bars (5 lb/sq in). Two completely separate hydraulic systems, using engine-driven pumps operating at 207 bars (3,000 lb/sq in). No. 1 system operates one side of tailplane, rudder and ailerons, also the automatic pitch control actuator and autopilot actuators. No. 2 system operates other half of tailplane, rudder and ailerons, also the landing gear, wheel brakes, airbrakes, nosewheel steering and constant-frequency electrical generator. Emergency ram-air turbine supplies emergency hydraulic pump and 4·5kVA 115/200V electric generator. Electrical system supplied by two engine-driven 20kVA 115/200V variable-frequency (320-520Hz) generators. Constant-speed hydraulic motor drives 2·5kVA 115/200V generator to supply fixed-frequency AC. 28V DC power supplied by two nickel-cadmium batteries and a 120A transformer-rectifier.

AVIONICS AND EQUIPMENT: Integrated avionics system in which various communications and navigation components may be installed as a series of interconnecting but self-sustaining units which may be varied to provide for different specific missions. Equipment includes autopilot with 'stick steering', which includes modes for pre-selecting and holding altitude, speed, heading and constant rate of turn; multi-purpose R21G/H radar for air-to-air interception, ground and contour mapping, and terrain avoidance modes of operation; fixed-reticle gunsight; bombing computer; air data computer; dead reckoning navigation device; Tacan radio air navigation system; provision for data link-time division set and AN/ARC-552 UHF radio; Litton LN-3-2A lightweight fully-automatic inertial navigation system; Sperry C-2G compass system; AN/APN-198 radar altimeter; AIC-18 intercom; and AN/APX-46 IFF/SIF. Provision for fitting a camera pod under the fuselage for reconnaissance duties.

ARMAMENT: Nine external attachment points, at wingtips, under wings and under fuselage, for bombs, rocket pods, auxiliary fuel tanks and air-to-air missiles. Normal primary armament consists of two AIM-7 Sparrow air-to-air missiles under wings and/or two Sidewinders under fuselage and either a Sidewinder or 645 litre (170 US gallon) fuel tank on each wingtip. Alternatively, an M-61 20 mm multi-barrel rotary cannon can be fitted in the port underside of the fuselage instead of the AIM-7 missile control package. Max external weapon load 3,402 kg (7,500 lb).

DIMENSIONS, EXTERNAL:

Wing span without tip-tanks	6·68 m (21 ft 11 in)
Wing chord (mean)	2·91 m (9 ft 6·6 in)
Wing aspect ratio	2·45
Length overall	16·69 m (54 ft 9 in)

Length of fuselage	15·62 m (51 ft 3 in)
Height overall	4·11 m (13 ft 6 in)
Tailplane span	3·63 m (11 ft 11 in)
Wheel track	2·74 m (9 ft 0 in)
Wheelbase	4·59 m (15 ft 0½ in)

AREAS:

Wings, gross	18·22 m² (196·1 sq ft)
Ailerons (total)	0·85 m² (9·2 sq ft)
Trailing-edge flaps (total)	2·11 m² (22·7 sq ft)
Leading-edge flaps (total)	1·51 m² (16·2 sq ft)
Airbrakes (total)	0·77 m² (8·25 sq ft)
Fin	3·50 m² (37·7 sq ft)
Ventral fin (centreline)	0·47 m² (5·1 sq ft)
Rear fuselage strakes (total)	0·71 m² (7·6 sq ft)
Rudder, incl tab	0·51 m² (5·5 sq ft)
Tailplane	4·48 m² (48·2 sq ft)

WEIGHTS AND LOADING:

Weight empty	6,760 kg (14,900 lb)
Max internal fuel load	2,641 kg (5,824 lb)
Max internal and external fuel load	5,153 kg (11,362 lb)
T-O weight ('clean')	9,840 kg (21,690 lb)
Max T-O weight	14,060 kg (31,000 lb)
Max zero-fuel weight ('clean')	6,806 kg (15,006 lb)
Max zero-fuel weight (fighter-bomber)	7,148 kg (15,760 lb)
Max wing loading	772 kg/m² (158 lb/sq ft)
Max power loading, with afterburning	176·6 kg/kN (1·73 lb/lb st)

PERFORMANCE (at 9,840 kg; 21,690 lb AUW except where indicated):

Never-exceed speed	Mach 2·2
Max level speed at 11,000 m (36,000 ft)	
Mach 2·2 (1,259 knots; 2,330 km/h; 1,450 mph)	
Max level speed at S/L	
Mach 1·2 (790 knots; 1,464 km/h; 910 mph)	
Max cruising speed at 11,000 m (36,000 ft)	
530 knots (981 km/h; 610 mph)	
Econ cruising speed	Mach 0·85
T-O speed at S/L, interceptor with two AIM-7 missiles	189 knots (350 km/h; 217 mph)
Typical landing speed at S/L	159 knots (295 km/h; 183 mph)
Max rate of climb at S/L	16,765 m (55,000 ft)/min
Service ceiling	17,680 m (58,000 ft)
Zoom altitude	more than 27,400 m (90,000 ft)
Time to accelerate from Mach 0·92 to Mach 2·0	2 min
Time to climb to 10,670 m (35,000 ft)	1 min 20 s
Time to climb to 17,070 m (56,000 ft)	2 min 40 s
T-O run at S/L, interceptor with two AIM-7 missiles	823 m (2,700 ft)
Typical landing run at S/L	762 m (2,500 ft)
Radius with max fuel	673 nm (1,247 km; 775 miles)
Ferry range (excl flight refuelling)	1,576 nm (2,920 km; 1,815 miles)

AERMACCHI
AERONAUTICA MACCHI SpA

HEAD OFFICE: Corso Vittorio Emanuele 15, 20122 Milan
OFFICES AND WORKS: Via Silvestro Sanvito 80, Casella Postale 246, 21100 Varese
Telephone: (0332) 283100
Telex: 380070 AERMAC
PRESIDENT: Dott Ing Paolo Foresio
VICE-PRESIDENT AND MANAGING DIRECTOR: Gen Ing Mario Matacotta
VICE-PRESIDENT AND GENERAL MANAGER: Dott Fabrizio Foresio
GENERAL MANAGER: Dott Ing Ermanno Bazzocchi
TECHNICAL MANAGER: Dott Ing Alberto Notari
SALES MANAGER: Dott Ing Gianni Cattaneo
MARKETING MANAGER: Dott Ing Ferruccio Tommasi

The Macchi company was founded in 1912 in Varese and its first aeroplane was built in 1913. In addition to its former factory area of 36,900 m² (397,200 sq ft), a new plant has been built at Venegono airfield, with a covered area of 20,000 m² (215,280 sq ft). Total work force in 1980 was more than 2,200.

Lockheed Aircraft International acquired a substantial minority interest in Aermacchi in December 1959.

The M.B. 339A two-seat trainer is in series production for the Italian Air Force and for export. A single-seat version, the M.B. 339K Veltro 2, is also available.

On 2 June 1978, Aermacchi and Aeritalia (which see) announced their intention to develop jointly new aircraft to meet the future needs of domestic and foreign markets.

AERMACCHI M.B. 326

The first prototype of the M.B. 326 jet trainer flew for the first time on 10 December 1957, powered by a Rolls-Royce Viper 8 turbojet engine. The more powerful Viper 11 powers six production versions of the aircraft built for the air forces of Italy (M.B. 326 and 326E), Tunisia (M.B. 326B), Ghana (M.B. 326F), Australia (M.B. 326H) and South Africa (M.B. 326M), and one version built for Alitalia (M.B. 326D).

The initial South African Air Force version, built by Atlas (which see), was the Impala Mk 1; an improved

version, the Impala Mk 2, is currently in production in that country.

Other versions with more powerful Viper engines, armament changes and other modifications are as follows:

M.B. 326E. Two-seat advanced trainer and weapons trainer: 12 built (including six conversions) for the Italian Air Force's Scuola di Volo Basico Iniziale at Lecce. Viper 11 engine (11·12 kN; 2,500 lb st), plus strengthened wings and six underwing hardpoints of the M.B. 326GB. New avionics and equipment include UHF radio, miniaturised Tacan, gyroscopic weapons sight and gun camera. Further details in 1978-79 Jane's.

M.B. 326GB. Two-seat dual-control advanced training and attack version, with airframe modifications and Viper 20 Mk 540 engine. M.B. 326G prototype flew for first time

in Spring 1967; similar M.B. 326GB is production version. Customers include Argentinian Navy (8), air forces of Zaïre (17) and Zambia (23). In addition, 182 similar **M.B.326GCs** are being assembled in Brazil under licence by EMBRAER (which see) for the Brazilian Air Force, as the **AT-26 Xavante**, and for the air forces of Paraguay (nine) and Togo (six). Currently in production only in Brazil.

M.B. 326K. Single-seat operational trainer and light ground attack version. Retains most of structure and systems of M.B. 326GB, but has more powerful Viper 632 engine, no second cockpit, additional fuselage fuel tanks, increased weapon-carrying capacity. Prototype with Viper 540 engine first flown 22 August 1970; second prototype, with Viper 632, first flew 1971. Delivered to Dubai

Well-camouflaged Aermacchi M.B. 326K single-seat training/attack aircraft for Tunisia

Aermacchi M.B. 326K single-seat training and light ground attack aircraft (*Pilot Press*)

Defence Force (nine), Ghana Air Force (six), South African Air Force (four reported), Tunisian Air Force (eight) and Zaîre Air Force (eight). In South Africa, Atlas Impala Mk 2 (which see) is a Viper 540 powered version based on the M.B. 326K.

M.B. 326L. Two-seat advanced trainer, combining airframe of single-seat M.B. 326K with standard two-seat dual control cockpit installation. Two delivered to Dubai and four to Tunisian Air Force.

A full description of these later models can be found in the 1978-79 *Jane's*. The principal characteristics are as follows:

TYPE: Two-seat basic and advanced trainer (GB, GC and L) or single-seat operational trainer (K); all versions have light ground attack capability.

POWER PLANT (GB): One Rolls-Royce Viper 20 Mk 540 turbojet engine, rated at 15·17 kN (3,410 lb st). Fuel in flexible rubber main tank in fuselage, capacity 782 litres (172 Imp gallons), and two 305 litre (67 Imp gallon) non-jettisonable wingtip tanks. Total standard fuel capacity 1,392 litres (306 Imp gallons). Provision for two 332 litre (73 Imp gallon) jettisonable underwing tanks, to give total capacity of 2,056 litres (452 Imp gallons). Single-point pressure refuelling receptacle under fuselage. Fuel dump valves permit quick emptying of tip-tanks.

POWER PLANT (K and L): One Rolls-Royce Viper Mk 632-43 turbojet engine, rated at 18·79 kN (4,000 lb st). M.B. 326L fuel capacity same as for GB. Fuel in M.B. 326K contained in three rubber fuselage tanks and two permanent wingtip tanks, total usable capacity 1,660 litres (366 Imp gallons). Provision to install self-sealing fuselage tanks and reticulated foam anti-explosive filling in all tanks, including those at wingtips. Two underwing stations equipped normally to carry jettisonable auxiliary tanks of up to 340 litres (75 Imp gallons) each. Single-point pressure refuelling receptacle and auxiliary gravity refuelling points.

ARMAMENT (GB and L): Provision for up to 1,814 kg (4,000 lb) of armament on six underwing attachments. Typical weapon loads include following alternatives: two LAU-3/A packs each containing nineteen 2·75 in FFAR rockets and two packs each containing eight Hispano-Suiza SURA 80 mm rockets; two 12·7 mm gun pods and four packs each containing six SURA 80 mm rockets; one 7·62 mm Minigun, one 12·7 mm gun pod, two Matra 122 rocket packs and two packs each containing six SURA 80 mm rockets; two 500 lb bombs and eight 5 in HVAR rockets; two AS.12 missiles; one 12·7 mm gun pod, one reconnaissance pack containing four Vinten cameras and two 272 kg (600 lb) drop-tanks, or two Matra SA-10 packs each containing a 30 mm Aden gun and 150 rounds. SFOM type 83 fixed gunsight or Ferranti LFS 5/102A gyro-sight. Gun camera in nose.

ARMAMENT (K): Standard fixed armament of two 30 mm DEFA electrically-operated cannon in lower front fuselage, with 125 rds/gun. Six underwing pylons, the inboard four stressed to carry up to 454 kg (1,000 lb) each and the outboard pair up to 340 kg (750 lb) each. Max external military load (with reduced fuel) is 1,814 kg (4,000 lb). Each pylon fitted with standard NATO 355 mm (14 in) MA-4A stores rack. Typical loads may include two 750 lb bombs, four 500 lb bombs, four napalm containers, two AS.11 or AS.12 air-to-surface missiles, two machine-gun pods, two Matra 550 air-to-air missiles, six SUU-11A/A 7·62 mm Minigun pods, and various Matra or other launchers for 37 mm, 68 mm, 100 mm, 2·75 in or 5 in rockets. A four-camera tactical reconnaissance pod can be carried on the port inner pylon without affecting the weapon capability of the other five stations.

DIMENSIONS, EXTERNAL:
Wing span over tip-tanks:
  GB   10·854 m (35 ft 7¼ in)
  K   10·850 m (35 ft 7 in)
Wing area, gross   19·30 m² (207·7 sq ft)
Length overall   10·673 m (35 ft 0¼ in)
Height overall   3·72 m (12 ft 2 in)

WEIGHTS AND LOADINGS (M.B. 326GB. A: Trainer; B: Attack):
Basic operating weight, excl crew:
  A   2,685 kg (5,920 lb)
  *B   2,558 kg (5,640 lb)
Max T-O weight (full internal fuel, wingtip and underwing tanks): A   4,577 kg (10,090 lb)
  B, no armament   4,447 kg (9,805 lb)
  B, with 769 kg (1,695 lb) armament
     5,216 kg (11,500 lb)

Max T-O weight (max armament):
  *B, with fuel in fuselage tank only and 1,962 kg (4,325 lb) armament   5,216 kg (11,500 lb)
Max wing loading   269·5 kg/m² (55·2 lb/sq ft)
Max power loading   343·8 kg/kN (3·37 lb/lb st)
* *Without tip-tanks and aft ejection seat*

WEIGHTS AND LOADINGS (M.B. 326K):
Weight empty, equipped   3,123 kg (6,885 lb)
T-O weight ('clean')   4,645 kg (10,240 lb)
Typical operational T-O weights:
  patrol and visual reconnaissance
     5,048 kg (11,130 lb)
  photographic reconnaissance 5,111 kg (11,270 lb)
Max T-O weight   5,897 kg (13,000 lb)
Max wing loading   305 kg/m² (62·4 lb/sq ft)
Max power loading   313·8 kg/kN (3·25 lb/lb st)

PERFORMANCE (M.B. 326GB. A: Trainer at typical weight of 3,937 kg (8,680 lb), representing max T-O weight without underwing tanks; B: Attack version at combat weight of 4,763 kg (10,500 lb); C: Attack version at max T-O weight):
Never-exceed speed:
  A Mach 0·82 (469 knots; 871 km/h; 541 mph EAS)
  B Mach 0·75 (419 knots; 778 km/h; 483 mph EAS)
Max level speed: A   468 knots (867 km/h; 539 mph)

Max cruising speed:
  A   430 knots (797 km/h; 495 mph)
Max rate of climb at S/L: A   1,844 m (6,050 ft)/min
  B   1,082 m (3,550 ft)/min
  C   945 m (3,100 ft)/min
Time to 3,050 m (10,000 ft): B   3 min 10 s
  C   4 min 0 s
Time to 6,100 m (20,000 ft): A   4 min 10 s
  B   8 min 0 s
  C   9 min 20 s
Time to 9,150 m (30,000 ft): A   7 min 40 s
  B   15 min 0 s
  C   18 min 40 s
Time to 12,200 m (40,000 ft): A   13 min 5 s
Service ceiling: A   14,325 m (47,000 ft)
  B   11,900 m (39,000 ft)
T-O run, ISA: A   412 m (1,350 ft)
  B   640 m (2,100 ft)
  C   845 m (2,770 ft)
T-O to 15 m (50 ft), ISA: A   555 m (1,820 ft)
  B   866 m (2,840 ft)
  C   1,140 m (3,740 ft)
Landing from 15 m (50 ft), ISA:
  A at landing weight of 3,175 kg (7,000 lb)
     631 m (2,070 ft)
  B at landing weight of 4,195 kg (9,250 lb)
     802 m (2,630 ft)
Range (A, with 113 litres; 25 Imp gallons reserve):
  fuselage and tip-tanks
     998 nm (1,850 km; 1,150 miles)
  fuselage, tip and underwing tanks
     1,320 nm (2,445 km; 1,520 miles)
Combat radius (C):
  max fuel, 769 kg (1,695 lb) armament, 90 kg (200 lb) fuel reserve, out at 6,100 m (20,000 ft), return at 7,620 m (25,000 ft)
     350 nm (648 km; 403 miles)
  fuselage tank only, 1,814 kg (4,000 lb) armament, 90 kg (200 lb) fuel reserve, cruise at 3,050 m (10,000 ft), five minutes over target
     69 nm (130 km; 80 miles)
  max fuel, 771 kg (1,700 lb) armament, 90 kg (200 lb) fuel reserve, cruise at 3,050 m (10,000 ft), 1 h 50 min patrol at 150 m (500 ft) over target
     49·5 nm (92 km; 57 miles)

Aermacchi M.B. 339A basic/advanced jet trainers of the Italian Air Force

PERFORMANCE (M.B. 326K. A: aircraft 'clean', at AUW of 4,390 kg; 9,680 lb; B: armed aircraft at 5,443 kg; 12,000 lb AUW):

Max design limit speed at S/L
  500 knots (927 km/h; 576 mph) EAS
Max limiting Mach number 0·82
Max level speed at 1,525 m (5,000 ft):
  A 480 knots (890 km/h; 553 mph)
Max level speed at 9,150 m (30,000 ft):
  B 370 knots (686 km/h; 426 mph)
Stalling speed, flaps up:
  A 102 knots (190 km/h; 118 mph) CAS
  B 113 knots (211 km/h; 131 mph) CAS
Stalling speed, flaps down:
  A 91 knots (169 km/h; 105 mph) CAS
  B 102 knots (190 km/h; 118 mph) CAS
Max rate of climb at S/L: A 1,980 m (6,500 ft)/min
  B 1,143 m (3,750 ft)/min
Time to 10,670 m (35,000 ft): A 9 min 30 s
  B 23 min 0 s
T-O run, ISA: A 411 m (1,350 ft)
  B 670 m (2,200 ft)
T-O run, ISA + 20°C: A 518 m (1,700 ft)
  B 815 m (2,675 ft)
T-O to 15 m (50 ft), ISA: A 572 m (1,875 ft)
  B 914 m (3,000 ft)
T-O to 15 m (50 ft), ISA + 20°C:
  A 709 m (2,325 ft)
  B 1,158 m (3,800 ft)
Typical combat radius:
  B (internal fuel and 1,280 kg; 2,822 lb external weapons), lo-lo-lo 145 nm (268 km; 167 miles)
  B (reduced fuel and 1,814 kg; 4,000 lb external weapons), lo-lo-lo 70 nm (130 km; 81 miles)
  visual reconnaissance with two external fuel tanks 400 nm (740 km; 460 miles)
  photo reconnaissance with two auxiliary tanks and camera pod, hi-lo-hi 560 nm (1,036 km; 644 miles)
Max ferry range (two underwing tanks)
  more than 1,149 nm (2,130 km; 1,323 miles)

AERMACCHI M.B. 339A

The M.B. 339 is a tandem two-seat trainer/ground attack aircraft, powered by a Fiat-built Rolls-Royce Viper 632 engine.

The first of two M.B. 339X flying prototypes (I-NOVE) was flown for the first time on 12 August 1976. The second aircraft (I-NINE), which made its first flight on 20 May 1977, was built to pre-production standard; the third and fourth airframes were used for static and fatigue testing respectively. They are being followed by 100 production M.B.339As for the Italian Air Force, of which the first 15 were ordered in FY 1978 and the next 40 in FY 1979; the final 45 were to be ordered in FY 1980. The first production aircraft (I-NEUF) flew for the first time on 20 July 1978, and the first examples were handed over to the Italian Air Force for pre-service trials on 8 August 1979. Later that year the M.B. 339A entered service with the Scuola di Volo Basico-Iniziale Aviogetti at Lecce-Galatina in southern Italy.

An unspecified number of M.B. 339As were ordered in 1980 by the Peruvian Air Force.

TYPE: Two-seat basic and advanced trainer and ground attack aircraft.

AIRFRAME: Structural design criteria based on MIL-A-8860A; 8g limit load factor in 'clean' configuration. Cockpit designed for 40,000 pressurisation cycles. Service life requirement 10,000 flying hours and 20,000 landings in the training role. Entire structure specially treated to prevent corrosion.

WINGS: Cantilever low/mid-wing monoplane. Wing section NACA 64A-114 (mod) at centreline, NACA 64A-212 (mod) at tip. Leading-edge swept back 11° 18'. Sweepback at quarter-chord 8° 29'. All-metal stressed-skin structure, with single main spar and auxiliary rear spar, built in two portions and bolted to fuselage. Skin stiffened by spanwise stringers, closely spaced ribs, and false ribs. Wingtip tanks permanently attached. Single fence on each wing at approx two-thirds span. Servo-powered ailerons embody 'Irving'-type aerodynamic balance provisions, and are statically balanced along their entire span. Electrically actuated balance tabs facilitate reversion to manual operation in the event of servo failure. Hydraulically actuated single-slotted flaps, operated by push/pull rods.

FUSELAGE: All-metal semi-monocoque structure, built in two main portions: forward (nose to engine mounting bulkhead), and rear (engine bulkhead to tailcone). Forward portion built of C-section frames, four C-section spars, longitudinal L-section stringers, and skin panels. Rear section manufactured entirely from aluminium alloy except for firewall and most of tailcone, which are of stainless steel; four-bolt attachment to forward fuselage to facilitate access to engine. Hydraulically actuated, electrically controlled airbrake under centre of fuselage, just forward of CG.

TAIL UNIT: Cantilever all-metal structure, of similar construction to wings. Slightly sweptback vertical surfaces. Rudder and elevators are statically balanced, each having an electrically actuated dual-purpose balance and trim tab. Two auxiliary fins under rear fuselage.

LANDING GEAR: Hydraulically-retractable tricycle type, with oleo-pneumatic shock-absorbers; suitable for operation from semi-prepared runways. Nosewheel retracts forward, main units outward into wings. Steerable nosewheel, fitted with shimmy damper. Low-pressure main-wheel tubeless tyres size 545 × 175-10 (12 ply rating); nosewheel tubeless tyre size 380 × 150-4 (6 ply rating). Emergency extension system. Hydraulic disc brakes with anti-skid system.

POWER PLANT: One Rolls-Royce Viper Mk 632-43 turbojet engine, rated at 17·8 kN (4,000 lb st). Engines built in Italy under Rolls-Royce/Fiat licence; final assembly by Piaggio. Fuel in two-cell rubber fuselage tank, capacity 781 litres (172 Imp gallons), and two integral wingtip tanks, combined capacity 632 litres (139 Imp gallons). Total internal capacity 1,413 litres (311 Imp gallons) usable. Single-point pressure refuelling receptacle in port side of fuselage, below wing trailing-edge. Gravity refuelling points on top of fuselage and each tip-tank. Provision for two drop-tanks, each of 325 litres (71·5 Imp gallons) capacity, on centre underwing stations. Anti-icing system for engine air intakes optional.

ACCOMMODATION: Crew of two in tandem, on Martin-Baker IT10F zero-zero ejection seats in pressurised cockpit. Rear seat elevated 32·5 cm (12¾ in). Rearview mirror for each occupant. Two-piece moulded transparent jettisonable canopy, opening sideways to starboard.

SYSTEMS: Hydraulic system, pressure 176 bars (2,600 lb/sq in), for actuation of flaps, aileron servos, airbrake, landing gear, wheel brakes and nosewheel steering. Backup system for wheel brakes and emergency extension of landing gear. Main electrical DC power from one 28V 9kW engine-driven starter/generator and one 28V 6kW secondary generator. Two 24V 22Ah nickel-cadmium batteries for engine starting. Fixed-frequency 115/26V AC power from two 600VA single-phase static inverters. External power receptacle. Pressurised cockpit, with max differential of 0·24 bars (3·5 lb/sq in). Bootstrap-type air-conditioning system, which also provides air for windscreen and canopy demisting. Low-pressure demand-type oxygen system, operating at 28 bars (400 lb/sq in).

AVIONICS AND EQUIPMENT: Typical avionics installation includes Perkin-Elmer/Magnavox AN/ARC-150(V) UHF or Perkin-Elmer/Magnavox SRT-194B VHF primary com transceiver; Collins 618M-3A VHF/AM or equivalent ARINC 566A, or Collins AN/ARC-186(V) VHF/AM and FM secondary com transceiver; Collins IA-210 interphone; Collins AN/ARN-118(V)1 Tacan or Collins 860E-5 DME nav system; Fiar/Bendix AN/APX-100(V) IFF; Collins 51RV-4D VOR/ILS, including localiser and glideslope receivers; Collins MKI-3 marker beacon receiver; Collins ADF-60A ADF; or (M.B.339A) Marconi Avionics AD-620C computerised area and dead reckoning navigation system. Standard instrumentation includes ARU-2B/A attitude director indicator, AQU-6/A HSI, Aeritalia-Sperry AS-339 attitude and heading reference system, AG-5 standby attitude indicator, and flight director system. Retractable landing light beneath port wing; taxying light on nosewheel leg.

ARMAMENT AND OPERATIONAL EQUIPMENT: Up to 1,815 kg (4,000 lb) of external stores can be carried on six underwing hardpoints, the inner four of which are stressed for loads of up to 454 kg (1,000 lb) each and the outer two for up to 340 kg (750 lb) each. Provisions are made, on the two inner stations, for the installation of two Macchi gun pods, each containing either a 30 mm DEFA cannon with 120 rds, or a 12·7 mm AN/M-3 machine-gun with 350 rds. Other typical loads can include two Matra 550 or AIM-9 Sidewinder air-to-air

missiles on the two outer stations; four 1,000 lb or six 750 lb bombs; six SUU-11A/A 7·62 mm Minigun pods with 1,500 rds/pod; six Matra 155 launchers, each for eighteen 68 mm rockets; six Matra F-2 practice launchers, each for six 68 mm rockets; six LAU-68/A or LAU-32/G launchers, each for seven 2·75 in rockets; six Aerea AL-25-50 or AL-18-50 launchers, each with twenty-five or eighteen 50 mm rockets respectively; six Aerea AL-12-80 launchers, each with twelve 81 mm rockets; four LAU-10/A launchers, each with four 5 in Zuni rockets; six Aerea BRD bomb/rocket dispensers; six Aermacchi 11B29-003 bomb/flare dispensers; or two 325 litre (71·5 Imp gallon) drop-tanks; or a photographic pod with four 70 mm Vinten cameras. Provision for Aeritalia 8.105.924 fixed reflector sight, Saab RGS 2 gunsight or Thomson-CSF RD-21 self-contained gyroscopic sight; a gunsight can also be installed in rear cockpit, to enable instructor to evaluate manoeuvres performed by student pilot. All gunsights can be equipped with fully automatic Teledyne TSC 116-2 gun camera. Head-up display system under study. Provision for towing type A-6B (1·83 × 9·14 m; 6 × 30 ft) aerial banner target; tow attachment point on inner surface of ventral airbrake.

DIMENSIONS, EXTERNAL:
Wing span over tip-tanks 10·858 m (35 ft 7½ in)
Wing aspect ratio 5·26
Length overall 10·972 m (36 ft 0 in)
Height overall 3·600 m (11 ft 9¾ in)
Tailplane span 4·164 m (13 ft 8 in)
Wheel track 2·483 m (8 ft 1¾ in)
Wheelbase 4·369 m (14 ft 4 in)
AREAS:
Wings, gross 19·30 m² (207·74 sq ft)
Ailerons (total) 1·328 m² (14·29 sq ft)
Trailing-edge flaps (total) 2·552 m² (27·47 sq ft)
Airbrake 0·520 m² (5·60 sq ft)
Fin 2·370 m² (25·51 sq ft)
Rudder, incl tab 0·610 m² (6·57 sq ft)
Tailplane 3·380 m² (36·38 sq ft)
Elevators (total, incl tabs) 0·979 m² (10·54 sq ft)
WEIGHTS:
Weight empty 3,075 kg (6,780 lb)
Weight empty, equipped 3,125 kg (6,889 lb)
Fuel load (internal, usable) 1,100 kg (2,425 lb)
T-O weight, 'clean' 4,400 kg (9,700 lb)
Max T-O weight, with external stores 5,897 kg (13,000 lb)
Landing weight with 10% fuel reserves 3,425 kg (7,550 lb)

PERFORMANCE (at 'clean' T-O weight, ISA, except where stated):
EAS limit/Mach limit
  Mach 0·82 (500 knots; 926 km/h; 575 mph)
Max level speed at S/L
  485 knots (898 km/h; 558 mph)
Max level speed at 9,150 m (30,000 ft)
  Mach 0·77 (441 knots; 817 km/h; 508 mph)
Max speed for landing gear extension
  170 knots (315 km/h; 195 mph) IAS
Approach speed over 15 m (50 ft) obstacle
  98 knots (182 km/h; 113 mph) IAS
Landing speed 89 knots (165 km/h; 102·5 mph) IAS
Stalling speed 80 knots (148·5 km/h; 92·5 mph)
Max rate of climb at S/L 2,010 m (6,595 ft)/min
Time to 9,150 m (30,000 ft) 7 min 6 s
Service ceiling (30·5 m; 100 ft/min rate of climb) 14,630 m (48,000 ft)
Min ground turning radius 8·45 m (27 ft 8¾ in)
T-O run at S/L:
  'clean' T-O weight 465 m (1,525 ft)
  max T-O weight 915 m (3,000 ft)

Aermacchi M.B. 339A two-seat jet trainer and light attack aircraft (Pilot Press)

T-O to, and landing from, 15 m (50 ft)
700 m (2,296 ft)

Landing run at S/L:
'clean' landing weight   415 m (1,362 ft)
ground attack mission landing weight of 3,630 kg
(8,000 lb)   427 m (1,400 ft)

Max range (internal fuel), 10% reserves
950 nm (1,760 km; 1,093 miles)

Max endurance at 9,150 m (30,000 ft) (internal fuel),
10% reserves   2 h 50 min

Max ferry range with two underwing drop-tanks, 10%
reserves   1,140 nm (2,110 km; 1,310 miles)

Max endurance at 7,620 m (25,000 ft) with two underwing drop-tanks, 10% reserves   3 h 45 min

g limits:
'clean' T-O weight   +8·0; −4·0
max T-O weight   +5·5; −2·0

WEIGHTS (armed configuration):
Typical T-O weights with crew of one and armament
indicated:
A: two Macchi 30 mm gun pods
4,822 kg (10,630 lb)
B: two Macchi 30 mm gun pods and two drop-tanks
5,475 kg (12,070 lb)
C: two Macchi 30 mm gun pods and four Mk 82
bombs   5,881 kg (12,965 lb)
D: four Mk 82 bombs and two drop-tanks
5,897 kg (13,000 lb)

E: six Mk 82 bombs   5,897 kg (13,000 lb)
F: two Macchi 30 mm gun pods, two LR-25-0 rocket
launchers and two drop-tanks 5,808 kg (12,805 lb)
G: four LR-25-0 launchers and two drop-tanks
5,642 kg (12,440 lb)
H: six LR-25-0 launchers   5,323 kg (11,735 lb)

PERFORMANCE (armed configuration, at T-O weights given
above):
Dash speed at S/L:
A   440 knots (815 km/h; 507 mph)
B   400 knots (741 km/h; 461 mph)
C, D   390 knots (723 km/h; 449 mph)
E   395 knots (732 km/h; 455 mph)
F, G, H   365 knots (676 km/h; 420 mph)
Radius of action, hi-lo-hi (no run-in or run-out):
A   223 nm (413 km; 257 miles)
B   323 nm (598 km; 372 miles)
C   176 nm (326 km; 203 miles)
D   320 nm (593 km; 368 miles)
E   212 nm (393 km; 244 miles)
F   275 nm (510 km; 317 miles)
G   305 nm (565 km; 351 miles)
H   165 nm (306 km; 190 miles)
Radius of action, lo-lo-lo (no run-in or run-out):
A   150 nm (278 km; 173 miles)
B   205 nm (380 km; 236 miles)
C   135 nm (250 km; 155 miles)
D   200 nm (371 km; 230 miles)

E   146 nm (271 km; 168 miles)
F   190 nm (352 km; 219 miles)
G   193 nm (358 km; 222 miles)
H   123 nm (228 km; 142 miles)
Radius of action, hi-lo-hi (30 nm; 56 km; 34·5 mile
run-in and run-out):
A   150 nm (278 km; 173 miles)
B   260 nm (482 km; 299 miles)
C   122 nm (226 km; 140 miles)
D   240 nm (445 km; 276 miles)
E   138 nm (256 km; 159 miles)
F   218 nm (404 km; 251 miles)
G   230 nm (426 km; 265 miles)
H   112 nm (208 km; 129 miles)
Radius of action, lo-lo-lo (30 nm; 56 km; 34·5 mile
run-in and run-out):
A   130 nm (241 km; 150 miles)
B   188 nm (348 km; 216 miles)
C   120 nm (222 km; 138 miles)
D   180 nm (334 km; 207 miles)
E   124 nm (230 km; 143 miles)
F   172 nm (319 km; 198 miles)
G   173 nm (321 km; 199 miles)
H   103 nm (191 km; 119 miles)

AERMACCHI M.B. 339K VELTRO 2 (GREYHOUND)

See Addenda.

AGUSTA
THE AGUSTA GROUP

HEAD OFFICES:
Viale del Ghisallo 20, 20151 Milan
Telephone: (0332) 30706
Telex: 333280
Via Abruzzi 11, 00187 Rome

Telephone: (06) 4756551
Telex: 614398
GROUP MANAGEMENT:
Cav del Lavoro Conte Corrado Agusta (Joint
President)
Dott Ing P. Fascione (Joint President)
Dott Ing G. Brazzelli (General Manager)
In 1977, four major Italian aerospace companies were

combined under a single management structure. They are
Costruzioni Aeronautiche Giovanni Agusta; SIAI-
Marchetti SpA (which see); Elicotteri Meridionali SpA
(see EM entry in this section); and Industria Aeronautica
Meridionale. There have since been added Fonderie e
Officine Meccaniche di Benevento SpA, and the
Brussels-based Agusta International. Together, they form
the Agusta Group.

COSTRUZIONI AERONAUTICHE GIOVANNI AGUSTA SpA

HEAD OFFICE AND WORKS: Casella Postale 480, 21017
Cascina Costa, Gallarate
Telephone: (0331) 220478
Telex: 332569
CHAIRMAN AND PRESIDENT: Conte Corrado Agusta
DEPUTY CHAIRMAN: E. Marelli
CHIEF EXECUTIVE OFFICER: P. Fascione
GENERAL MANAGER: A. Antichi
TECHNICAL DIRECTOR: L. Passini
DIRECTOR, INTERNATIONAL MARKETING: Enrico Guerra
PUBLIC RELATIONS: Francesco Lami

This company was established in 1907 by Giovanni
Agusta and built many experimental and production aircraft before the second World War.

In 1952 Agusta acquired a licence to manufacture the
Bell Model 47 helicopter and the first Agusta-built Model
47G made its maiden flight on 22 May 1954.

Agusta is producing under licence in Italy the Bell Models 205, 206 and 212. It is also collaborating with Bell
Helicopter Textron (see US section) in developing the
Model 412 version of the Bell 212, fitted with a new
four-blade rotor system. Under licence from Sikorsky,
production of SH-3 helicopters began in 1967, and production of the HH-3F (S-61R) started in 1974. Details are
given hereafter, following the descriptions of the A 109A
and A 129 helicopters designed by Agusta.

Agusta is also engaged, together with Meridionali,
SIAI-Marchetti and other Italian companies, in production under licence of the Boeing Vertol CH-47C Chinook
helicopter (see EM entry). It is collaborating with Westland Helicopters of the UK in developing the EH 101 Sea
King replacement (see under EHI in International section).

AGUSTA A 109A

The Agusta A 109A is a high-speed, high-performance
twin-engined helicopter. The basic version accommodates
a pilot and seven passengers, and has a large baggage
compartment in the rear of the fuselage. Alternatively, the
A 109A can be adapted for freight-carrying, as an ambulance, or for search and rescue. Military and naval versions
are described separately.

The first of three A 109 flying prototypes (NC7101)
flew for the first time on 4 August 1971. RAI and FAA
certification, including single-pilot IFR operation, was
announced on 1 June 1975; certification has since been
granted in Canada, France, West Germany, Sweden, Switzerland and the UK. Deliveries of production aircraft,
designated A 109A, started in early 1976 and had reached
a total of about 80 by the beginning of 1980. About half of
these are for customers in the USA; the Italian Carabinieri
and highway police have each ordered 10.

Agusta has successfully carried out trials of a four-unit
flotation gear for the A 109A, manufactured by Garrett
Air Cruisers of New Jersey.

The following description applies to the standard A
109A, production of which was at the rate of six to seven
per month in 1979.

TYPE: Twin-engined general-purpose helicopter.
ROTOR SYSTEM AND DRIVE: Fully-articulated four-blade
single main rotor and two-blade semi-rigid delta-hinged
tail rotor. Main transmission assembly is housed in fairing above the passenger cabin, driving the main rotor
through a coupling gearbox and main reduction gearbox, and the tail rotor through a 90° gearbox. Main rotor
blades can be folded back for stowage. Main
rotor/engine rpm ratio 1 : 15·62. Tail rotor/engine rpm
ratio 1 : 2·88. Rotor brake optional.

FUSELAGE AND TAIL UNIT: Pod and boom type, of
aluminium alloy construction, built in four main sections: nose, cockpit, passenger cabin and tailboom.
Sweptback vertical fins (above and below fuselage), and
non-swept elevators, mounted on rear of tailboom. Tail
rotor on port side.

LANDING GEAR: Retractable tricycle type, with single main
wheels and self-centering steerable nosewheel. Hydraulic retraction, nosewheel forward, main wheels
upward into fuselage. Hydraulic emergency retraction.
Brakes on main wheels, locking mechanism on nosewheel. All tyres are of tubeless type, size 360 × 135-6,
pressure 5·9 bars (85 lb/sq in). Emergency flotation gear
optional.

POWER PLANT: Two Allison 250-C20B turboshaft engines
(each 313 kW; 420 shp for T-O, 287 kW; 385 shp max
continuous power, 276 kW; 370 shp max cruise power,
derated to 258 kW; 346 shp for twin-engine operation),
mounted side by side in upper rear fuselage and separated from passenger cabin and from each other by
firewalls. Fuel tank in lower rear fuselage, usable capacity 550 litres (121 Imp gallons). Oil capacity 7·7 litres
(1·7 Imp gallons) for each engine and 9·5 litres (2·1 Imp
gallons) for transmission.

ACCOMMODATION: Crew of one or two on flight deck, which
has a door on each side. Dual controls. Main cabin seats
up to six passengers, in two rows of three at 81 cm (32
in) pitch, with large space at rear for baggage. A seventh
passenger can be carried in lieu of second crew member.
Door to passenger cabin on each side. First row of seats
removable to permit use as freight transport. Ambulance version can accommodate two stretchers, one
above the other, and two medical attendants, in addition
to the pilot. An external freight load of 907 kg (2,000 lb)
can be transported on a centre-of-gravity hook. A
side-mounted hoist and sliding doors can be installed for
rescue missions.

SYSTEMS: Utility hydraulic system, with emergency
accumulators, for landing gear operation, wheel and
rotor braking and nosewheel locking. Two separate
hydraulic systems provide for dual flight servo-controls.
28V DC electrical system, using two 30V 150A star-
ter/generators, and one 24V 22Ah battery. Single-
phase AC power supplied at 400 Hz from two 115/26V
250VA solid-state static inverters. Third inverter as
emergency backup.

AVIONICS AND EQUIPMENT: Additional instrumentation for
IFR operations and equipment to customer's require-
ments, including provision for VHF/FM, UHF/AM,
VOR (with Area Navigation if required), ILS, DME,
ADF, autopilot, and automatic stabilisation equipment.

DIMENSIONS, EXTERNAL:
Diameter of main rotor   11·00 m (36 ft 1 in)
Diameter of tail rotor   2·03 m (6 ft 8 in)
Length overall, rotors turning 13·08 m (42 ft 11 in)
Length of fuselage   11·11 m (36 ft 5½ in)
Height overall   3·32 m (10 ft 10¾ in)
Elevator span   2·88 m (9 ft 5½ in)

Agusta A 109A general-purpose helicopter (two Allison 250-C20B turboshaft engines)

Agusta A 109A twin-engined general-purpose helicopter *(Pilot Press)*

Wheel track	2·45 m (8 ft 0½ in)
Wheelbase	3·535 m (11 ft 7¼ in)
Passenger doors (each): Height	1·06 m (3 ft 5¾ in)
Width	1·15 m (3 ft 9¼ in)
Height to sill	0·65 m (2 ft 1½ in)

DIMENSIONS, INTERNAL:

Cabin, excl flight deck: Length	1·62 m (5 ft 3¾ in)
Width	1·42 m (4 ft 8 in)
Height	1·29 m (4 ft 2¾ in)
Volume	2·82 m³ (100 cu ft)
Baggage compartment volume	0·52 m³ (18·4 cu ft)

AREAS:

Main rotor blades (each)	1·84 m² (19·8 sq ft)
Tail rotor blades (each)	0·203 m² (2·185 sq ft)
Main rotor disc	95·00 m² (1,022·6 sq ft)
Tail rotor disc	3·23 m² (34·75 sq ft)

WEIGHTS AND LOADINGS:

Weight empty	1,415 kg (3,120 lb)
Max T-O weight	2,600 kg (5,730 lb)
Max disc loading	27·4 kg/m² (5·60 lb/sq ft)
Max power loading	4·15 kg/kW (6·82 lb/shp)

PERFORMANCE (at AUW of 2,450 kg; 5,400 lb. A: ISA, B: ISA + 22°C):

Never-exceed speed	168 knots (311 km/h; 193 mph)
Max cruising speed at max continuous power:	
A	144 knots (266 km/h; 165 mph)
Optimum cruising speed at S/L:	
A	125 knots (231 km/h; 143 mph)
Max rate of climb at S/L:	
A	488 m (1,600 ft)/min
Rate of climb at S/L, one engine out:	
A	103 m (340 ft)/min
Max operating height	4,572 m (15,000 ft)
Service ceiling: A	4,968 m (16,300 ft)
Service ceiling, one engine out: A	1,370 m (4,500 ft)
Hovering ceiling IGE: A	2,987 m (9,800 ft)
B	1,951 m (6,400 ft)
Hovering ceiling OGE: A	2,073 m (6,800 ft)
B	1,036 m (3,400 ft)
Max range at 2,000 m (6,560 ft):	
A	332 nm (615 km; 382 miles)
Max endurance at S/L: A	3 h 30 min

AGUSTA A 109 MILITARY VERSION

Five military A 109s were ordered by the Italian Army for evaluation, and delivery of these began in early 1977. Three of these are equipped to carry four TOW air-to-surface missiles each, the other two being equipped for transport and liaison duties. General configuration, structure and power plant are similar to those of the A 109A (which see). Changes in the military version include dual controls and instrumentation; rotor brake; tail rotor control magnetic brake; sliding doors; environmental control system; emergency flotation gear; armoured seats; crashworthy fuel tanks; heavy-duty battery; particle separator; external cargo hook; multi-purpose universal supports for external loads; rescue hoist; high-load cargo floor; and infra-red suppression system.

The military A 109 has been ordered by the Argentinian Army and other foreign operators.

ACCOMMODATION: Standard seating for a pilot and seven troops. Ambulance version can accommodate two stretcher patients and two medical attendants.

ARMAMENT: Basically two 7·62 mm flexibly-mounted machine-guns, with stabilised sight system, and two XM-157 rocket launchers, each with seven 2·75 in rockets. Alternative weapons include Hot or TOW missiles; an electrically-operated 7·62 mm Minigun on flexible mounting, with 1,000 rounds; a fully-automatic MG3 7·62 mm machine-gun with 5,000 rounds; an XM-159C launcher for nineteen 2·75 in rockets, Agusta launcher for seven 81 mm rockets, or 200A-1 launcher for nineteen 2·75 in rockets.

AGUSTA A 109 NAVAL VERSION

A naval version of the A 109A is in an advanced stage of development for several navies. The main missions to be carried out by the A 109 in the naval configuration are: anti-surface-vessel, anti-submarine, electronic warfare, armed patrol (stand-off missile guidance, TG-2), coast-guard patrol, SAR, aerial ambulance and utility.

The naval A 109, maintaining the general configuration, structure, power plant, reliability and performance of the A 109A, has been specially designed for shipboard compatibility. Besides the weapon systems appropriate to specific missions, the helicopter is equipped with four-axis ASE, radar altimeter, internal auxiliary fuel tanks, rotor brake, dual controls and instrumentation, particle separator, heavy duty battery, non-retractable landing gear, rescue hoist, universal supports for external loads, search radar, emergency flotation gear, anchorage points for deck lashings, and an automatic navigation system.

ACCOMMODATION: Standard seating for a crew of three or four. Ambulance version accommodates two stretchers and two medical attendants.

SYSTEMS: Standard duplicated hydraulic systems for flight controls, as in A 109A, and for automatic stabilisation equipment. Third, self-contained system for MAD and other utilities. Electrical system capacity increased to cater for higher power demand.

AVIONICS AND EQUIPMENT: Complete instrumentation for day and night sea operation in all weathers. Equipment common to all roles includes navigation, cabin and cockpit lights, two fixed landing lights, two anti-collision beacons, first aid kits, and hand-type fire extinguisher for cabin. Optional equipment common to all roles includes a four-axis cross-country autopilot system, UHF/VHF transceiver with homing, AG 03 crew intercom, VOR/ILS, DME, LF/ADF, radar altimeter, tactical air navigation system with Doppler radar, dual controls, and emergency flotation gear.

ARMAMENT AND OPERATIONAL EQUIPMENT: For the ASW role specialised equipment includes two homing torpedoes and six marine markers. Detection of the submarine can be carried out either by the parent ship (in which case the A 109 is acting as a weapon carrier system) or by the helicopter's onboard retractable classification and localisation equipment (MAD). For the ASV role the naval A 109 carries a high-performance long-range search radar with high discrimination in rough sea conditions. The surface attack is performed with AS.12 or AM-10 air-to-surface wire-guided missiles. For the TG-2 mission, the helicopter is equipped with a special guidance system to control and guide a ship-launched Otomat missile. Provisions are also incorporated for the installation of the most advanced ESM systems. A special ECM version of the naval A 109 has been studied by Agusta, and the equipment that can be installed in the helicopter includes a radar warning display, direction finder equipment, an interferometer, an electromagnetic emission analyser, and jamming equipment. For armed patrol, the naval A 109 is equipped with a search radar and armament to customer's requirements. The coastguard patrol configuration includes a search radar, a low light level TV camera and a special installation for external high efficiency loudspeakers. For the search and rescue role, the naval A 109 is fitted with a 150 kg (330 lb) capacity electrically operated hoist, emergency flotation gear and search radar. The naval A 109 can be equipped for several other duties including firefighting and crash rescue, reconnaissance, military command post, and liaison.

AGUSTA A 129 MANGUSTA (MONGOOSE)

This light anti-tank helicopter is at the final design stage for the Italian Army, which has ordered three prototypes. First flight is expected in 1982.

A narrow fuselage, 0·95 m (37·5 in) wide, accommodates the pilot's and co-pilot/gunner's seats in tandem, with the pilot to the rear. Each crew position is fitted with

Military Agusta A 109 for the Argentinian Army, armed with two rocket launchers and two machine-gun pods

Agusta A 109 naval version, with 360° radar search capability

Model of the Agusta A 129 Mangusta twin-turboshaft anti-tank helicopter

flying controls, instruments and an armoured seat. Two stub wings are standard, each with two external stores stations. The airframe has a ballistic tolerance against 12·7 mm armour-piercing ammunition, and meets the crash-worthiness standards of MIL-STD-1290. Mission equipment, in addition to weapons, includes radar warning receiver, chaff/flare dispenser, radar deceiver/jammer, and infra-red jammer.

ROTOR SYSTEM: Fully-articulated four-blade main rotor. Blades each have a glassfibre spar, Nomex honeycomb leading- and trailing-edge, and skin of composite materials. Hub has a swashplate of glassfibre composites; all mechanical linkages and moving parts are housed inside rotor mast.

POWER PLANT: Two Avco Lycoming LTS101-850A-1 turboshaft engines, each rated at 596 kW (800 shp) for T-O and derated to 429 kW (575 shp) for normal operations. In the event of failure of one engine, the remaining engine can be operated at 596 kW (800 shp) to provide adequate single-engined performance.

ARMAMENT: Eight TOW anti-tank missiles; eight TOW with either two 7·62 mm or 12·7 mm machine-gun pods, or two seven-tube launchers for 2·75 in air-to-surface rockets; eight Hellfire anti-tank missiles plus target acquisition and designation system, pilot's night vision equipment and integrated helmet and display system; or two machine-gun pods plus two 19-tube launchers for 2·75 in rockets; or two 19-tube plus two seven-tube launchers for 2·75 in rockets. Inner stores stations can each carry 300 kg (661 lb) loads; outer stations can each carry 200 kg (441 lb). Telescopic sight unit for TOW missiles, fitted with laser rangefinder and FLIR for target acquisition/designation.

DIMENSIONS, EXTERNAL:
Diameter of main rotor	11·90 m (39 ft 0½ in)
Diameter of tail rotor	2·14 m (7 ft 0¼ in)
Wing span	3·10 m (10 ft 2 in)
Length of fuselage	12·16 m (7 ft 1 in)
Fuselage: Max width	0·95 m (3 ft 1½ in)
Height over tail fin, tail rotor horizontal	2·65 m (8 ft 8¼ in)
Height to top of rotor hub	3·42 m (11 ft 2¾ in)
Tailplane span	3·00 m (9 ft 10 in)
Wheel track	2·20 m (7 ft 3½ in)
Wheelbase	7·14 m (23 ft 5 in)

WEIGHTS:
Weight empty, equipped	2,400 kg (5,291 lb)
Fuel load (max internal)	650 kg (1,433 lb)
Max mission T-O weight	3,554 kg (7,835 lb)

PERFORMANCE (estimated, at max mission T-O weight):
Max permissible diving speed, with 28 rockets	168 knots (311 km/h; 193 mph)
Max level speed at S/L, ISA + 20°C	
'clean'	142 knots (263 km/h; 163 mph)
with 8 TOW	154 knots (285 km/h; 177 mph)
Cruising speed	135 knots (250 km/h; 155 mph)
Max rate of climb at S/L, ISA + 20°C	576 m (1,890 ft)/min
Max rate of climb at S/L, one engine out	120 m (394 ft)/min
Hovering ceiling IGE, ISA + 20°C	1,675 m (5,495 ft)
Hovering ceiling OGE, ISA + 20°C	1,100 m (3,610 ft)
Endurance (anti-tank mission), no reserves	2 h 30 min
Max endurance at 70 knots (130 km/h; 81 mph)	3 h 0 min, plus 20 min reserves
Max self-ferry range at 135 knots (249 km/h; 155 mph)	
internal fuel	340 nm (629 km; 391 miles)
internal plus 400 kg (882 lb) external fuel	600 nm (1,112 km; 691 miles)

AGUSTA-BELL 205

The Agusta-Bell 205 is a multi-purpose utility helicopter, corresponding to the UH-1D/UH-1H versions adopted by the US armed forces. The cabin will accommodate a pilot and 13 or 14 passengers, and there is a 0·8 m³ (28·25 cu ft) baggage compartment in the tailboom. The AB 205 is fitted with IFR and night flying instruments,

and for normal operation only one pilot is needed. Power plant is a 1,044 kW (1,400 shp) Avco Lycoming T53-L-13B turboshaft engine, derated to 932 kW (1,250 shp) for take-off.

The AB 205 is in service with the Italian armed forces and has been ordered by many other countries. Recent customers include Tunisia (six).

DIMENSIONS, EXTERNAL: As Bell Model 205 except:
Main rotor diameter	14·72 m (48 ft 3½ in)
Width overall	2·76 m (9 ft 0½ in)
Height overall	4·48 m (14 ft 8 in)

WEIGHTS: As Bell Model 205 except:
Weight empty (standard)	2,240 kg (4,940 lb)
Normal T-O weight (internal load)	4,309 kg (9,500 lb)

PERFORMANCE (at Normal T-O weight, ISA):
Max level speed at S/L	120 knots (222 km/h; 138 mph)
Cruising speed	110 knots (204 km/h; 127 mph)
Max rate of climb at S/L	512 m (1,680 ft)/min
Service ceiling	4,570 m (15,000 ft)
Hovering ceiling IGE	4,115 m (13,500 ft)
Max range, standard tanks, no reserves	312 nm (580 km; 360 miles)
Max endurance, standard tanks, no reserves	3 h 48 min

AGUSTA-BELL 206B JETRANGER III

The Agusta-Bell 206 JetRanger has been manufactured under licence from Bell since the end of 1967; deliveries began in 1972 of the Agusta-Bell 206B JetRanger II, and of the current production version, the JetRanger III, at the end of 1978. Powered by a 313 kW (420 shp) Allison 250-C20B turboshaft engine, the JetRanger III incorporates many improvements derived from the production of, and operating experience with, many thousands of earlier commercial and military JetRangers. A description of the JetRanger III appears under the Bell Helicopter Textron entry in the US section.

AGUSTA-BELL 206L-1 LONGRANGER II

This aircraft is a seven-seat single-engined light helicopter, derived from the AB 206B and powered by a 373 kW (500 shp) Allison 250-C28B turboshaft engine, as described under the Bell Helicopter Textron entry in the US section.

AGUSTA-BELL 212

The Agusta-Bell 212 is a twin-engined utility transport helicopter particularly suited to military or civilian passenger transport duties. Its general configuration is similar to that of the Bell Model 212 Twin Two-Twelve, described in the US section.

Recent customers for the AB 212 include the Austrian Army, which ordered 24 to replace its AB 204s that entered service in 1957. They will be used for transport, rescue and casualty evacuation duties, some carrying armament.

The extensively-modified AB 212ASW naval version produced by Agusta is described separately.

DIMENSIONS, EXTERNAL:
Diameter of main rotor	14·63 m (48 ft 0 in)
Diameter of tail rotor	2·59 m (8 ft 6 in)
Length overall, rotors turning	17·40 m (57 ft 1 in)
Fuselage length	14·02 m (46 ft 0 in)
Height to top of cabin roof	2·34 m (7 ft 8 in)
Height overall, tail rotor turning	4·40 m (14 ft 5 in)
Elevator span	2·84 m (9 ft 4 in)
Width over skids	2·64 m (8 ft 8 in)

WEIGHTS:
Weight empty (standard)	2,676 kg (5,900 lb)
Max T-O weight	5,080 kg (11,200 lb)

PERFORMANCE (at AUW of 4,536 kg; 10,000 lb, ISA):
Cruising speed at S/L	110 knots (204 km/h; 127 mph)
Max rate of climb at S/L	567 m (1,860 ft)/min
Service ceiling	5,180 m (17,000 ft)
Hovering ceiling IGE	3,960 m (13,000 ft)
Hovering ceiling OGE	3,050 m (10,000 ft)
Max range at 1,525 m (5,000 ft) with standard fuel, no reserves	
on two engines	267 nm (494 km; 307 miles)
on one engine	318 nm (589 km; 366 miles)

AGUSTA-BELL 212ASW

The AB 212ASW is an extensively modified version of the AB 212, intended primarily for anti-submarine search and attack missions, and for attacks on surface vessels, but suitable also for search and rescue and utility roles. It benefits from considerable naval operational experience gained with the single-engined AB 204AS, and because of its similarity in size to the 204AS can operate from the same small ship decks.

The AB 212ASW is produced at a rate of approximately four to five per month and is being delivered to meet orders from several navies. Recent customers include also the Iraqi Air Force (eight).

Apart from some local strengthening and the provision of deck-mooring equipment, the airframe structure remains essentially similar to that of the commercial Model 212 and military UH-1N, described under the Bell Helicopter Textron entry in the US section. Main differences from the Agusta-Bell 212 are as follows:

TYPE: Twin-engined anti-submarine and anti-surface-vessel helicopter.

POWER PLANT: One Pratt & Whitney Aircraft of Canada PT6T-6 Turbo Twin Pac, rated at 1,398 kW (1,875 shp). Protection against salt water corrosion. Provision for one internal or two external auxiliary fuel tanks.

ACCOMMODATION: Normal crew of three or four. Volume of cabin is 6·1 m³ (215 cu ft), with floor area of 5·0 m² (54 sq ft). With sonar installed, volume is reduced to 5·1 m³ (180 cu ft). Naval 212 can accommodate two pilots and seven passengers; or two pilots, four stretcher patients and attendant. Single sliding door, with jettisonable emergency exit panel, on each side.

SYSTEMS: Standard duplicated hydraulic systems for flight controls, as in AB 212. The hydraulic system operates the automatic flight control system. Self-contained hydraulic system for operation of sonar, rescue hoist and

Agusta-Bell 212ASW anti-submarine and anti-surface-vessel helicopter

other utilities. Electrical system capacity increased to cater for higher power demand (28V DC, and three-phase 200/115V or single-phase 26V AC at 400Hz); the two standard generators are integrated with a 20kVA alternator.

AVIONICS AND EQUIPMENT: Complete instrumentation for day and night sea operation in all weathers. Avionics installed are AN/ARC-159 UHF transceiver, Collins SSB/DSB 718 U-5 HF transceiver, and Agusta AG-03-M intercom, for communications; Marconi Avionics AD 370B ADF, Hoffman AN/ARN-91 Tacan and Collins AN/ARA-50 homing UHF, for navigation assistance; Aeritalia (Honeywell) AN/APN-171 radar altimeter, Canadian Marconi AN/APN-208(V)2 Doppler radar, Canadian Marconi CMA-708B/ASW navigation computer, and automatic flight control system with General Electric SR-3 gyro platform, Agusta ASE-531A automatic stabilisation equipment and Agusta AATH-547A automatic approach to hover, for automatic navigation; Siemens AN/APX-77 IFF/SIF transponder; SMA/APS series search radar and Motorola SST-119X radar transponder; and Bendix AN/AQS-13B sonar for ASW search.

ARMAMENT AND OPERATIONAL EQUIPMENT: Weapons may consist of two homing torpedoes, depth charges or two air-to-surface missiles. Rescue hoist, capacity 270 kg (600 lb), standard. Provisions for auxiliary installations such as a 2,270 kg (5,000 lb) capacity cargo sling, inflatable emergency pontoons, internal and external auxiliary fuel tanks, according to mission.

ASW MISSION: The basic sensor system employed for the ASW search and attack mission is a low-frequency variable-depth sonar, with a max operating depth of 137 m (450 ft). The automatic navigation system permits the positioning of the helicopter over any desired 'dip' point of a complex search pattern. The position of the helicopter, computed by the automatic navigation system, is integrated with sonar target information in the radar tactical display where both the surface and the underwater tactical situations can be continuously monitored. Additional navigation and tactical information is provided by accurate UHF direction-finding equipment, from an A/A mode-capable Tacan and from a radar transponder. The automatic flight control system (AFCS) integrates the basic automatic stabilisation equipment with signal output from the radar altimeter, the Doppler radar, sonar cable angle signals and outputs from the dry cable transducer. The effectiveness of this system results in hands-off flight from cruise condition to sonar hover in all weathers and under rough sea conditions. A specially designed cockpit display shows the pilots all flight parameters for each phase of the ASW operation. The attack mission is carried out with two homing torpedoes, or with depth charges.

ASV MISSION: For this mission the AB 212ASW carries a high-performance long-range search radar, with a very efficient scanner design and installation possessing high discrimination in rough sea conditions. Provisions have also been made to permit incorporation of future radar system developments. The automatic navigation systems and the search radar are integrated to permit a continuously updated picture of the tactical situation. Provisions are also incorporated for the installation of the most advanced ECM systems. The surface attack is performed with air-to-surface wire-guided missiles. In operation, the co-pilot aims and 'flies' the missiles to the target through an XM-58 gyro-stabilised sight system.

STAND-OFF MISSILE GUIDANCE MISSION: In this mission the AB 212ASW, with special equipment, can provide mid-course passive guidance for the ship-launched Otomat 2 surface-to-surface missile. Equipment includes an SMA/APS series search radar and a TG-2 real-time target data transmission system for guidance of the missile.

DIMENSIONS, EXTERNAL: As AB 212, except:
Max width:
with torpedoes	3·95 m (12 ft 11½ in)
with missiles	4·17 m (13 ft 8¼ in)

WEIGHTS (A: ASW mission with Mk 46 torpedoes; B: ASV mission with AS.12 missiles; C: search and rescue mission; all at S/L, ISA):
Weight empty, equipped:	
A, B, C	3,420 kg (7,540 lb)
Crew of three: A, B, C	240 kg (529 lb)
Mission equipment:	
A (two Mk 46 torpedoes)	490 kg (1,080 lb)
B (AS.12 installation and XM-58 sight)	180 kg (396 lb)
C (rescue hoist)	40 kg (89 lb)
Full fuel (normal tanks)	1,021 kg (2,250 lb)
Auxiliary external tanks	32 kg (70 lb)
Auxiliary fuel	356 kg (785 lb)
Mission T-O weight: A	5,070 kg (11,176 lb)
B	4,973 kg (10,961 lb)
C	4,937 kg (10,883 lb)

PERFORMANCE (at max T-O weight, except where indicated, ISA):
Never-exceed speed	130 knots (240 km/h; 150 mph)
Max level speed at S/L	106 knots (196 km/h; 122 mph)

Agusta-Sikorsky SH-3D ASW/ASV helicopter, armed with the Marte (Sea Killer) missile system

Max cruising speed with armament	100 knots (185 km/h; 115 mph)
Max rate of climb at S/L: A	396 m (1,300 ft)/min
Rate of climb at S/L, one engine out:	
A	61 m (200 ft)/min
Hovering ceiling IGE: A	3,200 m (10,500 ft)
Hovering ceiling OGE:	
A at AUW of 4,763 kg (10,500 lb)	396 m (1,300 ft)
Search endurance (A) with 50% at 90 knots (167 km/h; 103·5 mph) cruise and 50% hovering out of ground effect, 10% reserve fuel	3 h 12 min
Search range (B) with 10% reserve fuel	332 nm (615 km; 382 miles)
Endurance (B), no reserves	4 h 7 min
Endurance (C) at 90 knots (167 km/h; 103·5 mph) search speed	5 h 4 min
Max range with auxiliary tanks, 100 knots (185 km/h; 115 mph) cruise at S/L, 15% reserves	360 nm (667 km; 414 miles)
Max endurance with auxiliary tanks, no reserves	5 h 0 min

AGUSTA-BELL 412

For sale primarily in Europe and the Middle East, Agusta is initiating production of the Bell Model 412 (see US section). First flight of an Italian-built aircraft is expected in 1980, with certification to follow a few months after that of the US version.

AGUSTA-SIKORSKY SH-3D

During 1967, Agusta began the construction under licence of Sikorsky SH-3D anti-submarine helicopters for the Italian Navy. Deliveries began in 1969. Additional orders have since been placed, both for the Italian armed forces and for other navies, in various configurations including ASW, VIP transport and rescue. The VIP transport version is designated **SH-3D/TS** (Trasporto Speciale), and serves with the 31° Stormo of the Italian Air Force.

Apart from some local strengthening and an improved horizontal tail surface, the Agusta-built airframe remains essentially similar to that of the SH-3D described under the Sikorsky heading in the US section of this edition of

Jane's. The Agusta SH-3D is capable of operation in the roles of anti-submarine search, classification and strike; anti-surface-vessel (ASV); anti-surface-missile defence (ASMD); electronic warfare (EW); tactical troop lift; search and rescue (SAR); vertical replenishment; and casualty evacuation.

POWER PLANT: Two 1,118 kW (1,500 shp) General Electric T58-GE-100 turboshaft engines, mounted side by side above the cabin. An optional anti-ice/sand shield can be provided. Fuel in underfloor bag tanks with a total capacity of 3,180 litres (840 US gallons). Internal auxiliary fuel tank may be fitted for long-range ferry purposes. Pressure and gravity refuelling points.

ACCOMMODATION: Crew of four in ASW role; accommodation for up to 31 paratroops in troop lift role, 15 stretchers and a medical attendant in casualty evacuation configuration, and up to 25 survivors in SAR role.

SYSTEMS: Three main hydraulic systems. Primary and auxiliary systems operate main rotor control. Utility system for landing gear, winches and blade folding, pressure 207 bars (3,000 lb/sq in). Electrical system includes two 20kVA 200V three-phase 400Hz engine-driven generators, a 26V single-phase AC supply fed from the aircraft's 22Ah nickel-cadmium battery through an inverter, and DC power provided as a secondary system from two 200A transformer-rectifier units.

OPERATIONAL EQUIPMENT (ASW/ASV role): As equipped for this role the Agusta SH-3D is a fully integrated all-weather weapon system, capable of operating independently of surface vessels, and has the following equipment and weapons to achieve this task: low-frequency 360° depth sonar; Doppler radar and ASW automatic navigation system; SMA/APS series radar with one or two transceivers, with ventral radome for 360° coverage; radio altimeter; AFCS; marine markers and smoke floats; four homing torpedoes or four depth charges. The AFCS provides three-axis stabilisation in pilot-controlled manoeuvres, attitude hold, heading hold and height hold in cruising flight; controlled transition manoeuvres to and from hover; automatic height control and plan position control in the hover; and trim facility. According to the threat, the Agusta SH-3D can

Agusta-Sikorsky HH-3F (S-61R) search and rescue helicopter of the Italian Air Force

be equipped with medium-range (four AS.12 air-to-surface wire-guided) missiles or long-range (two Sea Killer Mk 2 or Exocet AM-39/Harpoon type) missiles. The Sistel Sea Killer Mk 2 is an all-weather day and night anti-ship missile with a range of 13·5 nm (25 km; 15·5 miles); guidance: sea skimming in elevation, radar in azimuth. The SMA/APS series radar has been specially designed to operate in a dense electronic emission environment and has a special interface to draw out target data to feed the computer for the long-range missiles. Provisions are also incorporated for the installation of the most advanced EW systems.

OPERATIONAL EQUIPMENT (Search and rescue and transport roles): The Agusta SH-3D has a variable-speed hydraulic rescue hoist of 272 kg (600 lb) capacity

mounted above the starboard side cargo door. With search radar fitted, a total of 25 survivors and medical staff can be seated. In the casualty evacuation role, 15 stretchers and medical attendant can be accommodated. In the troop transport role the Agusta SH-3D can accommodate 31 troops and carry this load over a range of 314 nm (582 km; 362 miles). As a cargo transport the aircraft has an internal capacity of 2,720 kg (6,000 lb) or a max external load capacity of 3,630 kg (8,000 lb) when a low-response sling is fitted.

PERFORMANCE (at max T-O weight of 9,525 kg; 21,000 lb):
Never-exceed speed 144 knots (267 km/h; 165 mph)
Max rate of climb at S/L 670 m (2,200 ft)/min
Service ceiling 3,720 m (12,200 ft)
Hovering ceiling IGE 2,500 m (8,200 ft)

Hovering ceiling OGE 1,130 m (3,700 ft)
Range with max standard fuel
680 nm (1,260 km; 783 miles)

AGUSTA-SIKORSKY AS-61A-4

Three AS-61A-4s were built for the Italian Air Force; brief details of these were given in the 1979-80 *Jane's*.

AGUSTA-SIKORSKY HH-3F (S-61R)

In 1974 Agusta began production of this multi-purpose rescue helicopter. Twenty are being built initially, 12 for SAR duties with the Italian Air Force and others for foreign operators. Deliveries started in 1976.

Details of the HH-3F can be found under the Sikorsky heading in the US section of this edition.

BREDANARDI
BREDANARDI COSTRUZIONI AERONAUTICHE SpA

OFFICES AND WORKS: Casella Postale 108, 63039 San Benedetto del Tronto (AP)

Telephone: (0735) 67246/7/8/9
Telex: 560165 BRENAR I

MARKETING OFFICES:
Aeroporto Forlanini, 20090 Milan
Telephone: (02) 7560241
Telex: 312666 NARDI I
Via XXIV Maggio 46, 00187 Rome
Telephone: (06) 6797360 and 6796834
Telex: 614111 BRENAR I
PRESIDENT: Ing Riccardo Baldini

MANAGING DIRECTOR: Dott Elto Nardi
MARKETING DIRECTOR: Dott Elio Nardi
BredaNardi, a partnership of Nardi and EFIM, a state-owned financial organisation, was established in 1971.
At Monteprandone (AP), BredaNardi produces, under licence from Hughes Heicopters of the USA, the NH-300C, NH-500D and NH-500MD light helicopters. Descriptions of these aircraft can be found under the Hughes heading in the US section of this edition.

CAPRONI VIZZOLA
CAPRONI VIZZOLA COSTRUZIONI AERONAUTICHE SpA

Via Montecchio 2, 21010 Vizzola Ticino (Va)
Telephone: (0331) 230 826
Telex: 332554 CAVIZ I
COMMERCIAL DIRECTOR: Dott Livio Sonzio

CAPRONI VIZZOLA C22J

The C22J is a two-seat lightweight training aircraft, developed by Caproni Vizzola as a private venture. Its configuration bears a close resemblance to that of the company's A-21SJ Calif jet-powered sailplane (which see); construction is largely of metal, with the forward fuselage skin, some fairings and other unstressed areas of glassfibre.

Intended primarily for student pilot screening, basic and proficiency training, the C22J is also suitable for ECM evaluation, ground and air navaid calibration, ecological survey and high-speed liaison. It can be converted easily for photographic survey duties, or for use as an RPV.

A prototype (I-CAVJ) made its first flight during the first half of 1980.

TYPE: Two-seat basic training aircraft.

WINGS: Cantilever shoulder-wing monoplane. Constant-chord wings, of Wortmann FX-67K-170 section. Dihedral 2°. Incidence 1° 9'. No sweepback. Single-spar structure, with aluminium alloy skin and extruded leading-edge. Electrically-actuated trailing-edge plain flaps can be set in any position throughout their full range of movement. Flaps operate in conjunction with aluminium alloy airbrakes/spoilers, of which there is one in the upper surface of each wing, forward of the flap. Airbrakes are opened manually, but move with the flaps to provide balanced control. Aerodynamically balanced ailerons operate differentially and can be drooped to provide additional flap area. All movable surfaces are of extruded aluminium alloy, and are operated by Aviac actuators. No tabs.

FUSELAGE: Tadpole-shaped structure, designed as a laminar lifting body. Primary load-bearing structure is of light alloy, forward portion having a moulded glassfibre skin. NACA-type flush engine air inlet in top of fuselage, aft of cockpits. Tailboom is of light alloy, with undersurface skin of glassfibre.

TAIL UNIT: Cantilever T tail, tailplane being of light alloy stressed-skin construction. Full-span balanced elevator is a chemically milled extrusion, and has spring trim, actuated by an Industria electrical system located in the fin. All-metal two-spar stressed-skin fin, bolted to tailboom. All control surfaces operated by push/pull rods. No tabs. Rudder pedals adjustable in flight.

LANDING GEAR: Retractable tricycle type, actuated electrically with manual backup. All units retract forward into fuselage. Cantilever sprung main legs, of glassfibre epoxy; rubber-in-compression shock-absorption on nose unit. Cleveland main wheels, with Goodyear size 5·00-5 tyres (6 ply rating), pressure 3·0 bars (43·5 lb/sq in). Tost nosewheel, with Tost tyre size 260 × 85 cm (4 ply rating), pressure 2·5 bars (36·3 lb/sq in). Cleveland independent hydraulic disc brakes on main wheels. Steerable nosewheel, linked to rudder pedals. Safety lock for up and down positions. Electrical warning system.

POWER PLANT: Two KHD T 317 turbojet engines, each rated at 1·1 kN (247 lb st), mounted side by side in fuselage aft of cockpits. Production version may be fitted with Microturbo TRS 18 turbojets. Integral fuel tank in each wing leading-edge, combined capacity 250 litres (55 Imp gallons). Fuel system incorporates fuselage collector tank which permits up to 30 s of inverted flight. Refuelling point at each wingtip. Oil capacity 0·8 litres (1·4 Imp pints).

ACCOMMODATION: Seats for two persons side by side under jettisonable canopy which is hinged at rear and opens upward. Seats are semi-supine. Dual flying controls. Single instrument panel and centre console, eliminating

Caproni Vizzola C22J two-seat basic training aircraft *(Pilot Press)*

need for dual instruments and avionics. Rearview mirror for each occupant. Cockpit heated, ventilated and defrosted.

SYSTEMS: Hydraulic system for main-wheel brakes only. No pneumatic system. Electrical system is 28V DC, incorporating two Microturbo 800W or KHD 1·2 kW starter/generators and a 24V 18Ah lead-acid battery. Cockpit ventilation and defrosting by heat exchangers on jetpipes. Demand-type low-pressure oxygen system, capacity 5·6 litres (1·25 Imp gallons), for each occupant.

AVIONICS AND EQUIPMENT: Avionics bay in top of fuselage, aft of cockpits. Collins Microline radio, Pro Line flight director, navigation, landing and anti-collision lights, standard.

ARMAMENT: Provision for two or four standard NATO underwing pylons, for a wide range of stores (max external load 200 kg; 440 lb) for gunnery/weapon training, photographic reconnaissance and target-towing missions. Typical loads include one auxiliary fuel tank and one three-camera pod; two auxiliary fuel tanks; two 7·62 mm gun pods and 500 rds of ammunition; two Simpres AL-18-50 pods with eighteen 2 in rockets; four SAMP EU70 50 kg general-purpose bombs; four Mk 70 11 kg or M38-A2 50 kg practice bombs; or two Dornier DATS 1 50 kg towed targets.

DIMENSIONS, EXTERNAL:
Wing span	10·00 m (32 ft 9¾ in)
Wing chord (constant)	0·90 m (2 ft 11½ in)
Wing aspect ratio	11·42
Length overall	6·188 m (20 ft 3½ in)
Fuselage: Max width	1·228 m (4 ft 0½ in)
Height overall	1·88 m (6 ft 2 in)
Tailplane span	2·66 m (8 ft 8¾ in)
Wheel track	1·81 m (5 ft 11¼ in)
Wheelbase	1·81 m (5 ft 11¼ in)

AREAS:
Wings, gross	8·75 m² (94·18 sq ft)
Ailerons (total)	0·718 m² (7·73 sq ft)
Trailing-edge flaps (total)	0·824 m² (8·87 sq ft)
Airbrakes/spoilers (total)	0·572 m² (6·16 sq ft)
Fin	0·808 m² (8·70 sq ft)

Prototype Caproni Vizzola C22J (two KHD T 317 turbojet engines)

Rudder	0·225 m² (2·42 sq ft)
Tailplane	1·40 m² (15·07 sq ft)
Elevator	0·338 m² (3·64 sq ft)

WEIGHTS AND LOADING:
Weight empty	510 kg (1,124 lb)
Max fuel load	220 kg (485 lb)
Max T-O and landing weight	1,100 kg (2,425 lb)
Max wing loading	126·0 kg/m² (25·8 lb/sq ft)

PERFORMANCE (estimated, at max 'clean' T-O weight):
Never-exceed speed
377 knots (700 km/h; 435 mph) EAS
Max cruising speed at S/L
286 knots (530 km/h; 329 mph)

Max cruising speed at 4,880 m (16,000 ft)
254 knots (470 km/h; 292 mph)
Max design manoeuvring speed
218 knots (405 km/h; 252 mph) EAS
Max design speed with airbrakes fully deployed
178 knots (330 km/h; 205 mph) EAS
Econ cruising speed at 3,050 m (10,000 ft)
162 knots (300 km/h; 186 mph)
Max landing gear extension speed
108 knots (200 km/h; 124 mph) EAS
Stalling speed, flaps down, power off
69 knots (128 km/h; 80 mph) EAS
Max rate of climb at S/L   552 m (1,810 ft)/min

Rate of climb at S/L, one engine out
177 m (580 ft)/min
Time to climb to 5,000 m (16,400 ft)   12 min
Service ceiling   9,000 m (29,525 ft)
Service ceiling, one engine out   6,500 m (21,325 ft)
T-O run at S/L, ISA, zero wind   350 m (1,150 ft)
T-O to 15 m (50 ft), conditions as above
550 m (1,805 ft)
T-O to 15 m (50 ft) at 1,500 m (4,920 ft), ISA, zero wind   800 m (2,625 ft)
Max range on internal fuel, 10% reserves
572 nm (1,060 km; 658 miles)
Max endurance   3 h 18 min
g limits   +7·0; −3·5

EM
ELICOTTERI MERIDIONALI SpA

WORKS: Via Giovanni Agusta 1, Frosinone
Telephone: (0775) 82801
Telex: Elmef 611377 and Emf 614171
CHAIRMAN AND PRESIDENT: Conte Corrado Agusta
PRESIDENT, CHIEF EXECUTIVE OFFICER: P. Fascione
GENERAL MANAGER: Piero Tana

This company was formed with assistance from Agusta (which see) and began to operate in October 1967. Initially, its activities consisted of overhauling helicopters of the Italian armed forces and other organisations, and the manufacture of helicopter components and sub-assemblies. In 1968 Meridionali acquired rights to the co-production, marketing and servicing of the Boeing Vertol CH-47C Chinook transport helicopter for customers in Italy and several foreign countries. Italian production of the CH-47C airframe is undertaken by SIAI-Marchetti, another member of the Agusta group.

Meridionali, whose works occupy a total area of more than 300,000 m² (3,229,170 sq ft), participates in the manufacturing programmes for the Agusta A 109A, Agusta-Bell 205, 206B and 212, and Agusta-Sikorsky SH-3D helicopters (see under Agusta in this section). Meridionali is also distributor in Italy for the Allison 250 series of turboshaft engines, and has complete facilities for

Italian-built Boeing Vertol CH-47C helicopter in the insignia of Italian Army Aviation

overhaul, repair and field assistance.

EM (BOEING VERTOL) CH-47C

Italian manufacture of the CH-47C began in the Spring

of 1970 initially to meet orders for the Iranian Army and Air Force. Production has since continued for other military customers, including Libya and Morocco.

GENERAL AVIA
GENERAL AVIA COSTRUZIONI AERONAUTICHE Srl

ADDRESS: Via Trieste 24, 20096 Pioltello, Milan
Telephone: (02) 9046774
TECHNICAL DIRECTOR: Dott Ing Stelio Frati
SECRETARY-TREASURER: Lamberto Frati
PRODUCTION: Enrico Fanoli
PUBLIC RELATIONS: Carla Bielli

Dott Ing Stelio Frati is well known for the many successful light aircraft which, as a freelance designer, he has evolved since 1950. These have been built in prototype and production series by several Italian manufacturers, and have included the Procaer F15 Picchio and the F.250, now manufactured by SIAI-Marchetti as the SF.260.

General Avia was established by Dott Ing Stelio Frati in early 1970, primarily to develop prototypes of his own design for production by other companies. These have included

the F15F, a derivative of the Procaer F15E Picchio which is to be placed in production by Procaer; and the F.20 Pegaso, originally intended for production by Italair (see 1975-76 *Jane's*).

General Avia also developed the Canguro transport aircraft now in production by SIAI-Marchetti as the SF.600.

GENERAL AVIA F.20 PEGASO

Design of the F.20 Pegaso six-seat light business twin was started in January 1970. Two prototypes were built by General Avia, these making their first flights on 21 October 1971 and 11 August 1972, as described in previous editions of *Jane's*. Following type certification by the RAI (19 November 1974) and FAA (14 May 1975), the first series-built example flew on 17 December 1979.

The production version introduces a number of improvements compared with the prototypes. These include better cabin heating and soundproofing, and the

use of three-blade propellers to improve certain aspects of performance.

The Pegaso is also offered in a four-seat military version, the F.20 **Condor**, suitable for weapon training, long-range maritime surveillance, and search and rescue. This has lower-powered engines and can be fitted with three stores pylons under each wing, the centre one on each side being capable of carrying a 250 litre (55 Imp gallon) auxiliary fuel tank.

The following description applies to the civil Pegaso, except where indicated:

TYPE: Twin-engined six-seat light executive transport aircraft.

WINGS: Cantilever low-wing monoplane. Wing section NACA 65₂-415. Dihedral 5° from roots. Incidence 1° 45'. All-metal single-spar structure in light alloy, with flush-riveted stressed skin. Differentially-operated all-metal ailerons and electrically actuated double-slotted metal trailing-edge flaps. No tabs. Anti-icing optional.

FUSELAGE: All-metal semi-monocoque structure, with flush-riveted aluminium alloy skin.

TAIL UNIT: Cantilever all-metal structure with flush-riveted skin. Fixed-incidence tailplane. Trim tabs in rudder and each elevator. Anti-icing optional.

LANDING GEAR: Retractable tricycle type, with single wheel on each unit. Nosewheel steerable 18° to left and right. Electrical actuation, with manual backup. Oleo-pneumatic shock-absorbers. Main wheels and tyres size 7·00-6, pressure 3·24 bars (47 lb/sq in); nosewheel and tyre size 6·00-6, pressure 1·86 bars (27 lb/sq in). Cleveland brakes.

POWER PLANT: Two 223·5 kW (300 hp) Rolls-Royce Continental IO-520-K flat-six engines, each driving a Hartzell PHC-C3YF-2UF three-blade constant-speed fully-feathering propeller. Fuel in two wing tanks, each of 124 litres (27·25 Imp gallons), and two wingtip tanks each of 126 litres (27·7 Imp gallons) capacity. Total capacity 500 litres (110 Imp gallons). Provision in Condor for further 500 litres to be carried in two underwing auxiliary tanks. Oil capacity 22·8 litres (5 Imp gallons). Electrical propeller de-icing available optionally.

ACCOMMODATION: Normal seating, in fully enclosed cabin, for six persons (four in Condor), including pilot. Space for up to 104 kg (230 lb) of baggage in four compartments in forward and rear fuselage and each engine nacelle. Access to cabin via large door on each side. Cabin heated, ventilated and soundproofed, with glass-wool insulation.

AVIONICS AND EQUIPMENT: IFR instrumentation and dual controls standard; other installations to customer's requirements.

DIMENSIONS, EXTERNAL:
Wing span over tip-tanks	10·34 m (33 ft 11 in)
Wing chord at root	1·65 m (5 ft 5 in)

Condor four-seat military version of the General Avia F.20 Pegaso *(Pilot Press)*

Wing chord at tip	1·50 m (4 ft 11 in)
Wing aspect ratio	6·67
Length overall	8·22 m (26 ft 11½ in)
Height overall	3·50 m (11 ft 5¾ in)
Tailplane span	4·10 m (13 ft 5½ in)
Wheel track	3·50 m (11 ft 5¾ in)
Wheelbase	2·40 m (7 ft 10½ in)
Propeller diameter	1·98 m (6 ft 6 in)
Min propeller ground clearance	0·20 m (8 in)
Distance between propeller centres	3·42 m (11 ft 2½ in)

DIMENSIONS, INTERNAL:

Cabin: Max length	3·66 m (12 ft 0 in)
Max width	1·17 m (3 ft 10 in)
Max height	1·13 m (3 ft 8½ in)
Baggage compartments (four):	
Total volume	0·70 m³ (25 cu ft)

AREAS:

Wings, gross	16·02 m² (172·4 sq ft)
Ailerons (total)	1·42 m² (15·28 sq ft)
Trailing-edge flaps (total)	1·59 m² (17·13 sq ft)
Fin	1·24 m² (13·35 sq ft)
Rudder, incl tab	0·79 m² (8·50 sq ft)
Tailplane	2·46 m² (26·48 sq ft)
Elevators, incl tabs	1·95 m² (20·99 sq ft)

WEIGHTS AND LOADINGS (A: Pegaso; B: Condor without underwing tanks; C: Condor with underwing tanks):

Weight empty, equipped: A	1,510 kg (3,330 lb)
B	1,500 kg (3,307 lb)
C	1,600 kg (3,527 lb)

Max payload: A	514 kg	(1,134 lb)
Max T-O and landing weight: A	2,250 kg	(4,960 lb)
B	2,200 kg	(4,850 lb)
C	2,500 kg	(5,511 lb)
Max wing loading: A	145·0 kg/m²	(29·7 lb/sq ft)
B	137·3 kg/m²	(28·12 lb/sq ft)
C	156·0 kg/m²	(31·95 lb/sq ft)
Max power loading: A	5·30 kg/kW	(8·71 lb/hp)
B	5·18 kg/kW	(8·51 lb/hp)
C	5·89 kg/kW	(9·66 lb/hp)

PERFORMANCE (at max T-O weight except where indicated):

Never-exceed speed (A, B, C)	232 knots	(431 km/h; 267 mph)
Max level speed at S/L:		
A	216 knots	(400 km/h; 249 mph)
B	208 knots	(385 km/h; 239 mph)
C	188 knots	(350 km/h; 217 mph)
Max cruising speed (75% power) at 2,440 m (8,000 ft):		
A	203 knots	(377 km/h; 234 mph)
B	194 knots	(360 km/h; 224 mph)
C	178 knots	(330 km/h; 205 mph)
Econ cruising speed (60% power) at 3,660 m (12,000 ft): A, B	183 knots	(340 km/h; 211 mph)
C	167 knots	(310 km/h; 193 mph)
Stalling speed, flaps down:		
A	66 knots	(121 km/h; 76 mph)
B at 2,000 kg (4,409 lb) AUW	62 knots	(115 km/h; 71·5 mph)
C at 2,000 kg (4,409 lb) AUW	68 knots	(125 km/h; 78 mph)

Max rate of climb at S/L: A	550 m	(1,805 ft)/min
B	600 m	(1,970 ft)/min
C	480 m	(1,575 ft)/min
Rate of climb at S/L, one engine out:		
A	120 m	(394 ft)/min
Service ceiling: A	6,250 m	(20,500 ft)
B	6,000 m	(19,685 ft)
C	5,000 m	(16,400 ft)
Service ceiling, one engine out:		
A	2,290 m	(7,515 ft)
B	1,900 m	(6,235 ft)
C	1,500 m	(4,920 ft)
T-O run: A	230 m	(755 ft)
B	220 m	(722 ft)
C	300 m	(984 ft)
T-O to 15 m (50 ft): A	320 m	(1,050 ft)
Landing from 15 m (50 ft): A	380 m	(1,250 ft)
Landing run: A, B	260 m	(853 ft)
C	300 m	(984 ft)
Range:		
A with max fuel	955 nm	(1,770 km; 1,100 miles)
A with max payload	547 nm	(1,013 km; 630 miles)
B at 75% power	809 nm	(1,500 km; 932 miles)
B at 60% power	917 nm	(1,700 km; 1,056 miles)
C at 75% power	1,511 nm	(2,800 km; 1,740 miles)
C at 60% power	1,618 nm	(3,000 km; 1,864 miles)
Max endurance: B		5 h
C		10 h

PARTENAVIA
PARTENAVIA COSTRUZIONI AERONAUTICHE SpA

HEAD OFFICE AND WORKS: Via Cava, CP 2179, 80026 Casoria (Naples)

Telephone: (081) 7596311 (PBX)

Telex: 73199 Partenav

PRESIDENT: Prof Ing Luigi Pascale

DIRECTORS:
Dott G. Bulgari
Dott G. Fiore
Dott D. Marchiorello
Ing G. Regazzoni

PRODUCTION DIRECTOR: Ing Nino Pascale

INTERNATIONAL MARKETING: Ian A. Forbes

This company was founded in 1957 by Prof Ing Luigi Pascale and his brother, Ing Nino Pascale, and has since built a series of light aircraft designed by Prof Ing Pascale.

Since 1974 the company has occupied a 12,000 m² (129,165 sq ft) facility on Capodichino Airport, Naples, where it is now concentrating on production and development of the P.68C Victor twin-engined seven-seat light aircraft and its derivatives, and on the P.66C Charlie.

PARTENAVIA P.66C-160 CHARLIE

This two/four-seat basic training aircraft is an improved version of the P.64B/P.66B Oscar series (see 1975-76 *Jane's*), and is certificated in the FAR Pt 23 Utility category, with clearance for all positive-*g* aerobatic manoeuvres and six-turn spins. The prototype P.66C, with a 112 kW (150 hp) Avco Lycoming O-360-A1A engine, flew in early January 1976, and was certificated in Spring 1976.

The P.66C was chosen by the Aero Club d'Italia as the standard basic trainer for aero clubs throughout Italy, and an order for 70 P.66C Charlies was placed, with an option to increase this order to 250. Deliveries began at the end of 1977, and had totalled 84 by June 1980, with production continuing. A further 12 were due to be delivered during the remainder of 1980.

TYPE: Two/four-seat light monoplane.

WINGS: Braced high-wing monoplane with single streamline-section bracing strut each side. Wing section NACA 63 series. Thickness/chord ratio 15%. Dihedral 1° 30′. Incidence at root 1° 40′. No sweepback. Stressed-skin single-spar torsion-box structure of aluminium alloy, with one-piece glassfibre-reinforced plastics moulded leading-edges. Ailerons and electrically-operated slotted trailing-edge flaps of similar construction to wings.

FUSELAGE: Forward portion, to rear of cabin, has a welded steel tube basic structure to which are attached light alloy skin panels. Rear fuselage is of conventional light alloy stressed-skin construction.

TAIL UNIT: Cantilever stressed-skin metal structure with sweptback vertical surfaces. All-moving tailplane in two symmetrical halves joined by steel cross-tube. Anti-balance tab in trailing-edge of tailplane, over 80% of span.

LANDING GEAR: Non-retractable tricycle type, with steerable nosewheel. Cantilever spring steel main legs. Oleo nosewheel shock-absorber. Cleveland main wheels type 40-28, with Pirelli tyres size 6·00-6. Goodyear nosewheel tyre size 5·00-5. Cleveland type 30-18 hydraulic disc brakes.

POWER PLANT: One 119 kW (160 hp) Avco Lycoming O-320-H2AD flat-four engine, driving a Hoffmann HO 23-183.150 two-blade fixed-pitch propeller. Two integral fuel tanks in wing roots, total usable capacity 130 litres (28·5 Imp gallons). Refuelling points above wings. Oil capacity 7·5 litres (1·66 Imp gallons).

ACCOMMODATION: Enclosed cabin seating two or four persons in pairs; front seats are of the adjustable sliding type. Three forward-hinged doors: one by each front seat and on starboard side at rear. Baggage space aft of rear seats, with separate door on starboard side. Dual controls, heating, ventilation and soundproofing standard.

AVIONICS AND EQUIPMENT: Optional items include full IFR instrumentation, Grimes rotating beacon, VHF radio, VOR and ADF.

DIMENSIONS, EXTERNAL:

Wing span	9·986 m (32 ft 9¼ in)
Wing chord (constant)	1·36 m (4 ft 5½ in)
Wing aspect ratio	7·45
Length overall	7·24 m (23 ft 9 in)
Height overall	2·77 m (9 ft 1 in)
Tailplane span	3·10 m (10 ft 2 in)
Wheel track	2·10 m (6 ft 10½ in)
Wheelbase	1·63 m (5 ft 4¼ in)
Propeller diameter	1·88 m (6 ft 2 in)

DIMENSIONS, INTERNAL:

Cabin: Max width	1·06 m (3 ft 5¾ in)
Max height	1·20 m (3 ft 11¼ in)

AREAS:

Wings, gross	13·40 m² (144·2 sq ft)
Ailerons (total)	1·29 m² (13·88 sq ft)
Trailing-edge flaps (total)	1·71 m² (18·40 sq ft)
Fin	0·73 m² (7·86 sq ft)
Rudder	0·45 m² (4·84 sq ft)
Tailplane, incl tab	2·17 m² (23·36 sq ft)

WEIGHTS AND LOADINGS:

Weight empty	600 kg (1,322 lb)
Max T-O and landing weight	990 kg (2,183 lb)
Max wing loading	73·88 kg/m² (15·13 lb/sq ft)
Max power loading	8·30 kg/kW (13·63 lb/hp)

PERFORMANCE (at max T-O weight, ISA):

Max level speed at S/L	130 knots	(241 km/h; 150 mph)
Max cruising speed (75% power) at 1,980 m (6,500 ft)	118 knots	(218 km/h; 135 mph)
Econ cruising speed (65% power) at 2,745 m (9,000 ft)	111 knots	(206 km/h; 128 mph)
Stalling speed at S/L:		
flaps up	53 knots	(98·5 km/h; 61·5 mph)
flaps down (T-O)	50 knots	(93 km/h; 58 mph)
flaps down (landing)	44 knots	(82 km/h; 51 mph)
Max rate of climb at S/L	289 m	(950 ft)/min
Service ceiling	4,570 m	(15,000 ft)
T-O run at S/L	245 m	(805 ft)
T-O to 15 m (50 ft) at S/L	420 m	(1,378 ft)
Landing from 15 m (50 ft) at S/L	350 m	(1,148 ft)
Landing run at S/L	150 m	(492 ft)
Range at 1,980 m (6,500 ft), 75% power, with reserves	370 nm	(685 km; 426 miles)
Range at 2,745 m (9,000 ft), 65% power, with reserves	422 nm	(782 km; 486 miles)
Endurance at 1,980 m (6,500 ft), 75% power, with reserves		3 h 8 min
Endurance at 2,745 m (9,000 ft), 65% power, with reserves		3 h 48 min

PARTENAVIA VICTOR

The original P.68, designed by Prof Ing Luigi Pascale in 1968, was described in the 1975-76 *Jane's*. From it was developed the P.68B Victor twin-engined light transport, which entered production in Partenavia's factory at Naples Airport in the Spring of 1974.

The following versions have been announced:

P.68B. Initial production version, described in 1979-80 *Jane's*. Max T-O weight increased to 1,990 kg (4,387 lb). Production phased out in late 1979 in favour of P.68C.

P.68C. Improved version of P.68B, with lengthened nose, increased fuel capacity, and several internal changes.

Partenavia P.66C Charlie two/four-seat basic training aircraft

Detailed description applies primarily to this current production version.

P.68C-R. Retractable landing gear version of P.68C. Not intended for production.

P.68C-TC. Similar to P.68C, but with 156·5 kW (210 hp) Avco Lycoming TO-360-C1A6D turbocharged engines. Certificated in June 1980; in production.

P.68 floatplane/amphibian. One P.68B, modified for the installation of both amphibious and non-amphibious floats. All known details in 1979-80 *Jane's*.

P.68 Observer. Special observation version; described separately.

P.68R. Retractable landing gear version of P.68B, first flown in December 1976. Certificated, but not intended for production. Described in 1978-79 *Jane's*.

P.68RTC. Proposed variant of P.68B incorporating the retractable landing gear of the P.68R and TO-360 turbocharged engines of the P.68C-TC. Not built.

AP.68/8. Turboprop-powered version of P.68R, being developed jointly with Aeritalia. Described separately.

P.68WB. Version of P.68B with wider fuselage; under development.

By mid-1980, approx 210 Victors had been delivered, the majority of them for export to operators in Australia, Austria, Belgium, Chile, Congo, Denmark, England, Finland, France, Gabon, Germany (Federal Republic), Israel, Kenya, the Middle East, Morocco, Netherlands, Papua New Guinea, Norway, South Africa, Sweden, Switzerland, Tanzania, the USA and Venezuela.

TYPE: Six/seven-seat light transport and trainer.

WINGS: Cantilever high-wing monoplane. Wing section NACA 63₃-515. Dihedral 1°. Incidence 1° 30'. No sweepback. Stressed-skin single-spar torsion-box structure, of aluminium alloy except for area forward of main spar (30% of total area) which is of GRP. All-metal ailerons and electrically-operated single-slotted trailing-edge flaps. Hoerner GRP wingtips. Trim tab on port aileron.

FUSELAGE: Conventional all-metal semi-monocoque structure of frames and longerons, with four main longerons and stressed-skin covering. Fuselage/wing intersection mainly of GRP.

TAIL UNIT: Cantilever stressed-skin metal structure. All-moving tailplane, in two symmetrical halves joined by steel cross-tube and of constant chord except for increase at leading-edge roots. Balance tab in tailplane trailing-edge, over 80% of span. Sweptback fin and rudder, with small dorsal fin. Trim tab in rudder.

LANDING GEAR: Non-retractable tricycle type, with steerable nosewheel. Cantilever spring steel main legs. Oleo-pneumatic shock-absorber on nosewheel. Cleveland main wheels, type 40-96, with Pirelli eight-ply tyres size 6·00-6. Goodyear six-ply nosewheel tyre, size 5·00-5. Cleveland type 30-61 hydraulic disc brakes. Parking brake. Streamline wheel fairings standard.

POWER PLANT (P.68C): Two 149 kW (200 hp) Avco Lycoming IO-360-A1B6 flat-four engines, each driving a Hartzell HC-C2YK-2C/C-7666A-4 two-blade constant-speed fully-feathering propeller with spinner. Integral fuel tank in each wing, total capacity 538 litres (118 Imp gallons), of which 520 litres (114 Imp gallons) are usable. Refuelling point above each wing. Oil capacity 15 litres (3·3 Imp gallons).

ACCOMMODATION: Seating for seven persons in cabin, including pilot, in two rows of two seats and a rear bench seat for three persons. A 'club' seating arrangement is available optionally, having the two middle seats facing rearward with a folding table between them and the bench seat. Front seats are of the adjustable sliding type. Access to all seats via large car-type door on port side of cabin. Up to 181 kg (400 lb) of baggage can be carried in compartment aft of rear bench seat. Access to baggage compartment from inside cabin, or via large forward-hinged door on starboard side, which serves also as emergency exit. Two stretchers or other loads can be carried when all passenger seats are removed. Dual controls, cabin heating, ventilation and soundproofing standard.

SYSTEMS: Electrical power supplied by two 24V 70A alternators and a 24V 17Ah battery. No hydraulic system. Goodrich pneumatic de-icing system optional.

AVIONICS AND EQUIPMENT (P.68C): Wide range of Collins Micro Line, Edo-Aire Mitchell Century III Autopilot,

Partenavia P.68C current production version of the Victor six/seven-seat light aircraft

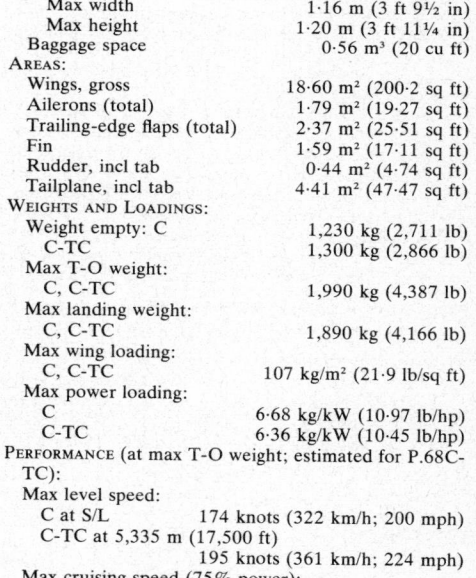
Partenavia P.68C Victor, with additional side view of P.68C-TC (centre) *(Pilot Press)*

or King Silver Crown avionics, to customer's requirements. Provision for Sunair ASB 100 HF radio. Standard equipment includes airspeed indicator, gyro horizon, directional gyro, two cylinder head temperature gauges, clock, exhaust gas temperature indicator, outside air temperature gauge, rate of climb indicator, sensitive altimeter, electrical turn rate indicator, inertia-reel shoulder harness for pilot and co-pilot, stall warning system, four upholstered seats with back pockets, and one bench seat with folding back (with safety belts on all seats), cabin fire extinguisher, six individual fresh-air outlets and six floor warm-air vents, windscreen defrosters, cabin soundproofing, annunciator panel warning lights, two map lights, individual reading lights, individual instrument panel floodlights with rheostat, anti-collision strobe light, two landing/taxying lights, navigation lights, anti-static kit, external power receptacle, oil coolers with thermostatic control, quick-drain fuel and oil valves, and towbar. Optional equipment includes Janitrol 45,000 BTU combustion heater, wing and tail pneumatic de-icing system, electrothermal propeller de-icing system, 0·46 × 0·58 m (18 × 23 in) floor panel for photogrammetric camera, including periscope sight hatch, second airspeed indicator, second gyro horizon, chronometer, second altimeter, vertically adjustable pilot's and co-pilot's seats, alcohol windscreen de-icing, heated stall warning indicator, all-leather interior, forced ventilation blower, ice light and second oil cooler.

DIMENSIONS, EXTERNAL:

Wing span	12·00 m (39 ft 4½ in)
Wing chord (constant)	1·55 m (5 ft 1 in)
Wing aspect ratio	7·75
Length overall	9·55 m (31 ft 4 in)
Height overall	3·40 m (11 ft 1¾ in)
Tailplane span	3·90 m (12 ft 9½ in)
Wheel track	2·40 m (7 ft 10½ in)
Wheelbase	3·50 m (11 ft 5¾ in)
Propeller diameter	1·88 m (6 ft 2 in)
Baggage door, stbd: Height	0·80 m (2 ft 7½ in)
Width	0·80 m (2 ft 7½ in)

DIMENSIONS, INTERNAL:

Cabin: Length	3·58 m (11 ft 9 in)
Max width	1·16 m (3 ft 9½ in)
Max height	1·20 m (3 ft 11¼ in)
Baggage space	0·56 m³ (20 cu ft)

AREAS:

Wings, gross	18·60 m² (200·2 sq ft)
Ailerons (total)	1·79 m² (19·27 sq ft)
Trailing-edge flaps (total)	2·37 m² (25·51 sq ft)
Fin	1·59 m² (17·11 sq ft)
Rudder, incl tab	0·44 m² (4·74 sq ft)
Tailplane, incl tab	4·41 m² (47·47 sq ft)

WEIGHTS AND LOADINGS:

Weight empty: C	1,230 kg (2,711 lb)
C-TC	1,300 kg (2,866 lb)
Max T-O weight: C, C-TC	1,990 kg (4,387 lb)
Max landing weight: C, C-TC	1,890 kg (4,166 lb)
Max wing loading: C, C-TC	107 kg/m² (21·9 lb/sq ft)
Max power loading: C	6·68 kg/kW (10·97 lb/hp)
C-TC	6·36 kg/kW (10·45 lb/hp)

PERFORMANCE (at max T-O weight; estimated for P.68C-TC):

Max level speed:	
C at S/L	174 knots (322 km/h; 200 mph)
C-TC at 5,335 m (17,500 ft)	195 knots (361 km/h; 224 mph)
Max cruising speed (75% power):	
C at 2,290 m (7,500 ft)	166 knots (307 km/h; 191 mph)
C-TC at 6,100 m (20,000 ft)	183 knots (339 km/h; 211 mph)
C-TC at 3,660 m (12,000 ft)	172 knots (318 km/h; 198 mph)
Cruising speed (65% power):	
C at 3,350 m (11,000 ft)	161 knots (298 km/h; 185 mph)
C-TC at 3,050 m (10,000 ft)	158 knots (293 km/h; 182 mph)
Cruising speed (55% power):	
C at 3,660 m (12,000 ft)	150 knots (278 km/h; 173 mph)
C-TC at 3,050 m (10,000 ft)	147 knots (272 km/h; 169 mph)
Stalling speed, flaps up: C, C-TC	65 knots (120 km/h; 75 mph)
Stalling speed, flaps down: C, C-TC	57·5 knots (106 km/h; 66 mph)

P.68C-TC turbocharged version of the Victor light transport aircraft

Max rate of climb at S/L:
C   457 m (1,500 ft)/min
C-TC   472 m (1,550 ft)/min

Rate of climb at S/L, one engine out:
C   82 m (270 ft)/min
C-TC   88 m (290 ft)/min

Service ceiling:
C   5,850 m (19,200 ft)
C-TC   7,620 m (25,000 ft)

Service ceiling, one engine out:
C   2,100 m (6,900 ft)
C-TC   4,420 m (14,500 ft)

T-O run:
C, C-TC   230 m (755 ft)

T-O to 15 m (50 ft):
C   396 m (1,300 ft)
C-TC   385 m (1,263 ft)

Landing from 15 m (50 ft):
C, C-TC   488 m (1,600 ft)

Landing run:
C, C-TC   215 m (705 ft)

Accelerate/stop distance:
C   473 m (1,550 ft)
C-TC   510 m (1,673 ft)

Optimum cruising range (C), 45 min reserves:
75% power at 2,290 m (7,500 ft)
      1,050 nm (1,945 km; 1,209 miles)
65% power at 3,350 m (11,000 ft)
      1,140 nm (2,112 km; 1,312 miles)
55% power at 3,660 m (12,000 ft)
      1,210 nm (2,242 km; 1,393 miles)

Optimum cruising range (C-TC) at 3,660 m (12,000 ft), 45 min reserves:
75% power   775 nm (1,436 km; 892 miles)
65% power   940 nm (1,742 km; 1,082 miles)
55% power   1,020 nm (1,890 km; 1,175 miles)

Range with max fuel (C-TC):
65% power at 6,400 m (21,000 ft)
      1,100 nm (2,037 km; 1,266 miles)

PARTENAVIA P.68 OBSERVER

Developed in collaboration with Sportavia-Pützer, Partenavia's West German distributor, the Observer has a forward and downward view for the crew equal to that of a helicopter.

The Plexiglas nose, cockpit and associated structure were designed by Sportavia-Pützer; the prototype (D-GERD) was constructed at that company's Dahlemer-Binz factory, and first flew on 20 February 1976.

With its good low-speed handling characteristics, the Observer is considered to be capable of performing many roles allocated normally to helicopters. It is intended particularly for patrol and observation operations. The prototype was evaluated in mid-1978 by the Rhineland-Palatinate police department.

The first Partenavia-built Observer was flown in the Spring of 1980, and certification was obtained in June of that year. Improvements have been made to the flight deck and instrument panel. A production line has been laid down to meet initial orders from Italy and West Germany, and other orders were being negotiated in mid-1980.

Turbocharged versions, with Avco Lycoming TO-360-C1A6D engines, will be made available. Military versions, with underwing stores capability, are planned.

DIMENSIONS, EXTERNAL: As P.68C except:
Length overall   9·35 m (30 ft 8 in)

WEIGHTS AND LOADINGS:
Weight empty   1,280 kg (2,822 lb)
Max T-O weight   1,960 kg (4,321 lb)
Max wing loading   105·3 kg/m² (21·58 lb/sq ft)
Max power loading   6·58 kg/kW (10·80 lb/hp)

PERFORMANCE (at max T-O weight):
Max level speed at S/L 174 knots (322 km/h; 200 mph)
Cruising speed:
75% power at 2,290 m (7,500 ft)
      165 knots (306 km/h; 190 mph)

Partenavia/Aeritalia AP 68TP seven-seat prototype for the eight-passenger AP 68/8

65% power at 3,350 m (11,000 ft)
      160 knots (296 km/h; 184 mph)
55% power at 3,660 m (12,000 ft)
      149 knots (276 km/h; 171 mph)
Stalling speed, flaps up 64 knots (118 km/h; 74 mph)
Stalling speed, flaps down 56 knots (101 km/h; 64 mph)
Max rate of climb at S/L   488 m (1,600 ft)/min
Rate of climb at S/L, one engine out
      98 m (320 ft)/min
Service ceiling   6,100 m (20,000 ft)
Service ceiling, one engine out   2,375 m (7,800 ft)
T-O run   229 m (750 ft)
T-O to 15 m (50 ft)   387 m (1,270 ft)
Landing from 15 m (50 ft)   479 m (1,570 ft)
Landing run   210 m (690 ft)
Accelerate/stop distance   473 m (1,550 ft)
Optimum cruising range, 45 min reserves:
75% power at 2,290 m (7,500 ft)
      1,015 nm (1,880 km; 1,168 miles)
65% power at 3,350 m (11,000 ft)
      1,108 nm (2,053 km; 1,275 miles)
55% power at 3,660 m (12,000 ft)
      1,180 nm (2,186 km; 1,358 miles)

PARTENAVIA/AERITALIA AP 68/8

This turbine-engined version of the P.68R, known originally as the P.68 Turbo, is being developed in association with Aeritalia. Multi-role versatility includes the ability to carry a wide variety of external stores on four underwing and two fuselage-side hardpoints, to cover a broad spectrum of possible missions. These include air taxi, liaison, executive or cargo transport, training, ground support, or (possibly with a 'goldfish bowl' nose similar to that of the P.68 Observer) for reconnaissance, coastal patrol and aerial survey.

The AP 68TP prototype (NC 6001; I-PAIT) flew for the first time on 11 September 1978, at Naples, piloted by Comm Lionello Bellio, an Aeritalia test pilot. Certification of the AP 68/8 was expected during 1980, with deliveries scheduled to begin in late 1980 or early 1981.

WINGS, FUSELAGE AND TAIL UNIT: As P.68C, except for local strengthening in vicinity of wing and fuselage hardpoints, lengthening of fuselage, and increased-area vertical tail surfaces.

LANDING GEAR: Retractable tricycle type, with single wheel on each unit. Electro-hydraulic actuation, nose-wheel retracting rearward, main units inward into fairings on fuselage sides. Available also with non-retractable tricycle gear.

POWER PLANT: Two Allison 250-B17C turboprop engines, each flat rated at 246 kW (330 shp) for T-O and max continuous operation, with a max cruise rating at 3,050 m (10,000 ft) of 232 kW (311 shp), and each driving a Hartzell HC-B3TF-7A/T10173-11R three-blade fully-feathering reversible-pitch metal propeller with

spinner. Fuel in two main and two auxiliary tanks in wings, total capacity 660 litres (145 Imp gallons) standard, 814 litres (179 Imp gallons) maximum.

ACCOMMODATION: Seating for up to nine persons in cabin, including pilot. Access to passenger seats via large car-type door on port side of cabin; pilot's door on starboard side. Access to baggage compartment (capacity 90 kg; 200 lb) via separate large door on starboard side. Dual controls, cabin heating, ventilation and soundproofing standard.

SYSTEMS: Primary electrical power from two 150A 28V DC starter/generators. Nickel-cadmium battery for engine starting. Inverter for 28V DC/115V AC power in event of loss of primary source. Pneumatic anti-icing system for wing and tail leading-edges; electrical anti-icing of propeller blades; engine intakes anti-iced by engine bleed air. Oxygen system optional.

AVIONICS: To customer's requirements. Typical installations may include dual VHF/AM com, HF, dual NAV/ILS, ADF, DME, ATC transponder, marker beacon receiver, Omega navigation system, weather radar, autopilot, audio control and gyro compass in civil version; or VHF/FM com with homing, UHF, Tacan and IFF/ATC in military version.

ARMAMENT AND OPERATIONAL EQUIPMENT (military version): Four underwing hardpoints, each of 182 kg (400 lb) capacity, with standard NATO MA-4A racks. Typical loads may include four SUU-11B/A 7·62 mm Minigun pods, four LAU-32B/A rocket launchers (each containing seven rockets), four 400 lb bombs, flare dispensers, air-to-surface missiles, supply containers, or auxiliary fuel tanks.

DIMENSIONS, EXTERNAL:
Wing span   12·00 m (39 ft 4½ in)
Wing chord, constant   1·55 m (5 ft 1 in)
Wing area, gross   18·60 m² (200·2 sq ft)
Wing aspect ratio   7·74
Length overall   9·844 m (32 ft 3½ in)
Height overall   3·48 m (11 ft 5 in)
Wheel track   2·115 m (6 ft 11¼ in)
Wheelbase   3·613 m (11 ft 10¼ in)
Propeller diameter   2·29 m (7 ft 6 in)

WEIGHTS (civil version):
Weight empty   1,392 kg (3,068 lb)
Operating weight empty   1,518 kg (3,346 lb)
Max payload   680 kg (1,500 lb)
Max T-O weight   2,600 kg (5,732 lb)
Max zero-fuel weight   2,180 kg (4,806 lb)
Max landing weight   2,500 kg (5,511 lb)

PERFORMANCE (at max T-O weight, ISA):
Max cruising speed at 3,050 m (10,000 ft)
      227 knots (421 km/h; 261 mph)
Econ cruising speed at 3,050 m (10,000 ft)
      202 knots (374 km/h; 233 mph)
Stalling speed, flaps and landing gear up
      74 knots (137·5 km/h; 85·5 mph) CAS
Stalling speed, flaps and landing gear down
      67 knots (124·5 km/h; 77·5 mph) CAS
Max rate of climb at S/L   646 m (2,120 ft)/min
Rate of climb at S/L, one engine out
      259 m (850 ft)/min
Service ceiling   7,620 m (25,000 ft)
Service ceiling, one engine out   5,500 m (18,050 ft)
T-O to 15 m (50 ft)   457 m (1,500 ft)
Landing from 15 m (50 ft)   448 m (1,470 ft)
Range at max cruising speed with 680 kg (1,500 lb) payload   440 nm (815 km; 506 miles)
Range at econ cruising speed with 454 kg (1,000 lb) payload   770 nm (1,427 km; 887 miles)

PARTENAVIA P.78

The P.78 is an enlarged version of the P.68C Victor, with increased carrying capacity and a number of airframe improvements. See Addenda for further details.

Prototype Partenavia P.68 Observer, modified from a standard P.68B by Sportavia-Pützer in Germany

PIAGGIO
INDUSTRIE AERONAUTICHE E MECCANICHE RINALDO PIAGGIO SpA

HEAD OFFICE: Viale Brigata Bisagno 14, Casella Postale 1396, 16129 Genoa
Telephone: 540 521
Telex: 270695 AERPIA I
BRANCH OFFICE: Via A. Gramsci 34, Rome
WORKS: Genoa-Sestri P. (Aircraft Division); Finale Ligure (Aero-Engine Division)
CHAIRMAN AND MANAGING DIRECTOR: Dott Rinaldo Piaggio
DIRECTOR GENERAL: Ing Umberto Barnato
DIRECTOR OF INTERNATIONAL PROGRAMMES: Ing B. Mori
TECHNICAL CONSULTANT: Ing Giovanni P. Casiraghi
TECHNICAL DIRECTOR: Ing Alessandro Mazzoni
MARKETING DIRECTOR: Commander G. B. Pizzinato

The original Piaggio company began the construction of aeroplanes in its Genoa-Sestri plant in 1916, and later in the Finale Ligure works. The present company was formed on 29 February 1964, and has since operated as an independent concern. It employs about 1,300 people and has a total covered works area (Genoa-Sestri and Finale-Ligure) of approx 100,000 m² (1,076,390 sq ft). In addition to building aircraft of its own design, Piaggio is producing components for the Aeritalia G222 and Panavia Tornado military aircraft.

The company is organised into two production Divisions: the activities of the Aero-Engine Division are described in the appropriate section of this edition.

R. PIAGGIO P.166-DL3

The P.166 has been produced in several basic versions, of which the original P.166 production version (32 built) was described in the 1963-64 *Jane's*; the military P.166M (51 built), the P.166B Portofino (5 built) and P.166C (2 built) in the 1971-72 *Jane's*; the P.166S search and surveillance version (20 built) in the 1974-75 *Jane's*; and the P.166-DL2 (4 built) in the 1978-79 *Jane's*.

The current version is:

P.166-DL3. Turboprop-powered version, first flown on 3 July 1976. FAA and RAI certification obtained in 1978. Twenty-two production aircraft being built. Two of these have been acquired by Alitalia for pilot training, each aircraft being equipped to accommodate two trainees.

TYPE: Twin-turboprop light transport.

WINGS: Shoulder gull-wing cantilever monoplane. NACA 230 wing section. Dihedral 21° 30′ on inner portion, 2° 30′ on outer wings. Incidence 2° 43′ at root. Aluminium alloy flush-riveted structure. All-metal slotted ailerons, with geared and trim tab in starboard aileron. All-metal slotted flaps. Rubber-boot leading-edge de-icing optional.

FUSELAGE: Aluminium alloy flush-riveted semi-monocoque structure.

TAIL UNIT: Cantilever aluminium alloy flush-riveted structure. Geared and trim tabs in elevators; trim tab in rudder.

LANDING GEAR: Retractable tricycle type. Magnaghi oleo-pneumatic shock-absorbers. Hydraulic retraction. Nosewheel retracts rearward, main units outward. Goodyear main wheels with size 25·65 × 8·70-10 tyres, pressure 3·59 bars (52 lb/sq in). Goodyear nosewheel with size 17·5 × 6·30-6 tyre, pressure 2·90 bars (42 lb/sq in). Goodyear or Magnaghi hydraulic brakes.

POWER PLANT: Two Avco Lycoming LTP 101-600 turboprop engines, each developing 438 kW (587 shp) at take-off, and each driving a Hartzell HC-B3TN-3/T10282-95 three-blade feathering constant-speed pusher propeller. Fuel in two internal tanks in outer wings and two external wingtip tanks, total capacity 1,024 litres (225·25 Imp gallons).

ACCOMMODATION: Standard seating for pilot, co-pilot and eight passengers. Alternative configurations include six-passenger layout, with toilet and bar at rear; cargo version, with stripped cabin and freight tiedowns; ambulance and air survey versions. Main door in centre of cabin on port side. Separate door to flight deck on each side. Emergency exit forward of wing on starboard side. Outside door to baggage compartment aft of cabin on port side. Dual controls standard.

SYSTEMS: Hydraulic system, pressure 127 bars (1,840 lb/sq in), operates landing gear, flaps and brakes. 28V engine-driven DC generator for electrical system.

AVIONICS AND EQUIPMENT: Optional avionics include VHF radio, VOR, ADF, marker beacon receiver, glideslope receiver and Collins AP 107 autopilot and horizon gyro unit.

DIMENSIONS, EXTERNAL:
Wing span: without tip-tanks	13·51 m (44 ft 4 in)
with tip-tanks	14·69 m (48 ft 2½ in)
Wing chord at root	2·40 m (7 ft 10½ in)
Wing chord at tip	1·15 m (3 ft 9¼ in)
Wing aspect ratio	7·3
Length overall	11·90 m (39 ft 3 in)

P.166-DL3 version of the Piaggio P.166, with two Avco Lycoming LTP 101 turboprop engines *(Pilot Press)*

R. Piaggio P.166-DL3 twin-turboprop light transport *(Giovanni Masino)*

Height overall	5·00 m (16 ft 5 in)
Tailplane span	5·10 m (16 ft 9 in)
Wheel track	2·66 m (8 ft 9 in)
Wheelbase	4·71 m (15 ft 5½ in)
Cabin door: Height	1·38 m (4 ft 6 in)
Width	1·28 m (4 ft 2 in)

DIMENSIONS, INTERNAL:
Cabin: Length	3·55 m (11 ft 8 in)
Max width	1·57 m (5 ft 2 in)
Max height	1·76 m (5 ft 9 in)
Floor area	5·14 m² (55·3 sq ft)
Volume	6·63 m³ (234·1 cu ft)
Baggage compartment (front)	0·77 m³ (27·2 cu ft)
Baggage compartment (rear)	1·80 m³ (63·6 cu ft)

AREAS:
Wings, gross	26·56 m² (285·9 sq ft)
Ailerons (total)	1·95 m² (21·00 sq ft)
Trailing-edge flaps (total)	2·38 m² (25·60 sq ft)
Fin	1·62 m² (17·44 sq ft)
Rudder, incl tab	1·23 m² (13·24 sq ft)
Tailplane	3·50 m² (37·67 sq ft)
Elevators, incl tabs	1·29 m² (13·88 sq ft)

WEIGHTS AND LOADINGS:
Weight empty, equipped	2,600 kg (5,732 lb)
Max payload	1,188 kg (2,619 lb)
Max T-O weight	4,300 kg (9,480 lb)
Max zero-fuel weight	3,800 kg (8,377 lb)
Max landing weight	3,800 kg (8,377 lb)
Max wing loading	162 kg/m² (33·2 lb/sq ft)
Max power loading	4·91 kg/kW (8·07 lb/shp)

PERFORMANCE (at AUW of 3,855 kg; 8,500 lb except where indicated):
Max level speed at 3,050 m (10,000 ft)	
	215 knots (400 km/h; 248 mph)
Max cruising speed at 3,050 m (10,000 ft)	
	205 knots (380 km/h; 236 mph)
Econ cruising speed at 3,050 m (10,000 ft)	
	162 knots (300 km/h; 186 mph)
Stalling speed, flaps and wheels down, at max landing weight	71 knots (131 km/h; 82 mph)
Max rate of climb at S/L	710 m (2,330 ft)/min
Rate of climb at S/L, one engine out	
	189 m (620 ft)/min
Service ceiling	8,840 m (29,000 ft)
Service ceiling, one engine out	3,960 m (13,000 ft)
T-O run	494 m (1,620 ft)
T-O to 15 m (50 ft)	640 m (2,100 ft)
Landing from 15 m (50 ft), at AUW of 3,400 kg (7,500 lb)	415 m (1,360 ft)

Range at cruising altitude of 4,875 m (16,000 ft), 30 min reserves:	
at max cruising speed	766 nm (1,420 km; 882 miles)
at max-range cruising speed	
	863 nm (1,600 km; 994 miles)

PIAGGIO P.166-DL3-MAR

The P.166-DL3-MAR is a medium-range maritime surveillance version of the standard P.166-DL3. Applications include coastguard, anti-smuggling, maritime traffic, fishery and pollution control, and search and rescue. The P.166-DL3-MAR is intended to be equipped with an integrated search/detection/identification/plotting and reporting system, plus four underwing pylons for external weapons or other stores. It is capable of operating from unprepared strips, day or night, in all weathers.

AIRFRAME AND POWER PLANT: As for standard P.166-DL3, except for specialised equipment changes.

AVIONICS AND EQUIPMENT: According to customer and mission requirements. Typical packages may include 180° scan search radar, two Vinten aerial cameras, Doppler or other suitable navigation system, and operator's console; or 360° search radar, low light level TV camera with monitor and recorder, Doppler/Omega navigation system and tactical co-ordinator's console.

WEIGHTS (estimated):
Weight empty, without operational equipment	
	2,460 kg (5,424 lb)
Operational equipment (conventional package)	
	400 kg (882 lb)

WEIGHTS:
Weight empty, equipped	2,860 kg (6,306 lb)
Operational weight	3,206 kg (7,069 lb)
Fuel	1,094 kg (2,411 lb)
Max T-O weight	4,300 kg (9,480 lb)

PERFORMANCE (estimated: typical mission with crew of three, cruising to search area at 170 knots; 315 km/h; 196 mph at 3,050 m; 10,000 ft, maintaining search at 140 knots; 259 km/h; 161 mph at 1,220 m; 4,000 ft, 30 min reserves):

At 40 nm (74 km; 46 miles) from base:	
time on station	6 h 0 min
total mission time	6 h 30 min
At 200 nm (370 km; 230 miles) from base:	
time on station	4 h 0 min
total mission time	6 h 20 min
At 360 nm (667 km; 415 miles) from base:	
time on station	2 h 0 min
total mission time	6 h 15 min
At 440 nm (815 km; 506 miles) from base:	
time on station	1 h 0 min
total mission time	6 h 0 min

PROCAER
PROGETTI COSTRUZIONI AERONAUTICHE SpA

Via Gramsci 2, 20091 Bresso (Milan)
Telephone: 6105742
PRESIDENT: Dott Ing Rico Neeff

Production by this company in recent years has concentrated on various versions of the F15 four-seat light aircraft. The latest of these are the all-metal F15E Picchio, and a developed version initiated by General Avia (which see) and known as the F15F. Both are part of a licence package offered by Procaer.

The production programmes for both aircraft had been delayed in early 1979, when licensing negotiations were pending. No subsequent news had been received at the time of closing for press.

PROCAER F15E PICCHIO

The F15E prototype (I-PROM) flew for the first time on 21 December 1968. The aircraft has been certificated by both the RAI and FAA, in November 1970 and July 1971 respectively. A second prototype, embodying modifications, was flight tested in 1976 and was the subject of a tender to the Aero Club d'Italia. The first production F15E (I-PROD) was certificated on 19 November 1977.

The following description applies to the first prototype:

TYPE: Four-seat light aircraft.
WINGS: Cantilever low-wing monoplane. NACA 64-215/64-210 wing sections. Dihedral 6° from roots. Incidence 4°. One-piece metal structure with single main spar, rear spar carrying aileron and flap hinges, and short front spar to carry landing gear loads. All-metal Frise ailerons and electrically actuated Fowler flaps.
FUSELAGE: All-metal semi-monocoque structure.
TAIL UNIT: Cantilever all-metal structure. Trim tab on rudder and in starboard elevator.
LANDING GEAR: Retractable tricycle type. Electrical or mechanical actuation. Oleo-pneumatic shock-absorbers. Inward-retracting main wheels, size 6·00-6. Steerable, rearward-retracting nosewheel, size 5·00-5. Hydraulic disc brakes.
POWER PLANT: One 224 kW (300 hp) Continental IO-520-F flat-six engine, driving a Hartzell HC-C2YF-1B/8475-6 two-blade constant-speed metal propeller. Fuel in two wing tanks and two wingtip tanks, total capacity 318 litres (70 Imp gallons). Oil capacity 11·5 litres (2·5 Imp gallons).
ACCOMMODATION: Four persons in pairs in enclosed cabin. Forward-opening door on each side. Space for 45 kg (100 lb) of baggage behind rear bench seat. Dual controls. Cabin soundproofed, heated and ventilated.
SYSTEMS AND EQUIPMENT: Two 12V 35Ah batteries, connected in series, provide power for landing gear and flap actuation. 600W engine-driven generator. Blind-flying instruments and radio optional.

DIMENSIONS, EXTERNAL:
Wing span over tip-tanks	9·90 m (32 ft 5¾ in)
Wing chord at root	1·72 m (5 ft 8 in)
Wing chord at tip	0·85 m (2 ft 9 in)
Wing aspect ratio	7·37
Length overall	7·50 m (24 ft 7¼ in)
Height overall	2·80 m (9 ft 2½ in)
Tailplane span	3·55 m (11 ft 8 in)
Wheel track	2·78 m (9 ft 1¼ in)
Wheelbase	1·73 m (5 ft 8½ in)
Propeller diameter	1·98 m (6 ft 6 in)

DIMENSIONS, INTERNAL:
Cabin: Length	2·75 m (9 ft 0 in)
Max width	1·20 m (3 ft 11¼ in)
Max height	1·35 m (4 ft 5¼ in)

AREAS:
Wings, gross	13·30 m² (143·2 sq ft)
Ailerons (total)	1·19 m² (12·81 sq ft)
Trailing-edge flaps (total)	1·72 m² (18·50 sq ft)
Fin	0·88 m² (9·50 sq ft)

First production example of the Procaer F15E Picchio four-seat light aircraft

Prototype of the F15F, with modified canopy, lower-powered engine and no tip-tanks

Rudder, incl tab	0·49 m² (5·27 sq ft)
Tailplane	1·67 m² (17·97 sq ft)
Elevators, incl tab	1·27 m² (13·67 sq ft)

WEIGHTS AND LOADINGS:
Weight empty	842 kg (1,856 lb)
Weight empty, equipped	861 kg (1,900 lb)
Max T-O weight: Normal	1,360 kg (3,000 lb)
Utility	1,225 kg (2,700 lb)
Max wing loading:	
Normal	101·8 kg/m² (20·85 lb/sq ft)
Utility	92·0 kg/m² (18·85 lb/sq ft)
Max power loading:	
Normal	6·42 kg/kW (10·55 lb/hp)
Utility	5·75 kg/kW (9·45 lb/hp)

PERFORMANCE (N: at max Normal T-O weight; U: at max Utility T-O weight):
Never-exceed speed:	
N	191 knots (354 km/h; 220 mph)
U	200 knots (370 km/h; 230 mph)
Max level speed:	
N	173 knots (320 km/h; 199 mph)
U	174 knots (322 km/h; 200 mph)
Max cruising speed:	
N, U	165 knots (306 km/h; 190 mph)
Econ cruising speed:	
N, U	144 knots (267 km/h; 166 mph)
Stalling speed, flaps and landing gear up:	
N	68 knots (127 km/h; 78·5 mph)
U	63 knots (118 km/h; 73 mph)
Stalling speed, flaps and landing gear down:	
N	60 knots (111 km/h; 69 mph)
U	56 knots (103 km/h; 64 mph)
Service ceiling: N	5,300 m (17,390 ft)
T-O run: N	360 m (1,181 ft)
T-O to 15 m (50 ft): N	560 m (1,837 ft)
Landing from 15 m (50 ft): N	625 m (2,050 ft)
Landing run: N	375 m (1,230 ft)
Max range (N), no reserves:	
at max cruising speed	647 nm (1,200 km; 746 miles)
at econ cruising speed	863 nm (1,600 km; 994 miles)
Max endurance (N):	
at max cruising speed	5 h 0 min
at econ cruising speed	6 h 0 min

PROCAER/GENERAL AVIA F15F

The F15F is a derivative of the F15E Picchio, designed by Dott Ing Frati of General Avia. The prototype (I-PROL), completed by General Avia, made its first flight on 20 October 1977. Manufacture of a pre-production series was to be undertaken by Procaer.

Principal differences from the F15E are as follows:

POWER PLANT: One 149 kW (200 hp) Avco Lycoming IO-360-A1B1 flat-four engine, driving a two-blade constant-speed metal propeller. Wingtip fuel tanks deleted.
ACCOMMODATION: Four seats, in two pairs, as in F15E; but fully-transparent moulded canopy instead of enclosed cabin.

DIMENSIONS, EXTERNAL:
Length overall	7·75 m (25 ft 5¼ in)

WEIGHTS AND LOADINGS:
Weight empty	765 kg (1,686 lb)
Max T-O weight (Utility)	1,225 kg (2,700 lb)
Max wing loading	92·0 kg/m² (18·85 lb/sq ft)
Max power loading	8·22 kg/kW (13·45 lb/hp)

PERFORMANCE (at max T-O weight):
Max level speed	164 knots (305 km/h; 189 mph)
Cruising speed	151 knots (280 km/h; 174 mph)
Stalling speed	55·5 knots (102 km/h; 63·5 mph)
Max rate of climb at S/L	270 m (885 ft)/min
Service ceiling	5,200 m (17,050 ft)

SIAI-MARCHETTI
SIAI-MARCHETTI SpA

MANAGEMENT: Via Indipendenza 2, 21018 Sesto Calende (Varese)
Telephone: (0331) 924421
Telex: 39601 Siaiavio
AERODROME AND MAIN WORKS: Vergiate (Varese)
OTHER WORKS: Sesto Calende (Varese), Malpensa and Borgomanero
ROME OFFICE: Via Barberini 36, 00187 Rome
Telephone: (06) 482811
PRESIDENT: Dott Ermenegildo Marelli
MANAGING DIRECTOR: Dott Ing Giovanni Angiola
ADVERTISING MANAGER: Alberto Menozzi

Founded in 1915, the SIAI-Marchetti company was known originally as Savoia-Marchetti. It has produced a wide range of military and civil landplanes and flying-boats, but is now increasingly involved in helicopter manufacture, in association with Agusta and Elicotteri Meridionali. Its current products include civil and military light aircraft of its own design or development, and co-production with Agusta (which see) of Boeing Vertol CH-47C (see EM entry in this section), Bell 212, and Sikorsky SH-3D and HH-3F helicopters. In 1980 it was preparing to launch production of the SF.600 Canguro.

SIAI-Marchetti is engaged in the overhaul and repair of various types of large aircraft (notably the C-130 Hercules) serving with the Italian Air Force. It also participates in national or multi-national programmes for the Aeritalia G222, Aeritalia (Lockheed) F-104S and Panavia Tornado.

The company's works at Vergiate, Sesto Calende, Malpensa and Borgomanero total 1,345,000 m² (14,477,450 sq ft) in area, of which 116,000 m² (1,248,600 sq ft) are covered, and employ more than 2,500 people.

SIAI-MARCHETTI SF.260 (MILITARY VERSIONS)

The prototype for the SF.260 series, known as the F.250, was designed by Dott Ing Stelio Frati and built by Aviamilano. Flown for the first time on 15 July 1964, it was powered by a 186·5 kW (250 hp) Avco Lycoming engine and was certificated for aerobatic flying. A description appeared in the 1965-66 *Jane's*.

The version developed initially, for civil production, was manufactured, at first under licence from Aviamilano, by SIAI-Marchetti, and is designated SF.260. It received FAA type approval on 1 April 1966. Subsequently SIAI-Marchetti became the official holder of the type certificate and of all manufacturing rights in the SF.260; it has continued to develop the civil version, described separately, and has also evolved three basic versions for military use. The three military models are as follows:

SF.260M. Two/three-seat military trainer, developed from the initial civil SF.260A and flown for the first time on 10 October 1970. Introduced a number of important structural and aerodynamic improvements, many of which were subsequently applied to the later civil versions. Meets the necessary requirements for basic flying training; instrument flying; aerobatics, including deliberate spinning and recovery; night flying; navigation flying; and formation flying.

Production to date of SF.260Ms has included orders from the Italian Air Force (25 SF.260AM), Belgian Air Force (36 SF.260M), Bolivian Air Force (6), Burmese Air Force (10 SF.260MB), Ecuadorean Air Force (12 SF.260ME), Libyan Arab Air Force (240 SF.260ML, of

SIAI-Marchetti SF.260M military trainer (Avco Lycoming O-540-E4A5 engine) *(Roy J. Grainge)*

which 160 are to be assembled in that country), Moroccan Air Force (2 SF.260MM), Philippine Air Force (32 SF.260MP), Singapore Air Defence Command (16 SF.260MS), Royal Thai Air Force (12 SF.260MT), Tunisian Air Force (6), Zaïre Air Force (23 SF.260MC) and Zambian Air Force (8 SF.260MZ). Singapore ordered six more in 1979.

SF.260W Warrior. Trainer/tactical support version of SF.260M, first flown (I-SJAV) in May 1972. Two or four underwing pylons, for up to 300 kg (661 lb) of external stores, and cockpit stores selection panel. Able to undertake a wide variety of roles, including low-level strike; forward air control; forward air support; armed reconnaissance; and liaison. Also meets same requirements as SF.260M for use as a trainer.

Customers to date include the Dubai Police Air Wing (1 SF.260WD), Irish Air Corps (10 SF.260WE, of which the first four were handed over on 4 March 1977), Philippine Air Force (16 SF.260WP), Somali Aeronautical Corps (6 SF.260WS), Tunisian Air Force (12 SF.260WT), Union of Burma Air Force (9) and Comoros (8 SF.260WC).

SF.260SW Sea Warrior. Version of SF.260W for surveillance, search and rescue, and supply missions. Retains the underwing pylons of the W, and is equipped also with specially designed enlarged tip-tanks containing a lightweight radar system (port) and photographic reconnaissance system (starboard). Operational flight testing of the SF.260SW has been completed. No orders had been announced up to mid-1980.

By mid-1980 more than 600 civil and military SF.260s of all models had been completed, of which most were for export. Total sales were then in excess of 700.

The following description applies primarily to the SF.260M, but is generally applicable to other military SF.260 models unless otherwise stated:

TYPE: Two/three-seat fully-aerobatic military light aircraft.

WINGS: Cantilever low-wing monoplane. Wing section NACA 64₁-212 (modified) at root, NACA 64₁-210 (modified) at tip. Dihedral 6° 20′ from roots. Incidence 2° 45′ at root, 0° at tip. No sweepback. Increased leading-edge radius compared with SF.260A, with lower datum line to improve stall characteristics. All-metal light alloy safe-life structure, with single main spar and auxiliary rear spar, built in two portions bolted together at centreline and attached to fuselage by six bolts. Press-formed ribs, with dimpled stiffening holes. Skin, which is butt-joined and flush-riveted, stiffened by stringers between main and rear spars. Differentially-operating Frise-type light alloy mass-balanced ailerons, and electrically-actuated light alloy single-slotted flaps. Flaps operated by torque tube and mechanical linkage, ailerons by pushrods and cables. Servo tab in each aileron.

FUSELAGE: Semi-monocoque safe-life structure of frames, stringers and flush-riveted skin, exclusively of light alloy except for welded steel tube engine mounting, glassfibre front panel of engine cowling, stainless steel firewall and detachable glassfibre tailcone.

TAIL UNIT: Cantilever light alloy safe-life structure, with sweptback vertical surfaces, fixed-incidence tailplane and one-piece elevator. Two-spar fin and one-piece tailplane, bolted to fuselage; single-spar elevator, statically and aerodynamically balanced, and balanced rudder. Military models have reinforced tail unit/fuselage joints compared with SF.260C. Rudder and elevator operated by cables. Controllable trim tab in starboard half of elevator; ground-adjustable tab on rudder.

LANDING GEAR: Electrically-retractable tricycle type, with manual emergency actuation. Inward-retracting main

gear, of trailing-arm type, and rearward-retracting nose unit, each embodying Magnaghi oleo-pneumatic shock-absorber (type 2/22028 on main units). Each welded steel tube main leg is hinged to the main and rear spars. Nose unit is of leg-and-fork type, with co-axial shock-absorber and torque strut. Cleveland P/N 3080A main wheels, with size 6·00-6 tube and tyre (6-ply rating), pressure 2·45 bars (35·5 lb/sq in). Cleveland P/N 40-77A nosewheel, with size 5·00-5 tube and tyre (6-ply rating), pressure 1·96 bars (28·4 lb/sq in). Cleveland P/N 3000-500 independent hydraulic single-disc brake and parking brake on each main wheel. Nosewheel steering (20° to left or right) is operated directly by the rudder pedals, to which it is linked by pushrods. Up-lock secures main gear in retracted position during flight; anti-retraction system prevents main gear from retracting whenever strut is compressed by weight of aircraft. Compared with SF.260C, the military models have a reinforced nosewheel drag brace attachment and landing gear retraction supports; increased use of light alloy forgings, instead of welded steel, in certain landing gear components; and an improved retraction locking mechanism. On all models, the mooring point beneath the rear fuselage acts as a tail bumper.

POWER PLANT: One 194 kW (260 hp) Avco Lycoming O-540-E4A5 flat-six engine, driving a Hartzell HC-C2YK-1BF/8477-8R two-blade constant-speed metal propeller with spinner. Fuel in two light alloy tanks in wings, capacity of each 49·5 litres (10·9 gallons); and two permanent wingtip tanks, capacity of each 72 litres (15·85 Imp gallons). Total internal fuel capacity 243 litres (53·5 Imp gallons), of which 235 litres (51·7 Imp gallons) are usable. Individual refuelling point on top of each tank. In addition, SF.260W and SW may be fitted with two 83 litre (18·25 Imp gallon) auxiliary tanks on underwing pylons. Oil capacity (all models) 11·4 litres (2·5 Imp gallons).

ACCOMMODATION (SF.260M; W and SW similar): Side-by-side front seats (for instructor and pupil in SF.260M), with third seat centrally at rear. Front seats are individually adjustable fore and aft, and have forward-folding backs and provision for back-type parachute packs. Dual controls standard. All three seats equipped with lap belts and shoulder harnesses. Baggage compartment aft of rear seat. One-piece fully-transparent rearward-sliding Plexiglas canopy, upper portion of which is tinted. Emergency canopy release handle for each front seat occupant. Steel tube windscreen frame for protection in the event of an overturn. Cabin carpeted, air-conditioned, heated and ventilated; walls thermally insulated and soundproofed by a glassfibre lining. Slots at base of windscreen admit air for windscreen defrosting.

SYSTEMS (SF.260M; other models generally similar): Hydraulic equipment for main-wheel brakes only. No pneumatic system. 24V DC electrical system of single-

conductor negative earth type, including 70A Prestolite engine-mounted alternator/rectifier and 24V 24Ah Varley battery, for engine starting, flap and landing gear actuation, fuel booster pumps, electronics and lighting. Sealed battery compartment in rear of fuselage on port side. Connection of an external power source automatically disconnects the battery. Heating system for carburettor air intake. Emergency electrical system for extending landing gear if normal electrical actuation fails; provision for mechanical extension in the event of total electrical failure. Cabin heating, and windscreen de-icing and demisting, by heat exchanger using engine exhaust air. Additional manually controlled warm-air outlets for general cabin heating. Oxygen system optional.

AVIONICS AND EQUIPMENT (SF.260M; W and SW generally similar): Basic instrumentation and military equipment to customer's requirements. Blind-flying instrumentation and communications equipment optional: typical selection includes dual Collins 20B VHF com; Collins VIR-31A VHF nav; Collins ADF-60A ADF; Collins TDR-90 ATC transponder; Collins PN-101 compass; ID-90-000 RMI; and Gemelli AG04-1 intercom. Landing light in nose, below spinner. Instrument panel can be slid rearward to provide access to rear of instruments. Compared with SF.260C, SF.260M has various improvements to flight controls, engine controls (duplicated propeller and throttle controls), electrical system, radio and other installations.

ARMAMENT (SF.260W): Two or four underwing hardpoints, able to carry external stores on NATO standard pylons up to a maximum of 300 kg (661 lb) when flown as a single-seater. Typical alternative loads can include one or two SIAI gun pods, each with one 7·62 mm FN machine-gun and 500 rds; two Matra MAC AAF1 7·62 mm gun pods; two Simpres AL-8-70 launchers each with eight 2·75 in FFAR rockets; two LAU-32 launchers each with seven 2·75 in FFAR rockets; two Simpres AL-18-50 launchers each with eighteen 2 in SNIA ARF/8M2 rockets; two Matra F2 launchers each with six 68 mm SNEB 253 rockets; two Matra 181 launchers each with eighteen 37 mm rockets; two SAMP EU 32 125 kg general purpose bombs or EU 13 120 kg fragmentation bombs; two SAMP EU 70 50 kg general purpose bombs; Mk 76 11 kg practice bombs; two Alkan 500B cartridge throwers for Lacroix 74 mm explosive cartridges, F 725 flares, or F 130 smoke cartridges; one Alkan 500B cartridge thrower and one photo-reconnaissance pod with two 70 mm automatic cameras; or two 83 litre (18·25 Imp gallon) auxiliary fuel tanks.

OPERATIONAL EQUIPMENT (SF.260SW): Retains the underwing pylons and gunsight of the SF.260W, but is equipped also with crew survival kit and specially designed enlarged tip-tanks incorporating a lightweight radar and a photographic reconnaissance system. Bendix RDR-1400 digital radar and transmitter-receiver in forward portion of port tip-tank for search, ground mapping, beacon identification and weather avoidance. Radar control and display units are mounted at co-pilot's station, but a radar reconnaissance can be flown without a separate radar operator. Forward-looking obliquely-mounted 70 mm camera in front portion of starboard tip-tank. Rear portion of each tip-tank contains same amount of fuel (72 litres; 15·85 Imp gallons) as the smaller tip-tanks of the SF.260W. The SW can also be used for search and rescue or air supply delivery with various underwing survival kits (land or sea type) and emergency packs. Survival kit, in droppable underwing containers, is parachute-stabilised and includes 10-place (or Matra Samar 8-place) life raft, tents, rations, signals, or other equipment, depending upon prevailing climatic conditions.

DIMENSIONS, EXTERNAL:
Wing span over tip-tanks:	
M, W	8·35 m (27 ft 4¾ in)
SW	8·70 m (28 ft 6½ in)
Wing chord at root	1·60 m (5 ft 3 in)
Wing mean aerodynamic chord	1·325 m (4 ft 4¼ in)
Wing chord at tip	0·784 m (2 ft 6⅞ in)
Wing aspect ratio (excl tip-tanks)	6·33
Wing taper ratio	2·24
Length overall	7·10 m (23 ft 3½ in)

SIAI-Marchetti SF.260M training aircraft of the Bolivian Air Force

Fuselage: Max width	1·10 m (3 ft 7¼ in)
Max depth	1·042 m (3 ft 5 in)
Height overall	2·41 m (7 ft 11 in)
Elevator span	3·01 m (9 ft 10½ in)
Wheel track	2·274 m (7 ft 5½ in)
Wheelbase	1·66 m (5 ft 5¼ in)
Propeller diameter	1·93 m (6 ft 4 in)
Propeller ground clearance	0·32 m (1 ft 0½ in)

DIMENSIONS, INTERNAL:

Cabin: Length	1·66 m (5 ft 5¼ in)
Max width	1·00 m (3 ft 3¼ in)
Height (seat cushion to canopy)	
	0·98 m (3 ft 2½ in)
Volume	1·50 m³ (53 cu ft)
Baggage compartment volume	0·18 m³ (6·36 cu ft)

AREAS:

Wings, gross	10·10 m² (108·70 sq ft)
Ailerons (total, incl tabs)	0·762 m² (8·20 sq ft)
Trailing-edge flaps (total)	1·18 m² (12·70 sq ft)
Fin	0·76 m² (8·18 sq ft)
Dorsal fin	0·16 m² (1·72 sq ft)
Rudder, incl tab	0·60 m² (6·46 sq ft)
Tailplane	1·46 m² (15·70 sq ft)
Elevator, incl tab	0·96 m² (10·30 sq ft)

WEIGHTS AND LOADINGS:

Manufacturer's basic weight empty:

W	770 kg (1,697 lb)
SW	775 kg (1,708 lb)
Weight empty, equipped: M	799 kg (1,761 lb)
W	814 kg (1,794 lb)
SW	857 kg (1,889 lb)

Fuel:

in-wing and wingtip tanks (all versions)	
	169 kg (372·5 lb)
underwing tanks (W and SW only)	114 kg (251·5 lb)

Typical mission weights:

M, trainer ('clean')	1,140 kg (2,513 lb)
W, two 47 kg (103·5 lb) machine-gun pods and full internal fuel	1,163 kg (2,564 lb)
W, one Alkan 500B cartridge thrower, one two-camera reconnaissance pod and full internal fuel	1,182 kg (2,605 lb)
W, trainer with 94 kg (207 lb) external stores	1,249 kg (2,753 lb)
W, self-ferry with two 83 litre (18·25 Imp gallon) underwing tanks	1,285 kg (2,833 lb)
W, two 125 kg bombs and 150 kg (331 lb) internal fuel	1,300 kg (2,866 lb)
W, two AL-8-70 rocket launchers and 160 kg (353 lb) internal fuel	1,300 kg (2,866 lb)
SW, reconnaissance patrol	1,246 kg (2,747 lb)
SW, search and rescue with two 90 kg (198·5 lb) survival kits, 60 kg (132 lb) of external weapons, and full internal fuel	1,264 kg (2,786 lb)
SW, armed patrol	1,300 kg (2,866 lb)
SW, surveillance with two 90 kg (198·5 lb) survival kits, two 47 kg (103·5 lb) gun pods, and full internal fuel	1,300 kg (2,866 lb)

Max T-O weight:

M, Aerobatic	1,100 kg (2,425 lb)
M, Utility	1,200 kg (2,645 lb)
W, SW, max permitted	1,300 kg (2,866 lb)
Max wing loading: M	119 kg/m² (24·4 lb/sq ft)
W, SW	129 kg/m² (26·4 lb/sq ft)

Max power loading:

M	6·19 kg/kW (10·17 lb/hp)
W, SW	6·70 kg/kW (11·01 lb/hp)

PERFORMANCE (M at AUW of 1,200 kg; 2,645 lb, W and SW at 1,300 kg; 2,866 lb, unless stated otherwise):

Never-exceed speed:

M	235 knots (436 km/h; 271 mph)

Max level speed at S/L:

M	183 knots (340 km/h; 211 mph)
W	170 knots (315 km/h; 196 mph)
SW	164 knots (304 km/h; 189 mph)

Max cruising speed (75% power) at 1,500 m (4,925 ft):

M	174 knots (322 km/h; 200 mph)
W	155 knots (287 km/h; 178 mph)
SW	148 knots (275 km/h; 171 mph)

Stalling speed, flaps and landing gear up:

M	74 knots (137 km/h; 85·5 mph)
W, SW	88 knots (163 km/h; 101·5 mph)

Stalling speed, flaps and landing gear down:

M	64 knots (118 km/h; 73·5 mph)
W, SW	75 knots (139 km/h; 86·5 mph)

Max rate of climb at S/L: M

M	475 m (1,558 ft)/min
W	335 m (1,099 ft)/min
SW	270 m (885 ft)/min

Time to 1,500 m (4,925 ft): M

M	4 min 0 s
W	6 min 20 s
SW	7 min 30 s

Time to 2,300 m (7,550 ft): M

M	6 min 50 s
W	10 min 20 s
SW	14 min 45 s

Time to 3,000 m (9,850 ft): M

M	10 min 0 s
W	18 min 40 s
Service ceiling: M	4,665 m (15,300 ft)
T-O run at S/L: M	384 m (1,260 ft)
T-O to 15 m (50 ft) at S/L: M	606 m (1,988 ft)
W, SW	825 m (2,707 ft)

Landing from 15 m (50 ft) at S/L:

M	539 m (1,768 ft)
W, SW	645 m (2,116 ft)
Landing run at S/L: M	345 m (1,132 ft)

Operational radius:

W, 6 h 25 min single-seat armed patrol mission at 1,163 kg (2,564 lb) AUW, incl 5 h 35 min over operating area, 20 kg (44 lb) fuel reserves
50 nm (92 km; 57 miles)

W, 3 h 38 min single-seat strike mission, incl two 5 min loiters over separate en-route target areas, 20 kg (44 lb) fuel reserves
250 nm (463 km; 287 miles)

W, 4 h 54 min single-seat strike mission, incl 5 min over target area, 20 kg (44 lb) fuel reserves
300 nm (556 km; 345 miles)

W, 4 h 30 min single-seat photo-reconnaissance mission at 1,182 kg (2,605 lb) AUW, incl three 1 h loiters over separate en-route operating areas, 20 kg (44 lb) fuel reserves
150 nm (278 km; 172 miles)

W, 6 h 3 min two-seat self-ferry mission with two 83 litre (18·25 Imp gallon) underwing tanks, at 1,285 kg (2,833 lb) AUW, 30 kg (66 lb) fuel reserves
926 nm (1,716 km; 1,066 miles)

SW, 5 h 17 min two-seat surveillance mission, incl 3 h 40 min over operating area at 105 knots (195 km/h; 121 mph), 20 kg (44 lb) fuel reserves
100 nm (185 km; 115 miles)

SW, 5 h 13 min two-seat surveillance mission, incl 2 h 0 min over operating area at 105 knots (195 km/h; 121 mph), 20 kg (44 lb) fuel reserves
200 nm (370 km; 230 miles)

SW, 5 h 27 min two-seat SAR mission at 1,264 kg (2,786 lb) AUW, incl 2 h 15 min over operating area, 5 kg (11 lb) fuel reserves
200 nm (370 km; 230 miles)

Range with max fuel:

M (two-seat)	890 nm (1,650 km; 1,025 miles)

g limits (M):

at max Aerobatic T-O weight	+6·0; —3·0
at max Utility T-O weight without external load	+4·4; —2·2

SIAI-MARCHETTI SF.260C (CIVIL VERSION)

As indicated in the preceding entry, the SF.260 was developed from the F.250 prototype originally as a civil aircraft.

Aircraft from the **SF.260A** first series, marketed in the USA under the name **Waco Meteor**, still hold two FAI Class C1b speed records set in 1969. The first of these is for a speed of 174 knots (322·52 km/h; 200·4 mph) over a 1,000 km closed circuit near Santa Monica, California, on 25 March 1969. The second, set up on 29 March 1969 near Los Angeles, is for a speed of 199·4 knots (369·43 km/h; 229·6 mph) over a 100 km closed circuit.

The second civil series (**SF.260B**), certificated by the FAA on 10 June 1974, incorporated many of the structural and aerodynamic improvements introduced by the SF.260M. Customers included Air France, Royal Air Maroc and Sabena, which ordered the SF.260 for airline crew training.

Approx 30-40 civil SF.260s, including SF.260As and SF.260Bs, had been built by the Spring of 1978.

The current civil version, certificated by the RAI and FAA on 23 October and 30 December 1976 respectively, is designated **SF.260C**. Four were delivered to Alitalia in 1980 for pilot training. The following description applies to the SF.260C:

TYPE: Three-seat fully-aerobatic light aircraft.

WINGS: As SF.260M/W/SW except dihedral 5°.

FUSELAGE: As SF.260M/W/SW.

TAIL UNIT: As SF.260M/W/SW, but without extra reinforcement.

LANDING GEAR: See description for SF.260M/W/SW.

POWER PLANT: As for SF.260M/W/SW, but driving a Hartzell HC-C2YK-1BF/8477-8R or HC-C2YK-4F/FC-8477-8R two-blade constant-speed metal propeller with spinner. Fuel capacity 49·5 litres (10·9 Imp gallons) in each wing tank and 72 litres (15·8 Imp gallons)

in each wingtip tank; total internal capacity 243 litres (53·4 Imp gallons). Oil capacity as for military versions.

ACCOMMODATION: Three seats in enclosed cockpit, two side by side in front, one at rear. Two children with a combined weight not exceeding 113 kg (250 lb) may occupy rear seat. One-piece fully-transparent rearward-sliding Plexiglas canopy, with rubber-cord canopy release. Baggage compartment, capacity 40 kg (88 lb), aft of rear seat. Cabin heated, ventilated and soundproofed with glassfibre.

SYSTEMS, AVIONICS AND EQUIPMENT: Generally similar to SF.260M.

DIMENSIONS, EXTERNAL: As SF.260M/W

DIMENSIONS, INTERNAL: As SF.260M/W/SW

AREAS: As SF.260M/W/SW

WEIGHTS AND LOADINGS:

Weight empty, equipped	755 kg (1,664 lb)
Max T-O weight: Aerobatic	1,000 kg (2,205 lb)
Utility	1,102 kg (2,430 lb)
Max wing loading	109 kg/m² (22·4 lb/sq ft)
Max power loading	5·68 kg/kW (9·33 lb/hp)

PERFORMANCE (at max Utility T-O weight):

Max level speed at S/L

	187 knots (347 km/h; 215 mph)

Max cruising speed (75% power) at 3,050 m (10,000 ft)

	178 knots (330 km/h; 205 mph)

Stalling speed, flaps and landing gear down

	60 knots (111 km/h; 70 mph)
Max rate of climb at S/L	546 m (1,791 ft)/min
Service ceiling	5,790 m (19,000 ft)
T-O run at S/L on concrete	250 m (820 ft)
T-O run at S/L on grass	290 m (952 ft)
T-O to 15 m (50 ft) at S/L	472 m (1,550 ft)
Landing from 15 m (50 ft) at S/L	490 m (1,608 ft)
Landing run at S/L	345 m (1,132 ft)

Range with max fuel (two persons)

	1,106 nm (2,050 km; 1,274 miles)
g limits: Aerobatic	+6·0; —3·0
Utility	+4·4; —2·2

SIAI-MARCHETTI S.205/20R and S.208A

Full details can be found in the 1972-73 Jane's of the S.205 light aircraft, and in the 1974-75 and 1976-77 editions of the S.208 series.

SIAI-Marchetti has offered, since early 1977, further-improved versions of these aircraft, which have the same basic airframe. Improvements applicable to both types include a new cockpit and cabin layout, with better cabin soundproofing; modified flaps and landing gear; and new heating and ventilation system.

Differences between the current versions are as follows:

S.205/20R. Four-seater, with 149 kW (200 hp) Avco Lycoming IO-360 engine. Selected as second-level trainer by Italian Aero Club, to which deliveries (of an order for 140 designated **S.205AC**) began in 1977.

S.208A. Five-seater, with 194 kW (260 hp) Avco Lycoming O-540 engine. Also available in cargo, ambulance or agricultural versions.

POWER PLANT (S.205/20R): One 149 kW (200 hp) Avco Lycoming IO-360-A1B6D flat-four engine, driving a Hartzell HC-C2YK-1BF/F7666A-2 two-blade constant-speed propeller with spinner. Fuel in two wing tanks, total capacity 210 litres (46·2 Imp gallons).

POWER PLANT (S.208A): One 194 kW (260 hp) Avco Lycoming O-540-E4A5 flat-six engine, driving a Hartzell HC-C2YK two-blade constant-speed propeller. Fuel in two wing tanks, total capacity 215 litres (47·3 Imp gallons), and two wingtip tanks, total capacity 115 litres (25·3 Imp gallons). Overall total fuel capacity 330 litres (72·6 Imp gallons).

ACCOMMODATION: Seats for four persons in S.205/20R (five in S.208A), in fully-enclosed cabin. Baggage space aft of rear seats. Forward-opening car-type door on starboard side of cabin. Additional small window at rear of cabin on each side, and door each side, in S.208A.

DIMENSIONS, EXTERNAL:

Wing span (S.205/20R)	10·86 m (35 ft 7½ in)
Wing span over tip-tanks (S.208A)	
	11·24 m (36 ft 10½ in)
Wing area, gross (both)	16·09 m² (173·2 sq ft)

SIAI-Marchetti SF.260C three-seat light aircraft (Avco Lycoming O-540 flat-six engine)

SIAI-Marchetti S.205/20R four-seat light aircraft

Length overall: S.205/20R	8·00 m (26 ft 3 in)
S.208A	8·10 m (26 ft 7 in)
Height overall (both)	2·89 m (9 ft 5¾ in)
DIMENSIONS, INTERNAL (both):	
Cabin: Max length	2·80 m (9 ft 2¼ in)
Max width	1·14 m (3 ft 9 in)
Max height	1·32 m (4 ft 4 in)
Volume	3·00 m³ (106 cu ft)
WEIGHTS AND LOADINGS:	
Weight empty, equipped:	
S.205/20R	761 kg (1,677 lb)
S.208A	835 kg (1,841 lb)
Max T-O weight: S.205/20R	1,300 kg (2,866 lb)
S.208A	1,505 kg (3,318 lb)
Max wing loading:	
S.205/20R	80·8 kg/m² (16·55 lb/sq ft)
S.208A	87·0 kg/m² (17·82 lb/sq ft)
Max power loading:	
S.205/20R	8·72 kg/kW (14·3 lb/hp)
S.208A	7·76 kg/kW (12·7 lb/hp)
PERFORMANCE (at max T-O weight):	
Max level speed at S/L:	
S.205/20R	119 knots (221 km/h; 137 mph)
S.208A	173 knots (320 km/h; 199 mph)
Max cruising speed:	
S.205/20R	107 knots (199 km/h; 124 mph)
S.208A	162 knots (300 km/h; 186 mph)
Stalling speed, flaps down:	
S.205/20R	41·5 knots (76 km/h; 47·5 mph)
S.208A	50 knots (92 km/h; 57·5 mph)
Max rate of climb at S/L:	
S.205/20R	252 m (826 ft)/min
S.208A	300 m (984 ft)/min
Service ceiling: S.205/20R	4,750 m (15,575 ft)
S.208A	5,400 m (17,725 ft)
T-O run: S.205/20R	260 m (853 ft)
S.208A	302 m (991 ft)
Landing run: S.205/20R	300 m (984 ft)
S.208A	171 m (561 ft)
Max range:	
S.205/20R	679 nm (1,258 km; 782 miles)
S.208A	971 nm (1,800 km; 1,118 miles)

SIAI-MARCHETTI SF.600 CANGURO (KANGAROO)

A prototype F.600 Canguro (I-CANG), built by General Avia and powered by 261 kW (350 hp) Avco Lycoming TIO-540-J flat-six engines, made its first flight on 30 December 1978. This aircraft was described under the General Avia heading in the 1979-80 *Jane's*.

SIAI-Marchetti began flight testing the Canguro in 1979, and in March 1980 was preparing to place the aircraft in production as the SF.600. The basic aircraft is offered with non-retractable landing gear and either Avco Lycoming piston engines or Allison turboprops. Retractable-gear, swing-tail, maritime surveillance and other versions are under development.

TYPE: Twin-engined freight, ambulance and general utility transport.

WINGS: Cantilever high-wing monoplane. Wing section NASA GAW-1, with 17% thickness/chord ratio. Dihedral 2°. Incidence (constant) 1° 30′. All-metal riveted structure in light alloy, with stressed skin. Centre-section has main spar and two auxiliary spars; outboard of engines, wings have two spars. All-metal ailerons and electrically-operated double-slotted flaps.

FUSELAGE: All-metal semi-monocoque structure, with stressed skin.

TAIL UNIT: Cantilever all-metal stressed-skin structure. Trim tabs in rudder and each elevator. Small dorsal and ventral fins.

LANDING GEAR: Non-retractable tricycle type, with oleo-pneumatic shock-absorption. Twin-wheel main units; single steerable nose unit. All five wheels and tyres same size, 7·00-6, tyre pressure 2·48 bars (36 lb/sq in). Retractable-gear version also available.

POWER PLANT: Two 261 kW (350 hp) Avco Lycoming TIO-540-J flat-six engines, each driving a Hartzell three-blade fully-feathering constant-speed propeller. Alternatively, may be powered by two 313 kW (420 shp) Allison 250-B17G turboprop engines. Fuel in four wing tanks, total capacity 1,100 litres (242 Imp gallons).

External tanks, total capacity 600 litres (132 Imp gallons), on turboprop version. Oil capacity 11·4 litres (2·5 Imp gallons).

ACCOMMODATION: Pilot and co-pilot or passenger on flight deck. Cabin accommodates up to nine passengers or 12 paratroops, or four stretcher patients and two medical attendants, or 907 kg (2,000 lb) of freight. Forward door on port side for crew; wider, sliding door at rear on port side for freight loading. Swing-tail rear-loading version also available.

DIMENSIONS, EXTERNAL:	
Wing span	15·00 m (49 ft 2½ in)
Wing chord (constant)	1·60 m (5 ft 3 in)
Wing aspect ratio	9·1
Length overall	12·15 m (39 ft 10½ in)
Height overall	4·60 m (15 ft 1 in)
Tailplane span	5·06 m (16 ft 7¼ in)
Wheel track	2·40 m (7 ft 10½ in)
Wheelbase	4·88 m (16 ft 0 in)
Propeller diameter	2·03 m (6 ft 8 in)
Crew door (fwd, port):	
Height	1·14 m (3 ft 9 in)
Width	0·86 m (2 ft 10 in)
Height to sill	0·90 m (2 ft 11½ in)
Cargo door (rear, port):	
Height	1·13 m (3 ft 8½ in)
Width	1·49 m (4 ft 10¾ in)
Height to sill	0·90 m (2 ft 11½ in)
DIMENSIONS, INTERNAL:	
Cabin, excl flight deck:	
Length	5·05 m (16 ft 6¾ in)
Width	1·23 m (4 ft 0½ in)
Height	1·27 m (4 ft 2 in)
Floor area	5·57 m² (60 sq ft)
Volume	7·80 m³ (275 cu ft)

WEIGHTS (A: TIO-540 engines; B: Allison 250 engines):	
Weight empty: A	1,950 kg (4,299 lb)
B	1,800 kg (3,968 lb)
Operating weight empty: A	2,090 kg (4,607 lb)
B	1,947 kg (4,292 lb)
Max external load: A, B	900 kg (1,984 lb)
Max T-O weight: A	3,200 kg (7,054 lb)
B	3,300 kg (7,275 lb)

PERFORMANCE (estimated, at max T-O weight. A: TIO-540 engines; B: Allison 250 engines):

Max level speed at 3,050 m (10,000 ft):	
A	176 knots (326 km/h; 203 mph)
B	178 knots (330 km/h; 205 mph)
Cruising speed (75% power) at 3,050 m (10,000 ft):	
A, B	159 knots (295 km/h; 183 mph)
Stalling speed, flaps down:	
A	58 knots (108 km/h; 67 mph)
B	59 knots (110 km/h; 68 mph)
Max rate of climb at S/L: A	381 m (1,250 ft)/min
B	396 m (1,300 ft)/min
Rate of climb at S/L, one engine out:	
A	85 m (280 ft)/min
B	91 m (300 ft)/min
Service ceiling: A	7,100 m (23,300 ft)
B	6,700 m (21,980 ft)
Service ceiling, one engine out:	
A	3,200 m (10,500 ft)
B	2,400 m (7,875 ft)
T-O run: A	240 m (788 ft)
B	220 m (722 ft)
T-O to 15 m (50 ft): A	395 m (1,296 ft)
B	350 m (1,150 ft)
Landing from 15 m (50 ft): A	340 m (1,115 ft)
B	320 m (1,050 ft)
Landing run: A	200 m (656 ft)
B	210 m (690 ft)
Cruising range, standard tanks:	
A (45 min reserves)	
	1,295 nm (2,400 km; 1,490 miles)
B	853 nm (1,580 km; 981 miles)

SIAI-MARCHETTI SM.1019E

The SM.1019 light STOL aircraft is suitable for observation, light ground attack or utility duties. Its design was started in January 1969, and construction of a prototype began two months later. This aircraft (I-STOL) flew for the first time on 24 May 1969, with an Allison 250-B15C engine, and was granted Normal and Utility category certification by the RAI on 25 October 1969.

A second prototype (I-SJAR), which flew for the first time on 18 February 1971, was designated SM.1019A. It had an improved fuel system, two doors and two instrument panels, and received RAI civil certification in the Normal and Utility categories.

Production began in 1974 of an initial series of 80 SM.1019EIs for the Aviazione Leggera dell'Esercito (ALE, or Italian Army Light Aviation), and all of these had been delivered by the Summer of 1978.

TYPE: Two-seat STOL light aircraft.

WINGS: High-wing monoplane, braced by single strut on each side. Wing section NACA 2412. Dihedral 2° 8′. Incidence 1° 30′. Washout 3°. Conventional all-metal structure, with detachable tapered outer panels. Metal Frise-type ailerons and electrically-actuated trailing-edge slotted flaps. Trim tab in starboard aileron. Tiedown point at each wingtip.

FUSELAGE: Conventional all-metal stressed-skin structure.

TAIL UNIT: Conventional cantilever all-metal structure, with horizontal surfaces mounted on top of fuselage. Dorsal fin. Fixed-incidence tailplane. Elevators and rudder horn-balanced. Manually-operated mechanically-actuated trim tab in starboard elevator; servo tab in port elevator. Ground-adjustable trim tab on rudder.

LANDING GEAR: Non-retractable tailwheel type, with cantilever leaf-type spring steel main-wheel legs. Goodyear 511960 main wheels, with low-pressure tyres, size 7·00-6, pressure 2·07 bars (30 lb/sq in); Scott 3200A tailwheel, with size 8-3·00 tyre, pressure 2·41 bars (35 lb/sq in). Goodyear independent hydraulic single-disc brakes on main wheels, controllable from either seat.

Prototype Canguro utility transport in SF.600 production configuration (*Giovanni Masino*)

SIAI-Marchetti SM.1019E demonstration aircraft fitted with wheel/ski landing gear

Parking brake. Combined wheel/ski gear, with hydraulic retraction and extension of skis, is optional.

POWER PLANT: One 298 kW (400 shp) Allison 250-B17 turboprop engine, driving a Hartzell HC-B3TF-7/T10173-11R three-blade constant-speed reversible-pitch metal propeller. Fuel in two tanks in each wing, each of 80 litres (17·5 Imp gallons) capacity; total capacity 320 litres (70 Imp gallons). Refuelling point for each tank on top of wings. Provision for two 80 litre (17·5 Imp gallon) auxiliary underwing tanks. Oil capacity 8 litres (1·75 Imp gallons).

ACCOMMODATION: Pilot and co-pilot or observer/systems operator seated in tandem in fully-enclosed and extensively-glazed cabin. Two forward-hinged doors on starboard side. Cabin heated, by engine bleed air, and ventilated. Dual controls standard.

SYSTEMS: 28V DC electrical power provided by 30V 150A Lear Siegler P/N230320020 engine-driven starter/generator and 24V 25Ah nickel-cadmium battery. External ground power receptacle. Windscreen defrosting and engine compressor inlet heating standard. Oxygen system optional.

AVIONICS AND EQUIPMENT: Choice of VHF/UHF/HF communication systems. VLF/Omega navigation. ADF; IFF; high-performance intercom and compass system. Provision for specialised avionics (VHF/FM, radar warning, Tacan and microwave landing system) to customer's requirements. Twin taxying and landing lights in port outer wing leading-edge. Anti-collision light on top of rudder.

ARMAMENT AND OPERATIONAL EQUIPMENT (SM.1019EI): Two hardpoints beneath each wing for 2·75 in rocket launchers, gun pods, missiles, bombs, auxiliary fuel tanks or a reconnaissance pod. Electronic, photographic and navigation equipment for use as day or night reconnaissance aircraft.

DIMENSIONS, EXTERNAL:

Wing span	10·972 m (36 ft 0 in)
Wing chord at root	1·63 m (5 ft 4¼ in)
Wing chord at tip	1·09 m (3 ft 7 in)
Wing aspect ratio	7·44
Length overall (tail up)	8·52 m (27 ft 11½ in)
Height overall (tail down)	2·86 m (9 ft 4½ in)
Tailplane span	3·42 m (11 ft 2¾ in)
Wheel track	2·29 m (7 ft 6¼ in)
Wheelbase	6·23 m (20 ft 5¼ in)
Propeller diameter	2·29 m (7 ft 6 in)
Propeller ground clearance	0·23 m (9 in)
Cabin doors, each: Height	1·06 m (3 ft 5¾ in)
Width	0·60 m (1 ft 11½ in)
Baggage door: Height	0·47 m (1 ft 6½ in)
Width	0·53 m (1 ft 9 in)
Height to sill	0·62 m (2 ft 0¼ in)

DIMENSIONS, INTERNAL:

Cabin: Max length	2·00 m (6 ft 6¾ in)
Max width	0·63 m (2 ft 0¾ in)
Max height	1·25 m (4 ft 1¼ in)
Volume	1·10 m³ (38·8 cu ft)
Baggage compartment volume	0·1 m³ (3·5 cu ft)

AREAS:

Wings, gross	16·16 m² (173·95 sq ft)
Ailerons (total)	1·70 m² (18·30 sq ft)
Trailing-edge flaps (total)	1·96 m² (21·10 sq ft)
Fin	0·957 m² (10·30 sq ft)
Rudder	1·295 m² (13·94 sq ft)
Tailplane	1·896 m² (20·41 sq ft)
Elevators (total)	1·584 m² (17·05 sq ft)

WEIGHTS AND LOADINGS (without external stores):

Weight empty, equipped	690 kg (1,521 lb)
Basic weight empty	730 kg (1,609 lb)
T-O weight:	
SM.1019A (Utility category), SM.1019EI (training)	1,300 kg (2,866 lb)
Max T-O weight:	
SM.1019A (Normal category), SM.1019EI (helicopter escort, reconnaissance)	1,450 kg (3,196 lb)
Wing loading at 1,300 kg (2,866 lb) AUW	80·4 kg/m² (16·5 lb/sq ft)
Max wing loading	89·7 kg/m² (18·4 lb/sq ft)
Power loading at 1,300 kg (2,866 lb) AUW	4·36 kg/kW (7·2 lb/shp)
Max power loading	4·87 kg/kW (8·0 lb/shp)

PERFORMANCE (A: Utility, AUW of 1,300 kg; 2,866 lb. B: helicopter escort, AUW of 1,450 kg; 3,196 lb. C: reconnaissance, AUW of 1,450 kg; 3,196 lb, except where indicated):

Never-exceed speed	169 knots (313 km/h; 194 mph)

Max cruising speed at S/L:

A	152 knots (281 km/h; 175 mph)
B, C	147 knots (272 km/h; 169 mph)

Max cruising speed at 1,525 m (5,000 ft):

A	159 knots (295 km/h; 183 mph)
B, C	154 knots (285 km/h; 177 mph)

Cruising speed (75% power) at 1,525 m (5,000 ft):

A	142 knots (263 km/h; 163 mph)
B, C	134 knots (248 km/h; 154 mph)

Stalling speed, flaps up, with fuel injection:

A	53 knots (98 km/h; 61 mph)
B, C	58 knots (107 km/h; 66·5 mph)

Stalling speed, flaps down, with fuel injection:

A	38 knots (70 km/h; 43·5 mph)

SIAI-Marchetti S.211 basic trainer and light attack aircraft *(Pilot Press)*

B, C	46 knots (85 km/h; 53 mph)

Max rate of climb at S/L:

A	499 m (1,640 ft)/min
B, C	439 m (1,440 ft)/min
Service ceiling: A, B, C	7,620 m (25,000 ft)

T-O run at S/L:

A	85 m (280 ft)
B, C	122 m (400 ft)

T-O to 15 m (50 ft) at S/L:

A	195 m (640 ft)
B, C	280 m (920 ft)

Landing from 15 m (50 ft) at S/L:

A	220 m (722 ft)
B, C	281 m (922 ft)

Landing run at S/L: A	91·5 m (300 ft)
B, C	135 m (443 ft)

Typical operational radius:

B, with two rocket launchers, at AUW of 1,400 kg (3,086 lb)	60 nm (111 km; 69 miles)

Max range at S/L:

A	499 nm (925 km; 575 miles)
B	421 nm (780 km; 485 miles)
C	610 nm (1,130 km; 702 miles)

Max range at 3,000 m (9,845 ft):

A	588 nm (1,090 km; 677 miles)
B	505 nm (935 km; 581 miles)
C	750 nm (1,390 km; 864 miles)

Max range with two external tanks, AUW of 1,400 kg (3,086 lb): C, at 610 m (2,000 ft)

	623 nm (1,154 km; 717 miles)
C, at 2,745 m (9,000 ft)	
	730 nm (1,352 km; 840 miles)

Max endurance at S/L:

A	5 h 45 min
B	5 h 0 min
C	7 h 20 min

Max endurance at 3,000 m (9,845 ft):

A	6 h 40 min
B	6 h 5 min
C, with auxiliary fuel tanks	8 h 45 min

SIAI-MARCHETTI S.211

Intended as a lightweight, low-cost basic trainer and light attack aircraft, the S.211 was first revealed in the form of a model at the Paris Air Show in May/June 1977. It is of tandem two-seat configuration, and is expected to make its first flight in mid-1981.

TYPE: Turbofan-engined basic trainer and light attack aircraft.

WINGS: Cantilever shoulder-wing monoplane, with supercritical section evolved by computer with the assistance of the US universities of New York and Kansas. Thickness/chord ratio 15% at root, 13% at tip. Incidence 2° 13′ at root, −1° 17′ at tip. Anhedral 2° from roots. Sweepback 15° 30′ at quarter-chord. Two-spar metal torsion box structure, forming integral fuel tank; attached to fuselage by four bolts. Upper and lower skins each formed by two one-piece panels joined along centreline and to the spars. Ailerons and large-area Fowler-type flaps on trailing-edges. Trim tab in each aileron.

FUSELAGE: Conventional metal semi-monocoque structure. Hydraulically actuated airbrake under centre-fuselage. Equipment bay in nose.

TAIL UNIT: Cantilever metal structure. Sweptback fin and rudder, tapered leading-edge on tailplane. No tabs.

LANDING GEAR: Hydraulically-retractable tricycle type. All units retract forward into fuselage (main units into undersides of engine air intake trunks). Main wheels size 6·50-8; nosewheel size 5·00-5. Designed for sink rate of 4 m (13 ft)/s. Provision for emergency free-fall extension.

POWER PLANT: One 11·12 kN (2,500 lb st) Pratt & Whitney Aircraft of Canada JT15D-4M non-afterburning turbofan engine mounted in rear of fuselage; lateral intake each side of fuselage. Fuel in 600 litre (132 Imp gallon) integral wing tank, 150 litre (33 Imp gallon) fuselage main tank and fuselage reserve tank; total usable capacity 832 litres (183 Imp gallons). Single-point gravity refuelling. Provision for two 350 litre (77 Imp gallon) drop-tanks on inboard underwing stores points. Oil capacity 10 kg (22 lb).

ACCOMMODATION: Seats for two persons in tandem in pressurised and air-conditioned cockpit under one-piece canopy opening sideways to starboard: pupil in front, instructor on rear seat elevated 28 cm (11 in). Martin-Baker Mk 8 ejection seats for both occupants, capable of operation at all altitudes and at speeds between 60-400 knots (111-741 km/h; 69-461 mph), including ejection through canopy; capable of conversion in field to Mk 10 zero-zero seats by addition of rocket assistance.

SYSTEMS: Environmental control system for cockpit pressurisation and air-conditioning, using engine bleed air. Max pressure differential 0·29 bars (4·2 lb/sq in). Hydraulic system, pressure 207 bars (3,000 lb/sq in), for landing gear and airbrake actuation. Primary electrical system is 28V DC, using an engine-driven starter/generator; nickel-cadmium battery; two static inverters supply AC power for instruments and avionics. Demand-type main oxygen system, sufficient to supply both occupants for 4 hours, plus emergency oxygen supply.

AVIONICS AND EQUIPMENT: To customer's requirements. Communications system has, as standard, dual U/VHF, and HF/SSB, all with dual control. Choice of ADF, Tacan or VOR/ILS nav. Provision for IFF, flight director, radio altimeter, Doppler radar, nose-mounted attack radar, head-up display, radar warning system and ECM.

ARMAMENT: Four underwing hardpoints, stressed for loads of up to 300 kg (660 lb) inboard, 150 kg (330 lb) outboard; max external load 600 kg (1,320 lb). Typical loads can include four SUU-11B 7·62 mm Minigun pods, four 12·7 mm gun pods, or (inboard only) two 20 mm gun pods; four AL-18-50 (18 × 50 mm), Matra F2 (6 × 68 mm), LAU-32 (7 × 2·75 in), or AL-6-80 (6 × 81 mm) rocket launchers, or (inboard only) two Matra 155 (18 × 68 mm) or SNORA RWK-020 (12 × 81 mm) launchers; two Sidewinder or Magic air-to-air, or two Maverick air-to-surface, missiles on the inboard points; four bombs or practice bombs of up to 150 kg size, or (inboard only) two bombs or napalm containers of up to 300 kg; four 74 mm cartridge throwers; or (inboard only) two photo-reconnaissance pods each with four cameras and infra-red linescan; or two 350 litre (77 Imp gallon) auxiliary fuel tanks.

DIMENSIONS, EXTERNAL:

Wing span	8·00 m (26 ft 3 in)
Wing chord at root	2·151 m (7 ft 0¾ in)
Wing chord at tip	1·00 m (3 ft 3¼ in)
Wing chord (mean aerodynamic)	1·646 m (5 ft 4¾ in)
Wing aspect ratio	5·08
Length overall	9·28 m (30 ft 5½ in)
Height overall	3·73 m (12 ft 2¾ in)
Tailplane span	3·96 m (13 ft 0 in)
Wheel track	2·29 m (7 ft 6 in)
Wheelbase	4·02 m (13 ft 2¼ in)

AREAS:

Wings, gross	12·60 m² (135·63 sq ft)
Airbrake	0·42 m² (4·52 sq ft)
Vertical tail surfaces (total)	1·936 m² (20·84 sq ft)
Horizontal tail surfaces (total)	3·378 m² (36·36 sq ft)

WEIGHTS:

Weight empty, equipped	1,445 kg (3,185 lb)
Max T-O weight: trainer, 'clean'	2,300 kg (5,070 lb)
armed version	2,800 kg (6,173 lb)

PERFORMANCE (estimated, at 2,200 kg; 4,850 lb AUW):

Never-exceed speed

	Mach 0·80 (400 knots; 740 km/h; 460 mph EAS)

Max level speed at 7,620 m (25,000 ft)

	386 knots (715 km/h; 444 mph)

Max cruising speed at 7,620 m (25,000 ft)		Service ceiling	12,800 m (42,000 ft)	Range at 9,145 m (30,000 ft) with max fuel, 30 min	
379 knots (703 km/h; 437 mph)		T-O and landing run	approx 305 m (1,000 ft)	reserves 1,030 nm (1,908 km; 1,186 miles)	
Stalling speed, flaps down		T-O to 15 m (50 ft)	347 m (1,140 ft)	Endurance, 30 min reserves	4 h 30 min
71 knots (131 km/h; 82 mph)		Landing from 15 m (50 ft)	649 m (2,130 ft)	Sustained g limit at 4,575 m (15,000 ft)	3·45
Max rate of climb at S/L 1,508 m (4,950 ft)/min		Min air turning radius at S/L	305 m (1,000 ft)	Design g limits	+6; −3

SSVV
SEZIONE SPERIMENTALE VOLO A VELA
Viale delle Rimembranze 22, 20068 Linate Paese (Peschiera Borromeo)
Telephone: 50 61 990
MANAGING DIRECTOR: Felice Gonalba

SSVV STINSON L-5 235 HP
In the early 1970s, SSVV was asked by the Aero Club Valle d' Aosta to produce a modified version of the Stinson L-5 Sentinel suitable for use at its airfield (which is situated in the Alps some 500 m; 1,640 ft above sea level) and capable of towing a 1,000 kg (2,205 lb) sailplane to an altitude of 1,000 m (3,280 ft).

The first such conversion was flown in the Spring of 1972, and 12 had been completed by the beginning of 1980.

The basic modification involves replacement of the original 138 kW (185 hp) Avco Lycoming O-435 with a 175 kW (235 hp) Avco Lycoming O-540-B1A5 flat-six engine, driving a Hoffmann two-blade fixed-pitch wooden propeller. The fuel, lubrication and electrical systems also are completely reworked.

A full description of the L-5 235 hp conversion can be found in the 1979-80 *Jane's.*
TYPE: Two-seat glider towing and touring aircraft.
WEIGHTS:

Weight empty	714 kg (1,574 lb)
Fuel	100 kg (220 lb)
Max T-O weight	1,021 kg (2,250 lb)

SSVV 235 hp conversion of the Stinson L-5 Sentinel, for glider towing

PERFORMANCE (at max T-O weight):
Max level speed at S/L
113 knots (209 km/h; 130 mph)

Max rate of climb at S/L 510 m (1,673 ft)/min
Rate of climb at 1,000 m (3,280 ft) with 520 kg (1,146 lb) glider 204 m (669 ft)/min

---

JAPAN

FUJI
FUJI HEAVY INDUSTRIES LTD (Fuji Jukogyo Kabushiki Kaisha)
HEAD OFFICE: Subaru Building, 7-2, 1-chome, Nishi-shinjuku, Shinjuku-ku, Tokyo
Telephone: Tokyo (03) 347 2505
Telex: 0-232-2268
AIRCRAFT FACTORY (UTSUNOMIYA MANUFACTURING DIVISION): Utsunomiya City, Tochigi Prefecture
Telephone: Utsunomiya (0286) 58 1111
CHAIRMAN OF THE BOARD: Eiichi Ohara
PRESIDENT: Sadamichi Sasaki
SENIOR EXECUTIVE VICE-PRESIDENT: Nobuhiro Sakata
EXECUTIVE MANAGING DIRECTORS:
Sukemitsu Irie
Shoji Nagashima
MANAGING DIRECTORS:
Iwao Shibuya
Kiyoyuki Kawabata
Yoshishige Suzuki
Hiroshi Yamamoto
Kiyoshi Ogawa

AIRCRAFT DIVISION MANAGEMENT:
Atsushi Kasai (General Manager)
Yasuo Kaneta (Deputy General Manager)
Kiichi Nomura (Asst General Manager, Commercial Marketing)
Takaaki Hosaka (Asst General Manager, Military Marketing)
MANAGER OF AIRCRAFT SALES DEPARTMENT: Kenshi Miura
SUPERINTENDENT OF UTSUNOMIYA AIRCRAFT FACTORY:
Yasumasa Honda

Fuji Heavy Industries Ltd was established on 15 July 1953. It is a successor to the Nakajima Aircraft Company, which was established in 1914 and built 29,925 aircraft up to the end of the second World War.

The present Utsunomiya Manufacturing Division (Aircraft and Rolling Stock Factories) occupies a site of 512,070 m² (5,511,870 sq ft) including a floor area of 161,532 m² (1,738,710 sq ft) and in 1980 employed 3,282 people.

Under licence from Cessna, Fuji produced 22 L-19E Bird Dog observation aircraft for the Japan Ground Self-Defence Force. Under licence from Beech, it built also the Beechcraft Mentor, and several modified versions

of the Mentor designated LM-1 Nikko, LM-2, KM and KM-2. Five additional KM-2s were ordered for the JMSDF in FY 1979; earlier details can be found in previous editions of *Jane's.* The modified KM-2B, combining features of the KM-2 and the Beechcraft T-34A, has been ordered by the JASDF as the T-3 primary trainer. An army version of the KM-2, designated TL-1, has been chosen by the JGSDF as an LM-1/2 replacement.

Fuji is also producing the Bell Model 204/205 series of helicopters. The first 204B covered by the agreement arrived in Japan in kit form in May 1962 for assembly.

Fuji is building wing assemblies for the Lockheed P-3C Orion maritime patrol aircraft which is being manufactured under licence in Japan for the JMSDF, and main landing gear doors and other airframe parts for McDonnell Douglas F-15 fighters delivered to the JASDF. As a part of Japan's YX civil transport aircraft programme, Fuji is responsible, under subcontract through the CTDC (Civil Transport Development Corporation), for building wing/fuselage body fairings for the Boeing 767 jet transport.

Fuji built the VTOL testbed designed by the National Aerospace Laboratory (1972-73 *Jane's),* and since 1972 has continued the study of VTOL research aircraft under contract to NAL.

Fuji is currently studying a proposal to meet the JASDF's MT-X requirement for a new jet trainer.

FUJI FA-200 AERO SUBARU
Fuji began detail design of this light aircraft in 1964 and the prototype flew for the first time on 12 August 1965. It went into production as the FA-200-160, FA-200-180 and FA-200-180AO, which differ as follows:

FA-200-160. Basic four-seat light aircraft, with 119 kW (160 hp) Avco Lycoming engine. Received JCAB and FAA Normal category type certificate as a four-seater, Utility category as a three-seater and Aerobatic category as a two-seater.

FA-200-180. Developed version with 134 kW (180 hp) Avco Lycoming engine.

FA-200-180AO. Version with 134 kW (180 hp) Avco Lycoming engine and fixed-pitch propeller.

Production of the FA-200 began in March 1968, and 294 had been completed by 1 February 1980, of which more than 170 were for export.

Production of the FA-200 was suspended in early 1980. A full description of all versions can be found in the 1979-80 *Jane's;* the following shortened description applies to the basic FA-200-160:
POWER PLANT: One 119 kW (160 hp) Avco Lycoming O-320-D2A flat-four engine, driving a McCauley 1C 160/FGM 7656 two-blade fixed-pitch metal propeller. Fuel in two integral tanks in inner wings with total capacity of 204·5 litres (45 Imp gallons).
ACCOMMODATION: Four seats in pairs in enclosed cabin. Individual adjustable front seats, with dual controls. Optional shoulder harness on each of the four seats.

Fuji FA-200-180 Aero Subaru four-seat light aircraft in inverted flight

Large rearward-sliding canopy, which can be opened in flight. Two tinted roof windows optional. Cabin heating and ventilation, and windscreen defrosting, standard. Baggage compartment in rear of fuselage, capacity 80 kg (176 lb). Baggage shelf aft of rear seats, capacity 20 kg (44 lb).

DIMENSIONS, EXTERNAL:

Wing span	9·42 m (30 ft 11 in)
Wing chord (constant)	1·525 m (5 ft 0 in)
Wing area, gross	14·0 m² (150·7 sq ft)
Wing aspect ratio	6·34
Length overall	8·17 m (26 ft 9½ in)
Height overall	2·59 m (8 ft 6 in)
Tailplane span	3·47 m (11 ft 4½ in)
Wheel track	2·63 m (8 ft 7½ in)
Wheelbase	1·75 m (5 ft 8¾ in)
Propeller diameter	1·93 m (6 ft 4 in)

WEIGHTS AND LOADINGS (N: Normal; U: Utility; A: Aerobatic category):

Weight empty	620 kg (1,366 lb)
Max T-O weight: N	1,060 kg (2,335 lb)
U	970 kg (2,138 lb)
A	880 kg (1,940 lb)
Max wing loading: N	75·7 kg/m² (15·5 lb/sq ft)
Max power loading: N	8·91 kg/kW (14·59 lb/hp)

PERFORMANCE (N: Normal category; A: Aerobatic category, at max T-O weight):

Max level speed at S/L:	
N	120 knots (222 km/h; 138 mph)
A	122 knots (225 km/h; 140 mph)
Max cruising speed (75% power):	
N at 1,525 m (5,000 ft)	106 knots (196 km/h; 122 mph)
A at 2,290 m (7,500 ft)	114 knots (211 km/h; 131 mph)
Econ cruising speed (55% power):	
N at 1,525 m (5,000 ft)	89 knots (164 km/h; 102 mph)
A at 2,290 m (7,500 ft)	96 knots (177 km/h; 110 mph)
Stalling speed, flaps down:	
N	49 knots (90 km/h; 56 mph)
A	45·5 knots (84 km/h; 52·5 mph)
Max rate of climb at S/L: N	207 m (680 ft)/min
A	302 m (991 ft)/min
Service ceiling: N	3,480 m (11,400 ft)
A	4,725 m (15,500 ft)
T-O run: A	160 m (525 ft)
T-O to 15 m (50 ft): N	465 m (1,530 ft)
A	310 m (1,020 ft)
Landing from 15 m (50 ft): N	340 m (1,115 ft)
A	315 m (1,033 ft)
Landing run: A	115 m (377 ft)
Range with max fuel (55% power at 2,290 m; 7,500 ft, no reserves): N	655 nm (1,215 km; 755 miles)
A	816 nm (1,512 km; 940 miles)

FUJI FA-300/MODEL 700

Design and development of the FA-300/Model 700 twin-engined six/eight-seat pressurised light aircraft began in Japan in the latter half of 1971. On 28 June 1974, Fuji and Rockwell International signed an agreement to establish further development of this aircraft as a collaborative venture.

For type certification, two prototypes were flown in Japan (first flight 13 November 1975) and three in the USA. Certification by the JCAB and FAA was granted on 16 May and 28 October 1977 respectively.

The first delivery of production aircraft was made in August 1978 by Rockwell International. Airframe major and subassemblies for the collaboration programme were built in Japan by Fuji; final assembly was undertaken by Rockwell's General Aviation Division.

Fuji and Rockwell ended their joint development and production agreement in early 1980, after a total of 42 shipsets had been delivered to Rockwell by Fuji.

A description of the Model 700 can be found under the Rockwell International heading in the 1979-80 edition of *Jane's*.

FUJI FA-300/MODEL 710

This more powerful version of the FA-300 family (335 kW; 450 hp engines) was a part of the collaboration agreement between Fuji and Rockwell International. The

Fuji T-3 (KM-2B) two-seat primary trainer of the JASDF (Avco Lycoming IGSO-480-A1F6 engine)

first flight was made on 22 December 1976. Two prototypes were flown in Japan, and after about 580 h of flight testing by these two aircraft JCAB certification was awarded on 26 February 1979. Two other Model 710s were used in a programme to obtain FAA certification under FAR Pts 21-29, but this had not been awarded at the time that Fuji and Rockwell ended their collaboration programme in early 1980.

The Model 710 also was described under the Rockwell International heading in the 1979-80 *Jane's*.

FUJI KM-2B

JASDF designation: T-3

The KM-2B is a modification of the original KM-2 development of the Beechcraft T-34A Mentor, described in the 1969-70 *Jane's*, combining the airframe and power plant of the KM-2 with the two-seat cockpit installation of the T-34A. The first KM-2B (JA3725) was flown for the first time on 26 September 1974, and received JCAB category A certification on 28 November 1974. A version for liaison and short-range rescue duties is under consideration.

In 1975 the JASDF selected the KM-2B to replace the T-34A in the primary trainer role. Purchase of 54 is planned as T-3s, of which 50 had been ordered by the Spring of 1980. The first of these made its first flight on 17 January 1978, and 24 had been delivered to the JASDF by 15 February 1980.

The following description applies to the T-3:

TYPE: Two-seat primary trainer.

WINGS: Cantilever low-wing monoplane. Wing section NACA 23016·5 at root, NACA 23012 at tip. Dihedral 6° from roots. Incidence 4° at root. 3° geometric twist. No sweep at quarter-chord. All-metal tapered two-spar structure with stressed skin. Aluminium alloy single-slotted flaps and plain ailerons. Servo tab in each aileron; port tab controllable for trim.

FUSELAGE: Conventional all-metal semi-monocoque structure.

TAIL UNIT: Cantilever all-metal structure. Fixed-incidence tailplane, with elevators. Controllable tab in each elevator; anti-servo tab in rudder.

LANDING GEAR: Electrically retractable tricycle type, with single wheel and oleo-pneumatic shock-absorber on each unit. Nosewheel retracts rearward, main wheels inward into wings. Goodyear wheels and Type III tyres on all units: size 6·50-8 (6 ply), pressure 2·34 bars (34 lb/sq in) on main units; size 5·00-5 (4 ply), pressure 2·76 bars (40 lb/sq in) on nose unit. Goodyear automatically adjustable single-disc brakes on main units.

POWER PLANT: One 254 kW (340 hp) Avco Lycoming IGSO-480-A1F6 flat-six engine, driving a Hartzell HC-A3V20-1F/V9333N-3 three-blade constant-speed propeller with spinner. One metal and one bladder-type fuel tank in each wing, total capacity 265 litres (70 US gallons; 58·3 Imp gallons). Refuelling points on top of wings. Oil capacity 11·35 litres (3 US gallons; 2·5 Imp gallons).

ACCOMMODATION: Crew of two in tandem, on adjustable seats in heated and ventilated cabin. Dual controls standard. Framed canopy, with rearward-sliding section over each seat. Space for 13·6 kg (30 lb) of baggage aft of rear seat.

SYSTEMS AND AVIONICS: Blind-flying instrumentation standard. Electrical system includes 28V 100A DC generator and two 160VA static inverters. Standard avionics include ICS, VHF, Tacan, and ATC transponder with Mode C.

DIMENSIONS, EXTERNAL:

Wing span	10·004 m (32 ft 10 in)
Wing chord at root	2·13 m (7 ft 0 in)
Wing chord at tip	1·07 m (3 ft 6 in)
Wing aspect ratio	6·1
Length overall	8·036 m (26 ft 4¼ in)
Height overall	3·023 m (9 ft 11 in)
Tailplane span	3·712 m (12 ft 2¼ in)
Wheel track	2·924 m (9 ft 7 in)
Wheelbase	2·266 m (7 ft 5¼ in)
Propeller diameter	2·286 m (7 ft 6 in)
Propeller ground clearance	0·25 m (9¾ in)

DIMENSIONS, INTERNAL:

Cabin: Max width	approx 0·90 m (2 ft 11½ in)
Max height	approx 1·30 m (4 ft 3¼ in)

AREAS:

Wings, gross	16·50 m² (177·6 sq ft)
Ailerons (total)	1·07 m² (11·52 sq ft)
Trailing-edge flaps (total)	1·98 m² (21·31 sq ft)
Fin	0·97 m² (10·44 sq ft)
Rudder, incl tab	0·61 m² (6·57 sq ft)
Tailplane	3·46 m² (37·24 sq ft)
Elevators, incl tab	1·39 m² (14·96 sq ft)

WEIGHTS AND LOADINGS:

Weight empty	1,136 kg (2,504 lb)
Normal operational T-O weight	1,510 kg (3,329 lb)
Max T-O weight	1,542 kg (3,400 lb)
Max wing loading	93·5 kg/m² (19·15 lb/sq ft)
Max power loading	6·07 kg/kW (10·00 lb/hp)

PERFORMANCE (at normal operational T-O weight):

Never-exceed speed	223 knots (413 km/h; 257 mph) EAS
Max level speed at 4,875 m (16,000 ft)	203 knots (377 km/h; 234 mph)
Max cruising speed at 2,440 m (8,000 ft)	177 knots (328 km/h; 204 mph)
Econ cruising speed at 2,440 m (8,000 ft)	137 knots (254 km/h; 158 mph)
Stalling speed, flaps up	66 knots (123 km/h; 76 mph)
Stalling speed, flaps down	54 knots (100 km/h; 62 mph)
Max rate of climb at S/L	463 m (1,520 ft)/min
Service ceiling	8,170 m (26,800 ft)
T-O run	265 m (870 ft)
T-O to 15 m (50 ft)	503 m (1,650 ft)
Landing from 15 m (50 ft)	436 m (1,430 ft)
Landing run	238 m (780 ft)
Range with max fuel	520 nm (965 km; 600 miles)

FUJI KM-2

JMSDF designation: KM-2
JGSDF designation: TL-1

Under the new designation TL-1, the Japan Ground Self-Defence Force has selected the Fuji KM-2 as a replacement for its LM-1s and LM-2s. The first order, for two aircraft, was due to be placed in FY 1980.

The TL-1 is almost identical to the KM-2 for the JMSDF (of which production has ended), except for minor changes of instrumentation and the installation of ARC-3 VHF radio, JARN-A-2 ADF, and JAN/APX-68 IFF.

FUJI-BELL 204B/204B-2 and 205A-1/UH-1H

Fuji is manufacturing Bell Model 204B and UH-1H helicopters under sub-licence from Mitsui and Co Ltd, Bell's Japanese licensee. By March 1980 a total of 47

One of the Japanese-built prototypes of the Fuji FA-300/Model 710

Fuji-Bell 204B/204B-2s had been produced for civilian operators.

Following the delivery of 90 UH-1Bs (military version of the 204B) to the Japan Ground Self-Defence Force by early 1973, Fuji production continued with the UH-1H version, of which the first example flew for the first time on 17 July 1973; 62 had been ordered by March 1980.

The Fuji-Bell 204B is identical with that built by Bell Helicopter Textron (see US section). It is powered by an 820 kW (1,100 shp) Kawasaki-built Avco Lycoming T53-K-11A turboshaft engine. The Fuji-Bell UH-1H has the same airframe and dynamic components as the Bell-built UH-1H, but has a tractor-type tail rotor and is powered by a 1,044 kW (1,400 shp) Kawasaki-built Avco Lycoming T53-K-13B turboshaft engine.

In October 1973 Fuji developed a higher-powered **204B-2** version of the 204B. Powered by a 1,044 kW (1,400 shp) Avco Lycoming T53-K-13B turboshaft engine, it has the same basic airframe and dynamic components as the 204B, but has a tractor-type tail rotor. The first example of this version was delivered in early 1974.

The following details apply to the standard Fuji-Bell 204B/204B-2/UH-1H:

DIMENSIONS, EXTERNAL:

Diameter of main rotor	14·63 m (48 ft 0 in)
Diameter of tail rotor	2·59 m (8 ft 6 in)
Length overall, tail rotor turning:	
204B/B-2	13·61 m (44 ft 7¾ in)
UH-1H	13·67 m (44 ft 10 in)
Length of fuselage: 204B/B-2	12·31 m (40 ft 4¾ in)
UH-1H	12·37 m (40 ft 7 in)
Height overall, tail rotor turning	4·42 m (14 ft 6 in)
Height to top of rotor hub:	
204B/B-2	3·77 m (12 ft 4½ in)

Fuji T-3 two-seat primary trainer, developed from the KM-2 and Beechcraft T-34A *(Pilot Press)*

UH-1H	3·98 m (13 ft 0¾ in)
Max width over landing skids:	
204B/B-2	2·64 m (8 ft 8 in)
UH-1H	2·60 m (8 ft 6½ in)
Tailplane span	2·84 m (9 ft 4 in)

WEIGHTS AND LOADINGS:

Weight empty: 204B/B-2	2,177 kg (4,800 lb)
UH-1H	2,390 kg (5,270 lb)

Max T-O weight:	
204B/B-2, internal load	3,855 kg (8,500 lb)
204B/B-2, external load	4,309 kg (9,500 lb)
UH-1H	4,309 kg (9,500 lb)
Max disc loading	25·6 kg/m² (5·25 lb/sq ft)
Max power loading:	
204B	5·25 kg/kW (8·64 lb/shp)
204B-2, UH-1H	4·13 kg/kW (6·78 lb/shp)

PERFORMANCE (at max T-O weight):

Max level and cruising speed	110 knots (204 km/h; 127 mph)
Max rate of climb at S/L:	
204B	463 m (1,520 ft)/min
204B-2	588 m (1,930 ft)/min
UH-1H	488 m (1,600 ft)/min
Service ceiling: 204B	4,480 m (14,700 ft)
204B-2	5,790 m (19,000 ft)
UH-1H	3,840 m (12,600 ft)
Hovering ceiling IGE: 204B	2,985 m (9,800 ft)
204B-2	4,635 m (15,200 ft)
UH-1H	4,145 m (13,600 ft)
Hovering ceiling OGE: 204B	1,310 m (4,300 ft)
204B-2	3,200 m (10,500 ft)
UH-1H	335 m (1,100 ft)
Range at S/L: 204B	206 nm (381 km; 237 miles)
204B-2	207 nm (383 km; 238 miles)
UH-1H	252 nm (467 km; 290 miles)

Fuji-Bell UH-1H medium helicopter of the JGSDF (Avco Lycoming T53-K-13B turboshaft engine)

KAWASAKI
KAWASAKI JUKOGYO KABUSHIKI KAISHA (Kawasaki Heavy Industries Ltd)

HEAD OFFICE: 2-16-1 Nakamachi-Dori, Ikuta-ku, Kobe
TOKYO AND AIRCRAFT GROUP OFFICE: World Trade Center Building, 4-1, Hamamatsu-cho 2-chome, Minato-ku, Tokyo
Telephone: Tokyo (03) 435 2971
Telex: 242-2851-3
CHAIRMAN: Kiyoshi Yotsumoto
PRESIDENT: Zenji Umeda
EXECUTIVE VICE-PRESIDENTS:
Tsuneo Ando
Toraichi Imai
WORKS: Gifu
MANAGING DIRECTOR, AND SENIOR GENERAL MANAGER, AIRCRAFT GROUP: Teruaki Yamada
DIRECTOR, AND ASST SENIOR GENERAL MANAGER, AIRCRAFT GROUP, AND GENERAL MANAGER, AIRCRAFT SALES DIVISION: Noriyasu Muroi

With effect from 1 April 1969, Kawasaki Aircraft Co Ltd was amalgamated with the Kawasaki Dockyard Co Ltd and the Kawasaki Rolling Stock Mfg Co Ltd, to form Kawasaki Heavy Industries Ltd. The Aircraft Division of the former Kawasaki Aircraft Co Ltd, which employs some 3,500 people, continues its activities as the Aircraft Group of this company. Kawasaki has a 31·77 per cent holding in Nippi (which see).

In addition to extensive overhaul work, Kawasaki has built many US aircraft under licence since 1953, including 48 Lockheed P2V-7 (P-2H) Neptune anti-submarine aircraft and 239 Bell Model 47 helicopters, plus another 211 Model KH-4 helicopters developed from the Bell 47 by its own design staff. From the Neptune it developed the P-2J anti-submarine aircraft, of which it delivered one prototype and 82 production examples (see 1978-79 *Jane's*).

In February 1977 Kawasaki was awarded a JDA contract to produce an experimental variable-stability aircraft (VSA) by converting a P2V-7 of the JMSDF. This aircraft has large direct side-force control panels on each wing, a fly-by-wire control system, direct-lift control flaps, and a miniature computer.

Design studies are being undertaken for a new intermediate jet trainer, provisionally designated KA-840, to succeed the Lockheed T-33A, of which the company built

210 under licence during 1956-59. The KA-840 is also intended as a possible replacement for the Fuji T-1.

Kawasaki is developing, jointly with MBB of West Germany, the BK-117 twin-engined multi-purpose helicopter described in the International section.

Kawasaki is prime contractor for the JASDF's C-1 transport; and for licence production of the Lockheed P-3C/Update II Orion, 45 of which are to be purchased by the JMSDF during the 1980s. The company is also a subcontractor for certain components of the McDonnell Douglas F-4EJ Phantom IIs and F-15J Eagles being licence-built in Japan by Mitsubishi (which see). As a part of Japan's YX civil transport aircraft programme, Kawasaki is subcontracted, through CTDC, to build forward and mid fuselage sections, and wing ribs, for the Boeing 767 jet transport. In late 1979 the company was nominated by the JASDF as prime contractor for overhaul of the four Grumman E-2C Hawkeye AEW aircraft which are to be introduced into service from 1982.

Kawasaki has exclusive rights to manufacture and sell the twin-engined Boeing Vertol 107 Model II helicopter and its own KV-107/IIA development of it. The Hughes Model 369 (500D and 500M) light observation helicopter is also being assembled by Kawasaki under a licence agreement concluded in October 1967. By 31 March 1980 a total of 123 KV-107 helicopters had been delivered to customers in Japan and other countries including Saudi Arabia, Sweden, Thailand and the USA; and approx 190 Hughes 500s to government and commercial operators in Japan.

Kawasaki is engaged in missile development and production; its aero-engine activities are described in the appropriate section of this edition.

KAWASAKI P-2J
JMSDF designations: P-2J and UP-2J

Work on the conversion of a standard P2V-7 Neptune as the P-2J prototype began in June 1965, and this aircraft flew for the first time on 21 July 1966.

The first production P-2J was flown on 8 August 1969, and was delivered to the JMSDF on 7 October. A further 81 P-2Js were built, and the last of these was delivered during March 1979.

A full description of the P-2J can be found in the 1978-79 *Jane's*.

By March 1980, two P-2Js had been converted to **UP-2J** configuration with equipment for target towing and ECM operations. It is planned to convert a third in FY 1980 and a fourth in FY 1981.

KAWASAKI P2V-7 (P-2H) VSA VARIABLE STABILITY AIRCRAFT

Under a $3 million contract awarded in February 1977 by the Technical Research and Development Institute of the Japan Defence Agency, Kawasaki modified the 39th production P2V-7 (P-2H) Neptune ASW aircraft to experimental configuration as a Variable Stability Aircraft (VSA).

The aircraft made its first flight at Gifu on 23 December 1977, and was handed over to the 51st Air Squadron of the JMSDF in 1978. Evaluation of direct lift control, direct side-force control, and the variable stability system, over a two-year period, has been completed. After demonstration at the 1979 Japan International Aerospace Show, the aircraft underwent minor modifications before being used for training at the JMSDF test pilots' school.

A description of the VSA can be found in the 1979-80 *Jane's*.

AREAS:

DLC flaps (two, each)	3·92 m² (42·19 sq ft)
SFS sections (on each wing)	5·50 m² (59·20 sq ft)
Airbrakes (two, each)	1·40 m² (15·07 sq ft)

WEIGHT:

Standard T-O weight for test	27,500 kg (60,627 lb)

KAWASAKI C-1

The C-1 medium-sized troop and freight transport was designed to meet the JASDF's requirement for a replacement for its former fleet of Curtiss C-46s. Preliminary design, and the construction of two XC-1 flying prototypes (plus one airframe for static tests), was undertaken by NAMC. The first flying prototype, assembled at Kawasaki's Gifu factory, made its first flight on 12 November 1970, followed by the second on 16 January 1971. These were handed over to the JDA on 24 February and 20 March 1971 respectively. Further development and evaluation tests by the JDA were completed in March 1973.

Two pre-production aircraft had been delivered by the end of February 1974. Airframe fatigue testing by the JDA was completed in November 1974.

Kawasaki C-1 medium-range military transport aircraft of the JASDF in camouflage finish

Kawasaki C-1 twin-turbofan medium-range military transport *(Pilot Press)*

Eleven production C-1s were delivered between December 1974 and the end of March 1976. An additional 13 C-1s were ordered during FY 1975; these had all been delivered by the end of February 1978, including two long-range aircraft with an additional 4,732 litre (1,250 US gallon) wing centre-section fuel tank. Two more long-range C-1s were ordered during FY 1977, and one in FY 1979; production is expected to end in 1981 with the delivery of the 31st aircraft. All C-1s are to be camouflaged by 1981.

The National Aerospace Laboratory (see NAL entry) is building an experimental STOL aircraft utilising the airframe of a C-1. The Technical Research and Development Institute of the Japan Defence Agency was, from FY 1980, to begin retrofitting one JASDF C-1 as a flying testbed for the XF-3 lightweight turbofan engine. This work is expected to be completed in 1982.

Prime contractor in the C-1 programme is Kawasaki, which builds the front fuselage and wing centre-section and undertakes final assembly and flight testing. Major subcontractors are Fuji (outer wing panels); Mitsubishi (centre and aft fuselage sections and tail surfaces); Nihon Hikoki (Nippi) (flaps, slats, spoilers, ailerons, engine pylons and pods); and Shin Meiwa (cargo loading equipment).

TYPE: Twin-turbofan medium-range transport.

WINGS: Cantilever high-wing monoplane. Wings have 20° sweepback at quarter-chord, with slightly increased leading-edge sweep inboard of the engine pylons. Thickness/chord ratio 12% at root, 11% at tip. Anhedral 5° 30' from centre-section. Conventional two-spar fail-safe structure of aluminium alloy, including control surfaces. Two quadruple-slotted flaps on each trailing-edge. Forward of these, on each wing, are three flight spoilers and a ground spoiler. Drooping leading-edge slats, in four sections, on each wing. Manually-operated aileron outboard of each outer flap. Trim tab in port aileron. Thermal anti-icing of leading-edges, using engine bleed air.

FUSELAGE: Conventional semi-monocoque fail-safe structure of aluminium alloy, with a circular cross-section.

TAIL UNIT: Aluminium alloy cantilever T tail, with sweepback on all surfaces (30° at fin quarter-chord, 25° at tailplane quarter-chord). Tailplane has 5° anhedral. Variable-incidence tailplane, with elevators. Balance tab in each elevator and anti-balance tab in rudder. Elevators and rudder are each operated by two independent hydraulic actuator systems; the elevators can be operated manually in an emergency. Thermal de-icing of tailplane, using electric heater mat.

LANDING GEAR: Hydraulically-retractable tricycle type, of Sumitomo design. Each main unit has two pairs of wheels in tandem, retracting forward into fairings built on to the sides of the fuselage. Forward-retracting nose unit has twin wheels. Main-wheel tyres size 35 × 10·7-16, nosewheel tyres size 28 × 9-12; tyre pressure (all units) 6·21 bars (90 lb/sq in). Oleo shock-absorbers. Kayaba wheels with Dunlop tyres, which on main units have pressure of 5·17 bars (75 lb/sq in). Kayaba hydraulic brakes (two-rotor on first 10 production aircraft, three-rotor from 11th aircraft onward); Sumisei anti-skid units.

POWER PLANT: Two 64·5 kN (14,500 lb st) Mitsubishi (Pratt & Whitney) JT8D-M-9 turbofan engines, installed in pylon-mounted underwing pods and fitted with thrust reversers. Four integral wing fuel tanks with total capacity of 15,200 litres (3,344 Imp gallons). Single pressure refuelling point for all tanks, plus overwing gravity refuelling point for each tank.

ACCOMMODATION: Crew of five, comprising pilot, co-pilot, navigator, flight engineer and load supervisor. Escape hatch in flight deck roof on starboard side. Flight deck and main cabin pressurised and air-conditioned. Standard complements are as follows: troops (max) 60, paratroops (max) 45, stretchers 36 plus attendants. As a cargo carrier, loads can include a 2½ ton truck, a 105 mm howitzer, two ¾ ton trucks or three jeeps. Up to three preloaded freight pallets, 2·24 m (7 ft 4 in) wide and 2·74 m (9 ft 0 in) long, can be carried. Floor is stressed for loads of up to 7 kg/cm² (100 lb/sq in). Access to flight deck via downward-opening door, with built-in stairs, on port side of forward fuselage. Paratroop door on each side of fuselage, aft of wing trailing-edge. For air-dropping, the rear-loading ramp/door can be opened in flight to the full cabin cross-section.

SYSTEMS: Pressurisation and air-conditioning systems utilise engine bleed air. APU in front section of starboard landing gear fairing supplies electrical power on ground and in the air, and bleed air on ground. Three independent hydraulic systems, each 207 bars (3,000 lb/sq in). No. 1 system actuates flight controls; No. 2 actuates flight controls, high-lift devices, landing gear, nosewheel steering and brakes; No. 3 system is used for cargo door operation, and provides emergency backup for brakes and high-lift devices. Electrical power supplied by three 40kVA AC generators, two engine-

driven and aircooled, and one driven by the APU. 28V DC power is obtained from AC source through a transformer-rectifier. One 24V 30Ah nickel-cadmium battery for emergency DC power.

AVIONICS AND EQUIPMENT: Standard avionics include autopilot, Doppler radar, radio altimeter, HF, VHF and UHF radio, ADF, UHF/DF, marker beacon, VOR/ILS, Tacan, SIF, dual compass system and flight director system. Optional avionics include Loran and weather radar.

DIMENSIONS, EXTERNAL:

Wing span	30·60 m (100 ft 4¾ in)
Wing chord at root	6·30 m (20 ft 8 in)
Wing chord at tip	2·00 m (6 ft 6¾ in)
Wing aspect ratio	7·8
Length overall	29·00 m (95 ft 1¾ in)
Length of fuselage	26·50 m (86 ft 11¼ in)
Height overall	9·99 m (32 ft 9¼ in)
Tailplane span	11·30 m (37 ft 1 in)
Wheel track	4·40 m (14 ft 5¼ in)
Wheelbase	9·33 m (30 ft 7¼ in)
Rear-loading ramp/door:	
Length	2·67 m (8 ft 9¼ in)
Width	2·70 m (8 ft 10¼ in)
Height to sill	1·25 m (4 ft 1¼ in)

DIMENSIONS, INTERNAL:

Cabin: Max length	10·80 m (35 ft 5¼ in)
Max width	3·60 m (11 ft 9¾ in)
Max height	2·55 m (8 ft 4½ in)
Floor area	28·6 m² (308 sq ft)
Volume (excl ramp area)	73·8 m³ (2,606 cu ft)

AREAS:

Wings, gross	120·5 m² (1,297 sq ft)
Ailerons (total)	3·4 m² (36·6 sq ft)
Trailing-edge flaps (total)	22·9 m² (246·5 sq ft)
Spoilers (total)	8·9 m² (95·8 sq ft)
Fin	15·8 m² (170·1 sq ft)
Rudder, incl tabs	6·4 m² (68·9 sq ft)
Tailplane	18·3 m² (197·0 sq ft)
Elevators, incl tabs	6·5 m² (70·0 sq ft)

WEIGHTS AND LOADINGS:

Weight empty	23,320 kg (51,410 lb)
Weight empty, equipped	24,300 kg (53,572 lb)
Normal payload	7,900 kg (17,416 lb)
Max payload	11,900 kg (26,235 lb)
Normal T-O weight	38,700 kg (85,320 lb)
Max T-O weight	45,000 kg (99,210 lb)
Max wing loading	373·4 kg/m² (76·48 lb/sq ft)
Max power loading	350 kg/kN (3·42 lb/lb st)

PERFORMANCE (at normal T-O weight except where indicated):

Max level speed at 7,620 m (25,000 ft) at 35,450 kg (78,150 lb) AUW	435 knots (806 km/h; 501 mph)
Econ cruising speed at 10,670 m (35,000 ft) at 35,450 kg (78,150 lb) AUW	354 knots (657 km/h; 408 mph)
Max rate of climb at S/L	1,065 m (3,500 ft)/min
Service ceiling	11,580 m (38,000 ft)
Service ceiling, one engine out	5,485 m (18,000 ft)
T-O run	640 m (2,100 ft)
T-O to 15 m (50 ft)	910 m (3,000 ft)
Landing from 15 m (50 ft) at 36,860 kg (81,260 lb) weight	823 m (2,700 ft)
Landing run at 36,860 kg (81,260 lb) weight	455 m (1,500 ft)
Range with max fuel and 2,200 kg (4,850 lb) payload	1,810 nm (3,353 km; 2,084 miles)
Range with 7,900 kg (17,416 lb) payload	700 nm (1,300 km; 807 miles)

KAWASAKI KA-840

Under the company designation KA-840, Kawasaki is developing an intermediate jet trainer to meet a JASDF requirement for a replacement for its Lockheed T-33As and Fuji T-1s. The KA-840 has a tandem two-seat cockpit arrangement, and will be powered by two approx 15·7 kN

(3,530 lb st) F-3 turbofan engines, the production version of the XF-3 currently under development by the Technical Research and Development Institute of the Japan Defence Agency. It will have an additional capability for light attack, carrying underwing 250 kg bombs.

The KA-840 is one of two designs being submitted for JASDF consideration, the other being a Fuji project known as the FT-20. The JASDF is expected to select one of these for development by mid-1981, with a prototype first flight scheduled for FY 1985.

The following details are provisional:

SPECIFICATION:
Wing area, gross   21·6 m² (232·5 sq ft)
Max T-O weight   approx 7,500 kg (16,535 lb)
Econ cruising speed at 7,620 m (25,000 ft)
    Mach 0·75 (450 knots; 834 km/h; 518 mph)
Max range with 454 litre (120 US gallon; 100 Imp gallon) external tanks
    900 nm (1,670 km; 1,035 miles)

KAWASAKI (BOEING VERTOL) KV-107/II and KV-107/IIA

Swedish Navy designation: HKP 4C

Kawasaki has exclusive rights to manufacture and sell the Boeing Vertol 107 Model II helicopter. The first KV-107 to be produced by Kawasaki under this licence agreement flew for the first time in May 1962.

In 1965, Kawasaki obtained world-wide sales rights in the KV-107 from The Boeing Company's Vertol Division. In November 1965, it was awarded a type certificate for the KV-107 by the FAA.

An improved model, the **KV-107/IIA**, is available in any of the KV-107/II forms, powered by two 1,044 kW (1,400 shp) General Electric CT58-140-1 or Ishikawajima-Harima CT58-IHI-140-1 turboshaft engines (max continuous rating 932 kW; 1,250 shp), which give improved performance during VTOL and in 'hot and high' conditions. Fuel capacity 1,324 litres; 350 US gallons (standard), 3,785 litres; 1,000 US gallons (max). A prototype (JA9509) was converted from a standard KV-107/II-2 and first flown on 3 April 1968. Type approval granted by JCAB on 26 September 1968 and by FAA on 15 January 1969.

The following versions of the KV-107/II and IIA have been announced:

KV-107/II-1. Basic utility helicopter. None yet built.

KV-107/II-2. Basic airline helicopter. Eleven built. Some now operated by Columbia Helicopters Inc of USA (five) and AirLift Inc of Japan (two). Prototype (JA9509) upgraded as IIA-2 prototype, currently used as a company test aircraft. One **KV-107/IIA-2** scheduled for delivery to AirLift Inc in November 1980.

KV-107/II-3. Mine countermeasures (MCM) helicopter for JMSDF with extended-range fuel tanks, towing hook and cargo sling. Nine ordered, all of which had been delivered by February 1975, including seven of the **KV-107/IIA-3** version with uprated power. All of these are fitted with minesweeping and retrieval equipment and serve with the 111th Air Wing of the JMSDF.

KV-107/II-4. Tactical cargo/troop transport for JGSDF, with foldable seats for 26 troops or 15 casualty litters. Strengthened floor for carrying heavy vehicles. Orders for 60 placed, of which 58 had been delivered by November 1979, including one equipped as a VIP transport for Cabinet use. The latest 17 aircraft are of the **KV-107/IIA-4** version with uprated power, and four of them are fitted with extended-range fuel tanks.

KV-107/II-5. Long-range search and rescue helicopter for JASDF. Orders for 32 placed, of which 28 had been delivered by December 1979, including 13 uprated **KV-107/IIA-5s**. Approval for three more to be requested in FY 1981. Extended-range fuel tank each side of fuselage, making total capacity 3,785 litres (1,000 US gallons). Extensive nav/com equipment, four searchlights, domed observation window and rescue hoist. The 27th aircraft is equipped with a Kawasaki/Boeing automatic flight control system, enabling it to cruise at preselected altitude and speed, descend at a programmed rate and distance, and come to hover at a preselected altitude. Also provided are automatic climb-out to the cruise mode; standard distance approach; a turns coupler to a preselected heading; altitude sensing, with dual radar altimeters, for added safety in IFR operations; and a vernier flight control to permit critical positioning during rescue hoist operations. Eight aircraft supplied to Swedish Navy in 1972-74 have Kawasaki-built airframes and rotor assemblies but were

fitted in Sweden with Rolls-Royce Gnome H.1200 turbo-shaft engines and a Decca navigation system. Details of other equipment fitted to Swedish aircraft as listed in 1977-78 *Jane's*.

KV-107/II-6. De luxe transport version. None yet built.

KV-107/II-7. De luxe VIP transport with 6-11 seats. One built: currently owned by Columbia Helicopters Inc of USA.

KV-107/IIA-17. Long-range passenger and cargo transport version for Tokyo Metropolitan Police Department; one delivered in February 1973. Cabin divided into two compartments: front section with 12 passenger seats, rear section capable of accommodating 2,268 kg (5,000 lb) of cargo, six stretcher patients or 12 passengers.

KV-107/IIA-SM-1. Firefighting version for Saudi Arabian government. Four delivered by early 1979. All can be fitted with specially designed equipment for various forms of firefighting (foam agent, chemical powder, water, and co-ordinated firefighting). Additional order for two anticipated.

KV-107/IIA-SM-2. Rescue and aeromedical version for Saudi Arabian government, with external rescue hoist, medical equipment, stretcher kit and other rescue gear; 303 litre (80 US gallon) additional fuel tank can be mounted on each side of fuselage. Two delivered by November 1978; additional order for one anticipated. For self-ferry flights. both SM-1 and SM-2 can be fitted with internally-mounted 1,893 litre (500 US gallon) auxiliary fuel tank.

The description which follows applies to the commercial KV-107/II-2, except where shown:

TYPE: Twin-engined transport helicopter.

ROTOR SYSTEM: Two three-blade rotors in tandem, rotating in opposite directions. Each blade is made up of a steel D spar to which is bonded a trailing-edge box constructed of aluminium ribs and glassfibre or aluminium skin.

ROTOR DRIVE: Power is transmitted from each engine through individually-overrunning clutches into the aft transmission, which combines the engine outputs, thereby providing a single power output to the interconnecting shaft which enables both rotors to be driven by either engine.

FUSELAGE: Basically square-section semi-monocoque structure built primarily of high-strength bare and Alclad aluminium alloy. Transverse bulkheads and built-up frames support transmission, power plant and landing gear. Loading ramp forms undersurface of upswept rear fuselage on utility and military models. Baggage container replaces ramp on airliner version. Fuselage is sealed to permit operation from water.

LANDING GEAR: Non-retractable tricycle type, with twin wheels on all three units. Oleo-pneumatic shock-

Kawasaki KV-107/II-2 making an approach to a construction site in a mountainous area

absorbers. Tubeless tyres, size 18 × 5·5, pressure 10·34 bars (150 lb/sq in), on all wheels. Disc brakes. Wheel/ski gear optional.

POWER PLANT (KV-107/II): Two 932 kW (1,250 shp) General Electric CT58-110-1 or Ishikawajima- Harima CT58-IHI-110-1 turboshaft engines, mounted side by side at base of rear rotor pylon. Alternatively, two Rolls-Royce Gnome H.1200 turboshafts (in HKP 4C). Fuel tanks in sponsons, capacity 1,324 litres (350 US gallons). KV-107/IIA has more powerful CT58 engines and provision for increased fuel capacity (see introductory copy).

ACCOMMODATION: Standard accommodation for two pilots, stewardess and 25 passengers in airliner version. Seats in eight rows, in pairs on port side and single seats on starboard side (two pairs at rear of cabin) with central aisle. Airliner fitted with parcel rack and a roll-out baggage container, with capacity of approximately 680 kg (1,500 lb), located in underside of rear fuselage. Ramp of utility model is power-operated on the ground or in flight and can be removed or left open to permit carriage of extra-long cargo.

AVIONICS AND EQUIPMENT: Standard avionics include stability augmentation system (SAS) and automatic speed trim system (AST). Optional avionics include automatic stabilisation equipment (ASE); automatic flight control system (AFCS); Doppler radar; radio altimeter; HF, VHF and UHF radio; ADF; VOR/ILS; Tacan; compass system and attitude director indicator system; and intercom system.

DIMENSIONS, EXTERNAL:
Rotor diameter (each)	15·24 m (50 ft 0 in)
Length overall, blades turning	25·40 m (83 ft 4 in)
Length of fuselage	13·59 m (44 ft 7 in)
Height to top of rear rotor hub	5·09 m (16 ft 8½ in)
Wheel track	3·92 m (12 ft 10½ in)
Wheelbase	7·57 m (24 ft 10 in)
Passenger door (fwd):	
Height	1·60 m (5 ft 3 in)
Width	0·91 m (3 ft 0 in)

DIMENSIONS, INTERNAL:
Cabin, excl flight deck:	
Length	7·37 m (24 ft 2 in)
Normal width	1·83 m (6 ft 0 in)
Max height	1·83 m (6 ft 0 in)
Floor area	13·47 m² (145 sq ft)
Volume (usable)	24·5 m³ (865 cu ft)

AREAS:
Rotor blades (each)	3·48 m² (37·50 sq ft)
Rotor discs (total)	364·6 m² (3,925 sq ft)

WEIGHTS AND LOADINGS:
Weight empty, equipped:	
II-2	4,868 kg (10,732 lb)
IIA-1	4,589 kg (10,118 lb)
IIA-2	5,250 kg (11,576 lb)
Max T-O and landing weight	8,618 kg (19,000 lb)
	or 9,706 kg (21,400 lb)
Max disc loading	23·6 kg/m² (4·84 lb/sq ft)
Max power loading	4·62 kg/kW (7·6 lb/shp)

PERFORMANCE (A: KV-107/II-2 at 8,618 kg; 19,000 lb AUW. B: KV-107/IIA at same AUW):
Never-exceed speed:	
A, B	146 knots (270 km/h; 168 mph)
Max speed at S/L, normal rated power:	
A	136 knots (253 km/h; 157 mph)
B	137 knots (254 km/h; 158 mph)
Cruising speed at 1,525 m (5,000 ft):	
A, B	130 knots (241 km/h; 150 mph)

Kawasaki KV-107/II-7 modified for offshore oil rig support duties

Kawasaki (Hughes) Model 369D helicopter

Max rate of climb at S/L:		
A, normal rated power	463 m (1,520 ft)/min	
B	625 m (2,050 ft)/min	
Max vertical rate of climb at S/L:		
B	381 m (1,250 ft)/min	
Service ceiling:		
A, normal rated power	4,570 m (15,000 ft)	
B	5,180 m (17,000 ft)	
Service ceiling, one engine out:		
A, military power, yaw, 248 rpm	107 m (350 ft)	
B	1,740 m (5,700 ft)	
Hovering ceiling IGE:		
A	2,895 m (9,500 ft)	
B	3,565 m (11,700 ft)	

Hovering ceiling OGE:
A   1,890 m (6,200 ft)
B   2,680 m (8,800 ft)
Min landing area (A, B):
Length   38 m (126 ft)
Width   23 m (75 ft)
T-O to 15 m (50 ft):
B   131 m (430 ft)
Landing from 15 m (50 ft), one engine out:
B   84 m (275 ft)
Range:
A with 3,000 kg (6,600 lb) payload, 10% reserves
   94 nm (175 km; 109 miles)
B with standard fuel   192 nm (357 km; 222 miles)
B with max fuel   592 nm (1,097 km; 682 miles)

KAWASAKI (HUGHES) 369/MODEL 500 and 500C
JGSDF and JMSDF designation: OH-6J

A total of 121 Model 369HM helicopters, manufactured by Kawasaki under licence from Hughes Helicopters, had been delivered to the JGSDF (117), JMSDF (3) and a civil operator (1) by the end of 1979; Japanese production of this model has now ceased.

Manufacture continues of the Model 369HS, of which 49 had been delivered to civil operators by the beginning of 1980, including 18 Model 500Cs.

DIMENSIONS AND AREAS: As for Hughes OH-6A/500/500C (see US section)

WEIGHTS AND LOADING: As for OH-6A/500/500C except:
Weight empty:
OH-6J, 500   537 kg (1,185 lb)
500C   545 kg (1,203 lb)

PERFORMANCE (at max T-O weight, ISA): As for OH-6A/500/500C except:
Max level and never-exceed speed
   130 knots (241 km/h; 150 mph)
Range with max fuel:
OH-6J, 500   307 nm (568 km; 353 miles)
500C   301 nm (557 km; 346 miles)
Max endurance:
OH-6J, 500   3 h 36 min
500C   3 h 24 min

KAWASAKI (HUGHES) 369D/MODEL 500D
JGSDF designation: OH-6D

The first Model 369D (500D) built by Kawasaki under licence from Hughes Helicopters was flown for the first time on 2 December 1977; JCAB Normal category certification was awarded on 20 April 1978. Four Model 500Ds had been delivered to civil operators in Japan by March 1980. The JGSDF ordered 22 as OH-6Ds, all of which have been delivered; it planned to order a further ten OH-6Ds in FY 1980.

MITSUBISHI
MITSUBISHI JUKOGYO KABUSHIKI KAISHA (Mitsubishi Heavy Industries Ltd)

HEAD OFFICE: 5-1, Marunouchi 2-chome, Chiyoda-ku, Tokyo 100
Telephone: Tokyo (03) 212 3111
Telex: J22282 and J22443
NAGOYA AIRCRAFT WORKS: 10, Oye-cho, Minato-ku, Nagoya 455
CHAIRMAN OF BOARD OF DIRECTORS: Gakuji Moriya
PRESIDENT: Masao Kanamori
EXECUTIVE VICE-PRESIDENTS:
   Kaname Taniguchi
   Soichiro Suenaga
   Masao Suzuki
   Teruo Tojo
MANAGING DIRECTOR AND GENERAL MANAGER OF AIRCRAFT AND SPECIAL VEHICLE HEADQUARTERS: Kenji Ikeda
ASST GENERAL MANAGER OF AIRCRAFT AND SPECIAL VEHICLE HEADQUARTERS: Yoshiaki Kato
GENERAL MANAGER, AIRCRAFT AND SPECIAL VEHICLE ADMINISTRATION DEPARTMENT: Yoshiaki Kato
GENERAL MANAGER, AIRCRAFT DEPARTMENT: Hideaki Ito
GENERAL MANAGER, AIRCRAFT EQUIPMENT DEPARTMENT: Naruo Taketa
GENERAL MANAGER, SPACE SYSTEM DEPARTMENT: Masahiko Hamada
DIRECTOR AND GENERAL MANAGER, SPECIAL VEHICLE DEPARTMENT: Takashi Tamaki
MANAGER OF MU-2 ADMINISTRATION SECTION: Yukiya Naramoto
GENERAL MANAGER, NAGOYA AIRCRAFT WORKS: Yoshio Sasaki

Mitsubishi began the production of aircraft in the present Oye plant of its Nagoya Engineering Works in 1921, and manufactured a total of 18,000 aircraft of approximately 100 different types during the 24 years prior to the end of the second World War in 1945. The company was also one of the leading aero-engine manufacturers in Japan, and produced a total of 52,000 engines in the 1,000-2,500 hp range. The conclusion of the Peace Treaty in 1952 enabled the aircraft industry in Japan to recommence, and in December of that year the company constructed its present Komaki South plant. This factory, together with Mitsubishi's Oye, Daiko and Komaki North plants, was later separated from the original Nagoya Engineering Works and consolidated as Nagoya Aircraft Works, with a combined floor area of 247,500 m² (2,750,000 sq ft).

In co-operation with Kawasaki as subcontractor, Mitsubishi is the JDA's prime contractor in producing F-4EJ Phantom fighters for the JASDF, under licence from McDonnell Douglas Corporation. The first two F-4EJs, built by McDonnell Douglas, were delivered and ferried to Japan in July 1971. The next eight were assembled from knock-down subassemblies, the first of these making its first flight on 12 May 1972. The remaining 130,

of which the first was delivered to the JASDF in September 1974, are being built entirely in Japan. A total of 128 F-4EJs had been delivered to the JASDF by 31 January 1980. Japanese production of the F-4EJ is due to end in May 1981.

Mitsubishi is prime contractor for 86 McDonnell Douglas F-15J Eagles (100 less 14 supplied as US Foreign Military Sales) to be ordered for the JASDF. Funds for the first 23 were approved in the FY 1978 budget. The first eight Eagles (including six two-seat F-15DJs), are imported (under FMS contract) US-built aircraft; the first of these made its initial flight on 4 June 1980 and was handed over to the JASDF on 15 July, in the USA. They are due to arrive in Japan in March 1981. The eight FMS Eagles will be followed by eight assembled in Japan from knock-down assemblies, the first of which is scheduled to fly in July 1981. The remaining 84 will be produced in Japan.

Mitsubishi's overhaul work on Sikorsky S-55 helicopters, started in 1954, led to licence manufacture of 44 helicopters of this type; 20 S-58/HSS-1s and 25 S-62As were subsequently assembled, mainly for Japanese customers, as detailed in previous editions of *Jane's*.

Today, Mitsubishi holds licence agreements to manufacture the Sikorsky S-61A, S-61A-1, S-61B (HSS-2) and S-61B-1 (HSS-2A and -2B) helicopters. By 31 March 1980, Mitsubishi had delivered three S-61As and one S-61A-1 (for the JMSDF, for use in support of the Japanese Antarctic Expedition) and had delivered four S-61A-1s (of six ordered) to the JMSDF for rescue duties. It had also delivered 87 of an order for 101 S-61Bs (HSS-2s) and S-61B-1s (HSS-2As and -2Bs) to the JMSDF for anti-submarine duties. From 1980, two S-61A-1s for rescue duties, and 14 S-61B-1s for anti-submarine duties with the JMSDF, are expected to be produced.

Mitsubishi is producing the MU-2 twin-turboprop utility transport; is prime contractor for the T-2 supersonic trainer and F-1 close-support combat aircraft for the JASDF, with Fuji, Nippi and Shin Meiwa as principal subcontractors; and is a subcontractor in the production programme for the Kawasaki C-1 (which see). As a part of

Japan's YX civil transport aircraft programme, Mitsubishi is subcontracted, through the CTDC, to build aft passenger cabin sections of the Boeing 767 jet transport. Part of this work is, in turn, subcontracted by Mitsubishi to Nippi and Shin Meiwa.

Current activities at the Daiko plant include various aero-engine activities; these are described in the appropriate section of this edition.

MITSUBISHI MU-2

The MU-2 is a twin-turboprop STOL multi-purpose transport, the basic design of which was begun in 1960. Prototype construction began in 1962 and the first aircraft was flown on 14 September 1963. By 1 January 1980, total orders for the MU-2 (all versions) had reached 623, including 574 for export and 49 for Japanese customers. Fifteen versions have been announced, of which the MU-2A (3 built), MU-2B (34 built), MU-2C (4 built), MU-2D (18 built), MU-2E (16 built), MU-2F (95 built), MU-2G (46 built), MU-2J (108 built), MU-2K (83 built), MU-2L (36 built), MU-2M (29 built), MU-2N (39 built) and MU-2P (40 built) have been described in the 1965-66 and subsequent editions of *Jane's*. The two current versions are the Marquise and Solitaire, of which 31 and 25 respectively had been built by 1 January 1980. These aircraft, for reasons explained in that entry, are now described under the heading of Mitsubishi Aircraft International in the US section of this edition.

MITSUBISHI MU-300

Mitsubishi completed two prototypes (JQ8001 and 8002) of the MU-300 twin-turbofan business aircraft, powered by 11·1 kN (2,500 lb st) Pratt & Whitney Aircraft of Canada JT15D-4 engines. First flight was made on 29 August 1978; in June and July 1979 the prototypes were transferred to the USA for an FAA certification programme.

The MU-300 is marketed worldwide (except in Japan), under the name **Diamond I**, by Mitsubishi Aircraft International in the USA. A full description of the aircraft can be found under that company's entry in this edition.

Mitsubishi-built F-4EJ Phantom II fighter of the Japan Air Self-Defence Force (*Katsumi Hinata*)

Length of fuselage	17·31 m (56 ft 9½ in)
Height overall	4·38 m (14 ft 4¼ in)
Wheel track	2·82 m (9 ft 3 in)
Wheelbase	5·72 m (18 ft 9 in)

AREAS:

Wings, gross	21·18 m² (228·0 sq ft)
Airbrakes (total)	0·952 m² (10·25 sq ft)
Vertical tail surfaces (total, excl ventral fins)	
	5·00 m² (53·82 sq ft)
Horizontal tail surfaces (total)	6·70 m² (72·12 sq ft)

WEIGHTS:

Operational weight empty	6,302 kg (13,893 lb)
Max T-O weight, 'clean'	9,805 kg (21,616 lb)

PERFORMANCE (at max 'clean' T-O weight except where indicated):

Max level speed at 11,000 m (36,000 ft)	Mach 1·6
Max rate of climb at S/L	10,670 m (35,000 ft)/min
Service ceiling	15,240 m (50,000 ft)
Required field length	1,525 m (5,000 ft)
Max ferry range with external tanks	
	1,400 nm (2,593 km; 1,610 miles)

Mitsubishi T-2 twin-turbofan supersonic jet trainer for the JASDF

MITSUBISHI T-2

The T-2, the first supersonic aircraft developed by the Japanese aircraft industry, is a twin-engined two-seat jet trainer designed to meet the requirements of the JASDF.

Mitsubishi was selected as prime contractor for the development programme in September 1967. Preliminary and detailed design, under the leadership of Dr Kenji Ikeda, were followed by the completion of two XT-2 flying prototypes plus a static test airframe. The first XT-2 (19-5101) flew for the first time on 20 July 1971, and the second (29-5102) on 2 December 1971. These two aircraft were delivered to the JASDF in December 1971 and March 1972 respectively for further flight testing. Two additional development aircraft made their first flights on 28 April and 20 July 1972; the flight test programme was completed in March 1974. A fatigue test airframe was delivered in January 1975.

Production orders have been placed for 77 T-2s (31 **T-2** advanced trainers, 44 **T-2A** combat trainers, and two as prototypes for the F-1 close-support fighter version, described separately). Sixty-three of the T-2/2As had been delivered by 31 March 1980, to the 4th Air Wing at Matsushima. The current schedule calls for the 14 remaining T-2/2As to be delivered by March 1982. Aircraft Nos. 5, 8-24 and 47-56 are unarmed; Nos. 25-46 and 57-66 are fitted with a 20 mm Vulcan multi-barrel cannon, for armament training. The T-2/2As are assigned to the 21st and 22nd Squadrons of the JASDF.

Mitsubishi, as prime contractor, is responsible for fuselage construction, final assembly and flight testing of production aircraft. Major programme subcontractors are Fuji (wings and tail unit), Nippi (pylons and launchers) and Shin Meiwa (drop-tanks).

Under contract to the Technical Research and Development Institute, Mitsubishi is to convert one T-2A as a CCV (control configured vehicle). Initially, this is to fly in 1981 with canard foreplanes and a fly-by-wire control system; later, it will be fitted with a completely new wing, and will flight test such other features as a head-up display, high-g ejection seat, manoeuvring flaps, electronic engine controls, and composite-structure components.

TYPE: Two-seat supersonic jet trainer.

WINGS: Cantilever all-metal shoulder-wing monoplane. Wing section NACA 65 series (modified). Thickness/chord ratio 4·66%. Anhedral 9° from roots. Sweepback on leading-edges 68° at root, 42° 29' inboard of outer extended-chord panels and 36° on outer panels; basic sweepback at quarter-chord 35° 47'. Multi-spar torsion box machined from tapered thick panels and constructed mainly of 7075 and 7079 aluminium alloy. Electrically-actuated aluminium honeycomb leading-edge flaps, the outer portions of which have extended chord. Electrically-actuated all-metal single-slotted flaps, with aluminium honeycomb trailing-edges over 70% of each half-span. No conventional ailerons. Lateral control by hydraulically-actuated all-metal two-section slotted spoilers ahead of flaps.

FUSELAGE: Conventional all-metal semi-monocoque structure, mainly of 7075 and 7079 aluminium alloy. Approx 10% of structure, by weight, is of titanium, mostly around engine bays. Two hydraulically-actuated door-type airbrakes under rear fuselage, aft of main-wheel bays.

TAIL UNIT: Cantilever all-metal structure. One-piece hydraulically-actuated all-moving swept tailplane, with 15° anhedral. Inner leading-edges of titanium; outer leading-edges of aluminium. Trailing-edges of aluminium honeycomb construction. Small ventral fin under each side of fuselage at rear. Hydraulically-actuated rudder.

LANDING GEAR: Hydraulically-retractable tricycle type, with pneumatic backup for emergency extension. Main units retract forward into fuselage, nose unit rearward. Single wheel on each unit. Nosewheel steerable through 72°. Oleo-pneumatic shock-absorbers. Hydraulic brakes and Hydro-Aire anti-skid units. Runway arrester hook beneath rear fuselage. Brake parachute in tailcone.

POWER PLANT: Two Rolls-Royce Turboméca Adour turbofan engines, each rated at 20·95 kN (4,710 lb st) dry and 31·45 kN (7,070 lb st) with afterburning, mounted side by side in centre of fuselage. (Engines licence-built by Ishikawajima-Harima, under designation TF40-IHI-801A.) Fixed-geometry air intake, with auxiliary 'blow-in' intake doors, on each side of fuselage aft of rear cockpit. Fuel in seven fuselage tanks with total capacity of 3,823 litres (841 Imp gallons; 1,010 US gallons). Pressure refuelling point in starboard side of fuselage, forward of main-wheel bay. Provision for carrying up to three 833 litre (183 Imp gallon; 220 US gallon) drop-tanks under wings and fuselage.

ACCOMMODATION: Crew of two in tandem on Daiseru-built Weber ES-7J zero-zero ejection seats in pressurised and air-conditioned cockpits, separated by windscreen. Rear seat elevated 0·28 m (11 in) above front seat. Individual manually-operated rearward-hinged jettisonable canopies. Liquid oxygen equipment.

SYSTEMS: Cockpit air-conditioning system. Two independent hydraulic systems, each 207 bars (3,000 lb/sq in), for flight controls, landing gear and utilities. Pneumatic bottle for landing gear emergency extension. Primary electrical power from two 12/15kVA AC generators.

AVIONICS AND EQUIPMENT: Mitsubishi Electric J/ARC-51 UHF. Nippon Electric J/ARN-53 Tacan and Toyo Communication J/APX-101 SIF/IFF. Mitsubishi Electric search and ranging radar in nose, with Mitsubishi Electric (Thompson-CSF) J/AWG-11 head-up display in cockpit. Lear 5010BL attitude and heading reference system.

ARMAMENT (combat trainer version): One Vulcan JM-61A-1 multi-barrel 20 mm cannon in lower fuselage, aft of cockpit on port side. Attachment point on underfuselage centreline and two under each wing for drop-tanks or other stores. Wingtip attachments for air-to-air missiles.

DIMENSIONS, EXTERNAL:

Wing span	7·88 m (25 ft 10¼ in)
Wing chord at root	4·172 m (13 ft 8¼ in)
Wing chord at tip	1·133 m (3 ft 8½ in)
Wing aspect ratio	3
Wing taper ratio	3·7
Length overall, incl probe	17·84 m (58 ft 6¼ in)

MITSUBISHI F-1

Following the JASDF's decision to develop a single-seat close air support fighter from the T-2 supersonic trainer, design began in 1972. During the development period the fighter was provisionally designated FS-T2-Kai, as described in previous editions of Jane's.

The second and third production T-2 trainers (59-5106 and 59-5107) were converted as prototypes, in which form they made their first flights on 7 and 3 June 1975 respectively. These aircraft retained the rear cockpit and canopy of the T-2, but this area was occupied by the fire control system and test equipment instead of a second occupant. Externally, they differed from the T-2 by the presence of a tubular fairing at the top of the fin, housing a passive warning radar antenna.

These prototypes were delivered to the JASDF Air Proving Wing at Gifu in July and August 1975, and after a year of flight test and evaluation the aircraft was type approved in November 1976 and officially designated F-1.

Production orders had been placed by March 1980 for 64 F-1s, of an anticipated total order for about 70. The first production F-1 (70-8201) made its first flight on 16 June 1977, and was delivered to the JASDF on 26 September 1977. Forty-four F-1s had been delivered, to the 3rd Squadron of the 3rd Air Wing at Misawa, by 31 March 1980.

TYPE: Single-seat close-support fighter.

AIRFRAME, POWER PLANT AND SYSTEMS: Generally similar to T-2, but with the rear cockpit area modified as electronics compartment for bombing computer, inertial navigationssystem and radar warning system. Up to three 821 litre (180 Imp gallon; 217 US gallon) auxiliary fuel tanks can be carried beneath the wings and fuselage.

ACCOMMODATION: Generally similar to T-2, but without rear seat and with 'solid' fairing in place of second canopy.

AVIONICS AND EQUIPMENT: Dual UHF; Tacan; IFF/SIF; Mitsubishi Electric nose-mounted air-to-air and air-to-ground radar, with Mitsubishi Electric (Thomson-CSF) J/AWG-12 head-up display; Ferranti 6TNJ-F inertial navigation system; radio altimeter; air data computer; Mitsubishi Electric fire control system and

Mitsubishi F-1 (two Rolls-Royce Turboméca Adour turbofan engines), with additional scrap view of two-seat nose of T-2 trainer (Pilot Press)

Mitsubishi F-1 single-seat close-support fighter of the JASDF

bombing computer; strike camera system; radar homing and warning system; attitude and heading reference system.

ARMAMENT: Single JM-61 multi-barrel 20 mm cannon. One underfuselage and four underwing hardpoints, as in T-2, with detachable multiple ejector racks. Bombs of 250, 500 or 750 lb can be carried on all five external stations, up to a maximum weight of 2,721 kg (twelve 500 lb bombs). The four underwing stations can each be used for rocket pods such as the JLAU-3A (with nineteen 70 mm), RL-7 (seven 70 mm) and RL-4 (four 125 mm). Primary weapon will be the Mitsubishi ASM-1

air-to-surface missile now under development; two of these can be carried on underwing stations. For air-to-air combat the F-1 can carry up to four AIM-9 Sidewinder missiles, one at each wingtip and one on each of the outboard underwing hardpoints. For long-range missions, the F-1 can carry up to three auxiliary fuel tanks (see 'Power Plant' paragraph).

DIMENSIONS AND AREAS:
As for T-2

WEIGHTS:
Operational weight empty	6,358 kg (14,017 lb)
Max T-O weight	13,674 kg (30,146 lb)

PERFORMANCE (at max 'clean' T-O weight except where indicated):
Generally similar to T-2 'clean', except for:
Time to 11,000 m (36,000 ft)	2 min
T-O run	1,280 m (4,200 ft)
Combat radius with four Sidewinders, internal fuel only, incl reserves	150 nm (278 km; 173 miles)
Combat radius (lo-lo-lo-hi) with eight 500 lb bombs and external tanks	190 nm (351 km; 218 miles)
Combat radius (hi-lo-hi) with two ASM-1s and one 821 litre drop-tank, incl reserves	300 nm (556 km; 346 miles)

NAL
NATIONAL AEROSPACE LABORATORY
1880 Jindaiji-machi, Chofu City, Tokyo
Telephone: Musashino (0422) 47 5911
DIRECTOR-GENERAL: Dr Toshio Kawasaki
DEPUTY DIRECTOR-GENERAL: Dr Shun Takeda
DIRECTOR OF V/STOL AIRCRAFT RESEARCH GROUP: Dr Norio Inumaru

The National Aerospace Laboratory (NAL) is a government establishment responsible for research and development in the field of aeronautical and space sciences. Since 1962 it has extended its activity in the field of V/STOL techniques.

NAL QSTOL RESEARCH AIRCRAFT
The NAL was allotted Y7,947 million in the FY 1980 budget for continuation of an 11-year programme to develop a large experimental Quiet STOL transport aircraft. This will be based upon the airframe of the Kawasaki C-1 tactical transport (which see), with the following modifications: replacement of the two Pratt & Whitney JT8D engines by four 48 kN (10,800 lb st) MITI/NAL FJR-710-600 high bypass ratio turbofan engines, installed above and far ahead of the wing leading-edges in nacelles with upper surface blowing, as on the Boeing YC-14 prototype STOL transport (see 1978-79 *Jane's*); installation of wing leading-edge and aileron BLC systems; replacement of the existing inboard flaps by USB flaps; fitting of a larger rudder, of the double-hinged type, and an increased-span tailplane; structural strengthening of the fuselage and landing gear; and installation of a digital stability and control augmentation system.

The basic and detailed design work is expected to take four years; aircraft modification began in 1979; first flight is due in 1983. Total cost of the development programme is estimated at Y23,000 million, including flight testing. Data obtained from this programme will, it is hoped, enable NAL to develop, in co-operation with the Japanese aerospace industry, a commercial STOL transport aircraft able to operate from 800 m (2,625 ft) runways with 150 passengers, and to cruise at around Mach 0·62. Tentative plans call for development of this to begin in mid-1980 and to be completed in 1990.

DIMENSIONS, EXTERNAL:
Wing span	30·60 m (100 ft 4¾ in)
Length overall	30·30 m (99 ft 5 in)
Height overall	10·10 m (33 ft 1¾ in)
Tailplane span	14·84 m (48 ft 8¼ in)
Wheel track (c/l of shock-struts)	4·40 m (14 ft 5¼ in)
Wheelbase (c/l of shock-struts)	9·33 m (30 ft 7¼ in)

WEIGHTS (estimated):
Weight empty	28,038 kg (61,813 lb)
Max T-O weight	38,700 kg (85,320 lb)

PERFORMANCE (estimated):
Cruising speed	Mach 0·62
Landing speed	72 knots (133 km/h; 83 mph)
T-O to 10·7 m (35 ft)	547 m (1,795 ft)
Landing from 10·7 m (35 ft)	488 m (1,600 ft)
Max range	1,400 nm (2,590 km; 1,610 miles)

NAL QSTOL research aircraft, based on a Kawasaki C-1 airframe *(Michael A. Badrocke)*

NIPPI
NIHON HIKOKI KABUSHIKI KAISHA (Japan Aircraft Manufacturing Co Ltd)
HEAD OFFICE AND SUGITA WORKS: No. 3175 Showa-machi, Kanazawa-ku, Yokohama 236
Telephone: Yokohama (045) 771 1251
Telex: (3822) 267 Nippi J
OTHER WORKS: Atsugi
PRESIDENT: Masao Nagahisa
PUBLIC RELATIONS MANAGER: Taketoshi Kitamura

Nippi's Sugita plant, to which the head office was transferred in early 1971, has a floor area of 49,144 m² (528,800 sq ft) and employs 913 persons. The Atsugi plant, which employs 744 persons, has a floor area of 36,334 m² (390,950 sq ft). Kawasaki has a 31·77 per cent holding in Nippi.

The Atsugi plant is engaged chiefly in the overhaul, repair and maintenance of various types of aircraft and helicopters, including those of the Japan Defence Agency and Maritime Safety Agency, and carrier-based aircraft of the US Navy. The Sugita plant manufactures in-spar ribs for the Boeing 767; components and assemblies for the Kawasaki C-1, Mitsubishi T-2, F-1, F-4EJ, F-15J (pylons and launchers) and Shin Meiwa PS-1; airframe and dynamic components for the Kawasaki KV-107; dynamic components for the Fuji-Bell UH-1B and Kawasaki-Hughes OH-6J; engine nacelles for Japanese licence-built examples of the Lockheed P-3C; body structures for Japanese satellites; tail units for Japanese-built rocket vehicles; and targets for the Japan Defence Agency.

The Nippi Pilatus B4 sailplane and NP-100A Albatross motor glider are described in the Sailplanes section.

SHIN MEIWA
SHIN MEIWA INDUSTRY Co Ltd
TOKYO OFFICE: c/o Shin Ohtemachi Building, 5th Floor, 2-1, 2-chome, Ohtemachi, Chiyoda-ku, Tokyo 100
Telephone: Tokyo (03) 279 3531
Telex: 222 2431 SMICAIR TOK
HEAD OFFICE: 1-5-25, Kosone-Cho, Nishinomiya-Shi, Hyogo-Ken
Telephone: Nishinomiya (0798) 47 0331
Telex: 5644493
WORKS (AIRCRAFT DIVISION): Konan and Itami
PRESIDENT: Yoshio Yagi
VICE-PRESIDENT: Itaru Morita
EXECUTIVE MANAGING DIRECTOR AND GENERAL MANAGER, AIRCRAFT DIVISION: Hajime Kawanishi
DIRECTOR AND ASST GENERAL MANAGERS:
Susumu Ishimoto
Kozo Kishikawa (Konan Works Manager)
Shigemi Matsui (Tokyo Office)

DIRECTOR, AND CHIEF OF ENGINEERING, HEAD OFFICE: Yukio Koya
SENIOR TECHNICAL CONSULTANT: Dr Shizuo Kikuhara
TECHNICAL CONSULTANT: Dr Koichi Tokuda
SALES MANAGER AND PUBLIC RELATIONS:
Motohiro Matsushita (Tokyo Office)

The former Kawanishi Aircraft Company became Shin Meiwa in 1949 and established itself as a major overhaul centre for Japanese and US military and commercial aircraft.

Shin Meiwa's principal current activities concern the series production of the PS-1 medium-range STOL flying-boat for the JMSDF, an amphibious search and rescue version, the US-1, and overhaul work on flying-boats and amphibians.

Shin Meiwa is engaged in the manufacture of components for other aircraft, including underwing drop-tanks for the Mitsubishi T-2 supersonic jet trainer and Japanese-built examples of the McDonnell Douglas F-15 Eagle jet fighter; the cargo loading system for the Kawasaki C-1 transport aircraft; nose and tail components, ailerons and trailing-edge flaps for Japanese licence-built examples of the Lockheed P-3C. Shin Meiwa will also take part in co-production of the Boeing 767, under subcontract to Mitsubishi.

SHIN MEIWA SS-2 and SS-2A
JMSDF designations: PS-1 and US-1
Shin Meiwa was awarded a contract in January 1966 to develop a new anti-submarine flying-boat for the Japan Maritime Self-Defence Force. Company designation for the basic flying-boat is **SS-2** and in ASW configuration this has the JMSDF designation **PS-1**. When adapted for amphibious operation the basic aircraft has the company designation **SS-2A**. The search and rescue version of this amphibian has the JMSDF designation **US-1**.

The first PS-1 prototype (5801) flew for the first time on 5 October 1967, and the second on 14 June 1968. These aircraft were delivered to the 51st Flight Test Squadron of the JMSDF at Iwakuni. JDA type approval was granted in Autumn 1970.

In addition to the two prototypes, Shin Meiwa had by March 1980 delivered 23 production PS-1s. These are in service with the 31st Air Group of the JMSDF for ASW duties, most of them with No. 31 Squadron at Iwakuni.

Design of the US-1 began in June 1970; the first example (9071) made its first flight, following a waterborne take-off, on 16 October 1974, and its first flight from a land base on 3 December 1974. The first US-1 was delivered on 5 March 1975, the second in July 1975 and the third in early February 1976. These amphibians are at present in service, for search and rescue duties, with No. 71 SAR Squadron of the JMSDF, also based at Iwakuni. The fourth was due to be delivered in March 1980; four more had been funded by early 1980.

In co-operation with the JMSDF and the National Fire Agency, Shin Meiwa converted the PS-1 first prototype into a water bombing testbed. The results of tests using tanks of 8·1 tons total capacity were analysed in 1978, and Shin Meiwa plans to achieve eventually a 14 ton water load capacity. The testbed aircraft can, in 3·6 h, deliver a maximum of 185 tonnes (182·1 tons) of water, picked up at 38 km (70 km; 43·5 miles) from base, to a site 5·2 nm (10 km; 6 miles) away. The proposed production version, with increased capacity, could deliver 315 tonnes (310 tons) to a site the same distance from its base before needing to refuel. Simulated operational tests were carried out by the National Fire Agency in 1979.

To make possible very low landing and take-off speeds, the PS-1 and US-1 have both a boundary layer control system and extensive flaps for propeller slipstream deflection. Control and stability in low-speed flight are enhanced by 'blowing' the rudder, flaps and elevators, and by use of an automatic flight control system.

The PS-1 is designed to dip its large sonar deep into the sea during repeated landings and take-offs, and can land on very rough water, in winds of up to 25 knots (47 km/h; 29 mph). Take-offs and landings have been made successfully in seas with wave heights of up to 3·0 m (10 ft). To resist salt-water corrosion, much of the structure is of 2024C-T3, 2024-T62, 7075-T73 and similar alloys, coated with a watertight polyurethane compound developed by Shin Meiwa.

The following description applies to both the PS-1 and US-1, except where a specific version is indicated:

TYPE: Four-turboprop STOL anti-submarine flying-boat (PS-1) or air/sea rescue amphibian (US-1).

WINGS: Cantilever high-wing monoplane. Conventional all-metal two-spar structure with rectangular centre-section and tapered outer panels. High-lift devices include outboard leading-edge slats extending over nearly 17% of the span and large outer and inner blown trailing-edge flaps extending 60° and 80° respectively. Two spoilers in front of outer flap on each wing. Powered ailerons. Leading-edge de-icing boots.

FUSELAGE: All-metal semi-monocoque hull, with high length/beam ratio. V-shaped single-step planing bottom, with curved spray suppression strakes along sides of nose and spray suppressor slots in fuselage undersides aft of inboard propeller line. Double-deck interior.

TAIL UNIT: Cantilever all-metal T tail. Large dorsal fin. Tailplane has slats and de-icing boots on leading-edge. Blown rudder and elevators. Tab in each elevator.

ALIGHTING AND BEACHING GEAR (PS-1): Hull; and fixed stabilising floats near wingtips. Retractable tricycle-type beaching gear installed, with aft-retracting single-wheel main gear unit on each side of hull and forward-retracting twin steerable nosewheels, making aircraft independent of ground beaching aids.

LANDING GEAR (US-1): Hull, as PS-1, plus hydraulically-retractable Sumitomo tricycle landing gear with twin wheels on all units. Steerable nose unit. Oleo-pneumatic shock-absorbers. Main units, which retract rearward into fairings on hull sides, have size 40 × 14-22 (Type VII) tyres, pressure 7·79 bars (113 lb/sq in). Nosewheel tyres size 25 × 6·75-18 (Type VII),

Shin Meiwa US-1 search and rescue amphibian, developed from the PS-1 *(Pilot Press)*

pressure 20·69 bars (300 lb/sq in). Three-rotor hydraulic disc brakes. No anti-skid units.

POWER PLANT: Four 2,282 kW (3,060 ehp) Ishikawajima-built General Electric T64-IHI-10 turboprop engines, each driving a Sumitomo-built Hamilton Standard 63E60-19 three-blade constant-speed reversible-pitch propeller. Additionally, one 1,044 kW (1,400 ehp) Ishikawajima-built General Electric T58-IHI-10 gas turbine (932 kW; 1,250 shp T58-IHI-10-M1 in US-1) is housed in the upper centre portion of the fuselage to provide power for boundary layer control system on rudder, flaps and elevators. Fuel in two bladder-type rear-fuselage tanks and five wing tanks, with total usable capacity of 19,500 litres (4,290 Imp gallons) in PS-1. US-1 fuel is in wing tanks (10,851 litres; 2,387 Imp gallons) and fuselage tanks (11,649 litres; 2,563 Imp gallons); total capacity 22,500 litres (4,950 Imp gallons). Pressure refuelling point on port side, near bow hatch. Oil capacity 152 litres (33·4 Imp gallons). The PS-1 and US-1 can both be refuelled on open sea, either from a surface vessel or from another PS-1 fitted with detachable at-sea refuelling equipment.

ACCOMMODATION (PS-1): Two pilots and flight engineer on flight deck, which has wide-view bulged windows at sides. Aft of this on the upper deck is a tactical compartment, housing two sonar operators, a navigator, MAD operator, radar operator, radio operator and a tactical co-ordinator. Electronic, magnetic and sonic equipment is installed on starboard side, with crew's rest area and bunks on port side. Aft of tactical compartment is the weapons compartment. On the lower deck, from nose to rear, are the avionics compartment, oxygen-bottle bay, main gear bay and two fuel tanks. Door on port side of rear fuselage.

ACCOMMODATION (US-1): Search and rescue version has accommodation for crew of nine and 20 seated survivors or 12 stretchers, one auxiliary seat and two observers' seats. Sliding rescue door on port side of fuselage, aft of wing. Transport version can seat up to 69 passengers in mainly four-abreast seating with centre aisle; rear portion of cabin convertible to cargo compartment.

SYSTEMS: Cabin air-conditioning system. Two independent hydraulic systems, each 207 bars (3,000 lb/sq in). No. 1 system actuates ailerons, outboard flaps, spoilers, elevators, rudder and control surface 'feel'; No. 2 system actuates ailerons, inboard and outboard flaps, wing leading-edge slats, elevators, rudder, landing gear extension/retraction and lock/unlock, nosewheel steering, main-wheel brakes and windscreen wipers.

Emergency system, also of 207 bars (3,000 lb/sq in), driven by 24V DC motor, for actuation of inboard flaps, landing gear extension/retraction and lock/unlock, and main-wheel brakes. Air/sea rescue version has oxygen system for all crew and stretcher stations. Garrett AiResearch GTCP85-131J APU provides power for starting main engines and shaft power for 40kVA emergency AC generator. BLC system includes a C-2 compressor, driven by T58-IHI-10 gas turbine, which delivers compressed air at 14 kg (30·9 lb)/s and pressure of 1·86 bars (27 lb/sq in) for ducting to inner and outer flaps, rudder and elevators. Electrical system includes 115/200V three-phase 400Hz constant-frequency AC and three transformer-rectifiers to provide 28V DC. Two 40kVA AC generators, driven by Nos. 2 and 3 main engines. Emergency 40kVA AC generator driven by APU. 24V emergency DC power from two 34Ah nickel-cadmium batteries. Anti-icing, air-conditioning, fire detection and extinguishing systems standard on US-1.

AVIONICS AND EQUIPMENT (PS-1): AN/ARA-50 UHF direction finder, HRN-105 Tacan, HRN-104 Loran, HPN-101B wave height meter, AN/APN-187C-N Doppler radar, A/A24G-9 TAS transmitter, AN/APS-80-N search radar, HGC-102 teletypewriter, AN/APN-125-N indicator group, HRN-101 ADF, N-PT-3 dead reckoning plotting board, AN/APX-68-N SIF, N-OA-35B/HSA tactical plotting group, HLR-102 countermeasure device, AN/ARR-52A sonobuoy receiver, HSQ-101 magnetic anomaly detector, HSA-103 error voltage monitor, HQS-101C dipping sonar, AN/ASA-20B recorder group, HQA-5 sonobuoy recorder, N-R-86/HRA OTPI (on top position indicator), HSA-116 integrated display system, HQH-101 sonobuoy data recorder, HSA-1B SDDS, RRC-15 emergency transmitter, HSA-102 automatic magnetic compensator device, N-CU-58/HRC antenna coupler, N-ID-66/HRN BDHI, HIC-3 interphone and HRC-107-3/4 HF.

AVIONICS AND EQUIPMENT (US-1): HIC-3 interphone, HRC-107 HF, N-CU-58/HRC antenna coupler, HGC-102 teletypewriter, HRC-106 radio, HRC-110 radio, HRN-101 ADF, AN/ARA-50 UHF/DF, HRN-105 Tacan, HRN-104 Loran, HRA-4 Loran signal processor, HRN-106 ILS marker beacon receiver, AN/APN-171 (N2) radar altimeter, HPN-101B wave height meter, AN/APN-187C Doppler radar, AN/AYK-2 navigation computer, A/A24G-9 TAS transmitter, N-PT-3 dead reckoning plotting board,

Shin Meiwa US-1 air/sea rescue amphibian (four Ishikawajima/General Electric T64-IHI-10 turboprop engines)

N-OA-35/HSA tactical plotter group, AN/APS-80N search radar, AN/APA-125N indicator group, AN/APX-68N IFF transponder, RRC-15 emergency transmitter and N-ID-66/HRN BDHI.

ARMAMENT AND OPERATIONAL EQUIPMENT (PS-1): Weapons bay on upper deck, aft of tactical compartment, in which are stored AQA-3 Jezebel passive long-range acoustic search equipment with 20 sonobuoys and their launchers, Julie active acoustic echo ranging with 12 explosive charges, four 330 lb anti-submarine bombs, and smoke bombs. External armament includes underwing pod between each pair of engine nacelles, each containing two homing torpedoes, and a launcher beneath each wingtip for three 5 in air-to-surface rockets. Searchlight below starboard outer wing.

OPERATIONAL EQUIPMENT (US-1): Marker launcher, 10 marine markers, 6 green markers, 2 droppable message cylinders, 10 float lights, pyrotechnic pistol, parachute flares, 2 flare storage boxes, binoculars, 2 rescue equipment kits, 2 droppable life-raft containers, rescue equipment launcher, lifeline pistol, lifeline, 3 lifebuoys, loudspeaker, hoist unit, rescue platform, lifeboat with outboard motor, camera, and 12 stretchers. Stretchers can be replaced by troop seats.

OPERATIONAL EQUIPMENT (water bomber): Water is picked up by two retractable ventral scoops just aft of the hull step and collected in a 'midships tank with a capacity of more than 8,100 litres (1,782 Imp gallons; 2,140 US gallons)—a water weight of more than 8,083 kg (17,820 lb). An injection system mounted on the water tank enables this to be mixed with a retardant compound which is carried in a separate container to the rear of the water tank. Dispersal is via two water dump doors in the underside of the hull, just forward of the step.

DIMENSIONS, EXTERNAL:
Wing span	33·15 m (108 ft 9 in)
Wing chord at root	5·00 m (16 ft 4¾ in)
Wing chord at tip	2·39 m (7 ft 10 in)
Wing aspect ratio	8
Length overall	33·46 m (109 ft 9¼ in)
Height overall:	
PS-1 (on beaching gear)	9·82 m (32 ft 4¾ in)
US-1	9·82 m (32 ft 2¾ in)
Tailplane span	12·36 m (40 ft 8½ in)
Wheel track: PS-1	3·10 m (10 ft 2 in)
US-1	3·56 m (11 ft 8¼ in)

Wheelbase: PS-1	8·20 m (26 ft 10¾ in)
US-1	8·33 m (27 ft 4 in)
Propeller diameter	4·42 m (14 ft 6 in)

Rescue hatch, US-1 (port side, rear fuselage):
Height	1·58 m (5 ft 2¼ in)
Width	1·46 m (4 ft 9½ in)

AREAS:
Wings, gross	135·8 m² (1,462 sq ft)
Ailerons (total)	6·40 m² (68·9 sq ft)
Inner flaps (total)	9·40 m² (101·18 sq ft)
Outer flaps (total)	14·20 m² (152·85 sq ft)
Leading-edge slats (total)	6·01 m² (64·7 sq ft)
Spoilers (total)	2·10 m² (22·60 sq ft)
Fin	17·56 m² (189 sq ft)
Dorsal fin	6·32 m² (68·03 sq ft)
Rudder	7·01 m² (75·5 sq ft)
Tailplane	23·05 m² (248 sq ft)
Elevators, incl tab	8·78 m² (94·5 sq ft)

WEIGHTS AND LOADINGS (PS-1):
Weight empty	26,300 kg (58,000 lb)
Normal T-O weight	36,000 kg (79,365 lb)
Max T-O weight	43,000 kg (94,800 lb)
Max wing loading	316·6 kg/m² (64·84 lb/sq ft)
Max power loading	4·71 kg/kW (7·74 lb/ehp)

WEIGHTS (PS-1 water bomber testbed):
Weight empty	25,200 kg (55,555 lb)
Water payload	8,100 kg (17,857 lb)
Max T-O and landing weight	43,000 kg (94,800 lb)

WEIGHTS AND LOADINGS (US-1, search and rescue):
Manufacturer's weight empty	23,300 kg (51,367 lb)
Weight empty, equipped	25,500 kg (56,218 lb)
Usable fuel: JP-4	17,518 kg (38,620 lb)
JP-5	18,397 kg (40,560 lb)
Max oversea operating weight	36,000 kg (79,365 lb)
Max T-O weight from water	43,000 kg (94,800 lb)
Max T-O weight on land	45,000 kg (99,200 lb)
Max wing loading	331·4 kg/m² (67·9 lb/sq ft)
Max power loading	4·93 kg/kW (8·11 lb/ehp)

PERFORMANCE (PS-1 at normal T-O weight):
Max level speed at 1,525 m (5,000 ft)	
	295 knots (547 km/h; 340 mph)
Cruising speed at 1,525 m (5,000 ft):	
4 engines	230 knots (426 km/h; 265 mph)
2 engines	170 knots (315 km/h; 196 mph)
Approach speed	47 knots (87 km/h; 54 mph)
Touchdown speed	41 knots (76 km/h; 47 mph)

Stalling speed	40 knots (75 km/h; 46 mph)
Max rate of climb at S/L	690 m (2,264 ft)/min
Service ceiling	9,000 m (29,500 ft)
Time to 3,050 m (10,000 ft)	5 min
T-O run	250 m (820 ft)
Landing run	180 m (590 ft)
Min ground turning radius	25·00 m (82 ft 0 in)
Normal range	1,169 nm (2,168 km; 1,347 miles)
Max ferry range	2,560 nm (4,744 km; 2,948 miles)
Endurance	15 h

PERFORMANCE (PS-1 water bomber testbed, estimated):
Max level speed	265 knots (491 km/h; 305 mph)

PERFORMANCE (US-1, search and rescue, at max T-O weight on land, except where indicated):
Max level speed	260 knots (481 km/h; 299 mph)
Max level speed at 3,050 m (10,000 ft), AUW of 36,000 kg (79,365 lb)	268 knots (496 km/h; 308 mph)
Cruising speed at 3,050 m (10,000 ft)	
	230 knots (426 km/h; 265 mph)
Max rate of climb at S/L, at max land T-O weight	460 m (1,510 ft)/min
Max rate of climb at S/L, AUW of 36,000 kg (79,365 lb)	725 m (2,380 ft)/min
Service ceiling at max land T-O weight	6,520 m (21,400 ft)
Service ceiling, AUW of 36,000 kg (79,365 lb)	8,230 m (27,000 ft)
T-O to 15 m (50 ft) from land, 30° flap, BLC on	620 m (2,035 ft)
T-O to 15 m (50 ft) from water, AUW of 43,000 kg (94,800 lb), 40° flap, BLC on	600 m (1,970 ft)
Landing from 15 m (50 ft) on land, AUW of 36,000 kg (79,365 lb), 50° flap, BLC on, with reverse pitch	810 m (2,655 ft)
Landing from 15 m (50 ft) on water, AUW of 43,000 kg (94,800 lb), 60° flap, BLC on	290 m (950 ft)
Min ground turning radius:	
self-powered	21·20 m (69 ft 6¾ in)
towed	18·80 m (61 ft 8¼ in)
Runway LCN requirement at AUW of 43,000 kg (94,800 lb)	42
Radius of search operation at AUW of 45,000 kg (99,200 lb), incl 2·3 h search	900 nm (1,665 km; 1,035 miles)
Max range at 230 knots (426 km/h; 265 mph) at 3,050 m (10,000 ft)	2,270 nm (4,207 km; 2,614 miles)

SHOWA
SHOWA HIKOKI KOGYO KABUSHIKI KAISHA
(Showa Aircraft Industry Co Ltd)

HEAD OFFICE AND SALES OFFICE: Mitsui Building, No. 3, 3-chome, Nihonbashi-Muromachi, Chuo-ku, Tokyo
Telephone: Tokyo (03) 270 1451 and 279 1451

WORKS: No. 600 Tanaka-machi, Akishima-shi, Tokyo
NARITA SERVICE CENTRE: 20 Araizumi, Naritasi, Chiba
PRESIDENT: Teiji Asano

Showa was the first Japanese aircraft manufacturing company to resume post-war operations when it undertook the overhaul and repair of US Air Force aircraft.

The company's present activities comprise mainly the manufacture of wingtip floats, tail fin, partition and other doors, torpedo pods and hatches for the Shin Meiwa PS-1 and US-1; and the supply of aluminium and non-metal honeycomb and honeycomb sandwich panels for aircraft floors and airframe construction. Showa also manufactures a variety of airborne equipment.

KOREA
(REPUBLIC)

KAL
KOREAN AIR LINES

KAL Building, CPO Box 864, Seoul
Telephone: 771 66 and 771 67
Telex: KALHO K27526
PRESIDENT: C. H. Cho

SENIOR VICE-PRESIDENT, SPECIAL PROJECT DEVELOPMENT: W. B. Lee

Following delivery by Hughes Helicopters of the USA of 34 Model 500MD Defender light helicopters to the Republic of Korea Air Force, Korean Air Lines is currently assembling both Defenders and Model 500D commercial helicopters from US-built components, and will proceed gradually to local manufacture. By early 1980,

KAL had completed more than 75 Model 500MD Standard Scouts and 25 Model 500 MD/TOW Defenders, in addition to a number of Model 500D commercial helicopters, for sale to customers in Korea.

Descriptions of the Defender and Model 500D can be found under the Hughes entry in the US section of this edition.

LIBYA

It was reported in 1978 that a new aircraft factory was under construction in Libya, approx 216 nm (400 km; 248 miles) from Tripoli, with assistance from SIAI-Marchetti

of Italy. Main purpose of the new factory was the licence assembly of 160 **SIAI-Marchetti SF.260s**, of an overall total of 240 ordered by Libya for its own and other Arab

air forces. Libyan production was expected to begin in 1980.

MEXICO

AAMSA
AERONAUTICA AGRICOLA MEXICANA SA
(Subsidiary of Industrias Unidas SA)

171 Oriente No. 398, Colonia Aragon, Apartado 14783, Mexico 14, DF
Telephone: 760 60 00
Telex: 17-74359
ADMINISTRATIVE MANAGER: Arnando Soto Ortega

As the result of an agreement between Rockwell International Corporation of the USA (which see) and Industrias Unidas SA of Mexico, this company was formed in 1971 to take over from the former's Commercial Products

Group the manufacture of Aero Commander Quail Commander and Sparrow Commander agricultural aircraft. AAMSA purchased the type design, tooling and all production materials for the Sparrow and Quail Commander agricultural aircraft, in order to build them at a new manufacturing complex in Pasteje, Mexico.

Up to the end of 1975, only a dozen of these aircraft had been completed in Mexico, and the Sparrow programme was terminated. The Quail Commander, now known as the AAMSA A9B-M Quail, supersedes an earlier version designated A-9 with a 175 kW (235 hp) Lycoming O-540-B2B5 engine and lower operating weights.

AAMSA A9B-M QUAIL

The A9B-M Quail agricultural aircraft has a 795 litre (210 US gallon) hopper and low operating cost. The entire primary structure is coated with Copon, an epoxy resin catalyst paint resistant to all known agricultural chemicals.

Component sets of the Quail are sent by AAMSA to its subsidiary, Aircraft Parts and Development Corporation of Laredo, Texas, which holds the FAA type certificate and is responsible for marketing the aircraft. A total of 43 AAMSA-built Quails had been completed by 1 January 1978. An output of 40 during 1980 was planned, all against firm orders, and a further 80 are scheduled to be built during 1981.

TYPE: Single-seat agricultural monoplane.

WINGS: Braced low-wing monoplane. Modified Clark Y wing section. Dihedral 5° 8′. Incidence 0° 20′. Composite structure with spruce spars, metal-covered leading-edge and Eonnex fabric covering on remainder of wing. Multiple steel tube overwing bracing struts on each side. Hoerner wingtips. Fabric-covered wooden ailerons. Flaps and drooping ailerons.

FUSELAGE: Steel tube structure with Eonnex fabric covering. Removable side panels.

TAIL UNIT: Wire-braced steel tube structure with Eonnex fabric covering. Trim tab in starboard elevator.

LANDING GEAR: Non-retractable tailwheel type. CallAir spring shock-absorbers. Cleveland main wheels, with Goodyear tyres, size 8·50-6 (6-ply). Scott 203 mm (8 in) steerable tailwheel. Cleveland toe-actuated brakes. Parking brake. Wire-cutters on main legs.

POWER PLANT: One 224 kW (300 hp) Avco Lycoming IO-540-K1A5 flat-six engine, driving a McCauley Type 1A200-DFA9050 two-blade fixed-pitch metal propeller. Two-position adjustable-pitch McCauley Type 2D34CT-84HF two-blade metal propeller optional. Fuel tank in each wing, combined capacity 151 litres (40 US gallons). Oil capacity 11 litres (3 US gallons).

ACCOMMODATION: Single seat in enclosed cockpit aft of hopper. Side doors. Steel tube overturn structure. Cabin heater standard.

SYSTEMS: Electrical system includes 12V 50A starter/generator and 30Ah battery.

AVIONICS AND EQUIPMENT: Radio and other avionics to customer's requirements. Standard equipment includes 0·64 m³ (22·5 cu ft) glassfibre/polyester hopper, capacity 643 litres (170 US gallons) of liquid or 545 kg (1,200 lb) of dry chemical; wing tiedown rings; landing gear and windscreen wire-cutters; canopy-to-fin deflector cable; and electrically-operated auxiliary fuel pumps. Optional equipment includes Transland Boommaster or Micronair spray system, Transland Swathmaster dry spreader system, lights for night flying, 0·17 m³ (6·0 cu

AAMSA A9B-M Quail single-seat agricultural monoplane, in spraying configuration

ft) hopper extension increasing capacity to 795 litres (210 US gallons) or 725 kg (1,600 lb), invert emulsion spray system or low volume spray system, bottom-loading equipment, rotating beacon, and 30 × 13-6 main wheels.

DIMENSIONS, EXTERNAL:

Wing span	10·59 m (34 ft 9 in)
Wing chord, constant	1·59 m (5 ft 2¾ in)
Length overall (tail up)	7·32 m (24 ft 0 in)
Height overall	2·34 m (7 ft 8 in)
Tailplane span	3·20 m (10 ft 6 in)
Wheel track	2·08 m (6 ft 10 in)
Wheelbase	5·21 m (17 ft 1 in)
Propeller diameter: standard	2·29 m (7 ft 6 in)
optional	2·13 m (7 ft 0 in)

AREAS:

Wings, gross	16·90 m² (182 sq ft)
Ailerons (total)	1·99 m² (21·4 sq ft)
Fin (A-9)	0·80 m² (8·6 sq ft)
Rudder (A-9)	0·84 m² (9·0 sq ft)
Tailplane	1·47 m² (15·8 sq ft)
Elevators (total)	1·30 m² (14·0 sq ft)

WEIGHTS AND LOADINGS:

Weight empty	817 kg (1,800 lb)
Max payload	725 kg (1,600 lb)
Max T-O weight	1,725 kg (3,800 lb)
Max wing loading	102 kg/m² (20·88 lb/sq ft)
Max power loading	7·70 kg/kW (12·67 lb/hp)

PERFORMANCE (at max T-O weight, except where indicated):

Max level speed at S/L	104 knots (193 km/h; 120 mph)
Max cruising speed (75% power) at 1,360 kg (3,000 lb) AUW	100 knots (185 km/h; 115 mph)
Normal operating speed	78-87 knots (145-161 km/h; 90-100 mph)
Stalling speed	52 knots (97 km/h; 60 mph)
Stalling speed as usually landed	35 knots (65 km/h; 40 mph)
Max rate of climb at S/L	259 m (850 ft)/min
Service ceiling	4,875 m (16,000 ft)
T-O run	328 m (1,000 ft)
Landing run at normal landing weight	136 m (447 ft)
Range at 50% power	260 nm (483 km; 300 miles)

ANAHUAC
FABRICA DE AVIONES ANAHUAC SA

ADDRESS: Calzada Adolfo López Mateos 478, Aeropuerto Internacional, Mexico 9, DF

Telephone: 558 27 57

PRESIDENT, FOUNDER AND GENERAL ADMINISTRATOR: Dr Alejandro Elizondo

CHIEF EXECUTIVES:

Ing Arno Gjumlich (Designer and Chief Engineer)

Capt Marcial Sanchez (Chief Production and Flight Test Pilot)

Capt Hector Mariscal (Sales Manager)

Luis Ortega (International Public Relations Manager)

This company was formed to initiate in Mexico the development of aircraft suited to the particular needs of agricultural aviation in that country, taking its name from the former Aztec valley where Mexico City is now situated. Anahuac's first product is a single-seat agricultural aircraft known as the Tauro.

ANAHUAC TAURO 350 (BULL)

Design of the Tauro was begun in January 1967, and the prototype first flew on 3 December 1968.

The first production Tauro was flown on 5 June 1970, following the award on 8 August 1969 of the Mexican DGAC's approved type certificate No. 1. By the end of 1971 Anahuac had built seven production aircraft, each powered by a 224 kW (300 hp) Jacobs R-755-A2M1 radial piston engine and designated Tauro 300; for a description and illustration see the 1974-75 Jane's.

During 1972 and part of 1973, studies were made for an improved version, incorporating a number of improvements suggested as a result of early operational use of the

Tauro 300. The result is the Tauro 350, to which the following description applies; this is in production, and three had been delivered by early 1978. A further six were scheduled for completion by the Spring of 1978, but no later news than this has been received from the company.

TYPE: Single-seat agricultural aircraft.

WINGS: Strut-braced low-wing monoplane. Wing section US 35B. Thickness/chord ratio approx 10%. Dihedral 5° from roots. Incidence 2°. No sweepback. Braced by inverted V-strut above each wing. All-metal (aluminium) spars and ribs, covered with Grade AA cotton fabric. Ailerons, of similar construction, actuated mechanically by push/pull rods. No flaps or tabs.

FUSELAGE: Basic structure of 4130 steel tube, covered with removable aluminium side panels. Impact-absorbing structure forward of cockpit.

TAIL UNIT: Single, slightly-sweptback fin and balanced rudder, and non-swept fixed-incidence tailplane and balanced elevators, of 4130 steel tube with fabric covering. Trim tab in port elevator. Horizontal surfaces wire-braced above and below.

LANDING GEAR: Non-retractable tailwheel type, with spring shock-absorbers on main units, leaf spring on tail unit. Main units have Cleveland 6·00-6 wheels with Goodyear 8·50-6 tyres, pressure 2·07 bars (30 lb/sq in). Cleveland plate-type brakes.

POWER PLANT: One 261 kW (350 hp) Jacobs R-755-SM turbocharged seven-cylinder radial aircooled engine, driving a Sensenich 5404/MA 96K two-blade ground-adjustable (or, optionally, constant-speed) propeller. Aluminium fuel tank in each wing root, total capacity 140 litres (31 Imp gallons; 37 US gallons). Refuelling point above tank in each wing. Provision for optional

auxiliary tank in fuselage. Oil capacity 20 litres (4·4 Imp gallons; 5·3 US gallons).

ACCOMMODATION: Single adjustable seat in fully-enclosed cockpit, with downward-hinged window/door on each side. Cabin ventilated.

SYSTEMS: Electrical system includes 12V 35Ah Rebat R-35 battery for engine starting.

AVIONICS AND EQUIPMENT: King VHF radio optional. No blind-flying instrumentation. Hopper in fuselage, forward of cockpit at CG, capacity 870 litres (191 Imp gallons; 230 US gallons) of liquid or 800 kg (1,764 lb) of dry chemical. Transland dispersal equipment.

DIMENSIONS, EXTERNAL:

Wing span	11·44 m (37 ft 6½ in)
Wing chord (constant)	1·77 m (5 ft 9¾ in)
Wing aspect ratio	6·4
Length overall	8·21 m (26 ft 11¼ in)
Height overall	2·34 m (7 ft 8 in)
Tailplane span	3·50 m (11 ft 5¾ in)
Wheel track	2·50 m (8 ft 2½ in)
Propeller diameter	2·44 m (8 ft 0 in)
Propeller ground clearance (in flying attitude)	0·30 m (1 ft 0 in)

DIMENSIONS, INTERNAL:

Cabin: Max length	1·12 m (3 ft 8 in)
Max width	0·86 m (2 ft 10 in)
Max height	1·295 m (4 ft 3 in)
Floor area	0·93 m² (10·0 sq ft)

AREAS:

Wings, gross	20·24 m² (217·89 sq ft)
Ailerons (total)	1·67 m² (18·00 sq ft)
Fin	1·02 m² (11·00 sq ft)
Rudder	1·30 m² (14·00 sq ft)
Tailplane	1·49 m² (16·00 sq ft)
Elevators, incl tab	1·39 m² (15·00 sq ft)

WEIGHTS AND LOADINGS:

Weight empty	958 kg (2,112 lb)
Max T-O and landing weight	2,064 kg (4,552 lb)
Max wing loading	101·98 kg/m² (20·89 lb/sq ft)
Max power loading	7·91 kg/kW (13·00 lb/hp)

PERFORMANCE (at max T-O weight):

Never-exceed speed	121 knots (225 km/h; 140 mph)
Max level speed at S/L	104 knots (193 km/h; 120 mph)
Max cruising speed at S/L	78 knots (145 km/h; 90 mph)
Econ cruising speed at 1,525 m (5,000 ft)	74 knots (137 km/h; 85 mph)
Stalling speed	36·5 knots (68 km/h; 42 mph)
Max rate of climb at S/L	259 m (850 ft)/min
Service ceiling	5,790 m (19,000 ft)
T-O run	275 m (900 ft)
T-O to, and landing from, 15 m (50 ft)	350 m (1,150 ft)
Landing run	250 m (820 ft)
Range with max fuel	202 nm (375 km; 233 miles)

Anahuac Tauro 350 (Jacobs R-755-SM turbocharged engine)

NETHERLANDS

FOKKER

FOKKER BV

HEAD OFFICE AND MAIN FACTORY: PO Box 7600, 1117 ZJ
Schiphol-Oost (Amsterdam Airport)

Telephone: Amsterdam (020) 5449111

Telex: 12227 SIFO NL

OTHER FACTORIES AND COMPANIES:

Drechtsteden Division, with plants at Papendrecht, Dordrecht and Hoogeveen

Avio-Fokker Division, with Ypenburg Works at Ypenburg Air Base, near the Hague; and Woensdrecht Works at Woensdrecht Air Base, near Bergen op Zoom

Trading Company Avio-Diepen BV

SUPERVISORY BOARD:

H. Buiter

Prof Dr W. H. J. Reynaerts

BOARD OF MANAGEMENT:

F. Swarttouw (Chairman)

H. J. Grobben (Vice-Chairman, Finance and Economy)

J. Cornelis (New Aircraft Projects)

J. Donders (Personnel and Social Affairs)

D. Krook (Marketing and Sales)

F. Nel (Technology)

HEAD OF DEPT OF CORPORATE RELATIONS: C. H. Verweij

PUBLIC RELATIONS AND PRESS OFFICER: L. J. N. Steijn

It was announced on 11 February 1980 that the merger between Fokker and the Federal German company VFW, which came into effect in 1969, was to be ended. The two companies will continue to pursue their own activities independently, though both intend to co-operate in future international programmes. Current joint programmes between Fokker and VFW are not affected.

Fokker forms the entire aircraft industry in the Netherlands, with six plants, in which about 7,800 people are employed. Earlier collaborative ventures, other than those with VFW, included participation in the manufacturing programmes for the Gloster Meteor, Hawker Hunter and Lockheed F-104G, with final assembly lines at Schiphol; and for the Breguet Atlantic and Canadair (Northrop) CF-5/NF-5. Fokker has an important share in the European manufacturing programme for the General Dynamics F-16 fighter, being responsible for centre-fuselages and wing moving surfaces for 589 aircraft (for the Dutch final assembly line for 174 F-16s for the Netherlands and Norway; and the remainder for the Belgian assembly line, and for General Dynamics, for aircraft to be delivered to the USAF). Delivery to the RNethAF of F-16s assembled by Fokker began in June 1979, following the first flight at Schiphol by a Dutch-assembled F-16 (J-259) on 3 May 1979. The first Dutch-assembled F-16 for the Royal Norwegian Air Force flew for the first time on 12 December 1979 and was handed over on 15 January 1980. The Norwegian F-16s are distinguished by a lengthened structure at the base of the rudder, housing a brake-chute.

Some 4,500 people are employed at the Schiphol-Oost works, which accommodates the company headquarters and administration together with the main F27, F28 and F-16 assembly lines and test flying facilities. Production is continuing of the F27 and F28, each in various versions, and wing moving surfaces are being produced for the Airbus A300. Also at Schiphol are the design offices, research department, numerically-controlled milling department, metal bonding department, electronics division, space division and scientific and administrative computer facilities.

The Drechtsteden plant, formed by the integrated production facilities at Dordrecht, Papendrecht and Hoogeveen, employs some 1,750 people. Most of these are engaged on detail production and component assembly for the General Dynamics F-16, Fokker F27 and F28 and

F-16 fighters for Norway are distinguished by the brake-chute housing under the rudder

Airbus A300; other work includes the manufacture of antennae and other specialised products.

Avio-Fokker is a Division of Fokker, employing some 1,500 people, and comprises the former Avio-Diepen plant at Ypenburg Air Base near the Hague and the former Aviolanda plant at Woensdrecht Air Base. At both facilities the installation of F-16 centre-fuselages, and maintenance, overhaul, repair and modification work on a wide variety of military and civil aircraft, are carried out. Production of outer wings and struts for the Shorts 330 has been undertaken at Woensdrecht since 1975.

Reinforced plastics components for the Friendship, Fellowship, Airbus A300 and Shorts 330, and radomes and fairings for the Westland Lynx helicopter, are manufactured at Ypenburg.

At Woensdrecht the ELMO division produces electrical and electronic systems and wire harnesses.

Hoogeveen Division, a facility of the Drechtsteden plant, is engaged in the manufacture of parts for the aerospace industry, radar and telecommunications and other industries. Quantity production of aluminium shelters is also undertaken in this factory.

FOKKER F27 FRIENDSHIP

The first of two F27 prototypes made its first flight on 24 November 1955, and was designed to accommodate 28 passengers in a 22·3 m (73 ft) long fuselage. The second, which flew on 29 January 1957, was representative of Series 100 production aircraft, with Dart 511 engines and 32 seats in a 23·1 m (76 ft) fuselage. Two further airframes were built for static and fatigue testing.

The F27 has been in series production for many years, both by Fokker and, for a period, by Fairchild Industries in the United States. Deliveries by Fokker began in November 1958. US production of the F-27 and FH-227 totalled 205; details have appeared in previous editions of *Jane's*. Fokker recently introduced a modernised flight deck and new-style cabin interior.

Outer wings for the F27 are manufactured in Belgium by SABCA; mid- and aft fuselage sections in France by Dassault-Breguet; dorsal fins, flaps and ailerons in West Germany by VFW.

The following F27 orders by airlines, air forces and government agencies had been announced by 2 September 1980:

Mk 100 (1967-68 *Jane's;* 83 built, incl 2 corporate; orders listed in 1971-72 *Jane's*)

Mk 200 (115 built, incl 1 corporate; orders listed in 1973-74 *Jane's*)

Mk 300 (1967-68 *Jane's;* 13 built; orders listed in 1971-72 *Jane's*)

Mk 400/600 (206 sold, incl 9 corporate; orders as listed in 1974-75 and 1977-78 *Jane's*, plus:

Air Ivoire (Mk 600)	2
Air Niger (Mk 600)	1
Air Tanzania (Mk 600)	1
Argentinian government	1
Bolivian government	6
Burma Airways (Mk 600)	1
GATL (Mk 400)	1
Lauda Air (Mk 600)	1
Libyan Arab Airlines (Mk 600)	2
Senegal government	6
Swift Aire Lines (USA) (Mk 600)	3
TAAG/Angola Airlines	1

Mk 500 (81 sold, incl 5 corporate); orders listed in 1974-75 and 1977-78 *Jane's*, plus:

Air New Zealand	6
KLM (NLM CityHopper)	3
Malaysian Airline System	2
Mississippi Valley Airlines	4
Sonangol (Angola)	1

Mk 700 (1 sold to Icelandair; see 1977-78 *Jane's*)

By 2 September 1980, total sales by Fokker had reached 510, bringing overall Dutch/US sales to 715. This total includes sales of the F27 Maritime, described separately.

Fokker is standardising currently on the Mks 200, 400M, 500 and 600, but any of the following versions of the F27 are available to order:

F27 Mk 200. Basic airliner or executive model with Dart RDa.7 Mk 536-7R turboprops. First flight 20 September 1959.

F27 Mk 400 Combiplane. Available on request only. Details in 1978-79 *Jane's*.

F27 Mk 400M. Military version, with accommodation for 46 parachute troops, 6,025 kg (13,283 lb) of freight or 24 stretchers and 9 attendants. Large cargo door and enlarged parachuting door on each side. First flight 24 April 1965. Four Imperial Iranian Air Force Mk 400Ms were modified by Fokker in 1977 for target towing duties.

F27 Mk 400M cartographic version. Aerial survey version with two super-wide-angle cameras, remotely controlled from central navigation station, and navigation sight. Inertial navigation system, with digital readout at navigation station and recorded on each picture. Photography through optical glass window panes. Electrically-operated window doors. First flight 24 August 1973.

F27 Mk 500. Similar to F27 Mk 200, but with lengthened fuselage and large cargo door. The 15 aircraft for the French Ministère des Postes et Télécommunications (Air France) have special large doors on both sides. First flight 15 November 1967.

F27 Mk 500M. Available on request only. Details in 1978-79 *Jane's*.

F27 Mk 600. Similar to Mk 200, but with a large cargo door. Does not have the reinforced and watertight flooring of the Combiplane. Can be fitted with quick-change interior, featuring roller tracks and palletised seats and/or cargo pallets. First flight 28 November 1968.

Any of the above models can be fitted, at customer's option, with a Dowty Rotol very-rough-field landing gear having two-stage oleos with a 100 mm (4 in) increase in stroke, giving increased overall height and propeller ground clearance. Rough-field gear versions are currently in operation with Air Tanzania, Aramco, Burma Airways and Somali Airlines.

TYPE: Twin-turboprop medium-range airliner.

WINGS: Cantilever high-wing monoplane. Wing section NACA 64-421 at root, 64-415 at tip. Dihedral 2° 30′. Incidence 3° 30′. All-metal riveted and metal-bonded two-spar stressed-skin structure, consisting of centre-section and two detachable outer sections. Detachable honeycomb-core sandwich leading-edges with Kléber-Colombes rubber-boot de-icers. GRP trailing-edges. Mechanically-operated single-slotted flaps, divided by engine nacelles. Electrically-operated trim tab in each aileron.

FUSELAGE: All-metal stressed-skin structure, built to fail-safe principles, with cylindrical portions metal bonded and conical parts riveted. Fuselage is pressurised between rear bulkhead of nosewheel compartment and circular pressure bulkhead aft of the baggage compartment. Length of pressurised section 16·16 m (53 ft 0 in), except for Mk 500 in which the pressurised section is 17·66 m (57 ft 11 in) long. The slightly flattened fuselage bottom is reinforced by underfloor members.

TAIL UNIT: Cantilever all-metal stressed-skin structure. Fin and tailplane, as well as leading-edges of surfaces,

Fokker F27 Friendship Mk 200, with additional side view (bottom) of Friendship Mk 500
(Pilot Press)

Fokker F27 Mk 600 Friendship in the insignia of Lauda Air, run by former Austrian racing driver Niki Lauda

are detachable. Trim tab in each elevator. Kléber-Colombes pneumatic-boot anti-icing.

LANDING GEAR: Retractable tricycle type. Pneumatic retraction. Dowty oleo-pneumatic shock-absorbers; Dunlop wheels, tyres and brakes. Twin-wheel main units retract backward into engine nacelles. Single-wheel steerable nose unit retracts forward into non-pressurised nosecone. Main-wheel tyre pressure 5·62 bars (81·5 lb/sq in), nosewheel tyre pressure 3·87 bars (56 lb/sq in). Pneumatic brakes on main wheels, with Dunlop Maxaret automatic anti-skid system. Provision on all currently-available models for Dowty Rotol very-rough-field landing gear in which, at 19,730 kg (43,500 lb) AUW, the total stroke in the main gear is lengthened from 305 mm (12 in) to 406 mm (16 in), increasing the aircraft's static height and propeller ground clearance by 76 mm (3 in). Low-pressure main-wheel tyres are fitted, pressure 4·2 bars (61 lb/sq in) below 18,143 kg (40,000 lb) AUW and 4·57 bars (66 lb/sq in) at higher operating weights. Nose unit is of levered-suspension type, with tyre pressure of 3·87 bars (56 lb/sq in).

POWER PLANT (all current versions): Two Rolls-Royce Dart Mk 536-7R (RDa.7 rating) turboprop engines, each developing 1,596 kW (2,140 shp) plus 2·34 kN (525 lb st) for take-off. Four-blade Dowty Rotol constant-speed propellers. Integral fuel tanks in outer wings, capacity 5,136 litres (1,130 Imp gallons). Optionally, fuel bag tanks for an additional 2,289 litres (503·5 Imp gallons) may be fitted. Overwing fuelling, but pressure refuelling optional. Provision for carrying two 950 litre (209 Imp gallon) external fuel tanks under wings. Methyl-bromide fire-extinguishing system with flame detectors.

ACCOMMODATION (Mks 200 and 600): Flight compartment seats two pilots side by side, with folding seat for third crew member if required. Main cabin has standard four-abreast seating for 44 passengers at 78/84 cm (31/33 in) pitch; alternative arrangements allow this number to be increased to 48 in Mk 200. Passenger door at rear of cabin, on port side, with toilet opposite. Standard cargo door at front of Mk 200 on port side; large cargo door in same position on Mk 600, with sill at truck-bed level. Cargo holds forward and aft of main cabin, size dependent on interior arrangement.

ACCOMMODATION (executive and VIP versions): Can be furnished to customer's specification, but a basic layout is available. In this, the cabin is divided into three sections: a conference room with six seats, a rest room with settee and divan, and a lounge with four seats. Toilet, galley, wardrobe, baggage space and seat for attendant in forward fuselage. Second toilet and baggage space at rear.

ACCOMMODATION (Mk 400M): Folding canvas seats, with safety harnesses, along cabin sides for up to 46 paratroops. Toilet and provision for medical supply box or pantry unit at rear. Ambulance version can accommodate 24 USAF-type stretchers, in eight tiers of three, with seats at front and rear for up to nine medical attendants or sitting casualties. All-cargo version fitted with skid strips, tiedown fittings, protection plates and hinged hatracks. Dispatch door on each side of fuselage at rear for dropping supplies and personnel.

ACCOMMODATION (Mk 500): Main cabin has standard seating for 52 passengers four abreast at 89·5 cm (35·25 in) seat pitch; alternative layouts enable up to 60 passengers to be carried at 72 cm (28·5 in) pitch.

SYSTEMS: Garrett-AiResearch pressurisation and air-conditioning system utilises two Rootes-type engine-driven blowers. Choke heating and air-to-air heat exchanger; optional bootstrap cooling system. Pressure differential 0·29 bars (4·16 lb/sq in) in Mks 500 and 600; 0·38 bars (5·5 lb/sq in) in Mk 200. No hydraulic system. Dunlop pneumatic system, pressure 235 bars (3,400 lb/sq in), for landing gear retraction, nosewheel steering and brakes. Emergency pneumatic circuits for landing gear extension and brakes. Bendix primary 28V electrical system supplied by two 375A 28V DC

engine-driven generators. Secondary system supplied via two 115V 400Hz AC constant-frequency inverters. Variable-frequency AC power supply, from 120/208V 15kVA engine-driven alternators, for anti-icing and heating. Two 24V 40Ah nickel-cadmium batteries. 1·12 m³ (39·4 cu ft) oxygen system for pilots.

AVIONICS AND EQUIPMENT: VHF and HF transceivers, VHF navigation system (including glideslope), ADF, ILS, marker beacon receiver, dual gyrosyn compass system, Fairchild flight data recorder, intercom system, Bendix weather radar and Smiths autopilot. Marquette windscreen wipers.

DIMENSIONS, EXTERNAL:
Wing span	29·00 m (95 ft 2 in)
Wing chord at root	3·45 m (11 ft 4 in)
Wing chord at tip	1·40 m (4 ft 7 in)
Wing aspect ratio	12
Length overall: except Mk 500	23·56 m (77 ft 3½ in)
Mk 500	25·06 m (82 ft 2½ in)
Fuselage: Max width	2·70 m (8 ft 10¼ in)
Max height	2·79 m (9 ft 1¾ in)
Height overall, standard landing gear:	
except Mk 500	8·50 m (27 ft 11 in)
Mk 500	8·71 m (28 ft 7¼ in)
Height overall, rough-field landing gear:	
except Mk 500	8·59 m (28 ft 2 in)
Tailplane span	9·75 m (32 ft 0 in)
Wheel track (c/l shock-absorbers)	
	7·20 m (23 ft 7½ in)
Wheelbase: except Mk 500	8·74 m (28 ft 8 in)
Mk 500	9·74 m (31 ft 11¼ in)
Propeller diameter	3·50 m (11 ft 6 in)
Propeller ground clearance:	
standard landing gear:	
except Mk 500	0·94 m (3 ft 1 in)
Mk 500	0·99 m (3 ft 3 in)
rough-field landing gear:	
except Mk 500	1·02 m (3 ft 4¼ in)
Passenger door (aft, port):	
Height	1·65 m (5 ft 5 in)
Width	0·74 m (2 ft 5 in)
Height to sill: except Mk 500	1·22 m (4 ft 0 in)
Mk 500	1·39 m (4 ft 6¾ in)
Service/emergency door (aft, stbd):	
Height	1·12 m (3 ft 8 in)
Width	0·74 m (2 ft 5 in)
Height to sill	0·99 m (3 ft 3 in)
Standard cargo door (Mk 200 only):	
Height	1·19 m (3 ft 11 in)
Width	1·04 m (3 ft 5 in)
Height to sill	0·99 m (3 ft 3 in)
Large cargo door (Mks 500 and 600):	
Height	1·78 m (5 ft 10 in)
Width	2·32 m (7 ft 7½ in)
Height to sill: except Mk 500	0·99 m (3 ft 3 in)
Mk 500	1·03 m (3 ft 4½ in)
Dispatch doors (Mk 400M only, aft, port and stbd,	
each): Height	1·65 m (5 ft 5 in)
Width	1·19 m (3 ft 11 in)
Height to sill	1·22 m (4 ft 0 in)

DIMENSIONS, INTERNAL:
Cabin, excl flight deck:	
Length: except Mk 500	14·46 m (47 ft 5 in)
Mk 500	15·96 m (52 ft 4 in)
Max width	2·55 m (8 ft 4½ in)
Max height	2·02 m (6 ft 7½ in)
Floor area (excl toilet):	
except Mk 500	26·0 m² (280 sq ft)
Mk 500	30·2 m² (325 sq ft)
Volume (excl toilet):	
except Mk 500	56·0 m³ (1,978 cu ft)
Mk 500	65·5 m³ (2,313 cu ft)
Freight hold (fwd), max: Mk 200	4·78 m³ (169 cu ft)
Mks 500, 600	5·58 m³ (197 cu ft)
Freight hold (aft), max:	
all versions	2·83 m³ (100 cu ft)

AREAS:
Wings, gross	70·00 m² (753·5 sq ft)
Ailerons (total)	3·51 m² (37·80 sq ft)
Trailing-edge flaps (total)	12·72 m² (136·90 sq ft)
Vertical tail surfaces (total)	14·20 m² (153 sq ft)
Horizontal tail surfaces (total)	16·00 m² (172 sq ft)

WEIGHTS AND LOADINGS:
Manufacturer's weight, empty:	
Mk 200, 44 seats	10,177 kg (22,436 lb)
Mk 400M	10,596 kg (23,360 lb)
Mk 500, 52-56 seats	10,695 kg (23,578 lb)
Mk 600, 44 seats	10,336 kg (22,786 lb)
Operating weight empty:	
Mk 200, 44 seats	11,164 kg (24,612 lb)
Mk 400M, all-cargo	10,862 kg (23,947 lb)
Mk 400M, medical evacuation	
	11,286 kg (24,880 lb)
Mk 400M, paratrooper	11,039 kg (24,336 lb)
Mk 500, 56 seats	11,950 kg (26,345 lb)
Mk 600, 44 seats	11,314 kg (24,943 lb)
Max payload (weight limited):	
Mk 200, 44 seats	5,846 kg (12,888 lb)
Mk 400M, all-cargo	6,148 kg (13,553 lb)
Mk 400M, medical evacuation	
	5,721 kg (12,612 lb)
Mk 400M, paratrooper	5,971 kg (13,164 lb)
Mk 500, 56 seats	5,967 kg (13,155 lb)
Mk 600, 44 seats	5,696 kg (12,557 lb)
Fuel load: standard	4,062 kg (8,955 lb)
with optional wing bag tanks (Mk 500)	
	5,885 kg (12,975 lb)
with optional wing bag tanks (Mk 600)	
	5,870 kg (12,941 lb)
Max T-O weight: all versions	20,410 kg (45,000 lb)
Max landing weight:	
Mks 200, 400M and 600	18,600 kg (41,000 lb)
Mk 500	19,731 kg (43,500 lb)
Max zero-fuel weight:	
Mks 200, 400M and 600	17,010 kg (37,500 lb)
Mk 500	17,900 kg (39,500 lb)
Max wing loading:	
all versions	291·5 kg/m² (59·7 lb/sq ft)
Max power loading:	
all versions	6·39 kg/kW (10·5 lb/shp)

PERFORMANCE (at weights indicated):
Normal cruising speed at 6,100 m (20,000 ft) and AUW	
of 17,237 kg (38,000 lb):	
all versions	259 knots (480 km/h; 298 mph)
Rate of climb at S/L, AUW of 18,143 kg (40,000 lb):	
all civil versions	451 m (1,480 ft)/min
military versions	494 m (1,620 ft)/min
Service ceiling at AUW of 17,237 kg (38,000 lb):	
all civil versions	8,990 m (29,500 ft)
military versions	9,145 m (30,000 ft)
Service ceiling, one engine out, at AUW of 17,237 kg	
(38,000 lb):	
all civil versions	3,565 m (11,700 ft)
military versions	4,055 m (13,300 ft)
Runway LCN at max T-O weight, hard runway, standard landing gear	16
Required T-O field length (ICAO-PAMC) at AUW of	
18,143 kg (40,000 lb), all civil versions:	
S/L, ISA	988 m (3,240 ft)
S/L, ISA +15°C	1,088 m (3,570 ft)
914 m (3,000 ft), ISA	1,210 m (3,970 ft)
Required T-O field length (military) at AUW of 18,143	
kg (40,000 lb), military versions:	
S/L, ISA	704 m (2,310 ft)
S/L, ISA +15°C	765 m (2,510 ft)
914 m (3,000 ft), ISA	838 m (2,750 ft)
Required landing field length (ICAO-PAMC) at AUW	
of 16,329 kg (36,000 lb), all civil versions:	
S/L	1,003 m (3,290 ft)
1,525 m (5,000 ft)	1,076 m (3,530 ft)
Required landing field length (military) at AUW of	
17,010 kg (37,500 lb), military versions:	
S/L	579 m (1,900 ft)
914 m (3,000 ft)	622 m (2,040 ft)

Range (ISA, zero wind conditions) with FAR 121.645 reserves for alternate, 30 min hold at 3,050 m (10,000 ft) and 10% flight fuel:

Mks 200 and 600, 44 passengers
    1,020 nm (1,926 km; 1,197 miles)
Mk 500, 52 passengers
    935 nm (1,741 km; 1,082 miles)

Military transport range (ISA, zero wind conditions) at max T-O weight, reserves for 30 min hold at S/L and 5% initial fuel:

Mk 400M, all-cargo, max standard fuel
    1,195 nm (2,213 km; 1,375 miles)
Mk 400M, all-cargo, max possible fuel
    2,370 nm (4,389 km; 2,727 miles)

Military combat radius, conditions as above:

Mk 400M, all-cargo, max standard fuel
    625 nm (1,158 km; 719 miles)
Mk 400M, all-cargo, max possible fuel
    1,230 nm (2,278 km; 1,416 miles)

Max endurance at 6,100 m (20,000 ft):

Mk 400M, max standard fuel   7 h 25 min
Mk 400M, max possible fuel   12 h 47 min

OPERATIONAL NOISE LEVELS (FAR Pt 36):

T-O   90·6 EPNdB
Approach (Mk 500)   98·9 EPNdB
Approach (Mk 600)   100·3 EPNdB
Sideline   92·2 EPNdB

FOKKER F27 MARITIME

The F27 Maritime is a medium-range maritime patrol version of the Friendship, designed to meet the requirements of various coastal agencies throughout the world which require a cost-effective surveillance aircraft for coastal patrol, fishery protection, search and rescue, and similar offshore duties. The basic design was defined in July 1975, and shortly afterwards Fokker began converting an ex-airline F27 to serve as a prototype/demonstration aircraft (PH-FCX). This prototype made its first flight in February 1976. Two Mk 400 F27 Maritimes have been delivered to the Peruvian government, and three Mk 200 Maritimes (for search and rescue duties) were delivered to the Spanish government during the first six months of 1979. Orders were received in 1980 from the governments of Angola (one), the Netherlands (two) and the Philippines (three).

The duties of the F27 Maritime include patrol of fishery areas and coastal shipping lanes, surveillance of offshore oil industry operations, search and rescue, environmental control and similar duties. It is operated by a crew of up to six persons, and the standard fuel capacity of 9,326 litres (2,051 Imp gallons; 2,463 US gallons) in centre-wing bag tanks and wing pylon tanks gives the aircraft an endurance of 10-12 h, or a range of up to 2,700 nm (5,000 km; 3,107 miles), depending on the mission to be flown.

TYPE: Twin-turboprop maritime patrol aircraft.

WINGS, FUSELAGE AND TAIL UNIT: As described for F27, except that airframe is heavily treated with anti-corrosive measures; in tail unit, only the port elevator has a trim tab; and 'teardrop' windows are fitted to flight deck.

LANDING GEAR: As described for F27, but with tyre pressures of 5·52 bars (80 lb/sq in) on main units and 3·80 bars (55 lb/sq in) on nose unit. With long-stroke main gear fitted, pressure in the low-pressure main-wheel tyres is 4·50 bars (65 lb/sq in), and in tyre on the levered-suspension nose unit is 3·80 bars (55 lb/sq in).

POWER PLANT: Two Rolls-Royce Dart Mk 536-7R (RDa.7 rating) turboprop engines, each developing 1,730 kW (2,320 shp) for T-O. Four-blade Dowty Rotol propellers. Integral fuel tanks in outer wings, total capacity 5,140 litres (1,130 Imp gallons; 1,357 US gallons). Overwing (gravity) and pressure refuelling. Additional centre-wing tank of 2,310 litres (508 Imp gallons; 610 US gallons) capacity, and two 938 litre (206·5 Imp gallon; 248 US gallon) tanks on underwing pylons, giving overall total fuel capacity of 9,326 litres (2,051 Imp gallons; 2,463 US gallons). Methyl bromide fire extinguishing system, with flame detectors. Water-methanol tank in each engine nacelle, combined capacity 303 litres (67 Imp gallons; 80 US gallons).

ACCOMMODATION: Flight compartment seats two pilots side by side, with folding seat for third crew member if required. Main cabin fitted out as tactical compartment (for a minimum of two operators), containing advanced avionics, galley, toilet and crew rest area. Bubble windows for observers are provided aft in main cabin. Rear cabin door is openable in flight. Standard cargo door at front on port side, with sill at truckbed height. Cargo holds forward and aft of main cabin.

SYSTEMS: Generally as described for F27, except that bootstrap cooling system is standard; cabin pressure differential is 0·38 bars (5·5 lb/sq in); secondary electrical system has a third 115V 400Hz AC constant-frequency inverter; and oxygen system includes individual supply for each tactical crew member.

AVIONICS AND EQUIPMENT: Com/nav equipment comprises Collins 618T-3 HF transceiver, two Collins 618M-3 VHF transceivers, Collins AN/ARC-159 UHF transceiver, interphone, Litton LTN-72 inertial navigation system, IDC air data computer, dual Sperry C-9 gyro compasses, Collins DF-206 radio compass, Collins 51Z-4 marker beacon receiver, Honeywell AN/APN-198 radar altimeter, Collins DF-301E VHF/UHF direction finder, two Collins 51RV-4 VOR/ILS receivers, two Collins HSIs, Smiths SEP-2E/M autopilot, Collins 621A-6A ATC transponder. Operational equipment includes Litton AN/APS-504(V)-2 search radar, with 360° coverage, mounted in ventral radome.

DIMENSIONS: As for F27 Mks 200/400/600, except:

Height overall   8·70 m (28 ft 6½ in)
Cabin volume (excl flight deck) 60·5 m³ (2,136 cu ft)

WEIGHTS AND LOADINGS:

Weight empty   12,212 kg (26,923 lb)
Normal max T-O weight 20,410 kg (45,000 lb)
Operational necessity weight 21,320 kg (47,500 lb)
Max landing weight   18,600 kg (41,000 lb)
Max zero-fuel weight   17,900 kg (39,500 lb)
Max wing loading 291·5 kg/m² (59·7 lb/sq ft)
Max power loading 6·39 kg/kW (10·5 lb/shp)

PERFORMANCE (at normal max T-O weight except where indicated):

Never-exceed speed, AUW of 17,237 kg (38,000 lb), S/L to 6,100 m (20,000 ft)
    259 knots (480 km/h; 298 mph) CAS
Normal cruising speed at 6,100 m (20,000 ft), AUW of 17,237 kg (38,000 lb)
    250 knots (463 km/h; 287 mph)
Normal operating speed at 6,100 m (20,000 ft), AUW of 17,237 kg (38,000 lb)
    227 knots (420 km/h; 261 mph) CAS
Patrol speed at 457 m (1,500 ft)
   150-180 knots (277-333 km/h; 172-207 mph)
Stalling speed, flaps up
    96 knots (178 km/h; 111 mph) CAS
Max rate of climb at S/L, ISA, AUW of 18,143 kg (40,000 lb)   442 m (1,450 ft)/min
Service ceiling   8,990 m (29,500 ft)
Service ceiling, one engine out 3,565 m (11,700 ft)
Runway LCN (42% tyre deflection) at 15,875 kg (35,000 lb) AUW:
 rigid pavement, L = 76·2 cm (30 in) 10·4
 flexible pavement, h = 25·4 cm (10 in) 11·4
 flexible pavement, h = 12·7 cm (5 in) 9·0
Runway LCN (42% tyre deflection) at 20,410 kg (45,000 lb) AUW:
 rigid pavement, L = 76·2 cm (30 in) 16·0
 flexible pavement, h = 25·4 cm (10 in) 14·8
 flexible pavement, h = 12·7 cm (5 in) 12·0
Runway CBR, unpaved soil, h = 25·4 cm (10 in), 3,000 passes:
 AUW of 15,875 kg (35,000 lb) 6·2%
 AUW of 20,410 kg (45,000 lb) 7·8%
T-O run at S/L: ISA   975 m (3,200 ft)
 ISA + 20°C   1,080 m (3,545 ft)
Landing distance (unfactored, ISA at S/L):
 AUW of 19,731 kg (43,500 lb) 610 m (2,000 ft)
 AUW of 13,607 kg (30,000 lb) 530 m (1,740 ft)
Transport range at 6,100 m (20,000 ft) with 4,536 kg (10,000 lb) payload, 30 min loiter and 5% reserves
    1,000 nm (1,850 km; 1,150 miles)

FOKKER F28 FELLOWSHIP

The F28 Fellowship twin-turbofan short/medium-haul transport was developed in collaboration with other European aircraft manufacturers and with equal financial support from the Netherlands Aircraft Development Board and through a loan guaranteed by the Dutch government.

Production is undertaken by Fokker in association with MBB and VFW in Germany and Short Bros in the UK. Fokker is responsible for the front fuselage, to a point just aft of the flight deck, the centre fuselage and wing-root fairings. MBB builds the fuselage from the wing trailing-edge to the rear pressure bulkhead, and the engine nacelles and support stubs. VFW is responsible for the rear fuselage and tail unit, and for the cylindrical fuselage section between the wing leading-edge and flight deck. Shorts are responsible for wings and other components, including main-wheel and nosewheel doors.

First flight of the first prototype F28 (PH-JHG) was made on 9 May 1967, and the second prototype, PH-WEV, flew on 3 August 1967. The third F28 (PH-MOL) flew for the first time on 20 October 1967 and was brought up to production standard in the early Summer of 1968.

The Dutch RLD granted a C of A to the F28 on 24 February 1969, and the first delivery (of the fourth aircraft, to LTU) was made on the same day. The aircraft received FAA type approval on 24 March 1969, German certification on 30 March 1969 and British CAA type approval in June 1979. RLD certification for operation from unpaved runways was granted in mid-1972. The Mk 1000 was granted FAA-approved noise certification on 31 December 1971. The 100th Fellowship, a Mk 1000 for the Peruvian Air Force, was delivered on 30 March 1976.

A total of 164 Fellowships had been ordered by 13 June 1980, as follows:

Mk 1000/1000C (97 ordered, incl 7 Mk 1000C; orders listed in 1975-76 Jane's, plus 5 Mk 1000 for Garuda)

Mk 2000 (10 ordered; orders listed in 1975-76 Jane's)

Mk 3000

Argentina	3
Cimber Air	2
Garuda Indonesian Airways	7
Ghanaian government	1
Royal Swazi National Airways	1
Tanzanian government	1

Mk 4000

Aerolineas Argentinas	1
Air Anglia	2
Altair Airlines	3
Bangladesh Biman	2
Burma Airways	1
East-West Airlines (Australia)	2
Empire Airlines	2
GATL/Air Ivoire	3
KLM-NLM	4
Linjeflyg (Sweden)	10 (plus 5 on option)
Nigeria Airways	2
Pelita Air Service	2
Undisclosed	8

Seven versions have been announced. Production of the Mks 1000 and 2000 (1976-77 Jane's) ended in 1976 in favour of the Mks 3000 and 4000, and these remained the current production versions in 1980. Details of the Mk 5000 can be found in the 1975-76 Jane's, and of the Mks 6000/6600 in the 1979-80 edition.

Mk 3000. Similar to Mk 4000, but with short fuselage seating up to 65 passengers. Available also in 15-passenger VIP or executive layout, with range of up to 2,200 nm (4,074 km; 2,533 miles). Two of those ordered by Garuda have the optional large cargo door.

Mk 4000. High-density long-fuselage version, first flown on 20 October 1976, to seat up to 85 passengers at 74 cm (29 in) pitch. Uprated Spey Mk 555-15H power plant. Two additional overwing emergency exits (making a total of four).

One Mk 4000 has been completed with uprated Mk 555-15 Spey engines, higher design weights, to enable more fuel to be carried, a strengthened wing of increased span, an engine noise reduction kit, new-look cabin decor and improved flight deck layout.

The following details apply to both the Mk 3000 and Mk 4000, except where a specific model is indicated:

TYPE: Twin-turbofan short/medium-range airliner.

Fokker F28 Mk 4000 short/medium-range transport, in the insignia of Nigeria Airways

WINGS: Cantilever low/mid-wing monoplane. Wing section NACA 0000-X 40Y series with camber varying along span. Thickness/chord ratio up to 14% on inner panels, 10% at tip. Dihedral 2° 30'. Sweepback at quarter-chord 16°. Single-cell two-spar light alloy torsion-box structure, comprising centre-section, integral with fuselage, and two outer panels. Fail-safe construction. Lower skin made of three planks. Taper-rolled top skin. Forged ribs in centre-section, built-up ribs in outer panels. Double-skin leading-edge with ducts for hot-air de-icing. Irreversible hydraulically-operated ailerons. Emergency manual operation of ailerons, through tabs. Hydraulically-operated Fowler double-slotted flaps over 70% of each half-span with electrical emergency extension. Five-section hydraulically-operated lift dumpers in front of flaps on each wing. Trim tab in each aileron.

FUSELAGE: Circular-section semi-monocoque light alloy fail-safe structure, made up of skin panels with Redux-bonded Z-stringers. Bonded doubler plates at door and window cutouts. Quickly-detachable sandwich (metal/end-grain balsa) floor panels. Hydraulically-operated petal airbrakes form aft end of fuselage.

TAIL UNIT: Cantilever light alloy structure, with hydraulically-actuated variable-incidence T tailplane. Electrical emergency actuation of tailplane. Hydraulically-boosted elevators. Hydraulically-operated rudder with duplicated actuators and emergency manual operation. Honeycomb sandwich skin panels used extensively, in conjunction with multiple spars. Double-skin leading-edges for hot-air de-icing.

LANDING GEAR: Retractable tricycle type of Dowty Rotol manufacture, with twin wheels on each unit. Hydraulic retraction, nosewheels forward, main units inward into fuselage. Oleo-pneumatic shock-absorbers. Goodyear wheels, tyres and electronically-controlled braking system. Steerable nosewheel. Main-wheel tyres size 39 × 13, 16-ply rating, pressure 7·59 bars (110 lb/sq in). Low-pressure tyres optional on all units (main-wheel tyre pressure 5·34 bars; 77·5 lb/sq in).

POWER PLANT: Two Rolls-Royce RB.183-2 Spey Mk 555-15H turbofan engines with blade-cooling (each 44 kN; 9,900 lb st, flat rated to 29·7°C), mounted in pod on each side of rear fuselage and fitted with acoustic liners and exhaust silencers. No water injection or thrust reversers. Thermal anti-icing for air intakes. Integral fuel tank in each outer wing panel with total usable capacity of 9,740 litres (2,143 Imp gallons). Optional seven bladder-type tank units in wing centre-section with total usable capacity of 3,300 litres (726 Imp gallons). Single refuelling point under starboard wing, near root.

ACCOMMODATION: Crew of two side by side on flight deck, with jump-seat for third crew member. Electrically-heated windscreen. Pantry/baggage space immediately aft of flight deck on starboard side, followed by entrance lobby with hydraulically-operated airstair door on port side, service and emergency door on starboard side, and seat for cabin attendant. Additional emergency door on each side of main cabin, over wing (two each side on Mk 4000). Main cabin layout of Mk 3000 can be varied to accommodate 55, 60 or 65 passengers five abreast at 94, 81/84 or 79 cm (37, 32/33 or 31 in) seat pitch respectively. In Mk 4000, layout can accommodate up to 85 passengers at 74 cm (29 in) pitch. Aft of cabin are a wardrobe (port), baggage compartment (port) and toilet compartment (starboard). Underfloor cargo compartments fore and aft of wing, with single door on starboard side of forward hold, with one door on rear hold of each version.

SYSTEMS: Garrett-AiResearch air-conditioning system, using engine bleed air. Max pressure differential 0·51 bars (7·45 lb/sq in). Two independent hydraulic systems, pressure 207 bars (3,000 lb/sq in). Primary system for flight controls, landing gear, nosewheel steering and brakes; secondary system for duplication of certain essential flight controls. Westinghouse all-AC electrical system utilises two 20kVA engine-driven generators to supply three-phase constant-frequency 115/200V 400Hz power. One 20Ah battery for starting APU and for emergency power. Garrett-AiResearch GTCP 36-4A APU, mounted aft of rear pressure bulkhead, for engine starting, ground air-conditioning and ground electrical power, and to drive a third AC generator for standby use on essential services in flight.

AVIONICS AND EQUIPMENT: Standard avionics include Collins VHF transceivers, Collins VHF navigation system (with glideslope), DME, marker beacon receiver, RCA weather radar, ADF, ATC transponder, dual compass system, interphone and public address systems, Smiths SEP6 autopilot, Collins FD 108 flight director, flight guidance caution system, Fairchild flight data recorder and Fairchild voice recorder. Menasco powered flight controls. Thermal bleed air system for wing leading-edges, tailplane leading-edge and engine air intakes. Optional equipment to customer's requirements, including equipment for operation in Cat. 2 weather minima.

Fokker F28 Fellowship Mk 4000 high-density short/medium-range transport aircraft *(Pilot Press)*

DIMENSIONS, EXTERNAL:

Wing span	25·07 m (82 ft 3 in)
Wing chord at root	4·80 m (15 ft 9 in)
Length overall: 3000	27·40 m (89 ft 10¾ in)
4000	29·61 m (97 ft 1¾ in)
Length of fuselage: 3000	24·55 m (80 ft 6½ in)
4000	26·76 m (87 ft 9½ in)
Fuselage: Max width	3·30 m (10 ft 10 in)
Height overall	8·47 m (27 ft 9½ in)
Tailplane span	8·64 m (28 ft 4¼ in)
Wheel track (c/l of shock-absorbers)	5·04 m (16 ft 6½ in)
Wheelbase: 3000	8·90 m (29 ft 2½ in)
4000	10·35 m (33 ft 11½ in)
Passenger door (fwd, port):	
Height	1·93 m (6 ft 4 in)
Width	0·86 m (2 ft 10 in)
Service/emergency door (fwd, stbd):	
Height	1·27 m (4 ft 2 in)
Width	0·61 m (2 ft 0 in)
Emergency exits (centre, each):	
Height	0·91 m (3 ft 0 in)
Width	0·51 m (1 ft 8 in)
Freight hold doors (each):	
Height (fwd, each)	0·90 m (2 ft 11½ in)
Height (aft)	0·80 m (2 ft 7½ in)
Width (fwd, each)	0·95 m (3 ft 1½ in)
Width (aft)	0·89 m (2 ft 11 in)
Height to sill (fwd, each)	1·47 m (4 ft 10 in)
Height to sill (aft)	1·59 m (5 ft 2½ in)
Baggage door (rear, port, optional):	
Height	0·60 m (1 ft 11½ in)
Width	0·51 m (1 ft 8 in)
Cargo door (fwd, port, optional):	
Height	1·87 m (6 ft 1¾ in)
Width	2·49 m (8 ft 2 in)
Height to sill	2·24 m (7 ft 4¼ in)

DIMENSIONS, INTERNAL:

Cabin, excl flight deck:	
Length: 3000	13·10 m (43 ft 0 in)
4000	15·31 m (50 ft 3 in)
Max length of seating area:	
3000	10·74 m (35 ft 2¾ in)
4000	12·95 m (42 ft 6¾ in)
Max width	3·10 m (10 ft 2 in)
Max height	2·02 m (6 ft 7¼ in)
Floor area: 3000	38·4 m² (413·3 sq ft)
4000	44·8 m² (482·2 sq ft)
Volume: 3000	71·5 m³ (2,525 cu ft)
4000	83·0 m³ (2,931 cu ft)
Freight hold (underfloor, fwd):	
3000	6·90 m³ (245 cu ft)
4000	8·70 m³ (308 cu ft)
Freight hold (underfloor, rear):	
3000	3·80 m³ (135 cu ft)
4000	4·80 m³ (160 cu ft)
Baggage hold (aft of cabin), max:	
3000, 4000	2·30 m³ (81·22 cu ft)

AREAS:

Wings, gross	79·00 m² (850 sq ft)
Ailerons (total)	2·67 m² (28·74 sq ft)
Trailing-edge flaps (total)	14·00 m² (150·7 sq ft)
Fuselage airbrakes (total)	3·62 m² (38·97 sq ft)
Fin (incl dorsal fin)	12·30 m² (132·4 sq ft)
Rudder	2·30 m² (24·6 sq ft)
Tailplane	19·50m² (209·9 sq ft)
Elevators (total)	3·84 m² (41·33 sq ft)

WEIGHTS AND LOADINGS:

Operating weight empty:	
3000, 65 seats	16,620 kg (36,642 lb)
4000, 85 seats	17,359 kg (38,269 lb)
Max weight-limited payload:	
3000	8,985 kg (19,810 lb)
4000	8,963 kg (19,760 lb)

Fuel load: standard	7,703 kg (16,982 lb)
with optional centre-section tanks	
	10,313 kg (22,736 lb)
Max T-O weight:	
3000, 4000	33,110 kg (73,000 lb)
Max zero-fuel weight:	
3000	25,400 kg (56,000 lb)
4000	28,118 kg (62,000 lb)
Max landing weight: 3000	29,030 kg (64,000 lb)
*4000	30,160 kg (66,500 lb)
Max wing loading:	
3000, 4000	407 kg/m² (83·4 lb/sq ft)
Max cabin floor loading:	
all passenger versions	366 kg/m² (75 lb/sq ft)
Max power loading:	
3000, 4000	367·5 kg/kN (3·6 lb/lb st)

*_in process of certification_

PERFORMANCE (Mks 3000 and 4000 at AUW of 29,000 kg; 63,934 lb, ISA, except where indicated):

Never-exceed speed	
Mach 0·83 (390 knots; 723 km/h; 449 mph) EAS	
Max permissible operating speed	
Mach 0·75 (330 knots; 611 km/h; 380 mph) EAS	
Max cruising speed at 7,000 m (23,000 ft)	
	455 knots (843 km/h; 523 mph)
Econ cruising speed at 9,150 m (30,000 ft)	
	366 knots (678 km/h; 421 mph)
Max cruising altitude	10,675 m (35,000 ft)
Min ground turning radius:	
3000	9·60 m (31 ft 6 in)
4000	10·90 m (35 ft 9 in)
Runway LCN at max T-O weight (hard runway):	
standard tyres: 3000	32
4000	31
low-pressure tyres: 3000, 4000	25
Runway LCN at max T-O weight (flexible runway):	
standard tyres: 3000, 4000	25
low-pressure tyres: 3000, 4000	20
FAR T-O field length at max T-O weight:	
S/L	1,590 m (5,217 ft)
S/L, ISA + 10°C	1,635 m (5,364 ft)
S/L, ISA + 15°C	1,710 m (5,610 ft)
610 m (2,000 ft)	1,710 m (5,610 ft)
915 m (3,000 ft)	1,940 m (6,365 ft)
FAR landing field length at max landing weight:	
S/L	965 m (3,166 ft)
1,525 m (5,000 ft)	1,090 m (3,576 ft)
Range, high-speed schedule, FAR 121.645 reserves:	
*3000, 65 passengers	
	975 nm (1,805 km; 1,122 miles)
4000, 85 passengers	
	900 nm (1,667 km; 1,036 miles)
Range, long-range schedule, FAR 121.645 reserves:	
*3000, 65 passengers	
	1,400 nm (2,593 km; 1,611 miles)
4000, 85 passengers	
	1,000 nm (1,853 km; 1,151 miles)

*_With wing centre-section tanks_

OPERATIONAL NOISE LEVELS (FAR Pt 36, estimated):

T-O	91·5 EPNdB
Approach	98 EPNdB
Sideline	97·5 EPNdB

FOKKER F29

As a further development of the F28 Fellowship, Fokker has for some time been studying various proposals for a 'stretched' version, with a new wing of increased span and more efficient section, and having a lengthened fuselage. Initial studies led by early 1979 to a 'Super F28', with seating for 115-130 passengers and retaining the rear-engined configuration of the F28.

Further studies during that year, however, led to the belief that market requirements would be served better by an aircraft with somewhat greater seating capacity,

Fokker F29 twin-turbofan short/medium-range transport *(Pilot Press)*

arranged in a six-abreast layout, instead of five abreast as in the Super F28 proposal. These conclusions resulted in the design of a totally new and larger aircraft, designated F29, with a wide-body fuselage and pod-mounted under-wing engines. Passenger capacity is increased to 138 (standard) and 156 (maximum), in a 'double bubble' fuselage identical in cross-section to that of the Boeing 737.

The largest aircraft ever designed by Fokker, the F29 will have two new-generation high bypass turbofan engines, offering a fuel consumption some 25 per cent lower, and direct operating costs per seat/mile at least 10 per cent better, than the current generation of 100/200-passenger twin-turbofan transports. Subject to an early go-ahead (expected in mid 1981), first flight is scheduled for 1983, with deliveries to begin in 1985.

TYPE: Twin-turbofan short/medium-range transport.
WINGS: Cantilever low/mid-wing monoplane. Sweepback 21° at quarter-chord. Dihedral from roots. Two-segment double-slotted Fowler-type flaps over approx three-quarters of each half-span. Four lift dumpers and three spoiler ailerons forward of flaps. Three-segment full-span leading-edge slats on each wing. Trim tab in each aileron.
FUSELAGE: Semi-monocoque pressurised structure, of 'double bubble' section identical to that of Boeing 737. Petal-type airbrakes form fuselage tailcone when closed.
TAIL UNIT: Cantilever T tail, generally similar to that of Fokker F28, with sweepback on all surfaces. Double-segment rudder.
LANDING GEAR: Retractable tricycle type, with twin wheels on each unit. Nose unit retracts forward, main units inward into wing centre-section/fuselage fairing.
POWER PLANT: Two turbofan engines in the 84·5/89 kN (19,000/20,000 lb st) class: either the Rolls-Royce/JAE RJ.500-01/D4 or the CFM International CFM56-3, mounted in underwing pods.
ACCOMMODATION: Crew of two or three on flight deck. Six-abreast seating in main cabin, with single aisle, for 138 passengers at 86 cm (34 in) pitch, or a maximum of 156 passengers at 76 cm (30 in) pitch. Passenger door at front and rear of cabin on each side. Underfloor cargo hold, accessible via one door forward and one aft of

wing on starboard side. Two overwing emergency exits on each side.
AVIONICS AND EQUIPMENT: Flight deck will be equipped with latest digital avionics, conforming to ARINC specifications.

DIMENSIONS, EXTERNAL:

Wing span	32·88 m (107 ft 10½ in)
Wing aspect ratio	10
Length overall	39·30 m (128 ft 11¼ in)
Length of fuselage	35·84 m (117 ft 7 in)
Fuselage: Max width	3·76 m (12 ft 4 in)
Max depth	4·01 m (13 ft 2 in)
Height overall	11·14 m (36 ft 6½ in)
Wheel track	6·85 m (22 ft 5¾ in)
Wheelbase	12·31 m (40 ft 4¾ in)

DIMENSIONS, INTERNAL:

Cabin: Length	25·84 m (84 ft 9¼ in)
Max width	3·56 m (11 ft 8¼ in)
Max height	2·10 m (6 ft 10¾ in)
Cargo hold volume	36·7 m³ (1,296 cu ft)

AREA:

Wings, gross	108·0 m² (1,162·5 sq ft)

WEIGHTS:
Typical operating weight empty:

RJ.500-01	33,720 kg (74,340 lb)
CFM56-3	34,000 kg (74,955 lb)
Fuel load	18,600 kg (41,005 lb)
Max T-O weight	59,770 kg (131,770 lb)
Max landing weight	55,300 kg (121,915 lb)
Max zero-fuel weight	50,800 kg (111,995 lb)

PERFORMANCE (estimated):
Max operating speed
Mach 0·79 (330 knots; 611 km/h; 380 mph EAS)
Econ cruising speed   Mach 0·75
Approach speed at max landing weight
120 knots (222 km/h; 138 mph)
Max cruising altitude   11,275 m (37,000 ft)
FAR T-O field length at max T-O weight (S/L, ISA + 15°C)
2,134 m (7,000 ft)
FAR landing field length at typical mission weight
1,220 m (4,000 ft)
Range with 138 passengers
1,700 nm (3,150 km; 1,957 miles)

OPERATIONAL NOISE LEVELS (estimated):
T-O   85 EPNdB

NEW ZEALAND

AEROSPACE
NEW ZEALAND AEROSPACE INDUSTRIES LIMITED
HEAD OFFICE AND WORKS: Hamilton Airport, R.D.2, Hamilton
Telephone: Hamilton 436 144 and 436 069
Telex: NZAIL 21242
GENERAL MANAGER: P. W. Goldsbro'
CHIEF DESIGNER: P. W. C. Monk
MARKETING MANAGER: H. J. I. Baxter
ENGINEERING MANAGER: L. C. Burrows
COMPANY SECRETARY: J. D. Linch

Aero Engine Services Ltd and Air Parts (NZ) Ltd (see *1972-73 Jane's*) amalgamated on 1 April 1973 to form New Zealand Aerospace Industries Ltd. This company has a share capital of $NZ 1·6 million, half of which is held by Air New Zealand (representing government support), one-third by New Zealand's largest agricultural operator, and the remainder by shareholders of the two constituent companies.

The company now produces the piston-engined Fletcher FU-24-954 and turboprop-powered Cresco agricultural aircraft, in a 5,574 m² (60,000 sq ft) main facility located at Hamilton Airport.

AEROSPACE FLETCHER FU-24-954
The FU-24 was developed by the Sargent-Fletcher Company of El Monte, California, USA, initially for agricultural top-dressing work in New Zealand. The prototype flew in July 1954, followed by the first production aircraft five months later. Type certification was granted on 22 July 1955. All manufacturing and sales rights for the FU-24 were acquired by Air Parts (NZ) Ltd in 1964, and production was undertaken subsequently in that company's factory at Hamilton Airport, New Zealand.

The initial production series of 100 was delivered to New Zealand operators for top-dressing work. By June 1979, a total of 272 completed Fletcher aircraft had been produced, including 56 for export to Australia, Bangladesh, Dubai, Iraq, Pakistan, Thailand, Uruguay and the USA. Up to early 1979 all foreign deliveries had been effected by solo delivery flights, but export then began of PKD and CKD (parts knock-down and component knock-down) aircraft to Frontier Aerospace Ltd, a subsidiary in Long Beach, California, USA.

The current model, to which the following description applies, is the FU-24-954. This now has a large cargo door as standard, the earlier small door (see *1979-80 Jane's*) having been discontinued.
TYPE: Agricultural and general-purpose aircraft.
WINGS: Cantilever low-wing monoplane. Constant-chord non-swept wings of NACA 4415 section. Dihedral (outer panels) 8°. Incidence 2°. Light alloy two-spar structure. Plain horn-balanced ailerons and single-slotted flaps, all of light alloy construction. Single row of vortex generators forward of each aileron.
FUSELAGE: All-metal semi-monocoque structure. Cockpit area stressed for 25g impact.
TAIL UNIT: Cantilever light alloy structure. All-movable horizontal tail with full-span anti-servo and trim tab. Ground-adjustable tab on rudder.

LANDING GEAR: Non-retractable tricycle type, with steer-able nosewheel. Fletcher air-oil shock-absorber struts. Cleveland wheels and hydraulic disc brakes on main units. Goodyear tyres, size 8·50-6 (6-ply), pressure range 0·76-2·07 bars (11-30 lb/sq in).
POWER PLANT: One 298 kW (400 hp) Avco Lycoming IO-720-A1A or A1B flat-eight engine, driving a Hartzell HC-C3YR-1R/847SR three-blade constant-speed variable-pitch metal propeller with spinner. Fuel tanks in wing leading-edges; total usable capacity 254 litres (67 US gallons), normal, 481 litres (127 US gallons) with optional long-range tanks.
ACCOMMODATION (Agricultural models): Enclosed cockpit for pilot and one passenger on side-by-side seats under rearward-sliding canopy. Cockpit reinforced for over-turn/crash protection. Large port-side cargo door,

Aerospace Fletcher FU-24-954, fitted with an Easton hopper box under the fuselage and showing the now-standard large port-side door

optional on early production aircraft, is now standard. Optional features include additional cargo floor area and dual controls.

ACCOMMODATION (Utility models): Enclosed cabin for pilot and up to seven passengers or equivalent freight. Dual controls optional. Rearward-sliding hood over front two seats. Large passenger/cargo door on port side.

AGRICULTURAL EQUIPMENT: Glassfibre hopper aft of cockpit, capacity 1,045 litres (230 Imp gallons; 276 US gallons) of liquid, 1,066 kg (2,350 lb) of dry chemicals. Hopper outlets for spreading of solids (fertiliser, dry ice, poison bait, etc). Transland Swathmaster for topdressing, seeding and high-volume spraying. Transland Boommaster for liquid spraying with booms, nozzles, fan-driven pump, etc, for low- and high-volume spraying. Micronair spraying equipment with electrically- or fan-driven pump, varied control systems, side-loading valve for liquids, and special adaptor plate for interchangeability of equipment.

OPTIONAL EQUIPMENT (all models): Full blind-flying instrumentation with ADF, VHF, VOR and DME. Full dual controls; dual main wheels and brakes, wheel and leg fairings; long-range fuel tanks; cabin heating and air-conditioning systems; metric instrumentation.

DIMENSIONS, EXTERNAL:

Wing span	12·81 m (42 ft 0 in)
Wing chord (constant)	2·13 m (7 ft 0 in)
Wing aspect ratio	6
Length overall	9·70 m (31 ft 10 in)
Height to top of fin	2·84 m (9 ft 4 in)
Fuselage: Max width	1·22 m (4 ft 0 in)
Max depth	1·52 m (5 ft 0 in)
Tailplane span	4·22 m (13 ft 10 in)
Wheel track	3·71 m (12 ft 2 in)
Wheelbase	2·28 m (7 ft 6 in)
Propeller diameter	2·18 m (7 ft 2 in)
Propeller ground clearance	0·33 m (12·8 in)

Passenger/cargo door (port, rear):

Height	0·97 m (3 ft 2 in)
Width	0·94 m (3 ft 1 in)

DIMENSIONS, INTERNAL:

Cabin: Length	3·18 m (10 ft 5 in)
Max width	1·22 m (4 ft 0 in)
Max height	1·27 m (4 ft 2 in)
Floor area	3·87 m² (41·7 sq ft)
Volume aft of hopper	3·37 m³ (119·0 cu ft)
Hopper volume	1·22 m³ (43·0 cu ft)

AREAS:

Wings, gross	27·31 m² (294 sq ft)
Ailerons (total)	1·82 m² (19·6 sq ft)
Trailing-edge flaps (total)	3·16 m² (34·0 sq ft)
Fin	1·26 m² (13·6 sq ft)
Rudder	0·64 m² (6·9 sq ft)
Tailplane	4·00 m² (43·1 sq ft)
Tailplane tab	0·45 m² (4·9 sq ft)

WEIGHTS AND LOADINGS:

Weight empty, equipped	1,188 kg (2,620 lb)
Max payload (agricultural)	1,052 kg (2,320 lb)
Normal max T-O weight	2,204 kg (4,860 lb)
Max agricultural T-O weight	2,463 kg (5,430 lb)
Cabin floor loading	1,885 kg (386 lb/m²)
Normal wing loading	80·6 kg/m² (16·5 lb/sq ft)
Normal power loading	7·40 kg/kW (12·15 lb/hp)

PERFORMANCE (at Normal max T-O weight):

Never-exceed speed	143 knots (265 km/h; 165 mph)
Max level speed at S/L	126 knots (233 km/h; 145 mph)
Max cruising speed (75% power)	113 knots (209 km/h; 130 mph)

Operating speed for spraying (75% power)
90-115 knots (167-212 km/h; 104-132 mph)

Stalling speed:

flaps up	55 knots (102 km/h; 63·5 mph)
flaps down	49 knots (91 km/h; 57 mph)
Max rate of climb at S/L	280 m (920 ft)/min
Service ceiling	4,875 m (16,000 ft)
T-O run	244 m (800 ft)
T-O to 15 m (50 ft)	372 m (1,220 ft)
Landing from 15 m (50 ft)	390 m (1,280 ft)
Landing run	207 m (680 ft)

Swath width (agricultural models):

oily	23 m (75 ft)
aqueous	21·3-24·4 m (70-80 ft)
dust	7·6-15·2 m (25-50 ft)

Range with max normal fuel, 45 min reserves
383 nm (709 km; 441 miles)

AEROSPACE CRESCO 600

Design of this turboprop development of the FU-24 began in 1977. Construction of a prototype started in the following year, and this aircraft (ZK-LTP) first flew on 28 February 1979. Powered by an Avco Lycoming LTP 101-600 turboprop engine, the Cresco 600 has many components interchangeable with the FU-24-954. Use of this engine, together with some structural refinement, permits a reduction in empty weight and a substantial increase in agricultural max T-O weight. The name Cresco is Latin for 'I grow'.

Aerospace Cresco 600 agricultural aircraft, with additional side view (bottom) of Fletcher FU-24-954
(Michael A. Badrocke)

Despite the later loss of the prototype in a flying accident, certification of the Cresco 600 was well under way in 1980, and the first production aircraft had flown by the Summer of that year. Five Cresco 600s had been ordered by the beginning of 1980.

The description of the FU-24-954 applies also to the Cresco 600, except in the following respects:

TYPE: Turboprop-powered agricultural and general-purpose aircraft.

WINGS: As FU-24-954, constructed mainly of 2014, 2024 and 6061 light alloys. Ground-adjustable tab in each aileron.

FUSELAGE: Similar to FU-24-954, with slight increase in length.

TAIL UNIT: As FU-24-954, but larger and constructed mainly of 2024, 6061 and L65 light alloys.

LANDING GEAR: As FU-24-954 but with NZ Aerospace Industries air-oil shock-absorber struts; tyres size 8·50-6 on nosewheel and size 8·50-10 on main wheels.

POWER PLANT: One 447 kW (600 shp) Avco Lycoming LTP 101-600A-1A turboprop engine, driving a Hartzell HC-B3TN-3D/T10282 H three-blade constant-speed metal propeller with spinner. Four fuel tanks in wing centre-section, total capacity 545·5 litres (120 Imp gallons). Two refuelling points in upper surface of each wing. Oil capacity 5·5 litres (1·2 Imp gallons). Variable-geometry inertia separating intake under nose.

ACCOMMODATION: Pilot only, or crew of two side by side, under rearward-sliding bulged cockpit hood. Tinted windscreen and canopy side panels standard. Dual controls available optionally. Large forward-hinged door, with window, aft of wing on port side. Generous cargo space immediately aft of hopper. Cockpit ventilated; heating system optional.

SYSTEMS: No air-conditioning, pressurisation, hydraulic, pneumatic or oxygen systems. Electrical system powered by 24V 150A Auxilec starter/generator and two 24V 25Ah lead-acid batteries.

AVIONICS: Range of Narco or Becker avionics available, including VHF, VOR, ADF and transponder. Stall warning system standard.

AGRICULTURAL EQUIPMENT: Generally similar to FU-24-954, except for substantially larger hopper, increasing capacity to 1,777 litres (391 Imp gallons) of liquid or 1,860 kg (4,100 lb) of dry chemical. Range of dispersal systems available to customer's requirements, from ultra-high-volume solids dispersal to ultra-low-volume spray.

DIMENSIONS, EXTERNAL: As FU-24-954 except:

Length overall	11·06 m (36 ft 3¼ in)
Length of fuselage	10·74 m (35 ft 2¾ in)
Height overall	3·42 m (11 ft 2½ in)
Tailplane span	4·61 m (15 ft 1½ in)
Wheelbase	2·77 m (9 ft 1¼ in)
Propeller diameter	2·59 m (8 ft 6 in)
Propeller ground clearance (static)	0·38 m (1 ft 3 in)

Cargo door (port):

Height	0·94 m (3 ft 1 in)
Width	0·94 m (3 ft 1 in)
Height to sill	0·91 m (3 ft 0 in)

DIMENSIONS, INTERNAL:

Cargo compartment volume (aft of hopper)
3·40 m³ (120·0 cu ft)

Hopper volume	1·77 m³ (62·5 cu ft)

AREAS:

Wings, gross	27·31 m² (294·0 sq ft)
Ailerons (total)	2·08 m² (22·4 sq ft)
Trailing-edge flaps (total)	3·06 m² (32·9 sq ft)
Fin	1·53 m² (16·5 sq ft)
Rudder, incl tab	0·63 m² (6·8 sq ft)
Tailplane, incl tab	5·08 m² (54·7 sq ft)

WEIGHTS AND LOADINGS:

Weight empty, equipped	1,161 kg (2,560 lb)

Max disposable load (Agricultural, incl fuel)
1,929 kg (4,254 lb)

Max fuel load	435 kg (960 lb)
Max T-O weight: Normal	2,925 kg (6,450 lb)
Agricultural	3,175 kg (7,000 lb)
Max landing weight	2,925 kg (6,450 lb)

Max wing loading:

Normal	107·07 kg/m² (21·94 lb/sq ft)
Agricultural	116·19 kg/m² (23·81 lb/sq ft)

Max power loading:

Normal	6·54 kg/kW (10·75 lb/shp)

PERFORMANCE (at max Normal T-O weight, ISA, except where indicated):

Never-exceed speed	177 knots (328 km/h; 204 mph)
Max level speed at S/L	148 knots (274 km/h; 170 mph)
Max cruising speed (75% power)	127 knots (235 km/h; 146 mph)

Stalling speed at 2,767 kg (6,100 lb) AUW, flaps down, power off 52 knots (96·5 km/h; 60 mph)

Max rate of climb at S/L	290 m (950 ft)/min
Service ceiling	6,400 m (21,000 ft)
T-O to 15 m (50 ft)	436 m (1,430 ft)
Landing from 15 m (50 ft)	500 m (1,640 ft)

Range with max fuel, no reserves
460 nm (852 km; 529 miles)

Aerospace Cresco 600 prototype during an early test flight

FLIGHT ENGINEERS
FLIGHT ENGINEERS LTD
PO Box 177, Papakura, Auckland
Telephone: Papakura 89 384

WORKS: Ardmore Aerodrome, Ardmore, Auckland
MANAGING DIRECTOR: J. T. Barr

Flight Engineers Ltd has terminated licence assembly in New Zealand of the Transavia PL-12 Airtruk, described in the Australian section. Further involvement in the Airtruk programme will be limited to a minor subassembly role.

PAKISTAN

According to the French magazine *Air et Cosmos*, a new aircraft overhaul and maintenance facility was inaugurated in the Summer of 1978 at Kamra, about 65 km (40 miles) from Rawalpindi. The factory, intended as the nucleus of a Pakistani aircraft manufacturing industry, was to overhaul Shenyang F-6 (MiG-19) and Dassault Mirage aircraft of the Pakistan Air Force, and was also, it was reported, to undertake production of the **Mushaak**, a training aircraft said to be of Swedish origin — presumably the Saab Supporter, a number of which were supplied to Pakistan by Sweden.

PHILIPPINES

PADC
PHILIPPINE AEROSPACE DEVELOPMENT CORPORATION
PADC Building, Domestic Terminal Avenue, Pasay, Metro Manila

Telephone: 839081 to 839088

Telex: 63883 PADC PN and 2114 AER PH

PRESIDENT: Roberto H. Lim
EXECUTIVE VICE-PRESIDENT: Pedro Q. Molina
TREASURER: Mila Abarro

CONTROLLER: Eloisa Valerio

DIRECTOR, MANAGEMENT SERVICES: Mario B. Antonio

BOARD OF DIRECTORS:
José Dans
Juan Ponce Enrile
Vicente Paterno
Geronimo Velasco
Panfilo Domingo
Roberto H. Lim
Placido Mapa Jr
Roman Cruz Jr

SUBSIDIARIES:
National Aero Manufacturing Corporation (NAM) (aircraft manufacture and assembly)
Philippine Aero Transport Inc (PATI) (air cargo operations)
Philippine Helicopter Services Inc (PHSI) (maintenance and overhaul of BO 105 helicopters)
Phillippine Resource Helicopters Inc (PRHI) (helicopter support and services for oil drilling operations)

PADC is a government corporation established in 1973 by President Ferdinand E. Marcos to promote the development of an aerospace industry in the Philippines.

NAM
NATIONAL AERO MANUFACTURING CORPORATION (A subsidiary of Philippine Aerospace Development Corporation)
PO Box 2023, Makati Commercial Centre; or Manila International Airport, Pasay City
WORKS: PADC Hangar No. 3, MIA Road, Pasay City; PADC Hangar No. 4, Sangley Point, Cavite City
PRESIDENT: Roberto H. Lim

PADC (MBB) BO 105
In 1974, PADC began an assembly and manufacturing programme for the BO 105C helicopter, under a licence agreement with MBB of West Germany. By mid-1979 a total of 38 had been assembled from knocked-down kits.

A new programme for six additional helicopters for export, and another six for PADC's own marketing needs, was then being negotiated; no further details of this programme have been received from the company, but the Philippine Navy is reported to have ordered an additional nine BO 105s.

NAM assembles/fabricates 45 per cent of the necessary components, importing the rest and exporting some components to MBB, including cargo and battery doors, oil drip pans, main relay boxes, overhead panels, nose doors, tailbooms, windscreen wipers and duct halves.

PADC (PILATUS BRITTEN-NORMAN) ISLANDER
Under a 1974 agreement between PADC and Britten-Norman, six Islanders were delivered to PADC from the UK. Fourteen unpainted aircraft, delivered to PADC without cabin trim, furnishings and avionics, were completed in 1975.

In 1976 NAM completed the assembly of 35 Islanders from completely knocked-down Britten-Norman kits. This phase included manufacture by NAM of ailerons, flaps, elevators, tailplanes, vertical fins, rudders, left centre boxes, fuselages and GRP parts.

The fourth phase, involving the assembly of 60 aircraft (of which 25 were to have been repurchased by Britten-Norman), was suspended when Pilatus acquired Britten-Norman in 1978. No further news of this programme has been received from the company, but it was reported in 1980 that PADC was to supply a further undisclosed number of Islanders/Maritime Defenders to the Philippine Navy.

PADC/NSDB FIXED-WING AIRCRAFT PROTOTYPE
This prototype development project is a joint venture between PADC and the Philippine government's National Science Development Board (NSDB); the Metals Industry Research and Development Center (MIRDC) is co-operating in the programme.

The aircraft is an all-metal, externally-braced high-wing monoplane, accommodating four persons including the pilot. It is intended to carry passengers or cargo, and will be easily convertible into an agricultural crop dusting or seeding aircraft, with the necessary manoeuvrability to carry out such operations over small field areas.

Phase 1 of the programme, which began in October 1975, covered the preliminary design and engineering studies necessary to ensure smooth development; phase 2, which began in January 1976, concerns the detail design, construction and flight testing of a prototype.

No recent news of this programme has been received.
TYPE: Four-seat light utility and agricultural aircraft.
WINGS: High-wing monoplane, braced by a single strut on each side. Wing section NACA 2415 (constant). No anhedral, dihedral or sweepback. Incidence 2°. Trailing-edge flaps and ailerons over virtually entire span. Turned-down wingtips.
FUSELAGE: All-metal pod and boom type.
TAIL UNIT: Cantilever all-metal structure, with slight sweepback on vertical surfaces. Shallow dorsal fin. Balanced rudder and balanced one-piece elevator.

LANDING GEAR: Non-retractable tricycle type. All three wheels same size. Streamline wheel fairing on each unit.
POWER PLANT: One 224 kW (300 hp) Avco Lycoming IO-540-K1B5 flat-six engine, driving a Hartzell constant-speed variable-pitch propeller with spinner. Fuel tank in each wing, combined capacity 189 litres (50 US gallons; 41·5 Imp gallons). Overwing refuelling point above each tank. Oil capacity 11·4 litres (3 US gallons; 2·5 Imp gallons).
ACCOMMODATION: Pilot and up to three passengers, in pairs, in fully-enclosed cabin. Forward-opening car-type door on each side, each with pull-in window for emergency exit. Freight/baggage space aft of rear pair of seats, access to which is via clamshell rear-loading doors. Cabin ventilated.
DIMENSIONS, EXTERNAL:

Wing span	11·66 m (38 ft 3 in)
Wing chord (constant)	1·52 m (5 ft 0 in)
Wing aspect ratio	7·65
Length overall	8·43 m (27 ft 8 in)
Height overall	3·55 m (11 ft 7¾ in)
Tailplane span	3·48 m (11 ft 5 in)
Wheel track	2·40 m (7 ft 10½ in)
Wheelbase	2·20 m (7 ft 2½ in)
Propeller diameter	1·95 m (6 ft 4¾ in)
Propeller ground clearance	0·25 m (10 in)

DIMENSIONS, INTERNAL:

Cabin: Length	2·95 m (9 ft 8 in)
Max width	1·04 m (3 ft 5 in)
Max height	1·22 m (4 ft 0 in)
Floor area	3·07 m² (33·0 sq ft)
Volume	3·82 m³ (135·0 cu ft)
Baggage compartment volume	0·85 m³ (30·0 cu ft)
Freight compartment volume	1·69 m³ (59·6 cu ft)

AREAS:

Wings, gross	17·77 m² (191·3 sq ft)
Ailerons (total)	2·14 m² (23·0 sq ft)
Trailing-edge flaps (total)	1·95 m² (21·0 sq ft)
Fin	1·67 m² (18·0 sq ft)
Rudder	0·84 m² (9·0 sq ft)
Tailplane	3·34 m² (36·0 sq ft)
Elevator	1·51 m² (16·2 sq ft)

WEIGHTS AND LOADINGS (estimated):

Weight empty	992 kg (2,188 lb)
Max T-O weight	1,496 kg (3,300 lb)
Max wing loading	84·2 kg/m² (17·25 lb/sq ft)
Max power loading	3·72 kg/kW (11·0 lb/hp)

PERFORMANCE (estimated, at max T-O weight):

Max level speed at S/L	168·5 knots (312 km/h; 194 mph)
Max cruising speed at S/L	154·5 knots (286 km/h; 178 mph)
Stalling speed, flaps up	55·5 knots (103 km/h; 64 mph)
Stalling speed, flaps down	46·5 knots (86 km/h; 53·5 mph)
Max rate of climb at S/L	372 m (1,220 ft)/min
Service ceiling	5,300 m (17,400 ft)
T-O run	204 m (669 ft)
T-O to 15 m (50 ft)	436 m (1,430 ft)
Landing from 15 m (50 ft)	568 m (1,865 ft)
Landing run	305 m (1,000 ft)
Max range	424 nm (785 km; 488 miles)

General arrangement of the PADC/NSDB prototype four-seat utility aircraft *(Michael A. Badrocke)*

PAF
PHILIPPINE AIR FORCE
Headquarters PAF, Nichols Air Base, Pasay City

PAF (AJI) T-610 CALI (SUPER PINTO)
The Self-Reliance Development Wing of the PAF acquired from American Jet Industries the prototype of the latter company's tandem two-seat COIN version of the Temco TT-1 Pinto, together with the works drawings and rights to the design and production of this aircraft.

The Super Pinto, last described in the 1972-73 edition of *Jane's*, is a light strike version of the TT-1 trainer, powered by a 12·7 kN (2,850 lb st) General Electric CJ610-4 turbojet engine (in place of the original Turboméca Marboré) and equipped with six underwing hardpoints for external stores.

No news of future plans for this aircraft has been received since the Autumn of 1978. All known details were given in the 1979-80 *Jane's*.

PATS/NSDB
PHILIPPINE AIR TRANSPORT & TRAINING SERVICES INC (PATS School of Aeronautics)/NATIONAL SCIENCE DEVELOPMENT BOARD
PRESIDENT: Ambrosio R. Valdez Sr

As a joint venture, the PATS School of Aeronautics and the National Science Development Board have undertaken two fairly simple aeronautical projects designed to utilise local raw materials. These are the Project 7307En light aircraft and the XG-001 two-seat aircraft.

PATS/NSDB RESEARCH PROJECTS
In a research programme, PATS and the NSDB conducted a project (No. 7307En) entitled 'Research on local fabric, local woods and local aluminium for aircraft use'. Tests were carried out, and the results of evaluation were utilised in the construction of the **PATS Bamboo Aircraft**, which logged more than 26 h of extensive testing. A proposal to continue with this project was awaiting approval in mid-1979.

In a related programme (No. 7714En, entitled 'Research on the utilisation of alcohol and/or alcohol/gasoline as fuel for light aircraft'), some 6½ h of flight testing were completed during the first year of research, using 100% alcohol as fuel in a Cessna 150 lightplane. This programme was then terminated by the NSDB owing to lack of funds.

However, in early 1980 the PATS School of Aeronautics had appealed for permission to continue the programme, with emphasis on flight performance under full load conditions and the resulting effects of prolonged usage of 100% alcohol fuel on the engine and its aluminium parts.

POLAND

PZL
POLSKIE ZAKLADY LOTNICZE, ZJEDNOCZENIE PRZEMYSLU LOTNICZEGO I SILNIKOWEGO PZL (Polish Aviation Works, Aircraft and Engine Industry Union)
HEAD OFFICE: ul. Miodowa 5, 00251 Warszawa
Telephone: Warszawa 279985

Telex: 814281

MANAGING DIRECTOR: Krzysztof Kuczynski, ME

VICE-DIRECTOR: Kazimierz Brejnak, ME

The Polish aircraft industry remains under the central management of the Zjednoczenie Przemyslu Lotniczego i Silnikowego PZL (Aircraft and Engine Industry Union).

The manufacture of aircraft in Poland began in 1910. In 1928 an industrial syndicate was established, grouping the existing aircraft factories into the Panstwowe Zaklady Lotnicze (State Aviation Works) to produce aircraft to meet domestic and export needs.

More than half a century of tradition in design and manufacture resulted in the production of several tens of thousands of aircraft, helicopters and gliders of various types, as well as of aero-engines and equipment.

The PZL Aircraft and Engine Industry Union currently comprises 24 factories, scientific and development units, technical and commercial organisations, which between them employ about 100,000 qualified workers. The work of the Union has a broad base which includes research, design, development, manufacture, foreign trade, agricultural aviation services, and technical support for its own products which are operated by other countries.

Production by the Polish aviation industry relies substantially on aircraft, engines and equipment of its own design, as well as on co-operation and co-production with leading foreign aircraft manufacturers in both the East and the West. These programmes currently include the PZL-104 Wilga, PZL-106 Kruk, PZL M-18 Dromader and PZL M-15 low/medium/high-capacity agricultural aircraft; component assembly (deliveries of which began in March 1979) for the Soviet Il-86 wide-bodied transport aircraft; the TS-11 Iskra, PZL-110 Koliber and PZL M-20 Mewa light multi-purpose, training and sporting aircraft; local-service passenger transports such as the Soviet-designed An-2 and An-28; the Mi-2, PZL-Sokól and PZL-Kania low/medium-capacity helicopters for agricultural, medical and transport operations; a wide range of sailplanes and motor gliders, including the Jantar, Puchacz and Ogar; piston, turbojet and turboprop engines; plus aircraft military equipment, propellers, and ground equipment for agricultural aircraft and helicopters, under the control of the PZL Union.

The export sales of all Polish aviation products are handled by Pezetel Foreign Trade Enterprise of the Aviation Industry, under the control of the Aircraft and Engine Industry Union.

Pezetel Foreign Trade Enterprise of the Aviation Industry
PO Box 6, 00-991 Warszawa
Telephone: 10 80 01
Telex: 813430
MANAGING DIRECTOR: Jerzy Krezlewicz, MSc
MANAGER OF AVIATION DEPARTMENT: Stanislaw Ferenstein

IL
INSTYTUT LOTNICTWA (Aeronautical Institute)
Al. Krakowska 110/114, 02-256 Warszawa-Okecie

Telephone: Warszawa 460993
Telex: 813537

MANAGING DIRECTOR: Dr Ing Andrzej Wierzba

CHIEF CONSULTANT FOR SCIENTIFIC AND TECHNICAL CO-OPERATION: Dipl Ing Jerzy Grzegorzewski

The Instytut Lotnictwa was founded in 1926. It belongs to the PZL Polish Aviation Works group, under the general management of the PZL Aircraft and Engine Industry Union. The IL is responsible for the control of all research and development work in the Polish aircraft industry. It conducts scientific research, including the investigation of problems associated with low-speed and high-speed aerodynamics, static and fatigue tests, development and testing of aero-engines, flight instruments and other equipment, flight tests, and materials technology. It is also responsible for the construction of experimental aircraft and aero-engines.

CNPSL-PZL WARSZAWA
CENTRUM NAUKOWO-PRODUKCYJNE SAMOLOTOW LEKKICH PZL WARSZAWA (Light Aircraft Science and Production Centre, PZL Warsaw)
HEAD OFFICE AND WORKS: 02-256 Warszawa-Okecie, Al. Krakowska 110/114
Telephone: Warszawa 461173 and 460031
Telex: 814649
MANAGERS:
Jozef Lipinski, Eng MSc (General Manager)
Andrzej Jaworowski, Eng (Technical)
Jacek Makles, Eng MSc (Sales)
PUBLIC RELATIONS: Jerzy Pasterski, Eng MSc

The Okecie factory, founded in 1928, is responsible for light aircraft development and production, and for the design and manufacture of associated agricultural equipment for its own aircraft and for those built at other factories in the Aircraft and Engine Industry Union. Formerly known as WSK-PZL-Okecie, it adopted its present title on 1 July 1976.

PZL-104 WILGA 80 (THRUSH)
The PZL-104 Wilga is a light general-purpose aircraft intended for a wide variety of general aviation and flying club duties. The prototype Wilga 1 flew for the first time on 24 April 1962. This aircraft, the Wilga 2, C and 3 prototypes, the 3A and 3S production versions and other early models, were described in the 1968-69 *Jane's*.

In 1967 the basic design was further modified, with improved cabin comfort, redesigned landing gear and glassfibre tailwheel leg. This version is known as the Wilga 35 (first flight 28 July 1967) when fitted with a 194 kW (260 hp) AI-14R engine, and as the Wilga 32 (first flown 12 September 1967) with a 171·5 kW (230 hp) Continental O-470-K, -L or -R engine and shorter landing gear. Both the Wilga 32 (see 1974-75 *Jane's*) and Wilga 35 received a Polish type certificate on 31 March 1969, having entered production in 1968. A modified version of the Wilga 32 was produced in Indonesia as the Lipnur Gelatik 32 (see 1975-76 *Jane's*). Details of the Wilga 40 and 43 experimental versions were given in the 1972-73 *Jane's*.

Major versions of the Wilga 35 (see 1979-80 *Jane's*) were the Wilga 35A (Aeroclub), 35P (Passenger/liaison), and 35R (agricultural version, described separately). Examples of the Wilga 35A were sold to customers in Austria, Belgium, Bulgaria, Czechoslovakia, Egypt, Germany (Democratic Republic), Germany (Federal Republic), Hungary, Romania, Spain, Switzerland, the UK, the USA, the USSR, Venezuela and Yugoslavia.

The Wilga 35H floatplane prototype (SP-WBK) was flown for the first time on 31 October 1979. Fitted with twin CAP Model 3000E floats, it successfully completed initial flight and water tests in Canada before the end of that year.

The generally-similar current production model of the Wilga, which conforms to FAR Pt 23 requirements, is known as the **Wilga 80**. It flew for the first time on 30 May 1979 and received Canadian government certification in March 1980. Four Wilga 80s, fitted with twin-float landing gear of the kind tested on the Wilga 35H, were delivered to Canada later in the same year.

By 1 January 1980 a total of 530 Wilgas, of all versions, had been built in Poland. Deliveries during 1979 totalled 110 Wilgas, of which 90% were for export. The 500th Wilga was completed on 22 November 1979.

The following description applies to the current Wilga 80:

TYPE: Single-engined general-purpose monoplane.

PZL-104 Wilga 35A general-purpose monoplane *(Pilot Press)*

Wilga 35H prototype of the Wilga 80 floatplane. Note the large dorsal fin

WINGS: Cantilever high-wing monoplane. Wing section NACA 2415. Dihedral 1°. All-metal single-spar structure, with leading-edge torsion box and beaded metal skin. Each wing attached to fuselage by three bolts, two at spar and one at forward fitting. All-metal aerodynamically and mass-balanced slotted ailerons, with beaded metal skin. Ailerons can be drooped to supplement flaps during landing. Manually-operated all-metal slotted flaps with beaded metal skin. Fixed metal slat on the leading-edge along the full span of the wing and over the fuselage. Tab on starboard aileron.

FUSELAGE: All-metal semi-monocoque structure in two portions, riveted together. Forward section incorporates main wing spar carry-through structure. Rear section is in the form of a tailcone. Beaded metal skin. Floor in cabin is of metal sandwich construction, with a paper honeycomb core, covered with foam rubber.

TAIL UNIT: Braced all-metal structure, with sweptback vertical surfaces. Stressed-skin single-spar tailplane attached to fuselage by a single centre fitting and supported by a single aluminium alloy strut on each side. Stressed-skin two-spar fin structure of semi-monocoque construction. Rudder and one-piece elevator are aerodynamically horn-balanced and mass-balanced. Trim tab at centre of elevator trailing-edge.

LANDING GEAR: Non-retractable tailwheel type. Semi-cantilever main legs, of rocker type, have oleo-pneumatic shock-absorbers. Low-pressure tyres size 500 × 200 mm on main wheels. Hydraulic brakes. Steerable tailwheel, tyre size 255 × 110 mm, carried on rocker frame with oleo-pneumatic shock-absorber. Metal ski landing gear, and CAP Model 3000E twin-float landing gear, optional.

POWER PLANT: One 194 kW (260 hp) PZL AI-14RA nine-cylinder supercharged radial aircooled engine, driving a PZL US-122000 two-blade constant-speed wooden propeller. Two removable fuel tanks in each wing, with total capacity of 195 litres (43 Imp gallons). Refuelling point on each side of fuselage, at junction with wing. Oil capacity 16 litres (3·5 Imp gallons).

ACCOMMODATION: Passenger version accommodates pilot and three passengers, in pairs, with adjustable front seats. Baggage compartment aft of seats, capacity 35 kg (77 lb). Upward-opening door on each side of cabin, jettisonable in emergency. In the parachute training version the starboard door is removed and replaced by two tubular uprights with a central connecting strap, and the starboard front seat is rearward-facing. Jumps are facilitated by a step on the starboard side and by a parachute hitch. A controllable towing hook can be attached to the tail landing gear permitting the Wilga, in this role, to tow a single glider of up to 650 kg (1,433 lb) weight or two or three gliders with a total combined weight of 1,125 kg (2,480 lb).

SYSTEMS: Hydraulic system pressure 39 bars (570 lb/sq in). Engine starting is effected pneumatically by a built-in system of 7 litres (427 cu in) capacity with a pressure of 49 bars (710 lb/sq in). Electrical system powered by DC generator and 24V 10Ah battery.

AVIONICS AND EQUIPMENT: Standard equipment includes VHF transceiver and blind-flying instrumentation. Optional avionics include RS-6102 (of Polish design), R-860 II, R860 IIM, King KY 195 or Bendix radio; and ARL-1601 VHF, ARK-9, King KR 85 or Bendix AV-200 ADF.

DIMENSIONS, EXTERNAL:

Wing span	11·12 m (36 ft 5¾ in)
Wing chord (constant)	1·40 m (4 ft 7¼ in)
Wing aspect ratio	7·95
Length overall	8·10 m (26 ft 6¾ in)
Height overall	2·94 m (9 ft 7¾ in)
Tailplane span	3·70 m (12 ft 1¾ in)
Wheel track	2·85 m (9 ft 4¼ in)
Wheelbase	6·70 m (21 ft 11¾ in)
Propeller diameter	2·65 m (8 ft 8 in)
Passenger doors (each): Height	1·00 m (3 ft 3¾ in)
Width	1·50 m (4 ft 11 in)

DIMENSIONS, INTERNAL:

Cabin: Length	2·20 m (7 ft 2½ in)
Max width	1·20 m (3 ft 10 in)
Max height	1·50 m (4 ft 11 in)

Floor area	2·20 m² (23·8 sq ft)
Volume	2·40 m³ (85 cu ft)
Baggage compartment	0·50 m³ (17·5 cu ft)

AREAS:

Wings, gross	15·50 m² (166·8 sq ft)
Ailerons (total)	1·57 m² (16·90 sq ft)
Trailing-edge flaps (total)	1·97 m² (21·20 sq ft)
Fin	0·97 m² (10·44 sq ft)
Rudder	0·92 m² (9·90 sq ft)
Tailplane	3·16 m² (34·01 sq ft)
Elevator, incl tab	1·92 m² (20·67 sq ft)

WEIGHTS AND LOADINGS:

Weight empty, equipped	900 kg (1,984 lb)
Max T-O and landing weight	1,300 kg (2,866 lb)
Max wing loading	83·9 kg/m² (17·18 lb/sq ft)
Max power loading	6·70 kg/kW (11·02 lb/hp)

PERFORMANCE (at max T-O weight):

Never-exceed speed	150 knots (279 km/h; 173 mph)
Max level speed	108 knots (201 km/h; 125 mph)
Max cruising speed	104 knots (193 km/h; 120 mph)
Econ cruising speed	69·5 knots (128 km/h; 80 mph)
Stalling speed, power on	
	37 knots (68 km/h; 42·5 mph)
Max rate of climb at S/L	300 m (985 ft)/min
Service ceiling	4,000 m (13,125 ft)
T-O run	80 m (260 ft)
T-O to 15m (50 ft)	186 m (610 ft)
Landing from 15 m (50 ft)	230 m (755 ft)
Landing run	95 m (310 ft)
Range with max fuel, 30 min reserves	
	366 nm (680 km; 422 miles)

PERFORMANCE AS GLIDER TUG:

Rate of climb at S/L: with 1 glider	234 m (770 ft)/min
with 2 gliders	204 m (670 ft)/min
with 3 gliders	132 m (435 ft)/min
Service ceiling: with 1 glider	4,000 m (13,125 ft)
with 2 gliders	3,900 m (12,800 ft)
with 3 gliders	2,500 m (8,200 ft)

Time to reach service ceiling:

with 1 glider	37 min 12 s
with 2 gliders	43 min 12 s
with 3 gliders	36 min 36 s

Range:

with 1 glider	344 nm (637 km; 395 miles)
with 2 gliders	272 nm (504 km; 313 miles)
with 3 gliders	227 nm (420 km; 260 miles)

PZL-104 WILGA 35R (AGRICULTURAL VERSION)

First flown on 13 February 1978, this agricultural version of the Wilga 35 takes advantage of the STOL capabilities of this aeroplane, its steep angles of climb and descent, and its ability to make tight turns, particularly over small fields where approach is a problem. Flight testing continued in 1979, and in early 1980 sets of equipment for five further conversions were under construction.

The agricultural equipment can be installed with any type of landing gear except floats, and is made entirely of materials resistant to chemical corrosion. Maximum chemical load, in addition to fuel for 1 hour's flying, is 270 kg (595 lb), and the limited carrying capacity qualifies the aircraft for ultra-low-volume spraying missions. With dual controls, this version can be used to give practical training to future agricultural pilots under genuine field conditions.

AGRICULTURAL EQUIPMENT: Glassfibre hopper for chemicals, attached beneath fuselage between main landing gear units; centrifugal pump, attached to port landing gear leg and driven by a six-blade fan; control valves; filter; spraybooms, supported well beneath wings on V struts and fitted with four Micronair atomisers or 40 pressurised spray outlets; fluid pressure gauges; Micronair flow meter. Pump brake actuated pneumatically; cut-off and release valves, and jettison system, operated manually.

PZL-106A KRUK (RAVEN)

The PZL-106 was designed in early 1972 by a team led by Andrzej Frydrychewicz. The first prototype (SP-PAS) flew for the first time on 17 April 1973, powered by a 298 kW (400 hp) Avco Lycoming IO-720 engine. It was followed in October of that year by a second Avco Lycoming-engined prototype (SP-PBG) and, from October 1974, by four prototypes fitted with the 441 kW (592 hp) PZL-3S radial engine that powers PZL-106A production aircraft. The latter also have a cruciform tail unit instead of the earlier T tail, and a greater chemical load, in a larger hopper. Manufacture of some 600 aircraft for the member countries of the CMEA (Council for Mutual Economic Aid) is anticipated.

Production of the PZL-106A began in 1976; the first export delivery, to Hungary, was made in 1977, and a total of 88 had been built by the beginning of 1980, of which 24 were delivered to the German Democratic Republic, two to Hungary, one to Cuba and two to Czechoslovakia. East Germany ordered 15 more for 1980 delivery, and during that year Egypt began to receive the first of an order for 40. A tropical version of the standard PZL-106A, with uncowled engine, is available.

Two aircraft have been equipped, for evaluation and certification, with a two-seat cockpit, dual controls, and a 400 litre (88 Imp gallon) hopper; this modification is available on any production PZL-106A. A version known as the **PZL-106AR**, first flown on 15 November 1978, is under development; this is powered by a geared PZL-3SR engine (gear ratio 0·7), driving a 3·10 m (10 ft 2 in) diameter PZL US-133000 propeller.

A **PZL-106AT Turbo-Kruk** version was exhibited at a Polish air show at Okecie in November 1979. This aircraft (SP-WUK) was fitted with a 567 kW (760 shp) Pratt & Whitney Aircraft of Canada PT6A-34AG turboprop engine, driving a 2·59 m (8 ft 6 in) diameter Hartzell HC-B3TN-3B/T10282 three-blade constant-speed fully-feathering reversible-pitch metal propeller with spinner.

TYPE: Single-engined agricultural aircraft.

WINGS: Braced low-wing monoplane with upward-cambered tips. Clark Y wing section throughout span, except at tips. Thickness/chord ratio 11·7%. Dihedral 4° from roots. Incidence 6° 6'. Sweepback 4° at quarter-chord. All-metal two-spar structure, of constant chord throughout most of span. Metal and polyester fabric covering. Glassfibre wingtips. Full-span six-section fixed leading-edge slats of glassfibre sandwich construction, with foam core. Three-section slotted ailerons of duralumin, with polyester fabric covering. No flaps or tabs. Streamline-section V bracing struts, with jury struts.

FUSELAGE: Welded steel tube structure, covered with quickly-removable panels of light alloy and GRP. Steel tube structure can be pressure-tested for crack detection.

Agricultural version of the Wilga 35, with underfuselage hopper and spraybooms

TAIL UNIT: Conventional duralumin structure, with single bracing strut each side. Fixed surfaces metal-covered; rudder and mass-balanced elevators polyester fabric-covered. Trim tab in port elevator, automatic tab in starboard elevator; ground-adjustable tab on rudder.

LANDING GEAR: Non-retractable tailwheel type, with oleo-pneumatic shock-absorber on each unit. Main wheels, with low-pressure tyres (size 800 mm × 260 mm), each carried on side V and half-axle. Main-wheel tyre pressure 2·0 bars (29 lb/sq in). Pneumatically-operated disc brakes on main wheels. Parking brake. Steerable tailwheel, with tubeless tyre size 350 mm × 135 mm, pressure 2·5 bars (36·25 lb/sq in).

POWER PLANT: One 441 kW (592 hp) PZL-3S seven-cylinder radial aircooled supercharged engine, driving a PZL US-132000/A four-blade constant-speed metal propeller. Fuel in two wing tanks, total capacity 300 litres (66 Imp gallons). Gravity refuelling point on each wing; semi-pressure refuelling point on starboard side of fuselage. Oil capacity 54 litres (11·9 Imp gallons) max, 7 litres (1·54 Imp gallons) min. Air filter fitted.

ACCOMMODATION: Pilot in enclosed, ventilated and heated cockpit. Second (mechanic's) rearward-facing seat to rear. Combined window/door on each side of cabin. Cockpit area strengthened to resist 40g impact.

SYSTEMS: Pneumatic system, rated at 49 bars (710 lb/sq in), for brakes and agricultural equipment. Electrical power, from 27·5V DC alternator and battery, for engine starting, pneumatic system control, aircraft lights, instruments, VHF transceiver and semi-pressure refuelling.

EQUIPMENT: VHF transceiver. Easily removable non-corrosive (GRP) hopper/tank, forward of cockpit, can carry 1,000 kg (2,205 lb) of dry or liquid chemical, and has a maximum capacity of 1,400 litres (308 Imp gallons). The hopper has a quick-dump system that can release 1,000 kg of chemical in less than 5 s. A pneumatically operated intake for the loading of dry chemicals is optional. Distribution system for liquid chemical is powered by a fan-driven centrifugal pump. A precise and reliable dispersal system, with positive on/off action for dry chemicals, gives effective swath widths of 10-35 m (33-115 ft). Hopper can be replaced easily by a special container with instructor's seat, controls, basic instruments and windscreen, to convert any version of the Kruk into a two-seat trainer.

DIMENSIONS, EXTERNAL (A, PZL-106A; B, PZL-106AR):
Wing span	14·80 m (48 ft 6½ in)
Wing chord (constant)	1·90 m (6 ft 2¾ in)
Wing aspect ratio	7·8
Length overall: A	9·10 m (29 ft 10¼ in)
B	9·16 m (30 ft 0¾ in)
Height overall	3·32 m (10 ft 10¾ in)
Tailplane span	5·77 m (18 ft 11¼ in)
Wheel track	3·10 m (10 ft 2¼ in)
Wheelbase	7·41 m (24 ft 3¾ in)
Propeller diameter	2·62 m (8 ft 7 in)
Propeller ground clearance (tail up)	0·36 m (1 ft 2¼ in)
Crew doors (each): Height	0·91 m (2 ft 11¾ in)
Width	1·06 m (3 ft 5¾ in)
Baggage door: Height	0·70 m (2 ft 3½ in)
Width	0·60 m (1 ft 11¾ in)

DIMENSIONS, INTERNAL:
Cabin: Length	1·37 m (4 ft 6 in)
Max width	1·25 m (4 ft 1¼ in)
Max height	1·30 m (4 ft 3¼ in)
Floor area	1·12 m² (12·05 sq ft)
Baggage compartment:	
Length	1·40 m (4 ft 7 in)
Width	1·00 m (3 ft 3¼ in)
Depth	0·60 m (1 ft 11¾ in)

AREAS:
Wings, gross	28·40 m² (305·7 sq ft)
Ailerons (total)	2·46 m² (26·50 sq ft)
Fin	1·26 m² (13·56 sq ft)
Rudder, incl tab	1·62 m² (17·44 sq ft)
Tailplane	3·34 m² (35·95 sq ft)
Elevators, incl tab	4·22 m² (45·42 sq ft)

WEIGHTS AND LOADINGS (A, PZL-106A; B, PZL-106AR):
Weight empty, equipped: A	1,610 kg (3,550 lb)
B	1,685 kg (3,715 lb)
Max chemical payload	1,000 kg (2,205 lb)
Normal T-O weight: A	2,800 kg (6,173 lb)
B	3,000 kg (6,614 lb)
Max T-O and landing weight: A, B	3,000 kg (6,614 lb)
*Max ramp weight: A, B	3,000 kg (6,614 lb)
Max wing loading	105·6 kg/m² (21·63 lb/sq ft)
Max power loading	6·7 kg/kW (11·02 lb/hp)

* Aircraft stressed for 3,000 kg (6,614 lb) T-O weight in Normal Category, BCAR Section K

PERFORMANCE (A, PZL-106A; B, PZL-106AR; at Normal T-O weight):
Never-exceed speed	140 knots (260 km/h; 161 mph)
Max level speed at S/L	114 knots (211 km/h; 131 mph)
Max cruising speed at S/L	97 knots (180 km/h; 112 mph)
Operating speed with 1,000 kg (2,205 lb) of chemical	65-86·5 knots (120-160 km/h; 74·5-99·5 mph)
Stalling speed at S/L	50 knots (92 km/h; 57·5 mph)
Max rate of climb at S/L with 1,000 kg (2,205 lb) of chemical: A	240 m (787 ft)/min
B	270 m (885 ft)/min
Service ceiling: A	4,000 m (13,125 ft)
B	4,200 m (13,780 ft)
*T-O run: A	220 m (722 ft)
B	240 m (788 ft)
*T-O to 15 m (50 ft): A	480 m (1,575 ft)
B	390 m (1,280 ft)
*Landing from 15 m (50 ft): A	410 m (1,345 ft)
B	370 m (1,215 ft)
*Landing run: A, B	210 m (689 ft)
Min ground turning radius	10·00 m (32 ft 10 in)
Range with max fuel: A	215 nm (400 km; 248 miles)
B	367 nm (680 km; 422 miles)

* with agricultural equipment

PZL-110 KOLIBER (HUMMING-BIRD)

Under this designation, CNPSL-PZL Warszawa is producing under licence a two/three-seat version of the Socata Rallye 100 ST, the lowest-powered model in the Rallye light aircraft family, and one which is no longer in production in France. The first PZL-110, modified to receive an 86·5 kW (116 hp) PZL-Franklin engine, made its initial flight on 18 April 1978.

The first production PZL-110 was flown on 8 May 1979, and by the beginning of 1980 a total of 10 Series I and 20 Series II aircraft had been completed. A Polish type certificate was awarded on 24 August 1979.

A description of the standard Rallye 100 ST can be found under the Socata heading in the French section of the 1978-79 Jane's. The PZL-110 version differs in the following details:

POWER PLANT: One 86·5 kW (116 hp) PZL-built Franklin 4A-235-B31 flat-four engine, driving a US 135 two-blade ground-adjustable propeller. Fuel system and capacity as for Rallye 100 ST. Oil capacity 6·2 litres (1·4 Imp gallons). Version with 164 kW (220 hp) PZL-Franklin 6A engine under development.

SYSTEMS AND EQUIPMENT: 12V electrical system, with alternator and 18Ah battery. VHF transceiver optional.

PZL-106A Kruk (PZL-3S engine), with scrap view of the two-seat version (Pilot Press)

PZL-106AR Kruk, with PZL-3SR geared engine (A. Glass)

Photograph and three-view drawing (Pilot Press) of the PZL-106AT Turbo-Kruk (Pratt & Whitney Aircraft of Canada PT6A-34AG turboprop engine)

Optional equipment includes ADF, and electrically powered gyro attitude indicator, turn and slip indicator and direction indicator.

DIMENSIONS, EXTERNAL: As Rallye 100 ST except:
Length overall   7·20 m (23 ft 7½ in)
Propeller diameter   1·78 m (5 ft 10 in)
AREAS: As Rallye 100 ST except:
Wings, gross   12·66 m² (136·3 sq ft)
WEIGHTS AND LOADING:
Weight empty, equipped   516 kg (1,137 lb)
Max T-O and landing weight (Normal category)
        850 kg (1,874 lb)
Max T-O weight (Utility category) 770 kg (1,700 lb)
Max wing loading   67·1 kg/m² (13·74 lb/sq ft)
PERFORMANCE (at 770 kg; 1,700 lb Utility max T-O weight except where indicated):
Never-exceed speed 145 knots (270 km/h; 167 mph)
Max level speed at S/L 105 knots (195 km/h; 121 mph)
Max cruising speed at S/L 92 knots (170 km/h; 106 mph)
Stalling speed, flaps up 43·5 knots (80 km/h; 50 mph)
Stalling speed, flaps down 40 knots (74 km/h; 46 mph)
Max rate of climb at S/L at AUW of 830 kg (1,830 lb)
        171 m (560 ft)/min
Service ceiling   3,500 m (11,480 ft)

PZL-110 Koliber, Polish-built version of the Socata Rallye 100 ST

T-O run at S/L   155 m (509 ft)
T-O to 15 m (50 ft) at S/L   380 m (1,247 ft)
Landing from 15 m (50 ft) at S/L 275 m (902 ft)

Landing run at S/L   113 m (371 ft)
Range at 500 m (1,640 ft) with max fuel, no reserves
      394 nm (730 km; 453 miles)

WSK-PZL MIELEC
WYTWORNIA SPRZETU KOMUNIKACYJ-NEGO-PZL MIELEC (Transport Equipment Manufacturing Centre, Mielec)

HEAD OFFICE AND WORKS: ul. Ludowego Wojska Polskiego 3, 39-301 Mielec
Telephone: Mielec 70
Telex: 83293
GENERAL MANAGER: Dipl Ing Tadeusz Ryczaj

Largest and best-equipped aircraft factory in Poland, the WSK factory at Mielec was founded in 1938. It currently has approx 278,700 m² (3 million sq ft) of floor area and a work force of some 18,000 people. It was engaged mainly in licence production of MiG single-seat jet fighters for several years. These aircraft carry the Polish designation of LiM, meaning Licence MiG, and included the LiM-1 (MiG-15), SBLiM-1 (MiG-15 UTI), LiM-2 (MiG-15 bis) and LiM-5 (MiG-17). Polish-developed versions of the LiM-5 were designated LiM-5M and LiM-6 bis. Licence production of MiG fighters ceased in Poland in about 1959.

Following a reduction in orders for combat aircraft in 1955, Mielec began production in 1956 of 240 TS-8 Bies basic trainers, described in the 1962-63 *Jane's*. Four years later, the Soviet-designed An-2 general utility biplane went into production at Mielec. In parallel production with the An-2 at the present time is the TS-11 Iskra jet trainer and light attack aircraft. In 1977 Mielec began to manufacture components, including fins, tailplanes, engine pylons, ailerons, and wing slats and flaps, for the Ilyushin Il-86 Soviet wide-bodied transport, and in 1978 it was announced that Mielec would assume responsibility for series production of the Soviet Antonov An-28 twin-turboprop light general-purpose aircraft. Mielec exported its 8,500th aircraft in January 1979.

There is a design office at the factory for development of original aircraft. Its most recent designs are the M-15 agricultural aircraft, M-17 light aircraft, and M-18 Dromader agricultural aircraft, of which the M-15 and M-18 are now in production.

PZL MIELEC (ANTONOV) An-2
NATO reporting name: Colt

The prototype of the An-2, designed to a specification of the Ministry of Agriculture and Forestry of the USSR, made its first flight on 31 August 1947. In 1948 the aircraft went into production in the USSR as the An-2, with a 746 kW (1,000 hp) ASh-62 engine.

By 1960, more than 5,000 An-2s had been built in the Soviet Union for service with the Soviet armed forces, Aeroflot and other civilian organisations; the various Soviet-built versions have been fully described in previous editions of *Jane's*. Many were exported, to all of the Socialist States, and to Greece, Afghanistan, Mali, Nepal, India and Cuba, and licence rights were granted to China, where the first locally-produced An-2 was completed in December 1957.

Since 1960, apart from a small Soviet-built quantity of a developed version known as the An-2M (see 1971-72 *Jane's*), the continued production of the An-2 has been the responsibility of the PZL factory at Mielec, the original licence arrangement providing for two basic versions: the An-2T transport and An-2R agricultural version. The first 10 Polish-built An-2s were completed in 1960 (first example flown on 23 October 1960). Mielec has since built considerable numbers of this aircraft for domestic use and for export to the USSR, Bulgaria, Czechoslovakia, Egypt, France, the German Democratic Republic, Hungary, North Korea, Mongolia, the Netherlands, Romania, Sudan, Tunisia and Yugoslavia. The 5,000th Polish-built An-2 was delivered, to the USSR, on 3 February 1973. Since beginning An-2 production, Mielec has made numerous improvements to the airframe of the An-2R, resulting in an increase in TBO from 900 hr in 1961 to 1,500 hr in 1970 and 2,000 hr in 1973.

By the beginning of 1980 about 9,000 An-2s (all versions) had been built at Mielec, including more than 3,800 of the An-2R agricultural version. More than 90 per cent of these were for export, including about 7,500 to the USSR.

The Polish-built versions have different designations from those built in the USSR. These are as follows:

An-2P. Passenger version, with seating for 12 adult passengers and two children. Compared with Soviet-built An-2P (see 1971-72 *Jane's*) has improvements in passenger cabin layout and comfort, better soundproofing, a new propeller and spinner, and weight-saving instrumentation and equipment. Entered production in 1968.

An-2PK. Five-seat executive version, having two seats on starboard side and three on port side, with foldaway table between pairs of seats on each side.

An-2P-Photo. Photogrammetry version.

An-2PR. Television relay version.

An-2R. Agricultural version, with 1,350 kg (2,976 lb) capacity glassfibre-reinforced epoxy-resin hopper or 1,400 litre (308 Imp gallon) capacity tank for dry or liquid chemicals. Similar to Soviet-built An-2S. Agricultural equipment being modernised.

An-2S. Ambulance version, equipped to carry six stretcher patients and their medical attendants.

An-2T. Basic general-purpose version, with accommodation for 12 passengers and baggage or 1,500 kg (3,306 lb) of cargo.

An-2TD. Paratroop transport and training version with six tip-up seats along each side of cabin. Granted French type certificate No. IM-55 (for import licence) in 1972.

An-2TP. Cargo/passenger version, similar to AN-2TD with six tip-up seats along each side of cabin.

An-2M. Twin-float version of An-2T, similar to Soviet-built An-2V. Built in small numbers only.

An-2 Geofiz. Geophysical survey version, developed for the State Prospecting Company in Warsaw.

The following details apply to the PZL Mielec An-2P:

TYPE: Single-engined general-purpose biplane.

WINGS: Unequal-span single-bay biplane. Wing section RPS 14% (constant). Dihedral, both wings, approx 2° 48'. All-metal two-spar structure, fabric-covered aft of front spar. I-type interplane struts. Differential ailerons and full-span automatic leading-edge slots on upper wings, slotted trailing-edge flaps on both upper and lower wings. Flaps operated electrically, ailerons mechanically by cables and push/pull rods. Electrically-operated trim tab in port aileron.

FUSELAGE: All-metal stressed-skin semi-monocoque structure of circular section forward of cabin, rectangular in the cabin section and oval in the tail section.

TAIL UNIT: Braced metal structure. Fin integral with rear fuselage. Fabric-covered tailplane. Elevators and rudder operated mechanically by cables and push/pull rods. Electrically-operated trim tab in rudder and port elevator.

LANDING GEAR: Non-retractable split-axle type, with long-stroke oleo shock-absorbers. Main-wheel tyres size 800 × 260 mm, pressure 2·25 bars (32·7 lb/sq in). Pneumatic shoe brakes on main units. Fully-castoring and self-centering PZL-Krosno tailwheel with electro-pneumatic lock. For rough-field operation the oleo-pneumatic shock-absorbers can be charged from a compressed air cylinder installed in the rear fuselage. Interchangeable ski landing gear available optionally.

POWER PLANT: One 746 kW (1,000 hp) Shvetsov ASz-62IR nine-cylinder radial aircooled engine, driving an AW-2 four-blade variable-pitch metal propeller. Six fuel tanks in upper wings, with total capacity of 1,200 litres (264 Imp gallons). Oil capacity 120 litres (26·4 Imp gallons).

ACCOMMODATION: Crew of two on flight deck, with access via passenger cabin. Standard accommodation for 12 passengers, in four rows of three with centre aisle. Two foldable seats for children in aisle between first and second rows, and infant's cradle at front of cabin on starboard side. Toilet at rear of cabin on starboard side. Overhead racks for up to 160 kg (352 lb) of baggage, with space for coats and additional 40 kg (88 lb) of baggage between rear pair of seats and toilet. Emergency exit on starboard side at rear. Walls of cabin are lined with glass-wool mats and inner facing of plywood to reduce internal noise level. Cabin floor is carpeted. Cabin heating and starboard windscreen de-icing by engine bleed air; port and centre windscreens are electrically de-iced. Cabin ventilation by ram-air intakes on underside of top wings. Air-conditioning system in An-2R.

SYSTEMS: Compressed air cylinder, of 8 litres (490 cu in) capacity, for pneumatic charging of shock-absorbers and operation of tailwheel lock at 49 bars (711 lb/sq in) pressure and operation of main-wheel brakes at 9·80 bars (142 lb/sq in). Contents of cylinder are maintained by AK-50 M engine-driven compressor, with AD-50 automatic relief device to prevent overpressure. DC

PZL Mielec (Antonov) An-2P in Romanian markings

electrical system is supplied with basic 27V power (and 36V or 115V where required) by an engine-driven generator and a storage battery. CO_2 fire extinguishing system with automatic fire detector.

AVIONICS AND EQUIPMENT: Dual controls and blind-flying instrumentation standard. R-842 short wave and R-860 ultra short wave lightweight radio transceivers, RW-UM radio altimeter, ARK-9 radio compass, MRP-56P marker, GB-1 gyro compass, GPK-48 gyroscopic direction indicator and SPU-7 intercom.

DIMENSIONS, EXTERNAL:

Wing span: upper	18·18 m (59 ft 8½ in)
lower	14·24 m (46 ft 8½ in)
Wing chord (constant): upper	2·40 m (7 ft 10½ in)
lower	2·00 m (6 ft 6¾ in)
Wing aspect ratio: upper	7·57
lower	7·12
Wing gap	2·17 m (7 ft 1½ in)
Length overall: tail up	12·74 m (41 ft 9½ in)
tail down	12·40 m (40 ft 8¼ in)
Height overall: tail up	6·10 m (20 ft 0 in)
tail down	4·00 m (13 ft 1½ in)
Tailplane span	7·20 m (23 ft 7½ in)
Wheel track	3·45 m (11 ft 3¾ in)
Wheelbase	3·36 m (11 ft 0¼ in)
Propeller diameter	3·60 m (11 ft 9¾ in)
Propeller ground clearance	0·70 m (2 ft 3½ in)
Emergency exit (stbd, rear):	
Height	0·65 m (2 ft 1½ in)
Width	0·51 m (1 ft 8 in)

AREAS:

Wings, gross: upper	43·6 m² (469 sq ft)
lower	28·0 m² (301 sq ft)
Ailerons (total)	5·90 m² (63·5 sq ft)
Trailing-edge flaps (total)	9·60 m² (103 sq ft)
Fin	5·85 m² (62·97 sq ft)
Rudder, incl tab	2·65 m² (28·52 sq ft)
Tailplane	12·28 m² (132·18 sq ft)
Elevators (total, incl tab)	4·72 m² (50·81 sq ft)

WEIGHTS AND LOADINGS:

Weight empty	3,450 kg (7,605 lb)
Max T-O weight	5,500 kg (12,125 lb)
Max landing weight	5,250 kg (11,574 lb)
Max wing loading	76·82 kg/m² (15·7 lb/sq ft)
Max power loading	7·38 kg/kW (12·13 lb/hp)

PERFORMANCE (at AUW of 5,250 kg; 11,574 lb):

Max level speed at 1,750 m (5,740 ft)	
	139 knots (258 km/h; 160 mph)
Econ cruising speed	100 knots (185 km/h; 115 mph)
Min flying speed	49 knots (90 km/h; 56 mph)
T-O speed	43 knots (80 km/h; 50 mph)
Landing speed	46 knots (85 km/h; 53 mph)
Max rate of climb at S/L	210 m (689 ft)/min
Service ceiling	4,400 m (14,425 ft)
Time to 4,400 m (14,425 ft)	30 min
T-O run: hard runway	150 m (492 ft)
grass	170 m (558 ft)
T-O to 10·7 m (35 ft): hard runway	300 m (984 ft)
grass	320 m (1,050 ft)
Landing run: hard runway	170 m (558 ft)
grass	185 m (607 ft)
Range at 1,000 m (3,280 ft) with 500 kg (1,102 lb) payload	485 nm (900 km; 560 miles)

PZL MIELEC (ANTONOV) An-28
NATO reporting name: Cash

Oleg Antonov first referred to planned production of an enlarged turboprop version of the piston-engined An-14 light general-purpose aircraft in the early 1960s, but until the Spring of 1972 there was no proof that such an aircraft had been built. Photographs of the prototype (CCCP-1968) were then published in the Polish press. It had flown for the first time in the USSR in September 1969, powered by two 604 kW (810 shp) Isotov TVD-850 turboprop engines, and was described in this form in the Soviet section of the 1974-75 and previous editions of *Jane's*.

Initially, the new aircraft was designated An-14M. Its official flight testing was completed in 1971, and during 1973 it was allocated the production designation An-28. The first pre-production An-28 (CCCP-19723) retained the original TVD-850 engines, but flight trials suggested that field performance and climb, in particular, could be improved by fitting more powerful engines. Thus, in April 1975, the same development aircraft (re-registered CCCP-19753) flew for the first time with 716 kW (960 shp) Glushenkov TVD-10 turboprop engines, which were specified also for production An-28s. It won a subsequent competitive evaluation against the Be-30, in which the emphasis was placed by the evaluators on concept rather than detail design.

Following Polish-Soviet talks in February 1978, it was announced that series production of the An-28 was to be entrusted to PZL Mielec. Mr Antonov stated at the Paris Air Show in June 1979 that the aircraft was at the final stages of testing for certification prior to production, which he expected to begin in 1980-81. The second pre-production aircraft (originally CCCP-19754, now CCCP-48105) was displayed at the Show. A total of 1,700 development flights had been completed by that time, including tests with ski landing gear. Subsequently, in September 1979, the Moscow representative of Pezetel stated that the first Polish-built An-28s would appear in

Antonov An-28 light general-purpose transport (Glushenkov TVD-10B turboprop engines) *(Tass)*

Antonov An-28 light transport, to be produced in Poland by WSK-PZL Mielec
(Pilot Press)

1982, with large-scale production beginning in 1983. An annual output of approx 200 is planned.

In general configuration the An-28 differs from the piston-engined An-14 mainly in having a much-enlarged fuselage to carry up to 20 passengers or equivalent alternative payloads. The original An-14M had a retractable landing gear, with small fairings on the sides of the fuselage into which the main units retracted. Subsequently it was decided that retraction was unnecessary for flights over short distances at low speeds, and the pre-production An-28s have fixed gear. The shape of the vertical tail surfaces was also changed as a result of early flight testing.

The Antonov design bureau evolved the An-28 for service on Aeroflot's shortest routes, particularly those operated by An-2 biplanes into places which are relatively inaccessible to other types of fixed-wing aircraft. The turboprop engines make possible full-payload operation under high-temperature conditions and in mountainous regions; and the An-28 is described as being suitable for carrying passengers, cargo and mail, for scientific expeditions, geological surveying, forest fire patrol, firefighting, air ambulance or rescue operations, and parachute training. In agricultural form it can carry an 800 kg (1,764 lb) chemical payload for dusting and spraying operations.

Mr Antonov has stated that Aeroflot pilots will begin their flying careers on the An-28, which will not stall, even with the control column held in the extreme rearward position, because of the action of its automatic slots. If an engine fails, the upper-surface spoiler forward of the aileron on the opposite wing is opened automatically; as a result, the wing bearing the 'dead' engine drops only 12° in 5 s instead of the 30° that it would drop through loss of lift without the action of the Antonov-patented spoiler. The fixed tailplane slot, also patented, improves handling during a high angle of attack climb-out. Under icing conditions, if the normal anti-icing system fails, ice collects on the slat rather than the tailplane, to retain controllability.

TYPE: Twin-turboprop light general-purpose aircraft.

WINGS: Braced high-wing monoplane, with single streamline-section bracing strut each side. Conventional two-spar structure. Full-span automatic leading-edge slots. Entire trailing-edges hinged, the single-slotted ailerons being designed to droop with the large double-slotted flaps. No tabs. Spoiler forward of each aileron. Short stub-wing extends from each side of the lower fuselage, carrying the main landing gear units, and providing lower attachments for the wing bracing struts. Anti-icing of wing leading-edges by engine bleed air.

FUSELAGE: Conventional all-metal semi-monocoque structure, longer, wider and deeper than that of the piston-engined An-14. Underside of rear fuselage upswept and made up of clamshell doors.

TAIL UNIT: Cantilever all-metal structure. Twin fins and rudders mounted vertically on an inverted-aerofoil tailplane that lacks the dihedral of that on the An-14. Fixed leading-edge slat under full span of tailplane leading-

edge. Anti-icing of leading-edges by engine bleed air. Twin tabs in each rudder.

LANDING GEAR: Non-retractable tricycle type, with single wheel on each unit. Wide-tread balloon tyres, size 720 × 320, pressure 3·5 bars (51 lb/sq in), on main units. Steerable and self-centering nosewheel, with size 595 × 185 tyre. Brakes on main wheels. Provision for skis or floats.

POWER PLANT: Two 715 kW (960 shp) Polish-built flat rated Glushenkov TVD-10B turboprop engines (Polish designation PZL-10W), each driving an AW-24AN three-blade reversible-pitch metal propeller. Two 310 litre (68 Imp gallon) centre-wing and two 670 litre (147 Imp gallon) outer-wing integral fuel tanks; total fuel capacity 1,960 litres (430 Imp gallons). Oil capacity 30 litres (6·5 Imp gallons) per engine. Electrical anti-icing of propellers and engine air intakes.

ACCOMMODATION: Crew of one or two on flight deck, which has bulged side windows and windscreen electrical anti-icing. Crew door forward of cabin on port side. Cabin of passenger version contains 15 seats in five rows at 72 cm (28 in) pitch, or up to 20 seats in high-density configuration, with double units on starboard side of aisle. Seats fold back against walls when aircraft is operated as a freighter or in mixed passenger/cargo role. Provision for baggage and toilet compartments and wardrobe space. Electrically-actuated ramp-door under upswept rear fuselage can slide forward under cabin to facilitate direct loading from trucks on to cabin floor. Overhead winch on rails, capacity 500 kg (1,102 lb) for handling cargo. Emergency exit at rear on starboard side. Six/seven-passenger executive version has four folding tables, which can be joined together in pairs to give working tops measuring 160 × 55 cm (63 × 21·5 in). Ambulance version accommodates six stretchers, five seated patients, a medical attendant and medical equipment. Can also be equipped to carry six parachutists and a dispatcher.

AVIONICS AND EQUIPMENT: Flight and navigation equipment includes blind-flying instrumentation; R-80W UHF, Karat short-wave, RSB-5 medium-wave, Landysz-5 and R-851 radios; Wint-2 navigation computer; DISS Maszt-FK and ARK-U2 'special installations'; ADF; emergency locator transmitter; DWS-8 airspeed indicator; AR-C7 turn indicator; MS-61 drift recorder; three-axis autopilot; and dual AK-59P astrocompasses. Landing light in nose. Current level of equipment is intended to permit operation in ICAO Category II conditions, with extension later to Category III.

DIMENSIONS, EXTERNAL:

Wing span	22·06 m (72 ft 4½ in)
Wing chord at root	2·20 m (7 ft 2½ in)
Wing area, gross	40·28 m² (433·5 sq ft)
Wing aspect ratio	12
Length overall	12·98 m (42 ft 7 in)

Height overall	4·60 m (15 ft 1 in)
Tailplane span	5·20 m (17 ft 0¾ in)
Wheel track	3·41 m (11 ft 2 ¼ in)
Wheelbase	4·35 m (14 ft 3¼ in)
Propeller diameter	2·80 m (9 ft 2¼ in)

DIMENSIONS, INTERNAL:

Cabin, excl flight deck: Length	5·26 m (17 ft 3 in)
Max width	1·66 m (5 ft 5 in)
Max height	1·70 m (5 ft 7 in)
Floor area	8·73 m² (93·97 sq ft)
Volume	14·84 m³ (524 cu ft)

AREA:

Wings, gross	40·28 m² (433·6 sq ft)

WEIGHTS AND LOADINGS:

Weight empty (approx)	3,500 kg (7,716 lb)
Normal payload	1,550 kg (3,415 lb)
Max payload	1,700 kg (3,750 lb)
Normal T-O weight	5,800 kg (12,785 lb)
Max T-O weight	6,100 kg (13,450 lb)
Max wing loading	151·4 kg/m² (31·03 lb/sq ft)
Max power loading	4·22 kg/kW (6·93 lb/shp)

PERFORMANCE (A: at normal T-O weight; B: at max T-O weight):

Max cruising speed:	
A, B	188 knots (350 km/h; 217 mph)
Econ cruising speed:	
A, B	162 knots (300 km/h; 186 mph)
Stalling speed, flaps up:	
A	70 knots (130 km/h; 81 mph)
B	73 knots (135 km/h; 84 mph)
Stalling speed, flaps down:	
A	65 knots (120 km/h; 75 mph)
B	67·5 knots (125 km/h; 78 mph)
Max rate of climb at S/L: A	750 m (2,460 ft)/min
B	708 m (2,320 ft)/min
Rate of climb at S/L, one engine out:	
A	192 m (630 ft)/min
B	174 m (570 ft)/min
T-O run: A	180 m (590 ft)
B	210 m (690 ft)
T-O to 15 m (50 ft): A	330 m (1,085 ft)
B	360 m (1,180 ft)
Landing from 15 m (50 ft): A	287 m (942 ft)
B	305 m (1,000 ft)
Landing run: A	150 m (492 ft)
B	170 m (558 ft)

Range at econ cruising speed at 3,000 m (9,850 ft), 30 min reserves:

A, 15 passengers	356 nm (660 km; 410 miles)
A, 18 passengers	202 nm (375 km; 233 miles)
B, 18 passengers	372 nm (690 km; 428 miles)
B, 20 passengers	275 nm (510 km; 317 miles)
A, max fuel	702 nm (1,300 km; 807 miles)
B, max fuel	696 nm (1,290 km; 801 miles)

PZL MIELEC TS-11 ISKRA (SPARK)

Designed in 1957 under the supervision of Docent Ing T. Soltyk, the TS-11 Iskra two-seat jet trainer was produced as a replacement for the piston-engined TS-8 Bies. Four prototypes were built during 1958-59, the first of these being used for static testing. First flight, on 5 February 1960, was made by the second aircraft, followed later in the same year by the third and fourth prototypes. Type approval was received in mid-1961, and quantity production began at Mielec in 1963. The formal handing over of the first Iskra to the Polish Air Force took place in March 1963, and the aircraft entered service in 1964. Iskras of the Polish Air Force logged a total of 100,000 flying hours by 1978. Another 30,000 flying hours had been accumulated in India.

Early production aircraft were powered by a 7·66 kN (1,720 lb st) HO-10 Polish-designed axial flow turbojet engine. In April 1964, flight testing began using the intended power plant, the more powerful SO-1; from the latter half of the 1960s, production Iskras were powered either by the SO-1 or by the modified but similarly rated SO-3.

About 500 Iskras had been built by mid-1979, in the following versions:

Iskra-Bis A. Basic two-seat version, for primary and advanced training. Two underwing hardpoints for external weapons.

Iskra-Bis B. Two-seat primary and advanced trainer, with four underwing attachments for missiles or other weapons. Prototype designated Iskra 100. In production.

Iskra-Bis C. Single-seat reconnaissance version. Prototype, designated Iskra 200, first flew in June 1972. Increased fuel capacity for greater range; camera pod on starboard side of nose.

Iskra-Bis D. Similar to Bis B, but able to carry a wider selection of external weapons. Prototype also designated Iskra 200. Export version supplied to Indian Air Force (50) in 1976. In production.

Iskra-Bis DF. Single-seat combat and reconnaissance trainer, with increased armament capability of Bis D, plus provision for three cameras in pod on starboard side of nose. In production.

The following description applies to the current production Iskra-Bis B, D and DF, except where indicated:

TYPE: Fully aerobatic two-seat jet primary and advanced trainer (A, B and D) and single-seat reconnaissance aircraft (C and DF).

WINGS: Cantilever mid-wing monoplane. Wing section NACA 64209 at root, NACA 64009 at tip. Sweepback at quarter-chord 7°. Marked dihedral. All-metal torsion box structure with two steel main spars and duralumin stressed skin. Hydraulically servo-assisted, aerodynamically-balanced ailerons. Hydraulically-actuated two-section double-slotted flaps and airbrakes (max deflection 87°). One boundary layer fence on each wing. Anti-flutter weight fairing projecting from each wing near tip.

FUSELAGE: All-metal semi-monocoque structure of pod and boom type.

TAIL UNIT: Cantilever all-metal structure. Two-spar fin, integral with fuselage. Variable-incidence two-spar tailplane, actuated electrically. Mass- and aerodynamically-balanced elevators and rudder. Anti-flutter weight fairing projecting from each half of tailplane at tip. Ground-adjustable tab on rudder; fixed balance tab in port elevator.

Standard two-seat Iskra-Bis D trainer

PZL Mielec Iskra-Bis D two-seat trainer, with four underwing pylons (*Pilot Press*)

LANDING GEAR: Retractable tricycle type with single wheel on each unit. Nosewheel retracts forward, main wheels inward into wing-root air intake trunks. Hydraulic actuation, with pneumatic emergency extension. Main wheels size 600 × 180, tyre pressure 5·38 bars (78 lb/sq in). Nosewheel size 400 × 150, tyre pressure 3·45 bars (50 lb/sq in). Oleo-pneumatic shock-absorbers. Disc brakes on main wheels. Castoring and self-centering nosewheel, with shimmy damper.

POWER PLANT: One SO-3 turbojet, rated at 9·81 kN (2,205 lb st), or higher-powered SO-3B, mounted in fuselage aft of cockpit section, with nozzle under tailboom. Fuel in two 315 litre (69 Imp gallon) integral wing tanks, one rubber 500 litre (110 Imp gallon) fuselage main tank (700 litre; 154 Imp gallon in single-seaters) and one rubber 70 litre (15·5 Imp gallon) fuselage collector tank. Total fuel capacity 1,200 litres (263·5 Imp gallons) in two-seaters, 1,400 litres (308 Imp gallons) in single-seaters. Fuel system permits up to 40 s of inverted flight.

ACCOMMODATION: Crew of one, or two in tandem, on lightweight ejection seat(s), under a one-piece hydraulically-actuated rearward-hinged upward-opening jettisonable canopy. Cockpit pressurised and air-conditioned. Rear seat of trainers slightly raised.

SYSTEMS: Hydraulic system, pressure 138 bars (2,000 lb/sq in), for actuation of ailerons, flaps, airbrakes, landing gear, canopy, and main-wheel brakes. Pneumatic system, pressure 118 bars (1,710 lb/sq in), for cockpit pressurisation, anti-icing and gun charging. Emergency pneumatic system for landing gear, flaps and emergency braking. Electrical power provided by 28·5V AW-30 generator and 24V 28Ah battery, for engine starting, instruments, lights and armament control system; 115V converter for AC power. Air-conditioning, oxygen, ethyl alcohol anti-icing and CO₂ fire extinguishing systems standard.

AVIONICS AND EQUIPMENT: Trainers have complete dual controls and instrumentation, including blind-flying panels. Standard avionics also include R-800, R-802G or R-802W VHF com; ARK-9 radio compass; RW-UM radio altimeter; MRP-56P marker beacon receiver; SPU-2P crew intercom in two-seaters; and IFF.

ARMAMENT: Forward-firing 23 mm cannon in nose on starboard side, with S-13 gun camera. Two or four attachments for a variety of underwing stores, including bombs of up to 100 kg (220 lb), eight-barrel rocket pods and 7·62 mm gun pods.

DIMENSIONS, EXTERNAL:

Wing span	10·06 m (33 ft 0 in)
Wing chord at root	2·254 m (7 ft 4¾ in)
Wing chord at tip	1·162 m (3 ft 9¾ in)
Wing aspect ratio	5·71
Length overall	11·15 m (36 ft 7 in)
Height overall	3·50 m (11 ft 5½ in)
Tailplane span	3·84 m (12 ft 7¼ in)
Wheel track	3·47 m (11 ft 4½ in)
Wheelbase	3·44 m (11 ft 3½ in)

Single-seat Iskra-Bis C reconnaissance version of the PZL Mielec TS-11

AREAS:
Wings, gross   17·50 m² (188·37 sq ft)
Ailerons (total)   1·48 m² (15·93 sq ft)
Trailing-edge flaps (total)   1·74 m² (18·73 sq ft)
Fin   1·55 m² (16·68 sq ft)
Rudder (incl tab)   0·70 m² (7·53 sq ft)
Tailplane   2·38 m² (25·62 sq ft)
Elevators (incl tab)   1·16 m² (12·48 sq ft)

WEIGHTS AND LOADINGS:
Weight empty (trainer versions):
B   2,494 kg (5,498 lb)
D/DF   2,560 kg (5,644 lb)
Normal T-O weight with 570 litres (125·5 Imp gallons)
internal fuel: B   3,184 kg (7,019 lb)
D/DF   3,243 kg (7,150 lb)
Normal T-O weight with 1,200 litres (263·5 Imp gallons) internal fuel: B   3,704 kg (8,166 lb)
D/DF   3,734 kg (8,232 lb)
T-O weight (reconnaissance version):
DF   3,787 kg (8,349 lb)
Max T-O weight with full external armament:
B   3,810 kg (8,400 lb)
D/DF   3,840 kg (8,465 lb)
Max wing loading:
D/DF   219 kg/m² (44·85 lb/sq ft)
Max power loading (SO-3):
D/DF   387·4 kg/kN (3·8 lb/lb st)

PERFORMANCE (at normal T-O weight with full internal fuel, except where indicated):
Never-exceed speed
Mach 0·8 (404 knots; 750 km/h; 466 mph)
Max level speed at 5,000 m (16,400 ft):
B, D/DF   388 knots (720 km/h; 447 mph)
Normal cruising speed:
B, D/DF   324 knots (600 km/h; 373 mph)
Unstick speed:
B, D/DF   102 knots (190 km/h; 118 mph)
Landing speed:
B, D/DF   92 knots (170 km/h; 106 mph)
Stalling speed, power off, flaps down:
B, D/DF   81 knots (150 km/h; 93·5 mph)
Max rate of climb at S/L:
B, D/DF   840 m (2,755 ft)/min
Time to 6,000 m (19,685 ft): B, D/DF   9 min 36 s
Time to 7,000 m (22,975 ft): B, D/DF   13 min 36 s
Service ceiling: B   11,140 m (36,550 ft)
D/DF   11,000 m (36,000 ft)
T-O run: B   725 m (2,380 ft)
D/DF   750 m (2,460 ft)
T-O to 15 m (50 ft), flaps down:
B   1,100 m (3,609 ft)
D/DF   1,190 m (3,904 ft)
Landing from 15 m (50 ft), flaps down:
B   1,000 m (3,280 ft)
D/DF   1,110 m (3,642 ft)
Landing run: B   660 m (2,165 ft)
D/DF   700 m (2,300 ft)
Range at 7,000 m (22,975 ft):
B with 570 litres fuel   235 nm (435 km; 270 miles)
D/DF with 570 litres fuel   243 nm (450 km; 280 miles)
B with 1,200 litres fuel   626 nm (1,160 km; 720 miles)
g limits (ultimate): B, D/DF   +8·0; −4·0

PZL MIELEC M-15 BELPHEGOR

As recorded in earlier editions of *Jane's*, the Polish and Soviet governments discussed in 1971 the development of a new, large agricultural aircraft known as the M-15, together with associated agricultural and ground support equipment. The Soviet government indicated a requirement for about 3,000 such aircraft, and on 2 December 1971 signed an agreement with the Polish government for large-scale production of the M-15.

Initial design of the M-15 was undertaken by a design bureau at Mielec under Soviet chief consulting engineer R. A. Ismailov and Polish designer K. Gocyla, and staffed by Polish and Soviet specialists. The agricultural equipment for the aircraft was developed jointly by the Instytut Lotnictwa at Warsaw (which see) and the Soviet Research Institute of Special and Utility Aviation at Krasnodar.

A prototype, designated LLP-M15, was flown on 30 May 1973; the first fully-representative M-15 prototype made its first flight on 9 January 1974. On 2 April 1975 five pre-series M-15s were sent to the USSR for evalua-

tion; Soviet acceptance tests were completed successfully in 1976 and were followed by the award of a provisional Soviet GosAvia certificate of airworthiness. Completion of the M-15 development programme, and the granting of a full Soviet certificate, was marked by a ceremony at the Mielec factory on 4 April 1979. The name Belphegor was registered for the M-15 at about the same time. One hundred M-15s had then been built, most of which had been exported to the USSR.

The prototype of a tandem two-seat training version, with large cabin side windows, was completed in 1980, and an improved standard model is under development for future production. Firefighting and cargo-carrying versions are expected to be developed.

The following description refers to the agricultural production version:

TYPE: Three-seat agricultural aircraft.
WINGS: Biplane wings, of mainly metal construction and unequal span, built chiefly of aluminium and steel alloys and glassfibre laminates. Wing section P-II-14. The upper wing has a constant-chord centre-section and tapered outer panels; dihedral at tips is increased on current aircraft. The centre-section is faired to the top of the engine pod. The shorter-span lower wings, which house the agricultural dispersal pipes, are of generally similar planform and are joined to the fuselage nacelle at floor level. The entire trailing-edge of the upper wing is hinged, and is made up of hydraulically-operated double-slotted flaps and single-slotted ailerons. There are automatically-operated slats on the leading-edge. In line with each tailboom, and occupying the full depth of the gap between the upper and lower wings, is a narrow streamlined hopper for agricultural chemical, and there is a single outward-sloping bracing strut outboard of each hopper fairing. Trim tab in port aileron.
FUSELAGE: Central semi-monocoque nacelle, of narrow rectangular section, built of same materials as wings.
TAIL UNIT: Cantilever metal/glassfibre structure, consisting of twin sweptback two-spar endplate fins and rudders, bridged by a high-mounted tailplane and full-span elevators, supported on two slender tailbooms located at approx one-quarter span on the upper wing. Trim tabs in elevator and starboard rudder.
LANDING GEAR: Non-retractable tricycle type, with single wheel and oleo-pneumatic shock-absorber on each unit. Main wheels and tyres size 720 × 320 mm, tyre pressure 3·0 bars (43 lb/sq in); nosewheel and tyre size 700 × 250 mm, tyre pressure 2·5 bars (36 lb/sq in). Nosewheel steerable hydraulically, 50° to left or right. Hydraulic disc brakes on main wheels.
POWER PLANT: One 14·7 kN (3,306 lb st) Ivchenko AI-25 turbofan engine, mounted in a pod on top of the fuselage. Eight rubber fuel tanks in upper wing, total capacity 1,460 litres (321 Imp gallons).
ACCOMMODATION: Seat for pilot in fully-enclosed cockpit in extreme nose of fuselage. Two seats in cabin, to rear of pilot's compartment, for carrying ground staff during ferry flights. Cockpit air-conditioning by engine compressor bleed air.

PZL Mielec M-15 turbofan-engined agricultural aircraft *(Pilot Press)*

Two-seat training version of the M-15 Belphegor, with larger side windows *(A. Glass)*

SYSTEMS: Hydraulic system, pressure 150 bars (2,175 lb/sq in), for actuation of nosewheel steering, brakes, flaps, and dispersal systems (including emergency jettison). Freon-type fire extinguishing system.
AVIONICS AND EQUIPMENT: Full flight and navigation instrumentation, including stall-warning indicator. VFR radio/navigation equipment optional. The two between-wings hoppers have a combined capacity for 2,900 litres (638 Imp gallons) of liquid or 2,200 kg (4,850 lb) of dry (powdered or granulated) chemical. Ivchenko AI-9 APU, normally removed from aircraft during agricultural operations, provides power for engine starting, ground refuelling and filling of hoppers with liquid chemical. Compressed air for chemical dispersal is bled from the AI-25 engine. Twin landing lights in nose.

DIMENSIONS, EXTERNAL:
Wing span: upper   22·33 m (73 ft 3 in)
lower   16·428 m (53 ft 10¾ in)
Wing mean aerodynamic chord (upper)
1·84 m (6 ft 0½ in)
Length overall   13·135 m (43 ft 1 in)
Height overall   5·339 m (17 ft 6¼ in)
Height of fuselage above ground
1·008 m (3 ft 3½ in)
Wheel track   4·319 m (14 ft 2 in)
Wheelbase   4·879 m (16 ft 0 in)
Distance between c/l of hoppers 5·20 m (17 ft 0¾ in)

AREAS:
Wings (total)   67·90 m² (730·9 sq ft)
Ailerons (total)   9·03 m² (97·20 sq ft)
Trailing-edge flaps (total)   4·99 m² (53·71 sq ft)
Fins (total)   5·53 m² (59·52 sq ft)
Rudders (total)   4·00 m² (43·06 sq ft)
Tailplane   5·92 m² (63·72 sq ft)
Elevators (total)   4·08 m² (43·92 sq ft)

WEIGHTS AND LOADINGS:
Weight empty: dusting   3,230 kg (7,120 lb)
spraying   3,270 kg (7,210 lb)
with atomisers   3,275 kg (7,220 lb)
Max hopper load   2,200 kg (4,850 lb)
Max T-O weight   5,750 kg (12,675 lb)
Max landing weight   4,000 kg (8,815 lb)
Max wing loading   85·19 kg/m² (17·44 lb/sq ft)
Max power loading   391·19 kg/kN (3·83 lb/lb st)

PERFORMANCE (at max T-O weight):
Max cruising speed   108 knots (200 km/h; 124 mph)
Normal operating speed
86-95 knots (160-175 km/h; 99-109 mph)
Stalling speed, flaps up
60·5 knots (112 km/h; 70 mph)
Stalling speed, flaps down
48 knots (89 km/h; 55·5 mph)
Max rate of climb at S/L   390 m (1,280 ft)/min
T-O run: on grass   380 m (1,247 ft)
on concrete   260 m (853 ft)

PZL Mielec M-15 Belphegor agricultural biplane (Ivchenko AI-25 turbofan engine)

Landing run: on grass 190 m (624 ft)
on concrete 330 m (1,083 ft)
Max range at 3,000 m (9,850 ft)
259 nm (480 km; 298 miles)
Swath width: dusting 65 m (213 ft)
spraying 40 m (131 ft)
with atomisers 70 m (230 ft)
Application rate:
dusting 10-50 kg (22-110 lb)/s
spraying 0-25 litres (0-5·5 Imp gallons)/s
with atomisers
0·2-6·5 litres (0·05-1·4 Imp gallons)/s

PZL MIELEC M-18 DROMADER (DROMEDARY)

Although superficially similar to the CNPSL-PZL Warszawa PZL-106A Kruk, the M-18 Dromader is an entirely different and much larger agricultural aircraft. Designed to meet the requirements of FAR Pt 23, it was developed with the co-operation of Rockwell International of the USA and utilises the outer wing panels and other components of the Thrush Commander S-2R. Particular attention was paid in the design to pilot safety, and all parts of the structure exposed to contact with chemicals are treated with polyurethane or epoxy enamels, or manufactured from stainless steel.

The M-18 was first flown on 27 August 1976, and a second flying prototype followed on 2 October 1976; a third was completed for static tests. The M-18 made its public debut at the Paris Air Show in May/June 1977. The prototypes were followed by seven pre-series aircraft, of which two were used for static and fatigue testing. The remainder were employed on operating trials, two of them spraying and dusting cotton in Egypt during the Summer of 1978, prior to the award of a Polish type certificate on 27 September 1978. Other pre-series aircraft were exhibited and demonstrated in 1978 in Hungary, Iraq, Italy, the USA and Yugoslavia. A total of 30 production Dromaders had been built by the Spring of 1980.

Future programmes are planned to include lighter-weight wings; development of new agricultural and other equipment, to decrease the reliance on imported items; and of a turboprop-powered version, probably with a PZL-10S (Glushenkov TVD-10) engine. A firefighting version of the Dromader was flown for the first time on 11 November 1978. Six were delivered to a customer in Canada in 1980, following Canadian certification of this version in March of that year.

The following description refers to the standard agricultural version:

TYPE: Single-seat agricultural aircraft; g limits +3·4/−1·4 (FAR 23); +2·8 (CAM 8).

WINGS: Cantilever all-metal low-wing monoplane, of constant chord, with 2° 30' dihedral on centre-section and 5° on outer panels. Wing sections NACA 4416 at root, NACA 4412 at tip. Incidence 3°. Single steel-capped duralumin spar. All-metal two-section trailing-edge slotted flaps, actuated hydraulically. All-metal slotted

ailerons, mass and aerodynamically balanced, actuated by pushrods. No tabs.

FUSELAGE: All-metal structure. Main frame, of helium-arc welded chrome-molybdenum steel tube, oiled internally against corrosion. Duralumin side panels, detachable for airframe inspection and cleaning. Fixed stainless steel bottom covering.

TAIL UNIT: All-metal structure, with braced tailplane. Corrugated skin on vertical surfaces. Aerodynamically and mass balanced rudder and elevators. Elevator actuated by pushrods; rudder by cables. Trim tab on each elevator.

LANDING GEAR: Non-retractable tailwheel type. Oleo-pneumatic shock-absorber on each unit. Main units have tyres size 720 × 320 mm, and are fitted with hydraulic disc brakes, parking brake and wire cutters. Fully-castoring tailwheel, lockable for take-off and landing, with size 318 × 114 mm tyre.

POWER PLANT: One 736 kW (987 hp) PZL Kalisz ASz-621R nine-cylinder radial aircooled supercharged engine, driving a PZL four-blade constant-speed aluminium propeller. Integral fuel tank in each outer wing panel, combined usable capacity 400 litres (88 Imp gallons; 105·7 US gallons). Gravity-feed header tank in fuselage.

ACCOMMODATION: Single adjustable seat in fully enclosed, sealed and ventilated cockpit which is stressed to withstand 40g impact. Glassfibre cockpit roof and rear fairing. Adjustable shoulder-type safety harness. Adjustable rudder pedals. Baggage compartment aft of seat. Quick-opening door on each side; port door jettisonable.

SYSTEMS: Hydraulic system, pressure 98-137 bars (1,421-1,987 lb/sq in), for flap actuation, disc brakes and dispersal system. Electrical system powered by 28·5V 100A generator, with 24V 25Ah nickel-cadmium battery and overvoltage protection relay.

AVIONICS AND EQUIPMENT: King KX 170B communications transceiver, KI 201C navigation receiver, VOR-OBS indicator, landing lights, taxi light and night working lights optional. Navigation lights, cockpit light, instrument panel lights and two rotating beacons standard. Built-in jacking and tiedown points in wings and aft fuselage; towing lugs on main landing gear. Cockpit fire extinguisher and first aid kit.

AGRICULTURAL EQUIPMENT: Glassfibre epoxy hopper, with stainless steel tube bracing, forward of cockpit; capacity 2,500 litres (550 Imp gallons; 660 US gallons) of liquid or 1,500 kg (3,306 lb) of dry chemical. Deflector cable from cabin roof to fin. Transland gatebox, control valve and strainer, Root pump, and 48/96-nozzle spraybooms for spraying; Transland gatebox, control valve and high output spreader for dusting with dry chemical; or eight AV 3000 atomisers for fine spraying. Aircraft can also be fitted with Rockwell International water bombing installation for fire suppression.

DIMENSIONS, EXTERNAL:
Wing span 17·70 m (58 ft 0¾ in)
Wing chord (constant) 2·286 m (7 ft 6 in)
Wing aspect ratio 7·83
Length overall 9·47 m (31 ft 1 in)
Height overall 3·70 m (12 ft 1¾ in)
Tailplane span 5·00 m (16 ft 4¾ in)
Wheel track 3·58 m (11 ft 9 in)
Propeller diameter 3·30 m (10 ft 10 in)
Propeller ground clearance (tail up) 0·23 m (9 in)

AREAS:
Wings, gross 40·00 m² (430·5 sq ft)
Ailerons and flaps (total) 9·53 m² (102·6 sq ft)
Vertical tail surfaces (total) 2·65 m² (28·5 sq ft)
Horizontal tail surfaces (total) 6·50 m² (70·0 sq ft)

WEIGHTS AND LOADINGS:
Weight empty 2,470 kg (5,445 lb)
Payload: FAR 23 1,500 kg (3,306 lb)
CAM 8 2,600 kg (5,732 lb)
Max T-O weight: FAR 23 4,200 kg (9,259 lb)
CAM 8 5,300 kg (11,684 lb)
Max landing weight 3,200 kg (7,055 lb)
Max wing loading (FAR 23)
105·0 kg/m² (21·51 lb/sq ft)
Max power loading (FAR 23)
5·63 kg/kW (9·26 lb/hp)

PERFORMANCE (at 4,200 kg; 9,259 lb max T-O weight, ISA. A: without agricultural equipment; B: with spreader equipment):
Never-exceed speed:
A 151 knots (280 km/h; 174 mph)
Max level speed: A 138 knots (256 km/h; 159 mph)
B 128 knots (237 km/h; 147 mph)
Cruising speed: A 110 knots (205 km/h; 127 mph)
B 102 knots (190 km/h; 118 mph)
Operating speed:
B 92-102·5 knots (170-190 km/h; 106-118 mph)
Stalling speed, power off, flaps up:
A, B 69 knots (127 km/h; 79 mph)
Stalling speed, power off, flaps down:
A, B 59 knots (109 km/h; 68 mph)
Max rate of climb at S/L: A 348 m (1,141 ft)/min
Service ceiling: A 6,500 m (21,325 ft)
T-O run: A 275 m (903 ft)
Landing run: A, B 330 m (1,085 ft)
Max range, no reserves:
A 280 nm (520 km; 323 miles)

PZL MIELEC M-20 MEWA (GULL)

It was announced in early 1977 that Pezetel had signed an agreement with Piper Aircraft Corporation of the USA whereby the Polish aircraft industry will assemble, manufacture and distribute in Eastern Europe the Piper Seneca II twin-engined business aircraft.

This work, which will be undertaken by PZL Mielec, will begin with the assembly of imported kits, and will progress eventually to full licence manufacture. The aircraft (production of 400 or more has been authorised by the US government) will be powered by 164 kW (220 hp) PZL-Franklin 6A-350C-1L/R engines, and will be known as the M-20 Mewa. The Polish prototype made its initial flight on 23 July 1979.

Prototype PZL Mielec M-20 Mewa, a version of the Piper Seneca II with PZL-Franklin engines

Three-view drawing (*Pilot Press*) **and photograph of the PZL Mielec M-18 Dromader agricultural aircraft**

WSK-PZL SWIDNIK
WYTWORNIA SPRZETU KOMUNIKACYJ-NEGO Im. ZYGMUNTA PULAWSKIEGO-PZL SWIDNIK (Zygmunt Pulawski Transport Equipment Manufacturing Centre, Swidnik)

HEAD OFFICE AND WORKS: 21-045 Swidnik k/Lublina
Telephone: Lublin 12061 and 12071
Telex: 84212 and 84212
GENERAL MANAGER: Dipl Ing Jan Czogala

The factory at Swidnik was built in 1951-52 and was engaged initially in manufacturing components for the LiM-1 (MiG-15) jet fighter.

In 1955, when the manufacture of combat aircraft was drastically reduced in Poland, the WSK at Swidnik began licence production of the Soviet-designed Mi-1 helicopter, some 1,700 of which were built under the designation SM-1. A small design office was formed subsequently at the factory to work on variants and developments of the basic SM-1 design and on original projects.

In September 1957, the Swidnik works was named after the famous pre-war PZL designer Zygmunt Pulawski, and currently employs about 10,000 people. Production is concentrated at present on various versions of the Soviet-designed Mil Mi-2 turbine-powered helicopter.

Swidnik, together with other PZL factories at Mielec and Kalisz, is manufacturing components for the Soviet Ilyushin Il-86 wide-bodied airliner.

PZL SWIDNIK (MIL) Mi-2
NATO reporting name: Hoplite

The Mil Mi-2, first flown in September 1961, was designed in the USSR by the Mikhail L. Mil bureau. It retains the basic configuration of Mil's earlier Mi-1 helicopter, but instead of a single piston engine has two Isotov turboshaft engines mounted side by side above the cabin.

Development of the Mi-2 prototype continued in the USSR until the helicopter had completed its initial State trials programme of flying. Then, in accordance with an agreement signed in January 1964, further development, production and marketing of the Mi-2 were assigned exclusively to the Polish aircraft industry, which flew its own first example of the Mi-2 on 4 November 1965.

Production at Swidnik began in 1965, and this factory has since built more than 3,000 in 24 different civil and military versions; the majority of these have been exported, including more than 2,000 to the USSR. Among the operators of the Mi-2 are the air forces of Czechoslovakia, Poland, Romania and the USSR, and civil operators in European and various developing countries. Production was continuing in 1979 at a rate of approx 300 a year.

In the 1970s Swidnik initiated a development programme to improve and modernise the original design. The first modernised version was powered by uprated engines of 335 kW (450 shp) each and was essentially similar to the basic Mi-2. It flew for the first time in 1974. On another version, the metal stabiliser, tail rotor blades and main rotor blades were replaced with similar components made of plastics, intended to simplify production and improve performance. The new rotor blades were designed, manufactured and tested at Swidnik.

There are several versions of the basic Mi-2, as follows:
(a) Convertible passenger/cargo transport;
(b) Passengers-only version, for six or eight passengers;
(c) Ambulance version (Mi-2R);
(d) Agricultural version, for conventional or ultra-low-volume spraying, known in Poland as the **Bazant** (Pheasant). In service in Bulgaria, Czechoslovakia, Denmark, Egypt, Finland, Iran, Iraq, Libya, Poland, Sudan, Sweden and USSR;
(e) Search and rescue version, with electrically-operated external hoist;
(f) Freighter version, with external cargo sling;
(g) Pilot training version, designed by WSK-Swidnik;
(h) Photogrammetric version, produced in small numbers only;
(i) Television version (for transmission from the air), produced in small numbers only;
(j) Version with 260 kg (573 lb) capacity hoist.
The following details apply specifically to the basic Mi-2, except where indicated:
TYPE: Twin-turbine general-purpose light helicopter.

ROTOR SYSTEM: Three-blade main rotor fitted with hydraulic blade vibration dampers. All-metal blades of NACA 230-13M section. Flapping, drag and pitch hinges on each blade. Main rotor blades and those of two-blade tail rotor each consist of an extruded duralumin spar with bonded honeycomb trailing-edge pockets. Anti-flutter weights on leading-edges, balancing plates on trailing-edges. Hydraulic boosters for longitudinal, lateral and collective pitch controls. Coil spring counterbalance mechanism in main and tail rotor systems. Pitch-change centrifugal loads on tail rotor carried by ribbon-type steel torsion elements. Rotors do not fold. Electrical blade de-icing system for main and tail rotors. Rotor brake fitted.

ROTOR DRIVE: Main rotor shaft driven via gearbox on each engine; three-stage WR-2 main gearbox, intermediate gearbox and tail rotor gearbox. Main rotor/engine rpm ratio 1 : 24·6; tail rotor/engine rpm ratio 1 : 4·16. Main gearbox provides drive for auxiliary systems and take-off for rotor brake. Freewheel units permit disengagement of a failed engine and also autorotation.

FUSELAGE: Conventional semi-monocoque structure of pod and boom type, made up of three main assemblies: the nose (including cockpit), central section and tailboom. Construction is of sheet duralumin, bonded and spot-welded or riveted to longerons and frames. Main load-bearing joints are of steel alloy.

TAIL UNIT: Variable-incidence horizontal stabiliser controlled by collective-pitch lever.

LANDING GEAR: Non-retractable tricycle type, plus tailskid. Twin-wheel nose unit. Single wheel on each main unit. Oleo-pneumatic shock-absorbers on all units, including tailskid. Main shock-absorbers designed to cope with both normal operating loads and possible ground resonance. Main-wheel tyres size 600 × 180, pressure 4·41 bars (64 lb/sq in). Nosewheel tyres size 300 × 125, pressure 3·45 bars (50 lb/sq in). Pneumatic brakes on main wheels. Metal ski landing gear optional.

POWER PLANT: Two 298 or 335 kW (400 or 450 shp) Polish-built Isotov GTD-350P turboshaft engines, mounted side by side above cabin. Fuel in single rubber tank, capacity 600 litres (131 Imp gallons), under cabin floor. Provision for carrying a 238 litre (52·4 Imp gallon) external tank on each side of cabin. Refuelling point in starboard side of fuselage. Oil capacity 25 litres (5·4 Imp gallons). Engine air intake de-icing by engine bleed air.

ACCOMMODATION: Normal accommodation for one pilot on flight deck (port side). Seats for up to eight passengers in air-conditioned cabin, there being back-to-back bench seats for three persons each, with two optional extra starboard side seats at the rear, one behind the other. All seats are removable for carrying up to 700 kg (1,543 lb) of internal freight. Access to cabin via forward-hinged doors on each side at front of cabin and aft on port side. Pilot's sliding window jettisonable in emergency. Ambulance version has accommodation for four stretchers and a medical attendant or for two stretchers and two sitting casualties. Side-by-side seats and dual controls in pilot training version. Cabin heating, ventilation and air-conditioning standard. Electrical de-icing of windscreen.

SYSTEMS: Cabin heating, by engine bleed air, and ventilation; heat exchangers warm atmospheric air for ventilation system during cold weather. Hydraulic system, pressure 59-78·6 bars (855-1,140 lb/sq in), for cyclic and collective pitch control boosters. Pneumatic system, pressure 49 bars (710 lb/sq in), for main-wheel brakes. AC electrical system, with two STG-3 3kW engine-driven starter/generators and 208V 16kVA three-phase alternator. 24V DC system, with two 28Ah lead-acid batteries.

AVIONICS AND EQUIPMENT: Standard equipment includes two transceivers (medium and short wave), gyro compass, radio compass, radio altimeter, intercom system and blind-flying panel. Electrically-operated wiper for pilot's windscreen. Fire extinguishing system, for engine bays and main gearbox compartment, is generally similar to, but simpler than, the Freon system fitted to the Soviet Mil Mi-8, and can be actuated automatically or manually.

OPERATIONAL EQUIPMENT: Bazant agricultural version carries a hopper on each side of the fuselage (total capacity 1,000 litres; 220 Imp gallons of liquid or 750 kg; 1,650

Armed version of the PZL Swidnik Mi-2, with four pylon-mounted air-to-surface missiles

lb of dry chemical) and either a spraybar to the rear of the cabin on each side or a distributor for dry chemicals under each hopper. Swath width covered by the spraying version is 40-45 m (130-150 ft). As a search and rescue aircraft, an electric hoist, capacity 120 kg (264 lb), is fitted. In the freight role an underfuselage hook can be fitted for suspended loads of up to 800 kg (1,763 lb).

ARMAMENT: Some Mi-2s of the Polish Air Force are equipped with rocket pods or air-to-surface missiles mounted on pylons on each side of the cabin.

DIMENSIONS, EXTERNAL:
Diameter of main rotor	14·56 m (47 ft 9¼ in)
Main rotor blade chord (constant, each)	0·40 m (1 ft 3¾ in)
Diameter of tail rotor	2·70 m (8 ft 10¼ in)
Length overall, rotors turning	17·42 m (57 ft 2 in)
Length of fuselage	11·94 m (39 ft 2 in)
Height to top of rotor hub	3·75 m (12 ft 3½ in)
Stabiliser span	1·85 m (6 ft 0¾ in)
Wheel track	3·05 m (10 ft 0 in)
Wheelbase	2·71 m (8 ft 10¾ in)
Tail rotor ground clearance	1·59 m (5 ft 2¾ in)
Cabin door (port, rear):	
Height	1·065 m (3 ft 5¾ in)
Width	1·115 m (3 ft 8 in)
Cabin door (stbd, front):	
Height	1·11 m (3 ft 7¾ in)
Width	0·75 m (2 ft 5½ in)
Cabin door (port, front):	
Height	approx 1·40 m (4 ft 7 in)
Width	approx 1·20 m (3 ft 11¼ in)

DIMENSIONS, INTERNAL:
Cabin:	
Length, incl flight deck	4·07 m (13 ft 4¼ in)
Length, excl flight deck	2·27 m (7 ft 5½ in)
Mean width	1·20 m (3 ft 11¼ in)
Mean height	1·40 m (4 ft 7 in)

AREAS:
Main rotor blades (each)	2·40 m² (25·83 sq ft)
Tail rotor blades (each)	0·22 m² (2·37 sq ft)
Main rotor disc	166·4 m² (1,791·11 sq ft)
Tail rotor disc	5·73 m² (61·68 sq ft)
Horizontal stabiliser	0·70 m² (7·53 sq ft)

WEIGHTS AND LOADING:
Weight empty, equipped:	
passenger version	2,402 kg (5,295 lb)
cargo version	2,372 kg (5,229 lb)
ambulance version	2,410 kg (5,313 lb)
Bazant	2,372 kg (5,229 lb)
Basic operating weight, empty:	
single-pilot versions	2,365 kg (5,213 lb)
dual-control version	2,424 kg (5,344 lb)
Max payload, excl pilot, oil and fuel	800 kg (1,763 lb)
Normal T-O weight (and max T-O weight of Bazant)	3,550 kg (7,826 lb)
Max T-O weight	3,700 kg (8,157 lb)
Max disc loading	22·4 kg/m² (4·6 lb/sq ft)

PERFORMANCE (at 3,550 kg; 7,826 lb T-O weight):
Never-exceed speed at 500 m (1,640 ft):		
Bazant		84 knots (155 km/h; 96·5 mph)
other versions		113 knots (210 km/h; 130·5 mph)
Max cruising speed at 500 m (1,640 ft):		
Bazant (without agricultural equipment)		102 knots (190 km/h; 118 mph)
other versions		108 knots (200 km/h; 124 mph)
Max level speed with agricultural equipment (Bazant)		84 knots (155 km/h; 96 mph)
Econ cruising speed for max range at 500 m (1,640 ft)		102 knots (190 km/h; 118 mph)
Econ cruising speed for max endurance at 500 m (1,640 ft)		54 knots (100 km/h; 62 mph)
Max rate of climb at S/L		270 m (885 ft)/min
Time to 1,000 m (3,280 ft)		5 min 30 s
Time to 4,000 m (13,125 ft)		26 min 0 s
Service ceiling		4,000 m (13,125 ft)
Hovering ceiling IGE		approx 2,000 m (6,560 ft)
Hovering ceiling OGE		approx 1,000 m (3,280 ft)

Agricultural version of the PZL Swidnik (Mil) Mi-2 twin-turbine helicopter

PZL Swidnik Kania twin-turboshaft light helicopter (left), and mockup (right) of the Taurus modified version for the North American market *(A. Glass and Brian M. Service)*

Min landing area	30 × 30 m (100 × 100 ft)

Range at 500 m (1,640 ft):

max payload, 5% fuel reserves	91 nm (170 km; 105 miles)
max internal fuel, no reserves	237 nm (440 km; 273 miles)
max internal and auxiliary fuel, 30 min reserves	313 nm (580 km; 360 miles)
max internal and auxiliary fuel, no reserves	430 nm (797 km; 495 miles)

Endurance at 500 m (1,640 ft), no reserves:

max internal fuel	2 h 45 min
max internal and auxiliary fuel	5 h 0 min

Endurance (Bazant), 5% reserves:

spraying	40 min
dusting	50 min

PZL SWIDNIK KANIA/KITTY HAWK AND TAURUS

In collaboration with the Detroit Diesel Allison Division of General Motors Corporation in the USA, PZL Swidnik is developing a modified export version of the Mi-2 light helicopter, known as the Kania or Kitty Hawk, powered by two Allison 250-C20B turboshaft engines. In addition to a standard passenger version, the Kania is intended for cargo, agricultural, ambulance and other roles, similar to those performed by the Mi-2. Two examples were scheduled for completion in 1979, and the first of these (SP-PSA) made its initial flight on 3 June that year.

In the USA, Spitfire Helicopters (which see) has rights to market a modified version of the Kania under the name **Taurus**. External differences in this version include a modified engine air intake cowling, with single orifice, revised nose contours, and a ventral tail fin. The power plant of the Taurus comprises two of the more powerful Allison 250-C28 turboshaft engines.

The following description applies to the standard Kania:

TYPE: Twin-turboshaft general-purpose light helicopter.

ROTOR SYSTEM: Three-blade fully articulated main rotor and two-blade seesaw tail rotor. Laminated plastics blades on both rotors. Three hydraulic boosters for longitudinal, lateral and collective pitch control of main rotor. Rotor brake fitted. Electrical anti-icing of rotor blades optional.

ROTOR DRIVE: Transmission driven via main rotor, intermediate and tail rotor gearboxes, each with oil sight gauge. Oil temperature gauge, oil cooling system, pressure indicator and tachometer for main gearbox. Antifriction bearings on tail rotor shaft.

FUSELAGE AND TAIL UNIT: Conventional semi-monocoque fuselage, with circular-section monocoque tailboom. Laminated horizontal stabiliser at end of tailboom. Hoist and cargo sling attachment points standard.

LANDING GEAR: Non-retractable tricycle type, plus laminated tailskid. Twin-wheel castoring nose unit; single wheel on each main unit. Pneumatic brakes on main wheels.

POWER PLANT: Two Allison 250-C20B turboshaft engines, mounted side by side above cabin; each rated at 313 kW (420 shp) for T-O and 30 min power, 298 kW (400 shp) max continuous, and 276 kW (370 shp) for max cruise. Standard usable fuel capacity of 600 litres (131 Imp gallons), with provision for additional 480 litres usable (105·5 Imp gallons) in optional auxiliary tanks.

ACCOMMODATION: Pilot (port side), and co-pilot or passenger, on adjustable and removable front seats, each fitted with safety belt. Dual controls optional. Accommodation for up to eight more persons, on two three-person bench seats and a single or double seat at rear of cabin, all with safety belts. Seats removable for carriage of 800 kg (1,764 lb) of cargo, stretchers, agricultural or other equipment. Access to cabin via jettisonable door on each side at front (port door of sliding type) and larger passenger/cargo door at rear on port side. Pilot's windscreen wiper standard. Cabin heating or air-conditioning, and electrical anti-icing of pilot's windscreen, optional.

SYSTEMS: Electrical system includes two 28V 150A DC starter/generators, two 115V 250A 400Hz static inverters, two 26V/115V 55VA 400Hz transformers, and a 25Ah nickel-cadmium battery. 16kVA alternator for anti-icing system optional. External power receptacle. Dual fire detection and extinguishing systems for engines; single system for transmission.

AVIONICS AND EQUIPMENT: King KX 175BE com/nav, KR 85 digital ADF, KT 76 transponder, and VFR instrumentation, all standard. Optional avionics include King KWX 50 digital weather radar, KRA 10 radar altimeter and KN 65A-03 DME. Dual instrument lighting systems, pilot's cabin extension light, cabin dome light, three hold dome lights, three position lights, adjustable landing light, and anti-collision light, are all standard, as are cargo and stretcher tiedown rings. Optional equipment includes dual controls, co-pilot's windscreen wiper, and auxiliary fuel tanks. Cabin carpet, standard or executive passenger seats, heating and air-conditioning systems, and sand filters, are also optional.

OPERATIONAL EQUIPMENT: According to mission, the Kania can be equipped with a 1,000 kg (2,205 lb) capacity stabilised cargo sling; 120 kg (265 lb) capacity hoist; stretchers and casualty care equipment; agricultural spraying or dusting gear.

DIMENSIONS, EXTERNAL:

Diameter of main rotor	14·56 m (47 ft 9¼ in)
Diameter of tail rotor	2·70 m (8 ft 10¼ in)
Length overall, rotors turning	17·41 m (57 ft 1½ in)
Length of fuselage	11·95 m (39 ft 2½ in)
Fuselage: Max width	1·60 m (5 ft 3 in)
Height to top of rotor hub	3·75 m (12 ft 3½ in)
Stabiliser span	1·84 m (6 ft 0½ in)
Wheel track	3·25 m (10 ft 8 in)
Wheelbase	2·71 m (8 ft 10¾ in)
Tail rotor ground clearance	1·80 m (5 ft 10¾ in)

DIMENSIONS, INTERNAL:

Cabin: Length, incl flight deck	4·07 m (13 ft 4¼ in)
Max width	1·50 m (4 ft 11 in)
Height at front	1·30 m (4 ft 3¼ in)
Mean height at rear	1·51 m (4 ft 11½ in)
Max height at rear	1·62 m (5 ft 3¾ in)
Floor area	5·68 m² (61·1 sq ft)
Volume	7·766 m³ (274·25 cu ft)

AREAS:

Main rotor disc	166·50 m² (1,792·2 sq ft)
Tail rotor disc	5·725 m² (61·6 sq ft)

WEIGHTS:

Weight empty, standard	2,140 kg (4,717 lb)
Normal T-O weight	3,350 kg (7,385 lb)
Max T-O weight	3,550 kg (7,826 lb)

PERFORMANCE (estimated, for 'clean' aircraft at S/L, ISA, zero wind. A: at 3,150 kg; 6,944 lb gross weight; B: at normal T-O weight; C: at max T-O weight):

Max cruising speed:

A, B, C	113 knots (210 km/h; 130 mph)

Econ cruising speed:

A, B	105 knots (195 km/h; 121 mph)
C	104·5 knots (194 km/h; 120·5 mph)

Rate of climb:

A	504 m (1,653 ft)/min
B	450 m (1,476 ft)/min
C	402 m (1,319 ft)/min

Rate of climb, one engine out:

A	96 m (315 ft)/min
B	66 m (216 ft)/min
C	42 m (138 ft)/min

Service ceiling (30·5 m; 100 ft/min climb rate):

A, B	above 4,000 m (13,125 ft)
C	4,000 m (13,125 ft)

Hovering ceiling IGE at T-O power:

A	2,560 m (8,400 ft)
B	1,940 m (6,365 ft)
C	1,320 m (4,330 ft)

Hovering ceiling OGE at T-O power:

A	1,860 m (6,100 ft)
B	1,240 m (4,070 ft)
C	480 m (1,575 ft)

PZL Swidnik W-3 Sokól (two PZL 10W turboshaft engines)

Max range at econ cruising speed, standard fuel, no

reserves: A	282 nm (522 km; 324 miles)
B	275 nm (510 km; 317 miles)
C	268 nm (497 km; 309 miles)

Max endurance, conditions as above:

A	3 h 41 min
B	3 h 27 min
C	3 h 15 min

PZL SWIDNIK W-3 SOKÓL (FALCON)

This all-new Polish helicopter was under development in 1978-79. Completion of the first prototype was achieved on 3 August 1979, and flight testing began on 16 November 1979. The design team was headed by S. Kaminski. Larger than the Mi-2/Kania, it accommodates a crew of two, and 12 passengers or up to 1,500 kg (3,306 lb) of freight. Power plant consists of two 746 kW (1,000 shp) PZL-10W (Polish-built Glushenkov TVD-10) turboshaft engines; fuel capacity is 1,100 litres (242 Imp gallons). Passenger, cargo, agricultural and ambulance versions are planned.

DIMENSIONS, EXTERNAL:

Main rotor diameter	15·70 m (51 ft 6 in)
Length overall, rotors turning	18·85 m (61 ft 10¼ in)
Height overall	4·15 m (13 ft 7½ in)

WEIGHTS:

Basic operating weight empty	2,490 kg (5,489 lb)
Max payload	1,500 kg (3,306 lb)
Normal T-O weight	5,810 kg (12,808 lb)
Max T-O weight	6,000 kg (13,227 lb)

PERFORMANCE (estimated):

Max level speed	140 knots (260 km/h; 161 mph)
Cruising speed	119 knots (220 km/h; 137 mph)
Max rate of climb at S/L	564 m (1,850 ft)/min
Max vertical rate of climb at S/L	120 m (394 ft)/min
Service ceiling	5,000 m (16,400 ft)

PZL Swidnik W-3 Sokól twin-turboshaft helicopter *(Pilot Press)*

Hovering ceiling OGE	1,850 m (6,070 ft)
Range: standard fuel	324 nm (600 km; 373 miles)
auxiliary fuel	593 nm (1,100 km; 683 miles)

PZL SWIDNIK SMALL HELICOPTER

Work has begun at Swidnik on a new 4/5-seat helicopter.

PORTUGAL

OGMA
OFICINAS GERAIS DE MATERIAL AERO-NÁUTICO (General Aeronautical Material Workshops)

WORKS: 2615 Alverca
Telephone: 2580 786; 2581 803, 882, 923 and 979
Telex: 14479 OGMA P
DIRECTOR: Maj Gen Eng Rui do Carmo da Conceição Espadinha
ASST DIRECTOR: Col Eng António Pedro da Silva Gonçalves

OGMA was founded in 1918 and has been in continuous operation since then. It is the Air Force department responsible for maintenance and repair, at depot level, of all aircraft, avionics, engines, structures, ground communications and radar equipment of the Portuguese Air Force.

OGMA has a total covered area of 110,000 m² (1,184,030 sq ft), and a work force of approx 3,000 people. It performs major overhaul and IRAN work on aircraft, aero-engines and components for the Portuguese

Air Force. Under a contract signed in 1959, it also undertakes IRAN, refurbishing and rehabilitation, periodic inspection and emergency maintenance and crash repair of US Air Force and US Navy aircraft.

Under contract to Aérospatiale of France, OGMA is manufacturing tail structures for the SA 315B Lama and SA 318 Alouette II helicopters, and small structural components for the SA 330 Puma. Other component manufacture is undertaken for Socata, SIAI-Marchetti, OMERA and Turboméca.

ROMANIA

CNIAR
CENTRUL NATIONAL AL INDUSTRIEI AERONAUTICE ROMÂNE (National Centre of the Romanian Aeronautical Industry)

HEADQUARTERS: 133 Calea Victoriei, Sector 1, 71102 Bucharest
GENERAL DIRECTOR: Teodor Zanfirescu

Romania has had a tradition of aviation since the earliest days of flying, dating from the first monoplane built in France in early 1906 by the Romanian engineer Traian Vuia, the original monoplane of Aurel Vlaicu which, in Bucharest on 17 June 1910, became the first nationally-designed aeroplane to be flown in Romania, and the aeroplanes designed and built in France and Britain by Henri Coanda in 1910-14.

Since that time the Romanian aircraft industry (IAR) has produced some 90 different types of landplane, including helicopters (of which 80 were Romanian-designed) and about 40 different types of sailplane. Many other achievements in the fields of theoretical and experimental aerodynamics have been made by teams of Romanian

engineers, led by Prof Elie Carafoli, Prof Ion Stroiescu, Prof Ion Grosu, Dipl Eng Radu Manicatide, Dipl Eng Iosif Silimon and others, using latterly the Canadian-licensed trisonic wind tunnel at INCREST in Bucharest.

The foundations for the present industry were laid at Brasov in 1926, and by 1939 the most important centre of the Romanian aircraft industry was the IAR (Industria Aeronautica Română) at Brasov, with 8,000 employees. Other factories included Astra, Arad, SET and ICAR. The IAR factory, destroyed by bombing in 1944, was rebuilt after the war for the manufacture of tractors. It resumed its aeronautical activities with the IAR-811 training aircraft, flown for the first time in March 1949, and the IAR-813, -814 and -817 utility, agricultural and ambulance aircraft. Known until 1959 as URMV-3 (aircraft component repair factory 3), the Brasov factory during that period produced more than 200 aircraft of different types and more than 20 types of sailplane. Two other repair factories were set up at Medias (ARMV-1) and Bucharest (ARMV-2).

In 1959 the URMV-3 was divided into two factories.

The Brasov team was renamed ICA (Intreprinderea de Constructii Aeronautice) Brasov-Ghimbav, and up to 1968 produced more than 100 sailplanes designed by Dipl Eng Iosif Silimon. The second team, relocated in Bucharest and combined with ARMV-2, became known as IRMA (Intreprinderea de Reparat Material Aeronautic), under the leadership of Dipl Eng Radu Manicatide. Here, up to 1968, were built more than 140 ambulance, training, agricultural and other aircraft.

The industry was again reorganised in 1968, and its activities are now undertaken, within the Ministry of Machine Building Industry, by the CNIAR, which combines the activities of the former CIAR and GAB (see 1979-80 *Jane's*). Major production activities of the CNIAR are carried out in five factories. The two main aircraft factories, details of whose products follow, are the ICA at Brasov and IAvB at Bucharest. A third factory, IRAvB at Bacau, builds the Soviet Yak-52 under licence and manufactures various components for the IAR-823, IAR-316B and SOKO/CNIAR Orao/IAR-93 (see International section); Viper 632-41 engines for the IAR-93 and Turmo IV CA engines for the IAR-330 (Puma) helicopter, are built by the Turbomecanica Enterprise in Bucharest. Exports and imports of aircraft and aero-engines are the responsibility of the CNA (see next entry), formed in 1979; avionics and electronic equipment sales are dealt with by Electronum and Electroexportimport. Aeronautical research and development are undertaken by INCREST (formerly IMFCA), the Aerospace Research and Design Institute at Bucharest. INCREST also designs and manufactures aerospace equipment, including anti-skid brakes, engine stands, fuel monitoring equipment, intercoms and various aviation raw materials. The flight test centre is the CIIAR (Centrul de Incercari In zbor) at Craiova.

The Baneasa area of Bucharest is being developed as the headquarters and main centre for CNIAR activities, and for the laboratories and design offices of INCREST.

Prototype of the IAR-93/Orao single-seat fighter, now in production for the air forces of Romania and Yugoslavia and described in the International section *(Front Magazine)*

CNA

CENTRUL NATIONAL AERONAUTIC (Intreprinderea Specializata pentru Comert Exterior) (National Centre for Aeronautical Foreign Trade)

Bulevardul Dacia 13, Bucharest
Telephone: 12 08 78
Telex: 10660
GENERAL DIRECTOR: Eng C. Zgavirdici
PUBLICITY: George Popescu

ICA

INTREPRINDEREA DE CONSTRUCTII AERONAUTICE (Aeronautical Construction Enterprise)

Ghimbav, near Brasov

ICA, created in 1968, continues the work that was begun in 1926 by IAR-Brasov and was then undertaken in 1950-59 as URMV-3 Brasov. Today, it manufactures the Romanian-designed IAR-823, the Alouette III and Puma helicopters under licence from Aérospatiale of France (as the IAR-316B and IAR-330 respectively), and the IS-28/29 series of Romanian sailplanes and motor gliders. It also produces aircraft components and equipment.

IAR-823

Design of the IAR-823 two/five-seat training and touring light aircraft was started at IMFCA in May 1970, by a team led by Dipl Ing Radu Manicatide. Construction of a prototype began at ICA-Brasov in the Autumn of 1971, and this aircraft made its first flight in July 1973. The first production aircraft flew in 1974, and at least 60 are reported to have been delivered to the Romanian Air Force and Romanian flying clubs by the beginning of 1980.

As a two-seater, the IAR-823 is fully aerobatic and is intended for training duties. With a rear bench seat for up to three more persons it is suitable as an executive, taxi or touring aircraft. Provision is made for two underwing pylons for the carriage of drop-tanks or practice weapons.

TYPE: Two/five-seat cabin monoplane.

WINGS: Cantilever low-wing monoplane. Wing section NACA 23012 (modified). Dihedral 7° from roots. Incidence 3° at root, 1° at tip. Conventional all-metal structure, with single main spar and rear auxiliary spar; three-point attachment to fuselage. Riveted spars, ribs and skin of corrosion-proof aluminium alloy. Leading-edges riveted, and sealed to ribs and main spar to form main torsion box and integral fuel tanks. Electrically-actuated fabric-covered metal single-slotted flaps and fabric-covered Frise-type slotted metal ailerons. Ground-adjustable tab.

FUSELAGE: All-metal semi-monocoque structure. Glassfibre engine cowling.

TAIL UNIT: Cantilever metal structure. Two-spar duralumin-covered fin and tailplane; fabric-covered duralumin horn-balanced rudder and elevators. Electrically-actuated automatic trim tabs in elevators; controllable tab in rudder.

LANDING GEAR: Retractable tricycle type, with steerable nosewheel. Electrical retraction, main units inward, nose unit rearward. Emergency manual actuation. Oleo-pneumatic shock-absorbers. Main-wheel tyres size 6·00-6, pressure 2·93 bars (42·5 lb/sq in). Nose-wheel tyre size 355 × 150 mm. Independent hydraulic main-wheel brakes, pedal-controlled from left front seat. Shimmy damper on nose unit. No wheel doors.

POWER PLANT: One 216 kW (290 hp) Avco Lycoming IO-540-G1D5 flat-six engine, driving a Hoffmann two-blade variable-pitch constant-speed metal propeller. Fuel in four integral wing tanks, total capacity 360 litres (79 Imp gallons). Provision for two 70 litre (15·4 Imp gallon) drop-tanks on underwing pylons.

ACCOMMODATION: Fully-enclosed cabin, seating two persons side by side on individual adjustable front seats, with removable bench seat at rear for up to three more people. Dual controls standard in training version, optional in other versions. Upward-hinged door (optionally jettisonable) on each side of cabin, which is soundproofed, heated and ventilated. Compartment at rear of cabin for up to 40 kg (88 lb) of baggage. Equipment and layout can be varied for use as air taxi, executive or freight transport, ambulance, liaison or photographic aircraft.

SYSTEMS AND AVIONICS: Electrical system, including 50A alternator and 24V 30Ah battery, for engine starting, elevator tab and landing gear actuation, radio communications, landing and navigation lights and cabin and instrument lighting. Standard avionics include VFR instrumentation and Bendix RT 221-AE transceiver. Optional equipment, according to mission, includes blind-flying instrumentation and, in civil transport version, marker beacon receiver, nav/com radio, VOR/ILS, ADF and autopilot.

IAR-823 two/five-seat light aircraft (Avco Lycoming IO-540 engine) *(Peter R. March)*

ICA IAR-823 light touring and training aircraft *(Pilot Press)*

DIMENSIONS, EXTERNAL:	
Wing span	10·00 m (32 ft 9¾ in)
Wing chord at c/l	2·00 m (6 ft 6¾ in)
Wing chord at tip	1·00 m (3 ft 3¼ in)
Wing aspect ratio	6·66
Length overall	8·24 m (27 ft 0¼ in)
Height overall	2·52 m (8 ft 3¼ in)
Wheel track	2·48 m (8 ft 1¾ in)
Wheelbase	1·86 m (6 ft 1¼ in)
Propeller diameter	2·23 m (7 ft 4 in)
AREAS:	
Wings, gross	15·00 m² (161·5 sq ft)
Ailerons (total)	1·20 m² (12·92 sq ft)
Trailing-edge flaps (total)	1·78 m² (19·16 sq ft)
Horizontal tail surfaces (total)	3·30 m² (35·52 sq ft)
Vertical tail surfaces (total)	1·50 m² (16·15 sq ft)

WEIGHTS AND LOADINGS (A: Aerobatic; U: Utility category):

Weight empty: A	900 kg (1,984 lb)
U	910 kg (2,006 lb)
Max T-O weight: A	1,190 kg (2,623 lb)
U	1,380 kg (3,042 lb)
Max permissible weight for special missions	1,500 kg (3,307 lb)
Max normal wing loading:	
A	79·0 kg/m² (16·2 lb/sq ft)
U	92·0 kg/m² (18·8 lb/sq ft)
Max normal power loading:	
A	5·51 kg/kW (9·15 lb/hp)

PERFORMANCE (at 1,400 kg; 3,086 lb AUW except where indicated):

Never-exceed speed	215 knots (400 km/h; 248 mph)
Max level speed at S/L	167 knots (310 km/h; 192·5 mph)
Max cruising speed (75% power) at 1,750 m (5,750 ft)	162 knots (300 km/h; 186 mph)
Econ cruising speed (60% power) at 3,050 m (10,000 ft)	156 knots (290 km/h; 180 mph)
Landing speed	56·5 knots (105 km/h; 65 mph)
Stalling speed, flaps up	62·5 knots (115 km/h; 71·5 mph)
Stalling speed, flaps down, power off	53 knots (98 km/h; 61 mph)
Max rate of climb at S/L	450 m (1,475 ft)/min
Time to 1,000 m (3,280 ft)	2 min 20 s
Service ceiling	5,600 m (18,375 ft)
T-O run	160 m (525 ft)
T-O to 15 m (50 ft)	310 m (1,017 ft)
Landing run	200 m (656 ft)
Range, according to mission and payload, 1 h reserves	431-970 nm (800-1,800 km; 497-1,118 miles)
Endurance, according to mission and payload	3-6 h
g limits (at 1,190 kg; 2,623 lb AUW)	+6; −3

IAR-824

Design of the IAR-824 began in the Winter of 1969, and a prototype, known as the IS-24 (YR-ISB), flew for the first time on 24 May 1971. It is believed to have been built in small numbers only, and production has now ended. A description can be found in the 1979-80 *Jane's*.

ICA (AÉROSPATIALE) IAR-316B ALOUETTE III

ICA and Aérospatiale concluded an agreement in 1971 for manufacture in Romania of SA 316B Alouette III helicopters. Production of these continues, and had totalled approx 175 by early 1980. Romanian-built components are also supplied for incorporation in French-built Alouette IIIs.

ICA (AÉROSPATIALE) IAR-330 PUMA

An agreement for licence production of the Aérospatiale SA 330 Puma in Romania was concluded in 1977, an initial quantity of 100 being involved. Approx 90 of these had been delivered by early 1980, most of them (and most Alouette IIIs) reportedly to the Romanian Air Force.

IAvB

INTREPRINDEREA DE AVIOANE BUCURESTI (Bucharest Aircraft Enterprise)

Baneasa Airport, Bd Ficusului 44, Bucharest

IAvB's predecessor, IRMA, was formed in 1959 from part of the former URMV-3 at Brasov (see 1979-80 and earlier editions of *Jane's*). The factory is currently responsible for manufacture of the BAe One-Eleven Srs 475 and 500 (components and complete aircraft), Pilatus Britten-Norman Islander, and Romanian-designed IAR-827A agricultural aircraft. It specialises in the development and manufacture of commercial and agricultural aircraft; in the repair and overhaul of various large and small aircraft; is agent and repair centre for Avco Lycoming engines; and manufactures aircraft equipment.

IAvB (BAe) ONE-ELEVEN

IAvB is the Romanian contractor for the manufacture in Bucharest of BAe One-Eleven Series 475 and 500 twin-turbofan transports under a licensing agreement signed initially in the UK on 15 June 1978 and confirmed by a series of contracts concluded in June 1979. British programme contractor is the Weybridge-Bristol Division

Pilatus Britten-Norman BN-2A-27 Islander built in Romania

IAvB IAR-827 single/two-seat agricultural aircraft, in original form with Avco Lycoming engine (Pilot Press)

of British Aerospace. A corresponding programme provides for Romanian manufacture of the Rolls-Royce Spey engines.

Initially, three complete aircraft are being delivered from British Aerospace's Hurn (Bournemouth) factory. The first of these was handed over on 22 February 1980. The transfer of industrial technology will take place in seven stages, permitting manufacture of the first 22 aircraft by 1985, after which production of complete aircraft will continue both to cover domestic requirements and for export. The first fuselage for a Romanian-assembled One-Eleven (a Srs 500) was delivered by Super Guppy transport aircraft in January 1980; two more fuselages were due to be delivered by the end of that year.

IAvB (PILATUS BRITTEN-NORMAN) ISLANDER

The Pilatus Britten-Norman Islander (see UK section) has been manufactured under licence in Romania, originally by IRMA, for several years. The first Romanian-built example flew for the first time at Baneasa Airport, Bucharest, on 4 August 1969, and the initial commitment to build 215 Islanders was completed in 1976. A total of

315 had been completed by June 1979, and production was continuing in 1980.

IAR-827A

The IAR-827A is a developed version of the all-metal IAR-826 (see 1978-79 *Jane's*), with increased payload, a Polish-built engine of higher power, and improved flying and operating characteristics.

Design of the basic IAR-827 began in the early part of 1973. The objective was to evolve an agricultural aircraft with an airframe life of 4,000 hours (equivalent to 22,000 flights) and able to carry a useful load equivalent to 2 kg (4·4 lb) for every horsepower. Particular attention was paid to minimising corrosion problems.

Static testing was completed before the first flight, which is believed to have taken place on or about 22 July 1976. A second aircraft was completed for fatigue testing. Initially, certification was anticipated during 1977, and five pre-series aircraft were to have been delivered by the end of that year; but early flight testing revealed the need for a more powerful engine, and the original 298 kW (400 hp) Avco Lycoming IO-720-DA1B flat-eight engine was replaced by a 447 kW (600 hp) PZL-3S radial engine.

A description of the Lycoming-engined IAR-827 prototype can be found in the 1979-80 *Jane's*. Certification of the IAR-827A, as the radial-engined production version is known, was received in 1979, and the first production IAR-827A was displayed at the Aero Technica '80 exhibition in Bucharest in June 1980.

The following description is applicable to the Avco Lycoming-engined prototype, amended where possible to refer to the production IAR-827A:

TYPE: Single/two-seat agricultural aircraft.

WINGS: Cantilever low-wing monoplane. Wing section NACA 23014. Constant-chord safe-life structure, with dihedral from roots. Welded chrome-molybdenum steel tube centre-section with duralumin skin. All-metal single-spar outer panels. Plain ailerons. Electrically-operated single-slotted Fowler-type flaps.

FUSELAGE: Forward structure of welded steel tube, with glassfibre skin panels attached by quick-release fastenings. Rear fuselage is an all-metal semi-monocoque.

TAIL UNIT: Cantilever all-metal structure, with slightly-sweptback fin and rudder. Balanced elevators, each with inset tab.

LANDING GEAR: Non-retractable tailwheel type. Main units comprise 140 mm stroke hydraulic shock-struts and side Vs, and are fitted with Dunlop wheels (tyre size 620 × 225) and brakes. Gear is of Romanian design and is designed to withstand a vertical velocity of 6 m (19·5 ft)/s or a free drop of 1·2 m (3 ft 11¼ in).

POWER PLANT (IAR-827A): One 447 kW (600 hp) PZL-3S seven-cylinder radial aircooled engine. Fuel tank in each wing leading-edge, each of 100 litres (22 Imp gallons) capacity in prototype.

ACCOMMODATION: Side-by-side seats for pilot and mechanic in fully-enclosed cockpit, with window/door on each side. Provision for dual controls and emergency door jettison. Seat height and rudder pedals adjustable. Crash pylon in fairing aft of seats. Cockpit is heated and ventilated and, on production aircraft, sealed and slightly pressurised to exclude dust.

EQUIPMENT: All-glassfibre hopper in forward fuselage, with a volume of 1·23 m³ (43·44 cu ft). Hopper stressed for loads of up to 1,000 kg (2,205 lb), but normal max load is 800 kg (1,763 lb) of dry or 1,200 litres (264 Imp gallons) of liquid chemical.

DIMENSIONS, EXTERNAL:

Wing span	14·00 m (45 ft 11¼ in)
Length overall (prototype)	9·60 m (31 ft 6 in)
Height overall (prototype)	2·60 m (8 ft 6½ in)
Tailplane span	approx 4·50 m (14 ft 9 in)
Wheel track	3·42 m (11 ft 2¾ in)
Wheelbase	6·20 m (20 ft 4 in)

AREA:

Wings, gross	29·00 m² (312·15 sq ft)

WEIGHTS (prototype):

Weight empty, with agricultural equipment	1,280 kg (2,822 lb)
Max T-O weight	2,350 kg (5,180 lb)

PERFORMANCE (prototype, estimated, with agricultural equipment, at max T-O weight):

Max level speed	113 knots (210 km/h; 130 mph)
Cruising speed	94 knots (175 km/h; 109 mph)
Operating speed range	75·5-92 knots (140-170 km/h; 87-106 mph)
Stalling speed, flaps up, power off	59·5 knots (110 km/h; 68·5 mph)
Max rate of climb at S/L	210 m (690 ft)/min
Service ceiling	3,500 m (11,475 ft)
T-O to 15 m (50 ft)	440 m (1,445 ft)
Max endurance	2 h 30 min

IRAvB
INTREPRINDEREA DE RAPARAT AVIOANE BACAU (Bacau Aircraft Repair Enterprise)
Bacau

This factory manufactures hydraulic, pneumatic, air-conditioning, fuel system and landing gear components for the ICA IAR-823 light aircraft and IAR-316B helicopter, and for the IAR-93 strike fighter. It is also building under

licence the Soviet Yakovlev Yak-52 light aircraft.

IRAvB (YAKOVLEV) Yak-52

After some two years of negotiation, arrangements were made in 1978 for the IRAvB factory at Bacau to build under licence the Yakovlev Yak-52 tandem two-seat trainer, described in the USSR section. At the beginning of these negotiations a total of 2,000 of these aircraft was planned to be built in Romania, with an eventual peak

production rate of 36 per month.

Manufacture began at Bacau in 1978, and in the Summer of 1979 a Yak-52 fuselage was installed in a structural test rig at INCREST in Bucharest. By September of that year, four complete airframes and two fuselages were on the final assembly line at Bacau, the aircraft at the head of the line being described as the third 'pre-production' example.

SOUTH AFRICA

AERONICS
AERONICS (PTY) LTD
PO Box 391090, Bramley 2018
Telephone: (011) 786 9600
DIRECTOR: J. M. Cohoe

Aeronics (Pty) Ltd has production rights to produce exclusively in South Africa the Sequoia Models 300 and 301 light aircraft, following an agreement signed in

November 1978 with Sequoia Aircraft Corporation of Richmond, Virginia, USA.

AERONICS (SEQUOIA) MODELS 300 and 301
Design of the Sequoia light aircraft, which began in 1975, was undertaken for Sequoia Aircraft Corporation by Mr David Thurston, a consultant whose other designs include the Teal and Marlin amphibians. In addition to planned availability for construction by homebuilders, it is

also to be a factory-produced aircraft, manufactured in South Africa by Aeronics (Pty) Ltd.

The Sequoia is configured basically as a two-seater in two forms, the Model 300 with side-by-side seating and the Model 301 with tandem seats; in addition, the Model 300 can be made available in a '2 + 2' layout.

A detailed description of the Sequoia 300/301 can be found in the Homebuilts section.

ATLAS
ATLAS AIRCRAFT CORPORATION OF SOUTH AFRICA (PTY) LIMITED

HEAD OFFICE AND WORKS: PO Box 11, Atlas Road, Kempton Park 1620, Transvaal
Telephone: 973 0111
Telex: 87965
GENERAL MANAGER: G. W. Ward
DIVISIONAL MANAGER (COMMERCIAL): A. J. Bester

Atlas built the Impala Mk 1 (M.B. 326M) jet trainer under licence from Aermacchi. Its present programmes include production of the Impala Mk 2 and of the Atlas C4M STOL light transport.

Atlas is manufacturing under licence components for Dassault Mirage F1-AZ and -CZ multi-purpose combat aircraft currently in service with Nos. 1 and 3 Squadrons respectively of the South African Air Force. It also undertakes maintenance and overhaul of SAAF aircraft.

ATLAS IMPALA Mk 2

The Impala Mk 2 is based on the single-seat Aermacchi M.B. 326K. It was developed by Atlas as an advanced trainer for the SAAF and is now in production. Four M.B. 326Ks are reported to have been delivered initially by Aermacchi. No details of the Impala Mk 2 have yet been released officially, except that it has a Rolls-Royce Viper Mk 540 turbojet engine; a brief description of the Aermacchi M.B. 326 series can be found in the Italian section. Impala Mks 1 and 2 are reported to equip Nos. 4, 5, 6, 7 and 8 Squadrons of the SAAF's Active Citizen Force, in addition to the Flying Training School at Langebaanweg.

ATLAS C4M
South African Air Force name: Kudu

The C4M is a six/eight-seat light transport aircraft, developed by Atlas, which can be converted rapidly from the passenger to the freight role, and vice versa, and can operate from unprepared surfaces. The prototype (ZS-IZF) flew for the first time on 16 February 1974, and certification to FAR Pt 23 was granted on 16 June 1975. The third C4M (ZS-IZG) flew shortly afterwards.

A military prototype flew for the first time on 18 June 1975, and was later handed over to the South African Air Force (SAAF serial number 961) for evaluation. A military C4M bearing the SAAF serial number 978, and belonging to No. 41 Squadron, was displayed at the Air Africa air show in 1977, indicating that the C4M is in production. No confirmation of its civil or military status has been given by Atlas, but the Kudu military version is believed now also to form part of the equipment of No. 42 Squadron of the SAAF. It is reported that the SAAF has ordered 40.

TYPE: Single-engined cabin monoplane.
WINGS: High-wing monoplane, with single elliptical-section bracing strut each side. Wing section NACA 23016 at root, NACA 4412 (modified) at tip. Dihedral 3°. Incidence 4° at root, 0° 27' at tip. All-metal D-spar torsion-box structure, bolted to fuselage. Electrically-operated Fowler flaps, of all-metal two-spar construction, interchangeable right with left. All-metal piano-hinged ailerons, with inset electrically-operated trim tab (port) and balance tab (starboard). Vortex generators forward of ailerons. Glassfibre wingtips.
FUSELAGE: All-metal stressed-skin structure, comprising a sturdy floor, bulkheads and stringers, of basically rectangular section. No longerons. Titanium alloy firewall. Glassfibre tailcone.
TAIL UNIT: Cantilever all-metal structure. Electrically-operated variable-incidence tailplane, with manual standby. Aerodynamically and mass balanced elevators and rudder. Balance tab in port elevator. Servo tab in each elevator. Vortex generators forward of elevators.
LANDING GEAR: Non-retractable tailwheel type. Main units each have an independent cantilever leg, and are connected to oleo-pneumatic shock-absorbers mounted below cabin floor level in small underfuselage blister fairings. Main-wheel tube-type tyres size 7·00-8, 6-ply rating, pressure 2·55 bars (37 lb/sq in). Single-disc hydraulic brakes. Steerable tailwheel, mounted on an oleo-pneumatic levered-suspension strut, has a size 5·00-4 6-ply tube-type tyre, pressure 2·45 bars (35·5 lb/sq in).
POWER PLANT: One 254 kW (340 hp) Piaggio-built Avco Lycoming GSO-480-B1B3 flat-six engine, driving a Hartzell HC-B3R20-4/R10160-1 three-blade constant-speed variable-pitch metal propeller with spinner. Three removable and partially self-sealing bag-type fuel tanks in each wing, total capacity 432

Atlas Impala Mk 2 single-seat light strike aircraft, based on the Aermacchi M.B. 326K

litres (95 Imp gallons). Overwing refuelling points. Oil capacity 11·3 litres (2·5 Imp gallons).
ACCOMMODATION: Pilot and co-pilot side by side at front, with four individual seats in pairs at rear, or two bench seats each for three persons. Baggage compartment aft of seats. Passenger seats can be removed to provide space for up to 560 kg (1,235 lb) of cargo. Heating, ventilation and windscreen demisting standard. Forward-hinged door on each side for pilot and co-pilot. Main cabin door is on port side, and is in two sections: forward-opening front section for passengers, rearward-opening rear section for loading cargo. A sliding door at the rear of the cabin on the starboard side may be opened in flight for parachuting and is available for emergency exit. A trap-door is provided in the cabin floor for aerial survey or supply dropping purposes.
SYSTEMS: Hydraulic system for main-wheel brakes only. 28V DC electrical system supplied by an engine-driven generator and a 24V 15Ah battery. Static inverter provides 115/26V AC power for instruments and radio.
AVIONICS AND EQUIPMENT: To customer's specification, but probably including two VHF transceivers, intercom, HF radio and ADF. Blind-flying instrumentation standard.

DIMENSIONS, EXTERNAL:
Wing span	13·075 m (42 ft 10¾ in)
Wing chord at root	1·727 m (5 ft 8 in)
Wing chord at tip	1·168 m (3 ft 10 in)
Wing aspect ratio	8·07
Length overall (tail down)	9·31 m (30 ft 6½ in)
Height overall (tail down)	3·66 m (12 ft 0 in)
Elevator span	4·79 m (15 ft 8½ in)
Wheel track (full fuel, no load)	2·935 m (9 ft 7½ in)
Wheelbase	6·625 m (21 ft 9 in)
Propeller diameter	2·54 m (8 ft 4 in)
Propeller ground clearance	0·233 m (9¼ in)
Crew doors (each): Height	1·16 m (3 ft 9¾ in)
Mean width	0·53 m (1 ft 9 in)
Double doors (port): Height	1·05 m (3 ft 5¼ in)
Width	1·42 m (4 ft 8 in)
Sliding door (stbd): Height	1·04 m (3 ft 5 in)
Width	0·74 m (2 ft 5 in)
Trap-door (floor): Length	0·70 m (2 ft 3½ in)
Width	0·50 m (1 ft 7¾ in)

DIMENSIONS, INTERNAL:
Cabin: Length, incl flight deck	3·20 m (10 ft 6 in)
Max width	1·14 m (3 ft 9 in)
Height at front	1·31 m (4 ft 3½ in)
Height at rear	1·14 m (3 ft 9 in)

AREAS:
Wings, gross	20·971 m² (225·7 sq ft)
Ailerons (total)	2·620 m² (28·19 sq ft)
Trailing-edge flaps (total)	3·774 m² (40·62 sq ft)
Fin	1·625 m² (17·49 sq ft)
Rudder	0·945 m² (10·17 sq ft)
Tailplane	3·430 m² (36·92 sq ft)
Elevators, incl tabs	2·063 m² (22·21 sq ft)

WEIGHTS AND LOADINGS:
Weight empty	1,230 kg (2,711 lb)
Max payload	560 kg (1,235 lb)
Max T-O and landing weight	2,040 kg (4,497 lb)
Max wing loading	97·3 kg/m² (19·93 lb/sq ft)
Max power loading	8·03 kg/kW (13·23 lb/hp)

PERFORMANCE (at max T-O weight):
Never-exceed speed	165 knots (305 km/h; 190 mph) IAS
Max level speed at 2,440 m (8,000 ft)	140 knots (259 km/h; 161 mph) TAS
Max cruising speed at 3,050 m (10,000 ft)	126 knots (233 km/h; 145 mph) TAS
Econ cruising speed at 3,050 m (10,000 ft)	108 knots (200 km/h; 124 mph) TAS
Stalling speed, flaps up, power on	65 knots (121 km/h; 75 mph) IAS
Stalling speed, flaps down, power on	48 knots (89 km/h; 55·5 mph) IAS
Max rate of climb at S/L	244 m (800 ft)/min
Service ceiling	4,270 m (14,000 ft)
T-O run	215 m (705 ft)
T-O to 15 m (50 ft)	370 m (1,214 ft)
Landing from 15 m (50 ft)	260 m (853 ft)
Landing run	140 m (460 ft)
Range with max fuel, 45 min reserves	700 nm (1,297 km; 806 miles)
Range with 400 kg (882 lb) payload, 45 min reserves	400 nm (740 km; 460 miles)
Endurance with max fuel, no reserves	8 h

Atlas C4M six/eight-seat light transport (Avco Lycoming GSO-480-B1B3 engine)

CSIR
COUNCIL FOR SCIENTIFIC AND INDUSTRIAL RESEARCH (National Institute for Aeronautics and Systems Technology)

PO Box 395, Pretoria 0001
Telephone: (012) 74 9111
Telex: 3-633 SA
HEAD OF AERONAUTICS DEPARTMENT: Dr C. G. van Niekerk, FRAeS

Initially, the CSIR concentrated on the spin-off from aeronautical research. This work led to the establishment in 1952 of a small aerodynamics division which grew into

the Aeronautics Research Unit, established in 1968. In 1978 this Unit joined another CSIR group to form the National Institute for Aeronautics and Systems Technology.

Current activities include research into lifting rotors, airframe fatigue, synthetic materials, separation of underwing stores, aircraft and missile stability, flutter, atmospheric turbulence, and aircraft noise problems.

The prototype CSIR (ARU) SARA II (South African Research Autogyro) made its first free flight in Pretoria during November 1972; a description of this can be found in the 1975-76 *Jane's*.

CSIR SARA 3

The modified SARA 3 (ZS-UIT) was designed and constructed during 1976-77, and techniques were developed for the design and manufacture of GRP rotor blades. This aircraft made its first flight on 1 August 1977, and its first public appearance three months later, at the Air Africa International display. Further development of GRP blade design was continuing in early 1980.

A detailed description of the SARA 3 can be found in the 1979-80 *Jane's*.

SPAIN

AISA
AERONAUTICA INDUSTRIAL SA

HEAD OFFICE, WORKS AND AIRFIELD: Cuatro Vientos
(Carretera del Aeroclub Carabanchel Alto), Apartado
984, Madrid 25
Telephone: 208 75 40 and 208 96 40
Telex: 23593 E Madrid
PRESIDENT: Gonzalo Suárez Alvarez
MANAGING DIRECTOR: José A. Delgado Vallina
PROJECT DIRECTOR: Juán del Campo Aguilera
PRODUCTION DIRECTOR: Angel Romero Benito

This company has been engaged since 1923 in the manufacture, repair and maintenance of fixed-wing aircraft
and helicopters. Its design office has been responsible for
several liaison, training and sporting aircraft for the
Spanish Air Force and aeroclub flying schools, including
the I-11, I-11B, AVD-12 and I-115. The Cuatro Vientos
factory has a covered area of 8,000 m² (86,110 sq ft) and
employs some 140 persons.

AISA is engaged in IRAN work and general overhaul of
several types of US aircraft, in particular the North
American T-6, Beechcraft B55, C90 and F33 Bonanza,
and Piper PA-23 aircraft operated by the Spanish Air
Force and the National School of Aeronautics. It is also
engaged in the repair and overhaul of Bell 47, 204, 205
and 206, and Boeing Vertol CH-47 helicopters, and their
dynamic components, for the Spanish Army, Spanish Air
Force and civilian operators. As a subcontractor to
Messier-Hispano-Bugatti, it is producing landing gear
shock-absorbers and hydraulic actuators for the
Dassault-Breguet Mirage and Falcon series, Das-
sault/Dornier Alpha Jet, and other European aviation
programmes.

AISA AUTOGYRO GN

AISA, which in 1927 built some of the earliest Cierva
Autogiros, is currently developing this four-seat autogyro.
Construction of two prototypes (one for ground testing)
began in 1978, and most structural static tests had been
completed by January 1980. First flight was scheduled for
1980.

The GN, which will have a jump take-off capability, is
powered by a 224 kW (300 hp) Avco Lycoming IO-540-
K1A5 flat-six engine, driving a two-blade constant-speed
Hartzell pusher propeller. It has accommodation for a
pilot and three passengers, with a single door on each side
of the cabin. A four-blade articulated rotor, with rotor
brake, is fitted, and the aircraft has short-span wings of
NACA 0024 section. The pod-shaped fuselage is an
aluminium alloy semi-monocoque structure, with
moulded Plexiglas transparencies; the twin tailbooms,

AISA autogyro GN (Avco Lycoming IO-540-K1A5 engine) *(Roy J. Grainge)*

tailplane, elevator and twin fins and rudders are also of
all-metal construction. A non-retractable tricycle landing
gear is fitted, with single wheel on each unit.

DIMENSIONS, EXTERNAL:

Rotor diameter	11·76 m (38 ft 7 in)
Rotor blade chord (each)	0·28 m (11 in)
Rotor disc area	108·62 m² (1,169·2 sq ft)
Wing span (incl tailbooms)	2·60 m (8 ft 6¼ in)
Wing chord (constant)	0·85 m (2 ft 9½ in)
Length of fuselage	6·50 m (21 ft 4 in)
Height overall	3·20 m (10 ft 6 in)
Propeller diameter	2·14 m (7 ft 0 in)
Doors (each): Height	1·085 m (3 ft 6¾ in)
Width	0·93 m (3 ft 0½ in)

WEIGHTS:

Weight empty	948 kg (2,090 lb)
Max payload	308 kg (679 lb)
Max T-O weight	1,400 kg (3,086 lb)

PERFORMANCE (estimated, at max T-O weight):
Max level speed at S/L
        129 knots (240 km/h; 149 mph)
Max cruising speed at S/L
        114 knots (212 km/h; 132 mph)
Min speed, power on 29 knots (54 km/h; 33·5 mph)
Max rate of climb at S/L   360 m (1,180 ft)/min
Landing run (zero wind)   0-5 m (0-16·5 ft)
Range with max fuel   431 nm (800 km; 497 miles)

CASA
CONSTRUCCIONES AERONAUTICAS SA

HEAD OFFICE: Rey Francisco 4, Apartado 193, Madrid 8
Telephone: 247 25 00
Telex: 27418
WORKS: Getafe, Seville, San Pablo, Cádiz, Madrid and
Ajalvir
HONORARY PRESIDENT: José Ortiz Echagüe
CHAIRMAN AND PRESIDENT: Dr Carlos Marin Ridruejo
VICE-CHAIRMAN OF THE BOARD: Dr Eugenio Aguirre
Castillo
GENERAL DIRECTOR: Dr Restituto Estirado
EXECUTIVE DIRECTOR, SALES/MARKETING: Pablo de Bergia
Gonzalez
DIRECTOR OF SALES: Juan Alonso Castro

This company was formed in March 1923 for the primary purpose of producing metal aircraft for the Spanish Air
Force. It began by building under licence the Breguet XIX
and has since manufactured many other aircraft of foreign
design, the most recent being the Northrop F-5 fighter. It
is assembling the 60 MBB BO 105 helicopters ordered for
the Spanish Army in July 1979.

CASA's own Project Office has designed several aircraft under contract to the Spanish Air Ministry, including
the C-212 Aviocar transport and the C-101 Aviojet jet
trainer, both of which are currently in production. It also
undertakes design and development work for foreign
companies and, for example, collaborated in the design of
the MBB HFB 320 Hansa executive transport; MBB in
turn co-operated in the design of the Aviocar. In order to
promote sales in the Far East, CASA established a C-212
assembly line in Indonesia, as well as full after-sales support in that area (see PT Nurtanio entry in Indonesian
section). It is now collaborating with Nurtanio to develop a
new 35-passenger transport.

Under contract to Dassault-Breguet (which see),
CASA is responsible for manufacturing outer wings for
the Falcon 10 light business aircraft. It is a full member
(4·2%) of Airbus Industrie (see International section), and
manufactures the horizontal tail surfaces, landing gear
doors and forward passenger doors for the Airbus A300
wide-bodied transport aircraft. It also manufactures
glassfibre honeycomb components, including underwing

fillets for McDonnell Douglas DC-10 and upper-rudder
segments for Boeing 727 jet transports, outboard flaps for
the Boeing 757, and wing units for the Otomat air-
launched missile.

CASA undertakes maintenance and modernisation
work for the Spanish Air Force and for the US Air Force in
Europe. Its principal current activities of this kind concern
overhaul and maintenance of McDonnell Douglas F-4
combat aircraft and Bell 47G, 204 and 205 and Sikorsky
H-19 helicopters.

In 1972 the former Hispano Aviación SA (see 1972-73
Jane's) was merged with CASA, the latter company taking
over all of Hispano's offices and other facilities, aircraft
production programmes and personnel. In June 1973
ENMASA (Empresa Nacional de Motores de Aviación)
was merged into CASA, and now constitutes the CASA
División de Motores (see Aero-Engines section). CASA
has six factories, employing about 7,950 people in early
1980. Including Hispano production, the company had by
then manufactured more than 3,500 aircraft and overhauled approx 6,250. CASA has a total covered area in
the region of 200,000 m² (2,152,780 sq ft); majority
shareholder in the company is the INI (Instituto Nacional
de Industria).

CASA C-212-5 AVIOCAR

The C-212 Aviocar twin-turboprop light utility STOL
transport was evolved by CASA to fulfil a variety of military or civil roles, but primarily to replace the mixed fleet of
Junkers Ju 52/3m (T.2), Douglas DC-3 (T.3) and
CASA-207 Azor (T.7) transport aircraft formerly in service with the Spanish Air Force. The first of two prototypes flew for the first time on 26 March 1971.

The C-212 is able to fill six main roles—as a 16-seat
paratroop transport, military freighter, ambulance,
photographic aircraft, crew trainer or 19-seat passenger
transport—and is certificated to joint military and civil
standards by the Instituto Nacional de Técnica Aeroespacial (INTA). It has a STOL capability that enables it to use
unprepared landing strips about 400 m (1,310 ft) in
length, and has been optimised for operation in remote
areas with a poor infrastructure.

Eight pre-production Aviocars were ordered by the
Spanish Air Ministry; the first made its first flight on 17

November 1972, and all had flown by February 1974.
They were eventually delivered to the Spanish Air Force,
six of them being brought up to C-212B standard and two
to C-212E standard.

A total of 154 Aviocars were completed to C-212-5
initial production standard, of which a description can be
found in the 1979-80 *Jane's*. Versions were as follows:

C-212A (Spanish Air Force designation T.12B).
Military utility transport, ordered by the air forces of
Indonesia (48), Jordan (3), Portugal (19) and Spain (55),
and for civil internal use by the governments of Nicaragua
(5) and Chile (10).

C-212AV. VIP transport operated by the air forces of
Jordan (1) and Spain (5).

C-212B (Spanish Air Force designation TR.12A).
Photographic survey version. Six pre-production Aviocars
completed to this configuration for the Spanish Air Force;
four delivered to Portuguese Air Force.

C-212C. Commercial transport, certificated by FAA to
FAR Pt 25 at AUW of 5,670 kg (12,500 lb) as C-212CA,
and at AUW of 6,500 kg (14,330 lb) as C-212CB.

C-212E. Navigation trainer. Two pre-production
Aviocars completed to this configuration for the Spanish
Air Force, which later increased its order to five of this
version. One delivered to Portuguese Air Force.

CASA C-212 SERIES 200 AVIOCAR

The current standard version of the Aviocar since 1979,
the Series 200 is an improved version of the original
C-212-5 (1979-80 *Jane's*) with more powerful TPE331-
10 engines and increased max T-O weight. Aircraft Nos.
138 and 139 served as prototypes for this version, making
their first flights on 30 April and 20 June 1978 respectively.

By 1 January 1980, 186 Aviocars had been sold, including 154 examples of the C-212-5 version. Sales by Nurtanio had reached a total of 28 (24 for Indonesian customers, plus two each for Royal Thailand Rain Industry and
Malaysian Airlines System).

TYPE: Twin-turboprop STOL utility transport.

WINGS: Cantilever high-wing monoplane. Wing section
NACA 653-218. Incidence 2° 30'. No dihedral or
sweepback. All-metal light alloy fail-safe structure.

CASA C-212 Series 200 Aviocar twin-turboprop transport aircraft in the insignia of MedAvia (Mediterranean Aviation) of Malta

CASA C-212 Series 200 Aviocar twin-turboprop light transport aircraft *(Pilot Press)*

All-metal ailerons and double-slotted trailing-edge flaps. Trim tab in port aileron. Rubber-boot de-icing of leading-edges.

FUSELAGE: Semi-monocoque fail-safe structure of light alloy construction.

TAIL UNIT: Cantilever two-spar all-metal structure, with dorsal fairing forward of fin. Tailplane mid-mounted on rear of fuselage. Trim tab in rudder and each elevator. Rubber-boot de-icing of leading-edges.

LANDING GEAR: Non-retractable tricycle type, with single main wheels and single steerable nosewheel. CASA oleo-pneumatic shock-absorbers. Goodyear wheels and tyres, main units size 11·00-12 Type III (10-ply rating), nose unit size 24-7·7 Type VII (8-ply rating). Tyre pressure 3·72 bars (54 lb/sq in) on main units, 3·52 bars (51 lb/sq in) on nose unit. Goodyear hydraulic disc brakes on main wheels.

POWER PLANT: Two Garrett-AiResearch TPE331-10-501C turboprop engines, each flat rated at 671 kW (900 shp) and driving a Hartzell HC-B4NM-5AL four-blade constant-speed propeller (Beta mode on ground). Fuel in four outer-wing tanks, with total capacity of 2,100 litres (462 Imp gallons). Oil capacity 6 litres (1·32 Imp gallons) per engine.

ACCOMMODATION: Crew of two on flight deck. For the troop transport role, the main cabin can be fitted with 21 inward-facing seats along the cabin walls, plus three forward-facing seats, to accommodate 23 paratroops with an instructor/jumpmaster; or seats for 24 fully-equipped troops. As an ambulance, the cabin would normally be equipped to carry 12 stretcher patients and two medical attendants. As a freighter, the Aviocar Srs 200 can carry up to 2,250 kg (4,960 lb) of cargo in the main cabin, including light vehicles. Photographic version is equipped with two Wild RC-10 vertical cameras and a darkroom. Navigation training version accommodation consists of individual desks for an instructor and five pupils, in two rows, fitted with appropriate instrument installations. The civil passenger transport version has standard seating for up to 26 persons at 79 cm (31 in) pitch, with provision for quick change to all-cargo or mixed passenger/cargo interior. Toilet and baggage compartment are not standard. VIP transport version can be furnished to customer's requirements. Access to main cabin is via two doors on the port side, one aft of (and providing access to) the flight deck and one aft of the wing trailing-edge. In addition, there is a two-section underfuselage loading ramp/door aft of the main cabin; this door is openable in flight for the discharge of paratroops or cargo, and is fitted with external wheels, to allow the door to remain open during ground manoeuvring. There is an emergency exit door aft of the wing trailing-edge on the starboard side. The interior of the rear-loading door can be used for additional baggage stowage.

SYSTEMS: Unpressurised cabin. Hydraulic system, pressure 138 bars (2,000 lb/sq in), operates main-wheel brakes, flaps, nosewheel steering and ventral cargo door. Electrical system is supplied by two 9kW starter/generators.

AVIONICS AND EQUIPMENT: Radio and radar equipment includes VHF, UHF, VOR/ILS and one ADF. Blind-flying instrumentation standard. Optional avionics include Tacan, SIF/IFF, and a second ADF.

DIMENSIONS, EXTERNAL:

Wing span	19·00 m (62 ft 4 in)
Wing chord at root	2·50 m (8 ft 2½ in)
Wing chord at tip	1·50 m (4 ft 11 in)
Wing aspect ratio	9
Length overall	15·16 m (44 ft 9 in)
Height overall	6·68 m (21 ft 11 in)
Tailplane span	8·40 m (27 ft 6¾ in)
Wheel track	3·10 m (10 ft 2 in)
Wheelbase	5·55 m (18 ft 2½ in)
Propeller diameter	2·79 m (9 ft 2 in)
Distance between propeller centres	5·30 m (17 ft 4¾ in)
Passenger door (port, aft):	
Max height	1·58 m (5 ft 2¼ in)
Max width	0·70 m (2 ft 3½ in)
Crew and servicing door (port, fwd):	
Max height	1·10 m (3 ft 7¼ in)
Max width	0·60 m (1 ft 11⅝ in)
Rear-loading door: Max length	3·66 m (12 ft 0 in)
Max width	1·70 m (5 ft 7 in)
Max height	1·80 m (5 ft 11 in)

DIMENSIONS, INTERNAL:

Cabin (between flight deck and rear-loading door):	
Length	6·50 m (21 ft 4 in)
Max width	2·10 m (6 ft 10¾ in)
Max height	1·80 m (5 ft 11 in)
Floor area	10·50 m² (113·0 sq ft)
Volume	22·00 m³ (776·9 cu ft)
Cabin: volume incl flight deck and rear-loading door	26·00 m³ (918·2 cu ft)

AREAS:

Wings, gross	40·0 m² (430·56 sq ft)
Ailerons (total)	2·45 m² (26·37 sq ft)
Trailing-edge flaps (total)	7·38 m² (79·44 sq ft)
Fin	4·25 m² (45·75 sq ft)
Rudder, incl tab	2·02 m² (31·74 sq ft)
Tailplane	12·57 m² (135·30 sq ft)
Elevators, incl tabs	4·36 m² (46·93 sq ft)

WEIGHTS:

Manufacturer's weight empty	3,915 kg (8,631 lb)
Weight empty, equipped	4,115 kg (9,072 lb)
Max payload (cargo)	2,250 kg (4,960 lb)
Fuel load	1,600 kg (3,527 lb)
Max T-O weight	7,300 kg (16,093 lb)
Max landing weight	7,000 kg (15,432 lb)
Max zero-fuel weight	6,550 kg (14,440 lb)

PERFORMANCE (at max T-O weight, ISA):

Max cruising speed at 3,050 m (10,000 ft)	208 knots (386 km/h; 240 mph)
Cruising speed (80% power) at 3,050 m (10,000 ft)	190 knots (353 km/h; 219 mph)
Max rate of climb at S/L	516 m (1,700 ft)/min
Rate of climb at S/L, one engine out	114 m (374 ft)/min
Service ceiling	8,535 m (28,000 ft)
Service ceiling, one engine out	3,660 m (12,000 ft)
T-O run	370 m (1,215 ft)
T-O to 15 m (50 ft)	565 m (1,855 ft)
Landing from 15 m (50 ft)	430 m (1,410 ft)
Landing run	280 m (920 ft)
Range at max cruising speed, no reserves:	
with max payload	410 nm (760 km; 472 miles)
with max fuel	875 nm (1,620 km; 1,007 miles)

CASA C-212 SERIES 200 AVIOCAR (ASW and MARITIME PATROL VERSION)

For service with the 22nd Wing of the Spanish Air Force, and for certain foreign countries, CASA has proposed a version of the C-212 Srs 200 equipped for anti-submarine and maritime patrol duties. As can be seen from the accompanying illustration, the principal external differences from the transport version are the addition of a nose radome and the appearance of various antennae on the fuselage and tail-fin. Underwing pylons are provided for the carriage of torpedoes, rocket pods and other weapons.

TYPE: Twin-turboprop ASW and maritime patrol aircraft.

AIRFRAME: Generally similar to standard C-212 Srs 200 except for addition of nose radome and various external antennae.

POWER PLANT: As for C-212 Srs 200.

ACCOMMODATION (ASW version): Pilot and co-pilot on flight deck, with OTPI and additional central console for radar repeater; control for radio-navigation, Doppler, DME, ADF, UHF/DF, Omega and VOR/ILS; weapons delivery controls; and intervalometer for rockets. Avionics rack on port side, aft of pilot, for com/nav equipment; second rack on starboard side, aft of co-pilot, contains avionics for mission equipment (radar, sonobuoys, MAD and ESM). Immediately aft of the latter rack, along the starboard side of the cabin, are three control consoles for the mission crew members. The first console has the radar control and display, ESM control and display, and ICS control. The second has the tactical display and control, MAD recorder and control, and ICS. The rearmost of the three incorporates ICS, sonobuoy receiver control unit, acoustic control panel, and HCU and ADU units.

ACCOMMODATION (maritime patrol version): Pilot and co-pilot on flight deck, with central console for radar repeater; control for radio-navigation, Doppler, DME, ADF, UHF/DF, Omega, VOR/ILS and searchlight. Avionics rack on port side, aft of pilot, for com/nav and radar equipment. On starboard side of cabin is a console for the radar operator that incorporates radar PPI and ICS controls. Posts for two observers are located at the rear of the cabin.

AVIONICS: Communications equipment includes two HF and two VHF transceivers, single UHF, and interphone. Navigation equipment includes automatic flight control system, flight director, VOR/ILS (including VOR/LOC), glideslope and marker beacon receiver, DME, two ADF, UHF/DF, radar altimeter, Doppler radar, VLF/Omega, autopilot and compass.

OPERATIONAL EQUIPMENT (ASW version): Search radar with 360° scan, electronic support measures (ESM), sonobuoy processing system (SPS), OTPI, MAD, tactical processing system (TPS), IFF/SIF transponder, sonobuoy and smoke marker launcher, torpedoes, rockets and other weapons.

OPERATIONAL EQUIPMENT (maritime patrol version): Search radar with 360° scan, searchlight, smoke markers and camera.

WEIGHTS:

Max T-O weight	8,400 kg (18,519 lb)
Max landing weight	7,000 kg (15,432 lb)

PERFORMANCE (at max T-O weight, ISA):

Max cruising speed at 3,050 m (10,000 ft)	190 knots (353 km/h; 219 mph)
Loiter speed at 457 m (1,500 ft)	105 knots (195 km/h; 121 mph)
Service ceiling	7,315 m (24,000 ft)

CASA C-101 AVIOJET
Spanish Air Force designation: E.25

On 16 September 1975, CASA and the Spanish Ministerio del Aire signed a contract for a new basic and advanced military jet trainer aircraft, the C-101. The contract covered design, development, and the construction of four prototype aircraft for flight test and two for static and fatigue testing. First flights were made on 27 June and 30 September 1977, and 26 January and 17 April 1978. All four were handed over to the Spanish Air Force, for service trials, in 1978.

To minimise cost and maintenance, the C-101 is built on modular lines, with ample space within the airframe for equipment for any training mission likely to be required in

1 Search radar
2 IFF
3 Sonobuoys
4 Doppler
5 Radar altimeter
6 ADF loop
7 ADF sense
8 Marker beacon
9 VHF Nav, VOR/LOC
10 Omega
11 Electronic warfare
12 HF Com
13 UHF/VHF Com
14 DME
15 Glideslope

Maritime patrol version of CASA C-212 Srs 200 (*Michael A. Badrocke*)

separated by internal windscreen. Rear seat elevated 0·325 m (1 ft 0¾ in). Cockpit pressurised and air-conditioned. Dual controls standard.

SYSTEMS: Hamilton Standard three-wheel bootstrap-type air-conditioning and pressurisation system, differential 0·28 bars (4·1 lb/sq in). Single hydraulic system, pressure 207 bars (3,000 lb/sq in), for landing gear, ailerons, flaps, airbrake and parking brake. Pneumatic system for air-conditioning, pressurisation and canopy seal. Electrical system includes 28V 8·4kW DC starter/generator, two 700VA inverters for AC power, and two 22Ah nickel-cadmium batteries. High-pressure oxygen system.

AVIONICS AND EQUIPMENT: Magnavox RT-1168/ARC-164 UHF; Wilcox AN/ARC-134 VHF; Bendix AN/ARN-127 VOR/ILS/marker; Collins AN/ARN-118 Tacan; Teledyne Electronic RT-1063B/APX-101 IFF/SIF; Sperry SPI-402 flight director system, including Tarsyn vertical and directional gyro package, dual HZ-444 attitude director indicators, RD-500A horizontal situation indicators with remote course selection, RH-405 radio magnetic indicators and 807A com transceivers.

ARMAMENT AND OPERATIONAL EQUIPMENT: Large bay below rear cockpit suitable for quick-change packages, including 30 mm DEFA cannon pod, a twin 12·7 mm gun pod, reconnaissance camera, ECM package or laser designator. Six underwing hardpoints, capacities 500 kg (1,102 lb) inboard, 375 kg (827 lb) centre and 250 kg (551 lb) outboard. Typical armament may include one 30 mm cannon or two 12·7 mm guns in the fuselage; and six LAU-10 pods of 5 in rockets, six LAU-68 pods of 2·75 in rockets, six BR-250 250 kg bombs, four BR-375 375 kg bombs, two BR-500 500 kg bombs, four BLU-27 napalm canisters or six SUU-25 flare pods under the wings.

DIMENSIONS, EXTERNAL:
Wing span	10·60 m (34 ft 9⅜ in)
Wing chord at c/l	2·36 m (7 ft 9 in)
Wing chord at tip	1·41 m (4 ft 7½ in)
Wing aspect ratio	5·6
Length overall	12·25 m (40 ft 2¼ in)
Height overall	4·25 m (13 ft 11¼ in)
Tailplane span	4·32 m (14 ft 2 in)
Wheel track	2·83 m (9 ft 3½ in)
Wheelbase	4·87 m (15 ft 11¾ in)

AREAS:
Wings, gross	20·00 m² (215·3 sq ft)
Ailerons (total)	1·60 m² (17·22 sq ft)
Trailing-edge flaps (total)	2·50 m² (26·91 sq ft)
Fin	1·90 m² (20·45 sq ft)
Rudder	1·30 m² (13·99 sq ft)
Tailplane	3·44 m² (37·03 sq ft)
Elevators	1·00 m² (10·76 sq ft)

WEIGHTS AND LOADINGS:
Basic operating weight	3,350 kg (7,385 lb)
Max internal fuel weight	1,850 kg (4,078 lb)

the 1980s. The C-101 is fully aerobatic, and is able to carry out such additional duties as ground attack, reconnaissance, escort, weapons training, electronic countermeasures (ECM), and photographic missions. The trainer version is designated **C-101EB**, the armed version **C-101ET**.

The C-101 was designed with the co-operation of MBB (West Germany) and Northrop (USA), the latter company providing assistance with the inlet design and that of the 'Norcasa' wing section. Manufacture of production aircraft is carried out entirely by CASA except for the nosewheel unit, which is produced in the UK by Dowty Rotol. Wings and main landing gear units are built at Getafe and fuselages at Seville.

Production of the first 10 aircraft started at the beginning of 1978, and the first of these flew for the first time on 8 November 1979. A total of 88 has been ordered by the Spanish Air Force, which has an overall requirement for about 120. The first four C-101EB trainers were delivered to the Spanish Air Force on 17 March 1980, and are in service with No. 793 Squadron.

TYPE: Tandem two-seat basic and advanced trainer and light tactical aircraft.

WINGS: Cantilever low-wing monoplane. Wing section Norcasa 15, thickness/chord ratio 15%. Dihedral 5°. Incidence 1°. Sweepback at quarter-chord 1° 53′. All-metal (aluminium alloy) three-spar fail-safe stressed-skin structure. Plain ailerons and slotted trailing-edge flaps, of glassfibre/honeycomb sandwich construction. Ailerons actuated hydraulically, with manual backup. Ground-adjustable tab on port aileron.

FUSELAGE: All-metal semi-monocoque fail-safe structure. Hydraulically-operated aluminium honeycomb airbrake under centre of fuselage.

TAIL UNIT: Cantilever all-metal structure, with variable-incidence tailplane. Aluminium honeycomb rudder and elevators, actuated manually. Electrically-actuated trim tab in rudder.

LANDING GEAR: Hydraulically-retractable tricycle type, with single wheel and oleo-pneumatic shock-absorber on each unit. Forward-retracting Dowty Rotol nose unit, with non-steerable nosewheel size 450 × 140-8. Inward-retracting main units, wheel size 615 × 225-10, with disc brakes.

POWER PLANT: One Garrett-AiResearch TFE731-2-2J non-afterburning turbofan engine (15·57 kN; 3,500 lb st) installed in rear fuselage. Lateral intake on each side of fuselage, abreast of second cockpit. Fuel in one 1,115 litre (245 Imp gallon) fuselage bag tank, one 552 litre (121·5 Imp gallon) integral tank in wing centre-section, and two outer-wing integral tanks each of 335 litres (74

Imp gallons). Total internal fuel capacity 2,337 litres (514·5 Imp gallons). Pressure-refuelling point in port air intake; gravity fuelling point above each tank. No provision for drop-tanks. Oil capacity 8·5 litres (1·8 Imp gallons).

ACCOMMODATION: Crew of two in tandem, on Martin-Baker Mk E10C zero-zero ejection seats, under individual canopies which open sideways to starboard and

CASA C-101EB (E.25) Aviojet trainer in Spanish Air Force service

CASA C-101 Aviojet basic advanced training and light strike aircraft (*Pilot Press*)

T-O weight: trainer, 'clean'	4,800 kg (10,582 lb)
ground attack	5,600 kg (12,345 lb)
Max landing weight:	
3·66 m (12 ft)/s sink rate	4,700 kg (10,361 lb)
3·05 m (10 ft)/s sink rate	5,400 kg (11,905 lb)
Wing loading: trainer	240 kg/m² (49·16 lb/sq ft)
ground attack	280 kg/m² (57·35 lb/sq ft)
Power loading: trainer	308 kg/kN (3·02 lb/lb st)
ground attack	359 kg/kN (3·53 lb/lb st)

PERFORMANCE (at 4,400 kg; 9,700 lb AUW):
Max limiting Mach No.   Mach 0·80
Max level speed at S/L 370 knots (685 km/h; 426 mph)
Max level speed at 8,230 m (27,000 ft)
                     Mach 0·69 (416 knots; 771 km/h; 479 mph)
Econ cruising speed at 9,145 m (30,000 ft)
                     Mach 0·56 (396 knots; 734 km/h; 456 mph)
Stalling speed, flaps up
                     99 knots (183 km/h; 114 mph)

Stalling speed, flaps down
                     88 knots (164 km/h; 102 mph)
Max rate of climb at S/L   1,097 m (3,600 ft)/min
Time to 7,620 m (25,000 ft)   10 min
Service ceiling   12,200 m (40,000 ft)
T-O run   670 m (2,200 ft)
T-O to and landing from 15 m (50 ft)
                                     900 m (2,955 ft)
Landing run   530 m (1,740 ft)
Typical combat radius:
  interdiction (lo-lo-hi) with four 250 kg bombs and 30
  mm gun, 3 min over target, 30 min reserves
                                210 nm (389 km; 242 miles)
  close air support (lo-lo-hi) with four 19 × 2·75 in
  rocket launchers and 30 mm gun, 1 h loiter over
  battle area, 8 min over target, 30 min reserves
                                150 nm (278 km; 173 miles)
  armed patrol with 30 mm gun or two 12·7 mm guns,

  no underwing stores, 3 h at 200 knots (370 km/h;
  230 mph) at S/L, 45 min reserves
                                175 nm (324 km; 201·5 miles)
  ECM, 3 h 15 min loiter over target, 30 min reserves
                                330 nm (611 km; 380 miles)
  photo-reconnaissance (hi-lo-lo), 30 min reserves
                                520 nm (964 km; 599 miles)
Ferry range, 30 min reserves
                          2,025 nm (3,750 km; 2,330 miles)
Typical endurance, training missions:
  two 1 h 10 min general handling missions, incl aerobatics, with 20 min reserves after second mission

CASA C-102

Under this designation CASA is developing a side-by-side two-seat primary training aircraft with a tricycle landing gear and a 149-186·5 kW (200-250 hp) engine.

SWEDEN

SAAB-SCANIA
SAAB-SCANIA AKTIEBOLAG

HEAD OFFICE: S-581 88 Linköping
Telephone: 46 13 11 54 00
Telex: 50040 SAABLGS
PRESIDENT: Sten Gustafsson
Aerospace Division
Telephone: 46 13 12 90 20
HEAD OF DIVISION: Dr Tore Gullstrand
HEAD OF MISSILE AND ELECTRONICS SECTOR: I. K. Olsson
INFORMATION: Hans G. Andersson

The original Svenska Aeroplan AB was founded at Trollhättan in 1937 for the production of military aircraft. In 1939 this company was amalgamated with the Aircraft Division (ASJA) of the Svenska Järnvägsverkstäderna rolling stock factory in Linköping. Following this merger, Saab moved its head office and engineering departments to Linköping, which is now the main aerospace factory.

In 1950, Saab acquired a factory at Jönköping for development and manufacture of airborne equipment. This factory is no longer part of the Aerospace Division. Other post-war expansions include a bombproof underground factory in Linköping, as well as important new production and engineering facilities in Linköping, Jönköping, Trollhättan and Gothenburg. The company's name was changed to Saab Aktiebolag in May 1965.

During 1968 Saab merged with Scania-Vabis, to strengthen the two companies' position in automotive product development, production and export. Malmö Flygindustri (MFI) was acquired in the same year.

Saab-Scania has nearly 40,000 employees, organised in four operating divisions. Of these, about 6,000 are employed by the Aerospace Division, including 4,400 at Linköping, 50 at Malmö, 35 at Norrköping and 25 at Gothenburg.

Saab-Scania's current aerospace products include the Saab 37 Viggen supersonic multi-purpose STOL combat aircraft and the Safari TS piston-engined light aircraft. Since 1949 Saab-Scania has delivered more than 2,000 military jet aircraft to the air forces of four nations. It has also delivered more than 1,500 piston-engined aircraft to military and civil customers around the world. Since 1962, Saab-Scania has had a dealership for Hughes helicopters in Scandinavia and Finland. In 1978 it received an order to manufacture the inboard wing flaps and vanes for the McDonnell Douglas DC-9 Super 80 twin-turbofan transport aircraft; the first set of flaps was delivered in January

1979. In December 1978 Saab-Scania signed an agreement to participate in certain design work and production of the BAe 146 four-turbofan feederliner. For this aircraft, it is manufacturing tailplanes, elevators, rudders, ailerons and spoilers.

In early 1980 an agreement was signed with Fairchild Industries of the USA, under which the two companies will jointly develop, produce and market the Saab/Fairchild Model 340 twin-turboprop commuter airliner (see International section). Deliveries of this aircraft are scheduled to begin in 1984.

Saab-Scania has greatly expanded its activities in the electronics field. Current production items include computer systems, autopilots, fire control and bombing systems for piloted aircraft, and electronics for guided missiles. A major production programme is the airborne computer for the Saab 37. The Saab RGS2 lead-computing optical sighting system has been selected for the Royal Netherlands Air Force Northrop NF-5A, the Italian Air Force Aermacchi M.B.339A, and the British Aerospace Hawks for the Finnish Air Force. Space-borne computers, optronic fire control systems and field artillery computer systems are also under development and in production.

Saab-Scania's guided missile activities are now conducted by Saab-Bofors Missile Corporation, formed jointly with AB Bofors. Initial task of this company is to develop a new anti-ship weapon, the RBS 15.

Saab-Scania is a member of the MESH space technology consortium which delivered the TD-1A solar research satellite to ESRO. In 1973 ESRO/ESA ordered from MESH the OTS satellite, and subsequently the MAROTS maritime communications satellite. For the French space organisation CNES, Saab-Scania delivered the OBC-AR compact guidance and control computer for Europe's largest space venture so far, the Ariane heavy launcher for satellites, the first successful launch of which took place in December 1979.

SAAB 37 VIGGEN (THUNDERBOLT)
Swedish Air Force designations: AJ 37, JA 37, SF 37, SH 37 and SK 37

The Saab 37 Viggen multi-mission combat aircraft is the major component in the System 37 manned weapon system for the Swedish Air Force. System 37 comprises the Saab 37 and its power plant, airborne equipment, armament, ammunition and photographic equipment; ground servicing equipment, including test equipment; and training equipment, including simulators. Particular attention

is paid to the optimum adaptation of System 37 to the SwAF base organisation and air defence control system (STRIL 60).

The Saab 37 is designed as a basic platform which can be readily adapted to fulfil the four primary roles of attack, interception, reconnaissance and training. The aircraft has an advanced aerodynamic configuration, using a foreplane, fitted with flaps, in combination with a main delta wing to confer STOL characteristics. Its Swedish development of the American Pratt & Whitney JT8D turbofan engine, with a very powerful Swedish-designed afterburner, enables the Viggen to cruise economically and to have the acceleration and climb performance required for interception duties; the combination of advanced aerodynamic features with this engine, thrust reverser, automatic speed control during landing, and head-up display, enables it to operate from narrow runways of about 500 m (1,640 ft) length.

The first of seven prototypes flew for the first time on 8 February 1967, and by April 1969 all six single-seat prototypes were flying. The seventh Viggen was the prototype for the two-seat SK 37 operational trainer. A number of airframe parts were also completed for static testing.

The following versions have been announced:

AJ 37. Single-seat all-weather attack version, with secondary interceptor capability. Initial production version, which began to replace the A 32A Lansen from mid-1971. First production AJ 37 flew on 23 February 1971 and deliveries began on 21 June 1971. First AJ 37 unit was F7 Wing at Såtenäs. The AJ 37 equips two squadrons of F6 Wing at Karlsborg, two squadrons of F7, and one squadron of F15 at Söderhamn.

JA 37. Single-seat interceptor, with Volvo Flygmotor RM8B engine. Improved performance, and secondary capability for attack missions. Preliminary design work began in 1968. Flight testing of selected systems, including the radar, was initiated in early 1973 in a modified Saab 32 Lansen development aircraft. Four modified AJ 37s were used in the JA 37 development programme, as detailed in the 1976-77 *Jane's*. The JA 37 has four elevon hydraulic actuators under each wing, instead of three as on other versions, and a modified, taller tail-fin similar to that of the SK 37.

An initial batch of 30 JA 37s was ordered in September 1974, out of a planned total procurement of 149 to re-equip eight Draken fighter squadrons of the Swedish Air Force in 1979-85. Two further batches, of 60 and 59, were ordered in 1978 and 1980. First flight by a production JA 37 (serial No. 301) was made on 4 November 1977. Deliveries, to a squadron of F13 Wing at Norrköping, began in 1979. Second squadron is with F17 Wing at Ronneby.

SF 37. Single-seat all-weather armed photographic reconnaissance version to replace the S 35E Draken. A production contract was awarded in early 1973. Intended normally for overland reconnaissance, the SF 37 has a modified nose containing cameras and other equipment, permitting reconnaissance at any hour of the day or night, at high or low altitudes and at long distances from its base. First flown on 21 May 1973. Deliveries, to F13 at Norrköping, began in April 1977. Also in service with two mixed (SF 37/SH 37) squadrons: F21 at Luleå and F17 at Kallinge. Last SF 37 delivered on 7 February 1980.

SH 37. Single-seat all-weather maritime reconnaissance version, to replace the S 32C version of the Lansen. Production ordered at same time as the SF 37. Primarily intended to survey, register, and report activities in the neighbourhood of Swedish territory. Can also be used for attack missions. Prototype first flown on 10 December 1973. First production SH 37 delivered on 19 June 1975. In service with F13 at Norrköping (one squadron); and in two mixed (SF 37/SH 37) squadrons: F17 at Kallinge and F21 at Luleå.

SK 37. Tandem two-seat dual-control training version, in which the rear cockpit takes the place of some electronics and the forward fuselage fuel tank, and is fitted

Saab SF 37 all-weather photographic reconnaissance version of the Viggen

with bulged hood and twin periscopes. Modified, taller tail-fin of increased area. Capable of secondary attack role, with full range of attack armament as in AJ 37. Prototype first flown on 2 July 1970. First production SK 37 delivered in June 1972. In service with conversion unit of F15 at Söderhamn.

Saab 37X. Proposed export version, essentially similar to JA 37.

Initially, 175 aircraft of the AJ 37, SF/SH 37 and SK 37 versions were ordered for the Swedish Air Force; in December 1973 it was announced that five more aircraft (AJ 37s) were to be built within the same overall budget cost. More than 200 of the 329 Viggens ordered by mid-1980 had been delivered by that time.

The following details refer generally to all versions of the Viggen, except where specific versions are indicated:

TYPE: Single-seat all-weather multi-purpose combat aircraft and (SK 37) two-seat operational trainer.

WINGS: Tandem arrangement of canard foreplane, with trailing-edge flaps, and a rear-mounted delta main wing with two-section hydraulically-actuated powered elevons on each trailing-edge, which can be operated differentially or in unison. Main wing has compound sweep on leading-edge. Outer sections have extended leading-edge. Extensive use of metal-bonded honeycomb panels for wing control surfaces, foreplane flaps and main landing gear doors.

FUSELAGE: Conventional all-metal semi-monocoque structure, using light metal forgings and heat-resistant plastics bonding. Local use of titanium for engine firewall and other selected areas. Four plate-type airbrakes, one on each side and two below fuselage. Metal-bonded honeycomb construction is used to a large extent. Quick-release handle permits nosecone to be pulled forward on tracks to give access to radar compartment.

TAIL UNIT: Vertical surfaces only, comprising main fin and powered rudder, supplemented by a small ventral fin. Rudder of metal-bonded honeycomb construction. The main fin can be folded downward to port.

LANDING GEAR: Retractable tricycle type of Saab origin, built by Motala Verkstad and designed for a max rate of sink of 300 m (985 ft)/min. Power-steerable twin-wheel nose unit retracts forward. Each main unit has two main wheels in tandem and retracts inward into main wing and fuselage. Main oleos shorten during retraction. Nosewheel tyres size 18 × 5·5, pressure 10·7 bars (155 lb/sq in). Main-wheel tyres size 26 × 6·6, pressure 14·8 bars (215 lb/sq in). Goodyear wheels and brakes. Dunlop anti-skid system.

POWER PLANT (AJ 37, SF/SH 37, SK 37): One Volvo Flygmotor RM8A (supersonic development of the Pratt & Whitney JT8D-22) turbofan engine, fitted with a Swedish-developed afterburner and thrust reverser. This engine is rated at 65·7 kN (14,770 lb st) dry and 115·7 kN (26,015 lb st) with afterburning. Thrust reverser doors are actuated automatically by the compression of the oleo as the nose gear strikes the runway, the thrust being deflected forward via three annular slots in the ejector wall. The ejector is normally kept open at subsonic speeds to reduce fuselage base drag; at supersonic speeds, with the intake closed, the ejector serves as a supersonic nozzle. Fuel is contained in one tank in each wing, a saddle tank over the engine, one tank in each side of the fuselage, and one aft of the cockpit. Electrically-powered pumps deliver fuel to the engine from the central fuselage tank, which is kept filled continuously from the peripheral tanks. Pressure refuelling point beneath starboard wing. Provision for jettisonable external auxiliary tank (normally perma-

Saab JA 37 version of the Viggen, in the markings of F13 Wing, Swedish Air Force

nent on SK 37) on underfuselage centreline pylon.

POWER PLANT (JA 37, Saab 37X): One Volvo Flygmotor RM8B turbofan engine, rated at 72·1 kN (16,203 lb st) dry and 125 kN (28,108 lb st) with afterburning. Thrust reverser and fuel system similar to other versions.

ACCOMMODATION: Pilot only, on Saab-Scania fully-adjustable rocket-assisted ejection seat beneath rearward-hinged clamshell canopy. Cockpit pressurisation, heating and air-conditioning by engine bleed air, via Delaney Gallay heat exchangers, cooling turbines and water separator. Birdproof windscreen. JA 37 cockpit redesigned and optimised for interceptor mission. SK 37 has twin periscopes, and tandem ejection seats under individual canopies.

SYSTEMS: Two independent hydraulic systems, each of 207 bars (3,000 lb/sq in) pressure, each with engine-driven pump; auxiliary electrically-operated standby pump for emergency use. Three-phase AC electrical system supplies 210/115V 400Hz power via a General Electric 60kVA liquid-cooled brushless generator (Westinghouse 75kVA in JA 37), which also provides 28V DC power via 24V nickel-cadmium batteries and rectifier. Emergency standby power from 6kVA turbogenerator, which is extended automatically into the airstream in the event of a power failure. External power receptacle on port side of fuselage. Graviner fire detection system.

AVIONICS AND FLIGHT EQUIPMENT: Altogether, about 50 avionics units, with a total weight of approx 600 kg (1,323 lb), are installed in the Saab 37. Flight equipment includes an automatic speed control system, a Marconi Avionics (in AJ 37) or Smiths (JA 37) electronic head-up display, AGA aircraft attitude instruments and radio, Phillips (AJ 37) or Garrett-AiResearch (JA 37) air data computer and instruments, L.M. Ericsson radar, Honeywell radar altimeter, Decca Doppler Type 72 navigation equipment, SATT radar warning system, Svenska Radio radar display system and electronic countermeasures, and AIL Tactical Instrument Landing System (TILS), a microwave scanning beam landing guidance system. Most of the avionics equipment in the Viggen is connected to the central digital computer, which is programmed to check out and monitor these systems both on the ground and during flight. The JA 37 has a ram-air intake on the underfuselage centreline, for cooling the avionics compartment.

ARMAMENT AND OPERATIONAL EQUIPMENT (AJ 37): All armament is carried externally on seven permanent attachment points, three under the fuselage and two under each wing, with standard 750 mm (29·5 in) store ejection racks. Each wing can be fitted with an additional hardpoint if required. Primary armament is the Swedish RB04E air-to-surface homing missile for use against naval targets; the Saab RB05A air-to-surface missile for use against ground, naval and certain airborne targets; or the TV-guided Hughes Maverick (RB 75). To these can be added pods of Bofors 135 mm air-to-surface rockets, up to 16 bombs, or 30 mm Aden gun pods. The AJ 37 version can be adapted to perform interception missions armed with RB24 (Sidewinder) or RB28 (Falcon) air-to-air missiles. Computations in connection with various phases of an attack, including navigation, target approach and fire control calculations, are handled by a Saab-Scania CK-37 miniaturised digital computer. This computer, which performs 48 specific tasks within the aircraft and is capable of 200,000 calculations per second, also provides data to the head-up display in the cockpit, thus freeing the pilot for concentration on other aspects of a flight. Continuous monitoring of the flight paths and fuel situation is

Saab JA 37 Viggen single-seat interceptor *(Pilot Press)*

provided throughout the mission; the computer can also, when required, release the weapons automatically.

ARMAMENT AND OPERATIONAL EQUIPMENT (JA 37): Permanent underbelly pack, offset to port side of centre-line, containing one 30 mm Oerlikon KCA long-range cannon with a muzzle velocity of 1,050 m (3,445 ft)/s, a rate of fire of 1,350 rds/min, and a projectile weight of 0·36 kg (0·79 lb). Improved fire control equipment. This gun installation permits retention of the three underfuselage stores attachment points, as in the AJ 37, in addition to the four underwing hardpoints. Advanced target search and acquisition system, based on a high-performance long-range L.M. Ericsson UAP-1023 X-band pulse-Doppler radar which is un-affected by variations of weather and altitude. This radar is not disturbed by ground clutter, and is highly resistant to ECM. Singer-Kearfott SKC-2037 central digital computer and Garrett-AiResearch LD-5 digital air data computer. Singer-Kearfott KT-70L inertial measuring equipment. Honeywell/Saab-Scania SA07 digital automatic flight control system. Armament can include a total of six BAe Dynamics Sky Flash (Swedish designation RB71) and Sidewinder (RB24) air-to-air missiles. For air-to-surface attack, a total of twenty-four 135 mm rockets can be carried in four pods.

ARMAMENT AND OPERATIONAL EQUIPMENT (SF 37 and SH 37): Both reconnaissance versions can carry two Sidewinder (RB24) air-to-air missiles, on the outboard wing stations, for self-defence. Equipment in the SF 37 includes a special optical sight, data camera, tape recorder and other registration equipment. The data camera collects and stores on its film co-ordination figures, aircraft position, course, altitude, target location and other data. Four vertical or oblique low-level cameras, two long-range vertical high-altitude cameras and a VKA 702 infra-red camera are installed in the nose, together with the camera sight, an infra-red sensor, and ECM registration equipment. Systems configuration also makes possible the detection of camouflaged targets and horizon-to-horizon (180°) photo coverage. Typical external mission equipment, in addition to air-to-air missiles, includes drop-tanks on the underfuselage stations, and an active or passive ECM pod on each of the inboard underwing pylons.

Internal equipment of the SH 37 includes a nose-mounted surveillance radar similar to that of the AJ 37, a camera for photographing the radar display, ECM registration equipment, and various other registration systems including a data camera and a tape recorder. The inboard and outboard wing pylons can be occupied, respectively, by active or passive ECM pods and air-to-air missiles, as on the SF 37. The underfuselage attachments can carry a drop-tank on the centreline station, a night reconnaissance pod on the port station and a long-range camera pod or a Red Baron night reconnaissance pod on the starboard station.

DIMENSIONS, EXTERNAL:
Main wing span	10·60 m (34 ft 9¼ in)
Main wing aspect ratio	2·45
Foreplane span	5·45 m (17 ft 10½ in)
Length overall (incl probe):	
except JA 37, Saab 37X	16·30 m (53 ft 5¾ in)
JA 37, Saab 37X	16·40 m (53 ft 9¾ in)
Length of fuselage:	
except JA 37, Saab 37X	15·45 m (50 ft 8¼ in)
JA 37, Saab 37X	15·58 m (51 ft 1½ in)
Height overall: AJ 37	5·80 m (19 ft 0¼ in)
JA 37	5·90 m (19 ft 4¼ in)
Height overall, main fin folded	4·00 m (13 ft 1½ in)
Wheel track	4·76 m (15 ft 7½ in)
Wheelbase (c/l of shock-absorbers):	
except JA 37, Saab 37X	5·60 m (18 ft 4½ in)
JA 37, Saab 37X	5·69 m (18 ft 8 in)

AREAS:
Main wings, gross	46·00 m² (495·1 sq ft)
Foreplanes, outside fuselage	6·20 m² (66·74 sq ft)

WEIGHTS (approx):
T-O weight:	
AJ 37	15,000-20,500 kg (33,070-45,195 lb)
JA 37 'clean'	15,000 kg (33,070 lb)
JA 37 (normal armament)	17,000 kg (37,478 lb)

PERFORMANCE (JA 37):
Max level speed: at high altitude	above Mach 2
at 100 m (300 ft)	Mach 1·2
Approach speed:	
	approx 119 knots (220 km/h; 137 mph)
Time to 10,000 m (32,800 ft) from brakes off, with afterburning	less than 1 min 40 s
T-O run	approx 400 m (1,310 ft)
Landing run	approx 500 m (1,640 ft)
Required landing field length:	
conventional landing	1,000 m (3,280 ft)
no-flare landing	500 m (1,640 ft)
Tactical radius with external armament:	
hi-lo-hi	over 540 nm (1,000 km; 620 miles)
lo-lo-lo	over 270 nm (500 km; 310 miles)

SAAB SAFARI TS

The prototype Safari (formerly Saab-MFI 15) flew for the first time on 11 July 1969 with a 119 kW (160 hp) engine. After being re-engined with a 149 kW (200 hp) Avco Lycoming IO-360-A1B6, it resumed flying on 26 February 1971. The initial production version with this engine was described and illustrated in the 1978-79 *Jane's*.

From August 1978 it was superseded in production by the Safari TS version with a turbocharged engine; the description which follows applies to this model, which is intended initially as a military trainer.

The Safari TS conforms to FAR Pt 23 in the Normal, Utility and Aerobatic categories, and can be adapted to carry up to 300 kg (660 lb) of external stores. Other typical missions include reconnaissance; liaison; rescue operations; ambulance role (with internally-stowed stretcher); coastal, forest fire or border patrol; road traffic control; and a wide range of basic flying training roles.

A tricycle landing gear is standard, but a tailwheel gear is available optionally, and conversion from one to the other can be accomplished quickly.

TYPE: Two/three-seat light aircraft.

WINGS: Braced shoulder-wing monoplane, with single bracing strut each side. Thickness/chord ratio 10%. Dihedral 1° 30′. All-metal structure, swept forward 5° from roots. Mass-balanced all-metal ailerons. Electrically-operated all-metal plain sealed flaps. Servo tab in starboard aileron.

FUSELAGE: Metal box structure. Glassfibre tailcone, engine cowling panels and wing strut/landing gear attachment fairings.

TAIL UNIT: Cantilever metal structure comprising swept fin and rudder and one-piece mass-balanced horizontal 'stabilator' with large anti-servo and trimming tab. Glassfibre fin tip. Trim tab in rudder.

LANDING GEAR: Non-retractable tricycle (standard) or tailwheel type. Cantilever composite spring main legs. Goodyear 6·00-6 main wheels and either a 5·00-5 steerable nosewheel or a tailwheel. Cleveland disc brakes on main units. Landes or Finncraft skis, or Edo floats, optional.

POWER PLANT: One 157 kW (210 hp) Continental turbo-charged flat-six engine, driving a two-blade constant-speed metal propeller with spinner. Two integral wing fuel tanks, total capacity 190 litres (41·8 Imp gallons). Oil capacity 7·5 litres (1·6 Imp gallons). From 10-20 s inverted flight (limited by oil system) permitted.

ACCOMMODATION: Side-by-side adjustable seats, with provision for back-type or seat-type parachutes, for two persons beneath fully-transparent upward-hinged canopy. Dual controls standard. Space aft of seats for 100 kg (220 lb) of baggage (with external access on port side) or, optionally, a rearward-facing third seat. Upward-hinged door, with window, beneath wing on port side. Cabin heated and ventilated.

SYSTEM: 28V 50A DC electrical system.

AVIONICS AND EQUIPMENT: Provision for full blind-flying instrumentation and radio. Six underwing attachments for up to 300 kg (660 lb) of external stores. Landing light in nose.

ARMAMENT: Six underwing hardpoints, the inner two stressed to carry up to 150 kg (330 lb) each and the outer four up to 100 kg (220 lb) each. Typical loads may include two 7·62 mm machine-gun pods, two Abel pods each with seven 75 mm air-to-surface rockets, four Abel pods each with seven 68 mm rockets, eighteen 75 mm Bofors rockets, or six Bofors Bantam wire-guided anti-tank missiles.

DIMENSIONS, EXTERNAL:
Wing span	8·85 m (29 ft 0½ in)
Wing chord (outer panels, constant)	
	1·36 m (4 ft 5½ in)
Length overall: nosewheel	7·10 m (23 ft 3½ in)
tailwheel	6·85 m (22 ft 5¾ in)
Height overall: nosewheel	2·60 m (8 ft 6½ in)
tailwheel (tail down)	1·90 m (6 ft 2¾ in)
Tailplane span	2·80 m (9 ft 2¼ in)
Wheel track: nosewheel	2·30 m (7 ft 6½ in)
tailwheel	2·025 m (6 ft 7¾ in)
Wheelbase: nosewheel	1·59 m (5 ft 2¾ in)
tailwheel	4·75 m (15 ft 7 in)
Propeller diameter	1·88 m (6 ft 2 in)
Cabin door (port): Height	0·78 m (2 ft 6¾ in)
Width	0·52 m (1 ft 8½ in)

DIMENSIONS, INTERNAL:
Cabin: Max width	1·10 m (3 ft 7¼ in)
Max height (from seat cushion)	1·00 m (3 ft 3¼ in)

AREAS:
Wings, gross	11·90 m² (128·1 sq ft)
Ailerons (total)	0·98 m² (10·55 sq ft)
Flaps (total)	1·55 m² (16·68 sq ft)
Fin	0·77 m² (8·29 sq ft)
Rudder, incl tab	0·73 m² (7·86 sq ft)
Horizontal tail surfaces (total)	2·10 m² (22·6 sq ft)

WEIGHTS AND LOADINGS:
Weight empty, equipped	680 kg (1,499 lb)
Max T-O weight: Normal	1,200 kg (2,645 lb)
Utility	1,125 kg (2,480 lb)
Aerobatic	900 kg (1,984 lb)
Max wing loading: Normal	101 kg/m² (20·7 lb/sq ft)
Utility	95 kg/m² (19·5 lb/sq ft)
Aerobatic	76 kg/m² (15·6 lb/sq ft)
Max power loading: Normal	7·64 kg/kW (12·6 lb/hp)
Utility	7·17 kg/kW (11·8 lb/hp)
Aerobatic	5·73 kg/kW (9·5 lb/hp)

PERFORMANCE (at max T-O weight, ISA; N: Normal category; U: Utility category; A: Aerobatic category):
Max level speed at S/L:	
N	137 knots (254 km/h; 158 mph)
U	138 knots (256 km/h; 159 mph)
A	142 knots (263 km/h; 163 mph)
Cruising speed (75% power) at 3,660 m (12,000 ft):	
N	131 knots (243 km/h; 151 mph)
U	133 knots (246 km/h; 153 mph)
A	138·5 knots (257 km/h; 160 mph)
Cruising speed (75% power) at S/L:	
N	120 knots (222 km/h; 138 mph)
U	121 knots (224 km/h; 139 mph)
A	125 knots (232 km/h; 144 mph)
Stalling speed, flaps up, power off:	
N	60 knots (111 km/h; 70 mph) IAS
U	58 knots (107 km/h; 67 mph) IAS
A	55·5 knots (102 km/h; 63·5 mph) IAS
Stalling speed, flaps down, power off:	
N	56·5 knots (104 km/h; 65 mph) IAS
U	54 knots (100 km/h; 62·5 mph) IAS
A	50·5 knots (93 km/h; 58 mph) IAS
Max rate of climb at S/L: N	288 m (945 ft)/min
U	324 m (1,063 ft)/min
A	462 m (1,516 ft)/min
Rate of climb at 3,660 m (12,000 ft):	
N	246 m (807 ft)/min
U	282 m (925 ft)/min
A	420 m (1,378 ft)/min
Time to 1,525 m (5,000 ft): N	5 min 30 s
U	5 min 0 s
A	3 min 30 s
Time to 3,660 m (12,000 ft): N	13 min 30 s
U	12 min 0 s
A	8 min 0 s
Service ceiling:	
N, U, A	above 6,100 m (20,000 ft)
T-O run at S/L: N	200 m (656 ft)
U	185 m (607 ft)
A	100 m (328 ft)
T-O to 15 m (50 ft) at S/L: N	375 m (1,230 ft)
U	345 m (1,132 ft)
A	210 m (689 ft)
Landing from 15 m (50 ft) at S/L:	
N	400 m (1,312 ft)
U	390 m (1,280 ft)
A	315 m (1,034 ft)
Landing run at S/L: N	160 m (525 ft)
U	155 m (509 ft)
A	125 m (410 ft)
g limits: A	+6·0; −3·0

Saab Safari TS two/three-seat light aircraft (Continental turbocharged engine)

SWITZERLAND

FFA
FLUG- UND FAHRZEUGWERKE AG ALTENRHEIN

HEAD OFFICE AND WORKS: CH-9423 Altenrhein
Telephone: (071) 43 01 01
Telex: 77 230 ffa ch
PRESIDENT, BOARD OF MANAGEMENT: Dr C. Caroni
VICE-PRESIDENT: Dr L. Caroni
DIRECTOR: Dipl Ing H. Eisenring
CHIEF ENGINEER: Dipl Ing P. Spalinger
MARKETING: R. Boehm

This company, known formerly as AG für Dornier Flugzeuge, was originally the Swiss branch of the West German Dornier company. It is now an entirely Swiss company.

FFA's current activities include production of the AS 202 Bravo light aircraft, and the overhaul, modification and servicing of military and civil aircraft. Marketing of the Bravo is undertaken by Repair AG, an FFA subsidiary.

The company had 860 employees in 1980, approximately one-quarter of whom were engaged in its aviation activities.

FFA AS 202 BRAVO

Following an agreement concluded with SIAI-Marchetti of Italy, FFA is engaged in production and development of the AS 202 Bravo light trainer and sporting aircraft.

The first Bravo to fly was a Swiss-assembled AS 202/15 prototype (HB-HEA), which flew for the first time on 7 March 1969. The Italian-built second prototype flew on 7 May 1969. The third aircraft (HB-HEC) made its first flight on 16 June 1969, and the first production aircraft on 22 December 1971.

Three versions are available, as follows:

AS 202/15. Two/three-seat initial production version, with 112 kW (150 hp) Avco Lycoming O-320-E2A engine. Optional third seat. Swiss certification granted on 15 August 1972; FAA certification awarded on 16 November 1973. In production: 32 delivered by January 1980.

AS 202/18A. Two/three-seat aerobatic version with a 134 kW (180 hp) Avco Lycoming engine, Hartzell constant-speed propeller and inverted oil system. First example (HB-HEY) flew for the first time on 22 August 1974. Swiss certification granted on 12 December 1975; FAA certification awarded on 17 December 1976. In production: 72 ordered by January 1980, including 48 AS 202/18A-1s for the Iraqi Air Force.

AS 202/26A. First flown in 1978. Two/three-seat training and aerobatic version with a 194 kW (260 hp) Avco Lycoming engine and systems for unlimited inverted flying.

Aircraft currently in production incorporate a number of modifications, including riveted wing skins, rubber fuel tanks, and a glassfibre engine cowling. About 150 Bravos had been sold by Summer 1980, in Switzerland and to foreign customers including Royal Air Maroc, the Royal Flight of Oman, the Uganda Central Flying School, and the air forces of Indonesia (20), Iraq (48) and Morocco (14).

The following description applies to all versions of the Bravo, except where a specific model is indicated:

TYPE: Two/three-seat light aircraft.

WINGS: Cantilever low-wing monoplane. Wing section NACA 63_2618 (modified) at centreline, 63_2415 at tip. Thickness/chord ratio 17·63% at root, 15% at tip. Dihedral 5° 43′ from roots. Incidence 3°. Sweepback at quarter-chord 0° 40′. Conventional aluminium single-spar fail-safe structure, with honeycomb laminate skin. Aluminium single-slotted flaps and single-slotted ailerons. Ground-adjustable tab on each aileron.

FUSELAGE: Conventional aluminium semi-monocoque fail-safe structure, with several glassfibre fairings.

TAIL UNIT: Cantilever aluminium single-spar structure with sweptback vertical surfaces. Rudder mass-balanced, with provision for anti-collision beacon. Fixed-incidence tailplane. Two-piece elevator with full-span trim tab on starboard half. (AS 202/26A has electrically-operated tailplane trim; elevator tab is retained for anti-balance purposes only). Ground-adjustable tab on rudder.

LANDING GEAR: Non-retractable tricycle type, with steerable nosewheel. Rubber-cushioned shock-absorber struts of SIAI-Marchetti design. Main-wheel tyres size 6·00-6; nosewheel tyre size 5·00-5. Tyre pressure (all units) 2·41 bars (35 lb/sq in). Independent hydraulically-operated disc brake on each main wheel.

POWER PLANT (AS 202/15): One 112 kW (150 hp) Avco Lycoming O-320-E2A flat-four engine, driving a McCauley 1C172 MGM two-blade fixed-pitch metal propeller with spinner. Two wing leading-edge fuel tanks with total capacity of 170 litres (37·4 Imp gallons). Refuelling point above each wing. Oil capacity 7·6 litres (1·6 Imp gallons). Additional exhaust muffler available optionally.

POWER PLANT (AS 202/18A): One 134 kW (180 hp) Avco Lycoming AEIO-360-B1F flat-four engine, driving a Hartzell HC-C2YK-1BF/F7666A-2 two-blade constant-speed propeller with spinner. Hoffmann three-blade propeller optional. Fuel capacity as for AS 202/15; starboard tank has additional flexible fuel intake for aerobatics. Christen 801 fully-aerobatic oil system, capacity 7·6 litres (1·6 Imp gallons).

POWER PLANT (AS 202/26A): One 194 kW (260 hp) Avco Lycoming fuel-injection engine, driving a Hartzell constant-speed propeller. Fuel capacity 174 litres (38·3 Imp gallons). Fuel and oil systems permit unrestricted inverted flight.

ACCOMMODATION: Seats for two persons side by side, in Aerobatic versions, under rearward-sliding jettisonable transparent canopy. Space at rear in Utility versions for a third seat or 100 kg (220 lb) of baggage. Dual controls, cabin ventilation and heating standard.

SYSTEMS: Hydraulic system for brake actuation. One 12V 60A engine-driven alternator and one 25Ah battery provide electrical power for engine starting, lighting, instruments, communications and navigation installations, and (AS 202/26A only) tailplane trim. 28V electrical system optional.

AVIONICS AND EQUIPMENT: Provision for VHF radio, VOR, ADF, Nav-O-Matic 200A autopilot, blind-flying instrumentation or other special equipment at customer's option. Clutch-and-release mechanism for glider towing optional.

FFA AS 202/18A-1 Bravo for the Iraqi Air Force

AS 202/26A version of the Bravo, showing different nose contours

DIMENSIONS, EXTERNAL:

Wing span	9·75 m (31 ft 11¾ in)
Wing chord at root	1·88 m (6 ft 2 in)
Wing chord at tip	1·16 m (3 ft 9½ in)
Wing aspect ratio	6·51
Length overall	7·50 m (24 ft 7¼ in)
Length of fuselage	7·15 m (23 ft 5½ in)
Height overall	2·81 m (9 ft 2¾ in)
Tailplane span	3·67 m (12 ft 0½ in)
Wheel track	2·25 m (7 ft 4½ in)
Wheelbase	1·78 m (5 ft 10 in)
Propeller diameter	1·88 m (6 ft 2 in)
Propeller ground clearance	0·31 m (1 ft 0¼ in)

DIMENSIONS, INTERNAL:

Cabin: Max length	2·15 m (7 ft 0½ in)
Max width	1·02 m (3 ft 4¼ in)
Max height	1·10 m (3 ft 7¼ in)
Floor area	2·15 m² (23·14 sq ft)

AREAS:

Wings, gross	13·86 m² (149·2 sq ft)
Ailerons (total)	1·09 m² (11·7 sq ft)
Trailing-edge flaps (total)	1·49 m² (16·04 sq ft)
Fin	0·45 m² (4·84 sq ft)
Rudder, incl tab	0·94 m² (10·12 sq ft)
Tailplane	1·88 m² (20·24 sq ft)
Elevators, incl tab	0·76 m² (8·18 sq ft)

WEIGHTS AND LOADINGS:

Weight empty, equipped: 15	630 kg (1,388 lb)
18A	700 kg (1,543 lb)
26A	793 kg (1,748 lb)
Max payload: 15, Aerobatic	175 kg (386 lb)
15, Utility	270 kg (595 lb)
18A, Aerobatic	172 kg (379 lb)
18A, Utility	258 kg (568 lb)
26A, Aerobatic	188 kg (414 lb)
26A, Utility	292 kg (643 lb)
Max T-O and landing weight:	
15, Aerobatic	885 kg (1,951 lb)
15, Utility	999 kg (2,202 lb)
18A, Aerobatic	950 kg (2,094 lb)
18A, Utility	1,050 kg (2,315 lb)
26A, Aerobatic	1,075 kg (2,370 lb)
26A, Utility	1,200 kg (2,645 lb)
Max wing loading: 15	72·1 kg/m² (14·8 lb/sq ft)
18A	75·8 kg/m² (15·52 lb/sq ft)
26A	86·6 kg/m² (17·75 lb/sq ft)
Max power loading:	
15, Utility	8·92 kg/kW (14·68 lb/hp)
18A, Utility	7·84 kg/kW (12·86 lb/hp)
26A, Utility	6·18 kg/kW (10·17 lb/hp)

PERFORMANCE (Utility category, at max T-O weight):

Never-exceed speed:		
	15, 18A	173 knots (320 km/h; 199 mph)
	26A	208 knots (385 km/h; 240 mph)
Max level speed at S/L:		
	15	114 knots (211 km/h; 131 mph)
	18A	130 knots (241 km/h; 150 mph)
Max cruising speed (75% power) at 2,440 m (8,000 ft):		
	15	114 knots (211 km/h; 131 mph)
	18A	122 knots (226 km/h; 141 mph)
	26A	138 knots (256 km/h; 159 mph)
Econ cruising speed at 3,050 m (10,000 ft):		
	15 (66% power)	109·5 knots (203 km/h; 126 mph)
	18A (55% power)	109·5 knots (203 km/h; 126 mph)
Stalling speed, flaps up, engine idling:		
	15	59·5 knots (110 km/h; 68·5 mph)
	18A	62 knots (114 km/h; 71 mph)
	26A	63·5 knots (117 km/h; 73 mph)
Stalling speed, flaps down, engine idling:		
	15	48·5 knots (89 km/h; 55·5 mph)
	18A	49 knots (90 km/h; 56 mph)
	26A	53 knots (98 km/h; 61 mph)
Max rate of climb at S/L:		
	15	193 m (633 ft)/min
	18A	276 m (905 ft)/min
	26A	360 m (1,181 ft)/min
Service ceiling: 15		4,265 m (14,000 ft)
	18A	5,490 m (18,000 ft)
	26A	5,670 m (18,600 ft)
T-O run at S/L: 15		235 m (771 ft)
	18A	210 m (689 ft)
	26A	185 m (607 ft)

Model of the FFA (Repair AG) AS 32T Turbo Trainer

T-O to 15 m (50 ft) at S/L: 15	475 m (1,558 ft)
18A	400 m (1,312 ft)
26A	340 m (1,115 ft)
Landing from 15 m (50 ft): 15	415 m (1,362 ft)
18A, 26A	465 m (1,525 ft)
Landing run: 15	130 m (427 ft)
18A, 26A	210 m (690 ft)
Range with max fuel, no reserves:	
15	480 nm (890 km; 553 miles)
18A	521 nm (965 km; 600 miles)
26A	459 nm (850 km; 528 miles)
Max endurance: 18A	5 h 30 min
26A	4 h 54 min

FFA AS 32T TURBO TRAINER

FFA's subsidiary Repair AG Altenrhein released preliminary details of the proposed AS 32T during the Paris Air Show in June 1979; detail design began in October of that year. The accompanying photograph illustrates the general configuration. The wing and tailplane are almost identical with those of the AS 202 Bravo, which Repair AG distributes for FFA, and it was proposed to fit an Allison 250-B17C engine, as specified for the AS 32T, into a standard Bravo for flight testing in the Summer of 1980.

TYPE: Tandem two-seat basic and advanced trainer.
WINGS: Identical geometrically to those of Bravo, except where it is necessary to modify them because of the narrower fuselage and retractable landing gear. Electrically-operated trim tab in port aileron.
FUSELAGE: Uses similar constructional techniques and materials to Bravo, but crew are seated in tandem.
TAIL UNIT: As AS 202/26A version of Bravo, except for electrically-operated trim tab in rudder.
LANDING GEAR: Retractable tricycle type, with single wheel and oleo-pneumatic shock-absorber on each unit. Nose unit retracts rearward, main units inward into wings. Tyre sizes 6·00-6 (main) and 5·00-5 (nose).
POWER PLANT: One 313 kW (420 shp) Allison 250-B17C turboprop engine, flat rated to 239 kW (320 shp) and driving a Hartzell HC-C3YF-2 three-blade constant-speed propeller. Fuel in one 130 litre (29 Imp gallon) centre-section tank and an 85 litre (18·5 Imp gallon) tank in each outer wing; total capacity 300 litres (66 Imp gallons). Overwing refuelling points. Oil capacity 5·7 litres (1·25 Imp gallons; 1·5 US gallons).
ACCOMMODATION: Instructor and pupil in tandem under fully-transparent rearward-sliding canopy. Dual controls standard.
SYSTEMS: No hydraulic or pneumatic systems; 24V electrical system; oxygen system.
AVIONICS AND EQUIPMENT: Instrumentation and avionics in production version to customer's requirements.

DIMENSIONS, EXTERNAL:
Wing span	9·65 m (31 ft 8 in)
Wing aspect ratio	6·9
Length overall	8·86 m (29 ft 0¾ in)
Height overall	3·04 m (9 ft 11¾ in)
Tailplane span	3·67 m (12 ft 0½ in)
Wheel track	2·60 m (8 ft 6½ in)
Propeller diameter	2·18 m (7 ft 2 in)

AREAS:
Wings, gross	13·67 m² (147·1 sq ft)
Ailerons (total)	1·09 m² (11·73 sq ft)
Trailing-edge flaps (total)	1·49 m² (16·04 sq ft)
Fin	0·45 m² (4·84 sq ft)
Rudder, incl tab	0·94 m² (10·12 sq ft)
Tailplane	1·88 m² (20·24 sq ft)
Elevators, incl tab	0·76 m² (8·18 sq ft)

WEIGHTS AND LOADINGS:
Weight empty	788 kg (1,737 lb)
Max fuel	240 kg (529 lb)
Max T-O weight	1,300 kg (2,866 lb)
Max landing weight	1,200 kg (2,645 lb)
Max wing loading	93·8 kg/m² (19·21 lb/sq ft)
Max power loading	5·45 kg/kW (8·95 lb/shp)

PERFORMANCE (estimated, at AUW of 1,200 kg; 2,645 lb, ISA, zero wind):
Never-exceed speed	
	243 knots (450 km/h; 280 mph) EAS
Cruising speed at 3,000 m (9,845 ft):	
80% power	188 knots (349 km/h; 217 mph)
55% power	175 knots (324 km/h; 201 mph)
Rate of climb at 500 m (1,640 ft)	552 m (1,811 ft)/min
Service ceiling	9,450 m (31,000 ft)
T-O run at 500 m (1,640 ft)	165 m (540 ft)
T-O to 15 m (50 ft)	330 m (1,080 ft)
Landing from 15 m (50 ft)	460 m (1,510 ft)
Landing run	210 m (690 ft)
Range with max fuel, 55% power, no reserves	
	777 nm (1,440 km; 895 miles)
Max endurance at 3,000 m (9,845 ft) 55% power, no reserves	4 h 30 min

PILATUS
PILATUS FLUGZEUGWERKE AG

HEAD OFFICE AND WORKS: CH-6370, Stans, near Lucerne
Telephone: (041) 63 11 33
Telex: 78 329
GENERAL MANAGER: H. Uehlinger
MANAGERS:
Aerospace Division:
H. Uehlinger
Dr A. Canal (Marketing and PR)
W. Damerum (Sales)
K. Bergius (Research and Development)
W. Volkart (Product Support)
K. G. Trautmann (Projects)
O. Masefield (Engineering)
Production: W. Gubler
Administration: P. Ebner

Pilatus Flugzeugwerke AG was formed in December 1939; details of its early history can be found in previous editions of *Jane's*. It is part of the Oerlikon-Bührle Group.

Current Pilatus products are the Turbo-Porter single-engined utility transport and the PC-7 Turbo-Trainer.

On 24 January 1979 Pilatus purchased the assets of Britten-Norman (Bembridge) Ltd of the UK, and the latter company is operated under the name Pilatus Britten-Norman Ltd (which see) as a subsidiary of Pilatus Aircraft Ltd.

PILATUS PC-6 TURBO-PORTER
US Army designation: UV-20 Chiricahua

The Pilatus PC-6 is a single-engined multi-purpose utility aircraft, with STOL characteristics permitting operation from unprepared strips under harsh environmental and terrain conditions. The aircraft can be converted rapidly from a pure freighter to a passenger transport, and can be adapted for a great number of different missions, including supply dropping, ambulance, aerial survey and photography, parachuting, crop spraying, water bombing and target towing as well as operation from soft ground, snow, glacier or water, and long-range operations.

The first of five PC-6 piston-engined prototypes made its first flight on 4 May 1959, and 20 pre-series PC-6s, with 253·5 kW (340 hp) Avco Lycoming engines, had been delivered by the Summer of 1961. Subsequent versions have included the piston-engined PC-6 and PC-6/350 Porters; the PC-6/A, A1, A2, B and C2-H2 Turbo-Porters, with various turboprop power plants. Descriptions of all these can be found in the 1974-75 and earlier editions of *Jane's*.

Swiss-built piston-engined variants have the name Porter, and turboprop-powered variants are known as Turbo-Porters. In the USA, where the PC-6 was manufactured by Fairchild, it is known simply as the Porter, irrespective of the type of power plant fitted.

The current production version is the **PC-6/B2-H2 Turbo-Porter**, certificated on 30 June 1970 and powered by a PT6A-27 turboprop engine. Other versions can be made available on request.

By 1 September 1980, more than 420 PC-6 aircraft, of all models, had been delivered (including US licence manufacture), and were operating in more than 50 countries. Military operators include the air forces of Angola, Argentina, Australia, Austria, Bolivia, Burma, Chad, Ecuador, Oman, Peru, Sudan, Switzerland, Thailand and the US Army. Production by Pilatus was continuing at a rate of two to three per month.

Pilatus markets a Q-STOL (Quiet STOL) conversion kit for the B1 and B2 Turbo-Porters fitted with PT6A-20 or -27 turbine engines. This includes a system whereby propeller speed can be altered independently of the engine power setting, and is claimed to reduce the noise level by more than 10 dB for T-O and 20 dB for landing.

The structural description which follows is applicable to the current B2-H2 version. Details of the agricultural Turbo-Porter are given separately.

TYPE: Single-engined STOL utility transport.
WINGS: Braced high-wing monoplane, with single streamline-section bracing strut each side. Wing section NACA 64-514 (constant). Dihedral 1°. Incidence 2°. Single-spar all-metal structure. Entire trailing-edge hinged, inner sections consisting of electrically-operated all-metal double-slotted flaps and outer sections of all-metal single-slotted ailerons. No airbrakes or de-icing equipment. Trim tabs and/or Flettner tabs on ailerons optional; ground-adjustable tabs are mandatory if these are not fitted.
FUSELAGE: All-metal semi-monocoque structure.
TAIL UNIT: Cantilever all-metal structure. Variable-incidence tailplane. Flettner tabs on elevator.
LANDING GEAR: Non-retractable tailwheel type. Oleo shock-absorbers of Pilatus design on all units. Steerable/lockable tailwheel. Goodyear Type II main wheels and GA 284 tyres size 24 × 7 or 7·50 × 10 (pressure 2·21 bars; 32 lb/sq in); oversize Goodyear Type III

Pilatus PC-6 Turbo-Porter, one of two operated by the US Army as the UV-20 Chiricahua

wheels and tyres optional, size 11·0 × 12, pressure 0·88 bars (12·8 lb/sq in). Goodyear tailwheel with size 5·00-4 tyre. Goodyear disc brakes. Pilatus wheel/ski gear or Edo 58-4580 or 679-4930 floats optional.

POWER PLANT (PC-6/B2-H2): One 507 kW (680 shp) Pratt & Whitney Aircraft of Canada PT6A-27 turboprop engine (flat rated to 410 kW; 550 shp at S/L), driving a Hartzell HC-B3TN-3D/T-10178 fully-feathering reversible-pitch propeller with Beta mode control. Standard fuel in integral wing tanks, capacity 480 litres (127 US gallons; 105·5 Imp gallons) normal, 644 litres (170 US gallons; 142 Imp gallons) maximum. Two underwing auxiliary tanks, each of 190 litres (50 US gallons; 42 Imp gallons), available optionally.

ACCOMMODATION: Cabin has pilot's seat forward on port side, with one passenger seat alongside, and is normally fitted with six quickly-removable seats, in pairs, to the rear of these for additional passengers. Up to 11 persons, including the pilot, can be carried in high-density layout. Floor is level, flush with door sill, and is provided with seat rails. Forward-opening door beside each front seat. Large rearward-sliding door on starboard side of main cabin. Double doors, without central pillar, on port side. Hatch in floor 0·58 × 0·90 m (1 ft 10¾ in × 2 ft 11½ in), openable from inside cabin, for aerial camera or for supply dropping. Hatch in cabin rear wall 0·50 × 0·80 m (1 ft 7 in × 2 ft 7 in) permits stowage of six passenger seats or accommodation of freight items up to 5·0 m (16 ft 5 in) in length. Walls lined with lightweight soundproofing and heat-insulation material. Adjustable heating and ventilation systems provided. Dual controls optional.

SYSTEMS: Cabin heated by engine bleed air. Scott 8500 oxygen system optional. 200A 30V starter/generator and 24V 34Ah nickel-cadmium battery.

EQUIPMENT: Generally to customer's requirements, but can include agricultural equipment (see separate description) or a 1,300 litre (286 Imp gallon) water tank in cabin, with quick-release system, for firefighting role.

DIMENSIONS, EXTERNAL:
Wing span	15·13 m (49 ft 8 in)
Wing span over navigation lights	
	15·20 m (49 ft 10½ in)
Wing chord (constant)	1·90 m (6 ft 3 in)
Wing aspect ratio	7·96
Length overall	10·90 m (35 ft 9 in)
Height overall (tail down)	3·20 m (10 ft 6 in)
Elevator span	5·12 m (16 ft 9½ in)
Wheel track	3·00 m (9 ft 10 in)
Wheelbase	7·87 m (25 ft 10 in)
Propeller diameter	2·56 m (8 ft 5 in)

Cabin double door (port) and sliding door (starboard):
Height	1·04 m (3 ft 5 in)
Width	1·58 m (5 ft 2¼ in)

DIMENSIONS, INTERNAL:
Cabin, from back of pilot's seat to rear wall:
Length	2·30 m (7 ft 6½ in)
Max width	1·16 m (3 ft 9½ in)
Max height (at front)	1·28 m (4 ft 2½ in)
Height at rear wall	1·18 m (3 ft 10½ in)
Floor area	2·67 m² (28·6 sq ft)
Volume	3·28 m³ (107 cu ft)

AREAS:
Wings, gross	28·80 m² (310 sq ft)
Ailerons (total)	3·83 m² (41·2 sq ft)
Flaps (total)	3·76 m² (40·5 sq ft)
Fin	1·70 m² (18·3 sq ft)
Rudder, incl tab	0·96 m² (10·3 sq ft)
Tailplane	4·03 m² (43·4 sq ft)
Elevator, incl tab	4·22 m² (45·4 sq ft)

WEIGHTS AND LOADINGS:
Weight empty, equipped	1,216 kg (2,680 lb)

Max T-O and landing weight:
Normal (CAR 3)	2,200 kg (4,850 lb)
Restricted (CAR 8)	2,770 kg (6,100 lb)
Max cabin floor loading	488 kg/m² (100 lb/sq ft)
Max wing loading (Normal)	
	76·4 kg/m² (15·65 lb/sq ft)
Max power loading (Normal)	
	5·37 kg/kW (8·82 lb/shp)

PERFORMANCE (at max T-O weight, Normal category):
Never-exceed speed	
	151 knots (280 km/h; 174 mph) IAS
Max cruising speed at 3,050 m (10,000 ft)	
	140 knots (259 km/h; 161 mph)
Econ cruising speed at 3,050 m (10,000 ft)	
	129 knots (240 km/h; 150 mph)
Max manoeuvring speed	
	106 knots (196 km/h; 122 mph)
Max speed with flaps extended	
	82 knots (152 km/h; 94·5 mph)
Stalling speed, power off, flaps up	
	50 knots (93·5 km/h; 58 mph)
Stalling speed, power off, flaps down	
	44 knots (82 km/h; 51 mph)
Normal rate of climb at S/L	387 m (1,270 ft)/min
Service ceiling	8,535 m (28,000 ft)
T-O run at S/L	110 m (360 ft)
T-O to 15 m (50 ft) at S/L	235 m (771 ft)
Landing from 15 m (50 ft) at S/L	218 m (715 ft)
Landing run at S/L	80 m (262 ft)

PC-6/B1 Turbo-Porter agricultural aircraft fitted with 46-nozzle sprayboom

Max range, no reserves:	
internal fuel only	560 nm (1,036 km; 644 miles)
with external fuel	875 nm (1,620 km; 1,007 miles)
Endurance, no reserves: internal fuel only	4 h 20 min
with external fuel	6 h 45 min
g limits	+3·72; −1·50

PILATUS PC-6 TURBO-PORTER (AGRICULTURAL VERSIONS)

The Turbo-Porter can, if required, be equipped for agricultural duties, the necessary equipment being easily removable when not required, to permit the use of the aircraft for other work.

For liquid spraying, a stainless steel tank (capacity 1,330 litres; 292·5 Imp gallons; 351·4 US gallons) is installed behind the two front seats, and 46- or 62-nozzle spraybooms are fitted beneath the wings. In this configuration the aircraft can cover a swath width of 45 m (148 ft). An ultra-low-volume system, using four to six atomisers or two to four Micronairs, is also available, permitting increase in swath width up to 400 m (1,310 ft).

For dusting with granulated materials, the lower part of the standard tank can be replaced by a discharge and dispersal door permitting coverage of a swath width of up to 20 m (66 ft). A Transland spreader can be fitted for dust application (swath up to 30 m; 100 ft). Effective swath width of these versions is 13-40 m (43-131 ft), the optimum being approx 20 m (66 ft).

Both versions are fitted with small doors in the fuselage sides, giving access to the tank/hopper for servicing, removal or replenishment, and two single seats or a bench seat for three persons can be installed aft of the tank. Optional items include an engine air intake screen and a loading door for chemical in the top of the fuselage.

AVIONICS AND EQUIPMENT: Optional avionics include Decca Mk 8A navigator, Decca Hi-Fix radio, Decca Doppler 72 radar, gyrosyn CL-11 compass and SR 54A radio altimeter.

WEIGHTS (L: liquid spray system; D: dry chemicals system):
Weight empty: L, D	1,215 kg (2,678 lb)
Agricultural installation: L	133 kg (293 lb)
D	105 kg (231 lb)
Chemical: L	1,132 kg (2,497 lb)
D	1,160 kg (2,559 lb)
Fuel, oil and pilot: L, D	286 kg (630 lb)

Max T-O and landing weight:
L, D	2,770 kg (6,100 lb)

PERFORMANCE (liquid spray version, PT6A-27 engine, at max T-O weight):
Never-exceed speed	
	120 knots (222 km/h; 138 mph)
Operating speed	
	approx 90 knots (167 km/h; 104 mph)
Operating height	6-8 m (20-26 ft)
Stalling speed, power off, flaps down	
	49 knots (91 km/h; 57 mph)

T-O run	180 m (590 ft)
T-O to 15 m (50 ft)	390 m (1,280 ft)
Landing from 15 m (50 ft)	345 m (1,132 ft)
Landing run	130 m (427 ft)
Spraying duration with full spray tank	6 min

PILATUS PC-7 TURBO-TRAINER

Pilatus announced in the Spring of 1975 details of the PC-7 Turbo-Trainer fully aerobatic two-seat training aircraft, fitted with a 410 kW (550 shp) Pratt & Whitney Aircraft of Canada PT6A-25A turboprop engine.

The PC-7 can be used for basic, transition and aerobatic training, and, with suitable equipment installed, for IFR and tactical training. It meets the requirements of FAR 23 (Aerobatic and Utility categories) and is also designed to comply with a selected group of US Air Force military specifications (Trainer category). As a single-seater, it is flown from the front seat. Six underwing hardpoints are standard, the inner pair stressed for 250 kg (551 lb) loads, the centre pair for 160 kg (353 lb) each and the outer pair for 110 kg (242·5 lb) each. Max external load comprises 1,040 kg (2,293 lb) of underwing stores.

Certification under FAR Pt 23 was awarded on 5 December 1978, following the first flight by a production PC-7 on 12 August that year. Deliveries to customers began immediately after certification, and had reached about 80 by the Summer of 1980. Orders have been placed by eight air forces for more than 160 PC-7s (including 12 for Bolivia, 34 for Burma, 4 for the Chilean Navy, 12 for Guatemala and 60 for Mexico), and the backlog of orders will absorb production capacity until 1982. The Swiss Air Force has integrated two leased PC-7s into its regular training course, for a final operational evaluation with a view to possible procurement in the early 1980s.

Production, at the rate of four to five a month in 1980, was scheduled to increase to six per month from 1981.

TYPE: Single-engined single/two-seat training aircraft.

WINGS: Cantilever low-wing monoplane. Wing section NACA 64₂A series at root, NACA 64₁A series at tip. Thickness/chord ratio 15% at root, 12% at tip. Dihedral 7° on outer panels. Sweepback 1° at quarter-chord. One-piece all-metal single-spar structure, with auxiliary spars and ribs. Constant-chord centre-section and tapered outer panels. Aluminium alloy (2022 or 2024) skin, reinforced by stringers. Some fairings of glassfibre-reinforced plastics. Plain mass-balanced ailerons; split trailing-edge flaps, extending under fuselage. Trim tab in port aileron; ground-adjustable tab on starboard aileron.

FUSELAGE: All-metal semi-monocoque structure, with aluminium alloy skin. Some fairings of glassfibre-reinforced plastics.

TAIL UNIT: Cantilever all-metal structure, of similar construction to wings. Trim tabs in rudder and starboard elevator. All control surfaces mass-balanced.

LANDING GEAR: Retractable tricycle type. Electrical actuation, with emergency manual extension. Main wheels retract inward, nosewheel rearward. Oleo-pneumatic

Pilatus PC-7 Turbo-Trainer (Pratt & Whitney Aircraft of Canada PT6A-25A turboprop engine) *(Pilot Press)*

shock-absorbers on all units. Castoring nosewheel, with shimmy dampers. Goodrich main wheels and tyres, size 6·50-8, pressure 4·83 bars (70 lb/sq in). Goodrich hydraulic disc brakes on main wheels. Parking brake.

POWER PLANT: One 485 kW (650 shp) Pratt & Whitney Aircraft of Canada PT6A-25A turboprop engine, flat rated at 410 kW (550 shp at S/L), driving a Hartzell HC-B3TN-2 three-blade constant-speed fully-feathering propeller with spinner. Fuel in integral tanks in wings, total usable capacity 476 litres (105 Imp gallons). Fuel system permits up to 30 s of inverted flight. Provision for underwing drop-tanks.

ACCOMMODATION: Adjustable seats for two persons in tandem, beneath rearward-sliding jettisonable Plexiglas canopy. Cockpits ventilated and heated by engine bleed air, which can also be used for windscreen de-icing. Space for 25 kg (55 lb) of baggage aft of seats, with external access.

SYSTEMS: Hydraulic system for main-wheel brakes only. No pneumatic system. 28V DC operational (24V nominal) electrical system, incorporating 30V 200A Lear Siegler starter/generator and 24V 34Ah or 40Ah nickel-cadmium battery. Ground power receptacle fitted.

AVIONICS AND EQUIPMENT: Dual controls, and Rosemount Srs 92 angle of attack indicator, are standard. Optional equipment includes IFR training shield, to screen rear cockpit, radio, oxygen and air-conditioning.

DIMENSIONS, EXTERNAL:
Wing span	10·40 m (34 ft 1½ in)
Wing mean aerodynamic chord	1·64 m (5 ft 4½ in)
Wing mean geometric chord	1·59 m (5 ft 2·6 in)
Wing aspect ratio	6·52
Length overall	9·775 m (32 ft 0¾ in)
Height overall	3·21 m (10 ft 6½ in)
Propeller diameter	2·36 m (7 ft 9 in)

AREA:
Wings, gross	16·60 m² (178·7 sq ft)

WEIGHTS AND LOADINGS:
Weight empty, equipped	1,270 kg (2,800 lb)
Max T-O weight:	
Aerobatic	1,900 kg (4,188 lb)
Utility	2,700 kg (5,952 lb)
Max landing weight:	
Aerobatic	1,900 kg (4,188 lb)
Utility (with underwing loads)	
	2,565 kg (5,655 lb)
Max wing loading:	
Aerobatic	114·5 kg/m² (23·44 lb/sq ft)
Utility	162·7 kg/m² (33·31 lb/sq ft)

Pilatus PC-7 Turbo-Trainer, ordered by eight of the world's air forces

Max power loading:
Aerobatic	4·63 kg/kW (7·61 lb/shp)
Utility	6·59 kg/kW (10·82 lb/shp)

PERFORMANCE (at max T-O weight, ISA. A: Aerobatic category, B: Utility category with underwing loads):
Never-exceed speed:	
A, B	270 knots (500 km/h; 310 mph) EAS
Max operating speed:	
A, B	270 knots (500 km/h; 310 mph) EAS
Max cruising speed at 6,100 m (20,000 ft):	
A	222 knots (412 km/h; 256 mph)
B	196 knots (364 km/h; 226 mph)
Econ cruising speed at 6,100 m (20,000 ft):	
A	171 knots (317 km/h; 197 mph)
B	165 knots (305 km/h; 190 mph)
Manoeuvring speed:	
A	175 knots (325 km/h; 202 mph) EAS
B	189 knots (350 km/h; 218 mph) EAS
Max speed with flaps and landing gear down:	
A, B	135 knots (250 km/h; 155 mph) EAS
Stalling speed, flaps up, power off:	
A	71 knots (131 km/h; 81·5 mph) EAS
B	85 knots (158 km/h; 98 mph) EAS
Stalling speed, flaps down, power off:	
A	64 knots (119 km/h; 74 mph) EAS
B	74 knots (137·5 km/h; 85·5 mph) EAS

Normal rate of climb at S/L:
A	610 m (2,000 ft)/min
B	364 m (1,195 ft)/min
Time to 5,000 m (16,400 ft): A	10 min
B	27 min
Service ceiling: A	9,755 m (32,000 ft)
B	7,925 m (26,000 ft)
T-O run at S/L: A	248 m (814 ft)
B	780 m (2,560 ft)
T-O to 15 m (50 ft) at S/L: A	365 m (1,198 ft)
B	1,080 m (3,543 ft)
Landing from 15 m (50 ft) at S/L:	
A	494 m (1,620 ft)
B	800 m (2,625 ft)
Landing run at S/L: A	336 m (1,100 ft)
B	505 m (1,655 ft)
Max range at cruise power at 5,000 m (16,400 ft), 5% plus 20 min reserves:	
A, B	810 nm (1,500 km; 932 miles)
Endurance, with reserves:	
A, at max speed	3 h 0 min
A, for max range	4 h 22 min
B, at max speed	2 h 36 min
B, for max range	3 h 54 min
g limits: A	+ 6·0; − 3·0
B	+ 4·5; − 2·25

SWISS FEDERAL AIRCRAFT FACTORY
EIDGENÖSSISCHES FLUGZEUGWERK—FABRIK FÉDÉRALE D'AVIONS—FABBRICA FEDERALE D'AEROPLANI

HEAD OFFICE AND WORKS: CH-6032 Emmen
Telephone: (041) 59 41 11
Telex: 7 84 80 fwead ch
DIRECTOR: Lucien Othenin-Girard
DEPUTY DIRECTOR: Dr Peter Burkhardt
CHIEF DESIGNERS:
  Hansjoerg Kobelt (Electronics)
  André Jordi (Structures)
HEAD OF RESEARCH DEPARTMENT: Heini Kamber
HEAD OF PRODUCTION: Hanspeter Arnold

The F+W is the Swiss government's official aircraft establishment for research, development, production, maintenance and modification of military aircraft. It employs about 600 people in a works located at Emmen, near Lucerne, covering 35,300 m² (380,000 sq ft). Included are four wind tunnels for speeds of up to Mach 4·5, test cells for piston and turbojet engines with or without afterburners, and a modern data acquisition and processing system.

The F+W is made up of six technical departments. Research Department operates the wind tunnel facilities and performs scientific research and development in the fields of aerodynamics, thermodynamics, systems analysis and flight mechanics. Engineering Department is responsible for the design and development of aircraft, aircraft subsystems and components, and the development of space hardware. Electronics Department undertakes maintenance and modification of the avionics of the Swiss Air Force's aircraft, and provides support for flight evaluations. Quality Assurance Department assures maintenance of high quality and adherence to standards in the production and maintenance of the aircraft and space hardware. The M & P Department maintains up-to-date awareness of new materials and processes, and develops its own process techniques to meet particular requirements. Thus, for example, fabrication of titanium parts and Inconel pressure vessels is undertaken at the F+W. Production Department is competent to undertake the fabrication of aircraft subassemblies and components, as well as final assembly and checkout of complete aircraft.

The Factory is taking part in the assembly programme of Northrop F-5E/F Tiger IIs for the Swiss Air Force, which began in 1976 and involves an initial total of 72 aircraft (see 1978-79 *Jane's*). Twenty-nine of these had been completed by December 1979. A second procurement, after delivery of the current batch, was under consideration in early 1980.

Since 1977, when purchase of the Dragon anti-tank weapon system was authorised by the Swiss government, the F+W has been responsible for licence manufacture of the tracker, its field test equipment, and the appropriate training equipment. The pilot quantity of these items had been completed by the beginning of 1980.

The F+W conducts wind tunnel programmes for foreign aircraft manufacturers, ground transportation developers and users, and for the building industry. It also offers proprietary products to potential customers, including an electronic audio warntone generator, water separators for aircraft conditioning systems, strain-gauge force measuring scales, and the POHWARO hot water rockets. Details of these rockets can be found in the 1977-78 *Jane's*.

TAIWAN

AIDC/CAF
AERO INDUSTRY DEVELOPMENT CENTER—CHINESE AIR FORCE

PO Box 8676-1, Taichung, Taiwan 400
Telephone: Taichung (042) 523051 and 523052
Telex: 51140
OTHER WORKS: Kang Shan
DIRECTOR: Lieutenant General Y. C. Lee
DEPUTY DIRECTORS:
  Dr Hsichun M. Hua (Engineering and Research)
  Major General E. Y. Chu (Manufacturing)

The Aero Industry Development Center was established on 1 March 1969 as a successor to the Bureau of Aircraft Industry (BAI), which was established in 1946 in Nanking and moved to Taiwan in 1948. It now employs approx 2,000 people.

In October 1968 the Aeronautical Research Laboratory, then a branch of BAI, constructed the first Chinese-built PL-1A (see 1970-71 *Jane's*), a slightly modified version of the US Pazmany PL-1 which flew for the first time on 26 October 1968. After further modifications, 35 PL-1B Chienshou production models were built by AIDC in 1970, and two further batches of 10 in 1972 and 1974. These aircraft have been used extensively as primary trainers for CAF air cadets. A full description and illustration of the PL-1B appeared in the 1975-76 *Jane's*.

Between 1969 and 1976, the AIDC produced in Taiwan 118 examples of the Bell UH-1H (Bell Model 205) helicopter under licence for the Chinese Nationalist Army.

The AIDC is currently engaged in licence building 212 Northrop F-5E Tiger II tactical fighter aircraft (see US section) and 36 two-seat F-5Fs for the Chinese Nationalist Air Force. The first Chinese-built F-5E (CAF name **Chung Cheng**) was rolled out on 30 October 1974, and more than 160 had been delivered by the beginning of 1980.

The AIDC designed and developed the T-CH-1 tandem two-seat turboprop trainer, and this is now in production for the Chinese Air Force. The Avco Lycoming T53 engines for the T-CH-1 are licence-built at Kang Shan. Under development are two other indigenous designs, the XC-2 twin-turboprop transport and a tandem two-seat twin-engined military trainer designated XAT-3.

AIDC T-CH-1

This aircraft is a tandem two-seat trainer, the design of which was started by AIDC in November 1970. Two prototypes were ordered, designated XT-CH-1A and XT-CH-1B; construction began in January 1972.

The first aircraft was completed in September 1973 and was flown for the first time on 23 November 1973; it was described and illustrated in the 1974-75 *Jane's*.

The second prototype (63-3002), designated XT-CH-1B, was a modified version able to perform weapon delivery training and counter-insurgency missions. It flew for the first time on 27 November 1974.

The following description applies to the T-CH-1, of which production began in May 1976. Fifty have been ordered for the Chinese Air Force, of which more than 35 had been delivered by early 1980.

TYPE: Turboprop-powered trainer and light ground attack aircraft.

WINGS: Cantilever low-wing monoplane. Wing section NACA 64-2A215 (constant). Dihedral 8° from roots. Incidence 2°. No sweepback. Conventional aluminium alloy stressed-skin structure, with aluminium alloy ailerons and slotted trailing-edge flaps. Link-balance type trim tab in each aileron.

FUSELAGE: Conventional semi-monocoque structure of aluminium alloy.

TAIL UNIT: Cantilever aluminium alloy structure, with fixed-incidence tailplane. Dorsal fin. Link-balance type trim tabs in rudder and each elevator.

LANDING GEAR: Retractable tricycle type. Hydraulic retraction, main wheels inward into wings, nosewheel rearward. Telescopic shock-absorbers. Goodyear brakes. Small tail bumper under rear fuselage.

POWER PLANT: One 1,082 kW (1,451 ehp) Taiwan-built Avco Lycoming T53-L-701 turboprop engine, driving a Hamilton Standard 53C51-27 three-blade metal propeller with spinner. Fuel in two tanks in each wing and one in fuselage, with total capacity of 963 litres (212 Imp gallons). Oil capacity 30 litres (6·6 Imp gallons).

ACCOMMODATION: Crew of two in tandem. Rearward-sliding fully-transparent canopy over each cockpit. Cockpits heated and ventilated.

SYSTEMS: Midland-Ross Corporation heating and ventilating system. 115V 300A system provides AC electrical power at 250VA 400Hz. 28V DC system includes 24V 34Ah battery. Oxygen bottle with volume of 3·5 litres (2,100 cu in).

AVIONICS AND EQUIPMENT: Collins AN/ARC-51BX UHF radio and Collins AN/ARN-83 ADF.

DIMENSIONS, EXTERNAL:

Wing span	12·19 m (40 ft 0 in)
Wing chord at root	2·44 m (8 ft 0 in)
Wing chord at tip	1·52 m (5 ft 0 in)
Wing aspect ratio	6
Length overall	10·26 m (33 ft 8 in)
Height overall	3·66 m (12 ft 0 in)
Tailplane span	5·56 m (18 ft 3 in)
Wheel track	3·86 m (12 ft 8 in)
Wheelbase	2·39 m (7 ft 10 in)
Propeller diameter	3·05 m (10 ft 0 in)
Propeller ground clearance	0·74 m (2 ft 5 in)

AREAS:

Wings, gross	25·18 m² (271·0 sq ft)
Ailerons (total)	2·42 m² (26·0 sq ft)
Flaps (total)	5·02 m² (54·0 sq ft)
Fin	1·67 m² (18·0 sq ft)
Rudder, incl tab	1·11 m² (12·0 sq ft)
Elevators, incl tabs	1·81 m² (19·5 sq ft)

WEIGHTS AND LOADINGS:

Weight empty	2,608 kg (5,750 lb)
T-O weight: 'clean'	3,402 kg (7,500 lb)
max	5,057 kg (11,150 lb)
Max wing loading	200·9 kg/m² (41·14 lb/sq ft)
Max power loading	4·68 kg/kW (7·68 lb/ehp)

PERFORMANCE (at AUW of 3,447 kg; 7,600 lb):

Never-exceed speed	370 knots (685 km/h; 426 mph)
Max level speed at 4,570 m (15,000 ft)	320 knots (592 km/h; 368 mph)
Max cruising speed at 4,570 m (15,000 ft)	220 knots (407 km/h; 253 mph)
Econ cruising speed at 4,570 m (15,000 ft)	170 knots (315 km/h; 196 mph)
Stalling speed	50 knots (93 km/h; 58 mph)
Max rate of climb at S/L	1,036 m (3,400 ft)/min
Service ceiling	9,755 m (32,000 ft)
T-O run	146 m (480 ft)
T-O to 15 m (50 ft)	244 m (800 ft)
Landing from 15 m (50 ft)	381 m (1,250 ft)
Landing run	183 m (600 ft)
Range with max fuel	1,085 nm (2,010 km; 1,250 miles)

AIDC/CAF-built Chung Cheng (Northrop F-5F) for the Chinese Nationalist Air Force

AIDC XC-2

The basic design of the XC-2 twin-turboprop transport, which was started in January 1973, incorporates features of common interest to military and civil operators, including quick-change capability and the ability to operate from short fields and unprepared surfaces. The XC-2 can carry up to 38 passengers or 3,855 kg (8,500 lb) of cargo.

The first prototype (serial number 68-5001) was rolled out on 31 October 1978, and made its first flight on 26 February 1979.

TYPE: Twin-turboprop transport aircraft.

WINGS: Cantilever high-wing monoplane. Wing section NACA 65₃-218. Incidence 4°. No dihedral or sweepback at quarter-chord. Light alloy three-spar fail-safe structure, in three sections: constant-chord centre-section and tapered outer panels. All-metal manually-operated ailerons and hydraulically-actuated Fowler-type trailing-edge flaps. Servo tab in each aileron.

FUSELAGE: Conventional all-metal semi-monocoque fail-safe structure, of basically rectangular section, upswept at rear to provide clearance for rear loading. Cabin pressurisation optional.

TAIL UNIT: Cantilever aluminium alloy three-spar structure, with sweptback fin and rudder and non-swept horizontal surfaces. Dorsal fin. Horizontal surfaces mounted halfway up fin. Trim and balance tab in rudder and each elevator.

LANDING GEAR: Retractable tricycle type, with hydraulically-steerable twin-wheel nose unit. Single-wheel main units retract into fairings on sides of fuselage.

POWER PLANT: Two 1,082 kW (1,451 ehp) Avco Lycoming T53-L-701A turboprop engines, each driving a Hamilton Standard 53C51-27 three-blade variable-pitch metal propeller with spinner. Fuel in rubber tanks in wings, with combined standard capacity of 3,028 litres (666 Imp gallons).

ACCOMMODATION: Crew of three (pilot, co-pilot and flight engineer) on flight deck. Standard seating in main cabin for 38 passengers, four abreast at 79 cm (31 in) pitch. Interior layout has quick-change capability to passenger/cargo or all-cargo configuration. Access to main cabin via forward and rear doors on port side; single door on starboard side; and a two-section loading ramp/door in underside of rear fuselage, aft of main cabin, which is openable in flight for airdrop operations. Provision for toilet, galley and baggage compartment in passenger version.

SYSTEMS: Anti-icing and cabin heating systems standard. Hydraulic system, pressure 207 bars (3,000 lb/sq in), for flaps, landing gear and nosewheel steering. 28V DC primary electrical system, with 300A starter/generator on each engine. Two nickel-cadmium batteries for engine starting and emergency power.

AVIONICS AND EQUIPMENT: Standard avionics include UHF and VHF com; and ADF, Tacan and transponder navigation equipment. Optional avionics include VOR/ILS and HF.

DIMENSIONS, EXTERNAL:

Wing span	24·90 m (81 ft 8·4 in)
Wing chord (centre-section, constant)	3·05 m (10 ft 0 in)
Wing aspect ratio	9·5
Length overall	20·10 m (65 ft 11·3 in)
Height overall	7·72 m (25 ft 3·8 in)
Tailplane span	9·12 m (29 ft 10·9 in)
Wheel track	3·86 m (12 ft 8 in)
Wheelbase	7·10 m (23 ft 3·5 in)
Propeller diameter	3·05 m (10 ft 0 in)
Propeller ground clearance	0·90 m (2 ft 11·5 in)

DIMENSIONS, INTERNAL:
Cabin, excl flight deck:

Length	8·095 m (26 ft 6·7 in)
Width	2·57 m (8 ft 5 in)
Height	2·23 m (7 ft 3·7 in)
Floor area	20·85 m² (224·4 sq ft)
Volume	45·45 m³ (1,605·0 cu ft)

AREAS:

Wings, gross	65·40 m² (704·00 sq ft)
Ailerons (total)	4·24 m² (45·63 sq ft)
Trailing-edge flaps (total)	11·69 m² (125·80 sq ft)
Fin (incl dorsal fin)	9·35 m² (100·64 sq ft)
Rudder (incl tabs)	4·75 m² (51·12 sq ft)
Tailplane	10·41 m² (112·05 sq ft)
Elevators (incl tabs)	8·97 m² (96·55 sq ft)

AIDC XC-2 twin-turboprop utility transport aircraft *(Pilot Press)*

Production line-up of AIDC/CAF T-CH-1 basic trainers for the Chinese Air Force

WEIGHTS AND LOADINGS:				
Weight empty	7,031 kg (15,500 lb)	Max zero-fuel weight	11,254 kg (24,810 lb)	Max level speed at S/L
Max payload	3,855 kg (8,500 lb)	Max wing loading	190·7 kg/m² (39·06 lb/sq ft)	212 knots (392 km/h; 244 mph)
Max T-O weight	12,474 kg (27,500 lb)	Max power loading	5·77 kg/kW (9·48 lb/ehp)	Max cruising speed at 3,050 m (10,000 ft)
Max landing weight	12,247 kg (27,000 lb)	PERFORMANCE (estimated, at max T-O weight):		200 knots (370 km/h; 230 mph)
		Never-exceed speed 250 knots (463 km/h; 287 mph)		Econ cruising speed at 3,050 m (10,000 ft)

Max level speed at S/L
212 knots (392 km/h; 244 mph)
Max cruising speed at 3,050 m (10,000 ft)
200 knots (370 km/h; 230 mph)
Econ cruising speed at 3,050 m (10,000 ft)
180 knots (333 km/h; 207 mph)
Stalling speed, flaps down
78 knots (145 km/h; 90 mph)
Max rate of climb at S/L   457 m (1,500 ft)/min
Service ceiling   8,015 m (26,300 ft)
Service ceiling, one engine out   2,740 m (9,000 ft)
T-O run   625 m (2,050 ft)
T-O to 15 m (50 ft)   778 m (2,550 ft)
Landing from 15 m (50 ft)   826 m (2,710 ft)
Landing run   582 m (1,910 ft)
Range with max payload, reserves for 87 nm (161 km;
    100 mile) alternate and 45 min hold
259 nm (480 km; 298 miles)
Range with max fuel, 45 min reserves
897 nm (1,661 km; 1,032 miles)

Prototype AIDC/CAF XC-2 twin-turboprop transport taking off for its first flight

TURKEY

TURKISH AIR FORCE

Air Reinforcement Centre, Kayseri

MAV ISIK 78-XA

This designation has been given to an agricultural air-craft which was undergoing flight test in the Summer of 1979 at the Turkish Air Force's Air Reinforcement Centre at Kayseri. Said to be of 85% Turkish design, the Mav Isik 78-XA is said to resemble current Cessna low-wing agricultural aircraft, except for a high-mounted two-seat cockpit, and is thought to be powered by a Continental flat-six engine. The objective is to produce the aircraft at an initial rate of 20 per year.

TUSAS

TÜRK UÇAK SANAYII ANONIM ORTAKLIGI (Turkish Aircraft Industries Inc)

HEAD OFFICE: Atatürk Bulvari 227, Kavaklidere, Ankara
Telephone: 27 81 25
Telex: 42127 TUS TR
BOARD:
  Saim Dilek (President and General Manager)
  Hulki Yanat, MSAeEng (representing Ministry of Industry and Technology)

Gen Cemal Tural, ret'd; former Chief of Staff (representing Ministry of Finance)
Gen Etem Ayan, ret'd; former Commander of Turkish Air Force (representing Air Force Foundation)
Gen Cengiz Sakaryali, ret'd (representing Ministry of Defence)
Yildirim Özdamar (Asst General Manager, Financial)

TUSAS is financed jointly by the Turkish government (55%) and the Turkish Air Force Foundation, a non-profit-making organisation (45%). It was officially estab-lished with effect from 11 July 1973 with an initial capital of 1,500 million Turkish liras. Its head office is in Ankara, and an area of 5 million m² (1·93 sq miles) near Ankara is provided for an aircraft manufacturing facility and aux-iliary buildings.

The jet trainer requirement referred to in the 1979-80 *Jane's* is no longer valid. In early 1980, TUSAS was await-ing proposals concerning combat aircraft from four friendly and allied nations; the deadline for receipt of these was the end of February 1980, after which final negotiations were to start.

UNION OF SOVIET SOCIALIST REPUBLICS

ANTONOV

GENERAL DESIGNER IN CHARGE OF BUREAU: Oleg Konstantinovich Antonov

After establishing his reputation with a series of success-ful glider and sailplane designs, Oleg K. Antonov became one of the Soviet Union's leading designers of transport aircraft, particularly those types intended for short-field operation.

In addition to the current products described in this section, his design bureau is studying the requirements of a large transport to replace the An-22.

ANTONOV An-2

NATO reporting name: Colt

Following manufacture of the An-2M specialised agricultural version of this large single-engined biplane, in the mid-sixties, production of the An-2 came to an end in the Soviet Union. Details of the various versions that were built can be found in the 1971-72 *Jane's*.

Several versions of the An-2 continue in production under licence in Poland (see WSK-PZL Mielec entry).

ANTONOV An-3

It was reported in the Spring of 1972 that the Antonov design bureau was engaged on design studies for a turbo-prop development of the An-2 biplane (see WSK-PZL Mielec in Polish section). Designated An-3, the aircraft was intended specifically for agricultural duties and was then expected to compete with the Polish turbofan-engined WSK-Mielec M-15 as the next-generation agricultural aircraft for use throughout the countries of eastern Europe and the Soviet Union.

At the 1979 Paris Air Show, Mr Antonov emphasised his continued interest in agricultural aircraft, and confirmed that a prototype of the An-3 (CCCP-30576) had been produced by converting an An-2 to have a 701 kW (940 shp) Glushenkov TVD-10B turboprop engine, driving a slow-turning large-diameter propeller optimised for an aircraft operating speed of 75-97 knots (140-180 km/h; 87-112 mph). He added that an important feature was the ability of the turboprop to ensure adequate cock-pit air-conditioning during operation in ambient tempera-tures of 40-45°C.

A photograph of the An-3 prototype, under test, was released to the East European press in 1979. This showed that it differs externally from the standard An-2 only in having a longer and slimmer nose, housing the TVD-10B turboprop. A chemical payload of 1,900 kg (4,188 lb) can be carried, representing a 40 per cent increase over that of the An-2.

ANTONOV An-12

NATO reporting name: Cub

About 850 An-12 freighters were built for military and civil use before production ended in 1973. Versions in service with the Soviet air forces, and identified by NATO reporting names, are as follows:

Cub-A. Standard Soviet military paratroop and freight transport for many years. At peak strength, 'Cub-As' could carry two full army divisions, totalling 14,000 men and their equipment, over a radius of 651 nm (1,207 km; 750 miles). In 1980, about 63 per cent of the 1,200 fixed-wing aircraft equipping the VTA (Military Transport Aviation) comprised 'Cub-As', designated **An-12BP** in the USSR, although replacement with Ilyushin Il-76s started in 1974. Others are operated by the air forces of Algeria, Bangladesh, India, Iraq, Poland, Sudan, Syria and Yugoslavia. Current Soviet Air Force An-12s have a larger undernose radome than that originally fitted. Civil An-12s serve with Aeroflot, Polish Airlines (LOT), Bal-kan Air, Air Guinée, Iraqi Airways and Cubana.

Cub-B. Conversion of 'Cub-A' for electronic intelli-gence (elint) duties. Example photographed off Sweden had four additional blister fairings under forward- and centre-fuselage, plus other antennae.

Cub-C. Used by Soviet Air Force and Navy for ECM duties. Ogival 'solid' fuselage tailcone, housing electronic equipment, instead of gun position. Additional electronic pods faired into forward fuselage and ventral surfaces. Glazed nose and undernose radar of other versions retained.

'Cub-A' has a tail gunner's position. In the converted military An-12 which Ghana Airways operated for a time, this was fitted out as a toilet. In the refined commercial version, first demonstrated at the 1965 Paris Air Show, the turret is removed and replaced by a streamlined fairing.

The following abbreviated details apply to the standard military An-12BP transport. A full description can be found in the 1979-80 *Jane's*.

TYPE: Four-engined cargo transport.
POWER PLANT: Four 2,983 kW (4,000 ehp) Ivchenko AI-20K turboprops, driving AV-68 four-blade reversible-pitch propellers. All fuel in 22 bag-type tanks

Antonov An-12 ('Cub-A') four-turboprop general-purpose commercial transport aircraft *(Pilot Press)*

in wings, total normal capacity 13,900 litres (3,058 Imp gallons). Max capacity 18,100 litres (3,981 Imp gallons).

ACCOMMODATION: Pilot and co-pilot side by side on flight deck. Engineer's station on starboard side, behind co-pilot. Radio operator in well behind pilot, facing outward. Navigator in glazed nose compartment. Rear gunner in tail turret. Crew door on port side forward of wing. Access to freight hold via ramp-door at rear, under upswept rear fuselage. Ramp-door is divided into two longitudinal halves, which can be hinged upward inside cabin to provide access for direct loading of freight from trucks. Undersurface of fuselage aft of ramp is formed by door which hinges upward into fuselage to facilitate loading and unloading. Equipped to carry 100 paratroops, all of whom can be despatched in under one minute, with ramp-doors folded upward.

ARMAMENT: Two 23 mm NR-23 guns in tail turret.

DIMENSIONS, EXTERNAL:

Wing span	38·00 m (124 ft 8 in)
Wing chord (mean)	3·452 m (11 ft 4 in)
Wing area, gross	121·70 m² (1,310 sq ft)
Wing aspect ratio	11·85
Length overall	33·10 m (108 ft 7¼ in)
Height overall	10·53 m (34 ft 6½ in)
Tailplane span	12·20 m (40 ft 0¼ in)
Wheel track	5·42 m (17 ft 9½ in)
Wheelbase	10·82 m (35 ft 6 in)
Propeller diameter	4·50 m (14 ft 9 in)
Rear loading hatch:	
Length	7·70 m (25 ft 3 in)
Width	2·95 m (9 ft 8 in)

DIMENSIONS, INTERNAL:

Cargo hold:	
Length	13·50 m (44 ft 3½ in)
Max width	3·50 m (11 ft 5¾ in)
Max height	2·60 m (8 ft 6¼ in)
Volume	97·2 m³ (3,432·6 cu ft)

WEIGHTS:

Weight empty	28,000 kg (61,730 lb)
Max payload	20,000 kg (44,090 lb)
Normal T-O weight	55,100 kg (121,475 lb)
Max T-O weight	61,000 kg (134,480 lb)

PERFORMANCE:

Max level speed	419 knots (777 km/h; 482 mph)
Max cruising speed	361 knots (670 km/h; 416 mph)
Min flying speed	88 knots (163 km/h; 101 mph)
Landing speed	108 knots (200 km/h; 124 mph)
Max rate of climb at S/L	600 m (1,970 ft)/min
Service ceiling	10,200 m (33,500 ft)
T-O run	700 m (2,300 ft)
Landing run	500 m (1,640 ft)
Range with max payload	
	1,942 nm (3,600 km; 2,236 miles)
Range with max fuel	
	3,075 nm (5,700 km; 3,540 miles)

ANTONOV An-14 PCHELKA (LITTLE BEE)
NATO reporting name: Clod

The An-14 Pchelka is a twin-engined light general-purpose aircraft, the first prototype of which made its first flight on 15 March 1958. Production began in 1965 at the Progress Plant at Arsenyev in the far east of the Soviet Union, for both Aeroflot and the Soviet armed forces, and continued for about four years. Several hundred were built; none had been involved in a fatal accident up to mid-1979.

The military An-14 was first seen at the Domodedovo air display in July 1967 and does not appear to differ externally from the civilian passenger version. It serves also with the air forces of Bulgaria, the German Democratic Republic and Guinea.

A full description of the An-14 can be found in the 1979-80 *Jane's*.

ANTONOV An-22 ANTHEUS
NATO reporting name: Cock

The prototype of this very large transport aircraft flew for the first time on 27 February 1965. Production aircraft

Electronic intelligence version of the Antonov An-12 known to NATO as 'Cub-B' *(Swedish Air Force)*

ECM version of the Antonov An-12 ('Cub-C'), operated temporarily in Egyptian Air Force insignia

were delivered to both the Soviet Air Force and Aeroflot, which uses the An-22 mainly in underdeveloped areas of the northern USSR, Siberia and the Far East. Deliveries were completed during 1974, after about 50 aircraft had been delivered to the military air transport force (VTA), and others to Aeroflot. In 1980 they remained the only Soviet transports capable of airlifting the T-62 tank.

A full list of the 27 FAI-homologated records for payload-to-height, and speed with payload, held currently by the An-22 can be found in the 1979-80 *Jane's*.

TYPE: Long-range heavy turboprop transport.

WINGS: Cantilever high-wing monoplane. Marked anhedral on outer panels. All-metal structure, appearing to have three main spars which attach to three strong fuselage ring-frames. Double-slotted trailing-edge flaps. Tab in each aileron.

FUSELAGE: All-metal semi-monocoque structure, with upswept rear fuselage containing loading-ramp/door for direct loading. Retractable jacks support rear fuselage at point where rear loading ramp is hinged.

TAIL UNIT: Cantilever all-metal structure. Twin fins and rudders (each in two sections, above and below tailplane) mounted outboard of mid-span. Bullet fairing forward of each fin tip. Tabs in each elevator and in each of the four rudder sections.

LANDING GEAR: Retractable tricycle type, designed to permit off-runway operation. Steerable twin-wheel nose unit. Each main gear consists of three twin-wheel levered-suspension units in tandem, each unit mounted at the bottom of one of the fuselage ring frames that also picks up a wing spar. Main units retract upward into fairings built on to sides of fuselage. Tyre pressure adjustable in flight or on ground to suit airfield surface.

POWER PLANT: Four 11,186 kW (15,000 shp) Kuznetsov NK-12MA turboprop engines, each driving a pair of four-blade contra-rotating propellers.

ACCOMMODATION: Crew of five or six. Navigator's station in nose. Cabin for 28-29 passengers aft of flight deck, separated from main cabin by bulkhead containing two doors. Uninterrupted main cabin, with reinforced titanium floor, tiedown fittings and rear loading ramp. When ramp lowers, a large door which forms the underside of the rear fuselage retracts upward inside fuselage to permit easy loading of tall vehicles. Rails in roof of cabin for four travelling gantries continue rearward on underside of this door. Two winches, used in conjunction with the gantries, each have a capacity of 2,500 kg (5,500 lb). Door in each landing gear fairing, forward of wheels, for crew and passengers.

AVIONICS AND EQUIPMENT: Pressurisation equipment and APU in forward part of starboard landing gear fairing. Two radars, in nose 'thimble' and undernose fairings.

DIMENSIONS, EXTERNAL:

Wing span	64·40 m (211 ft 4 in)
Length overall	approx 57·92 m (190 ft 0 in)
Height overall	12·53 m (41 ft 1½ in)
Propeller diameter	6·20 m (20 ft 4 in)

DIMENSIONS, INTERNAL:

Main cabin: Length	33·0 m (108 ft 3 in)
Max width	4·4 m (14 ft 5 in)
Max height	4·4 m (14 ft 5 in)

AREA:

Wings, gross	345 m² (3,713 sq ft)

WEIGHTS:

Weight empty, equipped	114,000 kg (251,325 lb)
Max payload	80,000 kg (176,350 lb)

Antonov An-22 Antheus long-range heavy transport aircraft (four Kuznetsov NK-12MA turboprop engines) *(Tass)*

Antonov An-22 Antheus long-range heavy transport aircraft (*Pilot Press*)

Max fuel	43,000 kg (94,800 lb)
Max T-O weight	250,000 kg (551,160 lb)

PERFORMANCE:

Max level speed	399 knots (740 km/h; 460 mph)
T-O run	1,300 m (4,260 ft)
Landing run	800 m (2,620 ft)
Range with max fuel and 45,000 kg (99,200 lb) payload	5,905 nm (10,950 km; 6,800 miles)
Range with max payload	2,692 nm (5,000 km; 3,100 miles)

ANTONOV An-24

NATO reporting name: Coke

Development of this twin-turboprop transport was started in 1958, to replace piston-engined types on Aeroflot's internal feederline routes. The first prototype flew in April 1960 and the An-24 entered service on Aeroflot's routes from Moscow to Voronezh and Saratov in September 1963. When production ended in 1978, a total of about 1,100 had been delivered. Aeroflot received several hundred; the last off the assembly line, delivered to the Romanian airline Tarom, was described as the 750th aircraft of the An-24/26 series to be exported.

A list of 15 airlines known to have operated An-24s can be found in the 1976-77 *Jane's*. The An-24 was also supplied for military service, usually in small numbers, with the air forces of the USSR, Bangladesh, Bulgaria, Congo (Brazzaville), Cuba, Czechoslovakia, Egypt, East Germany, Hungary, Iraq, North Korea, Mongolia, Romania, the Somali Republic, Sudan, North Viet-Nam and South Yemen. Six were acquired by the Laotian government, for unspecified duties, in 1977.

A full description of the An-24 can be found in the 1979-80 *Jane's*.

ANTONOV An-26

NATO reporting name: Curl

First displayed in public at the 1969 Paris Air Show, the An-26 is generally similar to the earlier An-24RT specialised freighter, with an auxiliary turbojet in the starboard engine nacelle, but has more powerful AI-24T turboprop engines and a completely redesigned rear fuselage of the 'beaver-tail' type. This embodies Oleg Antonov's new-type loading ramp, which forms the underside of the rear fuselage when retracted, in the usual way, but can be slid forward under the rear of the cabin to facilitate direct loading, or when the cargo is to be air-dropped.

Although intended primarily for cargo-carrying, the An-26 can be adapted easily for passenger-carrying, ambulance or paratroop transport duties. Production was continuing in 1980.

The Air Wing of the Bangladesh Defence Force has a small number of An-26s, as well as one An-24. Other An-26s serve with the Afghan, Angolan, Benin, Bulgarian, Cuban, Czechoslovak, East German, Hungarian, Iraqi, Peruvian, Polish, Romanian, Somali, Yugoslav and Soviet Air Forces. Aeroflot has more than 100, and three are operated by Tarom of Romania.

TYPE: Twin-turboprop short-haul transport.

WINGS: Cantilever high-wing monoplane, with 2° anhedral on outer panels. Incidence 3°. Sweepback at quarter-chord on outer panels 6° 50'. All-metal two-spar structure, built in five sections: centre-section, two inner wings and two detachable outer wings. Wing skin is attached by electrical spot-welding. Mass-balanced servo-compensated ailerons, with large trim tabs of glassfibre construction. Hydraulically-operated Fowler flaps along entire wing trailing-edges inboard of unpowered ailerons; single-slotted flaps on centre-section, double-slotted outboard of nacelles. Electrically-operated trim tab in each aileron. Thermal de-icing system.

FUSELAGE: All-metal semi-monocoque structure in front, centre and rear portions, of bonded/welded construction. Skin on lower portion of fuselage is made of 'bimetal' (duralumin-titanium) sheet for protection during operations from unpaved airfields.

TAIL UNIT: Cantilever all-metal structure, with ventral fin strake on each side of rear ramp. 9° dihedral on tailplane. All controls manually operated. Manually-operated trim tab in each elevator. Electrically-operated combined trim/servo tab in rudder. All leading-edges incorporate thermal de-icing system.

LANDING GEAR: Retractable tricycle type, with twin wheels on each unit. Hydraulic retraction. Emergency extension by gravity. All units retract forward. Shock-absorbers of oleo-nitrogen type on main units; nitrogen-pneumatic type on nose unit. Main-wheel tyres size 1,050 × 400, pressure 5·86 bars (85 lb/sq in). Nosewheel tyres size 700 × 250, pressure 3·93 bars (57 lb/sq in). Main wheels are fitted with hydraulic disc brakes and anti-skid units. Nosewheels can be steered hydraulically through 45° each side while taxying and are controllable through ±10° during take-off and landing.

POWER PLANT: Two 2,103 kW (2,820 ehp) Ivchenko AI-24VT turboprop engines, each driving a four-blade constant-speed fully-feathering propeller. Electrical de-icing system for propeller blades and hubs; hot air system for engine air intakes. One 7·85 kN (1,765 lb st) RU 19A-300 auxiliary turbojet in starboard nacelle for use, as required, at take-off, during climb and in level flight, and for self-contained starting of main engines. Fuel load 5,500 kg (12,125 lb), contained in integral tanks in inner wings and ten bag-type tanks in centre-section. Pressure refuelling socket in starboard engine nacelle. Gravity fuelling point above each tank area. Carbon dioxide inert gas system to create fireproof condition inside fuel tanks.

ACCOMMODATION: Basic crew of five (pilot, co-pilot, radio operator, flight engineer and navigator), with station at rear of cabin on starboard side for loading supervisor or load dispatcher. Electrical de-icing system for

Antonov An-26 twin-turboprop short-haul transport (*Pilot Press*)

One of five Antonov An-26 transports which passed through Gatwick Airport, en route to Cuba, in December 1978 (*Austin J. Brown*)

windscreens. Toilet on port side aft of flight deck; small galley and oxygen bottle stowage on starboard side. Emergency escape hatch in floor immediately aft of flight deck. Large downward-hinged rear ramp/door, which can also slide forward under fuselage for direct loading on to cabin floor or for airdropping of freight. Electrically-powered mobile winch, capacity 2,000 kg (4,409 lb), hoists crates through rear entrance and runs on a rail in the cabin ceiling to position payload in cabin. Electrically- or manually-operated conveyor, capacity 4,500 kg (9,920 lb), built-in flush with cabin floor, facilitates loading and airdropping of freight. Can accommodate a variety of motor vehicles, including GAZ-69 and UAZ-469 military vehicles, or cargo items up to 1·50 m (59 in) high by 2·10 m (82·6 in) wide. Height of rear edge of cargo door surround above the cabin floor is 1·50 m (4 ft 11 in). Cabin is pressurised and air-conditioned, and is fitted with a row of tip-up seats along each wall to accommodate 38 to 40 persons. Conversion to troop transport role, or to an ambulance for 24 stretcher patients and a medical attendant, takes 20 to 30 min in the field.

SYSTEMS: Air-conditioning system uses hot air tapped from the 10th compressor stage of each engine, with a heat exchanger and turbocooler in each nacelle. Cabin pressure differential 0·29 bars (4·27 lb/sq in). Main and emergency hydraulic systems, pressure 151·7 bars (2,200 lb/sq in), for landing gear retraction, nosewheel steering, flaps, brakes, windscreen wipers, propeller feathering and operation of cargo ramp and emergency escape doors. Handpump to operate doors only and build up pressure in main system. Electrical system includes two 27V DC starter/generators on engines, a standby generator on the auxiliary turbojet, and three storage batteries for emergency use. Two engine-driven alternators provide 115V 400Hz single-phase AC supply, with standby inverter. Basic source of 36V 400Hz three-phase AC supply is two inverters, with standby transformer. Permanent oxygen system for pilot, installed equipment for other crew members and three portable bottles for personnel in cargo hold.

AVIONICS AND EQUIPMENT: Standard com/nav avionics comprise two VHF transceivers, HF, intercom, two ADF, radio altimeter, glidepath receiver, glideslope receiver, marker receiver, weather/navigation radar, directional gyro and flight recorder. Optional equipment includes a flight director system, astrocompass and autopilot. Standard operational equipment includes parachute static line attachments and retraction devices, tiedowns, jack to support ramp sill, flight deck curtains, sun visors and windscreen wipers. Optional items include a navigator's observation blister on port side of flight deck, OPB-1R sight for pinpoint dropping of freight, medical equipment, and liquid heating system.

DIMENSIONS, EXTERNAL:

Wing span	29·20 m (95 ft 9½ in)

Wing aspect ratio	11·7
Length overall	23·80 m (78 ft 1 in)
Height overall	8·575 m (28 ft 1½ in)
Width of fuselage	2·90 m (9 ft 6 in)
Depth of fuselage	2·50 m (8 ft 2½ in)
Tailplane span	9·973 m (32 ft 8¾ in)
Wheel track (c/l shock-struts)	7·90 m (25 ft 11 in)
Wheelbase	7·651 m (25 ft 1¼ in)
Propeller diameter	3·90 m (12 ft 9½ in)
Propeller ground clearance	1·227 m (4 ft 0¼ in)
Crew door (stbd, front):	
Height	1·40 m (4 ft 7 in)
Width	0·60 m (1 ft 11¾ in)
Height to sill	1·47 m (4 ft 9¾ in)
Loading hatch (rear): Length	3·40 m (11 ft 1¾ in)
Width at front	2·40 m (7 ft 10½ in)
Width at rear	2·00 m (6 ft 6¾ in)
Height to sill	1·47 m (4 ft 9¾ in)
Height to top edge of hatchway	
	3·014 m (9 ft 10¾ in)
Emergency exit (in floor at front):	
Length	1·02 m (3 ft 4¼ in)
Width	0·70 m (2 ft 3½ in)
Emergency exit (top):	
Diameter	0·65 m (2 ft 1½ in)
Emergency exits (one each side of hold):	
Height	0·60 m (1 ft 11¾ in)
Width	0·50 m (1 ft 7½ in)

DIMENSIONS, INTERNAL:

Cargo hold: Length of floor	11·50 m (37 ft 8¾ in)
Width of floor	2·40 m (7 ft 10½ in)
Max height	1·91 m (6 ft 3 in)

AREAS:

Wings, gross	74·98 m² (807·1 sq ft)
Horizontal tail surfaces (total)	19·83 m² (213·45 sq ft)
Vertical tail surfaces (total, incl dorsal fin)	
	15·85 m² (170·61 sq ft)

WEIGHTS:

Weight empty	15,020 kg (33,113 lb)
Normal payload	4,500 kg (9,920 lb)
Max payload	5,500 kg (12,125 lb)
Normal T-O and landing weight	23,000 kg (50,706 lb)
Max T-O and landing weight	24,000 kg (52,911 lb)

PERFORMANCE (at normal T-O weight):

Cruising speed at 6,000 m (19,675 ft)	
	237 knots (440 km/h; 273 mph)
T-O speed	108 knots (200 km/h; 124 mph) CAS
Landing speed	102 knots (190 km/h; 118 mph) CAS
Max rate of climb at S/L	480 m (1,575 ft)/min
Service ceiling	7,500 m (24,600 ft)
T-O run, on concrete	780 m (2,559 ft)
T-O to 15 m (50 ft)	1,240 m (4,068 ft)
Landing from 15 m (50 ft)	1,740 m (5,709 ft)
Landing run, on concrete	730 m (2,395 ft)
Min ground turning radius	22·3 m (73 ft 2 in)

Range with max payload, no reserves	
	594 nm (1,100 km; 683 miles)
Range with max fuel, no reserves	
	1,376 nm (2,550 km; 1,584 miles)

ANTONOV An-28
NATO reporting name: Cash

Responsibility for An-28 production has been allocated to the WSK-PZL Mielec works in Poland (see Polish section).

ANTONOV An-30
NATO reporting name: Clank

Described as the first specialised aerial survey aeroplane produced in the Soviet Union, the An-30 is evolved from the An-24RT and An-26 twin-turboprop transports, to which it is generally similar. The major modifications are made to the nose, which is extensively glazed to give the navigator a wide field of view, and to the flight deck, which is raised to improve the pilots' view and increase the size of the navigator's compartment. There are fewer windows in the main cabin, which contains a darkroom and film storage cupboard, as well as survey cameras and a control desk. Other amenities include a toilet, buffet and crew rest area with armchairs and couches. All accommodation is pressurised and air-conditioned.

Photography can be automatic or semi-automatic if required, but two photographer/surveyors are normally carried, in addition to a flight crew of five (pilot, co-pilot, flight engineer, radio operator and navigator).

For the primary task of air photography for map-making, the An-30 is equipped with large survey cameras. These are mounted in the cabin above glazed apertures, of which there are five, each covered by a door. A crew photographer uncovers the apertures, as required, by remote control from his desk in the aircraft.

Standard equipment includes radio topographic distance measuring equipment and a radio altimeter, with recording units. The pre-programmed flight path of the aircraft over the area to be photographed is fed into an onboard computer, controlled from the navigator's station, which maintains the correct speed, altitude and direction of flight throughout the mission. The cartographic An-30 has an AFA-41/7·5 wide-angle camera, in a TAU-M gyro-stabilised mounting, over No. 1 aperture; and an A54/50-FK long focal-length camera over No. 3 aperture, each mounted vertically. Two further A54/50-FK cameras take oblique photographs at 28° to the vertical, port and starboard, through Nos. 4 and 5 apertures, and an SU-5 lightmeter is positioned over No. 2 window. One photogrammetric version has a vertically mounted AFA-41/7·5 camera in a TAU-M mount and an AFA-41/10 or AFA-41/20 camera in a fixed vertical mount. Another has the same installation without the gyroscopic mounting. A fourth variation offers an AFA-41/7·5 and an AFA-42/20, both in fixed mountings.

If required, the cameras can be replaced by other kinds of survey equipment, such as those used for mineral prospecting or for microwave radiometer survey, which measures the heat emission of land and ocean to obtain data on ocean surface characteristics, sea and lake ice, snow cover, flooding, seasonal vegetation changes, and soil types.

The power plant comprises two 2,103 kW (2,820 ehp) Ivchenko AI-24VT turboprop engines, with water injection, each driving an AV-72T four-blade constant-speed fully-feathering and reversible-pitch propeller. Main engines are supplemented by a 7·85 kN (1,765 lb st) RU 19A-300 auxiliary turbojet in the rear of the starboard engine nacelle. The latter is used for engine starting, and for take-off, climb and cruise power in the event of failure of the primary power plant. Engine TBO was 4,000 h in 1977. Max fuel capacity is 6,200 litres (1,364 Imp gallons).

Conversion into a transport aircraft is provided for, with cover plates to place over the camera apertures. The standard An-24 cabin door, on the port side of the fuselage at the rear, is retained, together with the standard forward freight compartment door on the starboard side and the load hoisting/conveying system.

The prototype An-30 flew for the first time in 1974. Operators include the Romanian Air Force, which has at least three.

DIMENSIONS, EXTERNAL:

Wing span	29·20 m (95 ft 9½ in)
Wing aspect ratio	11·4
Length overall	24·26 m (79 ft 7 in)
Height overall	8·32 m (27 ft 3½ in)
Tailplane span	9·973 m (32 ft 8¾ in)
Fuselage, nominal diameter	2·90 m (9 ft 6¼ in)
Wheel track (c/l of oleos)	7·90 m (25 ft 11 in)
Wheelbase	7·65 m (25 ft 1¼ in)
Propeller diameter	3·90 m (12 ft 9½ in)
Propeller ground clearance	1·20 m (3 ft 11¼ in)

WEIGHTS:

Basic operating weight	15,590 kg (34,370 lb)
Weight of aerial photography equipment	
	650 kg (1,433 lb)
Max T-O and landing weight	23,000 kg (50,705 lb)

PERFORMANCE:

Max level speed	291 knots (540 km/h; 335 mph)
Cruising speed at 6,000 m (19,675 ft)	
	232 knots (430 km/h; 267 mph)

Antonov An-30 (two AI-24VT turboprops and RU 19A-300 auxiliary turbojet) *(Pilot Press)*

Antonov An-30 aerial survey development of the An-24 twin-turboprop transport *(M. D. West)*

Antonov An-32, a version of the An-26 transport with a major increase in engine power for take-off from 'hot and high' airfields

Antonov An-32 short/medium-range transport (two Ivchenko AI-20M turboprop engines) *(Pilot Press)*

Landing speed   95 knots (175 km/h; 109 mph)
Service ceiling with APU operating
                            8,300 m (27,230 ft)
Service ceiling without APU   7,300 m (23,950 ft)
T-O run on concrete   710 m (2,330 ft)
Landing run on concrete   670 m (2,198 ft)
Range with max fuel, no reserves
                            1,420 nm (2,630 km; 1,634 miles)

ANTONOV An-32
NATO reporting name: Cline

This short/medium-range transport, of which first details were released in May 1977, is a developed version of the An-26, intended for operation in high-temperature or high-altitude environments. Except for having much enlarged ventral fins and a full-span slotted tailplane, the airframe appears to be generally similar to that of the An-26.

The An-32 is powered by two 3,862 kW (5,180 ehp) Ivchenko AI-20M turboprop engines, each driving a four-blade propeller. The large increase in power is intended specifically to improve take-off performance, service ceiling and payload. Thus, the An-32 is able to operate from airfields 4,000-4,500 m (13,125-14,750 ft) above sea level in an ambient temperature of ISA+25°C, and can transport 3 tonnes of freight over a 594 nm (1,100 km; 683 mile) stage length, with fuel reserves. The overwing location of the engines requires nacelles of considerable depth, as the main landing gear units continue to retract into the underwing portions.

A rear loading hatch and forward-sliding ramp/door, similar to those of the An-26, are retained, as well as a hoist, capacity 2,000 kg (4,409 lb), to facilitate handling of the maximum payload of 6 tonnes of freight. Alternative payloads include 39 passengers or 30 parachutists on a row of tip-up seats along each cabin wall, or 24 stretcher patients and a medical attendant; the normal crew of five comprises pilot, co-pilot, navigator, radio operator and flight engineer.

Low-pressure tyres (of the same sizes as those on the An-26) permit operation from unpaved strips; and the high position of the engines reduces the possibility of stone or debris ingestion. A TG-16M APU, housed in the rear of the starboard landing gear fairing, helps to make the An-32 independent of ground servicing equipment by providing onboard engine starting capability at airfields up to 4,500 m (14,750 ft) above sea level.

Only a single prototype of the An-32 had been built by mid-1980. It was exhibited at the 1977 Paris Air Show; at the 1979 Show, Mr Antonov commented that production would be undertaken only if sufficient orders were received in advance to justify such a move. Subsequently, it became known that the Indian Air Force was studying the An-32 as one solution to its requirement for a new general-purpose transport aircraft. If ordered, the An-32s would be assembled at the Kanpur plant of Hindustan Aeronautics, following delivery of an initial quantity from the Soviet Union. A total of as many as 95 aircraft could be involved.

DIMENSIONS, EXTERNAL AND INTERNAL:
As for An-26, except:
  Tailplane span   10·01 m (32 ft 10 in)
  Propeller diameter   4·70 m (15 ft 5 in)
WEIGHT:
  Max T-O weight   26,000 kg (57,320 lb)
PERFORMANCE:
  Normal cruising speed 275 knots (510 km/h; 317 mph)
  Optimum cruising height   8,000 m (26,250 ft)
  Service ceiling   9,500 m (31,150 ft)
  Service ceiling, one engine out 5,000 m (16,400 ft)
  T-O run   500 m (1,640 ft)
  Range with max payload, 45 min reserves
                            432 nm (800 km; 497 miles)
  Range with max fuel, 45 min reserves
                            1,188 nm (2,200 km; 1,367 miles)

ANTONOV An-72
NATO reporting name: Coaler

Two prototypes of this twin-turbofan STOL transport had been built by mid-1979, with a third airframe nearing completion for static testing. First photographs of one of these aircraft (CCCP-19774) were released by the Soviet Tass news agency about five months after the first flight of an An-72 on 31 August 1977. By the time of the 1979 Paris Air Show the two An-72s had logged a total of just over 1,000 h in about 300 flights, and were described by Mr Antonov as "progressing faster than the An-28", which was itself to enter production at Mielec in Poland.

Production of the An-72 is believed to be under way, following its evaluation as a STOL replacement for the An-26 twin-turboprop transports flown by Aeroflot and other airlines. The military potential of a transport able to utilise natural landing areas in undeveloped countries, or even small fields in Europe, is obvious. In particular, the An-72 might be an ideal aircraft with which to support operations by the new generation of V/STOL combat aircraft that will follow the Yak-36. Its low-pressure tyres and bogie landing gear are well suited to such tasks, enabling it to operate from unprepared airfields, or from surfaces covered with ice or snow; and the high-set engines avoid problems caused by foreign object ingestion.

The exhaust efflux is ejected over the upper surface of the wing and down over the very large multi-slotted flaps. By taking advantage of the so-called 'Coanda effect', which causes the airflow to 'attach to' the extended flaps, a considerable increase in lift can be achieved.

Mr Antonov anticipated few changes to the design if a decision were taken to put the An-72 into series production. However, he was not convinced that so small a transport had much to gain from complications such as the deflector doors at the rear of the engine nacelles which 'spread' the exhaust flow for optimum effectiveness during take-off and landing.

Particular care was taken to ensure easy handling of the An-72 in the air, and the designer commented that the aircraft had proved outstanding in this respect. Its Doppler-based automatic navigation system, linked to an onboard computer, is preprogrammed before take-off on a push-button panel to the right of the large cockpit map display. Failure warning panels above the windscreen display red lights for critical failures, yellow lights for non-critical failures, to minimise the time that needs to be spent on monitoring instruments and equipment.

TYPE: Twin-turbofan light STOL transport.

WINGS: Cantilever high-wing monoplane, with approx 25° sweepback on leading-edges and straight trailing-edges. Short constant-chord centre-section, without dihedral or anhedral. Approx 10° anhedral on outer panels. Wing upper-surface blowing requires engines to be mounted above and forward of wings, to exhaust over upper surface. Hydraulically-actuated full-span leading-edge flaps outboard of nacelles. Wide-span trailing-edge flaps, double-slotted inboard in exhaust efflux, triple-slotted on outer panels. Normal T-O flap setting 25-30°; max deflection 60°. Five-section spoilers forward of flaps on each side; some sections opened automatically on touchdown by sensors actuated by

Second prototype of the Antonov An-72 twin-turbofan STOL transport *(Brian M. Service)*

weight on main landing gear. Conventional ailerons outboard of flaps, with tab in port aileron.

FUSELAGE: Conventional all-metal semi-monocoque structure of circular cross-section. Underside of upswept rear fuselage made up of two outward-hinged clamshell doors and downward-opening ramp-door.

TAIL UNIT: Cantilever all-metal T tail, with wide-chord sweptback vertical surfaces. Double-hinged rudder, with tab in lower portion of two-section aft panel. Tailplane leading-edge sweep slightly greater than that of wings, with straight trailing-edge on horn-balanced elevators. Two tabs in each elevator. Tapered fairing forward of fin/tailplane junction. Two large outward-canted ventral fins, probably associated with airdrop testing from open ramp, on CCCP-19774; not fitted on CCCP-83966 (second prototype) when shown in Paris, June 1979.

LANDING GEAR: Retractable tricycle type. Twin wheels on rearward-retracting steerable nose unit. Each main unit comprises two trailing-arm legs in tandem, retracting inward through 90° so that wheels lie horizontally in bottom of large fairings, outside fuselage pressure cell. Low-pressure tyres, size 720 × 310 on nosewheels, 1050 × 400 on main wheels.

POWER PLANT: Two Lotarev D-36 high bypass ratio turbofan engines, each rated at 63·74 kN (14,330 lb st).

ACCOMMODATION: Pilot and co-pilot/navigator side by side on very roomy flight deck. Optional flight engineer's seat, at rear on starboard side, slides forward on tracks to position between and slightly aft of pilots, to give access to controls on central console. Main cabin designed primarily for freight, but with folding seats for 32 passengers along side walls and provision for carrying 24 casualties and attendant in ambulance configuration. Large downward-hinged rear ramp-door for loading trucks and tracked vehicles. As on An-26, ramp-door can be arranged to slide forward under fuselage to facilitate direct loading from a truck on to cabin floor, or for airdropping of freight. Winch, capacity 2,500 kg (5,510 lb), assists loading of containers up to 1·90 × 2·44 × 1·46 m (6 ft 3 in × 8 ft × 4 ft 9½ in) in size, pallets 1·90 × 2·42 × 1·46 m (6 ft 3 in × 7 ft 11 in × 4 ft 9½ in) in size, and other bulky items. Provision for building roller conveyors into floor. Main crew and passenger door at front of cabin on port side. Small

Antonov An-72 (two Lotarev D-36 turbofan engines), with scrap view of rear fuselage of first prototype *(Pilot Press)*

emergency exit and servicing door at rear of cabin on starboard side.

SYSTEM: Air-conditioning system provides comfortable environment to altitude of 10,000 m (32,800 ft), and can also be used to refrigerate main cabin when perishable goods are carried.

AVIONICS AND EQUIPMENT: Large radome over navigation/weather radar in nose. Doppler-based automatic navigation system, with map display on flight deck.

DIMENSIONS, EXTERNAL:
Wing span 25·83 m (84 ft 9 in)
Length overall 26·576 m (87 ft 2¼ in)
Height overall 8·235 m (27 ft 0¼ in)
DIMENSIONS, INTERNAL:
Main cabin: Length 9·00 m (29 ft 6¼ in)
Width at floor level 2·10 m (6 ft 10¾ in)
Height 2·20 m (7 ft 2½ in)
WEIGHTS:
Max payload 7,500 kg (16,535 lb)

Max T-O weight:
from 1,000 m (3,280 ft) runway 26,500 kg (58,420 lb)
from 1,200 m (3,935 ft) runway 30,500 kg (67,240 lb)
PERFORMANCE:
Max cruising speed 388 knots (720 km/h; 447 mph)
T-O speed with light load 81 knots (150 km/h; 94 mph)
T-O speed with heavier load 92 knots (170 km/h; 106 mph)
Max operating height 11,000 m (36,100 ft)
Normal operating height 8,000-10,000 m (26,250-32,800 ft)
T-O run 470 m (1,542 ft)
T-O run, one engine out 1,200 m (3,940 ft)
Range with max fuel, 30 min reserves 1,725 nm (3,200 km; 1,985 miles)
Range with max payload, 30 min reserves 540 nm (1,000 km; 620 miles)

Second prototype of the An-72, with modified rear fuselage and other changes, as shown at the 1979 Paris Air Show *(Tass)*

BERIEV

Georgi Mikhailovich Beriev, whose death at the age of 77 was reported in July 1979, was a graduate of the Leningrad Polytechnic Institute. He took up seaplane design in 1928 and became subsequently the best-known Soviet designer of water-based aircraft. He was appointed chief designer of the seaplane group at the TsKB (Central Design Bureau of Aviatrust) in 1930, and his first complete design, the single-engined MBR-2 flying-boat, was flown for the first time two years later, entering production in 1934. Other pre-war designs included the KOR-1 twin-float shipboard reconnaissance seaplane and the KOR-2 flying-boat, later redesignated Be-2 and Be-4 respectively.

In 1945 the Beriev bureau at Taganrog became the centre for all Soviet seaplane development, and the piston-engined Be-6 (first flown in 1947) was a standard military flying-boat during the 1950s. It was described in the 1959-60 *Jane's*. Only limited production was undertaken of the Be-8, also flown in 1947; and Beriev's next major flying-boat was the sweptwing twin-jet Be-10, based on the Be-R-1 prototype of 1949. A more recent maritime aircraft of Beriev design is the M-12 (Be-12) twin-turboprop amphibian, which is in standard service

with Soviet Naval Air Force units as a successor to the Be-6.

BERIEV M-12 (Be-12) TCHAIKA (SEAGULL)
NATO reporting name: Mail

This twin-turboprop medium-range maritime reconnaissance amphibian was displayed for the first time in the 1961 Aviation Day flypast at Tushino Airport, Moscow. Subsequently, during the period 23-27 October 1964, it established six officially-recognised international height records in Class C3 Group II. Data submitted in respect of these records revealed that the designation of the aircraft was M-12 and the power plant two 4,000 shp Ivchenko AI-20D turboprop engines. The aircraft was also, clearly, able to lift a payload of around 10 tons under record conditions.

The records set by the M-12 in 1964 were altitude of 12,185 m (39,977 ft) without payload, altitude of 11,366 m (37,290 ft) with payloads of 1,000 kg and 2,000 kg, altitude of 10,685 m (35,055 ft) with 5,000 kg payload, altitude of 9,352 m (30,682 ft) with 10,000 kg payload, and maximum payload of 10,100 kg (22,266 lb) lifted to a height of 2,000 m (6,560 ft).

These 1964 records have never been bettered. Subsequent record attempts have ensured that the M-12 retains

all 21 FAI records listed in Class C3 Group II for turboprop-powered amphibians, and all 19 current records in Class C2 Group II, for turboprop flying-boats. A list of these records can be found in the 1979-80 *Jane's*, except for two confirmed more recently, as follows: a C2/II sustained altitude record of 9,493 m (31,145 ft) set by E. Kolkov on 2 November 1978; and a height record of 9,407 m (30,863 ft) with 2,000 kg payload set by N. Chkourko on 6 November 1978.

Layout and construction of the M-12 are conventional. The single-step hull has a high length-to-beam ratio and is fitted with two long strakes, one above the other, on each side of the nose to prevent spray from enveloping the propellers at take-off. There is a glazed observation and navigation station in the nose, with a long radar 'thimble' built into it, and an astrodome type of observation position above the nose fuselage. The nose radome on current aircraft is wider and somewhat flatter in section than that on early M-12s. A long MAD (magnetic anomaly detection) 'sting' extends from the tail, and there appears to be an APU exhaust on the port side of the rear fuselage.

The sharply-cranked high-set wing, with non-retractable wingtip floats, is reminiscent of that of the Be-6, and is intended to raise the AI-20 turboprop engines well clear of the water. The cowlings of the turboprops open downward in two halves, so that they may be used as servicing platforms. The tail unit, with twin fins and rudders at the tips of a 'dihedral' tailplane, is also similar to that of the Be-6.

The tailwheel landing gear consists of single-wheel main units, which retract upward through 180° to lie flush within the sides of the hull, and a rearward-retracting tailwheel.

In addition to an internal bomb bay aft of the step, there is provision for one large and one small external stores pylon under each outer wing panel.

When three M-12s took part in the 1967 air display at Domodedovo, the commentator said that the unit to which they belonged was "one of those serving where the country's military air force began", implying that the aircraft were then in operational service. M-12s have since been identified in standard service at Soviet Northern and Black Sea Fleet air bases and were operational for a period from bases in Egypt, in Egyptian insignia. About 100 are believed to have been built, of which about 80 remain in service.

DIMENSIONS, EXTERNAL:
Wing span	29·71 m (97 ft 5¾ in)
Length overall	30·17 m (99 ft 0 in)
Height overall	7·00 m (22 ft 11½ in)
Propeller diameter	4·85 m (16 ft 0 in)

AREA:
Wings, gross	105 m² (1,130 sq ft)

WEIGHT:
Max T-O weight	29,450 kg (64,925 lb)

PERFORMANCE:
Max level speed	328 knots (608 km/h; 378 mph)

Beriev M-12 (Be-12) Tchaika twin-turboprop maritime reconnaissance amphibian (*Pilot Press*)

Normal operating speed		Service ceiling	11,280 m (37,000 ft)
	172 knots (320 km/h; 199 mph)	Max range	2,158 nm (4,000 km; 2,485 miles)
Rate of climb at S/L	912 m (2,990 ft)/min		

Beriev M-12 (Be-12) Tchaika maritime patrol amphibian flying-boat of the Soviet Naval Air Force (*Swedish Air Force*)

ILYUSHIN

DESIGN BUREAU HEADQUARTERS: Moscow Central Airport, Khodinka, Moscow
GENERAL DESIGNER: G. Novozhilov

This design bureau is named after its former leader, Sergei Vladimirovich Ilyushin, who died on 9 February 1977, at the age of 83. Ilyushin began his aviation career as a member of the ground staff at an airport. One of the aircraft he designed in the 'thirties made a record flight from Moscow to North America, but he is best remembered for his Il-2 and Il-10 Shturmovik close support aircraft of the second World War. He was awarded the Order of Lenin and a third Hammer and Sickle gold medal on 29 March 1974, in recognition of his service in the development of aviation technology and the Soviet aircraft industry.

Aircraft designed by Ilyushin and currently in service include the Il-14 piston-engined light transport and four-turboprop Il-18 transport, of which details have been given in earlier editions of *Jane's*, and the Il-28 twin-jet bomber, still in production in China (see pages 35-37). More recent types from the Ilyushin bureau include an anti-submarine variant of the Il-18, designated Il-38; a four-turbofan rear-engined airliner known as the Il-62; the Il-76 turbofan-engined heavy freighter, AWACS and flight refuelling tanker aircraft; and a large wide-bodied transport designated Il-86.

ILYUSHIN Il-18
NATO reporting name: Coot

The Il-18 prototype, named Moskva (Moscow), flew for the first time on 4 July 1957 and production models entered service with Aeroflot in 1959. In the following 20 years they logged 12 million flying hours with Aeroflot, carrying 235 million passengers on 5·5 million flights. Production is believed to have exceeded 700 aircraft, of which more than 100 were exported for use by commercial airlines. Known civilian operators were listed in the 1975-76 *Jane's*. Military operators of the Il-18s include the air forces of Afghanistan, Algeria, Bulgaria, China, Czechoslovakia, Poland, the Soviet Union, Syria and Yugoslavia, mostly in small numbers.

An anti-submarine derivative, the **Il-38** (NATO reporting name 'May'), is in service and is described separately. Another military variant of the Il-18, seen for the first time in 1978, is the ECM or elint aircraft known to NATO as **Coot-A** and shown in an accompanying illustration. In this case, the airframe appears to be basically unchanged by comparison with the transport. It carries under its fuselage a container about 10·25 m long and 1·15 m deep (33 ft 7½ in × 3 ft 9 in), which is assumed to house side-looking radar. There is a further container, about 4·4 m long and 0·88 m deep (14 ft 5 in × 2 ft 10½ in) on each side of the forward fuselage, containing a door over a camera or other sensor. Numerous other antennae and blisters can be seen, about eight of them on the undersurface of the centre and rear fuselage, with two large plates projecting above the forward fuselage. Further variants of the Il-18, adapted for military support tasks, will probably appear as the airliners are replaced by jets.

A detailed description of the commercial airliner versions of the Il-18 can be found in the 1979-80 and earlier editions of *Jane's*. The following abbreviated details of the Il-18D are retained as an indication of likely features of the military 'Coot-A':

WINGS: Cantilever low-wing monoplane. Mean thickness/chord ratio 14%. All-metal structure. Three spars in centre-section, two in outer wings. All-metal ailerons are mass-balanced and aerodynamically-compensated, and fitted with spring tabs. Manually-operated flying controls. Electrically-actuated double-slotted flaps. Electro-thermal de-icing.

FUSELAGE: Circular-section all-metal monocoque structure. The structure is of the fail-safe type, and appears to employ rip stop doublers around window cutouts, door frames and the more-heavily loaded skin panels.

TAIL UNIT: Cantilever all-metal structure. Trim tabs in rudder and elevators. Additional spring tab in rudder. Manually-operated flying controls. Electro-thermal de-icing.

LANDING GEAR: Retractable tricycle type. Hydraulic actuation. Four-wheel bogie main units, with 930 mm × 305 mm tyres and hydraulic brakes. Steerable (45° each way) twin nosewheel unit, with 700 mm × 250 mm tyres. Tyre pressures: main 7·86 bars (114 lb/sq in), nose 5·86 bars (85 lb/sq in). Hydraulic brakes and nosewheel steering. Pneumatic emergency braking.

POWER PLANT: Four 3,169 kW (4,250 ehp) Ivchenko AI-20M turboprop engines, each driving an AV-68I four-blade reversible-pitch propeller. Ten flexible bag-type fuel tanks in inboard panel of each wing and integral tank in outboard panel, with a total capacity of 23,700 litres (5,213 Imp gallons). Some Il-18 airliners have additional bag tanks in centre-section, giving a total capacity of 30,000 litres (6,600 Imp gallons). Pressure fuelling through four international standard connections in inner nacelles. Provision for overwing fuelling. Oil capacity 58·5 litres (12·85 Imp gallons) per engine.

ACCOMMODATION: Airliner was designed for a crew of five, comprising two pilots, navigator, wireless operator and flight engineer. Flight deck is separated from remainder of fuselage by a pressure bulkhead to reduce the hazards following a sudden decompression of either.

SYSTEMS: Cabin pressurised to max differential of 0·49 bars (7·1 lb/sq in). Electrical system includes eight 12kW DC generators and 28·5V single-phase AC inverters. Hydraulic system, pressure 207 bars (3,000 lb/sq in), for landing gear actuation, nosewheel steering, brakes and flaps.

DIMENSIONS, EXTERNAL:
Wing span	37·4 m (122 ft 8½ in)
Wing chord at root	5·61 m (18 ft 5 in)
Wing chord at tip	1·87 m (6 ft 2 in)
Wing aspect ratio	10
Length overall	35·9 m (117 ft 9 in)
Height overall	10·17 m (33 ft 4 in)
Tailplane span	11·8 m (38 ft 8½ in)
Wheel track	9·0 m (29 ft 6 in)
Wheelbase	12·78 m (41 ft 10 in)
Propeller diameter	4·50 m (14 ft 9 in)
Cabin doors (each): Height	1·40 m (4 ft 7 in)
Width	0·76 m (2 ft 6 in)
Height to sill	2·90 m (9 ft 6 in)

DIMENSIONS, INTERNAL:
Flight deck: Volume	9·36 m³ (330 cu ft)
Cabin, excl flight deck:	
Length	approx 24·0 m (79 ft 0 in)
Max width	3·23 m (10 ft 7 in)

ECM or electronic intelligence (elint) version of the Ilyushin Il-18 (NATO 'Coot-A'), photographed in early 1978 *(Royal Air Force)*

Max height	2·00 m (6 ft 6¾ in)
Volume	238 m³ (8,405 cu ft)

AREAS:

Wings, gross	140 m² (1,507 sq ft)
Ailerons (total)	9·11 m² (98·05 sq ft)
Trailing-edge flaps (total)	27·15 m² (292·2 sq ft)
Vertical tail surfaces (total)	17·93 m² (193·0 sq ft)
Rudder	6·83 m² (73·52 sq ft)
Horizontal tail surfaces (total)	
	27·79 m² (299·13 sq ft)
Elevators (total)	11·80 m² (127·0 sq ft)

WEIGHTS (Il-18D airliner):

Max payload	13,500 kg (29,750 lb)
Max T-O weight	64,000 kg (141,100 lb)

PERFORMANCE (Il-18D airliner, at max T-O weight):

Max cruising speed	364 knots (675 km/h; 419 mph)
Econ cruising speed	337 knots (625 km/h; 388 mph)
Operating height	8,000-10,000 m (26,250-32,800 ft)
T-O run	1,300 m (4,265 ft)
Landing run	850 m (2,790 ft)
Range with max fuel, 1 h reserves	
	3,508 nm (6,500 km; 4,040 miles)
Range with max payload, 1 h reserves	
	1,997 nm (3,700 km; 2,300 miles)

ILYUSHIN Il-38
NATO reporting name: May

This anti-submarine/maritime patrol development of the Il-18 airliner represents a conversion similar to that by which the US Navy's P-3 Orion was evolved from the Lockheed Electra transport. It has a lengthened fuselage fitted with an undernose radome similar in shape to that of the Ka-25 ASW helicopter but housing a different radar, an MAD tail 'sting', other specialised electronic equipment, and a weapon-carrying capability.

The main cabin of the Il-38 has few windows. The complete wing assembly is much further forward than on the Il-18, to cater for the effect on the CG position of internal equipment and stores. A crew of 12 is reported to be carried.

The Il-38 is a standard shore-based maritime patrol aircraft of the Soviet Naval Air Force, operating widely over the Atlantic and Mediterranean. In the latter area, some aircraft carried Egyptian Air Force insignia for a period, but are believed to have been manned by Soviet aircrew, operating from North African bases such as Matru, near Cairo. More recently, Il-38s of the Soviet Navy have operated over the Indian Ocean from an airfield in the People's Democratic Republic of Yemen.

In 1975, the Indian Navy ordered an initial batch of three Il-38s, of which delivery began in 1977, to equip INAS 315 at Dabolim, Goa. About 60 are believed to be operational with Soviet naval units.

DIMENSIONS, EXTERNAL:

Wing span	37·4 m (122 ft 8½ in)
Length overall	39·6 m (129 ft 10 in)
Height overall	10·17 m (33 ft 4 in)

PERFORMANCE (estimated):

Max cruising speed at 8,230 m (27,000 ft)	
	347 knots (645 km/h; 400 mph)
Max range	3,910 nm (7,240 km; 4,500 miles)

ILYUSHIN Il-62
NATO reporting name: Classic

Announced on 24 September 1962, when the first prototype (CCCP-06156) was inspected by the late Premier Krushchev, the standard Il-62 is a long-range airliner, with four Kuznetsov turbofan engines mounted in horizontal pairs on each side of the rear fuselage. It accommodates up to 186 passengers and was designed to fly on ranges equivalent to Moscow-New York (about 4,155 nm; 7,700 km; 4,800 miles) with more than 150 passengers and reserve fuel.

The Kuznetsov engines were not ready in time for the first flight of the first prototype, which took place in January 1963, with four 73·55 kN (16,535 lb st) Lyulka AL-7 engines installed. This aircraft was followed by a second prototype and three pre-production aircraft. Series production then started at Kazan, and Aeroflot introduced the Il-62 on to its Moscow-Montreal service on 15 September 1967, as a replacement for the Tu-114.

The Il-62 inaugurated Aeroflot's Moscow-New York service in July 1968, and has been used subsequently on many other routes, including Moscow-Paris and Moscow-Tokyo. Production is reported to have totalled at least 165 (including Il-62M/MKs), with export sales to CSA Czechoslovakian Airlines (8), Interflug of East Germany (6), Polish Airlines LOT (8), CAAC of China (5), Tarom of Romania (5), Cubana (1) and the Czechoslovakian government for VIP operation (1).

The Il-62's automatic flight control system is capable of taking over from a height of 200 m (650 ft) after take-off to a similar height during the landing approach. It can maintain a predetermined speed during climb and descent, and a selected cruising height, and can follow automatically a programmed track under command of the navigation computer.

The Il-62 is designed for an airframe service life of 25,000-30,000 flying hours, including 7,000-8,000 take-offs and landings.

A re-engined version, designated Il-62M, was flown for the first time in 1971. Details of this aircraft, and the further developed Il-62MK, are given separately, after the following description of the standard Il-62:

TYPE: Four-turbofan long-range airliner.

WINGS: Cantilever low-wing monoplane. Sweepback 35° at quarter-chord. Extended-chord leading-edge on outer two-thirds of each wing. All-metal structure, with four spars inboard, two at tip. Removable leading-edge. Each wing fitted with three-section manually-operated ailerons, electrically-actuated double-slotted flaps and two hydraulically-operated spoiler sections forward of flaps. Trim tab and spring-loaded servo tab in each centre aileron, spring-loaded servo tab in each inner aileron. Hot-air anti-icing of leading-edges.

FUSELAGE: Conventional all-metal semi-monocoque structure. Frames are duralumin stampings and pressings. Integrally pressed skin panels at highly-stressed areas. Floors are sandwich panels with foam plastics filler. Nosecone hinges upward for access to radar.

Ilyushin Il-38 anti-submarine/maritime patrol aircraft (four Ivchenko AI-20 turboprop engines), photographed from a Nimrod of No. 120 Squadron, RAF Kinloss

Ilyushin Il-38 anti-submarine/maritime patrol derivative of the Il-18 airliner *(Pilot Press)*

TAIL UNIT: Cantilever all-metal structure, with electrically-actuated variable-incidence T tailplane. All surfaces sweptback. Manually-operated rudder, fitted with yaw damper, trim tab and spring servo tab. Manually-operated elevators have two automatic trim tabs and two manual trim tabs. Hot-air leading-edge anti-icing system.

LANDING GEAR: Hydraulically-retractable tricycle type. Forward-retracting twin-wheel steerable nose unit. Emergency extension by gravity. Oleo-nitrogen shock-absorber on each unit. Each main unit carries a four-wheel bogie and retracts inward into wing-roots. Main-wheel tyres size 1450 × 450, pressure 9·31 bars (135 lb/sq in). Nosewheel tyres size 930 × 305, pressure 7·86 bars (114 lb/sq in). Hydraulic disc brake and inertia-type electric anti-skid unit on each main wheel, supplemented by large tail parachute. Parking brakes. Hydraulic twin-wheel strut is extended downward to support rear fuselage during loading and unloading.

POWER PLANT: Four Kuznetsov NK-8-4 turbofan engines, each rated at 103 kN (23,150 lb st), mounted in horizontal pairs on each side of rear fuselage. Thrust reverser on each outboard engine. Hot-air anti-icing system for engine intakes. Automatically-controlled fuel system, with seven integral tanks, three in wing centre-section, two in each outer panel. Each engine has its own independent fuel system, with cross-feed. Total fuel capacity 100,000 litres (21,998 Imp gallons). Four standard international underwing pressure refuelling sockets. Eight gravity refuelling sockets. Total oil capacity 204 litres (45 Imp gallons).

ACCOMMODATION: Crew of five (two pilots, navigator, radio operator and flight engineer) on flight deck. Provision for two supernumerary pilot/navigators. Basic two-cabin layout, and galley, toilet and wardrobe facilities, are unchanged in the three main versions, only the width and pitch of the seats being varied. In the 186-passenger version, there are 72 seats in the forward cabin and 114 in the rear cabin, all six-abreast and all at a seat pitch of 86 cm (34 in). In the 168-seat configuration, increased pitch reduces capacity to 66 in the forward cabin and 102 in the rear cabin. The 114-passenger version has 45 seats in the forward cabin and 69 in the rear cabin, all five-abreast, except for four-abreast rear row by door. A first class/de luxe version for 85 passengers is available, with 45 seats in forward cabin and 40 four-abreast sleeperette chairs with footrests in rear cabin. Passenger doors forward of front cabin and

between cabins on port side. Total of five toilets, opposite forward door, between cabins (starboard) and aft of rear cabin (both sides). Electrically-powered galley/pantry amidships and wardrobes in each version. Two pressurised baggage and freight compartments under cabin floor, forward and aft of wing. Unpressurised baggage/cargo compartment at extreme rear of fuselage. All compartments have tiedown fittings and rails in floor, and removable nets to restrain cargo.

SYSTEMS: Air-conditioning and pressurisation system maintains sea level conditions up to 7,000 m (23,000 ft) and gives equivalent of 2,100 m (6,900 ft) at 13,000 m (42,600 ft). Pressure differential 0·62 bars (9·0 lb/sq in). Hydraulic system, pressure 207 bars (3,000 lb/sq in), for landing gear retraction, nosewheel steering, brakes, spoilers and windscreen wipers. Emergency hydraulic system, powered by electric motor, for nosewheel steering, main-wheel extension and spoiler control. Three-phase 200/115V AC electrical supply from four 40kVA engine-driven generators (optional 27V DC system with eight 18kW engine-driven generators). Four transformer-rectifiers and four batteries for DC supply. Electrical windscreen de-icing. Type TA-6 APU in tailcone.

AVIONICS: Standard avionics include two-channel autopilot, navigation computer, air data system, HF and UHF radio, VOR/ILS, RMI, Doppler, radio altimeter and weather radar. Polyot automatic flight control system optional.

DIMENSIONS, EXTERNAL:

Wing span	43·20 m (141 ft 9 in)
Length overall	53·12 m (174 ft 3½ in)
Length of fuselage	49·00 m (160 ft 9 in)
Height overall	12·35 m (40 ft 6¼ in)
Tailplane span	12·23 m (40 ft 1½ in)
Fuselage width	4·10 m (13 ft 5½ in)
Fuselage height	3·75 m (12 ft 3½ in)
Wheel track	6·80 m (22 ft 3½ in)
Wheelbase	24·49 m (80 ft 4½ in)
Passenger doors (each): Height	1·83 m (6 ft 0 in)
Width	0·86 m (2 ft 9¾ in)
Height to sill	3·55 m (11 ft 8 in)
Emergency exit (galley service) door:	
Height	1·38 m (4 ft 6¼ in)
Width	0·61 m (2 ft 0 in)
Emergency exits (overwing):	
Height	0·91 m (2 ft 11¾ in)
Width	0·51 m (1 ft 8 in)

Front cargo hold door: Height	1·31 m (4 ft 3½ in)
Width	1·26 m (4 ft 1½ in)
Height to sill	1·90 m (6 ft 3 in)
Second cargo hold door: Height	1·00 m (3 ft 3½ in)
Width	1·26 m (4 ft 1½ in)
Height to sill	1·90 m (6 ft 3 in)
Third cargo hold door: Height	0·70 m (2 ft 3½ in)
Width	0·70 m (2 ft 3½ in)
Height to sill	2·26 m (7 ft 5 in)
Rear cargo hold door: Height	1·15 m (3 ft 9 in)
Width	1·07 m (3 ft 6 in)
Height to sill	3·68 m (12 ft 0¾ in)

DIMENSIONS, INTERNAL:

Cabin: Max height	2·12 m (6 ft 11½ in)
Max width	3·49 m (11 ft 5¼ in)
Volume	163 m³ (5,756 cu ft)
Total volume of pressure cell	396 m³ (13,985 cu ft)
Cargo hold volume:	
Front	22·7 m³ (801 cu ft)
Second	12·6 m³ (445 cu ft)
Third	6·9 m³ (243 cu ft)
Rear	5·8 m³ (205 cu ft)

AREAS:

Wings, gross	279·6 m² (3,010 sq ft)
Ailerons (total)	16·25 m² (174·9 sq ft)
Spoilers (total)	9·54 m² (102·7 sq ft)
Flaps (total)	43·48 m² (468·0 sq ft)
Horizontal tail surfaces (total)	40·00 m² (430·5 sq ft)
Vertical tail surfaces (total)	35·60 m² (383·2 sq ft)

WEIGHTS AND LOADING:

Weight empty	66,400 kg (146,390 lb)
Operating weight, empty	69,400 kg (153,000 lb)
Max payload	23,000 kg (50,700 lb)
Max fuel	83,325 kg (183,700 lb)
Max ramp weight	167,000 kg (368,000 lb)
Max T-O weight	162,000 kg (357,150 lb)
Max landing weight	105,000 kg (231,500 lb)
Max zero-fuel weight	93,500 kg (206,130 lb)
Max wing loading	572 kg/m² (117·2 lb/sq ft)

PERFORMANCE (at max T-O weight):

Normal cruising speed
    442-486 knots (820-900 km/h; 510-560 mph)
Normal cruising height
    10,000-12,000 m (33,000-39,400 ft)
Landing speed
    119-129 knots (220-240 km/h; 137-149 mph)
Max rate of climb at S/L   1,080 m (3,540 ft)/min
FAR T-O field length:
    ISA at S/L   3,250 m (10,660 ft)
    ISA+20°C at S/L   3,915 m (12,840 ft)
FAR landing field length:
    ISA at S/L   2,800 m (9,185 ft)
    ISA+20°C at S/L   2,950 m (9,680 ft)
Range with max payload, 66,700 kg (147,050 lb) fuel,
    1 h fuel reserves 3,612 nm (6,700 km; 4,160 miles)
Range with 80,000 kg (176,370 lb) fuel and 10,000
    kg (22,045 lb) payload, 1 h fuel reserves
        4,963 nm (9,200 km; 5,715 miles)

ILYUSHIN Il-62M / MK

First displayed publicly at the 1971 Paris Air Show, the **Il-62M** is a developed version of the Il-62, with no dimensional changes to the airframe. It is fitted with more powerful turbofans, of a different type, with clamshell thrust reversers on the outboard engine of each pair, offering a lower approach speed and improved airflow over the rear of the nacelles. An additional fuel tank is installed in the tail-fin, contributing (with the improved specific fuel consumption of the engines) to the longer range of this version.

Revised layout of the flight deck equipment, and new navigation and radio communications equipment, are features of the Il-62M. Control wheels of new design allow the pilots a better field of view, and the aircraft's automatic flight control system permits automatic landings in ICAO Category II conditions, with extension to Category III

Ilyushin Il-62M long-range airliner (four Soloviev D-30KU turbofan engines) of Cubana *(Harold G. Martin)*

conditions envisaged later. The wing spoilers of this version can be utilised differentially to enhance roll control.

Additional emergency and rescue equipment is installed on the Il-62M. Unlike the Il-62, it has a containerised baggage and freight system, with mechanised loading and unloading.

The Il-62M exhibited in Paris in 1971 and 1973 was the prototype (CCCP-86673). Production models entered service on Aeroflot's Moscow-Havana route in 1974 and have taken over progressively all of the airline's very-long-distance services. Four have been acquired by Cubana de Aviacion.

A variant announced in 1978 is the **Il-62MK,** still dimensionally unchanged and with the same power plant as the Il-62M, but with a strengthened wing for longer airframe life. Although the output of each engine is derated to 107·9 kN (24,250 lb st), max T-O weight is increased to 167,000 kg (368,170 lb) and max landing weight to 110,000 kg (242,500 lb), permitting the carriage of up to 195 passengers. To ensure adequate cabin service with so many passengers, the interior has been redesigned to permit the more efficient use of service trolleys. Range with max fuel and 10,000 kg (22,045 lb) payload is 5,180 nm (9,600 km; 5,965 miles). Max payload is 25,000 kg (55,115 lb).

The basic structural description of the Il-62 applies also to the Il-62M. The main innovations are as follows:

POWER PLANT: Four Soloviev D-30KU turbofan engines, each rated at 107·9 kN (24,250 lb st), mounted in horizontal pairs on each side of rear fuselage. Clamshell-type thrust reverser on each outboard engine. Remainder of power plant installation basically as for Il-62, but additional fuel tank in tail-fin, giving total capacity of 105,300 litres (23,162 Imp gallons).

ACCOMMODATION: Alternative configurations for up to 174 economy class, 168 tourist class or 140 mixed class passengers. In the basic tourist class version there are two toilets opposite the forward door, on the starboard side, aft of the flight deck. The forward cabin contains 66 seats, all six-abreast in threes with centre aisle. Galley/pantry, coat stowage and toilet amidships. Rear cabin contains 102 seats, six-abreast in threes with centre aisle. Two toilets and wardrobe to rear of this cabin. Doors as on Il-62. Forward underfloor baggage and freight hold accommodates nine containers, each weighing approximately 45 kg (100 lb) empty and with a capacity of 600 kg (1,322 lb) and 1·6 m³ (56·5 cu ft). Rear hold accommodates five similar containers. Two compartments for non-containerised cargo. Total baggage and freight capacity 48 m³ (1,695 cu ft)

SYSTEMS AND EQUIPMENT: See introductory notes.

AVIONICS: Duplicated SAU-1T automatic flight control system provides for automatic control from a height of 200 m (660 ft) after take-off to a height of 30 m (100 ft) on the approach to land. DISS-013 Doppler indicator and NV-PB-1 navigation computer. TKS-P course sensing system. TsGV-10P vertical master gyros. SVS-PN-15 air data system. Kurs-MP-2 radio navigation system, utilising VOR, ILS or SP-50 beacons. GROZA radar. SD-67 DME. ARK-15 ADF. RV-5 radio altimeter. SO-70 IFF transponder. MIKRON 2-24MHz HF radio. LANDASH 118-135MHz VHF radio. VESHANIE public address and in-flight entertainment system.

DIMENSIONS AND AREAS:
Same as for Il-62

WEIGHTS (Il-62M):
Max payload	23,000 kg (50,700 lb)
Max T-O weight	165,000 kg (363,760 lb)
Max landing weight	105,000 kg (231,500 lb)
Max zero-fuel weight	94,600 kg (208,550 lb)

PERFORMANCE (Il-62M, at max T-O weight):
Normal cruising speed
442-486 knots (820-900 km/h; 509-560 mph)
Normal cruising height
10,000-12,000 m (33,000-39,400 ft)
Balanced T-O distance (ISA, S/L) 3,300 m (10,830 ft)
Landing run (ISA, S/L) 2,500 m (8,200 ft)

Ilyushin Il-62M long-range four-turbofan transport *(Pilot Press)*

Range with max payload, with 5,100 kg (11,240 lb) fuel reserves	4,210 nm (7,800 km; 4,846 miles)
Range with 10,000 kg (22,045 lb) payload, with reserves	5,400 nm (10,000 km; 6,215 miles)

ILYUSHIN Il-76T
NATO reporting name: Candid

Towards the end of the 1960s, the Ilyushin design bureau, under the leadership of Mr. G. V. Novozhilov, began design of a heavy transport aircraft for operation over long distances in the Siberian regions of the USSR. Nominal task for the aircraft was to transport 40 tonnes of freight for a distance of 2,700 nm (5,000 km; 3,100 miles) in less than six hours, as a replacement for the turboprop An-12. It had to be capable of operation from short unprepared airstrips, in the most difficult weather conditions in Siberia, the north of the Soviet Union and the Far East, while being much simpler to service and flying much faster than the An-12.

The prototype of the new transport, known as the Il-76 (CCCP-86712), flew for the first time on 25 March 1971 and made its public debut at the 29th Salon de l'Aéronautique et de l'Espace in Paris in May 1971. Test flying continued until 1975, when the improved Il-76T, with increased hold capacity, entered series production. Subsequent operation in the most difficult weather and ground conditions of Central and Eastern Siberia revealed operating costs more than 25 per cent lower per tonne/km than for the An-12. This suggested that the Il-76T would be competitive with river transport, even during Summer months.

It was clear from the start that the Il-76 had considerable potential as a military transport. Evaluation by the Soviet Air Force had reached an advanced stage by 1974, when an official film depicted Il-76s with twin-gun rear turrets in use as vehicles for Soviet airborne troops. About 100 are believed to have been delivered subsequently to first-line squadrons of the Transport Aviation force, as An-12 replacements. Other customers for the military version are reported to include the air forces of Iraq, Czechoslovakia and Poland.

A version of the Il-76 was evaluated as a flight refuelling tanker for the 'Backfire' supersonic strategic bombers of the Soviet Air Force and Naval Air Fleet, as a successor to modified Myasishchev M-4 ('Bison') aircraft, and is expected to enter service in this role at an early date. A few are believed to be under evaluation in an AWACS role.

It was announced in 1978 that, following extensive testing of the commercial Il-76T in Siberia, the type was to be introduced into service on the Moscow-Japan route of

Aeroflot. By the beginning of 1980, this airline was reported to have about 40 Il-76Ts. Libyan Arab Airlines has two, and up to six of the basic military models are operated in airline insignia by Iraqi Airways, with the guns removed from the rear turret.

In July 1975, the Il-76 set a total of 25 officially recognised records for speed and altitude with payload. Piloted by Yakov I. Vernikov, on 4 July, it raised to 70,121 kg (154,590 lb) the record for greatest payload carried to a height of 2,000 m. The same flight recorded an altitude of 11,875 m (38,960 ft) with payloads of 60,000 kg, 65,000 kg and 70,000 kg. Also on 4 July, Alexander Turumine averaged 462·283 knots (856·697 km/h; 532·327 mph) around a 2,000 km circuit in an Il-76 carrying a payload of 60,000 kg, qualifying for additional records with 35,000 kg, 40,000 kg, 45,000 kg, 50,000 kg and 55,000 kg. On 7 July, Turumine averaged 462·801 knots (857·657 km/h; 532·923 mph) around 1,000 km, claiming nine records for payloads from 30,000 kg to 70,000 kg. The same pilot averaged 440·305 knots (815·968 km/h; 507·019 mph) around a 5,000 km circuit on 10 July, claiming records with 15,000 kg, 20,000 kg, 25,000 kg, 30,000 kg, 35,000 kg and 40,000 kg payloads. In the same year, a group of Soviet parachutists raised the world record for a high-altitude jump to 15,386 m (50,479 ft) from an Il-76.

TYPE: Four-turbofan medium/long-range freight transport.

WINGS: Cantilever monoplane, mounted above fuselage to leave interior unobstructed, and with constant anhedral from junction with centre-section on each side. Sweepback 25° at quarter-chord. All-metal five-piece structure, comprising centre-section, two inner panels carrying engines, and two outer panels. Leading-edge sweepback constant. Trailing-edge sweep increases outboard of joint between each inner and outer panel. Multi-spar fail-safe construction. Centre-section integral with fuselage. Mass-balanced ailerons, with balance/trim tabs. Two-section triple-slotted flaps over approx 75 per cent of each semi-span, from wing root to inboard edge of aileron. Upper-surface spoilers forward of flaps in 16 segments, four on each inner and outer wing panel. Ten-segment leading-edge slats over almost entire span, two on each inner panel, three on each outer panel.

FUSELAGE: All-metal semi-monocoque fail-safe structure of basically circular section. Underside of upswept rear fuselage made up of two outward-hinged clamshell doors, upward-hinged panel between these doors, and downward-hinged loading ramp.

Ilyushin Il-76T freight transport (four Soloviev D-30KP turbofan engines) *(Tass)*

Ilyushin Il-76T four-turbofan heavy freight-carrying transport *(Pilot Press)*

Parachute troops preparing to embark on a Soviet military Il-76. Note the rear gun turret

TAIL UNIT: Cantilever all-metal structure, with variable-incidence T tailplane. All surfaces sweptback. All control surfaces aerodynamically balanced. Tabs in rudder and each elevator.

LANDING GEAR: Hydraulically-retractable tricycle type, designed for operation from prepared and unprepared runways. Nose unit made up of two pairs of wheels, side by side, with central oleo. Each main-wheel bogie made up of four pairs of wheels in two rows. Low-pressure tyres size 1,300 × 480 on main wheels, 1,100 × 330 on nosewheels. Nosewheels retract forward. Main units retract inward into two large ventral fairings under fuselage, with an additional large fairing on each side of lower fuselage over actuating gear. During retraction main-wheel axles rotate around leg, so that wheels stow with axles parallel to fuselage axis (ie: wheels remain vertical but at 90° to direction of flight). All doors on wheel wells close when gear is down, to prevent fouling of legs by snow, ice, mud, etc. Oleo-pneumatic shock-absorbers. Tyre pressure can be varied in flight from 2·5 to 5 bars (36-73 lb/sq in) to suit different landing strip conditions. Hydraulic brakes on main wheels.

POWER PLANT: Four Soloviev D-30KP turbofan engines, each rated at 117·7 kN (26,455 lb st), in individual underwing pods. Each pod is carried on a large forwardly-inclined pylon and is fitted with a clamshell thrust reverser. Integral fuel tanks between spars of inner and outer wing panels. Total fuel capacity reported to be 81,830 litres (18,000 Imp gallons).

ACCOMMODATION: Crew of seven, including two freight handlers. Conventional side-by-side seating for pilot and co-pilot on spacious flight deck. Station for navigator below flight deck in glazed nose. Forward-hinged door on each side of fuselage forward of wing. Two windows on each side of hold serve as emergency exits. Hold has reinforced floor of titanium alloys, with folding roller-type conveyors, and is loaded via rear ramp. Entire accommodation is pressurised, and advanced mechanical handling systems are provided for containerised and other freight, which can include stan-

dard ISO containers, each 12 m (39 ft 4½ in) long, building machinery, heavy crawlers and mobile cranes. Quick configuration changes can be made by the use of modules, each able to accommodate 30 passengers in four-abreast seating, litter patients and medical attendants, or cargo. Three such modules can be carried, each approx 6·10 m (20 ft) long, 2·4 m (8 ft) wide and 2·4 m (8 ft) high. They are loaded through the rear doors by means of two overhead travelling cranes, and are secured to the cabin floor with cargo restraints. Cranes can utilise two hoists, each with capacity of 3,000 kg (6,615 lb), or four hoists, each with capacity of 2,500 kg (5,510 lb). Ramp can be used as additional hoist, with capacity of up to 30,000 kg (66,140 lb) to facilitate loading of large vehicles and those with caterpillar tracks. Wipers on pilot's windows.

SYSTEMS: Hydraulic system includes servo motors and motors to drive the flaps, slats, landing gear and its doors, ramp, rear fuselage clamshell doors and load hoists. Flying control boosters are supplied by electric pumps and are independent of the central hydraulic supply. Manual control is possible after booster failure. Electrical system includes engine-driven generators, auxiliary generators driven by an APU, DC converters and batteries. It powers the pumps for the flying control system boosters, radio and avionics, and lighting systems.

AVIONICS AND EQUIPMENT: Full equipment for all-weather operation by day and night, including a computer for automatic flight control and automatic landing approach. Large meteorological and ground-mapping radar in undernose radome. APU in port side landing gear fairing for engine starting and to supply all aircraft systems on ground, making aircraft independent of ground facilities.

DIMENSIONS, EXTERNAL:
Wing span	50·50 m (165 ft 8 in)
Wing aspect ratio	8·5
Length overall	46·59 m (152 ft 10½ in)
Height overall	14·76 m (48 ft 5 in)

Rear loading aperture:
Width	3·40 m (11 ft 1¾ in)
Height	3·45 m (11 ft 4 in)

DIMENSIONS, INTERNAL:
Cabin: Length, excl ramp	20·00 m (65 ft 7½ in)
Length, incl ramp	24·50 m (80 ft 4½ in)
Width	3·40 m (11 ft 1¾ in)
Height	3·46 m (11 ft 4¼ in)
Volume	235·3 m³ (8,310 cu ft)

AREA:
Wings, gross	300·0 m² (3,229·2 sq ft)

WEIGHTS AND LOADINGS:
Max payload	40,000 kg (88,185 lb)
Max T-O weight	170,000 kg (374,785 lb)
Permissible floor loading	1,450-3,100 kg/m² (297-635 lb/sq ft)
Permissible axle load (vehicles)	7,500-11,000 kg (16,535-24,250 lb)
Max wing loading	566·7 kg/m² (116·05 lb/sq ft)
Max power loading	361 kg/kN (3·54 lb/lb st)

PERFORMANCE:
Max level speed	459 knots (850 km/h; 528 mph)
Cruising speed	405-432 knots (750-800 km/h; 466-497 mph)
T-O speed	114 knots (210 km/h; 131 mph)
Approach and landing speed	119-130 knots (220-240 km/h; 137-149 mph)
Normal cruising height	9,000-13,000 m (29,500-42,650 ft)
Absolute ceiling	approx 15,500 m (50,850 ft)
T-O run	850 m (2,790 ft)
Landing run	450 m (1,475 ft)
Nominal range with max payload	2,700 nm (5,000 km; 3,100 miles)
Max range, with reserves	3,617 nm (6,700 km; 4,163 miles)

ILYUSHIN Il-86
NATO reporting name: Camber

First indication that this aircraft was under development was given at the 1971 Paris Air Show. Mr Genrikh Novozhilov, successor to the late Sergei Ilyushin as chief of the Ilyushin design bureau, told visitors that a new wide-bodied transport known as the Il-86 was then in the early project design stage.

No final decision on the configuration, or number of engines, had been taken at that time; but in the Spring of 1972 a model of one projected configuration was displayed publicly in Moscow. This design was similar in layout to the Il-62, with four rear-mounted turbofan engines and a T tail, but was intended to be much larger, with a two-deck fuselage. It was described and illustrated in the 1972-73 *Jane's*.

Simultaneously with the display of this original model, it became known that the Il-86 had been chosen for development, after a competition in which it was matched against proposals from the Antonov and Tupolev design teams.

By the end of 1972, it was evident that the design of the Il-86 had evolved along different lines to those suggested by the model displayed six months earlier. In particular the engines had been repositioned into four underwing pods, permitting the tailplane to be lowered on to the rear fuselage. The first of two prototypes (CCCP-86000), in this form, made a first flight of about 40 min after taking off in 1,700 m (5,575 ft) from an 1,820 m (5,970 ft) runway at the old Moscow Central Airport of Khodinka, where the Ilyushin Bureau has its headquarters, to the official flight test centre on 22 December 1976, piloted by Hero of the Soviet Union A. Kuznetsov.

The Novosti official press agency announced in September 1977 that more than 100 test flights had been made and that basic testing was expected to be completed by 7 November 1977, the 60th anniversary of the October Revolution. The Soviet Civil Air Minister, Mr Boris Bugayev, said that the Il-86 would enter service with Aeroflot in time to carry visitors from Prague, Sofia and Berlin to the 1980 Olympic Games in Moscow. This does not appear to have been achieved, although the first flight over an Aeroflot route, from Moscow to Mineralnye Vody, was made in September 1978, three months ahead of schedule. US reports suggest that the aim was to complete 1,200 h of flight testing before deliveries began in late 1979. Other routes which are to be served on entry into scheduled service include Moscow to Sotchi, Simferopol, Tashkent and Alma-Ata. Aircraft CCCP-86002, which flew for the first time at Voronezh on 24 October 1977, was described as the first production Il-86.

The Il-86 is likely to be used also by the Soviet Air Force, and the evolution of an AWACS version has been suggested as a possibility by Western sources. The airframe is believed to be designed for 40,000 flying hours or 20,000 landings.

For production aircraft, wings, including flaps and slats, pylons to carry the engine pods, and vertical and horizontal tail surfaces are being manufactured in Poland. Final assembly is centred at Voronezh.

TYPE: Four-turbofan wide-bodied passenger transport.

WINGS: Cantilever monoplane of all-metal construction (made at Voronezh). Wings mounted in low-mid position on fuselage. Dihedral from roots. Sweepback 35° at

Ilyushin Il-86 wide-bodied transport at 1979 Paris Air Show (*Brian M. Service*)

quarter-chord. Large double-slotted trailing-edge flaps, in two sections along entire span of each wing inboard of aileron. Multi-section spoilers in top surface, forward of all four flap sections. Full-span leading-edge slats, with small cutaway to clear each inboard engine pylon. Shallow fence on top surface in line with each pylon.

FUSELAGE: Conventional semi-monocoque light alloy structure of circular cross-section. Floors of main and lower decks of honeycomb and carbonfibre reinforced plastics.

TAIL UNIT: Conventional sweptback cantilever structure, with tailplane dihedral. Each control surface in two sections. (Tail unit made at Kiev.)

LANDING GEAR: Retractable four-unit type. Forward-retracting steerable twin-wheel nose unit, and three four-wheel bogie main units. Two of the latter retract inward into the wing-root fairings; the third unit is mounted centrally under the fuselage, slightly forward of the others, and retracts forward. (Main landing gear made at Kuibyshev.) Main-wheel tyres size 1300 × 480; nosewheel tyres size 1120 × 450.

POWER PLANT: Four Kuznetsov NK-86 turbofan engines, each rated at 127·5 kN (28,660 lb st), mounted on pylons forward of wing leading-edges. Engines fitted with combined thrust reversers/noise attenuators. Fuel capacity 70,000-80,000 litres (15,400-17,600 Imp gallons). Provision for APU in tailcone (space occupied by three-stage parachute for stall tests in prototype).

ACCOMMODATION: Standard flight crew comprises two pilots and a flight engineer, with provision for a navigator if required. Flight engineer's seat normally faces to starboard, aft of co-pilot, but can pivot to central forward-facing position to enable the engineer to operate the throttles. Upper deck, on which all seats are located, is divided into three separate cabins by wardrobes, a serving area connected by elevator to the lower-deck galley, and cabin staff accommodation, with a total of eight toilets at front (2) and rear (6) of the aircraft. Cabins feature unusually large windows, indirect lighting in walls and in ceiling panels, and enclosed baggage lockers at top of side walls. Preponderance of metal and natural fibre materials rather than plastics throughout cabins to enhance safety in an emergency. Up to 350 passengers in basic nine-abreast seating throughout, with two aisles, each 55 cm (21·6 in) wide. Suggested mixed-class alternative layout provides for 28 passengers six-abreast in the front cabin, and 206 passengers eight-abreast in the other two cabins. Passengers enter via three airstair-type doors (made in Kharkov), which hinge down from the port side of the lower deck. One of these doors is forward of the wing; the others are aft of the wing. Four further doors at upper-deck level on each side, for emergency use (using dual inflatable escape slides) and for use at airports where the utilisation of high-level boarding steps or bridges is preferred. Coats and hand baggage are stowed on the lower deck before passengers climb one of three fixed staircases to the main deck. Cargo holds are

Ilyushin Il-86 four-turbofan wide-bodied passenger transport (*Pilot Press*)

designed to accommodate heavy or registered baggage and freight in 8 standard LD3 containers, or 16 LD3 containers if some of the carry-on baggage racks are omitted. Access is via upward-hinged doors forward of the starboard wing-root leading-edge and at the side of the rear hold. Containers can be loaded and unloaded by means of a self-propelled truck with built-in roller conveyor. Films will be shown in flight, and there will be a choice of 12 tape-recorded audio programmes. A bar can be provided on the lower deck in place of the baggage and freight accommodation in the forward vestibule.

SYSTEMS: Four completely self-contained hydraulic systems, each operated by one of the engines. All avionics equipment located within pressurised part of fuselage. All hot pipelines of air-conditioning system, and all fuel supply lines, outside pressure cell. New-type smoke detection system, with sensors in baggage, freight and equipment stowage areas. New-type pulse-generating de-icing system consuming 500 times less energy than a conventional hot air or electrical system.

AVIONICS: Flight control and nav systems provide for automatic climb to the selected height, control of the rate of climb and automatic descent, and permit automatic landing in ICAO Cat IIIA conditions. Pre-programmable Doppler nav system with readout display screen on flight deck, on which microfilmed maps can be projected. Position of aircraft is indicated by cursor, driven by system computer. Nav system is updated automatically by inputs from VOR or VOR/DME radio beacons.

DIMENSIONS, EXTERNAL:
Wing span	48·06 m (157 ft 8¼ in)
Length overall	60·21 m (197 ft 6½ in)
Diameter of fuselage	6·08 m (19 ft 11½ in)
Height overall	15·68 m (51 ft 5½ in)
Tailplane span	20·57 m (67 ft 6 in)
Wheel track (c/l of outer shock-struts)	
	11·15 m (36 ft 7 in)
Wheelbase	21·34 m (70 ft 0 in)

DIMENSIONS, INTERNAL:
Main cabins: Height	2·61 m (8 ft 7 in)
Max width	approx 5·70 m (18 ft 8½ in)

AREA:
Wings, gross	320 m² (3,444 sq ft)

WEIGHTS:
Max payload	42,000 kg (92,600 lb)
Max fuel	86,000 kg (189,600 lb)
Max T-O weight (dependent on size and type of runway)	190,000-206,000 kg (418,875-454,150 lb)
Max landing weight	175,000 kg (385,800 lb)

PERFORMANCE (estimated):
Normal cruising speed at 9,000-11,000 m (30,000-36,000 ft)
485-512 knots (900-950 km/h; 560-590 mph)
Approach speed
130-141 knots (240-260 km/h; 149-162 mph)
Field length for take-off and landing
2,300-2,600 m (7,550-8,530 ft)
Range with max payload
1,944 nm (3,600 km; 2,235 miles)
Range with max fuel
2,480 nm (4,600 km; 2,858 miles)

KAMOV
CHIEF OF DESIGN BUREAU: S. Mikhéev

Nikolai I. Kamov, who died on 24 November 1973, aged 71, had been a leading designer of rotating-wing aircraft since the late 1920s and, with N. K. Skrzhinskii, was responsible for the first successful Soviet rotorcraft, the KaSkr-I, in 1929. He became well known internationally when he designed a series of one-man lightweight helicopters of the 'flying motorcycle' type in the late 1940s.

The Ka-15 and Ka-18 helicopters, developed by Kamov and his design team, under chief engineer Vladimir Barshevskii, were both put into large-scale production and service. Details of them can be found in the 1962-63 and 1963-64 editions of *Jane's* respectively.

Later Kamov types are the Ka-25 turbine-powered anti-submarine helicopter; a flying-crane version of the same design, designated Ka-25K; and a twin-engined

general-purpose helicopter designated Ka-26. All available details of these types follow:

KAMOV Ka-25
NATO reporting name: Hormone

The prototype of this military helicopter was first shown in public in the Soviet Aviation Day flypast over Tushino Airport, Moscow, in July 1961. It was allocated the NATO code name 'Harp', but this was changed to 'Hormone' for the production versions, of which about 460 were built in 1966-75. Together with the newer Mil helicopters known to NATO as 'Haze-A', these have largely replaced piston-engined Mi-4s in the Soviet Navy's ship and shore based force of around 275 helicopters. Nine are operated on coastal anti-submarine duties by the Syrian Air Force and others by India and Yugoslavia.

As well as serving as an anti-submarine and missile guidance aircraft, the Ka-25 fulfils a variety of other military roles. Only two versions may be identified at present by NATO reporting names:

Hormone-A. Basic ship-based anti-submarine version, operated from cruisers of 'Kresta' and 'Kara' classes, carrier/cruisers *Kiev* and *Minsk*, each of which carries 27 'Hormone-As' and 3 'Bs', and helicopter carrier/cruisers *Moskva* and *Leningrad*, each of which accommodates about 18 Ka-25s. Search radar in undernose radome, diameter 1·25 m (4 ft 1 in), towed magnetic anomaly detector, dipping sonar housed in compartment at rear of cabin, and electro-optical sensor. A major shortcoming is said to be lack of night and all-weather sonar-dipping capability.

Hormone-B. Special electronics variant, able to acquire targets for ship-launched missiles. Larger undernose radome with more spherical undersurface. Cylindrical radome under rear of cabin. Data link equipment.

TYPE: Twin-turbine anti-submarine and general-purpose helicopter.

Kamov Ka-25 ('Hormone-A') anti-submarine helicopter (two Glushenkov turboshaft engines) *(US Navy)*

'Hormone-B' target acquisition variant of ship-based Ka-25, with enlarged undernose radome and cylindrical radome under rear of cabin, but without belly weapon-bay doors *(US Navy)*

ROTOR SYSTEM: Two three-blade coaxial contra-rotating rotors. Automatic blade-folding.

FUSELAGE: Conventional all-metal semi-monocoque structure of pod and boom type.

TAIL UNIT: Cantilever all-metal structure, with central fin, ventral fin and twin endplate fins and rudders which are toed inward.

LANDING GEAR: Four-wheel type. Oleo-pneumatic shock-absorbers. Nosewheels are smaller than main wheels and are of castoring type. Each wheel can be enclosed in an inflatable pontoon surmounted by inflation bottles to provide flotation in event of an emergency alighting on water. Rear legs are pivoted to retract upward about their wishbone supports, so that the wheels can be moved to a position where they offer least interference to signals from the nose radar.

POWER PLANT: Two 671 kW (900 shp) Glushenkov GTD-3 turboshaft engines, mounted side by side above cabin, forward of rotor driveshaft, on early aircraft. Later aircraft believed to have two 738 kW (990 shp) GTD-3BM turboshafts. Provision for carrying external fuel tank on each side of cabin.

ACCOMMODATION: Pilot and co-pilot side by side on flight deck, with rearward-sliding door on each side. Entry to main cabin is via a rearward-sliding door to rear of main landing gear on port side. Cabin accommodates two or three systems operators in ASW role, but is large enough to contain 12 folding seats for passengers.

AVIONICS AND EQUIPMENT: Equipment available for all versions includes autopilot, navigational system, radio compass, radio communications installations, and lighting system for all-weather operation by day or night. Dipping sonar housed in compartment at rear of main cabin, immediately forward of tailboom, and search radar under nose of anti-submarine version, which carries also a towed magnetic anomaly detector. Some aircraft have a blister fairing over equipment mounted at the base of the centre tail-fin; others have a cylindrical housing, with a transparent top, above the central point of the tailboom (see illustration), with a shallow blister fairing to the rear of this. Doors under the fuselage of

some aircraft enclose a weapons bay for ASW torpedoes, nuclear depth charges and other stores. Two so-called 'air-to-surface missiles' carried on outriggers on each side of cabin of prototype during its Tushino appearance were dummies, but there is reason to believe that Ka-25s are being armed with newly-developed 'fire-and-forget' air-to-surface guided missiles.

DIMENSIONS, EXTERNAL:

Diameter of rotors (each)	15·74 m (51 ft 8 in)
Length of fuselage	9·75 m (32 ft 0 in)
Height to top of rotor head	5·37 m (17 ft 7½ in)
Width over tail-fins	3·76 m (12 ft 4 in)

Wheel track: front	1·41 m (4 ft 7½ in)
rear	3·52 m (11 ft 6½ in)
Cabin door: Height	1·10 m (3 ft 7¼ in)
Width	1·20 m (3 ft 11¼ in)

DIMENSIONS, INTERNAL:

Cabin, excl flight deck:

Length	3·95 m (12 ft 11½ in)
Max width	1·50 m (4 ft 11 in)
Max height	1·25 m (4 ft 1¼ in)

WEIGHTS (approx):

Weight empty	4,765 kg (10,500 lb)
Max T-O weight	7,500 kg (16,500 lb)

PERFORMANCE:

Max level speed	113 knots (209 km/h; 130 mph)
Normal cruising speed	104 knots (193 km/h; 120 mph)
Service ceiling	3,500 m (11,500 ft)
Range with standard fuel, with reserves	217 nm (400 km; 250 miles)
Range with external tanks, with reserves	351 nm (650 km; 405 miles)

KAMOV Ka-25K

The Ka-25K flying-crane helicopter, based on the military Ka-25, was shown publicly for the first time at the 1967 Paris Air Show. It did not enter production and service. Details can be found in the 1979-80 and earlier editions of *Jane's*.

KAMOV Ka-26
NATO reporting name: Hoodlum

First details of this twin-engined light helicopter were announced in January 1964, and the prototype flew for the first time in the following year. Kamov described it as an ideal helicopter for agriculture, possessing all the virtues of the Ka-15 (which was used in about a dozen countries) but able to lift three times as much chemical payload, and the Ka-26 entered large-scale service as an agricultural aircraft in the Soviet Union in 1970, being used primarily over orchards and vineyards. It is also used widely on Aeroflot's air ambulance services and is suitable for many other applications, including cargo and passenger transport, forest firefighting, mineral prospecting, pipeline construction and laying transmission lines.

The usual Kamov contra-rotating coaxial three-blade rotor system is retained, with hydraulic dampers fitted to each rotor head and the rotor shafts inclined forward at 6° to the vertical. The blades, made of glass-textolyte (plastics) materials, weigh only 25 kg (55 lb) each and are completely interchangeable. They, and the cabin windscreen, are equipped with an anti-icing system, activated automatically by a radioisotope ice warning device and utilising an alcohol glycerine mixture.

A powered control system is standard. The jacks are actuated by a single hydraulic system, with manual override in case of system failure.

The fully-enclosed cabin, with a door on each side, is fitted out normally for operation by a single pilot, but a second seat and dual controls are optional. The cabin is warmed and demisted by air from a combustion heater, which also heats the passenger compartment when fitted.

The tailplane, with twin fins and rudders toed inward at 15°, is carried on two plastics tailbooms. Short high-mounted stub-wings carry the two podded 242·5 kW (325 hp) M-14V-26 aircooled radial piston engines, designed by I. M. Vedeneev, and the main units of the non-retractable four-wheel landing gear. Each engine is cooled by a fan in the front of its nacelle, which absorbs about 18·6 kW (25 hp) from the engine output. Dust filters are fitted in the air delivery ducts, to protect the engines, each of which is connected to the rotor transmission by a shaft and two flexible couplings. Both rotors can be driven by either engine if the other fails; disengagement of the failed

'Hormone-A' anti-submarine version of the Kamov Ka-25 helicopter. Scrap view shows optional blister fairing at base of central tail-fin *(Pilot Press)*

engine is automatic, and an autorotative landing can be made if both engines fail.

All four landing gear units embody oleo-pneumatic shock-absorbers. The forward wheels are of the castoring type and are not fitted with brakes. The rear wheels are fitted with pneumatically-operated brakes. Tyre size is 595 × 185 on the main wheels, 300 × 125 on the forward wheels.

The space aft of the cabin, between the main landing gear units and under the rotor transmission, is able to accommodate a variety of interchangeable payloads. For agricultural work the chemical hopper (capacity 900 kg; 1,985 lb) and dust-spreader or spraybars are fitted in this position, on the aircraft's centre of gravity. This equipment is quickly removable and can be replaced by a cargo/passenger pod accommodating six persons, with provision for a seventh passenger beside the pilot. Alternatively, the Ka-26 can be operated with either an open platform for hauling freight or a hook for slinging bulky loads at the end of a cable or in a cargo net.

A version for geophysical survey has an electromagnetic pulse generator in the cabin and is encircled by a huge 'hoop' antenna. It carries on the port side of the fuselage a mounting for the receiver 'bird' which is towed at the end of a cable, beneath the helicopter, when in use. The receiver is lowered by an electric winch and the cable is cut by automatic shears if its traction should exceed the authorised limit.

An aerial survey model is available with an AFA-31-MA camera mounted in the cabin. This aircraft can photograph 5 km² (2 sq miles) per hour at a scale of 1 : 10,000.

As an air ambulance, the Ka-26 can carry two stretcher patients, two seated casualties and a medical attendant. A winch, with a capacity of up to 150 kg (330 lb), enables it to be used for rescue duties.

When operating as an agricultural sprayer, the Ka-26 discharges its chemical payload at 1·5-12 litres/s (0·33-2·65 Imp gallons/s). The rate of discharge in a dusting role is 1·5-12 kg/s (3·3-26·5 lb/s). Up to 120 hectares (296 acres) can be sprayed during each flying hour at the rate of 50 kg/ha (44·5 lb/acre). As a duster, 140 ha (346 acres) can be treated at the same discharge rate. 50 ha (123 acres) can be topdressed with chemical fertilisers each flying hour, at a rate of 100 kg/ha (89 lb/acre).

To protect the pilot against toxic chemicals in the agricultural role, the cabin is lightly pressurised by a blower and air filter system which ensures that the cabin air is always clean. The flying and navigation equipment are adequate for all-weather operation, by day and night. VHF and HF radio are fitted, together with a radio compass and radio altimeter.

Because of its small size and manoeuvrability, the Ka-26 can be operated from platforms on small ships such as whalers and icebreakers, and a Soviet fishing boat operating in the North Atlantic in early 1970 carried a Ka-26 for fish-spotting duties. This aircraft was equipped with inflated pontoons to permit alighting on the water. In mid-1969, a Ka-26 was tested in Siberia and the north-west USSR in a forest protection version able to deliver six firemen and their equipment speedily to the site of a forest fire. In the Spring of 1972, Ka-26s joined Mi-1,

Kamov Ka-26 used by Asahi Helicopter Co of Japan, mainly for crop-spraying in rice fields

Mi-2 and Mi-4 helicopters in operations to clear ice from Soviet rivers, by landing demolition teams on thick ice-floes and destroying thinner ice-fields from the air.

More than 600 Ka-26s had been produced by 1977. They are in civilian service in Bulgaria, East Germany, West Germany, Hungary, Japan, Romania and Sweden, as well as in the USSR. Military operators include the air forces of Hungary and Sri Lanka.

Mr S. Mikhéev, chief of the Kamov design bureau, stated that a new version of the Ka-26 was under development in 1979. This is probably turbine-powered.

DIMENSIONS, EXTERNAL:
Diameter of rotors (each)	13·00 m (42 ft 8 in)
Vertical separation between rotors	1·17 m (3 ft 10 in)
Length of fuselage	7·75 m (25 ft 5 in)
Height overall	4·05 m (13 ft 3½ in)
Width over engine pods	3·64 m (11 ft 11½ in)
Width over agricultural spraybars	11·20 m (36 ft 9 in)
Tailplane span	4·60 m (15 ft 1 in)
Wheel track: Main wheels	2·42 m (7 ft 11½ in)
Nosewheels	0·90 m (2 ft 11½ in)
Wheelbase	3·48 m (11 ft 5 in)
Passenger pod door: Height	1·40 m (4 ft 7 in)
Width	1·25 m (4 ft 1¼ in)

DIMENSIONS, INTERNAL:
Passenger pod:
Length, floor level	1·83 m (6 ft 0 in)
Width, floor level	1·25 m (4 ft 1¼ in)
Headroom	1·40 m (4 ft 7 in)

WEIGHTS:
Operating weight, empty:	
Stripped	1,950 kg (4,300 lb)
Cargo/platform	2,085 kg (4,597 lb)
Cargo/hook	2,050 kg (4,519 lb)
Passenger	2,100 kg (4,630 lb)
Agricultural	2,216 kg (4,885 lb)
Fuel weight: Transport	360 kg (794 lb)
Other versions	100 kg (220 lb)
Payload: Transport	900 kg (1,985 lb)
Agricultural duster	1,065 kg (2,348 lb)
Agricultural sprayer	900 kg (1,985 lb)
With cargo platform	1,065 kg (2,348 lb)
Flying crane	1,100 kg (2,425 lb)
Normal T-O weight: Transport	3,076 kg (6,780 lb)
Agricultural	2,980 kg (6,570 lb)
Max T-O weight: all versions	3,250 kg (7,165 lb)

PERFORMANCE (at max T-O weight):
Max level speed	91 knots (170 km/h; 105 mph)
Max cruising speed	81 knots (150 km/h; 93 mph)
Econ cruising speed	49-59 knots (90-110 km/h; 56-68 mph)
Agricultural operating speed range	16-62 knots (30-115 km/h; 19-71 mph)
Service ceiling	3,000 m (9,840 ft)
Service ceiling, one engine out	500 m (1,640 ft)
Hovering ceiling IGE at AUW of 3,000 kg (6,615 lb)	1,300 m (4,265 ft)
Hovering ceiling OGE at AUW of 3,000 kg (6,615 lb)	800 m (2,625 ft)
Range with 7 passengers, 30 min fuel reserves	215 nm (400 km; 248 miles)
Max range with auxiliary tanks	647 nm (1,200 km; 745 miles)
Endurance at econ cruising speed	3 h 42 min

MiG

GENERAL DESIGNER IN CHARGE OF BUREAU: Rostislav A. Belyakov

Colonel-General Artem I. Mikoyan, who died on 9 December 1970 at the age of 65, was head of the design bureau responsible for the MiG series of fighter aircraft. With Mikhail I. Gurevich, a mathematician, he collaborated in the design of the first really-modern Soviet jetfighter, the MiG-15, which began to appear in squadron service in numbers in 1949.

The MiG-17, a progressive development of the MiG-15, appeared in Soviet squadrons in 1953 or 1954, and was followed into service by the supersonic MiG-19, which appeared in 1955 and has been manufactured also in large numbers in China (which see).

All available details of aircraft designed by the Mikoyan bureau which are currently in production or known to be under development follow:

'Fishbed-H' reconnaissance version of MiG-21, with underbelly sensor pack, underwing fuel tanks and wingtip ECM (Flug Revue)

MIKOYAN MiG-21
NATO reporting names: Fishbed and Mongol

The MiG-21 air superiority fighter was developed on the basis of experience of jet-to-jet combat between MiG-15s and US aircraft during the war in Korea. The emphasis was placed on good transonic and supersonic handling, high rate of climb, small size and light weight, using a turbojet engine of medium power, in contrast with the heavier and much more powerful Sukhoi Su-7 and Su-9 fighters that were developed simultaneously. The first versions of the MiG-21 were, therefore, day fighters of limited range, with comparatively light armament and limited avionics. Subsequent development of the type has been aimed primarily at improvements in range, weapons and all-weather capability, and the MiG-21 has become the most widely-used fighter in the world, as well as forming for many years the backbone of Soviet tactical air power.

The E-5 aerodynamic prototype of the MiG-21 flew for the first time on 16 June 1956, and made its public debut during the flypast in the Soviet Aviation Day display at Tushino Airport, Moscow, on 24 June. The initial production version (NATO 'Fishbed-A') was built in only limited numbers, with a Tumansky R-11 turbojet engine rated at 38·25 kN (8,600 lb st) dry and 50 kN (11,240 lb st) with afterburning, and with an armament of two 30 mm NR-30 cannon. Meanwhile, the Soviet Union had been developing a small infra-red homing air-to-air missile, designated K-13 (NATO 'Atoll') and generally similar to the US AIM-9B Sidewinder 1A. Underwing pylons for two K-13s were fitted on the MiG-21F, the suffix 'F' standing for Forsirovanny (boosted) and indicating that this model also had a slightly more powerful turbojet. To save weight and provide room for avionics associated with the missiles, the port NR-30 cannon was removed and its blast-tube fairing on the lower fuselage was blanked off. Further details of this and subsequent operational versions of the MiG-21 are as follows:

MiG-21F (Fishbed-C). First major production version, built also in Czechoslovakia. Short-range clear-weather fighter, with radar ranging equipment and a Tumansky R-11 turbojet rated at 42·25 kN (9,500 lb st) dry and 56·4 kN (12,676 lb st) with afterburning (designation of engine given in Soviet press statements as TDR Mk R37F). Two underwing pylons for UV-16-57 pods, each containing sixteen 57 mm rockets, or K-13 air-to-air missiles, and one NR-30 cannon in starboard side of fuselage (one each side on early aircraft and on the ten supplied to India). Internal fuel capacity of 2,340 litres (515 Imp gallons), plus underfuselage pylon for external fuel tank of 490 litres (108 Imp gallons) capacity. Small nose air intake of approximately 69 cm (27 in) diameter, with small movable three-shock centrebody housing the radar ranging equipment. Undernose pitot boom, which folds upward on the ground to reduce risk of ground personnel walking into it. Transparent blister cockpit canopy which hinges upward about base of integral flat bulletproof windscreen. Transparent rear-view panel (not on aircraft built in Czechoslovakia) aft of canopy at front of shallow dorsal spine fairing. Large blade antenna at rear of this panel, with small secondary antenna midway along spine. Fowler-type flap between fuselage and aileron on each trailing-edge, with fairing plate under wing at outer extremity. Small forward-hinged airbrake under fuselage, forward of ventral fin; two further forward-hinged airbrakes, on each side of underfuselage in line with wing-root leading-edges, integral with part of cannon fairings. Brake-parachute housed inside small door on port underside of rear fuselage, with cable attachment near rear part of ventral fin. Semi-encapsulated escape system, in which canopy is ejected with seat, forming shield to protect pilot from slipstream, until the seat has been slowed by its drogue chute. Leading-edge of fin extended forward on all but early aircraft, to increase chord.

MiG-21PF (Fishbed-D). Basic model of second series of operational versions with forward fuselage of less-tapered form. Intake enlarged to diameter of approximately 91 cm (36 in) and housing larger centrebody for R1L search/track radar (NATO 'Spin Scan A') to enable all-weather capability (designation suffix letter 'P', standing for *Perekhvatchik,* is applied to aircraft adapted for all-weather interception from an earlier designed role). Remainder of airframe generally similar to that of MiG-21F, but pitot boom repositioned above air intake; cannon armament and fairings deleted, permitting simplified design for forward airbrakes; larger main wheels and tyres, requiring enlarged blister fairing on each side of fuselage, over wing, to accommodate wheel in retracted position; dorsal spine fairing widened and deepened aft of canopy, to reduce drag and house additional fuel tankage, and rear-view panel deleted; primary blade antenna repositioned to mid-spine and secondary antenna deleted. Uprated R-11 turbojet, giving 58·4 kN (13,120 lb st) with afterburning. Internal fuel capacity increased to 2,850 litres (627 Imp gallons) in seven fuselage tanks. Late production aircraft have attachments for a rocket-assisted take-off unit (RATOG) aft of each main landing gear bay, and provision for a flap-blowing system known as *Sduva Pogranichnovo Sloya* (SPS), which reduces the normal landing speed by some 22 knots (40 km/h; 25 mph). Flaps are larger than original Fowler type, do not move aft, and lack outboard fairing plates. Prototype shown at Tushino in 1961 had dummy metal centrebody. Production aircraft in service with many air forces.

Fishbed-E. Basically similar to 'Fishbed-C' with broad-chord vertical tail surfaces. Parachute-brake repositioned into acorn fairing, made up of clamshell doors, at base of rudder, above jet nozzle. Provision for GP-9 underbelly pack, housing GSh-23 twin-barrel 23 mm gun, in place of centreline pylon, with associated predictor sight and electrical ranging system. Identified in 1964.

MiG-21FL. Export version of late-model MiG-21PF series, with broad-chord vertical tail surfaces and parachute-brake housing at base of rudder but no provision for SPS or RATOG. About 200 were initially assembled and later built under licence in India by Hindustan Aeronautics Ltd (which see), with the IAF designation Type 77. R-11-300 turbojet rated at 38·25 kN (8,598 lb st) dry and 60·8 kN (13,668 lb) with afterburning. Suffix letter 'L' (*Lokator*) indicates the installation of Type R2L ('Spin Scan B') search/track radar. Can be fitted with GP-9 underbelly gun pack. Identified in 1966.

MiG-21PFS or MiG-21PF(SPS). Similar to 'Fishbed-D', but with SPS as standard production installation.

MiG-21PFM (Fishbed-F). Successor to interim MiG-21PFS, embodying all the improvements introduced progressively on the PF and PFS, the suffix letter 'M' indicating an exportable version of an existing design. Leading-edge of fin extended forward a further 45 cm (18 in). Small dorsal fin fillet eliminated. Additional refinements, including sideways-hinged (to starboard) canopy and conventional windscreen quarter-lights; simple ejection seat instead of semi-encapsulated type; and large dielectric portion at tip of tail-fin. R2L radar reported to have lock-on range of under 7 nm (13 km; 8 miles) and to be ineffective at heights below about 915 m (3,000 ft) because of ground 'clutter'. Max permissible speed at low altitude is reported to be 593 knots (1,100 km/h; 683 mph). Built also in Czechoslovakia.

MiG-21PFMA (NATO 'Fishbed-J') with four 'Atoll' missiles under its wings

MiG-21PFMA (Fishbed-J). Multi-role version. Basically similar to MiG-21PFM but with deeper dorsal fairing containing fuel tankage above fuselage, giving straight line from top of canopy to fin. Improved radar (NATO 'Jay Bird'). Pitot tube remains above air intake but is offset to starboard. Provision for GP-9 underbelly gun pack as alternative to centreline fuel tank. Four underwing pylons, instead of former two, for a variety of ground attack weapons and stores, as alternative or supplementary to two or four air-to-air missiles. Latter can include radar-homing 'Advanced Atoll' as well as infra-red K-13A 'Atoll'. Able to carry two underwing tanks in addition to standard underbelly tank, offsetting reduced internal fuel capacity of 2,600 litres (572 Imp gallons). Zero-zero ejection seat. Small boat-shape fairing with angle-of-attack indicator on port side of nose. Later production aircraft can have the GSh-23 gun installed inside the fuselage, with a shallow underbelly fairing for the twin barrels and splayed cartridge-ejection chutes to clear each side of centreline store.

MiG-21R. Generally similar to MiG-21PFMA, but belly gun replaced by a pack of three reconnaissance cameras mounted on a side-hinged (to starboard) door which protrudes from underfuselage, immediately aft of nosewheel leg. First identified in service with Egyptian Air Force in 1980.

MiG-21M. Generally similar to MiG-21PFMA with internal GSh-23 gun pack. R-11F2S-300 engine. Has superseded MiG-21FL on Hindustan Aeronautics production line in India, with IAF designation Type 88. First Indian-built MiG-21M was handed over officially to IAF on 14 February 1973.

MiG-21R (Fishbed-H). Tactical reconnaissance version, basically similar to MiG-21PFMA. Equipment includes an external pod for forward-facing or oblique cameras, infra-red sensors or ECM devices, and fuel, on fuselage centreline pylon. Suppressed antenna at mid-fuselage and optional ECM equipment in wingtip fairings.

MiG-21MF (Fishbed-J). Generally similar to MiG-21PFMA but re-engined with a Tumansky R-13-300 turbojet, lighter in weight and with higher performance ratings. Small rearview mirror above cockpit canopy. Debris deflector beneath each suction relief door forward of wing root. Entered service with Soviet Air Force in 1970.

MiG-21RF (Fishbed-H). Tactical reconnaissance version of MiG-21MF. Equipment as for MiG-21R.

MiG-21SMT (Fishbed-K). Similar to MiG-21MF, except for having deep dorsal spine extended rearward as

far as parachute-brake housing, to provide maximum possible fuel tankage and optimum aerodynamic form. Able to carry ECM equipment in small removable wingtip pods. Deliveries to Warsaw Pact air forces reported to have begun in 1971. Like the MiG-21PFMA and MiG-21MF, this version can carry K-13A 'Atoll' infra-red missiles and/or radar-homing 'Advanced Atolls'.

MiG-21bis (Fishbed-L). Third-generation multi-role air combat/ground attack version, with updated avionics and generally improved construction standards. Wider and deeper dorsal fairing. Max fuel capacity of seven internal self-sealing tanks 2,900 litres (638 Imp gallons).

MiG-21bis (Fishbed-N). Advanced version of 'Fishbed-L' with Tumansky R-25 turbojet engine, rated at 73·6 kN (16,535 lb st) with afterburning. Further improvement of avionics indicated by 'bow and arrow' antenna under nose. Radar detection range believed to be 16 nm (30 km; 18·5 miles). Standard equipment in Soviet Air Force for several years. Empty weight reported to be 5,200 kg (11,465 lb), normal T-O weight 7,960 kg (17,550 lb). Rate of climb at AUW of 6,800 kg (15,000 lb), with 50% fuel and two 'Atoll' missiles, is reported to be 17,700 m (58,000 ft)/min.

MiG-21U (Mongol). Two-seat training versions. Initial version, 'Mongol-A', is generally similar to the MiG-21F but has two cockpits in tandem with sideways-hinged (to starboard) double canopy, larger main wheels and tyres of MiG-21PF, one-piece forward airbrake, and pitot boom repositioned above intake. Cannon armament is deleted. Later models, 'Mongol-B', have the broader-chord vertical tail surfaces and under-rudder brake-parachute housing of the later operational variants, with a deeper dorsal spine and no dorsal fin fillet.

MiG-21US (Mongol-B). Similar to later MiG-21U but with provision for SPS flap-blowing, and retractable periscope for instructor in rear seat.

MiG-21UM (Mongol-B). Two-seat trainer counterpart of MiG-21MF with R-13 turbojet and four underwing stores pylons.

Alternative designations, allocated by the Soviet authorities to MiG-21s used to set up FAI-recognised international records, are as follows:

E-33. This designation has been applied to MiG-21U 'Mongol' trainers used to establish women's records. Those confirmed by the FAI include an altitude of 24,336 m (79,842 ft) set up by Natalya Prokhanova on 22 May 1965, which has not been beaten.

E-66. Aircraft of basic MiG-21F series, used by Col

Mikoyan MiG-21SMT ('Fishbed-K') single-seat multi-role fighter (*Pilot Press*)

MiG-21bis multi-role fighter (NATO 'Fishbed-N')

MiG-21R of Egyptian Air Force, with belly reconnaissance pack (*Denis Hughes*)

Two-seat training version of the MiG-21, known as 'Mongol-B', in Egyptian Air Force service *(Denis Hughes)*

Georgi Mossolov to set up a world absolute speed record (since beaten) of 1,288·6 knots (2,388 km/h; 1,484 mph) over a 15/25 km course on 31 October 1959. Engine described as a 58·35 kN (13,120 lb st) Type TDR Mk R37F.

E-66A. Variant of E-66 used by Mossolov to set a world height record (since beaten) of 34,714 m (113,892 ft) on 28 April 1961, from an aerodrome near Moscow. Powered additionally by a 29·4 kN (6,615 lb st) GRD Mk U2 rocket engine in underbelly pack, exhausting between twin ventral fins. Other changes compared with then-standard operational model included a widened dorsal spine and repositioned blade antenna, as standardised for the MiG-21PF, and a blister fairing above the nose.

E-66B. Used by Svetlana Savitskaya to set four women's time-to-height records on 15 November 1974, from an aerodrome near Moscow. Described as having one 68·7 kN (15,432 lb st) PDM engine (presumably afterburning turbojet) and two 22·6 kN (5,070 lb st) TTPDs (possibly assisted take-off rockets). Times recorded were 41·2 s to 3,000 m, 1 min 0·1 s to 6,000 m, 1 min 21 s to 9,000 m, and 1 min 59·3 s to 12,000 m.

E-76. Designation allocated to apparently-standard MiG-21PFs used by Soviet women pilots to establish international records. Those confirmed by the FAI and still unbeaten are for a speed of 485·78 knots (900·267 km/h; 559·40 mph) over a 2,000 km closed circuit by Yevgenia Martova on 11 October 1966; and a speed of 1,148·7 knots (2,128·7 km/h; 1,322·7 mph) over a 100 km closed circuit by the same pilot on 18 February 1967.

There is reason to believe that the similar designations E-74, E-77 and E-88 apply to versions of the export MiG-21F, MiG-21FL and MiG-21M respectively.

About 1,300 of the 4,350 aircraft estimated to equip Soviet tactical air forces are MiG-21s, including 300 of the reconnaissance versions ('Fishbed-H'). In addition, MiG-21s have been supplied to the Afghan, Algerian, Angolan, Bangladesh, Bulgarian, Chinese, Cuban, Czechoslovak, Egyptian, Ethiopian, Finnish, East German, Hungarian, Indian, Indonesian, Iraqi, North Korean, Laotian, Malagasy, Mozambique, Nigerian, Polish, Romanian, Somali, Sudanese, Syrian, Tanzanian, Viet-Namese, Yemen Arab Republic, People's Democratic Republic of Yemen, Yugoslav and Zambian air forces.

A version of the MiG-21 has been built in China under the designation F-7.

The Chinese industry is assisting with spares and overhaul services for the MiG-21s, MiG-17s and MiG-19s operated by Egypt. Ferranti and Smiths Industries of the UK are collaborating in a scheme to provide the Egyptian MiG-21s with a digital inertial navigation, weapon aiming and head-up display system (Hudwac).

The following details refer to the MiG-21MF ('Fishbed-J'):

TYPE: Single-seat multi-role fighter.

WINGS: Cantilever mid-wing monoplane of clipped-delta planform, with slight anhedral from roots. No leading-edge camber. Sweepback approximately 57°. Small pointed fairing on each side of fuselage forward of wing-root leading-edge. Small boundary-layer fence above each wing near tip. All-metal construction. Inset ailerons, actuated hydraulically. Large 'blown' plain trailing-edge flaps, actuated hydraulically.

FUSELAGE: Circular-section all-metal semi-monocoque structure. Ram-air intake in nose, with three-position movable centrebody. Large dorsal spine fairing along top of fuselage from canopy to fin. Forward-hinged door-type airbrake on each side of underfuselage below wing leading-edge. A further forward-hinged airbrake under fuselage forward of ventral fin. All airbrakes actuated hydraulically. Blister fairings above and below wing on each side to accommodate main wheels when retracted.

TAIL UNIT: Cantilever all-metal structure, with all surfaces sharply swept. Conventional fin and hydraulically-powered rudder. Hydraulically-actuated one-piece all-moving horizontal surface, with two gearing ratios for use at varying combinations of altitude and airspeed. Tailplane trim switch on control column. No trim tabs. Single large ventral fin.

LANDING GEAR: Hydraulically-retractable tricycle type, with single wheel on each unit; all units housed in fuselage when retracted. Forward-retracting non-steerable nosewheel unit; inward-retracting main wheels which turn to stow vertically inside fuselage. Tyres on main wheels inflated to approximately 7·93 bars (115 lb/sq in), ruling out normal operation from grass runways.

Pneumatic braking on all three wheels, supplied by compressed-air bottles. Steering by differential main-wheel braking. Wheel doors remain open when legs are extended. Brake parachute housed inside acorn fairing at base of rudder.

POWER PLANT: One Tumansky R-13-300 turbojet engine, rated at 50 kN (11,240 lb st) dry and 64·73 kN (14,550 lb st) with afterburning. Fuel tanks in fuselage, with total capacity of 2,600 litres (572 Imp gallons), of which approx 1,800 litres (396 Imp gallons) are usable within CG limits at low speed. Provision for carrying one finned external fuel tank, capacity 490 litres (108 Imp gallons), on underfuselage pylon and two similar drop-tanks on outboard underwing pylons. Two jettisonable solid-propellant JATO rockets can be fitted under rear fuselage, aft of wheel doors.

ACCOMMODATION: Pilot only, on ejection seat with spring-loaded arm at top which ensures that seat cannot be operated unless hood is closed. Canopy is sideways-hinged, to starboard, and is surmounted by a small rearview mirror. Flat bullet-proof windscreen. Cabin air-conditioned. Armour plating forward and aft of cockpit.

SYSTEMS: Duplicated hydraulic system, supplied by engine-driven pump, with backup by battery-powered electric pump, and emergency electric tailplane trim and manual operation of flying controls. Autostabilisation in pitch and roll only.

AVIONICS AND EQUIPMENT: Search and track radar (NATO 'Jay Bird') in intake centrebody, with search range of approx 15 nm (29 km; 18 miles). Other standard avionics include VOR/ADF and warning radar with an indicator marked in 45° sectors in front of and behind the aircraft. Gyro gunsight is reported to topple at 2·75*g*. Automatic ranging can be fed into gunsight. Full blind-flying instrumentation, with attitude and heading indicators driven by remote central gyro platform.

ARMAMENT: One twin-barrel 23 mm GSh-23 gun, with 200 rounds, in belly pack. Four underwing pylons for weapons or drop-tanks. Typical loads for interceptor role include two K-13A 'Atoll' air-to-air missiles on inner pylons and two radar-homing 'Advanced Atolls' or two UV-16-57 rocket packs (each sixteen 57 mm rockets) on outer pylons; four K-13As 'Advanced Atolls'; or two drop-tanks and two K-13As or 'Advanced Atolls'. Typical loads for ground attack role are four UV-16-57 rocket packs; two 500 kg and two 250 kg bombs; or four S-24 240 mm air-to-surface missiles.

DIMENSIONS, EXTERNAL:
Wing span	7·15 m (23 ft 5½ in)
Length, incl pitot boom	15·76 m (51 ft 8½ in)
Length, excl pitot boom and intake centrebody	13·46 m (44 ft 2 in)
Height overall	4·10 m (13 ft 5½ in)
Wheel track	2·69 m (8 ft 10 in)

AREA:
Wings, gross	23 m² (247 sq ft)

WEIGHTS:
T-O weight:
with four K-13A missiles	8,200 kg (18,078 lb)
with two K-13A missiles and two 108 Imp gallon drop-tanks	8,950 kg (19,730 lb)
with two K-13As and three drop-tanks	9,400 kg (20,725 lb)

PERFORMANCE:
Max level speed above 11,000 m (36,000 ft)	
	Mach 2·1 (1,203 knots; 2,230 km/h; 1,385 mph)
Max level speed at low altitude	
	Mach 1·06 (701 knots; 1,300 km/h; 807 mph)
Landing speed	146 knots (270 km/h; 168 mph)
Design ceiling	18,000 m (59,050 ft)
Practical ceiling	about 15,250 m (50,000 ft)
T-O run at normal AUW	800 m (2,625 ft)
Landing run	550 m (1,805 ft)

Two views of the MiG-23MF 'Flogger-B' single-seat variable-geometry air combat fighter of the Soviet Air Force. Note the large splitter plates forward of variable-geometry intakes on this version, on the two-seat MiG-23U and on all export models of this family of fighters. Stripes on the stores under the wings of the aircraft in the lower picture imply that they are missile simulators

Range, internal fuel only
            593 nm (1,100 km; 683 miles)
Ferry range, with three external tanks
            971 nm (1,800 km; 1,118 miles)

MIKOYAN MiG-23
NATO reporting names: Flogger-A, B, C, E, F and G

The prototype of this variable-geometry air combat fighter was first displayed in public during the 1967 Aviation Day flypast at Domodedovo Airport, Moscow. Initial deliveries of pre-series aircraft to the Soviet Air Force were made in 1970, but deployment of the MiG-23 in large numbers did not begin until 1973. Two Soviet fighter regiments, with a total of about 75 aircraft, were based in East Germany in 1973/74, and deliveries to the Soviet Air Force of all versions of the MiG-23 and the related MiG-27 were estimated to total more than 1,850 aircraft by the Spring of 1980. Others have been supplied to the Bulgarian, Czechoslovak, East German, Hungarian and Polish air forces. Export versions, with a lower equipment standard, are operated by the Algerian, Cuban, Egyptian, Ethiopian, Iraqi, Libyan and Syrian air forces.

US press reports suggest that two former Egyptian-operated MiG-23s are being flown by the US Air Force in the USA. At least one other is believed to have been presented to China.

There are six versions of the MiG-23 of which details can be published in 1980:

MiG-23 (Flogger-A). Prototype shown at Domodedovo on 9 July 1967. Illustrated in 1973-74 and preceding editions of *Jane's*. It is now known that one or two development squadrons of 'Flogger-As' entered service with the Soviet Air Force. Experience with these dictated almost total redesign of the major production versions which followed.

MiG-23MF (Flogger-B). Single-seat air combat fighter which is rapidly displacing the MiG-21 as the primary air-to-air tactical aircraft of the Soviet Air Forces, deployed in both forward areas and the interior of the USSR. Design changes compared with prototype include movement further rearward of all tail surfaces except ventral fin, giving much increased gap between wing and tailplane; a much larger dorsal fin; and the introduction of fixed inboard wing leading-edges. The US *Military Posture* statement for FY 1979 described 'Flogger-B' as "the first Soviet aircraft with a demonstrated ability to track and engage targets flying below its own altitude". Operated also by air forces of Czechoslovakia, East Germany and Hungary.

MiG-23U (Flogger-C). Tandem two-seat version suitable for both operational training and combat use. Individual canopy over each seat. Rear seat slightly higher than forward seat, with retractable periscopic sight for occupant. Dorsal fairing of increased depth aft of rear canopy. Otherwise identical to early MiG-23MF (with R-27 engine). In service with Soviet Air Force and air forces of other countries, including Cuba, Czechoslovakia and Egypt.

MiG-23 (Flogger-E). Export version of 'Flogger-B'. Generally similar to Soviet Air Force version, but equipped to a lower standard. Smaller radar (NATO 'Jay Bird': search range 15 nm; 29 km; 18 miles, tracking range 10 nm; 19 km; 12 miles) in shorter nose radome. No under-nose laser rangefinder or Doppler navigation equipment. Armed with 'Atoll' missiles and GSh-23 gun.

MiG-23BM (Flogger-F). Export counterpart of Soviet Air Force's MiG-27 ('Flogger-D') ground attack/interdictor version. Has the nose shape, raised seat, cockpit external armour plate and larger, low-pressure tyres of MiG-27, but retains the power plant, variable-geometry intakes and GSh-23 twin-barrel gun of the MiG-23MF interceptor. Operated by Algerian, Bulgarian, Cuban, Czechoslovak, Egyptian, Ethiopian, Iraqi, Libyan, Polish and Syrian Air Forces.

MiG-23 (Flogger-G). First identified when six aircraft from the air base of Kubinka made goodwill visits to Finland and France in the Summer of 1978. Although basically similar to 'Flogger-B', these aircraft had a much smaller dorsal fin. Absence of operational equipment, such as underwing pylons and infra-red and tracking pods, suggested that only a few aircraft had been modified to this standard for improved aerobatic capability as a display team. 'Flogger-G' has, however, been seen with an under-nose sensor pod of new design, and is almost certainly an operational variant.

Early production aircraft were powered by a Tumansky R-27 turbofan engine, rated at 68·65 kN (15,430 lb st) dry and 100·0 kN (22,485 lb st) with afterburning. This power plant continues in use in the two-seat MiG-23U, but the current MiG-23MF and MiG-27 have a Tumansky R-29B turbojet.

The following description refers specifically to the single-seat MiG-23MF ('Flogger-B') as supplied to the Soviet Air Force:

TYPE: Single-seat variable-geometry air combat fighter.

WINGS: Cantilever shoulder wing. Sweepback of main panels variable in flight or on the ground by manual control, reportedly at 16°, 45° or 72°. Fixed triangular inboard panels, with leading-edges swept at approximately 72°. Full-span trailing-edge single-slotted flaps, each in three sections, permitting independent actuation of outboard sections when wings are fully swept. Top-surface spoilers/lift dumpers forward of flaps, for differential operation in conjunction with horizontal tail surfaces, and for collective operation for improved runway adherence and braking after touchdown. Leading-edge flap on outboard two-thirds of each main (variable-geometry) panel.

FUSELAGE: Conventional semi-monocoque structure of basic circular section; flattened on each side of cockpit, forward of lateral air intake trunks which blend into circular shape of rear fuselage. Large flat boundary layer splitter plate forms inboard face of each intake. Two small rectangular 'blow-in' air intakes in each trunk, under inboard wing leading-edge. Perforations under rear fuselage, aft of main-wheel bays, are pressure-relief vents. Four door-type airbrakes, mounted two on each side of rear fuselage.

TAIL UNIT: All-moving horizontal surfaces, swept back at approximately 57° on leading-edge, operate both differentially and symmetrically to provide aileron and elevator function respectively. Conventional fin, swept back at approximately 65° on leading-edge, with inset rudder. Large dorsal fin. No tabs. Large ventral fin in

The two-seat MiG-23U, identical to the MiG-23MF except for second cockpit *(Flug Revue)*

'Flogger-E', the export version of 'Flogger-B', with smaller radome and other changes

Top to bottom: Side views of the 'Flogger-B', 'Flogger-C', 'Flogger-D' and 'Flogger-E' variants of the MiG-23/27 series *(Pilot Press)*

MiG-23 with modified tail ('Flogger-G') photographed during a goodwill visit to France in 1978 *(Colair)*

A shorter dorsal fin identifies the 'Flogger-G' version of the MiG-23 *(Pilot Press)*

two portions. Lower portion is hinged to fold to starboard when landing gear is extended, to increase ground clearance.

LANDING GEAR: Retractable tricycle type, with single wheel on each main unit and steerable twin-wheel nose unit. Main units retract inward into rear of air intake trunks. Main fairings to enclose these units are attached to legs. Small inboard fairing for each wheel bay hinged to fuselage belly. Nose unit, fitted with small mudguard, retracts rearward. Brake parachute housed in cylindrical fairing at base of rudder.

POWER PLANT: One Tumansky R-29B turbojet engine, rated at 78·45 kN (17,635 lb st) dry and 112·8 kN (25,350 lb st) with max afterburning. Max internal fuel capacity 5,750 litres (1,265 Imp gallons). Variable-geometry air intakes and variable nozzle. Provision for carrying external fuel tank, capacity 800 litres (176 Imp gallons), on underfuselage centreline pylon.

ACCOMMODATION: Single seat in air-conditioned cockpit, under small rearward-hinged canopy.

AVIONICS AND EQUIPMENT: J-band radar dish (NATO 'High Lark': search range 46 nm; 85 km; 53 miles, tracking range 29 nm; 54 km; 34 miles) behind dielectric nosecone. ILS antenna (NATO 'Swift Rod') under radome; yaw sensor above fuselage forward of windscreen; angle of attack sensor on port side. Small cylindrical fairings forward of starboard underwing pylon and above rudder are believed to contain ECM equipment. Undernose laser rangefinder, Sirena 3 radar warning system, and Doppler equipment, standard on Soviet Air Force version. Dr Robert C. Seamans, then US Secretary of the Air Force, stated his belief in early 1973 that the contemporary radar and missile systems were comparable with those of the US Air Force's F-4 Phantom II. Retractable landing light under nose, aft of radome.

ARMAMENT: One 23 mm GSh-23 twin-barrel gun in fuselage belly pack, with large flash eliminator around muzzles. One pylon under centre-fuselage, one under each engine air intake duct, and one under each fixed inboard wing panel, for rocket packs, air-to-air missiles (NATO 'Apex' and 'Aphid') or other external stores.

DIMENSIONS, EXTERNAL (estimated):
Wing span:
  fully spread   14·25 m (46 ft 9 in)
  fully swept   8·17 m (26 ft 9½ in)
  Length overall   16·80 m (55 ft 1½ in)
WEIGHT (estimated):
  T-O weight   12,700-15,000 kg (28,000-33,050 lb)
PERFORMANCE (estimated):
  Max level speed at height with external stores
                              Mach 2·3
  Max level speed at S/L   Mach 1·1
  Service ceiling   18,600 m (61,000 ft)
  T-O and landing run   900 m (2,950 ft)
  Combat radius   520 nm (960 km; 600 miles)

MIKOYAN MiG-27

NATO reporting name: Flogger-D

Although the single-seat ground attack aircraft known to NATO as 'Flogger-D' has many airframe features in common with the MiG-23, it differs in important respects and is designated MiG-27. Use of fixed air intakes and a fixed nozzle is consistent with the primary requirement of high subsonic speed at low altitude.

The forward portion of the fuselage is completely redesigned by comparison with the MiG-23. Instead of an ogival radome, 'Flogger-D' has a nose that is sharply-tapered in side elevation, with a small sloping window covering a laser rangefinder and marked target seeker, and additional armour on the flat sides of the cockpit. The seat and canopy are raised to improve the view from the cockpit. A six-barrel 23 mm Gatling-type underbelly gun replaces the GSh-23 of the interceptor, and there is a bomb rack under each side of the rear fuselage in addition to five pylons for external stores, which can include tactical nuclear weapons and, probably, the air-to-surface missile known to NATO as 'Kerry'. There is provision for carrying an external fuel tank for ferry flights under each outer wing, which must be kept in a fully-forward position when the tank is in place. Equipment includes an ECM antenna above the port glove pylon.

The somewhat similar aircraft known to NATO as 'Flogger-F' is a member of the MiG-23 series, with variable-geometry intakes and a GSh-23 twin-barrel gun,

although having the nose-shape, raised seat and larger, low-pressure tyres of 'Flogger-D'. It represents the export counterpart of 'Flogger-D', with lower standards of equipment and performance, and is described under the MiG-23 entry.

The following data are estimated for the MiG-27 as operated by the Soviet and East German Air Forces.

POWER PLANT: Generally similar to MiG-23S. Provision for three external tanks, each of 800 litres (176 Imp gallons) capacity, under fuselage and each outer wing.

DIMENSIONS, EXTERNAL: As MiG-23, plus:
  Wing aspect ratio (spread)   7·45
  Tailplane span   5·75 m (18 ft 10¼ in)
AREAS:
  Wings, gross (spread)   27·26 m² (293·4 sq ft)
  Horizontal tail surfaces   6·88 m² (74·06 sq ft)
WEIGHTS:
  Max weapon load   3,000 kg (6,610 lb)
  Max T-O weight, 'clean'   15,500 kg (34,170 lb)
  Max T-O weight   20,100 kg (44,310 lb)
PERFORMANCE (estimated):
  Max level speed at height   Mach 1·75
  Max level speed at S/L   Mach 0·95
  T-O to 15 m (50 ft) at AUW of 15,700 kg (34,600 lb)
                         800 m (2,625 ft)
  Max ferry range with three external tanks
                1,350 nm (2,500 km; 1,550 miles)

MIKOYAN MiG-25 (E-266)

NATO reporting name: Foxbat

Development of the MiG-25 was initiated as a high-priority programme to counter the threat of the US Air Force's Mach 3 B-70 strategic bomber, for which North American Aviation Inc was chosen as prime contractor in December 1957. When the B-70 was cut back to a research project by President Kennedy, in March 1961, work on the MiG-25 continued, with increasing emphasis on the reconnaissance potential of the design.

First indication that the prototype had flown came with a Soviet claim, in April 1965, that a twin-engined aircraft designated E-266 had set a 1,000 km closed-circuit speed record of 1,251·9 knots (2,320 km/h; 1,441·5 mph), carrying a 2,000 kg payload. The attempt was made at a height of 21,000-22,000 m (69,000-72,200 ft) by Alexander Fedotov, who had earlier set a 100 km record in the Mikoyan E-166 research aircraft.

The same pilot set a payload-to-height record of 29,977 m (98,349 ft) with a 2,000 kg payload in the E-266 on 5 October 1967, after a rocket-assisted take-off. This qualified also for the record with a 1,000 kg payload. Photographs of the E-266 issued subsequently in the Soviet Union identified it as the twin-finned single-seat fighter of which four examples had taken part in the Domodedovo display in July 1967, and the designation MiG-25 was confirmed later. NATO had, meanwhile, allocated the reporting name 'Foxbat' to the type.

The aircraft's performance in level flight was demonstrated further on 5 October 1967, when M. Komarov set a speed record of 1,608·83 knots (2,981·5 km/h; 1,852·61 mph) over a 500 km closed circuit. On 27 October, P. Ostapenko raised the 1,000 km closed-circuit record to 1,576·00 knots (2,920·67 km/h; 1,814·81 mph) in an E-266, carrying a 2,000 kg payload and qualifying also for records with 1,000 kg payload and no payload. On 8 April 1973, Fedotov achieved a speed of 1,405·741 knots (2,605·1 km/h; 1,618·734 mph) over a 100 km closed circuit. Next, on 25 July 1973, he set an absolute height record by climbing to 36,240 m (118,898 ft) in an E-266.

Three time-to-height records were established by the E-266 on 4 June 1973, when Boris Orlov climbed to 20,000 m in 2 min 49·8 s, and P. Ostapenko climbed to 25,000 m in 3 min 12·6 s and 30,000 m in 4 min 3·86 s. All three records were beaten by the McDonnell Douglas F-15 *Streak Eagle* in January-February 1975; but two of

MiG-27 ('Flogger-D') landing, with wings extended and ventral fin folded *(Flug Revue)*

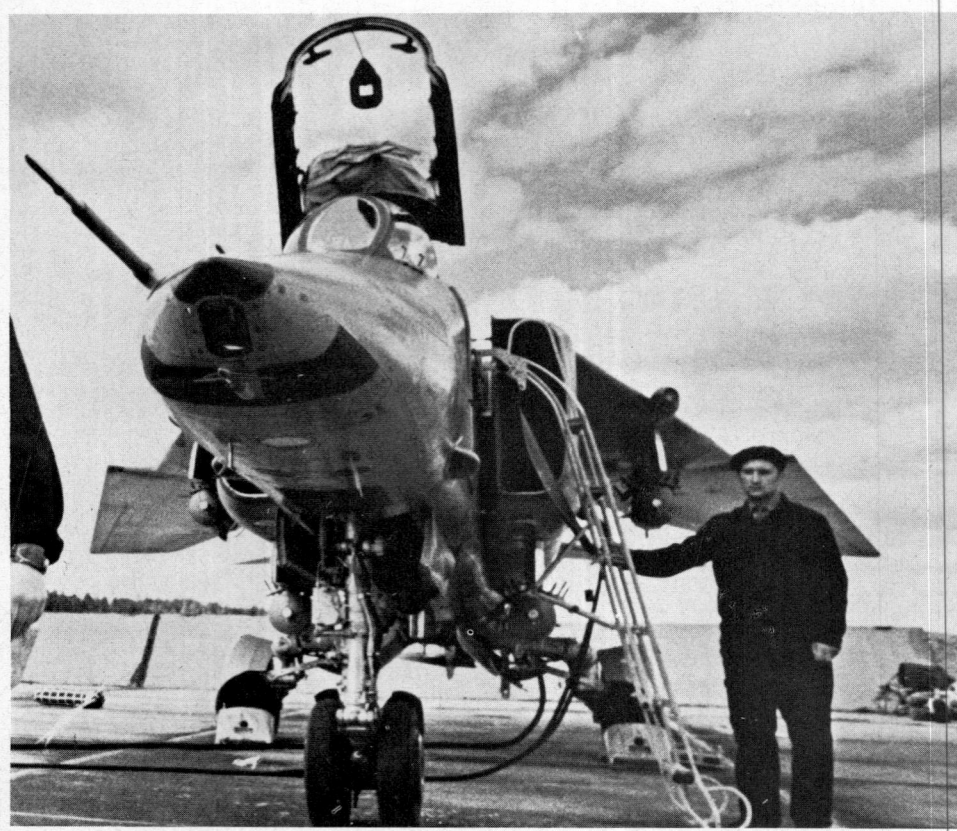

MiG-27 variable-geometry interdictor ('Flogger-D') of the Soviet Air Force. Note the fixed-geometry intakes, laser rangefinder in nose, and dielectric panels *(Tass)*

them were recaptured by an E-266M (with uprated power plant) on 17 May 1975. Fedotov climbed to 25,000 m in 2 min 34·2 s and Ostapenko reached 30,000 m in 3 min 9·85 s. Fedotov also set a new record by climbing to 35,000 m in 4 min 11·7 s.

The current absolute height record was set by Fedotov on 31 August 1977, when he climbed to 37,650 m (123,524 ft) in an E-266M. He had, on 22 July, climbed to 37,080 m (121,654 ft) carrying a 2,000 kg payload, qualifying also for the record with 1,000 kg.

Four MiG-25 reconnaissance aircraft were deployed with Soviet Air Force units in Egypt in the Spring of 1971, having been airlifted to that country in An-22 transports. Between the Autumn of 1971 and the Spring of 1972, these aircraft were despatched in pairs from Cairo West airfield on at least four occasions to carry out high-speed reconnaissance missions off the Israeli coastline or down the full length of the Israeli-occupied Sinai Peninsula. Phantom interceptors sent up by the Israeli defence forces failed to make contact with the MiGs, which remained in Egypt until September 1975. In 1977, MiG-25 reconnaissance aircraft were based in the Soviet Union, at Brieg in Silesia, and in Syria. First foreign operators, in 1979, were the Algerian and Syrian Air Forces.

In early 1973 Dr Robert C. Seamans, then US Secretary of the Air Force, described the MiG-25 as "probably the best interceptor in production in the world today", and added "This Mach 3 aircraft performs both interceptor and reconnaissance missions, can operate at 24,400 m (80,000 ft), and has a highly capable avionics and missile system". In his FY 1975 US Defense Department Report, then-Secretary Schlesinger commented: "Should the Soviet Union develop and deploy an AWACS/'Foxbat' 'look-down, shoot-down' air defence system, we would have to counter it with new penetration devices and techniques such as the cruise missile, bomber defence missiles and improved ECM".

A first opportunity to study the MiG-25 interceptor outside the Soviet Union came when Lt Viktor Belenko defected in one from the Soviet air base of Sikharovka, 200 km (120 miles) from Vladivostok, to Hakodate airport, Japan, on 6 September 1976. Statements attributed to this pilot suggest that more than 400 MiG-25s had been built by that time, and that his particular aircraft left the production line less than three years earlier. Japanese and US military technicians who examined the aircraft reported that the airframe is constructed mainly of steel, with titanium only in places subjected to extreme heating such as the wing leading-edges. The inevitable weight penalty restricts the amount of equipment that can be carried. Belenko said that the aircraft took a considerable time to accelerate to high speeds, which were then difficult to maintain.

Examination of the aircraft is said to have shown that the fuselage weighs about 13,600 kg (30,000 lb) with the wings, tail surfaces and afterburners removed; the fire control system is bulky and lacking in advanced technology, with its very high power (600 kW) devoted to

anti-jamming capability rather than range, and with vacuum tubes rather than solid-state circuitry throughout the avionics; the number of cockpit instruments was described as 50 per cent of those in F-4EJ Phantoms of the JASDF, with a smaller and less versatile weapon sight; and the Machmeter has a 'red-line' limit at Mach 2·8, which almost certainly represents a never-exceed speed when carrying missiles and pylons rather than the maximum speed of which the 'clean' aircraft is capable. Of particular interest is the aircraft's high-quality airborne computer which, in conjunction with a ground-based flight control system, enables the interceptor to be vectored automatically on to its target over long ranges.

There are now five variants of the MiG-25, as follows:

MiG-25 (Foxbat-A). Basic interceptor, with large radar (NATO 'Fox Fire') in nose and armed with four air-to-air missiles on underwing attachments. Slightly reduced wing leading-edge sweep towards tips. CW target illuminating radar in nose of wingtip anti-flutter bodies. In service also in Algeria and Syria.

MiG-25R (Foxbat-B). Basic reconnaissance version, with five camera windows and various flush dielectric panels aft of very small dielectric nosecap for radar. Equipment believed to include Doppler navigation system and side-looking airborne radar (SLAR). No armament. Slightly reduced span. Wing leading-edge sweep constant from root to tip. In service also in Algeria.

MiG-25U (Foxbat-C). Trainer, of which first photographs were published towards the end of 1975. Generally similar to operational versions, but with new nose, containing separate cockpit with individual canopy, forward of standard cockpit and at a lower level. No search radar or reconnaissance sensors in nose. The aircraft designated **E-133** in which Svetlana Savitskaya set a women's world speed record of 1,448·942 knots (2,683·44 km/h; 1,667·412 mph) on 2 June 1975 is believed to have been a MiG-25U. She has since set a women's sustained height record of 21,209·9 m (69,586 ft) in an E-133 on 31 August 1977, and a women's speed record of 1,331·70 knots (2,466·31 km/h; 1,532·49 mph) around a 500 km closed circuit on 21 October 1977.

MiG-25R (Foxbat-D). Generally similar to 'Foxbat-B', but with larger SLAR (side-looking airborne radar) dielectric panel, further aft on starboard side of nose, and no cameras.

E-266M. Designation of experimental aircraft which set three time-to-height records in 1975 and now holds also the absolute height record. Lt Belenko has referred to a developed interceptor in which the airframe has been strengthened to permit supersonic flight near the ground; the engines have been uprated to give 137·3 kN (30,865 lb st) with afterburning; the avionics have been improved; and two fuselage attachments have been added to make possible the carriage of a total of six air-to-air missiles. Installation of a gun is also likely.

In tests against simulated cruise missiles, a MiG-25 flying at 6,000 m (19,685 ft) has detected a target flying below 60 m (200 ft) at a range of 11 nm (20 km; 12·5 miles), fired an unarmed missile against it and achieved a theoretical 'kill'.

The following description of the MiG-25 ('Foxbat-A') interceptor should be regarded as provisional:

TYPE: Single-seat interceptor.

WINGS: Cantilever high-wing monoplane. Anhedral 4° from roots. Sweepback on leading-edge approx 42° inboard, 40° outboard of each outer missile attachment. Wing structure basically of steel, with titanium leading-edge. Upper surface fence in line with each inboard weapon attachment; shorter shallow fence in line with each outer attachment. Long anti-flutter body at each wingtip. Light alloy aileron at centre of each semi-span, with simple light alloy flap on inboard 37% of trailing-edge. No other movable wing surfaces.

FUSELAGE: Basic fuselage is quite slim, but is blended into the rectangular air intake trunks, which have wedge inlets. Inner walls of intakes are curved at top and do not run parallel with outer walls; a hinged panel forms the lower lip of each intake, enabling intake area to be varied electronically. Structure mainly of steel.

TAIL UNIT: Cantilever structure comprising twin outward-canted fins with inset rudders, and all-moving horizontal surfaces. All surfaces sweptback, without

MiG-25 ('Foxbat-A') interceptor, armed with four air-to-air missiles (NATO 'Acrid')

Mikoyan MiG-25 single-seat fighter (NATO 'Foxbat-A'), with additional side view (top) of two-seat MiG-25U
(Pilot Press)

The reconnaissance version of the MiG-25 known to NATO as 'Foxbat-B'. Note the camera-carrying nose and dielectric panels *(Flug Revue)*

Close-up of tandem cockpits in nose of MiG-25U ('Foxbat-C') *(Flug Revue)*

tabs. Main structures of steel, with titanium leading-edges and light alloy rear sections. Two outward-canted ventral fins. Large areas of each main and ventral fin form flush antennae.

LANDING GEAR: Retractable tricycle type. Single wheel, with high-pressure tyre of 1·20 m (47·25 in) diameter, on each forward-retracting main unit. Wheel stows vertically between air intake duct and outer skin of each trunk. Twin-wheel nose unit. Twin brake-chutes in fairing above and between jet nozzles.

POWER PLANT: Two Tumansky R-31 (R-266) single-shaft turbojet engines, each rated at 107·9 kN (24,250 lb st) with afterburning. Water-methanol injection standard. Fuel in two structural tanks in fuselage, between cockpit and engine bay, in saddle tanks around intake ducts, and in integral tank in each wing, filling almost the entire volume inboard of outer fence. Total fuel capacity approx 14,000 kg (30,865 lb).

ACCOMMODATION: Pilot only, on KM-1 zero-height, 80 knot (150 km/h; 93 mph) ejection seat similar to that fitted to some versions of MiG-21. Canopy hinged to open sideways, to starboard.

AVIONICS AND EQUIPMENT: Main fire-control radar (NATO 'Fox Fire': range believed to be 54 nm; 100 km; 62 miles) in nose, forward of electronics compartment housing navigation radar. SRZO-2 IFF and SOD-57M ATC/SIF, with antennae in starboard fin tip. Sirena 3 360° radar warning system with receivers in centre of each wingtip anti-flutter body and starboard fin tip.

Unidentified ECCM, decoys and jammers. RSB-70/RPS HF, RSIU-5 VHF, R-831 UHF communications equipment, SP-50 ILS, and MRP-56P marker beacon receiver. Retractable landing light under front of each intake trunk.

ARMAMENT: Four air-to-air missiles on underwing attach-

ments. These may comprise one infra-red and one radar homing example of the missile known to NATO as 'Acrid' under each wing. More usually, it is believed that one 'Apex' and one 'Aphid' are carried under each wing. Backup optical weapon sight.

DIMENSIONS, EXTERNAL (estimated):

Wing span:		
'Foxbat-A'		13·95 m (45 ft 9 in)
'Foxbat-B'		13·40 m (44 ft 0 in)
Wing aspect ratio		3·3
Length overall		23·82 m (78 ft 1¾ in)
Height overall		6·10 m (20 ft 0¼ in)

AREA:

Wings, gross:	
'Foxbat-A'	56 m² (603 sq ft)

WEIGHTS (estimated):

Basic operating weight, empty:		
'Foxbat-A'	at least	20,000 kg (44,100 lb)
'Foxbat-B'		19,600 kg (43,200 lb)
Max T-O weight:		
'Foxbat-A'		36,200 kg (79,800 lb)
'Foxbat-B'		33,400 kg (73,635 lb)

PERFORMANCE (estimated):

Max level speed at height:	
'Foxbat-B', 'clean'	Mach 3·2
Never-exceed combat speed:	
'Foxbat-A', with missiles	Mach 2·8
Max level speed at low altitude:	
'Foxbat-A'	Mach 0·85
Max rate of climb at S/L:	
'Foxbat-A'	12,480 m (40,950 ft)/min
Time to 11,000 m (36,000 ft) with afterburning:	
'Foxbat-A'	2 min 30 s
Service ceiling:	
'Foxbat-A'	24,400 m (80,000 ft)
T-O run:	
'Foxbat-A'	1,380 m (4,525 ft)
Landing run:	
'Foxbat-A'	2,180 m (7,150 ft)
Normal combat radius:	
'Foxbat-A'	610 nm (1,130 km; 700 miles)
Max combat radius, econ power:	
'Foxbat-A'	700 nm (1,300 km; 805 miles)

NEW MIKOYAN FIGHTER

Inevitably, there have been persistent reports in recent years concerning new fighter designs emanating from the Mikoyan bureau. The accompanying three-view drawing depicts an air superiority fighter in the class of the projected Northrop F-18L which is said to have been at the advanced flight testing stage in Spring 1979. US reports suggest that it is known in Washington as Ram L, having been identified initially on a photograph taken by reconnaissance satellite over Ramenskoye flight test centre in the USSR.

The drawing of this single-seat twin-jet fighter should be regarded as highly provisional. The aircraft's T-O weight is said to be in the 11,340 kg (25,000 lb) class.

Provisional drawing of the single-seat twin-jet fighter said to have been identified by reconnaissance satellite and to be known in Washington as Ram L *(Pilot Press)*

MIL

GENERAL DESIGNER IN CHARGE OF BUREAU: Marat N. Tishchenko

M. L. Mil was connected with Soviet gyroplane and helicopter development from at least 1930. His achievements were recognised by the award of the Order of Lenin on his 60th birthday in November 1969. He died on 31 January 1970.

His original Mi-1, which was designed in 1949, first flown in 1950 and introduced into squadron service in 1951, was the first helicopter to enter series production in the Soviet Union and was also produced in Poland. It was followed by the larger Mi-4 in a number of variants, and these types are still in service, in civil and military forms.

Subsequent products of the bureau that was headed by Mikhail Mil include the Mi-6, a very large passenger and

freight helicopter, the Mi-10 (V-10) and Mi-10K crane versions of the Mi-6, the smaller turbine-powered Mi-2 (V-2) and Mi-8 (V-8) passenger helicopters, the Mi-12 (V-12), which is the largest helicopter yet flown anywhere in the world, the Mi-14 coastal patrol development of the Mi-8, and the Mi-24 military assault helicopter. Aviaexport has sold helicopters of Mil design in 38 countries.

MIL Mi-2 (V-2)

Built exclusively in Poland and described under Polish aircraft industry entry for WSK-PZL Swidnik.

MIL Mi-4
NATO reporting name: Hound

Although Mi-4s have been largely replaced by turbine-powered helicopters in their original transport and anti-submarine roles, they continue in service with

support units. A version first identified in 1977 is shown in an accompanying illustration. The multiple antennae projecting from the front and rear of the cabin, on each side, are communications jammers.

The designations given by NATO to military variants of the Mi-4 may now be listed, as follows:

Hound-A. Basic transport helicopter.

Hound-B. ASW version, with undernose radar, etc.

Hound-C. ECM version, shown in an accompanying illustration.

The Mil Mi-4 was last described in the 1971-72 *Jane's*. About 3,500 were built in 1952-69.

MIL Mi-6
NATO reporting name: Hook

First announced in the Autumn of 1957, the Mi-6 was then the largest helicopter flying anywhere in the world.

Mil Mi-4 helicopter ('Hound-C') fitted with communications jamming equipment

Military version of Mil Mi-6 heavy general-purpose helicopter (*Pilot Press*)

From it were evolved the Mi-10 and Mi-10K flying crane helicopters, and its dynamic components were used in duplicated form on the V-12 (Mi-12).

Layout of the Mi-6 is conventional. Clamshell rear loading doors and folding ramps facilitate the loading of bulky freight and vehicles. Freight can also be carried externally, suspended from a hook on the CG. When the aircraft is operated in this flying crane role, the small wings which normally offload the rotor in flight can be removed, permitting an increase in payload.

The stub-wings are deleted also from the firefighting version. First demonstrated at the 1967 Paris Air Show, this carries several tons of water in tanks inside its cabin and can either spray this slowly from nozzles or dump it through the hoist cutout in its belly.

In setting up 14 FAI-recognised records in Class E1, the Mi-6 has lifted payloads of up to 20,117 kg (44,350 lb). Records still standing in mid-1980 included a 100 km closed-circuit speed record of 183·54 knots (340·15 km/h; 211·36 mph), set up by Boris Galitsky on 26 August 1964. On 15 September 1962 the same pilot, and crew, in an Mi-6 had flown at 162·08 knots (300·377 km/h; 186·64 mph) over a 1,000 km circuit, setting the current records for speed with payload of 1,000 kg and payload of 2,000 kg. On 11 September 1962 Vasily Kolochenko and crew of four averaged 153·44 knots (284·354 km/h; 176·69 mph) over a 1,000 km closed circuit, with a payload of 5,000 kg.

Five Mi-6s are reported to have been built for development testing, followed by an initial pre-series of 30 and subsequent manufacture of some 800 for military and civil use. Six were supplied to the Indonesian Air Force; many others have been delivered to the Bulgarian, Egyptian, Iraqi, Syrian and Viet-Namese air forces and to the government of Peru. Current production version is the **Mi-6A**, to which the following details apply.

TYPE: Heavy transport helicopter.

ROTOR SYSTEM: Five-blade main rotor and four-blade tail rotor. Main rotor blades each have a tapered steel tube spar, to which are bonded built-up metal aerofoil sections. Blades have coincident flapping and drag hinges and fixed tabs. Main rotor shaft inclined forward at 5° to vertical. Control via large welded swashplate. Hydraulically-actuated powered controls. Main rotor collective-pitch control interlocked with throttle controls. Main rotor blades incorporate electro-thermal

anti-icing system. Tail rotor embodies a fluid-type anti-icing system.

ROTOR DRIVE: Conventional transmission. Main reduction gearbox drives tail rotor, fan, AC generators and hydraulic pumps. Intermediate reduction gearbox fitted with special fan.

FUSELAGE: Conventional all-metal riveted semi-monocoque structure of pod and boom type.

WINGS: Two small cantilever shoulder wings, mounted above main landing gear struts, offload rotor by providing some 20% of total lift in cruising flight. Removed when aircraft is operated as flying crane.

TAIL UNIT: Tail rotor support acts as vertical stabiliser. Variable-incidence horizontal stabiliser, near end of tailboom, for trim purposes.

LANDING GEAR: Non-retractable tricycle type, with castoring twin-wheel nose unit and single wheel on each main unit. Twin-chamber oleo-pneumatic (high-pressure and low-pressure) main landing gear shock-struts. High-pressure chambers interconnected through overflow system incorporating spring damper, to damp out oscillations at full landing gear loading and so eliminate ground resonance. Main wheels size 1,325 × 480 mm. Nosewheels size 720-310 mm. Brakes on main wheels. Small tail-bumper under end of tailboom.

POWER PLANT: Two 4,101 kW (5,500 shp) Soloviev D-25V (TV-2BM) turboshaft engines, mounted side by side above cabin, forward of main rotor shaft. Electro-thermal anti-icing system for air intakes. Eleven internal fuel tanks, with total capacity of 6,315 kg (13,922 lb), and two external tanks, on each side of cabin, with total capacity of 3,490 kg (7,695 lb). Provision for two additional ferry tanks inside cabin, with total capacity of 3,490 kg (7,695 lb). Automatic fuel-flow control system with manual override. Side panels of engine cowlings are opened and closed hydraulically and are used as platforms for inspection and maintenance of engines and rotor head.

ACCOMMODATION: Crew of five, consisting of two pilots, navigator, flight engineer and radio operator. Four jettisonable doors on flight deck. Electro-thermal anti-icing system for glazing of flight deck and navigator's compartment. Equipped normally for cargo operation, with easily-removable tip-up seats along side walls. When these seats are supplemented by additional seats installed in centre of cabin, 65-90 passengers can be carried,

with cargo or baggage in the aisles. As an air ambulance, 41 stretcher cases and two medical attendants on tip-up seats can be carried. One of attendant's stations is provided with intercom to flight deck, and provision is made for portable oxygen installations for the patients. Cabin floor is stressed for loadings of 2,000 kg/m² (410 lb/sq ft), with provision for cargo tiedown rings. Rear clamshell doors and ramps are operated hydraulically. Standard equipment includes an electric winch of 800 kg (1,765 lb) capacity and pulley block system. External cargo sling system for bulky loads. Central hatch in cargo floor. Three jettisonable doors, fore and aft of main landing gear on port side and aft of landing gear on starboard side.

SYSTEMS: Main, standby and auxiliary hydraulic systems, each with separate pump mounted on main gearbox. Operating pressure 118-152 bars (1,705-2,205 lb/sq in). Main 27V DC electrical system, supplied by two 12kW starter/generators, with batteries for 30 min emergency supply. De-icing system and some radio equipment supplied by three-phase 360V 400Hz AC system, utilising two 90kVA generators. Trolley-mounted APU, consisting of 74·5 kW (100 hp) AI-8 gas turbine and 24kW generator, carried on board.

AVIONICS AND EQUIPMENT: Standard equipment includes VHF and HF communications radio, intercom, radio altimeter, radio compass, three-channel autopilot, marker beacon, directional gyro and full all-weather instrumentation.

ARMAMENT: A few Mi-6s are fitted with a gun of unknown calibre in the fuselage nose.

DIMENSIONS, EXTERNAL:

Diameter of main rotor	35·00 m (114 ft 10 in)
Diameter of tail rotor	6·30 m (20 ft 8 in)
Distance between rotor centres	21·09 m (69 ft 2½ in)
Length overall, rotors turning	41·74 m (136 ft 11½ in)
Length of fuselage	33·18 m (108 ft 10½ in)
Height overall	9·86 m (32 ft 4 in)
Wing span	15·30 m (50 ft 2½ in)
Span of horizontal stabiliser	5·04 m (16 ft 6½ in)
Wheel track	7·50 m (24 ft 7¼ in)
Wheelbase	9·09 m (29 ft 9¾ in)
Rear loading doors:	
Height	2·70 m (8 ft 10¼ in)
Width	2·65 m (8 ft 8¼ in)

Mil Mi-6 heavy general-purpose helicopter, with nose gun, in service with the Egyptian Air Force (*Denis Hughes*)

Passenger doors:
Height: front door	1·70 m (5 ft 7 in)
rear doors	1·61 m (5 ft 3½ in)
Width	0·80 m (2 ft 7½ in)
Sill height: front door	1·40 m (4 ft 7¼ in)
rear doors	1·30 m (4 ft 3¼ in)

Central hatch in floor
1·44 m (4 ft 9 in) × 1·93 m (6 ft 4 in)

DIMENSIONS, INTERNAL:
Cabin:
Length	12·00 m (39 ft 4½ in)
Max width	2·65 m (8 ft 8¼ in)
Max height:	
at front	2·01 m (6 ft 7 in)
at rear	2·50 m (8 ft 2½ in)
Cabin volume	80 m³ (2,825 cu ft)

WEIGHTS:
Weight empty	27,240 kg (60,055 lb)
Max internal payload	12,000 kg (26,450 lb)
Max slung cargo	8,000 kg (17,637 lb)
Fuel load, internal	6,315 kg (13,922 lb)
Fuel load, with external tanks	9,805 kg (21,617 lb)

Max T-O weight with slung cargo at altitudes under
1,000 m (3,280 ft)	38,400 kg (84,657 lb)
Normal T-O weight	40,500 kg (89,285 lb)
Max T-O weight for VTO	42,500 kg (93,700 lb)

PERFORMANCE (at max T-O weight):
Max level speed	162 knots (300 km/h; 186 mph)
Max cruising speed	135 knots (250 km/h; 155 mph)
Service ceiling	4,500 m (14,750 ft)

Range with 8,000 kg (17,637 lb) payload
334 nm (620 km; 385 miles)
Range with external tanks and 4,500 kg (9,920 lb)
payload 540 nm (1,000 km; 621 miles)
Max ferry range (tanks in cabin)
781 nm (1,450 km; 900 miles)

MIL Mi-8 (V-8)

NATO reporting name: Hip

This turbine-powered helicopter was shown in public for the first time during the 1961 Soviet Aviation Day display. Since then, more than 6,000 Mi-8s have been delivered for military and civil use, and production continues at a reported rate of about 750 a year. With Mi-24s, they form the standard equipment of Soviet tactical helicopter regiments, in a variety of forms, some carrying extremely heavy weapon loads. Military Mi-8s have also been supplied to the Afghan, Algerian, Anguilla, Bangladesh, Bulgarian, Czechoslovak, Egyptian, Ethiopian, Finnish, East German, Hungarian, Indian, Iraqi, North Korean, Laotian, Libyan, Malagasy, Pakistani, Peruvian, Polish, Romanian, Sudanese, Syrian, Viet-Namese, North Yemen, South Yemen and Yugoslav armed forces.

The commercial Mi-8, with larger, square windows in place of the circular cabin windows of the military version, is in service with Aeroflot for transport and air ambulance duties, and is operated by this airline in support of Soviet activities in the Antarctic. Standard Mi-8s are used there for ice patrol and reconnaissance, for rescue operations, and for carrying supplies and equipment to Vostok Station, near the South Pole.

Three international women's helicopter records for dis-

Mil Mi-8 ('Hip-E') military helicopter. This differs from the commercial version in having circular cabin windows, a nose gun and weapon-carriers on outriggers

tance and speed in a 2,000 km closed circuit were still credited to the Mi-8 in mid-1980.

The original prototype (NATO **Hip-A**) had a single 2,013 kW (2,700 shp) Soloviev turboshaft engine and four-blade main rotor. When fitted with the five-blade rotor that became standard on subsequent aircraft, it was redesignated **Hip-B**. The second prototype, which flew for the first time on 17 September 1962, introduced the now-standard Isotov twin-turbine power plant and became **Hip-C** to NATO in both civil and military forms.

There are three civil versions, as follows:

Mi-8. Passenger version, with standard seating for 28-32 persons in main cabin.

Mi-8T. General utility version, equipped normally to carry internal or external freight, but able to accommodate 24 tip-up passenger seats along the cabin walls.

Mi-8 Salon. De luxe version. Main cabin is furnished normally for eleven passengers, with an eight-place couch facing inward on the port side, and two chairs and a swivelling seat on the starboard side. There is a table on the starboard side. An air-to-ground radio telephone and removable ventilation fans are standard equipment. Forward of the main cabin is a compartment for a hostess, with buffet and crew wardrobe. Aft of the main cabin are a toilet (port) and passenger wardrobe (starboard), to each side of the entrance. An alternative nine-passenger layout is available. The Mi-8 Salon has a max T-O weight of 10,400 kg (22,928 lb) and range of 205 nm (380 km; 236 miles) with 30 min fuel reserve. In other respects it is similar to the standard Mi-8.

Military versions are identified by the following NATO reporting names:

Hip-C. Basic assault transport. Twin-rack for stores on each side of cabin, able to carry total of 128 × 57 mm rockets in four packs, or other weapons.

Hip-D. Rectangular-section canisters on outer stores

racks; added antennae. For electronic duties.

Hip-E. Described by US Department of Defense as world's most heavily armed helicopter. Standard equipment of Soviet tactical air forces. One flexibly-mounted 12·7 mm machine-gun in nose. Triple stores rack on each side of cabin, able to carry up to 192 rockets in six suspended packs, plus four 'Swatter' infra-red homing anti-tank missiles above racks.

Hip-F. Export counterpart of 'Hip-E'. Missile armament changed to six 'Saggers'.

TYPE: Twin-engined transport helicopter.

ROTOR SYSTEM: Five-blade main rotor and three-blade tail rotor. Transmission comprises a type VR-8 two-stage planetary main reduction gearbox giving main rotor shaft/engine rpm ratio of 0·016 : 1, intermediate and tail gearboxes, main rotor brake and drives off the main gearbox for the tail rotor, fan, AC generator, hydraulic pumps and tachometer generators. Main rotor shaft inclined forward at 4° 30′ to vertical. All-metal main rotor blades of basic NACA 230 section; solidity 0·0777. Each main blade is made up of an extruded light alloy spar carrying the blade root fitting, 21 trailing-edge pockets and the blade tip. Pockets are honeycomb-filled. Main rotor blades are fitted with balance tabs, embody a spar failure warning system, and are interchangeable. Their drag and flapping hinges are a few inches apart, and they are carried on a machined spider. Control system utilises irreversible hydraulic boosters. Main rotor collective-pitch control is interlocked to throttle controls. All-metal tail rotor blades, each made up of a spar and honeycomb-filled trailing-edge. Automatically-controlled electro-thermal de-icing system on all blades. In an emergency, the rotor blades of the Mi-8 and intermediate and tail gearboxes are interchangeable with those of the piston-engined Mi-4, although this prevents use of the de-icing system.

FUSELAGE: Conventional all-metal semi-monocoque structure of pod and boom type.

TAIL UNIT: Tail rotor support acts as small vertical stabiliser. Horizontal stabiliser near end of tailboom.

LANDING GEAR: Non-retractable tricycle type, with steerable twin-wheel nose unit, which is locked in flight, and single wheel on each main unit. All units embody oleo-pneumatic (gas) shock-absorbers. Main-wheel tyres size 865 × 280; nosewheel tyres size 595 × 185. Pneumatic brakes on main wheels. Pneumatic system can also recharge tyres in the field, using air stored in main landing gear struts. Optional main-wheel fairings.

POWER PLANT: Two 1,267 kW (1,700 shp) Isotov TV2-117A turboshaft engines. Main rotor speed governed automatically, with manual override. Single flexible internal fuel tank, capacity 445 litres (98 Imp gallons), and two external tanks, one each side of cabin, with capacity of 745 litres (164 Imp gallons) in the port tank and 680 litres (149·5 Imp gallons) in the starboard tank. Total standard fuel capacity 1,870 litres (411·5 Imp gallons). Provision for carrying one or two additional ferry tanks in cabin, raising max total capacity to 3,700 litres (814 Imp gallons). Fairing over starboard external tank houses optional cabin air-conditioning equipment at front. Engine cowling side panels form maintenance platforms when open, with access via hatch on flight deck. Engine air intake de-icing standard. Total oil capacity 60 kg (132 lb).

ACCOMMODATION: Two pilots side by side on flight deck, with provision for a flight engineer's station. Windscreen de-icing standard. Basic passenger version is furnished with 28 four-abreast track-mounted tip-up seats at a pitch of 72-75 cm (28-29·5 in), with a centre aisle 32 cm (12·5 in) wide, a wardrobe and baggage compartment; or 32 seats without wardrobe. Seats and bulkheads of basic version are quickly removable for cargo-carrying. Mi-8T has cargo tiedown rings in floor, a winch of 200 kg (440 lb) capacity and pulley block

'Hip-C' military version of Mil Mi-8 twin-turbine helicopter, with additional side view (bottom) of commercial version *(Pilot Press)*

system to facilitate the loading of heavy freight, an external cargo sling system (capacity 3,000 kg; 6,614 lb), and 24 tip-up seats along the side walls of the cabin. All versions can be converted for air ambulance duties, with accommodation for 12 stretchers and a tip-up seat for a medical attendant. The large windows on each side of the flight deck slide rearward. The sliding, jettisonable main passenger door is at the front of the cabin on the port side. An electrically-operated rescue hoist (capacity 150 kg; 330 lb) can be installed at this doorway. The rear of the cabin is made up of large clamshell freight-loading doors, with a downward-hinged passenger airstair door inset centrally at the rear. Hook-on ramps are used for vehicle loading.

SYSTEMS: Standard heating system can be replaced by full air-conditioning system. Two independent hydraulic systems, each with own pump; operating pressure 44-64 bars (640-925 lb/sq in). DC electrical supply from two 27V 18kW starter/generators and six 28Ah storage batteries. AC supply for de-icing system and some radio equipment supplied by 208/115/36/7·5V 400Hz generator, with 36V three-phase standby system. Provision for oxygen system for crew and, in ambulance version, for patients. Freon fire-extinguishing system in power plant bays and service fuel tank compartments, actuated automatically or manually. Two portable fire extinguishers for use in cabin.

AVIONICS AND EQUIPMENT: Standard equipment includes a type R-842 HF transceiver with frequency range of 2 to 8 MHz and range of up to 540 nm (1,000 km; 620 miles), type R-860 VHF transceiver operating on 118 to 135·9 MHz over ranges of up to 54 nm (100 km; 62 miles), intercom, radio telephone, type ARK-9 automatic radio compass, type RV-3 radio altimeter with 'dangerous height' warning, and four-axis autopilot to give yaw, roll and pitch stabilisation under any flight conditions, stabilisation of altitude in level flight or hover, and stabilisation of pre-set flying speed, navigation equipment and instrumentation for all-weather flying by day and night, including two gyro horizons, two airspeed indicators, two main rotor speed indicators, turn indicator, two altimeters, two rate of climb indicators, magnetic compass, radio altimeter, radio compass and astro-compass for Polar flying.

ARMAMENT: See individual model descriptions of military versions.

DIMENSIONS, EXTERNAL:

Diameter of main rotor	21·29 m (69 ft 10¼ in)
Diameter of tail rotor	3·90 m (12 ft 9½ in)
Distance between rotor centres	12·65 m (41 ft 6 in)
Length overall, rotors turning	25·24 m (82 ft 9¾ in)
Length of fuselage	18·31 m (60 ft 0¾ in)
Width of fuselage	2·50 m (8 ft 2½ in)
Height overall	5·65 m (18 ft 6½ in)
Wheel track	4·50 m (14 ft 9 in)
Wheelbase	4·26 m (13 ft 11¾ in)
Fwd passenger door: Height	1·41 m (4 ft 7¼ in)
Width	0·82 m (2 ft 8¼ in)
Rear passenger door: Height	1·70 m (5 ft 7 in)
Width	0·84 m (2 ft 9 in)
Rear cargo door: Height	1·82 m (5 ft 11½ in)
Width	2·34 m (7 ft 8¼ in)

DIMENSIONS, INTERNAL:

Passenger cabin: Length	6·36 m (20 ft 10¼	in)
Width	2·34 m (7 ft 8¼	in)
Height	1·80 m (5 ft 10¾	in)
Cargo hold (freighter):		
Length at floor	5·34 m (17 ft 6¼	in)
Width	2·34 m (7 ft 8¼	in)
Height	1·80 m (5 ft 10¾	in)
Volume	approx 23 m³ (812 cu	ft)

AREA:

Main rotor disc	355 m² (3,828 sq ft)

WEIGHTS:

Weight empty:	
Passenger version	6,799 kg (14,990 lb)
Cargo version	6,624 kg (14,603 lb)
Max payload: internal	4,000 kg (8,820 lb)
external	3,000 kg (6,614 lb)
Fuel, standard tanks	1,450 kg (3,197 lb)
Fuel, with 2 auxiliary tanks	2,870 kg (6,327 lb)
Normal T-O weight	11,100 kg (24,470 lb)
T-O weight with 28 passengers, each with 15 kg (33 lb) of baggage	11,570 kg (25,508 lb)
T-O weight with 2,500 kg (5,510 lb) of slung cargo	11,428 kg (25,195 lb)
Max T-O weight for VTO	12,000 kg (26,455 lb)

PERFORMANCE:

Max level speed at 1,000 m (3,280 ft):		
Normal AUW	140 knots (260 km/h; 161 mph)	
Max level speed at S/L:		
Normal AUW	135 knots (250 km/h; 155 mph)	
Max AUW	124 knots (230 km/h; 142 mph)	
With 2,500 kg (5,510 lb) of slung cargo	97 knots (180 km/h; 112 mph)	
Max cruising speed:		
Normal AUW	122 knots (225 km/h; 140 mph)	
Max AUW	97 knots (180 km/h; 112 mph)	
Service ceiling	4,500 m (14,760 ft)	
Hovering ceiling IGE at normal AUW	1,900 m (6,233 ft)	
Hovering ceiling OGE at normal AUW	800 m (2,625 ft)	

RANGES:

Cargo version at 1,000 m (3,280 ft), with standard fuel, 5% reserves:

Normal AUW	251 nm (465 km; 289 miles)
Max AUW	240 nm (445 km; 276 miles)

With 28 passengers at 1,000 m (3,280 ft), with 20 min fuel reserves 270 nm (500 km; 311 miles)

Ferry range of cargo version, with auxiliary fuel, 5% reserves 647 nm (1,200 km; 745 miles)

MIL Mi-10 (V-10)
NATO reporting name: Harke

This flying crane development of the Mi-6 was demonstrated at the 1961 Soviet Aviation Day display at Tushino, having flown for the first time in the previous year. Above the line of the cabin windows the two helicopters are almost identical, but the depth of the fuselage is reduced considerably on the Mi-10, and the tailboom is deepened so that the flattened undersurface runs unbroken to the tail. The Mi-10 also lacks the fixed wings of the Mi-6.

Items which are interchangeable between the Mi-6 and Mi-10 include the power plant, transmission system and reduction gearboxes, swashplate assembly, main and tail rotors, control system and most items of equipment. The power of the Soloviev turboshaft engines remains constant up to 3,000 m (9,850 ft) and to an ambient air temperature of 40°C at sea level. The aircraft will maintain level flight on one engine. Full navigation equipment and an autopilot permit all-weather operation, by day and night.

The tall long-stroke quadricycle landing gear, with wheel track exceeding 6·0 m (19 ft 8 in) and clearance under the fuselage of 3·75 m (12 ft 3½ in) with the aircraft fully loaded, enables the Mi-10 to taxi over a load it is to carry and to accommodate loads as bulky as a prefabricated building.

Use can be made of interchangeable wheeled cargo platforms which are held in place by hydraulic grips controllable from either the cockpit or a remote panel. Using these grips without a platform, cargoes up to 20 m (65 ft 7 in) long, 10 m (32 ft 9½ in) wide and 3·1 m (10 ft 2 in) high can be lifted and secured in 1½ to 2 minutes. The cabin can accommodate additional freight or passengers.

A closed-circuit TV system, with cameras scanning forward from under the rear fuselage and downward through the sling hatch, is used to observe the payload and main landing gear, touchdown being by this reference. The TV system replaces the retractable undernose 'dustbin' fitted originally.

The following details refer to the standard Mi-10, which has been operated by both Aeroflot and the Soviet armed forces and is available for export. About 55 are believed to have been delivered by 1977, with production resuming at a modest rate after a six-year break. Some have been exported to Iraq.

TYPE: Heavy flying-crane helicopter.

ROTOR SYSTEM: Same as for Mi-6, except that main rotor shaft is inclined forward at an angle of only 0° 45'.

FUSELAGE: Conventional all-metal riveted semi-monocoque structure.

TAIL UNIT: Same as for Mi-6.

LANDING GEAR: Non-retractable quadricycle type, with twin wheels on each unit. All units fitted with oleo-pneumatic shock-absorbers. Telescopic main legs. Main wheels size 1,230 × 260 mm, each with brake. Levered-suspension castoring nose units. Nosewheels size 950 × 250 mm. All landing gear struts are faired. The port nose gear fairing incorporates steps to the crew door. Despite the height of the gear, the Mi-10 can make stable landing and take-off runs at speeds up to 54 knots (100 km/h; 62 mph).

POWER PLANT: Two 4,101 kW (5,500 shp) Soloviev D-25V turboshaft engines, mounted side by side above cabin, forward of main rotor drive-shaft. Single fuel tank in fuselage and two external tanks, on sides of cabin, with total capacity of 6,340 kg (13,975 lb). Provision for carrying two auxiliary tanks in cabin, to give total fuel capacity of 8,260 kg (18,210 lb). Engine cowling side panels (opened and closed hydraulically) can be used as maintenance platforms when open.

ACCOMMODATION: Two pilots and flight engineer accommodated on flight deck, which has bulged side windows to provide an improved downward view. Flight deck is heated and ventilated and has provision for oxygen equipment. Crew door is immediately aft of flight deck on port side. Main cabin can be used for freight and/or passengers, 28 tip-up seats being installed along the side walls. Freight is loaded into this cabin through a door on the starboard side, aft of the rear landing gear struts, with the aid of a boom and 200 kg (440 lb) capacity electric winch. In addition to the cargo platform described earlier, the Mi-10 has external sling gear as standard equipment. This can be used in conjunction with a winch controlled from a portable control panel inside the cabin. The winch can be also used to raise loads of up to 500 kg (1,100 lb) while the aircraft is hovering on rescue and other duties, via a hatch in the cabin floor.

AVIONICS, EQUIPMENT AND SYSTEMS: Generally as for Mi-6, including APU.

DIMENSIONS, EXTERNAL:

Diameter of main rotor	35·00 m (114 ft 10 in)
Diameter of tail rotor	6·30 m (20 ft 8 in)
Distance between rotor centres	21·24 m (69 ft 8 in)
Length overall, rotors turning	41·89 m (137 ft 5½ in)
Length of fuselage	32·86 m (107 ft 9¾ in)
Ground clearance under fuselage	3·75 m (12 ft 3½ in)
Height overall	9·80 m (32 ft 2 in)
Wheel track (c/l of shock-struts):	
nosewheels	6·01 m (19 ft 8¾ in)
main wheels	6·92 m (22 ft 8½ in)
Wheelbase	8·29 m (27 ft 2½ in)
Cargo platform: Length	8·53 m (28 ft 0 in)
Width	3·54 m (11 ft 7¼ in)
Crew door: Height	1·35 m (4 ft 5¼ in)
Width	0·78 m (2 ft 6¾ in)
Height to sill	3·91 m (12 ft 10¼ in)
Freight loading door: Height	1·56 m (5 ft 1½ in)
Width	1·26 m (4 ft 1½ in)
Height to sill	3·92 m (12 ft 10½ in)
Cabin floor hatch:	
Diameter	1·00 m (3 ft 3¼ in)

Mil Mi-10 flying crane derivative of the Mi-6, with additional side view (bottom) of Mi-10K *(Pilot Press)*

DIMENSIONS, INTERNAL:

Cabin: Length	14·04 m (46 ft 0¾ in)
Width	2·50 m (8 ft 2½ in)
Height	1·68 m (5 ft 6 in)
Volume	approx 60 m³ (2,120 cu ft)

WEIGHTS:

Weight empty	27,300 kg (60,185 lb)
Max payload on platform, incl platform	15,000 kg (33,070 lb)
Max slung payload	8,000 kg (17,635 lb)
T-O weight with slung cargo	38,000 kg (83,775 lb)
Max T-O weight	43,700 kg (96,340 lb)

PERFORMANCE:

Max level speed at max T-O weight	108 knots (200 km/h; 124 mph)
Cruising speed at max T-O weight	97 knots (180 km/h; 112 mph)
Service ceiling (limited)	3,000 m (9,850 ft)
Range with platform payload of 12,000 kg (26,455 lb)	135 nm (250 km; 155 miles)

MIL Mi-10K

First displayed publicly in Moscow on 26 March 1966, the Mi-10K is a development of the Mi-10 with a number of important design changes, most apparent of which are a reduction in the height of the landing gear and a more slender tail rotor support structure.

It can be operated by a crew of only two pilots. This is made possible by the provision of an additional cockpit gondola under the front fuselage, with full flying controls and a rearward-facing seat. By occupying this seat, one of the pilots can control the aircraft in hovering flight and, at the same time, have an unrestricted view of cargo loading, unloading and hoisting, which are also under his control.

In the Mi-10K, the maximum slung payload is 11,000 kg (24,250 lb) and is expected to be increased further to 14,000 kg (30,865 lb) by using Soloviev D-25VF turboshaft engines, uprated to 6,500 shp each, in due course. Fuel capacity of the Mi-10K, in standard internal and external tanks, is 9,000 litres (1,980 Imp gallons). The rotor turns at 120 rpm.

DIMENSIONS, EXTERNAL:

Generally as for Mi-10, except:

Height overall	7·80 m (25 ft 7 in)
Wheel track	5·00 m (16 ft 4¾ in)
Wheelbase	8·74 m (28 ft 8 in)
Door sill heights:	
Crew door	1·81 m (5 ft 11 in)
Freight door	1·82 m (5 ft 11½ in)

WEIGHTS:

Weight empty	24,680 kg (54,410 lb)
Max payload, slung cargo	11,000 kg (24,250 lb)
Max fuel load with ferry tanks in cabin	8,670 kg (19,114 lb)
Max T-O weight with slung cargo	38,000 kg (83,775 lb)

PERFORMANCE:

Cruising speed, empty	135 knots (250 km/h; 155 mph)
Max cruising speed with slung load	109 knots (202 km/h; 125 mph)
Service ceiling	3,000 m (9,850 ft)
Ferry range with auxiliary fuel	428 nm (795 km; 494 miles)

MIL Mi-14 (V-14)
NATO reporting name: Haze

An accompanying photograph shows a shore-based anti-submarine helicopter which is in standard service with the Soviet Navy as a replacement for the Mi-4. Clearly derived from the Mi-8, it is known to NATO as 'Haze'.

No details are available officially. Features evident in

Mil Mi-10K preparing to lift a 10-tonne sheet steel drum to the top of a tower at the Sinarski pipe works in Kamenski Uralski *(Tass)*

the photograph include a boat-hull planing bottom on the fuselage, and a sponson on each side at the rear, to provide a degree of amphibious capability; a large undernose radome; and a towed magnetic anomaly detection (MAD) bird stowed against the rear of the fuselage pod. The landing gear of 'Haze' is fully retractable.

Dimensions, power plant and dynamic components

must be generally similar to those of the Mi-8.

It is generally assumed that 'Haze' is the 'float-equipped version of the Mi-8' which was reported to be under test in the Soviet Union in early 1974, with the designation V-14. About 50 are believed to have been delivered, with production continuing at a rate of 25 per year. A few were reported to have been delivered to Bulgaria in 1979.

Photograph and three-view drawing *(Pilot Press)* **of the Mil Mi-14 (V-14) ASW helicopter (NATO 'Haze')**

Mil Mi-24 assault helicopter, in the form known to NATO as 'Hind-A' *(Pilot Press)*

'Hind-A', first major production version of the Mil Mi-24 with original starboard-side tail rotor

MIL Mi-24 (and A-10)
NATO reporting name: Hind

This assault helicopter was known to exist for some two years before photographs became available to the technical press in early 1974. The two versions shown in those first photographs were each capable of carrying a squad of eight combat-equipped troops, and had attachments under their auxiliary wings for a variety of ordnance, to keep down the heads of enemy troops in the drop zone and to attack ground targets, including tanks. At least two units of approximate squadron strength were based in eastern Europe by the Spring of 1974. Since that time the Mi-24 has developed in two basic forms, one configured for optimum efficiency as an assault transport, while retaining heavy armament; the other as an advanced gunship, able to engage in air-to-air combat with other helicopters, and with secondary transport capability. Deliveries of all models are believed to exceed 1,000, with production continuing at a rate of more than 15 a month. Well over 450 of the gunship versions were deployed in 1979 by the Soviet air forces, including full regiments of Mi-24s based at Parchim and Stendal, northwest and west of Berlin, near the border with West Germany. Other operators include the Warsaw Pact Air Forces of Bulgaria, Czechoslovakia, East Germany, Hungary and Poland. Export deliveries have been made to Afghanistan (at least 30), Algeria, Iraq (41), Libya (26) and South Yemen (6), all of the gunship version. Many have been operated by Soviet forces in Afghanistan since December 1979.

The basic airframe, power plant and transmission system appear to be common to all versions of the Mi-24, with differences in armament, operational equipment and tail rotor location. In addition, the gunship has completely new crew accommodation forward of the engine inlets and above the fuselage floor. Five major variants of which details may be published are known by the following NATO reporting names:

Hind-A. Armed assault helicopter, with large enclosed flight deck for crew of four, comprising pilot, co-pilot, gunner/navigator and forward observer. Auxiliary wings, with considerable anhedral, each carry three weapon stations for heavy armament, supplemented by large-calibre machine-gun in nose. Anti-torque rotor, originally on starboard side of offset tail pylon, repositioned to port side on later and converted aircraft. Initial production Mi-24s were of this version.

Hind-B. Similar to 'Hind-A' except that auxiliary wings have neither anhedral nor dihedral, and carry only the two inboard weapon stations on each side. This version is believed to have preceded 'Hind-A' and was not built in large numbers.

Hind-C. Generally similar to late-model 'Hind-A' but without nose gun and undernose blister fairing, and no missile rails at wingtips.

Hind-D. Basically similar to late-model 'Hind-A', with tail rotor on port side, but with front fuselage completely redesigned for primary gunship role. Tandem stations for weapon operator (in nose) and pilot have individual canopies. Front canopy hinged to open sideways, to starboard; footstep under starboard side of fuselage for access to pilot's rearward-hinged door. Rear seat raised to give pilot an unobstructed forward view. Probe fitted forward of top starboard corner of bulletproof windscreen at extreme nose may be part of low-airspeed sensing equipment, to indicate optimum conditions for minimum dispersion of 57 mm rockets. Under nose is a four-barrel Gatling-type large-calibre machine gun in a turret with a wide range of movement in azimuth and elevation, providing air-to-air as well as air-to-surface capability. Undernose pack for sensors, possibly including radar and low-light-level TV. (Reports that forward-looking infra-red might be fitted were premature, as such equipment is not expected to be ready for service in the Soviet Union for several years). Wing armament of 'Hind-A' retained, but forward-looking (electro-optical?) sensor transferred from top of port inner pylon to wingtip. Many small antennae and blisters. Extended nosewheel leg to increase ground clearance of sensor pack; nosewheels semi-exposed when retracted.

Hind-E. As 'Hind-D', for Soviet armed forces, but with four laser-homing tube-launched anti-tank missiles (NATO 'Spiral') instead of 'Swatters', and structural hardening by substitution of steel and titanium for aluminium in critical components.

The helicopter known to the Soviet authorities as **A-10**, in which various FAI-approved records in class E1 have been set since 1975, is now known to be an Mi-24, with the 'Hind-A/C' type of front fuselage.

Pilot on all 1975 record flights was Galina Rastorgoueva, a test pilot and engineer. She was accompanied by Ludmila Polyanskaya, who is employed as navigator on Il-18 airliners of Aeroflot. On 18 July 1975, they averaged 180·480 knots (334·464 km/h; 207·826 mph) around a 100 km circuit, setting a new women's speed record. On 1 August, a speed of 178·624 knots (331·023 km/h; 205·688 mph) around 500 km set both general and women's records, as did an average speed of 179·500 knots (332·646 km/h; 206·697 mph) over 1,000 km on 13 August. Two women's time-to-height helicopter records followed, with a time of 2 min 33·5 s to 3,000 m on 8 August, and 7 min 43 s to 6,000 m on 26 August. At this period, the A-10 was powered by two 1,118·5 kW (1,500 shp) Isotov TV2-117A turboshaft engines, as fitted to the Mi-8.

Latest A-10 record confirmed by the FAI is a speed of 198·9 knots (368·4 km/h; 228·9 mph) set by Gourguen Karapetyan over a 15/25 km course near Moscow on 21 September 1978. This A-10 had two TV3-117 turboshaft engines, each rated at 1,640 kW (2,200 shp).

Except where indicated, the following details apply to all current operational versions of the Mi-24:

ROTOR SYSTEM: Five-blade main rotor and three-blade tail rotor; latter now on port side of offset tail fin. Main rotor blades, with glassfibre skin, on cast titanium head. Balance tab and electrical leading-edge de-icing on each blade.

FUSELAGE: Conventional all-metal semi-monocoque structure of pod and boom type. Forward portion, above shallow floor structure, differs with role.

AUXILIARY WINGS: Cantilever shoulder wings of tapered planform, with marked anhedral and incidence. No movable surfaces.

The completely redesigned nose of the Mi-24 ('Hind-D') gunship is shown in this close-up *(Camera Press)*

TAIL UNIT: Swept fin, offset a few degrees, serves also as tail rotor pylon. Variable-incidence horizontal stabiliser at base of fin.

LANDING GEAR: Tricycle type, with rearward-retracting twin-wheel nose unit, and single-wheel main units with oleo-pneumatic shock-absorbers and low-pressure tyres. Main units retract rearward and inward into the aft end of the fuselage pod, turning through 90° to stow almost vertically, discwise to the longitudinal axis of the fuselage, under prominent blister fairings. Tubular tripod skid assembly protects tail rotor in a tail-down take-off or landing.

POWER PLANT: Two 1,118·5 kW (1,500 shp) Isotov turbo-shaft engines, related to the TV2-117A engines of the Mi-8 but shorter, mounted side by side above the cabin, with their output shafts driving rearward to the main rotor shaft through a combining gearbox. (These may have been superseded by 1,640 kW; 2,200 shp TV3-117s in later aircraft; see paragraphs on A-10.)

ACCOMMODATION ('Hind-A'): Crew of four; eight fully-equipped troops in main cabin. Access to flight deck via large rearward-sliding blistered transparent panel which forms the aft flight deck window on the port side, and a large upward-hinged window forward of this. At front of passenger cabin on each side is a large door, divided horizontally into two sections which are hinged to open upward and downward respectively. Optically flat bulletproof glass window in nose, with wiper, for gunner. Armour protection for crew and some vital components.

SYSTEMS: Dual electrical system, with three generators. Stability augmentation system. Electro-thermal de-icing system for main and tail rotor blades.

AVIONICS: Include ADF navigation system with map display.

ARMAMENT ('Hind-A'): One 12·7 mm machine-gun in nose, probably slaved to undernose sighting system. Rails for four 'Swatter' anti-tank missiles under end-plate pylons at wingtips. Four underwing pylons for rocket pods (each thirty-two 57 mm rockets), special bombs, or other stores.

DIMENSIONS, EXTERNAL (estimated):
Diameter of main rotor 17·00 m (55 ft 9 in)
Diameter of tail rotor 3·90 m (12 ft 9½ in)
Length overall 17·00 m (55 ft 9 in)
Height overall 4·25 m (14 ft 0 in)

The gunship version of the Mil Mi-24, known to NATO as 'Hind-D' *(Pilot Press)*

WEIGHTS (estimated):
Max external weapons 1,275 kg (2,800 lb)
Normal T-O weight 10,000 kg (22,000 lb)

MIL HEAVY-LIFT HELICOPTER
NATO reporting name: Halo

A statement to Congress on the US Army's FY 1980 budget appropriations contained a comment that the Russians "may be on the verge of developing an operational heavy-lift helicopter—a system we do not possess. They have been flying prototypes of a helicopter called 'Homer' for several years (see 1977-78 *Jane's*). This is capable of carrying company-size units and is the same size as a Boeing 727. They have never deployed this system for reasons known only to themselves (probably technical). They now, however, have developed prototypes of a new

heavy-lift helicopter called 'Halo'".

No details of 'Halo' have been released officially, but it is reported to have a single main rotor/tail rotor configuration, with clamshell rear loading doors. Representatives of the Mil bureau have discussed their current involvement in heavy-lift helicopters with a total installed power of around 18,650 kW (25,000 shp). A standard training textbook by the late Mikhail Mil stated, significantly, that a single-rotor heavy-lift helicopter could have eight blades on its main rotor.

MIL NAVAL HELICOPTER

The US *Military Posture* statement for FY 1979 contained the remark: "Another new (Soviet) naval helicopter is projected in the mid-1980s for ASW and reconnaissance roles". No details were given.

MYASISHCHEV

This design bureau was formed in 1951, under the leadership of Professor Vladimir Mikhailovich Myasishchev, who died on 14 October 1978, at the age of 76. Although his work was little publicised, he had been responsible for 'translating into Russian' the drawings of the Douglas DC-3 transport, acquired from the USA under a licence agreement in 1936-38, and for the development of several important original types. First product of his own design bureau was the four-jet M-4 bomber (known in the West by the reporting name of 'Bison') which remains in service as a strategic bomber, maritime reconnaissance aircraft and flight refuelling tanker.

Myasishchev later designed a long-range four-jet heavy bomber known as the M-50 to replace the M-4. This was allocated the NATO code name of 'Bounder' and was described in the 1964-65 *Jane's*. Changing requirements limited 'Bounder' to a research role. Myasishchev spent the period from 1960 to 1967 as Director of TsAGI,

before returning to design.

MYASISHCHEV M-4
NATO reporting name: Bison

Three major production versions of this four-jet aircraft were identified by NATO code names, as follows:

Bison-A. The Soviet Union's first operational four-jet strategic bomber. Design work began in 1951. The last drawing was despatched to the works on 1 May 1952, and the prototype bomber was displayed initially over Moscow on 1 May 1954. Comparable with early versions of Boeing B-52 Stratofortress. Powered by four 85·3 kN (19,180 lb st) Mikulin AM-3D turbojets, buried in wing-roots. Defensive armament of ten 23 mm cannon in twin-gun turrets in tail, above fuselage fore and aft of wing and under fuselage fore and aft of bomb bays, believed necessary because of aircraft's limited operational ceiling. About 31 'Bison A's are serving currently as flight refuelling tankers for the 43 remaining M-4 bombers and the

Tu-95 'Bears' of the Soviet strategic bomber force, carrying a hose-reel unit in the bomb bay.

Bison-B. Maritime reconnaissance version, described in 1979-80 *Jane's*. Few remain.

Bison-C. Improved maritime reconnaissance version, described in 1979-80 *Jane's*. Few remain.

DIMENSIONS, EXTERNAL ('Bison-A'):
Wing span 50·48 m (165 ft 7½ in)
Length overall 47·20 m (154 ft 10 in)
Tailplane span 15·00 m (49 ft 2½ in)
WEIGHT ('Bison-A'):
Max T-O weight 158,750 kg (350,000 lb)
PERFORMANCE ('Bison-A', estimated):
Max level speed at 11,000 m (36,000 ft):
485 knots (900 km/h; 560 mph)
Service ceiling 13,700 m (45,000 ft)
Range at 450 knots (835 km/h; 520 mph) with 4,500 kg (10,000 lb) of bombs
6,075 nm (11,250 km; 7,000 miles)

SUKHOI

Pavel Osipovich Sukhoi, who headed this design bureau until his death in September 1975, helped to design the ANT-25 and had a share in the construction of the 'Rodina' before the second World War; his Su-2 attack aeroplane was used in the war. He was also responsible for one of the jet aircraft in the 1947 Soviet Aviation Day display.

Nearly a decade later, on 24 June 1956, there appeared over Tushino new sweptwing and delta-wing fighters from Sukhoi's design team. Both aircraft subsequently entered squadron service with the Soviet Air Force, as the Su-7 and Su-9, and have been followed by other Sukhoi designs.

SUKHOI Su-7B
NATO reporting names: Fitter-A and Moujik

The **Su-7B** single-seat ground attack fighter (NATO reporting name **Fitter-A**) was first seen in prototype form during the 1956 Soviet Aviation Day Display and appeared in formations of up to 21 aircraft at the 1961 Tushino display. It subsequently became the standard tactical fighter-bomber of the Soviet Air Force, with which about 200 continue in service. Others have been supplied to Afghanistan, Algeria, Czechoslovakia, Egypt, Hungary, India, Iraq, North Korea, Poland, Romania, Syria and Viet-Nam.

The fuselage and tail unit of the Su-7B are almost identical with those of the delta-wing Su-11. Early production models had the pitot boom mounted centrally above the air intake, but it is offset to starboard on current versions.

Another change was made in the brake-chute installation. Early aircraft had a single ribbon-type parachute, attached under the rear fuselage; later Su-7Bs have twin brake-chutes, in a housing at the base of the rudder. The size of the blast panels on the sides of the front fuselage by the wing-root guns was also increased, implying that the cannon now fitted have a higher muzzle velocity or rate of fire.

Among further changes that led to use of the revised designation **Su-7BM** (for *Modifikatsirovanny:* modified) was the introduction of a low-pressure nosewheel tyre, requiring blistered doors to enclose it when retracted.

A variant of the Su-7 seen first at Domodedovo in 1967 is the two-seat **Su-7U**, with the second cockpit in tandem, aft of the standard cockpit and with a slightly raised

Sukhoi Su-7B single-seat close support fighter of the Soviet Air Force

Su-7U two-seat training aircraft (NATO 'Moujik'), in service with the Egyptian Air Force *(Denis Hughes)*

Sukhoi Su-7BM single-seat close support fighter, with additional side view (bottom) of two-seat Su-7U
(Pilot Press)

canopy. A prominent dorsal spine extends from the rear of the aft canopy to the base of the tail fin. The two-seater is a standard operational trainer and has the NATO reporting name **Moujik**.

The following description applies to the standard Su-7BM:

TYPE: Single-seat ground attack fighter.

WINGS: Cantilever mid-wing monoplane. No dihedral or anhedral. Sweepback approx 60° on leading-edges. Conventional all-metal construction. Wing-root chord is extended, giving a straight trailing-edge on inboard section of each wing. Very large area-increasing flaps over entire trailing-edge from root to inboard end of aileron on each wing. No slats or tabs. Two boundary-layer fences on each wing, at approx mid-span and immediately inboard of tip.

FUSELAGE: Conventional all-metal semi-monocoque structure of circular section. Two slim duct fairings along top of centre-fuselage. Two door-type airbrakes, at top and bottom, on each side of rear fuselage.

TAIL UNIT: Cantilever all-metal structure, with sweepback on all surfaces. All-moving horizontal surfaces, with anti-flutter bodies projecting forward from tips. Conventional rudder. No tabs.

LANDING GEAR: Retractable tricycle type, with single wheel on each unit. Nosewheel retracts forward, main units inward into wings. Twin brake-chutes in large fairing at base of rudder.

POWER PLANT: One Lyulka AL-7F-1 turbojet engine, rated at 68·65 kN (15,432 lb st) dry and 98·1 kN (22,046 lb st) with afterburning. Total internal fuel capacity 3,175 kg (7,000 lb). Provision for two external tanks, side by side under fuselage, with total capacity of 952 kg (2,100 lb). Two JATO solid-propellant rocket units can be attached under rear fuselage to shorten T-O run.

ACCOMMODATION: Pilot only, on rocket-powered ejection seat, under rearward-sliding blister canopy.

ARMAMENT: Two 30 mm NR-30 guns, each with 70 rounds, in wing-root leading-edges. Four underwing attachments for rocket pods or bombs (usually two 750 kg and two 500 kg), including nuclear weapons. When underbelly fuel tanks are fitted, max external weapon load is 1,000 kg (2,200 lb).

DIMENSIONS, EXTERNAL:
Wing span	8·93 m (29 ft 3½ in)
Length overall, incl probe	17·37 m (57 ft 0 in)
Height overall	4·57 m (15 ft 0 in)

WEIGHTS:
Weight empty	8,620 kg (19,000 lb)
Normal T-O weight	12,000 kg (26,450 lb)
Max T-O weight	13,500 kg (29,750 lb)

PERFORMANCE:
Max level speed at 11,000 m (36,000 ft):
'clean'
　　Mach 1·6 (917 knots; 1,700 km/h; 1,055 mph)
with external stores
　　Mach 1·2 (685 knots; 1,270 km/h; 788 mph)
Max level speed at S/L without afterburning
　　approx 460 knots (850 km/h; 530 mph)
Max rate of climb at S/L
　　approx 9,120 m (29,900 ft)/min
Service ceiling　　15,150 m (49,700 ft)

Combat radius
　　172-260 nm (320-480 km; 200-300 miles)
Max range　　780 nm (1,450 km; 900 miles)

SUKHOI Su-9 and Su-11
NATO reporting names: Fishpot and Maiden

First seen at Tushino during the 1956 Aviation Day Display, the prototype of these single-seat all-weather fighters (allocated the NATO reporting name 'Fishpot-A') had a small conical radome above its engine air intake. This was replaced by a centrebody air intake on the production version, which entered standard service in the Soviet Air Force in two forms as follows:

Su-9 (Fishpot-B). Initial version, operational since 1959 and still in service. Powered by 88·25 kN (19,840 lb st) Lyulka AL-7F afterburning turbojet. Small-diameter air intake and centrebody housing R1L (NATO 'Spin Scan') S-band radar. Examples included in the Tushino display of 1961 carried four of the Soviet Air Force's then-standard radar-homing air-to-air missiles (NATO reporting name 'Alkali') on underwing attachments, plus two underfuselage fuel tanks side by side. No fixed armament.

Su-11 (Fishpot-C). First seen publicly at the Domodedovo Aviation Day display in 1967, the Su-11 is a much-improved development of the Su-9, with a Lyulka AL-7F-1 turbojet (98·1 kN; 22,046 lb st with afterburning) and a standard armament of two underwing missiles (NATO 'Anab'), one with radar homing head and one with infra-red homing head. It also has a lengthened nose of less-tapered form than that of the Su-9, with an enlarged centrebody for the Uragan 5B (NATO 'Skip Spin') X-band radar, and two slim duct fairings along the top of the centre-fuselage, as on the Su-7B. The fuselage and tail unit of the two types are, in fact, almost identical.

There is also a tandem two-seat training version (NATO reporting name **Maiden**), with a cockpit layout similar to that of the two-seat Su-7U ('Moujik').

Although the Su-9 and Su-11 are generally similar in layout to their Mikoyan contemporary, the MiG-21, they are larger and heavier aircraft, with a much more powerful afterburning turbojet. They are less limited in all-weather capability than early versions of the MiG-21. The Sukhoi and Mikoyan 'tailed deltas' were, therefore, regarded as complementary rather than competitive when ordered into production in the late 'fifties. In 1980, the Su-9 and Su-11 continued to form nearly 20 per cent of the Soviet home defence interceptor force of 2,600 aircraft.

The Su-9 and Su-11 can be distinguished from the MiG-21 by their cleaner airframe, and the absence of both a ventral stabilising fin and fairings on the fuselage forward of the wing-root leading-edges. The cockpit canopy of the single-seat versions is rearward-sliding, whereas that of the MiG-21 is hinged to open either forward about the base of the windscreen or sideways.

The tricycle landing gear of the Su-9 and Su-11 has a wide track, with a single wheel on each unit. The main units retract inward into the wings, the nosewheel forward. Control surfaces appear to be conventional, with a one-piece all-moving tailplane, carrying the anti-flutter body projection at each tip that is found on many Soviet combat aircraft. There are four petal-type airbrakes, in pairs on each side of the rear fuselage.

DIMENSIONS, EXTERNAL (Su-11, estimated):
Wing span	8·43 m (27 ft 8 in)
Length overall, incl probe	17·0 m (56 ft 0 in)

WEIGHT (Su-11, estimated):
Max T-O weight	13,600 kg (30,000 lb)

PERFORMANCE (Su-11, estimated):
Max level speed at 11,000 m (36,000 ft)
　　Mach 1·8 (1,033 knots; 1,915 km/h; 1,190 mph)
Service ceiling　　17,000 m (55,700 ft)

SUKHOI Su-15
NATO reporting name: Flagon

Ten examples of this twin-jet delta-wing fighter participated in the flying display at Domodedovo in July 1967. First to appear was a single black-painted machine, piloted by Vladimir Ilyushin, son of the famous designer and known to be a test pilot for Sukhoi. When a formation of nine similar aircraft appeared later, the identity of the

Sukhoi Su-9 all-weather fighter, with four underwing mountings for 'Alkali' missiles *(Tass)*

Sukhoi Su-11 single-seat fighter, armed with two of the missiles known to NATO as 'Anab' *(Novosti)*

Sukhoi Su-11 single-seat all-weather interceptor *(Pilot Press)*

design bureau responsible for them was confirmed by the obvious 'family likeness' to the Su-9 and Su-11 in the shape of the wings and tail unit.

It is now clear that this aircraft was developed to meet a Soviet Air Force requirement for a Mach 2·5 interceptor to replace the Su-11. It is in service with the Soviet Air Force in several forms:

Flagon-A. Basic single-seater, with simple delta wings (estimated span 9·15 m; 30 ft), identical in form to those of the Su-11. Conical nose radome. Turbojets reported to be Tumansky R-11F2-300s, as used in MiG-21 series, each rated at 60·8 kN (13,668 lb st) with afterburning. Probably restricted to small initial quantity.

Flagon-C. Two-seat training version of 'Flagon-D', with probable combat capability. Individual rearward hinged canopy over each seat. Periscope fitted above rear canopy for forward view.

Flagon-D. Generally similar to 'Flagon-A', but with longer-span wings of compound sweep, produced by reducing the sweepback at the tips via a very narrow unswept section. Conical radome. First major production version.

Flagon-E. Wings similar to those of 'Flagon-D'. New and more powerful propulsion system, increasing speed and range. Turbojets reported to be Tumansky R-13F-300s, as used in second-generation MiG-21MF, each rated at 64·73 kN (14,550 lb st). Uprated avionics. Major production version; operational since second half of 1973.

Flagon-F. Latest version in service. Can be identified by ogival nose radome. Generally similar to 'Flagon-E', but with uprated engines.

About 1,000 Su-15s were believed to form the backbone of the PVO-Strany's force of 2,600 interceptors in 1980, all based in the Soviet Union.

The following details apply to 'Flagon-F':

TYPE: Single-seat twin-jet all-weather interceptor.

WINGS: Cantilever mid-wing monoplane, basically similar to those of Su-11, but with new and extended tips. Sweepback approx 53° on inner wings, 37° on tips. No dihedral or anhedral. All-metal structure. Single boundary-layer fence above each wing at approx 70% span. Large area-increasing flap extends from inboard end of aileron to fuselage on each side.

FUSELAGE: Cockpit section is basically circular with large ogival dielectric nosecone. Centre fuselage is faired into rectangular-section air intake ducts. Two door-type airbrakes at top and bottom on each side of rear fuselage, forward of tailplane.

TAIL UNIT: Cantilever all-metal structure, with sweepback on all surfaces. All-moving tailplane, with anhedral, mounted slightly below mid position and fitted with anti-flutter bodies near tips. Conventional rudder. No trim tabs.

LANDING GEAR: Tricycle type, with single wheel on each unit. Main wheels retract inward into wings and intake ducts; nosewheel retracts forward.

POWER PLANT: Two turbojets, with variable-area nozzles, mounted side by side in rear fuselage. These are reported to be Tumansky R-13F2-300s, each rated at 70·6 kN (15,875 lb st) with afterburning. Ram-air intakes, with variable ramps on splitter plates, embodying vertical slots for boundary layer control. Blow-in auxiliary inlets midway between main intake and wing leading-edge in each duct.

ACCOMMODATION: Single seat in enclosed cockpit, with rearward-sliding blister canopy. Rear-view mirror above canopy of some aircraft.

ARMAMENT: Single pylon for external store under each wing, in line with boundary-layer fence. Normal armament comprises one radar homing and one infra-red homing air-to-air missile (NATO 'Anab'). Side-by-side pylons under centre-fuselage for further weapons or external fuel tanks.

AVIONICS AND EQUIPMENT: Large X-band radar (NATO 'Skip Spin') in nose, SOD-57M ATC/SIF nav system, SRO-2 (NATO 'Odd Rods') IFF, Sirena 3 radar warning system.

DIMENSIONS, EXTERNAL (estimated):
Wing span	10·53 m (34 ft 6 in)
Length overall	20·5 m (68 ft 0 in)

WEIGHT (estimated):
Max T-O weight	16,000 kg (35,275 lb)

PERFORMANCE (estimated):
Max level speed above 11,000 m (36,000 ft):	
with external stores	Mach 2·3
'clean'	Mach 2·5
Time to 11,000 m (36,000 ft)	2 min 30 s
Service ceiling	20,000 m (65,600 ft)
Combat radius	390 nm (725 km; 450 miles)

'Flagon-F' version of the Su-15, armed with 'Anab' missiles *(Swedish Air Force)*

Sukhoi Su-15, 'Flagon-F', with additional side views of two-seat 'Flagon-C' (centre) and 'Flagon-D' (top)
(Pilot Press)

Two views of the tandem two-seat combat trainer version of the Sukhoi Su-15, known to NATO as 'Flagon-C'

Sukhoi Su-17 single-seat variable-geometry fighter with wings extended *(Flug Revue)*

SUKHOI Su-17, Su-20 and Su-22
NATO reporting names: Fitter-C, D, E, F, G and H

The variable-geometry Su-17, with more powerful engine and improved avionics, is in a completely different class from the veteran Su-7 ('Fitter-A'). The prototype was an R & D aircraft shown at the Soviet Aviation Day display at Domodedovo Airport, Moscow, in July 1967, and was allocated the NATO reporting name 'Fitter-B'. Only some 4·0 m (13 ft) of each wing was pivoted, outboard of a very large fence, the remainder of the airframe being virtually identical with that of the Su-7. An attachment for an external store was built into each wing fence, but the power plant appeared to be unchanged and there was no reason to expect 'Fitter-B' to form the basis of a production aircraft, in view of the modest improvement in overall performance offered by such minimal modification.

Discovery of at least one or two squadrons of "improved Fitter-Bs" in service with the Soviet tactical air forces in 1972 came as a surprise, suggesting that even a small improvement in range and endurance by comparison with the Su-7 was considered worthwhile. Only after several years did the true measure of improvement become apparent. The combination of a more powerful engine and the variable-geometry wings permitted a doubled external load to be lifted from strips little more than half as long as those needed by the Su-7, and to be carried about 30 per cent further. Added to new avionics, this made the Su-17 so attractive that about 650 are deployed currently by Soviet tactical air forces, and by Soviet Naval aviation units assigned to anti-shipping strike and amphibious support roles in the Baltic Sea area. Differences between the various versions identified to date are as follows:

Su-17 (Fitter-C). Basic single-seat attack aircraft for Soviet Air Force, with Lyulka AL-21F-3 turbojet, offering better specific fuel consumption than AL-7F-1 of Su-7.

Su-17 (Fitter-D). Generally similar to 'Fitter-C', but forward fuselage lengthened by about 0·38 m (1 ft 3 in). Added undernose radome. Laser marked target seeker in intake centrebody.

Su-20 (Fitter-C). Export counterpart of Soviet basic

'Fitter-C', with reduced equipment standard. Variations in rear fuselage contours by comparison with Su-17 suggest a different engine, possibly the Su-7's AL-7F-1 afterburning turbojet (98·1 kN; 22,046 lb st). Supplied to Algeria, Czechoslovakia, Egypt, Iraq and Poland.

Su-22 (Fitter-C). Variant of Su-20 first delivered to Peru in 1977 (48 single-seat, 4 two-seat) and subsequently to Syria. Further reduced equipment standard, with Sirena 2 limited-coverage radar warning receiver, virtually no navigation aids, and IFF incompatible with Peru's SA-3 (NATO 'Goa') surface-to-air missiles. Weapons include 'Atoll' air-to-air missiles.

Additional versions, with the NATO reporting names 'Fitter-G and H', were revealed in US Department of Defense documents concerned with the FY 1981 budget requests. Taken in conjunction with photographs published in the Soviet Union and Eastern Europe during 1980, this has permitted compilation of the following provisional list of further versions:

Fitter-E. Tandem two-seat trainer for Soviet Air Force. Generally similar to 'Fitter-C' but entire fuselage forward of wing drooped slightly to improve view from rear seat. Port wing-root gun deleted.

Fitter-F. Export counterpart of 'Fitter-D'. Increased-diameter rear fuselage. Longer dorsal fin.

Fitter-G. Developed two-seater, with combat capability. Taller fin with straight top. Shallow ventral fin. Starboard gun only. Laser target seeker fitted.

Fitter-H. As 'Fitter-G' with drooped nose, but single-seat.

In early 1980, the accompanying photograph of a tandem two-seat version was published in the Soviet press. This has the increased-diameter rear fuselage and fin shape of 'Fitter-F', and the front fuselage droop of 'Fitter-E'. However, the rearward-hinged canopy on the rear cockpit is 'solid' except for a window at the front on each side, which would not be compatible with a normal training role. The width and depth of the dorsal spine are increased aft of the rear canopy. Other features include a ventral fin, and a laser seeker in the intake centrebody like that of 'Fitter-D'.

The following description applies to the Su-17 ('Fitter-C'):

TYPE: Single-seat ground attack fighter.
WINGS: Cantilever mid-wing monoplane, with wide-span fixed centre-section and manually-actuated variable-geometry outer panels, with min sweep angle of 28° and max sweep angle of 62° approx. Centre-section appears to be generally similar to inner wings of Su-7, except for slight sweepback on trailing-edge of area-increasing centre-section flaps. Outboard of these flaps, centre-section trailing-edge is swept to align with trailing-edge of outer panels when they are fully swept. Full-span leading-edge slats on movable panels. Entire trailing-edge of each movable panel made up of a slotted flap, operable only when the wings are spread, and a slotted aileron operable at all times. Large main fence on each side, at junction of fixed and movable panels, is square-cut at front and incorporates attachments for external stores. Shorter fence above centre-section on each side, inboard of main fence.
FUSELAGE: Conventional all-metal semi-monocoque structure of circular section. Large dorsal spine fairing along top of fuselage, from canopy to fin. Ram-air intake in nose, with variable shockcone centrebody. Four door-type airbrakes, at top and bottom on each side of rear fuselage, forward of tailplane. Pitot on port side of nose; transducer to provide data for fire control computer on starboard side.
TAIL UNIT: Cantilever all-metal structure, with sweepback on all surfaces. All-moving horizontal surfaces, with anti-flutter body projecting forward on each side near tip. Conventional rudder. No tabs.
LANDING GEAR: Retractable tricycle type, with single wheel on each unit. Nosewheel retracts forward, requiring blistered door to enclose it. Main units retract inward into centre-section. Container for twin brakechutes between the base of the rudder and the tailpipe.
POWER PLANT: One Lyulka AL-21F-3 turbojet engine, rated at 80·1 kN (18,000 lb st) dry and 109 kN (24,500 lb st) with afterburning. Fuel capacity increased to 4,550 litres (1,000 Imp gallons) by added tankage in dorsal spine fairing. Provision for carrying up to four 800 litre (176 Imp gallon) drop tanks on outboard wing pylons and under fuselage. When underfuselage tanks are carried, only the two inboard wing pylons may be used for ordnance to a total weight of 1,000 kg (2,204 lb).
ACCOMMODATION: Pilot only, on ejection seat, under rearward-hinged transparent canopy. Rearview mirror above canopy.
ARMAMENT: Two 30 mm NR-30 guns, each with 70 rds, in wing-root leading-edges. Total of eight weapon pylons (two tandem pairs under fuselage, one under each centre-section leading-edge, one under each main wing fence) for up to 5,000 kg (11,023 lb) of bombs, rocket pods and guided missiles such as the air-to-surface AS-7 (NATO 'Kerry').
AVIONICS AND EQUIPMENT: SRD-5M (NATO 'High Fix') radar in intake centrebody; ASP-5ND fire control system; Sirena 3 radar homing and warning system providing 360° coverage, with antennae in slim cylindrical housing above brake-chute container and in each centre-section leading-edge, between fences; SRO-2M IFF; SOD-57M ATC/SIF, with transponder housing beneath brake-chute container; RSIU-5/R-831 VHF/UHF and R5B-70 HF.
DIMENSIONS, EXTERNAL (estimated):
  Wing span: fully spread   14·00 m (45 ft 11¼ in)
           fully swept   10·60 m (34 ft 9½ in)

**Left:
Sukhoi Su-17 ('Fitter-D') with undernose radar**

**Right:
Unidentified two-seat version of the Sukhoi Su-17/20/22 series**

Wing aspect ratio: fully spread	4·9
fully swept	3·0
Length overall, incl probes	18·75 m (61 ft 6¼ in)
Fuselage length	15·40 m (50 ft 6¼ in)
Height overall	4·75 m (15 ft 7 in)
AREAS (estimated):	
Wings, gross: fully spread	40·1 m² (431·6 sq ft)
fully swept	37·2 m² (400·4 sq ft)
WEIGHTS (estimated):	
Weight empty	10,000 kg (22,046 lb)
Max internal fuel	3,700 kg (8,157 lb)
T-O weight, 'clean'	14,000 kg (30,865 lb)
Max T-O weight	17,700 kg (39,020 lb)

PERFORMANCE (estimated for 'clean' aircraft, 60% internal fuel, except where indicated):

Max level speed at height	Mach 2·17
Max level speed at S/L	Mach 1·05
Touchdown speed 143 knots (265 km/h; 165 mph)	
Max rate of climb at S/L 13,800 m (45,275 ft)/min	
Service ceiling	18,000 m (59,050 ft)
T-O run at AUW of 17,000 kg (37,478 lb)	620 m (2,035 ft)
T-O to 15 m (50 ft) at AUW of 17,000 kg (37,478 lb)	835 m (2,740 ft)
Landing run	600 m (1,970 ft)
Combat radius with 2,000 kg (4,409 lb) external stores:	
hi-lo-hi	340 nm (630 km; 391 miles)
lo-lo-lo	195 nm (360 km; 224 miles)

Sukhoi Su-20 variable-geometry ground attack fighter in service with the Polish Air Force

Sukhoi Su-20 variable-geometry tactical combat aircraft ('Fitter-C'), with scrap view of 'Fitter-D' nose
(*Pilot Press*)

SUKHOI Su-24
NATO reporting name: Fencer

This variable-geometry attack aircraft was identified as a major new operational type by Admiral Thomas H. Moorer, Chairman of the US Joint Chiefs of Staff, in early 1974, when he described it as "the first modern Soviet fighter to be developed specifically as a fighter-bomber for the ground attack mission". In the same class as the US Air Force's F-111, it was believed initially to be designated Su-19 in the Soviet Union, but the FY 1981 US Department of Defense Annual Report refers to it as the Su-24.

No clear photographs or officially-released details of 'Fencer' had been made available by mid-1980. However, it is believed that the accompanying drawing reflects the aircraft's major characteristics.

Seating for the crew of two (pilot and weapon systems officer) is shown to be side by side in a slim and clean fuselage typical of Sukhoi designs. The wings are pivoted much further inboard than on the Su-17/20 or Tupolev 'Backfire'. Each is shown with full-span leading-edge and trailing-edge flaps. This implies that the all-moving horizontal tail surfaces operate both differentially and symmetrically to provide aileron and elevator functions, although the outboard flap sections may function as drooping ailerons when the wings are spread.

Wing leading-edge sweep appears to be approximately 23° in the fully-spread position, and 70° fully swept. The

wings are shown with slight anhedral.

'Fencer' may be powered by two Lyulka AL-21F turbojets of the kind fitted to the single-engined Su-17. Armament includes more than 4,535 kg (10,000 lb) of guided and unguided air-to-surface weapons on six pylons under the fuselage, wing-root gloves and outer wings, in addition to a GSh-23 twin-barrel 23 mm gun. The pivoting pylons under the outer wings are the first observed on a Soviet aircraft.

Lt Gen Donald R. Keith, US Army Deputy Chief of Staff for Research, Development and Acquisition, has said that 'Fencer' is credited with having terrain-

avoidance radar, in addition to nav/attack radar, and "has the capability to deliver ordnance in all weather within 55 m (180 ft) of its target".

'Fencer' entered squadron service in December 1974. In the Spring of 1980 at least 250 were serving with first-line squadrons in the European theatre, including units in Lusatia and a regiment at Chernyakhovsk, near Kaliningrad on the Soviet Baltic coast. None has been seen outside the Soviet Union or its home waters.

DIMENSIONS, EXTERNAL (estimated):

Wing span: spread	17·15 m (56 ft 3 in)
swept	9·53 m (31 ft 3 in)
Length overall	21·29 m (69 ft 10 in)

WEIGHT (estimated):

Max T-O weight	30,850 kg (68,000 lb)

PERFORMANCE (estimated):

Max speed at height	above Mach 2
Combat radius, lo-lo-lo	over 174 nm (322 km; 200 miles)

Sukhoi Su-24 variable-geometry attack aircraft (*Pilot Press, provisional*)

Best photograph yet released of the Sukhoi Su-24

TUPOLEV

CHIEF DESIGNER (Tu-144): Dr Alexei A. Tupolev
CHIEF DESIGNER (Tu-154): Dmitry Markov
DEPUTY CHIEF OF BUREAU: Andrei Kandolov

Andrei Tupolev, born in 1888, was a leading figure in the Central Aero-Hydrodynamic Institute (TsAGI) in Moscow from the time when it was founded, in 1929, until his death on 23 December 1972. He was for long the Soviet Union's outstanding designer, and the recent products of his design team range from turbofan civil transports to the first Soviet supersonic bomber to enter service and the first supersonic transport aircraft. Also in production in the Soviet Union are small amphibious aerosleighs of Tupolev design, powered by aircraft piston engines and

capable of travelling over both water and snow. Current chief designers of the Tupolev bureau include Andrei Tupolev's son, Dr Alexei A. Tupolev.

TUPOLEV Tu-16
NATO reporting name: Badger

This bomber, which has the Tupolev design bureau designation Tu-88, made its first major public appearance on 1 May 1954; yet nearly half of the 2,000 that were built remain operational. About 300 are deployed with medium-range units of the Soviet strategic bomber force, able to deliver nuclear or conventional weapons, and supported by a few Tu-16 in-flight refuelling tankers, using a unique wingtip-to-wingtip transfer technique, more than 90 of various versions equipped for ECM duties, and 15

for reconnaissance. Naval units have about 275 Tu-16s for maritime attack, 70 tankers, and 40 reconnaissance and ECM models.

Ten versions of the Tu-16 have been identified by unclassified NATO reporting names. All except 'Badger-B' (see 1975-76 *Jane's*) remain in first-line service, as follows:

Badger-A. Basic strategic jet bomber, able to carry nuclear or conventional free-fall weapons. Glazed nose, with small undernose radome. Defensive armament of seven 23 mm cannon. Some equipped as flight refuelling tankers, using a unique wingtip-to-wingtip transfer technique. Nine supplied to Iraq. More than 80 operational with Chinese Air Force, mostly built in China under designation B-6.

'Badger-H' version of the Tupolev Tu-16 twin-jet bomber, for stand-off or escort ECM duties

Tupolev Tu-16, in the form known to NATO as 'Badger-F', with additional side view (bottom) of 'Badger-D'
(Pilot Press)

POWER PLANT: Two Mikulin AM-3 turbojet engines, each rated at 85·8 kN (19,285 lb st) at sea level. Fuel in wing and fuselage tanks, with total capacity of approx 45,450 litres (10,000 Imp gallons). Provision for underwing auxiliary fuel tanks and for flight refuelling. Tu-16 tankers trail hose from starboard wingtip; receiving equipment is in port wingtip extension.

ACCOMMODATION: Normal crew of six, with two pilots side by side on flight deck. Navigator in glazed nose of all versions except 'Badger-C and D'. Manned tail position plus lateral observation blisters in rear fuselage under tailplane.

ARMAMENT: Forward dorsal and rear ventral barbettes each containing two 23 mm NR-23 cannon. Two further cannon in tail position controlled by an automatic gun-ranging radar set. Seventh, fixed, cannon on starboard side of nose of versions without nose radome. Bomb load of up to 9,000 kg (19,800 lb) delivered from weapons bay about 6·5 m (21 ft) long in standard bomber. Naval versions can carry air-to-surface winged stand-off missiles.

AVIONICS AND EQUIPMENT: Radio and radar aids probably include HF and VHF R/T equipment, as well as IFF and a radio compass and radio altimeter. Other equipment differs according to role.

DIMENSIONS, EXTERNAL:
Wing span	32·93 m (108 ft 0½ in)
Length overall	34·80 m (114 ft 2 in)
Height overall	10·80 m (35 ft 6 in)
Tailplane span	11·75 m (38 ft 6½ in)
Wheel track	9·775 m (32 ft 0¾ in)

Badger-C. Anti-shipping version, first seen at 1961 Soviet Aviation Day display. Large air-to-surface winged missile (NATO reporting name 'Kipper') carried under fuselage. Wide nose radome, in place of glazing and nose gun of 'Badger-A'.

Badger-D. Maritime/electronic reconnaissance version. Nose similar to that of 'Badger-C'. Enlarged undernose radome; three blister fairings in tandem under centre-fuselage.

Badger-E. Similar to 'Badger-A' but with cameras in bomb bay.

Badger-F. Basically similar to 'Badger-E' but with electronic intelligence pod on a pylon under each wing.

Badger-G. Similar to 'Badger-A' but with underwing pylons for two rocket-powered air-to-surface missiles (NATO reporting name 'Kelt'). One photographed by pilot of Japanese F-86F in December 1977 carried a new missile (NATO 'Kingfish') on port underwing pylon. Others seen subsequently with a 'Kingfish' under each wing (see Air-Launched Missiles section). Majority serve with anti-shipping squadrons of Soviet Naval Air Force. Others were included in the 25 Tu-16s supplied to Egypt as replacements for aircraft lost in the October 1973 war with Israel.

Badger-H. Stand-off or escort ECM aircraft, with primary function of chaff dispensing. The chaff dispensers are probably located in the weapons bay area. Hatch aft of weapons bay. Two teardrop radomes, fore and aft of weapons bay. Two blade antennae aft of weapons bay.

Badger-J. Specialised ECM jamming aircraft, with at least some of the equipment located in a canoe-shape radome inside the weapons bay.

Badger-K. Electronic reconnaissance variant. Two teardrop radomes, inside and forward of weapons bay.

Maritime reconnaissance versions of 'Badger' make regular flights over units of the US Navy and other NATO naval forces at sea in the Atlantic, Pacific and elsewhere, and have been photographed while doing so. The aircraft often operate in pairs, with one 'Badger-F' accompanied by a different version. They also make electronic intelligence (elint) sorties around the coastlines of NATO and other non-Communist countries.

TYPE: Twin-jet medium bomber and maritime reconnaissance/attack aircraft.

WINGS: Cantilever high mid-wing monoplane with slight anhedral and with 35° of leading-edge sweep on outer panels; 42° sweep on inboard panels. Thickness/chord ratio 12½%.

FUSELAGE: All-metal semi-monocoque structure of circular cross-section.

TAIL UNIT: Cantilever all-metal structure, with sweepback on all surfaces. Trim tabs in rudder and each elevator.

LANDING GEAR: Retractable tricycle type. Twin-wheel nose unit retracts rearward. Main four-wheel bogies retract into housings projecting beyond the wing trailing-edge.

The latest electronic reconnaissance variant of the Tupolev Tu-16 ('Badger-K')

The version of the Tupolev Tu-142 known to NATO as 'Bear-D' *(Pilot Press)*

Camera ports under the bomb bay are a recognition feature of the 'Bear-E' version of the Tu-142 (*Royal Air Force*)

AREA:
Wings, gross   164·65 m² (1,772·3 sq ft)
WEIGHTS:
Weight empty   37,200 kg (82,000 lb)
Normal T-O weight   72,000 kg (158,730 lb)
PERFORMANCE (estimated, at max T-O weight):
Max level speed at 6,000 m (19,700 ft)
     535 knots (992 km/h; 616 mph)
Service ceiling   12,300 m (40,350 ft)
Range with max bomb load
     2,605 nm (4,800 km; 3,000 miles)
Range with max fuel 3,110 nm (5,760 km; 3,579 miles)

TUPOLEV Tu-95 and Tu-142
NATO reporting name: Bear

Documents issued in Washington concerning the SALT 2 negotiations, in 1979, revealed that the Soviet authorities use the designation Tu-95 for the 113 'Bear-A/Bs' that form the mainstay of Dalnaya Aviatsiya's current strategic bomber force, but that the assorted 'Bears', totalling about 75, used by the Soviet Naval Air Force are known as **Tu-142s**. The Naval aircraft, being employed only for anti-submarine warfare, are not subject to SALT restrictions. Those operated from bases made available in Cuba and Angola are capable of covering the North and South Atlantic from the Mediterranean approaches westward to the US east coast, and southward to the Cape of Good Hope.

Long range and endurance are only two of the attributes that have kept the huge four-turboprop Tu-95s and Tu-142s in first-line service for a quarter of a century. Their high speed, exceeding that once considered possible for propeller-driven aircraft, eclipsed the contemporary four-jet Myasishchev M-4. Their size and payload potential enabled them to accommodate the largest air-to-surface missiles and radars yet carried by operational aircraft. Thus, the six versions identified by NATO reporting names all remain in service, as follows:

Bear-A. Basic strategic bomber, first flown in late Summer of 1954 and shown in Aviation Day display at Tushino in July 1955. Internal stowage for two nuclear or a variety of conventional free-fall weapons. Fitted with chin radar, and defensive armament comprising three pairs of 23 mm cannon in remotely-controlled dorsal and ventral barbettes and manned tail gun turret. Two glazed blisters on rear fuselage, under tailplane, are used for sighting by the gunner controlling all these weapons. The dorsal and ventral barbettes can also be controlled from a station aft of the flight deck.

Bear-B. First seen in 1961 Aviation Day flypast. As 'Bear-A' but able to carry a large air-to-surface aeroplane-type missile (NATO reporting name 'Kangaroo') under fuselage, with associated radar equipment in wide undernose radome, replacing the original glazing. Some 'Bears' of Dalnaya Aviatsiya now carry 'Kitchen' air-to-surface missiles. Defensive armament retained. A few 'Bear-Bs' operate in maritime reconnaissance role, with flight refuelling nose-probe and, sometimes, a streamlined blister fairing on the starboard side of the rear fuselage. One was observed in 1978 with a pointed canister under each wing, presumably for air sampling.

Bear-C. Maritime patrol version, first identified when it appeared in vicinity of NATO naval forces during Exercise Teamwork in September 1964. Generally similar to 'Bear-B' but with streamlined blister fairing on *both* sides of rear fuselage. Refuelling probe standard.

Bear-D. This version was first photographed extensively when several examples (together with Tu-16s) made low passes over the US Coast Guard icebreakers *Edisto* and *Eastwind* off Severnaya Zemlya, in the Soviet Arctic, in August 1967. These aircraft differed in detail, but each had a glazed nose, an undernose radar scanner, a large underbelly radome for X-band radar, a blister fairing on each side of the rear fuselage like 'Bear-C', a nose refuelling probe, and a variety of other blisters and antennae, including a streamlined fairing on each tailplane tip. The

housing for I-band tail-warning radar above the tail turret is much larger than on previous versions. 'Bear-D' has an important function in support of operations involving surface-to-surface and air-to-surface missiles. It provides data on the location and nature of potential targets to missile launch crews on board ships and aircraft which are themselves too distant from the target to ensure precise missile aiming and guidance. About 40 serve with the Soviet Naval air fleet.

A 'Bear-D' photographed in the second half of 1978, after interception by US Navy F-4s, had in place of the normal tail turret and associated radome a faired tail housing special equipment (see accompanying illustration).

Bear-E. Maritime reconnaissance version, basically similar in configuration to 'Bear-A' but with refuelling probe and rear fuselage blister fairings as on 'Bear-C'. Six camera windows in bomb bay, in pairs in line with the wing flaps, sometimes with a seventh window to the rear on the starboard side.

Bear-F. First identified in 1973, this much-refined anti-submarine version has enlarged and lengthened fairings aft of its inboard engine nacelles, for purely aerodynamic reasons. The undernose radar of 'Bear-D' is missing on some aircraft; others have a radome in this position, but of considerably modified form. On both models the main underfuselage X-band radar housing is considerably further forward than on 'Bear-D' and smaller in size; the forward portion of the fuselage is longer; there are no large blister fairings under and on the sides of the rear fuselage; and the nosewheel doors are bulged prominently, suggesting the use of larger or low-pressure tyres. 'Bear-F' has two stores bays in its rear fuselage, one of them replacing the usual rear ventral gun turret and leaving the tail turret as the sole defensive gun position. About 30 of this version were operational in early 1980.

Examples of all versions of the Tu-142 have made reconnaissance flights over units of the US Fleet at sea and have been photographed by US naval fighters while doing so. They are also encountered frequently over the North Sea by the RAF and Royal Navy, and off the US east coast during transits between Murmansk and Cuba, and elint missions from Cuba.

TYPE: Four-turboprop long-range bomber and maritime reconnaissance aircraft.
WINGS: Cantilever mid-wing monoplane. Sweepback 37° at quarter-chord on inner panels, 35° at quarter-chord on outer panels. All-metal three-spar structure. All-metal hydraulically-powered ailerons and Fowler flaps. Trim tabs in ailerons. Spoilers in top surface of wing

forward of inboard end of ailerons. Three boundary layer fences on top surface of each wing. Thermal anti-icing system in leading-edges.
FUSELAGE: All-metal semi-monocoque structure of circular section, containing three pressurised compartments. Those forward and aft of the weapons bay are linked by a crawlway tunnel. The tail gunner's compartment is not accessible from the other compartments.
TAIL UNIT: Cantilever all-metal structure, with sweepback on all surfaces. Adjustable tailplane incidence. Hydraulically-powered rudder and elevators. Trim tabs in rudder and each elevator.
LANDING GEAR: Retractable tricycle type. Main units consist of four-wheel bogies, with tyres of approx 1·50 m (5 ft) diameter and hydraulic internal expanding brakes. Twin wheels on nose unit. All units retract rearward, main units into nacelles built on to wing trailing-edge. Retractable tail bumper consisting of two small wheels. Braking parachute may be used to reduce landing run.
POWER PLANT: Four Kuznetsov NK-12MV turboprop engines, each originally with max rating of approx 8,948 kW (12,000 ehp) but now uprated to 11,033 kW (14,795 ehp) and driving eight-blade contra-rotating reversible-pitch Type AV-60N propellers. Fuel in wing tanks, with normal capacity of 72,980 litres (16,540 Imp gallons).
ACCOMMODATION AND ARMAMENT: See notes applicable to individual versions and under 'Fuselage'.
OPERATIONAL EQUIPMENT ('Bear-D'): Large X-band radar in blister fairing under centre fuselage, for reconnaissance and to provide data on potential targets for anti-

The faired tail, housing special equipment, on a 'Bear-D' photographed in 1978

The version of 'Bear-F' with an undernose radome

The Tu-126 airborne warning and control system (AWACS) aircraft, known to NATO as 'Moss'

Tupolev Tu-126 (four Kuznetsov NK-12MV turboprops) *(Pilot Press)*

shipping aircraft or surface vessels. In latter mode, PPI presentation is data-linked to missile launch station. Four-PRF range J-band circular and sector scan bombing and navigation radar (NATO 'Short Horn'). I-band tail warning radar (NATO 'Bee Hind') in housing at base of rudder.

DIMENSIONS, EXTERNAL ('Bear-F', approx):
Wing span 51·10 m (167 ft 8 in)
Length overall 49·50 m (162 ft 5 in)
Height overall 12·12 m (39 ft 9 in)
WEIGHT ('Bear-F', estimated):
Max T-O weight 188,000 kg (414,470 lb)
PERFORMANCE ('Bear-A'):
Over-target speed at 12,500 m (41,000 ft)
435 knots (805 km/h; 500 mph)
Max range with 11,340 kg (25,000 lb) bomb load
6,775 nm (12,550 km; 7,800 miles)

TUPOLEV Tu-126
NATO reporting name: Moss

An officially-released Soviet documentary film, shown in the West in 1968, included sequences depicting a milit-

ary version of the Tu-114 four-turboprop transport (see 1972-73 *Jane's*), carrying above its fuselage a rotating 'saucer' type early warning radar with a diameter of about 11 m (36 ft). This was a logical development, as the Tu-114 had a fuselage of larger diameter than the military Tu-95, and could accommodate more easily the extensive avionic equipment and crew of 12 required by this long-endurance early-warning and fighter control aircraft. Designated Tu-126 in the Soviet Union, the aircraft also has wings similar to those of the Tu-114, with extended-chord trailing-edge flaps, rather than the 'straight' trailing-edge of the Tu-95. Its power plant comprises four 11,033 kW (14,795 ehp) Kuznetsov NK-12MV turbo-prop engines.

The general appearance of the Tu-126, which has the NATO reporting name 'Moss', is shown in the accompanying illustrations. It can be seen to have a flight refuelling nose-probe, ventral tail-fin and numerous additional antennae and blisters for electronic equipment.

In the AWACS (airborne warning and control system) role, the Tu-126 is intended to work in conjunction with advanced interceptors. After locating incoming low-level

strike aircraft, the Tu-126 would ideally direct towards them fighters armed with 'snap-down' air-to-air missiles able to be fired from a cruising height of 6,100 m (20,000 ft) or higher. It has a further, obvious application in assisting strike aircraft to elude enemy interceptors picked up by its radar.

At least 10 or 12 Tu-126s are operational with the Soviet air defence forces.They are said, by US defence experts, to have worked in overwater exercises but to be ineffective over land at the present stage of development.

DIMENSIONS, EXTERNAL:
Wing span 51·20 m (168 ft 0 in)
Wing aspect ratio 10·4
Length overall 55·20 m (181 ft 1 in)
Height overall 16·05 m (52 ft 8 in)
Wheel track 13·70 m (44 ft 11½ in)
Propeller diameter 5·60 m (18 ft 4½ in)
AREA:
Wings, gross 311·1 m² (3,349 sq ft)
WEIGHT (estimated):
Max T-O weight 170,000 kg (374,785 lb)
PERFORMANCE:
Max level speed 459 knots (850 km/h; 528 mph)
Normal operating speed
351 knots (650 km/h; 404 mph)
Max range without flight refuelling
6,775 nm (12,550 km; 7,800 miles)

TUPOLEV Tu-22
NATO reporting name: Blinder

First shown publicly in the 1961 Aviation Day flypast over Moscow, the Tu-22 was the first operational Soviet supersonic bomber. Of the ten examples which took part in that display, only one carried visible weapons, in the form of an air-to-surface missile (NATO reporting name 'Kitchen'), some 11 m (36 ft) long, semi-submerged in the underside of its fuselage. This aircraft had also a wider nose radome.

A total of 22 Tu-22s took part in the 1967 display at Domodedovo. One was escorted by six MiG-21PFs, permitting a more accurate calculation of its overall dimensions than had previously been possible. Most carried 'Kitchen' missiles; all had a partially-retractable nose refuelling probe and the wide radome seen on the single missile-armed aircraft in 1961.

About 250 Tu-22s were built, in four versions, as follows:

Blinder-A. Basic reconnaissance bomber, with fuselage weapon bay for free-fall bombs. 'Blinder-A' entered only limited service, its max range of 1,215 nm (2,250 km; 1,400 miles) being inadequate for the originally intended strategic role. Twelve supplied to Iraq.

Tupolev Tu-22 photographed from an investigating interceptor of the Swedish Air Force

Blinder-B. Generally similar to 'Blinder-A' but equipped to carry air-to-surface nuclear missile (NATO reporting name 'Kitchen') recessed in weapons bay. Larger radar and partially-retractable flight refuelling probe on nose. About 125 'Blinder-As' and 'Blinder-Bs' are believed to remain operational with the Soviet bomber force, plus 12 equipped for reconnaissance and 17 serving with the Libyan Air Force.

Blinder-C. Maritime reconnaissance version, with six cameras in weapons bay and camera windows in weapons bay doors. Modifications to nosecone, dielectric panels, etc, suggest possible electronic intelligence role or equipment for electronic countermeasures (ECM) duties. About 60 delivered, of which 40 remain in service, for operation primarily over sea approaches to the Soviet Union, from bases in the Southern Ukraine and Estonia.

Blinder-D. Training version. Cockpit for instructor in raised position aft of standard flight deck, with stepped-up canopy.

The following details apply to 'Blinder-A and B' but are generally applicable to all versions except as noted under model descriptions:

TYPE: Twin-jet supersonic bomber and maritime patrol aircraft.

WINGS: Cantilever mid-wing monoplane. Constant slight anhedral from roots. Sweepback approx 45° on leading-edge outboard of fence and 50° inboard of fence, increasing to acute sweep at roots. Conventional all-metal structure. Fully-powered two-section ailerons, with tab on each inboard section. Fowler flaps inboard and outboard of wheel pod on each wing trailing-edge.

FUSELAGE: All-metal semi-monocoque structure of circular section, with area-rule 'waisting' at wing-roots.

TAIL UNIT: Cantilever all-metal structure, with sweepback on all surfaces. Fully-powered slab-type horizontal surfaces at bottom of fuselage. Aerodynamically balanced rudder, with inset tab.

LANDING GEAR: Retractable tricycle type. Wide-track four-wheel bogie main units retract rearward into pods built on to wing trailing-edges. Oleo-pneumatic shock-absorbers. Main legs also designed to swing rearward for additional cushioning during taxying and landing on rough runways. Twin-wheel nose unit retracts rearward. Small retractable skid to protect rear fuselage in taildown landing or take-off.

POWER PLANT: Two turbojet engines, each reportedly rated at 120·1 kN (27,000 lb st) with afterburning, mounted in pods above rear fuselage, on each side of tail fin. Lip of each intake is in the form of a ring which can be translated forward by jacks for take-off. Air entering ram intake is then supplemented by air injected through annular slot between ring and main body of pod. Original nozzles had short fluted final section aft of short fixed section, with annular space between this and outer fairing. Current nozzles have longer-chord convergent-divergent nozzle inside the outer fairing, believed to have resulted in increased thrust and range. Semi-retractable flight refuelling probe on nose, with triangular guard underneath to prevent drogue damaging fuselage nosecone.

ACCOMMODATION: Crew of three in tandem. Row of windows in bottom of fuselage, aft of nose radome, at navigator/systems operator's station. Pilot has upward-ejection seat; other crew members have downward-ejection seats.

ARMAMENT AND OPERATIONAL EQUIPMENT: Weapons bay in centre-fuselage, with double-fold doors. Special doors with panels shaped to accommodate recessed 'Kitchen' missile on 'Blinder-B' version. Single 23 mm NS-23 gun in radar-directed tail turret, beneath 'Bee Hind' tail-warning radar antenna. Radar in nose (larger type in 'Blinder-B'). Chaff/flare countermeasures dispensers and bombing assessment cameras carried in rear of wheel pods of some aircraft.

Tupolev Tu-22 twin-jet supersonic bomber ('Blinder-A') with additional view of nose of 'Blinder-D' training version *(Pilot Press)*

DIMENSIONS, EXTERNAL (estimated):

Wing span	27·70 m (90 ft 10½ in)
Length overall	40·53 m (132 ft 11½ in)
Height overall	10·67 m (35 ft 0 in)

WEIGHT (estimated):

Max T-O weight	83,900 kg (185,000 lb)

PERFORMANCE (estimated):

Max level speed at 12,200 m (40,000 ft)	Mach 1·4 (800 knots; 1,480 km/h; 920 mph)
Service ceiling	18,300 m (60,000 ft)
Max range	1,215 nm (2,250 km; 1,400 miles)

TUPOLEV Tu-26 (Tu-22M)
NATO reporting name: Backfire

Official NATO sources first acknowledged the existence of a Soviet variable-geometry ('swing-wing') medium bomber in the Autumn of 1969. Such an aircraft was not unexpected, as the Tu-22 (NATO 'Blinder') was clearly incapable of fulfilling the long-range strategic bombing role for which it had been intended.

A prototype of the new bomber is said to have been observed in July 1970, on the ground near the Tupolev works at Kazan in Central Asia. Subsequent official statements confirmed the aircraft as a twin-engined design by the Tupolev bureau. At least two prototypes were built; up to twelve pre-production models followed, for development testing, weapons trials and evaluation, by the beginning of 1973. The official designation was said to be **Tu-26**, but the Soviet Union referred to the type as **Tu-22M** in the SALT 2 treaty talks. This seems illogical if 'Blinder' is the Tu-22, as the suffix 'M' normally signifies a modification of an existing type, and is clearly inapplicable

Tupolev Tu-26/Tu-22M (NATO 'Backfire-B') bomber and maritime reconnaissance/attack aircraft *(Pilot Press)*

'Backfire-B' version of the Tupolev Tu-26/Tu-22M photographed from an interceptor of the Swedish Air Force

'Kitchen' air-to-surface missile under fuselage of 'Backfire-B'

in the case of these very different aircraft. The NATO reporting name allocated to the aircraft is 'Backfire'.

When drawing up the basic parameters for the bomber, the Tupolev bureau is believed to have aimed at a maximum unrefuelled range of 4,775-5,200 nm (8,850-9,650 km; 5,500-6,000 miles) at high altitude. Unwillingness to depart from the Tupolev practice of retracting the main landing gear bogies into fairings on the wing trailing-edges limited the variable geometry to the outer wings, as on the Sukhoi Su-17 and Su-20. There is evidence to believe that the large size of these fairings, with the wheels stowed beneath the wing, caused excessive drag, so that 'Backfire's' range fell short of what had been planned. Redesign almost eliminated the fairings from later aircraft, after the main landing gear had been revised to retract inward into the fuselage. This accounts for the two versions of the Tu-26/Tu-22M currently identified by NATO reporting names:

Backfire-A. Initial version, with large landing gear fairing pods on the wing trailing-edges. Believed to equip only one squadron.

Backfire-B. Developed version, with landing gear fairing pods eliminated except for shallow underwing fairings, no longer protruding beyond the trailing-edge. Increased wing span. To stress the peripheral/theatre range capability which excludes 'Backfires' from SALT 2 restrictions, the aircraft are now flown usually with the standard flight refuelling nose-probe removed, although the housing remains. External stores racks under the air intake trunks of aircraft shown in accompanying illustrations must impose speed limitations and may be fitted only for exercises or for short-range ground support missions.

A further version has been reported, with wedge-type engine intakes similar in form to those of the MiG-25. This could imply use of new engines, giving a further increase in range.

Performance data given at the end of this entry conform with the latest estimates published openly by the Swedish Air Force and by other agencies. Some expert opinion continues to credit the 'Backfire' with a maximum speed in the Mach 2·25/2·5 bracket and a range adequate to cover virtually all of the continental USA with the aid of Arctic staging and flight refuelling, from bases in the USSR. US State Department document 12A on the SALT 2 agreement states: "Under certain flight conditions, the Backfire is assessed to have an intercontinental capability".

More than 150 'Backfire-Bs' are in service, with production continuing at the rate of 30 aircraft per year. Many of them have been allocated to medium-range bomber squadrons of the Soviet Strategic Nuclear Forces; but at least 70 are deployed in a maritime role by Soviet Naval Aviation, and the FY 1979 Annual Report of the US Department of Defense stated: "There is increasing evidence that the Soviet bomber and cruise missile force may be overtaking their submarine force as a threat to our fleet and to our forces necessary for the resupply of Europe. They can concentrate aircraft, co-ordinate attacks with air, surface, or submarine-launched missiles, and use new technology to find our fleet units, jam our defences and screen their approach". It is expected that the 'Backfire' strategic/maritime force will be built up gradually to a total of 250-400 aircraft. One unit was reported to be based at Komsomol'sk, about 430 nm (800 km; 500 miles) north of Vladivostok, in the Far East of the USSR, in Spring 1979.

TYPE: Twin-engined medium bomber and maritime reconnaissance/attack aircraft.

WINGS: Cantilever mid-wing monoplane, made up of a large-span fixed centre-section and two variable-geometry outer panels. No anhedral or dihedral, but wing section is so thin that considerable flexing of the outer panels takes place in flight. Leading-edge fence towards tip of centre-section on each side. Each outer wing panel is believed to be fitted with a full-span leading-edge slat, aileron, and slotted trailing-edge flaps aft of spoilers/lift dumpers. Wing sweep is believed to be variable from fully spread (20°) to fully swept (55°), rather than limited to one intermediate position as on the MiG-23.

FUSELAGE: Forward of wings, fuselage is basically circular with large ogival dielectric nosecone. Centre-fuselage is faired into rectangular-section air intake trunks, each fitted with a large splitter plate and assumed to embody complex variable-geometry ramps. There is no evidence to suggest external area-rule 'waisting' of these trunks.

TAIL UNIT: Cantilever structure, with sweepback on all surfaces. All-moving horizontal surfaces; conventional inset rudder.

LANDING GEAR: Retractable tricycle type, of which details remain largely speculative. Each main unit is assumed to carry a multi-wheel bogie, which pivots inward from the vestigial fairing under the centre-section into the bottom of the adjacent intake trunk.

POWER PLANT: Two turbofan engines with afterburners, mounted side by side in the rear fuselage. It is not yet possible to identify positively the type of engine fitted, but US sources have suggested the use of Kuznetsov turbofans similar to those installed in Tupolev's Tu-144 supersonic transport. This would be logical, as each

engine is rated at 196·1 kN (44,090 lb st) with afterburning in the Tu-144. Uprated for military use, such engines would give an increase of at least 70% over the installed power in the Tu-22. A less-likely alternative is the turbofan evolved by the Koliesov bureau as a backup for the Tu-144, and which is said to be capable of supporting supersonic cruise without use of reheat. Fuel tankage is believed to include integral tanks in the entire fixed portion of the wings and much of the centre-fuselage above the weapon bay. A flight refuelling nose-probe can be fitted; after one observed refuelling, a 'Backfire' prototype is said to have remained airborne for a further 10 h.

ACCOMMODATION: Pilot and co-pilot side by side on flight deck. Other crew members further aft, as indicated by position of windows between flight deck and air intakes.

AVIONICS AND EQUIPMENT: Large bombing and navigation radar (NATO 'Down Beat') inside dielectric nosecone. Radar (NATO 'Fan Tail') for tail turret, above guns.

ARMAMENT: Aircraft observed to date have usually carried a primary armament of one of several different versions of 'Kitchen' air-to-surface missile semi-submerged in the underside of the centre-fuselage. Aircraft shown in accompanying photograph has multiple racks for stores under the air intake trunks. US reports have suggested that the Soviet Union is developing decoy missiles to assist penetration of advanced defence systems, in addition to very advanced ECM and ECCM. Twin 23 mm guns in radar-directed tail mounting.

DIMENSIONS, EXTERNAL:

Wing span: fully spread	34·45 m (113 ft)
fully swept	26·21 m (86 ft)
Length overall	40·23 m (132 ft)
Height overall	10·06 m (33 ft)

WEIGHTS:

Nominal weapon load	9,435 kg (20,800 lb)
Max T-O weight	122,500 kg (270,000 lb)

PERFORMANCE (estimated):

Max speed at high altitude*	Mach 2·0
Max speed at low altitude	Mach 0·9
Max unrefuelled combat range*	
	4,350 nm (8,050 km; 5,000 miles)

*See introductory copy

TUPOLEV Tu-28P/Tu-128
NATO reporting name: Fiddler

Largest fighter ever put into squadron service, this supersonic twin-jet interceptor was seen for the first time at Tushino in July 1961, with a large delta-wing air-to-air missile (NATO 'Ash') mounted under each wing. It is thought to have the service designation Tu-28P (US Department of Defense has used Tu-128); its NATO reporting name is 'Fiddler'.

The Tu-28P has a large ogival nose radome and carries a crew of two in tandem. The shoulder intakes for its two afterburning turbojet engines have half-cone shock-bodies, and the jetpipes are side by side in the bulged tail. Each engine is estimated to have a max rating of about 120·1 kN (27,000 lb st).

The sharply-swept wings are mid-set, with slight anhedral, and have considerably increased chord on the inboard panels, which have both increased sweep and a straight trailing-edge. The wide-track main landing gear units, comprising four-wheel bogies, retract into large fairings built on to the wing trailing-edges.

The tail unit is also sharply swept, and the two aircraft seen in 1961 were each fitted with two ventral fins. These

Tu-28P all-weather interceptor with 'Ash' infra-red missiles on inboard underwing pylons and 'Ash' radar homing missiles on outboard pylons

were missing on the three Tu-28Ps which flew past at Domodedovo in July 1967, as was the large bulged fairing fitted under the fuselage in 1961.

The current armament is double that seen in 1961, each aircraft being equipped to carry two 'Ash' missiles under each wing, one usually of the radar homing type and the other of the infra-red homing type. This was confirmed as the standard armament of first-line service aircraft in a film released in 1969, showing units of the Soviet armed forces taking part in defence exercises.

About 130 'Fiddlers' are thought to be in service with the Soviet Union's PVO-Strany home defence fighter force.

DIMENSIONS, EXTERNAL (estimated):
Wing span	20·00 m (65 ft 0 in)
Length overall	26·00 m (85 ft 0 in)

WEIGHT (estimated):
Max T-O weight	45,000 kg (100,000 lb)

PERFORMANCE (estimated):
Max speed at 11,000 m (36,000 ft)	Mach 1·75
(1,000 knots; 1,850 km/h; 1,150 mph)	
Service ceiling	20,000 m (65,620 ft)
Range with max fuel 2,692 nm (4,989 km; 3,100 miles)	

'NEW TUPOLEV HEAVY BOMBER'

In the Department of Defense Annual Report for Fiscal Year 1979, Secretary Harold Brown stated: "The Soviet heavy bomber capability continues to rest principally in the small and ageing 'Bison-Bear' force consisting of 100 turboprop 'Bears' and 40 'Bisons'. However, we now expect to see the first prototype of a new modern heavy bomber in the near future". There was no evidence of the existence of such an aircraft by the Summer of 1980.

TUPOLEV Tu-134
NATO reporting name: Crusty

Known originally as the Tu-124A, this aircraft is a rear-engined twin-turbofan development of the Tu-124 (described in earlier editions of *Jane's*). It had completed more than 100 test flights when first details and photographs were released in mid-September 1964. The prototype was followed by five pre-production aircraft and the Tu-134 then went into series production at Kharkov. It entered international service on Aeroflot's Moscow-Stockholm route in September 1967, after a period on internal services, and was joined by the 'stretched' Tu-134A in the Autumn of 1970. The two versions differ as follows:

Tu-134. Initial version, with Soloviev D-30 turbofans, accommodating 64-72 passengers. Export orders included eleven for Interflug (East Germany), six for Balkan Bulgarian Airlines, five for LOT (Poland), six for Malev (Hungary) and three for Aviogenex (Yugoslavia). Described in detail in 1978-79 *Jane's*.

Tu-134A. Fuselage lengthened by 2·10 m (6 ft 10½ in) to accommodate 76-80 passengers and increase baggage space by 2·0 m³ (71 cu ft). Wider seats. Wings strengthened locally. Main landing gear units strengthened and fitted with Il-18 wheels and brakes. Thrust reversers on Soloviev D-30-II engines. New radio and navigation equipment to international standards. APU for self-contained engine starting, electrical power supply and air-conditioning on the ground. More than 200 Tu-134s and Tu-134As are believed to be in service with Aeroflot. Export orders for the Tu-134A have included 13 for CSA (Czechoslovakia), 20 for Interflug, three for Malev, seven for Balkan Bulgarian Airlines, seven for LOT, and six for Aviogenex. In some cases these replaced Tu-134s operated earlier.

The third aircraft delivered to Aviogenex differed from all Tu-134s seen previously in having the original glazed nose and undernose radome replaced by a more conventional conical nose radome. Subsequently this became optional on both the Tu-134 and the Tu-134A.

The following details apply to the Tu-134A:

Tupolev Tu-28P taking off, with underwing armament of two 'Ash' missiles

Tupolev Tu-28P supersonic twin-jet all-weather interceptor *(Pilot Press)*

TYPE: Twin-turbofan short/medium-range transport aircraft.

WINGS: Cantilever low-wing monoplane. Sweepback at quarter-chord 35°. Anhedral 1° 30′. Conventional light alloy two-spar structure, comprising centre-section, inner wings and detachable outer wings. Two-section aileron on each wing, operated manually through geared tabs, and fitted also with trim tabs. Electro-mechanically-actuated all-metal double-slotted flaps. Hydraulically-actuated spoilers. Hot-air de-icing system.

FUSELAGE: Conventional all-metal semi-monocoque structure of circular section. Electro-mechanically-actuated airbrake under fuselage, to steepen angle of approach.

TAIL UNIT: Cantilever all-metal structure, with variable-incidence T tailplane. Elevators operated manually through geared tabs. Rudder control is hydraulically powered, with yaw damper and Flettner/trim tab. Trim tab in each elevator. Fin leading-edge de-iced by hot air; tailplane leading-edge de-iced electrically.

LANDING GEAR: Retractable tricycle type. All units retract rearward. Main units consist of four-wheel bogies retracting into fairings built on to wing trailing-edge. Oleo-pneumatic shock-absorbers, supplemented by ability of legs to swing rearward to cushion taxying and landing on rough runways. Main wheels size 930 × 305, tyre pressure 5·86 bars (85 lb/sq in). Steerable twin nosewheels size 660 × 200, tyre pressure 6·38-6·90 bars (92·5-100 lb/sq in). Disc brakes and anti-skid units standard.

POWER PLANT: Two Soloviev D-30 Srs II turbofan engines, each rated at 66·7 kN (14,990 lb st), in pod on each side of rear fuselage, with thrust reversers, constant-speed drives and AC generators. Standard capacity of Tu-134A integral fuel tanks in inner wings is 16,600 litres (3,650 Imp gallons), with optional increase to 18,000 litres (3,960 Imp gallons). Single-point refuelling socket in starboard wing-root leading-edge. Gravity fuelling point above each tank. Hot-air de-icing system for nacelle intakes. Fire-warning and freon extinguishing system.

ACCOMMODATION: Flight crew of three, consisting of two pilots and a navigator, plus two stewardesses. All configurations have 28 seats in four-abreast rows in rear cabin. In standard configuration, front cabin seats 48 passengers, four-abreast at a seat pitch of 75 cm (29·5 in), with tables between front two rows. Alternative arrangements include an economy layout for a total of 84 passengers and a mixed-class layout for a total of 68, including 12 first class in a separate cabin at the front, with increased seat pitch. In each version there is a galley on the starboard side and baggage compartment on the port side immediately aft of the flight deck, two toilets at the rear and a large baggage and freight compartment aft, in line with the engines. Wardrobes between cabins. Reduced forward baggage space on 84-seater. Max loading on floor of freight compartment 400 kg/m² (82 lb/sq ft). The passenger door is on the port side, forward of the front cabin. There are two service doors, on the starboard side by the baggage compartments, and two emergency exits on each side over the wing. Crew cabin and canopy observation panel de-iced by electric heater and hot air.

SYSTEMS: Air-conditioning system, pressure differential 0·56 bars (8·10 lb/sq in), fed with bleed air from engine compressors. Hydraulic system operating pressure 207 bars (3,000 lb/sq in). Electrical system includes 27V DC

Tupolev Tu-134A medium-range transport (two Soloviev D-30 turbofan engines) of Aeroflot with glazed nose and undernose radar

Tupolev Tu-134A twin-turbofan short/medium-range transport with conical nose radome *(Pilot Press)*

supply from four 12kW starter/generators and two batteries, single-phase 115V 400Hz AC supply from two inverters and three-phase 36V 400Hz AC supply. APU available for main engine starting, electric power supply and operation of the air-conditioning system. Oxygen available continuously for pilot, from 92 litre bottle, with 1 h supply for other crew members and portable supply for emergency use by passengers.

AVIONICS AND EQUIPMENT: Typical installation includes autopilot, two ARK-15 radio compasses, Mikron HF communications radio, two UHF transceivers, RV-5 radio altimeter, two 'Course MP-2' VOR/ILS, two SO-70 transponders, ROZ-1 weather radar and DISS-013 Doppler.

DIMENSIONS, EXTERNAL (Tu-134A):

Wing span	29·00 m (95 ft 1¾ in)
Wing chord at root	8·66 m (28 ft 5 in)
Wing chord at tip	1·92 m (6 ft 3½ in)
Wing aspect ratio	7·3
Length overall	37·05 m (121 ft 6½ in)
Length of fuselage	33·17 m (108 ft 10 in)
Fuselage max diameter	2·90 m (9 ft 6 in)
Height overall	9·14 m (30 ft 0 in)
Tailplane span	11·80 m (38 ft 8½ in)
Wheel track	9·45 m (31 ft 0 in)
Wheelbase	16·04 m (52 ft 7½ in)
Passenger door: Height	1·61 m (5 ft 3¼ in)
Width	0·70 m (2 ft 3½ in)
Height to sill	2·60 m (8 ft 6½ in)
Service door (fwd): Height	1·25 m (4 ft 1¼ in)
Width	0·75 m (2 ft 5½ in)
Rear door (stbd): Height	1·22 m (4 ft 0 in)
Width	0·90 m (2 ft 11½ in)
Emergency exits (each): Height	0·59 m (1 ft 11¼ in)
Width	0·60 m (1 ft 11½ in)

DIMENSIONS, INTERNAL:

Cabin (portion containing seats only):	
Length	15·93 m (52 ft 3 in)
Width	2·71 m (8 ft 10½ in)
Height	1·96 m (6 ft 5 in)
Volume	68·0 m³ (2,400 cu ft)
Baggage compartment (fwd):	
Volume	4·0-6·0 m³ (141-212 cu ft)
Baggage compartment (aft):	
Height (mean)	1·75 m (5 ft 9 in)
Length (mean)	2·80 m (9 ft 2 in)
Width (mean)	1·75 m (5 ft 9 in)
Floor area	4·5 m² (48·4 sq ft)
Volume	8·50 m³ (300 cu ft)

AREAS:

Wings, gross	127·3 m² (1,370·3 sq ft)
Ailerons (total)	9·68 m² (104·2 sq ft)
Trailing-edge flaps (total)	22·50 m² (242·2 sq ft)
Spoilers (total)	4·48 m² (48·2 sq ft)
Vertical tail surfaces (total)	21·25 m² (228·7 sq ft)
Horizontal tail surfaces (total)	30·68 m² (330·2 sq ft)
Elevators	6·42 m² (69·1 sq ft)

WEIGHTS (Tu-134A):

Operating weight empty	29,050 kg (64,045 lb)
Max fuel	14,400 kg (31,800 lb)
Max payload	8,200 kg (18,075 lb)
Max ramp weight	47,200 kg (104,000 lb)
Max T-O weight	47,000 kg (103,600 lb)
Max landing weight	43,000 kg (94,800 lb)

PERFORMANCE (Tu-134A, at max T-O weight except where indicated):

Max cruising speed at AUW of 42,000 kg (92,600 lb) at 10,000 m (32,800 ft)
477 knots (885 km/h; 550 mph)

Normal cruising speed
405-458 knots (750-850 km/h; 466-528 mph)

Service ceiling at max T-O weight
11,900 m (39,000 ft)

T-O runway length (BCAR, at S/L)
2,400 m (7,875 ft)

Landing runway length at max landing weight (BCAR, at S/L)
2,200 m (7,218 ft)

Range at max AUW, cruising at 432 knots (800 km/h; 497 mph) at 11,000 m (36,100 ft):

with max payload
1,020 nm (1,890 km; 1,174 miles)

with payload of 5,000 kg (11,025 lb)
1,630 nm (3,020 km; 1,876 miles)

TUPOLEV Tu-144
NATO reporting name: Charger

A detailed history of the development of this supersonic transport aircraft can be found in the 1977-78 *Jane's*.

The first of the two prototypes of the Tu-144 (CCCP-68001) flew for the first time on 31 December 1968, this being the first flight by a supersonic airliner anywhere in the world. On 5 June 1969 the Tu-144 exceeded Mach 1 for the first time, at a height of 11,000 m (36,000 ft), half-an-hour after take-off. On 26 May 1970 it became the first commercial transport to exceed Mach 2, by flying at 1,160 knots (2,150 km/h; 1,335 mph) at a height of 16,300 m (53,475 ft) for several minutes. Highest speed reported subsequently was Mach 2·4, probably with the

aircraft in its almost totally redesigned production form.

Supersonic proving flights by Aeroflot began on 26 December 1975, between Moscow's Domodedovo Airport and Alma-Ata, capital of Kazakhstan. Carrying a payload of freight and mail, Tu-144 No. CCCP-77106 took 1 h 59 min for the journey of about 1,760 nm (3,260 km; 2,025 miles), flying for most of the time at 1,187 knots (2,200 km/h; 1,367 mph) at a height of 16,000-18,000 m (52,500-59,000 ft). This aircraft was retired to the Soviet Air Force Museum at Monino, near Moscow, in early 1980.

A total of 50 flights were made between the two cities and between Moscow and Khabarovsk (first on 22 February 1977). Another eight flights were cancelled and one returned to base after take-off.

Scheduled passenger flights began on 1 November 1977, when aircraft CCCP-77109 flew from Moscow to Alma-Ata in just under two hours, with 80 of its 140 seats occupied. A public holiday and bad weather led to cancellation or postponement of five of the next six services; but reliability improved from 20 December and a total of 102 flights was made by 1 June 1978. However, the service was then terminated, following an accident to one of the Tu-144s on a non-commercial flight. There was no further news of route flying by the aircraft until the Tu-144D, with new engines, made a proving flight from Moscow to Khabarovsk in June 1979 (see separate entry on Tu-144D).

Thirteen Tu-144s were built, including prototypes.

Construction of the Tu-144 is mainly of VAD-23 light alloy, with extensive use of integrally-stiffened panels, produced by both chemical milling and machining from solid metal. Stainless steel and titanium are used for the leading-edges, elevons, rudder and undersurface of the rear fuselage, and the aircraft is stated to embody 10,000 parts made of plastics.

The wings have a double-delta planform, with a sweepback in the order of 76° on the inboard portions and 57° on the main panels. They are cambered over the full area, with a downward-curving trailing-edge like that of the Concorde. The structure is multi-spar, with large honeycomb panels. The powered control surfaces consist of four separate elevons on each wing and a two-section rudder, each operated by two separate actuators.

The fuselage blends with the low-set wings, giving a flat undersurface which contributes to fuselage lift and directional stability. There are doors forward of the passenger cabins and in the centre on the port side, and six emergency exits.

The 'moustache' foreplanes are pivoted from points near the top of the fuselage, immediately aft of the flight deck. Each is fitted with a double-slotted trailing-edge flap and a fixed leading-edge double-slat. The foreplanes retract rearward, protruding only a little externally but restricting to a narrow passage the space between flight deck and cabin. When extended, during take-off and landing only, they have anhedral but no sweep.

The twin-wheel steerable nose unit of the landing gear retracts forward into the fuselage. Each main eight-wheel bogie (two rows of four) retracts forward and up into one of the engine ducts, between the divided air-intake trunks. This requires the bogie first to pivot sideways through 90° about the base of the leg, before retraction. Nosewheel tyres are size 950 × 300. The main wheels are fitted with size 950 × 400 tyres and quadruple steel disc brakes. All wheel-bays are thermally insulated, and the nosewheel tyres are blown with cooling air after retraction, throughout cruising flight.

The first flight of the Tu-144 prototype was also the first time that the Kuznetsov NK-144 turbofan engine, selected for the original version of the aircraft, had been tested in the air. At that time the engine max ratings were 127·5 kN (28,660 lb st) without afterburning and 171·6 kN (38,580 lb) with full afterburning. On production aircraft the rating with full afterburning was raised to 196·1

Tupolev Tu-144 supersonic transport, in initial production form. This aircraft was displayed at the 1977 Paris Air Show *(Brian M. Service)* kN (44,090 lb st). The engines were paired in two separate ducts; each intake trunk contained a central vertical wall, giving an individual flow of air to each engine. The intakes had fully-automatic movable ramps, with manual reversion, and with airflow dump doors midway from the inlet to the engines. Afterburning was normally maintained at 30 to 40 per cent of its maximum additional thrust throughout cruising flight. No thrust reversers were installed, but a twin brake-parachute was fitted solely for use on short runways.

Total fuel capacity was about 95,000 kg (209,440 lb), with a transfer tank in the fuselage tailcone to counterbalance CG movement in flight.

A flight crew of three is normally carried by both versions of the aircraft, consisting of two pilots and a flight engineer. The pilots have fully-adjustable armchair seats. During cruising flight, their windscreen is faired in by a retractable visor which has birdproof side windows and a 'solid' top. The entire nose can be drooped for improved view during take-off and landing.

The basic interior layout is for a total of 140 passengers in three cabins. The front cabin contains 11 seats for first class passengers, basically three-abreast, with tables between the front two rows. It is divided by a movable partition from the forward tourist class cabin, which contains six rows of five-abreast seats, with the three-seat units on the port side of the centre aisle. The rear tourist class cabin contains 15 rows of five-abreast seating at the front and six rows of four-abreast seating at the rear. Seat pitch is normally 102 cm (40 in) for first class and 87 cm (34·25 in) for tourist class; but alternative layouts are available.

Forward of the passenger accommodation there are toilet (starboard) and cloakroom compartments (port), with a bench seat for two cabin staff by the forward door. A second cloakroom, toilet and buffet kitchen are located between the two tourist class cabins, with two further toilets at the rear. Aft of these, in line with the engines, is a large compartment for containerised baggage and freight, which are loaded and unloaded semi-automatically through a large door on the starboard side of the hold, at the rear. There are no underfloor holds.

Little information is yet available on aircraft systems. The prototype had three independent hydraulic systems and two separate systems for pressurisation and air-conditioning. Preparation for flight, ground air-conditioning and engine starting can be performed independently of airport services. Advanced automatic flight control and navigation systems are standard, with the intention of progressing eventually to full automatic landing under all weather conditions. Six landing and taxi lights are mounted on the nosewheel leg.

DIMENSIONS, EXTERNAL:
Wing span	28·80 m (94 ft 6 in)
Length overall	65·70 m (215 ft 6½ in)
Height, wheels up	12·85 m (42 ft 2 in)
Wheel track	6·05 m (19 ft 10¼ in)
Wheelbase	19·60 m (64 ft 3½ in)

DIMENSIONS, INTERNAL:
Cabin: Headroom	1·93 m (6 ft 4 in)
Baggage/cargo hold capacity	20 m³ (706 cu ft)

AREA:
Wings, gross	438 m² (4,714·5 sq ft)

WEIGHTS:
Operating weight empty	85,000 kg (187,400 lb)
Max fuel	95,000 kg (209,440 lb)
Max payload (space limited)	14,000 kg (30,865 lb)
Max payload (structure limited)	15,000 kg (33,070 lb)
Max ramp weight	185,000 kg (407,850 lb)
Max T-O weight	180,000 kg (396,830 lb)
Max zero-fuel weight	100,000 kg (220,460 lb)
Max landing weight	110,000-120,000 kg (242,500-264,550 lb)

PERFORMANCE (nominal):
Max cruising speed
  Mach 2·35 (1,350 knots; 2,500 km/h; 1,550 mph)
Normal cruising speed
  Mach 1·98-2·2 (1,134-1,240 knots; 2,100-2,300 km/h; 1,305-1,430 mph)
Landing speed   151 knots (280 km/h; 174 mph)
Cruising height 16,000-18,000 m (52,500-59,000 ft)
Balanced field length at max T-O weight (approx):
  ISA, S/L   3,000 m (9,845 ft)
  ISA+15°C, S/L   3,200 m (10,500 ft)
  Landing run   2,600 m (8,530 ft)
Max range with 140 passengers, at an average speed of Mach 1·9 (1,080 knots; 2,000 km/h; 1,243 mph)
  3,500 nm (6,500 km; 4,030 miles)

TUPOLEV Tu-144D
Nato reporting name: Charger
First news of the development of this improved version of the Tu-144 was given after it had completed its first route proving flight from Moscow to Khabarovsk, in the Soviet Far East, on 23 June 1979. Time taken for the 3,340 nm (6,185 km; 3,840 mile) flight was 3 h 21 min. Passengers included the aircraft's designer, Dr Alexei A. Tupolev.

After this proving operation, Mr Ivan Razumovsky, Soviet Deputy Minister for Civil Aviation, said that the Tu-144D has new engines by comparison with the original

Tupolev Tu-154 medium/long-range three-turbofan transport aircraft (*Pilot Press*)

Tu-144. Reported to be the Koliesov variable bypass engines first mentioned briefly in *Jane's* in 1973-74, these were said by the Minister to be 50 per cent more economical in operation, making possible a max range of 3,780 nm (7,000 km; 4,350 miles), and to meet international requirements in terms of noise emission.

No other details of the Tu-144D had become available by mid-September 1980. It was not in regular service at that time, but was stated to be ready for series production.

TUPOLEV Tu-154
NATO reporting name: Careless
The three-engined Tu-154, announced in the Spring of 1966, was intended to replace the Tu-104, Il-18 and An-10 on medium/long stage lengths of up to 3,240 nm (6,000 km; 3,725 miles). It is able to operate from airfields with a class B surface, including packed earth and gravel. Normal flight can be maintained after shutdown of any one engine. Single-engine flight is possible at a lower altitude.

The first of six prototype and pre-production models flew for the first time on 4 October 1968. The seventh Tu-154 was delivered to Aeroflot for initial route proving and crew training in early 1971. Mail and cargo flights began in May. Initial passenger-carrying services were flown for a few days in the early Summer of 1971 between Moscow and Tbilisi. Regular services began on 9 February 1972, over the 700 nm (1,300 km; 800 mile) route between Moscow and Mineralnye Vody, in the North Caucasus. International services began with a proving flight between Moscow and Prague on 1 August 1972.

The following details apply to the basic Tu-154. This version was superseded in production successively by the Tu-154A and Tu-154B, which are described separately.
TYPE: Three-engined medium/long-range transport aircraft.
WINGS: Cantilever low-wing monoplane. Sweepback 35° at quarter-chord. Conventional all-metal three-spar fail-safe structure; centre spar extending to just outboard of inner edge of aileron on each wing. Five-section slat on outer 80% of each wing leading-edge. Triple-slotted flaps. Four-section spoilers forward of flaps on each wing. Outboard sections supplement ailerons for roll control. Section inboard of landing gear housing serves as airbrake and lift dumper; two middle sections can be used as airbrakes in flight. All control surfaces hydraulically actuated and of honeycomb construction. Hot-air de-icing of wing leading-edge. Slats are electrically heated.
FUSELAGE: Conventional all-metal semi-monocoque fail-safe structure of circular section.
TAIL UNIT: Cantilever all-metal structure, with variable-incidence T tailplane. Rudder and elevator of honeycomb construction. Sweepback of 40° at quarter-chord on horizontal surfaces, 45° on leading-edge of vertical surfaces. Control surfaces hydraulically actuated by irreversible servo-controls. Leading-edges of fin and tailplane and engine air intake de-iced by hot air.
LANDING GEAR: Retractable tricycle type. Hydraulic actuation. Main units retract rearward into fairings on wing trailing-edge. Each consists of a bogie made up of three pairs of wheels, size 930 × 305, in tandem; tyre pressure 7·86 bars (114 lb/sq in). Steerable anti-shimmy twin-wheel nose unit has wheels size 800 × 225 and retracts forward. Disc brakes and anti-skid units on main wheels.
POWER PLANT: Three Kuznetsov NK-8-2 turbofan engines, each rated at 93·2 kN (20,950 lb st), one on each side of rear fuselage and one inside extreme rear of fuselage. Two lateral engines fitted with upper and lower thrust-reversal grilles. Integral fuel tanks in wings; standard capacity 41,140 litres (9,050 Imp gallons). Max fuel capacity 46,825 litres (10,300 Imp gallons). Single-point refuelling standard.
ACCOMMODATION: Flight crew of two pilots and flight engineer; provision for navigator aft of pilot and folding

seats for additional pilots or instructors. There are basic passenger versions for a total of 167, 158, 152, 146 and 128 passengers. Each has a toilet at the front (starboard), removable galley amidships and three toilets aft. Coat storage, folding seat and inflatable evacuation chute in each entrance lobby. Standard economy class version has 54 seats in six-abreast rows, with two tables between front rows, in forward cabin; and 104 seats in six-abreast rows (rear two rows four-abreast) in rear cabin at seat pitch of 75 cm (29·5 in). The 167-seat high-density version differs in having one further row of six seats in the forward cabin and reduced galley facilities. The tourist class versions carry 146 passengers at a seat pitch of 81 cm (32 in) or 152 at a pitch of 87 cm (34·25 in) with reduced galley facilities. The 128-seat version has only 24 first class seats, four-abreast at a pitch of 102 cm (40 in), in the forward cabin. There is also an all-cargo version. Passenger doors are forward of front cabin and between cabins on the port side, with emergency and service doors opposite. All four doors open outwards. Four emergency exits, two over wing on each side. Two pressurised baggage holds under main cabin floor, with two inward-opening doors. Normal provision for mechanised loading and unloading of baggage and freight in containers. Smaller unpressurised hold under rear cabin for carrying spare parts or special cargo such as radioactive isotopes.
SYSTEMS: Air-conditioning system pressure differential 0·62 bars (9·0 lb/sq in). Three independent hydraulic systems; working pressure 207 bars (3,000 lb/sq in). No. 1 system, powered by two pumps driven by centre engine and port engine, operates landing gear, brakes and all control surfaces. No. 2 system, powered by a pump driven by centre engine, actuates nosewheel steering, the second flying controls circuit and landing gear emergency extension. No. 3 system, powered by pump on starboard engine, actuates the third flying controls circuit and second landing gear emergency extension circuit. Three-phase 200/115V AC electrical system, supplied by three 40kVA alternators. 28V DC system. APU standard, driving 40kVA alternator and 12kW starter/generator.
AVIONICS AND EQUIPMENT: Automatic flight control system standard, including automatic navigation on pre-programmed route under control of navigational computer with en-route checks by ground radio beacons (including VOR, VOR/DME) or radar, and automatic approach by ILS to ICAO Category II standard (development to Category III standard in hand). Moving-map ground position indicator, HF and VHF radio, and radar standard. Safety equipment includes four inflatable life-rafts, each for 26 persons.

DIMENSIONS, EXTERNAL:
Wing span	37·55 m (123 ft 2½ in)
Length overall	47·90 m (157 ft 1¾ in)
Height overall	11·40 m (37 ft 4¾ in)
Diameter of fuselage	3·80 m (12 ft 5½ in)
Tailplane span	13·40 m (43 ft 11½ in)
Wheel track	11·50 m (37 ft 9 in)
Wheelbase	18·92 m (62 ft 1 in)
Passenger doors (each): Height	1·73 m (5 ft 7 in)
Width	0·80 m (2 ft 7½ in)
Height to sill	3·10 m (10 ft 2 in)
Servicing door: Height	1·28 m (4 ft 2½ in)
Width	0·61 m (2 ft 0 in)
Emergency door: Height	1·28 m (4 ft 2½ in)
Width	0·64 m (2 ft 1¼ in)
Emergency exits (each): Height	0·90 m (2 ft 11½ in)
Width	0·48 m (1 ft 7 in)
Main baggage hold doors (each):	
Height	1·20 m (3 ft 11¼ in)
Width	1·35 m (4 ft 5 in)
Height to sill	1·80 m (5 ft 11 in)
Rear (unpressurised) hold:	
Height	0·90 m (2 ft 11½ in)

Width	1·10 m (3 ft 7¼ in)
Height to sill	2·20 m (7 ft 2½ in)

DIMENSIONS, INTERNAL:

Cabin: Width	3·58 m (11 ft 9 in)
Height	2·02 m (6 ft 7½ in)
Volume	163·2 m³ (5,763 cu ft)
Main baggage holds: front	21·5 m³ (759 cu ft)
rear	16·5 m³ (582 cu ft)
Rear underfloor hold	5·0 m³ (176 cu ft)

AREAS:

Wings, gross	201·45 m² (2,169 sq ft)
Horizontal tail surfaces	40·55 m² (436·48 sq ft)
Vertical tail surfaces	31·72 m² (341·43 sq ft)

WEIGHTS:

Operating weight empty	43,500 kg (95,900 lb)
Normal payload	16,000 kg (35,275 lb)
Max payload	20,000 kg (44,090 lb)
Max fuel	33,150 kg (73,085 lb)
Max ramp weight	90,300 kg (199,077 lb)
Normal T-O weight	84,000 kg (185,188 lb)
Max T-O weight	90,000 kg (198,416 lb)
Normal landing weight	68,000 kg (149,915 lb)
Max landing weight	80,000 kg (176,370 lb)
Max zero-fuel weight	63,500 kg (139,994 lb)

PERFORMANCE (at max T-O weight, except where indicated):

Max level speed:
above 11,000 m (36,000 ft)   Mach 0·90
at low altitudes 283 knots (525 km/h; 326 mph) IAS

Max cruising speed at 9,500 m (31,150 ft)
526 knots (975 km/h; 605 mph)

Best-cost cruising speed at 11,000-12,000 m (36,000-39,350 ft)
Mach 0·85 (486 knots; 900 km/h; 560 mph)

Long-range cruising speed at 11,000-12,000 m (36,000-39,350 ft)
Mach 0·80 (459 knots; 850 km/h; 528 mph)

Approach speed   127 knots (235 km/h; 146 mph)
Min ground turning radius   24·60 m (80 ft 8½ in)
T-O run at normal T-O weight, ISA   1,140 m (3,740 ft)
Balanced runway length at max T-O weight, FAR
standard: ISA, S/L   2,100 m (6,890 ft)
ISA+20°C, S/L   2,420 m (7,940 ft)
Landing field length, at max landing weight, FAR
standard: ISA, S/L   2,060 m (6,758 ft)
ISA+20°C, S/L   2,217 m (7,273 ft)

Range at 11,000 m (36,000 ft) with standard fuel, reserves for 1 hour and 6% of total fuel:
at 486 knots (900 km/h; 560 mph), with T-O weight of 84,000 kg and max payload (158 passengers, baggage and 5 tonnes of cargo and mail)
1,360 nm (2,520 km; 1,565 miles)
as above, T-O weight of 90,000 kg
1,867 nm (3,460 km; 2,150 miles)
at 459 knots (850 km/h; 528 mph) with T-O weight of 84,000 kg and max payload as above
1,510 nm (2,800 km; 1,740 miles)
as above, T-O weight of 90,000 kg
2,050 nm (3,800 km; 2,360 miles)
max range with 13,650 kg (30,100 lb) payload
2,850 nm (5,280 km; 3,280 miles)

Range at 11,000 m (36,000 ft) with optional centre-wing tanks, reserves as above:
with 9,000 kg (19,840 lb) payload (95 passengers)
3,453 nm (6,400 km; 3,977 miles)
with 6,700 kg (14,770 lb) payload (70 passengers)
3,723 nm (6,900 km; 4,287 miles)

TUPOLEV Tu-154A and Tu-154B
NATO reporting name: Careless

A developed version of the Tu-154, with the designation **Tu-154A**, was reported in early 1973, with the first flight scheduled for later that year. An article in the April 1975 issue of the Soviet magazine *Grazhdanskaya Aviatsiya* recorded that this aircraft had entered service with Aeroflot in April 1974 and that production Tu-154As were to be put into scheduled operation during 1975.

The Tu-154A is dimensionally unchanged by comparison with the original model, and is able to carry a normal payload of 152 passengers in Summer and 144 in Winter. Alternative configurations provide seats for 168 passengers on high-density routes, or 12 first class and 128 tourist class. Changes have centred mainly on the power plant, equipment and systems, to permit an increased gross weight, improve performance and reliability, and reduce servicing requirements.

The power plant consists of three Kuznetsov NK-8-2U turbofan engines, each uprated to 103 kN (23,150 lb st). Increased max take-off and landing weights allow extra fuel to be carried, raising the maximum capacity to 39,750 kg (87,630 lb). An additional tank, capacity 6,600 kg (14,550 lb), is mounted between the front and centre spars in the centre-section. It is intended primarily as a ballast tank for ferrying, and the fuel it contains can be pumped into the main system only on the ground. When the aircraft carries less than a full payload, this tank can be filled and its contents can be transferred to the main tanks at a destination airport, so reducing purchases of fuel outside the operator's home country. Other fuel system improvements have been made to the anti-icing fluid additive system; the centre-section tanks can be purged with CO₂ in the event of a forced landing with the wheels retracted.

The controls for the flaps, leading-edge slats and tailplane are interconnected, so that when the flaps are operated the tailplane is trimmed 3° down. An override switch caters for CG conditions which require a movement of more than 3°.

Additional emergency exits in the rear fuselage meet international requirements. The floor of the baggage holds has been strengthened to prevent damage by sharp-edged packages and baggage; and a smoke warning system has been introduced in the holds.

The electrical system has been modified by comparison with the Tu-154 and employs three alternators, on separate supply circuits, to provide 200/115V AC power. Two circuits supply all electrical services; the third supplies the electrical anti-icing system for the leading-edge slats. If one alternator fails, the remaining primary alternator can provide for all essential services, supplemented by the alternator on the APU. The duplicated DC electrical system embodies three rectifiers, of which one is for emergency use in the event of a failure of either of the others.

An ABSU automatic approach and landing system is fitted. This met ICAO Category I requirements initially, but was to be uprated to Category II later. Other equipment changes include the provision of duplicated radio compass, radio altimeter and DME; and the introduction of two-speed windscreen wipers and a system to indicate angle-of-bank limitations. An MSRP-64 flight recorder covers some 80 parameters, and a Mars-B voice recorder with open microphone is standard.

Servicing requirements and costs were reduced considerably on the Tu-154A, for which the servicing cycle is 300/900/1,800 h.

In 1977, production was switched to a further-improved version, designated **Tu-154B**, since refined as the **Tu-154B-2**. This retains the NK-8-2U turbofans of the Tu-154A, but is fitted with Thomson-CSF/SFIM automatic flight control and navigation equipment approved for ICAO Category II automatic landings. Max take-off and zero-fuel weights have been increased; and rearward extension of the usable cabin space enables up to 169 passengers to be carried despite the introduction of two more emergency exits, immediately forward of the engine nacelle on each side, making a total of six.

The 169 passengers are seated mostly six-abreast with centre aisle at a pitch of 75 cm (29·5 in), with 68 in the forward cabin and 101 in the rear cabin. The forward door, on the port side between the flight deck and passenger accommodation, leads into a vestibule with a galley/pantry on the port side and a toilet opposite. There are three more toilets at the rear of the cabin, and each of the two doorways contains three seats for cabin staff. The basic all-tourist version differs in having 62 seats forward and 98 aft, with added coat stowage opposite the forward door and a further galley amidships. In the 150-seat mixed-class layout, the forward cabin is divided in two, for eight first class (with 96 cm; 38 in seat pitch) and 44 tourist passengers.

Improvements have been made to the avionics, notably to simplify take-off and landing procedures. A different radar is fitted, and the fuel tank used as ballast on the Tu-154A can be used normally, as part of the standard fuel system of the Tu-154B/B-2.

Production of all versions of the Tu-154 exceeded 350 by mid-1979. More than 300 were operated by Aeroflot, others by Balkan Bulgarian Airlines (13), Malev (9) and Tarom (9).

WEIGHTS (A, Tu-154A; B, Tu-154B):

Basic operating weight: B	50,775 kg (111,940 lb)	
Normal payload: A	16,000 kg (35,275 lb)	
Max payload: A, B	18,000 kg (39,680 lb)	
Max fuel: B	39,700 kg (87,525 lb)	
Max T-O weight: A	94,000 kg (207,235 lb)	
B	96,000 kg (211,650 lb)	
Max zero-fuel weight: B	71,000 kg (156,525 lb)	
Max landing weight (normal): A, B	78,000 kg (171,960 lb)	
Max landing weight (emergency): A	92,000-94,000 kg (202,825-207,235 lb)	

PERFORMANCE (A, Tu-154A; B, Tu-154B, at max T-O weight, except where indicated):

Max level speed:
A   310 knots (575 km/h; 357 mph) IAS, except with less than 7,150 kg (15,763 lb) fuel at heights above 7,000 m (23,000 ft)

Normal cruising speed at up to 12,000 m (39,370 ft):
A   Mach 0·85 (486 knots; 900 km/h; 560 mph)
B   486-513 knots (900-950 km/h; 560-590 mph)

Required runway length: B   2,200 m (7,218 ft)
Range with payload of 16,000 kg (35,275 lb):
A   1,725-1,780 nm (3,200-3,300 km; 1,985-2,050 miles)

Range with 160 passengers and baggage:
B   1,755 nm (3,250 km; 2,019 miles)

Range with max payload:
B   1,485 nm (2,750 km; 1,708 miles)

Tupolev Tu-154B medium/long-range transport aircraft (three Kuznetsov NK-8-2U turbofan engines) in service with Aeroflot *(R. Killen)*

YAKOVLEV

GENERAL DESIGNER IN CHARGE OF BUREAU:
Alexander Sergeivich Yakovlev

Alexander Yakovlev is one of the most versatile Soviet designers, and products of his design bureau have ranged from transonic long-range fighters to the Yak-24 tandem-rotor helicopter, an operational VTOL carrier-based fighter and a variety of training and light general-purpose aircraft. Types in current production and service, or under development, are described hereafter.

YAKOVLEV Yak-18T

Details of this extensively-redesigned cabin version of the Yak-18 were given for the first time at the 1967 Paris Air Show, where an unregistered example was displayed statically. The first prototype flew for the first time in the Summer of that year, powered, like the Yak-18A and 18PM, with a 224 kW (300 hp) Ivchenko AI-14RF nine-cylinder radial engine, driving a two-blade variable-pitch propeller.

An initial evaluation programme of 450 test flights was completed by two prototypes during 1968-69. Together with experience gained during several months of operation at the Sasov flying school, this suggested that a number of improvements would be worthwhile. Most important of these was the installation of a more powerful M-14P radial engine of the type evolved by Vedeneev from the AI-14 and chosen also for the Kamov Ka-26 helicopter. In addition, improvements were made to the cabin layout and ventilation, and elevator effectiveness was reduced.

An aircraft embodying the modifications was approved by the Research Institute of the Soviet Ministry of Civil Aviation. Four others logged 605 flying hours, including 1,591 take-offs and landings, over a five-month period of testing on every kind of airfield, under a wide variety of weather conditions. The Yak-18T was pronounced superior to earlier versions of the Yak-18 for basic training, and far more economical to operate than the An-2, which was also widely used.

Full production was ordered at Smolensk, and by 1974 it was possible to train the complete intake of 100 pupil pilots at Sasov on the new aircraft. Seventeen were then available for use at the school, of which two were being flown at double the normal rate of utilisation under a Research Institute programme.

As the standard basic trainer at Aeroflot flying schools, the Yak-18T is used for circuits, instrument training and navigation training, and as a flying classroom for an instructor and three pupils. Only one pupil accompanies the instructor on aerobatic flights.

Next to enter service, as a successor to the Yak-12, will be the ambulance version, with light communications and forest fire patrol versions under consideration. A floatplane version is under development and the Yak-18T will also operate eventually on skis.

Designer responsible for this variant of the Yak-18 was Mr Y. Yankievich.

TYPE: Four-seat multi-purpose light aircraft.

WINGS: Cantilever low-wing monoplane, in three sections: a constant-chord centre-section, integral with the fuselage, and two tapered outer panels. Wing section Clark YH, with thickness/chord ratio of 14·5% at root and 9·3% at tip. Dihedral on outer panels only. Two-spar light alloy construction. Light alloy covering on centre-section and on leading-edges of outer panels; inboard 25% of outer panels covered with light alloy, remainder with fabric. Slotted ailerons of light alloy construction, each hinged at three points and partly fabric-covered. Light alloy split flap across entire span of centre-section, actuated by two pneumatic servo-motors. Fixed step at port wing-root trailing-edge, with corrugated upper surface walkway to door on each side. Ailerons operated by pushrods. Ground-adjustable tab on each aileron.

FUSELAGE: Conventional light alloy semi-monocoque structure, of basically square section. Skin on rear fuselage spot welded to frames and stringers.

TAIL UNIT: Braced light alloy structure, with wire bracing above tailplane and strut bracing below. All surfaces fabric-covered. Control surfaces operated by both pushrods and cables. Controllable trim tab in each elevator.

LANDING GEAR: Fully-retractable tricycle type, with single wheel on each unit. Pneumatic retraction, nosewheel rearward, main units inward into centre-section. No main-wheel doors. Oleo-nitrogen shock-absorbers. Castoring but non-steerable self-centering nosewheel with shimmy damper. All three tyres size 500 × 150. Differential pneumatic brakes on main wheels, with override button on instructor's control wheel.

POWER PLANT: One 269 kW (360 hp) Vedeneev M-14P nine-cylinder aircooled radial engine, driving a two-blade variable-pitch metal propeller, without spinner. Louvres in front of cowling to regulate cooling. Two-part cowling, split on horizontal centreline. Fuel tanks in wing roots.

ACCOMMODATION: Car-type cabin, seating four persons in pairs. Large forward-hinged door on each side, jettisonable in emergency. Provision for upholstered or parachute-type front seats. Bench-type rear seat

Yakovlev Yak-18T basic trainer (Vedeneev M-14P engine)

removable for freight carrying. Ambulance configuration available, for pilot, stretcher patient and medical attendant. Large baggage compartment aft of rear seat, with external access on port side. Stretcher of ambulance version is loaded through this large baggage door. Cabin furnishings of non-inflammable synthetic materials. Dual control wheels. Glareshield above panel. Heating and ventilation standard.

SYSTEMS: Pneumatic system for actuating landing gear and flaps. Electrical system includes instrument panel red lighting, navigation and landing lights, and anti-collision beacon at top of fin.

AVIONICS AND EQUIPMENT: Standard equipment includes UHF radio, intercom, radio compass, radio altimeter and flight recorder.

DIMENSIONS, EXTERNAL:
Wing span	11·16 m (36 ft 7¼ in)
Length overall	8·35 m (27 ft 4¾ in)

AREA:
Wings, gross	18·75 m² (201·8 sq ft)

WEIGHTS AND LOADINGS (A, with instructor and one pupil; B, with instructor and three pupils):
Max payload: A	306 kg (675 lb)
B	436 kg (960 lb)
Max T-O weight: A	1,500 kg (3,307 lb)
B	1,650 kg (3,637 lb)
Max wing loading: A	80 kg/m² (16·4 lb/sq ft)
B	88 kg/m² (18·0 lb/sq ft)
Max power loading: A	5·59 kg/kW (11·0 lb/hp)
B	6·15 kg/kW (12·1 lb/hp)

PERFORMANCE (at max T-O weight: A, with instructor and one pupil; B, with instructor and three pupils):
Max level speed:	
A, B	159 knots (295 km/h; 183 mph)

Max cruising speed:
B	135 knots (250 km/h; 155 mph)
Max rate of climb at S/L: B	300 m (985 ft)/min
Service ceiling: A, B	5,500 m (18,000 ft)
T-O run: A	330 m (1,085 ft)
B	400 m (1,315 ft)
Landing run: A	400 m (1,315 ft)
B	500 m (1,640 ft)
Range with max fuel, with reserves:	
A	350 nm (650 km; 403 miles)
B	485 nm (900 km; 560 miles)

YAKOVLEV Yak-28

NATO reporting names: Brewer, Firebar and Maestro

First seen in considerable numbers in the 1961 Soviet Aviation Day flypast were three successors to the Yak-25/27 series (see 1971/72 *Jane's*), described by the commentator as supersonic multi-purpose aircraft and identified subsequently by the designation Yak-28. These aircraft are shoulder-wing monoplanes, whereas all versions of the Yak-25, 26 and 27 were mid-wing. The Yak-28 series were, in fact, produced as entirely new designs, following only the general configuration of the earlier types.

The landing gear comprises two twin-wheel units in tandem, with the forward unit under the pilot's cockpit and the rear unit moved further aft than on the Yak-25/27, to a point immediately in front of the ventral fin. Wingtip balancer wheels are retained. The entire wing-root leading-edge is extended forward and the height of the fin and rudder increased. Tailplane sweep is also increased.

Several versions of the basic design have been identified, with the following NATO reporting names:

Version of the Yak-28 known to NATO as 'Brewer-C' *(Flug Revue)*

The long-nose version of the Yakovlev Yak-28P two-seat all-weather fighter ('Firebar') *(Pilot Press)*

Yak-28P ('Firebar') fitted with original short radome and carrying two 'Anab' missiles *(Flug Revue)*

The version of the Yak-28 two-seat tactical attack aircraft known to NATO as 'Brewer-C', with additional side views of 'Brewer-B' (top) and the Yak-28U ('Maestro') tandem-cockpit trainer (centre) *(Pilot Press)*

Brewer-A to C (Yak-28). Two-seat tactical attack versions. Single cockpit for pilot, with blister canopy, and glazed nose for navigator/bomb aimer. Corresponding to Yak-26 ('Mangrove') and produced to replace the Il-28 in the Soviet Air Force. Most examples have blister radome under fuselage just forward of wings. On some aircraft, long engine nacelles extend forward as far as the front of this radome. Others have shorter nacelles. Guns semi-submerged in each side of the fuselage on some aircraft; on starboard side only on others. Internal bomb bay between the underfuselage radome and the rear main landing gear unit. Now used only in places of secondary importance.

Brewer-D. Reconnaissance version, with cameras in bomb bay.

Brewer-E. First Soviet operational ECM escort aircraft, deployed in 1970. Underfuselage radome deleted. Active ECM pack built into bomb bay, from which it projects in form of a semi-cylindrical pack. Attachment under each outer wing, outboard of external fuel tank, for a rocket pod.

Firebar. Tandem two-seat all-weather fighter derivative of Yak-28, corresponding to Yak-27. Nose radome. Internal weapons bay deleted. 'Anab' air-to-air missile under each wing instead of guns. Identified as **Yak-28P** (Perekhvatchik; interceptor) at 1967 Domodedovo display, the suffix 'P' indicating that the design had been *adapted* for the fighter role. Example shown in static park had a much longer dielectric nosecone than the standard operational 'Firebars' in the flying display and had two missile pylons under each wing, one for an 'Atoll' and one for an 'Anab'. This suggested that it was a weapons development aircraft. However, the lengthened nosecone has since been fitted retrospectively on many Yak-28Ps in squadron service. This does not indicate any increase in radar capability or aircraft performance.

Maestro (Yak-28U). Trainer version of 'Firebar'. Normal cockpit layout replaced by two individual single-seat cockpits in tandem, each with its own canopy. Front canopy sideways-hinged to starboard; rear canopy rearward-sliding.

About 300 Yak-28P 'Firebars' continue to form a significant component of the Soviet home defence interceptor force. The Yak-28 'Brewer' series is changing gradually from first-line attack to support roles, with the emphasis on ECM, reconnaissance and operational training.

The following details refer specifically to the Yak-28P, but are generally applicable to the other versions of the Yak-28:

TYPE: Two-seat transonic all-weather interceptor.

WINGS: Cantilever shoulder-wing monoplane of basically constant chord. Extended leading-edge on outer wings and also between fuselage and each engine nacelle.

Outer extensions are drooped. Slotted flap, with unswept trailing-edge, between fuselage and each engine nacelle. Basic wing sweepback 45°. Anhedral from root. Single fence on upper surface of each wing, between fuselage and engine nacelle. Large trailing-edge flap and short aileron, with tab, outboard of nacelle on each wing. Balancer-wheel fairings, inset from wingtips, are extended forward as lead-filled wing balance weights.

FUSELAGE: All-metal semi-monocoque structure of basically circular section. Finely-tapered dielectric nosecone over radar scanner.

TAIL UNIT: Cantilever all-metal structure. Variable-incidence tailplane mounted midway up fin. All surfaces sweptback. Trim tab in rudder. Dorsal fin fairs into spine along top of fuselage. Shallow ventral stabilising fin.

LANDING GEAR: Two twin-wheel main units in tandem, retracting into fuselage. Front unit retracts forward, rear unit rearward. Small balancer wheel near each wingtip, retracting rearward under wing; fairing integral with leg.

POWER PLANT: Two afterburning turbojet engines, believed to be of same basic type as Tumansky R-11 fitted to some versions of MiG-21, with rating of 58.35 kN (13,120 lb st). Each fitted with centrebody shock-cone. A pointed slipper-type external fuel tank can be carried under the leading-edge of each wing, outboard of the engine nacelle.

ACCOMMODATION: Crew of two in tandem on ejection seats in pressurised cabin under long transparent blister canopy.

OPERATIONAL EQUIPMENT: Reported to include tail warning radar.

ARMAMENT: Pylon under each outer wing for 'Anab' air-to-air missile, with alternative infra-red or semi-active radar homing heads.

DIMENSIONS, EXTERNAL (estimated):
Wing span   12·95 m (42 ft 6 in)
Length overall: Yak-28   21·65 m (71 ft 0½ in)
Height overall   3·95 m (12 ft 11½ in)

WEIGHT (estimated):
Max T-O weight: Yak-28P   15,875 kg (35,000 lb)

PERFORMANCE (Yak-28P, estimated):
Max level speed at 10,670 m (35,000 ft)
          Mach 1·1 (636 knots; 1,180 km/h; 733 mph)
Cruising speed   496 knots (920 km/h; 571 mph)
Service ceiling   16,750 m (55,000 ft)
Max combat radius   500 nm (925 km; 575 miles)
Max range   1,040-1,390 nm
          (1,930-2,575 km; 1,200-1,600 miles)

YAKOVLEV Yak-36MP
NATO reporting name: Forger

This is the VTOL combat aircraft deployed by the Soviet Navy on the *Kiev* and *Minsk*, the first two of its 40,000 ton carrier/cruisers to put to sea. Two versions have been observed on the ships, as follows:

Forger-A. Basic single-seat combat aircraft. At least nine appear to be operational on each ship, in addition to about 15 Kamov Ka-25 anti-submarine and missile targeting helicopters. Primary operational roles are assumed to be reconnaissance, strikes against small ships, and fleet defence against shadowing, unarmed maritime reconnaissance aircraft.

Forger-B. Two-seat training version, of which one example was seen on the *Kiev* and another on the *Minsk*. A second cockpit is located forward of the normal cockpit, with the ejector seat at a lower level, under a continuous transparent canopy. To compensate for the longer nose, a 'plug' is inserted in the fuselage aft of the wing, lengthening the constant-section portion without requiring modification of the tapering rear fuselage assembly. In other respects this version appears to be identical to 'Forger-A', but has no ranging radar or weapon pylons.

The 1975-76 *Jane's* contained the remark that a strike/reconnaissance V/STOL aircraft was thought to have been developed by the Yakovlev bureau from the experimental VTOL aircraft known as 'Freehand', utilising a mixture of vectored thrust and direct jet-lift. This belief was confirmed when the *Kiev* entered the Mediterranean in July 1976 and subsequently operated its complement of 'Forgers' extensively during passage through that sea and the Atlantic en route to Murmansk. These aircraft, and those seen subsequently on the sister-ship *Minsk*, are assumed to be operated by a development squadron.

The general appearance of the single-seat 'Forger-A' is shown in the accompanying illustrations. Its basic configuration is conventional, except that VTOL capability has permitted the mid-set wings to be made relatively small in area. They fold upward at approximately mid-span, for stowage on board ship. No leading-edge devices

Yakovlev Yak-36MP single-seat VTOL carrier-based combat aircraft (NATO 'Forger-A') *(Pilot Press)*

are fitted, but the entire trailing-edge of each wing is made up of an aileron on the outboard (folding) panel and a large Fowler-type flap on the inboard panel. Sweepback is approximately 45° on the leading-edge, and there is considerable anhedral from the wing roots.

All tail surfaces are swept, with conventional rudder and elevators. 'Puffer-jet' stability control orifices are apparent above and below the tailcone and at each wingtip.

Each leg of the trailing-link tricycle landing gear carries a single wheel. The nose gear retracts rearward, the main units forward into the fuselage. A small bumper is fitted under the upward-curving rear fuselage.

Primary propulsion is by a single large turbojet, exhausting through a single pair of vectoring side-nozzles aft of the wing. No afterburner is fitted. The large lateral air intake ducts do not appear to embody splitter plates.

Two lift-jets are installed in tandem in the fuselage immediately aft of the cockpit, under a rearward-hinged louvred door of the kind fitted to the Mikoyan and Sukhoi STOL prototypes demonstrated in 1967. The position of the corresponding underfuselage doors implies that the lift-jets are mounted at an angle, in such a way that their thrust is exerted both upward and slightly forward. As the main vectored-thrust nozzles also turn up to 10° forward of vertical during take-off and landing, the total of four exhaust effluxes can be envisaged as forming a V under the fuselage. There is a small intake for cooling air at the front of the dorsal fin fairing.

Observers of deck flying by 'Forger-As' report that the aircraft appear to be extremely stable during take-off and landing. Take-offs are made vertically, with a smooth conversion about 5 to 6 m (15-20 ft) above the deck, initiated by lowering the aircraft's nose about 5° below the horizon and maintaining this attitude until the aircraft has accelerated to 30-40 knots (55-75 km/h; 35-46 mph). At this speed, a 5° nose-up attitude is assumed, and the accelerating transition is continued by vectoring aft the nozzles of the propulsion engine.

Landing procedure begins with a gradual descent from far astern, with the last 400 m (1,300 ft) flown essentially level, about 30 m (100 ft) above the water. The aircraft crosses the ship's stern with about a 5 knot (10 km/h; 6 mph) closure rate, 10-14 m (35-45 ft) above the flight deck, then flares gently to a hover and descends vertically. Landings are so precise that some form of control from the ship during take-off and approach has been suggested, perhaps in association with laser devices lining each side of the rear deck.

At no time was a STOL take-off observed, as practised by the Harrier/AV-8A combat aircraft of the Royal Air Force and US Marine Corps to increase their load-carrying capability. It is suggested that anything but direct vertical take-off might be difficult for the pilot of 'Forger-A', as take-off with forward speed over the deck would impose formidable stability and safety problems. The Soviet aircraft must also lack the Harrier's ability to increase its combat manoeuvrability by the use of thrust vectoring in forward flight (VIFF).

Estimates put the thrust of 'Forger-A's' primary power plant (based possibly on the Lyulka AL-21) at around 78 kN (17,500 lb), and the thrust of each Koliesov lift-jet at 25 kN (5,600 lb). This would appear adequate to permit a considerable weight of fuel and weapons to be carried. Gun pods and rocket packs have been photographed on four pylons under the aircraft's inner wing panels. Operational equipment includes radar ranging and an infra-red sensor.

DIMENSIONS, EXTERNAL (estimated):
Wing span   7·00 m (23 ft 0 in)
Length overall: 'Forger-A'   15·00 m (49 ft 3 in)
              'Forger-B'   17·66 m (58 ft 0 in)

Yakovlev Yak-36MP (NATO 'Forger-A') hovering over the flight deck on the *Kiev* (*Tass*)

The two-seat training version of the Yak-36 ('Forger-B')

WEIGHT (estimated):
  Max T-O weight:
    'Forger-A'   10,000 kg (22,050 lb)
PERFORMANCE (estimated):
  Max level speed at height   Mach 1·3
  Max rate of climb at S/L   4,500 m (14,750 ft)/min
  Service ceiling   12,000 m (39,375 ft)

YAKOVLEV Yak-40
NATO reporting name: Codling

This three-turbofan short-haul jet transport was designed to replace the Li-2 (Soviet-built DC-3) and to operate from Class 5 (grass) airfields. The prototype flew for the first time on 21 October 1966 and the Yak-40 made its first passenger flight in Aeroflot service on 30 September 1968.

By the Summer of 1976, more than 800 Yak-40s had been built. Most are in service with Aeroflot, some as air ambulances carrying patients to medical centres and to Black Sea convalescent centres. Others have been sold in Afghanistan, Bulgaria, Czechoslovakia, France, West Germany, Italy, Poland and Yugoslavia. Military operators include the Soviet, Bangladesh, Polish, Syrian and Yugoslav air forces. Production in the Soviet Union has ended, but a company named ICX Aviation Inc (which see) has announced plans to manufacture a re-engined version in the USA, as the X-Avia.

All Soviet production Yak-40s are structurally similar, with AI-25 engines, and differ only in their standard of accommodation, usually for 27 or 32 airline passengers in a single class, 16 or 20 passengers in two-class layouts, or up to 11 passengers in an executive layout. All have clamshell thrust reversers aft of the centre engine.

A freighter version is in service, with a cargo door, size approximately 1·50 m × 1·60 m (5 ft × 5 ft 2½ in), in the port side of the fuselage.

A full description of the Yak-40 can be found in the 1978-79 *Jane's*.

POWER PLANT: Three Ivchenko AI-25 turbofan engines, each rated at 14·7 kN (3,300 lb st). Fin and boundary layer splitter beneath and forward of intake for centre engine. Clamshell thrust reverser fitted to airframe aft of this engine. Hot-air anti-icing system for all three engine air intakes. Fire warning and extinguishing systems standard. Fuel in integral tanks between front auxiliary spar and main spar in each wing, from outboard of the fuselage to the inner end of the aileron, total capacity 3,910 litres (860 Imp gallons). Type AI-9 turbine APU mounted in rear of top engine intake fairing for engine starting. Provision for starting from ground compressed air supply.

ACCOMMODATION: Two pilots side by side on flight deck, on adjustable seats, with dual controls. Central jump seat

Yakovlev Yak-40 short-range transport (three Ivchenko AI-25 turbofan engines) in Aeroflot markings

at rear for third person. Automatically-actuated electrical windscreen de-icing system. Main cabin normally laid out for 27 passengers in three-abreast rows, with two-chair units on starboard side of aisle. Seat pitch 75·5 cm (29·7 in). Individual ventilator by each seat. Rack for hand baggage on starboard side of cabin ceiling. Cloakroom (port), buffet, baggage compartment and toilet (starboard) aft of main cabin. Seat for stewardess against rear face of partition separating cabin from rear compartments, on port side. Normal access via hydraulically-actuated ventral airstair door at rear. Service door on port side of cabin, at front. For high-density services, nine twin-seat units can be installed on the port side of the aisle and seven on the starboard side, giving a total of 32 seats. Pitch is unchanged, enabling the rear cabin partition to be moved forward and so giving a larger baggage compartment. The 18-seat mixed class version has two passenger cabins, separated by a partition. The forward cabin has two swivelling chairs, on each side of a table, on the port side; and an inward-facing four-place settee on the starboard side, with small cupboards fore and aft. Alternatively, two more swivelling seats and a table can replace the settee. The rear cabin contains 14 seats in basically four-abreast rows. A lobby between the flight deck and forward cabin provides access for the crew without passing through the main cabins, and contains a cloakroom (starboard) and seat for the stewardess. Compartments aft of the rear cabin are as in the standard 27-seat version. The executive version has a toilet and other facilities in a large compartment aft of the flight deck; a centre lounge furnished with a four-place settee, three armchairs, a writing desk and a sideboard; and rear cabin containing six seats, three-abreast. There is a further toilet aft, and the galley is equipped to special standards. A bar with two adjustable tables is built into the wall between the flight deck and lounge, on the port side. A freight-carrying version is in service.

AVIONICS AND EQUIPMENT: Standard equipment includes full blind-flying instrumentation, two Landysh-5 VHF radio communications installations, an ARK-10 automatic radio compass, KURS-MP-2 VOR/ILS system, RV-5 radio altimeter, Type SO 70 transponder, Grosa-40 weather radar, PRIVOD-ANE-1 flight director system, Kremenj 40E autopilot, AGD 1 artificial horizon and GMK-1GE gyro-compass, permitting automatic approach to ICAO Category II standards.

DIMENSIONS, EXTERNAL:
Wing span	25·0 m (82 ft 0¼ in)
Wing aspect ratio	9
Length overall	20·36 m (66 ft 9½ in)
Length of fuselage	17·00 m (55 ft 9 in)
Diameter of fuselage	2·40 m (7 ft 10½ in)
Height overall	6·50 m (21 ft 4 in)
Tailplane span	7·50 m (24 ft 7¼ in)
Wheel track	4·52 m (14 ft 10 in)
Wheelbase	7·47 m (24 ft 6 in)
Rear cabin door: Height	1·74 m (5 ft 8½ in)
Width	0·94 m (3 ft 1 in)
Service door: Height	1·20 m (3 ft 11¼ in)
Width	0·55 m (1 ft 9½ in)

DIMENSIONS, INTERNAL:
Cabin: Length	7·07 m (23 ft 2½ in)
Max width	2·15 m (7 ft 0¾ in)
Max height	1·85 m (6 ft 0¾ in)

AREA:
Wings, gross	70·00 m² (753·5 sq ft)

WEIGHTS AND LOADINGS (A: 27 seats, B: 32 seats, C: 16 seats, D: executive version):
Weight empty:	
A	9,010-9,400 kg (19,865-20,725 lb)
B	9,400 kg (20,725 lb)
D	9,560-9,850 kg (21,075-21,715 lb)
Max payload: A	2,300 kg (5,070 lb)
B	2,720 kg (6,000 lb)
C	1,360 kg (3,000 lb)
D	990 kg (2,180 lb)

Yakovlev Yak-42 three-turbofan medium-range passenger transport *(Pilot Press)*

Max fuel weight:	
A	2,125-4,000 kg (4,685-8,820 lb)
B	4,000 kg (8,820 lb)
D	3,000-4,000 kg (6,615-8,820 lb)
Normal T-O weight:	
A	12,360-15,500 kg (27,250-34,170 lb)
B	15,500 kg (34,170 lb)
D	12,360-15,000 kg (27,250-33,070 lb)
Max T-O weight: A, B	16,000 kg (35,275 lb)
C	15,310 kg (33,750 lb)
D	15,400 kg (33,950 lb)
Max wing loading: A, B	230 kg/m² (47·1 lb/sq ft)

PERFORMANCE (corresponding to weights given above):
Max level speed at S/L
Mach 0·7 (324 knots; 600 km/h; 373 mph) IAS
Max cruising speed at 7,000 m (23,000 ft)
297 knots (550 km/h; 342 mph)
T-O speed: A, B	86 knots (160 km/h; 100 mph)
D	81-84 knots (150-156 km/h; 93-97 mph)
Max rate of climb at S/L 480 m (1,575 ft)/min
Normal T-O run: A, B	700 m (2,297 ft)
C	650 m (2,133 ft)
D	660 m (2,165 ft)
Normal landing run: A, C, D	320 m (1,050 ft)
B	360 m (1,182 ft)
Range with max payload at 254 knots (470 km/h; 292 mph) at 8,000 m (31,500 ft), with reserves:
A, C, D	971 nm (1,800 km; 1,118 miles)
B	782 nm (1,450 km; 900 miles)
Range with max fuel at 254 knots (470 km/h; 292 mph) at 8,000 m (26,250 ft), with reserves:
All versions 971 nm (1,800 km; 1,118 miles)
Max range at 254 knots (470 km/h; 292 mph) at 8,000 m (26,250 ft), no reserves:
All versions 1,080 nm (2,000 km; 1,240 miles)

YAKOVLEV Yak-42
NATO reporting name: Clobber

On the basis of experience with the Yak-40, the Yakovlev design bureau is developing for Aeroflot this larger civil airliner with a similar three-engined layout. According to Alexander Yakovlev, the basic design objectives were simple construction, reliability in operation, economy and the ability to operate in remote areas with widely differing climatic conditions. Up to 2,000 aircraft in this category are needed, for use particularly on feederline

services extending north and south from the main east-west trans-Siberian trunk routes.

Three prototypes of the Yak-42 were ordered initially. The first of these (CCCP-1974) flew for the first time on 7 March 1975, with a wing sweepback of 11°, and was furnished as a 100-passenger local-service version with carry-on baggage and coat stowage fore and aft of the cabin. The second prototype (CCCP-1975) had 23° of wing sweep, and cabin windows which extended further forward and rearward on each side, indicating that it was representative of the 120-seat version with three more rows of seats and no carry-on baggage areas. The third prototype (CCCP-1976; re-registered subsequently as CCCP-42303) differed from the second only in detail, having hot-air de-icing on the tail surfaces as well as the wings; fairing discs over the main wheels and longer leg fairings to improve airflow over the doorless main landing gear when retracted; and movement further forward of the overwing emergency exits.

It was made known that a decision on the degree of wing sweep to be standardised for production aircraft would be taken after simultaneous evaluation of the prototypes, in terms of high-speed cruise, economy and low-speed handling characteristics. The 23° wing showed itself superior, and aircraft No. CCCP-42303, exhibited at the 1977 Paris Salon, was typical of the first series of 200 production Yak-42s, which will replace Tu-134s currently in Aeroflot service.

The Yak-42 is intended to use all three engines at cruise power during flight. It can, however, continue take-off after the failure of any one engine, and can maintain level cruising flight on a single engine.

Design is in accordance with the latest airworthiness standards of the Soviet civil authorities and US FAR 25 requirements. Special care has been taken during design to ensure that the D-36 will conform with national and international limits on smoke and noise; and the Yak-42 is intended to operate in temperatures ranging from −50°C to +50°C. An APU will be standard, for engine starting and ground services, making the aircraft independent of airport equipment.

TYPE: Three-turbofan medium-range passenger transport.
WINGS: Cantilever low-wing monoplane, consisting of a centre-section and two outer panels. No dihedral or anhedral. Sweepback 23° at quarter-chord. All-metal two-spar torsion-box structure. Two-section aileron on each wing, with servo tab on inner section and trim tab

Yakovlev Yak-42 medium-range transport (three Lotarev D-36 turbofan engines) *(Brian M. Service)* on outer section. Two-section single-slotted flaps on each wing. Multi-section spoilers forward of flaps. No leading-edge control surfaces. Ailerons and flaps actuated hydraulically.

FUSELAGE: All-metal riveted, bonded and welded semi-monocoque structure, of basic circular section, blending into an oval-section rear fuselage.

TAIL UNIT: Cantilever all-metal T-tail structure, with sweepback on all surfaces. One-piece tailplane; incidence variable from 4° upward to 8° downward. Trim tab in each elevator. Trim tab and spring servo tab in rudder. Control surfaces actuated hydraulically.

LANDING GEAR: Hydraulically-retractable tricycle heavy-duty type, with twin wheels on each unit. Main wheels retract inward into flattened fuselage undersurface. Nosewheels retract forward. Hydraulic backup system for extension only. Emergency extension by gravity. Oleo-nitrogen shock-absorbers. Steerable nose unit of levered-suspension type. Low-pressure tyres size 1,300 × 480 on main wheels, 930 × 305 on nosewheels. Hydraulic disc brakes on main wheels. Nosewheel brakes to stop wheel rotation after take-off.

POWER PLANT: Three Lotarev D-36 three-shaft turbofan engines, each rated at 63·74 kN (14,330 lb st). Centre engine, mounted inside rear fuselage, has S-duct air intake. Outboard engines are mounted in pod on each side of rear fuselage. Integral fuel tanks between spars in wings. APU standard.

ACCOMMODATION: Crew of two side by side on flight deck. Single passenger cabin, with total of 120 seats in six-abreast rows, at pitch of 80 cm (31·5 in), with centre aisle, in high-density configuration. Alternative 100-passenger local-service configuration, with carry-on baggage and coat stowage compartments fore and aft of cabin. Main airstair door hinges down from undersurface of rear fuselage. Second door forward of cabin on port side, with integral airstairs. Service door opposite. Galley and crew coat stowage between flight deck and front vestibule. Passenger coat stowage and toilet between vestibule and cabin. Second coat stowage and toilet at rear of cabin. Two underfloor holds for cargo, mail and baggage in standard containers, loaded through a large door on the starboard side, forward of wing. Chain-drive handling system for containers built into cabin floor. Forward hold accommodates six containers, each with capacity of 2·2 m³ (77·7 cu ft); rear hold takes three similar containers. Provision for convertible passenger/cargo interior, with enlarged loading door on port side of front fuselage. Two emergency exits overwing on each side. All passenger and crew accommodation pressurised and air-conditioned.

AVIONICS AND EQUIPMENT: Flight and navigation equipment for operation by day and night under adverse weather conditions, with landings on concrete or unpaved runways in weather minima down to 40 m (131 ft) visibility at 300 m (985 ft). Type SAU-42 automatic flight control system and area navigation system standard.

DIMENSIONS, EXTERNAL:
Wing span	34·20 m (112 ft 2½ in)
Wing aspect ratio	7·8
Length overall	36·38 m (119 ft 4¼ in)
Fuselage diameter	3·80 m (12 ft 5½ in)
Height overall	9·80 m (32 ft 1¾ in)
Tailplane span	10·80 m (35 ft 5 in)
Wheel track	5·63 m (18 ft 5¾ in)
Wheelbase	14·78 m (48 ft 6 in)
Passenger door (fwd):	
Height	1·81 m (5 ft 11¼ in)
Width	0·83 m (2 ft 8½ in)
Passenger entrance (rear): Height	1·78 m (5 ft 10 in)
Width	0·81 m (2 ft 7¾ in)
Cargo door (convertible version):	
Height	2·20 m (7 ft 2½ in)
Width	3·25 m (10 ft 8 in)
Baggage/cargo hold door: Height	1·35 m (4 ft 5 in)
Width	1·145 m (3 ft 9 in)
Height to sill	1·45 m (4 ft 9 in)

DIMENSIONS, INTERNAL:
Cabin: Length	19·89 m (65 ft 3 in)
Max width	3·60 m (11 ft 9¾ in)
Height	2·08 m (6 ft 9¾ in)
Forward baggage compartment volume (100-seater)	19·8 m³ (700 cu ft)
Rear baggage compartment volume (100-seater)	9·5 m³ (335 cu ft)

AREAS:
Wings, gross	150 m² (1,615 sq ft)
Horizontal tail surfaces (total)	27·60 m² (297·1 sq ft)
Vertical tail surfaces (total)	23·29 m² (250·7 sq ft)

WEIGHTS:
Weight empty	28,960 kg (63,845 lb)
Max payload	14,500 kg (32,000 lb)
Max T-O weight	52,000 kg (114,640 lb)

PERFORMANCE:
Normal cruising speed at 7,600 m (25,000 ft)	442 knots (820 km/h; 510 mph)
Approach speed	114-119 knots (210-220 km/h; 131-137 mph)
T-O field length	1,800 m (5,900 ft)
Landing from 15 m (50 ft)	1,100 m (3,610 ft)

Yakovlev Yak-50 single-seat aerobatic and sporting aircraft

Range with max fuel	1,620 nm (3,000 km; 1,860 miles)
Range with normal 10,500 kg (23,150 lb) payload, with reserves	1,000 nm (1,850 km; 1,150 miles)
Range with max payload, with reserves	540 nm (1,000 km; 620 miles)

YAKOVLEV Yak-50

A Novosti Press Agency bulletin, dated 30 June 1975, stated that tests of a new Yakovlev sporting aircraft, designated Yak-50, had been carried out near Arsenyev in the Soviet Far East. Mr Nikolai Sazykin, director of the Progress Engineering Works in which all Yakovlev sporting aircraft are assembled, was quoted as saying that the Yak-50 was intended to participate in the 1976 world aerobatic championships.

No descriptive details, specification or illustrations of the new aircraft were released. Test pilot Anatoly Sergeyev stated only that it was more advanced than the familiar Yak-18 training and aerobatic monoplane, with a more powerful engine, better manoeuvrability, a speed of over 215 knots (400 km/h; 248 mph) in a dive, and the ability to perform all aerobatics with its landing gear retracted or extended.

When six Yak-50s participated in the 1976 world aerobatic championships at Kiev, their evolution from the Yak-18 was apparent, but with significant changes. Basic configuration is little different from that of the single-seat Yak-18PS, with tailwheel-type landing gear. This was deliberate, to keep the handling characteristics of the two types as similar as possible. However, overall dimensions are reduced; control surface hinge-lines have been moved to keep control forces light; and overall structural strength has been increased by switching entirely to metal covering. In particular, the fuselage is now semi-monocoque instead of steel tube with fabric covering to the rear of the cockpit. Designers responsible for these and other changes were Sergei Yakovlev (son of Alexander Yakovlev) and Yuri Yankievich.

The wings dispense with the Yak-18's centre-section and have 2° dihedral and 2° incidence, and retain an asymmetric section. To ensure a high power/weight ratio in such a large aircraft, the power plant is a 268 kW (360 hp) Vedeneev (Ivchenko) M-14P aircooled radial piston engine, driving a V-530TA-D35 two-blade variable-pitch propeller, instead of the 224 kW (300 hp) Ivchenko AI-14RF of the Yak-18PS. Main-wheel tyre size is 500 × 150, nosewheel tyre size 200 × 80. The main fuel tank, capacity 55 litres (12 Imp gallons), is aft of the engine firewall, the electrical system battery behind the pilot's seat. A Zyablik radio transceiver is standard.

Observers at the world championships at Kiev reported that the Yak-50s performed the all-important Aresti manoeuvres with smooth precision, their primary shortcoming being excessive directional stability. Yak-50s flown by V. Letsko and I. Egorov finished first and second

in the men's competition. Others came fifth, seventh and ninth, to win the team prize. First five places in the women's championship were taken by Yak-50s.

DIMENSIONS, EXTERNAL:
Wing span	9·50 m (31 ft 2 in)
Length overall	7·676 m (25 ft 2¼ in)
Tailplane span	3·16 m (10 ft 4½ in)
Wheel track	2·00 m (6 ft 6¾ in)
Wheelbase	5·10 m (16 ft 8¾ in)
Propeller diameter	2·00 m (6 ft 6¾ in)

AREAS:
Wings, gross	15·00 m² (161·5 sq ft)
Ailerons (total)	1·95 m² (21·00 sq ft)
Vertical tail surfaces (total)	1·48 m² (15·93 sq ft)
Horizontal tail surfaces (total)	2·86 m² (30·78 sq ft)

WEIGHTS AND LOADINGS:
Weight empty, equipped	765 kg (1,686 lb)
Max T-O weight	900 kg (1,984lb)
Max wing loading	60 kg/m² (12·29 lb/sq ft)
Max power loading	3·36 kg/kW (5·51 lb/hp)

PERFORMANCE:
Never-exceed speed	226 knots (420 km/h; 261 mph)
Max level speed	173 knots (320 km/h; 199 mph)
T-O speed	65 knots (120 km/h; 75 mph)
Rate of climb at S/L	960 m (3,150 ft)/min
Service ceiling	5,500 m (18,045 ft)
T-O run	200 m (657 ft)
Landing run	250 m (820 ft)
Max range at 1,000 m (3,280 ft), with 120 litres (26·4 Imp gallons) auxiliary fuel, reserve of 10 litres (2·2 Imp gallons)	267 nm (495 km; 307 miles)
Endurance at 500 m (1,640 ft) with 52 litres (11·4 Imp gallons) auxiliary fuel, reserve of 10 litres (2·2 Imp gallons)	48 min
g limits	+9; −6

YAKOVLEV YAK-52

Announced in late 1978, the Yak-52 is a tandem-cockpit variant of the Yak-50, with unchanged span and length, but with a semi-retractable tricycle landing gear. Although aesthetically unattractive, this last feature is intended to reduce damage in a wheels-up landing.

The Yak-52 is expected to replace the Yak-18, which has been the standard ab initio trainer for Soviet pilots since the mid-1940s. Alexander Yakovlev has believed for many years that aeroplanes to be flown by young people should be designed by members of the Komsomol youth brigades and light aircraft enthusiasts, under experienced leadership. The enthusiasm engendered by this policy led to first flight of the prototype Yak-52 less than a year after its design was started. Flight testing was then undertaken by pilots qualified as Soviet Masters of Sport, as well as professional test pilots. Production has been entrusted to

Yakovlev Yak-52 tandem two-seat primary trainer (Pilot Press)

The semi-retractable landing gear of the Yak-52 can be seen clearly in this photograph

the Romanian aircraft industry, under the COMECON (Council for Mutual Economic Assistance) programme, and the first Romanian-built Yak-52s were nearing completion at Bacau in late 1979.

TYPE: Tandem two-seat piston-engined primary trainer.

WINGS: Cantilever low-wing monoplane of single-spar stressed-skin all-metal construction. Each wing comprises a single straight-tapered panel, attached directly to the side of the fuselage. Fabric-covered slotted ailerons. Light alloy split trailing-edge flaps. Ground-adjustable tab on each aileron.

FUSELAGE: Conventional light alloy semi-monocoque structure.

TAIL UNIT: Cantilever light alloy structure. Fixed surfaces metal covered; control surfaces fabric covered. Horn-balanced rudder, with ground-adjustable tab. Mass-balanced elevators. Controllable tab in port elevator.

LANDING GEAR: Semi-retractable tricycle type, with single wheel on each unit. Pneumatic retraction, nosewheel rearward, main units forward. All three wheels remain fully exposed to airflow, against the undersurface of the fuselage and wings respectively, to offer greater safety in the event of a wheels-up emergency landing. Oleo-pneumatic shock-absorbers. Main-wheel tyre size 500 × 150; nosewheel tyre size 400 × 150. Pneumatic brakes. Skis can be fitted in place of wheels for Winter operations, permissible at temperatures down to −42°C.

POWER PLANT: One 269 kW (360 hp) Vedeneev M-14P nine-cylinder aircooled radial engine, driving a two-blade variable-pitch propeller type V-530TA-D35, without spinner. Louvres in front of cowling to regulate cooling. Two-part cowling, split on horizontal centre-line. Two fuel tanks, in wing roots forward of spar, each with capacity of 65 litres (14·25 Imp gallons). Additional tank of 5·5 litres (1·25 Imp gallons) capacity supplies engine during inverted flight. Oil capacity 20 litres (4·5 Imp gallons).

ACCOMMODATION: Tandem seats for pupil and instructor (at rear) under long 'glasshouse' canopy, with separate rearward-sliding hood over each seat. Seats and dual flying controls are adjustable. Sides of cockpit have a soft synthetic lining. Heating and ventilation standard.

SYSTEMS: No hydraulic system. Independent main and emergency pneumatic systems, for flap actuation, landing gear retraction, engine starting, and wheel brake control. Pneumatic systems supplied by two compressed air bottles, mounted behind rear seat and recharged in flight by an AK-50T compressor. GSR-3000M engine-driven generator supplies 27V electrical system. Battery in port wing.

AVIONICS AND EQUIPMENT: Dual engine and flying instruments. Equipment includes GMK-1A gyro-compass, ARK-15M automatic radio compass, Landysh-5 VHF com and SPU-9 intercom.

DIMENSIONS, EXTERNAL:

Wing span	9·50 m (31 ft 2 in)
Length overall	7·676 m (25 ft 2¼ in)
Height overall	2·95 m (9 ft 8¼ in)
Propeller diameter	2·40 m (7 ft 10½ in)

AREA:

Wings, gross	15·00 m² (161·5 sq ft)

WEIGHTS AND LOADINGS:

Basic operating weight	1,000 kg (2,205 lb)
Max T-O weight	1,290 kg (2,844 lb)
Max wing loading	86·0 kg/m² (17·61 lb/sq ft)
Max power loading	4·80 kg/kW (7·90 lb/hp)

PERFORMANCE:

Never-exceed speed	194 knots (360 km/h; 223 mph)
Max level speed	154 knots (285 km/h; 177 mph)
Landing speed	60 knots (110 km/h; 69 mph)
Max rate of climb at S/L	600 m (1,970 ft)/min
Service ceiling	6,000 m (19,700 ft)
T-O run	170 m (558 ft)
Landing run	200 m (656 ft)
Range with max fuel	297 nm (550 km; 341 miles)
Endurance with max fuel	2 h 50 min
g limits	+7; −5

UNITED KINGDOM

AIRCRAFT DESIGNS

AIRCRAFT DESIGNS (BEMBRIDGE) LTD

Bembridge Fort, Sandown, Isle of Wight
Telephone: 0983 406124
Telex: 86448 Micair G
CHAIRMAN AND CHIEF EXECUTIVE: R. C. Britten
DIRECTORS:
J. M. McMahon
N. J. R. James, MA (Cantab)
F. H. Mann
TECHNICAL DIRECTOR:
M. J. Brennan, BSc, CEng, FIMechE, FRAeS
CHIEF DESIGNER:
J. Allan, DipAe(Hull), CEng, FRAeS

Founded in 1978 to design and construct the Sheriff lightweight twin-engined aircraft, Aircraft Designs (Bembridge) Ltd has since expanded to become a consultant in all aspects of light aviation, gaining CAA approval in October 1979. A separate company, Sheriff Aerospace Ltd, has been formed, with Mr Denis Berryman, CEng, FRAeS, as Technical Director, to finance the Sheriff; but all design and marketing continue to be handled by Aircraft Designs (Bembridge) Ltd.

The initial Sheriff project, for an economical twin-engined trainer, has now developed into a lower/middle range four-seat touring or air taxi aircraft, while still retaining the originally conceived option of a lower-powered twin-engined trainer, particularly suitable for low-cost military training.

Prototype construction has been subcontracted to Micronair (Aerial) Ltd, a company also situated at Bembridge Fort.

BRITTEN SHERIFF

TYPE: Two/four-seat lightweight training and utility aircraft.

WINGS: Cantilever low-wing monoplane. Wing section NACA 23015. Conventional single-spar structure of 2024 light alloy. The main spar is a built-up I-section, and the basic structure includes light alloy ribs and a stressed leading-edge skin, part of which forms an integral fuel tank in each wing. Frise-type light alloy ailerons with corrugated skins. Plain light alloy trailing-edge flaps with corrugated skins, actuated by a patented feature, the flap retracting step. No tabs.

FUSELAGE: Simple single-curvature rectangular box structure of 2024 light alloy. Four longerons and light alloy formers. Nosecone and fairings of glassfibre. Electronics/equipment bay in nose.

TAIL UNIT: Cantilever structure of 2024 light alloy, with twin endplate fins and rudders. Elevator and rudders have corrugated skins. Trim tab in centre of elevator.

LANDING GEAR: Retractable (optionally non-retractable) tricycle type with single wheel on each unit. Trailing-link main legs, with shock-absorption by air/oil struts. Nosewheel has oleo-pneumatic shock-strut and is fully castoring. Main wheels and tyres size 6·00-6. Nosewheel and tyre size 5·00-5.

POWER PLANT: Tourer has two 119 kW (160 hp) Avco Lycoming O-320-H flat-four engines, each driving a two-blade constant-speed fully-feathering metal propeller with spinner. Club trainer has two 85·7 kW (115 hp) Avco Lycoming O-235-L2C flat-fours, each driving a two-blade fixed-pitch metal propeller. Integral wing fuel tanks with total capacity of 277 litres (61 Imp gallons). Refuelling point in leading-edge of each wing.

ACCOMMODATION: Tourer has four forward-facing seats. Trainer has two side-by-side seats, with dual controls as standard. Two 'gull-wing' doors provide access.

DIMENSIONS, EXTERNAL:

Wing span	10·06 m (33 ft 0 in)
Wing chord (constant)	1·40 m (4 ft 7 in)
Wing aspect ratio	7·26
Length overall	6·98 m (22 ft 11 in)
Propeller diameter	1·83 m (6 ft 0 in)

AREAS:

Wings, gross	13·94 m² (150·0 sq ft)
Vertical tail surfaces (total)	2·60 m² (28·0 sq ft)
Horizontal tail surfaces (total)	3·25 m² (35·0 sq ft)

WEIGHTS AND LOADINGS (estimated. A: four-seat tourer/air taxi with non-retractable landing gear; B: four-seat tourer/air taxi with retractable landing gear; C: two-seat club trainer):

Weight empty:	A	810 kg (1,785 lb)
	B	855 kg (1,885 lb)
	C	716 kg (1,579 lb)
Max T-O weight:	A	1,270 kg (2,800 lb)
	B	1,338 kg (2,950 lb)
	C	975 kg (2,150 lb)
Max wing loading:	A	91·3 kg/m² (18·7 lb/sq ft)
	B	96·0 kg/m² (19·7 lb/sq ft)
	C	69·8 kg/m² (14·3 lb/sq ft)
Max power loading:	A	5·34 kg/kW (8·75 lb/hp)
	B	6·08 kg/kW (9·95 lb/hp)
	C	5·69 kg/kW (9·35 lb/hp)

PERFORMANCE (estimated, A: engines 110 kW; 148 hp at 2,500 rpm at 1,270 kg; 2,800 lb T-O weight; B: engines 110 kW; 148 hp at 2,500 rpm at 1,338 kg; 2,950 lb T-O weight; C: engines 85·7 kW; 115 hp at 975 kg; 2,150 lb T-O weight):

Max level speed:		
	A	139 knots (257 km/h; 160 mph)
	B	150 knots (278 km/h; 173 mph)
	C	127 knots (235 km/h; 146 mph)
Cruising speed at 75% power:		
	A	127 knots (235 km/h; 146 mph)
	B	137 knots (254 km/h; 158 mph)
	C	122 knots (225 km/h; 140 mph)
Cruising speed at 60% power:		
	A	115 knots (212 km/h; 132 mph)
	B	123 knots (229 km/h; 142 mph)

Aircraft Designs (Britten) Sheriff two/four-seat training and utility aircraft *(Pilot Press)*

Max rate of climb at S/L: A	405 m (1,330 ft)/min	C		49 m (160 ft)/min	C	369 m (1,210 ft)
B	396 m (1,300 ft)/min	T-O to 15 m (50 ft): A		367 m (1,205 ft)	Range with max fuel, no reserves:	
C	350 m (1,150 ft)/min	B		421 m (1,380 ft)	A	540 nm (1,000 km; 621 miles)
Rate of climb at S/L, one engine out:		C		381 m (1,250 ft)	B	580 nm (1,075 km; 668 miles)
A	91 m (300 ft)/min	Landing from 15 m (50 ft): A		480 m (1,575 ft)	C (132 litres; 29 Imp gallons)	
B	94 m (310 ft)/min	B		501 m (1,645 ft)		310 nm (575 km; 357 miles)

BAe
BRITISH AEROSPACE

HEADQUARTERS: Brooklands Road, Weybridge, Surrey KT13 0SJ

Telephone: 0932 45522
Telex: 27111

LONDON OFFICE: 100 Pall Mall, London SW1Y 5HR
Telephone: 01 930 1020
Telex: 24353

CORPORATION BOARD:
Sir Austin Pearce, CBE, PhD (Chairman)
A. H. C. Greenwood, CBE, JP, CEng, FRAeS (Deputy Chairman)
K. Bevins (part-time member)
L. W. Buck (Industrial Relations)
Kenneth Durham (part-time member)
Air Chief Marshal Sir Peter Fletcher, KCB, OBE, DFC, AFC, RAF(Retd) (Corporate Strategy and Planning)
B. E. Friend, FCA (Financial Director)
D. O. Gladwin, CBE, JP (part-time member)
H. A. Hitchcock (part-time member)
Admiral Sir Raymond Lygo, KCB, FBIM, RN (Retd) (Chairman and Chief Executive, Dynamics Group)
Sir Frederick Page, KB, CBE, FRS, MA, CEng, FRAeS, FBIM (Chairman and Chief Executive, Aircraft Group)

E. G. Rubython, CBE (Deputy Chief Executive, Aircraft Group)
J. T. Stamper, MA, CEng, FRAeS (Technical Director)
Sir Jack Wellings (part-time member)

SECRETARY/LEGAL ADVISER: B. Cookson, LLB
TREASURER: J. D. Hanson, LLB, FCA
CORPORATE PUBLIC RELATIONS MANAGER:
 D. W. Bainbridge
CHIEF PRESS OFFICER: D. A. Dorman

British Aerospace was established by the Aircraft and Shipbuilding Industries Act 1977, as a result of which, on 29 April 1977, the ownership of British Aircraft Corporation (Holdings) Ltd, Hawker Siddeley Aviation Ltd, Hawker Siddeley Dynamics Ltd and Scottish Aviation Ltd was vested in the Corporation. Initially, these four companies continued to trade under their existing names. With effect from 1 January 1978, a new structure for British Aerospace was implemented, whereby the Corporation functions through two operating groups, an Aircraft Group and a Dynamics Group (see Air-launched Missiles section).

As a result of legislation being implemented in Parliament in 1980, British Aerospace will become a limited liability company to be called British Aerospace Ltd. Shares in the new company, which will retain the existing structure of British Aerospace, will be offered for sale when market conditions dictate.

British Aerospace has the following overseas subsidiaries: British Scandinavian Aviation AB, British Aerospace Australia Ltd, British Aerospace Inc; and the following UK subsidiaries: British Aerospace (Insurance Brokers) Ltd, British Aerospace (Insurance) Ltd, British Aircraft Corporation (Pension Fund Trustees) Ltd and HSA/HSD (Pension Fund Trustees) Ltd.

Its associated companies are SEPECAT (formed in May 1966 by BAC and Breguet Aviation to control the development and production of the Jaguar tactical strike fighter and trainer), Panavia Aircraft GmbH (formed in March 1969 by BAC, MBB and Aeritalia to manage the development and production of the Tornado multi-role combat aircraft), Dulles International Aeroservices Inc (formed in 1976 by BAC (USA) Inc and Rolls-Royce Aero Engines of the USA to build and operate a new facility at Washington's Dulles International Airport to supply customers in North America with spares and engineering support), Arab-British Dynamics Ltd (inaugurated in 1977 by BAC Guided Weapons Division and the Arab Organisation for Industrialisation to manufacture the Swingfire missile in Egypt), Frames Travel (Fylde) Ltd and Remploy Services Ltd. In January 1980 British Aerospace Dynamics Group announced, simultaneously with Messerschmitt-Bölkow-Blohm and Aérospatiale's Division Engins Tactiques, the formation of a new European guided weapons company called Euromissile Dynamics Group (EMDG).

BRITISH AEROSPACE AIRCRAFT GROUP

HEADQUARTERS: Richmond Road, Kingston upon Thames, Surrey KT2 5QS
Telephone: 01 546 7741
Telex: 23726
GROUP BOARD:
Sir Frederick Page, KB, CBE, FRS, MA, CEng, FRAeS, FBIM (Chairman & Chief Executive)
E. G. Rubython, CBE (Deputy Chief Executive)
A. F. Atkin, CBE, BSc (Hons), DipAe (Hull), FEng, FIMechE, FRAeS (Managing Director, Military)
J. L. Thorne (Managing Director, Civil)
G. W. Carr, FCIS, MRAeS (Administration Director)
J. L. Glasscock, BA, FCIS, JP (Commercial Director)
P. Jefferson, CEng, MRAeS, MIMechE (Production Director)
F. E. Roe, DIC, BSc, CEng, ACGI, FRAeS (Resources Director)
R. H. Sawyer, FCA, FCMA, JDip, MA (Financial Director)
J. T. Stamper, MA, CEng, FRAeS (Technical Director)
A. S. Watson (Marketing Director, Military)
N. V. Barber, BA, MSc (Divisional Managing Director, Manchester Division)
C. M. Chandler, ACWA (Divisional Managing Director, Kingston-Brough Division)

M. J. Goldsmith, DIC, CEng, FRAeS (Divisional Managing Director, Hatfield-Chester Division)
L. Phillimore, BSc, CEng, FRAeS (Divisional Managing Director, Scottish Division)
J. Ferguson Smith, FCA (Deputy Managing Director, Civil; Divisional Chairman, Weybridge-Bristol Division; and Marketing Director, Civil)
M. G. Wilde, OBE, BSc, DipAe, CEng, FRAeS (Divisional Managing Director, Weybridge-Bristol Division)
I. R. Yates, BEng, CEng, FRAeS, FIMechE (Divisional Managing Director, Warton Division)
GROUP SECRETARY: H. T. Fream
MILITARY ADVISER: Air Chief Marshal Sir Denis Smallwood, GBE, KCB, DSO, DFC, (RAF Ret'd)
PUBLIC RELATIONS MANAGER: R. A. C. Gardner
PUBLIC RELATIONS OFFICER: D. M. Stroud

British Aerospace Aircraft Group was formed officially on 1 January 1978 by the reorganisation of the airframe interests of British Aircraft Corporation, Hawker Siddeley Aviation and Scottish Aviation. The Group is organised into six Divisions: Kingston-Brough; Manchester; Warton; Hatfield-Chester; Weybridge-Bristol; and Scottish.

Civil aircraft programmes include development and production of the British Aerospace 146 four-turbofan feederliner, the twin-turbofan HS 125 business aircraft and BAC One-Eleven transport, and the twin-turboprop HS 748 and Jetstream transports. Military aircraft programmes include manufacture of the Harrier and Sea Harrier V/STOL combat aircraft, Hawk ground attack/trainer and Bulldog basic and aerobatic trainer. Development of the Nimrod for anti-submarine warfare and airborne early warning duties continues. BAe also offers HS 748 variants for military transport and maritime patrol missions.

Major international collaborative programmes include the AV-8B development of the Harrier with McDonnell Douglas in the USA, the Tornado multi-role combat aircraft with MBB of Germany and Aeritalia of Italy, the Jaguar with Dassault-Breguet of France, and the One-Eleven with Romania. In 1978, British Aerospace became a full 20% risk-sharing partner in the Airbus Industrie wide-body airliner programme.

In defence support, British Aerospace holds large contracts in the Middle East, notably in Saudi Arabia where a continuing programme of training and maintenance for the Royal Saudi Air Force involves more than 2,000 expatriate employees.

BRITISH AEROSPACE AIRCRAFT GROUP, HATFIELD/CHESTER DIVISION

Hatfield, Hertfordshire AL10 9TL
Telephone: 07072 62345
Telex: 22411
OTHER WORKS: Broughton, near Chester, Clwyd
DIVISIONAL BOARD:
J. L. Thorne (Chairman)
M. J. Goldsmith, DIC, CEng, FRAeS, (Managing Director)
C. F. Bethwaite (Project Director, BAe 146)

B. J. Champion, CA(SA) (Resources Director; and Finance Director, Chester)
P. Edwards, OBE (Director; and General Manager, Chester)
J. Humphreys, ACCA (Financial Director)
J. A. Johnstone, OBE, CEng, FRAeS, FSLAET (Marketing Director, Civil)
R. M. McKinlay (Director, Airbus)
R. C. Meakins, MBIM (Administration Director; and Commercial Director, Chester)
P. R. Owen, CEng, FRAeS (Technical Director)
J. S. Paterson, CA (Commercial Director)

A. E. Rowland (Director and Deputy General Manager, Chester)
G. R. Wilkinson (Production Director)
SECRETARY: R. F. Kirkby
PUBLIC RELATIONS MANAGER: J. E. Scott, DSC, MRAeS

Main activities of this Division include development of the HS 125 and variants; design, development and production of A300 and A310 wings for Airbus Industrie; development and production of the British Aerospace 146, work on which is also taking place at other Group factories; responsibility for Trident aircraft in service.

BRITISH AEROSPACE AIRCRAFT GROUP, KINGSTON/BROUGH DIVISION

Richmond Road, Kingston upon Thames, Surrey KT2 5QS
Telephone: 01 546 7741
Telex: 23726
OTHER WORKS: Dunsfold Aerodrome, Godalming, Surrey; Hamble, Hampshire; Brough, North Humberside; Holme-on-Spalding Moor Aerodrome, Yorkshire; Bitteswell Aerodrome, Lutterworth, Leicestershire
DIVISIONAL BOARD:
A. F. Atkin, CBE, BSc, DipAe, FEng, FIMechE, FRAeS (Chairman)

C. M. Chandler, ACWA (Managing Director)
R. G. Adolphus, BSc, CEng, FRAeS (Production Director)
D. F. Corbett (Director and General Manager, Hamble)
K. Essex-Crosby, DipAe, CEng, FRAeS (Director)
J. W. Fozard, DCAe, BSc, CEng, FRAeS, FIMechE (Marketing Director)
R. H. Hill, CEng, MRAeS (Director)
R. S. Hooper, DCAe, DAe, CEng, MIMechE, FRAeS (Technical Director)
V. H. Lidstone (Commercial Director)
L. W. Milsom (Divisional Resources Director; and General Manager, Brough)

A. C. Spencer (Director)
J. F. White, FCA, MBIM, MRAeS (Financial Director)
A. H. Whitehouse, TEng, MRAeS (Administration Director; and General Manager, Bitteswell)
SECRETARY: T. A. Fletcher
PUBLIC RELATIONS MANAGER: A. D. F. Lewis

Main activities of this Division include design, development and production of the Harrier, Sea Harrier and Hawk; production of components for the BAe 146 and A300 Airbus; product support of the Buccaneer and Phantom; Phantom wing modifications; overhaul and conversion of Hunter, Shackleton, Vulcan and Buccaneer aircraft.

BRITISH AEROSPACE AIRCRAFT GROUP, MANCHESTER DIVISION

Greengate, Middleton, Manchester M24 1SA
Telephone: 061 681 2020
Telex: 667015
OTHER WORKS: Woodford Aerodrome, Woodford, Cheshire

DIVISIONAL BOARD:
A. F. Atkin, CBE, BSc, DipAe, FEng, FIMechE, FRAeS (Chairman)
N. V. Barber, BA, MSc (Managing Director)
H. T. Healy, ACMA (Financial Director)
J. E. Perry, BSc, MSc, CEng, MIMechE, MIProdE (Production Director)
J. B. Scott-Wilson, MA, FRAeS (Technical Director)

S. C. Ward, BSc (Commercial Director)
SECRETARY: W. A. Hayhoe
PUBLIC RELATIONS MANAGER: J. R. Gray

Main activities of this Division include design, development and production of the HS 748 and Nimrod; development of the AEW Nimrod; production of A300 and A310 Airbus components.

BRITISH AEROSPACE AIRCRAFT GROUP, SCOTTISH DIVISION

Prestwick International Airport, Ayrshire KA9 2RW
Telephone: 0292 79888
Telex: 77432
DIVISIONAL BOARD:
J. L. Thorne (Chairman)

L. Phillimore, BSc, CEng, FRAeS (Managing Director)
W. Agnew (Production Director)
D. McConnell (Commercial Director)
J. R. Woods (Administration Director)

SECRETARY: J. W. Connell
MARKETING MANAGER: R. A. Watt

PUBLICITY: R. Frost
Main activities of this Division include Bulldog and Jetstream production; production of fuselage sections for Lockheed C-130 Hercules and components for Lockheed TriStars; engine production and overhaul.

BRITISH AEROSPACE AIRCRAFT GROUP, WARTON DIVISION

Warton Aerodrome, Preston, Lancashire PR4 1AX
Telephone: 0772 633333
Telex: 67627
OTHER WORKS: Preston, Lancashire; Samlesbury Aerodrome, Blackburn, Lancashire
DIVISIONAL BOARD:
A. F. Atkin, CBE, BSc, DipAe, FEng, FIMechE, FRAeS (Chairman)
I. R. Yates, BEng, CEng, FIMechE, FRAeS (Managing Director)
F. E. Roe, DIC, BSc, CEng, ACGI, FRAeS (Deputy Managing Director)

A. H. Baxter (Deputy Production Director)
R. Dickson, MA (Cantab), CEng, FRAeS (Research Director)
R. H. Evans (Commercial Director and Director-in-charge, India)
S. Gillibrand, MSc, CEng, FRAeS (Production Director)
J. Glover, FCMA (Financial Director)
B. O. Heath, OBE, BSc, DIC, CEng, MRAeS, Hon MIED (Technical Director and Panavia Director of Systems Engineering; Warton)
Air Chief Marshal Sir John Nicholls, KCB, CBE, DFC, AFC (Director, Saudi Arabia)

T. O. Williams, MA, CEng, FIMechE, MIEE (Administration Director)
F. G. Willox (Director, Tornado Project)

SECRETARY: L. F. Trueman, FCCA
PUBLICITY MANAGER: A. F. Johnston

Main activities of this Division include design, development and production with MBB and Aeritalia of the Panavia Tornado; joint development and production with Dassault-Breguet of the SEPECAT Jaguar; marketing of the Strikemaster; product support of the Jet Provost and Lightning; conversion programmes for the Canberra; provision of advanced defence support programmes.

BRITISH AEROSPACE AIRCRAFT GROUP, WEYBRIDGE/BRISTOL DIVISION

Brooklands Road, Weybridge, Surrey KT13 0SF
Telephone: 0932 45522
Telex: 27111
OTHER WORKS: Filton House, Filton, Bristol; Bournemouth (Hurn) Airport, Christchurch, Dorset
DIVISIONAL BOARD:
J. L. Thorne (Chairman)
M. G. Wilde, OBE, BSc, DipAe, CEng, FRAeS (Managing Director)
K. Bentley, MA, CEng, MRAeS (Technical Director and General Manager, Weybridge)
G. Hanby, FCA, FCWA (Commercial Director)
J. A. Johnstone, OBE, CEng, FRAeS, FSLAET (Marketing Director, Civil)
B. G. Thomas (Production Director and Rombac Project Director)
E. B. Trubshaw, CBE, MVO, FRAeS (Director of Flight Test and Concorde; and General Manager, Filton)
D. Wynne, FCWA (Financial and Resources Director)
SECRETARY: H. T. Fream
DIVISIONAL PUBLIC RELATIONS MANAGER: N. A. Barfield
PUBLIC RELATIONS MANAGER, FILTON: H. Berry
Main activities of this Division include development and production of the One-Eleven; support for the Concorde, One-Eleven, VC10, Vanguard, Viscount, Britannia and Bristol Freighter; major subcontract work; major compo-nent manufacture for the BAe 146. Another major contract is for the conversion of five VC10 and four Super

Artist's impression of one of the VC10 flight refuelling tankers to be produced at Weybridge/Bristol Division by conversion of ex-airline transports

VC10 commercial transports to tanker configuration for the RAF.

BAe JETSTREAM 31

The decision to proceed with development and production of this new version of the Jetstream was announced by British Aerospace on 5 December 1978. It will be available in three versions, as follows:

Commuter. Basic version, designed to carry 18/19 passengers and baggage, and able to operate three 87 nm (160 km; 100 mile) stage lengths without refuelling.

Corporate. Executive version, designed for eight to ten passengers, and able to carry eight passengers for 870 nm (1,610 km; 1,000 miles). Cabin design for North American market undertaken by Dave Ellies Industrial Design Inc, for fitting out at completion centres in the USA.

Special. Intended for military communications, casualty evacuation, multi-engine training and cargo operations, and for specialist roles such as airfield calibration, resources survey and protection.

It is intended to obtain FAA certification to FAR Pt 25; the Jetstream 31 will qualify for the currently proposed amendment to FAR Pt 23, and also the longer-term proposal for FAR Pt 24 which applies to commuter airlines. The development aircraft (G-JSSD), converted from a Handley Page-built Jetstream 1, flew for the first time on 28 March 1980; certification and initial production deliveries are scheduled for 1981.

TYPE: Light commuter/executive transport.

WINGS: Cantilever low-wing monoplane. Wing section NACA 63A418 at root, NACA 63A412 at tip. Dihedral 7° from roots. Incidence 2° at root, 0° at tip. Sweepback 0° 34' at quarter-chord. Aluminium alloy fail-safe structure. Aluminium alloy manually-operated Frise-type ailerons. Hydraulically-operated aluminium alloy double-slotted flaps. No slats or leading-edge flaps. Trim tab in each aileron. Goodrich pneumatic rubber-boot de-icing system for leading-edges.

FUSELAGE: Conventional aluminium alloy semi-monocoque fail-safe structure, with chemically-milled skin panels. Fully pressurised.

TAIL UNIT: Cantilever two-spar aluminium alloy structure. Fixed-incidence tailplane. Manually-operated control

BAe Jetstream 31 twin-turboprop light commuter/executive transport *(Pilot Press)*

surfaces. Trim tabs in rudder and each elevator. Goodrich pneumatic rubber-boot de-icing system for leading-edges.

LANDING GEAR: Retractable tricycle type, with nosewheel steering. Hydraulic retraction, main wheels inward into wings, twin nosewheels forward. British Aerospace oleo-pneumatic shock-absorbers on all units. Dunlop wheels and tyres: main-wheel tyres size 28 × 9·00-12, pressure 3·93 bars (57 lb/sq in); nosewheel tyres size 6·00-6, pressure 2·34 bars (34 lb/sq in). No brake cooling. Anti-skid units.

POWER PLANT: Two 671 kW (900 shp) Garrett-AiResearch TPE331-10 turboprop engines, each driving a Dowty Rotol four-blade variable- and reversible-pitch fully-feathering metal propeller. Fuel in integral tank in each wing, total capacity 1,745 litres (384 Imp gallons; 461 US gallons). Refuelling point on top of each outer wing.

ACCOMMODATION: Two seats side by side on flight deck, with provision for dual controls, though aircraft can be approved (subject to local regulations) for single-pilot operation. Main cabin can be furnished in commuter layout for up to 18 passengers, or with executive interior for 8/10 passengers, but optional layouts are available. Downward-opening passenger door, with integral airstairs, at rear of cabin on port side. Emergency exit over wing on starboard side. Baggage compartment in rear of cabin, aft of main door. Entire accommodation pressurised, heated, ventilated and air-conditioned. Toilet, galley and bar optional.

SYSTEMS: Air-conditioning system with cabin pressurisation at max differential of 0·38 bars (5·5 lb/sq in), providing a 2,440 m (8,000 ft) cabin altitude at 7,620 m (25,000 ft). Single hydraulic system, pressure 138 bars (2,000 lb/sq in), with dual engine-driven pumps, for actuation of flaps, landing gear, brakes and nosewheel steering. Details of electrical and oxygen systems not finalised. APU optional.

DIMENSIONS, EXTERNAL:

Wing span	15·85 m (52 ft 0 in)
Wing chord at root	2·19 m (7 ft 2½ in)
Wing chord at tip	0·80 m (2 ft 7¼ in)
Wing aspect ratio	10
Length overall	14·37 m (47 ft 1½ in)
Length of fuselage	13·40 m (43 ft 11½ in)
Height overall	5·32 m (17 ft 5½ in)
Fuselage: Max diameter	1·98 m (6 ft 6 in)
Tailplane span	6·60 m (21 ft 8 in)
Wheel track	5·94 m (19 ft 6 in)
Wheelbase	4·60 m (15 ft 1 in)
Propeller diameter	2·69 m (8 ft 10 in)
Passenger door: Height	1·42 m (4 ft 8 in)
Width	0·86 m (2 ft 10 in)
Emergency exit: Height	0·91 m (3 ft 0 in)
Width	0·56 m (1 ft 10 in)

DIMENSIONS, INTERNAL:

Cabin, excl flight deck: Length	7·32 m (24 ft 0 in)
Max width	1·83 m (6 ft 0 in)
Max height	1·80 m (5 ft 11 in)
Floor area	8·35 m² (90 sq ft)
Volume	16·92 m³ (598 cu ft)
Baggage compartment volume (according to layout)	1·94-2·53 m³ (68·5-89·5 cu ft)

AREAS:

Wings, gross	25·08 m² (270 sq ft)
Ailerons, aft of hinge line (total)	1·52 m² (16·4 sq ft)
Trailing-edge flaps (total)	3·25 m² (35·0 sq ft)
Vertical tail surfaces (total)	7·72 m² (83·1 sq ft)
Horizontal tail surfaces (total)	7·80 m² (84·0 sq ft)

WEIGHTS AND LOADINGS (estimated):

Manufacturer's weight empty	3,450 kg (7,606 lb)
Max T-O and landing weight	6,400 kg (14,110 lb)
Max ramp weight	6,450 kg (14,220 lb)
Max zero-fuel weight	6,100 kg (13,448 lb)
Max wing loading	255·18 kg/m² (52·26 lb/sq ft)
Max power loading	4·73 kg/kW (7·78 lb/shp)

PERFORMANCE (estimated, at max T-O weight):

Max cruising speed: max continuous power	263 knots (488 km/h; 303 mph)
Max cruise power	253 knots (469 km/h; 291 mph)
Stalling speed, flaps down	96 knots (179 km/h; 111 mph)
Max rate of climb at S/L	680 m (2,230 ft)/min
Rate of climb at S/L, one engine out	163 m (535 ft)/min
Service ceiling	9,630 m (31,600 ft)
Service ceiling, one engine out	4,665 m (15,300 ft)
T-O to 15 m (50 ft)	858 m (2,815 ft)
Landing from 15 m (50 ft)	818 m (2,684 ft)
Range with max fuel, six passengers, 30 min reserves at cruising power at optimum altitude, plus 5%	1,108 nm (2,053 km; 1,275 miles)
Range with 18 passengers, reserves as above	420 nm (778 km; 484 miles)

BAe HS 125 SERIES 700

The BAe HS (formerly de Havilland) 125 Srs 700 is a twin-turbofan business aircraft which is also suitable for use by armed forces in the communications role, as a troop carrier, as an ambulance aircraft, for airways inspection,

BAe Jetstream 31 development aircraft (two Garrett-AiResearch TPE331-10 turboprop engines)

and as an economical trainer for pilots, navigators and specialised radio and radar operators. All Series of HS 125s can operate from unpaved runways without modification.

The HS 125 was developed as a private venture, and the first of two prototypes flew for the first time on 13 August 1962. Deliveries to customers began in September 1964. By 24 September 1980 a total of 500 HS 125s had been sold, approx 80 per cent of them for export.

Production of the Hawker Siddeley 125 Series 1 (8 built), 1A (64 built), 1B (13 built), 2 (RAF Dominie T. Mk 1, 20 built), 3 (2 built), 3A (12 built), 3B (15 built), 3A-R and 3A-RA (20 built), 3B-RA (16 built), 400A (69 built), 400B (47 built), 600A (33 built) and 600B (39 built) has ended, and these versions have been described in previous editions of *Jane's*. The current versions are:

HS 125 Srs 700A and 700B. Introduced in 1976. Use of Garrett-AiResearch TFE 731-3-1H turbofan engines gives an improved specific fuel consumption by comparison with that of the turbojets in earlier versions of the HS 125. The Series 700 also meets all existing and proposed international noise regulations. The prototype (G-BFAN) was produced by conversion of a Series 600 airframe and flew for the first time on 28 June 1976. Similar conversions of existing turbojet-powered HS 125s are offered; but new-production Series 700 aircraft embody many refinements in addition to the change of power plant. As in the case of earlier versions, the intended market is indicated by a suffix letter: the **Series 700A** is for the North American market, **Series 700B** for the rest of the world.

Improvements to the airframe, to reduce drag and enhance its appearance, include redesign of the wing keel skid, use of countersunk rivets instead of mushroom-head types in the flap bottom skin, replacement of the lower airbrake leading-edge castellations by internal castellations, replacement of the mushroom-head bolts and rivets in the inner tank doors and aileron trailing-edges by countersunk types, redesign of the ventral fin and adjacent fairings in glassfibre and enlargement of the area of the ventral fin to improve directional stability, deletion of the NACA cooling air intake introduced in the nose of the Series 600, addition of fairings over the windscreen wiper blades and two ADF loop aerials, and use of Harper radius countersunk rivets instead of mushroom-head rivets in the fuselage and tail unit.

New interior equipment and furnishings include the use of figured walnut veneer on cabin tables and toilet consoles, leather trim, provision of a Blaupunkt Bamberg combined radio/cassette stereo player and recorder, a luxury toilet compartment, digital cabin clock, slide-out portable bar box, full harness on sideways-facing seats, improved life-jacket stowage under seats, improved plug-in meal tray for divan occupants, and a new range of interior colour schemes.

The first flight of a production HS 125 Series 700 was made on 8 November 1976. UK certification was received on 7 April 1977. The first sale had been made before completion of the prototype, and by 24 September 1980 the sale of 142 Series 700s had been announced, including more than 90 for customers in North America. Military operators include the Irish Air Corps.

The following description applies specifically to the Series 700:

TYPE: Twin-turbofan business transport aircraft.

WINGS: Cantilever low-wing monoplane. Thickness/chord ratio 14% at root, 11% at tip. Dihedral 2°. Incidence 2° 6' at root, −0° 24' at tip. Sweepback 20° at quarter-chord. Wings built in one piece and dished to pass under fuselage, to which they are attached by four vertical links, a side link and a drag spigot. All-metal two-spar fail-safe structure, with partial centre spar of approx two-thirds span, sealed to form integral fuel tankage which is divided into two compartments by centreline rib. Skins are single-piece units on each of the upper and lower semi-spans. Detachable leading-edges. Fence on each upper surface at approx two-thirds span. Mass-balanced ailerons, operated manually by cable linkage. Trim tab and geared tab in port aileron, two geared tabs in starboard aileron. Aileron fences to improve lateral stability. Large, four-position double-slotted flaps, actuated hydraulically via a screwjack on each flap. Mechanically-operated hydraulic cutout prevents asymmetric operation of the flaps. Airbrakes above and below each wing, forming part of flap shrouds, provide lift-dumping facility during landing, and have interconnected controls to prevent asymmetric operation. TKS liquid system, using porous stainless steel leading-edge panels, for de-icing or anti-icing.

FUSELAGE: All-metal semi-monocoque fail-safe structure, making extensive use of Redux bonding. Constant circular cross-section over much of its length.

TAIL UNIT: Cantilever all-metal structure, with fixed-incidence tailplane mounted on fin. Small fairings on tailplane undersurface to eliminate turbulence around elevator hinge cutouts. Triangular ventral fin, and extended dorsal fin. Control surfaces operated manually via cable linkage. Tabs in rudder and each elevator. TKS liquid de-icing or anti-icing of fin and tailplane leading-edges.

LANDING GEAR: Retractable tricycle type, with twin wheels on each unit. Hydraulic retraction of all units; nosewheels forward, main wheels inward into wings. Oleo-pneumatic shock-absorbers. Fully-castoring nose unit, steerable 45° to left or right. Dunlop main wheels and 10-ply tyres, size 23 × 7-12, pressure 8·75 bars (127 lb/sq in). Dunlop nosewheels and 6-ply tyres, size 18 × 4.25-10, pressure 5·51 bars (80 lb/sq in). Dunlop double-disc hydraulic brakes with Maxaret anti-skid units on all main wheels.

BAe HS 125 Series 700 twin-turbofan business transport (*Pilot Press*)

BAe HS 125 Series 700 twin-turbofan business transport (two Garrett-AiResearch TFE731 engines)

POWER PLANT: Two 16·46 kN (3,700 lb st) Garrett-AiResearch TFE731-3-1H turbofan engines, mounted in rear fuselage pods designed and manufactured by Grumman Aerospace. Engine intake anti-icing by engine bleed air. Integral fuel tanks in wings, with total capacity of 4,628 litres (1,018 Imp gallons). Single pressure refuelling point in lower starboard side of rear fuselage. Overwing refuelling point near each wingtip. Rear underfuselage tank of 509 litres (112 Imp gallons) capacity, with refuelling point on starboard side, and 232 litre (51 Imp gallon) dorsal fin tank, raising overall total capacity to 5,369 litres (1,181 Imp gallons; 1,418 US gallons) of which 5,323 litres (1,171 Imp gallons; 1,406 US gallons) are usable.

ACCOMMODATION: Crew of two on flight deck, which is fully soundproofed, insulated and air-conditioned. Dual controls standard. Seat provided for third crew member. Standard executive layout has seating for eight passengers, with forward baggage compartment, refreshment bar and coat compartment (forward) and toilet (aft). There are individual recessed lights and air louvres. Cabin styling offers the operator a choice of interchangeable furnishing units to suit individual requirements. The wide seats, which on the Srs 700A swivel through 180°, are adjustable fore and aft and sideways, have adjustable lumbar support, and can be reclined hydraulically up to 40°. Typical executive furnishing includes a couch for three persons, five individual seats, and individual foldaway wall tables. Alternative high-density layout is available, seating up to 14 passengers. Outward-opening door at front on port side, with integral airstairs. Emergency exit over wing on starboard side. Edge-heating for windscreen. Electrical windscreen anti-icing, with methanol spray backup.

SYSTEMS: Garrett-AiResearch air-conditioning and pressurisation system. Max cabin differential 0·58 bars (8·35 lb/sq in), maintaining S/L cabin pressure up to 6,550 m (21,500 ft). Oxygen system standard, with dropout masks for passengers. Hydraulic system, pressure 186-207 bars (2,700-3,000 lb/sq in), for operation of landing gear, main-wheel doors, flaps, spoilers, nosewheel steering, main-wheel brakes and anti-skid units. Two accumulators provide emergency hydraulic power for wheel brakes in case of a main system failure. Independent auxiliary system for lowering landing gear and flaps in the event of a main system failure. DC electrical system utilises two 12kW engine-driven starter/generators and two 24V 25Ah nickel-cadmium batteries. A 24V 3·5Ah battery provides separate power for igniter and starter control circuits. AC electrical system includes two 115V 2·5kVA 400Hz three-phase static inverters and one 250VA solid-state standby inverter for avionics, and one engine-driven 120V 4·4kVA frequency-wild alternator for windscreen anti-

icing. Ground power receptacle on starboard side at rear of fuselage for 28V external DC supply. Garrett-AiResearch GTCP-30-92 auxiliary power unit is standard on Srs 700B. Engine ice protection system supplied by engine bleed air. Graviner triple FD Firewire fire warning system and two BCF engine fire extinguishers.

AVIONICS AND EQUIPMENT: Standard avionics include dual Collins VHF-20A com transceivers, Collins VIR-30A VHF nav receivers with dual marker indicators, dual Collins DF-206 ADF, dual Collins MC-103 compasses, Collins DME-40 DME, Marconi AD1540 audio control and passenger address system, RCA Primus 400 weather radar, Collins TDR-90 ATC transponder and Blaupunkt Bamberg stereo tape and AM/FM radio. Provisions for Collins 718U-5 HF com transceiver and second transponder and DME. Collins APS-80 autopilot and FDS-80 flight director system standard, to provide altitude hold, altitude pre-select, airspeed hold, Mach number hold, vertical speed hold, aircraft heading, VOR/LOC, ILS approach and pitch with electric trim.

DIMENSIONS, EXTERNAL:
Wing span	14·33 m (47 ft 0 in)
Wing chord (mean)	2·29 m (7 ft 6¼ in)
Wing aspect ratio	6·25
Length overall	15·46 m (50 ft 8½ in)
Height overall	5·36 m (17 ft 7 in)
Fuselage: Max diameter	1·93 m (6 ft 4 in)
Tailplane span	6·10 m (20 ft 0 in)
Wheel track (c/l of shock-absorbers)	2·79 m (9 ft 2 in)
Wheelbase	6·34 m (20 ft 9½ in)

Passenger door (fwd, port):
Height	1·30 m (4 ft 3 in)
Width	0·69 m (2 ft 3 in)
Height to sill	1·07 m (3 ft 6 in)

Emergency exit (overwing, stbd):
Height	0·91 m (3 ft 0 in)
Width	0·51 m (1 ft 8 in)

DIMENSIONS, INTERNAL:
Cabin (excl flight deck): Length	6·50 m (21 ft 4 in)
Max width	1·80 m (5 ft 11 in)
Max height	1·75 m (5 ft 9 in)
Floor area	5·11 m² (55·0 sq ft)
Volume	17·10 m³ (604·0 cu ft)
Baggage compartment	0·84 m³ (29·6 cu ft)

AREAS:
Wings, gross	32·8 m² (353·0 sq ft)
Ailerons (total)	2·76 m² (29·76 sq ft)
Trailing-edge flaps (total)	5·21 m² (56·06 sq ft)
Fin, incl dorsal fin	5·31 m² (57·15 sq ft)
Ventral fin	0·61 m² (6·61 sq ft)
Horizontal tail surfaces (total)	9·29 m² (100 sq ft)

WEIGHTS AND LOADINGS:
Weight empty	5,826 kg (12,845 lb)
Typical operating weight empty	6,270 kg (13,822 lb)
Max payload	1,010 kg (2,228 lb)
Max ramp and T-O weight	11,566 kg (25,500 lb)
Max zero-fuel weight	7,280 kg (16,050 lb)
Max landing weight	9,979 kg (22,000 lb)
Max wing loading	352·5 kg/m² (72·2 lb/sq ft)
Max power loading	351 kg/kN (3·45 lb/lb st)

PERFORMANCE (at max T-O weight except where indicated):
Never-exceed speed	Mach 0·85
Max level speed at S/L	
	320 knots (592 km/h; 368 mph) IAS
Max cruising speed at 8,380 m (27,500 ft)	
	436 knots (808 km/h; 502 mph)
Econ cruising speed at 11,275-12,500 m (37,000-41,000 ft)	
	390 knots (723 km/h; 449 mph)
Stalling speed, flaps down	
	83 knots (155 km/h; 96 mph) EAS
Service ceiling	12,500 m (41,000 ft)
T-O run	1,367 m (4,484 ft)
T-O to 10·7 m (35 ft), unfactored	1,448 m (4,750 ft)
T-O balanced field length	2,042 m (6,700 ft)
Landing from 15 m (50 ft) at landing weight of 7,167 kg (15,800 lb), unfactored	619 m (2,030 ft)
Landing run at landing weight of 6,804 kg (15,000 lb)	1,143 m (3,750 ft)
Range with max fuel and max payload, allowances for T-O, approach, landing, taxiing and 45 min reserves	2,420 nm (4,482 km; 2,785 miles)

OPERATIONAL NOISE LEVELS (FAR Pt 36):
T-O	87·6 EPNdB
Approach	96·3 EPNdB
Sideline	88·9 EPNdB

BAe HS 748 SERIES 2B

Design of the HS 748 short/medium-range turboprop airliner started in January 1959. The first prototype flew on 24 June 1960, followed by a second on 10 April 1961. UK production of the Series 1 (18 built) and Series 2 (including two Andover CC.Mk 2s for The Queen's Flight and four for Air Support Command), described in previous editions of *Jane's*, has been completed. These models were followed by the Series 2A (see 1977-78 *Jane's*), which continues to be available to order.

In early 1979 the BAe HS 748 Series 2A was replaced as the standard version by a new **Series 2B** basic model, with improved 'hot and high' Dart 536-2 engines, a 1·22 m (4 ft) greater span wing with reduced drag, modified tail surfaces, and other refinements. Prototype for this version was G-BCDZ, flown earlier as the demonstration model of the Coastguarder. The Srs 2B is available in the same civil, military and Coastguarder configurations as the Srs 2A (see following paragraphs), and modification kits are available to existing Srs 2A operators. First production Srs 2B (G-BGJV) made its initial flight on 22 June 1979, and seven had been ordered by 22 May 1980. First delivery of a Srs 2B was made to Air Madagascar in January 1980. On 4 March 1980 BAe, in conjunction with Rolls-Royce, began flight testing hush-kits for the Dart engines. Preliminary tests showed a minimum noise reduction of 5 EPNdB on approach, and useful attenuation levels achieved for ramp departure, taxi and take-off.

HS 748 Civil Transport. In addition to the basic transport configuration, the Series 2B is available optionally with a large rear freight door which has an opening of 2·67 m by 1·72 m (8 ft 9 in × 5 ft 7¾ in), together with a

BAe HS 748 Series 2B, the first of three for the government of Madagascar

BAe HS 748 Series 2A military transport aircraft with large rear freight door, in Belgian Air Force insignia

strengthened cabin floor capable of supporting an overall floor loading of 976 kg/m² (200 lb/sq ft).

HS 748 Military Transport. The military transport version has the large rear freight door and strengthened floor that are available for the civil transport and has, in addition, fixed fittings to undertake a wide range of military roles. Optional military overload take-off and landing weights give improved payload/range capabilities. A total of 52 military HS 748 Srs 2As had been exported by the Summer of 1980, of which 28 were fitted with the rear freight door and strengthened floor. These were for the air forces of Belgium (3), Brazil (12), Ecuador (5), three undisclosed air forces (6), the Royal Brunei Army (1), and the Nepal Royal Flight (1).

HS 748 Coastguarder. Variant for search and rescue and maritime surveillance roles. Described separately.

Sales of all Series (including 31 Andover C.Mk 1s for the RAF: see 1968-69 *Jane's*) totalled 350 by 31 July 1980, including more than 290 for export. Of these, over 335 had been delivered. Nine aircraft were sold with Dart RDa.8 engines, seven being supplied to Bundesanstalt für Flugsicherung (West Germany) with calibration equipment for radio navigational aids and two to the Royal Australian Navy with navigational and electronic training equipment. Six Andover C.Mk 1s were modified for flight checking and calibration duties, and redelivered to the RAF from 1977 to replace Argosy E.Mk 1 aircraft in this role. The modified Andovers are designated **E.Mk 3.**

The HS 748 is the subject of a manufacturing agreement with the Indian government, and 89 aircraft (included in above overall totals) are being assembled from British-built components by Hindustan Aeronautics Ltd. Of these, 17 are for Indian Airlines and 72 for the Indian Air Force.

The following description applies to the current production HS 748 Series 2B, except where indicated:

TYPE: Twin-engined passenger or freight transport.

WINGS: Cantilever low-wing monoplane. Wing section NACA 23018 at root, NACA 4412 at tip. Dihedral 7°. Incidence 3°. Sweepback 2° 54′ at quarter-chord. All-metal two-spar fail-safe structure. No cutouts in spars for engines or landing gear. All-metal set-back hinge, shielded horn-balance, manually-operated ailerons and electrically-actuated Fowler flaps. Geared tab in each aileron. Trim tab in starboard aileron. Pneumatic leading-edge de-icing boots.

FUSELAGE: All-metal semi-monocoque riveted fail-safe structure, of circular section.

TAIL UNIT: Cantilever all-metal structure. Fixed-incidence tailplane. Manually-operated controls. Trim tabs in elevators and rudder. Spring tab in rudder.

LANDING GEAR: Retractable tricycle type, with hydraulically-steerable nose unit. All wheels retract forward hydraulically. Main wheels retract into bottom of engine nacelles forward of front wing spar. Dowty Rotol shock-absorbers. Twin wheels, with Dunlop tyres, on all units. Main wheels size 32 × 10·75-14. Nosewheels size 25·65 × 8·5-10. Standard tyre pressures: main wheels 5·03 bars (73 lb/sq in); nosewheels 3·79 bars (55 lb/sq in). Minimum tyre pressures: main wheels 4·48 bars (65 lb/sq in); nosewheels 3·45 bars (50 lb/sq in). Dunlop disc brakes with Maxaret anti-skid units. No brake cooling.

POWER PLANT (Srs 2B): Two 1,700 kW (2,280 ehp) Rolls-Royce Dart RDa.7 Mk 536-2 turboprop engines, each driving a Dowty Rotol four-blade constant-speed fully-feathering propeller. Engine hush-kits available, externally evident by forward extension of nose cowl by approx 7·5 cm (3 in). Provision for automatic injection of water methanol into live engine in the event of an engine failure on take-off. Fuel in two integral wing tanks, with total capacity of 6,550 litres (1,440 Imp gallons). Tanks modified to provide increased wing bending relief. Underwing pressure refuelling and

overwing gravity refuelling. Oil capacity 14·2 litres (25 Imp pints) per engine.

ACCOMMODATION (commercial): Crew of two on flight deck, and cabin attendant. Accommodation for 40-58 passengers in paired seats on each side of central gangway. Baggage compartment forward of cabin, with provision for steward's seat. Galley, toilet and baggage compartment aft of cabin. Forward baggage compartment and steward's seat can be replaced by freight hold with moving partition between hold and passenger cabin. Main passenger door, on port side at rear, with smaller door on starboard side to serve as baggage door and emergency exit. Crew and freight door on port side at front. Hydraulically-operated stairs.

ACCOMMODATION (military transport): Up to 58 troops in airline type seats. Provision for forward and aft baggage compartments and hydraulically-operated airstairs. In paratroop role up to 48 paratroops and dispatchers can be accommodated on sidewall folding seats with safety harness. Dropping by static line or free fall. For casualty evacuation up to 24 stretchers and nine nursing staff can be carried, with provision for medical supplies and equipment. For supply dropping a guided roller conveyor system allows twelve 340 kg (750 lb) or six 680 kg (1,500 lb) loads to be dropped within six seconds. Capacity for 5,886 kg (12,976 lb) freight. Large cargo door will accept items up to 1·42 m × 1·42 m × 3·66 m (4 ft 8 in × 4 ft 8 in × 12 ft) or small diameter pipes over 12 m (39 ft 4 in) in length. Onboard freight hoist and palletised freight system available. Quickly-removable VIP cabin available, and a variety of VIP layouts, with separate toilet, telephone and wide range of options.

SYSTEMS: Normalair automatic pressurisation and air-conditioning system, giving equivalent altitude of 2,440 m (8,000 ft) at 7,620 m (25,000 ft). Pressure differential 0·38 bars (5·5 lb/sq in). Hydraulic system, pressure 172 bars (2,500 lb/sq in), for landing gear retraction, nose-wheel steering, brakes and propeller brakes. No pneumatic system. One 9kW 28V DC generator and one 22kVA alternator on each engine. Two 1,800VA static inverters.

AVIONICS AND EQUIPMENT: Collins or Bendix solid-state radio and radar. Blind-flying instrumentation and Bendix RDR colour weather radar. Standard equipment by Sperry includes SPZ-500 multi-mode autopilot/flight

director system, air data computer, SPI-402 10 cm (4 in) flight director instruments, VG-14A vertical gyro and C-14 Gyrosyn compass systems. Provision for flight data recorder. Marconi ARC 340 communications and homing system in Royal Brunei Army aircraft.

DIMENSIONS, EXTERNAL:

Wing span: Srs 2A	30·02 m (98 ft 6 in)
Srs 2B	31·23 m (102 ft 5½ in)
Wing chord at root	3·49 m (11 ft 5¼ in)
Wing chord at tip: Srs 2A	1·34 m (4 ft 5 in)
Wing aspect ratio: Srs 2A	11·967
Srs 2B	12·668
Length overall	20·42 m (67 ft 0 in)
Fuselage: Max diameter	2·67 m (8 ft 9 in)
Height overall	7·57 m (24 ft 10 in)
Tailplane span	10·97 m (36 ft 0 in)
Wheel track	7·54 m (24 ft 9 in)
Wheelbase	6·30 m (20 ft 8 in)
Propeller diameter	3·66 m (12 ft 0 in)
Propeller ground clearance	0·61 m (2 ft 0 in)
Passenger door (port, rear):	
Height	1·57 m (5 ft 2 in)
Width	0·76 m (2 ft 6 in)
Height to sill	1·84 m (6 ft 0½ in)
Freight and baggage door (fwd):	
Height	1·37 m (4 ft 6 in)
Width	1·22 m (4 ft 0 in)
Height to sill	1·84 m (6 ft 0½ in)
Baggage door (rear, stbd):	
Height	1·24 m (4 ft 1 in)
Width	0·64 m (2 ft 1 in)
Height to sill	1·84 m (6 ft 0½ in)
Optional freight door (rear, port):	
Height	1·72 m (5 ft 7¾ in)
Width	2·67 m (8 ft 9 in)

DIMENSIONS, INTERNAL:

Cabin, excl flight deck: Length	14·17 m (46 ft 6 in)
Max width	2·46 m (8 ft 1 in)
Max height	1·92 m (6 ft 3½ in)
Floor area	27·5 m² (296 sq ft)
Volume	56·35 m³ (1,990 cu ft)
Max total freight holds	9·54 m³ (337 cu ft)

AREAS:

Wings, gross: Srs 2A	75·35 m² (810·75 sq ft)
Srs 2B	77·00 m² (828·87 sq ft)

BAe HS 748 Series 2B twin-turboprop transport aircraft *(Pilot Press)*

Ailerons (total)	3·98 m² (42·90 sq ft)
Trailing-edge flaps (total)	14·83 m² (159·80 sq ft)
Fin	9·81 m² (105·64 sq ft)
Rudder, incl tabs	3·66 m² (39·36 sq ft)
Tailplane	17·55 m² (188·9 sq ft)
Elevators, incl tabs	5·03 m² (54·10 sq ft)

WEIGHTS AND LOADINGS (A: standard Srs 2A; B: Srs 2A military transport; C: standard Srs 2B; D: Srs 2B military transport):

Basic operating weight, incl crew:

A	12,159 kg (26,806 lb)
B	11,577 kg (25,524 lb)
C	12,206 kg (26,910 lb)
D	11,671 kg (25,730 lb)
Max payload: A	5,304 kg (11,694 lb)
B	5,886 kg (12,976 lb)
B, optional overload	7,927 kg (17,476 lb)
C	5,257 kg (11,590 lb)
D	5,819 kg (12,829 lb)
D, optional overload	7,833 kg (17,270 lb)
Max T-O weight: A, B, C, D	21,092 kg (46,500 lb)
B, D, optional overload	23,133 kg (51,000 lb)

Max zero-fuel weight:

A, B, C, D	17,463 kg (38,500 lb)
B, D, optional overload	19,504 kg (43,000 lb)
Max landing weight: A, B, C, D	19,504 kg (43,000 lb)
B, D, optional overload	21,546 kg (47,500 lb)
Max wing loading: A	279·8 kg/m² (57·3 lb/sq ft)
C	273·9 kg/m² (56·1 lb/sq ft)
Max power loading: A, C	6·20 kg/kW (10·2 lb/ehp)

PERFORMANCE (A: standard Srs 2A at max T-O weight unless otherwise indicated; B: military Srs 2A at normal max T-O weight with 20% fuel reserves; C: military Srs 2A at optional overload T-O weight with 20% fuel reserves; D: standard Srs 2B at max T-O weight unless otherwise indicated):

Cruising speed:

A, D at 17,236 kg (38,000 lb)
244 knots (452 km/h; 281 mph)

Max rate of climb at S/L:

A, D at 17,236 kg (38,000 lb) 433 m (1,420 ft)/min
Service ceiling: A, D   7,620 m (25,000 ft)

Min ground turning radius:

A, B, C, D   11·82 m (39 ft)
Runway LCN: A, D   9 to 18
T-O run: A (BCAR)   1,225 m (4,020 ft)
B   756 m (2,480 ft)
C   945 m (3,100 ft)
D (BCAR)   1,134 m (3,720 ft)

Balanced field length:

A (BCAR)   1,640 m (5,380 ft)
A (BCAR, 650 nm; 1,203 km; 748 mile sector, 40 passengers and reserves for 200 nm; 370 km; 230 miles plus 45 min hold)   892 m (2,925 ft)
D (BCAR)   1,393 m (4,570 ft)
D (BCAR, 840 nm; 1,557 km; 967 mile sector, 44 passengers and reserves for 200 nm; 370 km; 230 miles plus 45 min hold)   963 m (3,160 ft)
T-O to 15 m (50 ft): B   927 m (3,040 ft)
C   1,158 m (3,800 ft)

Landing field length:

A, D (BCAR)   1,036 m (3,400 ft)
Landing from 15 m (50 ft): B 567 m (1,860 ft)
C   625 m (2,050 ft)
Landing run: B   347 m (1,140 ft)
C   387 m (1,270 ft)

Radius of action:

B, supply drop mission with 12 × 340 kg (750 lb) containers   625 nm (1,158 km; 720 miles)

Range with max payload:

A, with reserves for 200 nm (370 km; 230 miles) plus 45 min hold   735 nm (1,361 km; 846 miles)
B   925 nm (1,714 km; 1,066 miles)
C   840 nm (1,556 km; 967 miles)
D, with reserves for 200 nm (370 km; 230 miles) plus 45 min hold   785 nm (1,455 km; 904 miles)

Range with max fuel:

A, with 3,662 kg (8,074 lb) payload, reserves for 200 nm (370 km; 230 miles) plus 45 min hold
1,340 nm (2,483 km; 1,543 miles)

B, with 4,321 kg (9,527 lb) payload
1,410 nm (2,613 km; 1,624 miles)
C, with 6,363 kg (14,027 lb) payload
1,280 nm (2,372 km; 1,474 miles)
D, with 3,660 kg (8,070 lb) payload, reserves for 200 nm (370 km; 230 miles) plus 45 min hold
1,420 nm (2,630 km; 1,635 miles)

OPERATIONAL NOISE LEVELS (FAR Pt 36):

T-O	92·5 EPNdB
Approach	103·8 EPNdB
Sideline	96·3 EPNdB

BAe HS 748 COASTGUARDER

The Coastguarder is a medium-range maritime patrol aircraft, based on the HS 748. Its development was initiated to meet the need for an aircraft in this category suitable for surface surveillance, fishery protection, pollution/contraband control, search and rescue, tactical surveillance and offshore oilfield patrol. A prototype/demonstration aircraft (G-BCDZ), constructed from an ex-airline HS 748 Series 2A, flew for the first time on 18 February 1977. Demonstration activity with this aircraft was intense during 1977-78, with visits to Europe, Scandinavia, South and Central America, and the Far East. It has since been modified as the prototype of the new HS 748 Series 2B.

The airframe of the Coastguarder is generally similar to that of the standard HS 748 civil and military transport; but there is crew accommodation for two pilots, two beam observers and a tactical navigator, to enable the Coastguarder to fulfil its primary roles. A 0·30 m (1 ft 0 in) diameter chute is mounted in the aft fuselage for the air launch of five-man rescue dinghies, and smoke or flame floats. Two optically flat, inward opening windows in the forward fuselage allow high definition photographs to be taken, with optional data annotation. The standard radio, radar and navigation equipment has been expanded to cover the normal naval radio frequencies, and to provide adequate navigation aids for long overwater flights.

The tactical navigator's station is situated midway down the cabin, on the starboard side, and is equipped with an MEL MAREC radar display and plotting board, Decca 72 Doppler, and a Decca 9447 TANS computer/display. The MAREC radar was chosen as standard on the basis of experience gained in previous ASV, ASW and SAR applications. It has an underfuselage antenna, a 0·43 m (1 ft 5 in) diameter main display and plotting board, with a 0·13 m (5 in) repeat display for the pilot. Used in conjunction with the Doppler, TANS computer and Marconi Omega VLF navigation system, the resulting tactical navigation system can, in addition to satisfying all normal search and navigation requirements, provide effective tactical plotting to control an exercise involving a group of friendly vessels and other radar targets, including aircraft. MAREC provides up to 210 nm (389 km; 242 miles) display range in all directions for the tactical navigator and up to 250 nm (460 km; 285 miles) for the pilot's repeater display. A choice of presentation scale between 1 and 30 nm (1·9-55·6 km; 1·2-34·5 miles) per inch allows enlargement of any selected part of the display.

To provide the additional range required for a maritime reconnaissance role, the fuel tankage has been increased to 10,047 litres (2,210 Imp gallons). The standard Coastguarder may be used for a number of maritime and other roles without any change to the basic configuration. Additional passengers can be accommodated by fitting seats to the standard rails which run the full length of the cabin. The optional rear freight door provides an airdropping capability, allowing the dispatch of large dinghies or supplies in an air/sea rescue role. As many as twelve 30-man dinghies can be transported and dropped for the rescue of a large number of aircraft/ship survivors. The Coastguarder can also be converted easily for cargo carrying, by removal of the tactical navigator's station and other equipment.

The description of the standard HS 748 Series 2B applies also to the Coastguarder, except as follows:
TYPE: Twin-turboprop maritime patrol aircraft.
POWER PLANT: Two 1,700 kW (2,280 ehp) Rolls-Royce Dart RDa.7 Mk 535-2 turboprop engines, each driving a Dowty Rotol four-blade metal constant-speed fully-feathering propeller. Fuel in integral wing tanks with a max combined capacity of 10,047 litres (2,210 Imp gallons). Underwing pressure refuelling and overwing gravity refuelling. Oil capacity 14·2 litres (25 Imp pints) per engine.
ACCOMMODATION: Standard Coastguarder layout has two pilots on flight deck; two beam observers seated at aft end of cabin, one each side, with domed windows; and tactical navigator approximately midway down cabin at tactical station on starboard side. Toilet on starboard side at aft end of cabin, with galley opposite. Main door on port side at rear of cabin; smaller door for emergency exit on starboard side. Crew door on port side at front of cabin. Large rear freight door optional. Four airline-type seats, forward of tactical navigator's station, on starboard side, serve as crew rest area.
AVIONICS AND EQUIPMENT: Avionics include Sylvania VHF/FM com transceiver, dual Collins 618M-3 VHF com transceivers, dual Collins 51RV-4B VHF nav receivers, Collins AN/ARC-159 UHF com transceiver, Collins 51Z-4 marker beacon receiver, dual Collins DF 206 ADF, Collins DF 301E UHF D/F, Collins 618T-3 HF transceiver, Collins 346D-1 address system, Ultra UA 60 interphone, Sperry RN 200 radio navigation display, Honeywell AN/APN-171 radio altimeter, MEL MAREC radar with 0·43 m (1 ft 5 in) main display and 0·13 m (5 in) pilot's repeat display, Marconi CMA 771 Omega VLF nav system, Decca 72 Doppler, and Decca 9447 TANS computer/display. Attitude stabilised antenna, size 0·91 m × 0·53 m (3 ft 0 in × 1 ft 9 in), in underfuselage radome provides 360° azimuth viewing, plus selected sector scan facilities. Provisions for optional ATC transponder, DME, and height encoding altimeter. Standard equipment includes a 0·30 m (1 ft 0 in) launch chute for five-man rescue dinghies and smoke or flame floats. Optional equipment includes large rear freight door, additional passenger seats, large dinghies, and other rescue equipment.

WEIGHTS AND LOADINGS:

*Typical operating weight empty
12,722 kg (28,048 lb)

Max T-O weight	21,092 kg (46,500 lb)
Max zero-fuel weight	17,463 kg (38,500 lb)
Max landing weight	19,504 kg (43,000 lb)
Max wing loading	279·8 kg/m² (57·3 lb/sq ft)
Max power loading	6·20 kg/kW (10·2 lb/ehp)

*depending upon customer requirements

PERFORMANCE (at max T-O weight, unless stated otherwise):

Cruising speed at 4,570 m (15,000 ft) at AUW of 18,144 kg (40,000 lb) 233 knots (431 km/h; 268 mph)
Typical search speed at 610 m (2,000 ft)
140 knots (259 km/h; 161 mph)
Service ceiling   7,620 m (25,000 ft)
T-O to 15 m (50 ft), unfactored:
S/L, ISA   951 m (3,120 ft)
S/L, ISA +20°C   1,045 m (3,430 ft)
Landing from 15 m (50 ft) at max landing weight, unfactored:
S/L, ISA   570 m (1,870 ft)
S/L, ISA +20°C   608 m (1,995 ft)
Range with 4,536 kg (10,000 lb) payload, 20% fuel reserves, ISA   960 nm (1,779 km; 1,105 miles)
Range with max fuel, 20% reserves, ISA
2,300 nm (4,262 km; 2,648 miles)
Time on station at 200 nm (370 km; 230 miles) radius of action, at 3,050 m (10,000 ft), 20% fuel reserves, ISA   9 h 24 min

BAe 146

In August 1973, Hawker Siddeley announced that it was to produce with government support a four-turbofan quiet-operating transport aircraft known as the HS (now BAe) 146. Within a few months economic problems in the UK halted this programme, but research and design continued on a limited basis. With the absorption of Hawker Siddeley into British Aerospace in April 1977, BAe continued to provide limited funding to allow the manufacture of assembly jigs, systems test rigs, and continuing design and wind tunnel testing. On 10 July 1978, the British Aerospace Board's decision to give the 146 programme a full go-ahead was approved by the government, and production is being undertaken in several BAe factories, including Brough, Filton, Manchester and Prestwick. Following the production decision, risk-sharing agreements were signed with Avco Aerostructures (USA) for the manufacture of 20 sets of wing boxes; and with Saab-Scania (Sweden) for 20 sets of tailplanes and control surfaces. Under an initial contract, Short Brothers (UK) is manufacturing 100 pods for the Avco Lycoming ALF 502 engines which power the 146. Final assembly takes place at BAe's Hatfield plant.

The basic aims of the BAe 146 are to provide a passenger seating standard comparable with present wide-bodied transports, combined with competitive operating costs, good airfield performance and low operating noise levels.

Two series are available:

Series 100. Designed to operate from short semi-prepared airstrips with minimal ground facilities, with a normal seating capacity of 71-93. A mixed passenger/freight version is planned.

BAe HS 748 Coastguarder twin-turboprop maritime patrol aircraft

Series 200. For operation from paved runways only, with seating capacity of 82-109 and greater range. Fuselage lengthened by five frame pitches (2·39 m; 7 ft 10 in). Increased maximum T-O weight and zero-fuel weight. Underfloor cargo volume increased by 35%. Reduced max operating speed.

The first flight of the Series 100 prototype is scheduled to be made in the Spring of 1981. Full transport category CAA certification of the Series 100 is expected to be obtained in August 1982, with initial deliveries of production aircraft in September and October. The eighth aircraft will be the first Series 200, with first flight scheduled for 1982 and certification and deliveries in 1983. LAPA of Argentina has ordered two Srs 100s and one Srs 200, with options for three more Srs 200s; two BAe 146s have been sold to an undisclosed US airline.

Freight-carrying and military versions are planned; the latter is described separately.

The following description applies to the BAe 146 Series 100, except where indicated:

TYPE: Four-turbofan short-range transport aircraft.

WINGS: Cantilever high-wing monoplane. British Aerospace high-lift aerofoil section. Thickness/chord ratio 15·3% adjacent to fuselage, 12·2% at tip. Anhedral 3° at trailing-edge. Incidence 3° 6' at fuselage side, 0° at tip. Sweepback 15° at quarter-chord. All-metal fail-safe structure of light alloy with machined skins, integrally machined spars and ribs. Single-section hydraulically-actuated tabbed Fowler flaps of light alloy, spanning 66% of each wing trailing-edge, with Dowty Rotol actuators. Mechanically-actuated balanced ailerons, with hydraulically-operated power boost spoilers on upper surfaces. Trim and spring tab in each aileron. No leading-edge lift devices. Hot-air anti-icing of leading-edges.

FUSELAGE: All-metal fail-safe pressurised semi-monocoque structure. Flight deck and tailcone areas free of stringers. Remainder of structure has 'top hat' stringers bonded to skins above keel area. 'Z' section stringers 'wet' assembled with bonding agent and riveted to skin in keel area. Chemically-etched skins of light alloy. Petal-type airbrakes form tailcone when closed.

TAIL UNIT: Cantilever sweptback T-tail, of all-metal construction. Chemically-etched light alloy skins bonded to 'top-hat' section stringers. Fixed-incidence tailplane. Manually-operated balanced elevators, each with trim and spring tab. Powered rudder. Hot-air anti-icing of tailplane leading-edges.

LANDING GEAR: Hydraulically-retractable tricycle type, of Dowty Rotol design, with twin Dunlop wheels on each unit. Main units retract inward into fairings on fuselage sides; steerable nose unit retracts forward. Oleopneumatic shock-absorbers with wheels mounted on trailing axle. Simple telescopic nosewheel strut. Mainwheel tyres size 13·00-16 Type III, pressure (Series 100) 7·59 bars (110 lb/sq in). Nosewheel tyres size 7·50-10 Type III, pressure (Series 100) 7·03 bars (102 lb/sq in). Low-pressure tyres optional. Dunlop multi-disc carbon brakes operated by duplicated hydraulic systems. Brake cooling and rudder pedal steering optional. Anti-skid units in both primary and secondary brake systems.

POWER PLANT: Four Avco Lycoming ALF 502R-3 turbofan engines, each rated at 29·8 kN (6,700 lb st), installed in pylon-mounted underwing pods. Fuel in two integral wing tanks and integral centre-section tank (the latter with a vented and drained sealing diaphragm above passenger cabin), having a combined capacity of 11,547 litres (2,540 Imp gallons). Optional auxiliary tanks in wing-root fairings, with combined capacity of 1,363 litres (300 Imp gallons), giving total optional capacity of 12,910 litres (2,840 Imp gallons). Single-point pressure refuelling, with coupling situated in starboard wing outboard of outer engine.

ACCOMMODATION: Crew of two pilots on flight deck, and two or three cabin staff. Optional observer's seat. Series 100 has accommodation in main cabin for 71 passengers with five-abreast seating at 84 cm (33 in) pitch, and a maximum of 93 seats six-abreast at 74 cm (29 in) pitch. Series 200 will have maximum capacity for 109 passengers with six-abreast seating at 74 cm (29 in) pitch. Various alternative layouts for mixed passenger/freight configurations. All seating layouts have two toilets, one forward and one aft, and a forward galley as standard. One outward-opening passenger door forward and one aft on port side of cabin. Built-in airstairs optional. Servicing doors, one forward and one aft, on starboard side of cabin. Freight and baggage holds under cabin floor. All accommodation air-conditioned. Windscreen electrical anti-icing and demisting standard. Rain repellent system optional.

SYSTEMS: BAe Dynamics cabin air-conditioning and pressurisation system, using engine bleed air. Electropneumatic pressurisation control with discharge valves at fore and aft of cabin. Max differential 0·45 bars (6·5 lb/sq in). Hydraulic system, duplicated for essential services, for landing gear, flaps, rudder, roll and lift spoilers, airbrakes, nosewheel steering, brakes and auxiliary fuel pumps; pressure 207 bars (3,000 lb/sq in). Electrical system powered by two 40 kVA integrated-drive

BAe 146 Series 200, with additional side view (centre right) of Series 100 (*Pilot Press*)

alternators to feed 115/200V 3-phase 400Hz primary systems. 28V DC power supplied by transformer-rectifier in each channel. Hydraulically-powered emergency electrical power unit. Garrett-AiResearch GTCP 36-100 APU for ground air-conditioning and electrical power generation. High-pressure gaseous oxygen system, pressure 124 bars (1,800 lb/sq in).

AVIONICS: Automatic flight control system incorporates a simplex Cat 1 autopilot with a flight director display and separate attitude reference for each pilot. Addition of extra equipment and wiring permits coupled approaches to Cat 2 minima. Standard ARINC interface with radio nav system allows choice of radio equipment. Basic avionics include dual VHF com, audio system, passenger address system, cockpit voice recorder, dual compass systems, dual ADIs with separate attitude reference driven by single computer, marker, weather radar, radio altimeter, ground proximity warning system, DME, ATC transponder, dual VHF nav and an ADF. Optional avionics include third VHF com, area navigation system, Selcal, tape reproducer, single or dual HF com, and second ADF, DME, transponder and radio altimeter.

DIMENSIONS, EXTERNAL:

Wing span	26·34 m (86 ft 5 in)
Wing aspect ratio	8·98
Length overall: Series 100	26·16 m (85 ft 10 in)
Series 200	28·55 m (93 ft 8 in)
Height overall	8·61 m (28 ft 3 in)
Fuselage diameter	3·56 m (11 ft 8 in)
Tailplane span	11·07 m (36 ft 4 in)
Wheel track	4·72 m (15 ft 6 in)
Wheelbase: Series 100	10·10 m (33 ft 1½ in)
Series 200	11·20 m (36 ft 9 in)
Passenger doors (port, fwd and rear):	
Height	1·83 m (6 ft 0 in)
Width	0·85 m (2 ft 9½ in)
Height to sill	1·93 m (6 ft 4 in)
Servicing doors (stbd, fwd and rear):	
Height	1·47 m (4 ft 10 in)
Width	0·85 m (2 ft 9½ in)
Height to sill	1·93 m (6 ft 4 in)
Underfloor freight hold door (stbd, fwd):	
Height	1·07 m (3 ft 6 in)
Width	1·22 m (4 ft 0 in)
Height to sill	0·86 m (2 ft 10 in)
Underfloor freight hold door (stbd, aft):	
Height	1·07 m (3 ft 6 in)
Width	0·91 m (3 ft 0 in)
Height to sill	1·07 m (3 ft 6 in)

DIMENSIONS, INTERNAL:

Cabin (excl flight deck, incl galley and toilets):	
Length: Series 100	15·42 m (50 ft 7 in)
Series 200	17·81 m (58 ft 5 in)
Max width	3·38 m (11 ft 1 in)
Max height	2·04 m (6 ft 8½ in)
Floor area: Series 100	49·24 m² (530 sq ft)
Baggage/freight holds, underfloor:	
Series 100	14·16 m³ (500 cu ft)
Series 200	18·69 m³ (660 cu ft)

AREAS:

Wings, gross	77·30 m² (832 sq ft)
Ailerons (total)	3·53 m² (38 sq ft)
Trailing-edge flaps (total)	19·32 m² (208 sq ft)
Spoilers (total)	9·66 m² (104 sq ft)
Fin	11·61 m² (125 sq ft)
Rudder	9·20 m² (99 sq ft)
Tailplane	15·61 m² (168 sq ft)
Elevators, incl tab	10·03 m² (108 sq ft)

WEIGHTS AND LOADINGS (estimated):

Typical operating weight, empty:	
Series 100	20,216 kg (44,570 lb)
Series 200	21,092 kg (46,500 lb)
Max payload: Series 100	8,133 kg (17,930 lb)
Series 200	9,979 kg (22,000 lb)
Max T-O weight:	
Series 100, standard	33,497 kg (73,850 lb)
Series 100, optional	36,287 kg (80,000 lb)
Series 200	39,690 kg (87,500 lb)
Max ramp weight: Series 100	33,724 kg (74,350 lb)
Series 200	39,916 kg (88,000 lb)
Max zero-fuel weight:	
Series 100	28,350 kg (62,500 lb)
Series 200	31,070 kg (68,500 lb)
Max landing weight:	
Series 100	32,590 kg (71,850 lb)
Series 200	34,926 kg (77,000 lb)
Max wing loading:	
Series 100, standard	433·6 kg/m² (88·8 lb/sq ft)
Series 200	513·6 kg/m² (105·2 lb/sq ft)
Max power loading:	
Series 100, standard	281 kg/kN (2·76 lb/lb st)
Series 200	333 kg/kN (3·26 lb/lb st)

PERFORMANCE (estimated, at max standard T-O weight, except where indicated):

Max operating speed:	
Series 100	
	Mach 0·70 (310 knots; 574 km/h; 357 mph CAS)
Series 200	
	Mach 0·70 (300 knots; 555 km/h; 345 mph CAS)
Max cruising speed:	
Series 100 at 6,705 m (22,000 ft)	
	434 knots (805 km/h; 500 mph)
Series 200 at 7,315 m (24,000 ft)	
	428 knots (793 km/h; 493 mph)
Econ cruising speed at 9,145 m (30,000 ft):	
Series 100	379 knots (702 km/h; 436 mph)
Series 200	386 knots (714 km/h; 444 mph)
Stalling speed, 40° flap:	
Series 100	91 knots (169 km/h; 105 mph) EAS
Series 200	99 knots (183 km/h; 114 mph) EAS
Stalling speed, 45° flap, at max landing weight:	
Series 100	87 knots (161 km/h; 100 mph) EAS
Series 200	90 knots (168 km/h; 104 mph) EAS
T-O to 10·7 m (35 ft), S/L, ISA:	
Series 100	1,128 m (3,700 ft)
Series 200	1,615 m (5,300 ft)
FAR landing distance from 15 m (50 ft), S/L, ISA, at max landing weight:	
Series 100	1,013 m (3,325 ft)
Series 200	1,061 m (3,480 ft)

Range with max fuel, incl 293 kg (645 lb) fuel for ground and airborne manoeuvres, plus fuel for 150 nm (278 km; 173 mile) diversion and 45 min hold at 1,525 m (5,000 ft):

Series 100	1,430 nm (2,650 km; 1,647 miles)
Series 200	1,238 nm (2,293 km; 1,425 miles)

Range with max payload, allowances as above:

Series 100	580 nm (1,075 km; 668 miles)
Series 200	1,085 nm (2,010 km; 1,249 miles)

OPERATIONAL NOISE LEVELS (FAR Pt 36-12, estimated):

T-O: Series 100	84 EPNdB
Series 200	90 EPNdB
Approach: Series 100 and 200	97 EPNdB
Sideline: Series 100 and 200	90 EPNdB

BAe 146M

This proposed military version of the BAe 146 is envisaged as a medium-lift aircraft suitable for the airlift of vehicles and palletised cargo; the delivery of heavy vehicles to forward airstrips, and casevac mission on the return flight; airdrop of paratroops and supplies, the latter by free-fall or parachute extraction technique; and troop or VIP transport, with mixed passenger/freight layouts optional.

BAe 146M, the proposed multi-role military transport version of the 146 *(Pilot Press)*

Generally similar to the civil BAe 146, the 146M differs primarily in having a changed landing gear to simplify operation from unprepared surfaces at forward landing strips, and in redesign of the aft fuselage to provide rear ramp loading.

TYPE: Short-range multi-role military transport.

WINGS: As for BAe 146.

FUSELAGE: All-metal fail-safe pressurised semi-monocoque structure, with a new aft fuselage which has a hydraulically-operated ramp, and doors which open outward and upwards, to permit straight-in loading of military vehicles and other cargo.

TAIL UNIT: As for BAe 146.

LANDING GEAR: Hydraulically-retractable tricycle type, specially designed for operation from unprepared surfaces. Nose unit, with twin wheels, retracts forward. Main landing gear has two large-diameter wheels with low-pressure tyres mounted in tandem on each side. Wheels are independently mounted on trailing arms which operate a dual-piston shock-absorber. Main units retract into a long fairing on each side of the lower fuselage. Anti-skid brake units standard.

POWER PLANT: As for BAe 146, except standard fuel capacity 12,910 litres (2,840 Imp gallons), contained in integral wing tanks and wing root fillet tanks. Provision for 5,455 litres (1,200 Imp gallons) of optional fuel.

ACCOMMODATION: Crew of two on flight deck, with seat for supernumerary crew member and provision for optional navigator's station. Constant-section cargo hold/cabin can accommodate a typical military load comprising a 105 mm light gun, a one ton truck and a half ton truck, plus their operating personnel. A Scorpion tank and its crew can be carried. A total of five 2·74 × 2·24 m (108 × 88 in) pallets can be loaded, using a side guidance system and rollers. A winch to simplify loading is available optionally. Accommodation is provided for up to 60 paratroops and two dispatchers, and two sticks of 30 men can be dispatched simultaneously through two rear paratroop exits. For supply drops the 146M can carry items ranging from two medium-stressed platforms, to 18 'one ton' type containers. As a troop transport, up to 70 seats can be provided in a five-abreast layout, which includes two toilets and 9·49 m³ (335 cu ft) of baggage space. A maximum of 84 passengers, seated six-abreast, can be accommodated in an all-passenger configuration, with two toilets and 9·63 m³ (340 cu ft) of baggage space.

SYSTEMS: Generally as for BAe 146. Optional APU in nose of starboard main landing gear fairing.

AVIONICS: Basic installation would include passenger address and audio systems, flight deck voice recorder, dual ADI, marker beacon receiver, weather radar, radio altimeter, DME, ADF, dual VHF nav, flight data recorder, dual VHF/UHF com, dual compass systems, Doppler, IFF with civil mode, TANS, and HF com. Options could add a second ADF, DME, IFF, radio altimeter and HF, Selcal, Tacan, Omega, DF/homer and an inertial navigation system.

DIMENSIONS, EXTERNAL:

Wing span	26·34 m (86 ft 5 in)
Length overall	27·38 m (89 ft 10 in)
Height overall	8·94 m (29 ft 4 in)
Wheel track	4·19 m (13 ft 9 in)
Wheelbase	10·95 m (35 ft 11 in)

DIMENSIONS, INTERNAL:
Cabin/hold:

Length (excl ramp)	12·50 m (41 ft 0 in)
Floor width	2·73 m (8 ft 11½ in)
Max width of doorway	2·82 m (9 ft 3 in)
Floor area (excl ramp)	34·19 m² (368 sq ft)
Volume	91·32 m³ (3,225 cu ft)

AREA:

Wings, gross	77·30 m² (832 sq ft)

WEIGHTS AND LOADINGS (estimated):

Max T-O weight	39,916 kg (88,000 lb)
Max landing weight	38,555 kg (85,000 lb)
Max zero-fuel weight	31,071 kg (68,500 lb)
Max wing loading	516·4 kg/m² (105·8 lb/sq ft)
Max power loading	335 kg/kN (3·28 lb/lb st)

PERFORMANCE (estimated, at max T-O weight except where indicated):

Max level speed above 6,100 m (20,000 ft)	more than 400 knots (742 km/h; 461 mph)
Max rate of climb at S/L at AUW of 36,287 kg (80,000 lb)	780 m (2,560 ft)/min
Max operating altitude	9,145 m (30,000 ft)
Service ceiling, one engine out, at AUW of 36,287 kg (80,000 lb)	6,920 m (22,700 ft)
T-O run, ISA + 20°C at S/L	1,317 m (4,320 ft)
T-O to 15 m (50 ft), ISA + 20°C at S/L	1,625 m (5,330 ft)
Landing from 15 m (50 ft) at max landing weight, ISA + 20°C at S/L	617 m (2,025 ft)
Landing run at max landing weight, ISA + 20°C at S/L	378 m (1,240 ft)
Range with max payload, standard fuel, 10% reserves	1,260 nm (2,335 km; 1,451 miles)

BAe (BAC) ONE-ELEVEN

Details of the One-Eleven were announced on 9 May 1961, simultaneously with the news that British United Airways had ordered ten. Design and manufacture are shared between three Weybridge/Bristol Division factories, at Weybridge, Filton and Hurn.

Five commercial versions have been produced, and details of the Series 200 (56 built), 300 (nine built) and 400 (69 built) can be found in the 1974-75 *Jane's*. Two versions are currently in production, as follows:

Series 475. Combines standard fuselage and accommodation of Series 400 with wings and power plant of Series 500 and a modified landing gear system, using low-pressure tyres, to permit operation from secondary low-strength runways with poorer-grade surfaces. The prototype flew for the first time on 27 August 1970. First production Series 475 flew on 5 April 1971. Certification and first production delivery (to Faucett of Peru) in July 1971. The three Srs 475s supplied to the Sultan of Oman's Air Force have a quick-change passenger/cargo interior layout and a 3·05 × 1·85 m (10 ft 0 in × 6 ft 1 in) forward freight door. The first executive Series 475, for a Saudi Arabian customer, was delivered in May 1978. Nine Srs 475s sold by mid-1980.

Series 500. Derived from Series 300/400, this version incorporates a lengthened fuselage (2·54 m; 100 in fwd of wing, 1·57 m; 62 in aft) which accommodates 97-119 passengers, with a flight crew of two. Wingtip extensions

increase span by 1·52 m (5 ft). Take-off performance improved by increased wing area and by installation of two Rolls-Royce Spey Mk 512 DW turbofans, each rated at 55·8 kN (12,550 lb st). Main landing gear strengthened and heavier wing planks used to cater for increased AUW. Prototype flew for first time on 30 June 1967. First production aircraft flew on 7 February 1968. ARB certification 15 August 1968. Deliveries to BEA (now British Airways) began on 29 August 1968. Total of 87 sold by mid-1980.

In addition, executive and freighter versions of the One-Eleven are available. More than 40 examples of the former are now in service, notably in the USA and with the Australian government, with interior and long-range tank conversions being made either by BAe or by specialist contractors. The One-Eleven freighter incorporates a 3·05 m by 1·85 m (10 ft 0 in by 6 ft 1 in) upward-opening hydraulically-powered loading door in the forward fuselage, together with a quickly-removable freight floor overlay and cargo handling system. First to be delivered, in November 1975, was one of three Series 475 freighters operated by the Sultan of Oman's Air Force.

In May 1977, BAe concluded an agreement with CNIAR of Romania (which see) for the Series 475 and Series 500 to be built under licence in Romania. Three complete aircraft (two Srs 500s and one Srs 475 freighter) are being delivered from Hurn, to be followed, up to 1985, by a further 22 aircraft in component form. Thereafter, production of complete aircraft will take place in Romania. Orders for 230 One-Elevens (not including those to be built in Romania) had been received by mid-1980.

A One-Eleven 'hush kit', comprising an intake duct lining, a bypass duct lining, an acoustically-lined jetpipe, and a six-chute exhaust silencer, was flown for the first time, on the Srs 475 development aircraft G-ASYD, on 14 June 1974. It is designed to reduce the area within the 90 EPNdB noise contour by approximately 50 per cent, giving a noise footprint equivalent to that of a twin-turboprop aircraft. The first production aircraft to be fitted with 'hush kits' were five One-Eleven 500s for Tarom, the Romanian state airline, which were delivered between March and August 1977. In May 1979 Monarch Airlines in the UK became the first operator to order 'hush kits' for retrospective fitting to its fleet of One-Eleven Srs 500s.

The following description applies to the Series 475 and 500:

TYPE: Twin-turbofan short/medium-range transport.

WINGS: Cantilever low-wing monoplane. Modified NACA cambered wing section. Thickness/chord ratio 12½% at root, 11% at tip. Dihedral 2°. Incidence 2° 30'. Sweepback 20° at quarter-chord. All-metal structure of copper-based aluminium alloy, built on fail-safe principles. Three-shear-web torsion box with integrally-machined skin/stringer panels. Ailerons of Redux-bonded light alloy honeycomb, manually operated through servo tabs. Port servo tab used for trimming. Light alloy Fowler flaps hydraulically operated through Hobson actuators. Light alloy spoiler/airbrakes on upper surface of wing, operated hydraulically through Dowty Boulton Paul actuators. Hydraulically-actuated lift dumpers, inboard of spoilers, are standard. Flaps on Series 475 have a glassfibre coating. Thermal de-icing of wing leading-edges with engine bleed air.

FUSELAGE: Conventional circular-section all-metal fail-safe structure with continuous frames and stringers. Skin made from copper-based aluminium alloy.

TAIL UNIT: Cantilever all-metal fail-safe structure, with variable-incidence T tailplane, controlled through duplicated Hobson hydraulic units. Fin integral with rear fuselage. Elevators and rudder actuated hydraulically through Dowty Boulton Paul tandem jacks. Leading-edges of fin and tailplane de-iced by engine bleed air.

LANDING GEAR: Retractable tricycle type, with twin wheels on each unit. Hydraulic retraction, nose unit forward, main units inward. Oleo-pneumatic shock-absorbers manufactured by BAC. Hydraulic nosewheel steering. Dunlop wheels, tubeless tyres and 5-plate heavy-duty hydraulic disc brakes. Hytrol Mk III anti-skid units. Main-wheel tyres size 40 × 12 on Srs 500, pressure 11·03 bars (160 lb/sq in). Dunlop 44 × 16 tyres on Srs 475, pressure 5·72 bars (83 lb/sq in). Nosewheel tyres size 24 × 7·25 on Srs 500, pressure 7·58 bars (110 lb/sq in). Dunlop 24 × 7·7 tyres on Srs 475, pressure

BAe (BAC) One-Eleven Series 400 in the insignia of Air UK

7·24 bars (105 lb/sq in). All tyre pressures are given for aircraft at mid-CG position and max taxi weight.

POWER PLANT: Two Rolls-Royce Spey Mk 512 DW turbofan engines, each rated at 55·8 kN (12,550 lb st), mounted in pod on each side of rear fuselage. Fuel in integral wing tanks of 10,160 litres (2,235 gallons) and centre-section tank of 3,864 litres (850 Imp gallons) capacity; total fuel capacity 14,024 litres (3,085 Imp gallons). Optional 1,591 litre (350 Imp gallon) and 3,182 litre (700 Imp gallon) fuel tanks are available to increase total fuel capacity. Pressure refuelling point in fuselage forward of wing on starboard side. Provision for gravity refuelling. Oil capacity (total engine oil) 13·66 litres (3 Imp gallons) per engine.

ACCOMMODATION (Srs 475): Crew of two on flight deck and up to 89 passengers in main cabin. Single class or mixed class layout, with movable divider bulkhead to permit any first/tourist ratio. Typical mixed class layout has 16 first class (four abreast) and 49 tourist (five abreast) seats. Galley units normally at front on starboard side. Coat space available on port side aft of flight deck. Ventral entrance with hydraulically-operated airstair. Forward passenger door on port side incorporates optional power-operated airstair. Galley service door forward on starboard side. Two baggage and freight holds under floor, fore and aft of wings, with doors on starboard side. Upward-opening forward freight door available at customer's option. Entire accommodation air-conditioned.

ACCOMMODATION (Srs 500): Crew of two on flight deck and up to 119 passengers in main cabin. Two additional overwing emergency exits, making two on each side. One toilet on each side of cabin at rear. Otherwise generally similar to Srs 475.

SYSTEMS: Fully-duplicated air-conditioning and pressurisation systems with main components by Normalair-Garrett. Air bled from engine compressors through heat exchangers. Max pressure differential 0·52 bars (7·5 lb/sq in). Hydraulic system, pressure 207 bars (3,000 lb/sq in), operates flaps, spoilers, rudder, elevators, tailplane, landing gear, brakes, nosewheel steering, ventral and forward airstairs and windscreen wipers. No pneumatic system. Electrical system utilises two 30kVA Plessey/Westinghouse AC generators, driven by Plessey constant-speed drive and starter units, plus a similar generator mounted on the APU and shaft-driven. Garrett-AiResearch gas-turbine APU in tailcone to provide ground electrical power, air-conditioning and engine starting, also some system checkout capability. APU is run during take-off to eliminate performance penalty of bleeding engine air for cabin air-conditioning.

AVIONICS AND EQUIPMENT: Communications and navigation avionics generally to customers' requirements. Typical installation includes dual VHF com to ARINC 546, dual VHF nav to ARINC 547A, including glideslope receivers, marker receiver, flight/service interphone system, Marconi AD 370, Bendix DFA 73 or Collins DF 203 ADF, ATC transponder to ARINC 532D, Collins 860 E2 DME, Ekco E 190 or Bendix RDR 1E weather radar. Sperry C9 or CL11 compass systems and Collins FD 108 flight director system (dual) are also installed. Elliott 2000 Series autopilot system. Provision on the Srs 500 for additional equipment, including automatic throttle control, for low weather minima operation.

DIMENSIONS, EXTERNAL:
Wing span	28·50 m (93 ft 6 in)
Wing chord at root	5·12 m (16 ft 9⅝ in)
Wing chord at tip	1·65 m (5 ft 5 in)
Wing aspect ratio	8·5
Length overall: Srs 475	28·50 m (93 ft 6 in)
Srs 500	32·61 m (107 ft 0 in)
Length of fuselage: Srs 475	25·55 m (83 ft 10 in)
Srs 500	29·67 m (97 ft 4 in)
Height overall	7·47 m (24 ft 6 in)
Tailplane span	8·99 m (29 ft 6 in)

BAe (BAC) One-Eleven Series 475 twin-turbofan short/medium-range airliner (*Pilot Press*)

Wheel track	4·34 m (14 ft 3 in)
Wheelbase: Srs 475	10·06 m (33 ft 0 in)
Srs 500	12·60 m (41 ft 4 in)
Passenger door (fwd, port):	
Height	1·73 m (5 ft 8 in)
Width	0·82 m (2 ft 8 in)
Height to sill	2·13 m (7 ft 0 in)
Ventral entrance: Height	1·83 m (6 ft 0 in)
Width	0·66 m (2 ft 2 in)
Height to sill	2·13 m (7 ft 0 in)
Freight door (fwd, starboard):	
Height (projected)	0·79 m (2 ft 7 in)
Width	0·91 m (3 ft 0 in)
Height to sill	1·09 m (3 ft 7 in)
Freight door (rear, starboard):	
Height (projected)	0·66 m (2 ft 2 in)
Width	0·91 m (3 ft 0 in)
Height to sill	1·30 m (4 ft 3 in)
Freight door (fwd, Srs 475 SOAF):	
Height	1·85 m (6 ft 1 in)
Width	3·05 m (10 ft 0 in)
Galley service door (fwd, starboard):	
Height (projected)	1·22 m (4 ft 0 in)
Width	0·69 m (2 ft 3 in)
Height to sill	2·13 m (7 ft 0 in)

DIMENSIONS, INTERNAL (Srs 475):
Cabin, excl flight deck:	
Length	17·31 m (56 ft 10 in)
Max width	3·16 m (10 ft 4 in)
Max height	1·98 m (6 ft 6 in)
Floor area	approx 47·0 m² (506 sq ft)
Freight hold, fwd	10·02 m³ (354 cu ft)
Freight hold, rear	4·42 m³ (156 cu ft)

DIMENSIONS, INTERNAL (Srs 500):
Cabin, excl flight deck:	
Length	21·44 m (70 ft 4 in)
Total floor area	approx 61·78 m² (665 sq ft)
Freight holds (total volume)	19·45 m³ (687 cu ft)

AREAS (Srs 475, 500):
Wings, gross	95·78 m² (1,031 sq ft)
Ailerons (total)	2·86 m² (30·8 sq ft)
Flaps (total)	15·89 m² (171 sq ft)
Spoilers (total)	2·30 m² (24·8 sq ft)
Vertical tail surfaces (total)	10·90 m² (117·4 sq ft)
Rudder, incl tab	3·05 m² (32·8 sq ft)
Horizontal tail surfaces (total)	23·90 m² (257·0 sq ft)
Elevators, incl tab	6·55 m² (70·4 sq ft)

WEIGHTS AND LOADINGS:
Operating weight empty:	
Srs 475	23,348 kg (51,473 lb)
Srs 500	24,454 kg (53,911 lb)
Max payload: Srs 475	9,764 kg (21,527 lb)
Srs 500	12,286 kg (27,089 lb)
Max T-O weight:	
Srs 475	41,730-44,678 kg (92,000-98,500 lb)
Srs 500	45,200-47,400 kg (99,650-104,500 lb)
Max ramp weight: Srs 475	44,905 kg (99,000 lb)
Srs 500	47,625 kg (105,000 lb)
Max landing weight:	
Srs 475	38,100-39,462 kg (84,000-87,000 lb)
Srs 500	39,462 kg (87,000 lb)
Max zero-fuel weight: Srs 475	33,112 kg (73,000 lb)
Srs 500	36,741 kg (81,000 lb)
Max wing loading:	
Srs 475	435·5 kg/m² (89·2 lb/sq ft)
Srs 500	472 kg/m² (96·7 lb/sq ft)
Max power loading:	
Srs 475	400·3 kg/kN (3·92 lb/lb st)
Srs 500	424·7 kg/kN (4·16 lb/lb st)

PERFORMANCE (at max T-O weight):
Never-exceed speed (structural)	410 knots (760 km/h; 472 mph) EAS
Max level and cruising speed at 6,400 m (21,000 ft)	470 knots (871 km/h; 541 mph)
Fuel econ cruising speed at 7,620 m (25,000 ft)	400 knots (742 km/h; 461 mph)
Stalling speed (T-O flap setting):	
Srs 475	99 knots (184 km/h; 114 mph) EAS
Srs 500	105 knots (195 km/h; 121 mph)
Rate of climb at S/L at 300 knots (555 km/h; 345 mph)	
EAS: Srs 475	756 m (2,480 ft)/min
Srs 500	695 m (2,280 ft)/min
Max cruising height	10,670 m (35,000 ft)
Min ground turning radius:	
Srs 475	17·07 m (56 ft 0 in)
Srs 500	17·98 m (59 ft 0 in)
Runway LCN at max weight, rigid pavement (1: 40):	
Srs 475	32
Srs 500	53
T-O run at S/L, ISA: Srs 475	1,676 m (5,500 ft)
Srs 500	1,981 m (6,500 ft)
Balanced T-O to 10·7 m (35 ft) at S/L, ISA:	
Srs 475	1,798 m (5,900 ft)
Srs 500	2,225 m (7,300 ft)

BAe (BAC) One-Eleven Series 500 in the insignia of British Airways

BAe Scottish Division Bulldog Model 121 trainer in service with the RAF

Landing distance (BCAR) at S/L, ISA, at max landing weight: Srs 475, Srs 500   1,463 m (4,800 ft)
Still-air range with max fuel, ISA, with reserves for 200 nm (370 km; 230 mile) diversion and 45 min hold:
Srs 475   1,997 nm (3,700 km; 2,300 miles)
Srs 500   1,880 nm (3,484 km; 2,165 miles)
Still-air range with typical capacity payload, ISA, reserves as above:
Srs 475 at 44,678 kg (98,500 lb)
          1,619 nm (3,000 km; 1,865 miles)
Srs 500 at 47,400 kg (104,500 lb)
          1,480 nm (2,744 km; 1,705 miles)
Srs 475 executive aircraft with additional 3,182 litres (700 Imp gallons) fuel has equivalent range of
          2,549 nm (4,725 km; 2,936 miles)

BAe SA-3-120 BULLDOG SERIES 120

First flight of the Beagle-built Bulldog prototype was made on 19 May 1969. A second prototype, completed by Scottish Aviation, was flown on 14 February 1971, and a third airframe was completed for static and fatigue tests.

All versions ordered so far are basically similar, except for the equipment fitted. The first production Bulldog, completed by Scottish Aviation, flew for the first time on 22 June 1971 and received full ARB certification on 30 June 1971. The first 98 production Bulldogs were of the Series 100 version, described in the 1972-73 *Jane's*. The second prototype was refurbished, issued with a Normal category C of A, and delivered to a private owner under the designation Model 104.

Production continued with the Series 120, which was awarded full CAA certification on 12 February 1973.

By March 1980 orders for the Bulldog Series 120 were as follows:

Model 121. For Royal Air Force, by whom it is designated **T. Mk 1.** Total of 130 ordered, of which the first (XX513) flew for the first time on 30 January 1973 and was delivered to the A & AEE at Boscombe Down on 20 February 1973. By February 1976, all had been delivered, and were in service with No. 2 FTS at Leeming, the CFS at Leeming, and University Air Squadrons.

Model 122. For Ghana Air Force. Six ordered initially, delivery of which was completed in September 1973. Further seven ordered in December 1973 (**Mk 122A**), delivery of which was completed by February 1976.

Model 123. For Nigerian Air Force. Twenty ordered initially. Delivery of these completed December 1974. Further 12 delivered in 1978.

Model 124. One aircraft (G-ASAL) used as company demonstration aircraft.

Model 125. Built for Jordanian Royal Academy of Aeronautics. Total of 13 delivered, in three batches, between 1974 and 1976. All transferred to Royal Jordanian Air Force in 1978.

Model 126. For Lebanese Air Force. Delivery of six completed in October 1975.

Model 127. For Kenya. Delivery of nine completed December 1976.

Model 128. For Royal Hong Kong Auxiliary Air Force. Two delivered in 1977.

Eleven more Bulldogs have been sold, to the Botswana Defence Force (six) and an unnamed Middle Eastern country (five). Production is scheduled to continue until at least 1982.

The following description applies to the Bulldog Series 120:

TYPE: Two/three-seat primary trainer.
WINGS: Cantilever low-wing monoplane. Wing section NACA 63₂615. Dihedral 6° 30′. Incidence 1° 9′ at root. Conventional single-spar riveted stressed-skin structure of light alloy. Electrically-operated slotted trailing-edge flaps and slotted ailerons of similar construction. Ground-adjustable tab on starboard aileron.
FUSELAGE: Conventional light alloy stressed-skin semi-monocoque structure.
TAIL UNIT: Cantilever two-spar light alloy stressed-skin structure. Fixed-incidence tailplane. Full-span trim tab in starboard elevator. Manually-operated trim tab in rudder. Ventral fin.
LANDING GEAR: Non-retractable tricycle type, with single wheel on each unit. Steerable nosewheel with Automotive Products oleo-pneumatic shock-absorber and

Goodyear wheel and tyre, size 5·00-5, pressure 2·76 bars (40 lb/sq in). Main units have Automotive Products oleo-pneumatic shock-absorbers and Goodyear wheels and tyres, size 6·00-6, pressure 2·07 bars (30 lb/sq in). Goodyear hydraulic disc brakes on main wheels. Optional ski landing gear.
POWER PLANT: One 149 kW (200 hp) Avco Lycoming IO-360-A1B6 flat-four engine, driving a Hartzell HC-C2YK-4F/FC7666A-2 two-blade constant-speed metal propeller with spinner. Avco Lycoming AEIO-360-A1B6 engine available optionally, permitting up to 20 s of inverted flight. Four removable metal fuel tanks, two in each wing, with total usable capacity of 145·5 litres (32 Imp gallons). Refuelling point on top of each wing. Oil capacity 7·6 litres (1·67 Imp gallons).
ACCOMMODATION: Enclosed cabin seating pilot and co-pilot or trainee side by side with dual controls, with space at rear for observer's seat or up to 100 kg (220 lb) of baggage. Rearward-sliding jettisonable transparent canopy. Cabin heated and ventilated.
SYSTEMS: Heat exchanger for cabin heating. Hydraulic system, pressure 40 bars (580 lb/sq in), for main-wheel brakes only. Vacuum-type pneumatic system available optionally. 24V DC power from engine-driven alternator and 24V 25Ah storage battery. No oxygen or de-icing systems.
AVIONICS AND EQUIPMENT: VHF, UHF or HF com radio to individual customer's requirements; panel can accommodate dual VHF nav, DME, ATC transponder, ADF and other navaids. Blind-flying instrumentation standard. Glider towing attachment optional.
ARMAMENT AND OPERATIONAL EQUIPMENT: Standard aircraft is unarmed, but has provision for installation of four underwing hardpoints to which can be attached various loads including unguided or wire-guided air-to-surface projectiles; 7.62 mm machine-gun pods; grenade launchers; practice or active bombs of up to 50 kg; markers; supply containers; leaflet dispensers; and rescue and survival equipment. Maximum underwing load 290 kg (640 lb).

DIMENSIONS, EXTERNAL:
Wing span	10·06 m (33 ft 0 in)
Wing chord at root	1·51 m (4 ft 11¼ in)
Wing chord at tip	0·86 m (2 ft 9¾ in)
Wing aspect ratio	8·4
Length overall	7·09 m (23 ft 3 in)
Height overall	2·28 m (7 ft 5¾ in)
Tailplane span	3·35 m (11 ft 0 in)
Wheel track	2·03 m (6 ft 8 in)
Wheelbase	1·40 m (4 ft 7 in)
Propeller diameter	1·88 m (6 ft 2 in)
Propeller ground clearance	0·26 m (10¼ in)

DIMENSIONS, INTERNAL:
Cabin: Length	2·11 m (6 ft 11 in)

Max width	1·14 m (3 ft 9 in)
Max height	1·02 m (3 ft 4 in)

AREAS:
Wings, gross	12·02 m² (129·4 sq ft)
Ailerons (total)	0·87 m² (9·4 sq ft)
Trailing-edge flaps (total)	1·30 m² (13·95 sq ft)
Vertical tail surfaces (total)	2·11 m² (22·72 sq ft)
Horizontal tail surfaces (total)	2·55 m² (27·50 sq ft)

WEIGHTS AND LOADINGS:
Weight empty, equipped	649 kg (1,430 lb)
Basic operating weight empty	669 kg (1,475 lb)
Max T-O weight:	
normal and semi-aerobatic	1,066 kg (2,350 lb)
fully aerobatic	1,015 kg (2,238 lb)
Max wing loading	88·6 kg/m² (18·15 lb/sq ft)
Max power loading	7·15 kg/kW (11·75 lb/hp)

PERFORMANCE (at max T-O weight):
Never-exceed speed (structural)	
	210 knots (389 km/h; 241 mph)
Max level speed at S/L	
	130 knots (241 km/h; 150 mph)
Max cruising speed at 1,220 m (4,000 ft)	
	120 knots (222 km/h; 138 mph)
Econ cruising speed at 1,220 m (4,000 ft)	
	105 knots (194 km/h; 121 mph)
Stalling speed, flaps down, power off	
	53 knots (98 km/h; 61 mph) EAS
Max rate of climb at S/L	315 m (1,034 ft)/min
Service ceiling	4,875 m (16,000 ft)
Min ground turning radius	9·75 m (32 ft 0 in)
T-O run	274 m (900 ft)
T-O to 15 m (50 ft)	427 m (1,400 ft)
Landing from 15 m (50 ft)	363 m (1,190 ft)
Landing run	153 m (500 ft)
Range with max fuel, 55% power, no reserves	
	540 nm (1,000 km; 621 miles)
Endurance with max fuel, conditions as above	
	5 h 0 min
g limits: semi-aerobatic	+4·4; −1·8
fully aerobatic	+6; −3

BAe (BAC 167) STRIKEMASTER

The BAe Strikemaster was developed from the BAC 145 series (see 1972-73 *Jane's*). It has the same airframe, but is powered by a Rolls-Royce Viper Mk 535 turbojet engine (15·2 kN; 3,410 lb st) and has four underwing hardpoints, enabling it to carry up to 1,360 kg (3,000 lb) of stores.

The first Strikemaster flew for the first time on 26 October 1967, and a total of 146 (including five BAC 145s) have been ordered. By the end of 1978 deliveries had been completed, including a further batch of 12 Mk 80As ordered by Saudi Arabia in 1977; but 10 aircraft are being built for stock in anticipation of further orders.

Details of the Strikemaster can be found in the 1978-79 *Jane's*.

BAe HAWK

RAF designation: Hawk T. Mk 1

After examining designs submitted by BAC and Hawker Siddeley to meet an RAF requirement for a basic and advanced jet trainer, the Ministry of Defence announced in October 1971 that the Hawker Siddeley 1182 had been selected to meet this requirement. Selection of a non-afterburning version of the Rolls-Royce Turboméca Adour to power the aircraft was announced on 2 March 1972, and later in the same month the Ministry of Defence confirmed an initial order for 176 HS 1182s, which were given the RAF name of Hawk. These were to consist of one pre-production aircraft (XX154), which first flew on 21 August 1974, and 175 production Hawks. There were no separate prototypes; instead, the first five production aircraft were allocated to the development programme. The first two production Hawks (XX162 and 163) were delivered to the Advanced Flying Training

BAe Hawk of the RAF Tactical Weapons Unit, Brawdy, firing folding-fin rockets from its Matra launchers

School at RAF Valley on 4 November 1976, and the 100th RAF Hawk was delivered on 27 March 1979. A follow-on order from the RAF for 18 Hawks was placed in April 1980.

The Hawk is designed to be fully aerobatic (it is stressed to +8 and −4g) and to have a fatigue life of 6,000 hours. It is replacing the Jet Provost, Gnat Trainer and Hunter in RAF service for advanced flying training, and for radio, navigation and weapons training. The basic design is capable of development for other operational roles, and studies of a number of variants have been made. One outcome of this is that a substantial number of RAF Hawks will be modified to carry two AIM-9L Sidewinder air-to-air missiles (see accompanying illustration) to supplement home defence fighter squadrons in an emergency. Under a continuing development programme the more powerful Adour Mk 861 engine of 25·35 kN (5,700 lb st) has been installed in BAe's demonstrator aircraft, this providing some 8% more thrust at take-off and, in conjunction with engine control refinements, more than 15% increase at high speeds. Wing development is continuing to improve both lift and stall characteristics, and the demonstrator has been flown with an enlarged braking parachute giving a drag increase of almost 50%. The RAF's premier aerobatic team, the Red Arrows, was re-equipped with the Hawk in 1979-80.

The Finnish government has ordered 50 Hawk **Mk 51** trainers to replace its Fouga Magisters, with initial deliveries scheduled for early 1980. Components for 46 of these, and final assembly, will be undertaken in Finland by Valmet (which see). British Aerospace announced on 5 April 1978 the receipt of a contract for the supply of eight **Mk 53** ground attack/trainer aircraft for the Indonesian Air Force. Kenya has ordered 12. Deliveries to all three export customers began in 1980.

In January 1979, it was announced that the US Naval Air Development Center had awarded BAe Aircraft Group a contract to study modification of the Hawk to meet the Navy's VTX-TS requirement for a replacement for the T-2C Buckeye and TA-4J Skyhawk. The modification would make the Hawk capable of operation from aircraft carriers. Since that time British Aerospace and McDonnell Douglas Corporation have finalised a partnership agreement under which BAe remains as prime contractor in the initial stages of VTX-TS bidding. Should the Hawk be selected for production for the US Navy, McDonnell Douglas would become prime contractor. The agreement also covers technical co-operation in making the Hawk carrier compatible, and in the integration of studies and proposals on the training systems and support-in-service aspects of VTX-TS.

By 1 July 1980 a total of 145 Hawks had flown, and had by then recorded a combined total of 60,000 flying hours.

TYPE: Two-seat basic and advanced jet trainer, with capability for close support role.

WINGS: Cantilever low-wing monoplane. Thickness/chord ratio 10·9% at root, 9% at tip. Dihedral 2°. Sweepback 26° on leading-edge, 21° 30′ at quarter-chord. One-piece wing, with six-bolt attachment to fuselage, employing a machined spars-and-skin torsion box, the greater part of which forms an integral fuel tank. Hydraulically-operated double-slotted flaps and ailerons, the latter operated by Automotive Products tandem actuators.

FUSELAGE: Conventional all-metal structure of frames and stringers, cut out to accept the one-piece wing. Large airbrake under rear of fuselage, aft of wing.

TAIL UNIT: Cantilever all-metal structure, with sweepback on all surfaces. One-piece all-moving power-operated anhedral tailplane, with Automotive Products tandem hydraulic actuators. Manually-operated rudder, with electrically-actuated trim tab.

LANDING GEAR: Wide-track retractable tricycle type, with single wheel on each unit. Hydraulic actuation, using Automotive Products jacks. Main units retract inward into wing, ahead of front spar; nosewheel retracts forward. Main wheels and tyres size 6·50-10, pressure 9·86 bars (143 lb/sq in). Nosewheel and tyre size 4·4-16, pressure 8·27 bars (120 lb/sq in). Tail bumper fairing under rear fuselage. Anti-skid wheel brakes. Tail braking parachute.

POWER PLANT: One Rolls-Royce Turboméca RT.172-06-11 Adour Mk 151 non-afterburning turbofan engine, rated at 23·13 kN (5,200 lb st). Air intake on each side of fuselage, forward of wing leading-edge. Engine starting by integral gas turbine starter. Fuel in one fuselage bag tank (841 litres; 185 Imp gallons) and integral wing tank (864 litres; 190 Imp gallons); total fuel capacity 1,705 litres (375 Imp gallons). Pressure refuelling point near front of port engine air intake trunk. Provision for carrying one 455 litre (100 Imp gallon) drop-tank on each inboard underwing pylon.

ACCOMMODATION: Crew of two in tandem under one-piece fully-transparent sideways-opening canopy. Fixed front windscreen and separate internal windscreen in front of rear cockpit. Rear seat elevated. Martin-Baker Mk 10B zero-zero rocket-assisted ejection seats, with MDC (miniature detonation cord) system to break canopy before seats eject. The MDC can also be operated from outside the cockpit in case of a ground emergency. Dual controls standard. Entire accommodation pressurised, heated and air-conditioned.

BAe Hawk Mk 53 for Indonesia (Rolls-Royce Turboméca Adour Mk 151 turbofan engine)

British Aerospace Hawk two-seat jet trainer/close support aircraft (*Pilot Press*)

SYSTEMS: BAe Dynamics cockpit air-conditioning and pressurisation systems, using engine bleed air. Duplicated hydraulic systems, each 207 bars (3,000 lb/sq in), for actuation of control jacks, flaps, airbrake, landing gear and anti-skid wheel brakes. Compressed nitrogen accumulators provide emergency power for flaps and landing gear. Hydraulic accumulator for emergency operation of wheel brakes. No pneumatic system. DC electrical power from single brushless generator, with two static inverters to provide AC power and two batteries for standby power. Gaseous oxygen system for crew. Pop-up Dowty Rotol ram-air turbine in upper rear fuselage provides emergency power for flying controls in the event of an engine or No. 2 pump failure.

AVIONICS AND EQUIPMENT: The RAF standard of flight instrumentation includes Ferranti gyros and inverter, two Sperry Gyroscope RAI-4 4 in remote attitude indicators and a magnetic detector unit, and Louis Newmark compass system. Radio and navigation equipment includes Sylvania UHF and VHF, Cossor CAT.7000 Tacan, Cossor ILS with CILS.75/76 localiser/glideslope receiver and marker receiver, and IFF/SSR (Cossor 2720 Mk 10A`IFF in aircraft for Finland).

ARMAMENT AND OPERATIONAL EQUIPMENT: Ferranti F.195 weapon sight and camera recorder in each cockpit. (Saab RGS2 sighting system in aircraft for Finland.) Trainer version has underfuselage centreline-mounted 30 mm Aden gun and ammunition pack, and two inboard underwing points each capable of carrying a nominal 454 kg (1,000 lb) stores load. Typical underwing armament training loads include two Matra 155 launchers, each with eighteen 2·75 in air-to-surface rockets, or two clusters of four practice bombs. Provision for two outboard underwing pylons, and a pylon in place of the ventral gun pack, also each capable of a 1,000 lb load (2,567 kg; 5,660 lb total external stores load), for close support role. The Hawk has demonstrated its ability to carry a total external load of 2,950 kg (6,500 lb). In RAF training roles the normal max external load is about 680 kg (1,500 lb). AIM-9L Sidewinder air-to-air missiles will be carried by RAF Hawks modified for operational use in an emergency.

DIMENSIONS, EXTERNAL:

Wing span	9·39 m (30 ft 9¾ in)
Wing chord at root	2·65 m (8 ft 8¼ in)
Wing chord at tip	0·90 m (2 ft 11½ in)
Wing aspect ratio	5·284
Length overall, excl probe	11·17 m (36 ft 7¾ in)
Height overall	3·99 m (13 ft 1¼ in)
Tailplane span	4·39 m (14 ft 4¾ in)
Wheel track	3·34 m (10 ft 11½ in)

AREAS:

Wings, gross	16·69 m² (179·6 sq ft)
Ailerons (total)	1·05 m² (11·30 sq ft)
Trailing-edge flaps (total)	2·50 m² (26·91 sq ft)
Airbrake	0·53 m² (5·70 sq ft)
Fin	2·51 m² (27·02 sq ft)

Rudder, incl tab	0·58 m² (6·24 sq ft)
Tailplane	4·33 m² (46·61 sq ft)

WEIGHTS:

Weight empty	3,647 kg (8,040 lb)
T-O weight:	
trainer, 'clean'	5,035 kg (11,100 lb)
trainer, armed	5,572 kg (12,284 lb)
Max T-O weight	7,750 kg (17,085 lb)
Max landing weight	4,649 kg (10,250 lb)

PERFORMANCE:

Max speed (in dive)	572 knots (1,060 km/h; 658 mph)
Max level speed	560 knots (1,038 km/h; 645 mph)
Max Mach number (in dive)	1·2
Max level speed Mach number	0·88
Max rate of climb at S/L	2,835 m (9,300 ft)/min
Time to 9,145 m (30,000 ft)	6 min 6 s
Service ceiling	15,240 m (50,000 ft)
T-O run	550 m (1,800 ft)
Landing run	488 m (1,600 ft)

Combat radius:
with 2,540 kg (5,600 lb) weapon load
300 nm (556 km; 345 miles)
with 1,360 kg (3,000 lb) weapon load
560 nm (1,038 km; 645 miles)
Ferry range 'clean' 1,313 nm (2,433 km; 1,510 miles)
Ferry range with two 455 litre (100 Imp gallon) drop-tanks   1,669 nm (3,093 km; 1,922 miles)
Endurance   approx 4 h 0 min

BAe HARRIER

RAF designations: Harrier GR. Mk 3, and T. Mk 2A and 4

USMC designations: AV-8A (Mk 50) and TAV-8A (Mk 54)

Spanish Navy designation: Matador (AV-8S and TAV-8S)

The Harrier was the world's first operational fixed-wing V/STOL strike fighter. Developed from six years of operating experience with the P.1127/Kestrel series of aircraft (see 1968-69 *Jane's*), it is an integrated V/STOL weapon system, incorporating a Ferranti FE 541 inertial navigation and attack system and Smiths head-up display. The first of six single-seat prototypes (XV276) flew for the first time on 31 August 1966; the following versions have since been built:

Harrier GR. Mk 1, 1A and 3. Single-seat close-support and tactical reconnaissance versions for the RAF. First of initial series of 78 production GR. Mk 1s (XV738) flew on 28 December 1967. Entered service with the Harrier OCU, No. 233 Squadron, at RAF Wittering, on 1 April 1969. Delivered to No. 1 Squadron at Wittering and Nos. 3, 4 and 20 in West Germany. These aircraft were designated Harrier GR. Mk 1 when fitted initially with Pegasus 101 engines. When retrofitted subsequently with the Pegasus 102 they were redesignated GR.Mk 1A. Aircraft

BAe Harrier GR.Mk 3 of No. 1 Squadron, RAF, with special camouflage for Exercise Cold Winter, held in Norway in 1979 *(Rolls-Royce)*

BAe Harrier GR.Mk 3 single-seat V/STOL close support and reconnaissance aircraft *(Pilot Press)*

now in service have Pegasus 103 engines and are designated GR. Mk 3. A further 36 GR. Mk 3s, making a total for the RAF of 114 single-seat Harriers, were ordered subsequently. By 1 September 1980 a total of 110 (including two-seaters) had been delivered to the RAF.

A Harrier GR. Mk 1A, piloted by Sqn Ldr T. L. Lecky-Thompson, set up two international time-to-height records after VTO, in Class H for jet-lift aircraft, on 5 January 1971. The aircraft reached 9,000 m (29,528 ft) in 1 min 44·7 s and 12,000 m (39,370 ft) in 2 min 22·7 s. The same RAF pilot also set up a Class H altitude record of 14,040 m (46,063 ft) in a Harrier GR. Mk 1A on 2 January 1971.

In early 1978 flight testing began of a Harrier GR. Mk 3 fitted with cushion augmentation devices (CADS) and wing leading-edge root extensions (LERX), both intended to improve lift capability. The CADS system consists of ventral strakes fitted to the underfuselage gun pods which, like the lift improvement devices (LIDS) employed on the McDonnell Douglas AV-8B Advanced Harrier, trap the exhaust air from the engine as it rebounds from the ground; the air is prevented from re-entering the intakes by a laterally-positioned surface fixed across the front of the two pods.

Harrier T. Mk 2, 2A, 4 and 6. Two-seat versions, retaining the full combat capability of the single-seater in terms of equipment fit and weapon carriage. There is a large degree of commonality in structure and system components, ground support equipment and flight and ground crew training. Differences include a new, longer nose section forward of the wing leading-edge, with two cockpits in tandem; a tailcone approx 1·83 m (6 ft) longer than that of the single-seat model; and enlarged fin surfaces. The two-seat Harrier may be used operationally with the rear seat and compensating tail ballast removed, thus minimising the weight penalty over its single-seat counterpart. First development aircraft (XW174) flew on 24 April 1969, and the first of 21 production aircraft for the RAF (XW264) on 3 October 1969. The two-seater entered RAF service in July 1970. Four are on order for the Royal Navy.

The RAF Harrier T. Mk 2, like the GR. Mk 1, was powered originally by the Pegasus 101 engine. The designations T. Mk 2A and T. Mk 4 apply to aircraft retrofitted with, respectively, the Pegasus 102 and 103. Royal Navy version is designated **T. Mk 6.**

Harrier Mk 50 (USMC designation AV-8A). Single-seat close-support and tactical reconnaissance version for the US Marine Corps, delivery of which began on 26 January 1971. Dimensionally as GR. Mk 3, but without laser ranger and marked target seeker, and with modifications to customer's specification, including provision for the carriage of Sidewinder missiles. Total of 102 ordered for US Marine Corps, plus eight Harrier **Mk 54s** (a two-seat version designated **TAV-8A**); all of those still in service now have Pegasus 103 engines.

The AV-8As equip three US Marine Corps combat squadrons: VMA 513, VMA 542 and VMA 231; and training squadron VMA(T) 203, at Cherry Point, North Carolina.

Beginning in 1979, and continuing until FY 1984, a total of 61 AV-8As are being upgraded to **AV-8C** standard. This involves a service life extension programme (SLEP) of structural improvements aimed at extending the airframe fatigue life to up to 4,000 h; and a CILOP (conversion in lieu of procurement) programme under which the AV-8As are fitted with forward-looking passive radar warning equipment at the wingtips, tail warning radar in the tail 'bullet' fairing, improved UHF com radio, a flare/chaff dispenser in the rear-fuselage equipment bay, the LIDS (lift improvement devices: underfuselage strakes and forward flap) developed for the AV-8B, an onboard oxygen generating system, and KY 58 secure voice system. Conversion of the first few AV-8As to AV-8C standard was undertaken by McDonnell Douglas, from kits supplied by BAe. The remaining conversions will be carried out by the US Marine Corps at NAS Cherry Point, North Carolina.

Harrier Mk 52. One aircraft built as a demonstrator using BAe and equipment suppliers' private funding. It is similar to the Harrier T. Mk 4, and is fitted with a Pegasus 103 engine; in recognition of its status as the first civil-registered jet V/STOL aircraft in the UK, it was granted the civil registration G-VTOL. First flight was made on 16 September 1971, with a Pegasus 102 fitted initially.

Harrier Mk 55. Eleven AV-8As and two TAV-8As ordered, through USA, for the Spanish Navy, by whom they are known as **Matadors** and designated **AV-8S** and **TAV-8S** respectively. Ten delivered by September 1980. These equip the 8a Escuadrilla of the Spanish Navy at Rota, Cadiz.

Harrier T. Mk 60. Two-seat operational trainer version for Indian Navy; two ordered by mid-1980.

Sea Harrier. Version for Royal Navy and Indian Navy. Described separately.

An Advanced Harrier study was completed in December 1973 by Hawker Siddeley, Rolls-Royce, McDonnell Douglas and Pratt & Whitney. This was funded jointly by the UK and US governments on behalf of the RAF, Royal Navy, US Marine Corps and US Navy, but in March 1975 the UK Secretary of State for Defence, Mr Roy Mason, stated that "there is not enough common ground on the Advanced Harrier for us to join in the programme with the US". The US **AV-8B** advanced version of the Harrier is, therefore, described under the McDonnell Douglas heading in this edition. A British proposal, known as the **Big Wing Harrier**, is described separately.

Following proposals by Lt Cdr D. R. Taylor, RN, tests were carried out successfully in 1977 with a 'ski-jump' launching ramp designed to boost the short take-off performance of vectored-thrust aircraft. This technique makes possible substantial benefits in Harrier operation both at sea and ashore, and will be a feature of all Royal Navy ships in which Sea Harriers are based. A ski-jump with a 20° angle enables the Harrier to take off at a 30 knot (55·5 km/h; 34·5 mph) lower speed than from a flat deck and at 60 knots (111 km/h; 69 mph) less than from a

runway, so conserving fuel for the flight itself. It also permits more than 907 kg (2,000 lb) of extra fuel or weapons to be carried than would be possible in the same distance with a flat-deck take-off.

The following details apply generally to the Harrier GR. Mk 3 and T. Mk 4, except where a specific version is indicated:

TYPE: V/STOL close support and reconnaissance aircraft.

WINGS: Cantilever shoulder-wing monoplane. Wing section of BAe (HS) design. Thickness/chord ratio 10% at root, 5% at tip. Anhedral 12°. Incidence 1° 45′. Sweepback at quarter-chord 34°. One-piece aluminium alloy three-spar safe-life structure with integrally-machined skins, manufactured by Brough factory of BAe, with six-point attachment to fuselage. Plain ailerons and flaps, of bonded aluminium alloy honeycomb construction. Ailerons irreversibly operated by Fairey tandem hydraulic jacks. Jet reaction control valve built into front of each outrigger wheel fairing. Entire wing unit removable to provide access to engine. For ferry missions, the normal 'combat' wingtips can be replaced by bolt-on extended tips to increase ferry range.

FUSELAGE: Conventional semi-monocoque safe-life structure of frames and stringers, mainly of aluminium alloy, but with titanium skins at rear and some titanium adjacent to engine and in other special areas. Access to power plant through top of fuselage, ahead of wing. Jet reaction control valves in nose and in extended tailcone. Large forward-hinged airbrake under fuselage, aft of main-wheel well.

TAIL UNIT: One-piece variable-incidence tailplane, with 15° of anhedral, irreversibly operated by Fairey tandem hydraulic jack. Rudder and trailing-edge of tailplane are of bonded aluminium honeycomb construction. Rudder is operated manually. Trim tab in rudder. Ventral fin under rear fuselage. Fin tip carries suppressed VHF aerial.

LANDING GEAR: Retractable bicycle type of Dowty Rotol manufacture, permitting operation from rough unprepared surfaces of CBR as low as 3% to 5%. Hydraulic actuation, with nitrogen bottle for emergency extension of landing gear. Single steerable nosewheel retracts forward, twin coupled mainwheels rearward, into fuselage. Small outrigger units retract rearward into fairings slightly inboard of wingtips. Nosewheel leg is of levered-suspension Liquid Spring type. Dowty Rotol telescopic oleo-pneumatic main and outrigger gear. Dunlop wheels and tyres, size 26·00 × 8·75-11 (nose unit), 27·00 × 7·74-13 (main units) and 13·50 × 6·4 (outriggers). GR. Mk 3 tyre pressures 6·21 bars (90 lb/sq in) on nose and main units, 6·55 bars (95 lb/sq in) on outriggers. T. Mk 4 tyre pressures 6·90 bars (100 lb/sq in) on nose unit, 6·55 bars (95 lb/sq in) on main and outrigger units. Dunlop multi-disc brakes and Dunlop-Hytrol adaptive anti-skid system.

POWER PLANT: One Rolls-Royce Pegasus Mk 103 vectored-thrust turbofan engine (95·6 kN; 21,500 lb st), with four exhaust nozzles of the two-vane cascade type, rotatable through 98° from fully-aft position. Engine bleed air from HP compressor used for jet reaction control system and to power duplicated air motor for nozzle actuation. The low-drag intake cowls, with outward-cambered lips, each have 8 automatic suction relief doors aft of the leading-edge to improve intake efficiency by providing extra air for the engine at low forward or zero speeds. Fuel in five integral tanks in fuselage and two in wings, with total capacity of approx 2,865 litres (630 Imp gallons). This can be supplemented by two 455 litre (100 Imp gallon) jettisonable combat tanks or two 1,500 litre (330 Imp gallon) ferry tanks on the inboard wing pylons. Ground refuelling point in port rear nozzle fairing. Provision for inflight refuelling probe above the port intake cowl.

ACCOMMODATION: Crew of one (Mk 3) or two (Mk 4) on Martin-Baker Type 9D zero-zero rocket ejection seats which operate through the miniature detonating cord equipped canopy of the pressurised, heated and air-conditioned cockpit. AV-8As of the US Marine Corps retrofitted with Stencel SIIIS-3 ejection seats. Manually-operated canopy, rearward-sliding on single-seat, sideways-opening (to starboard) on two-seat versions. Birdproof windscreen, with hydraulically-actuated wiper. Windscreen de-icing.

SYSTEMS: Three-axis limited-authority autostabiliser for V/STOL flight. Pressurisation system of BAe design, with Normalair-Garrett and Marston major components; max pressure differential 0·24 bars (3·5 lb/sq in). Duplicated hydraulic systems, each of 207 bars (3,000 lb/sq in), actuate Fairey flying control and general services and include a retractable ram-air turbine inside top of rear fuselage, driving a small hydraulic pump for emergency power. AC electrical system with transformer-rectifiers to provide required DC supply. One 12kVA Lucas alternator. Two 28V 25Ah batteries, one of which energises a 24V motor to start Lucas gas-turbine starter/APU. This unit drives a 6kVA auxiliary alternator for ground readiness servicing and standby. Normalair-Garrett liquid oxygen system of 5 litres (1 Imp gallon) capacity. Bootstrap-type cooling unit for equipment bay, with intake at base of dorsal fin.

AVIONICS AND EQUIPMENT: Plessey U/VHF, Ultra standby UHF, Hoffman Tacan and Cossor IFF, Ferranti FE 541 inertial navigation and attack system (INAS), with Sperry C2G compass, Smiths electronic head-up display of flight information and Smiths air data computer. INAS can be aligned equally well at sea or on land. The weapon aiming computer provides a general solution for manual or automatic release of free-fall and retarded bombs, and for the aiming of rockets and guns, in dive and straight-pass attacks over a wide range of flight conditions and very considerable freedom of manoeuvre in elevation. Communication equipment ranges through VHF in the 100-156MHz band to UHF in the 220-400MHz band. Ferranti Type 106 laser ranger and marked target seeker (LRMTS) retrofitted to all RAF Harriers.

ARMAMENT AND OPERATIONAL EQUIPMENT: Optically-flat panel in nose, on port side, for F.95 oblique camera, which is carried as standard. A cockpit voice recorder with in-flight playback facility supplements the reconnaissance cameras, and facilitates rapid debriefing and mission evaluation. No built-in armament. Combat load is carried on four underwing and one underfuselage pylons, all with ML ejector release units. The inboard wing points and the fuselage point are stressed for loads of up to 910 kg (2,000 lb) each, and the outboard underwing pair for loads of up to 295 kg (650 lb) each; the two strake fairings under the fuselage can each be replaced by a 30 mm Aden gun pod and ammunition. At present, the Harrier is cleared for operations with a maximum external load exceeding 2,270 kg (5,000 lb), but has flown with a weapon load of 3,630 kg (8,000 lb). The Harrier is able to carry 30 mm guns, bombs, rockets and flares of UK and US designs, and in addition to its fixed reconnaissance camera can also carry a five-camera reconnaissance pod on the underfuselage pylon. A typical combat load comprises a pair of 30 mm Aden gun pods, a 1,000 lb bomb on the underfuselage pylon, a 1,000 lb bomb on each of the inboard underwing pylons, and a Matra 155 launcher with 19 × 68 mm SNEB rockets on each outboard underwing pylon. A Sidewinder installation is provided in the AV-8A version, to give the aircraft an effective air-to-air capability in conjunction with the two 30 mm Aden guns.

DIMENSIONS, EXTERNAL:
Wing span: combat   7·70 m (25 ft 3 in)
        ferry   9·04 m (29 ft 8 in)
Wing chord at root   3·56 m (11 ft 8 in)
Wing chord at tip   1·26 m (4 ft 1½ in)
Wing aspect ratio: combat   3·175
        ferry   4·08
Length overall: single-seat   13·87 m (45 ft 6 in)
        single-seat (laser nose) 13·91 m (45 ft 7·8 in)
        two-seat   17·00 m (55 ft 9½ in)
Height overall:
        single-seat   3·45 m (11 ft 4 in)
        two-seat   4·17 m (13 ft 8 in)
Tailplane span   4·24 m (13 ft 11 in)
Outrigger wheel track   6·76 m (22 ft 2 in)
Wheelbase, nosewheel to main wheels
                    approx 3·45 m (11 ft 4 in)
AREAS:
Wings, gross: combat   18·68 m² (201·1 sq ft)
        ferry   20·1 m² (216 sq ft)
Ailerons (total)   0·98 m² (10·5 sq ft)
Trailing-edge flaps (total)   1·29 m² (13·9 sq ft)
Fin (excl ventral fin):
        single-seat   2·40 m² (25·8 sq ft)
        two-seat   3·57 m² (38·4 sq ft)
Rudder, incl tab   0·49 m² (5·3 sq ft)
Tailplane   4·41 m² (47·5 sq ft)

BAe Harrier T.Mk 4 two-seat combat trainer of the RAF's No. 4 Squadron, based at Gutersloh in Germany

British Aerospace's Big Wing as it would appear on a new-production Harrier with Pegasus 11-35 engine
(Pilot Press)

WEIGHTS AND LOADING:
Basic operating weight, empty, with crew:
        GR.Mk 3 and Mk 50   5,580 kg (12,300 lb)
        T.Mk 4 (solo for combat) 5,896 kg (13,000 lb)
        T.Mk 4 (dual)   6,237 kg (13,750 lb)
Internal fuel   2,295 kg (5,060 lb)
Max T-O weight (single-seat)
                    over 11,340 kg (25,000 lb)
Max wing loading (single-seat)
                    610 kg/m² (125 lb/sq ft)
PERFORMANCE:
Max speed at low altitude
        over 640 knots (1,186 km/h; 737 mph) EAS
Max Mach number (in a dive)   1·3
Time to 12,200 m (40,000 ft) from vertical T-O
                    2 min 22·7 s
Ceiling   more than 15,240 m (50,000 ft)
Range with one in-flight refuelling
        more than 3,000 nm (5,560 km; 3,455 miles)
Endurance with one in-flight refuelling
                    more than 7 h

BAe BIG WING HARRIER

British Aerospace Kingston/Brough Division has a research contract to design an advanced wing for the Harrier V/STOL combat aircraft, which will provide high subsonic performance, good manoeuvring capability and increased internal fuel capacity. Known simply as the Big Wing, the new structure embodies the latest UK supercritical technology and has a much greater thickness/chord ratio (12·5% at centreline, 9·2% at tip) than the wing of the current operational versions of the Harrier. This reduces the structural weight penalty of the increased-area wing and accommodates a further 1,114 litres (245 Imp gallons) of fuel.

The Big Wing, with a span of 9·75 m (32 ft 0 in) and area of 23·2 m² (250 sq ft), is designed to fit on to the existing Harrier GR. Mk 3 or T. Mk 4 fuselage with a minimum of modification. Changes are limited mainly to the addition of wiring and controls for the outboard stores pylons, and the provision of new wing fairings, engine access doors and hardpoints to locate the forward ends of the leading-edge root extensions (LERX). Addition of cushion augmentation devices (CADS), to improve VTOL performance and handling, also necessitates some modification of the underfuselage. The LERX and CADS have both been flight tested on an existing Harrier.

During the 1980 Defence Estimates debate, the UK Secretary of State for Defence stated that the Big Wing was "unlikely to be any part of an improvement programme of the GR. 3". He did, however, state that the British government intended to purchase 60 improved Harriers of some kind, though no further details of this intention were available at the time of closing for press.

BAe SEA HARRIER
RN designation: FRS. Mk 1
Indian Navy designation: FRS. Mk 51

On 15 May 1975, the British government announced its decision to proceed with full development of a maritime version of the Harrier, subsequently designated Sea Harrier **FRS. Mk 1**. The initial Royal Navy order is for 34 aircraft, of which 12 had been delivered by 1 September 1980. The Naval Intensive Flying Trials Unit for the Sea Harrier (No. 700A Squadron) was commissioned at RNAS Yeovilton on 19 September 1979. It will eventually become the shore-based HQ squadron, with eight aircraft. Front-line units, each with five aircraft, will be Nos. 800, 801 and 802 Squadrons, forming in 1980-81; these squadrons will operate from the anti-submarine cruisers HMS *Invincible*, *Illustrious* and *Ark Royal*, and the assault carrier HMS *Hermes*. Six similar Sea Harriers, designated **FRS. Mk 51**, have been ordered by the Indian Navy. Four standard, non-navalised T. Mk 4 two-seaters are to be procured by the Royal Navy for land-based training, and two T. Mk 60s by the Indian Navy.

A 7° 'ski-jump' T-O ramp is fitted to HMS *Invincible*. Ramps on later ships of the 'Invincible' class may be more steeply angled, and that which was scheduled for installation on HMS *Hermes* during the Summer of 1980 is set at 12°.

The first Sea Harrier to fly (XZ450) made its first flight on 20 August 1978, and the first for the Royal Navy (XZ451) was handed over on 18 June 1979. The first Sea Harrier ship trials were carried out on board HMS *Hermes* during November 1979.

Major changes compared with the Harriers in service with the RAF, Spanish Navy and US Marine Corps comprise the elimination of magnesium components, introduction of a raised cockpit, revised operational avionics, and installation of multi-mode Ferranti radar in a redesigned nose that folds to port for carrier stowage. Known by the name Blue Fox, this radar has been under development since March 1973, when the Electronic Systems Department of Ferranti was awarded a study and preliminary development contract. It is a derivative of the frequency-agile Sea Spray radar fitted in the Lynx helicopter, but embodies changes to suit its different role, with air-to-air intercept and air-to-surface modes of operation.

BAe Sea Harriers operating from HMS *Hermes* **during November 1979**

BAe Sea Harrier FRS.Mk 1 for the Royal Navy *(Pilot Press)*

Two specially modified Hawker Hunter T. Mk 8s, re-designated T.Mk 8M, were fitted with nose-mounted Blue Fox radars. Intended initially to speed the development of this radar and a new nav/attack system, they will continue in use for radar training. Equipment of the Sea Harrier includes ECM in a fairing near the tip of the tail-fin, and underwing attachments for air-to-air missiles of the Sidewinder type.

The Royal Navy's Sea Harrier FRS. Mk 1 has a Rolls-Royce Pegasus 104 vectored-thrust turbofan engine, with the same rating as the Pegasus 103 fitted to current RAF Harriers. The two variants differ little in design, except that the Pegasus 104 incorporates additional anti-corrosion features and has the capability to generate more electrical power.

Estimated weights, loadings and detailed performance figures are not yet available for the Sea Harrier. It is expected that the Navy's FRS.Mk 1 will operate at approximately the same weights as the GR.Mk 3, and will be capable of lifting a full military load with a 152 m (500 ft) flat deck run into an overdeck wind of 30 knots (55·5 km/h; 34·5 mph).

The description of the GR.Mk 3 applies also to the FRS.Mk 1, except as follows:

TYPE: V/STOL fighter, reconnaissance and strike aircraft.
POWER PLANT: As GR.Mk 3, except one Rolls-Royce Pegasus Mk 104 vectored-thrust turbofan engine of 95·6 kN (21,500 lb st). Internal fuel capacity 2,277 kg (5,060 lb). External combat fuel capacity 730 kg (1,600 lb).
ACCOMMODATION: As GR.Mk 3, but with pilot raised 28 cm (11 in), on Martin-Baker Type 10 rocket ejection seat.
SYSTEMS: As GR.Mk 3, except autopilot function on Fairey Hydraulics, giving throughput to aileron and tailplane power controls as well as to three-axis auto-stabs. Pressurisation system of BAe design with major components from Normalair-Garrett and Delaney Gallay. British Oxygen liquid oxygen system of 5 litres (1 Imp gallon) capacity. Lucas Mk 2 GTS/APU.
AVIONICS AND EQUIPMENT: Ferranti Blue Fox multi-mode nose-mounted radar, with TV-raster daylight-viewing tube which conveys flight information, as well as radar data, to pilot. New and larger Smiths electronic head-up display and digital weapon aiming computer. Decca Doppler 72. Ferranti self-aligning attitude reference platform and digital navigation computer. Radio nav aids include UHF homing, Tacan with offset facility and I-band transponder. Radio com by multi-channel Plessey PTR 377 U/VHF, with VHF standby via D 403M transceiver. Passive electronic surveillance and warning of external radar illumination by receiver with forward and rear hemisphere antennae in fin and tailcone respectively.
ARMAMENT AND OPERATIONAL EQUIPMENT: As GR.Mk 3, except for addition of Sidewinder installation similar to that of AV-8A, and provision for two air-to-surface missiles of Martel or Harpoon type.
DIMENSIONS, EXTERNAL: As GR.Mk 3 except:
Wing span   7·70 m (25 ft 3¼ in)
Length overall   14·50 m (47 ft 7 in)
Length overall, nose folded   12·88 m (42 ft 3 in)
Height overall   3·71 m (12 ft 2 in)
WEIGHT:
Max weapon load   3,630 kg (8,000 lb)
PERFORMANCE:
Max Mach No.   Mach 1·25
Max level airspeed
                 above 640 knots (1,185 km/h; 736 mph)

Typical cruising speed:
High altitude, for well over 1 h on internal fuel
                                                      above Mach 0·8
Low altitude 350-450 knots (650-833 km/h; 404-518 mph), with rapid acceleration to
                         600 knots (1,110 km/h; 690 mph)
Time from alarm to 30 nm (55 km; 35 miles) combat area
                                                          under 6 min
High altitude intercept radius, with 3 min combat and reserves for VL
                         400 nm (750 km; 460 miles)
Strike radius   250 nm (463 km; 288 miles)

BAe HS NIMROD

The Nimrod was developed to replace the Shackleton maritime reconnaissance aircraft of RAF Strike Command, with which it is scheduled to serve until well into the 1990s. Design of the Nimrod, as the Hawker Siddeley 801, began in June 1964, and government authority to proceed was announced in June 1965.

Based substantially upon the airframe of the Hawker Siddeley (de Havilland) Comet 4C, the Nimrod is a new-production aircraft with a 1·98 m (6 ft 6 in) shorter, modified pressurised fuselage; an unpressurised, under-slung pannier for operational equipment and weapons; and Rolls-Royce Spey turbofan engines (instead of the Avon turbojets of the Comet), with wider air intakes to allow for the greater mass flow. Other external changes include enlarged flight deck main windows and 'eyebrow' windows; ESM and MAD equipment, in glassfibre fairings on top of the fin and in the tailboom respectively; and a searchlight in the starboard wing external fuel tank. The search radar is housed in a streamlined glassfibre fairing which forms the nose section of the unpressurised lower fuselage.

The Nimrod was designed to combine the advantages of high-altitude, fast transit speed with low wing loading and good low-speed manoeuvring capabilities when operating in its primary roles of anti-submarine warfare, surveillance and anti-shipping strike. When required, two of the four Spey engines can be shut down to extend endurance, and the aircraft can cruise and climb on only one engine. A wide range of weapons can be carried in the 14·78 m (48 ft 6 in) long bomb bay, and large numbers of sonobuoys and markers can be carried and released from the pressurised rear fuselage area.

In addition to its surveillance and ASW roles, the Nimrod can be used for day and night photography. As supplied originally to the RAF, these aircraft had a stand-off surface missile capability. This has since been deleted but could be reactivated if required. The Nimrod MR. Mk 1 can carry 16 additional personnel in the self-support role; the MR. Mk 2 can also carry support personnel, but only 10 without the removal of equipment.

Two prototypes were built, both utilising existing Comet 4C airframes. The first of these (XV148), fitted with Spey engines, flew for the first time on 23 May 1967 and was used for aerodynamic testing. The second (XV147) retained its original Avon engines, was first flown on 31 July 1967, and was used for development of the nav/tac system and special maritime equipment.

The following versions have been produced:

Nimrod MR. Mk 1. Initial production version, to which the detailed description applies. Thirty-eight ordered initially (XV226-263), the first of which was flown on 28 June 1968. Deliveries began on 2 October 1969 and were completed in August 1972. The MR. Mk 1 was delivered initially to No. 236 OCU, RAF Strike Command, at St Mawgan, Cornwall, and is in service with No. 42 Squadron, also at St Mawgan; and Nos. 120, 201 and 206 Squadrons at Kinloss, Scotland. An order for eight additional Nimrods was announced in January 1972 and delivery of

BAe HS Nimrod R. Mk 1 of No. 51 Squadron, RAF. Note the modified tailcone in place of the MAD boom and the revised contours of the port wing leading-edge pod *(Swedish Air Force)*

BAe HS Nimrod MR. Mk 1 four-turbofan maritime patrol aircraft *(Pilot Press)*

these began in 1975. Only the first five were delivered to Mk 1 standard; three others were diverted as development aircraft for the Nimrod AEW. Mk 3.

Nimrod R. Mk 1. Designation of three aircraft (additional to the 46 MR. Mk 1s ordered for RAF Strike Command) delivered in 1971 to No. 51 Squadron at Wyton, Huntingdonshire. These aircraft (XW664-666), which replaced Comet 2s, are said to be employed for electronic reconnaissance and to monitor hostile radio and radar transmissions, although official statements have referred only to radio/radar calibration duties connected with RAF equipment. They can be identified by the absence of an MAD tailboom.

Nimrod MR. Mk 2. Thirty-two aircraft of the RAF's Nimrod MR. Mk 1 fleet are being refitted with new communications equipment, and advanced tactical sensor, ESM and navigation systems, under a programme which was started in 1975. Redelivery began on 23 August 1979 with XV236, the first completely refitted aircraft. After refit these aircraft are redesignated MR. Mk 2, and are being repainted in a new NATO-approved camouflage colour scheme. Equipment in this version includes an advanced search radar, offering greater range and sensitivity coupled with a higher data processing rate; a new acoustic processing system, developed by Marconi Avionics Systems, which is compatible with a wide range of existing and projected sonobuoys, and an early warning support measures (EWSM) pod at each wingtip. Armament includes Stingray homing torpedoes.

Nimrod AEW. Mk 3. Airborne early warning version; described separately.

Ample space and power is available in the basic Nimrod design to accept additional or alternative sensors such as sideways-looking radar, forward-looking infra-red, infra-red linescan, low light level TV, digital processing of intercepted ESM signals, and other new developments.

TYPE: Four-turbofan maritime patrol aircraft.

WINGS: Cantilever low/mid-wing monoplane, of metal construction. Sweepback 20° at quarter-chord. All-metal two-spar structure, comprising a centre-section, two stub-wings and two outer panels. Extensive use of Redux metal-to-metal bonding. All-metal ailerons, operated through duplicated hydraulic and mechanical units. Trim tab in each aileron. Plain flaps outboard of engines, operated hydraulically. Hot-air anti-icing system.

FUSELAGE: All-metal semi-monocoque structure. The circular-section cabin space is fully pressurised. Below this is an unpressurised pannier housing the bomb bay, radome and additional space for operational equipment. Segments of this pannier are free to move relative to each other, so that structural loads in the weapons bay are not transmitted to the pressure-cell. A glassfibre nose radome and tailboom are provided.

TAIL UNIT: Cantilever all-metal structure. Rudder and elevators operated through duplicated hydraulic and mechanical units. A glassfibre pod on top of the fin houses ESM equipment. Trim tab in each elevator. Hot-air anti-icing system.

LANDING GEAR: Retractable tricycle type. Four-wheel tandem-bogie main units, with size 36 × 10-18 Dunlop tyres, pressure 12·76 bars (185 lb/sq in). Twin-wheel nose unit, with size 30 × 9-15 Dunlop tyres, pressure 6·21 bars (90 lb/sq in).

POWER PLANT: Four Rolls-Royce RB. 168-20 Spey Mk 250 turbofan engines, each rated at 54 kN (12,140 lb st). Reverse thrust fitted on two outer engines. Fuel in fuselage keel tanks, integral wing tanks, and permanent external tank on each wing leading-edge, with total capacity of 48,780 litres (10,730 Imp gallons). Provi-

sion for up to six removable tanks in weapons bay.

ACCOMMODATION: Normal crew of 12, comprising pilot, co-pilot, and flight engineer on flight deck; routine navigator, tactical navigator, radio operator, radar operator, two sonics systems operators, ESM/MAD operator, and two observers/stores loaders in main (pressurised) cabin, which is fitted out as a tactical compartment. In this compartment, from front to rear, are a toilet on the port side; stations for the two navigators (stbd), radio and radar operators (port), and sonics systems operators (stbd) in the forward section; ESM/MAD operator's station, galley, four-seat dining area, rest quarters and sonobuoy stowage in the middle section; and buoy and marker launch area in the rear section. Three hemispherical observation windows forward of wings (one port, two stbd), giving 180° field of view. Two normal doors, emergency door, and four overwing emergency exits. Weapons bay can be utilised for additional fuel tanks (see under 'Power Plant') or for the carriage of freight. Provision is made for a trooping role, in which configuration 45 passengers can be accommodated if some rear-fuselage equipment is removed.

SYSTEMS: Air-conditioning by engine bleed air; Smith-Kollsman pressurisation system, with additional Normalair-Garrett conditioning pack on Mk 2 aircraft, max differential 0·603 bars (8·75 lb/sq in). Anti-icing and bomb-bay heating by engine bleed air. Lockheed hydraulic system, pressure 172 bars (2,500 lb/sq in), for duplicated flying control power units, landing gear shock-absorbers, steering and door jacks, weapons bay door jacks, camera aperture door jacks, and self-sealing couplings for water charging, ground test, engine bay and ancillary services. Lucas APU provides high-pressure air for engine starting. Electrical system utilises four 60kVA engine-driven alternators, with English Electric constant-speed drives, to provide 200V 400Hz three-phase AC supply. Secondary AC comes from two 115V three-phase static transformers, with duplicate 115V/26V two-phase static transformers which also feed a 1kVA frequency changer providing a 115V 1,600Hz single-phase supply for radar equipment. Emergency supplies for flight instruments are provided by a 115V single-phase static inverter. DC supply is by four 28V transformer-rectifier units backed up by two nickel-cadmium batteries.

AVIONICS AND EQUIPMENT (MR. Mk 1): Routine navigation by Decca Doppler Type 67M/Marconi E3 heading reference system, with reversionary heading from a Sperry GM7 duplicated gyro compass system, operating in conjunction with a Ferranti routine dynamic display. Tactical navigation, and stores selection and release, by Marconi nav/attack system utilising an 8K Marconi 920B digital computer. Tactical display station provides continually-updated information about aircraft position, with present and past track, sonobuoy positions, range circles from sonobuoys, ESM bearings, MAD marks, radar contacts and visual bearings. Course information can be displayed automatically to the pilots on the flight director system; alternatively, the computer can be coupled to the autopilot to allow the tactical navigator to direct the aircraft to a predicted target interception, weapon release point, or any other point on the tactical display. ASW equipment includes Sonics 1C sonar and a new long-range sonar system; EMI ASV-21D air-to-surface-vessel detection radar in nose; Thomson-CSF ESM (electronic support measures) equipment in pod on top of fin; and Emerson Electronics ASQ-10A MAD (magnetic anomaly detector) in extended tailboom. Strong Electric 70 million

candlepower searchlight at front of starboard external wing fuel tank. Aeronautical and General Instruments F.126 and F.135 cameras for day and night photography respectively, the latter having Chicago Aero Industries electronic flash equipment. Smiths SFS.6 automatic flight control system, embodying SEP.6 three-axis autopilot, integrated with the navigation and tactical system. Twin Plessey PTR 175 UHF/VHF, and Marconi AD 470 HF, communications transceivers; twin Marconi AD 260 VOR/ILS; Hoffman ARN 72 Tacan; Decca Loran C/A; Marconi AD 360 ADF; Honeywell AN/APN-171(V) radar altimeter. Yaw damper and Mach trim standard.

AVIONICS AND EQUIPMENT (MR. Mk 2): New and more flexible operational system, using three separate processors for tactical navigation, radar and acoustics. Marconi central tactical system, based on a 920 ATC computer with a greater storage capacity than that of MR. Mk 1, to provide improved computing and display facilities and, in conjunction with a Ferranti inertial navigation system, improved navigation capabilities. EMI Searchwater long-range air-to-surface-vessel radar, with its own data processing subsystem incorporating a Ferranti FM 1600D digital computer. This system presents a clutter-free picture, can detect and classify surface vessels, submarine snorts and periscopes at extreme ranges, can track several targets simultaneously, and is designed to operate in spite of countermeasures. AQS 901 acoustics processing and display system, based on twin Marconi 920 ATC computers, is compatible with a wide range of passive and active sonobuoys, either in existence or under development, including the Australian BARRA passive directional sonobuoy, the Canadian TANDEM, the US SSQ-41 and SSQ-53, and the new Ultra A-size X17255 Command Active Multi-Beam Sonobuoys (CAMBS), with a performance similar to that of helicopter-mounted dipping sonars. Communications are being improved by the installation of twin Marconi AD 470 HF transceivers (instead of the original single AD 470), and a radio teletype and encryption system. EWSM equipment in two wingtip pods.

ARMAMENT (MR. Mk 1): 14·78 m (48 ft 6 in) long weapons bay, with two pairs of doors, in unpressurised lower fuselage pannier, able to carry up to six lateral rows of ASW weapons, including up to nine torpedoes as well as bombs. (Capability of carrying depth charges and mines is not used by RAF.) Alternatively, to give greater range and endurance, up to six auxiliary fuel tanks can be fitted in the weapons bay, or a combination of fuel tanks and weapons can be carried. To ensure weapon serviceability, the weapons bay is heated when the ambient temperature falls below +5°C. Bay approx 9·14 m (30 ft) long in rear pressurised part of fuselage for storing and launching of active and passive sonobuoys and marine markers. Two rotary launchers, each capable of holding six size A sonobuoys, are used when the cabin is unpressurised; two single-barrel launchers are used when the aircraft is pressurised. A hardpoint is provided beneath each wing, just outboard of the main-wheel doors, on which can be carried air-to-surface missiles, rocket or cannon pods, or mines, according to mission requirements. The missile capability has been deleted from RAF Nimrods, but could be reactivated if required.

DIMENSIONS, EXTERNAL:

Wing span	35·00 m (114 ft 10 in)
Wing chord at root	9·00 m (29 ft 6 in)
Wing chord at tip	2·06 m (6 ft 9 in)
Wing aspect ratio	6·2

BAe HS Nimrod MR. Mk 2 four-turbofan maritime patrol aircraft of RAF Strike Command

Length overall	38·63 m (126 ft 9 in)
Height overall	9·08 m (29 ft 8½ in)
Tailplane span	14·51 m (47 ft 7¼ in)
Wheel track	8·60 m (28 ft 2½ in)
Wheelbase	14·24 m (46 ft 8½ in)

DIMENSIONS, INTERNAL:
Cabin (incl flight deck, navigation and ordnance areas, galley and toilet): Length	26·82 m (88 ft 0 in)
Max width	2·95 m (9 ft 8 in)
Max height	2·08 m (6 ft 10 in)
Volume	124·14 m³ (4,384 cu ft)

AREAS:
Wings, gross	197·0 m² (2,121 sq ft)
Ailerons (total)	5·63 m² (60·6 sq ft)
Trailing-edge flaps (total)	23·37 m² (251·6 sq ft)
Fin and rudder (above tailplane centreline)	10·96 m² (118 sq ft)
Dorsal fin	5·67 m² (61 sq ft)
Tailplane	40·41 m² (435 sq ft)
Elevators (incl tabs)	12·57 m² (135·3 sq ft)

WEIGHTS (MR. Mk 1):
Typical weight empty	39,000 kg (86,000 lb)
Max disposable military load	6,120 kg (13,500 lb)
Fuel load:	
standard tanks	38,940 kg (85,840 lb)
max, with six auxiliary tanks in weapons bay	45,785 kg (100,940 lb)
Normal max T-O weight	80,510 kg (177,500 lb)
Max overload T-O weight	87,090 kg (192,000 lb)
Typical landing weight	54,430 kg (120,000 lb)

PERFORMANCE (MR. Mk 1):
Max operational necessity speed, ISA + 20°C	500 knots (926 km/h; 575 mph)
Max transit speed, ISA + 20°C	475 knots (880 km/h; 547 mph)
Econ transit speed, ISA + 20°C	425 knots (787 km/h; 490 mph)
Typical low-level patrol speed (two engines)	200 knots (370 km/h; 230 mph)
Operating height range S/L to 12,800 m (42,000 ft)	
Min ground turning radius	27·1 m (89 ft 0 in)
Runway LCN at T-O weight of 82,550 kg (182,000 lb)	50
T-O run at 80,510 kg (177,500 lb) AUW, ISA at S/L	1,463 m (4,800 ft)
Unfactored landing distance at 54,430 kg (120,000 lb) landing weight, ISA at S/L	1,615 m (5,300 ft)
Typical ferry range	4,500-5,000 nm (8,340-9,265 km; 5,180-5,755 miles)
Typical endurance	12 h

BAe HS NIMROD AEW. Mk 3

This airborne early warning (AEW) version of the Nimrod was designed by Hawker Siddeley Aviation specifically for European defence. On 31 March 1977 the British Defence Secretary announced the government's intention to proceed with the procurement of 11 of the aircraft for the RAF, under the designation Nimrod AEW. Mk 3. Such a programme was made possible by the development by Marconi Avionics of a new radar system which, in addition to an essential maritime capability, satisfies also the air defence requirements of central Europe. Using this equipment, the Nimrod AEW. Mk 3 can provide, at long range and at low or high altitude,

The AEW. Mk 3 version of the BAe HS Nimrod (Pilot Press)

detection, tracking and classification of aircraft, missiles and ships; interceptor control; direction of strike aircraft; air defence; air traffic control; and search and rescue facilities. In doing so, it will be compatible with the USAF's Boeing E-3A Sentry AWACS, and with the E-3As that will be operated directly by NATO.

Designed specifically for installation in this modified version of the maritime reconnaissance Nimrod, the radar has made necessary some modifications to the nose and tail to permit installation of the newly developed and identically-shaped dual-frequency twisted cassegrain antennae in fore and aft positions. The aircraft's performance is affected only marginally by the structural changes, and a reduction in directional stability is compensated by a 0·91 m (3 ft 0 in) increase in fin height.

Mounting the scanners at the extremities of the airframe ensures good all-round coverage, and they do not suffer from airframe obscuration effects. Designed for very low sidelobe level, each sweeps through 180° in azimuth, the Cossor Jubilee Guardsman IFF interrogator using the same scanners to aid correlation of IFF and radar returns.

The associated radar is a pulsed Doppler system that, in addition to the detection of aircraft, has a ship surveillance capability. The rate at which pulses are transmitted can be varied to provide maximum detection in differing terrain conditions or sea states. The system has also highly sophisticated anti-jamming features to cope with the growing efficiency of electronic countermeasures.

The radar passes target plots in terms of range, azimuth, radial velocity and altitude to the advanced digital data handling system; this is based on an airborne computer that controls the flow of data from the scanners and correlates track information between the AEW aircraft and a surface control station. Six operator consoles are provided. Each has a tactical situation display, showing the tracks selected by the operator, and a tabular display for the selective presentation of detailed track and control information. Much of the data control is fully automatic;

thus, association of radar, IFF and EWSM, track initiation, tracking and data storage requires no action from the operator. Control of the data handling system is achieved by rolling ball and functionally arranged keyboards, the operator interfacing with the system to carry out system control, track classification, fighter control and data link management.

High standards of communications and navigation are essential to complement the advanced radar and data handling system. For communications the AEW Nimrod carries tactical UHF transceivers, SIMOP HF transceivers, pilot's U/VHF, RATT, secure voice com, LF receiver and data links. Primary navigation avionics consist of dual inertial navigation systems (INS), plus a gyro magnetic compass, air data computer, twin VOR/ILS, ADF, Tacan, autopilot and a flight director. EWSM (early warning support measures) equipment is housed in the two pods at the wingtips. Other features of special significance for this role are the spacious cabin for avionics and crew, high transit speed and good low-speed characteristics.

The first of four development aircraft, a converted Comet 4C (XW626), was rolled out at Woodford on 1 March 1977 and made its first flight on 28 June 1977. This aircraft carries nose-mounted radar only. The other three development aircraft were diverted from the batch of eight extra Nimrod MR. Mk 1s ordered in 1972, and are being completed instead as AEW. Mk 3s. The first of these (XZ286), which made its initial flight on 16 July 1980, is the first aerodynamically representative AEW. Mk 3 airframe. The Nimrod AEW.Mk 3 is expected to enter RAF service, with No 8 Squadron at RAF Waddington, Lincolnshire, in early 1982.

DIMENSIONS, EXTERNAL:
Wing span	35·08 m (115 ft 1 in)
Length overall	41·97 m (137 ft 8½ in)
Height overall	10·67 m (35 ft 0 in)

PERFORMANCE: Generally similar to Nimrod MR.Mk 2
Endurance	in excess of 10 h

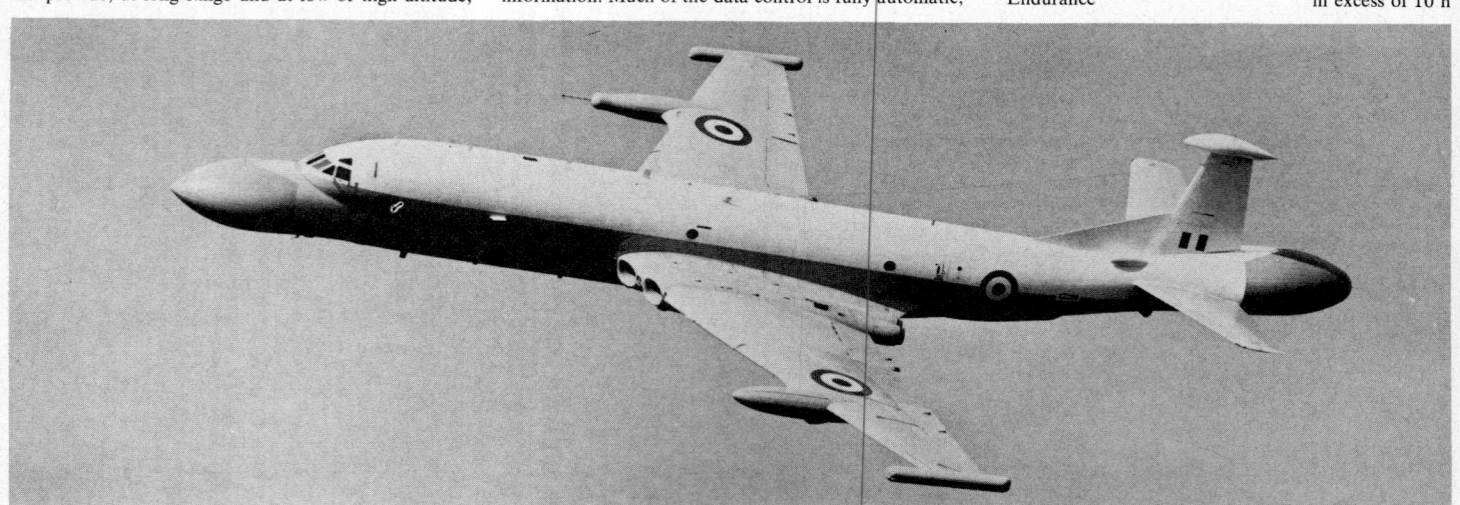

First aerodynamically representative BAe HS Nimrod AEW. Mk 3 airborne early warning aircraft (Brian M. Service)

BGA
BRITISH GLIDING ASSOCIATION
Kimberley House, Vaughan Way, Leicester
Telephone: 0533 51051
CHIEF TECHNICAL OFFICER: R. B. Stratton

BGA SUPERMUNK

First flown on 20 August 1979, the Supermunk (G-BBNA) is a conversion of a British-built de Havilland

Chipmunk Mk 22 to accept an Avco Lycoming flat-four engine in place of the original Gipsy Major in-line power plant. The conversion was started in April 1979 by officers of the BGA, and was undertaken in order to improve the performance and serviceability of the aircraft in the role of glider tug. By the Autumn of 1979, the aircraft had already satisfied expectations in regard to improvements in take-off performance and in turnround time during towing trials.

A description of the Chipmunk has appeared in previous editions of *Jane's*. The following details summarise the airframe, power plant and other changes embodied in the Supermunk version:

AIRFRAME: Basically as standard Chipmunk Mk 22 aft of firewall. Forward of firewall, engine is installed on a US-built welded teel tube dynafocal mounting, and is encased in a new two-piece cowling of fire-resistant polyester GRP. Not cleared for spinning or aerobatics; other limitations as for Chipmunk Mk 22.

POWER PLANT: One 134 kW (180 hp) Avco Lycoming O-360-A4A flat-four engine, driving a Sensenich two-blade metal propeller from a Piper Cherokee 180. Fuel system incorporates both mechanical and electrical pumps.

ACCOMMODATION: Seats for two persons in tandem, as in Chipmunk, under one-piece rearward-sliding framed canopy. Front cockpit instrumentation altered to accommodate different engine instruments. Original flight instruments retained in rear cockpit, but some engine instruments have been removed.

SYSTEMS: 12V (instead of 24V) electrical system includes generator, starter and single 35Ah battery. Vacuum pump to drive gyro instruments.

DIMENSIONS, EXTERNAL:
Wing span	10·46 m (34 ft 4 in)
Wing area, gross	15·98 m² (172 sq ft)
Length overall	7·84 m (25 ft 8½ in)
Height overall	2·13 m (7 ft 0 in)
Propeller diameter	1·93 m (6 ft 4 in)

BGA Supermunk, a converted Chipmunk 22 with Avco Lycoming O-360 engine

WEIGHTS:
Weight empty	652 kg (1,438 lb)
Max T-O weight	952 kg (2,100 lb)

PERFORMANCE (established up to Autumn 1979):
Cruising speed at 2,450 rpm
106 knots (196 km/h; 122 mph) IAS
Cruising speed at 2,300 rpm
97 knots (180 km-h; 112 mph) IAS
Max rate of climb at S/L (pilot only, plus max fuel)
360 m (1,180 ft)/min
Rate of climb as glider tug, depending on type and weight of glider 152-244 m (500-800 ft)/min

CRANFIELD
CRANFIELD INSTITUTE OF TECHNOLOGY

College of Aeronautics, Cranfield Institute of Technology, Cranfield, Bedford MK43 0AL
Telephone: 0234 750911
Telex: 825072
PROFESSOR OF AIRCRAFT DESIGN: D. Howe, PhD, SM, DCAe, CEng, FIMechE, FRAeS

CRANFIELD A1 Mk 2

Designed and built originally to the requirements of the late Neil Williams, for use by the British aerobatic team, the A1 was flown for the first time on 23 August 1976. The Rolls-Royce Continental IO-360-D engine which powered the aircraft in its Mk 1 form (see 1977-78 *Jane's*) was then replaced by an Avco Lycoming IO-540-D. The aircraft first flew with this power plant at the end of August

1977, and all aspects of performance and handling were considerably improved. Subsequently, the aircraft was fitted with modified ailerons and a rudder with increased height and horn balance, and in this form is known as the Mk 2. A description and illustration of the Mk 2 appeared in the 1979-80 *Jane's*.

CRANFIELD WINGTIP SAILS

Under the leadership of Mr John J. Spillman of the College of Aeronautics, Cranfield has developed sets of wingtip 'sails' which can be made integrally with new plastics wingtips for the Piper Pawnee agricultural aircraft. Flight testing of the three-sail tips illustrated has confirmed that they offer reductions in drag, fuel consumption and wake vortex effects, as well as reducing wasteful spray drift at the extremities of the spraybars.

In the Summer of 1979, NASA was testing in a wind

Wingtip 'sails' on a Piper Pawnee

tunnel a set of five-sail tips on a Pawnee model. The British National Research Development Corporation retains the patents for the sails, which it is hoped to market to Pawnee operators.

EDGLEY
EDGLEY AIRCRAFT LTD

31 Smith Street, Elsworth, Cambridgeshire CB3 8HY
Telephone: 09547 402
ALSO AT: Cranfield Institute of Technology, Cranfield, Bedford MK43 0AL
Telephone: 0234 750911 extn 479/294
DIRECTORS:
J. K. Edgley, BSc, DIC, AMRAeS (Chairman)
F. M. Edgley
CONSULTANT: D. Kent

Edgley Aircraft Ltd was formed in 1974 to design, build and market an unorthodox observation aircraft, the EA7 Optica. Its designer, Mr John Edgley, was a director of Scenic Flying Ltd, which in 1972 projected and subsequently patented a slow-flying touring aircraft in which the pilot sat behind the two passengers. In 1974 Mr Edgley began the final aerodynamic design of what eventually became the Optica, and this underwent wind tunnel testing at the Imperial College of Science and Technology, London, where Mr Edgley was then a post-graduate student, in the Summer of 1975. The Optica's three-abreast seating configuration was introduced in 1977, and since Scenic Flying did not wish to be concerned directly in its production Edgley Aircraft Ltd was formed to continue its development. Mr David Kent, who was connected with the Tawney Owl light aircraft last described in the 1961-62 *Jane's*, joined Edgley Aircraft in 1976, assisting Mr

Edgley in the final stages of design, stress analysis and construction of the Optica prototype, which began in August of that year in a London workshop. In mid-1978, with most of the airframe complete, the project was moved to the College of Aeronautics at Cranfield for final assembly.

EDGLEY EA7 OPTICA

First flown on 14 December 1979, the Optica (G-BGMW) is a most unusual design for a three-seat observation aircraft, particularly in the fields of pipeline and powerline inspection; forestry and coastal patrol; police traffic patrol; frontier patrol; aerial photography; film, TV and press reporting; and touring. The cabin configuration is based upon that of an insect's eye, to give the best possible all-round view from a fixed-wing aircraft. Power plant is a ducted propulsor unit, offering excellent quietness, both within the cabin and from the ground. A low wing loading, pre-set inboard flaps and a low stalling speed, facilitate continuous en-route flight at low speeds, and the generous flap area confers STOL capability from both hard and soft strips. Stability increases at low speed.

The Optica is intended for low volume production (up to 100 a year), using a minimum of sophisticated tooling. Methods of achieving this, under consideration in 1980, included extending the present company into a full production company; having a specific number of Opticas built initially by another company under subcontract or licence; and setting up a direct link with an existing man-

ufacturing organisation. In September 1980, negotiations were under way for subcontract construction of an initial batch of 26 by a company in the south of England.

TYPE: Three-seat slow-flying observation aircraft; stressed to BCAR Section K (non-aerobatic category) and FAR Pt 23 (Normal category).

WINGS: Cantilever mid-wing monoplane. Wing section NASA GAW-1, thickness/chord ratio 17%. Dihedral 3° on outer panels. Incidence 0°. Constant-chord single-spar non-swept wings of aluminium alloy stressed-skin construction. Wingtips (also fin/tailplane fillets, nosewheel mudguard and some power plant fairings) of glassfibre. Fowler trailing-edge flaps (29% of total wing chord) inboard and outboard of tailbooms. Electrically actuated outboard flaps can be set at angles up to 40° for landing; inboard flaps set permanently at 10°, giving the effect of a slotted wing, for continuous low-speed flying. Bottom-hinged, mass-balanced slotted ailerons outboard of outer flaps. No spoilers, air-brakes or tabs.

CABIN: 'Insect eye' shaped structure, built of aluminium alloy with Suntex vacuum formed acrylic windows. Cabin attached to fan shroud and rest of airframe by six stators of steel tube and aluminium alloy shear web construction. Steel tube and aluminium alloy nose beam supporting cabin floor. Horizontal window frame member just above floor level, designed to act in combination with forward-running nosewheel box to act as skid in case of nosewheel failure, is designed to withstand 9g impact. Depending upon number of occupants, the CG position can be adjusted by adding ballast weight; one possible means of accomplishing this is by installing a water tank in the nose, but the method to be adopted had not been finally decided up to early 1980.

TAIL UNIT: Twin-tailboom configuration, of aluminium alloy stressed-skin tubular construction. Tailboom pickup points at extremities of wing centre-section. Angular, inward-canted fins and balanced rudders. Fixed-incidence tailplane, with elevator, bridging space between tops of fins. Inset trim tab occupies port half of elevator trailing-edge; no rudder tabs.

LANDING GEAR: Non-retractable tricycle type, with steerable nosewheel offset to port. Modified Piper main-wheel legs, with rubber-in-compression shock-absorption. Nosewheel shock-absorption by bungee rubber in tension. Single wheel on each unit, tyre sizes 6·00-6 (main) and 5·00-5 (nose). Hydraulic disc brakes on main wheels. Retractable parking strut, operated from cabin, extends below fan shroud to keep aircraft level when empty on the ground, and to protect shroud in the event of main-wheel leg failure.

POWER PLANT: Ducted propulsor unit, with engine and fan forming a power pod separate from the main shroud. Pod is attached to fan shroud with four Lord rubber mountings, and supported by four stators of steel channel and aluminium alloy shear web construction, with steel tube engine bearers. Five-blade fixed-pitch birch

Edgley EA7 Optica three-seat slow-flying observation aircraft *(Crown copyright)*

Edgley EA7 Optica (Avco Lycoming IO-360 engine) *(Michael A. Badrocke)*

Height over tailplane	2·31 m (7 ft 7 in)
Tailplane span:	
c/l of tailbooms	3·40 m (11 ft 1¾ in)
intersection fin chord	2·60 m (8 ft 6½ in)
Wheel track	3·40 m (11 ft 1¾ in)
Wheelbase	2·73 m (8 ft 11½ in)
Doors (each): Long axis	1·34 m (4 ft 4¾ in)
Short axis	0·96 m (3 ft 1¾ in)
Height to sill	0·50 m (1 ft 7¾ in)

DIMENSIONS, INTERNAL:

Cabin: Length	2·45 m (8 ft 0½ in)
Max width (to door Perspex)	1·69 m (5 ft 6½ in)
Max height	1·35 m (4 ft 5¼ in)
Floor area	approx 0·72 m² (7·53 sq ft)

AREAS:

Wings, gross	15·84 m² (170·5 sq ft)
Ailerons (total)	1·55 m² (16·68 sq ft)
Trailing-edge flaps:	
inboard (total)	0·61 m² (6·57 sq ft)
outboard (total)	1·49 m² (16·04 sq ft)
Fins (total)	2·59 m² (27·88 sq ft)
Rudders (total)	1·38 m² (14·85 sq ft)
Tailplane	1·62 m² (17·44 sq ft)
Elevator, incl tab	1·26 m² (13·56 sq ft)

WEIGHTS:

Weight empty	895 kg (1,973 lb)
Max T-O weight	1,220 kg (2,690 lb)

fan, driven by a 134 kW (180 hp) Avco Lycoming IO-360 flat-four engine (119 kW; 160 hp O-320 for early test flights) mounted in a duct downstream of the fan. Fuel tank of 91 litres (20 Imp gallons) in each wing leading-edge, immediately outboard of tailbooms and forward of wing spar. Tanks are of full wing section, but are designed not to be stressed by wing bending and torsion. Total fuel capacity 182 litres (40 Imp gallons). Refuelling point in upper surface of each wing. Oil capacity 7·6 litres (1·7 Imp gallons).

ACCOMMODATION: Cabin designed to seat up to three persons side by side, with either single- or two-pilot operation (left hand and centre seats). Dual controls optional. Fixed seats in prototype; adjustable seats optional. Baggage space aft of seats. Alternative accommodation for two stretchers, or one stretcher and one medical attendant, in addition to pilot. Single elliptical door on each side, hinged at front and opening forward. Cabin heated, by hot air from engine, and ventilated.

SYSTEMS: Hydraulics for main-wheel brakes only. Prototype has 12V electrical system (battery and alternator) for engine starting, flap actuation and undershroud strut; it has no lights. 24V system under consideration for production version.

DIMENSIONS, EXTERNAL:

Wing span	12·16 m (39 ft 10¾ in)
Wing chord (basic, constant)	1·32 m (4 ft 4 in)
Wing chord (over 10° fixed flaps)	1·52 m (5 ft 0 in)
Wing aspect ratio	9·1
Length overall	8·16 m (26 ft 9¼ in)
Height over fan shroud (excl aerial)	
	1·92 m (6 ft 3½ in)
Diameter of fan shroud	1·68 m (5 ft 6¼ in)
Diameter of fan	1·20 m (3 ft 11¼ in)
Shroud ground clearance: at front	0·24 m (9½ in)
to aft leg mechanism	0·16 m (6¼ in)

PERFORMANCE:

Never-exceed speed	142 knots (264 km/h; 164 mph)
Max level speed	109·5 knots (203 km/h; 126 mph)
Cruising speed (65% power)	
	94 knots (174 km/h; 108 mph)
Loiter speed	50 knots (92 km/h; 57 mph)
Stalling speed, flaps up	
	40 knots (74 km/h; 46 mph)
Stalling speed, flaps down	
	37·5 knots (69·5 km/h; 43 mph)
Max rate of climb at S/L	219 m (720 ft)/min
Service ceiling	2,440 m (8,000 ft)
T-O to 15 m (50 ft)	198 m (650 ft)
Landing from 15 m (50 ft)	259 m (850 ft)
Range at 65% power cruising speed	
	538 nm (1,000 km; 620 miles)
Endurance at loiter speed	13 h

LEARFAN
LEARFAN LTD

POSTAL ADDRESS: 16 Church Road, Carnmoney, Co Antrim, Northern Ireland
Telephone: Whiteabbey (0231) 68862
WORKS: Aldergrove Airport, near Belfast, Co Antrim, Northern Ireland
MANAGING DIRECTOR AND CHIEF EXECUTIVE: Linden S. Blue

DIRECTOR OF ADMINISTRATION: William Murphy
DIRECTOR OF PRODUCTION: Oslam Haque

LearAvia Corporation of the USA (which see) has signed an agreement with the British government for sole-source production of the **LearFan 2100** twin-turboprop business aircraft at the former RAF base at Aldergrove, near Belfast, Northern Ireland. To manage this programme, LearFan Ltd has been established, with an initial investment of approx £3·5 million from each participant. LearAvia Corporation retains a 51 per cent holding in the new company.

As outlined in the US section, the first of four LearFan 2100 prototypes was scheduled to fly in October 1980, and deliveries are expected to begin shortly after certification in mid-1982. In the second half of that year LearFan Ltd is scheduled to deliver 29 aircraft, rising to an output of 219 in calendar year 1985. By that time, LearFan Ltd is expected to have a work force of some 1,250 persons.

LOCKSPEISER
LOCKSPEISER AIRCRAFT LTD

Registered Office: Royal Chambers, High Street, Weston-super-Mare, Avon BS23
Telephone: Weston-super-Mare (0934) 29467
MANAGING DIRECTOR: David Lockspeiser, MRAeS, CEng
COMPANY SECRETARY: Christopher E. Bean, FCA

LOCKSPEISER LDA-01

Mr David Lockspeiser designed a utility aeroplane known as the LDA, or Land Development Aircraft, the production version of which is intended for operation as a passenger, freight or vehicle transport, as an agricultural, ambulance, survey or firefighting aircraft, or for other duties. In a military version, for use as a light troop transport or battlefield support aircraft, the initials stand for Light Defence Aircraft.

The basic concept of the LDA is that of an 'aerial Land-Rover', offering a wide variety of applications, low initial cost and economy of operation, and capable of being easily assembled, inspected and repaired. Many of the major components are interchangeable, and the aircraft can carry a complete set of its own spares, including wings. A primary design consideration was ease of construction for licensed manufacture and assembly. A flush-fitting removable ventral container serves as an interchangeable 'mission pack' and facilitates the quick conversion of the aircraft from one role to another.

A 70% scale prototype, registered G-AVOR and known as the LDA-01, was flown for the first time by Mr Lockspeiser on 24 August 1971. Development flying with the LDA-01 defined the proposed full-size LDA-1 as a 12·04 m (39 ft 6 in) span aircraft, with 7·08 m³ (250 cu ft) of usable cargo space, a disposable load of 907 kg (2,000 lb) and a max T-O weight of 1,814 kg (4,000 lb). As an alternative to the removable mission pack the LDA-01, of which a full description can be found in the 1979-80 *Jane's*, has been flown with a side-loading double door on the port side.

TYPE: Single-engined general utility aeroplane.
POWER PLANT: One 119 kW (160 hp) Avco Lycoming O-320-D1A flat-four engine, at rear of fuselage, driving a Hoffmann HO-V-72 two-blade constant-speed metal pusher propeller with spinner. Two fuel tanks in fuselage, one forward and one aft of cargo bay, each of 69 litres (15·2 Imp gallons) capacity.

ACCOMMODATION: Pilot in enclosed cabin. Sideways-opening canopy, hinged on port side. Side-opening doors in fuselage for passengers or freight. Floor is fitted with lashing points, and has apertures for vertical photography. Production LDA-1 would have either the optional side-loading double doors, 1·98 m (6 ft 6 in) wide and 1·22 m (4 ft 0 in) in height, or the removable container, and would also have access via the roof so that conventional loaders could be used when the aircraft was employed in an agricultural role. Proposed Light Defence Aircraft military version capable of carrying six soldiers and their equipment, or of being fitted with anti-tank missiles or machine-gun pods.

DIMENSIONS, EXTERNAL:

Main wing span	9·27 m (30 ft 5 in)
Foreplane span	4·39 m (14 ft 5 in)
Length overall	7·14 m (23 ft 5¼ in)
Fuselage: Max width	0·91 m (3 ft 0 in)
Max depth	1·07 m (3 ft 6 in)
Height overall	2·77 m (9 ft 1 in)
Wheel track	2·08 m (6 ft 10 in)
Wheelbase	3·91 m (12 ft 10 in)
Propeller diameter	1·80 m (5 ft 11 in)
Fuselage floor/ground clearance	0·57 m (1 ft 10½ in)
Removable payload container:	
Length	1·98 m (6 ft 6 in)
Width	0·91 m (3 ft 0 in)
Depth	0·38 m (1 ft 3 in)

DIMENSION, INTERNAL:

Centre fuselage: total internal volume	
	1·7 m³ (60 cu ft)

WEIGHTS AND LOADINGS:

Basic weight empty	561 kg (1,236 lb)
Operating weight empty	635 kg (1,401 lb)
Normal T-O weight	733 kg (1,617 lb)
Normal operating weight	771 kg (1,700 lb)
Design max T-O weight	1,043 kg (2,300 lb)
Max wing loading	99·7 kg/m² (20·43 lb/sq ft)

Lockspeiser LDA-01 prototype Land Development or Light Defence Aircraft *(Anthony Young)*

Normal max power loading at 771 kg (1,700 lb) AUW
6·48 kg/kW (10·6 lb/hp)
Max power loading at design max T-O weight
8·76 kg/kW (14·3 lb/hp)

PERFORMANCE:
Cruising speed   92 knots (170 km/h; 106 mph)
Optimum climbing speed
68 knots (126 km/h; 78 mph)

Stalling speed   42 knots (78 km/h; 49 mph)
T-O run, flaps up   183 m (600 ft)
Landing run, flaps up   116 m (380 ft)
Range   260 nm (481 km; 299 miles)

MARSHALL
MARSHALL OF CAMBRIDGE (ENGINEERING) LTD (Aircraft Division)

HEAD OFFICE AND WORKS: Airport Works, Cambridge CB5 8RX
Telephone: 0223 61133
Telex: 81208
MANAGING DIRECTOR: Sir Arthur Marshall, OBE
COMMERCIAL DIRECTOR: R. D. Horsbrough
EXECUTIVE DIRECTOR, ENGINEERING: R. O. Gates
SALES MANAGER: Norman Sellars

The Aircraft Division of this company (known as Marshalls Flying School Ltd until 1962) has specialised for many years in the modification, overhaul and repair of military and commercial aircraft, including the design and installation of interior furnishing for executive transports and of avionics fits up to and including the complete outfitting of various aircraft for calibration and electronic countermeasures roles.

The company's design department is both CAA and MoD(PE) approved. As an approved service and repair centre for the Lockheed Hercules, Gulfstream American and Cessna Citation aircraft, Marshall of Cambridge also has FAA approval covering most types of American aircraft. The company's conversion, modification and overhaul facilities, which include some of the largest heated hangars in England, with workshop support to full aircraft factory standard, have enabled it to undertake numerous major programmes of work on Viscounts, Britannias, Comets, VC10s, Canberras and a vast number of other civil and military aircraft. It has a separate hangar for specialised painting of the largest aircraft, and a sculpture milling shop for manufacture of major aircraft components.

In 1966, Marshall of Cambridge was appointed the designated centre for the Royal Air Force Hercules C. Mk 1 transport aircraft, and in 1973 the company completed the conversion of an RAF Hercules C. Mk 1 to W. Mk 2 configuration, as detailed in the 1979-80 and earlier editions of *Jane's*.

MARSHALL (LOCKHEED) HERCULES CONVERSIONS

The **Hercules W. Mk 2** long-range meteorological aircraft was adapted by Marshall from a Hercules C. Mk 1; full details of the equipment and other changes involved were given in the 1974-75 *Jane's*.

It was announced in 1978 by the Ministry of Defence that a contract had been signed with Lockheed Corporation to modify 30 Hercules C. Mk 1s (C-130Ks) of the Royal Air Force to **Hercules C. Mk 3** configuration. The modification involves 'stretching' the fuselage by the insertion of a 2·54 m (8 ft 4 in) plug forward of the wings and a 2·03 m (6 ft 8 in) plug aft of the wings, thus producing the same fuselage dimensions and capacity as those of the L 100-30 Commercial Hercules (see US section). The first aircraft (XV 223) was modified by Lockheed in Marietta, Georgia, in 1979; the remaining 29 are being modified by Marshall of Cambridge in 1980-83.

Examples of volumetric and load differences include:
Cabin volume, incl ramp:

C. Mk 1	127·4 m³ (4,500 cu ft)
C. Mk 3	171·5 m³ (6,057 cu ft)

Palletised loads:

C. Mk 1	5
C. Mk 3	7

Land-Rovers plus trailers:

C. Mk 1	3 + 2
C. Mk 3	4 + 3

MARSHALL (SHORTS) BELFAST CONVERSION

In March 1980 the first of five Shorts Belfast ex-RAF military transports, purchased by HeavyLift Air Cargoes Ltd of Stansted Airport, Essex, entered civilian service. Intended for all-cargo use carrying unusual, outsize or heavy payloads, the Belfasts are being converted to HeavyLift requirements by Marshall of Cambridge. The programme involves an increase in minimum control speed of 10 knots (19 km/h; 12 mph); revision of the stall warning speeds; a reduction of max T-O weight to 104,325 kg (230,000 lb) from the normal military T-O weight of 104,780 kg (231,000 lb) and military operating standard T-O weight of 113,400 kg (250,000 lb); introduction of two-engine climb data to permit use of the fuel

Shorts Belfast modified by Marshall for civil freight operation *(Rolls-Royce)*

First 'stretched' Hercules C. Mk 3 for the Royal Air Force, modified by Lockheed

jettison system with 15° flap; changes to the watermethanol usage data for T-O; and a reassessment of aircraft performance standard.

In addition, in order to gain civil certification, changes include revision of the autopilot, avionics and electrical power installations; replacement of the liquid oxygen system by a gaseous system; introduction of a watermethanol contents indication system and a stall protection system; and other modifications to meet mandatory civil requirements. At the customer's request, the Belfasts are also being fitted with a dual Omega navigation system and an electrically driven auxiliary hydraulic pump.

DIMENSIONS, EXTERNAL:

Wing span	48·41 m (158 ft 10 in)
Length overall	41·58 m (136 ft 5 in)
Height overall	14·33 m (47 ft 0 in)
Height to ramp sill	1·63 m (5 ft 4 in)
Width of ramp	3·66 m (12 ft 0 in)
Height of rear loading entrance, ramp lowered	4·06 m (13 ft 4 in)
Height of rear loading entrance, ramp horizontal	3·12 m (10 ft 3 in)
Forward freight door: Height	1·98 m (6 ft 6 in)
Width	2·44 m (8 ft 0 in)

DIMENSIONS, INTERNAL:
Cargo compartment:

Length overall, incl ramp	25·70 m (84 ft 4 in)
Length overall, excl ramp	19·35 m (63 ft 6 in)
Max width	4·90 m (16 ft 1 in)
Max height	4·06 m (13 ft 4 in)
Max usable volume	321·4 m³ (11,350 cu ft)

WEIGHTS:

Typical operating weight empty	58,967 kg (130,000 lb)
Max payload	34,000 kg (75,000 lb)
Usable fuel	37,376 kg (82,400 lb)
Max T-O weight	104,325 kg (230,000 lb)
Max landing weight	97,520 kg (215,000 lb)
Max zero-fuel weight	92,986 kg (205,000 lb)

PERFORMANCE (at max T-O weight, except where stated):

Average cruising speed
275 knots (510 km/h; 316 mph)
T-O runway length   2,500 m (8,200 ft)
Landing runway length at max landing weight
2,075 m (6,800 ft)
Range with max payload, standard reserves
approx 850 nm (1,575 km; 975 miles)
Range with 10,000 kg (22,000 lb) payload, standard reserves approx 3,350 nm (6,200 km; 3,855 miles)

NASH—*See Addenda*

NDN
NDN AIRCRAFT LTD

Goodwood Aerodrome, nr Chichester, Sussex
Telephone: 0243 784337/8
Telex: 86501 NDNAIR G
DIRECTORS:
  N. D. Norman, CBE, MRAeS (Managing Director)
  K. A. F. Burke, ACA
  A. J. Coombe, BSc (Technical)
  B. E. Norman

Mr N. D. Norman founded NDN Aircraft Ltd in the early months of 1977 to develop and subsequently produce or arrange licence production of a new two-seat basic military trainer known as the NDN 1 Firecracker.

NDN 1 FIRECRACKER

The first prototype Firecracker (G-NDNI) made its initial flight on 26 May 1977, and a British type certificate in the Aerobatic category was issued by the CAA on 24 May 1979. The aircraft's design meets the requirements of FAR Pt 23-14. Negotiations for manufacture under licence were taking place in 1980.

The following description applies to the first prototype:
TYPE: Two-seat training aircraft.
WINGS: Cantilever low-wing monoplane. Wing section NACA 23012 (modified). Dihedral 5° on outer wing panels only. Incidence 3°. Leading-edge of inner wing panels swept back approximately 20°. Light alloy structure, including aerodynamically and mass balanced ailerons and hydraulically-operated single-slotted trailing-edge flaps. Trim tab in starboard aileron; geared tab in each aileron. All controls manually operated.
FUSELAGE: Semi-monocoque stressed-skin structure of light alloy. Hydraulically-operated light alloy door-type airbrake in fuselage undersurface, at wing trailing-edge.
TAIL UNIT: Cantilever stressed-skin structure of light alloy. Fixed-incidence tailplane. Trim tab in starboard half of elevator and in rudder.
LANDING GEAR: Hydraulically retractable tricycle type, steerable nosewheel retracting aft, main units inward. Oleo-pneumatic shock-absorber and single wheel on each unit. Cleveland type 551-751 main wheels, with size 6·00-6 Goodyear tyres. Cleveland type 551-753 nosewheel, with size 5·00-5 Goodyear tyre. Cleveland type 551-705 hydraulically-operated disc brakes.
POWER PLANT: One 194 kW (260 hp) Avco Lycoming AEIO-540-B4D5 flat-six engine, driving a Hoffmann HO-V123K/200AH5 three-blade constant-speed propeller. Also offered with 224 kW (300 hp) Avco Lycoming AEIO-540-L flat-six engine. Four integral wing fuel tanks with a combined capacity of 427 litres (94 Imp gallons). Refuelling points on wing upper surface. Fuel and Christen oil systems permit inverted flight.
ACCOMMODATION: Two seats in tandem beneath sideways-opening (to starboard) transparent canopy. Canopy can be jettisoned in emergency. Rear seat is raised 10 cm (4 in) above level of forward seat for improved view. Baggage space (0·25 m³; 9 cu ft) aft of rear seat. Accommodation heated and ventilated.
SYSTEMS: Hydraulic system, pressure 103·5 bars (1,500 lb/sq in), supplied by electro-hydraulic pump with hand-operated emergency pump. Gas bottle for emergency nosewheel extension. Electrical system powered by a Prestolite engine-driven 24V 70A alternator. 12V 35Ah battery for aerobatics. Air-conditioning and oxygen systems optional.

Prototype NDN 1 Firecracker two-seat military training aircraft with underwing SURA rockets

AVIONICS AND EQUIPMENT: Typical avionics will include dual VHF com/nav, plus ILS, DME, ADF, transponder and marker beacon receiver. Blind-flying instrumentation is standard. Optional equipment includes target towing facilities, underwing weapon pylons, gunsight, survey camera and autopilot.

DIMENSIONS, EXTERNAL:
Wing span	7·92 m (26 ft 0 in)
Wing chord at root	1·83 m (6 ft 0 in)
Wing chord at tip	1·45 m (4 ft 9 in)
Wing aspect ratio	5·36
Length overall	7·70 m (25 ft 3 in)
Height overall	3·00 m (9 ft 10 in)
Tailplane span	2·90 m (9 ft 6 in)
Wheel track	3·05 m (10 ft 0 in)
Wheelbase	2·08 m (6 ft 10 in)
Propeller diameter	1·93 m (6 ft 4 in)

AREAS:
Wings, gross	11·71 m² (126 sq ft)
Ailerons (total)	1·23 m² (13·2 sq ft)
Trailing-edge flaps (total)	1·23 m² (13·2 sq ft)
Fin	0·60 m² (6·5 sq ft)
Rudder, incl tab	0·65 m² (7·0 sq ft)
Tailplane	1·28 m² (13·8 sq ft)
Elevator, incl tab	1·11 m² (12·0 sq ft)

WEIGHTS AND LOADINGS (260 hp engine):
Weight empty, equipped	875 kg (1,930 lb)
Max T-O weight, fully aerobatic	1,288 kg (2,840 lb)
Max landing weight	1,225 kg (2,700 lb)
Max wing loading	109·9 kg/m² (22·5 lb/sq ft)
Max power loading	6·64 kg/kW (10·9 lb/hp)

WEIGHTS AND LOADINGS (estimated, 300 hp engine):
Weight empty	902 kg (1,990 lb)
Max T-O weight, fully aerobatic	1,288 kg (2,840 lb)
Max landing weight	1,224 kg (2,700 lb)
Max wing loading	109·8 kg/m² (22·5 lb/sq ft)
Max power loading	5·76 kg/kW (9·47 lb/hp)

PERFORMANCE (with 260 hp engine, at max landing weight, ISA at S/L, zero wind, unless otherwise stated):
Never-exceed speed
  238 knots (441 km/h; 274 mph) EAS
Max level speed at S/L
  176 knots (326 km/h; 203 mph)
Max cruising speed, 75% power at 2,285 m (7,500 ft)
  167 knots (309 km/h; 192 mph)
Stalling speed, flaps down
  56·5 knots (105 km/h; 65 mph) EAS
Max rate of climb at S/L   442 m (1,450 ft)/min
Service ceiling   5,485 m (18,000 ft)
Absolute ceiling   6,100 m (20,000 ft)
T-O run   271 m (890 ft)
T-O to 15 m (50 ft)   360 m (1,180 ft)
Landing from 15 m (50 ft)   396 m (1,300 ft)
Landing run   259 m (850 ft)
Range with max fuel, no reserves
  1,220 nm (2,260 km; 1,405 miles)
PERFORMANCE (estimated, with 300 hp engine, at max landing weight, ISA at S/L, zero wind, unless otherwise stated):
Never-exceed speed
  247 knots (458 km/h; 285 mph) EAS
Max level speed at S/L
  185 knots (343 km/h; 213 mph)
Max cruising speed, 75% power at 2,285 m (7,500 ft)
  175 knots (323 km/h; 201 mph)
Stalling speed   56·5 knots (105 km/h; 65 mph) EAS
Max rate of climb at S/L   527 m (1,730 ft)/min
Service ceiling   6,700 m (22,000 ft)
Absolute ceiling   7,315 m (24,000 ft)
T-O and landing distances   as 260 hp version
Range with max fuel, no reserves
  1,116 nm (2,068 km; 1,285 miles)

NDN 5

It was reported in early 1980 that NDN Aircraft was developing a turboprop version of the Firecracker with a 432·5 kW (580 shp) Pratt & Whitney Aircraft of Canada PT6A-25 engine, and that the prototype, designated NDN 5, would fly before the end of the year. No confirmation has been received from the manufacturer.

NDN 6 FIELDMASTER

A description of this newly-designed agricultural aircraft can be found in the Addenda.

PILATUS BRITTEN-NORMAN
PILATUS BRITTEN-NORMAN LTD (a subsidiary of Pilatus Aircraft Ltd)

HEAD OFFICE: Bembridge Airport, Bembridge, Isle of Wight PO35 5PR
Telephone: 098387 2511/5
Telex: 86277
DIRECTORS:
  D. C. Kloeckner (Managing)
  P. Desai (Marketing)
  J. Keller (Production)
  D. A. Berryman (Technical)

The previous history of this company can be found in the 1978-79 and earlier editions of *Jane's*. It produces the Islander and Trislander transport aircraft; the Islander is manufactured also in Romania by IAvB (which see). In addition to the Bembridge and Romanian production lines, Philippine Aerospace Development Corporation has an Islander production line in Manila, for the production of 115 aircraft under licence in four phases during the period 1974-1980. This programme is described under the NAM entry in the Philippines section.

By mid-1978, Britten-Norman had begun production of the latest series of the Islander, the BN-2B. Development of the Turbo Islander, Defender, Trislander and other versions of this widely used family of aircraft is continuing at Bembridge.

On 25 July 1978 it was announced that Pilatus Aircraft Ltd of Switzerland was to acquire all assets of Britten-Norman (Bembridge) Ltd, including the facilities on the Isle of Wight and the former Fairey SA Islander/Trislander production hardware at Gosselies in Belgium. Final takeover took place in September 1979. Part and licence production of Islanders in the Philippines and Romania is continuing under the new agreements.

PILATUS BRITTEN-NORMAN BN-2B ISLANDER and BN-2T TURBINE ISLANDER

The Islander is a modern replacement for aircraft in the class of the de Havilland Dragon Rapide. Detail design work began in April 1964 and construction of the prototype (G-ATCT) was started in September of the same year. It flew for the first time on 13 June 1965, powered by two 157 kW (210 hp) Rolls-Royce Continental IO-360-B engines and with wings of 13·72 m (45 ft) span. Subsequently, the prototype was re-engined with more powerful Avco Lycoming O-540 engines, with which it flew for the first time on 17 December 1965. The wing span was also increased by 1·22 m (4 ft) to bring the prototype to production standard.

Pilatus Britten-Norman BN-2A Islander for the Desert Locust Control Organisation

The production prototype BN-2 Islander (G-ATWU) flew for the first time on 20 August 1966. The Islander received its domestic C of A on 10 August 1967 and an FAA Type Certificate on 19 December 1967.

Deliveries of Islanders began in August 1967, and by early 1980 more than 900 aircraft of the various models had been delivered to operators in approx 120 countries.

Large-scale production in the Philippines began in 1974.

Initial production aircraft were designated **BN-2**. Those built from 1 June 1969 until 1978 had the designation **BN-2A**, as described in the 1977-78 *Jane's*. The current standard piston-engined model is the **BN-2B** Islander, which has a higher max landing weight and improved interior design. Features include a new range of passenger seats and covers, more robust door locks, improved door seals, improved stainless steel sills, redesigned fresh air system to improve ventilation in hot and humid climates, smaller diameter propellers to decrease cabin noise, and redesigned flight deck and instrument panel.

On 2 August 1980 the prototype (G-BPBN) was flown of the **BN-2T Turbine Islander**, powered by two Allison 250-B17C turboprop engines each flat rated to 238·5 kW (320 shp). Offering increased payload capability and a significant improvement in altitude performance, this version becomes available for customer deliveries from early 1981.

Military versions known as the **Defender** and **Maritime Defender**, and the three-engined civil **Trislander**, are described separately.

The basic Islander is available with a choice of two piston-engine power plants, or turboprops, and either standard 14·94 m (49 ft 0 in) span wings or wingtip extensions having raked tips and containing auxiliary fuel tanks. A series of modification kits is available as standard or as an option for new production aircraft, and can also be supplied to operators in the field for retrospective fitting to existing aircraft. The version with 224 kW (300 hp) fuel-injection engines was introduced in 1970, deliveries beginning in November of that year. An extended nose, incorporating 0·62 m³ (22 cu ft) of additional baggage space, was introduced as an optional feature in 1972.

A Rajay turbocharging installation was developed in the United States by Jonas Aircraft, the New York based distributors for Britten-Norman aircraft. The Rajay installation is a bolt-on unit, for manual operation, which can be fitted on to standard 194 kW (260 hp) engines. The superchargers have the effect of increasing the single-engined ceiling to 3,810 m (12,500 ft) and twin-engined ceiling to 7,925 m (26,000 ft). Cruising speed is also increased, from 139 knots (257 km/h; 160 mph) at 2,135 m (7,000 ft) to 146 knots (270 km/h; 168 mph) at 3,050 m (10,000 ft).

The following description applies to the standard piston-engined landplane BN-2B, unless otherwise stated:

TYPE: Twin-engined feederline transport.

WINGS: Cantilever high-wing monoplane. NACA 23012 constant wing section. No dihedral. Incidence 2°. No sweepback. Conventional riveted two-spar torsion-box structure in one piece, using L72 aluminium-clad aluminium alloys. Raked-back extended wingtips optional. Slotted ailerons and single-slotted flaps of metal construction. Flaps operated electrically, ailerons by pushrods and cables. Ground-adjustable tab on starboard aileron. BTR-Goodrich pneumatic de-icing boots optional.

FUSELAGE: Conventional riveted four-longeron semi-monocoque structure of pressed frames and stringers and metal skin, using L72 aluminium-clad aluminium alloys. Optional 1·15 m (3 ft 9¼ in) nose extension for baggage stowage.

Prototype of the Pilatus Britten-Norman BN-2B Islander

TAIL UNIT: Cantilever two-spar structure, with pressed ribs and metal skin, using L72 aluminium-clad aluminium alloys. Fixed-incidence tailplane and mass-balanced elevator. Rudder and elevator are actuated by pushrods and cables. Trim tabs in rudder and elevator. Pneumatic de-icing of tailplane and fin optional.

LANDING GEAR: Non-retractable tricycle type, with twin wheels on each main unit and single steerable nose-wheel. Cantilever main legs mounted aft of rear spar. All three legs fitted with Lockheed oleo-pneumatic shock-absorbers. All five wheels and tyres size 16 × 7-7, supplied by Goodyear. Tyre pressure: main 2·41 bars (35 lb/sq in); nose 2·00 bars (29 lb/sq in). Foot-operated aircooled Cleveland hydraulic brakes on main units. Parking brake. Wheel/ski gear available optionally.

POWER PLANT: Two Avco Lycoming flat-six engines, each driving a Hartzell HC-C2YK-2B or -2C two-blade metal constant-speed feathering propeller. Propeller synchronisers optional. Standard power plant is the 194 kW (260 hp) O-540-E4C5, but the 224 kW (300 hp) IO-540-K1B5 or 238·5 kW (320 shp) Allison 250-B17C turboprops can be fitted at customer's option. Optional Rajay turbocharging installation on 194 kW (260 hp) engines, to improve high-altitude performance. Integral fuel tank between spars in each wing, outboard of engine. Total fuel capacity (standard) 518 litres (114 Imp gallons; 137 US gallons). With auxiliary tanks in wingtip extensions, total capacity is increased to 741 litres (163 Imp gallons; 196 US gallons). Additional pylon-mounted underwing auxiliary tanks, each of 227 litres (50 Imp gallons; 60 US gallons) capacity, available optionally. Refuelling point in upper surface of wing above each internal tank. Total oil capacity 22·75 litres (5 Imp gallons).

ACCOMMODATION: Up to 10 persons, including pilot, on side-by-side front seats and four bench seats. No aisle. Seat backs fold forward. Access to all seats via three forward-opening doors, forward of wing and at rear of cabin on port side and forward of wing on starboard side. Baggage compartment at rear of cabin, with port-side loading door in standard versions. Exit in emergency by removing door windows. Special executive layouts available. Can be operated as freighter, carrying more than a ton of cargo; in this configuration the passenger seats can be stored in the rear baggage bay. In ambulance role, up to three stretchers and two attendants can be accommodated. Other layouts possible, including photographic and geophysical survey,

parachutist transport or trainer (with accommodation for up to eight parachutists and a dispatcher), firefighting, public health spraying and crop spraying.

SYSTEMS: Southwind cabin heater standard. 45,000 BTU Stewart Warner combustion unit, with circulating fan, provides hot air for distribution at floor-level outlets and at windscreen demisting slots. Fresh air, boosted by propeller slipstream, is ducted to each seating position for on-ground ventilation. Electrical DC power, for instruments, lighting and radio, from two engine-driven 24V 50A self-rectifying alternators and a controller to main busbar and circuit-breaker assembly in nose bay. Emergency busbar with automatic changeover provides a secondary route for essential services. One 24V 17Ah heavy-duty lead-acid battery for independent operation. Ground power receptacle provided. Optional electrical de-icing of propellers and windscreen, and pneumatic de-icing of wing and tail unit leading-edges. Intercom system, including second headset, and passenger address system are standard. Oxygen system available optionally for all versions.

AVIONICS AND EQUIPMENT: Standard items include blind-flying instrumentation, autopilot, dual flying controls and brake system, and a wide range of VHF and HF communications and navigation equipment.

DIMENSIONS, EXTERNAL:

Wing span: standard	14·94 m (49 ft 0 in)
with extended tips	16·15 m (53 ft 0 in)
Wing chord (constant)	2·03 m (6 ft 8 in)
Wing aspect ratio: standard	7·4
with extended tips	7·95
Length overall: standard	10·86 m (35 ft 7¾ in)
optional nose extension	12·02 m (39 ft 5¼ in)
Fuselage: Max width	1·21 m (3 ft 11½ in)
Max depth	1·46 m (4 ft 9¾ in)
Height overall	4·18 m (13 ft 8¾ in)
Tailplane span	4·67 m (15 ft 4 in)
Wheel track (c/l of shock-absorbers)	
	3·61 m (11 ft 10 in)
Wheelbase: standard	3·99 m (13 ft 1¼ in)
optional nose extension	4·90 m (16 ft 0¾ in)
Propeller diameter	1·98 m (6 ft 6 in)
Cabin door (front, port):	
Height	1·10 m (3 ft 7½ in)
Width: top	0·64 m (2 ft 1¼ in)
Height to sill	0·59 m (1 ft 11¼ in)
Cabin door (front, starboard):	
Height	1·10 m (3 ft 7½ in)
Max width	0·86 m (2 ft 10 in)
Height to sill	0·57 m (1 ft 10½ in)
Cabin door (rear, port):	
Height	1·09 m (3 ft 7 in)
Width: top	0·635 m (2 ft 1 in)
bottom	1·19 m (3 ft 11 in)
Height to sill	0·52 m (1 ft 8½ in)
Baggage door (rear, port):	
Height	0·69 m (2 ft 3 in)

DIMENSIONS, INTERNAL:

Passenger cabin, aft of pilot's seat:	
Length	3·05 m (10 ft 0 in)
Max width	1·09 m (3 ft 7 in)
Max height	1·27 m (4 ft 2 in)
Floor area	2·97 m² (32 sq ft)
Volume	3·68 m³ (130 cu ft)
Baggage space aft of passenger cabin:	
standard	0·85 m³ (30 cu ft)
maximum	1·39 m³ (49 cu ft)
Nose baggage compartment (optional)	
	0·62 m³ (22 cu ft)
Freight capacity:	
aft of pilot's seat, incl rear cabin baggage space	
	4·70 m³ (166 cu ft)
with four bench seats folded into rear cabin baggage space	
	3·68 m³ (130 cu ft)

AREAS:

Wings, gross: standard	30·19 m² (325·0 sq ft)
with extended tips	31·31 m² (337·0 sq ft)

Pilatus Britten-Norman BN-2T Turbine Islander (*Brian M. Service*)

Ailerons (total)	2·38 m² (25·6 sq ft)
Flaps (total)	3·62 m² (39·0 sq ft)
Fin	3·41 m² (36·64 sq ft)
Rudder, incl tab	1·60 m² (17·2 sq ft)
Tailplane	6·78 m² (73·0 sq ft)
Elevator, incl tabs	3·08 m² (33·16 sq ft)

WEIGHTS AND LOADINGS (A: standard wings, B: extended wings, C: 194 kW; 260 hp and D: 224 kW; 300 hp engines):

Weight empty, equipped (without avionics):
C	1,638 kg (3,612 lb)
D	1,695 kg (3,738 lb)

Max T-O and landing weight (A, B)
2,993 kg (6,600 lb)

Max zero-fuel weight (BCAR):
A/C, A/D	2,855 kg (6,300 lb)
B/C, B/D	2,810 kg (6,200 lb)
Max wing loading: A	99·1 kg/m² (20·3 lb/sq ft)
B	95·7 kg/m² (19·6 lb/sq ft)

Max floor loading, without cargo panels
586 kg/m² (120 lb/sq ft)

Max power loading: C	7·71 kg/kW (12·7 lb/hp)
D	6·68 kg/kW (11·0 lb/hp)

PERFORMANCE (C: at 2,855 kg; 6,300 lb AUW, ISA, 194 kW; 260 hp engines. D: at max T-O weight, ISA, 224 kW; 300 hp engines):

Never-exceed speed:
C, D (standard wings)
177 knots (327 km/h; 203 mph) IAS
C, D (extended wings)
184 knots (340 km/h; 211 mph) IAS

Max level speed at S/L:
C	148 knots (274 km/h; 170 mph)
D	151 knots (280 km/h; 173 mph)

Max cruising speed (75% power) at 2,135 m (7,000 ft):
C	139 knots (257 km/h; 160 mph)
D	142 knots (264 km/h; 164 mph)

Cruising speed (67% power) at 2,750 m (9,000 ft):
C	134 knots (248 km/h; 154 mph)
D	137 knots (254 km/h; 158 mph)

Cruising speed (59% power) at 3,660 m (12,000 ft):
C	130 knots (241 km/h; 150 mph)
D	132 knots (245 km/h; 152 mph)

Stalling speed, flaps up:
C 50 knots (92 km/h; 57 mph) IAS

Stalling speed, flaps down:
C, D 43 knots (79 km/h; 49 mph) IAS

Max rate of climb at S/L: C 290 m (950 ft)/min
D 344 m (1,130 ft)/min

Rate of climb at S/L, one engine out:
C	58·5 m (192 ft)/min
D	61 m (200 ft)/min

Absolute ceiling: C 4,938 m (16,200 ft)
D 5,974 m (19,600 ft)

Service ceiling: C 4,450 m (14,600 ft)
D 5,485 m (18,000 ft)

Service ceiling, one engine out:
C, standard wings	1,737 m (5,700 ft)
C, extended wings	1,981 m (6,500 ft)
D, standard wings	1,890 m (6,200 ft)
D, extended wings	2,133 m (7,000 ft)

Min ground turning radius 9·45 m (31 ft 0 in)

T-O run at S/L, zero wind, hard runway:
C	169 m (555 ft)
D	203 m (665 ft)

T-O run at 1,525 m (5,000 ft):
D 296 m (970 ft)

T-O to 15 m (50 ft) at S/L, zero wind, hard runway:
C	332 m (1,090 ft)
D	335 m (1,100 ft)

Pilatus Britten-Norman Maritime Defender fishery protection aircraft

T-O to 15 m (50 ft) at 1,525 m (5,000 ft):
D 475 m (1,560 ft)

Landing from 15 m (50 ft) at S/L, zero wind, hard runway:
C	292 m (960 ft)
D	299 m (980 ft)

Landing from 15 m (50 ft) at 1,525 m (5,000 ft):
D 357 m (1,170 ft)

Landing run at 1,525 m (5,000 ft):
D 168 m (550 ft)

Landing run at S/L, zero wind, hard runway:
C	137 m (450 ft)
D	140 m (460 ft)

Range at 75% power at 2,135 m (7,000 ft):
C, standard wings	622 nm (1,153 km; 717 miles)
C, extended wings	903 nm (1,673 km; 1,040 miles)
D, standard wings	555 nm (1,028 km; 639 miles)
D, extended wings	816 nm (1,513 km; 940 miles)

Range at 67% power at 2,750 m (9,000 ft):
C, standard wings	713 nm (1,322 km; 822 miles)
C, extended wings	1,036 nm (1,920 km; 1,193 miles)
D, standard wings	577 nm (1,070 km; 665 miles)
D, extended wings	847 nm (1,569 km; 975 miles)

Range at 59% power at 3,660 m (12,000 ft):
C, standard wings	755 nm (1,400 km; 870 miles)
C, extended wings	1,096 nm (2,032 km; 1,263 miles)
D, standard wings	613 nm (1,136 km; 706 miles)
D, extended wings	905 nm (1,677 km; 1,042 miles)

PILATUS BRITTEN-NORMAN DEFENDER

The Defender is a variant of the civil Islander which can be adapted for a wide variety of government and military roles such as search and rescue, internal security, long-range patrol, forward air control, troop transport, logistic support and casualty evacuation. It is available with the same choice of wing configuration as the current civil versions and can be equipped with a wide range of highly sophisticated avionics, including nose-mounted weather radar, providing the aircraft with a marine search capability. Optional equipment includes four NATO standard underwing pylons for a variety of external stores, the inboard pair each carrying up to 317·5 kg (700 lb) and the outboard pair up to 204 kg (450 lb).

Typical underwing loads include twin 7·62 mm machine-guns in pod packs, 250 lb or 500 lb GP bombs, Matra rocket packs, SURA rocket clusters, wire-guided missiles, 5 in reconnaissance flares, anti-personnel grenades, smoke bombs, marker bombs and 227 litre (50 Imp gallon; 60 US gallon) drop-tanks.

Internal capacity for passengers, stretcher cases or cargo is the same as that of the civil Islander.

Britten-Norman Defenders/Islanders are in service with the Abu Dhabi Defence Force, Belgian Army, Botswana Defence Force, British Army Parachute Association, Ghana Air Force, Guyana Defence Force, Indian Navy, Jamaica Defence Force, Malagasy Air Force, Philippine Navy, Presidential Flight of the Mexican Air Force, Royal Hong Kong Auxiliary Air Force, Panamanian Air Force, Sultan of Oman's Air Force, Mauritania Islamic Defence Force, and in Malawi and Rwanda. Those operated by the air forces of Iraq, Israel and Qatar are military Islanders, and are not equipped to carry offensive weapons. Those supplied to the Indian Navy are Maritime Defenders.

The description given for the BN-2B Islander applies also to the Defender, except as follows:

POWER PLANT: Two 224 kW (300 hp) Avco Lycoming IO-540-K1B5 flat-six engines standard.

AVIONICS: Typical installation comprises King 360-channel VHF nav/com transceivers with VOR/LOC and VOR/ILS, ADF, marker beacon receiver, KT 76 transponder, SunAir ASB 500 HF com transceiver, Bendix radar and Collins autopilot.

WEIGHTS AND LOADINGS:
Weight empty, equipped (excl avionics)
1,824 kg (4,020 lb)
Max T-O and landing weight 2,993 kg (6,600 lb)
Max wing loading 95·7 kg/m² (19·6 lb/sq ft)
Max power loading 6·68 kg/kW (11·0 lb/hp)

PERFORMANCE (at max T-O weight, ISA. A: no stores on pylons; B: pylons loaded):

Max level speed:
A	151 knots (280 km/h; 174 mph)
B	144 knots (266 km/h; 166 mph)

Cruising speed, 67% power at 3,050 m (10,000 ft):
A	138 knots (255 km/h; 159 mph)
B	131 knots (242 km/h; 150 mph)

Cruising speed, 59% power at 610 m (2,000 ft):
A	123 knots (227 km/h; 141 mph)
B	116 knots (215 km/h; 133 mph)

Stalling speed, flaps down:
A, B 39 knots (73 km/h; 45 mph)
Max rate of climb at S/L: A 396 m (1,300 ft)/min
B 357 m (1,170 ft)/min
Service ceiling: A, B 5,180 m (17,000 ft)
Absolute ceiling: A, B 6,100 m (20,000 ft)
T-O to 15 m (50 ft): A, B 320 m (1,050 ft)
Landing from 15 m (50 ft): A, B 303 m (995 ft)

Range with max payload:
A	363 nm (672 km; 418 miles)
B	326 nm (603 km; 375 miles)

Range with standard fuel:
A	1,096 nm (2,027 km; 1,260 miles)
B	1,000 nm (1,850 km; 1,150 miles)

Max range with auxiliary fuel, no reserves, at full mission weight with max endurance power setting
1,497 nm (2,772 km; 1,723 miles)

PILATUS BRITTEN-NORMAN MARITIME DEFENDER

Generally similar to the Defender, the Maritime Defender differs by having a modified nose with a larger search radar, capable of detecting a 100 m² (1,076 sq ft) target in sea state 4-5 at a range of 36 nm (67 km; 41·5 miles). Scanning 60° on each side of the flight path, the radar provides a search width of 60 nm (111 km; 69 miles) at optimum altitude. The interior layout provides for pilot and co-pilot, a radar operator at a mid-cabin position on the starboard side, and two observers in the rear of the cabin, one aft of the radar operator, and one adjacent to a window on the port side.

Intended for coastal patrol, fishery and oil rig protection duties, as well as search and rescue support, the Maritime Defender is suitable for all-weather operation, by day or night, and carries the equipment necessary to fulfil such roles. This can include Collins PN 101 compass/HSI, horizon gyro (radar stabilisation), autopilot, Bendix RDR 1400 radar, Marconi CMA 734 Omega, Plessey PVI 712 radio altimeter, dual Collins VHF 20 com, dual Collins VIR 30M VHF nav/ILS, VHF marine band com, Collins ADF 60, Collins TDR 90 transponder, Collins DME 40, encoding altimeter, and SunAir ASB 500 SSB HF com. Specialised equipment includes a searchlight installation and hand-held camera; the four underwing pylons can be used to carry a loudspeaker pod, flares, parachute dinghy packs and a variety of weapons.

The description of the Defender applies also to the Maritime Defender, except that overall length is increased to 11·07 m (36 ft 3¾ in).

PILATUS BRITTEN-NORMAN BN-2A Mk III TRISLANDER

In the Autumn of 1970 Britten-Norman introduced an enlarged development of the twin-engined Islander, having a third engine mounted at the rear and a lengthened fuselage seating up to 17 passengers.

The prototype Trislander was produced by converting the second prototype of the twin-engined Islander (G-ATWU), adding a 2·29 m (7 ft 6 in) length of parallel-section fuselage forward of the wing, reinforcing the rear fuselage and fitting a new main landing gear with larger wheels and tyres. The tail unit was modified to act as a mount for the third engine. This aircraft made its first flight on 11 September 1970, appearing at the SBAC Display at Farnborough later the same day. Production aircraft have additional fin area above the rear engine.

The prototype was later dismantled and its fuselage used for structural testing. By the end of 1970 construction had begun of three production aircraft by converting standard Islander airframes from the current production line. The first production Trislander (G-AYTU) was flown on 6 March 1971, and the first delivery (to Aurigny Air Services in the Channel Islands) was made on 29 June 1971.

ARB certification of the Trislander, granted on 14 May 1971, approved the aircraft for both VFR and IFR operation and for full public transport with one pilot and up to 17 passengers. FAA certification followed on 4 August 1971, to FAR Pt 23 and to the latest air taxi requirements of SFAR Pt 23 and Appendix A of FAR Pt 135.

By mid-1980 orders had been received for more than 80 Trislanders. Of these more than 70 had been delivered, to customers in the UK, Africa, Australasia, USA, Canada, Indonesia and South America.

The following versions of the Trislander are currently in production:

BN-2A Mk III-2. Standard version with extended nose containing baggage compartment.

BN-2A Mk III-3. As Mk III-2, with an autofeather system which feathers the propeller automatically should an engine fail on take-off.

BN-2A Mk III-4. As Mk III-3, plus a standby rocket engine to provide additional thrust should an engine fail on take-off.

TYPE: Three-engined feederline transport.

WINGS: Cantilever high-wing monoplane. NACA 23012 constant wing section. No dihedral. Incidence 2°. No sweepback. Conventional riveted two-spar torsion-box structure in one piece, using aluminium-clad aluminium alloys. Increases in skin gauges and spar laminates compared with twin-engined versions. Structure is strictly 'safe-life', but exhibits several fail-safe features and principles. Flared-up wingtips of Britten-Norman design, with raked tips. Slotted ailerons and electrically-operated single-slotted permanently-drooped flaps of metal construction. Ground-adjustable tab in starboard aileron. BTR-Goodrich pneumatic de-icing boots optional.

FUSELAGE: Conventional riveted four-longeron semi-monocoque structure of pressed frames and stringers and metal skin, using L72 aluminium-clad aluminium alloys. Some reinforcement of fuselage aft of wing to support weight of rear engine. Structure is strictly 'safe-life', but has several fail-safe features and principles.

TAIL UNIT: Cantilever structure, using L72 aluminium-clad aluminium alloys, with low aspect ratio main fin which also acts as mount for the third engine. Fixed-incidence tailplane (with raked tips) and elevators are similar in construction to those of Islander. Trim tab in rudder. BTR-Goodrich pneumatic de-icing boots for tailplane optional.

LANDING GEAR: Non-retractable tricycle type, with twin-wheel main units and single steerable nosewheel. Cantilever main legs mounted aft of rear spar. All five wheels and tyres are Cleveland size 7·00-6. Tyre pressure 3·10 bars (45 lb/sq in) on main units, 2·00 bars (29 lb/sq in) on nose unit. Cleveland foot-operated air-cooled hydraulic disc brakes on main units. Parking brake. No anti-skid units. Fairings fitted to main gear extension tubes below the engine nacelle and above the shock-absorber attachment bolts.

POWER PLANT: Three 194 kW (260 hp) Avco Lycoming O-540-E4C5 flat-six engines (two mounted on wings and one on vertical tail), each driving a Hartzell HC-C2YK-2G/C8477-4 two-blade constant-speed fully-feathering metal propeller. Automatic feathering device available as an option. Standby rocket engine, mounted just below rear of tail-engine nacelle, is available as an option; weighing 21 kg (46·2 lb), this provides 1·56 kN (350 lb st) for 12 seconds. Fuel in two integral tanks between front and rear wing spars, outboard of the engine nacelles, and two tanks in wingtips. Total fuel capacity 746 litres (164 Imp gallons; 197 US gallons). Overwing refuelling point above each tank. Oil capacity 34 litres (7·5 Imp gallons; 9 US gallons).

ACCOMMODATION: Up to 18 persons, including pilot, in pairs on bench seats at approx 79 cm (31 in) pitch. Access to all seats provided by five doors, two on port side and three on starboard side. Baggage compartment at rear of cabin, with external baggage door on port side. Exit in emergency by removing window panels in front four passenger doors. Heating, ventilation and sound insulation standard. Ambulance or VIP interior layouts at customer's option. Dual controls standard.

SYSTEMS: One Southwind cabin heater fitted as standard. DC electrical system includes two 24V 50A self-rectifying alternators, supplying the instruments, lighting and radio, and a 24V 17Ah battery. No hydraulic or pneumatic systems, except for self-contained hydraulic brakes.

AVIONICS AND EQUIPMENT: Optional avionics include Collins autopilot, a wide range of Collins, Bendix, King or Narco VHF nav/com equipment, including ADF, DME, and Collins or SunAir HF transceiver. Optional equipment includes windscreen de-icing, second cabin heater, cargo tiedowns, anti-collision strobe beacons, emergency exit beta lights, electric propeller de-icing and pneumatic airframe de-icing systems.

DIMENSIONS, EXTERNAL:

Wing span	16·15 m (53 ft 0 in)
Wing chord (constant)	2·03 m (6 ft 8 in)
Wing aspect ratio	7·95
Length overall	15·01 m (49 ft 3 in)
Fuselage: Max width	1·21 m (3 ft 11½ in)
Max depth	1·46 m (4 ft 9¾ in)
Height overall	4·32 m (14 ft 2 in)
Tailplane span	6·48 m (21 ft 3 in)
Wheel track (c/l of shock-absorbers)	
	3·35 m (11 ft 0 in)
Wheelbase	7·12 m (23 ft 4¼ in)
Propeller diameter	2·03 m (6 ft 8 in)
Propeller ground clearance	0·69 m (2 ft 3 in)

Pilatus Britten-Norman BN-2A Mk III-2 Trislander three-engined feederline transport (*Brian M. Service*)

Pilatus Britten-Norman BN-2A Mk III-2 Trislander feederline transport (*Pilot Press*)

Distance between propeller centres (wing engines)	
	3·61 m (11 ft 10 in)
Passenger doors (stbd, fwd and centre):	
Height	1·10 m (3 ft 7½ in)
Max width	0·89 m (2 ft 10·9 in)
Height to sill	0·57 m (1 ft 10½ in)
Passenger doors (port, fwd and rear):	
Height	1·09 m (3 ft 7 in)
Max width	1·21 m (3 ft 11·9 in)
Height to sill	0·57 m (1 ft 10½ in)
Passenger door (stbd, rear):	
Height	1·09 m (3 ft 7 in)
Width	0·75 m (2 ft 5½ in)
Baggage compartment door (rear, port):	
Height	0·66 m (2 ft 1·95 in)
Width	0·44 m (1 ft 5·2 in)
Nose baggage compartment door (port, optional):	
Width	0·79 m (2 ft 7 in)

DIMENSIONS, INTERNAL:

Cabin: Length, excl flight deck but incl rear baggage compartment	8·24 m (27 ft 0½ in)
Max width	1·09 m (3 ft 7 in)
Max height	1·27 m (4 ft 2 in)
Floor area	7·85 m² (84·45 sq ft)
Volume	9·54 m³ (337 cu ft)
Rear baggage compartment volume	
	0·71 m³ (25·0 cu ft)
Nose baggage compartment volume (optional)	
	0·62 m³ (22·0 cu ft)

AREAS:

Wings, gross	31·31 m² (337·0 sq ft)
Ailerons (total)	2·38 m² (25·6 sq ft)
Trailing-edge flaps (total)	3·62 m² (39·0 sq ft)
Fin	5·83 m² (62·7 sq ft)

Rudder, incl tab	1·13 m² (12·2 sq ft)
Tailplane	8·36 m² (90·0 sq ft)
Elevators	2·42 m² (26·0 sq ft)

WEIGHTS AND LOADINGS:

Weight empty, equipped (without avionics)	
	2,650 kg (5,843 lb)
Max T-O and landing weight	4,536 kg (10,000 lb)
Max wing loading	144·8 kg/m² (29·67 lb/sq ft)
Max power loading	7·79 kg/kW (12·8 lb/hp)

PERFORMANCE (at max T-O weight, ISA):

Max level speed at S/L	
	156 knots (290 km/h; 180 mph)
Cruising speed (75% power) at 1,980 m (6,500 ft)	
	144 knots (267 km/h; 166 mph)
Cruising speed (67% power) at 2,470 m (9,000 ft)	
	138 knots (256 km/h; 159 mph)
Cruising speed (59% power) at 3,960 m (13,000 ft)	
	130 knots (241 km/h; 150 mph)
Max rate of climb at S/L	298 m (980 ft)/min
Rate of climb at S/L, one engine out	
	86 m (283 ft)/min
Absolute ceiling	4,450 m (14,600 ft)
Service ceiling	4,010 m (13,150 ft)
Service ceiling, one engine out	2,105 m (6,900 ft)
T-O run at S/L, zero wind, hard runway	
	393 m (1,290 ft)
T-O to 15 m (50 ft) at S/L, zero wind, hard runway	
	594 m (1,950 ft)
Landing from 15 m (50 ft) at S/L, zero wind, hard runway	
	440 m (1,445 ft)
Landing run at S/L, zero wind, hard runway	
	259 m (850 ft)
Max still-air range at 59% cruising power	
	868 nm (1,610 km; 1,000 miles)

SHORTS
SHORT BROTHERS LIMITED

HEAD OFFICE, WORKS AND AERODROME: PO Box 241, Airport Road, Belfast BT3 9DZ, Northern Ireland
Telephone: 0232 58444
Telex: 74688
OTHER FACTORIES: Newtownards, Castlereagh, Belfast (3)
LONDON OFFICE: Berkeley Square House, Berkeley Square, London W1X 5LB
CHAIRMAN: Sir George Leitch, KCB
MANAGING DIRECTOR: P. F. Foreman, CBE
DIRECTORS:
  Sir Sidney Bacon
  F. F. H. Charlton
  D. W. G. L. Haviland, CB
  R. W. R. McNulty
  A. F. C. Roberts, OBE
  James Sim
  Dr Llewellyn Smith, CBE
  H. E. Trevan-Hawke
SECRETARY: Gordon Bruce
EXECUTIVE DIRECTORS:
  B. Carlin (Manufacturing)
  B. P. Laight, OBE (Engineering)
  A. R. Manvell (Missiles)
  K. W. Tyson (Commercial)
  M. I. Wild
CHIEF TEST PILOT: L. L. Cumming
MANAGER, PUBLIC RELATIONS SERVICES: Derek S. Jones
PUBLICITY MANAGER: G. H. Edgar

Short Brothers were first established, as aeronauts, in 1898, and in 1901 they began the manufacture of balloons at Hove, Sussex. Works were later established in London, first at premises off the Tottenham Court Road and, in 1906, at Battersea. In March 1909 Shorts opened the United Kingdom's first purpose-built aircraft factory at Shellbeach, Isle of Sheppey. (The Short No. 1 had been ordered by F. T. McClean in January 1909.) The contract placed with Shorts by the Wright brothers in March 1909, for six Flyers, was the first aircraft production contract to be placed in the UK. The main aircraft works moved to Eastchurch in 1909-10, and to Rochester in 1913-14.

In June 1936 Short Brothers, in collaboration with Harland & Wolff Ltd, formed a new company known as Short & Harland Ltd to build aircraft in Belfast, and in 1947 activities were concentrated in Belfast under the name Short Bros & Harland Ltd. The name Short Brothers Ltd was re-adopted on 1 June 1977.

The British government now owns, directly or indirectly, 100 per cent of the issued shareholding. In 1979 the company received the Queen's Award to Industry for the 10th time. It had 6,600 employees in April 1980.

The company's current products include the Shorts 330, a 30-seat commuter airliner, and the Skyvan turboprop STOL light transport, in use throughout the world for passenger, freight, survey, military and miscellaneous operations.

Internationally, Shorts is collaborating as risk-sharing partner with Fokker, MBB and VFW in production of the Fokker F28 Fellowship transport, with responsibility for the wings; and holds contracts to produce ailerons, spoilers, wingtips, landing gear doors, galley doors, environmental control system doors and tail unit rib assemblies for the Lockheed L-1011 TriStar, and landing gear doors for the Boeing 747. During 1967, Shorts began the design and manufacture of pods for Rolls-Royce jet engines, and is responsible for podding Rolls-Royce RB.211 turbofan engines for the TriStar. Deliveries of these direct to Lockheed at Palmdale began in the early Summer of 1970. The company is also podding RB.211 engines for the Boeing 747 and 757, and has produced pods for more than 500 RB.211s. A contract to produce pods for the Avco Lycoming ALF 502 turbofans of the British Aerospace 146 was announced in January 1979.

To cope with its involvement in the TriStar programme, Shorts installed some of Europe's most advanced facilities for the hot-forming of titanium and the manipulation of high-temperature creep-resistant alloys. It is conducting advanced research into jet-engine noise reduction and metal bonding. Shorts is also quality-approved subcontractor to many major US and UK aerospace companies. Conversely, production of the wings for the Shorts 330 is undertaken jointly by British Aerospace and Fokker, and production of the 330 landing gear by Menasco in Canada.

In addition to its activities in the field of piloted aircraft, Shorts is engaged in missile development and production, production of supersonic target drones, and production to MoD contract of the MATS-B and Skeet target drones.

The company's Flying Services Division operates maintenance units and airfields for various civil and military organisations, and flies and maintains aircraft and target drones for the Ministry of Defence. This includes operation of the Llanbedr target aircraft base, and the target service, supply and recovery flight at the Woomera range in Australia.

SHORTS 330

The Shorts 330 (originally SD3-30) is a 30-passenger twin-turboprop transport aircraft designed primarily for commuter and regional air service operators whose current 18/20-seat aircraft require replacement by larger aircraft.

Design of the 330 is derived from that of the Skyvan STOL utility transport, and it retains many of the latter type's well-proven characteristics, including the large

Shorts 330 twin-turboprop commuter and utility transport *(Pilot Press)*

cabin cross-section. The same safe-life concept and design philosophy is employed in the structural components. The cabin, including the toilet and galley compartments, is 3·78 m (12 ft 5 in) longer than that of the Skyvan Srs 3.

Two prototypes and the first production aircraft were used for the development programme. The first prototype (G-BSBH) flew for the first time on 22 August 1974. Eight days earlier, the first order for the 330 was placed by Command Airways of Poughkeepsie, New York, for three aircraft. CAA certification to full Transport Category requirements was granted on 18 February 1976; this was followed on 18 June 1976 by US FAR Pt 25 and Pt 36 approval, and subsequently by approvals from the Canadian Dept of Transport and the West German LBA. The 330 conforms with CAB Pt 298 (US) and meets the noise requirements of FAR Pt 36 by a substantial margin. Initial deliveries began in June 1976; first to enter service, on 24 August 1976, was a Time Air 330.

Firm orders for 60 Shorts 330s had been placed by 10 July 1980 as follows:

Aeronaves del Centro (Venezuela)	3
Air North (Vermont)	2
ALM Antillean Airlines (Curaçao)	2
Chautauqua Airlines (New York)	2
Command Airways (New York)	4
Crown Airways (Pennsylvania)	2
DLT (Germany)	7
Golden West Airlines (California)	5
Hawaiian Air	3
Henson Aviation (Maryland)	4
LAPA (Argentina)	2
Loganair (Scotland)	2
Metro Airlines (Texas)	5
Mississippi Valley Airlines (Wisconsin)	4
Olympic Airways (Greece)	2
Pennsylvania Commuter Airlines	1
Royale Airlines (Louisiana)	1
Suburban Airlines (Pennsylvania)	6
Time Air (Canada)	3

Of these, approx 30 had been delivered. They had carried one million passengers by 9 March 1979.

Shorts 330 wide-bodied commuter airliner in the insignia of Mississippi Valley Airlines, Wisconsin, USA

A military version, the **SD3-M**, has also been proposed. This would be capable of a variety of roles, including the tactical transportation of troops, cargo and vehicles, paratrooping, supply dropping, casualty evacuation and search and rescue, and would be able to carry up to 32 troops or 3,630 kg (8,000 lb) of cargo.

The following description applies to both the 330 and the SD3-M:

TYPE: Twin-turboprop transport aircraft.

WINGS: Braced high-wing monoplane, of all-metal safe-life construction, built in three sections. Wing sections NACA 63A series (modified). Thickness/chord ratio 18% at root, 14% on outer panels. Dihedral 3° on outer panels. Centre-section, integral with top of centre-fuselage, has taper on leading- and trailing-edges, and is a two-spar single-cell box structure of light alloy with conventional skin and stringers. The strut-braced outer panels, which are pin-jointed to the centre-section, are reinforced Skyvan constant-chord units, built of light alloy, and each consists of a two-cell box having wing skins made up of a smooth outer skin bonded to a corrugated inner skin. All-metal single-slotted ailerons. Geared trim tabs in ailerons. All-metal single-slotted flaps, each in three sections. Primary control surfaces are rod-actuated.

FUSELAGE: Light alloy structure, built in two main portions: nose (including flight deck, nosewheel bay and forward baggage compartment); and the centre (including main wing spar attachment frames and lower transverse beams which carry the main landing gear and associated fairings) and rear portion (including aft baggage compartment and tail unit attachment frames). The nose and rear underfuselage are of conventional skin/stringer design. The remainder is composed of a smooth outer skin bonded to a corrugated inner skin and stabilised by frames.

TAIL UNIT: Cantilever all-metal two-spar structure with twin fins and rudders, basically similar to that of the Skyvan. Fixed-incidence tailplane, with reinforced leading-edge. Full-span elevator, aerodynamically balanced by set-back hinges. Rudders each have an unshielded horn aerodynamic balance. Primary control surfaces are rod-actuated. Geared trim tabs in elevator and starboard rudder (port rudder, trim only).

LANDING GEAR: Menasco retractable tricycle type, with single wheel on each unit. Main units carried on short sponsons, into which the wheels retract hydraulically. Oleo-pneumatic shock-absorbers. Nosewheel is steerable. Normal tyre pressures: main units 5·38 bars (78 lb/sq in), nose unit 3·79 bars (55 lb/sq in). Special requirements for rough-field operation have been catered for in the design.

POWER PLANT: Two 862 kW (1,156 shp) (max continuous rating 761 kW; 1,020 shp) Pratt & Whitney Aircraft of Canada PT6A-45B turboprop engines, each driving a Hartzell five-blade low-speed propeller. Fuel in main tanks in wing centre-section/fuselage fairing, total capacity 2,182 litres (480 Imp gallons). Normal cross-feed provisions to allow for pump failure. Provision to increase total fuel capacity for special requirements.

ACCOMMODATION (330): Crew of two on flight deck, plus cabin attendant. Dual controls standard. Standard seating for 30 passengers, in ten rows of three at 76 cm (30 in) pitch, with wide aisle. Seat rails fitted to facilitate changes in configuration. Galley, toilet and cabin attendant's seat at rear. Large overhead baggage lockers. Entire accommodation soundproofed and air-conditioned. Baggage compartments in nose (1·27 m³; 45 cu ft) and to rear of cabin (2·83 m³; 100 cu ft), each with external access and capable of holding a combined total of 454 kg (1,000 lb) of baggage. Passenger door is at rear of cabin on port side. Passenger version has two emergency exits on the starboard side, two on the port side (including passenger door) and one in the flight deck roof. Mixed-traffic version has full access to these emergency exits. For mixed passenger/freight operation a partition divides the cabin into a rear passenger area (typically for 18 persons) and a forward cargo compartment, the latter being loaded through a large port-side door, capable of admitting ATA 'D' type containers. In all-cargo configuration the cabin can accommodate up to seven 'D' type containers, with ample space around them for additional freight. Cabin floor is flat throughout its length, and is designed to support loadings of 181 kg (400 lb) per foot run at 610·3 kg/m² (125 lb/sq ft). Locally-reinforced areas of higher strength are also provided. Seat rails can be used as cargo lashing points. Freight loading is facilitated by the low-level cabin floor.

SYSTEMS: Hydraulic system of 207 bars (3,000 lb/sq in), supplied by engine-driven pumps, operates landing gear, nosewheel steering, flaps and brakes (at lower pressure) and includes emergency accumulators. Main electrical system, for general services, is 28V DC and is of the split busbar type with cross-coupling for essential services. Lucas 28V 250A DC starter/generator for engine starting and aircraft services, with separate 1·5kW 200V AC output for windscreen anti-icing and demisting. Special AC sources of 115V and 26V available at 400Hz for certain instruments. De-icing/anti-icing system for wing and tail leading-edges; optional

inertial anti-icing system for engine intake ducts; electric mat de-icing for inlet lips and propellers. Full air-conditioning system.

AVIONICS AND EQUIPMENT: Passenger safety equipment standard. Wide range of radio and navigation equipment available to customer's requirements. Typical standard avionics comprise duplicated VHF communications and navigation systems, two glideslope/markers, two ILS repeaters, two radio magnetic indicators, one ADF, one transponder, one DME, PA system and weather radar. Flight data recorder and voice recorder available as standard options.

DIMENSIONS, EXTERNAL:

Wing span	22·76 m (74 ft 8 in)
Wing chord (standard mean)	1·85 m (6 ft 0·7 in)
Length overall	17·69 m (58 ft 0½ in)
Height overall	4·95 m (16 ft 3 in)
Tailplane span	5·68 m (18 ft 7¾ in)
Wheel track	4·24 m (13 ft 11 in)
Wheelbase	6·15 m (20 ft 2 in)
Propeller diameter	2·82 m (9 ft 3 in)
Propeller ground clearance	1·83 m (6 ft 0 in)
Cabin floor: height above ground	0·94 m (3 ft 1 in)
Passenger door (port, rear):	
Height	1·57 m (5 ft 2 in)
Width	0·71 m (2 ft 4 in)
Forward cargo door (port):	
Height	1·68 m (5 ft 6 in)
Width	1·42 m (4 ft 8 in)

DIMENSIONS, INTERNAL:

Cabin: Max length, incl toilet	9·47 m (31 ft 1 in)
Max width	1·93 m (6 ft 4 in)
Max height	1·93 m (6 ft 4 in)
Floor area	18·77 m² (202 sq ft)
Volume (all-cargo)	34·83 m³ (1,230 cu ft)
Baggage compartments volume (total usable)	
	4·11 m³ (145 cu ft)
Cabin overhead lockers (total)	1·13 m³ (40 cu ft)

AREAS:

Wings, gross	42·1 m² (453·0 sq ft)
Ailerons (total, aft of hinges)	2·55 m² (27·5 sq ft)
Trailing-edge flaps (total)	7·74 m² (83·3 sq ft)
Fins (total)	8·65 m² (93·1 sq ft)
Rudders (total, aft of hinges)	2·24 m² (24·1 sq ft)
Tailplane	7·77 m² (83·6 sq ft)
Elevator (total, aft of hinges)	2·54 m² (27·3 sq ft)

WEIGHTS AND LOADINGS:

Weight empty, equipped (incl crew of three):	
330 for 30 passengers	6,690 kg (14,750 lb)
Fuel: standard tanks	1,741 kg (3,840 lb)
Max payload for normal max T-O weight:	
30 passengers and baggage	2,653 kg (5,850 lb)
cargo	3,400 kg (7,500 lb)
Max T-O weight	10,250 kg (22,600 lb)
Max landing weight	10,115 kg (22,300 lb)
Max wing loading	243·6 kg /m² (49·89 lb/sq ft)
Max power loading	5·95 kg/kW (9·8 lb/shp)

PERFORMANCE (at max T-O weight, ISA at S/L, except where indicated):

Max cruising speed at 3,050 m (10,000 ft), AUW of 9,525 kg (21,000 lb)	
	190 knots (352 km/h; 218 mph)
Econ cruising speed at 3,050 m (10,000 ft), AUW of 9,525 kg (21,000 lb)	
	160 knots (296 km/h; 184 mph)
Stalling speed, flaps and landing gear up	
	91 knots (168 km/h; 104 mph)
Stalling speed at max landing weight, flaps and landing gear down	74 knots (137 km/h; 85 mph)
Max rate of climb at S/L	353 m (1,160 ft)/min
Service ceiling, one engine out, AUW of 9,072 kg (20,000 lb)	3,500 m (11,500 ft)
T-O distance (FAR Pt 25 and BCAR Gp A):	
ISA	1,160 m (3,800 ft)
ISA + 15°C	1,295 m (4,250 ft)

Landing distance, AUW of 9,072 kg (20,000 lb):

BCAR	1,143 m (3,750 ft)
FAR	1,030 m (3,380 ft)
Runway LCN at max T-O weight	10·4
Range with max passenger payload, cruising at 3,050 m (10,000 ft), no reserves	
	435 nm (805 km; 500 miles)
Range with max fuel, cruising at 3,050 m (10,000 ft), no reserves:	
passenger version, 1,830 kg (4,035 lb) payload	
	758 nm (1,403 km; 872 miles)
cargo version, 2,170 kg (4,785 lb) payload	
	758 nm (1,403 km; 872 miles)

OPERATIONAL NOISE LEVELS (FAR Pt 36):

Take-off	88·9 EPNdB
Sideline	84·1 EPNdB
Approach	92·8 EPNdB

SHORTS SD3-MR SEEKER

Shorts have proposed a version of the 330, known as the SD3-MR Seeker, for fishery protection, search and rescue, and various other maritime operations. Performance figures would be basically as for the 330/SD3-M but with greatly enhanced range/endurance capabilities afforded by an internal fuel tank which would virtually double the existing capacity.

Other changes from the standard specification would include blister windows at the forward cabin stations, observers' seats, long-range VLF/Omega navigation, search/weather radar, installation of a data-recording oblique camera, and a crew rest area. Full 360° scan radar, navigator and radar operator stations, flare launch tube and survival equipment stowage and deployment facilities, could readily be installed. The existing 330 galley/toilet and interior soundproofing and trim would be retained to ensure low crew fatigue on long sorties.

Allowing reserves for a 50 nm (92·5 km; 57·5 mile) diversion and 45 min holding, a typical on-station endurance would be 8·5 h at 610 m (2,000 ft) at 200 nm (370 km; 230 miles) from base. This represents a total endurance capability of over 12 h.

SHORTS 360

On 10 July 1980, Shorts released first details of this 'stretched' development of the Model 330, seating six more passengers in a lengthened fuselage and having a new tail unit, as well as more powerful and more fuel-efficient engines. The 360 is planned to enter airline service before the end of 1982. A prototype is scheduled to fly during September 1981, with certification following about a year later. First customer was Suburban Airlines of Reading, Pennsylvania, which has ordered four.

Designed specifically for short-haul airline operation, over typical commuter average stage lengths of about 104 nm (193 km; 120 miles), the Shorts 360 retains the basic configuration of the Model 330, the major external differences being the lengthened fuselage (a 0·91 m; 3 ft plug is inserted forward of the wings) and the introduction of a sweptback single fin and rudder instead of the latter's twin assembly. Power plant is a higher-rated version of the proven PT6A turboprop engine.

Pressurisation is considered unnecessary in view of the short stage lengths over which the aircraft will operate, and this enables the Shorts 360 to retain the same 'walk-about' headroom, square-section wide-bodied interior, seating comfort, air-conditioning and other amenities as its predecessor. The new rear fuselage/tail configuration is designed to reduce drag, improve fuel efficiency, and provide even greater baggage capacity. Considerable emphasis is placed on the 360's ability to provide more than 0·20 m³ (7 cu ft) of baggage space for each of its 36 passengers, a feature which Shorts claim is unique among today's commuter aircraft.

TYPE: Twin-turboprop commuter transport.

WINGS: As Shorts 330.

Shorts 360 commuter transport (two P&WC PT6A-65R turboprop engines) *(Pilot Press)*

FUSELAGE: As Shorts 330, but lengthened by insertion of 0·91 m (3 ft) plug forward of wings. Rear fuselage modified to cater for redesigned tail unit.

TAIL UNIT: Cantilever all-metal two-spar structure, with single sweptback fin and rudder and constant-chord non-swept tailplane. Trim tabs in each elevator.

LANDING GEAR: Similar to Shorts 330, but with higher tyre pressures to cater for increased operating weights.

POWER PLANT: Two 965 kW (1,294 shp) Pratt & Whitney Aircraft of Canada PT6A-65R turboprop engines, each driving an advanced technology propeller with spinner. Fuel capacity as for Shorts 330.

ACCOMMODATION: Crew of two on flight deck, plus cabin attendant. Dual controls standard. Main cabin accommodation as for Shorts 330, but seating a total of 36 passengers in 12 rows of three. Large overhead baggage lockers. Baggage compartments in nose and to rear of cabin, each with external access, giving equivalent of almost 0·17 m³ (6 cu ft) of baggage space per passenger (0·20 m³; 7·2 cu ft per passenger if locker space is included).

SYSTEMS: Generally as for Shorts 330. De-icing/anti-icing systems standard.

AVIONICS: Typical standard avionics comprise duplicated VHF com and nav systems (VOR/ILS and marker), two ATC transponders, one DME, one ADF, two gyromagnetic compass systems, two RMI, two ILS repeater indicators, flight director, HSI, weather radar, PA and stereo music systems, flight data recorder, voice recorder and GPWS.

DIMENSIONS, EXTERNAL: As for Shorts 330 except:

Length overall	21·49 m (70 ft 6 in)
Height overall	6·88 m (22 ft 7 in)
Tailplane span	7·12 m (23 ft 4½ in)
Wheelbase	7·06 m (23 ft 2 in)

DIMENSIONS, INTERNAL:

Cabin: Length	11·02 m (36 ft 2 in)
Max width	1·93 m (6 ft 4 in)
Max height	1·93 m (6 ft 4 in)
Passenger compartment volume	41·06 m³ (1,450 cu ft)

Baggage compartment volume:

forward	1·27 m³ (45 cu ft)
rear	4·81 m³ (170 cu ft)
lockers	1·27 m³ (45 cu ft)

AREAS: As for Shorts 330 except:

Vertical tail surfaces (total)	7·52 m² (81·0 sq ft)
Horizontal tail surfaces (total)	9·66 m² (104·0 sq ft)

WEIGHTS:

Typical operating weight empty	7,480 kg (16,490 lb)
Max payload (36 passengers)	3,184 kg (7,020 lb)
Max baggage load	635 kg (1,400 lb)
Max fuel load	1,741 kg (3,840 lb)
Max T-O weight	11,657 kg (25,700 lb)
Max ramp weight	11,702 kg (25,800 lb)
Max landing weight	11,521 kg (25,400 lb)

PERFORMANCE (estimated, at max T-O weight except where indicated):

Cruising speed at max recommended cruise power
211 knots (391 km/h; 243 mph)

T-O run at S/L: ISA	1,320 m (4,330 ft)
ISA + 20°C	1,440 m (4,720 ft)

Landing run at S/L at max landing weight, ISA
1,198 m (3,930 ft)

Range at 3,050 m (10,000 ft), cruising at 211 knots (391 km/h; 243 mph), ISA, reserves for 87 nm (161 km; 100 mile) diversion and 45 min hold:

with max passenger payload	230 nm (425 km; 265 miles)
with max fuel	570 nm (1,055 km; 655 miles)

SHORTS SC.7 SKYVAN

Design of the SC.7 Skyvan was started as a private venture in 1959, and construction of the first prototype began in 1960. This aircraft (G-ASCN) flew for the first time on 17 January 1963, with two 290 kW (390 hp) Continental GTSIO-520 piston engines, and completed its flight trials by mid-1963. It was then re-engined with 388 kW (520 shp) Astazou II turboprops and first flew in its new form on 2 October 1963.

The following versions of the Skyvan have been built:

Skyvan Srs 1 and Srs 1A. Designation of first prototype, with Continental engines (Srs 1) and later with Astazou IIs (Srs 1A).

Skyvan Srs 2. Three development and 16 initial production aircraft, with Astazou XII turboprop engines. Several subsequently re-engined to Srs 3 standard. Descriptions in 1968-69 and 1970-71 *Jane's*.

Skyvan Srs 3. Current civil version, which superseded Srs 2 in 1968. First Srs 3 to fly was the second development aircraft, G-ASZI, which had been equipped originally with Astazous. The first flight with Garrett-AiResearch engines was made on 15 December 1967, and a second aircraft (G-ASZJ) re-engined with TPE331s flew on 20 January 1968. Total of 69 ordered by July 1980, recent customers including Air Malawi, Gulf Air and the government of Saudi Arabia.

Skyvan Srs 3A. Introduced in September 1970. Complies with BCAR Passenger Transport Category, in Performance Group A: max T-O weight 6,215 kg (13,700 lb), max landing weight 6,075 kg (13,400 lb). Two ordered.

Skyvan Srs 3M. Military version of Srs 3, modified internally to accept optional equipment for typical military missions. Prototype (G-AXPT) flew for the first time in early 1970. Suitable for paratrooping and supply dropping, assault landing, troop transport, casualty evacuation, staff transport, and vehicle or ordnance transport.

A total of 54 had been ordered by March 1980, for armed services including the Argentinian Naval Prefectura (5), Austrian Air Force (2), Botswana Defence Force (2), Ecuador Army Air Force (1), Ghana Air Force (6), Indonesian Air Force (3), Lesotho Police (2), Malawi Police (1), Mauritanian Air Force (2), Royal Nepalese Army (2), No. 2 Squadron of the Sultan of Oman's Air Force (16), Panama National Guard (1), Singapore Air Force (6), Royal Thai Police (3) and Yemen Arab Republic Air Force (2). Three of the Singapore aircraft are equipped for search and rescue duties. Those of the Indonesian Air Force are equipped to civil standard and operate social services on behalf of the Ministry of the Interior.

Skyliner. Limited-production de luxe all-passenger version of Series 3/3A. Total of nine sold (orders listed in 1976-77 *Jane's*).

Total orders for Series 3/3A/3M Skyvans and Skyliners had reached 134 by July 1980. In February 1970 the Skyvan became the first aircraft to be certificated under the British Air Registration Board's new Civil Airworthiness Requirements for STOL operations.

The following description applies to the standard current civil Srs 3 and military Srs 3M:

TYPE: Light civil or military STOL utility transport.

WINGS: Braced high-wing monoplane. Wing section NACA 63A series (modified). Thickness/chord ratio 14%. Dihedral 2° 2′. Incidence 2° 30′. Light alloy structure consisting of a two-cell box with wing skins made up of a uniform outer sheet bonded to a corrugated inner sheet. All-metal single-slotted ailerons. Geared tabs on port and starboard ailerons, with manual trim on starboard aileron. All-metal single-slotted flaps. Provision

for sintered leading-edge de-icing system.

FUSELAGE: Light alloy structure. Nose and crew cabin section is of conventional skin/stringer design. Elsewhere, the fuselage structure consists of double-skin panels (flat outer sheets bonded to inner corrugated sheets), stabilised by frames.

TAIL UNIT: Cantilever all-metal two-spar structure, with twin fins and rudders. Fixed-incidence tailplane. Geared trim tabs in outer elevators and rudders. Provision for sintered leading-edge de-icing system.

LANDING GEAR: Non-retractable tricycle type. Single wheel on each unit. Steerable nosewheel. Main units carried on short sponsons. Electro-Hydraulics oleo-pneumatic shock-absorbers. Main-wheel tyres size 11·00-12, nosewheel tyre size 7·50-10. Tyre pressure (all units) 2·76 bars (40 lb/sq in). Hydraulically-operated disc brakes, with differential braking for steering. Low-pressure tyres available optionally.

POWER PLANT: Two 533 kW (715 shp) Garrett-AiResearch TPE331-201 turboprop engines, each driving a Hartzell HC-B3TN-5/T10282H three-blade (optionally four-blade) variable-pitch propeller. Fuel in four tanks in pairs on top of fuselage between wing roots, each pair consisting of one tank of 182 litres (40 Imp gallons) capacity and one of 484 litres (106·5 Imp gallons) capacity. Total fuel capacity of 1,332 litres (293 Imp gallons). Provision for increase in total fuel capacity to 1,773 litres (390 Imp gallons) by installing four specially-designed tanks in spaces between fuselage frames on each side, beneath main fuel tank. Oil capacity 7·73 litres (1·7 Imp gallons).

ACCOMMODATION: Crew of one, with provision for two. Accommodation (Srs 3) for up to 19 passengers, or 12 stretcher patients and attendants, or 2,085 kg (4,600 lb) of freight, vehicles or agricultural equipment. Srs 3M can accommodate 22 equipped troops; 16 paratroops and a dispatcher; 12 stretcher cases and two medical attendants, or 2,358 kg (5,200 lb) of freight. It carries its own lightweight vehicle loading ramps and has a one-piece door which leaves the fuselage threshold entirely clear of appendages. Executive version provides luxury accommodation and equipment for nine passengers. Full-width rear loading door, and forward door on each side of crew compartment. Rear door can be opened in flight to permit the parachuting of loads up to 1·37 m (4 ft 6 in) in height. Cockpit and cabin heated by engine bleed air mixed with fresh air from intake in nose. Cabin unpressurised. Some aircraft fitted with Rolamat cargo loading equipment.

SYSTEMS: Hydraulic system, pressure 172 bars (2,500 lb/sq in), operates flaps, wheel brakes and nosewheel steering. No pneumatic system. Electrical system utilises two busbars, operating independently, each connected to a 28V 125A DC starter/generator, a battery and a 115V 400Hz static inverter. General services are 28V DC; some radio and instruments 115V AC.

AVIONICS AND EQUIPMENT: Radio optional. Typical installation for operations in Europe and USA consists of duplicated VHF, duplicated VOR/ILS, marker beacon and ADF. Provision for HF, DME, transponder, Bendix M4D autopilot and weather radar. Blind-flying instrumentation standard.

EQUIPMENT (Srs 3M): Port-side blister window for an air dispatcher; two anchor cables for parachute static lines; a guard rail beneath the tail to prevent control surface fouling by the static lines; inward-facing paratroop seats with safety nets; parachute signal light; mounts for NATO-type stretchers; and roller conveyors for easy loading and paradropping of pallet-mounted supplies.

Shorts Skyvan Srs 3 twin-turboprop STOL transport aircraft in the insignia of Hornbill Skyways of Malaysia

DIMENSIONS, EXTERNAL:
Wing span	19·79 m (64 ft 11 in)
Wing chord (constant)	1·78 m (5 ft 10 in)
Wing aspect ratio	11
Length overall: without radome	12·21 m (40 ft 1 in)
with radome	12·60 m (41 ft 4 in)
Height overall	4·60 m (15 ft 1 in)
Tailplane span	5·28 m (17 ft 4 in)
Wheel track	4·21 m (13 ft 10 in)
Wheelbase	4·52 m (14 ft 10 in)
*Propeller diameter	2·59 m (8 ft 6 in)
Propeller ground clearance	1·52 m (5 ft 0 in)
Crew and passenger doors (fwd, port and stbd):	
Height	1·52 m (5 ft 0 in)
Width	0·51 m (1 ft 8 in)
Height to sill	1·14 m (3 ft 9 in)
Rear loading door: Height	1·98 m (6 ft 6 in)
Width	1·96 m (6 ft 5 in)
Height to sill	0·74 m (2 ft 5 in)

*Optional four-blade propellers of 2·51 m (8 ft 3 in)
diameter

DIMENSIONS, INTERNAL:
Cabin, excl flight deck: Length	5·67 m (18 ft 7 in)
Max width	1·98 m (6 ft 6 in)
Max height	1·98 m (6 ft 6 in)
Floor area	11·15 m² (120 sq ft)
Volume	22·09 m³ (780 cu ft)

AREAS:
Wings, gross	34·65 m² (373 sq ft)
Ailerons (total)	3·00 m² (32·3 sq ft)
Trailing-edge flaps (total)	5·86 m² (63·1 sq ft)
Fins	7·62 m² (82·0 sq ft)
Rudders, incl tabs	2·41 m² (25·9 sq ft)
Tailplane	7·53 m² (81·0 sq ft)
Elevators, incl tabs	3·62 m² (39·0 sq ft)

WEIGHTS AND LOADINGS (with 1,332 litres; 293 gallons of fuel):
Basic operating weight: 3	3,331 kg (7,344 lb)
3M	3,356 kg (7,400 lb)
Typical operating weight as freighter:	
3	3,447 kg (7,600 lb)
3M	3,456 kg (7,620 lb)
Typical operating weight with passengers or troops:	
3	3,674 kg (8,100 lb)
3M	3,778 kg (8,330 lb)
Max payload for normal T-O weight:	
3	2,086 kg (4,600 lb)
3M	2,358 kg (5,200 lb)
Max payload for overload T-O weight:	
3M	2,721 kg (6,000 lb)
Max T-O weight: 3, normal	5,670 kg (12,500 lb)
3M, normal	6,214 kg (13,700 lb)
3M, overload	6,577 kg (14,500 lb)
Max landing weight: 3	5,670 kg (12,500 lb)
3M	6,123 kg (13,500 lb)
Max wing loading: 3	163·6 kg/m² (33·5 lb/sq ft)
3M	179·1 kg/m² (36·7 lb/sq ft)

Shorts Skyvan Srs 3 transport aircraft with nose radome (Pilot Press)

Max power loading: 3	5·32 kg/kW (8·74 lb/shp)	
3M	6·17 kg/kW (9·58 lb/shp)	

PERFORMANCE (at max T-O weight, with 1,332 litres; 293 Imp gallons of fuel):
Never-exceed speed	217 knots (402 km/h; 250 mph) EAS
Max cruising speed at 3,050 m (10,000 ft):	
max cont power	176 knots (327 km/h; 203 mph)
cruise power	169 knots (314 km/h; 195 mph)
Econ cruising speed at 3,050 m (10,000 ft)	150 knots (278 km/h; 173 mph)
Stalling speed, flaps down:	
3	60 knots (111 km/h; 69 mph) EAS
3M	62 knots (115 km/h; 71 mph) EAS
Max rate of climb at S/L: 3	500 m (1,640 ft)/min
3M	466 m (1,530 ft)/min
Service ceiling (30 m; 100 ft/min climb):	
3	6,858 m (22,500 ft)
3M	6,705 m (22,000 ft)
Service ceiling, one engine out (15 m; 50 ft/min climb):	
3	3,810 m (12,500 ft)
3M	2,895 m (9,500 ft)
Min ground turning radius	3·76 m (12 ft 4 in)
Runway LCN at AUW of 5,670 kg (12,500 lb):	
standard tyres	3·5
low-pressure tyres	3·0
T-O run, STOL, unfactored: 3	213 m (700 ft)
3M	238 m (780 ft)
T-O run (normal): 3 (BCAR)	512 m (1,680 ft)

T-O to 10·7 m (35 ft), Transport Group A, ISA at S/L	1,020 m (3,350 ft)
T-O to 15 m (50 ft), STOL, unfactored:	
3	320 m (1,050 ft)
3M	384 m (1,260 ft)
T-O to 15 m (50 ft):	
3 (BCAR, normal)	610 m (2,000 ft)
3 (BCAR, STOL)	482 m (1,580 ft)
3 (FAR Pt 23)	488 m (1,600 ft)
Landing from 15 m (50 ft):	
3 (BCAR, normal)	622 m (2,040 ft)
3 (BCAR, STOL)	567 m (1,860 ft)
3 (FAR Pt 23)	451 m (1,480 ft)
3M (STOL, unfactored)	425 m (1,395 ft)
Landing from 15 m (50 ft), Transport Group A, ISA at S/L	1,010 m (3,320 ft)
Landing from 9 m (30 ft):	
3 (STOL, unfactored)	351 m (1,150 ft)
3 (BCAR, STOL)	500 m (1,640 ft)
Landing run: 3M (STOL, unfactored) 212 m (695 ft)	
Range at long-range cruising speed, 45 min reserves:	
3	600 nm (1,115 km; 694 miles)
3M	580 nm (1,075 km; 670 miles)
Range (typical freighter) at long-range cruising speed, 45 min reserves:	
3 with 1,814 kg (4,000 lb) payload	162 nm (300 km; 187 miles)
3M with 2,268 kg (5,000 lb) payload	208 nm (386 km; 240 miles)

TO

SOLAR-POWERED AIRCRAFT DEVELOPMENTS

5A Lyndhurst Gardens, London NW3

This company was formed by Mr Freddie To, in order to build a solar-powered aircraft that he had devised. Design of the aircraft, known as the Solar One, was undertaken by Mr David Williams, and the first short hop was claimed on 19 December 1978. A flight of nearly three-quarters of a mile (1,200 m) was made by Mr Ken Stewart at Lasham Airfield, Hampshire, on 13 June 1979. The flight was made at a maximum height of about 25 m (80 ft) and at a maximum speed of about 35 knots (65 km/h; 40 mph). A second flight was made on the same day by Mr Bill Maidment.

SOLAR ONE

This first successful British solar-powered aircraft has a glider configuration. The built-up framework structure is of wood, covered with a thin heat-shrunk plastics material known as Solarfilm. To simplify stowage and transport, the long-span cantilever wing is made in three sections, with a laminated spruce girder main box-spar. A Wortmann FX-180 wing section is used. The all-moving fin and tailplane are detachable.

A two-blade propeller, at the top of a pylon in front of the cockpit, is driven through 3:1 reduction gearing by four 0·75 kW (1 hp) Bosch permanent magnet electric motors, linked by a chain drive. The batteries to power the motors consist of 24 nickel-cadmium cells, with a combined capacity of 25Ah, which store the energy supplied by 750 solar cells, each 76 mm (3 in) in diameter, attached

The solar cells above the wing roots are visible in this view of Solar One (Flight International)

to the upper surface of the root section of the wings, aft of the spar.

DIMENSIONS, EXTERNAL:
Wing span	20·73 m (68 ft 0 in)
Wing area, gross	24·15 m² (260 sq ft)
Solar cell area	3·44 m² (37 sq ft)
Length overall	6·71 m (22 ft 0 in)

Propeller diameter	1·60 m (5 ft 3 in)

WEIGHT:
Weight empty, equipped	105 kg (230 lb)

PERFORMANCE (estimated):
Never-exceed speed	50 knots (92 km/h; 58 mph)
Design cruising speed	25 knots (46 km/h; 29 mph)
Max rate of climb at S/L	21 m (70 ft)/min

TRAGO MILLS
TRAGO MILLS LTD (AIRCRAFT DIVISION)

Treswithick Farm, Cardinham, Bodmin, Cornwall PL30 4BU
Telephone: Cardinham (020 882) 485
CHIEF DESIGNER: Sydney A. Holloway

Trago Mills sponsored and owns the MW2 Excalibur single-seat ultralight aircraft, designed by Mr Michael Whittaker and last described in the 1977-78 *Jane's.* More recently, the company has been building the prototype of Mr Sydney Holloway's SAH-1 two-seat light aircraft.

TRAGO MILLS SAH-1

Design of the SAH-1 started in October 1977, and construction of a prototype began in January 1978. Both design and construction are to full CAA and FAR Pt 23 standards, and production is intended after certification

Trago Mills SAH-1 side-by-side two-seat light aircraft *(Michael A. Badrocke)*

Wing aspect ratio	7·5
Length overall	6·58 m (21 ft 7¼ in)
Height overall	2·38 m (7 ft 9·6 in)
Tailplane span	2·74 m (9 ft 0 in)
Wheel track	2·26 m (7 ft 4·8 in)
Wheelbase	1·46 m (4 ft 9·6 in)
Propeller diameter	1·68 m (5 ft 6 in)
Propeller ground clearance	0·25 m (10 in)

DIMENSIONS, INTERNAL:
Cockpit: Length	1·52 m (5 ft 0 in)
Max width	1·19 m (3 ft 10·8 in)
Baggage space	0·4 m³ (14·0 cu ft)

AREAS:
Wings, gross	11·15 m² (120·0 sq ft)
Ailerons (total)	0·89 m² (9·6 sq ft)
Trailing-edge flaps (total)	1·30 m² (14·0 sq ft)
Fin	0·96 m² (10·3 sq ft)
Rudder	0·63 m² (6·8 sq ft)
Tailplane	1·11 m² (12·0 sq ft)
Elevators, incl tab	0·93 m² (10·0 sq ft)

WEIGHTS AND LOADINGS:
Weight empty, equipped	445 kg (982 lb)
Max fuel load	85 kg (188 lb)
Max T-O weight	725 kg (1,600 lb)
Max wing loading	65·05 kg/m² (13·33 lb/sq ft)
Max power loading:	
O-200-A	9·74 kg/kW (16·0 lb/hp)
O-240	7·48 kg/kW (12·3 lb/hp)

PERFORMANCE (estimated, at max T-O weight. A: O-200-A engine; B: O-240):
Never-exceed speed:	
A, B	198 knots (367 km/h; 228 mph)
Max level speed at S/L:	
A	120 knots (222 km/h; 138 mph)
B	135 knots (250 km/h; 155 mph)
Max cruising speed at S/L:	
A	120 knots (222 km/h; 138 mph)
B	133 knots (246 km/h; 153 mph)
Econ cruising speed at S/L:	
A	109 knots (202 km/h; 125 mph)
B	120 knots (222 km/h; 138 mph)
Stalling speed, flaps down, engine idling:	
A, B	46·5 knots (86·5 km/h; 54 mph)
Max rate of climb at S/L: A	228 m (750 ft)/min
B	280 m (921 ft)/min
Service ceiling: A	5,275 m (17,300 ft)
B	6,920 m (22,700 ft)
T-O run: A	275 m (901 ft)
B	229 m (751 ft)
T-O to 15 m (50 ft): A	422 m (1,385 ft)
B	328 m (1,077 ft)
Landing from 15 m (50 ft): A, B	262 m (858 ft)
Landing run: A, B	121 m (397 ft)
Min ground turning radius	8·53 m (28 ft 0 in)
Range (A, B):	
with max payload	312 nm (578 km; 359 miles)
with max fuel	497 nm (921 km; 572 miles)

has been obtained. It is hoped to make the first flight in the Summer of 1981.

TYPE: Two-seat fully-aerobatic light aircraft.

WINGS: Cantilever low-wing monoplane. Wing section NACA 2413·6 (constant). Dihedral 5° from roots. Incidence 3° at root, 1° at tip. Tapered, non-swept aluminium alloy wings, with L65 spar booms and L72 sheet skins, stabilised with PVC foam. Trailing-edge single-slotted flaps and slotted ailerons of similar construction.

FUSELAGE: Aluminium alloy fail-safe stressed-skin structure, with radiused corners, incorporating centre-section spars.

TAIL UNIT: Aluminium alloy cantilever structure, stabilised with PVC foam. Constant-chord tailplane, attached to fuselage, with horn-balanced elevators; full-span trim tab in starboard elevator. Sweptback fin and horn-balanced rudder.

LANDING GEAR: Non-retractable tricycle type, with single Cleveland 5·00-5 wheel and tyre on each unit. Oleo-pneumatic shock-absorber on nosewheel leg; spring steel main legs. Tyre pressures 1·93 bars (28 lb/sq in) on nose unit, 2·07 bars (30 lb/sq in) on main units. Cleveland hydraulic brakes.

POWER PLANT: One flat-four engine, driving a two-blade fixed-pitch propeller with spinner. Aircraft will be offered with choice of 75 kW (100 hp) Rolls-Royce Continental O-200-A or 97 kW (130 hp) Rolls-Royce Continental O-240. Integral fuel tank in each leading-edge, total capacity 114 litres (25 Imp gallons). Refuelling point in upper surface of each wing. Oil capacity 5·7 litres (1·25 Imp gallons).

ACCOMMODATION: Two seats side by side under rearward-sliding bubble canopy. Baggage space aft of seats. Cockpit heated and ventilated.

SYSTEM: 60A engine-driven alternator.

AVIONICS AND EQUIPMENT: Blind-flying instrumentation standard. Radio to customer's specification.

DIMENSIONS, EXTERNAL:
Wing span	9·36 m (30 ft 8·4 in)
Wing chord at root	1·515 m (4 ft 11⅔ in)
Wing chord at tip	0·81 m (2 ft 8 in)

WALLIS
WALLIS AUTOGYROS LTD

HEAD OFFICE: Reymerston Hall, Norfolk NR9 4QY
Telephone: 0362 850418
DIRECTORS:
Wg Cdr K. H. Wallis, CEng, FRAeS, FRSA, RAF (Retd)
P. M. Wallis

The first Wallis single-seat ultralight autogyro (G-ARRT, flown for the first time in August 1961) introduced many patented features, including a rotor head with offset gimbal system to provide hands and feet off stability and to eliminate pitch-up and 'tuck-under' hazards; a high-speed flexible rotor spin-up shaft with positive disengagement during flight; an automatic system of controlling rotor drive on take-off which allows power to be applied until the last moment; centrifugal stops to control rotor blade teetering; and a novel safe starting arrangement.

Many other Wallis autogyros have since been completed. All of these were built for special purposes, and are not on public sale.

WALLIS WA-116 and WA-116-T

The WA-116 represents the original Wallis design, of which the prototype (G-ARRT) flew for the first time on 2 August 1961, powered by a 54 kW (72 hp) modified McCulloch 4318 piston engine. Four more WA-116s were built by Beagle and five by Wg Cdr Wallis, as described in the 1973-74 *Jane's*. The last of these was later dismantled for construction of the two-seat G-AXAS, a WA-116-T.

WA-116/Mc. The prototype (G-ARRT) currently holds the height record for autogyros in Classes E3 and E3a, at 4,639 m (15,220 ft), set on 11 May 1968 with its original 54 kW (72 hp) McCulloch engine; and the Class E3 and E3a records for speed in a straight line (96·589 knots; 179·000 km/h; 111·225 mph), set on 12 May 1969 after being re-engined with a 67 kW (90 hp) McCulloch. This aircraft, and the 'James Bond' WA-116/Mc (G-ARZB), continue to perform well. The latter has now appeared in more than 500 displays, as far afield as Australia and the USA.

The photographic workhorse G-ASDY, a Wallis WA-116/F fitted with a Vinten 360 camera installation

First flown in 1961, the WA-116/Mc prototype G-ARRT is still in use and still in excellent flying order

Photographed in May 1980, the WA-116/F G-ATHM then held nine autogyro records and had a tenth awaiting confirmation

Rolls-Royce-engined Wallis WA-117/R-R, with Vinten 751 panoramic camera pack

The Wallis WA-118/M, designed to fly at altitudes of more than 9,145 m (30,000 ft)

Wallis WA-120/R-R, on display at the Science Museum, London
(Science Museum)

WA-116/F.

Designation applied following the refitting of G-ASDY in 1971 with a 44 kW (60 hp) Franklin 2A-120-A engine. It is currently fitted with a Franklin 2A-120-B engine, driving a specially-designed two-blade propeller, and has carried out a considerable amount of specialised aerial photographic work, as detailed in earlier editions of *Jane's*. This work is continuing, currently using a Vinten 360 camera with a 500-frame magazine of 70 mm film. The viewfinder, which is special to the fixed beam installation, can be adjusted to suit the different focal lengths of lens. With this fixed mounting, it is easy for the pilot to hold a subject in the centre of the viewfinder for 360° coverage, literally 'flying the camera'. The pilot can thus concentrate on the photographic task, since rotor revolutions are maintained automatically, while airspeed is relatively unimportant. Changes in airspeed are easily sensed, and adjusted by power changes.

A particularly successful WA-116/F is G-ATHM which currently holds nine world rotorcraft records; a tenth was awaiting certification in mid-1980. This aircraft underwent more extensive conversion than its predecessors, mainly to increase fuel capacity and pilot comfort to fit it for special long-range flights. It has a 50 litre (11 Imp gallon) internal fuel tank, and began test flying, for range, in April 1974. Fitted also with a 36 litre (8 Imp gallon) jettisonable long-range ventral tank, it set up on 13 July 1974 new Class E3 and E3a world records, for nonstop distance in a closed circuit, of 361·91 nm (670·26 km; 416·48 miles). Additionally, this flight set new 100 km (Class E3a only) and 500 km (Class E3 and E3a) closed-circuit speed records of 70·51 knots (130·67 km/h; 81·19 mph) and 68·07 knots (126·14 km/h; 78·38 mph) respectively. A 91 litre (20 Imp gallon) ventral tank was next fitted, and on 28 September 1975, with this tank containing some 70 litres (15·5 Imp gallons), Wg Cdr Wallis made a nonstop flight from Lydd, Kent, to Wick, Caithness. This flight set Class E3 and E3a records for nonstop distance in a straight line of 472·092 nm (874·315 km; 543·274 miles). In fact, the actual distance flown, to avoid airfield zones and other hazardous areas, was in the order of 521 nm (966 km; 600 miles), flown in 6 h 25 min at an average speed of approx 81 knots (150 km/h; 93 mph). The ventral tank was not jettisoned after being emptied, and G-ATHM landed with sufficient fuel remaining for a further 65 nm (121 km; 75 miles). Its time of 6 h 25 min was later confirmed by the FAI as a record for duration in both Class E3 and Class E3a. Thus, WA-116s now hold all the major autogyro world records for speed, height, range and endurance.

It was hoped during 1980 to fit G-ATHM with a prototype experimental British light aircraft engine, in collaboration with Weslake and Co of Rye, Sussex. This more economical and efficient engine was expected to enhance G-ATHM's performance, possibly leading to further record attempts; at the same time, the aircraft would serve as a flying testbed for the prototype engine.

WA-116-T/Mc.

The McCulloch-engined WA-116-T/Mc, G-AXAS, is a tandem two-seat autogyro which flew for the first time on 3 April 1969. It remains the lightest two-seater in the Wallis range, and is expected to improve even further upon the 3·14 : 1 ratio of all-up weight to empty weight, which it established at RAE Bedford in 1971. It made more than 130 flights in a programme of multi-spectral experiments by Plessey Radar on behalf of the Home Office, as described in the 1979-80 *Jane's*. More recently it has been operating on the volcanic island of Lanzarote, in the Canary Islands, during filming of the science-fiction motion picture *The Martian Chronicles*. In addition to its part in the film, as the vehicle carried on the 'Zeus 3' manned mission to Mars, the aircraft was used to carry a 35 mm Arriflex camera for some of the aerial photography.

DIMENSIONS (WA-116/F):
Rotor diameter	6·20 m (20 ft 4 in)
Length of fuselage	3·38 m (11 ft 1 in)
Height to top of rotor head	1·85 m (6 ft 1 in)
Wheel track	1·63 m (5 ft 4 in)
Wheelbase	1·07 m (3 ft 6 in)

WEIGHTS (WA-116/F):
Weight empty	143 kg (316 lb)
Max T-O weight	317·5 kg (700 lb)

PERFORMANCE (WA-116/F):
Max level speed	not fully explored
Cruising speed without long-range tank	
	87 knots (161 km/h; 100 mph)
Max rate of climb at S/L	305 m (1,000 ft)/min
Max range with long-range tank (estimated)	
	651 nm (1,207 km; 750 miles)

WALLIS WA-117/R-R

Started in 1964, the WA-117 combines the proven features of the WA-116 airframe with a fully-certificated engine, the 74 kW (100 hp) Rolls-Royce Continental O-200-B. An experimental test vehicle (G-ATCV) flew for the first time on 24 March 1965; this was later dismantled for the construction of a true WA-117 prototype (G-AVJV), which made its first flight on 28 May 1967. This aircraft took part in the Loch Ness investigations in 1970, and has since undertaken considerable evaluation of infra-red linescan and low light level TV systems. With a BAe Dynamics Type 213 Linescan and a photographic pack containing an electric-drive 70 mm wide-angle camera, it carried out experimental detection of leaks in main water pipelines buried 2·45 m (8 ft) underground. As shown in an accompanying photograph, it has also been fitted with a Vinten Type 751 panoramic camera, with which it recently made a photographic coverage of the Liverpool-Manchester railway on the occasion of the line's 150th anniversary celebrations. For that mission, the Vinten camera was used in the beam mode; it can also be used in a cross-track mode, as demonstrated during the 1979 Paris Air Show. With its special silencers and special four-blade 'quiet' propeller, G-AVJV is one of the quietest powered aircraft of any kind yet built.

WEIGHT:
Max T-O weight	approx 317·5 kg (700 lb)

PERFORMANCE:
Max level speed	104 knots (193 km/h; 120 mph)
Cruising speed	78 knots (145 km/h; 90 mph)
Max rate of climb	approx 305 m (1,000 ft)/min

WALLIS WA-118/M METEORITE

The WA-118 Meteorite flew for the first time on 6 May 1966, having at that time the registration G-ATPW. Its 89 kW (120 hp) supercharged Italian Meteor Alfa 1 engine was brought up to then-current standards during 1969-70. The aircraft was also fitted with a bubble canopy, reclining cockpit and other modifications, and was rebuilt as G-AVJW, making its first flight in this form on 9 August 1969. Intended for a long-term test programme, it was then completely redesigned and rebuilt with the latest features of the Wallis range. The aircraft has a partially stress-bearing GRP cockpit nacelle capable of being used as an open cockpit or, in inclement weather, of accepting an optional hardtop (not yet tested). The nacelle is being tested for a planned Franklin-powered autogyro of even better performance than the WA-116/F G-ATHM. The objective is to provide more space and comfort for the pilot, without sacrificing performance, and the cockpit will permit the internal stowage of oxygen equipment and an approved recording barograph. The WA-118/M is intended eventually to achieve altitudes in excess of 9,145 m (30,000 ft). Trials were continuing at a low priority in 1980, and will continue thus unless the present world altitude records for autogyros are broken by substantial margins.

WALLIS WA-120/R-R

The WA-120 (G-AYVO) is powered by a 97 kW (130 hp) Rolls-Royce Continental O-240-A flat-four engine and cruises at a fuel consumption of 15·9 litres (3·5 Imp gallons)/h. Construction began under the original designation WA-117-S. It subsequently developed into more than a re-engined version of the WA-117, justifying the use of a new designation. It flew for the first time on 13 June 1971.

The WA-120 has a forward-sliding transparent cockpit canopy, and can be flown at speeds of up to 60 knots (111 km/h; 69 mph) with this canopy partly open.

During 1977 the WA-120/R-R was loaned to the Science Museum in London, where in mid-1980 it still formed part of an exhibition on the theme of 'Exploration', fitted with four Vinten 70 mm reconnaissance cameras in a multi-band pack. Still in flying order, the WA-120/R-R is expected to remain in this exhibition for a further three years.

WALLIS WA-121

The WA-121 is the smallest and lightest Wallis autogyro to date. Three versions are envisaged: a high-speed **WA-121/Mc** with a Wallis-McCulloch engine of about 74 kW (100 hp); a cross-country **WA-121/F** with a 44·5 kW (60 hp) Franklin 2A-120-B engine; and a high-altitude **WA-121/M Meteorite 2** with a supercharged 89 kW (120 hp) Meteor Alfa 1 radial two-stroke engine and transistorised ignition.

The prototype WA-121/Mc (G-BAHH) has a high-mounted tailplane and an open cockpit, and made its first flight on 28 December 1972. It has already exceeded

unofficially the speed and altitude records held by the WA-116 prototype G-ARRT. It employs a number of improvements in control system design, resulting in greater stability at speed, better head resistance and greater pilot comfort. Special features in the rotor head suspension, originally incorporated in the WA-117 prototype G-AVJV, are incorporated also in the WA-120 and WA-121. Now fitted with a wider-track main landing gear, to standardise it with other autogyros in the Wallis range, the WA-121 was expected to begin experimental flying in 1980 using rotor blades designed for high speeds. The results so gained may be used in the design of a further autogyro, to be powered by the new Weslake engine referred to in the WA-116/F entry.

WALLIS WA-122/R-R

The basic layout of the open-frame, two-seat WA-116-T has proved very successful in providing a passenger

with autogyro air experience. In addition, dual controls can be fitted when required, and other controls (eg, throttle and spin-up drive lever) can be reached by both occupants. However, the high noise level of the modified McCulloch engine would preclude the use of this aircraft for ab initio instruction, and reliability of this uncertificated engine could not be accepted for regular training use.

In consequence, a slightly larger two-seat aircraft (G-BGGW), known as the WA-122/R-R, has been built, and began flight testing on 16 July 1980. Powered by a 119 kW (160 hp) Rolls-Royce Continental O-240 flat-four engine, the WA-122/R-R retains the main characteristics of the WA-116-T, keeping the tandem layout but with more space between the seats. The rear seat is higher than the one in front. Rotor diameter is increased to approx 7·0 m (23 ft); the blades, and also the landing gear legs, can be quickly folded, for ease of transportation in a container.

The Wallis WA-121/Mc, which has already exceeded unofficially the world speed and altitude records for autogyros held by the WA-116/Mc prototype since 1968-69

Wg Cdr Wallis demonstrating the 'hands and feet off' stability of the WA-122/R-R at a preselected and trimmed airspeed

WESTLAND
WESTLAND AIRCRAFT LTD

HEAD OFFICE, WORKS AND AIRFIELD: Yeovil, Somerset BA20 2YB
LONDON OFFICE: 8 The Sanctuary, Westminster, London SW1P 3JU
PRESIDENT: Sir Eric Mensforth, CB, DSc, FEng
CHAIRMAN: The Rt Hon Lord Aldington, PC, KCMG, CBE, DSO
DEPUTY CHAIRMAN: The Rt Hon Lord Aberconway
VICE-CHAIRMAN AND CHIEF EXECUTIVE: B. D. Blackwell, MA, BSc(Eng), FEng, FIMechE, FRAeS, FBIM
DIRECTORS:
Sir Christopher Hartley, KCB, CBE, DFC, AFC, BA
Sir Ronald Melville, KCB
W. T. C. Miller, OBE, MA, CEng, MIMechE, MInstM
J. Speechley, OBE, MSc, FEng, FRAeS
Sir John Treacher, KCB, FRAeS
S. W. Wiltshire
SECRETARY: J. R. Bayley, LLB
PUBLIC RELATIONS EXECUTIVE: John Teague, CEng, MRAeS, MIM

Westland Aircraft Ltd was formed in July 1935, to take over the aircraft branch of Petters Ltd, previously known as the Westland Aircraft Works, which had been engaged

in aircraft design and construction since 1915.

Westland entered the helicopter industry in 1947 by acquiring the licence to build the Sikorsky S-51, of which it produced 133 under the name Westland Dragonfly. This technical association with Sikorsky has continued, and it was decided subsequently to concentrate on the design, development and construction of helicopters.

In 1959, Westland acquired Saunders-Roe Ltd. In 1960 it acquired the Helicopter Division of Bristol Aircraft Ltd and Fairey Aviation Ltd, and is now the only major helicopter design and manufacturing organisation in the United Kingdom.

Since 1 October 1966, the company's helicopter business has been conducted through a wholly-owned company named Westland Helicopters Ltd.

Through the British Hovercraft Corporation Ltd, Westland is continuing development of the Hovercraft type of vehicle pioneered by Saunders-Roe.

One of Westland's subsidiary companies, Normalair-Garrett Ltd, specialises in the design, development and production of aircraft pressure control, air-conditioning, oxygen breathing and hydraulic systems. Most British pressurised aircraft, civil and military, use Normalair-Garrett equipment, as do the Panavia Tornado and many aircraft of foreign design. In addition, this company produces data loggers, trace readers and hydraulic equipment for aircraft flying controls.

WESTLAND HELICOPTERS LTD

HEAD OFFICE, WORKS AND AIRFIELD: Yeovil, Somerset BA20 2YB
Telephone: Yeovil (0935) 5222
Telex: 46277
EXECUTIVE CHAIRMAN: B. D. Blackwell, MA, BSc(Eng), FEng, FIMechE, FRAeS, FBIM
ACCOUNTING DIRECTOR AND SECRETARY: A. R. B. Hobbs, FCCA
FINANCE DIRECTOR: Malcolm Jones, BSc(Econ), FCMA, MBIM
DIRECTOR OF ADVANCED ENGINEERING: J. P. Jones, PhD, BSc(Eng), CEng, FRAeS
COMMERCIAL DIRECTOR: A. V. N. Reed, BSc(Tech), CEng, FRAeS, AMBIM
SALES AND PRODUCT SUPPORT DIRECTOR: A. M. Cundick, BSc(Eng), CEng, FRAeS, MBIM
WORKS DIRECTOR: J. W. Bower, CEng, MIMechE, MBIM
TECHNICAL DIRECTOR: V. A. B. Rogers, MSc, CEng, FRAeS, FIMechE
PUBLIC RELATIONS MANAGER: Michael J. Farlam

Helicopters in current production at the Yeovil headquarters of Westland Helicopters are the Sea King, Commando, Gazelle and Lynx. The Gazelle and Lynx, together with the Puma, form part of the Anglo-French helicopter co-operation programme.

Gazelles are in production for the British and French armed forces. Production of the Lynx began in 1975, and Westland is actively involved with production of component sets for Pumas built by Aérospatiale.

In another international programme, Westland Helicopters and Agusta of Italy have formed jointly a company named EH Industries to develop and produce the EH 101 anti-submarine helicopter (see page 100).

WESTLAND SEA KING

The Sea King was developed originally by Westland to meet the Royal Navy's requirement for an advanced anti-submarine helicopter with prolonged endurance. It can also undertake secondary roles, such as search and rescue, tactical troop transport, casualty evacuation, cargo carrying and long-range self-ferry. A land-based general-purpose version, the Commando, is described separately.

The Sea King development programme stemmed from a licence agreement for the S-61 helicopter concluded originally with Sikorsky in 1959. This permitted Westland to utilise the basic airframe and rotor system of the Sikorsky SH-3D, of which a description can be found in the US section. Considerable changes were made in the power plant and in specialised equipment, to meet British requirements.

The fuselage is essentially similar to that of the basic Sikorsky aircraft, with a watertight hull which allows water

Westland Sea King HAS.Mk 2 anti-submarine helicopter *(Pilot Press)*

landing in an emergency. The retractable main landing gear is housed in sponsons braced to the fuselage by fixed struts. To improve the lateral stability and flotation capability of the helicopter with the rotor stopped, inflatable buoyancy bags are fitted to the outside of each sponson.

The following versions of the Sea King had been announced up to mid-1980:

Sea King HAS. Mk 1. ASW version for Royal Navy, ordered in 1967. First production HAS. Mk 1 (XV642) flown for the first time on 7 May 1969. Total of 56 built, delivery of which was completed in May 1972. In service with Nos. 814, 819, 820, 824 and 826 Squadrons. Described in previous editions of *Jane's*. Currently being uprated by Royal Navy to Mk 2 standard.

Sea King HAS. Mk 2. Uprated version for ASW and SAR duties with the Royal Navy. Twenty-one ordered; first flown (XZ570) on 18 June 1976. Equipment includes search radar and dunking sonar. To be upgraded to **Mk 5** standard by introduction of Marconi Avionics LAPADS (Lightweight Acoustic Processing And Display System) passive sonobuoy processor to improve detection capability, MEL improved radar, Decca TANS and other modifications (see Addenda).

Sea King HAR. Mk 3. Uprated version for SAR duties with the Royal Air Force. Provision for flight crew of two pilots, air electronics/winch operator and loadmaster/winchman; up to six stretchers, or two stretchers and 11 seated survivors, or 19 persons. Nav system includes Decca TANS F computer, accepting inputs from Mk 19 Decca nav receiver and Type 71 Doppler. MEL radar. Sixteen ordered, to equip No. 202 Squadron at Lossiemouth, Scotland. First HAR. Mk 3 flew on 6 September 1977; deliveries completed in 1979.

Sea King HC. Mk 4. Utility version of Commando Mk 2 (which see) for Royal Navy.

Sea King Mk 4X. Two aircraft of this type, based on the Sea King Mk 4, are to be built for RAE Farnborough. The first of these aircraft, due for delivery in 1982, is to be used as a radar development vehicle for the EH 101 programme.

Sea King Mk 41. Search and rescue version for Federal German Navy. First example (89 + 50) flown for the first time on 6 March 1972. Twenty-two ordered, of which production and delivery were completed in 1974. First unit to equip with these aircraft was MFG.5, based at Kiel-Holtenau.

Sea King Mk 42. ASW version for Indian Navy. Original order for six, which are in service with No. 330 Squadron. Delivery of a further six was completed in 1974, and these are in service with Nos. 330 and 336 Squadrons. Follow-on order announced in June 1977 for three uprated aircraft, designated **Mk 42A**, with hauldown capability for small-ship operation.

Sea King Mk 43. SAR version for Norwegian Air Force. Eleven delivered. In service with No. 330 Squadron at Bodo.

Sea King Mk 45. ASW version for Pakistan Navy. Six ordered, delivery of which was completed during 1975.

Sea King Mk 47. ASW version. Six ordered by Saudi Arabia on behalf of Egyptian Navy. Delivery completed in 1976.

Sea King Mk 48. SAR version for Belgian Air Force. Five ordered, including one aircraft with VIP interior capability. Delivery completed in November 1976. In service with No. 40 Squadron at Coxyde.

Westland Sea King HAR. Mk 3 search and rescue helicopter of the Royal Air Force

Sea King Mk 50. Version, developed from Mk 1, for No. 817 Squadron of the Royal Australian Navy, which ordered 10. First flight 30 June 1974. Production included offset manufacture in Australia to 30% of the contract value. Deliveries began in the Autumn of 1974. The Mk 50 was the first fully-uprated version of the Sea King to fly. It is capable of operation in the roles of anti-submarine search and strike, vertical replenishment, tactical troop lift, search and rescue, casualty evacuation, and self-ferry.

A total of 239 Sea King and Commando aircraft had been ordered by 19 May 1980.

A description of the Sea King Mk 1, which is applicable also to most export versions except the Mks 47, 48 and 50, has appeared in previous editions of *Jane's*. Current production Sea Kings (Mk 2/3 standard) have uprated Gnome engines and transmission, a six-blade tail rotor, increased max T-O weight and other detail improvements; the following description applies to the current version. Most of the improvements are incorporated also in the Mk 50s built for Australia, and in certain other export versions.

POWER PLANT (all current versions): Two 1,238 kW (1,660 shp) (max contingency rating) Rolls-Royce Gnome H.1400-1 turboshaft engines, mounted side by side above cabin. Transmission rating 2,012 kW (2,700 shp). Fuel in underfloor bag tanks, total capacity (SAR versions) 3,636 litres (800 Imp gallons). Internal auxiliary tank may be fitted for long-range ferry purposes. Pressure refuelling point on starboard side, two gravity points on port side.

ACCOMMODATION: Crew of four in ASW role; accommodation for up to 22 survivors in SAR role. Two-section airstair door at front on port side, cargo door at rear on starboard side. Entire accommodation heated and ven-

tilated. Cockpit doors and windows, and two windows each side of cabin, can be jettisoned in an emergency.

SYSTEMS: Three main hydraulic systems. Primary and auxiliary systems operate main rotor control. Utility system (207 bars; 3,000 lb/sq in) for main landing gear, sonar and rescue winches and blade folding. Pressure for windscreen wipers 86 bars (1,250 lb/sq in). Electrical system includes two 20kVA 200V three-phase 400Hz engine-driven generators, a 26V single-phase AC supply fed from the aircraft's 22Ah nickel-cadmium battery through an inverter, and DC power provided as a secondary system from two 200A transformer-rectifier units.

OPERATIONAL EQUIPMENT (ASW models): As equipped for this role, the Sea King is a fully-integrated all-weather hunter-killer weapon system, capable of operating independently of surface vessels, and has the following equipment and weapons to achieve this task: Plessey Type 195 dipping sonar, Bendix AN/AQS-13B dipping sonar (Mk 50), Marconi AD 580 Doppler navigation system, AW 391 search radar in dorsal radome, transponder beneath rear fuselage, Honeywell AN/APN-171 radio altimeter, Sperry GM7B Gyrosyn compass system, Louis Newmark Mk 31 automatic flight control system, two No. 4 marine markers, four No. 2 Mk 2 smoke floats, Ultra Electronics mini-sonobuoys, up to four Mk 46 homing torpedoes, or four Mk 11 depth charges or one Clevite simulator. Observer/navigator has tactical display on which sonar contacts are integrated with search radar and navigational information. Radio equipment comprises Plessey PTR 377 UHF/VHF and homer, Ultra D 403M standby UHF, Collins 618-T3 HF radio, Ultra UA 60M intercom, Telebrief system and IFF provisions. For secondary role a mounting is provided on the aft frame of the starboard door for a general-purpose machine-gun. The Mk 31 AFCS provides radio altitude displays for both pilots; artificial horizon displays; three-axis stabilisation in pilot-controlled manoeuvres; attitude hold, heading hold and height hold in cruising flight; controlled transition manoeuvres to and from the hover; automatic height control and plan position control in the hover; and an auxiliary trim facility.

OPERATIONAL EQUIPMENT (non-ASW models): A wide range of radio and navigation equipment may be installed, including VHF/UHF communications, VHF/UHF homing, radio compass, Doppler navigation system, radio altimeter, VOR/ILS, radar and transponder, of Collins, Plessey, Honeywell and Marconi manufacture. A Sperry compass system and a Louis Newmark automatic flight control system are also installed. Sea Kings equipped for search and rescue have in addition a Breeze BL 10300 variable-speed hydraulic rescue hoist of 272 kg (600 lb) capacity mounted above the starboard-side cargo door. Automatic main rotor blade folding and spreading is standard with this version, and for shipboard operation the tail pylon can also be folded. With search radar fitted, a total of 18 survivors and medical staff can be carried; this total can be increased to 22 if the search radar is omitted . In the casualty evacuation role, the Sea King can accommodate up to 9 stretchers and two medical attendants, or intermediate combinations of seats and stretchers; a typical layout might provide for 14 seats and two stretchers. In the troop transport role, the Sea King can accommodate 22 troops, with the majority of seats at 42 cm (16·5 in) pitch, and can carry this load over a range of 300 nm (555 km; 345 miles) under ISA sea level conditions. As a cargo transport, the aircraft has an internal

Westland Sea King HC. Mk 4 utility version of the Commando for the Royal Navy

capacity of 2,720 kg (6,000 lb) or a max external load capacity of 2,948 kg (6,500 lb) when a low-response sling is fitted.

DIMENSIONS, EXTERNAL:

Diameter of main rotor	18·90 m	(62 ft 0 in)
Diameter of tail rotor	3·16 m	(10 ft 4 in)
Length overall (rotors turning)	22·15 m	(72 ft 8 in)
Length of fuselage	17·01 m	(55 ft 9¾ in)
Length overall (main rotor folded)		
	17·42 m	(57 ft 2 in)
Length overall (rotors and tail folded)		
	14·40 m	(47 ft 3 in)
Height overall (rotors turning)	5·13 m	(16 ft 10 in)
Height overall (rotors spread and stationary)		
	4·85 m	(15 ft 11 in)
Height to top of rotor hub	4·72 m	(15 ft 6 in)
Width overall (rotors folded):		
with flotation bags	4·98 m	(16 ft 4 in)
without flotation bags	4·77 m	(15 ft 8 in)
Wheel track (c/l of shock-absorbers)		
	3·96 m	(13 ft 0 in)
Cabin door (port): Height	1·68 m	(5 ft 6 in)
Width	0·91 m	(3 ft 0 in)
Cargo door (stbd): Height	1·52 m	(5 ft 0 in)
Width	1·73 m	(5 ft 8 in)
Height to sill	1·14 m	(3 ft 9 in)

DIMENSIONS, INTERNAL:

Cabin: Length:		
ASW	5·87 m	(19 ft 3 in)
SAR	7·59 m	(24 ft 11 in)
Max width	1·98 m	(6 ft 6 in)
Max height	1·92 m	(6 ft 3½ in)
Floor area (incl area occupied by radar, sonar etc):		
ASW	12·08 m²	(130 sq ft)
SAR	13·94 m²	(150 sq ft)

WEIGHTS AND LOADINGS (A: anti-submarine, B: SAR, C: troop transport, D: casualty evacuation, E: internal cargo):

Basic weight (depending on version)		
	approx 5,896 kg	(13,000 lb)
Weight, equipped: A	6,201 kg	(13,672 lb)
B, C	5,613 kg	(12,376 lb)
D	5,797 kg	(12,781 lb)
E	5,558 kg	(12,253 lb)
Max T-O weight:		
all current versions	9,525 kg	(21,000 lb)
Max disc loading	34·62 kg/m²	(7·09 lb/sq ft)
Max power loading	4·73 kg/kW	(7·77 lb/shp)

PERFORMANCE (at max T-O weight, all current versions):

Cruising speed at S/L		
	112 knots	(208 km/h; 129 mph)
Max rate of climb at S/L	616 m	(2,020 ft)/min
Max vertical rate of climb at S/L	119 m	(390 ft)/min
Service ceiling, one engine out	1,220 m	(4,000 ft)
Hovering ceiling IGE	1,525 m	(5,000 ft)
Hovering ceiling OGE	975 m	(3,200 ft)
Range with max standard fuel		
	664 nm	(1,230 km; 764 miles)
Ferry range with max standard and auxiliary fuel		
	814 nm	(1,507 km; 937 miles)

WESTLAND COMMANDO

First flown on 12 September 1973, the Commando is a tactical helicopter based on the Sea King.

The payload/range performance and endurance capabilities of the Sea King have been optimised in the design of the Commando, which is intended to operate with maximum efficiency in the primary roles of tactical troop transport, logistic support and cargo transport, and casualty evacuation. In addition, the Commando can operate effectively in the secondary roles of air-to-surface strike and search and rescue.

The following versions have been announced:

Commando Mk 1. Designation of first five Commandos, part of a larger order placed on behalf of the Egyptian Air Force by the Saudi Arabian government. Minimally-modified version able to transport up to 21 troops. First two delivered to Egypt in January/February 1974. All five now delivered.

British Army Westland Lynx during firing trials with TOW anti-tank missiles

Commando Mk 2. Major production version, to which the following description applies. Flew for first time (G-17-12) on 16 January 1975. The Saudi Arabian order for Sea King/Commando helicopters included 17 Mk 2s and two VIP Mk 2Bs for the Egyptian Air Force. In addition, four Mk 2s (three Mk 2As and one VIP Mk 2C) were ordered by the Qatar Emiri Air Force.

Sea King HC. Mk 4. Utility version of Commando Mk 2 for Royal Navy. Incorporates folding main rotor blades and folding tail pylon of Sea King, but retains non-retractable wheeled landing gear of Commando. Designed to carry up to 27 fully-equipped troops in cabin, or 2,720 kg (6,000 lb) of cargo, and to operate in arctic and tropical conditions. Max slung load 3,400 kg (7,500 lb). Equipped for parachuting and abseiling. Revised avionics, including Decca TANS with chart display and Decca 71 Doppler navigation system. For service with Nos. 845 and 846 (Naval Air Commando) Squadrons. First flight (by ZA290) 26 September 1979. Fifteen ordered, of which the first was handed over to the Royal Navy in November 1979.

TYPE: Twin-turboshaft tactical military helicopter.

ROTOR SYSTEM: Five-blade single main rotor and six-blade tail rotor. Main rotor blades, of NACA 0012 section, attached to hub by multiple bolted joint. Blade construction consists of a light alloy extruded spar, with light alloy trailing-edge pockets. Tail rotor blades are of similar construction. Rotor brake fitted. Tail section folds for stowage; main rotor blades do not.

ROTOR DRIVE: Twin input four-stage reduction main gearbox, with single bevel intermediate and tail gearboxes. Main rotor/engine rpm ratio 93·43; tail rotor/engine rpm ratio: 15·26.

FUSELAGE: Light alloy stressed-skin structure, unpressurised. Sea King sponsons replaced by stub-wings.

TAIL UNIT: Similar to Sea King, with starboard-side half-tailplane at top of tail rotor pylon.

LANDING GEAR: Non-retractable tailwheel type, with twin-wheel main units. Oleo-pneumatic shock-absorbers. Mainwheel tyres size 6·50-10, tailwheel tyre size 6·00-6.

POWER PLANT: As for current versions of Sea King (which see).

ACCOMMODATION: Crew of two on flight deck. Seats along cabin sides, and single jump seat, for up to 28 troops. Two-piece airstair door at front on port side, cargo door at rear on starboard side. Entire accommodation heated and ventilated. Cockpit doors and windows, and two windows each side of main cabin, are jettisonable in an emergency.

SYSTEMS: Primary and secondary hydraulic systems for flight controls. No pneumatic system. Electrical system includes two 20kVA alternators.

AVIONICS AND EQUIPMENT: Blind-flying instrumentation standard. Wide range of radio, radar and navigation equipment available to customer's requirements. Cargo sling and rescue hoist optional.

ARMAMENT: Wide range of guns, missiles, etc may be carried, according to customer's requirements.

DIMENSIONS, EXTERNAL:

Diameter of main rotor	18·90 m	(62 ft 0 in)
Diameter of tail rotor	3·16 m	(10 ft 4 in)
Distance between rotor centres	11·10 m	(36 ft 5 in)
Main rotor blade chord	0·46 m	(1 ft 6¼ in)
Length overall (rotors turning)	22·15 m	(72 ft 8 in)
Length of fuselage	17·02 m	(55 ft 10 in)
Height overall (rotors turning)	5·13 m	(16 ft 10 in)
Height to top of rotor hub	4·72 m	(15 ft 6 in)
Wheel track (c/l of shock-absorbers)		
	3·96 m	(13 ft 0 in)
Wheelbase	7·21 m	(23 ft 8 in)
Passenger door (fwd, port):		
Height	1·68 m	(5 ft 6 in)
Width	0·91 m	(3 ft 0 in)
Cargo door (aft, stbd): Height	1·52 m	(5 ft 0 in)
Width	1·73 m	(5 ft 8 in)

DIMENSIONS, INTERNAL: As Sea King (SAR version)

AREAS:

Main rotor disc	280·5 m²	(3,019 sq ft)
Tail rotor disc	7·79 m²	(83·86 sq ft)
Main rotor blades (each)	4·14 m²	(44·54 sq ft)
Tail rotor blades (each)	0·23 m²	(2·46 sq ft)
Tailplane	1·80 m²	(19·40 sq ft)

WEIGHTS:

Operating weight empty (troop transport, 2 crew)		
	5,700 kg	(12,566 lb)
Max T-O weight	9,525 kg	(21,000 lb)

PERFORMANCE (at max T-O weight): As given for Sea King, plus:

Range with max payload (28 troops), reserves for 30 min stand-off and T-O

240 nm (445 km; 276 miles)

WESTLAND LYNX

The Lynx is one of three types of aircraft (Puma, Gazelle and Lynx) covered by the Anglo-French helicopter agreement first proposed in February 1967 and confirmed on 2 April 1968. Westland has design leadership in the Lynx, which is a medium-sized helicopter intended to fulfil general-purpose, naval and civil transport roles. It is the first British aircraft to be designed entirely on a metric basis.

The first of 13 Lynx prototypes (XW835) flew for the first time on 21 March 1971 and was followed by XW837, the third prototype (second Lynx to fly), on 28 September 1971.

Details of the subsequent development aircraft can be found in the 1975-76 *Jane's*. One example of the Army version and two of the naval version began final type testing and certification trials at the A & AEE, Boscombe Down, in mid-1975.

A Lynx intensive flying trials unit, No. 700L Naval Air Squadron, was formed in September 1976 at RNAS Yeovilton, Somerset, as a joint Royal Navy/Royal Netherlands Navy operational evaluation unit. Deck handling tests, on board HMS *Birmingham* off Portland, were completed in February 1977. Another Lynx intensive flying trials unit was formed at the British Army Air Corps headquarters at Middle Wallop, Hampshire, in mid-1977. The Army intensive flight trials were completed in December 1977.

The following versions of the Lynx have been announced:

Lynx AH. Mk 1. General-purpose and utility version for the British Army. Capable of operation on tactical troop transport, logistic support, armed escort of troop-carrying helicopters, anti-tank strike, search and rescue, casualty evacuation, reconnaissance and command post duties. Total of 114 ordered by 1 September 1980. First production aircraft (XZ170) flown on 11 February 1977; 52 delivered by early 1980.

A Westland-owned aircraft (G-LYNX, first flown in May 1979), has demonstrated the helicopter's multi-role capability with a wide range of weapons which have included Hughes TOW and Euromissile Hot anti-tank guided missiles; SURA 80 mm, SNEB 68 mm and FZ 2·75 in rockets; twin 7·62 mm machine-gun pods and 20 mm automatic cannon; Matra Magic 550 air-to-air missiles; an AN/ALE-39 countermeasures dispenser with ECM chaff; and ECM warning equipment. It can also carry mine dispensers, or anti-tank teams armed with Milan missiles.

Westland Commando Mk 2 twin-turboshaft tactical military helicopter (*Pilot Press*)

Lynx HAS. Mk 2. Version for Royal Navy, for advanced shipborne anti-submarine and other duties. Ferranti Sea Spray search and tracking radar in modified nose. Capable of operation on anti-submarine classification and strike, air to surface vessel search and strike, search and rescue, reconnaissance, troop transport, fire support, communication and fleet liaison, and vertical replenishment duties. Total of 80 ordered by 1 September 1980. First production aircraft (XZ229) flown on 10 February 1976; 38 delivered by early 1980. First operational RN unit, No. 702 Squadron, formed on completion of Navy intensive flight trials in December 1977. Serving in 1980 with nine Ships' Flights (five in Type 21 frigates, two in 'Leander' class frigates, and two in Type 42 destroyers). May be fitted with additional submarine detection gear, possibly of the dipping sonar type.

Lynx (French Navy). Navy version, generally similar to British HAS. Mk 2 but with Alcatel dunking sonar, French radar and radio, and AS.12 wire-guided missiles. Total of 26 ordered initially. First example delivered on 28 September 1978; delivery of all 26 due for completion by late 1980. A further 14 were ordered in May 1980: these will be fitted with uprated engines and transmission to permit an increase in AUW to 4,763 kg (10,500 lb).

In addition to orders from the British and French armed forces, 24 naval Lynx were ordered by the Royal Netherlands Navy, of which 18 are at the increased AUW of 4,763 kg (10,500 lb). The first batch of six (Dutch naval designation **UH-14A**) have been delivered, and are being used for search and rescue (with No. 7 Squadron), communications and training duties. Ten for use in the ASW role (designation **SH-14B**) have been delivered and are equipped with Alcatel dunking sonar. The first SH-14B was handed over on 3 September 1979. The other eight (designation **SH-14C**) are to be equipped with MAD.

Nine naval Lynx have been delivered to the Brazilian Navy, two to the Argentinian Navy (which has ordered eight more), and three military general-purpose Lynx with uprated engines to the state of Qatar. The Royal Danish Navy and Royal Norwegian Air Force have ordered eight and six naval Lynx, the Federal German Navy 12 incorporating Bendix AN/AQS-18 sonar. The first for Denmark was handed over on 15 May 1980.

In addition to the Westland demonstrator, a total of 306 Lynx had been ordered by October 1980. Production is shared in the ratio of 70% by Westland to 30% by Aérospatiale, and was at an approximate rate of six per month in early 1980.

The following description applies to both the military general-purpose and naval versions with the standard Gem power plant, except where otherwise indicated:

TYPE: Twin-engined multi-purpose helicopter.

ROTOR SYSTEM: Single four-blade semi-rigid main rotor and four-blade tail rotor. The main rotor blades, which are interchangeable, are of cambered aerofoil section and embody mass taper. Each blade consists of a two-piece, two-channel stainless steel D-shaped box-spar, to which is bonded a GRP rear skin stabilised by a Nomex plastics honeycomb core. Blade tips are of moulded GRP, with a stainless steel anti-erosion sheath forward of the 50% chord line. Each blade is attached to the main rotor hub by titanium root attachment plates and a flexible arm; the inboard portion of each arm accommodates most of the flapping movement of each blade, while the outer portion provides freedom in the lag plane. The rotor hub and inboard portions of the flexible arms are built as a complete unit, in the form of a titanium monobloc forging. A feathering hinge, comprising double needle bearings, is incorporated between the inboard and outboard flexible arms. The feathering hinge bearings are relieved of centrifugal loading by a flexible torsion bar which joints the inboard and outboard section of each arm. A two-pin jaw for blade attachment and manual blade folding is provided. Each of the tail rotor blades has a light alloy spar, machined integrally with the root attachment, which forms the nose portion of the aerofoil section and has a flush-fitting stainless steel sheath on the leading-edge. The rear section of each blade is of similar construction to that of the main rotor blades. The tail rotor hub has conventional flapping and feathering hinges, and incorporates torsionally flexible tiebars which carry the centrifugal loads inboard to the flapping hinges. Tail rotor blades are replaceable in opposing pairs, and each blade is attached to the hub by the outboard tiebar pin and a six-bolt root-end flanged joint. Main rotor blades of both versions can be folded, and tail rotor pylon of naval version can be folded and spread manually, to reduce overall length for stowage.

ROTOR DRIVE: Transmission consists of three interconnected gearboxes, transmitting power to the main and tail rotors. The engines are mounted from extensions of the gearbox casing through gimbal and flexible couplings which permit a degree of angular misalignment. The drives are taken from the front of the engines into the main gearbox, which is mounted above the cabin forward of the engines. This gearbox interconnects the two engines, with the speed reduction being carried out in two stages. The first stage uses an involute-form spiral bevel pinion and gear. The second stage comprises a conformal pinion meshing with a gear fixed directly to

Westland Lynx AH.Mk 1 helicopter, with additional side view (top) of Lynx HAS. Mk 2 *(Pilot Press)*

the main rotor drive-shaft. In flight, the accessory gears, which are all at the front of the main gearbox, are driven by one of the two through shafts from the first-stage reduction gears. For system checking on the ground without the rotor turning, the accessories can be driven by the port engine via a through shaft, a lockout freewheel unit being selected manually to isolate the main rotor transmission from the port engine input drive. Freewheel units are mounted in each engine gearbox shaft, and also within the accessory drive chain of gears. In the uprated gearbox, a load-sharing input gear wheel is introduced, which allows the tail rotor drive conformal pinion to act also as a third paralleled input drive to the conformal gear wheel. This arrangement permits the increase in transmission rating necessary for uprated Lynx which have an AUW increased to 4,763 kg (10,500 lb). Rotor head controls are actuated by three identical tandem servojacks, trunnion-mounted from the main rotor gearbox and powered by two independent hydraulic systems. The collective jack is mounted centrally on the forward end of the main gearbox, with the cyclic jacks positioned at 45° on each side. Duplex autostabiliser actuators are integral with each jack. Cyclic and collective inputs from the three control jacks are translated to the lower bearing housing of a four-arm spider which is located within, and rotates with, the main rotor shaft. The spider is mounted universally within a splined section of the main shaft, above its bearing housing, and is linked to the blade pitch-change levers by four adjustable-length track rods. Rod and lever control runs are employed on both the cyclic and collective systems, and are carried within protective ducts below the cockpit floor, up to cabin roof level on both sides of the aircraft, and finally to the rotor head. Yaw control runs are initially by rod and lever, and then to cables which transmit pedal movements along the tailboom to the tail rotor control jacks, which in turn effect blade pitch changes. Spring feel units and electric trim motors for the cyclic control channels are installed below the cockpit floor. Yaw control pedals are adjustable separately over a wide range. Control system incorporates a simple stability augmentation system, which acts in a single channel to provide improved stability in pitch. Provision is made for in-flight blade tracking. Each engine embodies an independent control system which provides full-authority rotor speed governing, pilot control being limited to selection of the desired rotor speed range. In the event of an engine failure, this system will restore power up to single-engine maximum contingency rating to maintain the power turbine/rotor governed speed within the prescribed limits. A single, centrally-mounted rotor speed select lever, with a limited authority, sets the datum of the power turbine/rotor speed governing system. This system meters fuel to maintain the selected speed throughout the flight condition range. A fine-adjustment trimming control is provided to facilitate accurate matching of each engine. On the naval versions, the main rotor can provide negative thrust to increase stability on deck after touchdown. Tail rotor drive is taken from the main ring gear. A hydraulically-operated rotor brake is mounted on the main gearbox at the tail rotor drive-shaft coupling, the shaft continuing aft to the single-stage, bevel reduction type intermediate and tail rotor gearboxes. Pitch variation of the tail rotor blades is controlled by a spider, actuated by hydraulic jack via a pushrod which extends through the centre of the tail rotor gearbox.

FUSELAGE AND TAIL UNIT: Conventional semi-monocoque pod and boom structure, mainly of light alloy, including a cantilever floor structure with unobstructed surface. Glassfibre components used for access panels, doors and fairings. The forward fuselage is free from bulkheads, giving an unrestricted field of view. Single large window in each of the main cabin sliding doors. Provision for internally-mounted defensive armament, and for universal flange mountings on each side of the

exterior to carry weapons or other stores. Tailboom is a light alloy monocoque structure bearing the sweptback vertical fin/tail rotor pylon, which has a half-tailplane near the tip on the starboard side. Tailplane leading-and trailing-edges, and bullet fairing over tail rotor gearbox, are of glassfibre.

LANDING GEAR (general-purpose military version): Non-retractable tubular skid type. Provision for a pair of adjustable ground handling wheels on each skid. Flotation gear optional.

LANDING GEAR (naval versions): Non-retractable oleo-pneumatic tricycle type. Single-wheel main units, mounted on sponsons near rear of main fuselage, are fixed at 27° toe-out for deck landing, and can be manually turned into line and locked fore and aft for movement of aircraft into and out of ship's hangar. Twin-wheel nose unit can be castored hydraulically through 90° by the pilot. Designed for high shock-absorption to facilitate take-off from, and landing on, small decks under severe sea and weather conditions. Sprag brakes (wheel locks) fitted to each wheel prevent rotation on landing or inadvertent deck roll. These locks are disengaged hydraulically and will automatically re-engage in the event of hydraulic failure. Friction brakes may be fitted for shore use. Flotation gear, and hydraulically-actuated harpoon deck-lock securing system, optional.

POWER PLANT: Two Rolls-Royce Gem 2 turboshaft engines in Lynx AH. 1, HAS. Mk 2 and early export variants. Each has a max continuous rating of 559 kW (750 shp), a take-off and inter-contingency rating of 619 kW (830 shp), and a max contingency rating (2½ min) of 671 kW (900 shp). Uprating modifications have been incorporated progressively into the Gem engine to meet requirements for the increase in Lynx AUW to 4,763 kg (10,500 lb) and for operation in high ambient temperatures. The most recent engine version is the Gem 41-1, which has a max continuous rating of 663·5 kW (890 shp), a T-O rating of 746 kW (1,000 shp), an inter-contingency rating of 790·5 kW (1,060 shp), and a max contingency rating of 835 kW (1,120 shp). Engines mounted side by side on top of the fuselage upper decking, aft of the main rotor shaft and gearbox, and separated from fuselage, transmission area and each other by firewalls. Engine air intakes de-iced electrically. Fuel in five crashproof bag-type tanks, all within the fuselage structure, comprising two main tanks each of 204 kg (450 lb) capacity, two side-by-side collector tanks each of 93 kg (204·5 lb) capacity, and a 148 kg (326 lb) capacity underfloor tank at the forward end of the cabin. Total fuel capacity 733 kg (1,616 lb). Cross-feed system allows fuel to be supplied from both collector tanks to one engine or from one tank to both engines. If required, ferry range can be increased by installing in rear of cabin two metal auxiliary tanks with a combined capacity of 654 kg (1,442 lb). Single-point pressure refuelling (3·79 bars; 55 lb/sq in max) and defuelling; two points for gravity refuelling. A removable 114 litres (25 Imp gallons)/min pressure refuelling/defuelling pack can be fitted in the cabin and, with port engine running, can be used to refuel aircraft from dump stocks on ground or containers suspended from hoist. It is also possible to raise fuel about 5 m (15 ft) while the aircraft is hovering. Fuel jettison capability for main and forward tanks. Provision for self-sealing of both collector tanks (except in Royal Navy version) to provide protection against small-arms fire. Engine oil tank capacity 6·8 litres (1·5 Imp gallons). Main rotor gearbox oil capacity 18 litres (4 Imp gallons). Engine access doors manufactured in Australia by Hawker Pacific.

ACCOMMODATION: Pilot and co-pilot or observer on side-by-side seats which can accommodate back-type dinghies and are adjustable fore and aft and for height. Inertia-reel shoulder harness for pilot and co-pilot. Dual controls optional. Additional crew members (eg, gunner, hoist operator) according to role. Individual forward-hinged cockpit door and large rearward-sliding

Westland naval Lynx, one of six search and rescue UH-14As for the Royal Netherlands Navy

cabin door on each side; all four doors jettisonable. Main cabin doors manufactured by Hawker Pacific in Australia. Cockpit accessible from cabin area. Maximum high-density layout (general-purpose version) for one pilot and 10 armed troops or paratroops, on lightweight bench seats in soundproof cabin. Alternative VIP layouts for four to seven passengers, with additional cabin soundproofing. Seats can be removed quickly to permit the carriage of up to 907 kg (2,000 lb) of freight internally. Tiedown rings are provided at approx 51 cm (20 in) intervals on main cabin floor, which is stressed for loads of up to 976 kg/m² (200 lb/sq ft). Alternatively, loads of up to 1,360 kg (3,000 lb) can be carried externally on freight hook mounted below the cabin floor and fitted, in naval version, with electrically-operated emergency release system. In the casualty evacuation role, with a crew of two, the Lynx can accommodate three standard stretchers and a medical attendant; electrically-heated casualty bags can be provided. Both versions have secondary capability for search and rescue (up to nine survivors) and other roles (see introductory copy and 'Equipment' paragraphs).

SYSTEMS: Two independent hydraulic systems in all versions, pressure 141 bars (2,050 lb/sq in). Pumps powered by accessory drive from main rotor gearbox, enabling full power to be drawn from both main systems in event of engine failure. If either No. 1 or No. 2 main system fails, the other maintains adequate flying control. No. 1 system, additionally, actuates tail rotor yaw control and rotor brake. Tail rotor operation reverts to mechanical control if No. 1 system fails. A third hydraulic system, at the same pressure, is provided in the naval version when Alcatel sonar equipment, MAD or a hydraulic winch system is installed. When this third hydraulic system is installed, the deck-lock harpoon is also operated by this system. When the Bendix AN/AQS sonar is installed, a 207 bar (3,000 lb/sq in) 'utility' hydraulic system is used. No pneumatic system. 28V DC electrical power supplied by two 6kW engine-driven starter/generators and an alternator. Engines can also be started from external 28V DC power source. 24V 23Ah (optionally 40Ah) nickel-cadmium battery fitted for essential services and emergency engine starting. 200V three-phase AC power available at 400Hz from two 15kVA transmission-driven alternators. AC and DC external ground power sockets on starboard side of fuselage. Graviner Triple FD engine fire detection system; two separate fire suppression systems fitted, but interconnected to permit contents of both bottles to be directed to one engine if neccessary. All versions fitted with centralised standard warning system which provides visual and audio warnings of major emergencies, visual warnings for secondary failure, and visual indications of an advisory nature. Optional cabin heating and ventilation system, using mixing unit combining engine bleed air with outside air. Optional supplementary cockpit heating system. Electrical anti-icing and demisting of windscreen, and electrically-operated windscreen wipers, standard; windscreen washing system optional.

AVIONICS AND FLIGHT EQUIPMENT: Main equipment bays are in nose (under upward-hinged door) and at rear of cabin. All versions equipped as standard with navigation, cabin and cockpit lights; adjustable landing light under nose; anti-collision beacon; first aid kit(s); and hand-type fire extinguishers for cabin. Avionics common to all roles (general-purpose and naval versions) include Marconi duplex three-axis automatic stabilisation equipment; Sperry GM9 gyrosyn compass system; Decca tactical air navigation system (TANS); Decca 71 Doppler, E2C standby compass; and S.G. Brown intercom system. Optional role equipment for both versions includes Marconi automatic flight control system (AFCS); Plessey PTR 377 UHF/VHF with homing; Collins ARC-159 UHF with homing; Plessey PTR 1751 UHF; Ultra D 403M standby UHF; Collins ARC-182 VHF/UHF; AM/FM with homing; Collins VHF-20B VHF/AM; Marconi AD 120 VHF/FM; Chelton 7 homer; Collins VOR/ILS; DME; Collins ARN-118 Tacan; I-band transponder (naval version only); Plessey PTR 446, APX-72, Siemens STR 700/375 or Italtel APX-77 IFF; Marconi AD 370 and AD 380 radio compass; and vortex-type sand filter for engine air intakes. Additional units are fitted in naval version, when sonar is fitted, to provide automatic transition to the hover and automatic Doppler hold in the hover. Other optional equipment (both versions) includes signal pistol and cartridges, Aldis lamp and stowage.

ARMAMENT AND OPERATIONAL EQUIPMENT: For armed escort, anti-tank or air-to-surface strike missions, general-purpose version can be equipped with one 20 mm Oerlikon or similar cannon mounted in the cabin with 1,500 rds; or two 20 mm cannon mounted externally so as to permit the carriage also of anti-tank missiles or a pintle-mounted 7·62 mm GEC Minigun inside the cabin; or a Minigun beneath cabin, in Emerson Minitat installation, with 3,000 rds. External pylon can be fitted on each side of cabin for a variety of stores, including two Minigun or other self-contained gun pods; two pods each carrying eighteen 68 mm SNEB, twelve 80 mm SURA, or nineteen 2·75 in rockets, the 2·75 in rockets containing illuminating flares if required; or up to six Aérospatiale AS.11, or eight Aérospatiale/MBB Hot or Hughes TOW, or similar air-to-surface missiles. An additional six or eight missiles can be carried in cabin, for rearming in forward areas, and a stabilised sight is fitted for target detection and missile direction. British Army Lynx aircraft equipped with TOW missiles have roof-mounted Hughes sight manufactured under licence by Dynamics Group of British Aerospace. The Lynx can also transport mobile anti-tank teams of three gunners with missiles and launchers. For search and rescue role, with a crew of three, both versions can be fitted with a waterproof floor, eight 4 in flares in utility version (or six 4·5 in flares in naval version), and a 272 kg (600 lb) capacity electrically-operated 'clip-on' hoist in starboard side of cabin. Alternative option of hydraulically-operated hoist in naval version when third hydraulic system is installed. Hoist, which can lift a load through 76 m (250 ft) at 30·5 m (100 ft)/min, can be swung back into cabin when not in use, permitting sliding door to be closed. General-purpose version can also be equipped for several other duties, including firefighting and crash rescue, reconnaissance, military command post, liaison, customs and border control, and pilot and operational training. Optional equipment, according to role, can include lightweight sighting system with alternative target magnification, vertical and/or oblique cameras, up to six 4·5 in flares for night operation, low light level TV, infra-red linescan, searchlight, and specialised communications equipment. Naval version can carry out a number of these roles, but has specialised equipment for its primary duties. For ASW role, this includes two Mk 44 or Mk 46 homing torpedoes, one each on an external pylon on each side of fuselage, and six marine markers; or two Mk 11 depth charges. Detection of submarines is by means of either Alcatel DUAV 4 or Bendix AN/AQS-18 dipping sonars or Texas Instruments AN/ASQ-81 magnetic anomaly detector. The dipping sonars are operated by a hydraulically-powered winch and cable hover mode facilities within the AFCS. Ferranti Sea Spray lightweight search and tracking radar, for detecting small surface targets in low visi-bility/high sea conditions. Armament includes four BAe Sea Skua semi-active homing missiles for attacking light surface craft; alternatively, four AS.12 or similar wire-guided missiles can be employed in conjunction with AF 530 or APX-334 lightweight stabilised optical sighting system.

DIMENSIONS, EXTERNAL (A: general-purpose version; N: naval version):

Diameter of main rotor (A, N)	12·802 m (42 ft 0 in)
Diameter of tail rotor (A, N)	2·21 m (7 ft 3 in)
Main rotor blade chord (A, N, constant, each)	0·395 m (1 ft 3½ in)
Tail rotor blade chord (A, N, constant, each)	0·18 m (7·1 in)
Length overall, both rotors turning (A, N)	15·163 m (49 ft 9 in)

Length overall:
A, main rotor blades folded	13·165 m (43 ft 2·3 in)
N, main rotor blades and tail folded	10·618 m (34 ft 10 in)

Length of fuselage, nose to tail rotor centre:
A	12·06 m (39 ft 6·8 in)
N	11·92 m (39 ft 1·3 in)

Width overall, main rotor blades folded:
A	2·94 m (9 ft 7¾ in)
N	3·75 m (12 ft 3¾ in)

Height overall, both rotors turning:
A	3·66 m (12 ft 0 in)
N	3·60 m (11 ft 9¾ in)

Height overall, both rotors stopped:
A	3·504 m (11 ft 6 in)
N	3·48 m (11 ft 5 in)
Height to top of rotor hub: A	2·964 m (9 ft 8·7 in)

Height overall, main rotor blades and tail folded:
N	3·20 m (10 ft 6 in)

Tail rotor ground clearance: A
A	1·41 m (4 ft 7½ in)
N	1·38 m (4 ft 6·3 in)

Tailplane half-span (from fuselage c/l):
A, N	1·776 m (5 ft 9·9 in)
Skid track: A	2·032 m (6 ft 8 in)
Wheel track: N	2·778 m (9 ft 1·4 in)
Wheelbase: N	2·94 m (9 ft 7¾ in)

Cabin door openings (A, N, each):
Mean width	1·372 m (4 ft 6 in)
Height	1·194 m (3 ft 11 in)

DIMENSIONS, INTERNAL:

Cabin, from back of pilots' seats:
Min length	2·057 m (6 ft 9 in)
Max width	1·778 m (5 ft 10 in)
Width at rear	1·409 m (4 ft 7½ in)
Max internal floor width	1·715 m (5 ft 7½ in)
Max height	1·422 m (4 ft 8 in)
Floor area	3·72 m² (40·04 sq ft)
Volume	5·21 m³ (184 cu ft)

WEIGHTS (A: general-purpose version, N: naval version):
Manufacturer's bare weight: A		2,578 kg (5,683 lb)
N		2,740 kg (6,040 lb)
Manufacturer's basic weight: A		2,658 kg (5,860 lb)
N		3,030 kg (6,680 lb)

Operating weight empty, equipped:
A, troop transport (pilot and 10 troops)	2,787 kg (6,144 lb)
A, anti-tank strike (incl weapon pylons, firing equipment and sight)	3,072 kg (6,772 lb)
A, search and rescue (crew of three)	2,963 kg (6,532 lb)
N, anti-submarine strike	3,343 kg (7,370 lb)
N, reconnaissance (crew of two)	3,277 kg (7,224 lb)
N, anti-submarine classification and strike	3,472 kg (7,654 lb)
N, air to surface vessel search and strike (crew of two and four Sea Skuas)	3,414 kg (7,526 lb)
N, search and rescue (crew of three)	3,416 kg (7,531 lb)
N, dunking sonar search and strike	3,650 kg (8,047 lb)
Max T-O weight: A	4,535 kg (10,000 lb)
N	4,763 kg (10,500 lb)

PERFORMANCE (at normal max T-O weight at S/L, ISA, except where indicated. A: general-purpose version; N: naval version):

Max continuous cruising speed:
A	140 knots (259 km/h; 161 mph)
N	125 knots (232 km/h; 144 mph)
A (ISA + 20°C)	130 knots (241 km/h; 150 mph)
N (ISA + 20°C)	114 knots (211 km/h; 131 mph)

Max continuous cruising speed (1 h), one engine out:
A	134 knots (248 km/h; 154 mph)
N	122 knots (225 km/h; 140 mph)
A (ISA + 20°C)	114 knots (211 km/h; 131 mph)
N (ISA + 20°C)	99 knots (184 km/h; 114 mph)

Speed for max endurance:
A, N (ISA and ISA + 20°C)	70 knots (130 km/h; 81 mph)

Min flying speed (max contingency rating, one engine out):
A	19 knots (35·5 km/h; 22 mph)
N	23 knots (43 km/h; 26·5 mph)
A (ISA + 20°C)	32 knots (60 km/h; 37 mph)
N (ISA + 20°C)	39 knots (73 km/h; 45 mph)

Max forward rate of climb: A   756 m (2,480 ft)/min
  N   661 m (2,170 ft)/min
  A (ISA + 20°C)   536 m (1,760 ft)/min
  N (ISA + 20°C)   469 m (1,540 ft)/min
Max forward rate of climb (1 h power), one engine out:
  A   277 m (910 ft)/min
  N   223 m (730 ft)/min
  A (ISA + 20°C)   72 m (235 ft)/min
  N (ISA + 20°C)   64 m (210 ft)/min
Max vertical rate of climb:
  A   472 m (1,550 ft)/min
  N   351 m (1,150 ft)/min
  A (ISA + 20°C)   390 m (1,280 ft)/min
  N (ISA + 20°C)   244 m (800 ft)/min
Hovering ceiling OGE: A   3,230 m (10,600 ft)
  N   2,575 m (8,450 ft)

Typical range, with reserves:
  A, troop transport   292 nm (540 km; 336 miles)
Radius of action, out and back at max sustained speed, allowances for T-O and landing, 30 min loiter in search area, 3 min hover for each survivor, and 10 % fuel reserves at end of mission:
  N, search and rescue (crew of 3 and 2 survivors)
    115 nm (212 km; 132 miles)
  N, search and rescue (crew of 3 and 7 survivors)
    96 nm (178 km; 111 miles)
Time on station at 50 nm (93 km; 58 miles) radius, out and back at max sustained speed, with 2 torpedoes, smoke floats and marine markers, allowances for T-O and landing and 10% fuel reserves at end of mission:
  N, anti-submarine classification and strike, loiter speed on station   2 h 0 min
  N, anti-submarine strike, loiter on station
    2 h 29 min
  N, dunking sonar search and strike, 50% loiter speed and 50% hover on station   1 h 5 min
Time on station at 50 nm (93 km; 58 miles) radius, out and back at max sustained speed, with crew of 2 and 4 Sea Skuas, allowances and reserves as above:
  N, air to surface vessel strike, en-route radar search and loiter speed on station   1 h 36 min
Max range: A   340 nm (630 km; 392 miles)
  N   320 nm (593 km; 368 miles)
  A (ISA + 20°C)   339 nm (628 km; 390 miles)
  N (ISA + 20°C)   320 nm (593 km; 368 miles)
Max endurance: A   2 h 57 min
  N (ISA + 20°C)   2 h 50 min
Max ferry range with auxiliary cabin tanks:
  A   724 nm (1,342 km; 834 miles)
  N   565 nm (1,046 km; 650 miles)

Westland WG 30 twin-turboshaft general-purpose helicopter, in military configuration and fitted with tailplane and endplate fins

Westland WG 30 (two Rolls-Royce Gem 41-1 turboshaft engines) *(Pilot Press)*

WESTLAND WG 30

Westland Helicopters first undertook studies leading to this enlarged, twin-engined development of the Lynx helicopter as a private venture in early 1976. Detail design of the bigger fuselage began about a year later, and the construction of two prototypes was authorised in January 1978. The first of these, registered G-BGHF, made its first flight on 10 April 1979, two weeks ahead of schedule. By February 1980 it had accumulated 150 h of flying in 178 flights. The second prototype made its public debut at the Paris Air Show in June 1979.

Main differences from the Lynx are the completely new and more spacious fuselage; retractable landing gear; increased-diameter main and (on the production version) tail rotor; a noise and vibration reducing 'raft' mounting for the twin engines and main rotor head; a dynamic system developed from that of the Lynx and retaining more than 85% of the proven system in that aircraft; increased fuel capacity; new automatic flight control system; and simplified electrical system. Payload/range capability is increased, and the manoeuvrability of the Lynx is retained.

Initially, the WG 30 is planned to meet military needs for a tactical transport, battlefield support and aeromedical helicopter. The basic aircraft is, however, also suitable for the civil market, for such roles as passenger and/or cargo transport, executive and VIP use, offshore rig support, and Arctic operation. Military approvals and full Category A civil certification were expected to be obtained during 1980, and deliveries to begin in mid-1982. British Airways has indicated its intention to purchase a number of WG 30s, chiefly for offshore oil rig support. An initial production batch of 20 is being laid down by Westland.

TYPE: Twin-turboshaft general-purpose military and civil helicopter.

ROTOR SYSTEM: Four-blade semi-rigid main rotor and four-blade tail rotor. Main rotor blades, which can be folded for stowage, are of constant chord and cambered section; each has a stainless steel spar and a bonded GRP skin. Forged titanium hingeless main rotor head. Main rotor system, engines and main rotor gearbox are mounted on a structural 'raft' which reduces rotor-induced vibration, so improving passenger comfort, and also improves structural and systems reliability. This raft comprises two fore-and-aft steel beams and three cross-beams, the latter (from front to rear) being of machined light alloy, fabricated light alloy and steel. The raft 'floats' on four Lord elastomeric suspension blocks which, in turn, are mounted on two pairs of

fore-and-aft beams bridging the main lift frames. The aircraft has a tail rotor of slightly larger diameter than that of the Lynx, with composite blades, which rotates in the opposite direction and is quieter.

ROTOR DRIVE: Engines drive directly into standard Lynx conformal main gearbox, thence by driveshafts to intermediate and tail rotor gearboxes.

FUSELAGE: Main cabin, which is of basically rectangular cross-section, is a conventional semi-monocoque structure of light alloy frames and stringers, with stringer spacing constant throughout the airframe. Roof panels, fuel tank surrounds and bulkheads are of aluminium honeycomb, floor panels of Ciba-Geigy Fibrelam GRP.

LANDING GEAR: Hydraulically retractable tricycle type, with oleo-pneumatic shock-absorber on each unit. Fairey Hydraulics main units each have a single Goodyear wheel and tyre of the size fitted to the Westland Sea King; they retract into fairings on the fuselage sides at the rear of the cabin, the wheels remaining partly exposed when retracted. Fairey nose unit, which is castoring, is fully retractable rearwards, and is fitted with twin Goodyear wheels and tyres.

POWER PLANT: Two Rolls-Royce Gem 41-1 turboshaft engines mounted side by side above cabin, each rated at 835 kW (1,120 shp) max contingency, 790 kW (1,060 shp) intermediate contingency, 746 kW (1,000 shp) for T-O, and 671 kW (900 shp) max continuous. Engine intakes as for Lynx. Fuel in two FPT tanks, each of 499 kg (1,100 lb) capacity, one under front seats and one under rear seats in cabin. Intertechnique booster pumps, with provision for crossfeed to either engine.

ACCOMMODATION: Crew of two on flight deck, with provision for one-pilot operation. Large flight deck windows provide excellent field of view for crew. Windscreen washers and wipers on both front transparencies. Main cabin can accommodate, in military version, 14 troops each weighing 127 kg (280 lb) including full equipment; 17 troops with less equipment; or a maximum of 22 troops in high-density configuration; or, in cargo configuration, ammunition, anti-tank missile launch teams, fuel, and supplies for battlefield support. Aeromedical version can accommodate six stretchers plus 8/10 sitting casualties/medical attendants. Civil passenger version can provide three/four-abreast seating for up to 17 persons in airline standards of comfort. This version, too, has a high-density layout, in which up to 22 passengers can be accommodated in two forward-facing rows of five and two inward-facing rows of six. Various other civil layouts include executive/VIP trans-

port (six/eight seats, toilet and galley unit), offshore oil support, all-cargo, and mixed passenger/cargo. Large rearward-sliding door on each side of cabin. Four large square cabin windows each side, including one in each door. Step each side to facilitate access to flight deck. Baggage compartment in port side of rear fuselage, aft of cabin, with external access door. Stowages for safety equipment, liferafts, lifejackets and aircraft flotation gear for overwater operation.

SYSTEMS: Two independent hydraulic systems (each 141 bars; 2,050 lb/sq in), as in Lynx; No. 1 system actuates landing gear. Electrical compartment in starboard side of rear fuselage, aft of cabin. DC system as in Lynx (28V from two 6kW engine-driven starter/generators, alternator and battery); AC power provided by two 500V static inverters, but alternators are available at customer's option. Air-conditioning system optional.

AVIONICS AND EQUIPMENT: Nose compartment for avionics and radio. Standard aircraft is VFR equipped, but IFR package (to include VOR/ILS, DME and ADF) is under development. Louis Newmark duplex automatic flight control system for all three axes, with computer-based control and duplex heading hold. SFENA spring feel units (one each for pitch and roll). Other flying controls essentially similar to Lynx; rods connecting hand and foot controls to operating jacks are of the type fitted to Wessex and Sea King. Duplicated three-axis automatic stabilisation equipment. Communications and security systems to customer's requirements.

DIMENSIONS, EXTERNAL:
Diameter of main rotor   13·31 m (43 ft 8 in)
Diameter of tail rotor   2·44 m (8 ft 0 in)
Length overall, rotors turning   15·90 m (52 ft 2 in)
Length overall, main rotor blades folded
   14·46 m (47 ft 5¼ in)
Width overall, main rotor blades folded
   3·25 m (10 ft 8 in)
Height overall, rotors turning   4·39 m (14 ft 5 in)
Height overall (minimum)   4·04 m (13 ft 3 in)
Cabin doors (each): Height   1·37 m (4 ft 6 in)
  Width   1·22 m (4 ft 0 in)
  Height to sill   0·58 m (1 ft 10¾ in)

DIMENSIONS, INTERNAL:
Cabin, excl flight deck: Length   4·42 m (14 ft 6 in)
  Width   1·98 m (6 ft 6 in)
  Height   1·68 m (5 ft 6 in)
  Volume   13·03 m³ (460 cu ft)
Baggage compartment volume (rear) 1·05 m³ (37 cu ft)

AREAS:
Main rotor disc   139·14 m² (1,497·7 sq ft)
Tail rotor disc   4·68 m² (50·4 sq ft)

WEIGHTS AND LOADING:
Manufacturer's bare weight, with basic minimum
    equipment   3,030 kg (6,680 lb)
Max fuel load   998 kg (2,200 lb)
Typical operating weights (tactical troop transport):
    1 crew, VFR equipped   3,192 kg (7,037 lb)
    2 crew, IFR equipped   3,362 kg (7,412 lb)
Max weight for hovering OGE, ISA + 10°C
                    5,443 kg (12,000 lb)
Max T-O weight   5,443 kg (12,000 lb)
Max cabin floor loading   976 kg/m² (200 lb/sq ft)

PERFORMANCE (estimated, at max T-O weight except
where indicated):
Max level and cruising speed at S/L:
    ISA   130 knots (241 km/h; 150 mph)
    ISA + 20°C   119 knots (220 km/h; 137 mph)
Max level speed at S/L, ISA, one engine out
                98 knots (182 km/h; 113 mph)
Min level speed at S/L, one engine out
                35 knots (65 km/h; 40·5 mph)
Hovering ceiling IGE   1,920 m (6,300 ft)
Hovering ceiling OGE   1,190 m (3,900 ft)
Radius of action (offshore oil support, IFR), 45 min
    hold, 5% fuel reserves
                145 nm (269 km; 167 miles)
Range with 1,815 kg (4,000 lb) internal payload
                123 nm (228 km; 142 miles)
Max ferry range (S/L, ISA), with reserves
                nearly 350 nm (648 km; 403 miles)

Modified air intakes on new-production Puma for the RAF

WESTLAND/AÉROSPATIALE SA 330 PUMA

Following the completion of 40 Puma HC.Mk 1s for the RAF in 1972, Westland is building Puma component sets for the French production line. The first of an additional batch of eight for the RAF was delivered on 23 May 1980. These aircraft have composite main rotor blades, new multi-purpose air intakes which prevent ice and sand ingestion, and a max T-O weight of 7,000 kg (15,432 lb).

The Puma is described fully under the Aérospatiale heading in the French section.

WESTLAND/AÉROSPATIALE SA 341 GAZELLE

The Gazelle, described fully under the Aérospatiale heading in the French section, is in joint production in Britain and France under the same Anglo-French agreement as the Puma. The Gazelle has been ordered by the British Army (158 **AH. Mk 1** initially; 29 more in 1978), Royal Navy (30 **HT. Mk 2**) and Royal Air Force (20 **HT. Mk 3**, one **HCC. Mk 4**). A further 38 were ordered in 1980.

The first Gazelle HT. Mk 2 (XW845) was flown on 6 July 1972. The first HT. Mk 3 was delivered to the RAF Central Flying School on 16 July 1973. The AH. Mk 1 entered service on 6 July 1974, with No. 660 Squadron of the Army Air Corps at Soest, Germany; and the HT. Mk 2 with No. 705 Squadron at RNAS Culdrose on 10 December 1974.

British Army Gazelles began to be equipped in 1977 with Decca Doppler 80 radar and automatic chart display.

WHE

W. H. EKIN (ENGINEERING) CO LTD

158 King's Gate, Aberdeen AB2 6BR, Scotland
Telephone: Aberdeen (0224) 33463
REGISTERED OFFICE: c/o 4 Malone Hill Park, Belfast BT9 6RL, Northern Ireland
DIRECTORS:
Dr William H. Ekin, PhD, BSc(Hons), CEng, MIMechE, DMS
Mrs M. J. H. Ekin

This company was formed in March 1969 to undertake the production of six McCandless Mk IV Gyroplanes (see 1972-73 *Jane's*), and the first of these made its first flight in February 1972. An extensive redesign was embarked upon by WHE in Autumn 1971 and a new prototype (G-AXXN) flew for the first time on 1 February 1973. The modified aircraft is known as the WHE Airbuggy.

WHE AIRBUGGY

The first production Airbuggy (G-AYYX) was delivered to an English customer in October 1975, and two more had been delivered by May 1979. The fourth Airbuggy, delivered in November 1979, was fitted with an 1,800 cc engine instead of the standard 1,600 cc unit. A fifth example was to be test-flown in the Spring of 1980.
TYPE: Single-seat light autogyro.
ROTOR SYSTEM AND DRIVE: Two-blade semi-rigid teetering rotor with an offset gimbal head, through the centre of which runs the rotor spin-up drive. Blades are secured to hub by bolts, and are of Rotordyne bonded metal construction. Rotor spin-up effected via Vee-belt drive to 9·667 : 1 worm reduction gearbox and universal and sliding joints. No rotor brake or blade folding.
FUSELAGE: Space-frame of T35 and T45 steel tube, assembled by sifbronze welding.
TAIL UNIT: Fin, rudder and tailplane formed from plywood sandwich. Ground-adjustable trim tab on rudder. Endplate auxiliary fins on tailplane of prototype.
LANDING GEAR: Non-retractable tricycle type. All three wheels have rubber bungee for shock-absorption. Nosewheel steerable. Main wheels with tyres sized from 12 × 2·5 to 13·5 × 5 and nosewheel from 12 × 2·5 to 12 × 3·8 according to surface from which aircraft operates. Internal expanding drum brake on nosewheel only.
POWER PLANT: One 56 kW (75 hp) 1,600-1,800 cc modified Volkswagen engine, driving a Hoffmann two-blade pusher propeller via a 1·5 : 1 reduction drive. Drive transmitted by 10 V-belts. Fuel capacity 29·5 litres (6·5 Imp gallons), in gravity tank mounted above engine, with refuelling point on top of tank. Oil capacity 2·5 litres (4·5 Imp pints).

WHE Airbuggy single-seat autogyro (modified Volkswagen engine)

ACCOMMODATION: Single seat in open cockpit behind large windscreen. Door on starboard side.
SYSTEM: A 12V 25Ah ground rechargeable battery is installed to power an electric engine starter motor and to supply instruments and radio. The starters have been removed from the first two aircraft, as the engines have been found to start satisfactorily without them, using only the hand lever.
AVIONICS: Prototype had Parkair Nipper 24-channel com transceiver.

DIMENSIONS, EXTERNAL:
Diameter of rotor   6·63 m (21 ft 9 in)
Rotor blade chord   0·188 m (7·4 in)
Propeller diameter   1·45 m (4 ft 9 in)
Length overall, excl rotor   3·51 m (11 ft 6 in)
Height overall   2·21 m (7 ft 3 in)
Wheel track   1·63 m-1·68 m (5 ft 4 in-5 ft 6 in)
Wheelbase   1·32 m (4 ft 4 in)

AREAS:
Rotor blades (each)   0·52 m² (5·6 sq ft)
Rotor disc   37·63 m² (405 sq ft)

Fin   0·31 m² (3·3 sq ft)
Rudder   0·49 m² (5·3 sq ft)

WEIGHTS AND LOADINGS:
Weight empty   161 kg (355 lb)
Max T-O and landing weight   295 kg (650 lb)
Max disc loading   8·5 kg/m² (1·75 lb/sq ft)
Max power loading   5·27 kg/kW (8·7 lb/hp)

PERFORMANCE (at max T-O weight):
Never-exceed speed   69 knots (128 km/h; 80 mph)
Max level speed at S/L 69 knots (128 km/h; 80 mph)
Max cruising speed   61 knots (113 km/h; 70 mph)
Econ cruising speed   52 knots (97 km/h; 60 mph)
Max rate of climb at S/L   305 m (1,000 ft)/min
T-O run   46-92 m (150-300 ft)
Landing run, still air   9 m (30 ft)
Landing run in 13 knot (24 km/h; 15 mph) wind Nil
Range with max fuel, no allowances
                121 nm (225 km; 140 miles)
Range with max payload, no allowances
                86 nm (161 km; 100 miles)

UNITED STATES OF AMERICA

AEROSPACE GENERAL
AEROSPACE GENERAL COMPANY

Route 1, Box 208, Odessa, Texas 79763
Telephone: (915) 332 8233
PRESIDENT: Gilbert Magill

This company was formed by Mr Gilbert Magill who, as former President of Rotor-Craft Corporation, was responsible for the RH-1 Pinwheel ultralight one-man helicopter described and illustrated in the 1960-61 *Jane's*. The same basic concept, including the use of rotor-tip rockets for propulsion, was embodied later in a powered pilot rescue vehicle known as the Mini-Copter. Three prototypes were ordered by the US Navy for evaluation and development, but the programme was terminated in 1977, when the prototypes were transferred to the US Army. In early 1979 four aircraft of this type were acquired by the Army for test and evaluation in an Individual Tactical Air Vehicle (ITAV) role. Details of this helicopter, and of a generally similar civil MC-8 Mini-Copter, can be found in the 1978-79 *Jane's*.

AHRENS
AHRENS AIRCRAFT INC

WORKS: Hangar 403 (PO Box 432), Ramey, Puerto Rico 00604
Telephone: (809) 891 2033
Telex: 385 9451
PRESIDENT: Peter W. Ahrens
VICE-PRESIDENTS:
   Kim K. Ahrens (Chief Engineer)
   Edd H. Ahrens (Production)

AHRENS AIRCRAFT CORPORATION

HEAD OFFICE: 2800 Teal Club Road, Oxnard, California 93030
Telephone: (805) 985 2000
Telex: 659 240 Ahrens Air ONX

Ahrens Aircraft Corporation provides subassembly and shipping services for the main production and assembly plant of Ahrens Aircraft Inc, located at the former Ramey AFB, Puerto Rico. Current labour force at Ramey is approximately 180, but with full production this is expected to increase to 450-500 personnel.

AHRENS AR 404

Ahrens Aircraft Corporation initiated the design of the AR 404 in January 1975; the aim was to evolve a simple and robust multi-purpose transport aircraft that would be easy to operate and maintain. A constant-section square fuselage was adopted to provide maximum volume and simplify the loading of containers; the wing was mounted on the fuselage upper surface, eliminating the need for any wing carry-through structure within the fuselage. A modular concept was chosen for all systems to simplify maintenance, and it is claimed that an engine can be removed for replacement within 20 minutes.

Construction of a prototype began in August 1975, and this aircraft (N404AR) made its first flight on 1 December 1976. The first flight of a production aircraft, built wholly in Puerto Rico, was made on 26 October 1979, and in early 1980 this was continuing its flight testing. The second and third production aircraft were due to fly during the early months of 1980, and after initial testing were to join the first prototype to expedite completion of the certification programme. It was anticipated that certification under FAR Pt 25 would be gained by the end of 1980.

The company expected to build six or seven aircraft during 1980; subject to certification, these were to be available for delivery in early 1981. Production is scheduled at one aircraft per month during 1981, increasing gradually to three or four per month. In January 1980 a total of 24 delivery positions had been confirmed, mostly for operators in the Caribbean area, but with deliveries scheduled also for Canada and mainland USA, including Alaska.

The details which follow apply to the production version of the AR 404, which has a longer cabin than the prototype:

TYPE: Passenger/cargo transport.
WINGS: Cantilever high-wing monoplane. Wing section NACA 64₃-618. Dihedral 0°. Incidence 0°. Three-spar fail-safe light alloy structure, with light alloy skins. Electrically-operated two-section single-slotted trailing-edge flaps of light alloy construction on each wing. Manually-actuated plain ailerons of light alloy construction, with electrically-operated trim tab in each. Modified Hoerner-type wingtips.
FUSELAGE: Semi-monocoque square constant-section fail-safe structure of light alloy.
TAIL UNIT: Cantilever structure of light alloy. Manually-actuated control surfaces. Trim tabs in elevator and rudder.
LANDING GEAR: Hydraulically-retractable tricycle type, all units retracting forward to simplify free-fall extension in emergency. Main units retract into sponson on each side of fuselage. Oleo-pneumatic shock-absorber and twin wheels on each unit. Hydraulically-steerable nose unit has wheels and tyres size 6·00-6. Main wheels and tyres size 7·00-8. Hydraulically-operated disc brakes.
POWER PLANT: Four 314 kW (420 shp) Allison 250-B17B turboprop engines, each driving a Hartzell three-blade fully-feathering constant-speed metal propeller. Four wing fuel tanks, capacity 1,892 litres (500 US gallons). Single-point refuelling optional. Two optional leading-edge auxiliary tanks, capacity 946 litres (250 US gallons). Propeller blades de-iced electrically.
ACCOMMODATION: Crew of two side by side on flight deck, with dual controls. Up to 30 passengers can be accommodated in commuter version, with a 'two and one'

First production example of the Ahrens AR 404 during early flight tests

Production version of the Ahrens AR 404 utility transport aircraft *(Michael A. Badrocke)*

seating arrangement having an aisle width of 0·38 m (1 ft 3 in). Most operators are expected to select a 27-passenger layout, with one flight attendant and full baggage load. Baggage can be carried in a single rear-loaded container with capacity of 4·5 m³ (160 cu ft). Five-track seat/cargo restraint system in cabin floor may be used for seat attachment, direct cargo tiedown, or for the fitting of rollers to facilitate the handling of palletised cargo. Four standard D-3 containers can be accommodated. Twelve cabin windows on each side. Passenger door aft of wing on each side. Crew door on port side; communicating door between flight deck and cabin. Split cargo door forms undersurface of aft fuselage, lower half serving also as a loading ramp, which can be left open to permit the carriage of outsize cargo or to allow the airdropping of paratroops and supplies. Accommodation air-conditioned and heated.
SYSTEMS: Hydraulic system for landing gear retraction, brakes and nosewheel steering. Electrical system powered by four Lear Siegler starter/generators, each rated at 150kVA; one 24V 36Ah lead-acid battery. A small APU driving a 28V 150A generator is housed in one sponson for emergency electricity supply and battery charging.
AVIONICS AND EQUIPMENT: Collins FD-112V flight director and HSI-84 horizontal situation indicator standard. A wide range of optional avionics by Collins is available to customer requirements. Standard equipment includes angle of attack indicator, clock, encoding altimeter, instant vertical speed indicators, outside air temperature gauge, dual turn and slip indicators, inertia-reel shoulder harnesses for pilot and co-pilot, alternate static source, dual heated pitot tubes, audible stall warning system, interior corrosion proofing; map, instrument panel post, overhead and floodlights; cabin, anti-collision, dual landing, navigation and taxi lights; engine fire-extinguishing system, jack pads and choice of exterior colour scheme.
DIMENSIONS, EXTERNAL:

Wing span	20·12 m (66 ft 0 in)
Wing chord, constant	1·98 m (6 ft 6 in)
Wing aspect ratio	10·1
Length overall	16·08 m (52 ft 9 in)
Height overall	5·64 m (18 ft 6 in)
Tailplane span	7·32 m (24 ft 0 in)
Wheel track	4·27 m (14 ft 0 in)
Propeller diameter	2·29 m (7 ft 6 in)
Propeller ground clearance	1·45 m (4 ft 9 in)

Cabin doors (each): Height	1·52 m (5 ft 0 in)
Width	0·76 m (2 ft 6 in)
Rear cargo doors (upper and lower):	
Width	1·63 m (5 ft 4 in)

DIMENSIONS, INTERNAL:

Cabin: Length	8·53 m (28 ft 0 in)
Max width	1·85 m (6 ft 1 in)
Max height	1·83 m (6 ft 0 in)
Floor area	15·8 m² (170 sq ft)
Volume	28·55 m³ (1,008 cu ft)

AREAS:

| Wings, gross | 39·20 m² (422 sq ft) |
| Ailerons (total, incl tabs) | 2·79 m² (30 sq ft) |

Trailing-edge flaps (total)	5·95 m² (64 sq ft)
Vertical tail surfaces (incl tab)	4·83 m² (52 sq ft)
Horizontal tail surfaces (incl tab)	11·15 m² (120 sq ft)

WEIGHTS AND LOADINGS:

Weight empty, equipped	4,309 kg (9,500 lb)
Max T-O weight	7,938 kg (17,500 lb)
Max wing loading	202·1 kg/m² (41·4 lb/sq ft)
Max power loading	6·32 kg/kW (10·4 lb/shp)

PERFORMANCE (estimated, at max T-O weight):

Max level speed at 1,525 m (5,000 ft)	
	190 knots (352 km/h; 219 mph)
Max cruising speed at 1,525 m (5,000 ft)	
	170 knots (315 km/h; 195 mph)

Stalling speed, flaps down

	75 knots (139 km/h; 86·5 mph)
Max rate of climb at S/L	366 m (1,200 ft)/min
Rate of climb at S/L, one engine out	
	183 m (600 ft)/min
Service ceiling	5,500 m (18,000 ft)
T-O run	488 m (1,600 ft)
Landing run	396 m (1,300 ft)
Balanced field length, T-O and landing	
	915 m (3,000 ft)
Range with standard fuel, no reserves	
	850 nm (1,574 km; 978 miles)
Range with auxiliary fuel, no reserves	
	1,200 nm (2,222 km; 1,380 miles)

AIR TRACTOR
AIR TRACTOR INC

PO Box 485, Municipal Airport, Olney, Texas 76374
Telephone: (817) 564 5641
PRESIDENT: Leland Snow

The Air Tractor series of agricultural aircraft are new designs embodying more than 20 years' experience by their designer, Mr Leland Snow, who designed, developed, certificated and put into production the earlier Snow S-2 series of agricultural aircraft. The latter, which later became the Rockwell S-2R Thrush, have been described in previous editions of *Jane's*.

Four versions of the Air Tractor series were available in 1980: the Model AT-301 with Pratt & Whitney radial engine, the Models AT-302 and AT-302A, each with an Avco Lycoming turboprop engine, and the AT-400 with a Pratt & Whitney Aircraft of Canada PT6A-15AG turboprop engine.

AIR TRACTOR MODEL AT-301 AIR TRACTOR

Design of the Model AT-301 Air Tractor was initiated in January 1971, and construction of the first prototype/pre-production aircraft started in August 1972. This aircraft flew for the first time in September 1973, and received FAA certification under FAR Pt 23 in November of that year. At that time the aircraft was also flight tested to meet FAR Pt 8 requirements. By 1 January 1980, a total of 327 AT-301s had been ordered, of which 247 had been completed, and production was continuing at a rate of seven aircraft per month.

TYPE: Single-seat agricultural aircraft.

WINGS: Cantilever low-wing monoplane. Wing section NACA 4415. Dihedral 3° 30'. Incidence 2°. No sweepback. Conventional two-spar structure of 2024-T3 light alloy. Ailerons of light alloy construction, interconnected with trailing-edge flaps to droop 10° at maximum flap deflection of 30°. Electrically-operated Fowlertype trailing-edge flaps of light alloy construction. No trim tabs. Wing ribs and skins zinc chromated before assembly. Wing roots and skin overlaps sealed against chemical entry.

FUSELAGE: Welded structure of 4130N steel tube, oven stress relieved and oiled internally. Quickly detachable skins of 2024-T3 light alloy.

TAIL UNIT: Light alloy structure, with cantilever fin and strut-braced tailplane. Fabric-covered rudder and elevators. Trim tab in each elevator.

LANDING GEAR: Non-retractable tailwheel type. Cantilever spring steel main gear; flat spring suspension for castoring and lockable tailwheel. Cleveland main wheels with tyres size 8·50-10, pressure 2·83 bars (41 lb/sq in). Tailwheel tyre size 12·50-4, pressure 2·42 bars (35 lb/sq in). Cleveland type 30-89 hydraulic disc brakes.

POWER PLANT: One 447·4 kW (600 hp) Pratt & Whitney R-1340 aircooled radial engine, driving a Hamilton Standard 12D40/6101A-12 two-blade constant-speed metal propeller. Fuel in two integral wing tanks with combined capacity of 288 litres (76 US gallons). Refuelling points on upper surface of wings at root. Oil capacity 30·3 litres (8 US gallons).

ACCOMMODATION: Single seat in enclosed cabin which is sealed to prevent chemical ingress. Cabin ventilation by 0·08 m (3 in) diameter airscoop.

SYSTEMS: Agricultural dispersal system comprises a 1,211 litre (320 US gallon) glassfibre hopper, mounted in the forward fuselage; Transland gatebox, Agrinautics valve

Air Tractor Model AT-301 Air Tractor single-seat agricultural aircraft

and strainer, 0·05 m (2 in) Root pump, 0·05 m (2 in) stainless steel plumbing, and up to 72 nozzles in spraybars mounted below and just aft of wing trailing-edges. Electrical system 24V, supplied by 30A engine-driven alternator.

AVIONICS AND EQUIPMENT: Optional avionics include Narco Com 120 radio and Nav 121/Com 120 nav/com; 600W retractable landing light in port wingtip; night-flying package of strobe/navigation, instrument, post, flexible cord utility and dome lights; and (AT-301/302 only) directional and attitude gyro instrument package. Optional equipment includes engine cowling ring, new Hartzell propeller blades (AT-301), Cleveland 29-11 high-flotation tyres and wheels, and ferry fuel system. Alternative agricultural equipment includes Transland high volume and extra high volume spreader systems, and six- or eight-unit Micronair installations.

DIMENSIONS, EXTERNAL:

Wing span	13·72 m (45 ft 0 in)
Wing chord, constant	1·83 m (6 ft 0 in)
Wing aspect ratio	7·5
Length overall	8·23 m (27 ft 0 in)
Height overall	2·59 m (8 ft 6 in)
Propeller diameter	2·77 m (9 ft 1 in)

AREAS:

Wings, gross	25·08 m² (270 sq ft)
Ailerons (total)	3·55 m² (38·2 sq ft)
Trailing-edge flaps (total)	3·34 m² (36·0 sq ft)
Fin	0·82 m² (8·8 sq ft)
Rudder	1·12 m² (12·1 sq ft)
Tailplane	2·42 m² (26·0 sq ft)
Elevators (incl tabs)	2·36 m² (25·4 sq ft)

WEIGHTS AND LOADINGS:

Weight empty, equipped	1,656 kg (3,650 lb)
Max T-O weight (CAM 8)	3,130 kg (6,900 lb)
Max wing loading	124·8 kg/m² (25·6 lb/sq ft)
Max power loading	7·0 kg/kW (11·5 lb/hp)

PERFORMANCE (at max T-O weight, unless stated otherwise):

Never-exceed speed	155 knots (286 km/h; 178 mph)
Max level speed at S/L	
	143 knots (266 km/h; 165 mph)
Max cruising speed at 1,830 m (6,000 ft)	
	130 knots (241 km/h; 150 mph)
Econ cruising speed at 2,440 m (8,000 ft)	
	122 knots (225 km/h; 140 mph)
Stalling speed, flaps down, at normal landing weight	
	46 knots (85·5 km/h; 53 mph)
Max rate of climb at S/L	488 m (1,600 ft)/min
T-O run	259 m (850 ft)

Landing run at normal landing weight 91 m (300 ft)
Range with max fuel, no allowances
304 nm (563 km; 350 miles)

AIR TRACTOR MODEL AT-302/302A AIR TRACTOR

Design of the basic **AT-302** turboprop-powered version of the Air Tractor was initiated in September 1976, and construction of the prototype started two months later. It flew for the first time in June 1977. The first flight of a production aircraft was made in November 1977, and certification under FAR Pt 23 was awarded during the following month. Apart from installation of the Avco Lycoming turboprop engine, and the structural modifications necessary to accept this power plant, the Model AT-302 is basically similar to the piston-engined AT-301. A total of 20 had been ordered by 1 January 1980, of which 14 had been delivered.

The Model **AT-302A**, introduced in 1979, is identical to the AT-302 except for the installation of a 1,514 litre (400 US gallon) hopper, with a 0·97 m (3 ft 2 in) wide gatebox for high application rates of dry chemicals.

WINGS, FUSELAGE, TAIL UNIT, LANDING GEAR: As for Model AT-301.

POWER PLANT: One 447·5 kW (600 shp) Avco Lycoming LTP 101-600A1A turboprop engine, driving a Hartzell three-blade constant-speed non-reversing metal propeller. Fuel system as for AT-301, except total capacity 477 litres (126 US gallons). Oil capacity 7·5 litres (2 US gallons). Air intake has two large dry paper type automobile air filters to avoid ingestion of chemicals.

ACCOMMODATION, SYSTEMS: As for Model AT-301, except electrical system supplied by 24V 150A engine-driven starter/generator.

EQUIPMENT: Optional equipment includes Transland high volume (AT-302) or extra high volume (AT-302A) dispersal system.

DIMENSIONS, EXTERNAL: As for Model AT-301, except:

| Length overall | 8·99 m (29 ft 6 in) |
| Propeller diameter | 2·74 m (9 ft 0 in) |

DIMENSIONS, INTERNAL, AND AREAS: As for Model AT-301

WEIGHTS AND LOADINGS (A: AT-302; B: AT-302A):

Weight empty:	
A, spray equipped	1,474 kg (3,250 lb)
B, duster equipped	1,520 kg (3,350 lb)
Max T-O weight: A	2,994 kg (6,600 lb)
B	3,266 kg (7,200 lb)
Max wing loading: A	119·4 kg/m² (24·44 lb/sq ft)
B	130·2 kg/m² (26·67 lb/sq ft)
Max power loading: A	6·7 kg/kW (11·0 lb/shp)
B	7·3 kg/kW (12·0 lb/shp)

PERFORMANCE (AT-302, at max T-O weight unless stated otherwise):

Never-exceed speed	155 knots (286 km/h; 178 mph)
Max level speed at S/L	
	148 knots (274 km/h; 170 mph)
Max cruising speed at 2,440 m (8,000 ft)	
	143 knots (266 km/h; 165 mph)
Econ cruising speed at 2,440 m (8,000 ft)	
	130 knots (241 km/h; 150 mph)
Stalling speed, flaps down, at normal landing weight	
	44·3 knots (82 km/h; 51 mph)
Max rate of climb at S/L (hopper empty)	
	610 m (2,000 ft)/min
Rate of climb at S/L (hopper full)	
	366 m (1,200 ft)/min
T-O run	238 m (780 ft)

Air Tractor's turboprop-powered Model AT-302 Air Tractor

Landing run at normal landing weight 91 m (300 ft)
Range with max fuel, no allowances
347 nm (644 km; 400 miles)

AIR TRACTOR MODEL AT-400 AIR TRACTOR

This version of the Air Tractor incorporates the larger hopper and wider gatebox of the AT-302A; is powered by a 507 kW (680 shp) Pratt & Whitney Aircraft of Canada PT6A-15AG turboprop engine, driving a Hartzell three-blade constant-speed reversible-pitch propeller; has size 29-11 high-flotation tyres and wheels as standard; and has a 250A starter/generator. Fuel capacity is as for the AT-302/302A. Optional equipment includes Transland extra high volume dispersal system.

AMES
AMES INDUSTRIAL CORPORATION

55 Orville Drive, Bohemia, NY 11716
Telephone: (516) 567 3780

President: M. Berlon
Vice-President and General Manager: H. A. Iversen

This company was awarded a NASA contract to develop and build a small manned aircraft embodying the pivoting-wing concept. This aircraft, which is designated **AD-1**, flew for the first time on 21 December 1979. Details can be found under the NASA entry in this section.

ARCTIC
ARCTIC AIRCRAFT COMPANY

PO Box 6-141, Anchorage, Alaska 99502
Telephone: (907) 243 1580
Secretary: C. J. Diehl

Arctic Aircraft is constructing and marketing, as the S1B2 Arctic Tern, an updated and improved version of the Interstate S1A, first flown more than 30 years ago.

ARCTIC AIRCRAFT INTERSTATE S1B2 ARCTIC TERN

Type: Two-seat sporting and general utility aircraft.
Wings: High-wing monoplane, with V bracing struts each side and auxiliary struts. Wing section NACA 23012. Composite structure with Sitka spruce spars, light alloy ribs and Dacron covering. Hoerner-type wingtips of glassfibre. Semi-Fowler-type single-slotted trailing-edge flaps. Plain inset ailerons.
Fuselage: Welded structure of 4130 chrome-molybdenum steel tube, Dacron covered. Two-piece engine cowling of glassfibre.
Tail Unit: Wire-braced structure of welded 4130 steel tube with Dacron covering. Trim tab in elevator.
Landing Gear: Non-retractable tailwheel type. Main wheels carried in two side Vs and half-axles hinged to fuselage. Shock-absorption by hydraulic/coil spring oleo unit. Cleveland main wheels with US Uniroyal tyres size 8·50-6. Maule tailwheel, diameter 203 mm (8 in). Scott tailwheel optional. Scott toe-operated brakes. Parking brake optional. Peekay 1800 or Edo 2000 floats or 2500 skis optional.
Power Plant: One 112 kW (150 hp) Avco Lycoming O-320 flat-four engine, driving a McCauley two-blade fixed-pitch metal propeller. One fuel tank in each wing, total capacity 151 litres (40 US gallons). Belly-mounted auxiliary fuel tank optional.
Accommodation: Two seats in tandem; rear seat removable to provide additional space for cargo. Cabin door on starboard side, beneath wing. Cabin step. Baggage space in rear fuselage, with external door on starboard side. Tinted windows and cabin skylight optional. Safety belts and fittings standard. Dual controls standard. Cabin soundproofed, heated and ventilated. Windscreen de-icing by hot air. Cabin floor carpeted.
System: Electrical system includes 55A engine-driven

Arctic Aircraft Interstate S1B2 Arctic Tern with optional float landing gear

alternator, 12V DC storage battery, engine starter and navigation lights.
Avionics and Equipment: A range of radios is available. Standard features include epoxy priming, ground manoeuvring handles and engine quick oil drain. Optional items include Alcor exhaust gas analyser, folding front seat, shoulder harness, dome light, instrument lights, landing light, three-colour external paint scheme, belly-mounted cargo pack, lumber rack and salt water corrosion proofing.

Dimensions, external:
Wing span	10·97 m (36 ft 0 in)
Length overall	7·32 m (24 ft 0 in)
Height overall	2·13 m (7 ft 0 in)

Dimensions, internal:
Cabin volume	1·38 m³ (48·7 cu ft)
Baggage volume	0·84 m³ (29·63 cu ft)

Area:
Wings, gross	17·28 m² (186·0 sq ft)

Weights and Loadings:
Weight empty	487 kg (1,073 lb)
Max T-O weight	862 kg (1,900 lb)
Max wing loading	49·9 kg/m² (10·2 lb/sq ft)
Max power loading	7·7 kg/kW (12·67 lb/hp)

Performance:
Never-exceed speed	152 knots (282 km/h; 175·5 mph)
Max cruising speed at S/L, 75% power	102 knots (188 km/h; 117 mph)
Cruising speed, 65% power at optimum altitude	96 knots (178 km/h; 111 mph)
Stalling speed, flaps down	30 knots (55 km/h; 34 mph)
Max rate of climb at S/L, at max T-O weight	389 m (1,275 ft)/min
Service ceiling	5,790 m (19,000 ft)
Absolute ceiling	6,400 m (21,000 ft)
T-O run at max T-O weight	99 m (325 ft)
T-O to 15 m (50 ft) at max T-O weight	152 m (500 ft)
Landing from 15 m (50 ft)	137 m (450 ft)

Range with max fuel, 45 min reserves:
75% power	479 nm (888 km; 552 miles)
65% power	566 nm (1,049 km; 652 miles)

ASTEC
ADVANCED SYSTEMS TECHNOLOGY INC

Head Office and Works: Snohomish County Airport, Everett, Washington 98204
Telephone: (206) 355 8700
Telex: Astec Evt 15 2954

ASTEC/CESSNA EAGLE

Advanced Systems Technology (ASTEC) was founded in 1971 to provide consulting services in aerodynamics and aircraft structural design, and continued this work until, in 1976, the company initiated studies for a major aircraft modification. The Cessna Citation 500 was chosen, with the initial object of increasing cruising speed; but a market survey showed the major requirement to be extended range. Using computerised design and analysis techniques, ASTEC developed a wing modification to reduce drag and increase fuel capacity. To test the flight characteristics of this wing, a Citation 500 was flown with the new wing contours fabricated by the addition of polyurethane foam and glassfibre; a metal production prototype wing was then constructed and flight tested. FAA approval and issue of an STC for modification of Cessna Citation 500 and Citation I aircraft to the same standard was awarded on 4 August 1978.

Changes to the basic Citation 500 wing include use of an advanced technology aerofoil section of increased thickness and length over the inboard portion of the wing; wingtip extensions of 0·51 m (1 ft 8 in), and the addition of cove seals to the trailing-edge flaps. The thickened wing and the wingtip extensions contain an additional 392 kg (865 lb) of fuel, accounting for some 77% of the approximate 600 nm (1,112 km; 691 mile) increase in range over the basic Citation 500. The remainder of the increase is due to improved aerodynamic efficiency of the ASTEC wing.

An STC was received in May 1979 for similar modification of the Cessna Citation 501, this being known

The third production example of the ASTEC/Cessna Eagle, a conversion of the Citation 500

as the ASTEC/Cessna **Eagle SP** after conversion. It is certificated under FAR Pt 23 and approved for single-pilot operation.

Production conversions are being carried out at a rate of 2½ per month. The description of the Citation I under Cessna's entry in this edition applies also to the Eagle, except as follows:
Wings: Thickness/chord ratio of inboard portions increased from 14% to 19%, and supercritical technology incorporated to improve wing/fuselage airflow. Span increased, by comparison with Citation 500, by addition of wingtip extensions.
Power Plant: As for Citation 500, except increased fuel capacity provided in the thicker wing centre-section and wingtip extensions.

Dimensions, external:
Wing span	14·35 m (47 ft 0½ in)
Wing chord at root	2·95 m (9 ft 8⅛ in)
Wing chord at tip	0·93 m (3 ft 0½ in)
Wing aspect ratio	7·92
Length overall	13·26 m (43 ft 6 in)
Height overall	4·36 m (14 ft 3¾ in)
Wheel track	3·84 m (12 ft 7⅛ in)
Wheelbase	4·78 m (15 ft 8¼ in)

Weights:
Weight empty	2,971 kg (6,550 lb)
Max fuel weight	2,045 kg (4,510 lb)
Max T-O weight	5,670 kg (12,500 lb)
Max zero-fuel weight	4,309 kg (9,500 lb)
Max landing weight	5,148 kg (11,350 lb)

Performance (at max T-O weight except as indicated, A: JT15D-1; B: JT15D-1A power plant):
Max cruising speed, average cruise weight, at 10,670 m (35,000 ft):
A	341 knots	(631 km/h; 392 mph)
B	357 knots	(661 km/h; 411 mph)

Cruising speed, average cruise weight, at 12,500 m
(41,000 ft): A   317 knots (587 km/h; 365 mph)
    B   336 knots (623 km/h; 387 mph)
Stalling speed at max landing weight:
    A, B   78 knots (145 km/h; 90 mph)
Max certificated altitude: A   10,670 m (35,000 ft)
    B   12,500 m (41,000 ft)

Balanced T-O field length: A, B   907 m (2,975 ft)
FAA landing field length: A, B   722 m (2,370 ft)
Range, VFR, with 454 kg (1,000 lb) payload
    A, B   1,800 nm (3,336 km; 2,073 miles)
Range, IFR, with 454 kg (1,000 lb) payload
    A, B   1,400 nm (2,594 km; 1,612 miles)

ASTEC/GRUMMAN EAGLE II

In 1978 ASTEC began development of a new wing for the Gulfstream American Gulfstream II. Work on this project has been suspended temporarily, but details can be found in the 1979-80 *Jane's*.

AYRES
AYRES CORPORATION
PO Box 3090, Albany, Georgia 31706
Telephone: (912) 883 1440
Telex: 547629

AYRES THRUSH

Ayres Corporation purchased the manufacturing and world marketing rights of the Rockwell Thrush Commander-600 and -800 from Rockwell International's General Aviation Division in late November 1977, and is now offering the following versions of this large agricultural aircraft:

Thrush-600. Basic version with Pratt & Whitney R-1340 Wasp or Pezetel PZL-3S aircooled radial engine.

Turbo-Thrush S-2R. As Thrush-600, but with a Pratt & Whitney Aircraft of Canada PT6A-34 , -15 or -11 turboprop engine. Described separately.

Ayres took over the facility in Albany covering 23,226 m² (250,000 sq ft) at which Rockwell formerly built the Thrush, and retained the supervisory management and production personnel, amounting to 150 persons, who worked previously for Rockwell's General Aviation Division. In early 1980 production was continuing at a rate of 10 aircraft per month.

The Thrush-600 has a 1·50 m³ (53 cu ft) hopper able to contain up to 1,514 litres (400 US gallons) of liquid or 1,487 kg (3,280 lb) of dry chemicals. Corrosion-proofing is of activated Copon, and it is certificated to both CAR 3 Normal category and CAM 8 Restricted category requirements.

The following details refer to the basic single-seat Thrush-600:

TYPE: Single-seat agricultural aircraft.

WINGS: Cantilever low-wing monoplane. Dihedral 3° 30′. Two-spar structure of light alloy throughout, except for main spar caps of heat-treated SAE 4000 Series steel. Leading-edge formed by heavy main spar and the nose-skin. Light alloy plain ailerons. Electrically-operated flaps. Wing roots sealed against chemical entry.

FUSELAGE: Welded chrome-molybdenum steel tube structure covered with quickly-removable light alloy panels. Underfuselage skin of stainless steel.

TAIL UNIT: Wire-braced welded chrome-molybdenum steel tube structure, fabric-covered. Streamline-section heavy-duty stainless steel wire bracing and heavy-duty stainless steel attachment fittings. Light alloy controllable trim tab in each elevator. Deflector cable from cockpit to fin-tip.

LANDING GEAR: Non-retractable tailwheel type. Main units have rubber-in-compression shock-absorption and 29 × 11·00-10 wheels with 10-ply tyres. Hydraulically-operated disc brakes. Parking brakes. Wire cutters on main gear. Steerable, locking tailwheel, size 12·5 × 4·5 in.

POWER PLANT: One 448 kW (600 hp) Pratt & Whitney R-1340 Wasp nine-cylinder aircooled radial engine, driving a Hamilton Standard type 12D40/EAC AG-100-2 two-blade constant-speed metal propeller, is standard. Available optionally is a 448 kW (600 hp) Pezetel PZL-3S seven-cylinder aircooled radial engine, driving a Dowty-Rotol type CR289-3 three-blade constant-speed metal propeller. One 200·5 litre (53 US gallon) integral tank in each wing, giving total fuel capacity of 401 litres (106 US gallons), of which 378·5 litres (100 US gallons) are usable.

ACCOMMODATION: Single adjustable seat in 'safety pod' sealed cockpit enclosure is standard, with steel tube overturn structure. (Second, tandem seat, with or without dual controls, is optional, to provide accommodation for additional crew member, passenger, or flying instructor.) Two overhead windows for improved view in turns. Downward-hinged door on each side. Tempered safety-glass windscreen. Dual inertia-reel safety

harness standard. Baggage compartment. Windscreen wiper and washer.

SYSTEM: Electrical system powered by a 24V 50A engine-driven alternator; 70A alternator optional. Lightweight 24V 35Ah battery.

AVIONICS AND EQUIPMENT: Hopper forward of cockpit with capacity of 1·50 m³ (53 cu ft) or 1,514 litres (400 US gallons). Hopper has a 0·33 m² (3·56 sq ft) lid, openable by two handles. Standard equipment includes Universal spray system with external 50 mm (2 in) stainless steel plumbing, 50 mm Root Model 67 pump with wooden fan, Transland gate, 50 mm valve, quick-disconnect pump mount and strainer. Streamlined spraybooms with outlets for 68 nozzles, 36 nozzles installed. Micro-adjust valve control (spray) and calibrator (dry). A 63 mm (2·5 in) side-loading system is installed on the port side. Navigation lights, instrument lights and two rotating beacons. Optional equipment includes a rear cockpit to accommodate aft-facing crew member, or forward-facing seat for passenger, or flying instructor if optional dual controls installed; space can be used alternatively for cargo. Other optional items are a Transland high-volume spreader, agitator installation, extra-high-density spray configuration with 70 nozzles installed; Agrinautics electrically-operated three-way valve, emergency shut-off valve, pump in lieu of Root pump and strainer in lieu of Transland strainer; Agevenco 6520 pump in lieu of Root pump. Six- or eight-unit AU3000 Micronair installation in lieu of standard booms and nozzles; Transland S-2 Boommaster with Q-D flange in lieu of standard gate and Root pump; night working lights including wingtip turn lights,

cockpit fire extinguisher, and water bomber configuration. Optional avionics include Bendix T-12C ADF or T-12D digital ADF; King KX 170B, KX 170BE, KX 175B or KX 175BE nav/com; KI 201C converter indicator; Narco Com-11A or Com-11B com transceiver; and Nav-11 nav receiver.

DIMENSIONS, EXTERNAL:
Wing span   13·54 m (44 ft 5 in)
Length overall (tail up)   8·34 m (27 ft 4½ in)
Height overall   2·79 m (9 ft 2 in)
Tailplane span   4·86 m (15 ft 11½ in)
Wheel track   2·72 m (8 ft 11 in)
Propeller diameter   2·74 m (9 ft 0 in)
AREA:
Wings, gross   30·34 m² (326·6 sq ft)
WEIGHTS AND LOADINGS:
Weight empty, equipped   1,678 kg (3,700 lb)
Max T-O weight (CAR 3)   2,721 kg (6,000 lb)
Max T-O weight (CAM 8)   3,130 kg (6,900 lb)
Max wing loading   103·0 kg/m² (21·1 lb/sq ft)
Max power loading   6·99 kg/kW (11·5 lb/hp)
PERFORMANCE (with spray equipment installed and at CAR 3 max T-O weight, unless indicated otherwise):
Max level speed   122 knots (225 km/h; 140 mph)
Max cruising speed, 70% power
    108 knots (200 km/h; 124 mph)
Working speed, 70% power
    91-100 knots (169-185 km/h; 105-115 mph)
Stalling speed, flaps up 61 knots (113 km/h; 70 mph)
Stalling speed, flaps down
    57·5 knots (107 km/h; 66 mph)
Stalling speed at normal landing weight, flaps up
    50 knots (92 km/h; 57 mph)
Stalling speed at normal landing weight, flaps down
    48 knots (89 km/h; 55 mph)
Max rate of climb at S/L   274 m (900 ft)/min
Service ceiling   4,575 m (15,000 ft)
T-O run   236 m (775 ft)
Landing run   152 m (500 ft)
Ferry range with max fuel at 70% power
    350 nm (648 km; 403 miles)

AYRES TURBO-THRUSH S-2R

This turbine-engined version of the Thrush has as standard a 559 kW (750 shp) Pratt & Whitney Aircraft of Canada PT6A-34 turboprop, driving a three-blade constant-speed and reversible-pitch metal propeller. The 507 kW (680 shp) PT6A-15 or 373 kW (500 shp) PT6A-11 engines are available optionally. To compensate for the

Ayres Thrush-600 agricultural aircraft (Pratt & Whitney R-1340 engine)

Ayres Thrush-600 agricultural aircraft (PZL-3S engine), showing optional two-seat accommodation

Ayres Turbo-Thrush S-2R (Pratt & Whitney Aircraft of Canada PT6A-34 turboprop engine) *(R. Kunert)*

small size and light weight of the turboprop, it is mounted well forward of the firewall, in a slender cowling. Current installations have cowlings which comprise individual panels to improve access. Innovations include an oil cooler with an airscoop on top of the cowling, new exhaust outlets for the PT6A, and a special air induction system utilising large perforated aluminium panels at the aft end of the cowling side panels. Air entering via these panels is ducted to large centrifugal air filters, able to remove 98 per cent of all foreign matter in the airflow before it enters the engine.

A 1,514 litre (400 US gallon) hopper is standard for the Turbo-Thrush, but a 1,893 litre (500 US gallon) hopper is available optionally, and is suitable for installation with either the standard or optional power plants. Standard and optional equipment are generally as detailed for the basic Thrush, except that the two-seat conversion is not available.

Advantages claimed for this conversion include greatly improved take-off and climb performance; improved short landing capability; a 454 kg (1,000 lb) increase in payload due to reduced power plant weight; ability to operate on aviation turbine fuel, avgas or diesel fuel; a TBO of more than 3,000 h; quieter operation; and the ability to feather the propeller during fuelling and loading operations without shutting down the engine, because of the free-turbine configuration.

First flight of the prototype was made on 9 September 1975. More than 125 Turbo-Thrushes were in operation in January 1980, at which time production was at a rate of four turbine-powered aircraft per month.

DIMENSIONS, EXTERNAL:

Wing span	13·54 m (44 ft 5 in)
Length overall	10·06 m (33 ft 0 in)
Height overall	2·79 m (9 ft 2 in)
Tailplane span	4·86 m (15 ft 11½ in)
Wheel track	2·72 m (8 ft 11 in)

AREA:

Wings, gross	30·34 m² (326·6 sq ft)

WEIGHTS AND LOADINGS (A: standard hopper; B: optional 1,893 litre: 500 US gallon hopper):

Weight empty: A	1,633 kg (3,600 lb)
B	1,769 kg (3,900 lb)
Max T-O weight (CAR 3):	
A, B	2,722 kg (6,000 lb)
Typical operating weight (CAM 8):	
A	3,719 kg (8,200 lb)
B	3,856 kg (8,500 lb)

Max wing loading	127·1 kg/m² (26·0 lb/sq ft)
Max power loading	7·6 kg/kW (14·17 lb/shp)

PERFORMANCE (A and B, at max T-O weight unless specified otherwise):

Max level speed, with spray equipment	138 knots (256 km/h; 159 mph)
Cruising speed, 50% power	130 knots (241 km/h; 150 mph)
Working speed, 30-50% power	82·5-130 knots (153-241 km/h; 95-150 mph)
Stalling speed, flaps up	61 knots (113 km/h; 70 mph)
Stalling speed, flaps down	57 knots (106 km/h; 66 mph)
Stalling speed at normal landing weight, flaps up	51 knots (95 km/h; 59 mph)
Stalling speed at normal landing weight, flaps down	49·5 knots (92 km/h; 57 mph)
Max rate of climb at S/L	530 m (1,740 ft)/min
Service ceiling	7,620 m (25,000 ft)
T-O run	183 m (600 ft)
Landing run	152 m (500 ft)
Landing run with propeller reversal	91 m (300 ft)
Ferry range at 40% power	391 nm (724 km; 450 miles)

BEECHCRAFT

BEECH AIRCRAFT CORPORATION (Subsidiary of Raytheon Company)

HEAD OFFICE AND MAIN WORKS: Wichita, Kansas 67201
Telephone: (316) 681 7111
BRANCH DIVISIONS: Liberal, Kansas; Salina, Kansas; Selma, Alabama; and Boulder, Colorado
CHAIRMAN OF THE BOARD: Mrs O. A. (Walter H.) Beech
PRESIDENT: Frank E. Hedrick
EXECUTIVE VICE-PRESIDENT: Edward C. Burns
SENIOR VICE-PRESIDENTS:
  Seymour Colman (Administration)
  Michael G. Neuburger (International Division)
VICE-PRESIDENTS:
  Stewart M. Ayton
  Harold W. Deets (Materiel)
  Charles W. Dieker (Treasurer)
  Max P. Eaton (Production)
  Glenn Ehling (Manufacturing)
  Gary M. Hanssen (Industrial Relations)
  E. C. Nikkel (Aerospace Programmes)
  John A. Pike (Research and Development)
  C. A. Rembleske (Engineering)
  Austin Rising
  William G. Robinson (Corporate Communications)
  George D. Rodgers (Domestic Commercial Marketing)
  William G. Rutherford (Government Relations)
  W. D. Wise (Commuter Division)
CORPORATE SECRETARY: Mrs Ila A. Alumbaugh
ASSISTANT SECRETARY: Miss Harriett E. Bulmer
ASSISTANT TREASURER AND CONTROLLER: L. R. Damon
ASSISTANT TREASURER AND CHIEF ACCOUNTANT:
  D. C. Cullinane
ASSISTANT TREASURER: Wey D. Kenny
DIRECTOR, ADVERTISING AND SALES PROMOTION:
  R. James Yarnell
DIRECTOR, PUBLIC RELATIONS: Stephen M. Caine

Beech Aircraft Corporation was founded jointly in 1932 by Mrs Olive Ann Beech and the late Walter H. Beech, pioneer designer and builder of light aeroplanes in the USA. On 8 February 1980, following approval by the stockholders of each company, the Raytheon Company and Beech Aircraft Corporation completed the signing of closing merger documents under which Beech became a wholly-owned subsidiary of Raytheon. Beech will continue to be operated as a separate entity under its present management, at its present locations; but the separate Board of Directors for Beech includes Mr D. Brainerd Holmes and Mr Thomas L. Phillips, respectively the President and the Chairman and Chief Executive Officer of Raytheon, as representatives of the parent company.

Beech Aircraft Corporation is currently engaged in the production of civil and military aircraft, missile targets, aircraft and missile components, and cryogenic equipment for spacecraft.

Deliveries by Beech in 1979 were made up of 338 King Airs, 36 Dukes, 308 Barons, 439 Bonanzas, 158 Duchesses, 81 Sierras, 125 Sundowners and 67 Skippers. By 1 January 1980 Beech had delivered 3,256 pressurised aircraft since introducing the King Air 90 in 1964, a record exceeding that of any other general aviation manufacturer. Total production of Beechcraft aeroplanes exceeded 43,000 by the beginning of 1980.

Deliveries of the Beechcraft C-12 twin-turboprop transport to the US Army continued in 1979. Contracts totalling $37 million awarded in early 1980 covered Army and Navy procurement, and will extend deliveries of UC-12Bs for the US Navy and C-12Ds for the Army.

During 1979 Beech continued deliveries of the US Navy T-34C turboprop trainer for student primary training at NAS Milton, Florida. Beech has received contracts totalling $90 million for 184 T-34Cs and provision of engineering services.

FAA certification of the Model 77 Skipper trainer was awarded in March 1979, and initial deliveries of production aircraft began in May 1979. Delivery of the company's only turbocharged single-engined aircraft, the Bonanza A36TC, also began in the Spring of 1979.

Production of airframes for the Bell Helicopter Textron JetRanger, continuous at Beech since 1967, was extended until December 1981 by receipt of a $12 million contract in August 1979 and a $14·5 million contract in January 1980. Contracts for the commercial JetRanger helicopter; the US Army OH-58A observation helicopter, built from 1967-74; and spares, now exceed $164 million. Beech builds the complete airframe, including fuselage, cowling, tailboom and skid landing gear, at Wichita and the Salina, Kansas, division.

In February 1980 Beech announced that it had formed a team with Grumman Aerospace Corporation to compete in the US Navy's VTXTS jet trainer competition.

In early 1977 Beech established a wholly-owned subsidiary, Beech Aerospace Services Inc (BASI), to expand worldwide support of Beechcraft aerospace products. Beech Aircraft has contracts for total logistics support from the US Army, Navy and Air Force, which includes responsibility for furnishing technicians, spares, and ground support equipment. BASI activities cover the Army and Air Force C-12A, USN T-34C and T-44A, Navy/Marines UC-12B, as well as subsonic and supersonic missile targets for the Army. At the beginning of 1980, BASI had 472 maintenance and service personnel stationed at 60 bases in 24 countries, and had established supply routes to each base. BASI headquarters for administration, spare parts, publications central supply and training is based at Jackson, Mississippi.

Beech production of subassemblies for the McDonnell Douglas F-4 Phantom II fighter ended in 1979 after 17 years.

Beech Aircraft occupies 299,535 m² (3,224,167 sq ft) of plant area at its five major facilities in Wichita, Liberal and Salina, Kansas; Boulder, Colorado; and Selma, Alabama.

The Salina division supplies all wings used in Wichita production and is responsible for manufacture and final assembly of the Beechcraft Duke, the pressurised Baron 58P, and the T-34C trainer.

All assembly, flight testing and delivery of the Duchess 76, Sierra, Sundowner and Skipper are carried out at the Liberal Division, which also manufactures control surfaces for all Beech aircraft.

Work at Boulder involves space vehicle or missile applications, and Boulder engineers have developed for NASA cryogenic tanks with the capacity of supporting manned space missions of as long as six months. These tanks can store 50 times as much oxygen and 120 times as much hydrogen as those used in the Apollo programme.

In January 1974 Beech was awarded a subcontract to produce the power reactant storage assembly for NASA's Space Shuttle Orbiter. The assembly includes two liquid oxygen and two liquid hydrogen tanks to supply the Orbiter's fuel cells and environmental control/life support system. Design, development, test and production are being carried out at the Boulder division. The first delivery of oxygen and hydrogen cryogenic tanks for the power reactant storage assembly was completed in November 1978. During 1975-76 Beech received three additional contracts to develop Space Shuttle ground support equipment systems, which will be used at both the Kennedy Space Center and Vandenberg AFB launch sites. Beech contracts on the Space Shuttle programme total $35·6 million.

Boulder also produces aircraft assemblies for other Beech divisions and AQM-37A and MQM-107 (VSTT) missile target systems for the US Army and Navy (see RPVs and Targets section). In 1979, it announced the development of a system using liquid natural gas (LNG) as an efficient, safe, and environmentally-clean alternative fuel for motor vehicles.

In late 1978, Beech announced the lease of a 5,388 m² (58,000 sq ft) facility at Craig Field, Selma, Alabama, for aircraft modification. Beech continues to manufacture basic aircraft at its Wichita facility, and flies them to its Selma Division for specialised work. First aircraft modified at Selma were special maritime versions of the Super King Air for Japan's Maritime Safety Agency.

In September 1979, Beech announced that Selma would be the production site for the Beechcraft Commuter C99, the company's initial product for re-entry into the commuter aircraft market.

Beechcraft Turbine Mentor 34C trainers for the national pilot training school of Algeria

In June 1978, Beech announced the introduction of an innovative charter service through the Beechcraft Aviation Centers. Known as the Beechcraft Executive Flight plan, it makes available to businessmen on a guaranteed annual charter basis such aircraft as the Baron 58P and 58TC, and the single-engined Bonanza series. The company's belief that this would make a new sector of the business community aware of the economic advantages of private air transport has been confirmed; by 1 January 1980, aircraft at the 57 Executive Flight plan charter centres had flown more than 28,000 charter hours.

Wholly-owned subsidiaries of the parent company include Beech Acceptance Corporation Inc, which is engaged in business aircraft retail finance and leasing; Beechcraft AG, which has its headquarters in Zurich, Switzerland, and supports in Europe the sales, liaison and other activities of the parent company; Travel Air Insurance Company Ltd, a Bermuda-based company organised during 1972 to provide aircraft liability insurance; Beech Holdings Inc, which provides marketing support to the parent company; Beech International Sales Corporation, Wichita, through which all Beech export sales are made; Beech Aerospace Services Inc, which provides world-wide support of Beechcraft military aircraft, missile targets and related products; Fuel and Line Service Inc, Wichita; and the following product sales outlets: Hedrick Beechcraft, Colorado Springs, Colorado; Houston-Beechcraft Inc, Houston, Texas; Denver-Beechcraft Inc, Denver, Colorado and Aircraftco Division, Broomfield, Colorado; United Beechcraft Inc, Wichita, Kansas; Beechcraft West Hayward, Van Nuys, Bakersfield and Fresno, California; Mission Beechcraft, Santa Ana, California; Indiana Beechcraft Inc, Indianapolis, Indiana; Beechcraft East Inc, Farmingdale, New York; Baton Rouge Aircraft, Baton Rouge, Louisiana; and Thompson Beechcraft, Salt Lake City, Utah.

BEECHCRAFT MODEL T-34C
US Navy designation: T-34C

In March 1953 the US Air Force selected the Beechcraft Model 45 as its new primary trainer and, under the designation T-34A Mentor, a total of 450 were eventually acquired. Power plant consisted of a 168 kW (225 hp) Continental O-470-13 flat-six engine. Just over a year later the US Navy reached a similar decision, and a total of 423 T-34B Mentors were built for that service.

In 1973 Beech received a US Navy R & D contract to modify two T-34Bs to see whether the type could be upgraded for a continuing training role. This involved the installation of a turboprop engine and the latest avionics equipment, the primary object being to let student pilots have experience of operating turbine-powered aircraft from the beginning of their flight training. The power plant selected was the PT6A-25, which has a torque limiter in this application to restrict engine output to 298 kW (400 shp), ensure long engine life, and provide constant performance over a wide range of temperature and altitude.

Design of the modifications to update the aircraft began in March 1973, and conversion of two T-34Bs (140784 and 140861) started in May 1973. Designated YT-34C, the first of these aircraft (described in previous editions of *Jane's*) flew for the first time on 21 September 1973.

Beech has received US Navy contracts totalling approx $90 million for 184 new-production T-34Cs, and the provision of engineering services and support. The first of the aircraft were delivered to Naval Air Training Command at Whiting Field, Milton, Florida, in November 1977. Student training in the T-34C began in January 1978. An export civil version, known as the **Turbine Mentor 34C**, is in service at the Algerian National Pilot Training School, which received six in 1979.

Production T-34Cs incorporate improvements developed during the flight test programme; structural strength was increased to permit high limit speeds and a fatigue life of 16,000 h in a primary flight training role.

A **T-34C-1** armament systems trainer version is also available and, in addition to its basic role, is capable of

Beechcraft Model T-34C-1 turboprop-powered training/attack aircraft *(Pilot Press)*

carrying out forward air control (FAC) and tactical strike training missions. Contracts were received for the supply of 12 T-34C-1s to the Air Force of Morocco, 20 for the Air Force of Ecuador, 3 for the Ecuadorean Navy, 16 for the Air Force of Indonesia, 6 for the Peruvian Navy, and 15 for the Navy of Argentina. Delivery of all of these has been completed.

TYPE: Two-seat turbine-powered primary training aircraft.

WINGS: Cantilever low-wing monoplane. Wing section NACA 23016·5 (modified) at root, NACA 23012 at tip. Dihedral 7°. Incidence 4° at root, 1° at tip. No sweepback. Conventional box beam structure of light alloy. Ailerons of light alloy construction. Single-slotted trailing-edge flaps of light alloy. Manually operated trim tab in port aileron. Servo tabs in both ailerons.

FUSELAGE: Semi-monocoque light alloy structure.

TAIL UNIT: Cantilever structure of light alloy. Fixed-incidence tailplane. Manually-operated trim tabs in elevators and rudder. Twin ventral fins under rear fuselage.

LANDING GEAR: Electrically-retractable tricycle type. Main units retract inward, nosewheel aft. Beech oleo-pneumatic shock-absorbers. Single wheel on each unit. Main wheels size 7·00-8. Nosewheel and tyre size 5·00-5. Goodyear multiple-disc hydraulic brakes.

POWER PLANT: One 533 kW (715 shp) Pratt & Whitney Aircraft of Canada PT6A-25 turboprop engine, torque limited to 298 kW (400 shp), driving a Hartzell three-blade constant-speed fully-feathering metal propeller. Version of same engine derated to 410 kW (550 shp) is available optionally. Two bladder-type fuel cells in each wing, with a total usable capacity of 492 litres (130 US gallons). Oil capacity 15·1 litres (4 US gallons).

ACCOMMODATION: Instructor and pupil in tandem beneath rearward-sliding cockpit canopy. Cockpit ventilated, heated by engine bleed air and air-conditioned. Dual controls standard. All armament controls in forward cockpit of T-34C-1.

SYSTEMS: Hydraulic system for brakes only. Pneumatic system for emergency opening of cockpit canopy. Diluter demand gaseous oxygen system, pressure 103·5 bars (1,500 lb/sq in). Electrical power supplied by 250A starter/generator. Freon-type air-conditioner for cockpit cooling.

AVIONICS AND EQUIPMENT: Standard avionics can include UHF or VHF com, VOR or Tacan nav, DME, trans-

ponder, angle of attack indicator, ADF, marker beacon, compass and intercom system. Area-NAV, Loran, HF and specialised tactical systems available to customer's requirements. Blind-flying instrumentation standard. Electrically-heated pitot.

ARMAMENT (T-34C-1): CA-513 fixed-reticle reflector gunsight. Four underwing hardpoints are provided for the carriage of stores. The inboard stations are rated at 272 kg (600 lb) each, the outboard stations at 136 kg (300 lb) each, with a maximum load of 272 kg (600 lb) each side and 544 kg (1,200 lb) total. Weapons which can be carried on MA-4 racks include AF/B37K-1 bomb containers with practice bombs or flares, LAU-32 or LAU-59 rocket pods, MK 81 bombs, SUU-11 Minigun pods, BLU-10/B incendiary bombs, AGM-22A wire-guided anti-tank missiles and TA8X towed target equipment.

DIMENSIONS, EXTERNAL:

Wing span	10·16 m (33 ft 3⅞ in)
Wing chord at root	2·55 m (8 ft 4½ in)
Wing chord at tip	1·05 m (3 ft 5¼ in)
Wing aspect ratio	6·22
Length overall	8·75 m (28 ft 8½ in)
Height overall	2·92 m (9 ft 7 in)
Tailplane span	3·71 m (12 ft 2⅛ in)
Wheel track	2·95 m (9 ft 8 in)
Wheelbase	2·41 m (7 ft 11 in)
Propeller diameter	2·29 m (7 ft 6 in)
Propeller ground clearance	0·29 m (11¼ in)

DIMENSIONS, INTERNAL:

Cabin: Length	2·74 m (9 ft 0 in)
Max width	0·86 m (2 ft 10 in)
Max height	1·22 m (4 ft 0 in)

AREAS:

Wings, gross	16·69 m² (179·6 sq ft)
Ailerons (total)	1·06 m² (11·4 sq ft)
Trailing-edge flaps (total)	1·98 m² (21·3 sq ft)
Fin	1·20 m² (12·9 sq ft)
Rudder, incl tab	0·64 m² (6·9 sq ft)
Tailplane	3·46 m² (37·2 sq ft)
Elevators, incl tabs	1·26 m² (13·6 sq ft)

WEIGHTS AND LOADING:

Weight empty: T-34C	1,342 kg (2,960 lb)
T-34C-1	1,356 kg (2,990 lb)
Max T-O and landing weight:	
T-34C	1,950 kg (4,300 lb)
T-34C-1, strike role	2,494 kg (5,500 lb)
Max wing loading: T-34C 108·3 kg/m² (22·2 lb/sq ft)	

PERFORMANCE (T-34C, preliminary results at max T-O weight):

Never-exceed speed	280 knots (518 km/h; 322 mph)
Max cruising speed at 5,335 m (17,500 ft)	
	227 knots (420 km/h; 261 mph)
Stalling speed, flaps up	
	55 knots (102 km/h; 63·3 mph) CAS
Max rate of climb at 3,050 m (10,000 ft)	
	411 m (1,350 ft)/min
Service ceiling	over 9,145 m (30,000 ft)
Range at 6,100 m (20,000 ft)	
	591 nm (1,094 km; 680 miles)

PERFORMANCE (T-34C-1 with 410 kW; 550 shp engine, estimated. A with two stores at AUW of 2,222 kg; 4,900 lb. B with four stores at AUW of 2,495 kg; 5,500 lb, except where indicated):

Max level speed at 5,500 m (18,000 ft):		
A	209 knots (387 km/h; 241 mph)	
B	206 knots (382 km/h; 237 mph)	
Stalling speed, flaps down, idle power:		
A	65 knots (120 km/h; 75 mph) CAS	
B	69 knots (128 km/h; 80 mph) CAS	
Max rate of climb at S/L: A	540 m (1,771 ft)/min	
B	436 m (1,431 ft)/min	

Beechcraft Model 77 Skipper lightweight training aircraft (Avco Lycoming O-235 engine)

Typical combat radius:

FAC mission at AUW of 2,429 kg (5,355 lb), with four stores and optional max fuel, incl 2·6 h loiter over target and 20 min +5% reserves
100 nm (185 km; 115 miles)

Strike mission at AUW of 2,473 kg (5,452 lb), with four stores and optional max fuel, incl 20 min +5% reserves
300 nm (555 km; 345 miles)

BEECHCRAFT MODEL 77 SKIPPER

Beech announced on 17 April 1979 that the Model 77 Skipper had received FAA certification in the Utility category, and deliveries of production aircraft began in May 1979. The first aircraft were allocated to Beech Aero Centers for flying training duties; a total of 67 Skippers had been delivered by 1 January 1980.

Following design definition, which began in late 1973, a five-year development programme had been undertaken to evolve an efficient and economical two-seat general aviation trainer. The prototype, designated PD 285, flew for the first time on 6 February 1975, and was described briefly in the 1975-76 *Jane's*. It was fitted after a time with a T-tail, which offered aerodynamic improvements. Inherent design features included a wing of NASA-developed GAW-1 section, which resulted from NASA/Beech research into supercritical aerofoils with high-lift characteristics; extensive use of bonded metal construction; a one-piece bonded door on each side of the cabin; and all-round tinted cabin windows.

TYPE: Two-seat training aircraft, approved for six-turn spins.

WINGS: Cantilever low-wing monoplane, of NASA GAW-1 section. Dihedral 6° from roots. Tubular spar formed of wrapped light alloy sheet and glassfibre adhesive to ensure required bonding stiffness at all wing stations; auxiliary rear spar, light alloy ribs and bonded light alloy skins. Plain ailerons with corrugated skins. Ground-adjustable trim tab on each aileron. Plain trailing-edge flaps with corrugated skins. Flaps and ailerons actuated via torque tubes.

FUSELAGE: Semi-monocoque structure of light alloy. Lower cabin section is of bonded construction.

TAIL UNIT: Cantilever T-tail of light alloy. Fixed-incidence tailplane, leading-edge of fin, large portion of tailplane, elevator trim tabs and rudder are of bonded construction. Trim tab in each elevator; rudder trim standard.

LANDING GEAR: Non-retractable tricycle type with single wheel on each unit. Cantilever main legs. Steerable nosewheel.

POWER PLANT: One 85·5 kW (115 hp) Avco Lycoming O-235-L2C flat-four engine, driving a Sensenich fixed-pitch two-blade metal propeller with spinner. Fuel in integral wing tanks with combined usable capacity of 110 litres (29 US gallons). Refuelling point on upper surface of each wing.

ACCOMMODATION: Two seats side by side in enclosed cabin. Door on each side. Tinted cabin windows. Carpeted floor. Dual controls standard.

DIMENSIONS, EXTERNAL:
Wing span	9·14 m (30 ft 0 in)
Length overall	7·32 m (24 ft 0 in)
Height overall	2·41 m (7 ft 11 in)
Tailplane span	3·00 m (9 ft 10 in)
Wheel track	2·54 m (8 ft 4 in)
Wheelbase	1·50 m (4 ft 11 in)
Propeller diameter	1·83 m (6 ft 0 in)

WEIGHTS:
Weight empty	499 kg (1,100 lb)
Max T-O and landing weight	760 kg (1,675 lb)
Max ramp weight	762 kg (1,680 lb)

PERFORMANCE (at max T-O weight):

Max cruising speed, 80% power at 1,370 m (4,500 ft)
105 knots (195 km/h; 121 mph)

Econ cruising speed, 53% power at 1,370 m (4,500 ft)
88 knots (163 km/h; 101 mph)

Cruising speed, 61% power at 2,590 m (8,500 ft)
96 knots (177 km/h; 110 mph)

Econ cruising speed, 51% power at 2,590 m (8,500 ft)
85 knots (158 km/h; 98 mph)

Stalling speed, flaps up
48·5 knots (89 km/h; 55·4 mph) CAS

Stalling speed, flaps down
47 knots (87 km/h; 54 mph) CAS

Max rate of climb at S/L 219 m (720 ft)/min

Beechcraft Model 77 Skipper two-seat training aircraft (*Pilot Press*)

Service ceiling	3,930 m (12,900 ft)
Absolute ceiling	4,570 m (15,000 ft)
T-O run	238 m (780 ft)
T-O to 15 m (50 ft)	390 m (1,280 ft)
Landing from 15 m (50 ft)	400 m (1,313 ft)
Landing run	204 m (670 ft)

Range, max cruising speed at 1,370 m (4,500 ft), with reserves
326 nm (605 km; 376 miles)

Range, econ cruising speed at 1,370 m (4,500 ft), with reserves
410 nm (760 km; 472 miles)

Range, cruising speed (61% power) at 2,590 m (8,500 ft), with reserves
388 nm (719 km; 447 miles)

Range, econ cruising speed at 2,590 m (8,500 ft), with reserves
412 nm (764 km; 475 miles)

BEECHCRAFT SIERRA 200 and SUNDOWNER 180

In December 1971, Beech introduced a new light aircraft marketing programme centred around three models, which were given individual exterior paint schemes and renamed from their previous Musketeer designations (see 1971-72 *Jane's*).

In 1974 these designations were changed again to indicate the engine horsepower rating, so becoming Beechcraft Sierra 200 (formerly Model A24R Musketeer Super R), Sundowner 180 (Model C23, formerly Musketeer Custom), and Sport 150 (Model B19, formerly Musketeer Sport). The fourth aircraft in the former Musketeer line, the Super, was discontinued at the end of 1971 after a total of 368 had been built; and production of the Sport 150 (Model B19) ended in September 1978 after 903 had been built. Details of the Sport 150 can be found in the 1978-79 *Jane's*.

The Sierra 200 was recertificated in 1974 and redesignated Model B24R, due to the installation of a new engine, improved cowling and redesign of control features. Designated Model C24R in 1977, improvements included a propeller of increased diameter to enhance performance, and wheel well fairings to reduce drag when the wheels are retracted.

Details of the two current models are as follows:

Sundowner 180. Basic four-seat version with 134 kW (180 hp) Avco Lycoming O-360-A4K engine, driving a Sensenich Type 76EM8S5-0-60 two-blade fixed-pitch metal propeller, and non-retractable landing gear. Aerobatic version is approved for rolls, Immelmann turns, loops, spins, chandelles and other manoeuvres, carrying two persons. Three windows standard on each side of cabin.

Sierra 200. Generally similar to the Sundowner but with accommodation for four to six persons, a 149 kW (200 hp) Avco Lycoming IO-360-A1B6 engine, driving a Hartzell Type HC-M2YR-1BF/F7666A two-blade constant-speed metal propeller, and retractable tricycle landing gear. Electrically-actuated hydraulic system based on a self-contained unit in the rear fuselage, comprising electrically-driven hydraulic pump, fluid reservoir and valves. An emergency valve, sited adjacent to the pilot's feet, allows selection of the landing gear to free-fall within three seconds. Main wheels retract outward into wings;

nosewheel turns through 90° as it retracts rearwards. Four windows standard on each side of cabin.

Factory-installed optional equipment packages are as follows:

Weekender. Includes sun visors; tinted windscreen and windows; dual controls and pedal-operated brakes for co-pilot; lighting group comprising rotating beacon, navigation, cabin dome, overhead instrument and map lights; cabin boarding steps; and acrylic enamel paint; adding 12·7 kg (28 lb) to basic empty weight.

Holiday. As above, plus instrument group comprising 3 in horizon and directional gyros with vacuum system, electric clock, outside air temperature gauge, rate of climb indicator and turn co-ordinator; coat hook and garment hanger in baggage compartment; wing-mounted landing light; and two 12V 25Ah batteries; adding 27·2 kg (60 lb) to basic empty weight.

Professional. As above, plus true airspeed indicator; electrically-operated tailplane trim and control wheel switch; two headrests; instrument post lights; wing-mounted taxi light; and heated pitot tube; adding 30·8 kg (68 lb) to basic empty weight.

Ten factory-installed avionics packages are available optionally, and include com transceiver, nav receiver-converter, ADF, transponder and audio panel from Collins, King, Edo-Aire Mitchell or Narco, plus cabin speaker, microphone with jack and related antennae. An extensive selection of additional avionics is also available optionally.

Production is centred in Beech's Liberal, Kansas, plant. A total of 5,004 Musketeers, Sundowners, Sports and Sierras had been delivered by 1 January 1980. They included 20 aircraft supplied to the Mexican government for military training, 25 for the Canadian Armed Forces, 21 for the Indonesian Department of Transportation, Communication and Tourism for its primary training programme, and 19 for the University of Illinois Institute of Aviation. Three Sierra 200s were delivered in 1979 to the national pilot training school of Algeria.

The following details apply to both current models:

TYPE: Four- or four/six-seat cabin monoplane.

WINGS: Cantilever low-wing monoplane. Wing section NACA 63₂A415. Dihedral 6° 30'. Incidence 3° at root, 1° at tip. Single extruded main spar at 50% chord. Aluminium skin and stringers are bonded to honeycomb Trussgrid ribs on forward 50% of wing; rear 50% of wing is riveted. Slotted all-metal riveted ailerons and mechanically-controlled (optionally electrically-actuated) flaps have corrugated skin. No trim tabs. Plastics wingtips.

FUSELAGE: Cabin section has basic keel formed by floor and lower skin, with rolled skin side panels, stringers, a minimum number of bulkheads and structural top. Conventional semi-monocoque rear fuselage.

TAIL UNIT: Cantilever all-metal structure, with swept vertical surfaces. One-piece all-moving horizontal surface with full-span anti-servo tab. Optional electric tailplane trim. Rudder and aileron controls interconnected for easy cross-country flying.

Beechcraft Sundowner 180 four-seat light aircraft

Beechcraft Sierra 200 four/six-seat light aircraft

LANDING GEAR (Sundowner): Non-retractable tricycle type. Beech rubber-disc shock-absorbers. Nosewheel with tube-type tyre size 15 × 6·00-6, pressure 2·76 bars (40 lb/sq in). Main wheels have tube-type tyres size 17·5 × 6·00-6, pressure 1·52 bars (22 lb/sq in). Cleveland disc-type hydraulic brakes with toe-operated control. Steerable nosewheel. Parking brake.

POWER PLANT: One flat-four engine (details given under model listings). Two fuel tanks in inboard wing leading-edges, with usable capacity of 216 litres (57 US gallons). Refuelling points above tanks. Oil capacity 7·5 litres (2 US gallons).

ACCOMMODATION: Pilot and three or five passengers (Sierra); pilot and three passengers (Sundowner); in pairs, in enclosed cabin with door on each side. Compartment for 122 kg (270 lb) baggage, with external door on port side. In-flight adjustable seats, pilot's storm window, windscreen defroster, instrument panel glareshield, air vents, map stowage, wall-to-wall carpeting. Optional aerobatic kit for Sundowner includes g meter and quick-release door.

SYSTEMS: Electrical system supplied by 60A alternator; 24V 15·5Ah battery standard, two 12V 25Ah batteries optional. Hydraulic system for brakes only, except on Sierra which has electro-hydraulic actuation system for landing gear. Vacuum system for instruments optional.

AVIONICS AND EQUIPMENT: Optional avionics as listed earlier. Standard equipment includes sensitive altimeter, fore and aft adjustable front seats with reclining backs, shoulder harness and lap belts, control locks, map stowage, pilot's storm window, emergency locator transmitter, stall warning device, and towbar. Optional equipment includes exhaust gas temperature gauge, Hobbs hour meter, outside air temperature gauge, true airspeed indicator, headrests, tinted windscreen and windows, alternate static source, heated pitot, rear cabin 'family' seat, internal corrosion proofing, instrument post lights, two-light strobe system, wing-mounted taxi light, external power socket and acrylic enamel exterior finish. An aerobatic kit is available for the Sundowner, and a 'Magic Hand' landing gear safety system for the Sierra.

DIMENSIONS, EXTERNAL:

Wing span	9·98 m (32 ft 9 in)
Wing chord, constant	1·34 m (4 ft 4¾ in)
Wing aspect ratio	7·4
Length overall	7·85 m (25 ft 9 in)
Height overall: Sundowner	2·51 m (8 ft 3 in)
Sierra	2·46 m (8 ft 1 in)
Tailplane span	3·30 m (10 ft 10 in)
Wheel track: Sundowner	3·61 m (11 ft 10 in)
Sierra	3·86 m (12 ft 8 in)
Wheelbase: Sundowner	1·93 m (6 ft 4 in)
Sierra	1·83 m (6 ft 0¼ in)
Propeller diameter	1·93 m (6 ft 4 in)
Propeller ground clearance:	
Sundowner	0·36 m (1 ft 2 in)
Sierra	0·33 m (1 ft 1 in)
Cabin doors: Height	0·91 m (3 ft 0 in)
Width	0·91 m (3 ft 0 in)
Baggage compartment door:	
Sundowner: Height	0·47 m (1 ft 6½ in)
Width	0·60 m (1 ft 11¾ in)
Sierra: Height	0·84 m (2 ft 9 in)
Width	0·56 m (1 ft 10 in)

DIMENSIONS, INTERNAL:
Cabin, aft of instrument panel:

Length	2·41 m (7 ft 11 in)
Max width	1·18 m (3 ft 8 in)
Max height	1·22 m (4 ft 0 in)
Floor area	2·4 m² (25·84 sq ft)
Volume	2·92 m³ (103·2 cu ft)
Baggage compartment	0·55 m³ (19·5 cu ft)

AREAS:

Wings, gross	13·57 m² (146 sq ft)
Ailerons (total)	0·93 m² (10·06 sq ft)
Flaps (total)	1·74 m² (18·76 sq ft)
Fin	0·93 m² (9·98 sq ft)
Rudder	0·43 m² (4·62 sq ft)
Tailplane, incl anti-servo tab	2·52 m² (27·08 sq ft)

WEIGHTS AND LOADINGS:
Weight empty (incl oil and unusable fuel):

Sundowner	681 kg (1,502 lb)
Sierra	777 kg (1,713 lb)
T-O weight, Utility category:	
Sundowner	920 kg (2,030 lb)
Max T-O weight: Sundowner	1,111 kg (2,450 lb)
Sierra	1,247 kg (2,750 lb)
Max wing loading:	
Sundowner	81·9 kg/m² (16·78 lb/sq ft)
Sierra	91·9 kg/m² (18·84 lb/sq ft)
Max power loading:	
Sundowner	8·29 kg/kW (13·61 lb/hp)
Sierra	8·37 kg/kW (13·75 lb/hp)

PERFORMANCE (at max T-O weight):
Max level speed at S/L:

Sundowner	123 knots (228 km/h; 141 mph)
Sierra	142 knots (262 km/h; 163 mph)

Cruising speed:
Sundowner, 84% power
                123 knots (228 km/h; 141 mph)

Sundowner, 59% power
                98 knots (182 km/h; 113 mph)
Sierra, 75% power 137 knots (254 km/h; 158 mph)
Sierra, 55% power 115 knots (213 km/h; 132 mph)
Stalling speed, flaps down, power off:

Sundowner	51 knots (94·5 km/h; 59 mph) CAS
Sierra	60 knots (111 km/h; 69 mph) CAS

Max rate of climb at S/L:

Sundowner	241 m (792 ft)/min
Sierra	283 m (927 ft)/min
Service ceiling: Sundowner	3,840 m (12,600 ft)
Sierra	4,690 m (15,385 ft)
Absolute ceiling: Sundowner	4,390 m (14,400 ft)
Sierra	5,315 m (17,430 ft)
Min ground turning radius	7·29 m (23 ft 11 in)
T-O run: Sundowner	344 m (1,130 ft)
Sierra	361 m (1,185 ft)
T-O to 15 m (50 ft): Sundowner	596 m (1,955 ft)
Sierra	506 m (1,660 ft)
Landing from 15 m (50 ft):	
Sundowner	452 m (1,484 ft)
Sierra	446 m (1,462 ft)
Landing run: Sundowner	214 m (703 ft)
Sierra	249 m (816 ft)

Range with max fuel, allowances for warm-up, T-O, climb and 45 min reserves:
Sundowner, 2,300 rpm at 1,370 m (4,500 ft)
                597 nm (1,106 km; 687 miles)
Sierra, 2,400 rpm at 3,050 m (10,000 ft)
                686 nm (1,271 km; 790 miles)

BEECHCRAFT BONANZA MODEL V35B

The prototype Bonanza flew for the first time on 22 December 1945 and the type went into production in 1947. In February 1977 the 10,000th V-tail Bonanza Model 35 was completed, and this aircraft entered its 34th year of production in 1980. The current version is designated Model V35B.

The Bonanza Model A36 and A36TC utility aircraft, and Model F33 series with conventional tail unit, are described separately.

The Bonanzas for 1980 are equipped with a dual-duct fresh air system to increase cabin airflow. Safety features include single diagonal strap shoulder harness with inertia reel for all occupants as standard equipment. Five optional factory-installed IFR avionics packages include dual communication, navigation, marker beacon, glideslope, DME, and transponder. Four packages meet FAA Technical Standard Order (TSO). Beech was in 1972 the first general aviation manufacturer to acquire approval for factory installation of area navigation equipment on production aircraft with IFR equipment.

In 1980 Beech was offering five 'Super Utility' packages of optional equipment, which includes a large cargo door on the Models V35B and F33A and club seating arrangement on the Models A36 and A36TC, gyro horizon and directional gyro with pressure system, heated pitot, alternate static source, super soundproofing and a choice of Edo-Aire Mitchell Century I, III or IV, Bendix FCS-810 or King KFC 200 autopilot.

Other optional extras available on the Bonanza include the Beech-designed 'Magic Hand' landing gear safety system. Designed to eliminate the possibility of wheels-up landing or inadvertent retraction of the landing gear on the ground, it lowers the gear automatically on approach when the engine manifold pressure falls below approximately 508 mm (20 in) and airspeed has been reduced to 104 knots (193 km/h; 120 mph). On take-off, it keeps the gear down until the aircraft is airborne and has accelerated to 78 knots (145 km/h; 90 mph) IAS. The system can be switched off by the pilot at will.

An optional 12,000 BTU refrigeration-type air-conditioning system was introduced during 1975, comprising an evaporator located beneath the pilot's seat, condenser mounted on the lower fuselage and an engine-mounted compressor. Air outlets are located on the centre console, and a two-speed blower is provided for air distribution (except on A36TC).

TYPE: Four/five-seat light cabin monoplane.

WINGS: Cantilever low-wing monoplane. Wing section Beech modified NACA 23016·5 at root, modified NACA 23012 at tip. Dihedral 6°. Incidence 4° at root, 1° at tip. Sweepback 0° at quarter-chord. Each wing is a two-spar semi-monocoque box-beam of conventional aluminium alloy construction. Symmetrical-section ailerons and single-slotted three-position flaps of aluminium alloy construction. Ground-adjustable trim tab in each aileron.

FUSELAGE: Conventional aluminium alloy semi-monocoque structure. Hat-section longerons and channel-type keels extend forward from cabin section, making the support structure for the engine and nosewheel an integral part of the fuselage.

TAIL UNIT: Cantilever V tail, with tailplane and elevators set at 33° dihedral angle. Semi-monocoque construction. Fixed surfaces have aluminium alloy structure and skin. Control surfaces, aft of the light alloy spar, are primarily of magnesium alloy, with large controllable trim tab in each. Tail surfaces are interchangeable port and starboard, except for tabs and actuator horns. Electrically-operated elevator trimming optional.

LANDING GEAR: Electrically-retractable tricycle type, with steerable nosewheel. Main wheels retract inward into wings, nosewheel aft. Beech oleo-pneumatic shock-absorbers on all units. Cleveland main wheels, size 6·00-6, and tyres, size 7·00-6, pressure 2·28-2·76 bars (33-40 lb/sq in). Cleveland nosewheel and tyre, size 5·00-5, pressure 2·76 bars (40 lb/sq in). Cleveland ring-disc hydraulic brakes. Parking brake. 'Magic Hand' landing gear system optional.

POWER PLANT: One 212·5 kW (285 hp) Continental IO-520-BB flat-six engine, driving a McCauley two-blade constant-speed metal propeller. Three-blade McCauley propeller optional. Manually-adjustable engine cowl flaps. Two standard fuel tanks in wing leading-edges, with total usable capacity of 280 litres (74 US gallons). Refuelling points above tanks. Oil capacity 11·5 litres (3 US gallons).

ACCOMMODATION: Enclosed cabin seating four or five persons on individual seats. Centre windows open for ventilation on ground and have release handles to permit their use as emergency exits. Pilot's storm window, port side. Cabin structure reinforced for protection in turnover. Space for up to 122·5 kg (270 lb) of baggage aft of seats. Passenger door and baggage access door both on starboard side. Cabin heated and ventilated.

SYSTEMS: Electrical system supplied by 28V 50A alternator, 24V 15·5Ah battery. A 100A alternator is available as an option, as is a standby generator. Hydraulic system for brakes only. Pneumatic system for instrument gyros and refrigeration-type air-conditioning system optional. Oxygen system optional.

AVIONICS AND EQUIPMENT: Standard avionics comprise King KX 170B 720-channel com transceiver, 200-channel nav receiver with KI 208 VOR/LOC converter-indicator, microphone, headset, cabin speaker, and nav/com/GS antenna. A wide range of optional avionics is available, by Bendix, Collins, Edo-Aire Mitchell, King and Narco. Standard equipment includes electric clock, outside air temperature gauge, rate of climb indicator, sensitive altimeter, turn co-ordinator, four fore and aft adjustable and reclining seats, armrests, headrests, shoulder harness and lap-belts, pilot's storm window, sun visors, ultraviolet-proof windscreen and windows, emergency locator transmitter, stall warning device, carpeted floor, coat hooks, glove compartment, in-flight storage pockets, utility shelf, cabin dome light, reading lights, instrument panel floodlights, electroluminescent sub-panel lighting, landing light, taxi light, full-flow oil filter, urethane exterior paint, and towbar. Optional equipment includes control wheel clock, 3 in horizon and directional gyros, exhaust gas temperature gauge, dual controls, co-pilot's wheel brakes, alternate static source, heated pitot, fifth seat, large cargo door, super soundproofing, control wheel map lights, entrance door courtesy light, instrument post lights, internally-lighted instruments, rotating beacons, three-light strobe system, external power socket, and static wicks.

DIMENSIONS, EXTERNAL:

Wing span	10·21 m (33 ft 6 in)
Wing chord at root	2·13 m (7 ft 0 in)

Beechcraft's V-tail V35B Bonanza four/five-seat light aircraft

Wing chord at tip	1·07 m (3 ft 6 in)
Wing aspect ratio	6·2
Length overall	8·05 m (26 ft 5 in)
Height overall	2·31 m (7 ft 7 in)
Tailplane span	3·10 m (10 ft 2 in)
Wheel track	2·92 m (9 ft 7 in)
Wheelbase	2·13 m (7 ft 0 in)
Propeller diameter: two-blade	2·13 m (7 ft 0 in)
three-blade	2·03 m (6 ft 8 in)
Passenger door: Height	0·91 m (3 ft 0 in)
Width	0·94 m (3 ft 1 in)
Baggage compartment door:	
Height	0·47 m (1 ft 6½ in)
Width	0·57 m (1 ft 10½ in)

DIMENSIONS, INTERNAL:

Cabin, aft of firewall: Length	3·07 m (10 ft 1 in)
Max width	1·07 m (3 ft 6 in)
Max height	1·27 m (4 ft 2 in)
Volume	3·31 m³ (117 cu ft)
Baggage space	0·99 m³ (35 cu ft)

AREAS:

Wings, gross	16·80 m² (181 sq ft)
Ailerons (total)	1·06 m² (11·4 sq ft)
Trailing-edge flaps (total)	1·98 m² (21·3 sq ft)
Fixed tail surfaces	2·20 m² (23·8 sq ft)
Movable tail surfaces, incl tabs	1·34 m² (14·4 sq ft)

WEIGHTS AND LOADINGS:

Weight empty, equipped	960 kg (2,117 lb)
Max T-O and landing weight	1,542 kg (3,400 lb)
Max wing loading	91·8 kg/m² (18·80 lb/sq ft)
Max power loading	7·26 kg/kW (11·93 lb/hp)

PERFORMANCE (at max T-O weight, except cruising speeds at mid-cruise weight):

Max level speed at S/L

182 knots (338 km/h; 209 mph)

Cruising speed:

75% power at 1,830 m (6,000 ft)

172 knots (319 km/h; 198 mph)

66% power at 3,050 m (10,000 ft)

168 knots (311 km/h; 193 mph)

55% power at 3,660 m (12,000 ft)

157 knots (291 km/h; 181 mph)

45% power at 2,440 m (8,000 ft)

136 knots (253 km/h; 157 mph)

Stalling speed, power off, flaps up

64 knots (118 km/h; 74 mph) IAS

Stalling speed, power off, 30° flap

51 knots (94 km/h; 59 mph) IAS

Max rate of climb at S/L	356 m (1,167 ft)/min
Service ceiling	5,445 m (17,860 ft)
T-O run	305 m (1,002 ft)
T-O to 15 m (50 ft)	539 m (1,769 ft)
Landing from 15 m (50 ft)	404 m (1,324 ft)
Landing run	233 m (763 ft)

Range with 280 litres (74 US gallons) usable fuel, allowances for engine start, taxi, T-O, climb and 45 min reserves at 45% power:

75% power at 1,830 m (6,000 ft)

716 nm (1,326 km; 824 miles)

66% power at 3,050 m (10,000 ft)

777 nm (1,440 km; 894 miles)

55% power at 3,660 m (12,000 ft)

838 nm (1,553 km; 964 miles)

45% power at 2,440 m (8,000 ft)

889 nm (1,648 km; 1,023 miles)

BEECHCRAFT BONANZA MODEL F33A/C

The **F33A** version of the Bonanza is a four/five-seat single-engined executive aircraft, similar in general configuration to the Bonanza Model V35B, but distinguished by a conventional tail unit with sweptback vertical surfaces. The prototype flew for the first time on 14 September 1959, and the production models were known as Debonairs until 1967.

The **F33C** is generally similar to the A, but approved for both aerobatic and utility operation.

The Model G33 was discontinued in early 1973 after 49 had been produced.

A total of 2,321 Model 33s had been built by 1 January 1980. Twenty-one were bought for pilot training by Lufthansa in West Germany; and Pacific Southwest Airlines acquired 12 F33As for airline crew training. Deliveries of F33As and aerobatic F33Cs to foreign air forces were as follows: Imperial Air Force of Iran, 16 F33Cs; Mexican Navy, 5 F33Cs; Netherlands Government Flying School, 16 F33Cs; and Spanish Air Ministry and Air Force, 74 F33s.

Optional extras include the 'Magic Hand' automatic landing gear control system, air-conditioning system and other items described under the Model V35B Bonanza entry, except that the large cargo door, air-conditioning and fifth seat are not available for the Bonanza F33C.

TYPE: Four/five-seat cabin monoplane.

WINGS: As for V35B Bonanza.

FUSELAGE: As for Bonanza V35B series.

TAIL UNIT: Conventional cantilever all-metal stressed-skin structure, primarily of aluminium alloy but with corrugated magnesium skin on elevators. Large trim tab in each elevator. Fixed tab in rudder.

LANDING GEAR: As for Bonanza V35B series. Main wheels size 6·00-6, with tyres size 7·00-6, pressure 2·28-2·76

bars (33-40 lb/sq in); nosewheel size 5·00-5, tyre pressure 2·76 bars (40 lb/sq in).

POWER PLANT: As for Bonanza V35B.

ACCOMMODATION: Enclosed cabin with four individual seats in pairs as standard, plus optional forward-facing fifth seat (F33A only). Baggage compartment and hat shelf aft of seats. Passenger door and baggage compartment door on starboard side. Heater standard. Large cargo door, on starboard side of fuselage, optional on F33A.

SYSTEMS: As for V35B.

AVIONICS AND EQUIPMENT: As for V35B.

DIMENSIONS, EXTERNAL: As for V35B except:

Length overall	8·13 m (26 ft 8 in)
Height overall	2·51 m (8 ft 3 in)
Tailplane span	3·71 m (12 ft 2 in)
Propeller diameter	2·13 m (7 ft 0 in)

DIMENSIONS, INTERNAL: As for V35B.

AREAS: As for V35B except:

Fin	0·85 m² (9·1 sq ft)
Rudder, incl tab	0·43 m² (4·6 sq ft)
Tailplane	1·75 m² (18·82 sq ft)
Elevators, incl tabs	1·24 m² (13·36 sq ft)

WEIGHTS AND LOADINGS:

Weight empty	967 kg (2,132 lb)
Max T-O and landing weight	1,542 kg (3,400 lb)
Max wing loading	91·8 kg/m² (18·8 lb/sq ft)
Max power loading	7·26 kg/kW (11·93 lb/hp)

PERFORMANCE: As for V35B

BEECHCRAFT BONANZA MODEL A36

This version of the Bonanza, introduced in mid-1968, is a full six-seat utility aircraft developed from the Bonanza Model V35B. It is generally similar to the V35B, but has a conventional tail unit with sweptback vertical surfaces, similar to that of the F33 series of Bonanzas. In addition, the A36 has large double doors on the starboard side of the fuselage aft of the wing root, to facilitate loading and unloading of bulky cargo when used in a utility role. The cabin volume is increased by 0·54 m³ (18·9 cu ft) compared with the V35B, due to a fuselage extension of 0·25 m (10 in), and an increase of 0·28 m³ (10 cu ft) in the baggage compartment volume.

Like all Bonanzas, the Model A36 is licensed in the FAA Utility category at full gross weight, with no limitation of performance.

The current version of the Bonanza Model A36 introduced the improvements noted for the Bonanza V35B as well as options which include a club-seating interior layout with rear-facing third and fourth seats, executive writing desk, reading lights and fresh air outlets for fifth and sixth seats. Optional extras include the 'Magic Hand' automatic landing gear control system, refrigeration-type air-conditioning system and all other items mentioned under the Model V35B Bonanza entry, except for the large cargo door.

TYPE: Four/six-seat utility light cabin monoplane.

WINGS: As for Model V35B.

FUSELAGE: As for Model V35B but lengthened by 0·25 m (10 in).

TAIL UNIT: Conventional cantilever all-metal stressed-skin structure, primarily of aluminium alloy but with corrugated magnesium skin on elevators. Large trim tab in each elevator. Fixed tab in rudder.

LANDING GEAR: Electrically-retractable tricycle type, similar to that of Baron. Main units retract inward into wings, nosewheel rearward. Beech oleo-pneumatic shock-absorbers. Steerable nosewheel. Cleveland main wheels, size 6·00-6, with tyres size 7·00-6, pressure 2·28-2·76 bars (33-40 lb/sq in). Cleveland nosewheel and tyre size 5·00-5, pressure 2·76 bars (40 lb/sq in). Cleveland ring-disc hydraulic brakes. Parking brake.

POWER PLANT: As for Model V35B.

ACCOMMODATION: Enclosed cabin seating four to six persons on individual seats. Two rear removable seats and two folding seats permit rapid conversion to utility

configuration. Optional club-seating layout with rear-facing third and fourth seats, executive writing desk, headrests for third and fourth seats, reading lights and fresh air outlets for fifth and sixth seats. Double doors of bonded aluminium honeycomb construction on starboard side facilitate loading of cargo. As an air ambulance, one stretcher can be accommodated with ample room for a medical attendant and/or other passengers. Extra windows provide improved view for passengers. Stowage for 181 kg (400 lb) of baggage.

SYSTEMS: Electrical system supplied by 28V 50A alternator, 24V 15·5Ah battery; a 100A alternator is available as an option. Hydraulic system for brakes only. Pneumatic system for instrument gyros and refrigeration-type air-conditioning system optional.

AVIONICS AND EQUIPMENT: Standard avionics include King KX 170B 720-channel nav/com, with KI 208 VOR/LOC Omni converter/indicator and Beechcraft antenna, but a wide range of optional avionics is available. Optional items of equipment are as detailed for the V35B Bonanza, except as noted.

DIMENSIONS, EXTERNAL: As for V35B except:

Length overall	8·38 m (27 ft 6 in)
Height overall	2·57 m (8 ft 5 in)
Wheelbase	2·39 m (7 ft 10¼ in)
Rear passenger/cargo door:	
Height	1·02 m (3 ft 4 in)
Width	1·14 m (3 ft 9 in)

DIMENSIONS, INTERNAL:

Cabin, aft of firewall: Length, incl extended baggage compartment	3·84 m (12 ft 7 in)
Max width	1·07 m (3 ft 6 in)
Max height	1·27 m (4 ft 2 in)
Volume	3·85 m³ (135·9 cu ft)

AREA:

Wings, gross	16·8 m² (181 sq ft)

WEIGHTS AND LOADINGS:

Weight empty, equipped	994 kg (2,191 lb)
Max T-O weight	1,633 kg (3,600 lb)
Max wing loading	97·2 kg/m² (19·9 lb/sq ft)
Max power loading	7·68 kg/kW (12·6 lb/hp)

PERFORMANCE (at max T-O weight, except cruising speeds at mid-cruise weight):

Max level speed 179 knots (332 km/h; 206 mph)

Cruising speed:

75% power at 1,830 m (6,000 ft)

168 knots (311 km/h; 193 mph)

66% power at 3,050 m (10,000 ft)

163 knots (303 km/h; 188 mph)

55% power at 3,660 m (12,000 ft)

150 knots (278 km/h; 173 mph)

45% power at 2,440 m (8,000 ft)

127 knots (235 km/h; 146 mph)

Stalling speed, flaps up, power off

62 knots (115 km/h; 71 mph) IAS

Stalling speed, 30° flap, power off

52 knots (96·5 km/h; 60 mph) IAS

Max rate of climb at S/L	314 m (1,030 ft)/min
Service ceiling	5,060 m (16,600 ft)
T-O run	347 m (1,140 ft)
T-O to 15 m (50 ft)	622 m (2,040 ft)
Landing from 15 m (50 ft)	442 m (1,450 ft)
Landing run	256 m (840 ft)

Range with 280 litres (74 US gallons) usable fuel, allowances for engine start, taxi, T-O, climb and 45 min reserves at 45% power:

75% power at 1,830 m (6,000 ft)

697 nm (1,292 km; 802 miles)

66% power at 3,050 m (10,000 ft)

748 nm (1,386 km; 861 miles)

55% power at 3,660 m (12,000 ft)

790 nm (1,464 km; 909 miles)

45% power at 2,440 m (8,000 ft)

824 nm (1,527 km; 948 miles)

Beechcraft Model F33A Bonanza four/five-seat cabin monoplane

BEECHCRAFT TURBO BONANZA MODEL A36TC

Beech introduced for 1979 a turbocharged version of the A36 Bonanza, following FAA certification on 7 December 1978. This addition to the Beechcraft range is generally similar to the A36, except as detailed:

WINGS, FUSELAGE, TAIL UNIT AND LANDING GEAR: As for Model A36.

POWER PLANT: One 223·7 kW (300 hp) Continental TSIO-520-UB turbocharged flat-six engine, driving a McCauley three-blade constant-speed metal propeller. Two fuel tanks in wing leading-edges, with total usable capacity of 280 litres (74 US gallons). Refuelling points above tanks. Oil capacity 11·5 litres (3 US gallons).

ACCOMMODATION AND SYSTEMS: As for Model A36, except that air-conditioning is not available as an option.

AVIONICS AND EQUIPMENT: As detailed for Model V35B, except that rear cabin utility shelf, exhaust gas temperature gauge and air-conditioning are not available. A turbine inlet temperature gauge is standard.

DIMENSIONS, EXTERNAL: As for Model A36, except:
Propeller diameter	2·03 m (6 ft 8 in)
Propeller ground clearance	0·24 m (9½ in)

DIMENSIONS, INTERNAL, AND AREAS: As for Model A36

WEIGHTS AND LOADINGS:
Max T-O and landing weight	1,655 kg (3,650 lb)
Max ramp weight	1,663 kg (3,666 lb)
Max wing loading	98·6 kg/m² (20·17 lb/sq ft)
Max power loading	7·40 kg/kW (12·17 lb/hp)

PERFORMANCE (at max T-O weight):
Never-exceed speed	214 knots (396 km/h; 246 mph) IAS
Max operating altitude	above 7,620 m (25,000 ft)

BEECHCRAFT DUCHESS 76

The Duchess 76, a four-seat twin-engined light aircraft, flew for the first time on 24 May 1977, and received FAA certification on 24 January 1978. A testbed version of this aircraft, designated PD 289, had been undergoing a comprehensive flight test programme since September 1974. Following certification in the Normal category for day and night VFR and IFR, the first production deliveries were made in May 1978, at which time more than 350 had been ordered. A total of 278 Duchesses had been delivered by 1 January 1980.

The Duchess 76 is planned for use by Beech Aero Centers, and is designed for the personal light twin, light charter and multi-engine flight trainer markets. Emphasis has, therefore, been placed on good low speed flight and single-engine handling characteristics, and opposite-rotating propellers are fitted.

Factory-installed optional equipment packages are available as follows:

Beechcraft A36TC turbocharged version of the four/six-seat Model A36 Bonanza

Weekender. Comprising sun visors; tinted windscreen and windows; landing, navigation, strobe, cabin dome, map, overhead instrument and instrument post lights; cabin boarding steps; propeller unfeathering accumulators; and acrylic enamel paint; adding 20·4 kg (45 lb) to basic empty weight.

Holiday. As above, plus coat hook and garment hanger in baggage compartment; instrument group comprising electric clock, 3 in horizon and directional gyros and pressure system, exhaust gas temperature gauge, outside air temperature gauge, rate of climb indicator, turn co-ordinator, and wing-mounted landing light; adding 37·6 kg (83 lb) to basic empty weight.

Professional. As above, plus true airspeed indicator; electric elevator trim with control wheel switch; two seat headrests; heated pitot tube; and wing-mounted taxi lights; adding 40·8 kg (90 lb) to basic empty weight.

Ten factory-installed avionics packages are also available optionally, and include com transceiver; nav receiver-converter, with VOR/LOC indicator; ADF; transponder; and audio panel; from Collins, Edo-Aire Mitchell, King and Narco. An extensive selection of additional avionics, including autopilot, DME, glideslope receiver and marker beacon systems, are available optionally from these manufacturers and also from Bendix.

TYPE: Four-seat cabin monoplane.

WINGS: Cantilever low-wing monoplane. Wing section NACA 63₂A415 with modified root section. Dihedral 6°30'. Incidence 3° at root, 0° 38' 28" at tip. Wings and modified Frise-type ailerons of light alloy bonded honeycomb construction. Electrically-operated single-slotted trailing-edge flaps of light alloy.

FUSELAGE: Semi-monocoque structure of light alloy.

TAIL UNIT: Conventional cantilever T-tail structure of light alloy with swept vertical surfaces. Fixed-incidence tailplane. Trim tab in rudder and each elevator.

LANDING GEAR: Hydraulically-retractable tricycle type, with single wheel on each unit. Self-centering steerable nosewheel retracts forward, main units inward. Oleo-pneumatic shock-absorbers. Main wheels with tube type tyres size 17·5 × 6·00-6. Nosewheel with tube type tyre size 5·00-5. Hydraulic brakes. Parking brake.

POWER PLANT: Two 134·2 kW (180 hp) Avco Lycoming O-360-A1G6D counter-rotating flat-four engines, each driving a Hartzell two-blade constant-speed fully-feathering metal propeller type HC-M2YR-2C(L)EUF/F(J)C 7666A. One fuel tank in each wing, with a combined usable capacity of 378·5 litres (100 US gallons). Refuelling point on upper surface of each wing. Oil capacity 15 litres (4 US gallons).

ACCOMMODATION: Two individual front seats, adjustable fore and aft, with reclining seatbacks. Rear bench seat for two passengers. Shoulder harness and lap belt for each seat. Door on each side of cabin. Baggage compartment (capacity 90 kg; 200 lb) with external access door on port side. Pilot's storm window. Accommodation heated and ventilated. Windscreen defroster.

SYSTEMS: Electrical system supplied by two 24V 60A engine-driven alternators, 24V 15·5Ah battery. Electrically-driven hydraulic pump for landing gear retraction. Separate hydraulic system for brakes. 45,000 BTU heater.

AVIONICS AND EQUIPMENT: Optional avionics as listed earlier. Standard equipment includes instrument panel glareshield, sensitive altimeter, control lock, map and storage pockets, emergency locator transmitter, stall warning device, armrests, carpeted floor, super sound-proofing, utility shelf, tiedown rings, and towbar. Optional equipment includes Hobbs hour meter, ventilation blower, third and fourth split seat in lieu of bench seat, internal corrosion proofing, and external power socket.

Beechcraft Duchess 76 light aircraft (two Avco Lycoming O-360-A1G6D engines)

DIMENSIONS, EXTERNAL:
Wing span	11·58 m (38 ft 0 in)
Wing chord at root	1·71 m (5 ft 7½ in)
Wing chord at tip	1·36 m (4 ft 5¾ in)
Wing aspect ratio	7·973
Length overall	8·86 m (29 ft 0½ in)
Height overall	2·90 m (9 ft 6 in)
Tailplane span	3·81 m (12 ft 6 in)
Wheel track	3·20 m (10 ft 6 in)
Wheelbase	2·13 m (7 ft 0 in)
Propeller diameter	1·93 m (6 ft 4 in)
Propeller ground clearance	0·25 m (10 in)
Cabin doors (port, stbd): Height	0·91 m (3 ft 0 in)
Width	0·91 m (3 ft 0 in)
Baggage door (port): Height	0·84 m (2 ft 9 in)
Width	0·56 m (1 ft 10 in)

DIMENSIONS, INTERNAL:
Cabin: Length	2·41 m (7 ft 11 in)
Max width	1·12 m (3 ft 8 in)
Max height	1·23 m (4 ft 0½ in)
Baggage compartment	0·55 m³ (19·5 cu ft)

AREAS:
Wings, gross	16·81 m² (181 sq ft)
Ailerons (total)	0·99 m² (10·7 sq ft)
Trailing-edge flaps (total)	2·29 m² (24·7 sq ft)
Fin	1·70 m² (18·27 sq ft)
Rudder (incl tab)	0·68 m² (7·3 sq ft)
Tailplane	3·66 m² (39·4 sq ft)
Elevators (incl tabs)	1·28 m² (13·77 sq ft)

WEIGHTS AND LOADINGS:
Weight empty	1,116 kg (2,460 lb)
Max T-O and landing weight	1,769 kg (3,900 lb)
Max ramp weight	1,776 kg (3,916 lb)
Max zero-fuel weight	1,587 kg (3,500 lb)
Max wing loading	105·2 kg/m² (21·5 lb/sq ft)
Max power loading	6·59 kg/kW (10·8 lb/hp)

PERFORMANCE (at max T-O weight):
Never-exceed speed	171 knots (317 km/h; 197 mph)
Max cruising speed at 1,830 m (6,000 ft)	
	166 knots (308 km/h; 191 mph)

Beechcraft Duchess 76 four-seat light twin (*Pilot Press*)

Recommended cruising speed at 3,050 m (10,000 ft)
158 knots (293 km/h; 182 mph)
Econ cruising speed at 3,660 m (12,000 ft)
151 knots (280 km/h; 174 mph)
Stalling speed, power off, flaps up
70 knots (130 km/h; 81 mph) IAS
Stalling speed, power off, flaps down
60 knots (111 km/h; 69 mph) IAS
Max rate of climb at S/L   380 m (1,248 ft)/min
Rate of climb at S/L, one engine out
72 m (235 ft)/min
Service ceiling   5,990 m (19,650 ft)
Service ceiling, one engine out   1,880 m (6,170 ft)
T-O run   310 m (1,017 ft)
T-O to 15 m (50 ft)   646 m (2,119 ft)
Landing from 15 m (50 ft)   573 m (1,881 ft)
Landing run   305 m (1,000 ft)
Range with max fuel, incl allowances for start, taxi, T-O, climb, and 45 min reserves at econ cruise power:
Max cruising speed at 1,830 m (6,000 ft)
623 nm (1,155 km; 717 miles)
Recommended cruising speed at 3,050 m (10,000 ft)
711 nm (1,317 km; 818 miles)
Econ cruising speed at 3,660 m (12,000 ft)
780 nm (1,445 km; 898 miles)

BEECHCRAFT BARON MODEL 95-B55
US Army designation: T-42A Cochise

The original Baron Model 95-55 was a four/five-seat cabin monoplane developed from the earlier Travel Air but with more power, better all-weather capability and airframe refinements that included a swept tail-fin. It first flew in prototype form on 29 February 1960 and was licensed in the FAA Normal category in November 1960. The Baron Model 95-B55 was similarly licensed in September 1963.

The current Barons are optional four-, five- or six-seaters, with interior features as described for the Bonanza.

In February 1965 the US Army selected the Model 95-B55 as winner of its competition for a twin-engined fixed-wing instrument trainer. Beech identified the military trainer as the Model 95-B55B, and this received FAA Type Approval in the Normal and Utility categories in August 1964. The US Army ordered 65, which were delivered under the designation T-42A. During 1971 Beech delivered five more T-42As to the US Army, for service with the army of Turkey, under the Military Assistance Programme. Export deliveries of the standard Model 95-B55 have also been made, including 19 for the Spanish Air Ministry and six for the Civil Air Bureau of Japan. These aircraft are used as instrument trainers.

A total of 2,371 civil and military Barons of the Model 95-55 series had been delivered by 1 January 1980.

TYPE: Four/six-seat cabin monoplane.

WINGS: Cantilever low-wing monoplane. Wing section NACA 23016·5 at root, NACA 23010·5 at tip. Dihedral 6°. Incidence 4° at root, 0° at tip. No sweepback. Each wing is a two-spar semi-monocoque box beam of conventional aluminium alloy construction. Symmetrical-section ailerons of light alloy construction, with beaded skins. Electrically-operated single-slotted light alloy trailing-edge flaps, with beaded skins. Manually-operated trim tab in port aileron. Pneumatic rubber de-icing boots optional.

FUSELAGE: Semi-monocoque aluminium alloy structure. Hat-section longerons and channel-type keels extend forward from the cabin section, making the support structure for the forward nose section and nosewheel gear an integral part of the fuselage.

TAIL UNIT: Cantilever all-metal structure. Elevators have smooth magnesium alloy skins. Manually-operated trim tab in each elevator and in rudder. Pneumatic rubber de-icing boots optional.

LANDING GEAR: Electrically-retractable tricycle type. Main units retract inward into wings, nosewheel aft. Beech oleo-pneumatic shock-absorbers on all units. Steerable nosewheel with shimmy damper. Cleveland wheels, with 6·50-8 main-wheel tyres, pressure 3·45-3·72 bars (50-54 lb/sq in). Nosewheel tyre size 5·00-5,

pressure 3·31-3·59 bars (48-52 lb/sq in). Cleveland ring-disc hydraulic brakes. Parking brake.

POWER PLANT: Two 194 kW (260 hp) Continental IO-470-L flat-six engines, each driving a Hartzell two-blade constant-speed fully-feathering propeller. Optional Hartzell three-blade propellers. Manually-operated cowl flaps. Standard fuel system comprises two interconnected tanks in each wing leading-edge, with total usable capacity of 378 litres (100 US gallons). Optional interconnected fuel tanks may be added in each wing to provide a total usable capacity of 515 litres (136 US gallons). Single refuelling point in each wing for the standard or optional fuel systems. Optional fuel system includes a mechanical sight gauge in each wing leading-edge to give partial fuelling information. Oil capacity 23 litres (6 US gallons). Propeller de-icing optional.

ACCOMMODATION: Standard model has four individual seats in pairs in enclosed cabin, with door on starboard side. Single diagonal strap shoulder harness with inertia reel standard on all seats. Optional wider door for cargo. Folding airline-style fifth and sixth seats optional, complete with shoulder harness and inertia reel. Baggage compartments aft of cabin and in nose, both with external doors on starboard side and with capacity of 181 kg (400 lb) and 136 kg (300 lb) respectively. An extended rear compartment providing for an additional 54 kg (120 lb) of baggage is optional. Pilot's storm window, port side. Openable windows adjacent to the third and fourth seats are used for ground ventilation and as emergency exits. Cabin heated and ventilated. Windscreen defrosting standard. Alcohol de-icing for port side of windscreen optional.

SYSTEMS: Cabin heated by Janitrol 50,000 BTU heater, which serves also for windscreen defrosting. Oxygen system of 1·41 m³ (49·8 cu ft) or 1·87 m³ (66 cu ft) capacity optional. Electrical system includes two 24V 25A generators. One 24V 13·5Ah battery. Two 24V 50A engine-driven alternators and/or two 12V 25Ah batteries optional. Hydraulic system for brakes only. Pneumatic pressure system for air-driven instruments, and optional wing and tail unit de-icing system. Oxygen system optional.

AVIONICS AND EQUIPMENT: Standard avionics comprise King KX 170B 720-channel com transceiver and 200-channel nav receiver with KI 208 VOR/LOC converter indicator, microphone, headset, cabin speaker and com, and nav/GS antennae. A wide range of optional avionics by Bendix, Collins, King, Edo-Aire Mitchell and Narco is available to customer's requirements. Standard equipment includes blind-flying instrumentation, clock, outside air temperature gauge, sensitive altimeter, turn co-ordinator, pilot's storm window, sun visors, ultraviolet-proof windscreen and windows, armrests, adjustable and retractable starboard side rudder pedals, emergency locator transmitter, heated pitot, carpeted floor, glove compartment, hatshelf, headrests for passenger seats, cabin dome light, instrument panel floodlights, map light, trim tab position indicator lights, passenger reading lights, navigation lights, position lights, dual landing lights, soundproofing, heated fuel vents, towbar, and engine winterisation kit. Optional equipment includes control wheel clock or chronograph, engine and flight hour recorders, vertical speed indicator, exhaust gas temperature gauge, dual tachometers with synchroscope, dual controls, alternate static source, cabin fire extinguisher, super soundproofing, entrance door courtesy light, instrument post lights, internally illuminated instruments, rotating beacon, strobe lights, taxi light, wing ice lights, propeller synchroniser, propeller unfeathering accumulator, external power socket, and static wicks.

DIMENSIONS, EXTERNAL:
Wing span	11·53 m (37 ft 10 in)
Wing chord at root	2·13 m (7 ft 0 in)
Wing chord at tip	0·90 m (2 ft 11·6 in)
Wing aspect ratio	7·16
Length overall	8·53 m (28 ft 0 in)
Height overall	2·92 m (9 ft 7 in)
Tailplane span	4·19 m (13 ft 9 in)

Wheel track	2·92 m (9 ft 7 in)
Wheelbase	2·13 m (7 ft 0 in)
Propeller diameter: two-blade	1·98 m (6 ft 6 in)
three-blade	1·93 m (6 ft 4 in)
Passenger door: Height	0·91 m (3 ft 0 in)
Width	0·94 m (3 ft 1 in)
Height to step	0·41 m (1 ft 4 in)
Baggage door (fwd): Height	0·56 m (1 ft 10 in)
Width	0·64 m (2 ft 1 in)
Baggage door (rear):	
Standard: Height	0·57 m (1 ft 10½ in)
Width	0·47 m (1 ft 6½ in)
Height to sill	0·71 m (2 ft 4 in)
Optional: Height	0·57 m (1 ft 10½ in)
Width	0·97 m (3 ft 2 in)

DIMENSIONS, INTERNAL:
Cabin: Length	3·07 m (10 ft 1 in)
Max width	1·07 m (3 ft 6 in)
Max height	1·27 m (4 ft 2 in)
Baggage compartment (fwd)	0·34 m³ (12 cu ft)
Baggage compartment (rear)	0·99 m³ (35 cu ft)

AREAS:
Wings, gross	18·5 m² (199·2 sq ft)
Ailerons (total)	1·06 m² (11·40 sq ft)
Trailing-edge flaps (total)	2·39 m² (25·70 sq ft)
Fin	1·02 m² (11·00 sq ft)
Rudder, incl tab	1·08 m² (11·60 sq ft)
Tailplane	4·46 m² (48·06 sq ft)
Elevators, incl tabs	1·51 m² (16·20 sq ft)

WEIGHTS AND LOADINGS:
Weight empty	1,466 kg (3,233 lb)
Max T-O and landing weight	2,313 kg (5,100 lb)
Max ramp weight	2,322 kg (5,121 lb)
Max wing loading	120·5 kg/m² (25·6 lb/sq ft)
Max power loading	5·96 kg/kW (9·8 lb/hp)

PERFORMANCE (at max T-O weight, except cruising speeds at average cruise weight):
Max level speed at S/L
201 knots (372 km/h; 231 mph)
Max cruising speed, 77% power at 1,830 m (6,000 ft)
188 knots (348 km/h; 216 mph)
Cruising speed, 66% power at 3,050 m (10,000 ft)
184 knots (341 km/h; 212 mph)
Econ cruising speed, 56% power at 3,660 m (12,000 ft)
173 knots (320 km/h; 199 mph)
Stalling speed, flaps up, power off
79 knots (146 km/h; 91 mph) IAS
Stalling speed, flaps down, power off
73 knots (135 km/h; 84 mph) IAS
Max rate of climb at S/L   516 m (1,693 ft)/min
Rate of climb at S/L, one engine out
121 m (397 ft)/min
Service ceiling   5,880 m (19,300 ft)
Service ceiling, one engine out   1,950 m (6,400 ft)
Min ground turning radius   9·00 m (29 ft 6 in)
Runway LCN   2
T-O run   427 m (1,400 ft)
T-O to 15 m (50 ft)   657 m (2,154 ft)
Landing from 15 m (50 ft)   655 m (2,148 ft)
Landing run   447 m (1,467 ft)
Range with 515 litres (136 US gallons) usable fuel, with allowances for engine start, taxi, T-O, climb and 45 min reserves at econ cruise power:
max cruising speed at 1,830 m (6,000 ft)
798 nm (1,479 km; 918 miles)
cruising speed at 3,050 m (10,000 ft)
907 nm (1,680 km; 1,044 miles)
econ cruising speed at 3,660 m (12,000 ft)
991 nm (1,836 km; 1,141 miles)

BEECHCRAFT BARON MODEL E55

The Baron E55 had its origin in the Baron 95-C55 when that model was added to the Baron series of twin-engined aircraft in August 1965. Compared to the B55, the 95-C55 had Continental IO-520-C engines, a pneumatic vacuum system for instrument gyros and the optional wing and tail unit de-icing system, two 24V 50A engine-driven alternators, increased tailplane span, swept vertical surfaces and an extended nose baggage compartment. It was followed by the D55 in October 1967, this model introducing a pneumatic pressure system in place of the pneumatic vacuum system. The subsequent Model E55, which has an improved interior and systems accessory refinements, was licensed in the FAA Normal category on 12 November 1969.

Beech had delivered a total of 1,170 of this Baron series by 1 January 1980.

TYPE: Four/six-seat cabin monoplane.

WINGS: As for Model 95-B55.

FUSELAGE: As for Model 95-B55, except nose extended by 0·305 m (1 ft 0 in).

TAIL UNIT: As for Model 95-B55, except tailplane span increased.

LANDING GEAR: As for Model 95-B55, except main-wheel tyre pressure 3·59-3·86 bars (52-56 lb/sq in); nosewheel tyre pressure 3·79-4·14 bars (55-60 lb/sq in).

POWER PLANT: Two 212·5 kW (285 hp) Continental IO-520-CB flat-six engines, each driving a Hartzell two-blade constant-speed fully-feathering metal propeller. Hartzell three-blade propellers optional. Fuel system as for Model 95-B55, except optional total usable capacity

Beechcraft Baron Model E55 four/six-seat cabin monoplane

628 litres (166 US gallons). Oil capacity 23 litres (6 US gallons). Full-flow oil filters standard; propeller de-icing optional.

ACCOMMODATION: As for Model 95-B55, except that extended rear compartment, providing for an additional 54 kg (120 lb) of baggage, is standard.

SYSTEMS: As for Model 95-B55, except standard electrical system supplied by two 24V 50A gear-driven alternators with alternator failure lights and one 24V 13·5Ah battery. Two 100A alternators and two 12V 25Ah batteries optional. Cabin air-conditioning system optional.

AVIONICS AND EQUIPMENT: Standard and optional avionics as for Model 95-B55, except that a King KR 87 ADF with KI 227 indicator is standard. Standard and optional equipment as for Model 95-B55, except cabin door courtesy light and extended rear baggage compartment standard. Electric elevator trim optional.

DIMENSIONS, EXTERNAL: As for Model 95-B55, except:

Length overall	8·84 m (29 ft 0 in)
Height overall	2·79 m (9 ft 2 in)
Tailplane span	4·85 m (15 ft 11 in)
Wheelbase	2·46 m (8 ft 1 in)

DIMENSIONS, INTERNAL: As for Model 95-B55, except:

Cabin: Length (incl extended rear baggage compartment)	3·58 m (11 ft 9 in)
Baggage compartment (fwd)	0·51 m³ (18 cu ft)
Baggage compartment (rear)	0·99 m³ (35 cu ft)
Extension to rear baggage compartment	0·28 m³ (10 cu ft)

AREAS: As for Model 95-B55, except:

Tailplane	4·95 m² (53·30 sq ft)
Elevators, incl tabs	1·84 m² (19·80 sq ft)

WEIGHTS AND LOADINGS:

Weight empty	1,490 kg (3,286 lb)
Max T-O and landing weight	2,405 kg (5,300 lb)
Max ramp weight	2,415 kg (5,324 lb)
Max wing loading	130·0 kg/m² (26·6 lb/sq ft)
Max power loading	5·66 kg/kW (9·3 lb/hp)

PERFORMANCE (at max T-O weight, except cruising speeds at average cruise weight):

Max level speed at S/L	208 knots (386 km/h; 239 mph)
Max cruising speed, 77% power at 1,830 m (6,000 ft)	200 knots (370 km/h; 230 mph)
Cruising speed, 66% power at 3,050 m (10,000 ft)	195 knots (362 km/h; 224 mph)
Econ cruising speed, 56% power at 3,660 m (12,000 ft)	184 knots (341 km/h; 212 mph)
Stalling speed, flaps up, power off	83 knots (154 km/h; 96 mph) IAS
Stalling speed, flaps down, power off	73 knots (135 km/h; 84 mph) IAS
Max rate of climb at S/L	513 m (1,682 ft)/min
Rate of climb at S/L, one engine out	118 m (388 ft)/min
Service ceiling	5,820 m (19,100 ft)
Service ceiling, one engine out	2,010 m (6,600 ft)
T-O run	401 m (1,315 ft)
T-O to 15 m (50 ft)	625 m (2,050 ft)
Landing from 15 m (50 ft)	671 m (2,202 ft)
Landing run	377 m (1,237 ft)

Range with 628 litres (166 US gallons) usable fuel, with allowances for engine start, taxi, T-O, climb and 45 min reserves at econ cruise power:

max cruising speed at 1,830 m (6,000 ft)	933 nm (1,728 km; 1,074 miles)
cruising speed at 3,050 m (10,000 ft)	1,032 nm (1,912 km; 1,188 miles)
econ cruising speed at 3,660 m (12,000 ft)	1,135 nm (2,103 km; 1,306 miles)

BEECHCRAFT BARON MODEL 58

In late 1969 Beech introduced a new version of the Baron, designated Model 58. Developed from the Baron D55, it differed by having the forward cabin section extended by 0·254 m (10 in), allowing the windscreen, passenger door, instrument panel and front seats to be moved forward and so provide a more spacious cabin. This change was made without affecting the wing main spar location, but the wheelbase was extended by moving the nosewheel forward, to improve ground handling. New features included double passenger/cargo doors on the starboard side of the cabin, extended propeller hubs, redesigned engine nacelles to improve cooling, and a fourth window on each side of the cabin. The Model 58 Baron was licensed by the FAA in the Normal category on 19 November 1969.

Beech had delivered 1,451 of this Baron series (including Baron 58Ps and 58TCs) by 1 January 1980.

TYPE: Four/six-seat cabin monoplane.

WINGS: As for Model 95-B55.

FUSELAGE: As for Model E55, except forward cabin section extended by 0·254 m (10 in).

TAIL UNIT: As for Model E55.

LANDING GEAR: As for Model E55, except wheelbase extended by 0·254 m (10 in).

POWER PLANT: As for Model E55, except that the standard and optional Hartzell propellers have extended hubs, and the engine nacelles are lengthened to accommodate these. The standard fuel system has a usable capacity of

514 litres (136 US gallons), with optional usable capacity of 628 litres (166 US gallons). Optional 'wet wingtip' installation also available, increasing usable capacity to 734 litres (194 US gallons).

ACCOMMODATION: As for Model E55, except that folding fifth and sixth seats, or club seating comprising folding fifth and sixth seats and aft-facing third and fourth seats, are optional. Executive writing desk available as option with club seating. Double passenger/cargo doors on starboard side of cabin provide access to space for 181 kg (400 lb) of baggage or cargo behind the third and fourth seats.

SYSTEMS: As for Model E55.

AVIONICS AND EQUIPMENT: Standard and optional avionics as for Model E55. Equipment as for Model E55, except double passenger/cargo doors with door-ajar warning light standard. Optional equipment includes club seating arrangement as described above, executive writing desk, and Hartzell three-blade propellers.

DIMENSIONS, EXTERNAL, AND AREAS:
As for Model E55, except:

Length overall	9·09 m (29 ft 10 in)
Height overall	2·90 m (9 ft 6 in)
Wheelbase	2·72 m (8 ft 11 in)
Rear passenger/cargo doors:	
Max height	1·02 m (3 ft 4 in)
Width	1·14 m (3 ft 9 in)

DIMENSIONS, INTERNAL: As for Model E55, except:

Cabin, incl rear baggage area:	
Length	3·84 m (12 ft 7 in)
Floor area	3·72 m² (40 sq ft)
Volume	3·85 m³ (135·9 cu ft)

WEIGHTS AND LOADINGS:

Weight empty	1,525 kg (3,363 lb)
Max T-O and landing weight	2,449 kg (5,400 lb)
Max wing loading	132·3 kg/m² (27·1 lb/sq ft)
Max power loading	5·76 kg/kW (9·5 lb/hp)

PERFORMANCE (at max T-O weight, except cruising speeds at average cruise weight):

Max level speed at S/L	208 knots (386 km/h; 239 mph)
Max cruising speed, 77% power at 1,830 m (6,000 ft)	200 knots (370 km/h; 230 mph)
Cruising speed, 66% power at 3,050 m (10,000 ft)	195 knots (362 km/h; 224 mph)
Econ cruising speed, 56% power at 3,660 m (12,000 ft)	184 knots (341 km/h; 212 mph)
Stalling speed, flaps up, power off	84 knots (156 km/h; 97 mph) IAS
Stalling speed, flaps down, power off	74 knots (137 km/h; 85 mph) IAS
Max rate of climb at S/L	506 m (1,660 ft)/min
Rate of climb at S/L, one engine out	119 m (390 ft)/min
Service ceiling	5,670 m (18,600 ft)
Service ceiling, one engine out	2,135 m (7,000 ft)
T-O run	407 m (1,336 ft)
T-O to 15 m (50 ft)	640 m (2,101 ft)
Landing from 15 m (50 ft)	761 m (2,498 ft)
Landing run	439 m (1,439 ft)

Range with 734 litres (194 US gallons) usable fuel, with allowances for engine start, taxi, T-O, climb and 45 min reserves at econ cruise power:

max cruising speed at 1,830 m (6,000 ft)	1,108 nm (2,054 km; 1,275 miles)
cruising speed at 3,050 m (10,000 ft)	1,224 nm (2,268 km; 1,409 miles)
econ cruising speed at 3,660 m (12,000 ft)	1,339 nm (2,482 km; 1,541 miles)

BEECHCRAFT BARON MODEL 58P

Design of this pressurised version of the Model 58 Baron started in June 1972; the first flight of the prototype was made in August 1973. Certification under FAR Part 23 was received in May 1974; the first production aircraft flew later the same year. Examples of the Model 58P produced prior to 1979 are powered by two 231 kW (310 hp) Continental TSIO-520-L (or -LB) engines. The production aircraft for 1980 have more powerful TSIO-520-WB engines.

Deliveries of production aircraft began in late 1975, and a total of 244 Baron 58Ps had been delivered by 1 January 1980. Four were delivered to the US Forest Service for use as lead aircraft in smoke-jumping operations, as well as for reconnaissance, administration and cargo missions.

TYPE: Four/six-seat cabin monoplane.

WINGS: As for Model 95-B55.

FUSELAGE: As for Model 58, except structural reinforcement to cater for pressurisation.

TAIL UNIT: As for Model 58.

LANDING GEAR: Main gear as for Duke, except mainwheel tyre pressure 5·24 to 5·66 bars (76 to 82 lb/sq in). Nosewheel unit as for Model 58. Goodrich single-disc hydraulic brakes. Parking brake.

POWER PLANT: Two 242 kW (325 hp) Continental TSIO-520-WB turbocharged flat-six engines, each driving a Hartzell three-blade constant-speed fully-feathering metal propeller. Electrically-operated engine cowl flaps. Integral fuel tanks in wings, with standard capacity of 651 litres (172 US gallons) of which 628 litres (166 US gallons) are usable. Optional maximum capacity of 742 litres (196 US gallons) of which 719 litres (190 US gallons) are usable. Refuelling points in outboard leading-edge of wings and, for optional maximum fuel, in wingtips. Oil capacity 22·7 litres (6 US gallons). Electrical anti-icing for propellers optional.

ACCOMMODATION: Standard accommodation has four individual seats in pairs, facing forward, with shoulder harness and inertia reel. Fifth and sixth seats optional, as is club layout. Doors on starboard side, adjacent to copilot, and at trailing-edge of wing on port side. Baggage space in aft cabin and in fuselage nose, with door on starboard side of nose. Openable storm window for pilot on port side. Cabin heated and pressurised. Air-conditioning optional. Windscreen defrosting by hot air. Windscreen electrical or alcohol anti-icing optional.

SYSTEMS: Garrett-AiResearch pressurisation system with max differential of 0·26 bars (3·7 lb/sq in) in aircraft manufactured prior to 1979, providing a 3,050 m (10,000 ft) cabin environment to an altitude of 6,460 m (21,200 ft). Aircraft manufactured subsequently have Garrett-AiResearch pressurisation system with max differential of 0·27 bars (3·9 lb/sq in), giving a 3,050 m (10,000 ft) cabin environment to a height of 6,705 m (22,000 ft). Beechcraft 14,000 BTU air-conditioning optional. Janitrol 35,000 BTU heater. Engine-driven compressors supply air for flight instruments, pressurisation control and optional pneumatic de-icing boots. Electrical system powered by two 24V 50A alternators, with two 12V 25Ah storage batteries. Two 24V 100A alternators optional. Hydraulic system for brakes only. Oxygen system of 0·42 m³ (15 cu ft) optional.

AVIONICS AND EQUIPMENT: Standard avionics package comprises King KX 170B nav/com (720-channel com transceiver and 200-channel nav receiver) with KI 208 VOR/LOC converter-indicator, KR 87 ADF with KI 227 indicator, King combined loop/sense antenna, microphone, headset, cabin speaker and B38 nav and B6 com antennae. Optional avionics by Bendix, Collins, King, Narco, Edo-Aire Mitchell, Sperry and RCA. Standard equipment as for Model E55, plus emergency locator transmitter, heated stall warning transmitter, nose baggage compartment light, door-ajar warning light, step light, dual rotating beacons, and exterior urethane paint. Optional equipment includes engine and flight hour recorders, control wheel chronometer, dual controls, electrically-operated elevator trim, cabin fire extinguisher, executive writing desk, instrument post lights, internally illuminated instruments, strobe lights, wing ice lights, propeller synchroniser and unfeathering accumulators, and static wicks.

DIMENSIONS, EXTERNAL:

Wing span	11·53 m (37 ft 10 in)
Wing chord at root	2·13 m (7 ft 0 in)
Wing chord at tip	0·90 m (2 ft 11½ in)
Length overall	9·12 m (29 ft 11 in)

Beechcraft Baron Model 58 four/six-seat cabin monoplane

Height overall	2·79 m (9 ft 2 in)
Tailplane span	4·85 m (15 ft 11 in)
Wheel track	2·92 m (9 ft 7 in)
Wheelbase	2·72 m (8 ft 11 in)
Propeller diameter	1·98 m (6 ft 6 in)
Propeller ground clearance	0·28 m (10¾ in)
Passenger door (stbd, fwd):	
Height	0·91 m (3 ft 0 in)
Width	0·94 m (3 ft 1 in)
Height to sill	0·51 m (1 ft 8 in)
Passenger door (port, aft):	
Height	0·89 m (2 ft 11 in)
Width	0·58 m (1 ft 11 in)
Height to sill	0·79 m (2 ft 7 in)
Baggage door (nose, stbd):	
Height	0·38 m (1 ft 3 in)
Width	0·64 m (2 ft 1 in)

DIMENSIONS, INTERNAL: As for Model 58
AREAS: As for Model 58
WEIGHTS AND LOADINGS:

Weight empty, equipped	1,823 kg (4,020 lb)
Max T-O and landing weight	2,812 kg (6,200 lb)
Max ramp weight	2,830 kg (6,240 lb)
Max zero-fuel weight	2,585 kg (5,700 lb)
Max wing loading	151·9 kg/m² (31·12 lb/sq ft)
Max power loading	5·81 kg/kW (9·54 lb/hp)

PERFORMANCE (at max T-O weight, except cruising speeds at average cruise weight):
Max level speed   260 knots (483 km/h; 300 mph)
Max cruising speed at approx 77% power:
  at 3,050 m (10,000 ft)
          212 knots (393 km/h; 244 mph)
  at 4,570 m (15,000 ft)
          222 knots (412 km/h; 256 mph)
  at 6,100 m (20,000 ft)
          232 knots (430 km/h; 267 mph)
  at 7,620 m (25,000 ft)
          241 knots (447 km/h; 277 mph)
Cruising speed at approx 75% power:
  at 3,050 m (10,000 ft)
          210 knots (389 km/h; 242 mph)
  at 4,570 m (15,000 ft)
          220 knots (407 km/h; 253 mph)
  at 6,100 m (20,000 ft)
          229 knots (425 km/h; 264 mph)
  at 7,620 m (25,000 ft)
          237 knots (439 km/h; 273 mph)
Cruising speed at approx 65% power:
  at 3,050 m (10,000 ft)
          198 knots (367 km/h; 228 mph)
  at 4,570 m (15,000 ft)
          210 knots (389 km/h; 242 mph)
  at 6,100 m (20,000 ft)
          215 knots (399 km/h; 248 mph)
  at 7,620 m (25,000 ft)
          222 knots (412 km/h; 256 mph)
Econ cruising speed at approx 53% power:
  at 3,050 m (10,000 ft)
          175 knots (325 km/h; 201 mph)
  at 4,570 m (15,000 ft)
          186 knots (344 km/h; 214 mph)
  at 6,100 m (20,000 ft)
          194 knots (359 km/h; 223 mph)
  at 7,620 m (25,000 ft)
          202 knots (375 km/h; 233 mph)
Stalling speed, flaps up, power off
          84 knots (156 km/h; 97 mph)
Stalling speed, flaps down, power off
          78 knots (145 km/h; 90 mph)
Max rate of climb at S/L   450 m (1,475 ft)/min
Rate of climb at S/L, one engine out
          82 m (270 ft)/min
Service ceiling   above 7,620 m (25,000 ft)
Service ceiling, one engine out   4,110 m (13,490 ft)
T-O run   474 m (1,555 ft)
T-O to 15 m (50 ft)   806 m (2,643 ft)
Landing from 15 m (50 ft)   740 m (2,427 ft)
Landing run   420 m (1,378 ft)
Range with 719 litres (190 US gallons) usable fuel, and allowances for engine start, taxi, T-O, climb and 45 min reserves at econ cruising speed:
  at approx 77% power:
    at 3,050 m (10,000 ft)
      884 nm (1,638 km; 1,017 miles)
    at 4,570 m (15,000 ft)
      916 nm (1,697 km; 1,054 miles)
    at 6,100 m (20,000 ft)
      958 nm (1,775 km; 1,102 miles)
    at 7,620 m (25,000 ft)
      1,008 nm (1,868 km; 1,160 miles)
  at approx 75% power:
    at 3,050 m (10,000 ft)
      900 nm (1,667 km; 1,036 miles)
    at 4,570 m (15,000 ft)
      930 nm (1,723 km; 1,071 miles)
    at 6,100 m (20,000 ft)
      971 nm (1,799 km; 1,118 miles)
    at 7,620 m (25,000 ft)
      1,019 nm (1,888 km; 1,173 miles)
  at approx 65% power:
    at 3,050 m (10,000 ft)
      1,005 nm (1,862 km; 1,157 miles)

Beechcraft Baron Model 58TC, turbocharged version of the Baron 58

  at 4,570 m (15,000 ft)
      1,027 nm (1,904 km; 1,183 miles)
  at 6,100 m (20,000 ft)
      1,062 nm (1,968 km; 1,223 miles)
  at 7,620 m (25,000 ft)
      1,093 nm (2,026 km; 1,259 miles)
  at approx 53% power:
    at 3,050 m (10,000 ft)
      1,179 nm (2,185 km; 1,357 miles)
    at 4,570 m (15,000 ft)
      1,198 nm (2,220 km; 1,379 miles)
    at 6,100 m (20,000 ft)
      1,217 nm (2,255 km; 1,400 miles)
    at 7,620 m (25,000 ft)
      1,229 nm (2,277 km; 1,414 miles)

BEECHCRAFT BARON MODEL 58TC

This turbocharged version of the Baron Model 58 is generally similar to the Model 58P, with the same power plant, but is unpressurised, with detail differences in the airframe and equipment. The design originated in July 1974, and construction of a prototype to production aircraft standard began in February 1975. The first flight of this aircraft was made on 31 October 1975 and FAA certification, in the Normal category, was granted on 23 January 1976. Deliveries began in June 1976, and a total of 110 had been delivered by 1 January 1980.

TYPE: Four/six-seat cabin monoplane.
WINGS: Generally similar to Model 58P.
FUSELAGE: Generally similar to Model 58.
TAIL UNIT: Generally similar to Model 58.
LANDING GEAR: Generally similar to Model 58P.
POWER PLANT: As Model 58P.
ACCOMMODATION: Generally similar to that of Model 58, except windscreen electrical anti-icing optional. Baggage/cargo space aft of 3rd and 4th seats for 272 kg (600 lb). By removing these seats 408 kg (900 lb) baggage/cargo can be stowed aft of pilot and co-pilot seats with restraining net.
SYSTEMS: Generally similar to Model 58P, except Beech Freon air-conditioning system optional. 50,000 BTU heater standard. Hydraulic system for brakes and propeller unfeathering only. Electrical power from two 24V 50A alternators, with 24V 13·5Ah storage battery. Two 100A alternators and two 12V 25Ah storage batteries optional. Oxygen system to supply crew and passengers.
AVIONICS AND EQUIPMENT: As for Baron 58P.
DIMENSIONS, EXTERNAL: As for Model 58P except:
  Utility double door (stbd, aft):
    Height   1·02 m (3 ft 4 in)
    Width   1·14 m (3 ft 9 in)
  Baggage door (nose, stbd):
    Height   0·56 m (1 ft 10 in)
    Width   0·64 m (2 ft 1 in)
  Emergency exit window (port and stbd):
    Height   0·53 m (1 ft 9 in)
    Width   0·61 m (2 ft 0 in)
DIMENSIONS, INTERNAL: As for Model 58
AREAS:

Wings, gross	17·47 m² (188·1 sq ft)
Ailerons (total, incl tabs)	1·08 m² (11·58 sq ft)
Trailing-edge flaps (total)	1·98 m² (21·3 sq ft)
Fin	1·46 m² (15·67 sq ft)
Rudder, incl tab	1·08 m² (11·6 sq ft)
Tailplane	5·11 m² (55·05 sq ft)
Elevators, incl tabs	1·84 m² (19·8 sq ft)

WEIGHTS AND LOADINGS:

Weight empty, equipped	1,720 kg (3,793 lb)
Max T-O and landing weight	2,812 kg (6,200 lb)
Max ramp weight	2,830 kg (6,240 lb)
Max zero-fuel weight	2,585 kg (5,700 lb)
Max wing loading	160·96 kg/m² (32·96 lb/sq ft)
Max power loading	5·81 kg/kW (9·54 lb/hp)

PERFORMANCE (at max T-O weight, except cruising speeds at average cruise weight):
As for Baron Model 58P except:
  Max rate of climb:
    at 4,575 m (15,000 ft)   366 m (1,201 ft)/min

Rate of climb, one engine out:
  at 1,525 m (5,000 ft)   67 m (220 ft)/min

BEECHCRAFT DUKE B60

Design work on the original version of this 4/6-seat pressurised and turbocharged light twin-engined transport started in early 1965. Construction of the prototype began in January 1966, and the first flight was made on 29 December 1966. FAA Type Approval was granted on 1 February 1968.

The current version of the B60 has a Garrett-AiResearch Lexan pressurisation system, with a mini controller that allows selection of cabin altitude prior to take-off or landing. This system can also change the aircraft cabin altitude at any desired rate from 15-610 m (50-2,000 ft)/min.

A total of 520 Dukes had been produced by 1 January 1980.

TYPE: Four/six-seat cabin monoplane.
WINGS: Cantilever low-wing monoplane. Wing section NACA 23016·5 at root, NACA 23010·5 at tip. Thickness/chord ratio 13·7% at root, 10·5% at tip. Dihedral 6°. Incidence 4° at root, 0° at tip. Each wing is a two-spar semi-monocoque box beam of conventional aluminium alloy construction. Overhang-balance ailerons constructed of aluminium alloy. Conventional hinged trim tab in port aileron. Electrically-operated single-slotted aluminium alloy flaps. Pneumatic rubber de-icing boots optional.
FUSELAGE: Semi-monocoque aluminium alloy structure. Heavy-gauge chemically-milled aluminium alloy skins.
TAIL UNIT: Cantilever all-metal structure. Aluminium spars and end ribs; magnesium alloy skins reinforced with metal bonded honeycomb stiffeners running chordwise. Dorsal fin. Swept vertical and horizontal surfaces. Tailplane dihedral 10°. Trim tabs in rudder and port elevator. Pneumatic rubber de-icing boots optional.
LANDING GEAR: Electrically-retractable tricycle type. Main units retract inward, nosewheel aft; all three units have fairing doors. Beechcraft oleo-pneumatic shock-absorbers. Goodrich main wheels and tyres size 19·50 × 6·75-8 10-ply rating, pressure 5·52 bars (80 lb/sq in). Goodyear steerable nosewheel with shimmy damper, tyre size 15 × 6·00-6, pressure 3·45 bars (50 lb/sq in). Goodrich single-disc hydraulic brakes. Parking brake.
POWER PLANT: Two 283 kW (380 hp) Avco Lycoming TIO-541-E1C4 turbocharged flat-six engines, each driving a Hartzell three-blade constant-speed fully-feathering metal propeller. Propeller unfeathering accumulators and electrical anti-icing optional. Electrically-operated engine cowl flaps. Two interconnected fuel cells in each wing containing 269 litres (71 US gallons); total usable capacity 538 litres (142 US gallons). Optionally, four interconnected fuel cells in each wing containing 382 litres (101 US gallons); total usable capacity 764 litres (202 US gallons); or five interconnected fuel cells in each wing containing 439 litres (116 US gallons), with total usable capacity 878 litres (232 US gallons). Refuelling points in each leading-edge, near wingtip. Oil capacity 24·5 litres (6·5 US gallons).
ACCOMMODATION: Standard model has four individual seats in pairs, each complete with headrest and inertia-reel shoulder harness, in enclosed cabin with centre aisle. Door, hinged at forward edge, on port side at rear of cabin. Baggage hold in the nose, capacity 0·91 m³ (32 cu ft), with external access door on port side of nose. Additional 0·80 m³ (28·25 cu ft) of baggage space at rear of cabin. Optional extras include fifth and sixth seats, rearward-facing third and fourth seats, curtain separating passenger and pilot seating, writing desks, refreshment cabinets, toilet, windscreen electrical anti-icing and cabin fire extinguishers.
SYSTEMS: Cabin pressurisation system, differential 0·32 bars (4·6 lb/sq in), supplied by engine turbocharger bleed air, maintains cabin altitude equivalent to 3,050 m (10,000 ft) at 7,560 m (24,800 ft). Combustion heater

Beechcraft Duke B60 four/six-seat pressurised transport

of 45,000 BTU standard. Ventilation system has provisions for optional engine-driven vapour-cycle air-conditioning system of 14,000 BTU. Automatic altitude controller for cabin pressurisation system standard. Oxygen system optional, with 0·31 m³ (11 cu ft), 0·62 m³ (22 cu ft) or 1·39 m³ (49 cu ft) bottle. Hydraulic system for brakes only. Pneumatic system for pressure-operated instruments and de-icing boots only. 24V 125A generators standard; two 12V 25Ah batteries.

AVIONICS AND EQUIPMENT: Standard avionics comprise Collins VHF-251 VHF transceiver with PWC-150 power adaptor and B3 com antenna, Collins VIR-351 Omni No. 1 receiver with IND-351A VOR/ILS indicator and B38 antenna, Collins AMR-350 audio panel, Collins marker beacon incorporated in AMR-350, with single set marker lights and B16 antenna, Collins ADF-650A ADF with IND-650A indicator and ANT-650A antenna, Collins GLS-350 glideslope receiver with A-326A antenna, Collins TDR-950 transponder with B18 antenna, Beech metal radio panel, radio accessories, static wicks, microphone key button in pilot's control wheel, white lighting, dual microphones and headsets, single cockpit speaker, and avionics master switch. Optional avionics include an extensive range of Bendix, Collins, King, Edo-Aire Mitchell, Sperry and RCA equipment. Standard equipment includes blind-flying instrumentation, LCD digital clock/chronometer, outside air temperature gauge, turn co-ordinator, pilot's storm window, sun visors, alternate static source, heated stall warning device, heated pitot, armrests, headrests, in-flight storage pockets, carpeted floor, tinted cabin side windows, baggage straps, super soundproofing, cabin dome light, entrance light, instrument floodlights, instrument post lights, map lights, nose baggage compartment light, reading lights, dual landing lights, navigation lights, rotating beacons, taxi light, retracting step, heated fuel vents, full-flow oil filters, external power socket, towbar, and polyurethane paint. Optional equipment includes de luxe instrument panel with duplicated blind-flying instrumentation for co-pilot, instantaneous vertical speed indicator, tachometer with synchroscope, flight and engine hour recorders, pilot's control wheel chronometer, pilot's relief tube, co-pilot's toe brakes, co-pilot's control wheel map light, internally lighted instruments, wing ice light, strobe lights, and propeller synchroniser.

DIMENSIONS, EXTERNAL:
Wing span	11·97 m (39 ft 3¼ in)
Wing chord at fuselage c/l	2·80 m (9 ft 2⅛ in)
Wing chord at tip	0·90 m (2 ft 11⅝ in)
Wing aspect ratio	7·243
Length overall	10·31 m (33 ft 10 in)
Height overall	3·76 m (12 ft 4 in)
Tailplane span	5·18 m (17 ft 0 in)
Wheel track	3·43 m (11 ft 3 in)
Wheelbase	2·82 m (9 ft 2⅜ in)
Propeller diameter	1·88 m (6 ft 2 in)
Passenger door: Height	1·21 m (3 ft 11½ in)
Width	0·67 m (2 ft 2½ in)
Height to sill	0·81 m (2 ft 8 in)
Baggage compartment door:	
Height	0·60 m (1 ft 11½ in)
Width	0·95 m (3 ft 1½ in)
Height to sill	0·95 m (3 ft 1½ in)

DIMENSIONS, INTERNAL:
Cabin: Length	3·61 m (11 ft 10 in)
Max width	1·27 m (4 ft 2 in)
Max height	1·32 m (4 ft 4 in)
Floor area	3·36 m² (36·2 sq ft)
Volume	4·80 m³ (169·6 cu ft)

AREAS:
Wings, gross	19·78 m² (212·9 sq ft)
Ailerons (total)	1·06 m² (11·4 sq ft)
Trailing-edge flaps (total)	2·76 m² (29·7 sq ft)
Fin	1·52 m² (16·38 sq ft)
Rudder, incl tab	1·15 m² (12·4 sq ft)
Tailplane	4·24 m² (45·6 sq ft)
Elevators, incl tab	1·52 m² (16·4 sq ft)

WEIGHTS AND LOADINGS:
Weight empty, equipped	1,998 kg (4,406 lb)
Max T-O and landing weight	3,073 kg (6,775 lb)
Max ramp weight	3,093 kg (6,819 lb)
Max wing loading	155·3 kg/m² (31·8 lb/sq ft)
Max power loading	5·43 kg/kW (8·9 lb/hp)

PERFORMANCE (at max T-O weight, except cruising speeds at average cruise weight):
Max level speed at 7,010 m (23,000 ft)
    246 knots (455 km/h; 283 mph)
Max cruising speed:
approx 78% power at 7,620 m (25,000 ft)
    239 knots (443 km/h; 275 mph)
approx 78% power at 6,100 m (20,000 ft)
    231 knots (428 km/h; 266 mph)
approx 78% power at 4,570 m (15,000 ft)
    220 knots (407 km/h; 253 mph)
Cruising speed:
approx 74% power at 7,620 m (25,000 ft)
    233 knots (431 km/h; 268 mph)
approx 74% power at 6,100 m (20,000 ft)
    225 knots (417 km/h; 259 mph)
approx 74% power at 4,570 m (15,000 ft)
    214 knots (396 km/h; 246 mph)
approx 68% power at 7,620 m (25,000 ft)
    225 knots (417 km/h; 259 mph)
approx 68% power at 6,100 m (20,000 ft)
    215 knots (399 km/h; 247 mph)
approx 68% power at 4,570 m (15,000 ft)
    205 knots (380 km/h; 236 mph)
approx 63% power at 7,620 m (25,000 ft)
    217 knots (402 km/h; 250 mph)
approx 63% power at 6,100 m (20,000 ft)
    209 knots (388 km/h; 241 mph)
approx 63% power at 4,570 m (15,000 ft)
    199 knots (369 km/h; 229 mph)
Stalling speed, wheels and flaps up, power off
    81 knots (150·5 km/h; 93 mph)
Stalling speed, wheels and flaps down, power off
    73 knots (135 km/h; 84 mph)
Max rate of climb at S/L   488 m (1,601 ft)/min
Rate of climb at S/L, one engine out
    94 m (307 ft)/min
Service ceiling   9,145 m (30,000 ft)
Service ceiling, one engine out   4,600 m (15,100 ft)
Runway LCN   4
T-O run   632 m (2,075 ft)
T-O to 15 m (50 ft)   800 m (2,626 ft)
Landing from 15 m (50 ft)   934 m (3,065 ft)
Landing run   402 m (1,318 ft)
Range with max optional fuel and allowances for engine start, taxi, take-off, climb to altitude and 45 min fuel reserves at 45% power, ISA:
approx 78% power at 7,620 m (25,000 ft)
    1,045 nm (1,936 km; 1,203 miles)
approx 78% power at 6,100 m (20,000 ft)
    967 nm (1,793 km; 1,113 miles)
approx 78% power at 4,570 m (15,000 ft)
    916 nm (1,698 km; 1,054 miles)
approx 74% power at 7,620 m (25,000 ft)
    1,072 nm (1,986 km; 1,234 miles)
approx 74% power at 6,100 m (20,000 ft)
    1,010 nm (1,872 km; 1,163 miles)
approx 74% power at 4,570 m (15,000 ft)
    964 nm (1,786 km; 1,110 miles)
approx 68% power at 7,620 m (25,000 ft)
    1,112 nm (2,060 km; 1,280 miles)
approx 68% power at 6,100 m (20,000 ft)
    1,070 nm (1,983 km; 1,232 miles)
approx 68% power at 4,570 m (15,000 ft)
    1,028 nm (1,905 km; 1,183 miles)
approx 63% power at 7,620 m (25,000 ft)
    1,168 nm (2,165 km; 1,344 miles)
approx 63% power at 6,100 m (20,000 ft)
    1,122 nm (2,079 km; 1,291 miles)
approx 63% power at 4,570 m (15,000 ft)
    1,083 nm (2,007 km; 1,247 miles)

BEECHCRAFT KING AIR MODEL C90
USAF designation: VC-6B

Introduced in September 1970, the King Air C90 is a pressurised 6/10-seat twin-turboprop business aircraft which superseded the original Models 90, A90 and B90 King Air. It is powered by Pratt & Whitney Aircraft of Canada PT6A-21 turboprop engines, which provide improved performance over a wide range of altitudes and temperatures. Increases in take-off and climb power offer improvements in high altitude and hot weather operation and, since these engines also run cooler, increases in useful life and lower overhaul costs result.

The C90 King Air utilises the more advanced cabin pressurisation and heating system of the King Air 100. This comprises a dual engine bleed air system for cabin pressurisation, with a max differential of 0·32 bars (4·6 lb/sq in).

The 1980 King Air C90 has as standard dual bleed air pressurisation and cabin heating, including supplementary electric heating, air-conditioning, super soundproofing, a full anti-icing system, four cabin seats in club arrangement, forward cabin partition with curtain, aft starboard cabin partition with curtain, polarised cabin windows, exterior urethane paint scheme and a comprehensive avionics package which includes dual nav/com, transponder, DME, ADF, marker beacon receiver, glideslope and dual blind-flying instrumentation.

A total of 1,448 commercial and military King Air 90s had been delivered by 1 January 1980. One was provided for the US Air Force's 1254th Special Air Missions Squadron at Andrews AFB, Maryland, for VIP transport duties under the designation **VC-6B**. Beech has delivered 10 King Air C90s to the Spanish Air Force and Civil Aviation School for instrument training and liaison. Delivery of five to the FAA, to replace Queen Airs which have been in service since 1963, began in early 1980.

TYPE: Six/ten-seat twin-turboprop business aircraft.
WINGS: Cantilever low-wing monoplane. Wing section NACA 23014·1 (modified) at root, NACA 23016·22 (modified) at outer end of centre-section, NACA 23012 at tip. Dihedral 7°. Incidence 4° 48′ at root, 0° at tip. No sweepback at quarter-chord. Two-spar aluminium alloy structure. All-metal ailerons of magnesium, with adjustable trim tab on port aileron. Single-slotted aluminium alloy flaps. Automatic pneumatic de-icing boots on leading-edges standard.
FUSELAGE: Aluminium alloy semi-monocoque structure.
TAIL UNIT: Cantilever all-metal structure with sweptback vertical surfaces. Fixed-incidence tailplane, with 7° dihedral. Trim tabs in rudder and each elevator. Automatic pneumatic de-icing boots on leading-edges of fin and tailplane.
LANDING GEAR: Electrically-retractable tricycle type. Nosewheel retracts rearward, main wheels forward into engine nacelles. Main wheels protrude slightly beneath nacelles when retracted, for safety in a wheels-up emergency landing. Steerable nosewheel with shimmy damper. Beech oleo-pneumatic shock-absorbers. B.F. Goodrich main wheels with tyres size 8·50-10, pressure 3·79 bars (55 lb/sq in). B.F. Goodrich nosewheel with tyre size 6·50-10, pressure 3·59 bars (52 lb/sq in). Goodrich heat-sink and aircooled multi-disc hydraulic brakes. Parking brakes.
POWER PLANT: Two 410 kW (550 ehp) Pratt & Whitney Aircraft of Canada PT6A-21 turboprop engines, each driving a Hartzell three-blade constant-speed fully-feathering propeller. Propeller electrothermal anti-icing, auto ignition system, environmental fuel drain collection system, and magnetic chip detector standard. Fuel in two tanks in engine nacelles, each with capacity of 231 litres (61 US gallons), and bladder type auxiliary tanks in outer wings, each with capacity of 496 litres (131 US gallons). Total fuel capacity 1,454 litres (384 US gallons). Refuelling points in top of each engine nacelle and in wing leading-edge outboard of each nacelle. Oil capacity 13·2 litres (3·5 US gallons). Engine anti-icing system standard.
ACCOMMODATION: Two seats side by side in cockpit with dual controls standard. Normally, four reclining seats are provided in the main cabin, in pairs facing each other fore and aft. Standard furnishings include cabin forward partition, with fore and aft partition curtain and coat rack, hinged nose baggage compartment door, seat belts and inertia-reel shoulder harness for all seats. Optional arrangements seat up to eight persons, some with two-or three-place couch, lateral tracking chairs, and refreshment cabinets. Baggage racks at rear of cabin on starboard side, with optional toilet on port side. Door on port side aft of wing, with built-in airstairs. Emergency exit on starboard side of cabin. Entire accommodation pressurised and air-conditioned. Electrically-heated windscreen, windscreen defroster and windscreen wipers standard.
SYSTEMS: Pressurisation by dual engine bleed air system with pressure differential of 0·32 bars (4·6 lb/sq in). Cabin heated by 45,000 BTU dual engine bleed air system and auxiliary electrical heating system. Electrical system utilises two 28V 250A starter/generators, 24V 45Ah aircooled nickel-cadmium battery with failure detector. Complete de-icing and anti-icing

equipment. Oxygen system, 0·62 m³ (22 cu ft), 1·39 m³ (49 cu ft) or 1·81 m³ (64 cu ft) capacity, optional. Vacuum system for flight instruments.

AVIONICS AND EQUIPMENT: Standard avionics package comprises dual Collins VHF-251 VHF transceivers with PWL-150 power adaptors and B3 antennae; dual Collins VIR-351 Omni nav receivers, one with Collins 331A-3G indicator and B17 antenna, the other with IND-351A on B17 antenna; Collins AMR-350 audio system; Collins ADF-650A ADF, with IND-650A indicator and ANT-650 antenna; Collins marker receiver integral with AMR-350, plus marker lights and B16 antenna; dual Collins GLS-350 glideslope receivers with B35 antenna; Collins DME-451, with IND-451 indicator, Nav1/Nav 2 switching, DME hold and B18 antenna; Collins PN-101 compass system (pilot); Standard Electric gyro horizon (pilot); CF gyro horizon and directional gyro (co-pilot); dual Flite-Tronics PC-125 125VA inverters with failure light; avionics transient protection; dual flight instrumentation; sectional instrument panel; white lighting; radio accessories, static wicks and Beech metal radio panel; microphone key button in pilot and co-pilot control wheels; dual microphones, headsets and cockpit speakers; and avionics master switch. Optional avionics include a wide range of equipment by Bendix, Collins, King, Edo-Aire Mitchell, RCA and Sperry. Standard equipment includes dual blind-flying instrumentation with sensitive altimeters, standby magnetic compass, outside air temperature gauge, LCD digital clock/chronometer, vacuum gauge, de-icing pressure gauge, cabin rate of climb indicator, cabin altitude and pressure differential indicators, pilot and co-pilot four-way adjustable seats with shoulder harness, map pockets, control locks, storm windows, sun visors, automatic fuel heater system, emergency locator transmitter, heated pitots, heated stall warning transmitter, stall warning device, cabin windows with adjustable polarised shades, carpeted floor, internal corrosion proofing, 'No smoking—Fasten seat belt' sign, fresh air outlets, dual map lights, primary and secondary instrument light systems, indirect cabin lighting, two overhead cabin spotlights, entrance door light, adjustable reading lights, aft compartment lights, dual landing lights, taxi light, position lights, dual rotating beacons, wing ice lights, heated fuel vents, external power socket, static wicks, and external polyurethane paint. Optional equipment includes control wheel mounted chronographs, flight hour recorder, instantaneous vertical speed indicator, cockpit and cabin fire extinguishers, a range of cabin seats, cabinets, storage drawers and toilets, entrance door step lights, strobe lights, wingtip recognition lights, engine fire detection and extinguishing system, automatic propeller feathering, reversible-pitch propellers and propeller synchrophaser.

DIMENSIONS, EXTERNAL:

Wing span	15·32 m (50 ft 3 in)
Wing chord at root	2·15 m (7 ft 0½ in)
Wing chord at tip	1·07 m (3 ft 6 in)
Wing aspect ratio	8·57
Length overall	10·82 m (35 ft 6 in)
Height overall	4·34 m (14 ft 3 in)
Tailplane span	5·26 m (17 ft 3 in)
Wheel track	3·89 m (12 ft 9 in)
Wheelbase	3·75 m (12 ft 3½ in)
Propeller diameter	2·36 m (7 ft 9 in)
Passenger door: Height	1·30 m (4 ft 3½ in)
Width	0·69 m (2 ft 3 in)
Height to sill	1·17 m (3 ft 10 in)

DIMENSIONS, INTERNAL:

Total pressurised length	5·43 m (17 ft 10 in)
Cabin: Length	3·86 m (12 ft 8 in)
Max width	1·37 m (4 ft 6 in)
Max height	1·45 m (4 ft 9 in)
Floor area	6·50 m² (70 sq ft)
Volume	8·89 m³ (314 cu ft)
Baggage compartment, aft	1·51 m³ (53·5 cu ft)

AREAS:

Wings, gross	27·31 m² (293·94 sq ft)
Ailerons (total)	1·29 m² (13·90 sq ft)
Trailing-edge flaps (total)	2·72 m² (29·30 sq ft)
Fin	2·20 m² (23·67 sq ft)
Rudder, incl tab	1·30 m² (14·00 sq ft)
Tailplane	4·39 m² (47·25 sq ft)
Elevators, incl tabs	1·66 m² (17·87 sq ft)

WEIGHTS AND LOADINGS:

Weight empty	2,621 kg (5,778 lb)
Max T-O weight	4,377 kg (9,650 lb)
Max ramp weight	4,402 kg (9,705 lb)
Max landing weight	4,159 kg (9,168 lb)
Max wing loading	160·1 kg/m² (32·8 lb/sq ft)
Max power loading	5·34 kg/kW (8·8 lb/ehp)

PERFORMANCE (at max T-O weight, except where indicated):

Max cruising speed at 3,660 m (12,000 ft)
222 knots (412 km/h; 256 mph)
Max cruising speed at 4,880 m (16,000 ft) at AUW of 3,794 kg (8,365 lb)
219 knots (406 km/h; 252 mph)
Max cruising speed at 6,400 m (21,000 ft) at AUW of 3,794 kg (8,365 lb)
216 knots (401 km/h; 249 mph)

Beechcraft King Air C90 six/ten-seat business aircraft

Stalling speed, wheels and flaps up, power off
89 knots (164 km/h; 102 mph) IAS
Stalling speed, wheels and flaps down, power off
76 knots (140 km/h; 87 mph) IAS
Max rate of climb at S/L 596 m (1,955 ft)/min
Rate of climb at S/L, one engine out
164 m (539 ft)/min
Service ceiling 8,565 m (28,100 ft)
Service ceiling, one engine out 4,587 m (15,050 ft)
Min ground turning radius 11·58 m (38 ft 0 in)
Runway LCN 4
T-O to 15 m (50 ft) 689 m (2,261 ft)
Accelerate/stop distance 1,066 m (3,498 ft)
Landing from 15 m (50 ft) without propeller reversal at AUW of 4,159 kg (9,168 lb) 613 m (2,010 ft)
Landing run, without propeller reversal, at AUW of 4,159 kg (9,168 lb) 328 m (1,075 ft)
Range with max fuel at max cruising speed, incl allowance for starting, taxi, take-off, climb, descent and 45 min reserves at max range power, ISA, at:
6,400 m (21,000 ft)
1,202 nm (2,227 km; 1,384 miles)
4,875 m (16,000 ft)
1,059 nm (1,962 km; 1,219 miles)
3,660 m (12,000 ft)
957 nm (1,773 km; 1,102 miles)
Max range at econ cruising power, allowances as above, at:
6,400 m (21,000 ft)
1,281 nm (2,374 km; 1,474 miles)
4,875 m (16,000 ft)
1,159 nm (2,147 km; 1,334 miles)
3,660 m (12,000 ft)
1,068 nm (1,979 km; 1,229 miles)

BEECHCRAFT KING AIR E90

On 1 May 1972 Beech announced an addition to the King Air range of business aircraft. Designated King Air E90, this combines the airframe of the King Air C90 with the 507 kW (680 ehp) Pratt & Whitney Aircraft of Canada PT6A-28 turboprop engines that power the King Air A100, each flat rated to 410 kW (550 ehp). The US Navy ordered King Air 90s in 1976 as **T-44A** advanced trainers to meet its VTAM (X) requirement, and this version is described separately.

The description of the King Air C90 applies also to the King Air E90, except as follows:

LANDING GEAR: As King Air C90, except main-wheel tyre pressure 3·93 bars (57 lb/sq in).

POWER PLANT: Two 507 kW (680 ehp) Pratt & Whitney Aircraft of Canada PT6A-28 turboprop engines, flat rated to 410 kW (550 ehp), each driving a Hartzell three-blade fully-feathering and reversible-pitch constant-speed metal propeller. Standard fuel capacity 1,794 litres (474 US gallons).

AVIONICS AND EQUIPMENT: Standard avionics include dual Collins VHF-20A VHF transceivers with Gables controls and B3 antennae; Collins VIR-30 MGM Omni No. 1 receiver, with 331A-3G indicator, Gables control and B17 antenna; Collins VIR-30MG Omni No. 2 receiver with 331H-3G indicator and Gables control; Collins 356C-4 isolation amplifier and 356F-3 speaker amplifier with single set of audio switches; Collins ADF-650A ADF with IND-650A indicator, Gables control, voice range filter and ANT-650 antenna; Collins marker beacon integral with VIR-30 No. 1, with marker lights and B16 antenna; Collins glideslope receiver integral with VIR-30 No. 1, with B35 antenna; dual flight instrumentation; Collins DME-40 with 339F-12 indicator, Nav 1/Nav 2 switching, DME hold, and 237Z-1 antenna; Collins TDR-950 transponder with 237Z-1 antenna; Collins PN-101 compass system (pilot); Standard Electric gyro horizon (pilot); CF gyro horizon and directional gyro (co-pilot); dual Flite-Tronics PC-125 125VA inverters with failure light; avionics transient protection; Beech edge-lighted radio panel, radio accessories and static wicks; white lighting; microphone key button in pilot and co-pilot control wheels; dual microphones, headsets and cockpit speakers; and avionics master switch. Optional avionics include a wide range of equipment by Bendix, Collins, King, Edo-Aire Mitchell, RCA and Sperry. Standard

and optional equipment generally as listed for King Air C90.

WEIGHTS AND LOADINGS:

Weight empty	2,745 kg (6,052 lb)
Max T-O weight	4,581 kg (10,100 lb)
Max ramp weight	4,608 kg (10,160 lb)
Max landing weight	4,400 kg (9,700 lb)
Max wing loading	168·0 kg/m² (34·4 lb/sq ft)
Max power loading	5·59 kg/kW (9·18 lb/ehp)

PERFORMANCE (at max T-O weight, except where indicated):

Max cruising speed at 3,660 m (12,000 ft)
249 knots (462 km/h; 287 mph)
Cruising speed at max recommended cruise power:
at 4,875 m (16,000 ft)
248 knots (460 km/h; 286 mph)
at 6,400 m (21,000 ft)
245 knots (454 km/h; 282 mph)
Cruising speed for max range
197 knots (365 km/h; 227 mph)
Stalling speed, power off, wheels and flaps up
86 knots (159 km/h; 99 mph) IAS
Stalling speed, power off, wheels and flaps down
77 knots (143 km/h; 89 mph) IAS
Max rate of climb at S/L 570 m (1,870 ft)/min
Rate of climb at S/L, one engine out
143 m (470 ft)/min
Service ceiling 8,420 m (27,620 ft)
Service ceiling, at 3,629 kg (8,000 lb) AUW
9,420 m (30,910 ft)
Service ceiling, one engine out 4,385 m (14,390 ft)
Service ceiling, one engine out, at 3,629 kg (8,000 lb) AUW 6,220 m (20,400 ft)
Min ground turning radius 11·58 m (38 ft 0 in)
Runway LCN 4·5
T-O run 473 m (1,553 ft)
T-O to 15 m (50 ft) 617 m (2,024 ft)
Landing distance, 5° approach angle, full flap, at max landing weight:
landing from 15 m (50 ft) 643 m (2,110 ft)
landing run 314 m (1,030 ft)
Accelerate/stop distance, incl 2 s failure recognition time 1,139 m (3,736 ft)
Cruising range at max recommended cruise power:
at 4,875 m (16,000 ft)
1,125 nm (2,084 km; 1,295 miles)
at 6,400 m (21,000 ft)
1,309 nm (2,425 km; 1,507 miles)
Cruising range at max range power:
at 4,875 m (16,000 ft)
1,480 nm (2,742 km; 1,704 miles)
at 6,400 m (21,000 ft)
1,625 nm (3,011 km; 1,871 miles)
Range at max T-O weight, max recommended power at 6,400 m (21,000 ft), 45 min reserves, five occupants, 37 kg (82 lb) baggage and 1,440 kg (3,176 lb) fuel before engine start
1,309 nm (2,425 km; 1,507 miles)

BEECHCRAFT T-44A (KING AIR 90)

In 1976 Beech Aircraft won an industry-wide competition for a twin-turboprop advanced pilot training aircraft to meet the US Navy's VTAM(X) requirement. The aircraft selected was a version of the King Air 90, incorporating features of both the Model C90 and E90, with modifications to meet Navy special requirements. This aircraft has the US Navy designation T-44A, and by the end of 1978 Beech had received contracts totalling $53 million to build 61 aircraft, of which completion of delivery was announced on 19 June 1980.

The first T-44A was delivered to US Navy Training Command at NAS Corpus Christi, Texas, on 5 April 1977, and student pilot training began in July 1977. T-44As replace TS-2As and TS-2Bs in the US Navy's training aircraft inventory.

The Navy's T-44As differ primarily from other King Air 90s by their power plant, consisting of two 560 kW (750 ehp) Pratt & Whitney Aircraft of Canada PT6A-34B turboprop engines, flat rated to 410 kW (550 ehp). They have also an engine compressor wash system. The fuel capacity is as for the civil King Air C90.

The avionics systems comprise a complete commercial

package, plus Tacan, UHF, and UHF/DF. A 'failure mode selector box' is provided also, enabling the instructor to initiate any of 10 avionics/instrument failures on the student's instrument panel.

The description of the civil King Air C90 applies generally to the T-44A, except as described above, and it has the same maximum T-O weight.

PERFORMANCE (at max T-O weight):

Cruising speed at 4,570 m (15,000 ft)
    240 knots (445 km/h; 276 mph)
Max rate of climb at S/L   597 m (1,960 ft)/min
Service ceiling   8,990 m (29,500 ft)
T-O to 15 m (50 ft)   625 m (2,050 ft)
Landing from 15 m (50 ft)   619 m (2,030 ft)
Range with max fuel at 7,620 m (25,000 ft)
    1,265 nm (2,344 km; 1,456 miles)

BEECHCRAFT SUPER KING AIR MODEL F90

Deliveries of the Super King Air F90 began in mid-1979, shortly after FAA certification of this sixth member of the King Air range of corporate transport aircraft. Basically, it combines the pressurised fuselage of the King Air 90 with reduced-span wings similar to those of the King Air 100, and a T tail assembly similar to that of the Super King Air 200.

New Beechcraft assemblies and technology are utilised throughout its construction, and the PT6A-135 turboprop engines drive slow-turning four-blade propellers to reduce airport and in-flight noise. Cabin pressurisation is increased to 0·34 bars (5·0 lb/sq in) to give a sea level environment at 3,375 m (11,065 ft), a 2,440 m (8,000 ft) environment at 7,050 m (23,120 ft), and a 3,050 m (10,000 ft) environment at an altitude of 8,075 m (26,500 ft).

TYPE: Seven/ten-seat twin-turboprop business aircraft.
WINGS: Similar to King Air 100. De-icing system standard.
FUSELAGE: Similar to King Air 90.
TAIL UNIT: Similar to Super King Air 200. Tailplane de-icing standard.
LANDING GEAR: Retractable tricycle type, with twin-wheel main units and single steerable nosewheel.
POWER PLANT: Two 559 kW (750 shp) Pratt & Whitney Aircraft of Canada PT6A-135 turboprop engines, each driving a Hartzell FT 101 73 four-blade propeller with optional reverse pitch. Automatic fuel transfer system, engine anti-icing, propeller de-icing, and ice-free fuel venting system, are standard.
ACCOMMODATION: Two seats side by side on flight deck. Seats for five to eight persons in main cabin, in deep-cushioned chairs. Passengers screened from flight deck and toilet by partitions at front and rear of cabin. Space for 172 kg (380 lb) of baggage. Windscreen anti-icing standard.
SYSTEM: Pressurisation system differential 0·34 bars (5·0 lb/sq in).
AVIONICS: Standard avionics package includes dual nav/com, marker beacon receiver, glideslope, DME and transponder.

DIMENSIONS, EXTERNAL:

Wing span   13·99 m (45 ft 10¾ in)
Wing area, gross   25·98 m² (279·7 sq ft)
Length overall   12·13 m (39 ft 9½ in)
Height overall   4·60 m (15 ft 1¼ in)
Tailplane span   5·61 m (18 ft 4¾ in)
Propeller diameter   2·34 m (7 ft 8 in)
Passenger door: Height   1·31 m (4 ft 3½ in)
   Width   0·69 m (2 ft 3 in)

DIMENSIONS, INTERNAL:

Cabin, excl flight deck: Length   3·86 m (12 ft 8 in)
   Width   1·37 m (4 ft 6 in)
   Height   1·45 m (4 ft 9 in)
Avionics compartment volume   0·45 m³ (16 cu ft)

Beechcraft Super King Air F90 T-tailed seven/ten-seat business aircraft

WEIGHTS AND LOADINGS:

Weight empty   3,012 kg (6,640 lb)
Max T-O and landing weight   4,966 kg (10,950 lb)
Max ramp weight   5,003 kg (11,030 lb)
Max wing loading   190·8 kg/m² (39·1 lb/sq ft)
Max power loading   4·4 kg/kW (7·3 lb/shp)

PERFORMANCE (A: at max T-O weight; B: at 4,309 kg/9,500 lb AUW; C: at 4,082 kg/9,000 lb AUW):

Max cruising speed (B):

at 3,660 m (12,000 ft) 267 knots (495 km/h; 307 mph)
at 5,490 m (18,000 ft) 260 knots (483 km/h; 300 mph)
at 7,925 m (26,000 ft) 251 knots (465 km/h; 289 mph)
Take-off speed (A)   107 knots (198 km/h; 123 mph)
Approach speed (A)   108 knots (200 km/h; 124 mph)

Stalling speed (A), power off:

flaps up   94 knots (174 km/h; 108 mph)
32·5% flap   84 knots (156 km/h; 97 mph)
100% flap   77 knots (143 km/h; 89 mph)

Max rate of climb at S/L: A   725 m (2,380 ft)/min
   C   947 m (3,108 ft)/min

Rate of climb at S/L, one engine out:

A   183 m (600 ft)/min
C   289 m (947 ft)/min

Service ceiling: A   9,084 m (29,802 ft)
   C   above 9,450 m (31,000 ft)

Service ceiling, one engine out: A 4,395 m (14,419 ft)
   C   5,919 m (19,420 ft)
T-O run (A), flaps up   637 m (2,090 ft)
T-O run to 15 m (50 ft) (A), flaps up 871 m (2,856 ft)
Landing from 15 m (50 ft) (A) without propeller reversal   907 m (2,977 ft)
Landing run (A), without propeller reversal
   578 m (1,895 ft)

Cruising range at max cruise power, with reserves:

at 3,660 m (12,000 ft)
   960 nm (1,779 km; 1,105 miles)
at 5,490 m (18,000 ft)
   1,168 nm (2,165 km; 1,345 miles)
at 7,925 m (26,000 ft)
   1,439 nm (2,667 km; 1,657 miles)

Cruising range at max range power, with reserves:

at 3,660 m (12,000 ft)
   1,179 nm (2,185 km; 1,357 miles)
at 5,490 m (18,000 ft)
   1,368 nm (2,535 km; 1,575 miles)
at 7,925 m (26,000 ft)
   1,576 nm (2,920 km; 1,814 miles)

BEECHCRAFT COMMUTER C99 and 1900

Beech announced on 7 May 1979 the company's intention to re-enter the commuter airliner market, initially with two aircraft. The first of these is an updated version of the Beechcraft 99 Airliner, last described in the 1977-78 *Jane's*. Improvements include new Pratt & Whitney Aircraft of Canada PT6A-34 engines, producing more power than the PT6A-27 turboprops which powered the B99 versions when production ended. It is anticipated that production aircraft will become available for delivery during 1981, as Beechcraft Commuter C99s.

The C99 prototype, converted from a 1969 Model 99, flew for the first time on 20 June 1980. Carrying a crew of two and 15 passengers, it has a cruising speed of 252 knots (467 km/h; 290 mph), a max rate of climb at S/L of 618 m (2,030 ft)/min, and a service ceiling, with one engine out, of 4,085 m (13,400 ft).

The Beechcraft Commuter 1900 will be a T-tailed 19-seat pressurised aircraft, of which the development period is estimated at 3 to 3½ years. An engineering mockup was under construction in mid-1980. Beech is also studying a new pressurised commuter airliner in the 35-seat category.

The Commuter 1900 will be powered by two PT6A-65 turboprop engines of approx 746 kW (1,000 shp), will cruise at about 260 knots (483 km/h; 300 mph), have a max T-O weight of 6,915 kg (15,245 lb), and a fully-loaded cruising range of 555 nm (1,028 km; 639 miles), with IFR reserves, under ISA conditions. Fore and aft airstair doors will be standard, seats will be designed for quick removal for conversion to cargo configuration, and options will include a 1·32 × 1·32 m (52 × 52 in) cargo door. An executive transport version is also under consideration.

BEECHCRAFT KING AIR A100

US Army designation: U-21F

Beech Aircraft announced on 26 May 1969 the addition of a new version of the King Air to its fleet of corporate transport aircraft. Designated King Air 100, this is a pressurised transport with increased internal capacity and more powerful engines, enabling it to carry a useful load of more than two short tons. By comparison with the King Air 90 series, it has a fuselage 1·27 m (4 ft 2 in) longer, reduced wing span, larger rudder and elevator and twin-wheel main landing gear. It is available in a variety of interior configurations, seating six to eight in executive versions, or up to 13 in high-density arrangement, plus crew of two.

The King Air 100 has been approved for Category 2 landing minima by the FAA. Initial deliveries were made

The new Beechcraft Commuter C99, photographed during its first flight

in August 1969, following FAA certification. A total of 327 commercial and military King Air 100s had been delivered by 1 January 1980.

First deliveries of the advanced Model A100, comprising five U-21Fs for the Department of the Army, began in October 1971. Supplied under a $2·5 million contract, they represented the first pressurised aircraft in the Army's inventory. Two A100s were supplied to the Spanish Air Force.

Two aircraft equipped with a Beech-developed UNACE package (Universal Aircraft Com/Nav Evaluation) have been delivered to Belgium and Indonesia. UNACE-configured aircraft, which provide an economical means of inspecting and calibrating aviation navigation aids, are operating also in Algeria, Canada, Malaysia, Mexico and the USA. Beech is able to modify King Airs for aerial photography, and deliveries of camera-equipped aircraft have been made to Canada, Chile, France, Jamaica, Saudi Arabia and Thailand, as well as to various US organisations.

TYPE: Twin-turboprop light passenger, freight or executive transport.

WINGS: Cantilever low-wing monoplane. Wing section NACA 23018 at root, NACA 23016·5 at centre-section joint with outer panel, NACA 23012 at tip. Dihedral 7°. Incidence 4° 48' at root, 0° at tip. Two-spar all-metal light alloy structure. All-metal ailerons of magnesium. Trim tab in port aileron. Single-slotted light alloy trailing-edge flaps. Pneumatic de-icing boots standard.

FUSELAGE: All-metal light alloy semi-monocoque structure.

TAIL UNIT: Cantilever all-metal structure with swept vertical surfaces and a ventral stabilising fin. Trim tab in rudder. Electrically-operated adjustment of tailplane incidence. Pneumatic de-icing boots standard.

LANDING GEAR: Retractable tricycle type with single steerable nosewheel and twin wheels on each main unit. Electrical retraction, nosewheel rearward, main units forward into engine nacelles. Hydraulic retraction system optional. Beech oleo-pneumatic shock-absorbers. Goodrich main wheels and tubeless tyres size 18 × 5·5, pressure 7·10 bars (103 lb/sq in). Nosewheel with tubeless tyre size 6·50 × 10, pressure 3·93 bars (57 lb/sq in). B. F. Goodrich heat sink and aircooled single-disc hydraulic brakes.

POWER PLANT: Two 507 kW (680 ehp) Pratt & Whitney Aircraft of Canada PT6A-28 turboprop engines, each driving a Hartzell four-blade fully-feathering and reversible-pitch constant-speed propeller. Rubber fuel cells in wings, with total capacity of 1,779 litres (470 US gallons). Automatic fuel heating systems; inertial engine inlet de-icing system; engine inlet lips de-iced by electro-thermally heated boots; auto ignition system; environmental fuel drain collector system; magnetic chip detector. Goodrich electrical propeller anti-icing system.

ACCOMMODATION: Crew of two side by side on flight deck, with full dual controls and instruments. Easily removable partition with sliding door between flight deck and cabin. Six fully-adjustable individual cabin chairs standard, with removable headrests, with a variety of alternative layouts, for up to 13 passengers in commuter role. Seat belts and inertia-reel shoulder harness for all seats. Polarised cabin windows. Dual storm windows. Fully-carpeted floor. External access door to forward radio compartment. Aft fuselage maintenance access door. Plug-type emergency exit at forward end of cabin on starboard side. Passenger door at rear of cabin on port side, with integral airstair. Easily removable aft cabin partition with sliding doors. Lavatory installation and stowage for up to 186 kg (410 lb) baggage in aft fuselage. Other standard cabin equipment includes reading lights and fresh air outlets for all passengers, cabin coat rack and dual 'No smoking—Fasten seat belt' signs. Electrothermally heated windscreen, hot air windscreen defroster and windscreen wipers standard. Optional equipment includes cabin fire extinguisher, additional cabin window, flush toilet and a variety of interior cabinets.

SYSTEMS: Cabin pressurisation by engine bleed air with a differential of 0·32 bars (4·6 lb/sq in). Cabin heated by 27,000 BTU electrical heating system. Oxygen system for flight deck and 0·62 m³ (22 cu ft) oxygen system for cabin standard. Cabin oxygen system of 1·39 m³ (49 cu ft), or 1·81 m³ (64 cu ft) optional. Dual vacuum system for instruments. Hydraulic system for brakes only. Pneumatic system for wing and tail unit de-icing only. Two 250A starter/generators. Aircooled nickel-cadmium 28V 45Ah battery with failure detector. Engine fire detection system.

AVIONICS AND EQUIPMENT: Standard avionics comprise dual King KTR 905 VHF transceivers, with Gables controls and B3 antennae; King KNR 630 Omni No. 1, with Collins 331A-3G indicator, Gables control and B17 antenna; King KNR 630 Omni No. 2, with Collins 331H-3G indicator and Gables control; dual Omni range filters; dual Collins 356F-3 audio amplifiers, each with 356C-4 isolation amplifiers and audio switches; King KDF 805 ADF less indicator, with KFS 580B control, voice range filter, and Beech flush sense antenna; King KMR 675 marker beacon receiver, with dual

marker lights and B16 antenna; dual glideslope receivers integral with No. 1 and No. 2 Omni, with B35 antenna; Bendix RDR-130 weather radar, with phased array antenna and digital scope; Sperry C-14-43 compass system with servo amplifier (pilot); King KNI 581 RMI with VOR-1/ADF on single needle, VOR-2/ADF on double needle; King KXP 755 transponder, with Gables control and B18 antenna; King KDM 706 DME with KDI 572 indicator, Nav-1/Nav-2 switching, DME hold and B18 antenna; dual Flite-Tronics PC-250 250VA inverters with failure light; avionics transient protection; sectional instrument panel; Standard Electric gyro horizon (pilot); CF gyro horizon and directional gyro (co-pilot); Beech edge-lighted radio panel, radio accessories, microphone button in pilot and co-pilot control wheels, static wicks and white lighting; dual microphones, headsets and cockpit speakers; and avionics master switch. A wide range of optional avionics equipment is available, by Bendix, Collins, King, RCA, Sperry and SunAir. Heated main landing gear brake de-icing and tail floodlight offered as optional equipment. Other standard and optional equipment generally as listed for King Air C90.

DIMENSIONS, EXTERNAL:
Wing span	14·00 m (45 ft 11 in)
Wing chord at root	2·15 m (7 ft 0½ in)
Wing chord at tip	1·07 m (3 ft 6 in)
Wing aspect ratio	7·51
Length overall	12·17 m (39 ft 11 in)
Height overall	4·70 m (15 ft 5 in)
Tailplane span	6·83 m (22 ft 5 in)
Wheel track	3·96 m (13 ft 0 in)
Wheelbase	4·55 m (14 ft 11 in)
Propeller diameter	2·29 m (7 ft 6 in)
Propeller ground clearance	0·34 m (1 ft 1½ in)

DIMENSIONS, INTERNAL:
Cabin: Length (excl flight deck)	5·08 m (16 ft 8 in)
Max width	1·37 m (4 ft 6 in)
Max height	1·45 m (4 ft 9 in)
Volume, avionics compartment in nose	0·45 m³ (16 cu ft)
Volume, aft baggage compartment	1·51 m³ (53·5 cu ft)

WEIGHTS AND LOADINGS:
Weight empty	3,083 kg (6,797 lb)
Max T-O weight	5,216 kg (11,500 lb)
Max ramp weight	5,247 kg (11,568 lb)
Max zero-fuel weight	4,354 kg (9,600 lb)
Max landing weight	5,084 kg (11,210 lb)
Max wing loading	201 kg/m² (41·2 lb/sq ft)
Max power loading	5·14 kg/kW (8·46 lb/ehp)

PERFORMANCE (at max T-O weight, unless otherwise quoted):
Max cruising speed at 4,762 kg (10,500 lb) AUW:
at 6,400 m (21,000 ft)
235 knots (436 km/h; 270 mph)
at 4,875 m (16,000 ft)
243 knots (450 km/h; 280 mph)
at 3,050 m (10,000 ft)
248 knots (459 km/h; 285 mph)
Stalling speed, power off, wheels and flaps up
89 knots (164 km/h; 102 mph)
Stalling speed, power off, wheels and flaps down
75 knots (139 km/h; 86 mph)
Max rate of climb at S/L 598 m (1,963 ft)/min
Rate of climb at S/L, one engine out
138 m (452 ft)/min
Service ceiling 7,575 m (24,850 ft)
Service ceiling, one engine out 2,835 m (9,300 ft)
Min ground turning radius 12·2 m (40 ft 0 in)
Runway LCN 4·5
T-O run: flaps up 628 m (2,060 ft)
30% flap 565 m (1,855 ft)
T-O to 15 m (50 ft): flaps up 989 m (3,245 ft)
30% flap 817 m (2,681 ft)
Landing from 15 m (50 ft) at max landing weight, without propeller reversal 897 m (2,944 ft)
Landing run at max landing weight, without propeller reversal 545 m (1,787 ft)

Beechcraft King Air B100 twin-turboprop light passenger, freight or executive transport

*Accelerate/stop distance, flaps up
1,303 m (4,275 ft)
*Accelerate/stop distance, 30% flap
1,182 m (3,877 ft)
Range at high cruise power, with 1,779 litres (470 US gallons) fuel, incl allowances for starting, taxi, take-off, climb, descent and 45 min reserves:
at 6,400 m (21,000 ft)
1,212 nm (2,247 km; 1,395 miles)
at 4,875 m (16,000 ft)
1,064 nm (1,971 km; 1,225 miles)
at 3,050 m (10,000 ft)
900 nm (1,667 km; 1,036 miles)
Range at long range cruise power, fuel and allowances as above:
at 6,400 m (21,000 ft)
1,340 nm (2,483 km; 1,542 miles)
at 4,875 m (16,000 ft)
1,272 nm (2,358 km; 1,464 miles)
at 3,050 m (10,000 ft)
1,152 nm (2,136 km; 1,326 miles)
*Includes allowance for failure recognition

BEECHCRAFT KING AIR B100

On 20 March 1975 Beech recorded the first flight of a new version of the King Air. Designated King Air B100, it is generally similar to its predecessors, except for the installation of two 533 kW (715 shp) Garrett-AiResearch TPE 331-6-252B turboprop engines, giving improved performance.

The description of the King Air A100 applies also to the B100, except as follows:

TYPE: Twin-turboprop light passenger, freight or executive transport.

WINGS, FUSELAGE, TAIL UNIT, LANDING GEAR: As for Model A100.

POWER PLANT: Two 533 kW (715 shp) Garrett-AiResearch TPE 331-6-252B turboprop engines, each driving a four-blade constant-speed fully-feathering metal propeller. Fuel system and anti-icing system as for Model A100.

ACCOMMODATION, SYSTEMS, AVIONICS AND EQUIPMENT: As for Model A100, except for slight variations in ancillary equipment associated directly with the power plant.

DIMENSIONS, EXTERNAL: As for Model A100, except:
Propeller ground clearance 0·39 m (1 ft 3½ in)
DIMENSIONS, INTERNAL, AND AREAS: As for Model A100

WEIGHTS AND LOADINGS:
Weight empty, equipped	3,226 kg (7,112 lb)
Max T-O weight	5,352 kg (11,800 lb)
Max ramp weight	5,386 kg (11,875 lb)
Max zero-fuel weight	4,354 kg (9,600 lb)
Max landing weight	5,085 kg (11,210 lb)
Max wing loading	206·0 kg/m² (42·2 lb/sq ft)
Max power loading	5·02 kg/kW (8·25 lb/shp)

PERFORMANCE (at max T-O weight):
Max level speed and max cruising speed:
at 3,660 m (12,000 ft)
265 knots (491 km/h; 305 mph)
at 6,400 m (21,000 ft)
262 knots (486 km/h; 302 mph)
Stalling speed, flaps up
93 knots (172·5 km/h; 107 mph) IAS
Stalling speed, flaps down
83 knots (154·5 km/h; 96 mph) IAS
Max rate of climb at S/L 652 m (2,139 ft)/min
Rate of climb at S/L, one engine out
152 m (501 ft)/min
Service ceiling 8,575 m (28,140 ft)
Service ceiling, one engine out 3,695 m (12,120 ft)
T-O run 579 m (1,898 ft)
T-O run, 30% flap 535 m (1,755 ft)
T-O to 15 m (50 ft) 899 m (2,951 ft)
T-O to 15 m (50 ft), 30% flap 821 m (2,694 ft)
Landing from 15 m (50 ft) without propeller reversal
1,040 m (3,413 ft)
Landing from 15 m (50 ft) with propeller reversal
817 m (2,679 ft)
Landing run without propeller reversal 503 m (1,651 ft)

Landing run with propeller reversal 393 m (1,290 ft)
Range with 1,779 litres (470 US gallons) usable fuel,
with allowances for start, taxi, T-O, climb, descent
and 45 min reserves at max range power, ISA:
at max cruising power at:
  3,660 m (12,000 ft)
            1,015 nm (1,881 km; 1,168 miles)
  4,875 m (16,000 ft)
            1,119 nm (2,074 km; 1,288 miles)
  6,400 m (21,000 ft)
            1,264 nm (2,343 km; 1,455 miles)
at econ cruising power at:
  3,660 m (12,000 ft)
            1,108 nm (2,053 km; 1,275 miles)
  4,875 m (16,000 ft)
            1,205 nm (2,232 km; 1,387 miles)
  6,400 m (21,000 ft)
            1,325 nm (2,456 km; 1,525 miles)

C-12A version of the Beechcraft Super King Air 200 for the USAF

BEECHCRAFT SUPER KING AIR 200
US military designations: C-12 and RU-21J

Design of the Super King Air 200 began in October
1970, construction of the first prototype and first pre-
production aircraft starting simultaneously a year later.
The first prototype, serial BB-1, flew for the first time on
27 October 1972, followed by the second aircraft, BB-2,
on 15 December 1972. While the flight tests and testing of
a static fuselage were under way, construction of the first
production aircraft began in June 1973. FAA certification
under FAR Part 23 was awarded on 14 December 1973,
the aircraft satisfying also the icing requirements of FAR
Part 25.

By comparison with the King Air 100, the Super King
Air 200 has increased wing span, basically the same fuselage, a T tail, more powerful engines, additional fuel capacity, increased cabin pressurisation and a higher gross
weight. The cargo door fitted to some military versions
became available as an option on civil Super King Airs in
1979; first deliveries were for air ambulance use in Libya
and commuter operations in Australia.

In August 1974, Beech received a military contract to
build and support 34 modified versions of the Super King
Air, designated **C-12A**. Subsequently, many more C-12s
have been ordered, in four versions, as follows:

C-12A. Initial version for US Army (81) and US Air
Force (30), with two 559 kW (750 shp) Pratt & Whitney
Aircraft of Canada PT6A-38 turboprop engines, each
driving a Hartzell three-blade constant-speed fully-
feathering reversible-pitch propeller. Total of 111
ordered by 1 January 1980.

UC-12B. US Navy/Marine Corps version, with 634 kW
(850 shp) PT6A-41 turboprop engines, cargo door and
high-flotation landing gear. Total of 66 ordered by
4 February 1980, which will extend deliveries into 1982.

C-12C. As C-12A, for US Army (14), but with PT6A-
41 engines.

C-12D. As C-12C, for US Army, but with cargo door.
Total of 21 ordered by 17 July 1980.

Contract value of all 212 C-12s (116 for the Army, 30
for the Air Force, and 66 for the Navy) totals $193 million.

Worldwide deployment of the C-12s began in July
1975. They are described as 'standard off-the-shelf Super
King Air types, modified slightly to meet military flight
requirements and to orient the control systems for two-
pilot operation which is standard military practice'.
Accommodation is provided for eight passengers, plus two
pilots, with easy conversion to cargo missions. The large
baggage area has provisions for storing survival gear.

In addition, during 1974 the US Army added three
Super King Airs to its fleet of special mission aircraft, with
the designation **RU-21J**. Under an R and D contract,
Beech had modified these antenna-laden aircraft for the
US Army's Cefly Lancer programme. They are approved
for take-off at a special AUW of 6,804 kg (15,000 lb).

In February 1977 Beech delivered to the French Institut
Géographique National two specially-modified Super
King Airs. These have twin Wild RC-10 Superaviogon
camera installations and Doppler navigation systems, and
were the first Super King Airs to be equipped with
optional wingtip fuel tanks, which increase the total usable

fuel capacity from 2,059 litres (544 US gallons) to 2,457
litres (649 US gallons) to provide a max endurance of
10·3 h. Designated **Model 200Ts**, they are fitted with
high-flotation main landing gear, and are being operated
under a special French airworthiness certificate which
allows max T-O and landing weights of 6,350 kg (14,000
lb) and 6,123 kg (13,500 lb) respectively. The aircraft can
be operated with or without the wingtip tanks, for high-
altitude photographic and weather observation missions.

Beech announced on 25 April 1977 the company's
intention to introduce a specially-equipped maritime patrol version of the Super King Air, the **Maritime Patrol
200T**, which is described separately.

During 1978 Beech announced supply to the Egyptian
government of a Super King Air which is being used to
continue water, uranium and other natural resources exploration in the Sinai and Egyptian deserts which was
originated by US ERTS-1 and Landsat satellites. In June
1978, the Japan Maritime Safety Agency announced
selection of the Super King Air for maritime patrol in
connection with Japan's 174 nm (322 km; 200 mile)
fishing limit. A total of 13 aircraft is required at a cost of
more than $26 million, and delivery of the first aircraft was
made in September 1979. Also in June 1978, Beech delivered to the government of Taiwan a Super King Air
equipped to check ground-based navigation systems. A
second special-mission aircraft was scheduled for delivery
to Taiwan's Ministry of the Interior in May 1979. In late
1978 Beech won an industry-wide competition for the
lease of four Super King Airs to the border patrol fleet of
the US Customs Service, and these were delivered in
Spring 1979.

By 1 January 1980 Beech had delivered 600 Super King
Airs to commercial and private operators and 117 military
C-12s to the US Air Force, US Navy and US Army.

TYPE: Twin-turboprop passenger or executive light transport.

WINGS: Cantilever low-wing monoplane. Wing section
NACA 23018·5 (modified) at root, NACA 23011·3 at
tip. Dihedral 6°. Incidence 3°48' at root, −1° 7' at tip.
No sweepback at quarter-chord. Two-spar light alloy
structure. Conventional ailerons of light alloy construction, with trim tab in port aileron. Single-slotted
trailing-edge flaps of light alloy construction. Pneumatic
de-icing boots standard.

FUSELAGE: Light alloy semi-monocoque structure of safe-
life design.

TAIL UNIT: Conventional cantilever T-tail structure of
light alloy with swept vertical and horizontal surfaces.
Fixed-incidence tailplane. Trim tab in each elevator.
Anti-servo tab in rudder. Pneumatic de-icing boots
standard, on leading-edge of tailplane only.

LANDING GEAR: Electrically-retractable tricycle type, with
twin wheels on each main unit. Single wheel on steerable nose unit, with shimmy damper. Main units retract
forward, nosewheel aft. Beech oleo-pneumatic shock-

absorbers. Goodrich main wheels and tyres size 18 ×
5·5, pressure 7·25 bars (105 lb/sq in). Goodrich nosewheel size 6·50 × 10, with tyre size 22 × 6·75-10,
pressure 3·93 bars (57 lb/sq in). Goodrich hydraulic
multiple-disc brakes. Parking brake.

POWER PLANT: Two 634 kW (850 shp) Pratt & Whitney
Aircraft of Canada PT6A-41 turboprop engines, each
driving a three-blade constant-speed fully-feathering
reversible-pitch metal propeller; PT6A-38 engines in
C-12A, as noted in introductory copy. Bladder type fuel
cells in each wing, with main system capacity of 1,461
litres (386 US gallons) and auxiliary system capacity of
598 litres (158 US gallons). Total fuel capacity 2,059
litres (544 US gallons). Two refuelling points in upper
surface of each wing. Oil capacity 29·5 litres (7·8 US
gallons). Anti-icing of engine air intakes by hot air from
engine exhaust is standard. Electrothermal anti-icing
for propellers. Wingtip tanks optional.

ACCOMMODATION: Pilot only, or crew of two side by side,
on flight deck, with full dual controls and instruments as
standard. Six cabin seats standard, each equipped with
seat belts and inertia-reel shoulder harness; alternative
layouts for a maximum of 13 passengers in cabin and
14th beside pilot. Partition with sliding door between
cabin and flight deck, and partition at rear of cabin.
Door at rear of cabin on port side, with integral airstair.
Large cargo door optional. Inward-opening emergency
exit on starboard side over wing. Lavatory and stowage
for up to 186 kg (410 lb) baggage in aft fuselage.
Maintenance access door in rear fuselage; radio compartment access doors in nose. Standard equipment
includes reading lights and fresh air outlets for all passengers, triple cabin windows with polarised glare control, fully-carpeted floor, 'No smoking—Fasten seat
belt' sign, cabin coat rack, fluorescent cabin lighting,
aisle and door courtesy lights. Electrically-heated
windscreens, hot air windscreen defroster, dual storm
windows, sun visors, map pockets and windscreen
wipers. Cabin is air-conditioned and pressurised, and
can be provided with optional radiant heat panels.

SYSTEMS: Cabin pressurisation by engine bleed air, with a
maximum differential of 0·41 bars (6·0 lb/sq in). Cabin
air-conditioner of 34,000 BTU capacity. Auxiliary
cabin heating by radiant panels optional. Oxygen system for flight deck, and 0·62 m³ (22 cu ft) oxygen system
for cabin, with automatic drop-down face masks; standard system of 1·39 m³ (49 cu ft), 1·81 m³ (64 cu ft), or
2·15 m³ (76 cu ft) optional. Dual vacuum system for
instruments. Hydraulic system for brakes only.
Pneumatic system for wing and tailplane de-icing. Electrical system has two 250A 28V starter/generators and
24V 45Ah aircooled nickel-cadmium battery with failure detector. AC power provided by dual 250VA inverters.

AVIONICS AND EQUIPMENT: Standard avionics include dual
Collins VHF-20A VHF transceivers, with Gables controls and B3 antennae; Collins VIR-30AGM automatic
Omni No. 1, with 331A-3G indicator, Gables control
and B17 antenna; Collins VIR-30AG automatic Omni
No. 2, with 331H-3G indicator and Gables control; dual
Omni range filters; Collins dual 356-F3 audio
amplifiers, each with 356C-4 isolation amplifiers and
audio switches; Collins ADF-60A ADF less indicator,
with Gables control, voice range filter and ANT-60
antenna; Collins marker beacon, integral with VIR-30
No. 1, with dual marker lights and B16 antenna; dual
Collins glideslopes, integral with VIR-30 No. 1 and No.
2, with B35 glideslope antenna; Bendix RDR-130
weather radar, with phased array antenna and digital
scope; Sperry C-14-43 compass system, with servo
amplifier (pilot); Collins 332C-10 RMI, with Nav
1/ADF on single needle, Nav 2/ADF on double needle;
Collins TDR-90 transponder, with Gables control and
237Z-1 antenna; Collins DME-40 with 339F-12 indicator, Nav 1/Nav 2 switching, DME hold and 237Z-1
antenna; dual Flite-Tronics PC-250 250VA inverters
with failure light; sectional instrument panel; dual flight
instrumentation; Standard Electric gyro horizon (pilot);
CF gyro horizon and directional gyro (co-pilot); Beech

**Beechcraft Super King Air 200 eight/fifteen-seat pressurised transport (two Pratt & Whitney Aircraft of
Canada PT6A-41 turboprop engines)**

edge-lighted radio panel, radio accessories, microphone key button in pilot's and co-pilot's control wheels, static wicks, and white lighting; dual microphones, headsets and cockpit speakers; and avionics master switch. A wide range of optional avionics by Bendix, Collins, King, RCA, Sperry and SunAir is available to customer's requirements. Standard equipment is generally as listed for King Air C90, plus dual max allowable airspeed indicators, control wheel mounted chronographs, toilet, fluorescent cabin lighting instead of indirect lighting, aisle courtesy light, transistor controlled blue/white cockpit lighting, entrance door light, engine fire detection system, rudder boost system, and yaw damper system. Optional equipment includes a flight hour recorder, instantaneous vertical speed indicator, cockpit and cabin fire extinguishers, a range of cabin chairs, cabinets and table, flushing toilet, aft cabin air-conditioning installation, radiant heating system, entrance door step lights, wingtip recognition lights, strobe lights, fin illumination lights, engine fire extinguishing system, automatic propeller feathering, propeller synchrophaser, electric pitch trim, oversize and/or 10-ply main-wheel tyres.

Beechcraft Super King Air 200 twin-turboprop transport, with additional side views of Maritime Patrol 200T (centre right); scrap views of wingtip tanks (left) and centre-fuselage of photo survey aircraft for IGN
(Pilot Press)

DIMENSIONS, EXTERNAL:

Wing span	16·61 m (54 ft 6 in)
Wing chord at root	2·18 m (7 ft 1¾ in)
Wing chord at tip	0·90 m (2 ft 11⅝ in)
Wing aspect ratio	9·8
Length overall	13·34 m (43 ft 9 in)
Height overall	4·57 m (15 ft 0 in)
Tailplane span	5·61 m (18 ft 5 in)
Wheel track	5·23 m (17 ft 2 in)
Wheelbase	4·56 m (14 ft 11½ in)
Propeller diameter	2·50 m (8 ft 2½ in)
Propeller ground clearance	0·37 m (1 ft 2½ in)
Distance between propeller centres	5·23 m (17 ft 2 in)
Passenger door: Height	1·31 m (4 ft 3½ in)
Width	0·68 m (2 ft 2¾ in)
Height to sill	1·17 m (3 ft 10 in)
Cargo door (optional):	
Height	1·32 m (4 ft 4 in)
Width	1·32 m (4 ft 4 in)
Nose avionics service doors (port and stbd):	
Max height	0·57 m (1 ft 10½ in)
Width	0·63 m (2 ft 1 in)
Height to sill	1·37 m (4 ft 6 in)
Emergency exit door (stbd):	
Height	0·66 m (2 ft 2 in)
Width	0·50 m (1 ft 7¾ in)

DIMENSIONS, INTERNAL:

Cabin (from forward to aft pressure bulkhead):	
Length	6·71 m (22 ft 0 in)
Max width	1·37 m (4 ft 6 in)
Max height	1·45 m (4 ft 9 in)
Floor area	7·80 m² (84 sq ft)
Volume	11·10 m³ (392 cu ft)
Baggage hold, rear of cabin:	
Volume	1·51 m³ (53·5 cu ft)

AREAS:

Wings, gross	28·15 m² (303 sq ft)
Ailerons (total)	1·67 m² (18·0 sq ft)
Trailing-edge flaps (total)	4·17 m² (44·9 sq ft)
Fin	3·46 m² (37·2 sq ft)
Rudder, incl tab	1·40 m² (15·1 sq ft)
Tailplane	4·52 m² (48·7 sq ft)
Elevators, incl tabs	1·79 m² (19·3 sq ft)

WEIGHTS AND LOADINGS:

Weight empty	3,421 kg (7,543 lb)
Max T-O and landing weight	5,670 kg (12,500 lb)
Max ramp weight	5,710 kg (12,590 lb)
Max zero-fuel weight	4,717 kg (10,400 lb)
Max wing loading	201·6 kg/m² (41·3 lb/sq ft)
Max power loading	4·47 kg/kW (7·35 lb/shp)

WEIGHTS AND LOADINGS (C-12A): As Super King Air, except:

Basic empty weight	3,538 kg (7,800 lb)
Max ramp weight	5,708 kg (12,585 lb)
Max power loading	5·07 kg/kW (8·33 lb/shp)

PERFORMANCE (at max T-O weight, ISA, unless specified):
Never-exceed speed
  Mach 0·52 (260 knots; 482 km/h; 299 mph) CAS
Max level speed, average cruise weight at 4,570 m
  (15,000 ft)   289 knots (536 km/h; 333 mph)
Max cruising speed, average cruise weight at 7,620 m
  (25,000 ft)   278 knots (515 km/h; 320 mph)
Econ cruising speed, average cruise weight at 7,620 m
  (25,000 ft)   272 knots (503 km/h; 313 mph)
Stalling, speed, flaps up
        99 knots (183 km/h; 114 mph) IAS
Stalling speed, flaps down
      75·5 knots (138·5 km/h; 86 mph) IAS
Max rate of climb at S/L   747 m (2,450 ft)/min
Rate of climb at S/L, one engine out
        226 m (740 ft)/min
Service ceiling   10,670 m (35,000 ft)
Service ceiling, one engine out 5,835 m (19,150 ft)
T-O run   592 m (1,942 ft)
T-O run, 40% flap   566 m (1,856 ft)
T-O to 15 m (50 ft), flaps up 1,020 m (3,345 ft)
T-O to 15 m (50 ft), 40% flap 786 m (2,579 ft)
Landing from 15 m (50 ft), full flap, without propeller
  reversal   867 m (2,845 ft)
Landing from 15 m (50 ft) with propeller reversal
        632 m (2,074 ft)
Landing run, full flap, without propeller reversal
        536 m (1,760 ft)
Landing run with propeller reversal 341 m (1,120 ft)
Range with 2,059 litres (544 US gallons) usable fuel, with allowances for start, taxi, climb, descent and 45 min reserves at max range power, ISA:
  max cruising power at:
  5,485 m (18,000 ft)
        1,190 nm (2,204 km; 1,370 miles)
  7,620 m (25,000 ft)
        1,485 nm (2,750 km; 1,709 miles)
  9,450 m (31,000 ft)
        1,757 nm (3,254 km; 2,022 miles)
  econ cruising power at:
  5,485 m (18,000 ft)
        1,487 nm (2,755 km; 1,712 miles)
  7,620 m (25,000 ft)
        1,737 nm (3,217 km; 1,999 miles)
  9,450 m (31,000 ft)
        1,887 nm (3,495 km; 2,172 miles)
PERFORMANCE (C-12A at max T-O weight, except as noted otherwise):
Max level speed at 4,265 m (14,000 ft) and AUW of 4,536 kg (10,000 lb) 260 knots (482 km/h; 299 mph)
Max cruising speed at 9,145 m (30,000 ft) and AUW of 4,536 kg (10,000 lb) 236 knots (437 km/h; 272 mph)
Service ceiling   9,450 m (31,000 ft)
Service ceiling, one engine out 5,365 m (17,600 ft)
T-O to 15 m (50 ft)   860 m (2,820 ft)
Landing from 15 m (50 ft)   766 m (2,514 ft)
Range at max cruising speed
      1,584 nm (2,935 km; 1,824 miles)

BEECHCRAFT MARITIME PATROL 200T

After investigating the potential market for a maritime patrol version of its Super King Air 200 twin-turboprop light transport, Beech announced on 9 April 1979 that it had begun to flight test such an aircraft for FAA certification as the Maritime Patrol 200T.

In production form, the 200T can be equipped for missions such as monitoring exclusive economic zones, detecting pollution, inspecting offshore installations, and conducting search and rescue flights. Special missions for which it could also be used include aerial photography, environmental and ecological research, airways and ground-based navigation equipment checks, and ambulance duties.

Modifications to the standard Super King Air to adapt it to Maritime Patrol 200T configuration include fitting new outboard wing assemblies, with mountings for a 200·5 litre (53 US gallon) removable fuel tank at each wingtip; strengthened landing gear to cater for higher take-off and landing weights; a bubble observation window in the aft cabin for visual search and photography; a hatch for dropping survival equipment; and a search radar with full 360° scan in a radome beneath the fuselage. Advanced navigation equipment is available, especially for maritime patrol use; standard avionics include VLF/Omega which provides ground stabilisation and is coupled with the autopilot. This permits a search pattern to be programmed before take-off or en route.

Seven of 13 Maritime Patrol 200Ts bought by Japan's Maritime Safety Agency had been delivered by 1 March 1980.

The description of the Super King Air 200 applies also to the 200T, except as follows:

TYPE: Twin-turboprop maritime patrol or multi-mission aircraft.

WINGS: As for Super King Air 200, except for new outboard wing panels redesigned to permit mounting of removable wingtip tanks.

LANDING GEAR: Strengthened to cater for higher operating weights.

POWER PLANT: As for Super King Air 200, plus provision for removable wingtip tanks to increase maximum fuel capacity by 401 litres (106 US gallons), to a total of 2,460 litres (650 US gallons).

AVIONICS AND EQUIPMENT: Standard items as detailed in introductory description. Optional avionics include INS, VHF/FM com, HF and VHF com, FLIR, LLLTV, multispectral scanner, tactical navigation computer, and two alternative search radar systems, both with 360° scan and weather avoidance capability.

DIMENSIONS, INTERNAL: As for Super King Air 200, except:
  Cabin: Length (excl flight deck) 5·08 m (16 ft 8 in)

DIMENSIONS, EXTERNAL: As for Super King Air 200, except:

Wing span over tip-tanks	17·25 m (56 ft 7 in)
Wing aspect ratio	10·5

WEIGHTS (A: Normal category; B: Restricted category):

Weight empty: A, B	3,744 kg (8,255 lb)
Max T-O weight: A	5,670 kg (12,500 lb)
B	6,350 kg (14,000 lb)
Max landing weight: A	5,670 kg (12,500 lb)
B	6,123 kg (13,500 lb)

PERFORMANCE (at max T-O weight):
Max cruising speed, AUW of 4,990 kg (11,000 lb) at 4,265 m (14,000 ft) 265 knots (491 km/h; 305 mph)
Typical patrol speed
        140 knots (259 km/h; 161 mph)
Range with max fuel, patrolling at 227 knots (420 km/h; 261 mph) at 825 m (2,700 ft), 45 min reserves
      1,790 nm (3,317 km; 2,061 miles)
Typical endurance at 140 knots (259 km/h; 161 mph), at 610 m (2,000 ft), 45 min reserves
        6 h 36 min

One of 13 Beechcraft Maritime Patrol 200Ts for service with Japan's Maritime Safety Agency

BELL

BELL HELICOPTER TEXTRON (Division of Textron Inc)

HEAD OFFICE: PO Box 482, Fort Worth, Texas 76101
Telephone: (817) 280 2011
PRESIDENT: James F. Atkins
SENIOR VICE-PRESIDENTS:
    Hans Weichsel Jr (Product Development)
    L. M. Horner (Marketing & Programmes)
    Robert R. Lynn (Research & Engineering)
    Richard K. May (Operations)
    Charles R. Rudning (Medium Helicopters)
VICE-PRESIDENTS:
    John A. Buyers (Model 222 Programme)
    James C. Fuller (Public Relations)
    George Galerstein (Law)
    William L. Humphrey (General Manager, Amarillo Facility)
    Webb F. Joiner (Finance)
    Dwayne K. Jose (Commercial Marketing)
    Clifford J. Kalista (International Marketing)
    Gainor J. Lindsey (Administration)
    Joseph Mashman (Special Projects)
    C. M. McKeen Jr (Procurement)
    Phil C. Norwine (Government Marketing)
    Warren T. Rockwell (Washington Operations)
    Edmund Szol (Employee Relations)
    Ted R. Treff (Treasurer)

Available details of the range of military and commercial helicopters in current production, or under development, by Bell Helicopter Textron are published in this entry. Some models are also built under licence by Agusta in Italy and Fuji in Japan (which see).

During 1972 Bell achieved a major breakthrough in the elimination of vibration in helicopters with what is known as the nodalisation concept, flight test data and analytical results suggesting that 70 to 90 per cent vibration isolation was practicable. This concept is based on the scientific fact that any beam subjected to vertical vibratory forces, such as those induced by a rotor, will develop flexing to produce a wave form. Points of no relative motion, called the nodal points, appear at equal distances from the centre of the induced wave form, and it is at these points that Bell suspends the helicopter fuselage. Since the nodes have no relative motion, the fuselage becomes virtually free from rotor-induced vibration. Flight tests of a Model 206 Jet-Ranger with its fuselage suspended from a nodalised beam were so convincing that Bell decided to utilise this 'Noda-Matic' technique on new production helicopters, beginning with the Models 206L LongRanger and 214.

Approximately 9,200 people were employed by Bell in 1980. The company has produced more than 24,000 helicopters.

BELL MODEL 205

US military designations: UH-1D/H, EH-1H and HH-1H Iroquois
Canadian military designation: CH-118 Iroquois

Although basically similar to the earlier Model 204 (see 1971-72 *Jane's*), the Model 205 introduced a longer fuselage, increased cabin space to accommodate a much larger number of passengers, and other changes. Details of the full range of military variants have been recorded in previous editions of *Jane's*. The final production version is the **UH-1H**. Deliveries of this version to the US Army began in September 1967 and 1,242 had been built by 1976, including nine for the RNZAF. Production of the UH-1H continued in 1978 to satisfy export orders and a new contract for 27 for the US Army.

The FY 1980 budget requests included $18·8 million to modify five UH-1Hs to **EH-1H** electronic countermeasures configuration, with the Phase II Quick Fix system, AN/APR-39V2 radar warning receiver, XM-130 chaff/flare dispenser and AN/ALQ-144 infra-red jammer. FY 1981 requests include $5·5 million to convert initial Quick Fix IA systems in the EH-1H to Phase IB configuration, and $3·2 million for survivability equipment to protect the aircraft against known and postulated threats, including hot metal/plume suppression.

Four aircraft have been modified for field evaluation of the US Army Standoff Target Acquisition System (SOTAS). General Dynamics Electronics Division is prime contractor for this system, which will give battlefield commanders real-time radar moving target information on the battle situation, relayed from the helicopters. Added equipment includes a large plank-like antenna under the fuselage and Sperry coupled four-axis autopilot and three-cue flight director for precise helicopter stabilisation at very low speeds.

Under a licensing agreement concluded in 1969, a total of 118 UH-1Hs were produced for the Nationalist Chinese Army, with much of the manufacturing and assembly carried out at Taichung, Taiwan.

The following details refer specifically to the military UH-1H. The commercial Model 205A-1 is described separately.

TYPE: Single-rotor general-purpose helicopter.
ROTOR SYSTEM: Two-blade all-metal semi-rigid main rotor with interchangeable blades, built up of extruded aluminium spars and laminates. Stabilising bar above

and at right angles to main rotor blades. Underslung feathering axis hub. Two-blade all-metal tail rotor of honeycomb construction. Blades do not fold.
ROTOR DRIVE: Shaft-drive to both main and tail rotors. Transmission rating 820 kW (1,100 shp). Main rotor rpm 294-324.
FUSELAGE: Conventional all-metal semi-monocoque structure.
TAIL SURFACE: Small synchronised elevator on rear fuselage is connected to the cyclic control to increase allowable CG travel.
LANDING GEAR: Tubular skid type. Lock-on ground handling wheels and inflated nylon float-bags available.
POWER PLANT: One 1,044 kW (1,400 shp) Avco Lycoming T53-L-13 turboshaft engine, mounted aft of the transmission on top of the fuselage and enclosed in cowlings. Five interconnected rubber fuel cells, total capacity 799 litres (211 US gallons). Overload fuel capacity of 1,935 litres (511 US gallons) obtained by installation of kit comprising two 568 litre (150 US gallon) internal auxiliary fuel tanks interconnected with the basic fuel system.
ACCOMMODATION: Cabin space of 6·23 m³ (220 cu ft) provides sufficient room for pilot and 11-14 troops, or six litters and a medical attendant, or 1,759 kg (3,880 lb) of freight. Crew doors open forward and are jettisonable. Two doors on each side of cargo compartment; front door is hinged to open forward and is removable, rear door slides aft. Forced air ventilation system.
AVIONICS AND EQUIPMENT: FM, UHF, VHF radio sets, IFF transponder, Gyromatic compass system, direction finder set, VOR receiver and intercom standard. Optional nav/com systems. Standard equipment includes bleed air heater and defroster, comprehensive range of engine and flight instruments, power plant fire detection system, 30V 300A DC starter/generator, navigation, landing and anti-collision lights, controllable searchlight, hydraulically-boosted controls. Optional equipment includes external cargo hook, auxiliary fuel tanks, rescue hoist, 150,000 BTU muff heater.

DIMENSIONS, EXTERNAL:

Diameter of main rotor	14·63 m (48 ft 0 in)
Diameter of tail rotor	2·59 m (8 ft 6 in)
Main rotor blade chord	0·53 m (1 ft 9 in)
Tail rotor blade chord	0·213 m (8·4 in)
Length overall (main rotor fore and aft)	17·62 m (57 ft 9⅝ in)
Length of fuselage	12·77 m (41 ft 10¾ in)
Height overall	4·42 m (14 ft 6 in)

AREAS:

Main rotor disc	168·06 m² (1,809 sq ft)
Tail rotor disc	5·27 m² (56·7 sq ft)

WEIGHTS AND LOADINGS:

Weight empty	2,363 kg (5,210 lb)
Basic operating weight (troop carrier mission)	2,520 kg (5,557 lb)
Mission weight	4,100 kg (9,039 lb)
Max T-O and landing weight	4,309 kg (9,500 lb)
Max zero-fuel weight	3,660 kg (8,070 lb)
Max disc loading	25·6 kg/m² (5·25 lb/sq ft)
Max power loading	4·13 kg/kW (8·63 lb/shp)

PERFORMANCE (at max T-O weight):

Never-exceed speed	110 knots (204 km/h; 127 mph)
Max level and cruising speed	110 knots (204 km/h; 127 mph)
Econ cruising speed at 1,735 m (5,700 ft)	110 knots (204 km/h; 127 mph)
Max rate of climb at S/L	488 m (1,600 ft)/min
Service ceiling	3,840 m (12,600 ft)
Hovering ceiling IGE	4,145 m (13,600 ft)

Bell UH-1H Iroquois, with additional side view (bottom) of UH-1N *(Pilot Press)*

Hovering ceiling OGE	1,220 m (4,000 ft)
Range with max fuel, no allowances, no reserves, at S/L	276 nm (511 km; 318 miles)

BELL MODEL 205A-1

The Model 205A-1 is a fifteen-seat commercial utility helicopter developed from the UH-1H, with a 1,044 kW (1,400 shp) Avco Lycoming T5313B turboshaft engine, derated to 932 kW (1,250 shp) for take-off. It is designed for rapid conversion for alternative air freight, flying crane, ambulance, rescue and executive roles. Total cargo capacity is 7·02 m³ (248 cu ft) including baggage space in tailboom, with 2·34 m (7 ft 8 in) by 1·24 m (4 ft 1 in) door openings on each side of the cabin to facilitate loading of bulky freight. External load capacity in flying crane role is 2,268 kg (5,000 lb). The ambulance version can accommodate six litter patients and one or two medical attendants.

Normal fuel capacity is 814 litres (215 US gallons); optional capacity is 1,495 litres (395 US gallons).

The Model 205A-1 is produced under licence in Italy by Agusta (which see) as the AB 205A-1.

The description of the Bell UH-1H applies also to the Model 205A-1, except for the following details:
TYPE: Fifteen-seat commercial utility helicopter.
AVIONICS AND EQUIPMENT: Standard avionics comprise 360-channel VHF transceiver and intercom system. Extensive range of optional nav/com systems available. Standard equipment includes vertical gyro system, 5 in gyro attitude indicator, gyro compass, master caution panel, force trim hydraulic boost controls, twin windscreen wipers, soundproof headliner, cabin fire extinguisher, map case, passenger retractable boarding steps, engine fire extinguishing system and bleed air heating. Optional items include dual controls, customised interiors, high-output cabin heater, litter installations, auxiliary fuel tanks, rescue hoist, rotor brake, float landing gear, external cargo suspension, and protective covers.

DIMENSIONS, EXTERNAL:

Length of fuselage	12·65 m (41 ft 6 in)
Height overall	4·39 m (14 ft 4¾ in)

WEIGHTS:

Weight empty, equipped	2,414 kg (5,323 lb)
Normal T-O weight	4,309 kg (9,500 lb)
Max T-O weight, external load	4,763 kg (10,500 lb)

Bell UH-1H Iroquois general-purpose helicopter

PERFORMANCE (at normal T-O weight):
Max level speed from S/L to 915 m (3,000 ft)
110 knots (204 km/h; 127 mph)
Max cruising speed at S/L
110 knots (204 km/h; 127 mph)
Max cruising speed at 2,440 m (8,000 ft)
96 knots (179 km/h; 111 mph)
Max rate of climb at S/L   512 m (1,680 ft)/min
Max vertical rate of climb at S/L 259 m (850 ft)/min
Service ceiling   4,480 m (14,700 ft)
Hovering ceiling IGE   3,170 m (10,400 ft)
Hovering ceiling OGE   1,830 m (6,000 ft)
Range at S/L, at max cruising speed
270 nm (500 km; 311 miles)
Range at 2,440 m (8,000 ft) at max cruising speed, no
reserves   298 nm (553 km; 344 miles)

BELL MODEL 206B JETRANGER III

In the Summer of 1977, Bell began delivery of the Model 206B JetRanger III, which subsequently replaced in production the lower-powered JetRanger II, of which 1,619 were delivered.

Power plant of the JetRanger III is the Allison 250-C20B turboshaft, which Bell was able to install with minimal modification of the original airframe to meet requests for higher performance under hot-day/high-altitude conditions. This enables Bell to offer modification kits to convert JetRanger IIs to JetRanger III standard.

The uprated power plant increases power-limited airspeeds in high altitude/temperature conditions. For example, at 3,050 m (10,000 ft) ISA, airspeed increases by 5 knots (9 km/h; 6 mph). Greater improvements are achieved at above-standard temperatures. Hovering weights are increased by up to 91 kg (200 lb) at the same altitude, and hovering ceilings by as much as 610 m (2,000 ft) at higher altitudes and temperatures.

Under a succession of major contracts, Beech Aircraft has produced airframes for all the commercial and military versions of the JetRanger, the first airframe being delivered to Bell on 1 March 1968. The work involves manufacture of the fuselage, skid gear, tailboom, spars, stabiliser and two rear fairing assemblies.

By January 1980, Bell and its licensees had manufactured well over 6,000 helicopters of the Model 206 series, more than 2,300 of them for commercial customers.

TYPE: Turbine-powered general-purpose light helicopter.
ROTOR SYSTEM: Two-blade semi-rigid see-saw type main rotor, employing pre-coning and underslinging to ensure smooth operation. Blades are of standard Bell 'droop-snoot' section. They have a D-shape aluminium spar, bonded aluminium alloy skin, honeycomb core and a trailing-edge extension. Each blade is connected to the hub by means of a grip, pitch-change bearings and a tension-torsion strap assembly. Two tail rotor blades have bonded aluminium skin but no core. Main rotor blades do not fold, but modification to permit manual folding is possible. Rotor brake available as optional kit.
ROTOR DRIVE: Rotors driven through tubular steel alloy shafts with spliced couplings. Initial drive from engine through 90° spiral bevel gear to single-stage planetary main gearbox. Shaft to tail rotor single-stage bevel gearbox. Freewheeling unit ensures that main rotor continues to drive tail rotor when engine is disengaged. Main rotor/engine rpm ratio 1 : 15; main rotor rpm 374-394. Tail rotor/engine rpm ratio 1 : 2·3.
FUSELAGE: Forward cabin section is made up of two aluminium alloy beams and 25 mm (1 in) thick aluminium honeycomb sandwich. Rotor, transmission and engine are supported by upper longitudinal beams. Upper and lower structures are interconnected by three fuselage bulkheads and a centrepost to form an integrated structure. Intermediate section is of aluminium alloy semi-monocoque construction. Aluminium monocoque tailboom.

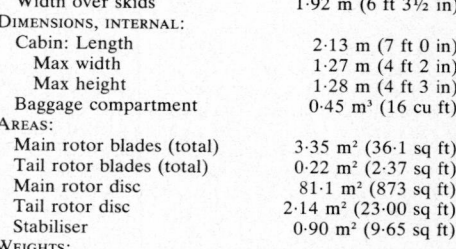

Bell 206B JetRanger III light utility helicopter (*Pilot Press*)

TAIL UNIT: Fixed stabiliser of aluminium monocoque construction, with inverted aerofoil section. Fixed vertical tail-fin in sweptback upper and ventral sections, made of aluminium honeycomb with aluminium alloy skin.
LANDING GEAR: Aluminium alloy tubular skids bolted to extruded cross-tubes. Tubular steel skid on ventral fin to protect tail rotor in tail-down landing. Special high skid gear (0·25 m; 10 in greater ground clearance) available for use in areas with high brush. Inflated bag-type pontoons or stowed floats, capable of in-flight inflation, available as optional kits.
POWER PLANT: One 313 kW (420 shp) Allison 250-C20B turboshaft engine. Fuel tank below and behind rear passenger seat, capacity 288 litres (76 US gallons). Refuelling point on starboard side of fuselage, aft of cabin. Oil capacity 5·2 litres (5·5 US quarts).
ACCOMMODATION: Two seats side by side in front and rear bench seat for three persons. Dual controls optional. Two forward-hinged doors on each side, made of formed aluminium alloy with transparent panels. Baggage compartment aft of rear seats, capacity 113 kg (250 lb), with external door on port side.
SYSTEMS: Hydraulic system, pressure 41·5 bars (600 lb/sq in), for cyclic, collective and directional controls. Electrical supply from 150A starter/generator. One 24V 13Ah nickel-cadmium battery.
AVIONICS AND EQUIPMENT: Full range of avionics available in form of optional kits, including VHF communications and omni navigation kit, Collins APS-841H autopilot, glideslope kit, ADF, DME, marker beacon, transponder and intercom and speaker system. Standard equipment includes cabin fire extinguisher, first aid kit, door locks, night lighting, and dynamic flapping restraints. Optional items include clock, engine hour meter, turn and slip indicator, stability and control augmentation system, custom seating, internal litter kit, cabin heater, camera access door, high-intensity night lights, engine fire detection and extinguishing system, engine oil vent, external cargo sling of 545 kg (1,200 lb) capacity, and fairing kit.
DIMENSIONS, EXTERNAL:
Diameter of main rotor   10·16 m (33 ft 4 in)
Main rotor blade chord   0·33 m (1 ft 1 in)
Distance between rotor centres 5·96 m (19 ft 6½ in)
Length overall, blades turning 11·82 m (38 ft 9½ in)
Length of fuselage   9·50 m (31 ft 2 in)
Height overall   2·91 m (9 ft 6½ in)
Stabiliser span   1·96 m (6 ft 5¼ in)

Width over skids   1·92 m (6 ft 3½ in)
DIMENSIONS, INTERNAL:
Cabin: Length   2·13 m (7 ft 0 in)
Max width   1·27 m (4 ft 2 in)
Max height   1·28 m (4 ft 3 in)
Baggage compartment   0·45 m³ (16 cu ft)
AREAS:
Main rotor blades (total)   3·35 m² (36·1 sq ft)
Tail rotor blades (total)   0·22 m² (2·37 sq ft)
Main rotor disc   81·1 m² (873 sq ft)
Tail rotor disc   2·14 m² (23·00 sq ft)
Stabiliser   0·90 m² (9·65 sq ft)
WEIGHTS:
Weight empty, equipped, incl oil and lubricants
732 kg (1,615 lb)
Max T-O weight   1,451 kg (3,200 lb)
PERFORMANCE (at max T-O weight, ISA):
Never-exceed speed at S/L
122 knots (225 km/h; 140 mph)
Max cruising speed at 1,525 m (5,000 ft)
116 knots (216 km/h; 134 mph)
Max cruising speed at S/L
115 knots (214 km/h; 133 mph)
Max rate of climb at S/L   384 m (1,260 ft)/min
Vertical rate of climb at S/L   91 m (300 ft)/min
Service ceiling   4,115 m (13,500 ft)
Hovering ceiling IGE   3,900 m (12,800 ft)
Hovering ceiling OGE   2,680 m (8,800 ft)
Range with max fuel and max payload at S/L, no
reserves   296 nm (549 km; 341 miles)
Range with max fuel and max payload at 1,525 m (5,000
ft), no reserves   328 nm (608 km; 378 miles)

BELL KIOWA

US Army designation: OH-58
Canadian military designation: CH-136

On 8 March 1968 the US Army named Bell as winner of its reopened light observation helicopter competition, and awarded the company the first increment of a total order for 2,200 **OH-58A** Kiowa aircraft, generally similar to the Model 206A and each powered by a 236·5 kW (317 shp) Allison T63-A-700 turboshaft engine. Major difference concerns the main rotor, that of the Kiowa having an increased diameter. There are also differences in the internal layout and avionics.

The first OH-58A was delivered to the US Army on 23 May 1969 and deployment in Viet-Nam began in the early Autumn of 1969.

Seventy-four similar COH-58As were delivered to the Canadian Armed Forces, and are now designated **CH-136**.

Under a co-production agreement with the Australian government 56 Model 206B-1 Kiowa military light observation helicopters (similar to the OH-58A) were delivered over an eight-year period. The initial 12 206B-1s were built by Bell. Commonwealth Aircraft Corporation was prime Australian licensee, with responsibility for final assembly of the remainder. Only the engines and avionics were supplied from US sources. Delivery of 12 **OH-58Bs** to the Austrian Air Force was completed in 1976.

Under a US Army development qualification contract placed on 30 June 1976, Bell converted an OH-58A to an improved standard, under the designation **OH-58C**. This involved installation of a flat glass canopy to reduce glint, an uprated Allison T63-A-720 turboshaft engine, and an IR reduction package. Two additional OH-58As were modified to OH-58C configuration, for pre-production flight testing by Bell and the US Army, and production modification of 275 OH-58As to OH-58C standard began in March 1978 at Bell Helicopter, Amarillo. The final configuration includes a new instrument panel, modifications to reduce vulnerability in combat, CONUS (Continental US) navigation equipment, day optics, improved avionics and improved maintenance features. The additional power significantly improves high-altitude, hot-weather performance.

Bell Model 206B JetRanger III light helicopter (Allison 250-C20B turboshaft engine)

A prototype mast-mounted sight, manufactured by Rockwell, was installed and flight tested on an OH-58C in 1979-80. The sight consists of a TV camera with automatic tracking, and a laser designator/rangefinder.

The following details apply specifically to the OH-58C:

TYPE: Turbine-powered light observation helicopter.

ROTOR SYSTEM: Two-blade semi-rigid see-saw type main rotor, employing pre-coning and underslinging to ensure smooth operation. Blades of standard Bell 'droop-snoot' section, with D-shape aluminium spar, bonded light alloy skin, honeycomb core and trailing-edge extension. Each blade is connected to the hub by means of a grip, pitch-change bearings and a tension-torsion strap assembly. The two tail rotor blades have bonded aluminium skin but no core. Main rotor blades do not fold, but modification to permit manual folding is possible. Rotor brake available as optional kit.

ROTOR DRIVE: Rotors driven through tubular steel alloy shafts with spliced couplings. Initial drive from engine through 90° spiral bevel gear to single-stage planetary main gearbox. On OH-58C, transmission improvements include a four-pinion planetary, with new thrust bearing and 'fly dry' capability. Shaft to tail rotor single-stage bevel gearbox protected by cover. Free-wheeling unit ensures that main rotor continues to drive tail rotor when engine is disengaged. Redundant tail rotor control for improved safety if primary system is disabled. Main rotor/engine rpm ratio 1 : 17·44; main rotor rpm 354. Tail rotor/engine rpm ratio 1 : 2·353.

FUSELAGE: Forward cabin section is made up of two aluminium alloy beams and 25 mm (1 in) thick aluminium honeycomb sandwich. Rotor, transmission and engine are supported by upper longitudinal beams. Upper and lower structures are interconnected by three fuselage bulkheads and a centrepost to form an integrated structure. Intermediate section is a light alloy semi-monocoque tailboom. A low-glare canopy design reduces the solar glint signature of the OH-58C. The windscreens are slightly convex to assist rain removal and increase their strength.

TAIL UNIT: Fixed stabiliser of aluminium monocoque construction, with inverted aerofoil section. Fixed vertical fin in sweptback upper and ventral sections, constructed of aluminium honeycomb with light alloy skins.

LANDING GEAR: Light alloy tubular skids bolted to extruded cross-tubes. Tubular steel skid on ventral fin to protect tail rotor in tail-down landing. Special high skid gear available, with 0·25 m (10 in) greater ground clearance, for use in areas with high brush. Inflated bag-type pontoons, or stowed floats capable of in-flight inflation, available as optional kits.

POWER PLANT: One 313 kW (420 shp) Allison T63-A-720 turboshaft engine. 'Black Hole' exhaust stacks and hot metal shroud for infra-red suppression. Fuel tank below and behind aft passenger seat, total usable capacity 276 litres (73 US gallons). Refuelling point on starboard side of fuselage, aft of cabin. Oil capacity 5·6 litres (1·5 US gallons).

ACCOMMODATION: Forward crew compartment seats pilot and co-pilot/observer side by side. Entrance to this compartment is provided by single door on each side of fuselage. The cargo/passenger compartment, which has its own doors, one on each side, provides approximately 1·13 m³ (40 cu ft) of cargo space, or provision for two passengers by installation of two seat cushions, seat belts and shoulder harnesses. A redesigned instrument panel on the OH-58C houses new avionics, and all flight instruments have been modified for night operations using night vision goggles. An improved defrost/defog air circulation system increases the aircraft's mission readiness.

SYSTEMS: Hydraulic system, pressure 41·5 bars (600 lb/sq in) for cyclic and collective controls. Electrical supply from 150A starter/generator. One 24V 13Ah nickel-cadmium battery.

AVIONICS: C-6533/ARC intercommunication subsystem, AN/ARC-114 VHF/FM, AN/ARC-115 VHF/AM, AN/ARC-116 UHF/AM, AN/ARN-89 ADF, AN/ASN-43 gyro magnetic compass, AN/APX-100 IFF transponder, TSEC/KY-28 communications security set, C-8157/ARC control indication, MT-3802/ARC mounting, TS-1843/APX transponder test set and mounting, KIT-1A/TSEC computer and mounting, duplicate AN/ARC-114, AN/APR-39 radar warning, ID-1351 C/A HBI, ID-1347 C/ARN CDI; and provisions for AN/ARN-123(V)1 CONUS nav, AN/APN-209 radar altimeter and YG-1054 proximity warning.

ARMAMENT: Standard equipment is the M-27 armament kit, utilising the 7·62 mm Minigun.

DIMENSIONS, EXTERNAL: As JetRanger III, except:
Diameter of main rotor   10·77 m (35 ft 4 in)
Length overall, blades turning
                                12·49 m (40 ft 11¾ in)
Length of fuselage   9·93 m (32 ft 7 in)

AREAS: As JetRanger III, except:
Main rotor blades (total)   3·55 m² (38·26 sq ft)
Main rotor disc   90·93 m² (978·8 sq ft)

WEIGHTS AND LOADINGS (A: OH-58A; C: OH-58C):
Weight empty: A   664 kg (1,464 lb)
              C   719 kg (1,585 lb)

Operating weight: A   1,049 kg (2,313 lb)
                  C   1,104 kg (2,434 lb)
Max T-O and landing weight: A   1,360 kg (3,000 lb)
                            C   1,451 kg (3,200 lb)
Max zero-fuel weight: A   1,145 kg (2,525 lb)
                      C   1,200 kg (2,646 lb)
Max disc loading: A   14·9 kg/m² (3·07 lb/sq ft)
                  C   15·9 kg/m² (3·27 lb/sq ft)

PERFORMANCE (OH-58A at observation mission gross weight of 1,255 kg; 2,768 lb, ISA, except where indicated):
Never-exceed speed at S/L
                    120 knots (222 km/h; 138 mph)
Cruising speed for max range
                    102 knots (188 km/h; 117 mph)
Loiter speed for max endurance
                    49 knots (90·5 km/h; 56 mph)
Max rate of climb at S/L   543 m (1,780 ft)/min
Service ceiling   5,760 m (18,900 ft)
Hovering ceiling IGE   4,145 m (13,600 ft)
Hovering ceiling OGE   2,682 m (8,800 ft)
Hovering ceiling OGE (armed scout mission at 1,360 kg; 3,000 lb)   1,828 m (6,000 ft)
Max range at S/L, 10% reserves
                    259 nm (481 km; 299 miles)
Max range at S/L, armed scout mission at 1,360 kg (3,000 lb), no reserves
                    264 nm (490 km; 305 miles)
Endurance at S/L, no reserves   3 h 30 min

BELL MODEL 206L-1 LONGRANGER II

Announced on 25 September 1973, Bell's LongRanger was intended to satisfy a requirement for a turbine-powered general-purpose light helicopter in a size and performance range between the five-seat JetRanger II and 15-seat Model 205A-1. The current LongRanger II, with more powerful engine and detail improvement, was certificated on 17 May 1978 and replaced the original model on the production line. It introduced a new version of the Allison 250 power plant, the 373 kW (500 shp) 250-C28B, which has a max continuous rating of 365 kW (489 shp), and includes in its design an integral particle separator. A new transmission is rated at 324 kW (435 shp) for take-off, its continuous rating remaining unchanged at 276 kW (370 shp). Main rotor rpm is 394. Fuel capacity remains the same, at 371 litres (98 US gallons). Production rate was increased to 170 a year in 1979, and deliveries were expected to total more than 600 by the end of 1980.

The LongRanger II incorporates Bell's Noda-Matic cabin suspension system, which gives a substantial reduction in rotor-induced vibration and results in a standard of comfort comparable with that of turboprop-powered fixed-wing aircraft.

With a cabin volume of 2·35 m³ (83 cu ft), compared with the 1·39 m³ (49 cu ft) of the JetRanger II, utility is enhanced by innovations that allow the maximum use of this space. For example, the port forward passenger seat has a folding back to allow loading of a container measuring 2·44 × 0·91 × 0·30 m (8 × 3 × 1 ft), making possible the carriage of such items as survey equipment, skis, and long components that cannot be accommodated in any other light helicopter. Double doors on the port side of the cabin provide an opening 1·52 m (5 ft 0 in) in width, for easy straight-in loading of litter patients or utility cargo; in an ambulance or rescue role two litter patients and two ambulatory patients/attendants may be carried. With a crew of two, the standard cabin layout accommodates five passengers in two canted aft-facing seats and three forward-facing seats. An optional executive cabin layout has four individual passenger seats.

Detail improvements introduced in the LongRanger II include a redesigned aft cabin to provide 0·05 m (2 in) more headroom for passengers in aft cabin seats; new cowlings, firewall, engine mountings, and engine deck area structure; new freewheeling unit, input shaft, forward tail rotor drive shaft, and increased diameter tail rotor; new engine oil system, oil tank, cooler, and transition duct;

Bell Model 206L-M LongRanger II equipped with experimental four-blade soft-in-plane glassfibre rotor

deletion of the water/alcohol system required formerly; and increased capacity 17Ah battery. Optional kits include emergency flotation gear, a 907 kg (2,000 lb) cargo hook, and an engine bleed air environmental control system. FAA certification was gained in December 1978 for the LongRanger II equipped with a Collins AP-107H autopilot, this providing single-pilot IFR capability. The Collins APS-841H autopilot is also available, featuring automatic heading, altitude, navigation, approach, and basic stabilisation modes of operation. A special turbulence mode improves response to handle rough air.

A LongRanger designated Model 206L-M was used in 1978 as testbed for Bell's experimental four-blade soft-in-plane rotor. A production rotor of this type is fitted to the new Bell Model 412 (which see).

DIMENSIONS, EXTERNAL:
Diameter of main rotor   11·28 m (37 ft 0 in)
Diameter of tail rotor   1·65 m (5 ft 5 in)
Length overall   12·46 m (40 ft 10½ in)
WEIGHTS:
Weight empty, standard configuration
                                978 kg (2,156 lb)
Max T-O weight   1,882 kg (4,150 lb)
PERFORMANCE (ISA at T-O weight of 1,837 kg; 4,050 lb):
Max level speed at S/L
                    130 knots (241 km/h; 150 mph)
Max cruising speed at 1,525 m (5,000 ft)
                    116 knots (215 km/h; 134 mph)
Max rate of climb at S/L   463 m (1,520 ft)/min
Service ceiling at max cruise power
                                5,945 m (19,500 ft)
Hovering ceiling IGE   4,025 m (13,200 ft)
Hovering ceiling OGE   2,470 m (8,100 ft)
Range at S/L, no reserves 297 nm (550 km; 342 miles)
Range at 1,525 m (5,000 ft), no reserves
                    335 nm (621 km; 386 miles)

BELL MODEL 209 HUEYCOBRA and SEACOBRA

US Army designations: AH-1G, AH-1Q and AH-1R
US Navy/Marine Corps designations: AH-1J and AH-1T
Spanish Navy designation: Z.14

Bell Helicopter Textron initiated the Model 209 in March 1965 as a company-funded development of the UH-1B/C Iroquois intended specifically for armed helicopter missions. The original design combined the basic transmission and rotor system and (in its standard form) the power plant of the UH-1C with a new, stream-lined fuselage designed for maximum speed, armament load and crew efficiency. Relatively small, its low silhouette and narrow profile make it easy to conceal with small camouflage nets or to move under cover of trees. Tandem seating provides the best possible field of view for the crew of two.

The Model 209 prototype made its first flight on 7 September 1965, and was sent to Edwards AFB in December 1965 for US Army evaluation. The Army's intention to order the aircraft was announced on 11 March 1966, the initial model being known as the AH-1G HueyCobra. Total orders to date exceed 1,800.

Versions announced so far are as follows:

AH-1G HueyCobra. Original version for US Army, powered by a single 1,044 kW (1,400 shp) Avco Lycoming T53-L-13 turboshaft engine, derated to 820 kW (1,100 shp) for T-O and max continuous rating. Development contract for two pre-production aircraft placed on 4 April 1966, followed on 13 April by an initial order for 110 aircraft plus long-lead-time spares. Subsequent contracts raised the total US Army order to 1,078 by mid-1971. Deliveries began in June 1967, and two months later the AH-1G was deployed operationally in Viet-Nam; it played a particularly important part in the Tet offensive in 1968, and in Laos in the Spring of 1971. The US Marine Corps acquired 38 AH-1Gs during 1969, for transition training and initial deployment pending deliveries of the AH-1J; these are included in the above total. The Spanish

Navy received 20, for anti-shipping strike duties, and six were supplied to Israel in 1974. A number of AH-1Gs have been converted to **TH-1G** dual-control trainers. Following the decision to equip the HueyCobra with TOW missiles, 93 AH-1Gs were converted to interim AH-1Q standard; all of these have been updated further to Mod AH-1S standard. One AH-1G was converted to **JAH-1G** as a testbed aircraft, initially for the Hellfire laser-guided air-launched missile. More recent tests with this aircraft have included demonstrations of a General Electric M-197 three-barrel 20 mm gun with an improved rate of fire of 1,500 rds/min. An increase to 3,000 rds/min is possible with this gun, and GE is also developing fast-firing 25 mm and 30 mm weapons for helicopter applications, with the emphasis on air-to-air anti-helicopter combat.

AH-1J SeaCobra. Initial twin-turboshaft version for US Marine Corps, powered by a 1,342 kW (1,800 shp) Pratt & Whitney Aircraft of Canada T400-CP-400 coupled free-turbine turboshaft engine, a military version of the PT6T-3 Turbo Twin Pac. Engine and transmission flat rated at 820 kW (1,100 shp) continuous output, with increase to 932 kW (1,250 shp) available for T-O or 5 min emergency power. Following an initial US Marine Corps order for 49, placed in May 1968, a pre-production example was displayed to representatives of the US armed forces at Enless, Texas, on 14 October 1969. Deliveries of these 49 began in mid-1970 and were completed in 1971; a further 20, ordered in early 1973, were delivered between April 1974 and February 1975. The last two of this batch were converted later as prototypes for the AH-1T. Under a $38.5 million contract announced on 22 December 1972, 202 TOW-capable AH-1Js were supplied to the Imperial Iranian Army Aviation from 1974, the US Army acting as purchasing agent.

AH-1Q HueyCobra. Interim anti-armour version for US Army, converted from AH-1G to fire Hughes TOW anti-tank missiles. First of eight 'pre-production' examples delivered in early 1973; first 'production' deliveries on 10 June 1975. Total of 93 converted; subsequently upgraded to Mod AH-1S standard.

AH-1R HueyCobra. As AH-1G, but with 1,342 kW (1,800 shp) T53-L-703 turboshaft engine. No TOW missile installation.

AH-1S HueyCobra. Advanced and modernised TOW-capable version for US Army; described separately.

AH-1T Improved SeaCobra. Improved version of twin-engined AH-1J for US Marine Corps. Last two of 69 AH-1Js modified as prototypes under a US Army Aviation Systems Command contract, with uprated components for significantly increased payload and performance. Incorporates features of AH-1J airframe, but embodies dynamic system of Bell Model 214, some technology developed for Bell Model 309 Kingcobra, and upgraded power plant (1,529 kW; 2,050 shp T400-WV-402) and transmission. Lengthened fuselage. Initial contract for 10 announced in June 1975; total of 57 ordered by 1979, of which 23 are scheduled to be modified to TOW configuration. First AH-1T (USN serial number 59228) delivered to US Marine Corps on 15 October 1977.

Under US Navy contract, Hughes is adapting its Black Hole infra-red suppression system (developed for the YAH-64) for interchangeable use on the AH-1J and AH-1T.

The following description applies primarily to the AH-1G and AH-1Q, except where indicated otherwise:
TYPE: Single-engined (AH-1G/Q/R/S) and twin-engined (AH-1J/T) close support and attack helicopters.
ROTOR SYSTEM AND DRIVE (AH-1G/J/Q/R): Model 540 two-blade wide-chord 'door-hinge' main rotor, similar to that of UH-1C. Interchangeable blades, built up of extruded aluminium spars and laminates. Rotor brake fitted. Blades do not fold. Two-blade all-metal flex-beam tractor tail rotor on starboard side, of honeycomb construction; blade chord increased on AH-1J, which also has push/pull tail rotor controls. Shaft drive to both main and tail rotors. Main rotor rpm 294-324.
ROTOR SYSTEM AND DRIVE (AH-1T): Similar to that of Bell Model 214, with strengthened main rotor hub incorporating Lord Kinematics Lastoflex elastomeric and

Bell AH-1S HueyCobra with flat plate canopy and missile launchers

Teflon-faced bearings. Main rotor blades have increased chord, and swept tips which reduce noise and improve high-speed performance. Tail rotor also similar to that of Model 214, with increased diameter and blade chord.
WINGS: Small mid-mounted stub-wings, to carry armament and offload rotor in flight.
FUSELAGE: Conventional all-metal semi-monocoque structure, with low silhouette and narrow profile. AH-1T has forward fuselage lengthened by insertion of a 0·305 m (1 ft 0 in) plug, to accommodate tankage for additional 181·5 kg (400 lb) of fuel, and tailboom lengthened by 0·79 m (2 ft 7 in).
TAIL UNIT: Sweptback vertical fin/tail rotor pylon, strengthened on twin-engined models to cater for increased power. Elevator, of inverted aerofoil section, mid-mounted on tailboom forward of fin.
LANDING GEAR: Non-retractable tubular skid type. Ground handling wheels optional.
POWER PLANT: Single or twin turboshaft engines, as detailed under model listings. Fuel capacity (G and J) 1,014 litres (268 US gallons). (Fuel loads, where known, are given under 'Weights' heading.) Refuelling point in port side of fuselage, aft of cockpits.
ACCOMMODATION: Crew of two in tandem, with co-pilot/gunner in front seat and pilot at rear. Crew are protected by seats and side panels of Norton Co 'Noroc' armour; other panels protect vital areas of aircraft.
SYSTEMS: Hydraulic system, with Abex pumps, for flight controls and other services. Battery-powered 28V DC electrical system. Environmental control and fire detection systems.
AVIONICS: Communications equipment in AH-1G includes AN/ARC-54/131 FM radio; AN/ARC-51 and AN/ARC-134 voice com; KY-28 secure voice system.
ARMAMENT AND OPERATIONAL EQUIPMENT (AH-1G): Initial production AH-1Gs were fitted with GAU-2B/A 7·62 mm Minigun in Emerson Electric TAT-102A undernose turret (see 1978-79 Jane's). This was superseded by an M-28 turret, able to mount either two Miniguns (each with 4,000 rds), or two M-129 40 mm grenade launchers (each with 300 rds), or one Minigun and one M-129. The Miniguns in these turrets have two rates of fire, controlled by the gunner's trigger: 1,600 rds/min for searching or registry fire, or 4,000 rds/min for attack. The M-129 fires at a single rate of 400 rds/min. Four external stores attachments under stub-wings can accommodate seventy-six 2·75 in rockets in four M-159 launchers, 28 similar rockets in four M-157 launchers, or two M-18E1 Minigun pods. An initial batch of six AH-1Gs were delivered to the US Army in December 1969 equipped with a Bell/General Electric M-35 armament subsystem. This unit consists of an M-61 six-barrel 20 mm automatic cannon on the port inboard wing station, having a firing rate of 750 rds/min. Two ammunition boxes faired flush to the fuselage below the stub-wings each accommodate 500 rds, and total installed weight of the system is 531 kg (1,172 lb). A total of 350 M-35 kits was ordered subsequently by the US Army. All wing stores are symmetrically or

totally jettisonable. In normal operation, the co-pilot/gunner controls and fires the turret armament, and the pilot (aided by an M-73 adjustable reflex rocket sight) normally fires the wing stores. The pilot can fire the turreted weapons only in the stowed (ie, dead ahead) position; the turret returns to the stowed position automatically when the gunner releases his grip on the slewing switch. The gunner also has the capability to fire the wing stores if required. Other operational equipment on the AH-1G includes an M-130 chaff dispenser.
ARMAMENT (AH-1J): Electrically operated General Electric undernose turret, housing an M-197 three-barrel 20 mm weapon (a lightweight version of the M-61 cannon). A 750-rd ammunition container is located in the fuselage directly aft of the turret; firing rate is 750 rds/min, but a 16-round burst limiter is incorporated in the firing switch. Barrel length of 1·52 m (5 ft) makes it imperative that the M-197 is centralised before wing stores are fired. Gun can be tracked 110° to each side, 18° upward, and 50° downward. Four attachments under stub-wings for various loads, including LAU-68A/A (seven-tube) or LAU-61A/A (19-tube) 2·75 in rocket launchers, or M-18E1 Minigun pods. Total possible armament load 245 kg (542 lb) internal, 998 kg (2,200 lb) external.
ARMAMENT (AH-1Q): M-28 turreted weapons as for AH-1G. Anti-armour configuration involves installation of eight Hughes TOW missile containers, disposed as two two-round pods on each of the outboard underwing stations. The inboard wing stations remain available for other stores, as listed for AH-1G. In the TOW configuration, a Sperry Univac helmet sight is used by both crew members to cue the turreted weapon or the TOW stabilised sight. In addition, the co-pilot/gunner may use the 2x or 13x magnification offered by the M-65 TOW system's telescopic sight unit for turret weapon engagements.

DIMENSIONS, EXTERNAL:
Diameter of main rotor: G, J, Q, R	13·41 m (44 ft 0 in)
T	14·63 m (48 ft 0 in)
Main rotor blade chord: G, J, Q, R	0·69 m (2 ft 3 in)
T	0·84 m (2 ft 9 in)
Diameter of tail rotor: G, J, Q, R	2·59 m (8 ft 6 in)
T	2·96 m (9 ft 8½ in)
Tail rotor blade chord: G, Q, R	0·21 m (8·4 in)
J	0·29 m (11½ in)
T	0·305 m (1 ft 0 in)
Wing span (all)	3·15 m (10 ft 4 in)
Length overall, main rotor fore and aft:	
G, Q, R	16·14 m (52 ft 11½ in)
J	16·26 m (53 ft 4 in)
T	17·68 m (58 ft 0 in)
Length of fuselage: G, J, Q, R	13·59 m (44 ft 7 in)
T	14·68 m (48 ft 2 in)
Width of fuselage: G, Q, R	0·965 m (3 ft 2 in)
J, T	0·98 m (3 ft 2½ in)
Height overall: G, Q, R	4·12 m (13 ft 6¼ in)
J	4·15 m (13 ft 8 in)
Elevator span (all)	2·11 m (6 ft 11 in)
Width over skids (all)	2·13 m (7 ft 0 in)
Width over TOW missile pods:	
G, Q	3·26 m (10 ft 8¾ in)

AREAS:
Main rotor disc: G, J, Q, R	141·26 m² (1,520·53 sq ft)
T	168·11 m² (1,809·56 sq ft)
Tail rotor disc: G, J, Q, R	5·27 m² (56·75 sq ft)
T	6·88 m² (74·03 sq ft)

WEIGHTS:
Operating weight empty, incl amounts shown for crew, fluids, avionics and armour:	
G (404 kg; 891 lb)	2,754 kg (6,073 lb)
J (398 kg; 877 lb)	3,294 kg (7,261 lb)
Weight empty: T	3,635 kg (8,014 lb)
Operating weight empty: T	3,904 kg (8,608 lb)
Mission fuel load:	
G (871 litres; 230 US gallons)	680 kg (1,500 lb)
J	725 kg (1,600 lb)
Max useful load (fuel and disposable ordnance):	
J	1,144 kg (2,523 lb)
T	2,445 kg (5,392 lb)

Bell AH-1T improved version of the Model 209 SeaCobra for the US Marine Corps

Mission weight: G   4,266 kg (9,407 lb)
J   4,523 kg (9,972 lb)
Max T-O and landing weight:
G, Q, R   4,309 kg (9,500 lb)
J   4,535 kg (10,000 lb)
T   6,350 kg (14,000 lb)
PERFORMANCE (at max T-O weight, ISA):
Never-exceed speed:
G, Q, R   190 knots (352 km/h; 219 mph)
J   180 knots (333 km/h; 207 mph)
Max level speed: G, Q 149 knots (277 km/h; 172 mph)
J   180 knots (333 km/h; 207 mph)
Max crosswind speed for hovering:
J   40 knots (74 km/h; 46 mph)
Max rate of climb at S/L, normal rated power:
G, Q   375 m (1,230 ft)/min
J   332 m (1,090 ft)/min
Service ceiling, normal rated power:
G, Q   3,475 m (11,400 ft)
J   3,215 m (10,550 ft)
Hovering ceiling IGE: G, Q 3,015 m (9,900 ft)
J   3,794 m (12,450 ft)
Range with max fuel:
G, Q, both at S/L, 8% reserves
                 310 nm (574 km; 357 miles)
J, no reserves   311 nm (577 km; 359 miles)

BELL MODEL 209 HUEYCOBRA (MODERNISED VERSION)

US Army designation: AH-1S

The AH-1S is an advanced version of the single-engined TOW-capable HueyCobra for the US Army, with upgraded power plant, gearbox, transmission and many other improvements. Current Army planning calls for the acquisition of 690 of this model by mid-1981, and the supply of an undisclosed number to Israel has been authorised. Two are being delivered to Japan in 1979-80, and will be evaluated by the JGSDF for potential large-scale procurement.

The first of a succession of US Army contracts was placed in 1975, and orders to the beginning of 1979 were as follows:

Mod AH-1S. This designation (the 'Mod' in this case indicating 'Modified') applies to 290 AH-1Gs already brought up to 'Production AH-1S' standard and redelivered to the US Army. These include the 93 AH-1Gs previously converted to AH-1Qs, which were further modified by Bell and Dornier to Mod AH-1S.

Production AH-1S. Under Step 1 of a three-step new-production programme, 100 Production AH-1S HueyCobras were built and delivered to the US Army between March 1977 and September 1978. These aircraft have a new flat-plate canopy, improved nap-of-the-earth (NOE) instrument panel layout, continental United States (CONUS) navigation equipment, radar altimeter, improved communication radios, uprated engine and transmission, push/pull anti-torque controls, and (from the 67th aircraft onwards) new Kaman-developed composite rotor blades. First unit to receive this version, in August 1977, was the 82nd Airborne Division at Fort Bragg, North Carolina.

Up-gun AH-1S. The next 98 new-production aircraft (Step 2) have all the improvements detailed for the Production AH-1S, plus a new universal 20/30 mm gun turret, an improved wing stores management system for the 2·75 in rockets, automatic compensation for off-axis gun firing, and a 10kVA alternator to provide the necessary additional electric power. Deliveries of this version began in September 1978 and were completed in October 1979.

Modernised AH-1S. This version, not to be confused with the 'Mod AH-1S' referred to earlier, represents the fully-upgraded AH-1S, and became standard from the 199th new-production aircraft. To the improvements already mentioned for the two preceding stages are being added, as Step 3, a new fire control subsystem (comprising a laser rangefinder and tracker, ballistics computer, low-airspeed sensor, and pilot's head-up display), air data system, Doppler navigation system, IFF transponder, infra-red jammer, hot-metal and plume infra-red suppressor, closed-circuit refuelling, and new secure voice communications. Deliveries of the 99 Modernised AH-1S so far ordered are taking place between November 1979 and June 1981.

Under a $13 million contract awarded by the US Army Missile Command, Hughes Aircraft Company began the manufacture of 44 Laser Augmented Airborne TOW (LAAT) stabilised sights for installation in Modernised AH-1S aircraft. The very small (13 × 13 × 4 cm; 5 × 5 × 1·5 in) laser transmitter has been developed to fit within the existing turret of the AH-1S; initial delivery of production sights was scheduled for July 1980.

Three engineering development models of the LAAT were used for flight testing by Bell at Yuma Proving Grounds, Arizona. They demonstrated that the LAAT can significantly improve first-burst accuracy of gun and rocket fire. In use, the gunner sights a target and fires the laser. Reflected from the target, the returning beam provides accurate and almost instantaneous range information, enabling the aircraft's fire control computer to integrate range, wind and ammunition ballistics data to direct weapon firing with great accuracy.

Bell Modernised AH-1S HueyCobra, fitted with the advanced rotor system designed for the Model 412

The US Army hopes eventually to bring all of its AH-1S HueyCobras up to the full Modernised AH-1S standard over a period of about five years. Current plans envisage, first, the conversion of a further 372 AH-1Gs to Modernised AH-1S in 1979-82; the 290 'Mod AH-1S' aircraft would then be upgraded to Modernised AH-1S in 1982-83; and finally, the 100 Step 1 aircraft (in 1983-84) and 98 Step 2 aircraft (in 1984) would be brought up to the full Step 3 standard. The US National Guard is to receive 12 Modernised AH-1S from April 1981, under a US Army contract announced in July 1980.

One Modernised AH-1S was tested in 1979-80 with the standard two-blade rotor replaced by a four-blade advanced rotor of the kind used on the Bell Model 412 transport helicopter. It had achieved speeds of up to 170 knots (315 km/h; 195 mph) by February 1980.

The major differences between the standard AH-1S and earlier single-engined HueyCobras may be summarised as follows:

TYPE: Anti-armour attack helicopter.

ROTOR SYSTEM AND DRIVE: Upgraded gearbox and transmission, the latter rated at 962 kW (1,290 shp). From 67th new-production AH-1S onward, new main rotor blades of composite construction are fitted, developed by Kaman Aerospace Corporation and equipped with tungsten carbide bearing sleeves. The outer 15% of these blades, which are tolerant of damage by weapons of up to 23 mm calibre, is tapered in both chord and thickness.

FUSELAGE: Tailboom strengthened to increase survivability against weapons of up to 23 mm calibre. Entire airframe has an anti-infra-red paint finish.

POWER PLANT: One 1,342 kW (1,800 shp) Avco Lycoming T53-L-703 turboshaft engine. Closed-circuit refuelling on Modernised AH-1S.

ACCOMMODATION: New flat-plate canopy has seven planes of viewing surfaces, designed to minimise glint and reduce possibility of visual detection during nap-of-the-earth (NOE) flying; it also provides increased headroom for pilot. Improved instrument layout and lighting, compatible with use of night vision goggles. Improved, independently-operating window/door ballistic jettison system to facilitate crew escape in emergency.

SYSTEMS: 10kVA AC alternator added to electrical system. Battery-driven Abex standby pump, for use in event of main hydraulic system failure, can be used for collective pitch control and for boresighting turret and TOW missile system. Improved environmental control and fire detection systems.

AVIONICS AND EQUIPMENT: Standard lightweight avionics equipment (SLAE) includes AN/ARC-114 FM, AN/ARC-164 UHF/AM voice com, and E-Systems (Memcor Division) AN/ARC-115 VHF/AM voice com (compatible with KY-58 single-channel secure voice system). Other avionics include AN/ARN-123 CONUS navigation system with VOR/ILS receivers, glideslope, marker beacon and indicator lights (Doppler navigation system in Modernised AH-1S); HSI; VSI; radar altimeter; push/pull anti-torque controls for tail rotor; co-pilot's standby magnetic compass.

ARMAMENT AND OPERATIONAL EQUIPMENT: M-65 system with eight TOW missiles on outboard underwing stations, as in AH-1Q. Beginning with the 101st new-production AH-1S (the first 'Up-gun' example), the M-28 (7·62/40 mm) turret in earlier HueyCobras is replaced by a new electrically-powered General Electric universal turret, designed to accommodate either a 20 mm or a 30 mm weapon and to improve stand-off capability. Initially, the 20 mm M-197 three-barrel Vulcan (with 750 rds) is mounted in this turret, with the 30 mm Hughes XM-230E1 single-barrel Chain Gun (with 500 rds) scheduled for installation in mid-1981. Rate of fire of both guns is 730 rds/min. Turret position is controlled by the pilot or co-pilot/gunner through helmet sights, or by the co-pilot using the M-65 TOW missile system's telescopic sight unit. Field of fire is up to 110° to each side of aircraft, 20·5° upward and 50° down-

ward. Also from the first 'Up-gun' AH-1S, the helicopter is equipped with a new Baldwin Electronics XM-138 wing stores management subsystem, providing the means to select and fire, singly or in groups, any one of five types of external 2·75 in rocket store. These are mounted in launchers each containing from 7 to 19 tubes, and are additional to the TOW missile capability. In addition to these installations the 199th new-built AH-1S (the first to full 'Modernised' standard) introduces a fire control subsystem which includes a Kaiser head-up display for the pilot, Teledyne Systems digital fire control computer for the turreted weapon and underwing rockets, omnidirectional airspeed system to improve cannon and rocket accuracy, Hughes laser rangefinder (accurate to 10,000 m; 32,800 ft), and AN/AAS-32 airborne laser tracker. Other operational equipment includes a Marconi Avionics air data subsystem, AN/APX-100 solid-state IFF transponder, Sanders AN/ALQ-144 infra-red jammer, suppressor for infra-red signature from engine hot metal and exhaust plume, AN/APR-39 radar warning receiver, AN/ALQ-136 radar jammer (with M-130 chaff system as backup), Perkin-Elmer laser warning receiver.

DIMENSIONS, EXTERNAL: As AH-1G except:
Main rotor blade chord (from 67th new-production
AH-1S)   0·76 m (2 ft 6 in)
Tail rotor blade chord   0·29 m (11½ in)
WEIGHTS:
Operating weight empty   2,939 kg (6,479 lb)
Mission weight   4,524 kg (9,975 lb)
Max T-O and landing weight   4,535 kg (10,000 lb)
PERFORMANCE (at max T-O weight, ISA):
Never-exceed speed (TOW configuration)
                 170 knots (315 km/h; 195 mph)
Max level speed (TOW configuration)
                 123 knots (227 km/h; 141 mph)
Max rate of climb at S/L, normal rated power
                 494 m (1,620 ft)/min
Service ceiling, normal rated power 3,720 m (12,200 ft)
Hovering ceiling IGE   3,720 m (12,200 ft)
Range at S/L with max fuel, 8% reserves
                 274 nm (507 km; 315 miles)

BELL MODEL 212 TWIN TWO-TWELVE

US military designation: UH-1N
Canadian military designation: CH-135

Bell announced on 1 May 1968 that the Canadian government had approved development of a twin-engined UH-1 helicopter to be powered by a Pratt & Whitney Aircraft of Canada PT6T power plant. Subsequently, the Canadian government ordered 50 of these aircraft (designated CUH-1N) for the Canadian Armed Forces, with options on 20 more. Simultaneously, orders totalling 141 aircraft for the US services were announced, comprising 79 for the US Air Force, 40 for the US Navy and 22 for the US Marine Corps, all having the designation **UH-1N**. Subsequent orders covered the delivery of 159 more UH-1Ns to the US Navy and Marine Corps in 1973-78.

Initial deliveries for the US Air Force began in 1970, and the first CUH-1N for the Canadian Armed Forces was handed over officially at Uplands Airport, Ottawa, on 3 May 1971; the Canadian order was completed one year later. Deliveries to the US Navy and US Marine Corps began during 1971. Canadian aircraft are now designated **CH-135**. Six were delivered to the air force of Bangladesh in early 1977, and the Argentinian Air Force ordered eight in 1978.

A commercial version, known as the Twin Two-Twelve, is also in full-scale production. This received FAA type certification in October 1970, and on 30 June 1971 the Twin Two-Twelve was granted FAA Transport Type Category A certification. The Model 212 has the capability of carrying an external load of 2,268 kg (5,000 lb), and the military UH-1N a load of 1,814 kg (4,000 lb).

Bell announced in January 1973 that two Twin Two-Twelves had been modified and flown in a programme to gain IFR certification from the UK's CAA and America's FAA. Conversion of the Model 212 from VFR to IFR

Bell UH-1N of Antarctic Development Squadron Six (VXE-6), US Navy

Bell Model 212 twin-turbine helicopter for the People's Republic of China

configuration requires a new avionics package, new instrument panel and aircraft stabilisation controls. The Model 212 has also qualified for IFR certification by the Norwegian DCA and the Canadian DoT. In June 1977, it became the first helicopter FAA-certificated for single-pilot IFR operations with fixed floats.

An order for eight Model 212s, to support energy and natural resources development in China, was received in early 1979, and all were delivered by the end of the year. Operated by the Civil Air Authority of China (CAAC), they represent the first order received from the People's Republic of China by a US helicopter manufacturer.

ROTOR SYSTEM: Two-blade all-metal semi-rigid main rotor with interchangeable blades, built up of extruded aluminium spars and laminates. Stabilising bar above and at right angles to main rotor blades. Underslung feathering axis hub. Two-blade all-metal tail rotor. Main rotor blades do not fold. Rotor brake standard.

ROTOR DRIVE: Shaft drive to both main and tail rotors.

FUSELAGE: Conventional all-metal semi-monocoque structure.

TAIL SURFACE: Small fixed stabiliser on rear fuselage.

LANDING GEAR: Tubular skid type. Lock-on ground handling wheels, fixed floats and inflatable nylon float-bags optional.

POWER PLANT: Pratt & Whitney Aircraft of Canada PT6T-3 Turbo Twin Pac, comprising two PT6 turboshaft engines coupled to a combining gearbox with a single output shaft. Producing 1,342 kW (1,800 shp), the Twin Pac is flat rated to 962 kW (1,290 shp) for T-O and 842 kW (1,130 shp) for continuous operation. In the event of an engine failure, the remaining engine can deliver 671 kW (900 shp) for 30 minutes or 596 kW (800 shp) continuously. Five interconnected rubber fuel cells, total capacity 814 litres (215 US gallons). Auxiliary fuel tanks optional, to provide a max total capacity of 1,495 litres (395 US gallons). Single-point refuelling on starboard side of cabin.

ACCOMMODATION: Pilot and up to 14 passengers. In cargo configuration there is a total internal volume of 7·02 m³ (248 cu ft), including baggage space in tailboom. Forward door on each side of fuselage, opening forward. Two doors on each side of cabin; forward door hinged to open forward, rear door sliding aft. Accommodation heated and ventilated. Garrett-AiResearch air-cycle environmental control unit available optionally.

SYSTEMS: Dual hydraulic systems. 28V DC electrical system supplied by two completely independent 30V 200A starter/generators. Secondary AC power supplied by two completely independent 250VA single-phase solid-state inverters. A third inverter can acquire automatically the load of a failed inverter.

AVIONICS AND EQUIPMENT: Optional IFR avionics include dual King KTR 900A com transceivers; dual King KNR 660A VOR/LOC/RMI receivers; King KDF 800 ADF; King KMD 700A DME; King KXP 750A transponder; King KGM 690 marker beacon/glideslope receiver; dual Sperry Tarsyn-444 three-axis gyro units; stability control augmentation system; and an automatic flight control system. Optional equipment includes a cargo sling, rescue hoist, emergency pop-out flotation gear and high skid gear.

DIMENSIONS, EXTERNAL:
Diameter of main rotor (with tracking tips)
14·69 m (48 ft 2¼ in)
Diameter of tail rotor 2·59 m (8 ft 6 in)
Main rotor blade chord 0·59 m (1 ft 11¼ in)
Tail rotor blade chord 0·292 m (11½ in)
Length overall (main rotor fore and aft)
17·46 m (57 ft 3¼ in)
Length of fuselage 12·92 m (42 ft 4¾ in)
Height overall 4·53 m (14 ft 10¼ in)
Width overall (main rotor fore and aft)
2·86 m (9 ft 4½ in)
AREAS:
Main rotor disc 168·06 m² (1,809 sq ft)
Tail rotor disc 5·27 m² (56·74 sq ft)

WEIGHTS:
VFR empty weight plus usable oil
2,787 kg (6,143 lb)
Max T-O weight and mission weight
5,080 kg (11,200 lb)
PERFORMANCE (at max T-O weight):
Never-exceed speed at S/L
140 knots (259 km/h; 161 mph)
Max cruising speed at S/L
124 knots (230 km/h; 142 mph)
Max rate of climb at S/L 402 m (1,320 ft)/min
Service ceiling 4,330 m (14,200 ft)
Hovering ceiling IGE 3,350 m (11,000 ft)
Max range with standard fuel at S/L, no reserves
227 nm (420 km; 261 miles)

BELL MODEL 214B BIGLIFTER

Bell announced its intention to develop the Model 214B on 4 January 1974, claiming that it would have a lift capability better than that of any existing commercial helicopter in the medium category. FAA certification was received on 27 January 1976.

Powered by a 2,185 kW (2,930 shp) Avco Lycoming T5508D turboshaft engine, the 214B has the same rotor drive and transmission system as the military Model 214A that was exported to Iran (see Model 214ST entry). The engine is flat rated at a maximum of 1,678 kW (2,250 shp) and the transmission is rated at 1,529 kW (2,050 shp) for take-off, with a maximum continuous power output of 1,379·5 kW (1,850 shp). The main rotor has a Wortmann blade section, swept tips, and an advanced rotor hub with elastomeric bearings on the flapping axis. The tail rotor hub requires no lubrication. Other features include an automatic flight control system, with stability augmentation and attitude retention; nodalised suspension; separate dual hydraulic systems; and a large engine deck that serves also as a maintenance platform. Differences from the military Model 214A include the addition of an engine fire extinguishing system, push-out escape windows in the cargo doors, and commercial avionics.

The standard **Model 214B** can cruise at 140 knots (259 km/h; 161 mph) with an internal load of 1,814 kg (4,000 lb). A passenger configuration provides seats for 14 persons, in addition to the crew of two. It is able to carry external loads in excess of 3,175 kg (7,000 lb) on its cargo hook, which is certificated for a maximum of 3,629 kg (8,000 lb). In an agricultural role this allows nearly four US tons of chemicals to be lifted, or 3,025 litres (800 US gallons) of water or suppressant in a firefighting role.

The **Model 214B-1** differs only in having its max T-O weight for internal load-carrying limited to 5,670 kg (12,500 lb) to meet different certification standards.

A new main rotor blade developed for the Model 214B became the first glassfibre blade of US manufacture to receive FAA certification on 24 July 1978. Assembled as a two-blade rotor for this helicopter, it has a diameter of 15.24 m (50 ft 0 in) and chord of 0.84 m (2 ft 9 in). Testing had exceeded 400 flying hours at the date of certification, and initial FAA approval is for a retirement life of 2,400 h. Bell is confident that a retirement life of at least 10,000 h will be achieved when in-plant and service testing have been completed.

Production glassfibre blades are being delivered initially as replacements for conventional blades in service on Model 214Bs. When full-scale manufacture is established, they will become standard on all 214Bs coming off the assembly line.

Bell Model 214B BigLifter utility helicopter (Avco Lycoming T5508D turboshaft engine)

The production version of the blade has a spar consisting entirely of machine-made elements. An orbital machine winds the spar caps, which are of spanwise-orientated S₂ glass fibres that carry bending loads and centrifugal force. The fibres of these spar caps wrap around the sleeve of the attachment bolt to the hub, forming integral attachment lugs to the hub. Torsional loads in the spar are carried by layers of filament-wound crossply material located inside and outside the spanwise spar caps.

The blade skins consist of layers of non-woven crossply E-glass. A layer of woven cloth is applied to the outside of the skin to minimise foreign object damage, and the skins are supported by a Nomex non-metallic honeycomb core. The leading-edge of the blade is protected by a full-length titanium abrasion strip. The paint finish incorporates a semi-conductive graphite layer to aid the dissipation of static electricity.

Tests have shown that this method of blade construction does not dent as easily as metal. A fatigue crack usually will not grow from a small hole or puncture, and skin patches can be applied with less risk of subsequent cracking. Blades tested by the Lightning and Transient Research Institute of St Paul, Minnesota, were not damaged structurally by lightning strikes of 200,000 amperes, which is equivalent to the highest strikes recorded on aircraft. In ballistic tolerance tests, one blade virtually 'swallowed' a 23 mm high-explosive impact round rather than permitting it to exit.

DIMENSIONS, EXTERNAL:
Main rotor diameter	15·24 m (50 ft 0 in)
Main rotor blade chord	0·84 m (2 ft 9 in)
Tail rotor diameter	2·95 m (9 ft 8 in)
Tail rotor blade chord	0·305 m (1 ft 0 in)

WEIGHTS:
Max T-O weight:
internal loading, 214B	6,260 kg (13,800 lb)
internal loading, 214B-1	5,670 kg (12,500 lb)
external loading, 214B and 214B-1	
	7,257 kg (16,000 lb)

BELL MODEL 214ST

Bell Helicopters announced on 22 December 1972 the receipt of an order for 287 advanced **Model 214A** 16-seat utility helicopters, which were being acquired by Iran through the US government; an additional six examples were ordered in March 1977. The first Model 214A for Iran flew for the first time on 13 March 1974, and deliveries began on 26 April 1975. In February 1976, 39 generally similar **Model 214Cs** were ordered, with equipment for search and rescue duties.

The Model 214A, of which brief details can be found in the 1978-79 *Jane's*, was to have been the first product of the Iranian Helicopter Industry, in which the Iranian government and Bell Helicopter Textron were in partnership. As a result of changed national policy, Bell has withdrawn from this partnership, and is to continue by itself development and production of the improved **Model 214ST**, which was being developed specifically for major production and service in Iran. This aircraft was expected to serve initially as a military transport helicopter; but Bell will now develop the 214ST as a commercial transport with multi-mission capability. Originally, the suffix ST indicated Stretched Twin: Bell is retaining these initials to represent Super Transport.

The prototype 214ST built by Bell flew for the first time in February 1977, and construction of three pre-production examples began in 1978. Certification under FAR Pt 29 was scheduled for early 1980, and the decision to manufacture an initial series of 100 production 214STs was announced in November 1979. Deliveries are due to begin in early 1982, at a rate of three per month.

TYPE: Twin-turboshaft commercial transport helicopter.
ROTOR SYSTEM: Two-blade advanced technology main rotor. Each blade has a unidirectionally laid glassfibre spar, with a ±45°-wound torque casing of glassfibre cloth. The trailing-edge is also of unidirectional glassfibre, and the space between spar and trailing-edge is filled by a Nomex honeycomb core. The entire blade is then bonded together by glassfibre wrapping, with the leading-edge protected by a titanium abrasion strip and the tip by a replaceable stainless steel cap. Two-blade tail rotor; interchangeable blades, each with a stainless

Bell Model 214B medium-size commercial heavy-lift helicopter *(Pilot Press)*

steel leading-edge spar and covering, aluminium honeycomb core and glassfibre trailing-edge strip. Main rotor hub incorporates elastomeric bearings. Second-generation Noda-Matic nodal suspension system. Nodal beam requires no lubrication. Main rotor brake standard.

ROTOR DRIVE: Main transmission, which has a one-hour run-dry capability, has a maximum rating of 1,678 kW (2,250 shp), maximum continuous rating of 1,380 kW (1,850 shp), and single-engine rating of 1,212 kW (1,625 shp). Combining, intermediate and tail rotor gearboxes, each with one-hour run-dry capability.

FUSELAGE: Conventional all-metal semi-monocoque structure, incorporating roll-over protection ring.

TAIL SURFACE: Electronically-controlled elevator, which minimises trim changes with alterations of power and CG, and improves longitudinal stability.

LANDING GEAR: Energy-absorbing non-retractable tubular skid type.

POWER PLANT: Two 1,212 kW (1,625 shp) General Electric CT7-2 turboshaft engines, connected to a combining gearbox. In the event of an engine failure, the remaining engine is able to provide continued flight capability. Standard fuel capacity 1,560 litres (412 US gallons), contained in seven interconnected cells, arranged to provide two independent fuel systems as required by FAR Pt 29. Single-point refuelling. Auxiliary fuel system optional, consisting of two tanks in rear of cabin.

ACCOMMODATION: Standard seating for pilot, co-pilot and 16 passengers, with alternative layout for 17 passengers. Dual controls under development. Crew seats adjustable. All seats have lap belt and shoulder harness. Jettisonable crew door each side. Large cabin door on port side for passengers or easy loading of cargo. Three emergency exits on each side. Baggage space aft of cabin, capacity 1·84 m³ (65 cu ft). Passenger seating removable to provide 8·95 m³ (316 cu ft) of cargo capacity. Cabin heated and ventilated.

SYSTEMS: Dual engine-driven hydraulic pumps for fully redundant hydraulic system. Redundant electrical system with dual engine-driven generators. Stability and control augmentation system (SCAS). Attitude/altitude retention system (AARS). Automatic elevator trim system.

AVIONICS AND EQUIPMENT: Avionics to provide full IFR capability, radar, and VLF navigation system, are under development. Equipment under development includes emergency flotation gear, external cargo suspension system, and internal rescue hoist.

DIMENSIONS, EXTERNAL:
Diameter of main rotor	15·85 m (52 ft 0 in)
Diameter of tail rotor	2·95 m (9 ft 8 in)
Main rotor blade chord	0·84 m (2 ft 9 in)
Tail rotor blade chord	0·36 m (1 ft 2 in)
Length overall, rotors turning	18·95 m (62 ft 2¼ in)
Length of fuselage	15·24 m (50 ft 0 in)
Height overall	4·84 m (15 ft 10½ in)
Skid track	2·64 m (8 ft 8 in)

DIMENSIONS, INTERNAL:
Cabin: Length, instrument panel to centre rear bulkhead
head	3·42 m (11 ft 2¾ in)
Length, max	4·13 m (13 ft 6¾ in)
Max width	2·41 m (7 ft 11 in)
Volume	7·73 m³ (273 cu ft)

AREAS:
Main rotor disc	197·32 m² (2,124 sq ft)
Tail rotor disc	6·82 m² (73·39 sq ft)

WEIGHTS:
Max T-O weight:
internal load	7,030 kg (15,500 lb)
external load	7,484 kg (16,500 lb)

PERFORMANCE (at internal load max T-O weight, unless detailed otherwise):
Max cruising speed at S/L
	142 knots (264 km/h; 164 mph)

Max cruising speed at 1,220 m (4,000 ft)
	140 knots (259 km/h; 161 mph)

Long-range average cruising speed
	140 knots (259 km/h; 161 mph)
Service ceiling, one engine out	2,865 m (9,400 ft)
Hovering ceiling IGE	3,840 m (12,600 ft)
Hovering ceiling OGE	1,005 m (3,300 ft)

Range, ISA, VFR, standard fuel, no reserves
	451 nm (835 km; 519 miles)

Ferry range with auxiliary fuel, pilot only, no payload,
no reserves   over 600 nm (1,112 km; 691 miles)

BELL MODEL 222

In April 1974, Bell announced its intention of developing the Model 222, described as the first commercial light twin-engined helicopter to be built in the USA. Construction of five prototypes began on 1 September 1974 and the first of these flew for the first time on 13 August 1976. FAA certification for a Model 222 in pre-production configuration was received on 16 August 1979. The production model received approval for VFR operation on 20 December, and the first delivery, to Petroleum Helicopters Inc, was made on 16 January 1980. Orders exceeded 150 at that date. FAA certification for single-pilot IFR operations in Category I weather conditions was granted on 15 May 1980.

The general appearance of the Model 222 is shown in the accompanying illustration. It was designed to meet FAR Pt 29 Transport Category requirements, and before taking a development decision Bell displayed a full-scale concept mockup at the annual convention of the Helicopter Association of America, in San Diego, in January 1974. The response of potential operators encouraged the development go-ahead, and customer suggestions were embodied in the definitive Model 222 design. In particular, the lower glazing of the flight deck was revised to provide increased field of view for rooftop landings, and the cabin was both lengthened and widened at the rear to give more spacious accommodation in high-density passenger-carrying configuration.

Production aircraft are offered in three configurations, as follows:

Basic 222. Standard model, as described.

222 Executive. Fully equipped for both single and dual pilot IFR flight. Sperry coupled automatic flight control system to provide stability augmentation and automatic hold for attitude, altitude, heading and airspeed, plus VOR/LOC course and glideslope hold during approach. Collins Proline avionics include dual VHF com, dual VOR nav with glideslope, ADF, marker beacon, transponder, DME and area navigation. Luxury accommodation for five or six passengers, with automatic temperature control, fluorescent and reading lights, window curtains and ceiling speakers. Optional stereo system and refreshment cabinet.

222 Offshore. Equipped for dual pilot IFR operations over water, with emergency flotation system, auxiliary fuel tanks and Collins Microline avionics.

TYPE: Twin-turbine light commercial helicopter.
ROTOR SYSTEM: Two-blade main rotor. Blade section Wortmann 090. Thickness/chord ratio 8%. Each blade

Bell Model 214ST twin-turbine transport helicopter, scheduled for certification in 1980

comprises a stainless steel spar with bonded glassfibre safety straps to retard crack propagation and offer secondary load path; replaceable stainless steel leading-edge; and afterbody of Nomex honeycomb covered with glassfibre skin. Each blade is attached to the hub by two chordwise bolts. Small trim tab on each blade. Completely dry titanium main rotor hub has conical elastomeric bearings. Two-blade tail rotor of stainless steel construction, with preconing, underslung feathering axis and skewed flapping axis. Rotor blades do not fold. A rotor brake is standard.

ROTOR DRIVE: Rotors shaft driven through gearbox with two spiral bevel reductions and one planetary reduction. Main rotor/engine rpm ratio 1 : 27·4; tail rotor/engine rpm ratio 1 : 5·08.

SPONSONS: Short-span cantilever sponson set low on each side of fuselage, serving also as work platform. Section NACA 0035. Dihedral 3° 12'. Incidence 5°. Sweepback at quarter-chord 3° 30'. All-metal structure of light alloy sheet and honeycomb. No movable surfaces.

FUSELAGE: Semi-monocoque structure of light alloy, with limited use of light alloy honeycomb panels. Fail-safe structure in critical areas. One-piece nosecone tilts forward and down for access to avionics and equipment bay.

TAIL UNIT: Cantilever structure of light alloy. Fixed vertical fin in sweptback upper and lower sections. Tailplane, with slotted leading-edge and endplate fins, mounted midway along rear fuselage. Small skid below ventral fin for protection in tail-down landing.

LANDING GEAR: Hydraulically-retractable tricycle type. All units retract forward, main wheels into sponsons. Free-fall extension in emergency. Oleo-pneumatic shock-absorbers, with scissored yoke. Self-centering nosewheel, swivelling through 360°. Single wheel and tyre on each unit. Main-wheel tyres size 6·00-6, pressure 5·18 bars (75 lb/sq in). Nosewheel tyre size 5·00-5, pressure 4·14 bars (60 lb/sq in). Hydraulic disc brakes. New-type water-activated emergency 'pop-out' floats on Offshore version, which eliminate the need for tips on the sponsons and thus save 40 kg (88 lb) in installed weight.

POWER PLANT: Two Avco Lycoming LTS 101-650C-2 turboshaft engines, mounted in a streamlined housing above the cabin and aft of the rotor pylon. Each engine is rated at 503·3 kW (675 shp) max for 2½ min, 469·8 kW (630 shp) for 30 min and 440 kW (590 shp) max continuous; transmission rated at 633·8 kW (850 shp) from two engines or 503·3 kW (675 shp) from one engine. Bell focused pylon with nodalisation. Fuel contained in three crash-resistant internal bladders, in fuselage and sponsons, with total capacity of 715 litres (189 US gallons). Single-point refuelling on starboard side of fuselage. Oil capacity 3·2 litres (6·85 US quarts) per engine.

ACCOMMODATION: Pilot and seven passengers in standard 2-3-3 layout; alternatively pilot, co-pilot and six passengers. Two additional passengers can be accommodated in a high-density 2-2-3-3 arrangement. Energy-attenuating seats, all with shoulder harness. Crew door at forward end of cabin on each side; cabin door on each side immediately forward of wing. Space for 1·05 m³ (37 cu ft) of baggage aft of cabin, with external door on starboard side. Ventilation standard; air-conditioning and heating optional.

SYSTEMS: Dual hydraulic systems, pressure 103·5 bars (1,500 lb/sq in). Electrical system supplied by dual 150A DC generators. Dual 250VA AC inverters, and 13Ah nickel-cadmium storage battery.

AVIONICS AND EQUIPMENT: VHF radio and Sperry IFR equipment standard. Other avionics, blind-flying instrumentation and equipment, including Bendix RDR-1400 weather radar and 1,588 kg (3,500 lb) capacity cargo hook kit, to customer's requirements.

DIMENSIONS, EXTERNAL:
Diameter of main rotor 12·12 m (39 ft 9 in)
Diameter of tail rotor 1·98 m (6 ft 6 in)
Main rotor blade chord 0·73 m (2 ft 4·6 in)
Tail rotor blade chord 0·254 m (10 in)
Sponson chord at root 1·55 m (5 ft 1 in)
Sponson chord at tip 1·49 m (4 ft 10¾ in)
Length of fuselage 10·98 m (36 ft 0¼ in)
Width overall 3·18 m (10 ft 5 in)
Height overall 3·51 m (11 ft 6 in)
Wheel track 2·77 m (9 ft 1 in)
Wheelbase 3·70 m (12 ft 1¾ in)
Passenger doors (each): Height 1·30 m (4 ft 3 in)
Width 0·99 m (3 ft 3 in)
Height to sill 0·46 m (1 ft 6 in)
Baggage door (stbd, aft): Height 0·62 m (2 ft 0½ in)
Width 0·89 m (2 ft 11 in)
Height to sill 1·14 m (3 ft 9 in)

DIMENSIONS, INTERNAL:
Cabin (passenger area): Length 2·01 m (6 ft 7 in)
Max width 1·41 m (4 ft 7½ in)
Max height 1·30 m (4 ft 3 in)
Volume, incl crew area 5·52 m³ (195 cu ft)
Baggage hold 1·05 m³ (37 cu ft)
Hat box (aft of cabin seats) 0·14 m³ (5 cu ft)

AREAS:
Main rotor blades (each) 4·40 m² (47·37 sq ft)

Bell Model 222 eight/ten-seat twin-turbine light commercial helicopter (*Brian M. Service*)

Tail rotor blades (each) 0·21 m² (2·29 sq ft)
Main rotor disc 115·29 m² (1,241 sq ft)
Tail rotor disc 2·15 m² (23·18 sq ft)
Vertical tail surfaces (total) 1·72 m² (18·53 sq ft)
Horizontal tail surfaces (total) 1·37 m² (14·8 sq ft)

WEIGHTS AND LOADING:
Weight empty, equipped 2,190 kg (4,828 lb)
Max T-O and landing weight 3,560 kg (7,850 lb)
Max disc loading 30·9 kg/m² (6·33 lb/sq ft)

PERFORMANCE (at max T-O weight):
Never-exceed speed and max cruising speed:
below 2,330 m (7,650 ft)
135 knots (250 km/h; 155 mph)
above 2,330 m (7,650 ft)
130 knots (241 km/h; 150 mph)
Max rate of climb at S/L 485 m (1,590 ft)/min
Service ceiling 6,100 m (20,000 ft)
Service ceiling, one engine out, ISA
1,705 m (5,600 ft)
Hovering ceiling IGE, ISA 2,680 m (8,800 ft)
Hovering ceiling OGE, ISA 1,770 m (5,800 ft)
Range with max fuel, 20 min reserves
282 nm (523 km; 325 miles)

BELL MODEL 301
US Army designation: XV-15
Bell Helicopter announced in May 1973 that it had been chosen by NASA and the US Army to build and test two twin-engined tilt-rotor research aircraft. Estimated cost of the six-year programme was $45 million.

The company has been working on tilt-rotor technology since the mid-1950s, proving the concept feasible with its XV-3 prototype, described in the 1962-63 *Jane's*. Since that time development of tilt-rotor systems has progressed steadily, leading to the Model 301 which Bell proposed to meet the NASA/Army requirement. The two research aircraft, on which design work was started in July 1973, have the official designation XV-15. The fuselages and tail units were built under subcontract by Rockwell International's Tulsa Division.

The airframe structure is basically that of a conventional fixed-wing aircraft. However, the hover lift and cruise propulsive force is provided by low-disc-loading rotors located at each wingtip. These rotors, together with their wingtip-mounted turboshaft engines, rotate from a vertical position for hover and helicopter flight to horizontal for the conventional propeller-driven flight mode. Hover control is provided by rotor-generated forces and moments. In the conventional mode of flight, control is provided primarily by use of normal aerodynamic control surfaces of the kind fitted to fixed-wing aircraft. A cross-shafting system interconnecting the rotors precludes a complete loss of power to either rotor due to failure of one engine, permits power transfer for transient conditions, and achieves rotational speed synchronisation. A conversion system interconnect shaft caters for rotor axis tilt synchronisation.

The Avco Lycoming turboshaft engines are mounted in rotatable wingtip nacelles to minimise the operational loads on the cross-shaft system. The use of a free-turbine engine permits the reduction of rotor turning speed for conventional forward flight, thus improving rotor performance and reducing cruise noise. The rotors have elastomeric flapping restraints to increase helicopter mode control power and damping. The forward-swept fixed wings provide blade clearance which is adequate to cater for blade flexion resulting from gusts or manoeuvres while operating in an aeroplane flight mode. Wing/rotor/pylon stability is accomplished by selecting a stiff wing and pylon-to-wing attachment, and by minimising the distance of the rotor hub from the wing.

For hover flight the wing trailing-edge flaps and flap/ailerons (flaperons) are deflected downward to reduce the wing download, thereby increasing hovering efficiency. Hover roll control is provided by differential rotor collective pitch, pitch control by cyclic pitch, and yaw control by differential cyclic pitch. Dual controls for use in the helicopter mode are similar to those of a conventional rotating-wing aircraft. Thus, dual collective control sticks provide power and collective pitch for height control, and dual control columns provide longitudinal and lateral control; dual rudder pedals provide directional control.

In the aeroplane flight mode, the control columns and rudder pedals are employed conventionally, while the collective stick/power lever continues in use for power management. An H-tail configuration, with twin endplate fins and rudders, was selected to provide optimum aircraft directional stability around a zero yaw angle. Control authority for the power lever, blade pitch governor, cyclic, differential cyclic, differential collective, and flap/flaperon relationship, are phased with rotor mast angle by mechanical mixing linkages.

At intermediate rotor axis tilt angles (between 60° and 75°) the aircraft can perform STOL operations at weights above the maximum VTOL gross weight of 5,897 kg (13,000 lb).

The XV-15 is fitted with a stability and control augmentation system to improve the handling qualities and enhance pilot efficiency. Ejection seats are installed as a safety feature during flight trials.

Future commercial and military aircraft which might be derived from the XV-15 would have a wing span of about 10·67 m (35 ft) and fuselage length of 12·50 m (41 ft). They would carry 15 troops in military service or 12 passengers as civil transports.

Initially, the programme was funded and managed jointly by the NASA Ames Research Center and the US Army's Air Mobility Research and Development Laboratory, but US Navy funding was also provided in 1979 and 1980. The two XV-15s are being used in a research programme to prove the concept, explore the limits of the operational flight envelope and assess its application to military and civil transport needs.

The first aircraft (702) made its first free hovering flight on 3 May 1977. The second aircraft was transferred to Bell's Arlington, Texas, flight test facility for systems checks in late August 1977. Wind tunnel tests of the first XV-15 were carried out at NASA's Ames Research Center in June/July 1978, up to tunnel maximum speeds of

Bell XV-15 tilt-rotor research aircraft in state of partial conversion

180 knots (333 km/h; 207 mph). Flight tests of the second XV-15 in helicopter mode began on 23 April 1979. The first full in-flight conversion to aeroplane mode was made by this second XV-15 (N703NA) on 24 July 1979. It achieved speeds of up to 160 knots (296 km/h; 184 mph) during the 40 min flight.

Testing carried out since that date has included flights at 1,525 m (5,000 ft) with in-flight conversions at speeds up to 207 knots (384 km/h; 238 mph), and roll-on landings at maximum speeds of 60 knots (111 km/h; 69 mph) with a 95° pylon angle. Emergency operation of the aircraft was also tested by simulated systems and engine failures, including autorotative descents. Noise and vibration levels were found to be lower than had been predicted.

Following completion of that phase of testing, N703NA underwent a planned 100 h inspection. Subsequent demonstrations of high-speed cruising flight have included a true airspeed of 301 knots (557 km/h; 346 mph) achieved on 17 June 1980.

Bell Helicopter announced in July 1979 the receipt of a contract from NASA-Ames covering preliminary design study of an advanced rotor blade for the XV-15. The purpose of the study is to select a design concept for a composite rotor blade of 0·43 m (17 in) blade chord, that will offer improved performance and extended life expectancy compared with the existing metal blades of the XV-15.

TYPE: Tilt-rotor research aircraft.
ROTOR SYSTEM: Two three-blade rotors, spring restrained, stiff in plane and gimballed, with an elastomeric hub spring to increase control power and damping. Stainless steel blades of high-twist design, suitable for both helicopter and high-speed aircraft flight modes. Blade section is Bell-modified NACA 6-series. Blades attached to titanium hub by tension-torsion straps and roller pitch bearings. Blades do not fold. No rotor brake.
ROTOR DRIVE: Each rotor is driven by individual engine via reduction gear, engine coupling, rotor planetary gear and shaft centrebox. Rotor/engine rpm ratio 1 : 35·11. Interconnected drive shafts and redundant tilting mechanisms permit single-engine operation and fail-operative tilt capability.
WINGS: Cantilever high-wing monoplane. Wing section Bell-modified NACA 64A223. Dihedral 2°. Incidence 3°. Forward sweep at quarter-chord 6° 30′. All-metal conventional structure, with light alloy ribs and honeycomb panels. Flap/aileron of light alloy construction on outer two-thirds of each wing trailing-edge, powered by HRT hydraulic actuators. Plain light alloy trailing-edge flap on inboard third of each wing, operated by Curtiss-Wright power hinges. No tabs.
FUSELAGE: Semi-monocoque fail-safe structure of light alloy.
TAIL UNIT: Cantilever structure of light alloy, with end-plate fin and rudder mounted at each tailplane tip. Tailplane incidence ground-adjustable. Elevators and rudders powered by HRT hydraulic actuators. No tabs.
LANDING GEAR: Hydraulically-retractable tricycle type, as used originally on Canadair CL-84, with twin wheels on each unit. Main units retract forward into fuselage-mounted landing gear pods, nose unit aft. Menasco oleo-pneumatic shock-absorbers. Nosewheel unit of self-centering type. Goodyear magnesium main wheels with Goodyear tyres size 6·50-8, pressure 3·8 bars (55 lb/sq in). Goodyear magnesium nosewheels with Goodyear tyres size 5·00-4, pressure 3·8 bars (55 lb/sq in). Goodyear hydraulically-operated magnesium/steel disc brakes.
POWER PLANT: Two 1,156 kW (1,550 shp) Avco Lycoming LTC1K-4K turboshaft engines, each with a two-minute contingency rating of 1,343 kW (1,800 shp), wingtip-mounted with tilt mechanism operated by SPECO interconnected double ballscrew actuators. Two fuel tanks in each wing, total capacity 867 litres (229 US gallons). Refuelling point on upper surface of each wing. Oil capacity 11·4 litres (3 US gallons).
ACCOMMODATION: Pilot and co-pilot on Rockwell-Columbus LW-3B ejection seats, side by side on flight deck, with access to cabin. Currently in austere test configuration for research equipment, cabin could accommodate nine personnel. Door on starboard side. Flight deck (only) is heated, ventilated and air-conditioned. Overhead and side windows jettisonable ballistically in emergency.
SYSTEMS: Garrett-AiResearch air-cycle environmental control unit. No pressurisation. Triplex hydraulic system, pressure 207 bars (3,000 lb/sq in): dual system for rotor and flight controls, with utility system as backup. Pneumatic system, pressure 207 bars (3,000 lb/sq in), for emergency actuation of landing gear. DC electrical system supplied by two 30V 300A generators. Two 28V 13Ah nickel-cadmium storage batteries. Oxygen system at pressure of 124 bars (1,800 lb/sq in). Engine inlet strut anti-icing.
AVIONICS AND EQUIPMENT: Stability control augmentation system and FFS. King VHF, UHF, VOR, ILS, marker beacon indication and DME. Blind-flying instrumentation fitted.
DIMENSIONS, EXTERNAL:
Diameter of rotors (each) 7·62 m (25 ft 0 in)
Distance between rotor centres 9·80 m (32 ft 2 in)

Bell XV-15 tilt-rotor research aircraft *(Pilot Press)*

Bell XV-15 in conventional flight mode. Slow-turning prop-rotors appear to be stationary

Rotor blade chord	0·36 m (1 ft 2 in)	
Wing span	10·72 m (35 ft 2 in)	
Wing aspect ratio	6·12	
Wing chord, constant	1·60 m (5 ft 3 in)	
Length overall, rotors turning	12·83 m (42 ft 1 in)	
Height overall	4·67 m (15 ft 4 in)	
Wheel track, c/l of shock-absorbers	2·64 m (8 ft 8 in)	
Wheelbase	4·80 m (15 ft 9 in)	
Cabin door (stbd): Height	1·37 m (4 ft 6 in)	
Width	0·81 m (2 ft 8 in)	
Height to sill	0·56 m (1 ft 10 in)	

DIMENSIONS, INTERNAL:
Cabin (excl flight deck):

Length	4·53 m (14 ft 10½ in)	
Max width	1·52 m (5 ft 0 in)	
Max height	1·52 m (5 ft 0 in)	
Floor area	5·40 m² (58·1 sq ft)	
Volume	8·50 m³ (300 cu ft)	

AREAS:

Rotor blades (each)	1·36 m² (14·6 sq ft)	
Rotor discs (each)	45·61 m² (491 sq ft)	
Wings, gross	15·70 m² (169 sq ft)	
Flap/ailerons (total)	1·88 m² (20·2 sq ft)	
Trailing-edge flaps (total)	1·02 m² (11·0 sq ft)	
Fins (total)	3·99 m² (43·0 sq ft)	
Rudders (total)	0·70 m² (7·5 sq ft)	
Tailplane	3·46 m² (37·25 sq ft)	
Elevators (total)	1·21 m² (13·0 sq ft)	

WEIGHTS AND LOADING:

Weight empty	4,341 kg (9,570 lb)	
Max payload (STOL)	1,542 kg (3,400 lb)	
Max fuel weight	676 kg (1,490 lb)	
Design T-O weight	5,897 kg (13,000 lb)	
Max T-O weight (STOL)	6,804 kg (15,000 lb)	
Max disc loading	74·2 kg/m² (15·2 lb/sq ft)	

PERFORMANCE (estimated, at design T-O weight):

Never-exceed speed	364 knots (674 km/h; 419 mph)	
Max level speed at 5,180 m (17,000 ft)		
	332 knots (615 km/h; 382 mph)	
Max cruising speed at 4,970 m (16,300 ft)		
	303 knots (561 km/h; 349 mph)	
Econ cruising speed at 6,100 m (20,000 ft)		
	200 knots (371 km/h; 230 mph)	
Max rate of climb at S/L	960 m (3,150 ft)/min	

Service ceiling	8,840 m (29,000 ft)	
Service ceiling, one engine out	4,570 m (15,000 ft)	
Min ground turning radius	6·83 m (22 ft 5 in)	
Hovering ceiling IGE	3,200 m (10,500 ft)	
Hovering ceiling OGE	2,635 m (8,650 ft)	
Range with max fuel	445 nm (824 km; 512 miles)	

BELL MODEL 412

Bell announced on 8 September 1978 its intention to develop a variant of the twin-turbine Model 212 with a four-blade main rotor of advanced design. The new aircraft, designated Model 412, is the first production helicopter with a four-blade rotor to be manufactured by Bell, although the company has flown many helicopters with multi-blade rotors for research purposes.

Two new fully-certificated Model 212s were modified for use in the development and certification programme for the Model 412. The first of these began its flight trials in early August 1979, and the second in December 1979. FAA type approval in accordance with FAR Pt 29 was expected in time to permit deliveries of the Model 412 to begin in 1981. CAA certification will also be obtained, and production will be undertaken simultaneously by Bell and its Italian licensee, Agusta. By September 1979, Bell had received provisional orders for 60 Model 412s.

Introduction of the new rotor has not only improved performance and reduced noise, but has reduced vibration significantly without requiring a costly redesign of the fuselage structure to introduce nodal suspension.

The description of the Model 212 applies also to the Model 412, except as follows:
ROTOR SYSTEM: Four-blade flex-beam soft-in-plane advanced technology main rotor. Blades are of similar construction to those described for the Model 214ST, but have lightning-protection mesh moulded into the structure and there are provisions for inclusion of de-icing heater elements. New-design main rotor hub of steel and light alloy construction, with elastomeric bearings and dampers. Main rotor can be folded. Rotor brake standard. Two-blade tail rotor of all-metal construction.
ROTOR DRIVE, FUSELAGE, TAIL SURFACE AND LANDING GEAR: As for Model 212, except for shorter main rotor mast. Transmission T-O rating 975 kW (1,308 shp).

POWER PLANT: Pratt & Whitney Aircraft of Canada PT6T-3B Turbo Twin Pac, comprising two PT6 turboshaft engines coupled to a combining gearbox with a single output shaft. Producing 1,342 kW (1,800 shp), the Twin Pac is flat rated to 975 kW (1,308 shp) for take-off and 843 kW (1,130 shp) for continuous operation. In the event of an engine failure the remaining engine can deliver up to 764 kW (1,025 shp) for 2½ minutes, or 723 kW (970 shp) for 30 minutes. Five interconnected rupture-resistant fuel cells, with automatic shut-off valves (breakaway fittings), have a combined capacity of 814 litres (215 US gallons). Optional auxiliary fuel tanks provide a maximum total capacity of 1,495 litres (395 US gallons). Single-point refuelling on starboard side of cabin.

ACCOMMODATION AND SYSTEMS: As for Model 212.

AVIONICS AND EQUIPMENT: Optional IFR avionics include dual King KTR 900A com transceivers, dual King KNR 660A VOR/LOC/RMI receivers, King KDF 800 ADF, King KMD 700A DME, King KXP 750A transponder, King KGM 690 marker beacon/glideslope receiver, dual three-axis gyro units, stability control augmentation system, and an automatic flight control system. A Sperry autopilot/nav coupler system was undergoing certification testing in Spring 1980. Optional equipment includes a cargo sling, rescue hoist, emergency pop-out flotation gear and high skid gear.

Prototype Bell Model 412, an improved 212 with four-blade advanced technology rotor

DIMENSIONS, EXTERNAL:

Diameter of main rotor	14·02 m (46 ft 0 in)	
Diameter of tail rotor	2·59 m (8 ft 6 in)	
Main rotor blade chord: at root	0·40 m (1 ft 3·9 in)	
at tip	0·22 m (8½ in)	
Tail rotor blade chord	0·29 m (11½ in)	
Length overall (rotors turning)	17·07 m (56 ft 0 in)	
Length of fuselage (excl rotors)	12·92 m (42 ft 4¾ in)	
Height overall	4·32 m (14 ft 2¼ in)	
Stabiliser span	2·86 m (9 ft 4½ in)	
Width over skids	2·59 m (8 ft 6 in)	

AREAS:

Main rotor disc	154·40 m² (1,662 sq ft)
Tail rotor disc	5·27 m² (56·75 sq ft)

WEIGHTS:

Weight empty plus usable oil	2,753 kg (6,070 lb)
Max T-O weight	5,216 kg (11,500 lb)

PERFORMANCE (estimated, at max T-O weight):
Never-exceed speed at S/L
140 knots (259 km/h; 161 mph)
Max cruising speed at S/L
124 knots (230 km/h; 143 mph)
Max rate of climb at S/L   433 m (1,420 ft)/min
Service ceiling   4,330 m (14,200 ft)
Hovering ceiling IGE   3,350 m (11,000 ft)
Max range with standard fuel at S/L, no reserves
227 nm (420 km; 261 miles)

BELLANCA

BELLANCA AIRCRAFT CORPORATION (subsidiary of Anderson, Greenwood and Co)

HEAD OFFICE AND WORKS: PO Box 69, Municipal Airport, Alexandria, Minnesota 56308
Telephone: (612) 762 1501
PRESIDENT AND CHIEF OPERATING OFFICER:
Robert E. Howard Jr
CHAIRMAN OF THE BOARD AND CHIEF EXECUTIVE OFFICER:
James Elder
VICE-PRESIDENTS:
John Hall (Marketing and General Manager)
James L. Brown
Lloyd Cox (Production)
Michael Sherbin (Finance, and Controller)

Known originally as International Aircraft Manufacturing Inc (Inter-air), Bellanca Sales Company (a subsidiary of Miller Flying Service) acquired the assets of Champion Aircraft Corporation on 30 September 1970. Following the merger, the name Bellanca Aircraft Corporation was adopted, and Bellanca has since marketed both its own products and those of Champion Aircraft.

The Anderson, Greenwood company of Houston, Texas, of which Bellanca Aircraft Corporation is a wholly-owned subsidiary, obtained FAA certification on 28 July 1976 for its T-250 prototype four-seat light aircraft, now known as the Aries. Bellanca also undertook responsibility for manufacture of the Eagle agricultural biplane (see Eagle Aircraft Company entry in this section).

For economic reasons, Bellanca halted production of its Viking four-seat light business aircraft, and suspended manufacture of the Citabria, Scout and Decathlon two-seat light aircraft, in the first months of 1980. Its remaining 60 production employees continued work on the Aries and Eagle.

BELLANCA MODEL 17-30A
SUPER VIKING 300A

By 1 January 1980 a total of 1,670 Vikings of all models had been built, including 72 completed in 1979. Manufacture has been halted. Full details of the aircraft can be found in the 1979-80 *Jane's*.

CHAMPION (BELLANCA) CITABRIA

By the beginning of 1980 a total of 5,186 Citabrias of all models had been built, including 210 completed in 1979. Manufacture has been suspended. Full details of the aircraft can be found in the 1979-80 *Jane's*.

BELLANCA MODEL 8GCBC SCOUT

By the beginning of 1980 a total of 329 Model 8GCBC Scouts had been produced, including 51 completed in 1979. Manufacture has been suspended. Full details of the aircraft can be found in the 1979-80 *Jane's*.

CHAMPION (BELLANCA) DECATHLON

By the beginning of 1980 a total of 552 Decathlons had been produced, including 146 completed in 1979. Manufacture has been suspended. Full details of the aircraft can be found in the 1979-80 *Jane's*.

The prototype Bellanca Aries T-250 five-seat light aircraft

BELLANCA ARIES T-250

Designed by Anderson, Greenwood and Company, the four-seat T-250 is the product of a research and development programme which had spanned approximately nine years by the time the aircraft received FAA certification on 28 July 1976. It first flew on 10 July 1973. Turbocharged and six-seat versions are under consideration.

The first production Aries T-250 was delivered to a Bellanca dealer on 17 April 1980, at which time it was hoped to maintain production at a rate of approximately one aircraft per month.

TYPE: Five-seat cabin monoplane.

WINGS: Cantilever low-wing monoplane. Wing section NACA 600412 modified. Dihedral 6°. Conventional structure of light alloy. Cambered leading-edge. Plain ailerons of light alloy construction. Spring servo-tab in each aileron. Electrically-operated trailing-edge flaps of light alloy construction. Flaps can be operated manually in emergency.

FUSELAGE: Conventional light alloy structure of basic rectangular cross-section.

TAIL UNIT: Cantilever structure of light alloy, with T tailplane. All-moving horizontal surfaces, with tab.

LANDING GEAR: Electrically-retractable tricycle type. Main wheels retract inward, nosewheel aft, and all wheels are enclosed when retracted. Wheels can be raised and lowered manually in emergency. Oleo-pneumatic shock-absorbers.

POWER PLANT: One 186·5 kW (250 hp) Avco Lycoming O-540-A4D5 flat-six engine, driving a Hartzell two-blade constant-speed metal propeller. Fuel tanks in wings, with total capacity of 288 litres (76 US gallons). Refuelling point in upper surface of each wing. Oil capacity 11·5 litres (3 US gallons).

ACCOMMODATION: Seats for pilot and up to four passengers. Dual controls standard. Door on starboard side. Space for 113 kg (250 lb) baggage at aft end of cabin when fifth seat is folded, with external access door on starboard side.

AVIONICS: Prototype has dual nav/com radio installations and a transponder.

DIMENSIONS, EXTERNAL:

Wing span	9·55 m (31 ft 4 in)
Wing chord (constant)	1·68 m (5 ft 6 in)
Length overall	7·98 m (26 ft 2 in)
Height overall	2·62 m (8 ft 7 in)
Tailplane span	3·81 m (12 ft 6 in)
Wheel track	1·68 m (5 ft 6 in)
Wheelbase	2·36 m (7 ft 9 in)
Propeller diameter	1·96 m (6 ft 5 in)
Propeller ground clearance	0·32 m (1 ft 0½ in)

DIMENSIONS, INTERNAL:

Cabin: Length	2·92 m (9 ft 7 in)
Max height	1·23 m (4 ft 0½ in)
Max width	1·14 m (3 ft 9 in)
Baggage compartment volume	0·76 m³ (27 cu ft)

AREA:

Wings, gross	15·79 m² (170 sq ft)

WEIGHTS AND LOADINGS:

Weight empty	839 kg (1,850 lb)
Max T-O weight	1,429 kg (3,150 lb)
Max wing loading	90·5 kg/m² (18·5 lb/sq ft)
Max power loading	7·67 kg/kW (12·6 lb/hp)

PERFORMANCE (at max T-O weight):
Never-exceed speed 211 knots (392 km/h; 244 mph)
Max level speed at S/L 187 knots (346 km/h; 215 mph)
Max cruising speed, 75% power
181 knots (335 km/h; 208 mph)
Cruising speed, 65% power
174 knots (322 km/h; 200 mph)
Stalling speed, wheels and flaps up
62·5 knots (116 km/h; 72 mph)
Stalling speed, wheels and flaps down
55·5 knots (103 km/h; 64 mph)
Max rate of climb at S/L   378 m (1,240 ft)/min
Service ceiling   5,515 m (18,100 ft)
Range with four occupants, max fuel, 45 min reserves at 45% power:
75% power   860 nm (1,593 km; 990 miles)
65% power   946 nm (1,754 km; 1,090 miles)
55% power 1,016 nm (1,883 km; 1,170 miles)
Range with five occupants, 189 litres (50 US gallons) fuel, reserves as above
586 nm (1,086 km; 675 miles)

BELLANCA
BELLANCA AIRCRAFT ENGINEERING INC

HEAD OFFICE AND WORKS: PO Box 70, Scott Depot, nr
  Charleston, West Virginia 25560
Telephone: (304) 755 4354
PRESIDENT: August T. Bellanca
MANAGING DIRECTOR: Henry E. Payne

The original Bellanca Aircraft Corporation of New
Castle, Delaware, merged with companies not engaged in
aircraft manufacture and lost its identity in 1959. The
present company, formed by Mr August Bellanca and his
father, the late G. M. Bellanca, bought all of the original
Bellanca aircraft designs with the exception of the Model
14-19. On 1 December 1971 the company was reorganised and acquired corporate offices and production
plant at Scott Depot, West Virginia.

BELLANCA MODEL 19-25 SKYROCKET II

Research and design of this aircraft were initiated in
1956 by the late G. M. Bellanca and his son, August T.
Bellanca. The early decision to fabricate this aircraft from
glassfibre composites resulted from much research and
testing. Basically, the advantages are that smooth
aerodynamic surfaces are obtained, together with high
strength. The materials used in the Model 19-25 Skyrocket have a higher strength-to-weight ratio than
aluminium, with better durability and fatigue resistance.

Prototype of the Bellanca Model 19-25 Skyrocket II six-seat light aircraft

Because of the extremely smooth surface finish, the
Skyrocket II has a very low drag coefficient ($C_{do} = 0.016$),
and was being tested by NASA in early 1979 to evaluate
application of these principles to general aviation.

Since the first flight in March 1975, the Skyrocket II
prototype has demonstrated its capabilities by setting
record speeds of 245·80 knots (455·23 km/h; 282·86 mph)
over a 100 km closed circuit, 257·64 knots (477·15 km/h;

296·49 mph) over 500 km, and 261·67 knots (484·62
km/h; 301·13 mph) over 1,000 km in the 1,000-1,750 kg
weight class; and speeds of 283·72 knots (525·45 km/h;
326·50 mph) over 500 km, and 272·84 knots (505·31
km/h; 313·98 mph) over 1,000 km in the 1,750-3,000 kg
class. A decision on production was still pending in early
1980; a description of the Skyrocket II can be found in the
1979-80 and earlier editions of *Jane's*.

BOEING
THE BOEING COMPANY

HEAD OFFICE: PO Box 3707, Seattle, Washington 98124
ESTABLISHED: July 1916
CHAIRMAN OF THE BOARD AND CHIEF EXECUTIVE OFFICER:
T. A. Wilson
PRESIDENT: Malcolm T. Stamper
SENIOR VICE-PRESIDENTS:
  H. W. Haynes (Executive Vice-President, Chief
    Financial Officer)
  W. M. Maulden
VICE-PRESIDENTS:
  R. R. Albrecht (Counsel and Secretary)
  R. E. Bateman (General Manager, Boeing Marine
    Systems)
  W. L. Hamilton (International Business)
  V. F. Knutzen (Controller)
  R. B. Light (Manager, Washington DC Office)
  S. M. Little (Industrial and Public Relations)
  H. W. Neffner (Contract Negotiations and Pricing)
  Clyde Skeen
  J. E. Steiner (Corporate Product Development)
  R. W. Tharrington (President, Boeing Computer
    Services)
  B. M. Wheat (Senior Vice-President, Boeing Computer
    Services)
  Other Vice-Presidents are listed under individual
    company headings
TREASURER: J. B. L. Pierce
PUBLIC RELATIONS AND ADVERTISING DIRECTOR:
  R. P. Bush

Boeing Commercial Airplane Company:
PO Box 707, Renton, Washington 98055
PRESIDENT: E. H. Boullioun
EXECUTIVE VICE-PRESIDENT: Richard W. Welch

VICE-PRESIDENTS:
  J. A. Blue (Product and Customer Support)
  W. W. Buckley (Operations)
  Ernest V. Fenn (General Manager, 757 Division)
  W. T. Hamilton (Research and Development)
  Kenneth F. Holtby (New Programmes)
  Donald McLaren (Finance and Contracts)
  V. C. Moe (Contracts)
  H. Carl Munson (Strategic Planning)
  George D. Nible (Customer Services)
  Lynn M. Olason (General Manager, 747 Division)
  O. M. Roetman (International Sales)
  William L. Shineman (General Manager, Fabrication
    Division)
  Frank A. Shrontz (General Manager, 707/727/737
    Division)
  Joseph F. Sutter (Operations and Product Develop-
    ment)
  John M. Swihart (Domestic and Canadian Sales)
  R. W. Taylor (Special Assistant to President)
  Dean D. Thornton (General Manager, 767 Division)
  C. F. Wilde (Sales and Marketing)
  H. W. Withington (Engineering)
  Brien S. Wygle (Flight Operations)

Boeing Aerospace Company:
Kent, Washington
PRESIDENT: H. K. Hebeler
VICE-PRESIDENTS:
  R. L. Brock (Army Systems Acquisition)
  C. P. Ekas (Requirements and Strategy Planning)
  J. H. Goldie (Executive Vice-President, Department
    Management)
  D. E. Graves (Aerospace Sales)
  R. W. Hager (Air Force Systems Acquisition)
  D. B. Jacobs (Science, Technology and Development)

  M. K. Miller (Systems Acquisition)
  Howard N. Stuverude (Programme Management)

Boeing Military Airplane Company:
3801 South Oliver, Wichita, Kansas 67210
PRESIDENT: L. D. Alford
VICE-PRESIDENTS:
  A. M. S. Goo (Military Systems Development and
    Management)
  Frank Verginia (Advanced Military Aeroplane)

Boeing Vertol Company:
PO Box 16858, Philadelphia, Pennsylvania 19142
PRESIDENT: Joseph Mallen
VICE-PRESIDENT: C. W. Ellis (Helicopter Development
  and Programme Management)

In May 1961 The Boeing Airplane Company changed
its proprietary name to The Boeing Company as a recognition of its diversified interests. On 19 December 1972 it
was announced that three of the company's operating
organisations had been designated as companies, comprising Boeing Commercial Airplane Company, Renton,
Washington; Boeing Aerospace Company, Kent,
Washington; and Boeing Vertol Company, Philadelphia,
Pennsylvania.

The Boeing Military Airplane Company at Wichita,
Kansas, was formed in Autumn 1979 to replace the former
Boeing Wichita Company and take over some aircraft
programmes from Boeing Aerospace Company. Its
responsibilities include modification programmes, 707,
727, 737 and 747 parts fabrication, research, programmes
on military aircraft currently in use with the armed forces
(B-52 and KC-135), and other support functions.

A factory with an area of 75,000 m² (807,300 sq ft) at St
James-Assiniboia Airport, near Winnipeg, produces 747
components.

BOEING COMMERCIAL AIRPLANE COMPANY (BCAC)

The Boeing Commercial Airplane Company, with
headquarters at the company's Renton, Washington, facility just south of Seattle, has five divisions. The
707/727/737 Division at Renton and the 747 Division at
Everett continue to manufacture aircraft of those series;
the 767 Division was established to develop this new

wide-body transport, which will be built at Everett; the
757 Division handles that programme at the Renton facility; and the Fabrication Division serves the other operating
groups with its massive NC machine capability. A separate
Engineering Organisation, reporting to company headquarters, is responsible for such functions as technology,
quality control and flight operations.

Including military derivatives, 6 Model 707s, 136

Model 727s, 77 Model 737s and 67 Model 747s were
delivered in 1979. Orders for 317 new air transports,
valued at approximately $9 billion, were announced by
Boeing customers during the year.

BOEING MODEL 707
USAF designation: VC-137

The prototype for the Boeing Model 707, designated

Boeing Model 707-320C four-turbofan commercial transport in the insignia of Libyan Arab Airlines

Model 367-80, was the first jet transport designed as such to be completed and flown in the United States. It made its first flight on 15 July 1954, and a developed version was ordered in large numbers as a flight refuelling tanker/transport for the US Air Force under the designation KC-135.

On 13 July 1955 Boeing was given clearance by the US Air Force to build commercial developments of the prototype concurrently with the production of KC-135s. These transport aircraft have the basic designations of Boeing 707 and 720, but were made available in many versions, of which a total of 962 had been sold and 938 delivered by 1 October 1980. These totals included five specially-equipped aircraft delivered to the US Air Force under the designations VC-137A (now VC-137B) and VC-137C, and 22 aircraft (10 delivered) for completion under the E-3A AWACS (Airborne Warning and Control System) programme.

Boeing and CFM International fitted a 707-320C airframe with CFM56 turbofan engines under the designation 707-700. The aim of this programme was to find additional military and commercial markets for the 707, and flight testing began on 27 November 1979. The test programme was successful, but plans to offer a CFM56 re-engining programme to commercial 707 operators were later suspended. The engine is, however, being fitted to US Air Force KC-135 tanker aircraft, in a programme described under the Boeing Military Airplane Co heading.

Production of the 707 for commercial operation has virtually ended, and current manufacture is providing airframes for the USAF/NATO military AWACS programmes. However, the following commercial version remained available in 1980:

707-320C Convertible. Certificated to carry up to 219 passengers, this version can also operate mixed passenger/cargo or all-cargo services. Loading is through a 2·34 m × 3·40 m (92 in × 134 in) forward cargo door, with cargo on pallets or in containers. A Boeing-developed cargo handling system is installed on seven rows of seat tracks in the floor. Upper-deck cargo space comprises 161·21 m³ (5,693 cu ft) palletised and lower deck 48·14 m³ (1,700 cu ft) bulk. The cargo system can carry thirteen 2·24 m × 3·18 m (88 in × 125 in) or 2·24 m × 2·74 m (88 in × 108 in) 'A' type containers. There is a crew rest area aft of the flight deck. Received FAA Type Approval on 30 April 1963, and first entered service with Pan American in June 1963. Five were delivered to the Canadian Armed Forces during 1970-71 to serve as troop and staff transports and military cargo carriers. Two of these are equipped as flight refuelling tankers, utilising wingtip pods containing a hinged boom and trailing hose and drogue manufactured by Beech.

TYPE: Four-turbofan airliner.

WINGS: Cantilever low-wing monoplane. Dihedral 7°. Incidence 2°. Sweepback at quarter-chord 35°. All-metal two-spar fail-safe structure. Centre-section continuous through fuselage. Normal outboard aileron and small inboard aileron on each wing, built of aluminium honeycomb panels. Two Fowler flaps and one fillet flap of aluminium alloy on each wing. Full-span leading-edge flaps. Four hydraulically-operated aluminium alloy spoilers on each wing, forward of flaps. Primary flying controls are aerodynamically balanced and manually operated through spring tabs. Lateral control at low speeds by all four ailerons, supplemented by spoilers which are interconnected with the ailerons. Lateral control at high speeds by inboard ailerons and spoilers only. Operation of flaps adjusts linkage between inboard and outboard ailerons to permit outboard operation with extended flaps. Spoilers may also be used symmetrically as speed brakes. Thermal anti-icing of wing leading-edges.

FUSELAGE: All-metal semi-monocoque fail-safe structure with cross-section made up of two circular arcs of different radii, the larger above, faired into smooth-contoured ellipse.

TAIL UNIT: Cantilever all-metal structure. Anti-balance tab and trim tab in rudder. Trim and control tabs in each elevator. Electrically and manually operated variable-incidence tailplane. Powered rudder.

LANDING GEAR: Hydraulically-retractable tricycle type. Main units are four-wheel bogies which retract inward into underside of thickened wing-root and fuselage.

Boeing 707-320C four-turbofan passenger/cargo transport aircraft (*Pilot Press*)

Dual nosewheel unit retracts forward into fuselage. Landing gear doors close when legs fully extended. Gear can be extended in flight to give maximum rate of descent of 4,570 m/min (15,000 ft/min) when used in conjunction with spoilers. Boeing oleo-pneumatic shock-absorbers. Main wheels and tyres size 46 × 16. Nosewheels and tyres size 39 × 13. Tyre pressures: main wheels 12·41 bars (180 lb/sq in), nosewheels 7·93 bars (115 lb/sq in). Multi-disc brakes by Goodyear. Hydro-Aire flywheel detector type anti-skid units.

POWER PLANT: Four Pratt & Whitney JT3D-7 turbofan engines, each developing 84·5 kN (19,000 lb st), in pods under wings. Fuel in four main, two reserve and one centre main integral wing tanks with total capacity of 90,299 litres (23,855 US gallons). Provision for both pressure and gravity refuelling. Total oil capacity 114 litres (30 US gallons).

ACCOMMODATION: Max accommodation for 219 passengers. Typical arrangement has 14 first class seats, a 4-seat lounge and 133 coach class seats, with four galleys and five toilets. There are two passenger doors, forward and aft on port side. Galley servicing doors forward and aft on starboard side. Baggage compartments fore and aft of wing in lower segment of fuselage below cabin floor. Entire accommodation, including baggage compartments, air-conditioned and pressurised.

SYSTEMS: Air-cycle air-conditioning and pressurisation system, using three Garrett-AiResearch engine-driven turbocompressors. Pressure differential 0·59 bars (8·6 lb/sq in). Hydraulic system, pressure 207 bars (3,000 lb/sq in), for landing gear retraction, nosewheel steering, brakes, flaps, flying controls and spoilers. Electrical system includes four 30kVA or 40kVA 115/200V 3-phase 400Hz AC alternators and four 75A transformer-rectifiers giving 28V DC. APU optional.

AVIONICS AND EQUIPMENT: To customer's specification.

DIMENSIONS, EXTERNAL:

Wing span	44·42 m (145 ft 9 in)
Wing chord at root	10·33 m (33 ft 10·7 in)
Wing chord at tip	2·84 m (9 ft 4 in)
Wing aspect ratio	7·056
Length overall	46·61 m (152 ft 11 in)
Length of fuselage	44·35 m (145 ft 6 in)
Width of fuselage	3·76 m (12 ft 4 in)
Height overall	12·93 m (42 ft 5 in)
Tailplane span	13·95 m (45 ft 9 in)
Wheel track	6·73 m (22 ft 1 in)
Wheelbase	17·98 m (59 ft 0 in)
Passenger doors (each): Height	1·83 m (6 ft 0 in)
Width	0·86 m (2 ft 10 in)
Height to sill: fwd	3·25 m (10 ft 8 in)
aft	3·20 m (10 ft 6 in)

Cargo door: Height	2·34 m (7 ft 8 in)
Width	3·40 m (11 ft 2 in)
Height to sill	3·20 m (10 ft 6 in)
Forward baggage compartment door:	
Height	1·27 m (4 ft 2 in)
Width	1·22 m (4 ft 0 in)
Height to sill	1·55 m (5 ft 1 in)
Rear baggage compartment door (fwd):	
Height	1·24 m (4 ft 1 in)
Width	1·22 m (4 ft 0 in)
Height to sill	1·47 m (4 ft 10 in)
Rear baggage compartment door (aft):	
Height	0·89 m (2 ft 11 in)
Width	0·76 m (2 ft 6 in)
Height to sill	1·93 m (6 ft 4 in)

DIMENSIONS, INTERNAL:

Cabin, excl flight deck:	
Length	33·93 m (111 ft 4 in)
Max width	3·55 m (11 ft 8 in)
Max height	2·34 m (7 ft 8 in)
Floor area	106·18 m² (1,143 sq ft)
Volume	228·6 m³ (8,074 cu ft)
Baggage compartment (fwd)	23·65 m³ (835 cu ft)
Baggage compartment (rear)	24·50 m³ (865 cu ft)

AREAS:

Wings, gross	283·4 m² (3,050 sq ft)
Ailerons (total)	11·24 m² (121 sq ft)
Trailing-edge flaps (total)	44·22 m² (476 sq ft)
Leading-edge flaps	14·31 m² (154 sq ft)
Fin	30·47 m² (328 sq ft)
Rudder, incl tabs	9·48 m² (102 sq ft)
Tailplane	58·06 m² (625 sq ft)
Elevators, incl tabs	14·03 m² (151 sq ft)

WEIGHTS AND LOADINGS:

Basic operating weight, empty:	
Passenger	66,406 kg (146,400 lb)
Cargo	64,000 kg (141,100 lb)
Max payload: Cargo	40,324 kg (88,900 lb)
Max T-O weight	151,315 kg (333,600 lb)
Max ramp weight	152,405 kg (336,000 lb)
Max zero-fuel weight	104,330 kg (230,000 lb)
Max landing weight	112,037 kg (247,000 lb)
Max wing loading	537·1 kg/m² (110·0 lb/sq ft)
Max power loading	448 kg/kN (4·39 lb/lb st)

PERFORMANCE (at average cruising weight, unless indicated otherwise):

Never-exceed speed	Mach 0·95
Max level speed	545 knots (1,010 km/h; 627 mph)
Max cruising speed at 7,620 m (25,000 ft)	
	525 knots (973 km/h; 605 mph)
Econ cruising speed	478 knots (886 km/h; 550 mph)
Stalling speed (flaps down, at max landing weight)	
	105 knots (195 km/h; 121 mph)
Max rate of climb at S/L	1,219 m (4,000 ft)/min
Service ceiling	11,885 m (39,000 ft)
CAR T-O to 10·7 m (35 ft)	3,054 m (10,020 ft)
CAR landing from 15 m (50 ft)	1,095 m (6,250 ft)
Landing run	785 m (2,575 ft)

Range with max fuel, 14 first class and 133 tourist class passengers, long-range step cruise, international reserves 5,000 nm (9,265 km; 5,755 miles)

Range with 36,287 kg (80,000 lb) cargo, long-range step cruise, international reserves 3,150 nm (5,835 km; 3,625 miles)

BOEING MODEL 727

Boeing announced its intention to supplement the four-jet 707/720 series with the three-engined short/medium-range 727 on 5 December 1960. The 727 switched to a rear-engined configuration, but has an upper fuselage section identical with that of the 707/720 and many parts and systems are interchangeable between the three types.

Boeing 707 testbed aircraft powered by CFM56 turbofan engines

Boeing Model 727-200 three-turbofan short/medium-range transport in the insignia of Yemen Airways

The original short-fuselage 727-100, 727-100C, 727-100QC and 727-100 Business Jet versions of the Model 727 are no longer in production; details of these can be found in the 1973-74 *Jane's*.

The only version currently available is the advanced model of the lengthened 727-200 announced by Boeing on 12 May 1971, at an initial ramp weight of 86,635 kg (191,000 lb), and first delivered in June 1972. This has a much greater fuel capacity and range than earlier 727-200s; the interior features the 'Superjet-look', and a large 'Carry-all' compartment is available at no extra cost. Availability of successively more powerful engines has made possible weight increases up to a current max ramp weight of 95,254 kg (210,000 lb) for aircraft with JT8D-15/17/17R turbofans. The current 727-200 is certificated for Category IIIA 15 m (50 ft) decision height, 213 m (700 ft) RVR landing. Improved overhead duct air-conditioning is now standard. A performance data computer system has been added as standard equipment to provide onboard information for optimisation of flight profile and fuel consumption.

A total of 1,807 Model 727s had been sold by 1 September 1980, of which 1,646 had been delivered. The 727 is the only commercial transport aircraft of which more than 1,500 have been delivered, the 1,500th example being handed over to United Air Lines on 2 July 1979. More than 1,000 of those sold are of the 727-200 series.

TYPE: Three-turbofan airliner.

WINGS: Cantilever low-wing monoplane. Special Boeing aerofoil sections. Thickness/chord ratio from 9% to 13%. Dihedral 3°. Incidence 2°. Sweepback at quarter-chord 32°. Primary structure is a two-spar aluminium alloy box with conventional ribs. Upper and lower surfaces are of riveted skin-stringer construction. There are no chordwise splices in the primary structure from the fuselage to the wingtip. Advanced 727-200s at gross weight options have modified stringers and in-spar webs, as well as upper and lower surface wing skins of increased gauge. Structure is fail-safe. Hydraulically-powered aluminium ailerons, in inboard (high speed) and outboard (low speed) units, operate in conjunction with flight spoilers. Triple-slotted trailing-edge flaps constructed primarily of aluminium and aluminium honeycomb. Four aluminium leading-edge slats on outer two-thirds of wing. Three Krueger leading-edge flaps on inboard third of wing, made from magnesium or aluminium castings. Seven spoilers on each wing, consisting of five flight spoilers outboard and two ground spoilers inboard. Spoilers function also as airbrakes. Balance tab in each outboard aileron; control tab in each inboard aileron. Controls are hydraulically-powered dual systems with automatic reversion to manual control. Actuators manufactured primarily by Weston, National Water Lift and Bertea. Thermal anti-icing of wing leading-edges by engine bleed air.

FUSELAGE: Semi-monocoque fail-safe structure, with aluminium alloy skin reinforced by circumferential frames and longitudinal stringers.

TAIL UNIT: Cantilever structure, built primarily of aluminium alloys, with tailplane mounted near tip of fin. Dual-powered variable-incidence tailplane, with direct manual reversion. Hydraulically-powered dual elevator control system with control tab manual reversion. Hydraulically-powered rudders, utilising two main systems with backup third system for lower rudder. Anti-balance tabs; rudder trim by displacing system neutral.

LANDING GEAR: Hydraulically-retractable tricycle type, with twin wheels on all three units. Nosewheels retract forward, main gear inward into fuselage. Boeing oleo-pneumatic shock-absorbers. B.F. Goodrich nose-gear wheels, tyres and brakes are standard on all models. Goodrich and Bendix are both approved suppliers of main-gear wheels, tyres and brakes for all Model 727s. Nosewheels and tyres are size 32 × 11·5 Type VIII. Main-gear wheels size 49 × 17, with tyres size 50 × 21 Type VII, are standard.

POWER PLANT: Three Pratt & Whitney JT8D-9A turbofan engines with thrust reversers and full sound attenuation, each flat rated at 64·5 kN (14,500 lb st) to 29°C, are standard. Optionally, JT8D-15s rated at 68·9 kN (15,500 lb st), JT8D-17s rated at 71·2 kN (16,000 lb st),

or JT8D-17Rs with automatic performance reserve (APR) and rated at 77·4 kN (17,400 lb st) can be fitted. The JT8D-17R engines are normally operated at an alternative rating of 72·9 kN (16,400 lb st); APR senses any significant loss in thrust by an engine during take-off and initial climb, automatically increasing thrust on the other engines to 77·4 kN (17,400 lb). This feature significantly improves performance from hot/high airports. Each engine has individual fuel system fed from integral tanks in wings, but all three tanks are interconnected. Optional fuselage fuel tanks can be installed, displacing forward and/or aft cargo compartment volume. Standard total fuel capacity 30,623 litres (8,090 US gallons). Modular design bladder cell tanks with dual fuel barrier can be installed to contain up to approximately 9,387 litres (2,480 US gallons). Single pressure fuelling point, rated at 2,271 litres (600 US gallons)/min, near leading-edge underside of starboard wing at mid-span. Total usable oil capacity 45·5 litres (12 US gallons).

ACCOMMODATION: Crew of three on flight deck. Basic accommodation for 145 passengers (14 first class, 131 tourist class, 4-6 abreast). Max capacity 189 passengers. Two galleys forward and two aft. One toilet forward and two aft. Other layouts to customer's specification. A 'Superjet-look' passenger interior design is standard. The wide-body effect is achieved (without any changes in cross-section dimensions) by lighting and architectural redesign. Retrofit kits for the 'Superjet-look' are offered, as are kits for larger 'Carry-all' compartments. Entry via hydraulically-operated integral aft stairway under centre engine and door at front on port side with optional Weber Aircraft electrically-operated airstairs. Two Type III emergency exits in mid-cabin on each side and aft service door on each side. The starboard forward service door is opposite the port forward passenger door. Two heated and pressurised baggage and freight compartments under floor, forward and aft of main landing gear bay. Each compartment has one outward-opening cargo door; a second cargo door is optional for the aft compartment.

SYSTEMS: Garrett-AiResearch air-conditioning and pressurisation system, using engine bleed air combined with air-cycle refrigeration. Pressure differential 0·59 bars (8·6 lb/sq in). Three independent 207 bar (3,000 lb/sq in) hydraulic systems, utilising Boeing Material Specification BMS 3-11 hydraulic fluid, provide power for flying controls, landing gear and aft airstairs. Electrical system includes three 40kVA 400Hz constant-frequency AC generators, three 50A transformer-rectifier units, one 22Ah battery. Garrett-AiResearch APU provides electrical power and compressed air for engine starting and air-conditioning on ground.

AVIONICS AND EQUIPMENT: Standard avionics include dual Wulfsberg 2000 VHF com installations, Motorola NA-134D2 Selcal, flight and service attendants' interphone, passenger address system, ARINC 542 flight recorder and remote encoder, Collins 642C1 voice recorder, dual King KNR 6030 VHF nav systems, ARINC 570 ADF, dual King KDM 7000 DME, dual King KXP ATC, Collins 51Z-4 marker beacon, RCA Primus 90 colour weather radar, Sperry SP-150 single-channel Mod Blk V autopilot, dual yaw dampers, dual vertical gyros, dual Sperry C-9D compasses, Honeywell HG 7502 radio altimeter, instrument comparison and warning system, ARINC 545 digital air data system, variable instrument switching, dual FD-108 flight directors, and Sundstrand ground proximity warning system. Optional avionics include FD-110 or Sperry Z-15 flight directors, Sperry C-11 compass system, HF com, Collins or King VHF, third VHF, Bendix weather radar, dual weather radar systems, Bendix DFA-73A-1 ADF, dual ADF, dual DME, autothrottles, speed command, dual autopilot channels, roll monitor and flare coupler, Omega and dual INS.

DIMENSIONS, EXTERNAL:

Wing span	32·92 m (108 ft 0 in)
Wing chord at root	7·70 m (25 ft 3 in)
Wing chord at tip	2·34 m (7 ft 8 in)
Wing aspect ratio	7·07
Length overall	46·69 m (153 ft 2 in)

Length of fuselage	41·51 m (136 ft 2 in)
Height overall	10·36 m (34 ft 0 in)
Tailplane span	10·90 m (35 ft 9 in)
Wheel track	5·72 m (18 ft 9 in)
Wheelbase	19·28 m (63 ft 3 in)
Passenger door (ventral): Height	1·93 m (6 ft 4 in)
Width	0·81 m (2 ft 8 in)
Passenger door (fwd): Height	1·83 m (6 ft 0 in)
Width	0·86 m (2 ft 10 in)
Height to sill	2·67 m (8 ft 9 in)
Service door (fwd): Height	1·65 m (5 ft 5 in)
Width	0·84 m (2 ft 9 in)
Service doors (aft, each): Height	1·52 m (5 ft 0 in)
Width	0·76 m (2 ft 6 in)
Baggage hold door (fwd): Height	1·07 m (3 ft 6 in)
Width	1·37 m (4 ft 6 in)
Baggage hold door (aft): Height	1·12 m (3 ft 8 in)
Width	1·37 m (4 ft 6 in)

DIMENSIONS, INTERNAL:

Cabin (aft of flight deck to rear pressure bulkhead):	
Length	28·24 m (92 ft 8 in)
Max width	3·55 m (11 ft 8 in)
Max height	2·11 m (6 ft 11 in)
Floor area	91·05 m² (980 sq ft)
Volume	188·4 m³ (6,652 cu ft)
Baggage hold (fwd)	20·1 m³ (710 cu ft)
Baggage hold (aft): standard	23·1 m³ (815 cu ft)
with optional 2nd door	21·1 m³ (745 cu ft)

AREAS:

Wings, gross	157·9 m² (1,700 sq ft)
Ailerons (total)	5·30 m² (57 sq ft)
Trailing-edge flaps, retracted (total)	26·10 m² (281 sq ft)
Trailing-edge flaps, extended (total)	36·04 m² (388 sq ft)
Flight spoilers (total)	7·41 m² (79·8 sq ft)
Fin	33·07 m² (356 sq ft)
Rudder, incl tabs	6·13 m² (66 sq ft)
Tailplane	34·93 m² (376 sq ft)
Elevators, incl tabs	8·83 m² (95 sq ft)

WEIGHTS AND LOADINGS (A: brake release weight of 83,820 kg; 184,800 lb, B: brake release weight of 86,405 kg; 190,500 lb, C: brake release weight of 95,027 kg; 209,500 lb):

Operating weight empty (basic specification):	
A	44,588 kg (98,300 lb)
B	45,132 kg (99,500 lb)
C	46,021 kg (101,460 lb)
Operating weight empty (typical airline):	
A	45,360 kg (100,000 lb)
Max payload (structural, based on airline operating weight empty): A	18,144 kg (40,000 lb)
Max T-O weight: A	83,820 kg (184,800 lb)
B	86,405 kg (190,500 lb)
C	95,027 kg (209,500 lb)
Max ramp weight: A	84,275 kg (185,800 lb)
B	86,635 kg (191,000 lb)
C	95,254 kg (210,000 lb)
Max zero-fuel weight: A	62,595 kg (138,000 lb)
B	63,500 kg (140,000 lb)
C	65,315 kg (144,000 lb)
Max landing weight: A, B	70,080 kg (154,500 lb)
C	73,028 kg (161,000 lb)
Max wing loading: A	530·7 kg/m² (108·7 lb/sq ft)
B	544·4 kg/m² (111·5 lb/sq ft)
C	595·7 kg/m² (122 lb/sq ft)
Max power loading: A	392 kg/kN (4·2 lb/lb st)
B	404·5 kg/kN (4·1 lb/lb st)
C	445 kg/kN (4·4 lb/lb st)

PERFORMANCE (A at brake release weight of 83,820 kg; 184,800 lb, B at brake release weight of 86,405 kg; 190,500 lb, and C at brake release weight of 95,027 kg; 209,500 lb, except where indicated):

Max operating speed	Mach 0·90
Max level speed: A at 6,585 m (21,600 ft)	549 knots (1,017 km/h; 632 mph)
B, C at 6,250 m (20,500 ft)	539 knots (999 km/h; 621 mph)
Max cruising speed: A at 6,705 m (22,000 ft)	514 knots (953 km/h; 592 mph)

B at 7,530 m (24,700 ft)
520 knots (964 km/h; 599 mph)
Econ cruising speed at 9,145 m (30,000 ft)
495 knots (917 km/h; 570 mph)
Stalling speed at S/L, flaps down:
at 72,575 kg (160,000 lb)
106 knots (197 km/h; 122 mph)
Initial cruise altitude   10,060 m (33,000 ft)
Min ground turning radius   24·49 m (80 ft 4 in)
Runway LCN at max weight of 86,635 kg (191,000 lb),
optimum tyre pressure and 0·51 m (20 in) flexible
pavement:
50 × 21 tyres   70
CAR T-O distance to 10·7 m (35 ft):
A   2,938 m (9,640 ft)
B   2,591 m (8,500 ft)
C   3,140 m (10,300 ft)
CAR landing distance from 15 m (50 ft):
at 71,668 kg (158,000 lb)   1,430 m (4,690 ft)
Range at long-range cruising speed, with fuel load as
specified and payload of 12,474 kg (27,500 lb), ATA
domestic reserves:
A with 30,623 litres (8,090 US gallons)
2,000 nm (3,706 km; 2,303 miles)
B with 33,878 litres (8,950 US gallons)
2,200 nm (4,077 km; 2,533 miles)
C with 36,831 litres (9,730 US gallons)
2,400 nm (4,447 km; 2,763 miles)
Range with 18,144 kg (40,000 lb) payload, at long-
range cruising speed, ATA domestic reserves:
A   1,450 nm (2,685 km; 1,670 miles)
B   1,605 nm (2,970 km; 1,845 miles)
C   approx 2,140 nm (3,966 km; 2,464 miles)
OPERATIONAL NOISE LEVELS (with JT8D-15 engines, FAR
Pt 36):
T-O noise level at brake release weight of 86,405 kg
(190,500 lb)   100 EPNdB
Approach noise level at 70,080 kg (154,500 lb) landing
weight and 30° flap   100·4 EPNdB
Sideline noise level   102·2 EPNdB

BOEING MODEL 737
USAF designation: T-43A

The decision to build this short-range transport was
announced by Boeing on 19 February 1965. Simultaneously, a first order for 21 aircraft was placed by Lufthansa.

The original Model 737 was designed to utilise many
components and assemblies already in production for the
Boeing 727. Design began on 11 May 1964, and the first
Model 737 flew on 9 April 1967. Deliveries began before
the end of 1967, following FAA certification on 15
December. Sales of the 737 totalled 840 by 1 October
1980, of which 693 had been delivered, including 19
Model 737-200s modified as T-43A navigation trainers
for the US Air Force (see 1975-76 *Jane's*). A production
increase to eight and a half aircraft per month was made in
1979.

Details of the early production versions of the Model
737, and of subsequent design development, can be found
in the 1974-75 *Jane's*. Versions currently available are as
follows:

Advanced 737-200. Current standard model, with max
ramp weight of 52,615 kg (116,000 lb) and max T-O
weight of 52,390 kg (115,500 lb). JT8D-9A engines (each
64·5 kN; 14,500 lb st) standard; JT8D-15 (68·9 kN;
15,500 lb st); JT8D-17 (71·2 kN; 16,000 lb st); or JT8D-
17R with Automatic Performance Reserve (75·6 kN;
17,000 lb st) engines optional; basic fuel capacity of
19,532 litres (5,160 US gallons). Accommodation for 115
passengers and baggage, with 86 cm (34 in) pitch seating,
or up to 130 passengers in 74 cm (29 in) pitch seating with
no reduction in cabin facilities. A gross weight option with
a max ramp weight of 53,295 kg (117,500 lb) and max
T-O weight of 53,070 kg (117,000 lb) is available.

Advanced 737-200C/QC. Standard convertible pas-
senger/cargo model with strengthened fuselage and floor,
and a large two-position upper-deck cargo door with
effective opening of 2·15 m × 3·40 m (7 ft 0½ in × 11 ft 2
in). The quick-change (QC) feature allows more rapid
conversion by using palletised passenger seating and other
special interior furnishings. A gross weight option with a
max ramp weight of 53,295 kg (117,500 lb) and max T-O
weight of 53,070 kg (117,000 lb) is available.

Advanced 737-200 Executive Jet. Same as standard
Advanced 737-200, except interiors are adapted to special
business and executive luxury requirements. Executive
interiors can be obtained from vendors. A limited kit
selection is available from Boeing. Additional fuel capacity offered by installation of fuel cells in lower cargo compartments. With max fuel this model can carry 15 passengers up to 3,000 nm (5,560 km; 3,455 miles).

Advanced 737-200 High Gross Weight Structure.
Higher gross weight models of the Advanced 737-
200/200C, for longer-range use, are available in two versions. One has a maximum taxi weight of 56,700 kg
(125,000 lb) and a maximum T-O weight of 56,472 kg
(124,500 lb) with JT8D-15, -17, or -17R engines, and a
fuel capacity of either 20,951 litres (5,535 US gallons) or
22,598 litres (5,970 US gallons). The additional capacity
for increased range capability is provided by a 1,419 litre
(375 US gallon) or a 3,066 litre (810 US gallon) fuel tank
installed in the aft lower cargo compartment. The second
version, with a maximum taxi weight of 58,332 kg
(128,600 lb), maximum T-O weight of 58,105 kg
(128,100 lb), design landing weight of 48,534 kg (107,000
lb), and maximum zero-fuel weight of 43,091 kg (95,000
lb), has approximately 650 nm (1,204 km; 748 miles)
greater range capability than the standard Advanced
737-200 (130 passenger payload). Sectors of 2,300 nm
(4,262 km; 2,648 miles) can be served with a 130 passenger payload and typical fuel reserves. Aircraft is identical to the current Advanced 737-200 except for the auxiliary fuel tank, new wheels, tyres and brakes, and
strengthened landing gear and wing structure.

All higher gross weight versions meet FAR Pt 36 and
ICAO Annex 16 in respect of noise characteristics.

An FAA-certificated kit is available which enables the
Model 737 to operate from unpaved or gravel runways.
The kit includes a vortex dissipator for each engine, consisting of a short hollow boom that protrudes from under
each engine's forward edge. The boom is capped by a plug
with downward-facing orifices. Pressurised engine bleed
air forced through these orifices destroys any ground-level
vortex and prevents small pieces of gravel being ingested
by the engines. Other items include a gravel deflection 'ski'

Boeing 727-200 three-turbofan short/medium-range transport (*Pilot Press*)

on the nosewheel, deflectors between the main landing
gear wheels, protective shields over hydraulic tubing and
speed brake cable on the main gear strut, glassfibre reinforcement of lower inboard flap surfaces, application of
Teflon-base paint to fuselage and wing undersurfaces and
provision of more robust DME, ATC and VHF antennae.

On 10 February 1980 British Airways began operations
with the first of 28 Advanced 737s which the airline calls
'Super 737s'. These aircraft are equipped with advanced
flight deck avionics, including a Sperry SP-177 digital
automatic flight control system. Lufthansa has ordered 32
Advanced 737s with similar equipment; these will also
have a Sperry RD-800J horizontal situation indicator and
an engine noise reduction 'mixer'. Category IIIA certification of these AFCS versions is expected by late Spring
1981.

The following version was under consideration in mid-
1980:

737-300. Projected 'stretched' version, with longer
fuselage and new high bypass ratio turbofan engines. Two
additional six-seat rows plus one half-row (three seats),
repositioned rear galley, made possible by insertion of
plugs totalling 2·13 m (7 ft 0 in) fore and aft of wings.
Engines under consideration include General Elec-
tric/SNECMA CFM56-3 and Rolls-Royce/Japanese
Aero-Engines RJ-500, both in the 89 kN (20,000 lb st)
class.

The description which follows applies to the versions of
the 737-200 in current production:

TYPE: Twin-turbofan short-range transport.

WINGS: Cantilever low-wing monoplane. Special Boeing
wing sections. Average thickness/chord ratio 12·89%.
Dihedral 6°. Incidence 1° at root. Sweepback at
quarter-chord 25°. Aluminium alloy dual-path fail-safe
two-spar structure. Ailerons of aluminium honeycomb
construction. Boeing-developed triple-slotted trailing-
edge flaps, all of aluminium with trailing-edges of
aluminium honeycomb. Aluminium alloy Krueger flaps
on leading-edge, inboard of nacelles. Three leading-
edge slats of aluminium alloy with aluminium honeycomb trailing-edge on each wing from engine to wingtip.
Two-section aluminium honeycomb flight spoilers on
each outer wing serve both as airbrakes in the air and for
lateral control, in association with ailerons. Two-section
aluminium honeycomb ground spoilers on each wing,
inboard of engine, are used only during landing. Ailerons are hydraulically powered by two hydraulic systems with manual reversion. Trailing-edge flaps are
hydraulically powered, with electrical backup.
Leading-edge slats and Krueger flaps are symmetrically
powered by one hydraulic system normally, and by a
second hydraulic system for alternate extension. Flight
spoilers are symmetrically powered by the two main
individual hydraulic systems. Engine bleed air for anti-
icing supplied to engine nose cowls and all wing
leading-edge slats.

FUSELAGE: Aluminium alloy semi-monocoque fail-safe
structure.

TAIL UNIT: Cantilever aluminium alloy multi-spar structure. Variable-incidence tailplane. Elevator has dual
hydraulic power, with manual reversion. Rudder is
powered by a dual actuator from two main hydraulic
systems, with a standby hydraulic actuator and system.
Tailplane trim has dual electric drive motors, with manual backup. Elevator control tabs for manual reversion
are locked out during hydraulic actuation.

LANDING GEAR: Hydraulically-retractable tricycle type,
with free-fall extension. Nosewheels retract forward,
main units inward. No main gear doors: wheels form
wheel-well seal. Twin wheels on each main and nose
unit. Boeing oleo-pneumatic shock-absorbers. Main
wheels and tyres size 40 × 14-16 (low-pressure 40 ×
18-17 tyres, or C40 × 14-21/H40 × 14·5-19 tyres with
heavy-duty wheel brakes, are available optionally).
Nosewheels and tyres size 24 × 7·7 (low-pressure 24·5
× 8·5 tyres available optionally). Bendix multi-disc
brakes. Hydro-Aire Mk III anti-skid units and automatic brakes standard.

POWER PLANT: Two Pratt & Whitney JT8D turbofan

Boeing 737-200 twin-turbofan short-range transport (*Pilot Press*)

Boeing Model 737-200 twin-turbofan short-range transport in the appropriate insignia of Air-Executive Norway Busy Bee

engines (details under individual model listings), in underwing pods. High-performance target-type thrust reversers, with full sound attenuation quiet nacelles. All models have standard fuel capacity of up to 19,532 litres (5,160 US gallons), with integral fuel cells in wing centre-section as well as two integral wing tanks. Long-range version has auxiliary fuel tank in aft lower cargo compartment, giving max fuel capacity of 22,598 litres (5,970 US gallons). Single-point pressure refuelling through leading-edge of starboard wing. Fuelling rate 1,135 litres (300 US gallons)/min. Auxiliary overwing fuelling points. Total oil capacity 41·5 litres (11 US gallons).

ACCOMMODATION: Crew of two side by side on flight deck. Details of passenger accommodation given under individual model descriptions. Passenger versions are equipped with forward airstair; an aft airstair is optional. Convertible passenger/cargo versions have the aft airstair as standard and forward airstair optional. One plug-type door at each corner of cabin, with passenger doors on port side and service doors on starboard side. Overwing escape hatches on each side. Basic passenger cabin has one lavatory and one galley at each end. Large-volume hand baggage overhead bins. Provision for a large variety of interior arrangements. Freight holds forward and aft of wing, under floor.

SYSTEMS: Air-conditioning and pressurisation system utilises engine bleed air. Max differential 0·52 bars (7·5 lb/sq in). Two independent hydraulic systems, using fire-resistant hydraulic fluid, for flying controls, flaps, slats, landing gear, nosewheel steering and brakes; pressure 207 bars (3,000 lb/sq in). No pneumatic system. Electrical supply provided by engine-driven generators. Garrett-AiResearch APU for air supply and electrical power in flight and on the ground, as well as engine starting.

AVIONICS AND EQUIPMENT: Equipment to satisfy FAA Category II low weather minimum criteria is standard, as well as a Lear Siegler performance data computer system. Autopilot, specially designed for ILS localiser and glideslope control, with control wheel steering. Optional equipment will permit Category IIIA capability. Very Low Frequency (VLF-Omega) navigation systems, and a range of flight management systems with various levels of automation, including autothrottle, automatic flight control, and a performance navigation computer system, are available as options.

DIMENSIONS, EXTERNAL:
Wing span	28·35 m (93 ft 0 in)
Wing chord at root	4·71 m (15 ft 5·6 in)
Wing chord at tip	1·60 m (5 ft 3 in)
Wing aspect ratio	8·83
Length overall	30·53 m (100 ft 2 in)
Length of fuselage	29·54 m (96 ft 11 in)
Height overall	11·28 m (37 ft 0 in)
Tailplane span	10·97 m (36 ft 0 in)
Wheel track	5·23 m (17 ft 2 in)
Wheelbase	11·38 m (37 ft 4 in)

Main passenger door (port, front):
Height	1·83 m (6 ft 0 in)
Width	0·86 m (2 ft 10 in)
Height to sill	2·62 m (8 ft 7 in)

Passenger door (port, rear):
Height	1·83 m (6 ft 0 in)
Width	0·76 m (2 ft 6 in)
Width with airstair	0·86 m (2 ft 10 in)
Height to sill	2·72 m (8 ft 11 in)

Galley service door (stbd, front):
Height	1·65 m (5 ft 5 in)
Width	0·76 m (2 ft 6 in)
Height to sill	2·62 m (8 ft 7 in)

Service door (stbd, rear):
Height	1·65 m (5 ft 5 in)
Width	0·76 m (2 ft 6 in)
Height to sill	2·72 m (8 ft 11 in)

Freight hold door (stbd, fwd):
Height	1·30 m (4 ft 3 in)
Width	1·22 m (4 ft 0 in)
Height to sill	1·30 m (4 ft 3 in)

Freight hold door (stbd, rear):
Height	1·22 m (4 ft 0 in)
Width	1·22 m (4 ft 0 in)
Height to sill	1·45 m (4 ft 9 in)

DIMENSIONS, INTERNAL:
Cabin, incl galley and toilet:
Length	20·88 m (68 ft 6 in)
Max width	3·52 m (11 ft 6½ in)
Max height	2·18 m (7 ft 2 in)
Floor area	63·8 m² (687 sq ft)
Volume	131·28 m³ (4,636 cu ft)
Freight hold (fwd) volume	10·48 m³ (370 cu ft)
Freight hold (rear) volume	14·30 m³ (505 cu ft)

AREA:
Wings, gross	91·04 m² (980 sq ft)

WEIGHTS AND LOADINGS (standard aircraft at brake release weight of 52,390 kg; 115,500 lb except where indicated):

Operating weight empty:
200	27,646 kg (60,950 lb)
200C all passenger	28,916 kg (63,750 lb)
200C all cargo	27,374 kg (60,350 lb)
200QC all passenger	30,422 kg (67,070 lb)
200QC all cargo	27,828 kg (61,350 lb)

Max payload:
200	15,445 kg (34,050 lb)
200C all passenger	14,175 kg (31,250 lb)
200C all cargo	17,531 kg (38,650 lb)
200QC all passenger	12,669 kg (27,930 lb)
200QC all cargo	17,078 kg (37,650 lb)
200 Executive Jet	2,268 kg (5,000 lb)

Max T-O weight:
All models, basic	52,390 kg (115,500 lb)
Optional	53,070 kg (117,000 lb)
	or 56,472 kg (124,500 lb)
	or 58,105 kg (128,100 lb)

Max ramp weight:
All models, basic	52,615 kg (116,000 lb)
Optional	53,295 kg (117,500 lb)
	or 56,700 kg (125,000 lb)
	or 58,332 kg (128,600 lb)

Max zero-fuel weight:
All models, basic	43,091 kg (95,000 lb)
Optional for 200C	up to 44,906 kg (99,000 lb)

Max landing weight:
All models, basic	46,720 kg (103,000 lb)
Optional	47,627 kg (105,000 lb)
	or 48,534 kg (107,000 lb)

Wing loading:
All models, basic	575·5 kg/m² (117·9 lb/sq ft)
Max optional	638·2 kg/m² (130·7 lb/sq ft)

Power loading (JT8D-17):
All models, basic	368 kg/kN (3·61 lb/lb st)
Max optional	408 kg/kN (4·00 lb/lb st)

WEIGHTS AND LOADINGS (at brake release weight of 56,472 kg; 124,500 lb):
Operating weight empty	27,760 kg (61,200 lb)
Max payload	15,331 kg (33,800 lb)
Max T-O weight	56,472 kg (124,500 lb)
Max ramp weight	56,700 kg (125,000 lb)
Max zero-fuel weight	43,091 kg (95,000 lb)
Max landing weight	48,534 kg (107,000 lb)
Max wing loading	620·24 kg/m² (127·04 lb/sq ft)
Max power loading (JT8D-17)	397 kg/kN (3·9 lb/lb st)

PERFORMANCE (ISA, with JT8D-15 engines):
Max operating speed, all models   Mach 0·84
Max level speed, all models, at 7,165 m (23,500 ft)
    509 knots (943 km/h; 586 mph)
Max cruising speed, 737-200 at an average cruise weight of 40,823 kg (90,000 lb) at 6,890 m (22,600 ft)   500 knots (927 km/h; 576 mph)
Econ cruising speed at 9,145 m (30,000 ft)
    Mach 0·73
Stalling speed, flaps down, at max landing weight
    99 knots (184 km/h; 114 mph)
Runway LCN (at max taxi weight of 52,615 kg; 116,000 lb, optimum tyre pressure and 20 in flexible pavement):
40 × 14-16 tyres	51
40 × 14-21 tyres	51
40 × 18-17 tyres	36

FAR T-O distance to 10·7 m (35 ft), 737-200 at 49,435 kg (109,000 lb) AUW and 28·9°C (84°F):
JT8D-9 engines	2,073 m (6,800 ft)
JT8D-17 engines	1,615 m (5,300 ft)

FAR landing distance from 15 m (50 ft), 737-200 at max landing weight   1,341 m (4,400 ft)
Min ground turning radius   17·58 m (57 ft 8 in)
Range, cruising at 10,060 m (33,000 ft), including 3,016 kg (6,650 lb) reserve fuel, 737-200 at 52,615 kg (116,000 lb) taxi weight with 115 passengers
    1,900 nm (3,521 km; 2,188 miles)
Range, all conditions as above, except 58,332 kg (128,600 lb) taxi weight
    2,400 nm (4,448 km; 2,764 miles)
Range, conditions as above, 737-200 with 130 passengers   2,300 nm (4,262 km; 2,648 miles)

OPERATIONAL NOISE LEVELS (JT8D-9 engines and nacelle acoustic treatment, FAR Pt 36):
T-O noise level at 52,390 kg (115,500 lb) brake release weight   95·3 EPNdB
Sideline noise level at 52,390 kg (115,500 lb) brake release weight   100·6 EPNdB
Approach noise level at 46,720 kg (103,000 lb) max landing weight   102·4 EPNdB

BOEING MODEL 747
USAF designation: E-4

First details of this wide-body commercial transport were announced on 13 April 1966, simultaneously with the news that Pan American had placed a $525 million contract for 25 Boeing 747s, including spares. Programme go-ahead date was officially 25 July 1966.

The first 747 (designated RA001) flew for the first time on 9 February 1969 and has been retained by Boeing as an experimental flight test vehicle for airframe, avionics and systems technology development, evaluation, and certification. FAA certification of the basic 747 was granted on 30 December 1969. The first 747 to be delivered was received by Pan American on 12 December 1969, and this company inaugurated commercial service with the type on its New York/London route on 22 January 1970. Orders

Boeing Model 747-200B four-turbofan commercial transport, the first of three for Thai International

for all versions of the 747 totalled 558 by 1 October 1980, of which 467 had been delivered. The total 747 fleet operating in Autumn 1980 carried about 4·3 million passengers each month, and had flown more than 8·5 million hours in revenue service.

Versions of the Boeing 747 are available currently as follows:

747-100B. The 747-100 was introduced into commercial service in January 1970. This aircraft, in versions with gross weights up to 334,751 kg (738,000 lb), more than doubled passenger and cargo payload capabilities by comparison with any previous commercial aircraft. A total of 167 was sold. The current replacement -100B incorporates strengthened wing, fuselage and landing gear structure. Versions with max taxi weights of 323,411 kg (713,000 lb), 334,751 kg (738,000 lb), and 341,555 kg (753,000 lb) allow for the installation of a variety of optional engines in addition to the basic 208·8 kN (46,950 lb st) Pratt & Whitney JT9D-7A. These include the 216 kN (48,570 lb st) JT9D-7AW, 213·5 kN (48,000 lb st) JT9D-7F, 222·4 kN (50,000 lb st) JT9D-7FW, 222·4 kN (50,000 lb st) JT9D-7J, 233·5 kN (52,500 lb st) General Electric CF6-50E/E1/E2, 206·8 kN (46,500 lb st) CF6-45A/A2 and CF6-45B/B2, 222·8 kN (50,100 lb st) Rolls-Royce RB.211-524B2, and 229·5 kN (51,600 lb st) Rolls-Royce RB.211-524C2. Initial order, with JT9D-7F engines, was placed by Iran Air in 1978, and this aircraft was delivered on 5 July 1979.

747SP. Lighter-weight, shorter-bodied derivative of the 747-100B. Described separately.

747SR. This short-range version of the 747-100B embodies structural changes required for high take-off and landing cycles. The initial purchase of four 747SRs by Japan Air Lines (later increased to seven) was announced on 30 October 1972, and All Nippon Airways has ordered 13. The JAL aircraft have max taxi weights of 273,515 kg (603,000 lb) and 237,225 kg (523,000 lb). The first 747SR flew on 4 September 1973 and was delivered on 26 September 1973. Thirteen had been delivered by early 1980. The 747SR is available at max taxi weights up to 341,555 kg (753,000 lb) with the same engines as available to the 747-100B.

747-200B. Passenger version, with same accommodation as 747-100B. First flown on 11 October 1970 and certificated on 23 December 1970; deliveries began on 15 January 1971. Basic version had max T-O weight of 351,535 kg (775,000 lb) and increased fuel capacity. Available now with 216 kN (48,570 lb st) JT9D-7AW engines and max T-O weight of 356,070 kg (785,000 lb); 222·4 kN (50,000 lb st) JT9D-7FW and max T-O weight of 365,140 kg (805,000 lb); 222·4 kN (50,000 lb st) JT9D-7J engines and max T-O weight of 362,875 kg (800,000 lb); 235·7 kN (53,000 lb st) JT9D-7Q engines and max T-O weight of 377,840 kg (833,000 lb); 235·7 kN (53,000 lb st) JT9D-70A engines and max T-O weight of 377,840 kg (833,000 lb); 233·5 kN (52,500 lb st) General Electric CF6-50E engines and max T-O weight of 371,945 kg (820,000 lb); 233·5 kN (52,500 lb st) CF6-50E1/E2 engines and max T-O weight of 377,840 kg (833,000 lb); 222·8 kN (50,100 lb st) Rolls-Royce RB.211-524B2 engines and max T-O weight of 371,945 kg (820,000 lb); 229·5 kN (51,600 lb st) RB.211-524C2 engines and max T-O weight of 377,840 kg (833,000 lb); and 236·25 kN (53,110 lb st) RB.211-524D4 engines and max T-O weight of 377,840 kg (833,000 lb).

During certification tests for the Pratt & Whitney JT9D-7Q engine, on 23 May 1979, a 747-200B took off from an airport near Glascow, Montana, at a gross weight of 385,970 kg (850,920 lb). This is the heaviest T-O weight ever recorded by an aeroplane, and while not certificated as an official record by Boeing, it was one of a series of take-offs at more than 385,553 kg (850,000 lb) made by this aircraft during heavy-weight noise certification tests.

747-200B Combi. A version of the basic 747-200B, modified by the installation of a 3·05 × 3·40 m (120 × 134 in) cargo door in the port side of the fuselage, aft of the wing. This permits main deck layouts for all passengers or

for passengers and up to 12 pallets/containers, with passenger and cargo areas separated by removable bulkhead. The first modification to Combi configuration was carried out on a Sabena 747-100, and redelivery was made in February 1974. The first 747-200B production Combi was delivered to Air Canada in March 1975.

747-200C Convertible. Version of 747-200B which can be converted from all-passenger to all-cargo, or a combination of both. The first 747-200C flew on 23 March 1973, was certificated on 17 April, and was delivered to World Airways on 27 April 1973. Max T-O weight of 356,070 kg (785,000 lb) with Pratt & Whitney JT9D-7AW engines; 365,140 kg (805,000 lb) with JT9D-7FW engines; 362,875 kg (800,000 lb) with JT9D-7J engines; 371,945 kg (820,000 lb) with General Electric CF6-50E or Rolls-Royce RB.211-524B2 engines; and 377,840 kg (833,000 lb) with JT9D-7Q, JT9D-70A, General Electric CF6-50E1/E2 or Rolls-Royce RB.211-524C2/D4 engines. Total of 13 ordered by 1 October 1980.

747-200F. Freighter version, capable of delivering 90,720 kg (200,000 lb) of palletised cargo over a range of 4,100 nm (7,600 km; 4,720 miles). Certification of the first 747-200F, which is described separately, was awarded by the FAA on 7 March 1972. T-O weights as detailed for 747-200C. Total of 44 ordered by 1 October 1980.

747SUD. Version with 'stretched' upper deck. Described separately.

E-4. Advanced Airborne Command Post version of 747, developed for US Air Force. Described separately under Boeing Aerospace heading.

The following details apply specifically to the basic Model 747 passenger airliner:

TYPE: Four-turbofan heavy commercial transport.

WINGS: Cantilever low-wing monoplane. Special Boeing wing sections. Thickness/chord ratio 13·44% inboard, 7·8% at mid-span, 8% outboard. Dihedral 7°. Incidence 2°. Sweepback 37° 30′ at quarter-chord. Aluminium alloy dual-path fail-safe structure. Low-speed outboard ailerons; high-speed inboard ailerons. Triple-slotted trailing-edge flaps. Six aluminium honeycomb spoilers on each wing, comprising four flight spoilers outboard and two ground spoilers inboard. Ten variable-camber leading-edge flaps outboard and three-section Krueger flaps inboard on each wing leading-edge. All controls fully powered.

FUSELAGE: Conventional semi-monocoque structure, consisting of aluminium alloy skin, longitudinal stiffeners and circumferential frames. Structure is of fail-safe design, utilising riveting, bolting and structural bonding.

TAIL UNIT: Cantilever aluminium alloy dual-path fail-safe

Boeing 747-200B four-turbofan heavy transport aircraft (*Pilot Press*)

structure. Variable-incidence tailplane. No trim tabs. All controls fully powered.

LANDING GEAR: Hydraulically-retractable tricycle type. Twin-wheel nose unit retracts forward. Main gear comprises four four-wheel bogies: two, mounted side by side under fuselage and aft, retract forward; two mounted under wings retract inward. Cleveland Pneumatic oleo-pneumatic shock-absorbers. All 18 wheels and tubeless tyres of Model 747-100B are size 46 × 16 Type VII. Tyre pressure: main wheels 14·49 bars (210 lb/sq in), nosewheels 13·11 bars (190 lb/sq in). Main wheels and tyres size 49 × 17 on 747-200B model, pressure 14·15 bars (205 lb/sq in). The high gross weight aircraft has 49 × 19 tyres at a pressure of 13·46 bars (195 lb/sq in). Disc brakes on all main wheels, with individually-controlled anti-skid units.

POWER PLANT: Four Pratt & Whitney, General Electric or Rolls-Royce turbofan engines, as detailed in model listings, in pods pylon-mounted on wing leading-edges. Fuel in seven integral tanks. Capacity of centre wing tank varies according to version: 747-100B: 49,966 litres (13,200 US gallons); 747-200B and 747-200F: 64,973 litres (17,164 US gallons). Remaining tanks common to all versions: two inboard main tanks, each 47,492 litres (12,546 US gallons); two outboard main tanks, each 16,966 litres (4,482 US gallons); two inboard reserve tanks, each 2,021 litres (534 US gallons). Outboard mains are reduced by 1,234 litres (326 US gallons) when CF6-50E or JT9D-70A engines are installed. 747-200B also available with two outboard reserve tanks, each 2,983 litres (788 US gallons). Total capacity, including manifolds, 747-100B: 183,380 litres (48,445 US gallons); 747-200B and 747-200F: 198,385 litres (52,409 US gallons). Refuelling point on each wing between inboard and outboard engines. Total usable oil capacity 19 litres (5 US gallons).

ACCOMMODATION: Normal operating crew of three, on flight deck above level of main deck. Observer station and provision for second observer station are provided. Basic accommodation for 442 passengers, made up of 28 first class and 414 economy class, which includes a 32-passenger upper deck. Alternative layouts accommodate 447 economy class passengers in nine-abreast seating or 516 ten-abreast, with 32 passengers on upper deck. All versions have two aisles. Five passenger doors on each side, of which two forward of wing on each side are normally used. Freight holds under floor, forward and aft of wing, with doors on starboard side. One door on forward hold, two on rear hold. Aircraft is designed for fully-mechanical loading of baggage and freight. An optional side cargo door is available for passenger, convertible and freighter versions of the Model 747. Installed aft of door 4 on the port side of the fuselage, it makes possible the carriage of main-deck cargo on passenger versions. Addition of this door to the freighter allows loads up to 3·05 m (10 ft) in height to be accommodated aft of the flight deck, and also makes possible simultaneous nose and side cargo handling.

SYSTEMS: Air-cycle air-conditioning system. Pressure differential 0·61 bars (8·9 lb/sq in). Four independent hydraulic systems, pressure 207 bars (3,000 lb/sq in), each with one engine-driven and one pneumatically-driven pump. The latter pumps supplement or substitute for engine-driven pumps. A small AC-powered electric pump is installed to charge the brake accumulator during towing of the aircraft. Electrical supply from four aircooled 60kVA generators mounted one on each engine. Two 60kVA generators (supplemental cooling allows 90kVA each) mounted on APU for ground operation and to supply primary electrical power when engine-mounted generators are not operating. Three-phase 400Hz constant-frequency AC generators, 115/200V output. 28V DC power obtained from transformer-rectifier units. 24V 36Ah nickel-cadmium battery for selected ground functions and as in-flight backup. Gas turbine APU for pneumatic and electrical supplies.

AVIONICS AND EQUIPMENT: Standard avionics include two ARINC 566 VHF communications systems, two ARINC 533A HF communications systems, one ARINC 531 Selcal, three ARINC 547 VOR/ILS navigation systems, two ARINC 570 ADF, marker beacon, two ARINC 568 DME, two ARINC 572 ATC, two ARINC 552 low-range radio altimeters, two ARINC 564 weather radar units, three ARINC 561 inertial navigation systems, two heading reference systems, ARINC 412 interphone, passenger address system, passenger entertainment system, ARINC 573 flight recorder, ARINC 557 cockpit voice recorder, integrated electronic flight control system with autothrottle and rollout guidance to provide automatic stabilisation, path control and pilot assist functions for category II and III landing conditions, two ARINC 565 central air data systems, stall warning system, central instrument warning system, ground proximity warning system, attitude and navigation instrumentation, and standby attitude indication.

DIMENSIONS, EXTERNAL:

Wing span	59·64 m (195 ft 8 in)
Wing chord at root	16·56 m (54 ft 4 in)
Wing chord at tip	4·06 m (13 ft 4 in)
Wing aspect ratio	6·96
Length overall	70·66 m (231 ft 10 in)
Length of fuselage	68·63 m (225 ft 2 in)
Height overall	19·33 m (63 ft 5 in)
Tailplane span	22·17 m (72 ft 9 in)
Wheel track	11·00 m (36 ft 1 in)
Wheelbase	25·60 m (84 ft 0 in)
Passenger doors (ten, each):	
Height	1·93 m (6 ft 4 in)
Width	1·07 m (3 ft 6 in)
Height to sill	approx 4·88 m (16 ft 0 in)
Baggage door (front hold):	
Height	1·68 m (5 ft 6 in)
Width	2·64 m (8 ft 8 in)
Height to sill	approx 2·64 m (8 ft 8 in)
Baggage door (forward door, aft hold):	
Height	1·68 m (5 ft 6 in)
Width	2·64 m (8 ft 8 in)
Height to sill	approx 2·69 m (8 ft 10 in)
Bulk loading door (rear door on aft hold):	
Height	1·19 m (3 ft 11 in)
Width	1·12 m (3 ft 8 in)
Height to sill	approx 2·90 m (9 ft 6 in)
Optional cargo door (port):	
Height	3·05 m (10 ft 0 in)
Width	3·40 m (11 ft 2 in)

DIMENSIONS, INTERNAL:

Cabin, incl toilets and galleys:	
Length	57·00 m (187 ft 0 in)
Max width	6·13 m (20 ft 1½ in)
Max height	2·54 m (8 ft 4 in)
Floor area, passenger deck	327·9 m² (3,529 sq ft)
Volume, passenger deck	789 m³ (27,860 cu ft)
Baggage hold (fwd, containerised) volume	
	78·4 m³ (2,768 cu ft)
Baggage hold (aft, containerised) volume	
	68·6 m³ (2,422 cu ft)
Bulk volume	28·3 m³ (1,000 cu ft)

AREAS:

Wings, reference area	511 m² (5,500 sq ft)
Ailerons (total)	20·6 m² (222 sq ft)
Trailing-edge flaps (total)	78·7 m² (847 sq ft)
Leading-edge flaps (total)	48·1 m² (518 sq ft)
Spoilers (total)	30·8 m² (331 sq ft)
Fin	77·1 m² (830 sq ft)
Rudder	22·9 m² (247 sq ft)
Tailplane	136·6 m² (1,470 sq ft)
Elevators	32·5 m² (350 sq ft)

WEIGHTS (letters are used to denote engine installations as follows: (A) JT9D-7A/7AW; (B) JT9D-7F/7FW/7FJ; (C) JT9D-7Q; (D) JT9D-70A; (E) CF6-50E; (F) CF6-50E1/E2; (G) CF6-45A/A2 or -45B/B2; (H) RB.211-524B2; (J) RB.211-524C2; and (K) RB.211-524D4):

Operating weight empty (approx) for max available gross weights:

747SR (516 pass):		
A, B	159,664 kg	(352,000 lb)
E, F, G	161,480 kg	(356,000 lb)
H, J	164,200 kg	(362,000 lb)
747-100B (442 pass):		
A, B	169,190 kg	(373,000 lb)
E, F, G	171,460 kg	(378,000 lb)
H, J	174,180 kg	(384,000 lb)
747-200B (442 pass):		
A, B	171,460 kg	(378,000 lb)
C	172,820 kg	(381,000 lb)
D	175,540 kg	(387,000 lb)
E, F	173,725 kg	(383,000 lb)
H, J	176,450 kg	(389,000 lb)
K	175,995 kg	(388,000 lb)
747-200B Combi (232 pass and 12 pallets):		
A, B	171,005 kg	(377,000 lb)
C	172,365 kg	(380,000 lb)
D	175,540 kg	(387,000 lb)
E, F	173,725 kg	(383,000 lb)
H, J	176,450 kg	(389,000 lb)
K	175,995 kg	(388,000 lb)
747-200C (442 pass):		
A, B	175,540 kg	(387,000 lb)
C	177,355 kg	(391,000 lb)
D	180,075 kg	(397,000 lb)
E, F	178,715 kg	(394,000 lb)
H, J	181,435 kg	(400,000 lb)
K	180,530 kg	(398,000 lb)
747-200C (28 pallets):		
A, B	162,385 kg	(358,000 lb)
C	164,200 kg	(362,000 lb)
D	167,375 kg	(369,000 lb)
E, F	165,560 kg	(365,000 lb)
H, J	168,285 kg	(371,000 lb)
K	167,830 kg	(370,000 lb)

Max payload:

747SR (516 pass):		
A, B	79,150 kg	(174,500 lb)
E, F, G	77,335 kg	(170,500 lb)
H, J	74,615 kg	(164,500 lb)
747-100B (442 pass):		
A, B	69,625 kg	(153,500 lb)
E, F, G	67,360 kg	(148,500 lb)
H, J	64,635 kg	(142,500 lb)
747-200B (442 pass):		
A, B	67,360 kg	(148,500 lb)
C	66,000 kg	(145,500 lb)
D	63,275 kg	(139,500 lb)
E, F	65,090 kg	(143,500 lb)
H, J	62,370 kg	(137,500 lb)
K	62,820 kg	(138,500 lb)
747-200B Combi (232 pass and 12 pallets):		
A, B	76,205 kg	(168,000 lb)
C	74,845 kg	(165,000 lb)
D	71,670 kg	(158,000 lb)
E, F	73,480 kg	(162,000 lb)
H, J	70,760 kg	(156,000 lb)
K	71,215 kg	(157,000 lb)
747-200C (442 pass):		
A, B	92,080 kg	(203,000 lb)
C	90,265 kg	(199,000 lb)
D	87,545 kg	(193,000 lb)
E, F	88,905 kg	(196,000 lb)
H, J	86,185 kg	(190,000 lb)
K	87,090 kg	(192,000 lb)
747-200C (28 pallets):		
A, B	105,235 kg	(232,000 lb)
C	103,420 kg	(228,000 lb)
D	100,245 kg	(221,000 lb)
E, F	102,060 kg	(225,000 lb)
H, J	99,335 kg	(219,000 lb)
K	99,790 kg	(220,000 lb)

Max T-O weight:

747SR (initial aircraft):		
A, B, E, F, G, H, J	235,870 kg	(520,000 lb)
	or 272,160 kg	(600,000 lb)
747-100B, 747SR (optional):		
A, B, E, F, G, H, J	322,050 kg	(710,000 lb)
	or 333,390 kg	(735,000 lb)
	or 340,195 kg	(750,000 lb)
747-200B, -200B Combi, -200C:		
A	351,535 kg	(775,000 lb)
	or 356,070 kg	(785,000 lb)
B	362,875 kg	(800,000 lb)
	or wet 365,140 kg	(805,000 lb)
E, H	362,875 kg	(800,000 lb)
	or 371,945 kg	(820,000 lb)
C, D, F, J, K	362,875 kg	(800,000 lb)
	or 371,945 kg	(820,000 lb)
	or 377,840 kg	(833,000 lb)

Models showing difference between stretched upper deck (above) and standard versions of Boeing 747

Max ramp weight:

747-100B, 747SR:		
A, B, E, F, G, H, J	341,555 kg	(753,000 lb)
747-200B, -200B Combi, -200C:		
A	357,430 kg	(788,000 lb)
B	366,500 kg	(808,000 lb)
E, H	373,305 kg	(823,000 lb)
C, D, F, J, K	379,200 kg	(836,000 lb)

Max zero-fuel weight:

747SR (initial aircraft):		
A, B, E, F, G, H, J	215,455 kg	(475,000 lb)
	or 219,990 kg	(485,000 lb)
747-100B, 747SR (optional):		
A, B, E, F, G, H, J	238,815 kg	(526,500 lb)
747-200B:		
A, B, C, D, E, F, H, J, K		
	238,815 kg	(526,500 lb)
747-200B Combi:		
A, B, C, D, E, F, H, J, K		
	247,205 kg	(545,000 lb)
747-200C:		
A, B, C, D, E, F, H, J, K		
	267,620 kg	(590,000 lb)

Max landing weight:

747SR (initial aircraft):		
A, B, E, F, G, H, J	229,065 kg	(505,000 lb)
	or 238,135 kg	(525,000 lb)
747-100B, 747SR (optional):		
A, B, E, F, G, H, J	255,825 kg	(564,000 lb)
	or 265,350 kg	(585,000 lb)
747-200B:		
A, B, C, D, E, F, H, J, K		
	255,825 kg	(564,000 lb)
	or 265,350 kg	(585,000 lb)
	or 285,765 kg	(630,000 lb)
747-200B Combi:		
A, B, C, D, E, F, H, J, K		
	265,350 kg	(585,000 lb)
	or 285,765 kg	(630,000 lb)
747-200C:		
A, B, C, D, E, F, H, J, K		
	285,760 kg	(630,000 lb)

PERFORMANCE (at max T-O weight except where indicated):

Max level speed:
747-100B, JT9D-7A engines and AUW of 272,160 kg (600,000 lb) at 9,145 m (30,000 ft)
    522 knots (967 km/h; 601 mph)
747-200B, CF6-50E engines and AUW of 317,515 kg (700,000 lb) at 9,145 m (30,000 ft)
    523 knots (969 km/h; 602 mph)

Cruise ceiling, all versions	13,715 m (45,000 ft)
Min ground turning radius	22·86 m (75 ft 0 in)

Runway LCN (A: 334,750 kg; 738,000 lb, B: 341,555 kg; 753,000 lb, C: 366,500 kg; 808,000 lb, D: 379,200 kg; 836,000 lb max taxi weight on h=0·51 m; 20 in flexible pavement):

A	81
B	83
C	86
D	88

Runway LCN (weights as above, on l=1·02 m; 40 in rigid pavement):

A	87
B	89
C	93
D	95

FAR T-O distance to 10·7 m (35 ft) at S/L, ISA:
747-100B (JT9D-7A engines at AUW of 332,480 kg (733,000 lb)   2,880 m (9,450 ft)
747-200B (JT9D-7FW engines at AUW of 365,140 kg (805,000 lb)   3,338 m (10,950 ft)
747-200B, C, F, CF6-50E1/E2 engines at AUW of 377,840 kg (833,000 lb)   3,298 m (10,820 ft)
747-200B, C, JT9D-7Q/-70A engines at AUW of 377,840 kg (833,000 lb)   3,225 m (10,580 ft)
FAR landing field length, at max landing weights:
747-100B, -200B at 255,825 kg (564,000 lb)
     1,881 m (6,170 ft)
747-100B, -200B at 265,350 kg (585,000 lb)
     1,942 m (6,370 ft)
747-200B, C, F at 285,765 kg (630,000 lb)
     2,109 m (6,920 ft)

Boeing Model 747SP four-turbofan special performance long-range transport in Braniff insignia

Range (long-range cruise, FAR 121.645 reserves):
747-100B at T-O weight of 340,195 kg (750,000 lb),
with 442 passengers and baggage
        4,700 nm (8,710 km; 5,412 miles)
747-200B at T-O weight of 365,140 kg (805,000 lb),
with 442 passengers and baggage
        5,300 nm (9,822 km; 6,103 miles)
747-200B at T-O weight of 377,840 kg (833,000 lb),
with 442 passengers and baggage
        5,700 nm (10,562 km; 6,563 miles)
Ferry range (long-range cruise, FAR 121.645
reserves):
747-200B 6,800 nm (12,600 km; 7,830 miles)
OPERATIONAL NOISE LEVELS (As per FAR Pt 36, A:
JT9D-7A engines at brake release weight (BRW) of
332,480 kg; 733,000 lb and landing weight of 255,825
kg; 564,000 lb, B: JT9D-7FW at BRW of 365,140 kg;
805,000 lb and landing weight of 255,825 kg; 564,000
lb, C: CF6-50E at BRW of 371,945 kg; 820,000 lb and
landing weight of 285,765 kg; 630,000 lb):

T-O noise level: A		106 EPNdB
B		109 EPNdB
C		107 EPNdB
Approach noise level: A		106 EPNdB
B		107 EPNdB
C		106 EPNdB
Sideline noise level: A		98 EPNdB
B		99 EPNdB
C		98 EPNdB

BOEING MODEL 747SP

The Boeing Company announced on 3 September 1973
that it intended to proceed 'incrementally' with development of a lower-weight longer-range version of the basic
Model 747, for use on lower-density routes. A week later
came the news that Pan American had placed an order for
10 747SP (Special Performance) aircraft, with an option
on 15 more. Other orders have been received from Braniff
(3), China Air (3), Iran Air (4), South African Airways
(6), Syrian Arab (2), Saudi Arabian government (1),
Saudia (1), Korean Air Lines (2), Qantas (2), TWA (3)
and CAAC (3).

Retaining a 90 per cent commonality of components
with the standard Model 747, the major change is a reduction in overall length of 14·35 m (47 ft 1 in). Construction
of the first production aircraft began in April 1974, with
rollout on 19 May 1975, first flight on 4 July 1975, and
FAA certification on 4 February 1976. First delivery was
made on 5 March that year.

On 23-24 March 1976, taking off at a gross weight of
323,547 kg (713,300 lb) with 50 passengers, the first
747SP for South African Airways made a delivery flight
from Paine Field, Washington, to Cape Town of 8,936 nm
(16,560 km; 10,290 miles), a world record for nonstop
distance flown by a commercial aircraft. The aircraft
landed with fuel remaining for a further 2 h 27 min of
flight.

A 747SP of Pan American, commanded by Capt Walter
H. Mullikin, set a round-the-world speed record of 436·95
knots (809·24 km/h; 502·84 mph), by circumnavigating
the globe in 1 day 22 h 50 s on 1-3 May 1976. The same
pilot circumnavigated the world via the North and South
Poles in a 747SP on 28-31 October 1977, covering 22,926
nm (42,459 km; 26,382·75 miles) in 54 h 7 min 12 s at an
average speed of 423·49 knots (784·31 km/h; 487·35
mph). Start and finish were at San Francisco, with en route
landings at London, Cape Town and Auckland, New
Zealand.

The description of the basic Model 747 applies also to
the 747SP, except for the following details:

WINGS: As Model 747, except that trailing-edge flaps are

of single-slotted variable pivot type, and wing structural
materials are of reduced gauge. Large flap track fairings
replaced by small link fairings. New wing/body fairings
and leading-edge fillets.

FUSELAGE: As Model 747, except length reduced.

TAIL UNIT: Similar to 747, but tailplane span increased by
3·05 m (10 ft). Two-segment elevators. Height of fin
increased by 1·52 m (5 ft 0 in). Double-hinged rudder.

LANDING GEAR: As Model 747, except structural weight
reduced. Main-wheel tyres size 46 × 16, pressure 12·63
bars (183 lb/sq in). Nosewheel tyres size 49 × 17, pressure 13·8 bars (200 lb/sq in). Higher gross weight aircraft uses 747-100 wheels and brakes. Modified 747-
100 steel brakes by Bendix.

POWER PLANT: Four Pratt & Whitney JT9D-7A turbofan
engines, each 208·8 kN (46,950 lb st); or JT9D-7F of
213·5 kN (48,000 lb st); JT9D-7AW of 216 kN (48,570
lb st); JT9D-7FW of 222·4 kN (50,000 lb st); JT9D-7J
of 222·4 kN (50,000 lb st); or four General Electric
CF6-45A/B turbofan engines, each of 206·8 kN
(46,500 lb st); four Rolls-Royce RB.211-524B2 turbofan engines, each of 222·8 kN (50,100 lb st), or
RB.211-524C2 engines, each of 229·5 kN (51,600 lb
st). Fuel system and oil capacity as for Model 747-100B,
except Model 747SP has an additional 5,966 litres
(1,576 US gallons) reserve fuel, providing a total
capacity of 190,625 litres (50,359 US gallons).

ACCOMMODATION: Normal operating crew of three on
flight deck above level of main deck. Observer station
and provision for second observer station are provided.
Accommodation for 289 passengers on main deck, with
28 first class seats in forward area and ten-abreast seating throughout the major part of the main cabin. Seating
for 32 passengers on upper deck, giving total capacity of
321 passengers. Max high-density accommodation for
440 passengers. Four doors on each side, two forward
and two aft of the wing. Crew door on starboard side
giving access to upper deck. Freight holds under floor,
forward and aft of wing box, each with one door on
starboard side.

SYSTEMS, AVIONICS AND EQUIPMENT: As for Model 747.

Boeing 747SP short-fuselage long-range version of the 747 *(Pilot Press)*

DIMENSIONS, EXTERNAL: As for Model 747 except:

Length overall	56·31 m (184 ft 9 in)
Height overall	19·94 m (65 ft 5 in)
Tailplane span	25·22 m (82 ft 9 in)
Wheelbase	20·52 m (67 ft 4 in)

DIMENSIONS, INTERNAL:
Cabin, incl toilets and galleys:

Length	42·27 m (138 ft 8 in)
Max width	6·13 m (20 ft 1½ in)
Max height	2·54 m (8 ft 4 in)
Floor area, passenger deck	253·2 m² (2,725 sq ft)
Volume, passenger deck	613·34 m³ (21,660 cu ft)
Baggage hold volume (fwd)	48·99 m³ (1,730 cu ft)
Baggage hold volume (aft, containerised)	
	48·99 m³ (1,730 cu ft)
Bulk compartment volume (aft)	11·33 m³ (400 cu ft)

AREAS: As for Model 747 except:

Ailerons (total)	20·37 m² (219·3 sq ft)
Trailing-edge flaps (total)	78·78 m² (848 sq ft)
Fin	82·22 m² (885 sq ft)
Tailplane	142·51 m² (1,534 sq ft)

WEIGHTS: (letters are used to denote engine installations
as follows: (A) JT9D-7A/7AW; (B) JT9D-
7F/7FW/7J; (C) CF6-45A/A2 or -45B/B2; (D)
RB.211-524B2; and (E) RB.211-524C2):

Operating weight empty (approx, with 321 passengers):

A, B	146,510 kg (323,000 lb)
C	148,780 kg (328,000 lb)
D, E	151,500 kg (334,000 lb)

Max T-O weight (dry engines):

A, B, C, D, E	285,765 kg (630,000 lb)
	or 299,370 kg (660,000 lb)
	or 303,905 kg (670,000 lb)
	or 312,980 kg (690,000 lb)
	or 315,700 kg (696,000 lb)
	or 318,420 kg (702,000 lb)

Max ramp weight:

A, B, C, D, E	288,485 kg (636,000 lb)
	or 302,095 kg (666,000 lb)
	or 306,630 kg (676,000 lb)
	or 315,700 kg (696,000 lb)
	or 318,875 kg (703,000 lb)

Max zero-fuel weight:
A, B, C, D, E   185,973 kg (410,000 lb)
     or 192,777 kg (425,000 lb)
Max landing weight:
A, B, C, D, E   204,117 kg (450,000 lb)
     or 210,920 kg (465,000 lb)

PERFORMANCE (at max T-O weight, except where indicated):
Never-exceed speed   Mach 0·92
Max level speed, AUW of 226,795 kg (500,000 lb) at 9,145 m (30,000 ft)
    529 knots (980 km/h; 609 mph)
Service ceiling   13,745 m (45,100 ft)
Min ground turning radius over outer wingtip
    22·25 m (73 ft 0 in)
Runway LCN (Y: 302,095 kg; 666,000 lb, Z: 318,875 kg; 703,000 lb max taxi weight on h = 0·51 m; 20 in flexible pavement):
Y   70
Z   75
Runway LCN (weights as above, on l = 1·02 m; 40 in rigid pavement):
Y   76
Z   80
FAR T-O distance to 10·7 m (35 ft) at S/L, ISA (Y: 299,370 kg; 660,000 lb, Z: 318,420 kg; 702,000 lb max T-O weight):
(A) Y   2,393 m (7,850 ft)
     Z   2,780 m (9,120 ft)
(B) Y   2,164 m (7,100 ft)
     Z   2,469 m (8,100 ft)
(C) Y   2,362 m (7,750 ft)
     Z   2,743 m (9,000 ft)
(D) Y   2,118 m (6,950 ft)
     Z   2,438 m (8,000 ft)
FAR landing field length:
at max landing weight   1,594 m (5,230 ft)
at optional max landing weight   1,646 m (5,400 ft)
Range (long-range step cruise, FAR 121.645 reserves, with 321 passengers and baggage at Y: 299,370 kg; 660,000 lb, Z: 318,420 kg; 702,000 lb):
Y   5,350 nm (9,915 km; 6,161 miles)
Z   6,050 nm (11,210 km; 6,966 miles)
Ferry range (long-range step cruise, FAR 121.645 reserves)   7,350 nm (13,620 km; 8,463 miles)

BOEING MODEL 747SUD

On 12 June 1980, Boeing announced a new option for the Model 747, which involves structural changes to the aircraft's upper deck area to increase passenger-carrying capacity. Identified initially as the 747SUD (stretched upper deck), the bulged upper forward fuselage will be extended aft by 7·01 m (23 ft 0 in) to increase upper-deck accommodation from 32 to 69 passengers in a standard economy class configuration. Seating will be six abreast, with a single aisle, and panniers between the outer seats and cabin wall will be provided for hand baggage. A further seven seats can be provided by replacing the standard circular stairway, which gives access to the forward end of the upper deck, with a new straight stairway at the rear of the upper deck area. Other structural changes include the provision of a new emergency exit and additional windows. The stretched upper deck modification is available initially on existing aircraft of the 747-200 series; maximum take-off weight is unchanged, but operating weight empty is increased by 3,630 kg (8,000 lb).

The stretched upper deck will be available to order on new 747-100B, 747SR, 747-200B and 747-200B Combi aircraft. It is not applicable to the 747SP.

Four 747s with stretched upper deck and 243·54 kN (54,750 lb st) JT9D-7R4G2 engines have been ordered by Swissair, for delivery between March 1983 and December 1984, and delivery of one previously-ordered 747 has been delayed so that the modification can be incorporated.

BOEING MODEL 747-200F FREIGHTER

The Boeing Model 747-200F is a freighter version of the standard Model 747-200, capable of delivering 90,720 kg (200,000 lb) of containerised or palletised cargo over a range of 4,100 nm (7,600 km; 4,720 miles).

The first 747-200F flew for the first time on 30 November 1971. It was certificated on 7 March 1972 and delivered to Lufthansa two days later.

To ensure maximum utilisation, the 747-200F has a special loading system that enables two men to handle and stow the maximum load of up to 113,400 kg (250,000 lb) in 30 min. This system was fully described in the 1977-78 *Jane's*.

The 747-200F can carry up to 29 containers measuring 3·05 m × 2·44 m × 2·44 m (10 ft long, 8 ft high and 8 ft wide), plus 30 lower-lobe containers, each of 4·90 m³ (173 cu ft) capacity, and 22·65 m³ (800 cu ft) of bulk cargo. The main deck can accommodate ANSI/ISO containers of up to 12·2 m (40 ft) in length, and many combinations of pallets and igloos. The lower hold can accommodate combinations of IATA-A1 or -A2, and ATA LD-1 or -3 half-width containers, full-width or main-deck baggage containers, and many combinations of pallets and igloos.

The nose loading door, which is hinged just below the flight deck to allow it to swing forward and upward, gives clear access to the main deck to facilitate the handling of long or large loads. A side cargo door is available as an option, allowing simultaneous nose and side loading. The side cargo door will accept palletised loads up to 3·05 m (10 ft 0 in) in height.

The description of the Model 747-200B applies also to the Model 747-200F except as follows:

TYPE: Four-turbofan heavy commercial freighter.
FUSELAGE: As for Model 747-200B, except nose cargo loading door, which is hinged at the top and opens forward and upward.
ACCOMMODATION: Normal operating crew of three on flight deck. Nose cargo loading door, hinged at top. Lower lobe cargo doors, on starboard side, one forward and one aft of wing. Bulk compartment cargo door, on starboard side, aft of lower lobe cargo door. Two doors for crew on port side of aircraft. Aircraft is designed for fully-mechanical loading of freight.
DIMENSIONS, EXTERNAL: As for Model 747-200B except:
Crew doors (two, each): Height   1·93 m (6 ft 4 in)
Width   1·07 m (3 ft 6 in)
Height to sill   approx 4·88 m (16 ft 0 in)
Nose cargo loading door: Height   2·49 m (8 ft 2 in)
Width at top (min)   2·67 m (8 ft 9 in)
Max width   3·81 m (12 ft 6 in)
Height to sill   approx 4·90 m (16 ft 1 in)
DIMENSIONS, INTERNAL:
Main cargo deck: Height   2·54 m (8 ft 4 in)
Max width at floor level   5·92 m (19 ft 5 in)
Lower lobe: Width at floor level   3·18 m (10 ft 5 in)
Total cargo volume   687·0 m³ (24,260 cu ft)
AREAS: As for Model 747-200B
WEIGHTS (letters are used to denote engine installations as follows: (A) JT9D-7A/7AW; (B) JT9D-7F/7FW/7J; (C) JT9D-7Q; (D) JT9D-70A; (E) CF6-50E; (F) CF6-50E1/E2; (G) RB.211-524B2; (H) RB.211-524C2; and (J) RB.211-524D4):
Operating weight empty (approx) for max available gross weights:
A, B   154,675 kg (341,000 lb)
C   156,035 kg (344,000 lb)
D   159,210 kg (351,000 lb)
E, F   157,395 kg (347,000 lb)
G, H   160,120 kg (353,000 lb)
J   159,665 kg (352,000 lb)
Max payload (29 pallets):
A, B   112,945 kg (249,000 lb)
C   111,585 kg (246,000 lb)
D   108,410 kg (239,000 lb)
E, F   110,220 kg (243,000 lb)
G, H   107,500 kg (237,000 lb)
J   107,955 kg (238,000 lb)
Max T-O weight:
A   351,535 kg (775,000 lb)
     or 356,070 kg (785,000 lb)
B   362,875 kg (800,000 lb)
     or (wet) 365,140 kg (805,000 lb)
E, G   362,875 kg (800,000 lb)
     or 371,945 kg (820,000 lb)
C, D, F, H, J   362,875 kg (800,000 lb)
     or 371,945 kg (820,000 lb)
     or 377,840 kg (833,000 lb)
Max ramp weight:
A   357,430 kg (788,000 lb)
B   366,500 kg (808,000 lb)
E, G   373,305 kg (823,000 lb)
C, D, F, H, J   379,200 kg (836,000 lb)
Max zero-fuel weight:
A, B, C, D, E, F, G, H, J   267,620 kg (590,000 lb)
Max landing weight:
A, B, C, D, E, F, G, H, J   285,765 kg (630,000 lb)
PERFORMANCE (at max T-O weight except where indicated):
Max level speed at AUW of 272,160 kg (600,000 lb), at 9,145 m (30,000 ft)
    528 knots (978 km/h; 608 mph)
Cruise ceiling   13,715 m (45,000 ft)
Min ground turning radius   22·86 m (75 ft 0 in)
FAR T-O distance to 10·7 m (35 ft) at S/L, ISA:
JT9D-7FW engines, at AUW of 365,140 kg (805,000 lb)   3,338 m (10,950 ft)
CF6-50E/E1/E2 engines, at AUW of 377,840 kg (833,000 lb)   3,298 m (10,820 ft)
JT9D-7Q/-70A engines, at AUW of 377,840 kg (833,000 lb)   3,225 m (10,580 ft)
FAR landing field length, at max landing weight
    2,103 m (6,900 ft)
Range, long-range step cruise, FAR 121.645 reserves, with 90,720 kg (200,000 lb) payload:
T-O weight of 356,070 kg (785,000 lb)
A, B   3,450 nm (6,390 km; 3,970 miles)
T-O weight of 377,840 kg (833,000 lb)
D, G, H   4,000 nm (7,410 km; 4,605 miles)
C, F   4,150 nm (7,690 km; 4,780 miles)
Ferry range with max fuel, long-range cruise, FAR 121.645 reserves
    7,300 nm (13,525 km; 8,405 miles)

BOEING MODEL 757

In the early months of 1978, The Boeing Company announced a proposal to develop a new family of advanced technology commercial aircraft, to which it gave the Model designations 757, 767 and 777. The short/medium-range 757 was intended to differ considerably from the other two, being based on the Boeing 727 fuselage. Improved performance would come from two new high bypass engines and an advanced technology wing, with less sweepback than that of the Model 727.

On 31 August 1978 Eastern Air Lines and British Airways announced their intention to purchase 21 (since increased to 27) and 19 Model 757s respectively, the former taking an option on an additional 24, and the latter on 18. Following the signature in early 1979 of formal contracts by both of these airlines, Boeing announced on 23 March 1979 that the company had initiated full production of the Model 757; the first metal was cut for the new aircraft on 10 December 1979. First flight is scheduled for February 1982, with first deliveries in January 1983. Aircraft for both British Airways and Eastern Air Lines will be designated **Model 757-200** and will be powered by two 166·4 kN (37,400 lb st) class Rolls-Royce RB.211-535C turbofan engines. This was the first time that Boeing had launched a new airliner with a non-American engine. On a

Boeing Model 747-200F freighter in service with Cargolux Airlines International. This aircraft was the first certificated for a max T-O weight of 377,840 kg (833,000 lb), the heaviest weight of any aircraft yet flown.

typical 400 nm (740 km; 460 mile) stage, the Model 757-200 with RB.211-535 engines is expected to use up to 37 per cent less fuel per passenger than current medium-range aircraft.

By 1 September 1980, orders totalled 52, the additional customers being Transbrasil (3) and Aloha Airlines of Hawaii (3). The Transbrasil and Aloha 757s will differ from others in being powered by General Electric CF6-32C1 turbofans.

The Model 757 retains the same fuselage cross-section as the 707/727/737 family. The original design provided for a T-tail configuration, but as a result of wind tunnel testing it was decided to mount the tailplane on the fuselage.

On 11 October 1979, more than $1,000 million worth of subcontracts for 757 components were awarded by Boeing, in each case for 200 ship-sets, with follow-on options for 200 more. Subcontracts for the wing centre-section and adjacent fuselage keel beam went to Avco Aerostructures; Fairchild Republic was selected to manufacture the overwing passenger cabin section (and, under a later subcontract, the wing leading-edge slats); Rockwell International's subcontract covered fuselage sections immediately forward and aft of the wing; Vought Corporation was made responsible for the tailplane, fin and extreme rear fuselage. Earlier subcontracts had gone to Short Brothers of Northern Ireland for inboard trailing-edge flaps; to Hawker de Havilland of Australia for wing in-spar ribs; to CASA of Spain for outboard trailing-edge flaps; and to Menasco of California for main and nose landing gear units. Other major subcontractors include Grumman (wing spoilers), Rohr Industries (engine pylons), and Heath Tecna (wing/fuselage fairings).

Avionics equipment will include a Honeywell inertial reference system (IRS). In this IRS, conventional mechanical gyroscopes are replaced by laser gyroscopes, and utilisation, in both the Models 757 and 767, will represent their first commercial application. The IRS will provide position, velocity, and attitude information to flight deck displays, and for the flight management computer system (FMCS) and digital air data computer (DADC), to be supplied by Sperry Flight Systems. The FMCS will provide automatic en-route and terminal navigation capability, and will also compute and command both lateral and vertical flight profiles for optimum fuel efficiency, maximised by electronic linkage of the FMCS with automatic flight control and thrust management systems.

LANDING GEAR: Retractable tricycle type, with main and nose units manufactured by Menasco. Each main unit comprises a four-wheel bogie, fitted with Goodrich wheels and brakes, and Dunlop tyres. Twin-wheel nose unit.

POWER PLANT: Two Rolls-Royce RB.211-535 or General Electric CF6-32 turbofan engines in the 160 kN (36,000 lb st) class, mounted in underwing pods. Fuel capacity 41,185 litres (10,880 US gallons).

ACCOMMODATION: Crew of two on flight deck, with provision for a third person. Typical accommodation for 178 mixed class or 196 tourist class passengers, in four/six-abreast seating with central aisle. Seat pitch in the all-tourist configuration is 86 cm (34 in). Max capacity 223 passengers at 76 cm (30 in) seat pitch.

SYSTEMS AND AVIONICS: Garrett-AiResearch environmental control system; General Electric engine thrust management system; Sundstrand electrical power generating system and ram-air turbines; and Garrett-AiResearch GTCP 331-200 APU. Honeywell inertial reference system (IRS); Sperry flight management computer system (FMCS) and digital air data computer (DADC); Collins FXS-700 flight control system, EFIS-700 electronic flight instruments system, RMI-743 radio distance magnetic indicator (RDMI) and optional radio magnetic indicator (RMI).

DIMENSIONS, EXTERNAL:
Wing span	37·95 m (124 ft 6 in)
Wing sweepback	25°
Wing area, gross	181·25 m² (1,951 sq ft)
Length overall	47·32 m (155 ft 3 in)
Length of fuselage	46·89 m (153 ft 10 in)
Height overall	13·56 m (44 ft 6 in)
Tailplane span	14·99 m (49 ft 2 in)
Wheel track	7·32 m (24 ft 0 in)
Passenger doors (two, fwd, port):	
Height	1·83 m (6 ft 0 in)
Width	0·89 m (2 ft 9 in)
Service door (fwd, stbd):	
Height	1·65 m (5 ft 5 in)
Width	0·76 m (2 ft 6 in)
Service door (stbd, opposite 2nd passenger door):	
Height	1·83 m (6 ft 0 in)
Width	0·89 m (2 ft 9 in)
Service doors (aft, port and stbd):	
Height	1·83 m (6 ft 0 in)
Width	0·76 m (2 ft 6 in)
Emergency exits (two, aft of wings):	
Height	1·32 m (4 ft 4 in)
Width	0·61 m (2 ft 0 in)

DIMENSIONS, INTERNAL:
Underfloor cargo volume (bulk loading):	
fwd	17·3 m³ (610 cu ft)
aft	31·5 m³ (1,112 cu ft)

Boeing Model 757 twin-turbofan short/medium-range transport aircraft *(Pilot Press)*

WEIGHTS (with 178 passengers. A: 166·4 kN/37,400 lb st RB.211-535C engines; B: 161·6 kN/36,330 lb st CF6-32s):
Operating weight empty:	A	59,430 kg (131,020 lb)
	B	57,920 kg (127,690 lb)
Max basic T-O weight: A, B		99,790 kg (220,000 lb)
Max T-O weight (medium range)		104,325 kg (230,000 lb)
Max T-O weight (optional)		108,860 kg (240,000 lb)
Max landing weight: A, B		89,810 kg (198,000 lb)
Max zero-fuel weight		83,460 kg (184,000 lb)

PERFORMANCE (with 178 passengers, US mixed class operations; at max basic T-O weight and with engines as above):
Cruising speed: A, B		Mach 0·80
Approach speed:		
A, B		134 knots (248 km/h; 154 mph)
Initial cruising height: A		11,340 m (37,200 ft)
B		11,765 m (38,600 ft)
T-O field length (S/L, 29°C): A		2,095 m (6,870 ft)
B		2,035 m (6,670 ft)
Max range: A		2,340 nm (4,336 km; 2,695 miles)
B		2,400 nm (4,447 km; 2,763 miles)

BOEING MODEL 767

On 14 July 1978, Boeing announced its intention to launch full-scale development of the twin-turbofan Model 767, following receipt of an order from United Air Lines for 30, with initial deliveries scheduled for August 1982. This airline had participated actively in defining the design of the Model 767, as it did with the design of the Model 727 in 1959-60. It is estimated that when these aircraft enter service with United, powered by Pratt & Whitney JT9D-7R4A engines, they will be 35 per cent more fuel-efficient than the aircraft they will replace, and will comply also with the stringent noise regulations which are foreseen for 1984.

Construction of the first Model 767 began on 6 July 1979. It has a completely new airframe, with a fuselage 1·24 m (4 ft 1 in) wider than that of the Model 757, permitting a two-aisle seating layout. It was proposed initially in two forms, as the 767-100 with accommodation for approximately 180 passengers, and the 767-200MR with accommodation for up to 255 passengers. Since that time, a 211-passenger version known as the **767-200** has been finalised as the basic model, with the first flight of the prototype scheduled for September/October 1981. It is intended to market an optional medium-range version with reduced fuel capacity, and a later option will cater for a version with a higher gross weight, although this is not expected to be available until late 1983.

By 8 October 1980, orders for the Model 767 totalled 161, with options on 129 more. Alternative engines for the basic model are the Pratt & Whitney JT9D-7R4D, rated at 212 kN (47,700 lb st), and General Electric CF6-80A, rated at 213 kN (47,900 lb st). The same engines are projected for the later models, except that the version of the Pratt & Whitney turbofan in the medium-range model will be the JT9D-7R4A, rated at 156 kN (44,000 lb st). Fuel capacity of this model will be 42,850 litres (11,320 US gallons). Boeing is also studying the Rolls-Royce RB.211 as an alternative option. The basic interior arrangements of all versions are identical.

Boeing has awarded manufacturing subcontracts to Grumman Aerospace Corporation (wing centre-section, an adjacent lower fuselage section, and fuselage bulkheads); to Vought Corporation (horizontal tail); and to Canadair Ltd (rear fuselage). In two other major work-sharing programmes announced in August and September 1978, Boeing gave details of co-production agreements whereby Aeritalia of Italy and member companies of the Civil Transport Development Corporation (CTDC) of Japan will participate as follows:

Aeritalia: Wing control surfaces, flaps and leading-edge slats; wingtips; elevators; fin, rudder; and nose radome.

Fuji: Wing fairings and main landing gear doors.

Kawasaki: Centre-fuselage body panels, exit hatches and wing in-spar ribs.

Mitsubishi: Rear-fuselage body panels, stringers, passenger and cargo doors, and dorsal fin.

The following details apply to the basic Model 767-200:

TYPE: Twin-turbofan medium-range commercial transport.

WINGS: Cantilever low-wing monoplane. Special Boeing wing sections. Thickness/chord ratio 15·1% at root, 10·3% at tip. Dihedral 6°. Incidence 3° 48'. Sweepback 31° 30' at quarter-chord. Fail-safe structure of 2324 and 7150 aluminium alloy. Plain inboard and outboard ailerons of graphite hybrid composites. Single-slotted linkage-supported aluminium honeycomb trailing-edge flaps. Conventional inboard and outboard spoilers of graphite composite construction are provided for roll control, to act as airbrakes, and for lift dumping. Track-mounted leading-edge slats of light alloy construction. Roll trim through spring feel system. All control surfaces are powered hydraulically. Anti-icing of outboard wing leading-edges.

FUSELAGE: Conventional semi-monocoque structure of 2024 light alloy, consisting of skin, longitudinal stringers and circumferential frames. Structure is of fail-safe design, and is pressurised except for tailcone aft of passenger cabin, landing gear wheel wells and air cycle machine wells.

TAIL UNIT: Cantilever fail-safe structure of 2024 light alloy and aluminium honeycomb. Variable-incidence tailplane. Elevators of single-hinge type with redundant parallel actuators. No trim tabs. All controls are powered hydraulically. Yaw trim through spring feel system. No tail unit anti-icing.

LANDING GEAR: Hydraulically-retractable tricycle type. Twin-wheel nose unit retracts forward. Cleveland Pneumatic main gear, comprising two four-wheel bogies which retract inward. Oleo-pneumatic shock-absorbers. Bendix wheels and brakes. Main-wheel tyres size 45 × 17-20, pressure 12·14 bars (176 lb/sq in). Nosewheel tyres size 37 × 14-15, pressure 8·28 bars (120 lb/sq in). Steel disc brakes on all main wheels. Electronically-controlled anti-skid units.

POWER PLANT: Two high bypass turbofan engines in the 177·9 to 222·4 kN (40,000 to 50,000 lb st) class, in pods pylon-mounted on the wing leading-edges. Pratt & Whitney JT9D-7R4D and General Electric CF6-80A engines had been specified by customers up to January 1980, and Boeing has alternative Rolls-Royce RB.211 engines under study. Fuel in one integral tank in each wing, with total capacity of 58,900 litres (15,560 US gallons). Refuelling point in port outer wing. Anti-icing of engine air inlets.

ACCOMMODATION: Normal operating crew of two or three on flight deck. Basic accommodation for 211 passengers, made up of 18 first class passengers forward in six-abreast seating at 96·5 cm (38 in) pitch, and 193 tourist class in mainly seven-abreast seating at 86 cm (34 in) pitch. Type A inward-opening plug doors are provided at both the front and rear of the cabin on each side of the fuselage, with a Type III emergency exit over the wing on each side. A total of five toilets is installed, two centrally in the main cabin, two aft in the main cabin, and one forward in the first class section. Galleys are situated at forward and aft ends of the cabin. With the two central toilets moved to the rear of the cabin, the number of tourist passengers can be increased to 198 in this mixed class, one meal service model. With an additional rear galley for one and one-half meal service, the rear centre row of three tourist class seats is removed in each configuration. Alternative single class layouts provide for 230 tourist passengers, seated mainly seven-abreast at 86 cm (34 in) pitch; 241 passengers seated seven-abreast at 81 cm (32 in) pitch; or 255 passengers mainly seven-abreast (two-three-two) at 76 cm (30 in)

Boeing Model 767-200 wide-bodied medium-range commercial transport aircraft *(Pilot Press)*

pitch, or eight-abreast (two-four-two) at 81 cm (32 in) pitch. Max seating capacity (requiring additional overwing emergency exit) for 289 passengers, mainly eight-abreast, at 76 cm (30 in) pitch. Underfloor cargo holds can accommodate, typically, up to 22 LD-2 or 11 LD-3 containers. Forward and aft cargo doors of equal size are standard, but a larger (1·75 by 3·40 m; 5 ft 9 in by 11 ft 2 in) forward cargo door is optional, to permit loading of Type 2 pallets. Bulk cargo door at rear on port side. Overhead stowage for carry-on baggage. Cabin is air-conditioned, cargo holds heated.

SYSTEMS: Hamilton Standard dual air-cycle air-conditioning system. Pressure differential 0·59 bars (8·6 lb/sq in). Electrical supply from two engine-driven 90kVA three-phase 400Hz constant-frequency AC generators, 115/200V output. 90 kVA generator mounted on APU for ground operation or for emergency use. Three hydraulic systems at 207 bars (3,000 lb/sq in), for flight control and utility functions, supplied from Garrett-AiResearch bleed air powered hydraulic pump or APU. Nitrogen chlorate oxygen generators plus gaseous oxygen. Anti-icing for air data sensors and windscreen. APU, to provide ground and in-flight electrical power and pressurisation, in tailcone.

AVIONICS AND EQUIPMENT: Standard avionics include ARINC 700 Series equipment, Collins caution annunciator, dual digital flight management systems, and triple digital flight control computers, including FCS-700 flight control system, EFIS-700 electronic flight instruments system and RMI-743 radio distance magnetic indicator. Honeywell IRS, and Sperry Flight Systems FMCS and DADC, as described in Boeing Model 757 entry.

DIMENSIONS, EXTERNAL:

Wing span	47·55 m (156 ft 4 in)
Wing chord at root	8·57 m (28 ft 1¼ in)
Wing chord at tip	2·29 m (7 ft 6 in)
Wing aspect ratio	7·9
Length overall	48·51 m (159 ft 2 in)
Length of fuselage	47·24 m (155 ft 0 in)
Fuselage width, max	5·03 m (16 ft 6 in)
Height overall	15·85 m (52 ft 0 in)
Tailplane span	18·62 m (61 ft 1 in)
Wheel track	9·30 m (30 ft 6 in)
Wheelbase	19·69 m (64 ft 7 in)

Passenger doors (two, fwd and aft, port):

Height	1·88 m (6 ft 2 in)
Width	1·07 m (3 ft 6 in)

Galley service door (fwd, stbd):

Height	1·83 m (6 ft 0 in)
Width	1·07 m (3 ft 6 in)

Galley service door (aft, stbd):

Height	1·88 m (6 ft 2 in)
Width	1·07 m (3 ft 6 in)

Emergency exits (two, each):

Height	0·97 m (3 ft 2 in)
Width	0·51 m (1 ft 8 in)

Cargo doors (two, fwd and aft, stbd):

Height	1·75 m (5 ft 9 in)
Width	1·78 m (5 ft 10 in)

Optional cargo door (fwd, port):

Height	1·75 m (5 ft 9 in)
Width	3·40 m (11 ft 2 in)

DIMENSIONS, INTERNAL:
Cabin, excl flight deck:

Length	33·93 m (111 ft 4 in)
Max width	4·72 m (15 ft 6 in)
Max height	2·87 m (9 ft 5 in)
Floor area	157·6 m² (1,696 sq ft)
Volume	428·2 m³ (15,121 cu ft)
Volume, flight deck	13·5 m³ (478 cu ft)

Baggage holds (containerised) volume

	74·8 m³ (2,640 cu ft)
Bulk cargo hold volume	12·2 m³ (430 cu ft)

AREAS:

Wings, gross	283·3 m² (3,050 sq ft)
Ailerons (total)	11·87 m² (127·8 sq ft)
Trailing-edge flaps (total)	36·19 m² (389·5 sq ft)
Leading-edge flaps (total)	28·37 m² (305·4 sq ft)
Spoilers (total)	15·83 m² (170·4 sq ft)
Fin	30·17 m² (324·7 sq ft)
Rudder	15·98 m² (172·0 sq ft)
Tailplane	77·69 m² (836·2 sq ft)
Elevators	17·47 m² (188·0 sq ft)

WEIGHTS (estimated, A: 767-200 basic/JT9D-7R4D engines; B: 767-200 basic/CF6-80A; C: medium-range version/JT9D-7R4A; D: medium-range version/CF6-80A; E: higher gross weight version/JT9D-7R4D; F: higher gross weight version/CF6-80A):

Manufacturer's weight empty:

A, E	74,205 kg (163,590 lb)
B, F	74,160 kg (163,500 lb)
C	74,120 kg (163,410 lb)
D	74,080 kg (163,320 lb)

Operating weight empty:

A, E	81,890 kg (180,540 lb)
B, F	81,850 kg (180,450 lb)
C	81,720 kg (180,160 lb)
D	81,680 kg (180,070 lb)

Max T-O weight: A, B	136,080 kg (300,000 lb)
C, D	127,910 kg (282,000 lb)
E, F	140,615 kg (310,000 lb)
Max ramp weight: A, B	136,985 kg (302,000 lb)
C, D	128,820 kg (284,000 lb)
E, F	141,520 kg (312,000 lb)

Max zero-fuel weight:

A, B, E, F	112,490 kg (248,000 lb)
C, D	109,770 kg (242,000 lb)

Max landing weight:

A, B, E, F	122,470 kg (270,000 lb)
C, D	116,575 kg (257,000 lb)

PERFORMANCE (estimated, at max T-O weight except where indicated):

Max cruising speed, all versions	Mach 0·80

Approach speed at max landing weight:

A, B, E, F	134 knots (248 km/h; 154 mph)
C, D	131 knots (243 km/h; 151 mph)

Service ceiling: A	11,920 m (39,100 ft)
B, E	11,705 m (38,400 ft)
C, D	12,100 m (39,700 ft)
F	11,520 m (37,800 ft)

Service ceiling, one engine out (weight for 1,000 nm; 1,850 km; 1,150 miles range):

A, E	6,490 m (21,300 ft)
B, D, F	6,250 m (20,500 ft)
C	6,190 m (20,300 ft)

T-O field length (S/L, 29°C): A	2,060 m (6,750 ft)
B	2,040 m (6,700 ft)
C	1,980 m (6,500 ft)
D	1,800 m (5,900 ft)
E	2,225 m (7,300 ft)
F	2,180 m (7,150 ft)

Design range: A	2,730 nm (5,058 km; 3,143 miles)
B	2,785 nm (5,161 km; 3,207 miles)
C	1,975 nm (3,660 km; 2,274 miles)
D	2,025 nm (3,753 km; 2,332 miles)
E	3,140 nm (5,819 km; 3,616 miles)
F	3,200 nm (5,930 km; 3,685 miles)

BOEING AEROSPACE COMPANY

The Boeing Aerospace Company has its headquarters at the company's space centre at Kent, Washington, some 12 miles south of Seattle. It consists of three major organisations: Systems Acquisitions, Department Management, and Program Management. Major programmes and activities include the E-3A Sentry Airborne Warning And Control System; Minuteman ICBM; MX ICBM ground support system; Inertial Upper Stage; E-4 Airborne Command Post; Roland: Air Launched Cruise Missile; Space Defense and Re-entry Systems Launch Branch; Technical Services; Automated Transportation System; Multiple Launch Rocket System; and Electrical Support. Responsible for much of Boeing's military, space and diversification efforts, it has a labour force of approximately 18,500.

BOEING E-3 SENTRY

USAF designations: EC-137D and E-3A

The E-3A Sentry AWACS (Airborne Warning And Control System) aircraft offers the potential of long-range high- or low-level surveillance of all air vehicles, manned or unmanned, in all weathers and above all kinds of terrain. Its data storage and processing capability can provide real-time assessment of enemy action, and of the status and position of friendly resources. By centralising the co-ordination of complex, diverse and simultaneous air operations in wartime, such an aircraft can command and control the total air effort: strike, air superiority, support, airlift, reconnaissance and interdiction.

In US Air Force service, the system has a dual use: as a command and control centre to support quick-reaction deployment and tactical operations by Tactical Air Command units; and as a survivable early-warning airborne command and control centre for identification, surveillance and tracking of airborne enemy forces, and for the command and control of NORAD (North American Air Defense) forces over the continental USA. The E-3A provides comprehensive surveillance out to a range of more than 200 nm (370 km; 230 miles) for low-flying targets, and still further for targets flying at higher altitudes.

Boeing's Aerospace Group was awarded an initial contract as prime contractor and systems integrator for the AWAC system on 23 July 1970. Its design submission was based on the airframe of the Model 707-320B commercial jet transport. Two of these aircraft, with the prototype designation EC-137D, were modified initially for comparative trials with prototype downward-looking radars designed by Hughes Aircraft Company and Westinghouse Electric Corporation.

After several months of airborne tests the Westinghouse radar was selected, on 5 October 1972. On 26 January 1973 the US Air Force announced that, following satisfactory completion of Phase 1, approval had been given for full-scale development of AWACS, and production was authorised in the Spring of 1975. The full-scale development test programme involved a fleet of three aircraft completely equipped with mission avionics, and a fourth aircraft equipped for airworthiness testing, and was completed at the end of 1976.

In December 1976 Boeing awarded Westinghouse a contract to develop a maritime surveillance capability that could be incorporated in the E-3A radar. This program began flight testing this system in June 1979. All E-3A aircraft, beginning with production system 22 scheduled for delivery in early 1981, will be equipped for maritime surveillance.

The first production E-3A Sentry was delivered on 24 March 1977 to Tactical Air Command's 552nd Airborne Warning and Control Wing, based at Tinker AFB, Oklahoma. A total of five were delivered by the end of 1977, followed by ten more during 1978, and five during 1979. E-3As achieved initial operational status in April 1978, and have since completed deployments to Alaska, Iceland, Saudi Arabia, the Mediterranean area, and the Pacific. They began assuming a role in US continental air defence on 1 January 1979, when 30 NORAD personnel started to augment TAC E-3A flight crews on all operational NORAD missions from Tinker AFB. This unit was expected to be fully operational by Summer 1979.

Funding for a total of 28 E-3As had been approved by the end of 1980, and two more will be requested under each Fiscal Year budget until the planned force of 34 USAF AWACS is complete. In addition, NATO has approved the acquisition of 18, under a cost-sharing agreement, to be based in the Federal Republic of Germany. For these, much of the avionics will be produced in West Germany, with Dornier as systems integrator; deliveries to NATO will begin in early 1982. These, too, will have a maritime surveillance capability. Avionics and equipment in the NATO aircraft are generally similar to those in US Air Force E-3As, though in some cases the supplier is different.

From aircraft No. 24, US Air Force and NATO E-3As will be to an upgraded standard of which the main ingredients include a joint tactical information distribution system (JTIDS), funded by the US Air Force, and improved data processing capability, funded by NATO.

TYPE: Airborne early-warning and command post aircraft.

WINGS, FUSELAGE, TAIL UNIT AND LANDING GEAR: Basically as Boeing 707-320B, with strengthened fuselage structure and installation of rotodome.

POWER PLANT: Four Pratt & Whitney TF33-PW-100/100A turbofan engines, each rated at 93·4 kN (21,000 lb st), mounted in pods beneath the wings.

ACCOMMODATION: Basic operational crew of 17 includes a flight crew complement of four plus thirteen AWACS specialists, though this latter number can vary for tactical and defence missions. Aft of flight deck, from front to rear of fuselage, are communications, data processing and other equipment bays; multi-purpose consoles; communications, navigation and identification equipment; and crew rest area.

SYSTEMS: A liquid cooling system provides protection for the radar transmitter. An air-cycle pack system and a closed-loop ram-cooled environmental control system ensure a suitable environment for crew and avionics equipment. Electrical power generation has a 600kVA capability. The distribution centre for mission equipment power and remote avionics is located in the lower forward cargo compartment. The aft cargo compartment houses the radar transmitter and an APU. External sockets allow intake of power when the aircraft is on the ground. Two separate and independent hydraulic systems power flight-essential and mission-essential equipment, but either system has the capability of satisfying the requirements of both equipment groups in an emergency.

AVIONICS AND EQUIPMENT: Prominent above the fuselage is the elliptical cross-section rotodome which is 9·14 m (30 ft) in diameter and 1·83 m (6 ft) in depth. It comprises four essential elements: a strut-mounted turntable, supporting the rotary joint assembly to which are attached sliprings for electrical and waveguide continuity between rotodome and fuselage; a structural centre section of aluminium skin and stiffener construction, which supports the AN/APY-1 surveillance radar and IFF/TADIL C antennae, radomes, auxiliary equipment for radar operation and environmental control of the rotodome interior; liquid cooling of the radar antenna; and two radomes constructed of multi-layer glassfibre sandwich material, one for the surveillance radar and one for the IFF/TADIL C array. For surveillance operations the rotodome is hydraulically driven at 6 rpm, but during non-operational flights it is rotated at only ¼ rpm, to keep the bearings lubricated. The Westinghouse radar operates in the S band; by use of pulse Doppler technology, with a high pulse repetition frequency, this radar features long range and accuracy in addition to a normal downlook capability. Its antenna, spanning about 7·32 m (24 ft), and 1·52 m (5 ft) deep, scans mechanically in azimuth, and electronically from ground level up into the stratosphere. Heart of the data processing in the first 23 aircraft is an IBM 4 Pi CC-1 high-speed computer, the entire group consisting of arithmetic control units, input/output units, main storage units, peripheral control units, mass memory drums, magnetic tape transports, punched tape reader, line printer, and an operator's control panel. Processing speed is in the order of 740,000 operations/s; input/output data rate has a maximum of 710,000 words/s; main memory size is 131,072 words (expandable to 180,224), and mass memory size 802,816 words (expandable to 1,204,224). An interface adapter unit developed by Boeing is the key integrating element interconnecting functional data between AWACS avionics subsystems, data processing group, radar, communications, navigation/guidance, display, azimuth and identification. From the 24th production aircraft, an improved IBM computer will be installed, with a main storage capacity of 665,360 words. Data display and control is provided by Hazeltine Corporation multi-purpose consoles (MPC) and auxiliary display units (ADU); in present configura-

Three-view drawing *(Pilot Press)* **and photograph of a Boeing E-3A Sentry airborne warning and control system (AWACS) aircraft for the USAF**

tion each AWACS aircraft carries nine MPCs and two ADUs. Navigation/guidance relies upon three principal sources of information: two Delco AN/ASN-119 (Carousel IV) inertial platforms; a Northrop AN/ARN-120 Omega navigation set; and a Ryan AN/APN-213 Doppler velocity sensor. Communications equipment, supplied by Collins Radio, Electronic Communications Inc, E-Systems, and Hughes Aircraft, provides HF, VHF and UHF communication channels by means of which information can be transmitted or received in clear or secure mode, in voice or digital form. Identification is based on an AN/APX-103 interrogator set developed by Cutler-Hammer's AIL Division. It is the first airborne IFF interrogator set to offer complete AIMS Mk X SIF air traffic control and Mk XII military identification friend or foe (IFF) in a single integrated system. Simultaneous Mk X and Mk XII multi-target and multi-mode operations allow the operator to obtain instantaneously the range, azimuth and elevation, code identification and IFF status of all targets within radar range.

DIMENSIONS, EXTERNAL:
Wing span	44·42 m (145 ft 9 in)
Length overall	46·61 m (152 ft 11 in)
Height overall	12·60 m (41 ft 4 in)

WEIGHT:
Max T-O weight	147,400 kg (325,000 lb)

PERFORMANCE:
Max level speed	460 knots (853 km/h; 530 mph)
Service ceiling	over 8,850 m (29,000 ft)
Endurance on station, 870 nm (1,610 km; 1,000 miles) from base	6 h

BOEING ADVANCED AIRBORNE COMMAND POST

USAF designation: E-4

On 28 February 1973 the US Air Force's Electronic Systems Division announced from its headquarters at Hanscom Field, Bedford, Massachusetts, that it had awarded The Boeing Company a $59 million fixed-price contract for the supply of two Model 747-200Bs to be adapted as **E-4A** airborne command posts under the 481B Advanced Airborne Command Post (AABNCP) programme. A contract valued at more than $27·2 million was awarded, in July 1973, for a third aircraft; in December 1973 the fourth aircraft was contracted at $39 million.

The third and fourth aircraft differed initially from the first two in having General Electric F103-GE-100 turbo-

Boeing E-4B advanced airborne command post operated by the USAF Strategic Air Command

fan engines, each rated at 233·5 kN (52,500 lb st), instead of the JT9Ds that were then fitted normally to aircraft of the 747 series; F103-GE-100s were fitted retrospectively to the first two aircraft during 1976. The fourth aircraft is fitted with more advanced equipment (see below) and is designated **E-4B**.

On 15 January 1976 it was stated that the total planned force was six E-4Bs, comprising the fourth aircraft, two more similar aircraft, and the three E-4As brought up to the same standard retrospectively. Contracts covering modification of one E-4A to E-4B configuration, with options to modify the other two, were announced on 26 June 1980. E-Systems Inc of Greenville, Texas, is teamed with Boeing Aerospace in the E-4A/B modification programme.

The E-4s are intended to replace EC-135 Airborne Command Posts of the National Military Command System and Strategic Air Command, which are military variants of the Model 707. E-Systems won the contract to install interim equipment in the three E-4As. This involved transfer and integration of equipment removed from EC-135s, providing aircraft with increased endurance and the ability to carry an expanded battle staff. The E-4A's 429·2 m² (4,620 sq ft) of floor space accommodates almost three times the payload of the EC-135. The main deck is divided into six areas: the National Command

Authorities' (NCA) work area, conference room, briefing room, battle staff work area, communications control centre and rest area. The flight deck accommodates the flight crew, navigation station and flight crew rest area. Lobe areas, beneath the main deck, house a technical control facility and a limited onboard maintenance storage area.

The first E-4A flew for the first time on 13 June 1973, and was delivered to Andrews AFB, Maryland, in December 1974. The second and third, also consigned to Andrews AFB, were received in May and September 1975. In their present form, they are able to operate as National Emergency Airborne Command Posts (NEACPs), and provided operational experience that proved invaluable in finalising the design of equipment installed in the E-4B. The E-4 is capable of remaining airborne for up to 72 hours.

Boeing, E-Systems and a team comprising Electrospace Systems Inc of Richardson, Texas; Collins Radio Division of Rockwell International Corporation, Dallas, Texas; RCA Corporation of Morristown, NJ; and Burroughs Corporation, Federal and Special Systems Group, of Paoli, Pennsylvania, are responsible for designing and installing the advanced command post equipment in the E-4B. The first E-4B was delivered to the US Air Force in August 1975 in testbed configuration, with flight refuel-

ling equipment installed but without the planned command, control and communications equipment. Next stage involved installation of the 1,200kVA electrical system (two 150kVA generators on each engine) that had been designed to support the advanced avionics. Finally the operational systems were added, and the first flight of the fully equipped E-4B took place in June 1978. US Air Force tests of operational capability began later that year.

The first E-4B (75-0125) was redelivered to the US Air Force on 21 December 1979, and entered service in January 1980. It has accommodation for a larger battle staff than that carried by the E-4A; an air-conditioning system of 226·5 m³ (8,000 cu ft)/min capacity to cool avionics components; nuclear thermal shielding; acoustic controls; an improved technical control facility; and new super high frequency (SHF) and Collins LF/VLF communications systems, the latter employing a trailing-wire antenna that is trailed several miles behind the aircraft in flight. The SHF antennae are housed in a dorsal fairing which is a recognition characteristic of the E-4B.

Strategic Air Command (SAC) is now sole operational manager of the AABNCP force. Transfer of operational responsibility from Headquarters Command USAF to SAC began in October 1975 and became effective as from 1 November 1975. The main operating base for the E-4 fleet is at Offutt AFB, Nebraska.

BOEING MILITARY AIRPLANE COMPANY

Boeing Military Airplane Company, the formation of which was announced on 23 October 1979, is responsible for all work on the B-52 Stratofortress bomber and KC-135 jet tanker-transport series. It manufactures parts and assemblies for the Boeing Model 707, 727, 737 and 747 series of commercial transports, and is preparing to produce the nose section of the new Models 757 and 767. It also undertakes conversion of Boeing aircraft from passenger to freight-carrying configurations, installs new interiors and embodies structural modifications.

Under a major US Air Force contract awarded in 1979, Boeing is developing a system known as the mission-adaptive wing. Instead of conventional flaps, this wing has a smooth and uninterrupted upper surface in all phases of flight, its camber being varied mechanically to bend, physically, flexible glassfibre-skinned leading- and trailing-edges. The technology is expected to increase dramatically the performance of a wide variety of military aircraft. The 54-month programme is a joint US Air Force/NASA development. Flight testing of the new wing, initially under manual control, is scheduled to begin in August 1982 at Edwards AFB, California. The NASA TACT F-111 (which see) will be modified as the test aircraft, and after the first year will be further modified to incorporate an automatic flight control system.

BOEING B-52 STRATOFORTRESS

Designed originally as an intercontinental, high-altitude nuclear bomber, the B-52, which first entered US Air Force service in 1955, has undergone numerous improvement programmes over the years to ensure that its operational capabilities meet changing defence needs. The US Air Force expects that more than 300 B-52s will remain in its active inventory for the remainder of this century.

The early development history of the B-52 has been recorded in previous editions of *Jane's*, and a structural description can be found in the 1964-65 edition. The three versions still in squadron service (other than the B-52F, which is used for training) are the B-52D, G and H, of which a combined total of 465 was built (170, 193 and 102 respectively). A total of 349 of these (including 270 of the G and H models) remain operational, serving with the 2nd, 7th, 19th, 42nd, 68th, 97th, 379th, 410th and 416th Bomb Wings of the Eighth Air Force; the 5th, 22nd, 28th, 92nd, 93rd, 96th, 319th and 320th Bomb Wings of the Fifteenth Air Force; and the 43rd Strategic Wing of the 3rd Air Division of SAC. An additional 187 B-52s are kept in inactive storage.

Several programmes involving the **B-52G** and **H** have been undertaken or are now in progress to improve the avionics, equipment and operational capability. Under a 1971 contract, 281 of these two models were modified to carry the Boeing SRAM (short range attack missile), which completely replaced the underwing Hound Dog missiles formerly carried. The first of these became operational on 4 August 1972.

The US Air Force's Rivet Ace programme, initiated in 1974, has progressively updated about 270 B-52Gs and B-52Hs which are currently receiving Phase VI ECM (electronic countermeasures). These aircraft have already an AN/ASQ-151 Electro-optical Viewing System (EVS) to improve low level penetration capability, the EVS sensors being housed in two steerable, side-by-side chin turrets. The starboard turret houses a Hughes Aircraft AAQ-6 forward-looking infra-red (FLIR) scanner, while the port turret contains a Westinghouse AVQ-22 low light level TV camera.

By 1981 the B-52G and H should be ready for flight test with Motorola ALQ-122 SNOE (Smart Noise Operation Equipment) countermeasures, and Northrop AN/ALQ-155(V) power management system; by 1982 with an

AFSATCOM kit permitting worldwide communication via satellite; and by 1984 with Northrop ALT-28 and ALT-32 jammers. Sedco Systems has an Air Force contract to design and develop the prototype of an electronically steerable antenna system (ESAS) for the onboard ALT-28s, to improve their defensive electronics (jamming) capability. Other Phase VI avionics include a Dalmo Victor ALR-46 digital radar warning receiver, Westinghouse ALQ-153 pulse-Doppler tail warning radar, and two tail-mounted ITT Avionics ALQ-117 noise/deception jammers.

Boeing has a US Air Force contract to define and design an Offensive Avionics System (OAS) to upgrade the navigation and weapons delivery of the B-52G and H. At a significantly reduced life-cycle cost, this will be a digital (instead of analogue) based, solid-state system, and will include Tercom (terrain comparison) guidance.

Phase I of this programme, to be completed by 1981, involves the equipment of a B-52G test aircraft with the new avionics, followed by 12 months of flight testing. The new equipment includes a Teledyne Ryan Doppler radar, Honeywell AN/ASN-131 gimballed electrostatic airborne inertial navigation system (GEANS), IBM/Raytheon ASQ-38 analogue bombing/navigation system with IBM digital processing, Lear Siegler attitude heading and reference system, Honeywell radar altimeter, Sperry controls and displays, and Norden Systems modernised radar. The programme will be completed in the late 1980s by a Phase II under which a percentage of the B-52 fleet will be equipped for better performance of low-level penetration missions. A major feature of Phase II is an electronically agile radar (EAR), modified from an existing Westinghouse radar, which has been under test since 1978. The EAR will be able to fulfil both mapping and terrain-following functions, and to update the GEANS by measuring ground speed. Automatic terrain-following guidance and a new flight control system also form a part of the Phase II programme, flight testing of which is scheduled for FY 1982-84. A production decision is due to be taken in FY 1983 or 1984.

Following the choice of Boeing's AGM-86B air-

launched cruise missile, as a result of its fly-off against the General Dynamics AGM-109 Tomahawk, the B-52G will be adapted as carrier aircraft for the AGM-86B, and development for this role is continuing. Full-scale development of B-52 carrier aircraft equipment, as an integral part of the cruise missile programme, began in early 1978, and three B-52Gs were modified for use in the fly-off programme at Edwards AFB, California.

The current programme calls for 173 B-52Gs each to be modified to carry 12 AGM-86Bs externally (six on each inboard underwing pylon), in addition to its internal load of SRAMs and other weapons. Initial operational capability in this form is scheduled for December 1982; later in the 1980s the aircraft will be further modified in order to carry eight AGM-86Bs internally. In addition, the US Air Force has an option to convert 96 B-52Hs to the same configuration, beginning in 1984, and development towards this possibility is continuing.

POWER PLANT (B-52D): Eight 44·5 kN (10,000 lb st) Pratt & Whitney J57-P-19W or -29W turbojet engines. Fuel capacity 135,140 litres (35,700 US gallons) internally, plus two 11,355 litre (3,000 US gallon) underwing drop-tanks.

POWER PLANT (B-52G): Eight 61·2 kN (13,750 lb st) J57-P-43WB turbojet engines. Fuel capacity 174,130 litres (46,000 US gallons) internally, plus two 2,650 litre (700 US gallon) underwing drop-tanks.

POWER PLANT (B-52H): Eight 75·6 kN (17,000 lb st) Pratt & Whitney TF33-P-3 turbofan engines. Fuel capacity as for B-52G.

ACCOMMODATION (B-52D/G/H): Crew of six (pilot and co-pilot, side by side on flight deck, navigator, radar navigator, ECM operator and gunner).

ARMAMENT (B-52D): Four 0·50 in machine-guns in occupied tail turret. Up to eighty-four 500 lb bombs in fuselage weapons bay, and a further twenty-four 750 lb bombs on underwing pylons: total bomb load 27,215 kg (60,000 lb).

ARMAMENT (B-52G): Four 0·50 in machine-guns in tail turret, remotely operated by AGS-15 fire control system, remote radar control, or closed circuit TV. Up to

Boeing B-52G fitted with AN/ASQ-151 Electro-optical Viewing System and with other recent modifications

20 Boeing AGM-69 SRAM short-range attack missiles: eight on rotary launcher in internal weapons bay, and six under each wing, plus nuclear free-fall bombs.

ARMAMENT (B-52H): As B-52G, except for single 20 mm Vulcan multi-barrel cannon in tail turret instead of four machine-guns.

DIMENSIONS, EXTERNAL:

Wing span	56·39 m (185 ft 0 in)
Wing area, gross	371·6 m² (4,000 sq ft)
Length overall: G, H	49·05 m (160 ft 10·9 in)
Height overall: D	14·74 m (48 ft 4½ in)
G, H	12·40 m (40 ft 8 in)
Width of fuselage	3·00 m (9 ft 10 in)
Tailplane span: G, H	15·85 m (52 ft 0 in)
Wheel track (c/l of shock-struts)	2·51 m (8 ft 3 in)
Wheelbase	15·48 m (50 ft 3 in)

DIMENSION, INTERNAL:

Weapons bay volume	29·53 m³ (1,043 cu ft)

WEIGHTS:

Max T-O weight:

D	more than 204,115 kg (450,000 lb)
G, H	more than 221,350 kg (488,000 lb)

PERFORMANCE (B-52G/H):

Max level speed at high altitude
Mach 0·90 (516 knots; 957 km/h; 595 mph)
Cruising speed at high altitude
Mach 0·77 (442 knots; 819 km/h; 509 mph)
Penetration speed at low altitude
Mach 0·53 to 0·55
(352-365 knots; 652-676 km/h; 405-420 mph)

Service ceiling	16,765 m (55,000 ft)
T-O run: G	3,050 m (10,000 ft)
H	2,900 m (9,500 ft)

Range with max fuel, without in-flight refuelling:
G more than 6,513 nm (12,070 km; 7,500 miles)
H more than 8,685 nm (16,093 km; 10,000 miles)

BOEING KC-135A STRATOTANKER

The first of 732 KC-135A tanker-transports built by Boeing for the US Air Force flew on 31 August 1956. In early 1979, a total of 615 remained operational to support Strategic Air Command aircraft and those of other US Air Force commands, the US Navy and Marine Corps, and other nations.

Since 1975 Boeing at Wichita has been engaged in a programme to extend the flying life of each KC-135A by

27,000 hours, by replacing the lower wing skins. This will enable the aircraft to remain fully operational well past the year 2000, and has justified a programme to retrofit modern technology engines, to improve fuel economy and reduce noise. Selection of the 97·86 kN (22,000 lb st) General Electric/SNECMA CFM56-1B1 turbofan for evaluation on a KC-135A testbed aircraft was announced in early 1980, and retrofit of an unspecified number of KC-135As will be undertaken by Boeing Military Airplane Company. The re-engined aircraft will have the new designation **KC-135RE**. Electrical, hydraulic and flight control systems will also undergo modification. Installation of the new engines will begin in 1982, after which the first KC-135RE will undergo seven months of US Air Force flight testing at Edwards AFB, California, followed by three months of operational trials.

On 10 June 1977, Boeing received a contract to design, install and flight test on a KC-135A a set of winglets that could reduce fuel consumption by an estimated 8 per cent. This would save 140 million litres (37 million US gallons) of fuel annually; the winglets are also expected to improve take-off performance, and slightly enhance fuel offload capability. Flight testing of the winglets on the KC-135A began in 1979 (see NASA entry).

BOEING VERTOL COMPANY

Boeing Vertol Company, established in 1960, has produced and delivered some 2,500 tandem-rotor helicopters to the US military services, as well as to many foreign nations. The CH-47 Chinook is the company's current production helicopter for the US Army, and is in service also with the armed forces of ten other nations. Marketing of the MBB BO 105 C helicopter has been transferred from Boeing Vertol to MBB's North American subsidiary during the past year.

BOEING VERTOL MODEL 107
USN and USMC designation: CH-46/UH-46 Sea Knight

Details of the Boeing Vertol Model 107, of which production by Boeing Vertol ended some years ago, can be found in the 1971-72 *Jane's*. A derivative, the KV-107, is being produced currently under licence in Japan by Kawasaki Heavy Industries Ltd (which see).

A total of 624 basically similar CH/UH-46 aircraft were delivered to the US Marine Corps and US Navy in the 1964-1971 period. With a view to modernising the Marine Corps' fleet of CH-46s, two prototypes were modified by Boeing Vertol in 1975 and have since completed flight testing. The US Marine Corps now plans to update 273 CH-46s to **CH-46E** configuration, this involving the installation of 1,394 kW (1,870 shp) General Electric T58-GE-16 turboshaft engines, each developing 33·6% more power than the 1,044 kW (1,400 shp) T58-GE-10s installed in production CH-46D/F aircraft. Other modifications include the provision of crash attenuating seats for pilot and co-pilot, a crash and combat resistant fuel system, and improved rescue system. Initial fleet modifications began during 1977, and the first CH-46E modified at the Cherry Point, NC, Naval Air Rework Facility was rolled out on 3 August 1977.

In April 1975 Boeing Vertol received a contract from Naval Air Systems Command to initiate the development of glassfibre main rotor blades for the H-46 fleet. In early 1977 glassfibre rotor blades for testing purposes were manufactured by Boeing Vertol, and these were bench tested, whirl tested and flight tested during the remainder of the year. Due to the satisfactory progress of this programme, the US Marine Corps began in-service testing of the blades in early 1978. The first production order for these glassfibre rotor blades was issued by the US Navy in December 1977, and by early 1980 a total of 811 blades had been ordered. Fifty-six CH-46s had been fitted with the new blades by August 1980. Follow-on orders for an additional 2,100 blades are programmed, to maintain deliveries up to the end of 1984. Boeing Canada (which see) is currently upgrading a number of Canadian Armed Forces CH-113/113As under a programme known as SARCUP.

BOEING VERTOL MODELS 114 and 414
US Army designation: CH-47 Chinook
Canadian Armed Forces designation: CH-147
Royal Air Force designation: Chinook HC. Mk 1

Development of the CH-47 Chinook series of helicopters began in 1956, and the first of five YCH-47As (formerly YHC-1B) made its initial hovering flight on 21 September 1961. Since then, effectiveness of the CH-47 has been increased by successive improvement programmes. A total of 949 Chinooks had been ordered by 1 January 1980, of which 868 had been delivered; of these, 147 orders and 108 deliveries were from licence production by the Agusta group in Italy (which see).

The CH-47 was designed to meet the US Army's requirement for an all-weather medium transport helicopter and, depending upon the series model, is capable of transporting specified payloads under severe combinations of altitude and temperature conditions. The primary mission radius criterion established by the US Army is 100 nm (185 km; 115 miles). The primary mission take-off

Boeing Vertol updated CH-46E, for the US Marine Corps, with General Electric T58-GE-16 turboshaft engines

The three Boeing Vertol CH-47D prototypes, converted from CH-47A/47B/47C Chinooks

gross weight is based on the capability of hovering out of ground effect at 1,830 m/35°C (6,000 ft/95°F). The CH-47C has demonstrated its ability to hover out of ground effect with a useful load of 11,453 kg (25,250 lb) at sea level under standard atmospheric conditions.

The following versions of the Chinook have been produced:

CH-47A. Initial production version, powered by two 1,640 kW (2,200 shp) Avco Lycoming T55-L-5 or 1,976 kW (2,650 shp) T55-L-7 turboshaft engines. Operation of the CH-47A by the Viet-Nam Air Force (VNAF) began in 1971. Four delivered to Royal Thai Air Force. Production completed. Transmissions uprated to CH-47C standard under 1978 Army contract.

CH-47B. Developed version with 2,125 kW (2,850 shp) T55-L-7C turboshaft engines, redesigned rotor blades with cambered leading-edge, blunted rear rotor pylon, and strakes along rear ramp and fuselage for improved flying qualities. First of two prototypes flew for the first time in early October 1966. Deliveries began on 10 May 1967. Production completed. Transmissions uprated to CH-47C standard under 1978 Army contract.

CH-47C. Increased performance from a combination of strengthened transmissions, two 2,796 kW (3,750 shp) T55-L-11A engines and increased integral fuel capacity. First flight of original CH-47C made 14 October 1967; production deliveries began in Spring 1968. First deployed in Viet-Nam in September 1968. Total of 210 US Army CH-47Cs currently undergoing retrofit with glassfibre rotor blades.

A Crash-worthy Fuel System (CWFS) and an Integral Spar Inspection System (ISIS) were made available during 1973. Incorporation of the CWFS on US Army CH-47Cs was accomplished by retrofit kits, deliveries of which began in March 1973. Chinooks delivered to Australia have this system, which provides a total fuel capacity of 3,944 litres (1,042 US gallons).

CH-147. Designation of nine CH-47Cs delivered to Canada from September 1974. These aircraft have T55-L-11C engines, ISIS, CWFS, forward door rescue hoist, ferry range tank kit, up to 44 troop seats, advanced flight control system, rear ramp with water dam, 12,700 kg (28,000 lb) cargo hook, T-O weight of 22,680 kg (50,000 lb), and weight for water operations of 16,330 kg (36,000 lb) normal or 20,865 kg (46,000 lb) emergency.

CH-47D. Three Chinooks (one each of the CH-47A, CH-47B, and CH-47C models) have been modernised to CH-47D configuration under a $75 million contract received from the US Army in June 1976. The three aircraft were stripped down to their basic airframes, and were then rebuilt with improved components and systems to provide three CH-47D prototypes.

Conversion included the installation of Avco Lycoming T55-L-712 engines, which have an emergency power rating; the introduction of improved rotor transmissions with a rating of 5,593 kW (7,500 shp); the introduction of integral lubrication and cooling for the transmission systems, and of glassfibre rotor blades. Other improvements include a redesigned cockpit to reduce the pilot's workload; the introduction of redundant and improved electrical systems, modularised hydraulic systems, an advanced flight control system, and improved avionics equipment. In addition, a T62T-2B APU and a triple cargo hook suspension system have been installed.

The first CH-47D, converted from a CH-47A airframe, was rolled out four months ahead of schedule on 6 March 1979. After flight testing had been completed by Boeing Vertol, this aircraft was accepted by the US Army, at Fort Rucker, Alabama, on 13 December 1979, and by mid-1980 the three prototypes had completed a 920-hour

First Boeing Vertol Chinook HC. Mk 1 for the Royal Air Force

programme of flight testing, as well as an extensive series of ground tests, by Boeing Vertol and the US Army. Two of the CH-47D prototypes were allocated to an operational test programme, conducted by the 101st Airborne Division (Air Assault) at Fort Campbell, Kentucky, which took place in April and May 1980. The third aircraft was then being used for climatic tests. A decision was due in August/September 1980 on US Army plans calling for 436 earlier-model Chinooks to be remanufactured to CH-47D standard. Meanwhile, what Boeing Vertol describes as "an orderly transition to the start of CH-47D production" has been under way since January 1979.

Chinook HC.Mk 1. Version for Royal Air Force, which ordered 33 for delivery by the end of 1981. First example (ZA670) made its initial flight on 23 March 1980. Deliveries were due to begin in September 1980. Generally similar to Canadian CH-147, with Avco Lycoming T55-L-11E turboshaft engines, but with provision for glassfibre/carbonfibre rotor blades and three external cargo hooks (capacity 12,700 kg; 28,000 lb on centre hook, or 9,072 kg; 20,000 lb total on forward and rear hooks); accommodation for up to 44 troops or 24 standard NATO stretchers; engine and windscreen de-icing; provision for two self-ferry fuel tanks in cabin; and amphibious capability in sea states of up to 3. Intended for use on logistic support, tactical troop lift, casualty evacuation, air-mobility, and external load-carrying duties. Will equip one squadron based in the UK, a small training unit (also in the UK), and No. 18 Squadron at RAF Gutersloh in West Germany. Extensive range of British avionics and equipment, including Decca tactical navigation system, Doppler Mk 71 radar and Mk 19 area navigation; Marconi Avionics ARC340 VHF/FM com and homing system, AD120 VHF/AM com, AD380 ADF, AD2770 Tacan and AD27733 interface unit; Lucas 40kVA generators; and UHF/AM, VOR/ILS, HF/SSB, radar altimeter, UHF/VHF homing, and IFF transceiver.

Model 234. Commercial version, described separately.

CH-47 helicopters are in service in many places, including Alaska, Australia, West Germany, Hawaii, Iran, Italy, Korea, Spain and Thailand, as well as at numerous US National Guard and US Army installations within the continental United States. Total US Army procurement of CH-47A/B/C models had reached 727 by 1 January 1980. Of these, 358 then equipped active Army units, with 94 more in Reserve/ANG service. Other customers for US-built CH-47Cs include Argentina (3), Australia (12),

Canada (9), Spain (10), Thailand (4), and the UK (33). Deliveries of Agusta/EM-built CH-47Cs have been made to the air forces of Italy (26), Iran (95, of which 60 delivered by the end of 1979), Libya (20, of which 16 delivered) and Morocco (6).

Details of the CH-47A and -47B can be found in the 1974-75 *Jane's*. Those which follow apply specifically to the CH-47C:

TYPE: Twin-engined medium transport helicopter.

ROTOR SYSTEM: Two three-blade rotors, rotating in opposite directions and driven through interconnecting shafts which enable both rotors to be driven by either engine. Rotor blades, of a modified NACA 0012 section, have cambered leading-edge, a strengthened steel spar structure and honeycomb-filled trailing-edge boxes. Two blades of each rotor can be folded manually. Rotor heads are fully articulated, with pitch, flapping and drag hinges. All bearings are submerged completely in oil.

ROTOR DRIVE: Power is transmitted from each engine through individual overrunning clutches, into the combiner transmission, thereby providing a single power output to the interconnecting shafts. Rotor/engine rpm ratio 64 : 1.

FUSELAGE: Square-section all-metal semi-monocoque structure. Loading ramp forms undersurface of upswept rear fuselage. Fairing pods along bottom of each side are made of metal honeycomb sandwich and are sealed and compartmented, as is the underfloor section of the fuselage, for buoyancy during operation from water.

LANDING GEAR: Menasco non-retractable quadricycle type, with twin wheels on each forward unit and single wheels on each rear unit. Oleo-pneumatic shock-absorbers on all units. Rear units fully castoring and steerable; power steering installed on starboard rear unit. All wheels are government-furnished size 24 × 7·7-VII, with tyres size 8·50-10-III, pressure 4·62 bars (67 lb/sq in). Two single-disc hydraulic brakes. Provision for fitting detachable wheel-skis.

POWER PLANT: Two 2,796 kW (3,750 shp) Avco Lycoming T55-L-11A turboshaft engines, mounted one each side of rear rotor pylon. Combined transmission rating 5,369 kW (7,200 shp); max single-engine transmission limit 3,430 kW (4,600 shp). Self-sealing fuel tanks in external pods on sides of fuselage. Total fuel capacity is 4,137 litres (1,093 US gallons), or 3,944 litres (1,042 US gallons) when equipped with Crashworthy Fuel System.

CH-47C CHINOOK WEIGHTS AND PERFORMANCE

	Condition 1	Condition 2	Condition 3	Condition 4
Weight empty	9,736 kg (21,464 lb)	9,736 kg (21,464 lb)	9,812 kg (21,633 lb)	9,599 kg (21,162 lb)
Payload	5,284 kg (11,650 lb)	2,903 kg (6,400 lb)	9,843 kg (21,700 lb)	—
T-O weight	17,463 kg (38,500 lb)	14,968 kg (33,000 lb)	20,593 kg (45,400 lb)	20,865 kg (46,000 lb)
Max speed, S/L, ISA at normal rated power	155 knots (286 km/h; 178 mph)	164 knots (304 km/h; 189 mph)	127 knots (235 km/h; 146 mph)	—
Average cruising speed	139 knots (257 km/h; 160 mph)	137 knots (254 km/h; 158 mph)	114 knots (211 km/h; 131 mph)	133 knots (246 km/h; 153 mph)
Max rate of climb, S/L, ISA at normal rated power	649 m (2,130 ft)/min	878 m (2,880 ft)/min	421 m (1,380 ft)/min	402 m (1,320 ft)/min
Service ceiling, ISA, normal rated power	3,290 m (10,800 ft)	4,570 m (15,000 ft)	2,560 m (8,400 ft)	2,440 m (8,000 ft)
Hovering ceiling OGE, ISA, max power	2,805 m (9,200 ft)	4,145 m (13,600 ft)	Sea level	—
Mission radius	100 nm (185 km; 115 miles)	100 nm (185 km; 115 miles)	20 nm (37 km; 23 miles)	—
Ferry range	—	—	—	1,156 nm (2,142 km; 1,331 miles)

Condition 1 Criteria: Take-off gross weight equals gross weight to hover OGE at 1,830 m/35°C (6,000 ft/95°F). Radius of action 100 nm (185 km; 115 miles). Fuel reserve 10%. Payload carried internally.

Condition 2 Criteria: Take-off gross weight equals design gross weight. Radius of action 100 nm (185 km; 115 miles). Fuel reserve 10%. Payload carried internally.

Condition 3 Criteria: Take-off gross weight equals gross weight to hover OGE at S/L ISA. Radius of action 20 nm (37 km; 23 miles). Fuel reserve 10%. Payload carried externally. Except for the mission average cruising speed, all other performance is predicated on internal loading of cargo.

Condition 4 Criteria: Take-off gross weight represents alternative design gross weight. Max ferry range (integral and internal auxiliary fuel only), cruise at optimum altitude and standard temperature, no payload, 10% fuel reserves.

Refuelling points above tanks. Total oil capacity 14 litres (3·7 US gallons).

ACCOMMODATION: Two pilots on flight deck, with dual controls. Jump seat is provided for crew chief or combat commander. Jettisonable door on each side of flight deck. Depending on seating arrangement, 33 to 44 troops can be accommodated in main cabin, or 24 litters plus two attendants, or vehicles and freight. Typical loads include a complete artillery section with crew and ammunition. All components of the Pershing missile system are transportable by Chinooks. Extruded magnesium floor designed for distributed load of 1,465 kg/m² (300 lb/sq ft) and concentrated load of 1,136 kg (2,500 lb) per wheel in tread portion. Floor contains eighty-three 2,270 kg (5,000 lb) tiedown fittings and eight 4,540 kg (10,000 lb) fittings. Rear loading ramp can be left completely or partially open, or can be removed to permit transport of extra-long cargo and in-flight parachute or free-drop delivery of cargo and equipment. Main cabin door, at front on starboard side, comprises upper hinged section which can be opened in flight and lower section with integral steps. Lower section is jettisonable. Up to 12,700 kg (28,000 lb) can be carried on external cargo hook.

SYSTEMS: Cabin heated by 200,000 BTU heater-blower. Hydraulic system provides pressures of 207 bars (3,000 lb/sq in) for flying controls, and 276 bars (4,000 lb/sq in) for engine starting. Electrical system includes two 20kVA alternators driven by transmission drive system. Solar T62 APU runs accessory gear drive, thereby operating all hydraulic and electrical systems.

AVIONICS AND EQUIPMENT: All government furnished, including UHF communications and FM liaison sets, transponder, intercom, omni-receiver, ADF and marker beacon receiver. Blind-flying instrumentation standard. Special equipment includes dual electro-hydraulic stability augmentation system, automatic/manual speed trim system, hydraulically-powered winch for rescue and cargo handling purposes, cargo and rescue hatch in floor, integral work stands and steps for maintenance, rearview mirror, provisions for paratroops' static lines and for maintenance davits for removal of major components.

DIMENSIONS, EXTERNAL:

Diameter of rotors (each)	18·29 m (60 ft 0 in)
Main rotor blade chord	0·64 m (2 ft 1¼ in)
Distance between rotor centres	11·94 m (39 ft 2 in)
Length overall, rotors turning	30·18 m (99 ft 0 in)
Length of fuselage	15·54 m (51 ft 0 in)
Width, rotors folded	3·78 m (12 ft 5 in)
Height to top of rear rotor hub	5·68 m (18 ft 7·8 in)
Wheel track (c/l of shock-absorbers)	3·20 m (10 ft 6 in)
Wheelbase	6·86 m (22 ft 6 in)
Passenger door (fwd, stbd):	
Height	1·68 m (5 ft 6 in)
Width	0·91 m (3 ft 0 in)
Height to sill	1·09 m (3 ft 7 in)
Rear loading ramp entrance:	
Height	1·98 m (6 ft 6 in)
Width	2·31 m (7 ft 7 in)
Height to sill	0·79 m (2 ft 7 in)

DIMENSIONS, INTERNAL:

Cabin, excl flight deck: Length		9·20 m (30 ft 2 in)
Width (mean)		2·29 m (7 ft 6 in)
Width at floor		2·51 m (8 ft 3 in)
Height		1·98 m (6 ft 6 in)
Floor area		21·0 m² (226 sq ft)
Usable volume		41·7 m³ (1,474 cu ft)

AREAS:

Rotor blades (each)	5·86 m² (63·1 sq ft)
Main rotor discs (total)	525·3 m² (5,655 sq ft)

WEIGHTS (CH-47C: see accompanying table. CH-47D as follows, A: guaranteed; B: estimated, based on whirl test results):

Internal payload over 100 nm (185 km; 115 miles) at 1,220 m (4,000 ft), hovering OGE at T-O:

A	5,896 kg (13,000 lb)
B	6,496 kg (14,322 lb)

External payload over 30 nm (55·5 km; 34·5 miles) at 1,220 m (4,000 ft), 61 m (200 ft)/min vertical climb at T-O, 35°C: A

A	6,803 kg (15,000 lb)
B	7,155 kg (15,775 lb)

Gross weight, hovering OGE at S/L, ISA:

A	22,680 kg (50,000 lb)
B	24,267 kg (53,000 lb)

PERFORMANCE (CH-47C: see accompanying table. CH-47D: as follows):

Max level speed at S/L, ISA, at AUW of 14,968 kg (33,000 lb): A 155 knots (287 km/h; 178 mph)
             B 161 knots (298 km/h; 185 mph)

Single-engine service ceiling at 14,968 kg (33,000 lb) AUW, ISA: A 3,050 m (10,000 ft)
           B 4,270 m (14,000 ft)

BOEING VERTOL MODEL 234 COMMERCIAL CHINOOK

Announced in the late Summer of 1978, this development of the military CH-47 Chinook is being produced for use as a commercial passenger transport, as a cargo carrier, and for specialised tasks such as servicing offshore oil and natural gas rigs, remote resources exploration and extraction, logging, and construction work.

The airframe of the Model 234 is based on that of the latest military Chinook, but has many new features. These include the use of wide-chord glassfibre rotor blades, instead of the usual metal blades; redesign of the fuselage-side fairings in two different forms; a lengthened nose to accommodate the weather radar antenna; and movement further forward of the front landing gear units.

Two basic versions of the commercial Model 234 are offered:

Long-range model. Identified by continuous fuselage-side fairings, approximately twice as large as those of the military Chinook and containing large fuel tanks. Equipped to airline standards as a passenger, passenger/freight 'combi' or all-cargo transport.

Utility model. Fuselage-side fuel tanks replaced by two drum-shape internal tanks, mounted longitudinally side by side at the front of the cabin. Fuselage-side fairings removed, leaving only an individual streamlined blister around each landing gear mounting. As well as reducing weight, this enhances the helicopter's lifting capability by

reducing the airframe surface area on which the rotor downwash impinges.

Conversion from one configuration of the Model 234 to another is estimated to take eight hours, and requires four persons to handle the fuel tanks of the utility model and the ramp baggage bins of the passenger-carrying helicopter. Initial cost of the glassfibre blades is significantly greater than that of metal blades, but manufacturing time is reduced by 25% and in-service maintenance costs by 71%. Mean time between blade removal is estimated at 3,200 h. The three blades of any one rotor are interchangeable, but blades cannot be interchanged from one hub to another. Current engine TBO is 1,800 h.

Initial order for the Model 234 was placed by British Airways Helicopters, which ordered three in 1978 (since increased to six), primarily for North Sea oil rig support operations. By the Summer of 1980 a total of 12 Commercial Chinooks had been ordered, including options. Assembly of the first aircraft began in mid-1979. First flight was made on 19 August 1980, and full certification is expected to be achieved by mid-1981.

TYPE: Twin-turbine commercial transport helicopter.

ROTOR SYSTEM: Two three-blade rotors in tandem, turning in opposite directions and driven through interconnecting shafts which enable both rotors to be driven by either engine. Wide-chord glassfibre blades, with VR7 section over inboard 85% of span, and VR8 section on outer 15% of span; thickness/chord ratio 12% and 8% respectively. Overall blade twist 12°. Each blade comprises a laminated glassfibre skin over a glassfibre D spar, forming the front half of the section, and with the rear half filled with Nomex honeycomb. An aluminium screen inserted in the skin provides lightning protection, discharging strikes via the titanium leading-edge. Outboard 25% of leading-edge capped with replaceable nickel section. Blade balancing by tracking weights in tips. Two blades of each rotor can be folded manually. Hubs fully articulated, with pitch, flapping and drag hinges. All bearings submerged completely in oil. Auxiliary transmission lubrication system enables flight to be completed after total loss of oil in primary system. Blades embody electrical de-icing blankets, permitting addition of a de-icing kit if required. Rotor rpm 225.

ROTOR DRIVE: Power is transmitted from each engine through individual overrunning clutches, into the combiner transmission, thereby providing a single power output to the interconnecting shafts.

FUSELAGE: All-metal semi-monocoque structure of basically square section. Loading ramp forms undersurface of upswept rear fuselage. External fuel pods of long-range model made of advanced composites, including glassfibre, graphite/epoxy and Nomex nylon honeycomb. These fairing pods provide flotation capability adequate to meet British airworthiness requirements applicable to a sea state seven (9·15 m; 30 ft waves. Wave length-to-height ratio 15) without added flotation gear.

LANDING GEAR: Non-retractable quadricycle type, with twin wheels on each forward unit and single wheels on each rear unit. All tyres size 8·50-10, Type III (12 ply), pressure 8·55 bars (124 lb/sq in) on forward gear, 7·20 bars (104·4 lb/sq in) on aft gear. Oleo-pneumatic

Three views on left depict the Boeing Vertol CH-47D military helicopter. Plan view at top right shows the Model 234 commercial utility model. Remaining three views depict the long-range commercial model (*Pilot Press*)

shock-absorbers on all units. Rear units fully castoring and steerable. Hydraulic disc brakes.

POWER PLANT: Two Avco Lycoming AL 5512 turboshaft engines, pod-mounted on each side of rear rotor pylon. Each engine has max T-O rating of 3,039 kW (4,075 shp), max continuous rating of 2,218·5 kW (2,975 shp), and 30 min contingency rating of 3,246 kW (4,353 shp). Transmission rated at 5,592 kW (7,500 shp) at 225 rotor rpm, and 3,430 kW (4,600 shp) for single-engine operation. Long-range model has two fuel tanks, one in each fuselage-side fairing, with total capacity of 7,911 litres (2,090 US gallons). Utility model has two drum-shape internal tanks, with total capacity of 3,785 litres (1,000 US gallons). Single-point pressure refuelling.

ACCOMMODATION: Two pilots side by side on flight deck, with dual controls. Passenger cabin of long-range model seats up to 44 persons four-abreast, with centre aisle. Each seat has overhead bin and underseat stowage for carry-on baggage; larger items are stowed over the rear ramp in the main baggage compartment. Galley, with cabin attendant's seat, and toilet, are standard, between flight deck and cabin. Typical 'combi' configuration accommodates 18 passengers forward and 7,250 kg (16,000 lb) of freight, loaded via rear ramp. All passenger facilities can be removed for freight-only service. Passenger door at front of cabin on starboard side. Crew door on each side of flight deck. Cabin floor supported by dynamically tuned fittings to reduce vibration. Hydraulically powered cargo ramp can be stopped at any intermediate position to match the level of the loading vehicle being used. Single central cargo hook is standard on utility model for carrying external loads of up to 12,700 kg (28,000 lb). Optional dual tandem hooks for precision operations and for load stability in high-speed flight; or three tandem hooks for delivering multiple loads.

SYSTEMS: Heating and ventilation systems maintain comfortable flight deck/cabin temperature in ambient temperatures down to −32°C. Duplicated flying control, hydraulic and electrical systems. Solar T62T-2B APU, rated at 71 kW (95 shp), drives auxiliary gearbox on rear transmission to start engines and provide power for two flying control system hydraulic pumps and two alternators. All critical systems heated to inhibit ice build-up.

AVIONICS AND EQUIPMENT: Duplicated full blind-flying instrumentation, weather radar, and dual four-axis automatic flight control system with built-in test equipment, provide all-weather capability. Optional equipment includes passenger interior furnishings for the utility model, 'combi' interior, downward-shining cargo load light, cargo winch of 5,440 kg (12,000 lb) capacity operable via floor hatch or loading ramp, rescue hoist of 272 kg (600 lb) capacity, a power-down rear loading ramp to drive the ramp below water when required, a water dam to prevent water entering the cabin when the ramp is down, glassfibre wheel-skis, an ice detector probe, and ditching equipment that includes two liferafts, each with an overload capacity of 36 persons. Standard items include integral work platforms, and a maintenance panel that allows 26 separate checks to be made from a single ground-level position.

DIMENSIONS, EXTERNAL:

Rotor diameter (each)	18·29 m (60 ft 0 in)
Rotor blade chord (constant)	0·813 m (2 ft 8 in)
Length overall, rotors turning	30·18 m (99 ft 0 in)
Length of fuselage	15·87 m (52 ft 1 in)
Height overall	5·68 m (18 ft 7·8 in)
Width over fuselage-side fairings	4·78 m (15 ft 8 in)
Wheel track:	
fwd gear	3·20 m (10 ft 6 in)
aft gear	3·40 m (11 ft 2 in)
Wheelbase	7·87 m (25 ft 9·9 in)

DIMENSIONS, INTERNAL:

Passenger cabin: Length	9·19 m (30 ft 2 in)
Max width	2·51 m (8 ft 3 in)
Max height	1·98 m (6 ft 6 in)
Baggage compartment volume	4·42 m³ (156 cu ft)
Utility model, cargo hold volume	41·03 m³ (1,449 cu ft)

WEIGHTS (L, long-range model; U, utility model):

Manufacturer's weight empty:	
L	11,090 kg (24,449 lb)
U	9,369 kg (20,655 lb)
Operating weight empty:	
L	11,566 kg (25,500 lb)
U	9,576 kg (21,112 lb)
Fuel load: L	6,361 kg (14,024 lb)
U	1,826 kg (4,026 lb)
Max payload: L	10,229 kg (22,551 lb)
U, internal	11,843 kg (26,109 lb)
L, U, external	12,700 kg (28,000 lb)
Max T-O weight:	
L and U, internal load	21,318 kg (47,000 lb)
L, external load	22,226 kg (49,000 lb)
U, external load	23,133 kg (51,000 lb)

PERFORMANCE (estimated: L, long-range model; U, utility model):

Never-exceed speed:	
L, U	165 knots (305 km/h; 190 mph)
Max cruising speed at 610 m (2,000 ft):	
L, U, internal load, at 21,318 kg (47,000 lb) AUW	145 knots (269 km/h; 167 mph)
Cruising speed for optimum range, at 610 m (2,000 ft):	
L, U, internal load, at 18,150 kg (40,000 lb) AUW	137 knots (253 km/h; 157 mph)
L, U, internal load, at 21,318 kg (47,000 lb) AUW	135 knots (250 km/h; 155 mph)
Max rate of climb at S/L:	
L, U, internal load	410 m (1,350 ft)/min
Service ceiling:	
L, U, internal load	4,570 m (15,000 ft)
Service ceiling, one engine out:	
L, U, internal load	457 m (1,500 ft)
Hovering ceiling IGE:	
L	2,790 m (9,150 ft)
U	3,155 m (10,350 ft)
Hovering ceiling OGE:	
L	1,495 m (4,900 ft)
U	2,195 m (7,200 ft)
Range with 45 min IFR reserves:	
L with 44 passengers	545 nm (1,010 km; 627 miles)
L with max fuel	740 nm (1,371 km; 852 miles)
U with max internal load	180 nm (333 km; 207 miles)
U with max external load	135 nm (250 km; 155 miles)
Max endurance:	
L	5 h 6 min
U, external load	2 h 24 min

Boeing 234 Commercial Chinook during first flight on 19 August 1980

BRANTLY-HYNES

BRANTLY-HYNES HELICOPTER INC

HEAD OFFICE AND WORKS: PO Box 697, Frederick, Oklahoma 73542
Telephone: (405) 335 2256
PRESIDENT: Michael K. Hynes

This company, formed on 1 January 1975, replaced Brantly Operators Inc which acquired all rights in Brantly helicopters in late 1970. Mr M. K. Hynes acquired also ownership of the Type Certificates for the Brantly B-2, B-2A, B-2B and Model 305.

Brantly-Hynes has put the two-seat B-2B back into production, and plans to introduce an agricultural version of the Model 305 in early 1981. Production of 18 B-2Bs was scheduled for 1980.

BRANTLY-HYNES MODEL B-2B

TYPE: Two-seat light helicopter.
ROTOR SYSTEM: Three-blade main rotor. Articulated inboard flapping hinges offset 0·07 m (2·67 in) from hub, and coincident flap and lag hinges offset 1·31 m (4 ft 3¾ in) from hub. Symmetrical blade section with 29% thickness ratio on inboard portion; NACA 0012 section outboard of hinge. Inboard portion of each blade is rigid, built around a steel spar blade. Outboard portion is flexible, with an extruded aluminium leading-edge spar and polyurethane core; aluminium skin is bonded to core and riveted to spar. Blades are attached to hub by flapping links and do not fold. A rotor brake is standard equipment. Two-blade all-metal anti-torque tail rotor.
ROTOR DRIVE: Through centrifugal clutch and planetary reduction gears. Bevel gear take-off from main transmission with flexible coupling to tail rotor drive-shaft. Main rotor/engine rpm ratio 1 : 6·158. Tail rotor/engine rpm ratio 1 : 1.
FUSELAGE: Stressed-skin all-metal structure with conical tail section. Tail rotor on swept-up boom extension.
LANDING GEAR: Alternative skid, wheel or float gear. Skid type has small retractable wheels for ground handling, fixed tailskid and four shock-absorbers with rubber in compression. Tyres size 10 × 3½, pressure 4·14 bars (60 lb/sq in). Alternative non-retractable tricycle landing gear has oleo-pneumatic shock-absorbers for all units, with single wheels on main units and twin nosewheels. Inflatable pontoons, which attach to standard skids, are available to permit operation from water.
POWER PLANT: One 134 kW (180 hp) Avco Lycoming IVO-360-A1A flat-four engine, mounted vertically, with dual fan cooling system. Rubber bag-type fuel tank under engine, capacity 117 litres (31 US gallons). Refuelling point on port side of fuselage. Oil capacity 5·7 litres (1·5 US gallons).
ACCOMMODATION: Totally-enclosed circular-section cabin for two persons seated side by side. Forward-hinged door on each side. Dual controls, cabin heater and demisting fan standard. Compartment for 22·7 kg (50 lb) baggage in forward end of tail section.
AVIONICS AND EQUIPMENT: Provision for all standard nav/com radios. Blind-flying instrumentation available as an option, but the Model B-2B is not certificated for instrument flight. Twin landing lights in nose.

DIMENSIONS, EXTERNAL:

Diameter of main rotor	7·24 m (23 ft 9 in)
Main rotor blade chord: inboard	0·225 m (8·85 in)
outboard	0·203 m (8·0 in)
Diameter of tail rotor	1·29 m (4 ft 3 in)
Length overall, rotor turning	8·53 m (28 ft 0 in)
Length of fuselage	6·62 m (21 ft 9 in)
Height overall	2·06 m (6 ft 9 in)
Skid track	1·73 m (5 ft 8¼ in)
Passenger doors (each): Height	0·79 m (2 ft 7 in)
Width	0·86 m (2 ft 9¾ in)
Baggage compartment door:	
Mean height	0·25 m (9¾ in)
Length	0·55 m (1 ft 9¾ in)

DIMENSIONS, INTERNAL:

Max width of cabin	1·27 m (4 ft 2 in)
Baggage compartment	0·17 m³ (6 cu ft)

AREAS:

Main rotor blades (each)	0·69 m² (7·42 sq ft)
Main rotor disc	41·06 m² (442 sq ft)
Tail rotor disc	1·21 m² (13 sq ft)

WEIGHTS AND LOADINGS:

Weight empty with skids	463 kg (1,020 lb)
Weight empty with floats	481 kg (1,060 lb)
Max T-O weight	757 kg (1,670 lb)
Max disc loading	18·4 kg/m² (3·77 lb/sq ft)
Max power loading	5·65 kg/kW (9·27 lb/hp)

PERFORMANCE (at max T-O weight):

Max level speed at S/L	87 knots (161 km/h; 100 mph)
Max cruising speed (75% power)	78 knots (145 km/h; 90 mph)
Max rate of climb at S/L	580 m (1,900 ft)/min
Service ceiling	3,290 m (10,800 ft)
Hovering ceiling IGE	2,040 m (6,700 ft)
Range with max fuel, with reserves	217 nm (400 km; 250 miles)

Brantly-Hynes Model B-2B light helicopter (Avco Lycoming IVO-360-A1A engine)

Brantly-Hynes Model 305 light helicopter carrying 181 kg (400 lb) underslung load

BRANTLY-HYNES MODEL 305

The Model 305 is a five-seat helicopter of similar configuration to the Model B-2B, but larger in every respect. The prototype of the original Model 305 flew for the first time in January 1964, and FAA Type Approval was received on 29 July 1965.
TYPE: Five-seat light helicopter.
ROTOR SYSTEM: Three-blade main rotor. Articulated inboard flapping hinges, offset 0·09 m (3·625 in) from hub, and coincident flap and lag hinges outboard. Inboard portion of each blade is rigid, built around a steel spar blade. All-metal outboard portion has a D-spar and is foam-filled. Two-blade all-metal tail rotor. Each blade has a forged aluminium leading-edge spar, ribs and riveted aluminium skin. Main rotor blades do not fold. Rotor brake is standard.
ROTOR DRIVE: Main rotor shaft-driven through centrifugal clutch and planetary reduction gears. Bevel gear take-off from main transmission, with flexible coupling, through tail rotor drive-shaft and intermediate gearbox to tail gearbox. Main rotor/engine rpm ratio 1 : 6·666. Tail rotor/engine rpm ratio 1 : 0·998.
FUSELAGE: Stressed-skin all-metal structure, with conical tail section. Tail rotor carried on swept-up boom extension.
TAIL UNIT: Small variable-incidence horizontal stabiliser of all-metal stressed-skin construction.
LANDING GEAR: Alternative skid, wheel or float gear. Skid landing gear has four oleo struts, two on each side, and small retractable ground handling wheels. The wheel gear has two main wheels and twin nosewheels, all on oleo-pneumatic shock-absorbers. Goodyear main wheels and tyres size 6·00-6, pressure 2·07 bars (30 lb/sq in). Goodyear nosewheels and tyres size 5·00-5, pressure 1·93 bars (28 lb/sq in). Goodyear single-disc hydraulic brakes on main wheels.
POWER PLANT: One 227·5 kW (305 hp) Avco Lycoming IVO-540-A1A flat-six engine, mounted vertically, with dual cooling fans. One rubber-cell fuel tank under engine, capacity 163 litres (43 US gallons). Refuelling point in port side of fuselage. Oil capacity 9·5 litres (2·5 US gallons).
ACCOMMODATION: Two individual seats side by side with dual controls. Rear bench seat for three persons. Door on each side. Rear compartment for 113 kg (250 lb) of baggage, with downward-hinged door on starboard side.
AVIONICS AND EQUIPMENT: King or Narco radio, to customer's specification. Blind-flying instrumentation is available, but helicopter is not certificated for instrument flight.

DIMENSIONS, EXTERNAL:

Diameter of main rotor	8·74 m (28 ft 8 in)
Main rotor blade chord (constant)	0·254 m (10 in)
Diameter of tail rotor	1·30 m (4 ft 3 in)
Length overall, rotor turning	10·03 m (32 ft 11 in)
Length of fuselage	7·44 m (24 ft 5 in)
Height overall	2·44 m (8 ft 0⅛ in)
Wheel track	2·10 m (6 ft 10¾ in)
Wheelbase	2·15 m (7 ft 0½ in)
Passenger doors (each): Height	0·82 m (2 ft 8⅛ in)
Width	1·02 m (3 ft 3⅞ in)
Baggage compartment door:	
Mean height	0·30 m (1 ft 0¼ in)
Width	0·69 m (2 ft 3 in)

DIMENSIONS, INTERNAL:

Cabin: Length	2·30 m (7 ft 6½ in)
Max width	1·39 m (4 ft 6¾ in)
Max height	1·22 m (4 ft 0½ in)
Baggage compartment volume	0·47 m³ (16·7 cu ft)

AREAS:

Main rotor blades (each)	1·09 m² (11·79 sq ft)
Tail rotor blades (each)	0·05 m² (0·50 sq ft)
Main rotor disc	3·33 m² (35·8 sq ft)
Tail rotor disc	1·32 m² (14·18 sq ft)

WEIGHTS AND LOADINGS:		PERFORMANCE (at max T-O weight):				
Weight empty	817 kg (1,800 lb)	Max level speed at S/L		Max rate of climb at S/L	297 m (975 ft)/min	
Max T-O and landing weight	1,315 kg (2,900 lb)		104 knots (193 km/h; 120 mph)	Service ceiling	3,660 m (12,000 ft)	
Max zero-fuel weight	1,224 kg (2,700 lb)	Max cruising speed at S/L		Hovering ceiling IGE	1,245 m (4,080 ft)	
Max disc loading	22·7 kg/m² (4·65 lb/sq ft)		96 knots (177 km/h; 110 mph)	Range with max fuel and max payload, with 15 min		
Max power loading	5·78 kg/kW (9·84 lb/hp)			reserves	191 nm (354 km; 220 miles)	

CALSPAN
CALSPAN ADVANCED TECHNOLOGY CENTER

HEAD OFFICE: PO Box 400, Buffalo, New York 14225
Telephone: (716) 632 7500
Telex: 91-270

Calspan Advanced Technology Center, a division of Arvin Industries' Applied Technology Group since 1978, carries out advanced research and development covering many technical disciplines. Its Flight Research Branch has specialised in the design, construction and operation of variable-stability systems and research/simulation/training aircraft. These modified aircraft are used primarily to investigate flying qualities, control systems and displays, using in-flight simulation techniques. This is made possible by the installation of programmable computer systems to vary stability, control, guidance, and electronic displays.

The aircraft operated by Calspan in 1980 include:

X-22A. Since 1970, under contract to the US Naval Air Systems Command, Calspan has been operating the Bell/Navy X-22A V/STOL research aircraft, last described in the 1970-71 *Jane's*. In this continuing programme, research is focused on the evaluation of desirable V/STOL flight qualities and display formats. It is being used currently in a programme to investigate advanced control systems for helicopters which are required to land on the decks of ships in heavy seas.

NT-33A. From 1958, under contract to the US Air Force Flight Dynamics Laboratory, Calspan has been operating the Lockheed/US Air Force NT-33A for varied studies into flying qualities and training simulations. These programmes have investigated recently the effects of digital flight control systems on handling qualities, and the development of side stick controllers. The NT-33A has been used also to familiarise pilots with the characteristics of new aircraft, prior to their first flights in types such as the F-15, YF-16, YF-17 and F-18.

Under a joint US Navy/Air Force programme, the NT-33A has been used since 1977 in a project known as Display Evaluation Flight Test (DEFT). The DEFT system, operational since September 1979, provides the necessary link between any new class of aircraft display/information hardware and software, and the pilot's needs. In this configuration the NT-33A is equipped with a programmable head-up display and associated sensors, in order to examine the interaction of display characteristics and handling qualities. Growth potential has been included for head-down vertical situation and energy manoeuvrability displays. The DEFT systems can be used also to investigate terminal area problems, manoeuvring performance, energy management, ground attack, and air-to-air combat.

TIFS. Since 1969, under contract to the US Air Force Flight Dynamics Laboratory, Calspan has been operating this extensively modified Convair/US Air Force NC-131H. It is called the Total In-Flight Simulator (TIFS) as it has an independent control for each degree of freedom, with computer-controlled side force surfaces, direct-lift flaps, and throttle, in addition to similarly controlled ailerons, elevators and rudder. It is used primarily to investigate the flying qualities of larger aircraft, and is involved currently in programmes to study for NASA the Space Shuttle Orbiter's landing control system, and advanced supersonic cruise transport handling qualities. Other current tasks for the TIFS include study of aircraft motion effects on pilots and passengers, and gathering of data on human orientation perception in space. Installation of a multi-purpose digital computer in 1979 has expanded

Bell/US Navy X-22A V/STOL research aircraft, in use for helicopter landing investigation

Lockheed/US Air Force NT-33A DEFT for investigation of display characteristics and handling qualities

Convair NC-131H TIFS, studying currently the Space Shuttle Orbiter's landing control system

greatly the aircraft's simulation capabilities.

Learjet. For the past 20 years, Calspan has been operating two variable-stability Douglas B-26s for training and demonstration of aircraft stability and control at the US Air Force and Navy Test Pilot Schools. In 1979, Calspan was awarded a contract to modify a Learjet 24F to replace these B-26s. The aircraft, purchased by Calspan,

was delivered to the company in December 1979. In early 1980, installation of the Calspan-designed variable-stability system, including three-axis moment control, variable feel system, and digital computer configuration control system, was in progress. First flight of the modified Learjet 24F was planned for the latter half of 1980, permitting operational use in 1981.

CAMAIR
CAMAIR AIRCRAFT CORPORATION

HEAD OFFICE: PO Box 600, Remsenburg, Long Island, New York 11960
Telephone: (516) 325 1838
PRESIDENT: Fred Garcia Jr

CAMAIR TWIN NAVION

The Camair Twin Navion is a twin-engined version of the North American/Ryan Navion light aircraft. It embodies structural modifications to cater for the

increased power and weight, together with design and aerodynamic refinements which provide improved performance, comfort and styling. Versions are as follows:

CTN-A. Prototype only. Built and flown in 1953 with two 168 kW (225 hp) Continental engines.

CTN-B. Powered by two 179 kW (240 hp) Continental O-470-B engines. First flown in early 1954. Total of 28 delivered in 1955-59.

CTN-C. First flown in 1960, with two 194 kW (260 hp) Continental IO-470-D engines. A number of Model Bs

have been converted to Model C configuration.

CTN-D. The prototype of this version was powered by two 224 kW (300 hp) Continental IO-520 engines

Production of new aircraft has been suspended; but Camair is able to modify B and C models to the later model D configuration, and continues to supply spares to Twin Navion owners.

Details of the CTN-D can be found in the 1978-79 *Jane's*. The CTN-A, -B and -C versions were described in earlier editions.

CESSNA
CESSNA AIRCRAFT COMPANY

HEAD OFFICE AND WORKS: Wichita, Kansas 67201
Telephone: (316) 685 9111
PRESIDENT, CHAIRMAN OF THE BOARD AND CHIEF EXECUTIVE OFFICER:
Russell W. Meyer Jr

SENIOR VICE-PRESIDENTS:
R. P. Bauer (Treasurer and Controller)
William A. Boettger (Pawnee Division)
Robert D. Dickerson (Wallace Division)
Malcolm S. Harned (Technology)
Charles B. Husick (Fluid Power and Aircraft Systems Division)

R. L. Lair (Commercial Aircraft Marketing)
J. Derek Vaughan (Commercial Jet Marketing Division)
William L. Worford (Personnel and Community Relations)
VICE-PRESIDENTS:
Pierre Clostermann (President, Reims Aviation)

John W. Dussault (McCauley Accessory Division)
Richard B. Foster (Aircraft Radio and Control Division)
L. C. Gartin (Commercial Aircraft Product Support)
Homer G. Nester (Controller and Assistant Treasurer)
Thane L. Woolsey (Fluid Power Division)
SECRETARY: David R. Edwards

Cessna Aircraft Company was founded by the late Clyde V. Cessna, a pioneer in US aviation in 1911, and was incorporated on 7 September 1927. It has four plants in Wichita engaged on production of commercial and military aircraft, and The Fluid Power Division in Hutchinson, Kansas, which manufactures fluid power systems.

Subsidiary companies owned by Cessna are Aircraft Radio and Control Division at Boonton, New Jersey, the McCauley Accessories Division of Dayton, Ohio, Cessna Fluid Power Ltd of Glenrothes, Fife, Scotland, Cessna Finance Corporation and Cessna International Finance Corporation in Wichita. It has a 49 per cent interest in Reims Aviation of France.

By the beginning of January 1980 the company had produced a total of 159,949 aircraft. During 1979, its commercial sales totalled 8,400 aircraft, including units assembled in France by Reims Aviation (which see).

Military subcontract programmes include manufacture of assemblies, including missile ejection racks, wing tank and missile pylons, for the McDonnell Douglas F-4 Phantom II, and crew door subassemblies for Bell helicopters.

CESSNA MODEL 152

During 1977 Cessna introduced a new two-seat cabin monoplane to replace the Model 150, which had been in production for almost 20 years. Designated Model 152, it differed primarily in having a more powerful engine using low-lead 100 octane fuel, an improved 'gull wing' propeller, and power plant installation and cowling changes to reduce engine noise and vibration.

Improvements introduced on the 1981 Model 152 include a spin-on oil filter for cleaner engine oil, improved battery contactors, main-wheel tyres of reduced frontal area and weight, and an avionics cooling system.

Four versions are available:

Model 152. Standard version, as described.

Model 152/II. As Model 152, but including as standard a factory installed avionics and equipment package which includes a Cessna Series 300 nav/com, dual controls, true airspeed indicator, navigation light detectors, heated pitot, courtesy lights, omni-flash beacon, alternate static source, and emergency locator transmitter.

Model 152 Trainer. Introduced in 1981 model range, with the most frequently ordered avionics and accessories installed as standard, at a package price. These include a cockpit intercom system with lightweight headset and 'hot' microphone, EGT indicator, all-purpose control wheel, oil quick-drain, flight hour recorder, refuelling steps and handles, tinted windows, dual controls, sun visors, Series 300 nav/com and transponder, basic avionics kit, attitude and directional gyros, outside air temperature indicator, vertical speed indicator, omni-flash beacon, cowl-mounted landing light, and variable-intensity light for radio stack.

Model 152 Aerobat. Described separately.

A total of 4,979 Model 152s had been built by 1 January 1980, including 271 F-152s built by Reims Aviation in France.

TYPE: Two-seat cabin monoplane.

WINGS: Braced high-wing monoplane. Wing section NACA 2412 (tips symmetrical). Dihedral 1°. Incidence 1° at root, 0° at tip. All-metal structure of light alloy. Conical camber glassfibre wingtips optional. Modified Frise-type ailerons and electrically-actuated NACA single-slotted trailing-edge flaps of light alloy construction. No trim tabs.

FUSELAGE: Conventional semi-monocoque structure of light alloy.

TAIL UNIT: Cantilever structure of light alloy with swept vertical surfaces. Trim tab in starboard elevator. Ground-adjustable rudder tab.

LANDING GEAR: Non-retractable tricycle type. Land-O-Matic cantilever main legs, each comprising a one-piece machined conically-tapered spring steel tube. Steerable nosewheel on oleo-pneumatic shock-absorber strut. Mainwheel tyres size 15 × 6·00-6. Nosewheel size 5·00-5 with nylon tube-type tyre, pressure 2·07 bars (30 lb/sq in). Toe-operated single-disc hydraulic brakes. Rudder pedal extensions and wheel fairings optional.

POWER PLANT: One 82 kW (110 hp) Avco Lycoming O-235-L2C flat-four engine, driving a McCauley two-blade metal fixed-pitch propeller with spinner. Fuel tanks in wings, with total capacity of 98 litres (26 US gallons), of which 92·75 litres (24·5 US gallons) are usable. Optional long-range tanks have a total capacity of 147·5 litres (39 US gallons), of which 142 litres (37·5 US gallons) are usable. Refuelling points on upper surface of wing. Oil capacity 6·6 litres (1·75 US gallons).

ACCOMMODATION: Enclosed cabin seating two side by side. Vertically-adjustable seats for pilot and co-pilot; inertia-reel shoulder harness and dual controls optional on standard model. Baggage compartment behind seats, backs of which hinge forward. Baggage capacity 54 kg (120 lb). Optional 'family seat' can be fitted in baggage

Cessna Model 152 for 1981 (Avco Lycoming O-235-L2C engine)

space, for two children not exceeding 54 kg (120 lb) in combined weight. Door, with opening window, on each side. Heating and ventilation standard. Dual windscreen defrosters standard. Cabin skylight windows optional.

SYSTEMS: Hydraulic system for brakes only. Electrical system includes a 28V 60A alternator and 28V battery.

AVIONICS AND EQUIPMENT: Optional avionics include Cessna Series 300 nav/com (standard on 152/II and Trainer), Series 300 transceiver, Series 300 nav/com with remote VOR/LOC or VOR/ILS indicator, Series 300 ADF, marker beacon with three lights and aural signal, transponder with 4096 code capability, single unit avionics control panel, slimline microphone, intercom, and padded headset with attached microphone and control wheel operating button. Standard equipment includes safety belts, map compartment, control locks, stall warning device, baggage retaining net, cabin dome lights, variable-intensity instrument panel red floodlights, navigation lights and spin-on oil filter. Optional equipment (standard on 152/II) includes true airspeed indicator, dual controls, alternate static source, emergency locator transmitter, heated pitot, courtesy lights, navigation light detectors, and omni-flash beacon. Other optional equipment includes artificial horizon, directional gyro, electric clock, economy mixture indicator, exhaust gas temperature indicator, outside air temperature gauge, flight hour recorder, rate of climb indicator, sensitive altimeter, turn and bank indicator, turn co-ordinator, cabin fire extinguisher, tinted windows, sun visors, control wheel map light, instrument post lights, cowl-mounted landing light, white strobe lights, anti-precipitation static kit, engine winterisation kit, external power socket, refuelling steps and handles, full-flow oil filter, and quick-drain oil valve.

DIMENSIONS, EXTERNAL:

Wing span: standard	9·97 m (32 ft 8½ in)
with optional conical wingtips	10·11 m (33 ft 2 in)
Wing chord at root	1·63 m (5 ft 4 in)
Wing chord at tip	1·13 m (3 ft 8½ in)
Wing aspect ratio	6·7
Length overall	7·34 m (24 ft 1 in)
Height overall	2·59 m (8 ft 6 in)
Tailplane span	3·05 m (10 ft 0 in)
Wheel track	2·32 m (7 ft 7¼ in)
Wheelbase	1·47 m (4 ft 10 in)
Propeller diameter	1·75 m (5 ft 9 in)
Passenger doors (each): Width	0·86 m (2 ft 10 in)

AREAS:

Wings, gross: standard	14·59 m² (157·0 sq ft)
with optional conical wingtips	14·82 m² (159·5 sq ft)

WEIGHTS AND LOADINGS (A: standard 152; B: 152/II):

Weight empty: A	502 kg (1,107 lb)
B	518 kg (1,141 lb)
Max T-O and landing weight: A, B	757 kg (1,670 lb)
Max ramp weight: A, B	760 kg (1,675 lb)
Max wing loading	51·3 kg/m² (10·5 lb/sq ft)
Max power loading	9·24 kg/kW (15·2 lb/hp)

PERFORMANCE (at max T-O weight):

*Max level speed at S/L
110 knots (204 km/h; 127 mph)
*Max cruising speed, 75% power at 2,440 m (8,000 ft)
107 knots (198 km/h; 123 mph)
Stalling speed, flaps up, power off
48 knots (89·5 km/h; 55·5 mph) CAS
Stalling speed, flaps down, power off
43 knots (80·5 km/h; 50 mph) CAS
Max rate of climb at S/L   218 m (715 ft)/min
Service ceiling   4,480 m (14,700 ft)
T-O run   221 m (725 ft)
T-O to 15 m (50 ft)   408 m (1,340 ft)
Landing from 15 m (50 ft)   366 m (1,200 ft)
Landing run   145 m (475 ft)
Range, recommended lean mixture, with allowance for start, taxi, T-O, climb and 45 min reserves at 75% power:
standard fuel, 75% power at 2,440 m (8,000 ft)
320 nm (592 km; 368 miles)
max fuel, 75% power at 2,440 m (8,000 ft)
545 nm (1,009 km; 627 miles)

Range, allowances as above, but with 45 min reserves at 45% power:
standard fuel, econ cruising power at 3,050 m (10,000 ft)   415 nm (769 km; 478 miles)
max fuel, econ cruising power at 3,050 m (10,000 ft)
690 nm (1,278 km; 794 miles)
*With wheel fairings which increase speeds by approximately 2 knots (3·7 km/h; 2·3 mph)

CESSNA MODEL 152 AEROBAT

The Model 152 Aerobat combines the economy and versatility of the standard Model 152 with aerobatic capability. Structural changes allow the Aerobat to perform 'unusual attitude' manoeuvres and it is licensed in the Aerobatic category for load factors of +6g and —3g at full gross weight, permitting the performance of barrel and aileron rolls, snap rolls, Immelmann turns, Cuban eights, spins, vertical reversements, lazy eights and chandelles.

Equipment of the aircraft differs only slightly from that of the standard 152. Quick-release cabin doors, removable seat cushions and backs, quick-release lapstraps, and shoulder harnesses, are standard, as are two tinted skylights in the cabin roof which offer extra field of view. Distinct external styling provides immediate recognition of the Aerobat's role. The improvements for 1981 and the 152/II package detailed for the Model 152 apply also to the Aerobat.

DIMENSIONS AND AREAS: As for Model 152
WEIGHTS AND LOADINGS: As for Model 152 except:
Weight empty   512 kg (1,129 lb)
PERFORMANCE (at max T-O weight): As for Model 152 except:
*Max level speed at S/L
109 knots (202 km/h; 126 mph)
*Max cruising speed, 75% power at 2,440 m (8,000 ft)
106 knots (196 km/h; 122 mph)
Range, recommended lean mixture, with allowance for engine start, taxi, T-O, climb and 45 min reserves at 75% power:
standard fuel, 75% power at 2,440 m (8,000 ft)
315 nm (583 km; 362 miles)
max fuel, 75% power at 2,440 m (8,000 ft)
540 nm (1,000 km; 621 miles)
Range, allowances as above, but with 45 min reserves at 45% power:
standard fuel, econ cruising power at 3,050 m (10,000 ft)   410 nm (760 km; 472 miles)
max fuel, econ cruising power at 3,050 m (10,000 ft)
680 nm (1,260 km; 783 miles)
*With wheel speed fairings which increase speeds by approximately 2 knots (3·7 km/h; 2·3 mph)

CESSNA SKYHAWK

Two versions of the Skyhawk are currently available:

Skyhawk. This improved version of the Skyhawk, powered by a 119 kW (160 hp) engine able to operate on 100 octane low-lead fuel, was introduced in 1977. Improvements for 1981 include an increase of 40 kg (89 lb) in useful load; a new engine which offers improved performance; a modified elevator with rounded leading-edge which improves handling; addition of an avionics cooling fan which eliminates an external airscoop; a changed max flap setting for better balked landing performance; larger battery contactors; a new anti-precipitation static nav antenna which suppresses undesired signals; availability of an extra long range integral wing fuel tank system; and optional intercom.

Skyhawk II. As Skyhawk, but including as standard a 300 Series nav/com with 360-channel com and 160-channel nav, dual controls, true airspeed indicator, navigation light detectors, heated pitot, courtesy lights, omni-flash beacon, alternate static source and emergency locator transmitter. It can be equipped optionally with a Nav Pac which adds a second nav/com, a 300 Series ADF and a transponder.

The Skyhawk is certificated for operation as a floatplane, and can be fitted with skis. A version designated F-172 is produced in France by Reims Aviation.

A total of 32,429 commercial aircraft in the Model 172/Skyhawk series had been built by 1 January 1980, including 1,803 F-172s built in France. In addition, 237 were built in 1966-67 as T-41A Mescalero military basic trainers.

TYPE: Four-seat cabin monoplane.

WINGS: Braced high-wing monoplane. NACA 2412 wing section. Dihedral 1° 44'. Incidence 1° 30' at root, −1° 30' at tip. All-metal structure, except for conical-camber glassfibre wingtips. Single bracing strut on each side. Modified Frise all-metal ailerons. Electrically-controlled NACA all-metal single-slotted flaps inboard of ailerons.

FUSELAGE: All-metal semi-monocoque structure.

TAIL UNIT: Cantilever all-metal structure. Sweepback on fin 35° at quarter-chord. Trim tab in starboard elevator. Ground-adjustable trim tab in rudder, in-flight adjustable trim tab optional.

LANDING GEAR: Non-retractable tricycle type. Cessna Land-O-Matic cantilever main legs, each comprising a one-piece machined conically-tapered spring steel tube. Nosewheel is carried on an oleo-pneumatic shock-strut and is steerable with rudder up to 10° and controllable up to 30° on either side. Cessna main wheels size 6·00-6 and nosewheel size 5·00-5 (optionally 6·00-6), with nylon cord tube-type tyres. Tyre pressure: main wheels 1·59 bars (23 lb/sq in), nosewheel 1·79 bars (26 lb/sq in). Hydraulic disc brakes. Optional wheel fairings. Alternative float and ski gear.

POWER PLANT: One 119 kW (160 hp) Avco Lycoming O-320-D2J flat-four engine, driving a two-blade fixed-pitch metal propeller. One fuel tank in each wing, total capacity 163 litres (43 US gallons). Usable fuel 151·4 litres (40 US gallons). Provision for long-range tanks, giving total capacity of 204 litres (54 US gallons), of which 189 litres (50 US gallons) are usable; or extra-long-range system, using integral tanks in wings to provide total capacity of 257 litres (68 US gallons), of which 234 litres (62 US gallons) are usable. Oil capacity 7·5 litres (2·0 US gallons). Oil cooler and full-flow oil filter standard.

ACCOMMODATION: Cabin seats four in two pairs, with optional fully-articulating front seats. Baggage space aft of rear seats, capacity 54 kg (120 lb). An optional fold-away seat can be fitted in baggage space, for one or two children not exceeding 54 kg (120 lb) total weight. Door on each side of cabin, giving access to all seats, simplifies loading if rear seats are removed and cabin used for freight. Pilot's window opens; co-pilot's opening side window and dual controls optional on Skyhawk; dual controls standard on Skyhawk II. Baggage door on port side. Combined heating and ventilation system; air-conditioning optional. Dual windscreen defrosters. Glassfibre soundproofing. Optional overhead skylights.

SYSTEMS: Electrical system of 28V includes electric engine starter and 24V battery. Air-conditioning system of 14,000 BTU capacity optional. Vacuum system for blind-flying instruments optional.

AVIONICS AND EQUIPMENT: Optional avionics include Cessna Series 300 720-channel transceiver, 720-channel nav/com with remote VOR indicator, 720-channel nav/com with remote VOR/LOC indicator or VOR/ILS indicator, ADF, marker beacon with three lights and aural signal, transponder with 4096 code capability, DME, 10-channel HF transceiver, Nav-O-Matic autopilot with heading control plus VOR, Series 400 glideslope receiver, intercom, boom microphone with control-wheel switch, padded headset with boom microphone, and speaker sidetone facility. Optional equipment (standard on Skyhawk II) includes true air-speed indicator, alternate static source, emergency locator transmitter, heated pitot, navigation light detectors, courtesy lights, and omni-flash beacon. Other optional equipment includes artificial horizon, directional gyro with movable heading index, carburettor air temperature gauge, electric clock, exhaust gas and outside air temperature gauges, flight hour recorder, rate of climb indicator, sensitive altimeter, turn and bank indicator, turn co-ordinator, reclining and vertically adjustable front seats, inertia reel shoulder harness, headrests, overhead skylights, rudder pedal extensions, starboard side storm window, sun visors, child's foldaway seat, fire extinguisher, portable stretcher, rear seats with individual reclining backs, safety belts for third and fourth seats, internal corrosion proofing, rear seat ventilation system, tinted windows, utility shelf, ventilation fan, control wheel map light, map and instrument panel lights, dual cowl-mounted landing lights, beacon, wing-tip strobe lights, anti-precipitation static kit, engine priming system, floatplane kit, full-flow oil filter, glider tow hook, external power socket, quick-drain oil valve, tailplane abrasion boots, towbar, wing-strut and fuselage steps and handles for refuelling, and winterisation kit.

DIMENSIONS, EXTERNAL (L: landplane; F: floatplane):
Wing span	10·92 m (35 ft 10 in)
Wing chord at root	1·63 m (5 ft 4 in)
Wing chord at tip	1·12 m (3 ft 8½ in)
Wing aspect ratio	7·52
Length overall: L	8·20 m (26 ft 11 in)
F	8·13 m (26 ft 8 in)
Height overall: L	2·68 m (8 ft 9½ in)
F	3·63 m (11 ft 11 in)

Cessna Skyhawk II four-seat lightplane for 1981 (Avco Lycoming O-320-D2J engine)

Tailplane span	3·45 m (11 ft 4 in)
Wheel track: L	2·53 m (8 ft 3½ in)
Wheelbase: L	1·63 m (5 ft 4 in)
Propeller diameter: L	1·91 m (6 ft 3 in)
F	2·03 m (6 ft 8 in)
Passenger doors (each): Height	1·01 m (3 ft 3¾ in)
Width	0·89 m (2 ft 11 in)

AREAS:
Wings, gross	16·17 m² (174 sq ft)
Ailerons (total)	1·70 m² (18·3 sq ft)
Trailing-edge flaps (total)	1·97 m² (21·20 sq ft)
Fin	1·04 m² (11·24 sq ft)
Rudder	0·69 m² (7·43 sq ft)
Tailplane	2·00 m² (21·56 sq ft)
Elevators, incl tab	1·35 m² (14·53 sq ft)

WEIGHTS AND LOADINGS (Skyhawk landplane: L; floatplane: F):
Weight empty, equipped: L	642 kg (1,414 lb)
F	723 kg (1,593 lb)
Skyhawk II: L	653 kg (1,440 lb)
Skyhawk II: F	735 kg (1,619 lb)
Max T-O and landing weight: L	1,089 kg (2,400 lb)
F	1,007 kg (2,220 lb)
Max ramp weight:	
L	1,092 kg (2,407 lb)
F	1,010 kg (2,227 lb)
Max wing loading: L	67·3 kg/m² (13·8 lb/sq ft)
F	62·0 kg/m² (12·7 lb/sq ft)
Max power loading: L	9·15 kg/kW (15·0 lb/hp)
F	8·44 kg/kW (13·9 lb/hp)

PERFORMANCE (L: Skyhawk and Skyhawk II landplane; F: floatplane, at max T-O weight):
Never-exceed speed:	
L	151 knots (280 km/h; 174 mph)
Max level speed at S/L:	
L	123 knots (228 km/h; 141 mph)
F	96 knots (178 km/h; 111 mph)
Max cruising speed (75% power):	
L, at 2,440 m (8,000 ft)	120 knots (222 km/h; 138 mph)
F, at 1,220 m (4,000 ft)	95 knots (176 km/h; 109 mph)
Stalling speed, flaps up:	
L	51 knots (95 km/h; 59 mph) CAS
F	48 knots (89 km/h; 55 mph) CAS
Stalling speed, flaps down:	
L	46 knots (85 km/h; 53 mph)
F	44 knots (82 km/h; 51 mph) CAS
Max rate of climb at S/L: L	213 m (700 ft)/min
F	226 m (740 ft)/min
Service ceiling: L	3,960 m (13,000 ft)
F	4,570 m (15,000 ft)
T-O run: L	272 m (890 ft)
F	427 m (1,400 ft)
T-O to 15 m (50 ft): L	556 m (1,825 ft)
F	658 m (2,160 ft)
Landing from 15 m (50 ft): L	390 m (1,280 ft)
F	410 m (1,345 ft)
Landing run: L	165 m (540 ft)
F	180 m (590 ft)

Range, at recommended lean mixture, with allowances for engine start, taxi, T-O, climb and 45 min reserves at 75% power:
Max cruising speed:	
L, standard fuel	440 nm (815 km; 506 miles)
F, standard fuel	360 nm (666 km; 414 miles)
L, 62 US gallons fuel	755 nm (1,398 km; 868 miles)
F, 50 US gallons fuel	475 nm (879 km; 546 miles)

Range, allowances as above, but with 45 min reserves at 45% power:
Econ cruising speed at 3,050 m (10,000 ft):	
L, standard fuel	520 nm (963 km; 598 miles)
F, standard fuel	435 nm (806 km; 501 miles)
L, 62 US gallons fuel	875 nm (1,620 km; 1,007 miles)
F, 50 US gallons fuel	565 nm (1,046 km; 650 miles)

CESSNA MODEL R172E

US Army designation: T-41B Mescalero
US Air Force designations: T-41C/D Mescalero

The Cessna Model R172E was a more powerful version of the original Model 172, of which civil and military production has ended. Details of this version can be found in the 1979-80 *Jane's*.

CESSNA MODEL R172 HAWK XP

On 23 June 1976, Cessna introduced the Model R172 Hawk XP, and a similar model is being produced by Reims Aviation in France (which see), known as the Model FR172/Reims Hawk XP. A total of 1,321 had been sold by 1 January 1980, this total including 67 Reims-built FR172s. Eighteen Hawk XPs were supplied to the Chilean Army in 1978.

Two versions are available:

Hawk XP. Standard version, powered by one 145·4 kW (195 hp) Continental IO-360-K engine. Available also as floatplane.

Hawk XP/II. Version of the above, equipped in a VFR and IFR configuration. It can be equipped optionally with Nav Pac which adds a second nav/com system and other avionics.

The 1981 versions of the Hawk XP introduce as standard a modified elevator with rounded leading-edge which improves handling; a changed max flap setting for better balked landing performance; larger battery contactors; and a new anti-precipitation static nav antenna.

The description of the Skyhawk applies also to the Hawk XP, except as follows:

POWER PLANT: One 145·4 kW (195 hp) Continental IO-360-KB flat-six fuel-injection engine, driving a McCauley two-blade constant-speed metal propeller type ZA34C203/90DCA-14, with spinner. Two fuel tanks in wings with a combined capacity of 197 litres (52 US gallons), of which 185 litres (49 US gallons) are usable. Optional integral fuel cells provide a maximum usable capacity of 250 litres (66 US gallons).

ACCOMMODATION: As for Skyhawk, except that Hawk XP has restyled sidewalls and overhead console to improve appearance. Overhead console change provides better access to overhead floodlighting. New control yokes and addition of control for constant-speed propeller. Baggage space has capacity of 91 kg (200 lb).

DIMENSIONS, EXTERNAL (L: landplane; F: floatplane): As for Skyhawk except:
Length overall: L	8·28 m (27 ft 2 in)
F	8·18 m (26 ft 10 in)
Height overall: F	3·78 m (12 ft 5 in)

WEIGHTS AND LOADINGS (L: Hawk XP landplane; F: floatplane):
Weight empty: L	701 kg (1,546 lb)
F	820 kg (1,808 lb)
Hawk XP II: L	713 kg (1,572 lb)
F	832 kg (1,834 lb)
Max T-O and landing weight	1,157 kg (2,550 lb)
Max ramp weight	1,160 kg (2,558 lb)
Max wing loading	71·8 kg/m² (14·7 lb/sq ft)
Max power loading	7·96 kg/kW (13·08 lb/hp)

PERFORMANCE (at max T-O weight):
Max level speed at S/L:	
L	133 knots (246 km/h; 153 mph)
F	118 knots (219 km/h; 136 mph)
Max cruising speed (80% power at 1,830 m; 6,000 ft):	
L	130 knots (241 km/h; 150 mph)
F	116 knots (215 km/h; 134 mph)
Stalling speed, flaps up, power off:	
L	52 knots (97 km/h; 60 mph) CAS
F	50 knots (93 km/h; 58 mph) CAS
Stalling speed, flaps down, power off:	
L	47 knots (87 km/h; 54 mph) CAS
F	44 knots (82 km/h; 51 mph) CAS
Max rate of climb at S/L:	
L, F	265 m (870 ft)/min
Service ceiling: L	5,180 m (17,000 ft)
F	4,725 m (15,500 ft)
T-O run: L	244 m (800 ft)
F	346 m (1,135 ft)

Cessna Model R172 Hawk XP II, a version of the four-seat Skyhawk with more powerful engine

T-O to 15 m (50 ft): L   415 m (1,360 ft)
F   564 m (1,850 ft)
Landing from 15 m (50 ft): L   410 m (1,345 ft)
F   424 m (1,390 ft)
Landing run: L   194 m (635 ft)
F   206 m (675 ft)
Range (recommended lean mixture, allowances for engine start, taxi, T-O, climb, and 45 min reserves at 45% power):
  80% power at 1,830 m (6,000 ft) with 185 litres (49 US gallons) usable fuel:
    L   440 nm (815 km; 506 miles)
    F   395 nm (731 km; 454 miles)
  80% power at 1,830 m (6,000 ft) with 250 litres (66 US gallons) usable fuel:
    L   635 nm (1,176 km; 730 miles)
    F   570 nm (1,055 km; 656 miles)
Econ cruising power at 3,050 m (10,000 ft) with 185 litres (49 US gallons) usable fuel:
    L   575 nm (1,065 km; 662 miles)
    F   495 nm (916 km; 569 miles)
Econ cruising power at 3,050 m (10,000 ft) with 250 litres (66 US gallons) usable fuel:
    L   815 nm (1,510 km; 938 miles)
    F   705 nm (1,305 km; 811 miles)

CESSNA CUTLASS RG

Cessna announced on 15 August 1979 the introduction of a new four-seat lightplane with retractable landing gear which it claimed to be the lowest-priced aircraft in this category. Known as the Cutlass RG, it combines the airframe of the Model 172 Skyhawk with the retractable landing gear developed for the Skylane RG. Power is provided by a 134 kW (180 hp) Avco Lycoming O-360-F1A6 flat-four engine, driving a two-blade constant-speed metal propeller. Two fuel tanks, one in each wing, have a combined usable capacity of 235 litres (62 US gallons).

The Cutlass RG became available in late 1979, together with a Cutlass RGII with avionics and equipment as detailed for the Skyhawk II, plus the optional Nav Pac. Equivalent versions designated F Cutlass RG and F Cutlass RGII are assembled under licence by Reims Aviation in France. Sales totalled 185 by 1 January 1980.

DIMENSIONS, EXTERNAL: As for Skyhawk except:
  Length overall   8·36 m (27 ft 5 in)
  Tailplane span   3·43 m (11 ft 3 in)
  Wheel track   2·59 m (8 ft 6 in)
  Propeller diameter   1·94 m (6 ft 4½ in)
WEIGHTS AND LOADINGS (A: Cutlass RG; B: Cutlass RGII):
  Weight empty: A   706 kg (1,555 lb)
    B   721 kg (1,590 lb)
  Max T-O and landing weight:
    A, B   1,202 kg (2,650 lb)
  Max ramp weight
    A, B   1,206 kg (2,658 lb)
  Max wing loading:
    A, B   74·4 kg/m² (15·2 lb/sq ft)
  Max power loading:
    A, B   8·97 kg/kW (14·7 lb/hp)
PERFORMANCE (at max T-O weight):
  Max level speed at S/L 145 knots (269 km/h; 167 mph)
  Max cruising speed (75% power) at 2,740 m (9,000 ft)
     140 knots (259 km/h; 161 mph)
  Stalling speed, flaps up, power off
     54 knots (100 km/h; 62 mph) CAS
  Stalling speed, flaps down, power off
     50 knots (93 km/h; 58 mph) CAS
  Max rate of climb at S/L   244 m (800 ft)/min
  Service ceiling   5,120 m (16,800 ft)
  T-O run   323 m (1,060ft)
  T-O to 15 m (50 ft)   541 m (1,775 ft)
  Landing from 15 m (50 ft)   408 m (1,340 ft)
  Landing run   191 m (625 ft)
  Range with max fuel at max cruising speed, recommended lean mixture, with allowances for engine start, taxi, T-O, climb and 45 min reserves
     720 nm (1,334 km; 829 miles)

Range with max fuel at econ cruising speed, allowances as above   840 nm (1,557 km; 967 miles)

CESSNA MODEL 180 SKYWAGON

The Model 180 Skywagon has a typical Cessna braced high-wing monoplane layout, but with a tailwheel type of landing gear. Two commercial versions are available:

Model 180 Skywagon. Basic model, as described, which introduced as standard improvements for 1980 a new audio panel with marker beacon, dim switching of marker and navigation annunciator lights, marker beacon muting switch, alternator circuit breaker, and new sun visors.

Model 180 Skywagon II. As Skywagon, plus factory-installed avionics package which includes Series 300 nav/com with remote VOR indicator, ADF and an emergency locator transmitter. Optional Nav Pac provides a second nav/com, with Series 400 glideslope and marker beacon. Standard equipment is as Skywagon, plus long-range fuel tanks with a total usable capacity of 284 litres (75 US gallons), artificial horizon, clock, directional gyro, exhaust gas temperature gauge, outside air temperature gauge, turn co-ordinator, vertical speed indicator, dual controls, sun visor, heated pitot, map light, quick-drain oil plug, and external power socket.

A total of 6,110 Model 180s had been built by 1 January 1980.

TYPE: One/six-seat cabin monoplane.
WINGS: Generally similar in construction to those of Skyhawk. Dihedral 1° 44'.
FUSELAGE: All-metal semi-monocoque structure. Identical to fuselage of Cessna 185, except for firewall and mounting brackets for dorsal fin.
TAIL UNIT: Unswept cantilever all-metal structure with adjustable-incidence tailplane. Normally no trim tabs; manually-operated rudder trim available optionally.
LANDING GEAR: Non-retractable tailwheel type. Cessna cantilever spring steel main legs. Tailwheel has tapered tubular spring. Main wheels and nylon tube-type tyres size 6·00-6 (optionally 8·00-6). Cessna tailwheel size 8·00 × 2·80. Tyre pressure, main wheels 2·07 bars (30 lb/sq in), tailwheel 3·79-4·48 bars (55-65 lb/sq in) according to load. Hydraulic disc brakes. Parking brake. Wheel and brake fairings optional. Alternative Edo Model 628-296 floats, snow ski or amphibian gear.
POWER PLANT: One 171·5 kW (230 hp) Continental O-470-U flat-six engine, driving a McCauley 2A34C203/90DA-8 two-blade constant-speed metal propeller. Two fuel tanks in wings, with total standard capacity of 333 litres (88 US gallons), of which 318 litres (84 US gallons) are usable. Oil capacity 11·5 litres (3 US gallons).
ACCOMMODATION: Standard seating is for a pilot only, with a choice of three optional arrangements. Maximum seating is for six persons in three pairs, without baggage space. With fewer seats there is space at rear of cabin for up to 181 kg (400 lb) of baggage. Door on each side of cabin, plus optional cargo door and baggage compartment door on port side. Starboard door has quick-release hinge pins so that it can be removed when loading bulky cargo. Fifth and sixth passenger seats, attached to aft wall of cabin, can be folded when space is required for cargo. Hinged window each side. Instrument lighting controls are transistorised. Heating, ventilation, and windscreen defroster standard. Fully-articulating seats for pilot and co-pilot, child's foldaway seat for the rear cabin and safety belts for rear-seat passengers are available optionally. Dual controls optional (standard on Skywagon II).
SYSTEMS: Hydraulic system for brakes only. Electrical system powered by 28V 60A alternator. 24V 33Ah battery. Oxygen system, 1·36 m³ (48 cu ft) capacity, optional.
AVIONICS AND EQUIPMENT: Optional avionics include Cessna Series 300 360-channel com transceiver, 360-channel nav/com with 160-channel nav and remote VOR indicator, 720-channel com and 200-channel nav with remote VOR/LOC indicator or VOR/ILS indicator, ADF with digital tuning, marker beacon with three lights and aural signal, transponder with 4096 code capability, DME, Nav-O-Matic single-axis autopilot with heading control and VOR intercept and track; or Series 400 720-channel com transceiver, 720-channel nav/com with remote VOR/LOC or VOR/ILS indicator, transponder with 4096 code capability, glideslope receiver and ADF with digital tuning. Standard avionics for Skywagon II include Cessna 300 Series nav/com with remote VOR indicator, ADF and an emergency locator transmitter. Standard equipment includes control locks, audible stall warning, baggage restraint net, cabin dome light, instrument panel red floodlights, and landing and taxi lights. Optional equipment (standard on Skywagon II) includes long-range fuel tanks, artificial horizon, clock, directional gyro, exhaust gas temperature gauge, outside air temperature gauge, turn co-ordinator, vertical speed indicator, dual controls, sun visor, heated pitot, map light, quick-drain oil valve and external power socket. Other optional equipment includes carburettor air temperature gauge,

Cessna Cutlass RG four-seat lightplane with retractable landing gear

Cessna Model 180 Skywagon one/six-seat cabin monoplane (Continental O-470-U engine)

economy mixture indicator, flight hour recorder, true airspeed indicator, turn and bank indicator, co-pilot's seat installation, pilot and co-pilot headrests, rudder pedal extensions, stowable starboard side rudder pedals, inertia reel shoulder harness, twin beverage pack, tailwheel lock, alternate static source, emergency locator transmitter, navigation light detectors, cargo tiedown fittings, bubble and tinted windows, de luxe interior, internal corrosion proofing, cabin fire extinguisher, photographic provisions, stretcher installation, courtesy lights, boom microphone, control wheel with map light and microphone switch, auxiliary instrument lights, instrument panel post lights, omni-flash beacon, strobe light, amphibian kit, floatplane kit, ski kit, engine winterisation kit, agricultural sprayer system, non-congealing oil cooler, oil dilution system, overall paint scheme, and tailplane abrasion boots.

DIMENSIONS, EXTERNAL:

Wing span	10·92 m (35 ft 10 in)
Wing chord at root	1·63 m (5 ft 4 in)
Wing chord at tip	1·11 m (3 ft 7¾ in)
Wing aspect ratio	7·52
Length overall: Landplane	7·81 m (25 ft 7½ in)
Skiplane	8·47 m (27 ft 9½ in)
Floatplane	8·23 m (27 ft 0 in)
Amphibian	8·38 m (27 ft 6 in)
Height overall:	
Landplane, skiplane	2·36 m (7 ft 9 in)
Floatplane	3·71 m (12 ft 2 in)
Amphibian	3·86 m (12 ft 8 in)
Tailplane span	3·35 m (11 ft 0 in)
Wheel track, landplane	2·33 m (7 ft 8 in)
Propeller diameter:	
Landplane, skiplane	2·08 m (6 ft 10 in)
Floatplane, amphibian	2·29 m (7 ft 6 in)
Passenger doors (each): Height	1·01 m (3 ft 3¾ in)
Width	0·89 m (2 ft 11 in)

AREAS:

Wings, gross	16·16 m² (174 sq ft)
Ailerons (total)	1·70 m² (18·3 sq ft)
Trailing-edge flaps (total)	1·97 m² (21·23 sq ft)
Fin	0·84 m² (9·01 sq ft)
Dorsal fin	0·19 m² (2·04 sq ft)
Rudder	0·68 m² (7·29 sq ft)
Tailplane	1·94 m² (20·94 sq ft)
Elevators	1·40 m² (15·13 sq ft)

WEIGHTS AND LOADINGS:

Weight empty, equipped:	
Skywagon landplane	746 kg (1,644 lb)
Skywagon II landplane	768 kg (1,694 lb)
Floatplane	885 kg (1,950 lb)
Skiplane	810 kg (1,786 lb)
Amphibian	1,000 kg (2,205 lb)
Max T-O weight:	
Landplane, skiplane	1,270 kg (2,800 lb)
Floatplane, amphibian	1,338 kg (2,950 lb)
Max ramp weight: Landplane	1,274 kg (2,810 lb)
Max wing loading:	
Landplane, skiplane	78·6 kg/m² (16·1 lb/sq ft)
Floatplane, amphibian	83·0 kg/m² (17·0 lb/sq ft)
Max power loading:	
Landplane, skiplane	7·41 kg/kW (12·2 lb/hp)
Floatplane, amphibian	7·80 kg/kW (12·8 lb/hp)

PERFORMANCE (at max T-O weight):

Never-exceed speed:	
Landplane	167 knots (309 km/h; 192 mph)
Max level speed at S/L:	
*Landplane	148 knots (274 km/h; 170 mph)
Floatplane, amphibian, skiplane	129 knots (240 km/h; 149 mph)
Max cruising speed (75% power) at 2,440 m (8,000 ft):	
*Landplane	142 knots (264 km/h; 164 mph)
Floatplane, amphibian	123 knots (228 km/h; 142 mph)
Skiplane	124 knots (230 km/h; 143 mph)
Econ cruising speed at 3,050 m (10,000 ft):	
Landplane	105 knots (195 km/h; 121 mph)
Floatplane, amphibian	99 knots (183 km/h; 114 mph)
Skiplane	88 knots (162 km/h; 101 mph)
Stalling speed, flaps up, power off:	
All versions	53 knots (98·5 km/h; 61 mph) CAS
Stalling speed, flaps down, power off:	
All versions	48 knots (88·5 km/h; 55 mph) CAS
Max rate of climb at S/L:	
Landplane	335 m (1,100 ft)/min
Floatplane, amphibian	296 m (970 ft)/min
Skiplane	277 m (910 ft)/min
Service ceiling: Landplane	5,395 m (17,700 ft)
Floatplane, amphibian	4,663 m (15,300 ft)
Skiplane	4,480 m (14,700 ft)
T-O run: Landplane	190 m (625 ft)
Floatplane	354 m (1,160 ft)
Amphibian, on land	213 m (700 ft)
Amphibian, on water	354 m (1,160 ft)
T-O to 15 m (50 ft): Landplane	367 m (1,205 ft)
Floatplane	579 m (1,900 ft)
Amphibian, on land	401 m (1,315 ft)
Amphibian, on water	579 m (1,900 ft)
Landing from 15 m (50 ft):	
Landplane	416 m (1,365 ft)

Floatplane	524 m (1,720 ft)
Amphibian, on land	442 m (1,450 ft)
Amphibian, on water	524 m (1,720 ft)
Landing run: Landplane	146 m (480 ft)
Floatplane	224 m (735 ft)
Amphibian, on land	226 m (740 ft)
Amphibian, on water	224 m (735 ft)

Range, at recommended lean mixture, with allowances for start, taxi, T-O, climb and 45 min reserves at 45% power:

Max fuel, max cruising speed at 2,440 m (8,000 ft):	
Landplane	785 nm (1,454 km; 903 miles)
Floatplane, amphibian	680 nm (1,260 km; 783 miles)
Skiplane	685 nm (1,270 km; 789 miles)
Max fuel, econ cruising speed at 3,050 m (10,000 ft):	
Landplane	1,010 nm (1,872 km; 1,163 miles)
Floatplane, amphibian, skiplane	815 nm (1,510 km; 938 miles)

These speeds are 1 knot (1·9 km/h; 1·2 mph) higher with optional speed fairings installed

CESSNA SKYLANE

Three variants of this aircraft were available, of which the Model 182 was the basic standard version. This was discontinued in 1976, leaving two commercial versions currently available:

Skylane. Standard version.

Skylane II. As Skylane, plus factory installed avionics package which includes Cessna Series 300 nav/com with 720-channel com and 200-channel nav with remote VOR/LOC, ADF, transponder and 200A Nav-O-Matic autopilot with VOR/LOC track and intercept. It is available optionally with a Nav Pac, which adds a second 300 nav/com plus VOR/ILS, Series 400 glideslope receiver with VOR/ILS indicator and Series 400 marker beacon. Standard equipment includes exhaust gas temperature gauge, true airspeed indicator, dual controls, alternate static source, heated pitot, navigation light detectors, emergency locator transmitter, courtesy lights, omni-flash beacon, and external power socket.

The 1980 versions of the Skylane embody the improvements listed for the Cessna Model 180. New options include a writing table, AM/FM stereo cassette entertainment centre, and wider range of interior and exterior finishes.

A version designated F182 Skylane is produced for the European market by Reims Aviation in France (which see).

A total of 18,542 Model 182/Skylanes had been built by 1 January 1980, including 129 F182s built by Reims Aviation.

TYPE: Four-seat cabin monoplane.

WINGS: Braced high-wing monoplane. Wing section NACA 2412, modified. Incidence at root 0° 47', at tip −2° 50'. Dihedral 1° 44'. Wing structure similar to Skyhawk, except metal-to-metal bonded leading-edge.

FUSELAGE: All-metal semi-monocoque structure.

TAIL UNIT: Cantilever all-metal structure with swept fin and rudder. Trim tab in starboard elevator. Electrically-operated elevator trim optional.

LANDING GEAR: Non-retractable tricycle type. Land-O-Matic cantilever main legs, each comprising a one-piece machined conically-tapered spring steel tube. Steerable nosewheel with oleo-pneumatic shock-absorption. Cessna main wheels and tyres size 6·00-6, pressure 2·90 bars (42 lb/sq in). Cessna nosewheel and tyre size 5·00-5, pressure 3·38 bars (49 lb/sq in). Cessna hydraulic disc brakes. Parking brake. Optional wheel fairings.

POWER PLANT: Similar to that of Model 180, except for McCauley propeller type 2A34C203/90DCA-8. Standard fuel capacity 348 litres (92 US gallons), of which 333 litres (88 US gallons) are usable. Refuelling point on upper surface of each wing. Oil capacity 11·5 litres (3 US gallons).

ACCOMMODATION: Generally similar to Skyhawk, with standard seating for four; four seat belts and two shoulder harnesses standard. Optional child's seat. Baggage space aft of rear seats and hatshelf with total capacity of

91 kg (200 lb), with external baggage door. Cargo tiedown net standard. Front seat inertia-reel shoulder harness, rear seat shoulder harness, leather seating, air vent for rear-seat passengers, and openable starboard window optional. Dual controls optional on Skylane. Heating, ventilation and windscreen defrosters standard.

SYSTEMS: Electrical system powered by 60A 28V engine-driven alternator. 24V battery. Hydraulic system for brakes only. Vacuum system optional. Oxygen system of 1·36 m³ (48 cu ft) capacity optional.

AVIONICS AND EQUIPMENT: Standard avionics for Skylane II, optional on Skylane, include Cessna 200 Series 200A Nav-O-Matic autopilot, 300 Series 720-channel nav/com with remote VOR/LOC or VOR/ILS indicator, ADF with digital tuning, marker beacon with three lights and aural signal, and transponder with 4096 code capability. Other optional avionics include DME, 10-channel HF transceiver, 300A Nav-O-Matic single-axis autopilot with heading control plus VOR intercept and track, 400 Series glideslope receiver, ADF with digital tuning, and transponder with 4096 code capability. Standard equipment includes control locks, armrests, tinted windscreen, audible stall warning, baggage restraint net, tinted windows, cabin dome light, adjustable cabin ventilators, variable-intensity instrument panel red floodlights, pedestal lights, navigation lights, and cabin steps. Optional equipment (standard for Skylane II) includes exhaust gas temperature gauge, true airspeed indicator, dual controls, alternate static source, heated pitot, emergency locator transmitter, navigation light detectors, courtesy lights, omni-flash beacon, and external power socket. Other optional equipment includes artificial horizon, carburettor air temperature gauge, directional gyro, electric clock, flight hour recorder, outside air temperature gauge, rate of climb indicator, sensitive altimeter, turn co-ordinator, inertia-reel shoulder harness for front seats, skylights, sun visors, heated stall warning transmitter, child's seat, headrests, shoulder harness for rear seats, leather seating, cabin fire extinguisher, internal corrosion proofing, rear window curtain, stretcher installation, utility shelf, writing table, stereo cassette entertainment centre, control wheel map light, instrument post lights, omni-flash beacon, wingtip strobe lights, engine priming system, engine winterisation kit, full-flow oil filter, non-congealing oil cooler, quick-drain oil valve, glider tow hook, overall paint scheme, tailcone lift handles, towbar, and tailplane abrasion boots.

DIMENSIONS, EXTERNAL:

Wing span	10·92 m (35 ft 10 in)
Wing chord at root	1·63 m (5 ft 4 in)
Wing chord at tip	1·09 m (3 ft 7 in)
Length overall	8·53 m (28 ft 0 in)
Height overall	2·82 m (9 ft 3 in)
Tailplane span	3·55 m (11 ft 8 in)
Wheel track	2·74 m (9 ft 0 in)
Wheelbase	1·69 m (5 ft 6½ in)
Propeller diameter	2·08 m (6 ft 10 in)
Passenger doors (each): Height	1·02 m (3 ft 4¼ in)
Width	0·90 m (2 ft 11¼ in)

AREAS:

Wings, gross	16·16 m² (174 sq ft)
Ailerons (total)	1·70 m² (18·3 sq ft)
Trailing-edge flaps (total)	1·97 m² (21·20 sq ft)
Fin	1·08 m² (11·62 sq ft)
Rudder	0·65 m² (6·95 sq ft)
Tailplane	2·13 m² (22·96 sq ft)
Elevators	1·47 m² (15·85 sq ft)

WEIGHTS AND LOADINGS:

Weight empty, equipped: Skylane	774 kg (1,706 lb)
Skylane II	799 kg (1,762 lb)
Max T-O and landing weight	1,338 kg (2,950 lb)
Max ramp weight	1,342 kg (2,960 lb)
Max wing loading	82·5 kg/m² (16·9 lb/sq ft)
Max power loading	7·80 kg/kW (12·8 lb/hp)

PERFORMANCE (at max T-O weight):

Max level speed at S/L	
	148 knots (273 km/h; 170 mph)

Cessna Skylane four-seat cabin monoplane (Continental O-470-U engine)

Max cruising speed, 75% power at 2,440 m (8,000 ft)
144 knots (267 km/h; 166 mph)

Stalling speed, flaps up
56 knots (103 km/h; 64 mph) CAS

Stalling speed, flaps down
50 knots (92 km/h; 57 mph) CAS

Max rate of climb at S/L 308 m (1,010 ft)/min

Service ceiling 5,030 m (16,500 ft)

T-O run 215 m (705 ft)

T-O to 15 m (50 ft) 411 m (1,350 ft)

Landing from 15 m (50 ft) 411 m (1,350 ft)

Landing run 180 m (590 ft)

Range, recommended lean mixture, with allowances for start, taxi, T-O, climb and 45 min reserves at 45% power:

Max fuel, 75% power at 2,440 m (8,000 ft)
840 nm (1,556 km; 967 miles)

Max fuel, econ cruising speed at 3,050 m (10,000 ft)
1,090 nm (2,020 km; 1,255 miles)

CESSNA SKYLANE RG and TURBO-SKYLANE RG

Introduced in late 1977, the retractable landing gear version of the Skylane is available in four models:

Skylane RG. Standard version, powered by Avco Lycoming O-540-J3C5D flat-six engine, derated to 175 kW (235 hp) and driving a two-blade metal constant-speed propeller with spinner.

Skylane RG II. As Skylane RG, plus additional avionics and equipment detailed for the Skylane II.

Turbo-Skylane RG. Generally similar to Skylane RG, but powered by a 175 kW (235 hp) Avco Lycoming O-540-L3C5D flat-six engine with turbocharger, driving a two-blade metal constant-speed propeller.

Turbo-Skylane RG II. As Turbo-Skylane RG, plus additional avionics and equipment detailed for the Skylane II, except that the Series 300 transponder is replaced by the Series 400 model. Optional Nav Pac provides IFR capability with addition of a second Series 300 nav/com and indicator, and Series 400 glideslope and marker beacon.

All versions of the Skylane RG introduced for 1980 a restyled nosecap that provides more engine cooling airflow, and have the standard and optional improvements detailed for the 1980 Skylane models. Air-conditioning is available optionally for all versions, together with an anti-icing system for the Turbo-Skylane RG/RG II. By 1 January 1980 a total of 1,341 Skylane RGs had been built, including 41 assembled by Reims Aviation in France as Reims 182 Skylane RGs.

The description of the Cessna Skylane applies also to the Skylane RG and Turbo-Skylane RG, except as follows:

LANDING GEAR: Hydraulically-retractable tricycle type. Tubular spring steel main gear struts, retracting rearward into fuselage. Nosewheel, which retracts forward, is carried on a short-stroke oleo-pneumatic shock-absorber with hydraulic damper, and is steerable. Nosewheel enclosed by doors when retracted. Hydraulic brakes. Parking brake.

POWER PLANT: One Avco Lycoming flat-six engine, as detailed in model listings. Standard fuel capacity 348 litres (92 US gallons), of which 333 litres (88 US gallons) are usable. Refuelling point on upper surface of each wing. Oil capacity 8·5 litres (2·25 US gallons).

SYSTEMS: As described for Skylane, except self-contained electro-hydraulic system for operation of landing gear and brakes, plus optional air-conditioning system for all versions, and anti-icing system for Turbo-Skylane RG versions.

DIMENSIONS, EXTERNAL: As for Skylane except:
Length overall 8·72 m (28 ft 7½ in)
Height overall 2·72 m (8 ft 11 in)

WEIGHTS AND LOADINGS (A: Skylane RG; B: Skylane RG II; C: Turbo-Skylane RG; D: Turbo-Skylane RG II):
Weight empty: A 794 kg (1,750 lb)
B 818 kg (1,804 lb)
C 812 kg (1,791 lb)
D 836 kg (1,844 lb)

Max T-O and landing weight:
All versions 1,406 kg (3,100 lb)

Max ramp weight:
All versions 1,412 kg (3,112 lb)

Max wing loading:
All versions 86·9 kg/m² (17·8 lb/sq ft)

Max power loading:
All versions 8·03 kg/kW (13·2 lb/hp)

PERFORMANCE (at max T-O weight):
Max level speed at S/L:
A, B 160 knots (296 km/h; 184 mph)

Max level speed at 6,100 m (20,000 ft):
C, D 187 knots (346 km/h; 215 mph)

Max cruising speed, 75% power at 2,285 m (7,500 ft):
A, B 156 knots (290 km/h; 180 mph)

Max cruising speed, 75% power at 6,100 m (20,000 ft):
C, D 173 knots (320 km/h; 199 mph)

Max cruising speed, 75% power at 3,050 m (10,000 ft):
C, D 158 knots (293 km/h; 182 mph)

Stalling speed, flaps up, power off:
All versions 54 knots (100 km/h; 62 mph)

Stalling speed, flaps down, power off:
All versions 50 knots (92·5 km/h; 57·5 mph)

Cessna Skylane RG with retractable landing gear *(Pilot Press)*

Cessna Skylane RG II, a retractable landing gear version of the extensively built Model 182/Skylane

Max rate of climb at S/L:
A, B 347 m (1,140 ft)/min
C, D 317 m (1,040 ft)/min

*Service ceiling: A, B 4,360 m (14,300 ft)

Max certificated operating altitude:
C, D 6,100 m (20,000 ft)

T-O run: All versions 250 m (820 ft)

T-O to 15 m (50 ft): All versions 479 m (1,570 ft)

Landing from 15 m (50 ft):
All versions 402 m (1,320 ft)

Landing run: All versions 183 m (600 ft)

Range with max fuel, recommended lean mixture, with allowances for start, taxi, T-O, climb and 45 min reserves at 45% power:
75% power at 2,285 m (7,500 ft):
A, B 845 nm (1,566 km; 973 miles)
75% power at 6,100 m (20,000 ft):
C, D 825 nm (1,529 km; 950 miles)
75% power at 3,050 m (10,000 ft):
C, D 800 nm (1,482 km; 921 miles)
econ cruising power at 3,050 m (10,000 ft):
A, B 1,135 nm (2,103 km; 1,307 miles)
econ cruising power at 6,100 m (20,000 ft):
C, D 1,010 nm (1,871 km; 1,163 miles)
econ cruising power at 3,050 m (10,000 ft):
C, D 1,030 nm (1,908 km; 1,186 miles)

* *Service ceiling is 5,485 m (18,000 ft) if optional EGT gauge is used to set best power mixture*

CESSNA MODEL 185 SKYWAGON

US military designation: U-17

The prototype of the Model 185 Skywagon flew for the first time in July 1960 and the first production model was completed in March 1961. It is generally similar to the Model 180 Skywagon, except for installation of a 224 kW (300 hp) Continental IO-520 engine.

Two versions are available:

Model 185 Skywagon. Standard version.

Model 185 Skywagon II. As Skywagon, plus factory-installed avionics package which includes Series 300 nav/com, ADF, and emergency locator transmitter. Optional Nav Pac provides a second nav/com with Series 400 glideslope and marker beacon. Standard equipment as for basic Model 185, plus artificial horizon, clock, directional gyro, exhaust gas temperature gauge, outside air temperature gauge, sensitive altimeter, turn co-ordinator, vertical speed indicator, dual controls, sun visor, heated pitot and stall warning transmitter, map light, quick-drain oil valve, and external power socket.

The Model 185 Skywagon can be fitted with Edo 628-2960 floats, or Edo Model 597 amphibious floats, or Fli-Lite skis, and can be used in an agricultural role, for aerial application or agricultural pilot training, with optional 571 litre (151 US gallon) capacity Sorensen fan-driven spray system. It can carry under its fuselage a detachable glassfibre Cargo-Pack, more than 2·75 m long and 0·79 m wide (9 ft × 2 ft 7 in), with a volume of 0·61 m³ (21·5 cu ft) and capacity of 136 kg (300 lb). The Pack incorporates loading doors on the side and at the rear.

The 1980 version has the improvements detailed for the Model 180 Skywagon, and introduces as standard a three-blade propeller.

Cessna has received important contracts to supply U-17A/B/C Skywagons to the US Air Force for delivery to overseas countries, under the US Military Assistance Programme.

A total of 3,869 Model 185 Skywagons, including U-17A/B/Cs, had been built by 1 January 1980. The 4,000th aircraft was delivered on 22 February 1980.

TYPE: One/six-seat cabin monoplane.

WINGS AND FUSELAGE: Similar to Model 180.

TAIL UNIT: Same as for Model 180, except for fin of increased area and manually-operated rudder trim as standard equipment.

LANDING GEAR: Similar to Model 180, except for tyre pressures: main wheels (6·00-6) 2·41 bars (35 lb/sq in), main wheels (8·00-6) 1·72 bars (25 lb/sq in), tailwheel 3·79-4·83 bars (55-70 lb/sq in) depending on load. Manual tailwheel lock standard. Wheel and brake fairings optional. Optional amphibian, float or ski gear.

POWER PLANT: One 224 kW (300 hp) Continental IO-520-D flat-six engine, driving a McCauley three-blade constant-speed metal propeller. Fuel in two tanks in wings, total capacity 333 litres (88 US gallons), of which 318 litres (84 US gallons) are usable. Oil capacity 11·5 litres (3 US gallons).

ACCOMMODATION, AVIONICS AND EQUIPMENT: Generally as for Model 180, except omni-flash beacon and manual tailwheel lock standard, plus availability of optional agricultural kit comprising 571 litre (151 US gallon) capacity Sorensen fan-driven spraygear with electric spray valve, deflector cable, windscreen and landing gear wire cutters, and external finish of Jet-flo polyurethane paint to provide extra corrosion protection.

DIMENSIONS: As for Model 180, except:
Propeller diameter 2·03 m (6 ft 8 in)

AREAS: As for Model 180, except:
Fin 1·29 m² (13·86 sq ft)

WEIGHTS AND LOADINGS:
Weight empty, equipped:
Skywagon landplane 765 kg (1,688 lb)
Floatplane 902 kg (1,990 lb)
Amphibian 1,018 kg (2,245 lb)
Skiplane 830 kg (1,830 lb)
Skywagon II landplane 789 kg (1,739 lb)

Max T-O and landing weight:
Landplane, skiplane 1,519 kg (3,350 lb)
Floatplane 1,506 kg (3,320 lb)
Amphibian, land take-off 1,481 kg (3,265 lb)
Amphibian, water take-off 1,406 kg (3,100 lb)

Max ramp weight:
Landplane 1,525 kg (3,362 lb)

Max wing loading:
Landplane, skiplane 94·2 kg/m² (19·3 lb/sq ft)
Floatplane 93·3 kg/m² (19·1 lb/sq ft)
Amphibian 91·8 kg/m² (18·8 lb/sq ft)

Max power loading:
Landplane, skiplane 6·78 kg/kW (11·2 lb/hp)
Floatplane 6·72 kg/kW (11·1 lb/hp)
Amphibian 6·61 kg/kW (10·9 lb/hp)

Cessna Model 185 Skywagon one/six-seat cabin monoplane (Continental IO-520-D engine)

PERFORMANCE (at max T-O weight):

Never-exceed speed:

Landplane	182 knots (338 km/h; 210 mph)	

Max level speed at S/L:

*Landplane	154 knots (285 km/h; 177 mph)
Floatplane	140 knots (259 km/h; 161 mph)
Amphibian	135 knots (249 km/h; 155 mph)
Skiplane	136 knots (252 km/h; 157 mph)

Max cruising speed (75% power) at 2,135 m (7,000 ft):

*Landplane	147 knots (272 km/h; 169 mph)
Floatplane	133 knots (246 km/h; 153 mph)
Amphibian	129 knots (240 km/h; 149 mph)
Skiplane	131 knots (243 km/h; 151 mph)

Stalling speed, flaps up, power off:

Landplane, skiplane, floatplane	
	56 knots (104 km/h; 64·5 mph) CAS
Amphibian	55 knots (102 km/h; 63 mph) CAS

Stalling speed, flaps down, power off:

Landplane, skiplane	
	49 knots (90·5 km/h; 56 mph) CAS
Amphibian	51 knots (94 km/h; 58 mph) CAS
Floatplane	52 knots (96 km/h; 60 mph) CAS

Max rate of climb at S/L:

Landplane	328 m (1,075 ft)/min
Floatplane	293 m (960 ft)/min
Amphibian	290 m (950 ft)/min
Skiplane	262 m (860 ft)/min

Service ceiling: Landplane 5,455 m (17,900 ft)

Floatplane	5,000 m (16,400 ft)
Amphibian	4,907 m (16,100 ft)
Skiplane	4,725 m (15,500 ft)

T-O run: Landplane 251 m (825 ft)

Floatplane	436 m (1,430 ft)
Amphibian, on land	238 m (780 ft)
Amphibian, on water	343 m (1,125 ft)

T-O to 15 m (50 ft): Landplane 436 m (1,430 ft)

Floatplane	648 m (2,125 ft)
Amphibian, on land	404 m (1,325 ft)
Amphibian, on water	521 m (1,710 ft)

Landing from 15 m (50 ft):

Landplane	427 m (1,400 ft)
Floatplane	477 m (1,565 ft)
Amphibian, on land	378 m (1,240 ft)
Amphibian, on water	450 m (1,480 ft)

Landing run: Landplane 186 m (610 ft)

Floatplane	253 m (830 ft)
Amphibian, on land	174 m (570 ft)
Amphibian, on water	236 m (775 ft)

Range with max fuel (recommended lean mixture, with allowances for engine start, taxi, T-O, climb and 45 min reserves at 45% power):

75% power at 2,135 m (7,000 ft):

Landplane	645 nm (1,196 km; 743 miles)
Floatplane	585 nm (1,085 km; 674 miles)
Amphibian	570 nm (1,056 km; 656 miles)
Skiplane	575 nm (1,065 km; 662 miles)

econ cruising power at 3,050 m (10,000 ft):

Landplane	850 nm (1,575 km; 979 miles)
Floatplane	745 nm (1,381 km; 858 miles)
Amphibian	715 nm (1,324 km; 823 miles)
Skiplane	665 nm (1,233 km; 766 miles)

These speeds are 1 knot (1·9 km/h; 1·2 mph) higher with optional speed fairings installed

CESSNA AGWAGON and AGTRUCK

On 8 December 1971, Cessna introduced three new agricultural aircraft based on the earlier AGwagon low-wing monoplane. Of these, the AGpickup (53 built) was discontinued in 1976.

The current AGwagon and AGtruck are of all-metal construction and have special corrosion proofing, heavy-duty spring steel Land-O-Matic landing gear and Cessna's Camber-Lift wing to provide better control during low-speed operations. Wing fences are used to smooth airflow over the wing. Special attention has been paid to safety features, and these include ensolite padding on the upper instrument panel, urethane padding on tubular structures in the cabin area and around doors, safe flush switch and control locations and quick-release door hinges. Other standard features include wide wing walks, large hopper loading doors, and fresh-air scoops that slightly pressurise the cockpit and tailcone to prevent the ingress of dust and fumes.

Optional equipment includes a special night operations package to provide brilliant illumination for night operations. This comprises a 100A 24V alternator, taxi/landing lights, instrument panel lights, overhead floodlight, two 600W retractable spray lights, lighting angle control for spray lights, wingtip turning lights, hopper quantity light and a control stick grip incorporating light switches.

Improvements introduced for 1980 include a simplified hydraulic system that is easier to maintain, addition of a circuit breaker for the alternator, deletion of the external scoop and relocation of the condenser coil of the optional air-conditioning system, addition of main landing gear jackpads for the optional jacking provisions, and introduction of a manual locking-type inertia-reel shoulder harness as an extra option.

Differences between the two models are as follows:

AGwagon. Basic model, powered by a 224 kW (300 hp) Continental IO-520-D flat-six engine, driving a constant-speed propeller. Standard equipment includes a 757 litre (200 US gallon) hopper, a liquid and dry material dispersal control system, cockpit canopy with all-round view, tailplane abrasion boots, oversize 8·00-8 × 22 main-wheel tyres, 10 in tailwheel tyre, wire cutters, cable deflector, tailcone lift handles, hopper side-loading system on port side, navigation lights, pilot's four-way adjustable seat, control stick lock, quick oil drain, auxiliary fuel pump, steerable tailwheel and remote fuel strainer drain control. Options include an automatic flagman and cockpit air-conditioning.

AGtruck. As AGwagon, except for 1,060 litre (280 US gallon) hopper. Additional standard equipment includes a 22-nozzle engine-driven hydraulic spray system with manually-controlled spray valve and gatebox without agitator, wing fuel tanks, extended conical-cambered wingtips, automatic inertia reel for the safety belt system, sensitive altimeter, pilot's foul weather windows, strobe lights, instrument panel lights, landing and taxi lights, three-colour exterior styling, and oversize 10 in main and tailwheel tyres. Options include air-conditioning and a six-way articulating seat.

By 1 January 1980 deliveries totalled 1,566 AGwagons and 1,780 AGtrucks.

TYPE: Single-seat agricultural monoplane.

WINGS: Braced low-wing monoplane, with single streamline-section bracing strut each side. Wing section NACA 2412, modified. Dihedral 9°. Incidence 1° 30' at root, −1° 30' at tip. All-metal structure with NACA all-metal single-slotted flaps inboard of Frise all-metal ailerons. Aileron leading-edge gaps sealed. Wing fences immediately outboard of bracing strut attachment points. Conical-cambered wingtips, extended on AGtruck.

FUSELAGE: Rectangular-section welded steel tube structure with removable metal skin panels forward of cabin. All-metal semi-monocoque rear fuselage.

TAIL UNIT: Cantilever all-metal structure. Fixed-incidence tailplane. Trim tab in starboard elevator.

LANDING GEAR: Non-retractable tailwheel type. Land-O-Matic cantilever main legs of heavy-duty spring steel. Tapered tubular tailwheel spring shock-absorber. Main wheels and tyres size 8·00-8 × 22 on AGwagon, with oversize 10 in main-wheel tyres on AGtruck. AGwagon has 10 in tailwheel tyre and AGtruck an oversize 10 in tailwheel tyre. Hydraulic disc brakes and parking brake. Wheel fenders optional.

POWER PLANT: One 224 kW (300 hp) Continental IO-520-D flat-six engine, driving a McCauley two-blade constant-speed metal propeller. Larger two-blade, or three-blade, propeller optional. Two fuel tanks in wings with combined capacity of 204 litres (54 US gallons), of which 197 litres (52 US gallons) are usable. Oil capacity 11·5 litres (3 US gallons).

ACCOMMODATION: Pilot only, on vertically and longitudinally adjustable seat, in enclosed cabin. Steel overturn structure. Combined window and door on each side, hinged at bottom. Heating and ventilation standard.

SYSTEM: Electrical system has a 60A 12V alternator and 12V 24Ah battery as standard. A 60A 24V or a 100A 24V alternator is available optionally.

EQUIPMENT: Standard equipment is as detailed in model listings. Optional equipment includes fan-driven or engine-driven hydraulic spray systems; 22, 44 or 64 nozzle spraybooms; two spreader systems for either medium or high-volume applications; electric spray control valve; a Cessna-designed gatebox; wing leading-edge repair kit, a manual locking-type inertia-reel shoulder harness, and main gear and tailcone jacking points.

DIMENSIONS, EXTERNAL (A: AGwagon; B: AGtruck):

Wing span: A	12·41 m (40 ft 8½ in)
B	12·70 m (41 ft 8 in)
Wing chord at root	1·63 m (5 ft 4 in)
Wing chord at tip	1·12 m (3 ft 8 in)
Length overall	7·90 m (25 ft 11 in)
Height overall	2·49 m (8 ft 2 in)
Tailplane span	3·35 m (11 ft 0 in)
Wheel track	2·16 m (7 ft 1 in)
Propeller diameter: standard	2·08 m (6 ft 10 in)
optional: 2-blade	2·18 m (7 ft 2 in)
3-blade	2·03 m (6 ft 8 in)

AREAS:

Wings, gross: A	18·77 m² (202 sq ft)
B	19·05 m² (205 sq ft)

WEIGHTS AND LOADINGS:

Weight empty, approx, with no dispersal equipment installed: A	906 kg (1,998 lb)
B	931 kg (2,052 lb)
Weight empty, with liquid dispersal system gatebox and engine-driven hydraulic pump:	
A	986 kg (2,175 lb)
B	1,010 kg (2,227 lb)
T-O weight, Normal category	1,496 kg (3,300 lb)
Max T-O weight, Restricted category:	
A	1,814 kg (4,000 lb)
B	1,905 kg (4,200 lb)
Max landing weight	1,496 kg (3,300 lb)
Wing loading, Normal category:	
A	79·6 kg/m² (16·3 lb/sq ft)
B	78·6 kg/m² (16·1 lb/sq ft)
Max wing loading, Restricted category:	
A	96·6 kg/m² (19·8 lb/sq ft)
B	100·0 kg/m² (20·5 lb/sq ft)
Power loading, Normal category:	
A, B	6·68 kg/kW (11·0 lb/hp)
Max power loading, Restricted category:	
A	8·10 kg/kW (13·3 lb/hp)
B	8·50 kg/kW (14·0 lb/hp)

PERFORMANCE (A: AGwagon, B: AGtruck. At max T-O weight with liquid dispersal equipment):

Max level speed at S/L:

A	107 knots (198 km/h; 123 mph)
B	106 knots (196 km/h; 122 mph)

Max cruising speed, 75% power at 1,980 m (6,500 ft):

A	101 knots (186 km/h; 116 mph)
B	99 knots (183 km/h; 114 mph)

Cessna AGwagon, the basic model of the company's series of agricultural aircraft

Stalling speed, flaps up, power off:
A   58 knots (108 km/h; 67 mph) CAS
B   60 knots (111 km/h; 69 mph) CAS
Stalling speed, flaps down, power off:
A   55 knots (101 km/h; 63 mph) CAS
B   56 knots (104 km/h; 65 mph) CAS
Max rate of climb at S/L: A   168 m (550 ft)/min
B   149 m (490 ft)/min
Service ceiling: A   2,775 m (9,100 ft)
B   2,470 m (8,100 ft)
T-O run: A   367 m (1,205 ft)
B   415 m (1,360 ft)
T-O to 15 m (50 ft): A   575 m (1,885 ft)
B   661 m (2,170 ft)
Landing from 15 m (50 ft): A, B   386 m (1,265 ft)
Landing run: A, B   128 m (420 ft)
Range, recommended lean mixture, allowances for engine start, taxi, T-O, climb, and 30 min reserves at 45% power:
Max fuel, 75% power at 1,980 m (6,500 ft):
A   252 nm (467 km; 290 miles)
B   247 nm (459 km; 285 miles)

CESSNA AGHUSKY

Cessna introduced for 1979 an addition to its line of agricultural aircraft. Named the AGhusky, it is a turbocharged version of the AGtruck, the 231 kW (310 hp) engine providing improved performance at varying operational altitudes.

By 1 January 1980 a total of 141 AGhusky aircraft had been delivered.

The description of the AGtruck applies also to the AGhusky, except as follows:

POWER PLANT: One 231 kW (310 hp) Continental TSIO-520-T turbocharged flat-six engine, driving a three-blade constant-speed metal propeller.

EQUIPMENT: Standard equipment includes a 1,060 litre (280 US gallon) hopper, a Cessna hydraulic dispersal system with electric spray valve and 22-nozzle sprayboom, and a special lighting package.

DIMENSIONS, EXTERNAL: As for AGtruck, except:
Length overall   8·08 m (26 ft 6 in)
Propeller diameter   2·03 m (6 ft 8 in)
WEIGHTS AND LOADINGS:
Weight empty, standard   1,047 kg (2,308 lb)
Max T-O weight, Restricted category
                            1,996 kg (4,400 lb)
Max landing weight   1,497 kg (3,300 lb)
Max wing loading   104·78 kg/m² (21·5 lb/sq ft)
Max power loading   8·64 kg/kW (14·2 lb/hp)
PERFORMANCE (at max T-O weight, unless detailed otherwise):
Max level speed at S/L 113 knots (209 km/h; 130 mph)
Max cruising speed, 75% power at 1,980 m (6,500 ft)
               106 knots (196 km/h; 122 mph)
Stalling speed, flaps up, power off
             62 knots (114 km/h; 71 mph) CAS
Stalling speed, flaps down, power off
             58 knots (108 km/h; 67 mph) CAS
Max rate of climb at S/L   155 m (510 ft)/min
Max certificated operating altitude
                            4,265 m (14,000 ft)
T-O run   393 m (1,290 ft)
T-O to 15 m (50 ft)   628 m (2,060 ft)
Landing from 15 m (50 ft)   386 m (1,265 ft)
Landing run   128 m (420 ft)
Range with max fuel, 75% power at 1,980 m (6,500 ft), recommended lean mixture, allowances for engine start, taxi, T-O, climb, and 30 min reserves at 45% power   217 nm (402 km; 250 miles)

CESSNA AGCARRYALL

Announced by Cessna on 8 December 1971, the AGcarryall represented a multi-purpose concept in the agricultural aircraft category. A total of 108 AGcarryalls had been delivered when production was terminated in 1979. Details of this aircraft can be found in the 1979-80 *Jane's*.

CESSNA STATIONAIR 6

Cessna first renamed the former U206 Skywagon and TU206 Turbo-Skywagon as the Stationair and Turbo-Stationair respectively. In 1978 a further name change to Stationair 6 and Turbo-Stationair 6 highlighted the six-seat capacity of these cargo/utility aircraft. Among their important features are double cargo doors on the starboard side of the fuselage which permit the easy loading and unloading of a crate more than 1·22 m long, 0·91 m wide and 0·91 m deep (4 ft × 3 ft × 3 ft). Differences between the two versions are as follows:

Stationair 6. Standard cargo utility model with 224 kW (300 hp) Continental IO-520-F engine, as described in detail.

Turbo-Stationair 6. Similar to the Stationair 6 but with 231 kW (310 hp) Continental TSIO-520-M turbocharged engine in modified cowling and with a manifold pressure relief valve to prevent overboost.

The 'II' package of optional avionics and equipment, as detailed for the Skylane, is available for both versions of the Stationair 6.

A utility version of the Stationair is also available, with a single seat for the pilot as standard, vinyl floor covering,

Photograph and three-view drawing *(Pilot Press)* **of the Cessna AGhusky, a turbocharged version of the extensively-built AGtruck**

two-colour paint scheme and no wheel fairings. Up to five passenger seats can be supplied optionally.

The 1980 models of the Stationair 6/Turbo-Stationair 6 introduce a number of improvements as standard, including a redesigned cabin door, new audio panel with marker beacon, marker beacon muting switch, an alternator circuit breaker, and new exterior styling. New optional items include an anti-icing system, writing desk, and AM/FM cassette stereo player.

A total of 6,076 Model 206 Skywagons and Stationairs had been built by 1 January 1980, including 643 de luxe Super Skylanes of similar basic design.

TYPE: Single-engined cargo/utility aircraft.

WINGS: Braced high-wing monoplane. Single streamlined-section bracing strut each side. Wing section NACA 2412, modified. Dihedral 1° 44'. Incidence 1° 30' at root, —1° 30' at tip. All-metal structure. Glassfibre conical camber tips. Modified Frise-type wide-chord ailerons. Electrically-operated wide-span NACA single-slotted flaps. No tabs.

FUSELAGE: Conventional all-metal semi-monocoque structure.

TAIL UNIT: Cantilever all-metal structure, with sweptback vertical surfaces. Large trim tab in starboard elevator. Electrical operation of trim tab optional.

LANDING GEAR: Non-retractable tricycle type. Cessna Land-O-Matic cantilever spring steel main legs. Steerable nosewheel with oleo-pneumatic shock-absorbers. Cessna wheels, tubeless tyres and hydraulic disc brakes. Parking brake. Main wheels and tyres size 6·00-6, pressure 2·90 bars (42 lb/sq in). Nosewheel and tyre size 5·00-5, pressure 3·10 bars (45 lb/sq in). Main-wheel tyres size 8·00-6, nosewheel tyre size 6·00-6 and oversize wheel fairings optional. Floats and wheel-skis optional.

POWER PLANT: One Continental flat-six engine (details given under model listings), driving a McCauley three-blade constant-speed metal propeller type D2A32C90/82NC-2 (Stationair) or D3A-32C88/82NC-2 (Turbo-Stationair). Two fuel cells in wings, with total standard capacity of 348 litres (92 US gallons), of which 333 litres (88 US gallons) are usable. Oil capacity 11·5 litres (3 US gallons).

ACCOMMODATION: Standard seating for pilot, co-pilot and up to four passengers, front seats with inertia safety belts. Club seating arrangement optional, with centre row of seats facing aft. Utility version has only pilot's seat as standard. Pilot's door on port side. Large double cargo doors on starboard side; forward door hinged to open forward, rear door hinged to open rearward. Aircraft can be flown with cargo doors removed for photography, airdropping of supplies or parachuting. Openable starboard window optional. Fully articulating seats for pilot and co-pilot and safety harness for four rear

seats optional. Cabin heated and ventilated.

SYSTEMS: Electrical system powered by an engine-driven 60A 28V alternator. 24V 33Ah battery. Hydraulic system for brakes and optional wheel-skis. Oxygen system of 2·10 m³ (74 cu ft) capacity standard on Turbo-Stationair 6; 1·36 m³ (48 cu ft) system optional for Stationair 6. Vacuum system optional.

AVIONICS AND EQUIPMENT: Optional avionics as detailed for the Skylane, plus Series 400 Nav-O-Matic two-axis autopilot with heading control, VOR intercept and track and altitude control, Series 400 nav/com, DME, RNAV, a non-slaved HSI (with autopilot installation), audio/marker beacon panel, padded headset and electro-luminescent panel lighting, plus the optional avionics detailed for the Skylane II. Standard equipment as for the Skylane, plus electric clock, glareshield, outside air temperature gauge, sensitive altimeter, turn co-ordinator, sun visors, and overall paint scheme. Optional equipment, less the above items, is as detailed for the Skylane, plus ambulance kits, casket kit, photographic provisions, glider towing provisions and sky-diving kit. The child's seat and skylights are not available for the Stationair 6. The Turbo-Stationair 6 has an overboost control valve, absolute pressure controller, pressurised fuel system, turbine access door, pilot's all-purpose control wheel, non-congealing oil cooler, full flow oil filter and alternate static source as standard.

DIMENSIONS, EXTERNAL (L: landplane; F: floatplane):
Wing span   10·92 m (35 ft 10 in)
Wing chord at root   1·63 m (5 ft 4 in)
Wing chord at tip   1·09 m (3 ft 7 in)
Wing aspect ratio   7·63
Length overall:
   Stationair 6: L   8·61 m (28 ft 3 in)
   Stationair 6: F   9·04 m (29 ft 8 in)
   Turbo-Stationair 6   8·61 m (28 ft 3 in)
Height overall: L   2·83 m (9 ft 3½ in)
   F   4·31 m (14 ft 1½ in)
Tailplane span   3·96 m (13 ft 0 in)
Wheel track: L   2·46 m (8 ft 1 in)
Propeller diameter: L   2·03 m (6 ft 8 in)
   F   2·18 m (7 ft 2 in)
Pilot's door (port):
   Height, mean   1·03 m (3 ft 4 in)
Cargo double door (stbd):
   Height   0·98 m (3 ft 2½ in)
   Width   1·13 m (3 ft 8½ in)
   Height to sill   0·64 m (2 ft 1 in)
DIMENSIONS, INTERNAL:
Cabin: Length   3·66 m (12 ft 0 in)
   Max width   1·12 m (3 ft 8 in)
   Max height   1·26 m (4 ft 1½ in)
   Volume available for payload
                           2·87 m³ (101·2 cu ft)

Cessna Stationair 6/II one/six-seat cargo/utility aircraft

AREAS:

Wings, gross	16·17 m² (174·0 sq ft)
Ailerons (total)	1·60 m² (17·32 sq ft)
Trailing-edge flaps (total)	2·63 m² (28·35 sq ft)
Fin	1·08 m² (11·62 sq ft)
Rudder, incl tab	0·65 m² (6·95 sq ft)
Tailplane	2·31 m² (24·84 sq ft)
Elevators, incl tab	1·86 m² (20·08 sq ft)

WEIGHTS AND LOADINGS (L: landplane; F: floatplane; A: amphibian):

Weight empty:

Utility Stationair 6:	L	854 kg (1,882 lb)
	F	1,016 kg (2,240 lb)
Utility Stationair 6/II:	L	880 kg (1,941 lb)
	F	1,043 kg (2,299 lb)
Stationair 6:	L	874 kg (1,927 lb)
	F	1,027 kg (2,264 lb)
Stationair 6/II:	L	901 kg (1,987 lb)
	F	1,055 kg (2,325 lb)
Utility Turbo-Stationair 6:	L	888 kg (1,957 lb)
	F	1,049 kg (2,313 lb)
	A	1,182 kg (2,605 lb)
Utility Turbo-Stationair 6/II:	L	914 kg (2,016 lb)
	F	1,076 kg (2,372 lb)
	A	1,208 kg (2,664 lb)
Turbo-Stationair 6:	L	908 kg (2,003 lb)
	F	1,060 kg (2,338 lb)
	A	1,193 kg (2,630 lb)
Turbo-Stationair 6/II:	L	935 kg (2,062 lb)
	F	1,087 kg (2,397 lb)
	F	1,220 kg (2,689 lb)

Max T-O and landing weight:

Stationair 6:	L	1,633 kg (3,600 lb)
	F	1,587 kg (3,500 lb)
Turbo-Stationair 6:	L, F, A	1,633 kg (3,600 lb)

Max ramp weight:

Stationair 6:	L	1,638 kg (3,612 lb)
Turbo-Stationair 6:	L, F, A	1,640 kg (3,616 lb)

Max wing loading:

Stationair 6:	L	101·1 kg/m² (20·7 lb/sq ft)
	F	98·1 kg/m² (20·1 lb/sq ft)
Turbo-Stationair 6:	L, F, A	101·1 kg/m² (20·7 lb/sq ft)

Max power loading:

Stationair 6:	L	7·29 kg/kW (12·0 lb/hp)
	F	7·08 kg/kW (11·7 lb/hp)
Turbo-Stationair 6:	L, F, A	7·07 kg/kW (11·6 lb/hp)

PERFORMANCE (L: landplane; F: floatplane; A: amphibian):

Max level speed:

Stationair 6 at S/L:		
	L	156 knots (290 km/h; 180 mph)
	F	138 knots (256 km/h; 159 mph)
Turbo-Stationair 6 at 5,180 m (17,000 ft):		
	L	174 knots (322 km/h; 200 mph)
	F	155 knots (287 km/h; 178 mph)
	A	150 knots (278 km/h; 173 mph)

Max cruising speed (75% power):

Stationair 6 at 1,980 m (6,500 ft):		
	L	147 knots (272 km/h; 169 mph)
	F	132 knots (245 km/h; 152 mph)
Turbo-Stationair 6, 80% power at 6,100 m (20,000 ft):		
	L	167 knots (309 km/h; 192 mph)
	F	147 knots (272 km/h; 169 mph)
	A	141 knots (261 km/h; 162 mph)
Turbo-Stationair 6, 80% power at 3,050 m (10,000 ft):	L	152 knots (282 km/h; 175 mph)
	F	135 knots (249 km/h; 155 mph)
	A	130 knots (241 km/h; 150 mph)

Stalling speed, flaps up, power off:

Stationair 6:	L	62 knots (115 km/h; 71·5 mph) CAS
	F	56 knots (104 km/h; 64·5 mph) CAS
Turbo-Stationair 6:		
	L	62 knots (115 km/h; 71·5 mph) CAS
	F, A	57 knots (106 km/h; 65·5 mph) CAS

Stalling speed, flaps down, power off:

Stationair 6:	L	54 knots (101 km/h; 62·5 mph) CAS
	F	51 knots (95 km/h; 59 mph) CAS
Turbo-Stationair 6:		
	L	54 knots (101 km/h; 62·5 mph) CAS
	F, A	52 knots (96·5 km/h; 60 mph) CAS

Max rate of climb at S/L:

Stationair 6:	L	280 m (920 ft)/min
	F	282 m (925 ft)/min
Turbo-Stationair 6:	L	308 m (1,010 ft)/min
	F	255 m (835 ft)/min
	A	247 m (810 ft)/min

Service ceiling:

Stationair 6:	L	4,511 m (14,800 ft)
	F	4,237 m (13,900 ft)
Turbo-Stationair 6:	L	8,230 m (27,000 ft)
	F	7,800 m (25,600 ft)
	A	7,650 m (25,100 ft)

T-O run:

Stationair 6:	L	274 m (900 ft)
	F	559 m (1,835 ft)
Turbo-Stationair 6:	L	255 m (835 ft)
	F, A water	552 m (1,810 ft)
	A land	288 m (945 ft)

T-O to 15 m (50 ft):

Stationair 6:	L	543 m (1,780 ft)
	F	860 m (2,820 ft)
Turbo-Stationair 6:	L	500 m (1,640 ft)
	F, A water	850 m (2,790 ft)
	A land	561 m (1,840 ft)

Landing from 15 m (50 ft):

Stationair 6:	L	425 m (1,395 ft)
	F	511 m (1,675 ft)
Turbo-Stationair 6:	L	425 m (1,395 ft)
	F, A water	533 m (1,750 ft)
	A land	430 m (1,410 ft)

Landing run:

Stationair 6:	L	224 m (735 ft)
	F	238 m (780 ft)
Turbo-Stationair 6:	L	224 m (735 ft)
	F, A water	258 m (845 ft)
	A land	229 m (750 ft)

Range, Stationair 6, recommended lean mixture, with allowances for start, taxi, T-O, climb, and 45 min reserves at 45% power:

Max cruising speed at 1,980 m (6,500 ft) with max fuel:		
	L	680 nm (1,260 km; 783 miles)
	F	615 nm (1,139 km; 708 miles)
Econ cruising speed at 3,050 m (10,000 ft) with max fuel:	L	900 nm (1,667 km; 1,036 miles)
	F	770 nm (1,427 km; 887 miles)

Range, Turbo-Stationair 6, allowances and reserves as above:

Max cruising speed at 6,100 m (20,000 ft) with max fuel:	L	640 nm (1,186 km; 737 miles)
	F	550 nm (1,019 km; 633 miles)
	A	530 nm (981 km; 610 miles)
Max cruising speed at 3,050 m (10,000 ft) with max fuel:	L	610 nm (1,130 km; 702 miles)
	F	535 nm (991 km; 616 miles)
	A	515 nm (954 km; 593 miles)
Econ cruising speed at 6,100 m (20,000 ft) with max fuel:	L	775 nm (1,435 km; 892 miles)
	F	660 nm (1,223 km; 760 miles)
	A	630 nm (1,167 km; 725 miles)
Econ cruising speed at 3,050 m (10,000 ft) with max fuel:	L	805 nm (1,492 km; 927 miles)
	F	690 nm (1,278 km; 794 miles)
	A	660 nm (1,223 km; 760 miles)

CESSNA STATIONAIR 8 and TURBO-STATIONAIR 8

For 1980, Cessna replaced the seven-seat Stationair 7 and Turbo-Stationair 7 (see 1979-80 *Jane's*) with the eight-seat Stationair 8 and Turbo-Stationair 8 respectively. Differences between the two new models are as follows:

Stationair 8. Standard passenger/cargo utility model with 224 kW (300 hp) Continental IO-520-F engine.

Turbo-Stationair 8. Generally similar to Stationair 8, but with 231 kW (310 hp) Continental TSIO-520-M turbocharged engine, driving a McCauley three-blade constant-speed metal propeller. Absolute pressure controller, pressurised fuel system, non-congealing oil cooler, full-flow oil filter, overboost control valve, alternate static source and oxygen system standard.

When production of the Stationair 7 and Turbo-Stationair 7 ended, a total of 564 had been built, including early Model 207 Skywagons and Turbo-Skywagons. Ten Stationair 8s and Turbo-Stationair 8s had been sold by 1 January 1980.

The following description applies to the Stationair 8, except where stated otherwise:

TYPE: Single-engined utility aircraft.

WINGS: Braced high-wing monoplane. Single streamline-section bracing strut each side. Wing section NACA 2412 from root to just inboard of tip; wingtip is symmetrical. Dihedral 1° 44'. Incidence 1° 30' at root, —1° 30' at tip. All-metal structure. Glassfibre conical-camber tips. Modified Frise-type all-metal wide-chord ailerons. Electrically-operated long-span NACA single-slotted all-metal flaps. No trim tabs.

FUSELAGE: Conventional all-metal semi-monocoque structure.

TAIL UNIT: Cantilever all-metal structure, with sweptback vertical surfaces. Tailplane fixed with —3° incidence. Large trim tab in starboard elevator. Electrical operation of trim tab optional. Rudder trimmed by adjustment of bungee.

LANDING GEAR: Non-retractable tricycle type. Improved Cessna Land-O-Matic cantilever main legs of one-piece tapered steel tube. Steerable nosewheel with Cessna oleo-pneumatic shock-absorber and hydraulic shimmy damper. Cessna wheels, tubeless tyres and hydraulic disc brakes. Main wheels and tyres size 6·00-6, pressure 3·79 bars (55 lb/sq in). Nosewheel and tyre size 5·00-5, pressure 3·38 bars (49 lb/sq in). Optional 8·00-6 main-wheel tyres, pressure 2·41 bars (35 lb/sq in), nosewheel tyre size 6·00-6, pressure 2·00 bars (29 lb/sq in). Wheel fairings standard; oversize wheel fairings optional.

POWER PLANT: One 224 kW (300 hp) Continental IO-520-F flat-six engine, driving a McCauley three-blade constant-speed metal propeller. A bladder-type fuel tank, capacity 115·5 litres (30·5 US gallons), is located in the inboard section of each wing. Total fuel capacity 231 litres (61 US gallons), of which 204 litres (54 US gallons) are usable. Optional tankage increases capacity to 151·5 litres (40 US gallons) in each wing, giving a total capacity of 303 litres (80 US gallons), of which 276 litres (73 US gallons) are usable. Refuelling points in upper surface of each wing. Oil capacity 11·5 litres (3 US gallons).

ACCOMMODATION: Standard seating is for a pilot and seven passengers, with individual seats arranged in four pairs. A six-seat club arrangement is optional. Seats removable individually to increase cargo space. Pilot's door on port side, co-pilot's door on starboard side at front. Large double cargo doors on starboard side at rear of cabin; forward door hinged to open forward, rear door hinged to open rearward. Aircraft can be flown with cargo doors removed for photography, airdropping of supplies or parachuting; optional equipment includes a spoiler for use when the aircraft is flown in this configuration. Openable window, port side; openable window starboard side optional. Separate baggage compartment, forward of cabin, capacity 54 kg (120 lb), accessible through top-hinged door on starboard side. External glassfibre cargo pack, capacity 136 kg (300 lb), carried beneath the fuselage, is available as an optional extra.

SYSTEMS: Hydraulic system for brakes. Electrical system powered by a 28V 60A engine-driven alternator. 24V 33Ah battery. Oxygen system of 2·15 m³ (76 cu ft) capacity standard on Turbo-Stationair 8; 1·36 m³ (48 cu ft) system optional on Stationair 8.

AVIONICS AND EQUIPMENT: Avionics detailed as standard and optional for the Stationair 6/Turbo-Stationair 6 apply also to the Stationair 8/Turbo-Stationair 8 respectively. Standard equipment is as described for the Model 180, plus electric clock, outside air temperature gauge, rate of climb indicator, sensitive altimeter, turn co-ordinator, sun visors, tinted windscreen and windows, emergency locator transmitter, baggage tiedown rings, electro-luminescent lights for switch and comfort control panels, instrument panel glareshield light, cabin dome lights, dual-beam landing lights, cabin steps and towbar. Additional optional items include articulating and vertically adjustable front seats, inertia-reel shoulder harness for two front seats, openable starboard window, heated pitot and stall warning transmitter, centre armrests, shoulder harness for six passenger seats, ambulance kit, skydiving kit, instrument post lights, anti-precipitation static kit, flush com antenna, and glider tow hook.

DIMENSIONS, EXTERNAL:

Wing span	10·92 m (35 ft 10 in)
Wing chord at root	1·63 m (5 ft 4 in)

Wing chord at tip	1·09 m (3 ft 7 in)
Wing aspect ratio	7·46
Length overall	9·80 m (32 ft 2 in)
Height overall	2·92 m (9 ft 7 in)
Tailplane span	3·96 m (13 ft 0 in)
Wheel track	3·09 m (10 ft 1¾ in)
Wheelbase	2·11 m (6 ft 11¼ in)
Propeller diameter	2·03 m (6 ft 8 in)
Forward cabin doors (each):	
Height	1·05 m (3 ft 5½ in)
Width	0·89 m (2 ft 11½ in)
Height to sill	0·71 m (2 ft 4 in)
Cargo double doors (stbd):	
Height	0·97 m (3 ft 2 in)
Width	1·13 m (3 ft 8½ in)
Height to sill	0·76 m (2 ft 6 in)
Baggage door (stbd): Height	0·61 m (2 ft 0 in)
Width	0·34 m (1 ft 1½ in)
Height to sill	1·02 m (3 ft 4 in)

DIMENSIONS, INTERNAL:

Cabin: Length	4·27 m (14 ft 0 in)
Max width	1·13 m (3 ft 8½ in)
Max height	1·24 m (4 ft 1 in)
Floor area	4·38 m² (47·1 sq ft)
Volume	4·40 m³ (155·5 cu ft)
Forward baggage compartment:	
Length	0·43 m (1 ft 5 in)
Max width	1·05 m (3 ft 5½ in)
Max height	0·69 m (2 ft 3 in)
Floor area	0·46 m² (4·9 sq ft)
Volume	0·27 m³ (9·5 cu ft)
Underfuselage cargo pack	0·34 m³ (12·0 cu ft)

AREAS:

Wings, gross	16·17 m² (174·0 sq ft)
Ailerons (total)	1·60 m² (17·32 sq ft)
Trailing-edge flaps (total)	2·66 m² (26·60 sq ft)
Fin	0·84 m² (9·04 sq ft)
Rudder	0·65 m² (6·95 sq ft)
Tailplane	2·31 m² (24·84 sq ft)
Elevators, incl tab	1·86 m² (20·08 sq ft)

WEIGHTS AND LOADINGS:

Weight empty: Utility Stationair 8	938 kg (2,067 lb)
Utility Stationair 8/II	968 kg (2,134 lb)
Stationair 8	955 kg (2,105 lb)
Stationair 8/II	985 kg (2,172 lb)
Utility Turbo-Stationair 8	973 kg (2,145 lb)
Utility Turbo-Stationair 8/II	1,003 kg (2,211 lb)
Turbo-Stationair 8	990 kg (2,183 lb)
Turbo-Stationair 8/II	1,020 kg (2,249 lb)
Max T-O and landing weight:	
Stationair 8 and Turbo-Stationair 8	1,723 kg (3,800 lb)
Max ramp weight: Stationair 8	1,729 kg (3,812 lb)
Turbo-Stationair 8	1,731 kg (3,816 lb)
Max wing loading:	
Stationair 8 and Turbo-Stationair 8	106·44 kg/m² (21·8 lb/sq ft)
Max power loading:	
Stationair 8	7·69 kg/kW (12·7 lb/hp)
Turbo-Stationair 8	7·46 kg/kW (12·3 lb/hp)

PERFORMANCE (at max T-O weight and without wheel fairings, which increase speed by 3-4 knots; 5·5-7·5 km/h; 3·5-4·5 mph, with corresponding difference in range. A: Stationair 8; B: Turbo-Stationair 8):

Never-exceed speed:	
A, B	182 knots (338 km/h; 210 mph)
Max level speed:	
A at S/L	150 knots (278 km/h; 173 mph)
B at 5,180 m (17,000 ft)	170 knots (315 km/h; 196 mph)
Max cruising speed:	
A, 75% power at 1,980 m (6,500 ft)	143 knots (266 km/h; 165 mph)
B, 80% power at 6,100 m (20,000 ft)	161 knots (298 km/h; 185 mph)
B, 80% power at 3,050 m (10,000 ft)	148 knots (274 km/h; 170 mph)
Stalling speed, flaps up, power off:	
A, B	65 knots (121 km/h; 75 mph) CAS
Stalling speed, flaps down, power off:	
A, B	58 knots (108 km/h; 67 mph) CAS
Max rate of climb at S/L: A	247 m (810 ft)/min
B	270 m (885 ft)/min
Service ceiling: A	4,054 m (13,300 ft)
B	7,925 m (26,000 ft)
T-O run: A	335 m (1,100 ft)
B	314 m (1,030 ft)
T-O to 15 m (50 ft): A	600 m (1,970 ft)
B	567 m (1,860 ft)
Landing from 15 m (50 ft): A, B	457 m (1,500 ft)
Landing run: A, B	233 m (765 ft)

Range, A at recommended lean mixture, with allowances for engine start, taxi, T-O, climb and 45 min reserves at 45% power:

Max cruising speed at 1,980 m (6,500 ft) with standard fuel	350 nm (649 km; 403 miles)
Max cruising speed at 1,980 m (6,500 ft) with max fuel	525 nm (972 km; 604 miles)
Econ cruising speed at 3,050 m (10,000 ft) with standard fuel	470 nm (871 km; 541 miles)
Econ cruising speed at 3,050 m (10,000 ft) with max fuel	690 nm (1,279 km; 795 miles)

Cessna Stationair 8/II, a one/eight-seat version of this utility aircraft

Cessna Stationair 8 utility aircraft *(Pilot Press)*

Range, B with allowances as above:

Max cruising speed at 3,050 m (10,000 ft) or 6,100 m (20,000 ft) with standard fuel	300 nm (556 km; 345 miles)
Max cruising speed at 6,100 m (20,000 ft) with max fuel	475 nm (880 km; 547 miles)
Max cruising speed at 3,050 m (10,000 ft) with max fuel	460 nm (853 km; 530 miles)
Econ cruising speed at 6,100 m (20,000 ft) with standard fuel	380 nm (703 km; 437 miles)
Econ cruising speed at 3,050 m (10,000 ft) with standard fuel	415 nm (769 km; 478 miles)
Econ cruising speed at 6,100 m (20,000 ft) with max fuel	580 nm (1,075 km; 668 miles)
Econ cruising speed at 3,050 m (10,000 ft) with max fuel	610 nm (1,130 km; 702 miles)

CESSNA CENTURION and CENTURION II

The original prototype Model 210, which flew in January 1957, followed the general formula of the Cessna series of all-metal high-wing monoplanes, but was the first to have a retractable tricycle landing gear.

Later versions of the Model 210 have a fully-cantilever wing, eliminating the bracing struts used on earlier models. Their design was started on 24 October 1964 and construction of a prototype began on 29 November 1964. The first T210 with the new wing flew on 18 June 1965.

On 3 December 1970 Cessna announced the introduction of two new versions of the Model 210 to be known as Centurion II and Turbo-Centurion II. These differ from the Centurion and Turbo-Centurion by having as standard equipment a factory-installed IFR avionics package which offers a cost saving on avionics equipment, plus a gyro panel, dual controls, articulating front seats and all-purpose control wheel. A Pressurised Centurion was introduced in late 1977, and is described separately.

Standard improvements for the 1980 versions of the Centurion include a new audio panel with marker beacon, dim switching of marker and navigation annunciator lights, marker beacon muting switch, alternator circuit breaker, and a redesigned cabin door. New options include a second Srs 400 glideslope receiver, Bendix RDR 160 colour radar, air-conditioning, writing desk, stereo entertainment centre, leather seats, fin lights, large capacity oxygen system, and new exterior finishes. An optional standby electric generator is available for Turbo- and Pressurised Centurions.

The six current production versions of the Centurion are as follows:

Centurion. Standard model, with 224 kW (300 hp) Continental IO-520-L flat-six engine, driving a McCauley D3A32C88/82NC-2 three-blade constant-speed metal propeller.

Centurion II. Identical to Centurion but with a 720-channel Cessna Series 300 nav/com, ADF, transponder, artificial horizon, directional gyro, economy mixture indicator, true airspeed indicator, reclining and vertically adjustable co-pilot's seat, all-purpose control wheel, dual controls, alternate static source, emergency locator transmitter, heated pitot and stall warning transmitter, navigation light detectors, courtesy lights, instrument post lights, omni-flash beacon, and external power socket as standard. Optional avionics include Nav-O-Matic 200A autopilot, Bendix RDR 160 colour weather radar, a second Srs 400 glideslope receiver, this last item included in the optional Nav Pac which includes also a second Series 300 nav/com.

Turbo-Centurion. Generally similar to Centurion, but powered by a 231 kW (310 hp) Continental TSIO-520-R turbocharged engine, driving a McCauley three-blade constant-speed metal propeller. Absolute pressure controller, full-flow oil filter, pressurised fuel system, oxygen system, non-congealing oil cooler and overboost control valve standard.

The Turbo-Centurion version holds an international altitude record for aircraft of this class with a height of 12,906·5 m (42,344 ft).

Turbo-Centurion II. Identical to Turbo-Centurion but with additional standard equipment as detailed for Centurion II, except that transponder is Series 400. The same optional avionics are available also.

Pressurised Centurion/Pressurised Centurion II. Introduced in late 1977, these pressurised versions of the Centurion are described separately.

The original versions received FAA Type Approval on 23 August 1966. A total of 7,194 Model 210/Centurions, plus an additional 419 Pressurised Centurions, had been delivered by 1 January 1980.

TYPE: Six-seat cabin monoplane.

WINGS: Cantilever high-wing monoplane. Wing section NACA 64₂A215 at root, NACA 64₁A412 (A=0·5) at tip. Dihedral 1° 30′. Incidence 1° 30′ at root, −1° 30′ at tip. All-metal structure, except for glassfibre conical-camber tips. All-metal Frise-type ailerons. Electrically-actuated all-metal Fowler-type flaps. Ground-adjustable tab in each aileron. Pneumatic de-icing system optional.

FUSELAGE: All-metal semi-monocoque structure.

TAIL UNIT: Cantilever all-metal structure with 36° sweepback on fin. Fixed-incidence tailplane. Controllable trim tabs in rudder and starboard elevator. Electrical operation of elevator tab optional. Pneumatic de-icing system optional.

LANDING GEAR: Hydraulically-retractable tricycle type with single wheel on each unit. Nose unit retracts forward, main units aft and inward. Chrome vanadium tapered steel tube main legs. Steerable nosewheel with oleo-pneumatic shock-absorber. Cessna main wheels and tube-type tyres, size 6·00-6, pressure 2·90 bars (42 lb/sq in). Cessna nosewheel and tyre, size 5·00-5, pressure 3·10 bars (45 lb/sq in). Cessna hydraulic disc brakes. Parking brake.

POWER PLANT: One flat-six engine, as described under model listings. Electrical de-icing system for propeller

Cessna Centurion II six-seat cabin monoplane with retractable landing gear

optional. Integral fuel tanks in wings, with max total capacity of 340 litres (90 US gallons). Refuelling points above wing. Oil capacity 9·5 litres (2·5 US gallons) in Centurions, 10·5 litres (2·75 US gallons) in Turbo-Centurions.

ACCOMMODATION: Six persons in pairs in enclosed cabin. Front two seats of fully-articulating type on Centurion II and Turbo-Centurion II (pilot's seat only on other versions). Fifth and sixth seats have folding backs to accommodate articles up to 2·01 m (6 ft 7 in) long. Openable window on port side standard; optional for starboard side. Dual controls standard on Centurion II and Turbo-Centurion II (optional on other models). Forward-hinged door on each side of cabin. Baggage space aft of rear seats, capacity 109 kg (240 lb), with outside door on port side. Combined heating and ventilation system. Windscreen defroster standard; electrical anti-icing optional.

SYSTEMS: Integral hydraulic-electric unit for landing gear operation. Hydraulic system for brakes. Electrical power supplied by 24V 60A engine-driven alternator. 24V battery; standby electric generator available optionally for Turbo-Centurions. Oxygen system standard on Turbo-Centurion, optional for Centurion. Vacuum system and air-conditioning system optional.

AVIONICS AND EQUIPMENT: Optional avionics as for Stationair, except that Series 300 or 400 integrated flight control system is available when the Series 200A, 300A, or 400 Nav-O-Matic autopilot is replaced by the Series 400A two-axis autopilot, which has automatic pitch trim and an optional ILS coupler. Automatic Radial Centering (ARC) is optional with Series 300 nav indicators. Series 400 avionics, including 400B Integrated Flight Control System, and a second glideslope receiver, Series 800 encoding altimeter with altitude alert system, and Bendix RDR-160 weather radar, are also available as options. Standard equipment includes electric clock, outside air temperature gauge, rate of climb indicator, sensitive altimeter, turn co-ordinator, armrests, control locks, tinted windscreen and windows, sun visors, stall warning device, baggage restraint net, adjustable fresh air vents, dome lights, electroluminescent lights for switch and comfort control panels, glareshield and map lights, variable-intensity instrument panel red floodlights, landing lights, taxi light, navigation lights, quick fuel drains and sampler cup, overall paint scheme, cabin steps and towbar. Optional equipment for all versions includes cabin fire extinguisher, headrests, internal corrosion proofing, stretcher installation, ice detector light, wingtip-mounted strobe lights, engine priming system, glider tow hook, tailplane abrasion boots, and static dischargers. Equipment detailed under Centurion II/Turbo-Centurion II model listings is available optionally for Centurion/Turbo-Centurion. Optional for the Centurion and Centurion II only are a full-flow oil filter, non-congealing oil cooler, and engine winterisation kit.

DIMENSIONS, EXTERNAL:

Wing span	11·20 m (36 ft 9 in)
Wing chord at root	1·68 m (5 ft 6 in)
Wing chord at tip	1·22 m (4 ft 0 in)
Wing aspect ratio	7·66
Length overall	8·59 m (28 ft 2 in)
Height overall	2·95 m (9 ft 8 in)
Tailplane span	3·96 m (13 ft 0 in)
Wheel track	2·64 m (8 ft 8 in)
Wheelbase	1·75 m (5 ft 9 in)
Propeller diameter	2·03 m (6 ft 8 in)
Passenger doors (each):	
Height	1·02 m (3 ft 4¼ in)
Width	0·90 m (2 ft 11¼ in)
Height to sill	0·91 m (3 ft 0 in)
Baggage compartment door:	
Height	0·57 m (1 ft 10½ in)
Width	0·74 m (2 ft 5 in)

DIMENSIONS, INTERNAL:

Cabin: Length	3·50 m (11 ft 6 in)
Max width	1·08 m (3 ft 6½ in)
Max height	1·23 m (4 ft 0½ in)
Floor area	2·69 m² (29·0 sq ft)
Volume	3·96 m³ (139·9 cu ft)
Baggage space	0·46 m³ (16·25 cu ft)

AREAS:

Wings, gross	16·25 m² (175 sq ft)
Ailerons (total)	1·75 m² (18·86 sq ft)
Trailing-edge flaps (total)	2·74 m² (29·50 sq ft)
Fin, incl dorsal fin	0·95 m² (10·26 sq ft)
Rudder, incl tab	0·65 m² (6·95 sq ft)
Tailplane	1·73 m² (18·57 sq ft)
Elevators, incl tab	1·87 m² (20·08 sq ft)

WEIGHTS AND LOADINGS:

Weight empty: Centurion	967 kg (2,133 lb)
Centurion II	997 kg (2,198 lb)
Turbo-Centurion	1,007 kg (2,221 lb)
Turbo-Centurion II	1,037 kg (2,286 lb)
Max T-O and landing weight:	
Centurion, Centurion II	1,724 kg (3,800 lb)
Max T-O weight:	
Turbo-Centurion, Turbo-Centurion II	1,814 kg (4,000 lb)
Max landing weight:	
Turbo-Centurion, Turbo-Centurion II	1,724 kg (3,800 lb)
Max ramp weight:	
Centurion, Centurion II	1,729 kg (3,812 lb)
Turbo-Centurion, Turbo-Centurion II	1,822 kg (4,016 lb)
Max wing loading:	
Centurion, Centurion II	106 kg/m² (21·7 lb/sq ft)
Turbo-Centurion, Turbo-Centurion II	111·6 kg/m² (22·8 lb/sq ft)
Max power loading:	
Centurion, Centurion II	7·69 kg/kW (12·7 lb/hp)
Turbo-Centurion, Turbo-Centurion II	7·85 kg/kW (12·9 lb/hp)

PERFORMANCE (at max T-O weight):

Max level speed:
Centurion, Centurion II at S/L
175 knots (325 km/h; 202 mph)
Turbo-Centurion, Turbo-Centurion II at 5,180 m (17,000 ft) 204 knots (378 km/h; 235 mph)

Max cruising speed:
Centurion, Centurion II, 75% power at 1,980 m (6,500 ft) 171 knots (317 km/h; 197 mph)
Turbo-Centurion, Turbo-Centurion II, 80% power: at 6,100 m (20,000 ft)
196 knots (364 km/h; 226 mph)
at 3,050 m (10,000 ft)
180 knots (333 km/h; 207 mph)

Stalling speed, flaps up, power off:
Centurion, Centurion II
65 knots (121 km/h; 75 mph) CAS
Turbo-Centurion, Turbo-Centurion II
67 knots (124 km/h; 77 mph) CAS

Stalling speed, flaps down, power off:
Centurion, Centurion II
56 knots (104 km/h; 64·5 mph) CAS
Turbo-Centurion, Turbo-Centurion II
58 knots (108 km/h; 67 mph) CAS

Max rate of climb at S/L:
Centurion, Centurion II   290 m (950 ft)/min
Turbo-Centurion, Turbo-Centurion II
283 m (930 ft)/min

Service ceiling:
Centurion, Centurion II   5,275 m (17,300 ft)
Turbo-Centurion, Turbo-Centurion II
8,230 m (27,000 ft)

T-O run:
Centurion, Centurion II   381 m (1,250 ft)
Turbo-Centurion, Turbo-Centurion II
396 m (1,300 ft)

T-O to 15 m (50 ft):
Centurion, Centurion II   619 m (2,030 ft)
Turbo-Centurion, Turbo-Centurion II
658 m (2,160 ft)

Landing from 15 m (50 ft):
All versions   457 m (1,500 ft)
Landing run: All versions   233 m (765 ft)

Range, Centurion and Centurion II with max fuel, at recommended lean mixture, with allowances for engine start, taxi, T-O, climb and 45 min reserves at 45% power:
Max cruising speed at 1,980 m (6,500 ft)
805 nm (1,492 km; 927 miles)
Econ cruising speed at 3,050 m (10,000 ft)
1,065 nm (1,973 km; 1,226 miles)

Range, Turbo-Centurion and Turbo-Centurion II with max fuel, allowances as above:
Max cruising speed at 3,050 m (10,000 ft)
725 nm (1,344 km; 835 miles)
Max cruising speed at 6,100 m (20,000 ft)
755 nm (1,398 km; 869 miles)
Econ cruising speed at 3,050 m (10,000 ft)
960 nm (1,778 km; 1,105 miles)
Econ cruising speed at 6,100 m (20,000 ft)
940 nm (1,741 km; 1,082 miles)

CESSNA PRESSURISED CENTURION and PRESSURISED CENTURION II

On 10 November 1977, Cessna announced the introduction of a pressurised version of the Centurion. It is available in two versions:

Pressurised Centurion. Standard model, generally similar to Centurion, except for installation of 231 kW (310 hp) Continental TSIO-520-P engine with a special high-capacity turbocharger to support the pressurisation system, and pressure cabin. Easily identified by four smaller windows on each side of cabin.

Pressurised Centurion II. Identical to Pressurised Centurion, with additional standard avionics and equipment as described for Centurion II, except that autopilot is Nav-O-Matic 300A and transponder is Series 400.

These Centurions have a cabin pressure differential of 0·23 bars (3·35 lb/sq in), providing a cabin altitude of 3,695 m (12,127 ft) at 7,010 m (23,000 ft). Cabin heat is provided by a double heat exchange system using exhaust system heat. Unlike the average combustion heating unit, this system uses no fuel and is reported to offer outstanding performance even in extremely cold temperatures. A total of 419 Pressurised Centurions had been delivered by 1 January 1980.

The description of the Centurion applies also to the Pressurised Centurion, except as follows:

FUSELAGE: Conventional semi-monocoque structure of light alloy, with fail-safe structure in the pressurised section.

POWER PLANT: One 231 kW (310 hp) Continental TSIO-520-P flat-six engine; otherwise as for Centurion. Oil capacity 10·5 litres (2·75 US gallons).

ACCOMMODATION: As for Centurion, except forward-hinged door on port side of cabin. Large emergency exit on starboard side. Baggage space aft of cabin area, capacity 91 kg (200 lb). Four windows each side of cabin, two overhead windows above the rear seats. Cabin pressurised, heated and ventilated.

SYSTEMS: As for Centurion, except cabin pressurisation system by engine bleed air, max differential 0·23 bars (3·35 lb/sq in). Cabin heated by double heat exchange system using exhaust system heat.

DIMENSIONS, INTERNAL: As for Centurion except:
Baggage space   0·52 m³ (18·3 cu ft)

Cessna Pressurised Centurion, with underwing weather radar

WEIGHTS AND LOADINGS (A: Pressurised Centurion; B: Pressurised Centurion II):

Weight empty: A	1,061 kg (2,340 lb)
B	1,091 kg (2,405 lb)
Max T-O weight: A, B	1,814 kg (4,000 lb)
Max landing weight: A, B	1,723 kg (3,800 lb)
Max ramp weight: A, B	1,821 kg (4,016 lb)
Max wing loading: A, B	111·8 kg/m² (22·9 lb/sq ft)
Max power loading: A, B	7·85 kg/kW (12·9 lb/hp)

PERFORMANCE (at max T-O weight, except where indicated):

*Max level speed at 5,180 m (17,000 ft)	
	206 knots (381 km/h; 237 mph)
*Max cruising speed, 80% power at 6,100 m (20,000 ft)	
	200 knots (370 km/h; 230 mph)
*Max cruising speed, 80% power at 3,050 m (10,000 ft)	
	182 knots (338 km/h; 210 mph)
Stalling speed, flaps up	
	67 knots (124 km/h; 77·5 mph) CAS
Stalling speed, flaps down	
	58 knots (108 km/h; 67 mph) CAS
Max rate of climb at S/L	283 m (930 ft)/min
Rate of climb at 3,050 m (10,000 ft)	
	248 m (815 ft)/min
Rate of climb at 6,100 m (20,000 ft)	
	157 m (515 ft)/min
Max certificated operating altitude	
	7,010 m (23,000 ft)
T-O run	396 m (1,300 ft)
T-O to 15 m (50 ft)	658 m (2,160 ft)
Landing from 15 m (50 ft)	457 m (1,500 ft)
Landing run	233 m (765 ft)

Range with max fuel, recommended lean mixture, with fuel allowance for engine start, taxi, T-O, climb and 45 min reserves at 45% power:

80% power at 6,100 m (20,000 ft)	
	705 nm (1,306 km; 812 miles)
80% power at 3,050 m (10,000 ft)	
	680 nm (1,260 km; 783 miles)
70% power at 6,100 m (20,000 ft)	
	805 nm (1,492 km; 927 miles)
70% power at 3,050 m (10,000 ft)	
	780 nm (1,445 km; 898 miles)
Econ cruising speed at 6,100 m (20,000 ft)	
	910 nm (1,687 km; 1,048 miles)
Econ cruising speed at 3,050 m (10,000 ft)	
	925 nm (1,714 km; 1,065 miles)

*Speeds based on estimated mid-cruise weight

CESSNA MODEL T303 CRUSADER

Cessna announced on 17 February 1978 the first flight, three days earlier, of a new lightweight twin-engined aircraft known as the Model 303. At that time, it was a four-seat aircraft, with 119 kW (160 hp) engines, and made use of bonded structures and a supercritical wing section. It has been superseded by the new Model T303, with six seats, 186 kW (250 hp) turbocharged engines and conventional construction. To be certificated to the latest FAR Pt 23 regulations, this aircraft was undergoing certification flight testing in early 1980. Deliveries of production aircraft are scheduled to begin during the 1981 model year. The name Clipper was applied temporarily to the T303 but was changed to Crusader because of a trademark dispute.

Only preliminary details of the T303's specification and performance had been released by mid-1980, and all available information follows:

TYPE: Twin-engined cabin monoplane.

WINGS: Cantilever low-wing monoplane. Wing section of NACA 23000 series. Structure is primarily of light alloy. Conventional trailing-edge flaps and ailerons. Trim tab in starboard aileron.

FUSELAGE: Oval-section semi-monocoque structure of light alloy.

TAIL UNIT: Cantilever structure, primarily of light alloy, with horizontal surfaces mounted partway up fin. All surfaces swept back. Long dorsal fin. Trim tab in rudder and each elevator.

LANDING GEAR: Retractable tricycle type, with single wheel on each unit. Main wheels retract inward, nosewheel forward. Main units of articulated (trailing-link) type.

POWER PLANT: Two 186 kW (250 hp) Continental TSIO-520-AE flat-six turbocharged engines, each driving a McCauley two-blade constant-speed metal propeller with spinner. Propellers are counter-rotating. Fuel in integral wing tanks with combined usable capacity of 549 litres (145 US gallons). Refuelling point on upper surface of each wing.

ACCOMMODATION: Standard seating for pilot and five passengers; or pilot, co-pilot and four passengers. Six individual forward-facing seats can be replaced by optional club arrangement. Outboard armrests are standard; inboard retractable armrests and adjustable headrests are normally optional, but are standard with club seating. Wide range of optional cabin furniture and equipment. Clamshell-type two-piece cabin door, with integral airstair, on port side at aft end of cabin. Baggage stowage in nose compartment, wing lockers, and at rear of cabin, with combined capacity of 267 kg (590 lb). Accommodation heated and ventilated.

Prototype of the new six-seat Cessna Model T303 Crusader

Cessna Model T303 Crusader (two Continental TSIO-520-AE engines) (Michael A. Badrocke)

EQUIPMENT: Fresh air vents in cabin standard. Optional equipment includes club seating with armrests and adjustable headrests, writing tables, refreshment units, storage drawer, ice chest, and stereo equipment.

WEIGHT (estimated):

Max useful load	more than 860 kg (1,900 lb)

PERFORMANCE (provisional, at max T-O weight, and in excess of figure quoted unless otherwise detailed):

Max level speed at 6,100 m (20,000 ft)	
	215 knots (398 km/h; 247 mph)
Max cruising speed at 3,050 m (10,000 ft)	
	180 knots (334 km/h; 207 mph)
Max rate of climb at S/L	427 m (1,400 ft)/min
Rate of climb at S/L, one engine out	
	61 m (200 ft)/min
Certificated operational ceiling	7,620 m (25,000 ft)
Service ceiling, one engine out	3,960 m (13,000 ft)
T-O to 15 m (50 ft)	less than 610 m (2,000 ft)
Landing from 15 m (50 ft)	less than 610 m (2,000 ft)
Range with max fuel	800 nm (1,482 km; 921 miles)

CESSNA MODEL 310 and 310 II

The Model 310 is a twin-engined five/six-seat cabin monoplane, the prototype of which flew on 3 January 1953. It went into production in 1954. The Turbo 310 was added in late 1968, and the first production model was delivered in December 1968. On 21 December 1973 Cessna announced two new versions of the Model 310, known as the 310 II and the Turbo 310 II, which have factory-installed IFR avionics plus other comfort and convenience features as standard. A total of 5,102 commercial examples of the Model 310 had been completed by 1 January 1980, plus 196 delivered to the US Air Force as U-3A/Bs.

There are four current versions of the Model 310, as follows:

310. Standard model, as described in detail, powered by two 212·5 kW (285 hp) Continental IO-520-MB flat-six engines, driving McCauley three-blade fully-feathering constant-speed metal propellers.

310 II. Identical to 310, but having as standard equipment dual 300 Series nav/com with 720-channel com, 200-channel nav, VOR/LOC and VOR/ILS indicators; 300 Series ADF with digital tuning; 400 Series glideslope receiver; marker beacon; transponder; 400B Nav-O-Matic autopilot with approach coupler; associated antennae; avionics cooling kit and panel; economy mixture indicator, outside air temperature gauge, dual controls, six individual seats, emergency locator transmitter, large baggage door, starboard landing light, rotating beacon, taxi light, auxiliary fuel system of 238·5 litres (63 US gallons) capacity, nosewheel fender, static wicks, and external power socket.

Turbo T310. Similar to 310, but with two 212·5 kW (285 hp) Continental TSIO-520-BB turbocharged engines, with automatic propeller synchronisation, full-flow oil filters, absolute and pressure ratio controllers, overboost control valves and engine cowl flaps as standard.

Turbo T310 II. Identical to T310, but with the additional standard equipment as detailed for the 310 II.

The 1980 versions of the Model 310 introduce as standard improvements better accessibility to elevator and rudder controls for routine maintenance, revised instrument layout, and new interior and exterior styling. New options include a cabin stereo system.

TYPE: Twin-engined five- or six-seat monoplane.

WINGS: Cantilever low-wing monoplane. Wing section NACA 23018 at centreline, NACA 23009 at tip. Dihedral 5°. Incidence 2° 30′ at root, −0° 30′ at tip. All-metal structure. Electrically-operated split flaps. Trim tab in port aileron. Pneumatic de-icing system optional.

FUSELAGE: All-metal semi-monocoque structure.

TAIL UNIT: Cantilever all-metal structure, with 40° sweepback on fin at quarter-chord. Small ventral fin. Trim tabs in rudder and starboard elevator. Electrically-operated elevator trim optional. Pneumatic de-icing system optional.

LANDING GEAR: Retractable tricycle type. Electro-mechanical retraction. Cessna oleo shock-absorber struts. Nosewheel steerable to 15° and castoring from 15° to 55° each side. Main wheels size 6·50-10, tyre pressure 4·14 bars (60 lb/sq in). Nosewheel size 6·00-6, tyre pressure 2·76 bars (40 lb/sq in). Goodyear single-disc hydraulic brakes. Hydraulic parking brake.

POWER PLANT: Two flat-six engines, as described under individual model listings, driving three-blade propellers. Automatic propeller unfeathering system and propeller de-icing optional; automatic propeller synchrophaser standard for T310 and T310 II, optional for 310 and 310 II. Standard fuel in two permanently attached canted wingtip tanks, each holding 193 litres (51 US gallons), of which 189 litres (50 US gallons) are usable. Cross-feed fuel system. Optional fuel in two 77·5 litre (20·5 US gallon) rubber fuel cells installed between the wing spars outboard of each engine nacelle, two 43·5 litre (11·5 US gallon) rubber fuel cells further outboard in each wing, and two 77·5 litre (20·5 US gallon) wing locker fuel tanks, providing a maximum fuel capacity of 783 litres (207 US gallons), of which 768 litres (203 US gallons) are usable. Oil capacity 24·6 litres (6·5 US gallons).

ACCOMMODATION: Cabin normally seats five, two in front and three on cross-bench behind. Four alternative seating arrangements are available, with up to six individual seats in pairs, all of which can tilt and have fore and aft adjustment, individual air vents, reading lights and magazine pockets. Dual controls optional. Inertia seatbelts for two front seats (optional for rear seats). Pilot's storm window, port side. Cabin windows are double-glazed to reduce noise level. Large door on starboard side giving access to all seats. Cargo door, 1·02 m (3 ft 4 in) wide, for loading of bulky items, standard on 310 II and T310 II, optional on 310 and T310. Baggage compartment at rear of cabin, capacity 163 kg (360 lb), with internal and external access; locker for a further 54·5 kg (120 lb) of baggage in the rear of each engine nacelle; and baggage compartment in extended nose with capacity of 158 kg (350 lb). Total baggage capacity 430 kg (950 lb). Optional cabin accessories include writing desk, window curtains, vertical adjustment of pilot and co-pilot seats, all-leather seats, oxygen system and photographic survey provisions. Windscreen defrosting standard; windscreen alcohol de-icing system, and electrically-heated windscreen panel optional.

SYSTEMS: Electrical system powered by two 50A 28V engine-driven alternators and 24V 25Ah battery. 100A alternators optional. Oxygen system of 2·17 m³ (76·6 cu ft) or 1·37 m³ (48·3 cu ft) capacity optional; an automatic altitude compensating regulator is standard with this installation. Janitrol 45,000 BTU thermostatically-controlled blower-type heater for cabin heating and windscreen defrosting. Cabin air-conditioning system rated at 12,000 BTU optional. Vacuum system supplied by two engine-driven pumps with adequate capacity to cater for the pneumatic de-icing boots and flight instruments. Hydraulic system for brakes only.

AVIONICS AND EQUIPMENT: Optional avionics include Series 300 nav/com transceiver with 720-channel com and 200-channel nav with remote VOR/LOC or VOR/ILS indicator, ADF with digital tuning, 10-channel HF and flight director system; Series 400 nav/com transceiver with 720-channel com and 200-channel nav with remote VOR/LOC or VOR/ILS indicator, 40-channel glideslope, ADF with digital tuning and BFO, transponder with 4096 code capability, encoding altimeter, Nav-O-Matic 400B two-axis autopilot and integrated flight control system with optional RMI or HSI; or Series 1000 com transceiver, nav receiver, ADF, and glideslope receiver, with Series 800 DME and RNAV system. Additional avionics options include Bendix RDR-160 colour weather radar, KNC 610 area nav, AVQ-75 DME, KN 65 DME, radar altimeter, locator beacon, yaw damper, boom microphone and headset. Standard equipment includes blind-flying instrumentation, quartz crystal clock, sensitive altimeter, control locks, pilot and co-pilot safety belts, sun visors, alternator failure warning, heated pitot, heated stall warning transmitter, heater overheat warning, landing gear warning device, armrests, cabin radio speaker, baggage straps, adjustable air vents, emergency exit window, aft omni-vision window, tinted dual-pane windows, hat shelf, super soundproofing, map light, instrument post lights, variable-intensity emergency floodlight, reading lights, navigation light detectors, landing light, navigation lights, full-flow oil coolers, heated fuel vents, nosewheel fender, overall paint scheme, quick-drain fuel valves, retractable cabin step, and towbar. Optional equipment for Model 310/Turbo T310, but standard for 310 II/Turbo T310 II, as detailed in model listings. Optional equipment for all versions includes angle of attack indicator, co-pilot's blind-flying instrumentation, digital clock, instantaneous rate of climb indicator, flight hour recorder, synchronous tachometer, true airspeed indicator, turn co-ordinator, heated static sources, vertically adjustable seats with inertia-reel shoulder harness for pilot and co-pilot, pilot's relief tube, rudder pedal locks, cabin curtain, rear window curtains, cabin fire extinguisher, 'total flood' cabin fire extinguisher, eight-track stereo with cabin speakers and stereo headsets, internal corro-

Cessna Model 310 II twin-engined five/six-seat cabin monoplane

sion proofing, electro-luminescent instrument panel lighting, baggage compartment courtesy lights, courtesy light timer, ice detection light, anti-collision light, second landing light, taxi light, three-light strobe system, carpet for nose baggage area, fuselage ice protection plates, photographic provisions, anti-icing kit, engine fire detection and extinguishing system, and radome nose. Additional optional items for the Model 310 and 310 II include automatic propeller synchrophaser and partial oxygen system plumbing.

DIMENSIONS, EXTERNAL:

Wing span	11·25 m (36 ft 11 in)
Wing chord at root	1·71 m (5 ft 7½ in)
Wing chord at tip	1·16 m (3 ft 9½ in)
Wing aspect ratio	7·3
Length overall	9·74 m (31 ft 11½ in)
Height overall	3·25 m (10 ft 8 in)
Tailplane span	5·18 m (17 ft 0 in)
Wheel track	3·59 m (11 ft 9½ in)
Wheelbase	2·80 m (9 ft 2¼ in)
Propeller diameter: 310, 310 II	1·94 m (6 ft 4½ in)
T310, T310 II	1·98 m (6 ft 6 in)

DIMENSIONS, INTERNAL:

Baggage compartment (cabin)	1·26 m³ (44·6 cu ft)
Baggage compartments (nacelles, total)	0·52 m³ (18·5 cu ft)
Baggage compartment (nose)	0·59 m³ (21 cu ft)

AREAS:

Wings, gross	16·63 m² (179 sq ft)
Ailerons (total)	1·32 m² (14·17 sq ft)
Trailing-edge flaps (total)	2·14 m² (23·06 sq ft)
Fin, incl ventral fin	1·74 m² (18·70 sq ft)
Rudder	1·09 m² (11·76 sq ft)
Tailplane	2·99 m² (32·15 sq ft)
Elevators	2·05 m² (22·10 sq ft)

WEIGHTS AND LOADINGS:

Weight empty: 310	1,520 kg (3,352 lb)
310 II	1,631 kg (3,597 lb)
T310	1,575 kg (3,473 lb)
T310 II	1,686 kg (3,717 lb)
Max ramp weight: All versions	2,511 kg (5,535 lb)
Max T-O weight: All versions	2,495 kg (5,500 lb)
Max landing weight: All versions	2,449 kg (5,400 lb)
Max zero-fuel weight:	
310, 310 II	2,223 kg (4,900 lb)
T310, T310 II	2,275 kg (5,015 lb)
Max wing loading:	
All versions	150 kg/m² (30·73 lb/sq ft)
Max power loading:	
All versions	5·87 kg/kW (9·65 lb/hp)

PERFORMANCE (at max T-O weight, except speeds at midcruise weight):

Never-exceed speed:	
All versions 227 knots (420 km/h; 261 mph) CAS	
Max level speed:	
310 at S/L	207 knots (383 km/h; 238 mph)
T310 at 4,875 m (16,000 ft)	237 knots (439 km/h; 273 mph)
Max cruising speed:	
310, 75% power at 2,285 m (7,500 ft)	195 knots (361 km/h; 225 mph)
T310, 73·6% power at 3,050 m (10,000 ft)	201 knots (372 km/h; 231 mph)
T310, 73·6% power at 6,100 m (20,000 ft)	223 knots (413 km/h; 257 mph)
Econ cruising speed with max fuel:	
310 at 3,050 m (10,000 ft)	144 knots (267 km/h; 166 mph)
T310 at 6,100 m (20,000 ft)	175 knots (325 km/h; 202 mph)
Min control speed (VMC):	
All versions	81 knots (150 km/h; 93 mph)
Stalling speed, flaps and landing gear up, power off:	
All versions 78 knots (145 km/h; 90 mph) CAS	
Stalling speed, flaps and landing gear down, power off:	
All versions 70 knots (130 km/h; 81 mph) CAS	
Max rate of climb at S/L:	
310	507 m (1,662 ft)/min
T310	518 m (1,700 ft)/min

Rate of climb at S/L, one engine out:

310	113 m (370 ft)/min
T310	119 m (390 ft)/min
Service ceiling: 310	6,020 m (19,750 ft)
T310	8,350 m (27,400 ft)
Service ceiling, one engine out:	
310	2,255 m (7,400 ft)
T310	5,245 m (17,200 ft)
T-O run: 310	407 m (1,335 ft)
T310	398 m (1,306 ft)
T-O to 15 m (50 ft): 310	518 m (1,700 ft)
T310	507 m (1,662 ft)
Landing from 15 m (50 ft):	
All versions, at 2,449 kg (5,400 lb)	546 m (1,790 ft)
Landing run:	
All versions, at 2,449 kg (5,400 lb) 195 m (640 ft)	

Range, recommended lean mixture, allowances for start, taxi, T-O, climb and 45 min reserves at selected cruise power:

310, 310 II, max cruising speed at 2,285 m (7,500 ft) with 272 kg (600 lb) usable fuel
440 nm (816 km; 507 miles)

310, 310 II, as above with 552 kg (1,218 lb) usable fuel
1,078 nm (1,997 km; 1,241 miles)

310, 310 II, econ cruising speed at 3,050 m (10,000 ft) with 272 kg (600 lb) usable fuel
631 nm (1,170 km; 727 miles)

310, 310 II, as immediately above with 552 kg (1,218 lb) usable fuel
1,534 nm (2,842 km; 1,766 miles)

T310, T310 II, max cruising speed at 6,100 m (20,000 ft) with 272 kg (600 lb) usable fuel
469 nm (869 km; 540 miles)

T310, T310 II, as immediately above with 552 kg (1,218 lb) usable fuel
1,197 nm (2,218 km; 1,378 miles)

T310, T310 II, econ cruising speed at 6,100 m (20,000 ft) with 272 kg (600 lb) usable fuel
586 nm (1,086 km; 675 miles)

T310, T310 II, as immediately above with 552 kg (1,218 lb) usable fuel
1,451 nm (2,689 km; 1,671 miles)

CESSNA MODEL 335

Cessna introduced for 1980 this new six-seat twin-engined aircraft, which is essentially a lighter-weight unpressurised version of the Model 340A. Development of the Model 335 began in September 1977; construction of the prototype started during July 1978, and it was first flown on 5 December 1978. The first flight of a production aircraft was made on 13 August 1979, and 11 had been delivered to customers by 1 January 1980.

Two versions are available:

Model 335. Basic version, to which the detailed description applies.

Model 335 II. Generally similar to the above, but fitted as standard with a factory-installed package of avionics and equipment which includes the following items: dual Cessna Series 300 nav/coms, one with VOR/ILS indicator, other with VOR/LOC indicator; Series 300 ADF; Series 400 glideslope, marker beacon, and transponder; 400B Nav-O-Matic autopilot; marker beacon audio muting switch; audio system; avionics cooling kit; basic avionics kit and all associated antennae; economy mixture indicator; outside air temperature gauge; dual controls; emergency locator transmitter; starboard landing, taxi, and strobe lights; auxiliary fuel system, with additional capacity of 238·5 litres (63 US gallons); external power socket; nosewheel fender; and static wicks.

TYPE: Six-seat twin-engined business aircraft.

WINGS: As for Model 340A.

FUSELAGE: All-metal fail-safe semi-monocoque structure.

TAIL UNIT, LANDING GEAR: As for Model 340A.

POWER PLANT: Two 224 kW (300 hp) Continental TSIO-520-EB flat-six turbocharged fuel-injection engines, each driving a three-blade constant-speed fully-feathering metal propeller. Fuel system, max usable capacity 768 litres (203 US gallons), as described for Model 310. Oil capacity 24·6 litres (6·5 US gallons).

ACCOMMODATION: As for Model 340A, except cabin not pressurised.

SYSTEMS: Generally as for Model 340A, except pressurisation system deleted. Air-conditioning optional. Optional oxygen system of 2·17 m³ (76·6 cu ft) capacity.

AVIONICS AND EQUIPMENT: Avionics and equipment as described for the Model 335 II are available optionally for the Model 335. A further range of optional avionics is available for both versions; standard and optional equipment is generally as detailed for the Model 340A.

DIMENSIONS, EXTERNAL:

Wing span over tip-tanks	11·61 m (38 ft 1¼ in)
Wing chord at root	1·71 m (5 ft 7½ in)
Wing chord at tip	1·16 m (3 ft 9½ in)
Wing aspect ratio	7·20
Length overall	10·46 m (34 ft 4 in)
Height overall	3·83 m (12 ft 6¾ in)
Tailplane span	5·18 m (17 ft 0 in)
Wheel track	3·93 m (12 ft 10¾ in)
Wheelbase	3·11 m (10 ft 2½ in)
Propeller diameter	1·94 m (6 ft 4½ in)
Passenger door: Height	1·25 m (4 ft 1¼ in)
Width	0·53 m (1 ft 9 in)

DIMENSIONS, INTERNAL: As for Model 340A.

AREAS:

Wings, gross	17·16 m² (184·7 sq ft)
Ailerons (total)	1·06 m² (11·44 sq ft)
Trailing-edge flaps (total)	2·14 m² (23·06 sq ft)
Fin	1·51 m² (16·20 sq ft)
Rudder, incl tab	1·09 m² (11·70 sq ft)
Tailplane	5·04 m² (54·24 sq ft)
Elevators (incl tab)	1·97 m² (21·25 sq ft)

WEIGHTS AND LOADINGS (A: Model 335; B: Model 335 II):

Weight empty: A	1,700 kg (3,749 lb)
B	1,797 kg (3,963 lb)
Max fuel weight: A, B	552 kg (1,218 lb)
Max T-O and landing weight: A, B	2,717 kg (5,990 lb)
Max ramp weight: A, B	2,733 kg (6,025 lb)
Max zero-fuel weight: A, B	2,553 kg (5,630 lb)
Max wing loading: A, B	158·9 kg/m² (32·55 lb/sq ft)
Max power loading: A, B	6·08 kg/kW (9·98 lb/hp)

PERFORMANCE (at max T-O weight, except speeds at midcruise weight):

Never-exceed speed
234 knots (433 km/h; 269 mph) CAS
Max level speed at 4,875 m (16,000 ft)
230 knots (427 km/h; 265 mph)
Max cruising speed, 73·7% power at 6,100 m (20,000 ft):
211 knots (391 km/h; 243 mph)
Econ cruising speed at 3,050 m (10,000 ft)
146 knots (270 km/h; 168 mph)
Econ cruising speed at 6,100 m (20,000 ft)
169 knots (314 km/h; 195 mph)
Stalling speed, flaps up, power off
79 knots (147 km/h; 91 mph) CAS
Stalling speed, flaps down, power off
71 knots (132 km/h; 82 mph) CAS
Max rate of climb at S/L 426 m (1,400 ft)/min
Rate of climb at S/L, one engine out
61 m (200 ft)/min
Service ceiling 8,170 m (26,800 ft)
Service ceiling, one engine out 3,505 m (11,500 ft)
T-O run 564 m (1,850 ft)
T-O to 15 m (50 ft) 721 m (2,365 ft)
Landing from 15 m (50 ft) 564 m (1,850 ft)
Landing run 235 m (770 ft)
Range, recommended lean mixture, with allowances for start, taxi, T-O, climb, descent and 45 min reserves at selected cruise power:
73·7% power at 3,050 m (10,000 ft) with 272 kg (600 lb) usable fuel 372 nm (689 km; 428 miles)
73·7% power at 3,050 m (10,000 ft) with 552 kg (1,218 lb) usable fuel
945 nm (1,751 km; 1,088 miles)
73·7% power at 6,100 m (20,000 ft) with 272 kg (600 lb) usable fuel 383 nm (710 km; 441 miles)
73·7% power at 6,100 m (20,000 ft) with 552 kg (1,218 lb) usable fuel
1,015 nm (1,881 km; 1,169 miles)
Econ cruising power at 3,050 m (10,000 ft) with 272 kg (600 lb) usable fuel 483 nm (895 km; 556 miles)
Econ cruising power at 3,050 m (10,000 ft) with 552 kg (1,218 lb) usable fuel
1,185 nm (2,196 km; 1,365 miles)
Econ cruising power at 6,100 m (20,000 ft) with 272 kg (600 lb) usable fuel 463 nm (858 km; 533 miles)
Econ cruising power at 6,100 m (20,000 ft) with 552 kg (1,218 lb) usable fuel
1,192 nm (2,208 km; 1,372 miles)

CESSNA MODEL 337 SKYMASTER and SKYMASTER II
USAF designation: O-2

This unorthodox all-metal 4/6-seat business aircraft resulted from several years of study by Cessna aimed at producing a twin-engined aeroplane that would be simple to fly, low in cost, safe and comfortable, while offering all the traditional advantages of two engines. Construction of a full-scale mockup was started in February 1960 and completed two months later. The prototype flew for the first time on 28 February 1961, followed by the first production model in August 1962. FAA Type Approval was

Cessna's new six-seat Model 335, an unpressurised version of the Model 340A

received on 22 May 1962 and deliveries of the original Model 336 Skymaster, with non-retractable landing gear, began in May 1963.

A total of 195 Model 336 Skymasters had been built by January 1965. In the following month, this version was superseded by the Model 337 Skymaster, with increased wing incidence, retractable landing gear, and other changes, making it virtually a new aeroplane. A total of 2,016 Model 336/337 Skymasters had been built by 1 January 1980, plus an additional 66 Reims Skymasters by Reims Aviation in France, and a total of 340 Pressurised Skymasters produced by Cessna and Reims.

In addition, 544 examples of two military versions (O-2A and O-2B) were delivered to the US Air Force and Imperial Iranian Air Force, as detailed in the 1977-78 and earlier editions of *Jane's*. Similar aircraft are now available from Summit Aviation (which see), by conversion of standard Skymasters.

Six commercial versions of the Model 337 Skymaster were available for 1980:

Skymaster. Basic version, powered by two 156·5 kW (210 hp) Continental IO-360-GB flat-six engines, each driving a McCauley two-blade constant-speed and fully-feathering metal propeller. Detailed description applies to this version.

Skymaster II. Generally similar to the Skymaster, but including the following equipment as standard: dual Series 300 nav/coms, Series 300 ADF, Series 400 transponder, glideslope, marker beacon, and 400A Nav-O-Matic autopilot (Series 400 IFCS offered as alternative exchange). Optional equipment includes attitude and directional gyros, true airspeed indicator, dual controls, all-purpose control wheel, electric elevator trim, emergency locator transmitter, heated stall warning transmitter, 560 litre (148 US gallon) total fuel capacity, external power socket, and static wicks.

Turbo-Skymaster. Generally similar to Skymaster, but powered by two 156·5 kW (210 hp) Continental TSIO-360-HB flat-six turbocharged engines, each driving a two-blade constant-speed and fully-feathering metal propeller.

Turbo-Skymaster II. Identical to Turbo-Skymaster, but with additional standard avionics and equipment as detailed for Skymaster II, plus full-flow oil filters, and turbocharger access door.

Pressurised Skymaster/Pressurised Skymaster II. Described separately.

The 1980 versions of the Skymaster/Turbo-Skymaster introduced as standard improvements a new flap position indicator, and a restyled instrument panel. New options include an AM/FM cassette stereo system, and a new audio/marker beacon control panel.

It was announced in 1980 that production of the Model 337 series by Cessna had been terminated, but that manufacture of specialised developments of the type would be continued in France by Reims Aviation (which see).

TYPE: Tandem-engined 4/6-seat cabin monoplane.

WINGS: Braced high-wing monoplane, with single streamlined bracing strut each side. Wing section NACA 2412 at root, NACA 2409 at tip. Dihedral 3°. Incidence 4° 30′ at root, 2° 30′ at tip. Conventional all-metal two-spar structure. Conical-camber glassfibre wingtips. All-metal Frise ailerons. Electrically-operated all-metal single-slotted flaps. Ground-adjustable tab in port aileron. Pneumatic de-icing system optional.

FUSELAGE: Conventional all-metal semi-monocoque structure.

TAIL UNIT: Cantilever all-metal structure with twin swept-back fins and horn-balanced rudders, carried on two slim metal booms. Trim tab in starboard side of elevator, with optional electrical actuation. Optional pneumatic de-icing system.

LANDING GEAR: Hydraulically-retractable tricycle type. Cantilever spring steel main legs. Steerable nosewheel with oleo-pneumatic shock-absorber. Main wheels and tyres size 6·00-6. Nosewheel and tyre size 15 × 6·00-6. Main-wheel tyre pressure 3·80 bars (55 lb/sq in). Hydraulic disc brakes. Parking brake. Oversize wheels and heavy-duty brakes optional.

POWER PLANT: Two Continental flat-six engines, as detailed in model listings. Electrically-operated cowl flaps. Propeller de-icing optional for forward propeller. Fuel in two main tanks in each wing, with total usable capacity of 333 litres (88 US gallons); two additional tanks in wings, with total usable capacity of 227 litres (60 US gallons), provide optional long-range system. Total usable capacity with optional tanks 560 litres (148 US gallons). Refuelling points above wings. Oil capacity (Skymaster/Skymaster II) 15 litres (4 US gallons); (Turbo-Skymaster/Turbo-Skymaster II) 17 litres (4·5 US gallons).

ACCOMMODATION: Standard accommodation for pilot and co-pilot on individual seats, with individual track-mounted seats for two passengers. Dual controls optional. Alternative arrangements include individual seats for fifth and sixth passengers. Optional cabin equipment includes fully-articulating individual seats for passengers and matching headrests. Optional centre seats can be moved fore and aft to ease access to other seats. Space for 165 kg (365 lb) of baggage in four-seat version, with external loading door. Emergency exit window on port side optional. Airstair door on starboard side. Cabin is heated, ventilated and soundproofed. Windscreen defroster standard, anti-icing panel optional. Adjustable air vents and reading lights available to each passenger.

SYSTEMS: Electrical system supplied by two 38A 28V engine-driven alternators. 24V battery. Hydraulic system for landing gear operation and brakes. Oxygen system optional.

AVIONICS AND EQUIPMENT: Optional avionics include Cessna Series 300 nav/com with 720-channel com and 200-channel nav with remote VOR/LOC or VOR/ILS indicator, ADF with digital tuning, marker beacon with three lights, aural signal, and audio muting capability, DME, Series 400 nav/com with 720-channel com and 200-channel nav with VOR/LOC or VOR/ILS indicator, 40-channel glideslope receiver, ADF with digital tuning and BFO, transponder with 4096 code capability, Nav-O-Matic 400A two-axis autopilot and integrated flight control system, non-slaved or slaved HSI, aural/visual altitude alert system with coupling to IFCS when installed, and Bendix RDR 160 weather radar, or RCA Weather Scout II radar. Standard equipment includes electric clock, engine synchronisation indicator, outside air temperature gauge, rate of climb indicator, sensitive altimeter, turn co-ordinator, control locks, storm windows, tinted windscreen and windows, sun visors, stall warning device, baggage net, map light, dome light, reading lights, navigation light detectors, omni-flash beacon, taxi light, quick-drain fuel valves, tiedown rings, towbar, and external polyurethane paint. Standard equipment for Skymaster II/Turbo-Skymaster II, optional for Skymaster and Turbo-Skymaster, includes attitude and directional gyros, true airspeed indicator, dual controls, all-purpose control wheel, electric elevator trim, emergency locator transmitter, heated stall warning transmitter, external power socket, and static wicks. Other optional equipment for all versions includes economy mixture indicator, flight-hour recorder, boom microphone switch, pitch trim switch, autopilot/electric trim disengage switch, heated pitot, cabin fire extinguisher, cargo tie-downs, safety belts for 3rd, 4th, 5th and 6th seats, internal corrosion proofing, wall-mounted table, instrument post lights, ice detection light, white strobe lights, engine winterisation kit, propeller synchrophaser, flush glideslope antenna and telescoping towbar. Full-flow oil filters are standard on Turbo-Skymaster II, but optional for other versions.

DIMENSIONS, EXTERNAL:

Wing span	11·63 m (38 ft 2 in)
Wing chord at root	1·83 m (6 ft 0 in)
Wing chord at tip	1·22 m (4 ft 0 in)
Wing aspect ratio	7·18
Length overall: Skymaster	9·07 m (29 ft 9 in)
Turbo-Skymaster	9·09 m (29 ft 10 in)
Height overall	2·79 m (9 ft 2 in)
Tailplane span	3·06 m (10 ft 0½ in)

Wheel track	2·49 m (8 ft 2 in)
Wheelbase	2·39 m (7 ft 10 in)
Propeller diameter: Front	1·98 m (6 ft 6 in)
Rear	1·93 m (6 ft 4 in)
Passenger door: Height	1·17 m (3 ft 10 in)
Width	0·91 m (3 ft 0 in)

DIMENSIONS, INTERNAL:

Cabin: Length	3·02 m (9 ft 11 in)
Max width	1·12 m (3 ft 8¼ in)
Max height	1·30 m (4 ft 3¼ in)
Volume	3·62 m³ (128 cu ft)
Baggage space	0·50 m³ (17 cu ft)

AREAS:

Wings, gross	18·81 m² (202·5 sq ft)
Ailerons (total)	1·43 m² (15·44 sq ft)
Trailing-edge flaps (total)	3·43 m² (36·88 sq ft)
Fins (total)	2·85 m² (30·68 sq ft)
Rudders (total)	0·99 m² (10·70 sq ft)
Tailplane	3·05 m² (32·82 sq ft)

WEIGHTS AND LOADINGS (A: Skymaster; B: Skymaster II; C: Turbo-Skymaster; D: Turbo-Skymaster II):

Weight empty: A	1,264 kg (2,787 lb)
B	1,327 kg (2,925 lb)
C	1,315 kg (2,899 lb)
D	1,378 kg (3,038 lb)
Max T-O weight: All versions	2,100 kg (4,630 lb)
Max ramp weight: A, B	2,108 kg (4,648 lb)
C, D	2,110 kg (4,652 lb)
Max landing weight: All versions	1,996 kg (4,400 lb)
Max wing loading: All versions	112 kg/m² (22·9 lb/sq ft)
Max power loading: All versions	6·71 kg/kW (11·0 lb/hp)

PERFORMANCE (at max T-O weight):

Max level speed:
- A, B at S/L 172 knots (319 km/h; 198 mph)
- C, D at 6,100 m (20,000 ft) 207 knots (383 km/h; 238 mph)

Max cruising speed:
- A, B, 75% power at 1,675 m (5,500 ft) 169 knots (314 km/h; 195 mph)
- C, D, 80% power at 6,100 m (20,000 ft) 200 knots (370 km/h; 230 mph)
- C, D, 80% power at 3,050 m (10,000 ft) 182 knots (338 km/h; 210 mph)

Stalling speed, flaps up, power off:
- All versions 70 knots (130 km/h; 81 mph) CAS

Stalling speed, flaps down, power off:
- All versions 61 knots (113 km/h; 70 mph) CAS

Max rate of climb at S/L: A, B 287 m (940 ft)/min
- C, D 354 m (1,160 ft)/min

Rate of climb at S/L, front engine only:
- A, B 91 m (300 ft)/min

Rate of climb at S/L, rear engine only:
- A, B 98 m (320 ft)/min

Single-engine rate of climb at S/L:
- C, D 102 m (335 ft)/min

Service ceiling: A, B 4,970 m (16,300 ft)
- A, B, front engine only 2,105 m (6,900 ft)
- A, B, rear engine only 2,165 m (7,100 ft)
- C, D, single-engine 5,030 m (16,500 ft)

Max certificated operating altitude:
- C, D, single- or twin-engine 6,100 m (20,000 ft)
- T-O run: All versions 305 m (1,000 ft)
- T-O to 15 m (50 ft): All versions 511 m (1,675 ft)
- Landing from 15 m (50 ft): All versions 503 m (1,650 ft)
- Landing run: All versions 213 m (700 ft)

Range, recommended lean mixture, allowances for start, taxi, T-O, climb, descent, and 45 min reserves at selected cruise power: A, B:
- 75% power at 1,675 m (5,500 ft) with 239 kg (528 lb) usable fuel 495 nm (917 km; 570 miles)
- 75% power at 1,675 m (5,500 ft) with 403 kg (888 lb) usable fuel 940 nm (1,741 km; 1,082 miles)
- Econ cruising power at 3,050 m (10,000 ft) with 239 kg (528 lb) usable fuel 675 nm (1,250 km; 777 miles)
- Econ cruising power at 3,050 m (10,000 ft) with 403 kg (888 lb) usable fuel 1,235 nm (2,288 km; 1,422 miles)

C, D:
- 80% power at 6,100 m (20,000 ft) with 239 kg (528 lb) usable fuel 465 nm (861 km; 535 miles)
- 80% power at 3,050 m (10,000 ft) with 239 kg (528 lb) usable fuel 440 nm (816 km; 507 miles)
- 80% power at 6,100 m (20,000 ft) with 403 kg (888 lb) usable fuel 925 nm (1,714 km; 1,065 miles)
- 80% power at 3,050 m (10,000 ft) with 403 kg (888 lb) usable fuel 855 nm (1,584 km; 984 miles)
- Econ cruising power at 6,100 m (20,000 ft) with 239 kg (528 lb) usable fuel 590 nm (1,093 km; 679 miles)
- Econ cruising power at 3,050 m (10,000 ft) with 239 kg (528 lb) usable fuel 580 nm (1,075 km; 668 miles)
- Econ cruising power at 6,100 m (20,000 ft) with 403 kg (888 lb) usable fuel 1,125 nm (2,084 km; 1,295 miles)
- Econ cruising power at 3,050 m (10,000 ft) with 403 kg (888 lb) usable fuel 1,080 nm (2,002 km; 1,244 miles)

CESSNA MODEL P337 PRESSURISED SKYMASTER and PRESSURISED SKYMASTER II

On 8 December 1971 Cessna introduced a pressurised version of the Skymaster. Design and construction of the prototype began in January 1971, and the first prototype made its initial flight on 23 July 1971. Construction of pre-production and production aircraft began simultaneously in May 1971, and FAA certification was granted on 2 February 1972. Deliveries began in May 1972.

The pressurised version is distinguished easily from the standard Skymaster in having four, instead of three, windows on each side of the cabin. Pressurisation is provided from the turbocharged engines, either of which can maintain full pressurisation and air-conditioning. With a maximum differential of 0·23 bars (3·35 lb/sq in), a cabin altitude of 3,050 m (10,000 ft) can be maintained to 6,100 m (20,000 ft). Pilot setting of departure and landing field altitudes on the pressurisation controls is all that is necessary for the system to begin automatic operation.

Two versions of the Model P337 were available for 1980:

Pressurised Skymaster. Basic version, to which the detailed description applies.

Pressurised Skymaster II. Pressurised version of Skymaster II, to which it is identical except for pressurisation installation; a Series 400A Nav-O-Matic autopilot is standard, with Series 400 IFCS offered in exchange.

The 1980 versions of the P337 introduced also the improvements detailed for the Model 337. A total of 313 Model P337 Skymasters had been built by 1 January 1980, plus an additional 27 Reims Pressurised Skymasters built by Reims Aviation in France. Production by Cessna has been terminated.

TYPE: Tandem-engine, pressurised 4/5-seat cabin monoplane.

WINGS: As Model 337 Skymaster.

FUSELAGE: Conventional all-metal semi-monocoque structure, with fail-safe structure in the pressurised section extending between the two engine bulkheads, but excluding aft lower area below cabin floor.

TAIL UNIT: As Model 337 Skymaster.

LANDING GEAR: Hydraulically-retractable tricycle type, main units retracting aft, nosewheel forward. Cantilever spring steel main units. Steerable nosewheel with oleo-pneumatic shock-absorber. Main-wheel tyres size 6·00-6, pressure 3·79 bars (55 lb/sq in). Nosewheel tyre size 15·00 × 6·00-6, pressure 2·90 bars (42 lb/sq in). Cleveland hydraulic disc brakes. Parking brake. Heavy-duty wheels, brakes and tyres optional.

POWER PLANT: Two 168 kW (225 hp) Continental TSIO-360-CB turbocharged flat-six engines, each driving a McCauley two-blade constant-speed fully-feathering metal propeller. Propeller anti-icing optional for forward propeller. Four interconnected fuel tanks in each wing with a combined usable capacity of 280 litres (74 US gallons). Total usable fuel capacity 560 litres (148 US gallons). Refuelling points in wing upper surfaces. Oil capacity 17 litres (4·5 US gallons).

ACCOMMODATION: Standard accommodation for pilot and co-pilot on individual seats, with rear bench seat for two passengers. A third passenger seat at rear of cabin is optional. Space for 165 kg (365 lb) of baggage in four-seat version. Bench seat slides forward and aft to provide easy access to baggage area. Two-section door on starboard side, lower half opening downward and incorporating airstairs. Upper half opens upward. Cabin is heated and ventilated. Double-pane windows. Individual adjustable air ventilators and reading lights for passengers. Windscreen defrosting standard. Windscreen anti-icing optional.

SYSTEMS: Electrical system powered by two 28V 38A engine-driven self-rectifying alternators. 24V battery. Electrically-driven hydraulic pump for landing gear retraction. Vacuum system optional for blind-flying instrumentation. Oxygen system optional. Cabin pressurised by engine bleed air, max differential 0·23 bars (3·35 lb/sq in). Cabin heated by 25,000 BTU gasoline heater and/or hot air from the compression section of the pressurisation system.

AVIONICS AND EQUIPMENT: Optional avionics are as detailed for the Model 337 Skymaster. Standard equipment is the same as for the Skymaster, plus a manual cabin altitude control, and cabin rate of climb, altitude, and differential pressure gauges, altitude warning light, and propeller synchrophaser. Optional equipment includes a true airspeed indicator, emergency locator transmitter, solid-state oxygen system, engine priming system, and automatic propeller unfeathering system, in addition to the options detailed for the Skymaster.

DIMENSIONS, EXTERNAL:
As for Model 337 except:
Length overall	9·09 m (29 ft 10 in)
Propeller ground clearance: Front	0·23 m (9 in)
Rear	0·51 m (1 ft 8 in)
Passenger door: Height	1·15 m (3 ft 9¼ in)
Width	0·90 m (2 ft 11¼ in)
Height to sill	0·56 m (1 ft 10 in)

DIMENSIONS, INTERNAL:
Cabin: Length	3·02 m (9 ft 11 in)
Max width	1·11 m (3 ft 7¾ in)
Max height	1·29 m (4 ft 2¾ in)
Floor area	2·10 m² (22·6 sq ft)
Volume	3·62 m³ (128 cu ft)
Baggage space	0·50 m³ (17 cu ft)

AREAS: As for Model 337

WEIGHTS AND LOADINGS:
Weight empty:	
Pressurised Skymaster	1,396 kg (3,078 lb)
Pressurised Skymaster II	1,444 kg (3,184 lb)
Max T-O weight	2,131 kg (4,700 lb)
Max ramp weight	2,142 kg (4,724 lb)
Max landing weight	2,025 kg (4,465 lb)
Max wing loading	113·3 kg/m² (23·2 lb/sq ft)
Max power loading	6·34 kg/kW (10·4 lb/hp)

PERFORMANCE (at max T-O weight):
Max level speed at 6,100 m (20,000 ft) 212 knots (393 km/h; 244 mph)
Max cruising speed, 75% power at 6,100 m (20,000 ft) 205 knots (380 km/h; 236 mph)
Max cruising speed, 75% power at 3,050 m (10,000 ft) 186 knots (344 km/h; 214 mph)
Stalling speed, flaps and wheels up, power off 70 knots (130 km/h; 81 mph) CAS
Stalling speed, flaps and wheels down, power off 62 knots (115 km/h; 71 mph) CAS
Max rate of climb at S/L 357 m (1,170 ft)/min
Rate of climb at S/L, one engine out 114 m (375 ft)/min
Max certificated operating altitude 6,100 m (20,000 ft)
Service ceiling, one engine out 5,700 m (18,700 ft)
Min ground turning radius 2·54 m (8 ft 4 in)
T-O run 288 m (945 ft)
T-O to 15 m (50 ft) 457 m (1,500 ft)
Landing from 15 m (50 ft) at max landing weight 511 m (1,675 ft)
Landing run at max landing weight 242 m (795 ft)
Range, recommended lean mixture, with allowances for start, taxi, T-O, climb, descent and 45 min reserves at selected cruise power:
- 75% power at 6,100 m (20,000 ft) with 403 kg (888 lb) usable fuel 935 nm (1,733 km; 1,077 miles)
- 75% power at 3,050 m (10,000 ft) with 403 kg (888 lb) usable fuel 865 nm (1,603 km; 996 miles)
- Econ cruising power at 6,100 m (20,000 ft) with 403 kg (888 lb) usable fuel 1,155 nm (2,140 km; 1,330 miles)
- Econ cruising power at 3,050 m (10,000 ft) with 403 kg (888 lb) usable fuel 1,110 nm (2,056 km; 1,278 miles)

CESSNA MODEL 340A, 340A II and 340A III

Cessna announced on 8 December 1971 the introduction of a pressurised twin-engined business aircraft designated Model 340. Developed from the Model 310, it had a wing and landing gear generally similar to those of the

Model P337 pressurised version of the Cessna Skymaster, with underwing weather radar

Model 414, a pressurised fuselage of fail-safe design, a tail unit similar to that of the Model 310 and 212·5 kW (285 hp) Continental TSIO-520-K engines. The Model 340 II followed, with factory-installed avionics as standard, and in 1978 a Model 340A III was introduced.

Versions of the Model 340 available in 1980 are as follows:

340A. Standard model, as described in detail.

340A II. Identical to Model 340A, but with dual Series 300 nav/coms with 720-channel com and 200-channel nav and VOR/LOC and VOR/ILS indicators, ADF, Series 400 DME, marker beacon, glideslope, transponder and 400B two-axis Nav-O-Matic autopilot, basic avionics kit, avionics cooling kit, audio system, marker beacon audio muting switch, and all necessary antennae for onboard avionics as standard. Other standard equipment includes economy mixture indicator, outside air temperature gauge, dual controls, electric elevator trim, emergency locator transmitter, cabin pressure control system, rear baggage compartment door, starboard landing light, taxi light, strobe lights, 238·5 litre (63 US gallon) auxiliary fuel system, nosewheel fender, static dischargers, and external power socket.

340A III. As Model 340A, plus an avionics package comprising dual Series 400 nav/coms, one with HSI and the other with Automatic Radial Centering (ARC), Series 400 dual glideslope, RNAV, ADF, marker beacon, DME, transponder, 400B IFCS, Series 800 encoding altimeter and altitude alerter, Series 1000 RMI, Bendix RDR-160 weather radar, yaw damper, basic avionics kit, avionics cooling, audio system, all essential antennae, hand fire extinguisher, and 100A alternators added and/or substituted for the equipment installed on the 340A II. Standard equipment is as detailed for the Model 340A II.

All 1980 models has as standard improvements better accessibility to elevator and rudder controls for routine maintenance, redesigned upper cabin door extender, and revised instrument layout. New options include lightweight 100A alternators, improved air-conditioning, and a cabin stereo system.

A total of 1,026 Model 340s had been delivered by 1 January 1980.

TYPE: Six-seat pressurised business aircraft.

WINGS: Cantilever low-wing monoplane, with 'Stabila-tip' fixed wingtip fuel tanks. Wing section NACA 23018 (modified) at aircraft centreline, NACA 23015 (modified) at centre-section/outer wing junction, NACA 23009 (modified) at tip. Dihedral 5° on outer panels. Incidence 2° 30′ at root, −0° 30′ at tip. All-metal two-spar structure. All-metal ailerons of single-spar construction; controllable trim tab in starboard aileron. Electrically-actuated all-metal trailing-edge split flaps, of single-spar construction with lower skin, comprising an inboard and outboard panel on each wing. Optional pneumatic de-icing system.

FUSELAGE: All-metal semi-monocoque structure. The pressurised cabin section, extending from station 100·00 aft to station 252·00, is of fail-safe construction. All openings are reinforced with doublers and frame members, and longitudinal continuity is provided by lightweight extruded T-section stringers.

TAIL UNIT: Cantilever all-metal structure with swept vertical surfaces. Fixed-incidence tailplane of conventional two-spar construction. Elevators of single-spar construction, with controllable trim tab in starboard elevator. Rudder, built up on a formed channel spar and transverse ribs, has a controllable trim tab. Optional pneumatic de-icing system.

LANDING GEAR: Retractable tricycle type, with single wheel on each unit. Electro-mechanical retraction, main units inward into wings and faired by doors when retracted, nose unit rearward into the fuselage nose and faired by two doors when retracted. Mechanically-operated emergency gear extension system. Cessna oleo-pneumatic shock-absorbers. Steerable nosewheel with shimmy damper and self-centering device. Main-wheel tyres size 6·50-10 (8-ply); nosewheel tyre size 6·00-6 (6-ply). Single-disc hydraulic brakes. Parking brake.

POWER PLANT: Two 231 kW (310 hp) Continental TSIO-520-NB flat-six turbocharged fuel-injection engines, each driving a McCauley three-blade constant-speed and fully-feathering metal propeller. Propeller anti-icing system optional. Fuel system, max usable capacity 768 litres (203 US gallons), as described for Model 310. Manifold pressure relief valves to prevent engines from overboosting are standard equipment. Oil capacity 24·6 litres (6·5 US gallons).

ACCOMMODATION: Standard seating for pilot and co-pilot on tilting and individually adjustable seats. Individual seats for four passengers, two forward-facing on the port side, one aft-facing and one forward-facing on starboard side. Door, on port side aft of wing, is two-piece type with built-in airstairs in bottom portion. Plug-type emergency escape hatch on starboard side of cabin, over wing. Foul-weather window for pilot. Baggage accommodated in nose compartment with external access doors, capacity 159 kg (350 lb), two wing lockers, capacity 54·5 kg (120 lb) each, and in rear cabin area, capacity 154 kg (340 lb). Total baggage capacity 422 kg (930 lb). Cabin pressurised, heated and ventilated.

Cessna Model 340A six-seat pressurised business aircraft

Air-conditioning optional. Windscreen defroster standard; windscreen alcohol de-icing system optional.

SYSTEMS: Electrical system powered by two 28V 50A engine-driven alternators and 24V 25Ah battery. 100A alternators optional, standard on 340A III. Vacuum system supplied by two engine-driven pumps. Hydraulic system for brakes only. Cabin pressurised by engine bleed air, max differential 0·29 bars (4·2 lb/sq in). Cabin heated by Stewart Warner 45,000 BTU gasoline heater. Lightweight air-conditioning system optional. Oxygen system, 0·31 m³ (11·0 cu ft) or 2·17 m³ (76·6 cu ft) capacity, optional.

AVIONICS AND EQUIPMENT: Optional avionics for the Model 340A are as detailed for the Model 310. Standard equipment of Model 340A includes attitude and directional gyros, quartz crystal clock, cabin altitude and differential pressure gauge, rate of climb indicator, sensitive altimeter, control locks, pilot and co-pilot safety belts, sun visors, 'Door not locked' warning light, heater overheat warning light, stall warning device, heated pitot, heated stall warning transmitter, cabin speaker, super soundproofing, courtesy lights, instrument post lights, variable intensity floodlights, reading lights, retractable landing light in port wing, navigation lights with flasher unit, two rotating beacons, full-flow oil filters, quick-drain fuel valves, heated fuel vents, propeller synchrophaser, towbar, and all-over paint scheme. Optional items, except as detailed in model listings, include angle of attack indicator, blind-flying instrumentation for co-pilot, digital clock, economy mixture indicator, flight hour recorder, instantaneous rate of climb indicator, true airspeed indicator, inertia-reel shoulder harness for pilot and co-pilot, rudder pedal lock, emergency locator transmitter, heated dual static source, flight deck divider curtain, all-leather seats, headrests, tinted double-pane cabin windows, window curtains, refreshment centre, writing desk, stereo system, internal corrosion proofing, cabin fire extinguisher, 'total flood' cabin fire extinguisher system, baggage compartment courtesy light, courtesy light timer, ice detection light, taxi light, white strobe lights, engine fire detection and extinguishing system, propeller unfeathering system, fuselage ice impact panels, radome nose and dual pitot system.

DIMENSIONS, EXTERNAL:

Wing span	11·62 m (38 ft 1·3 in)
Wing chord at root	1·714 m (5 ft 7·4 in)
Wing chord, mean aerodynamic	1·57 m (5 ft 1·68 in)
Wing chord at tip	1·156 m (3 ft 9·6 in)
Wing aspect ratio	7·2
Length overall	10·46 m (34 ft 4 in)
Height overall	3·84 m (12 ft 7 in)
Tailplane span	5·18 m (17 ft 0 in)
Wheel track	3·93 m (12 ft 10·7 in)
Wheelbase	3·12 m (10 ft 2·7 in)
Propeller diameter	1·94 m (6 ft 4½ in)
Passenger door: Height	1·25 m (4 ft 1¼ in)
Width	0·53 m (1 ft 9 in)
Emergency hatch: Height	0·50 m (1 ft 7½ in)
Width	0·66 m (2 ft 2 in)

DIMENSIONS, INTERNAL:

Cabin: Length, incl baggage compartment	3·86 m (12 ft 8 in)
Max width	1·18 m (3 ft 10½ in)
Max height	1·24 m (4 ft 1 in)
Volume (total)	4·6 m³ (162·4 cu ft)
Baggage space: Cabin	0·52 m³ (18·5 cu ft)
Nose	0·44 m³ (15·5 cu ft)
Engine nacelles (each)	0·13 m³ (4·625 cu ft)

AREAS:

Wings, gross	17·09 m² (184 sq ft)
Ailerons (total)	1·06 m² (11·44 sq ft)
Trailing-edge flaps (total)	2·14 m² (23·06 sq ft)
Fin	1·51 m² (16·20 sq ft)
Ventral fin	0·54 m² (5·80 sq ft)
Rudder, incl tab	1·09 m² (11·76 sq ft)
Tailplane	2·99 m² (32·15 sq ft)
Elevators, incl tab	2·05 m² (22·10 sq ft)

WEIGHTS AND LOADINGS:

Weight empty: 340A	1,774 kg (3,911 lb)
340A II	1,879 kg (4,142 lb)
340A III	1,919 kg (4,232 lb)
Max T-O and landing weight	2,717 kg (5,990 lb)
Max ramp weight	2,733 kg (6,025 lb)
Max zero-fuel weight	2,554 kg (5,630 lb)
Max wing loading	158·9 kg/m² (32·55 lb/sq ft)
Max power loading	5·88 kg/kW (9·66 lb/hp)

PERFORMANCE (at max T-O weight, except speeds are those at mid-cruise weight):

Never-exceed speed
234 knots (433 km/h; 269 mph) CAS
Max level speed at 6,100 m (20,000 ft)
244 knots (452 km/h; 281 mph)
Max cruising speed, 74·8% power:
at 7,470 m (24,500 ft)
229 knots (425 km/h; 264 mph)
at 3,050 m (10,000 ft)
198 knots (367 km/h; 228 mph)
Econ cruising speed:
at 7,620 m (25,000 ft) with 272 kg (600 lb) usable fuel
170 knots (315 km/h; 196 mph)
at 7,620 m (25,000 ft) with 552 kg (1,218 lb) usable fuel
172 knots (319 km/h; 198 mph)
Stalling speed, flaps up, power off
79 knots (146 km/h; 91 mph) CAS
Stalling speed, flaps down, power off
71 knots (132 km/h; 82 mph) CAS
Max rate of climb at S/L 503 m (1,650 ft)/min
Rate of climb at S/L, one engine out
96 m (315 ft)/min
Service ceiling 9,085 m (29,800 ft)
Service ceiling, one engine out 4,815 m (15,800 ft)
T-O run 492 m (1,615 ft)
T-O to 15 m (50 ft) 663 m (2,175 ft)
Landing from 15 m (50 ft) 564 m (1,850 ft)
Landing run 235 m (770 ft)
Range, recommended lean mixture, with allowances for start, taxi, T-O, climb, descent and 45 min reserves at selected cruise power:
74·8% power at 7,470 m (24,500 ft) with 272 kg (600 lb) usable fuel 418 nm (774 km; 481 miles)
74·8% power at 7,470 m (24,500 ft) with 552 kg (1,218 lb) usable fuel
1,106 nm (2,049 km; 1,273 miles)
74·8% power at 3,050 m (10,000 ft) with 272 kg (600 lb) usable fuel 391 nm (724 km; 450 miles)
74·8% power at 3,050 m (10,000 ft) with 552 kg (1,218 lb) usable fuel
986 nm (1,827 km; 1,135 miles)
Econ cruising power at 7,620 m (25,000 ft) with 272 kg (600 lb) usable fuel
530 nm (982 km; 610 miles)
Econ cruising power at 7,620 m (25,000 ft) with 552 kg (1,218 lb) usable fuel
1,377 nm (2,551 km; 1,585 miles)
Econ cruising power at 3,050 m (10,000 ft) with 272 kg (600 lb) usable fuel
579 nm (1,073 km; 667 miles)
Econ cruising power at 3,050 m (10,000 ft) with 552 kg (1,218 lb) usable fuel
1,405 nm (2,603 km; 1,618 miles)

CESSNA MODEL 402C, 402C II and 402C III

The original Model 402 was intended for the third-level airline market, with a convertible cabin and reinforced cabin floor of bonded crushed honeycomb construction, enabling it to be changed quickly from a ten-seat commuter to a light cargo transport. On 8 December 1971 Cessna renamed the original Model 402 as the Model 402 Utililiner and introduced a version designated Model 402 Businessliner. On 29 October 1975 Mk II versions of both aircraft were made available, each including a package of factory-installed equipment and avionics as standard; Model 402 III versions of both aircraft were introduced for 1978.

The 1980 versions of the Model 402C introduce a number of improvements as standard, including a 7·5 litre (2 US gallon) increase in fuel capacity, better fuel system inspection facilities, relocation of the tail navigation light, redesigned upper cabin door extender, relocation of the ADF indicator or RMI, and new interior and exterior styling. New options include simplified nacelle fire extinguisher inspection, lighter-weight 100A alternators, improvements to the optional air-conditioning system, and a stereo system.

Five versions of the Model 402C are available for 1980:
Model 402C Utililiner. Basic version, as described in detail.

Model 402C Businessliner. As basic version, except six/eight seats and optional side-hinged door, next to standard cabin door, to provide a total loading door width of 1·02 m (3 ft 4 in). Other options include folding business desks, stereo equipment, refreshment centre and cabin dividers.

Model 402C II Utililiner. As basic version, plus the following factory-installed equipment and avionics as standard: economy mixture indicator, flight hour recorder, dual controls, electric elevator trim, marker beacon audio muting switch, emergency locator transmitter, cabin fire extinguisher, starboard landing light, taxi light, nosewheel fender, external power socket, static wicks, dual Cessna Series 300 nav/com with 720-channel com, 200-channel nav and VOR/ILS and VOR/LOC indicators, Series 300 ADF, Series 400 marker beacon, glideslope and transponder, Series 400B Nav-O-Matic autopilot, and basic avionics kit comprising antennae, avionics cooling kit and audio system.

Model 402C II Businessliner. As Model 402C Businessliner, plus standard factory-installed equipment and avionics detailed for Model 402C II Utililiner.

Model 402C III Businessliner. As Model 402C II Businessliner, except that standard equipment includes 100A instead of 50A engine-driven alternators, and the avionics package comprises Series 400 nav/com with HSI; second Series 400 nav/com with ARC; dual Series 400 glideslope; Series 400 ADF, DME, marker beacon, RNAV, transponder; Series 800 encoding altimeter and altitude alerter; Series 1000 RMI; Bendix RDR-160 weather radar; Series 400B IFCS; yaw damper; and basic avionics kit, audio system, avionics cooling and antennae.

The same prototype served for Models 401 and 402, and the FAA Type Certificate, awarded on 20 September 1966, also covered both types. A total of 1,220 Model 402s had been built by 1 January 1980. Twelve Model 402s were delivered in 1975 to the Royal Malaysian Air Force, which uses ten of them for multi-engine training and the other two for photographic and liaison missions.

TYPE: Ten-seat (optional nine-seat) convertible passenger/freight transport (Utililiner) or six/eight-seat business aircraft (Businessliner).

WINGS: Cantilever low-wing monoplane. Wing section NACA 23018 (modified) at aircraft centreline, NACA 23015 (modified) at centre-section/outer wing junction, NACA 23009 (modified) at tip. All-metal two-spar structure of light alloy with stamped ribs and surface skins reinforced with spanwise stringers. Outer wing panels of bonded construction. All-metal ailerons and electrically-actuated split flaps. Trim tab in port aileron. Optional pneumatic de-icing system.

FUSELAGE: All-metal semi-monocoque structure.

TAIL UNIT: Cantilever all-metal structure, with 40° sweepback on fin at quarter-chord. Fixed-incidence tailplane. Trim tabs in rudder and starboard elevator. Electrical operation of trim tabs optional. Optional pneumatic de-icing system.

LANDING GEAR: Hydraulically-retractable tricycle type. Main units retract inward into wings, nosewheel unit rearward. No doors over main wheels when retracted. Emergency extension system. Oleo-pneumatic shock-absorbers. Steerable nosewheel. Cleveland heavy-duty wheels. Main-wheel tyres size 6·50-10, nosewheel tyre size 6·00-6. Cleveland heavy-duty hydraulic brakes. Parking brakes.

POWER PLANT: Two 242 kW (325 hp) Continental TSIO-520-VB flat-six turbocharged engines, each driving a three-blade constant-speed fully-feathering metal propeller. Propeller synchrophaser, automatic unfeathering and electrical de-icing optional. Integral wing fuel tanks with total capacity of 808 litres (213 US gallons), of which 780 litres (206 US gallons) are usable. Oil capacity 24·6 litres (6·5 US gallons).

ACCOMMODATION: Two seats side by side in pilot's compartment. Dual controls standard on Model 402C II/III versions, optional for Model 402C versions. The Utililiner cabin has four individual seats in pairs and two double seats. Passenger seats are 'Enviro-form' moulded honeycomb, glassfibre reinforced. Businessliner has four individual seats as standard, two additional seats optional, in the main cabin. Refreshment centre at aft end of cabin. Passenger reading lights standard on Businessliner, optional on Utililiner. Door with built-in airstair on port side of cabin at centre. Storm windows for pilot and co-pilot. Tinted cabin windows. An emergency escape hatch is provided on the starboard side of the cabin. Optional cargo door and crew access door available. Baggage contained in area at rear of cabin, nose compartment, and wing locker at rear of each engine nacelle, with combined capacity of 680 kg (1,500 lb). Rear double seat on Utililiner can have fold-down back to facilitate access to rear baggage shelf. Cabin heated and ventilated. Windscreen defrosting standard. Electrical anti-icing of pilot's window or alcohol anti-icing of pilot's and co-pilot's windows optional.

SYSTEMS: Electrical system powered by two 24V 50A alternators. 24V 25Ah battery. Battery can be sited optionally in nose baggage area. 100A alternators optional, standard on 402C III version. Hydraulic system for brakes only. Vacuum system provided by two engine-driven pumps. Oxygen system of 1·25 m³ (44 cu ft) or 3·25m³ (115 cu ft) capacity optional. Air-conditioning system optional. Heating and ventilation system with 45,000 BTU gasoline heater standard.

AVIONICS AND EQUIPMENT: Optional avionics as detailed for Model 310, plus radio telephone. Standard equipment includes attitude and directional gyros, quartz crystal clock, outside air temperature gauge, sensitive altimeter, pilot and co-pilot safety belts, control locks, sun visors, alternator failure lights, door 'Not locked' light, heater overheat warning light, emergency locator transmitter, stall warning device, armrests, cabin speaker, cabin air ventilators, super soundproofing, courtesy lights, map light, variable-intensity floodlight and instrument post lights, navigation light detectors, navigation lights, retractable landing light, towbar, and all-over paint scheme. Optional equipment, unless part of Model 402C II or III packages, includes co-pilot's blind-flying instrumentation, digital clock, economy mixture indicator, flight hour recorder, instantaneous rate of climb indicator, true airspeed indicator, pilot's and co-pilot's inertia-reel harness, rudder lock, dual heated static source, cabin hand fire extinguisher, 'total flood' cabin fire extinguisher, stereo system, Utililiner or Businessliner interiors (including flight deck divider curtains, window curtains, headrests, reading lights, 'Seat Belt' and 'No Smoking' signs and various arrangements of seats, tables, refreshment units and toilets), internal corrosion proofing, ice detection light, second retractable landing light, taxi light, three-light strobe system, vertical tail floodlight and photographic provisions.

Photograph and three-view drawing *(Pilot Press)* of the Cessna Model 402C, latest version of the Businessliner/Utililiner

DIMENSIONS, EXTERNAL:

Wing span	13·45 m (44 ft 1½ in)
Wing chord at root	1·77 m (5 ft 9¾ in)
Wing chord at tip	1·05 m (3 ft 5½ in)
Length overall	11·09 m (36 ft 4½ in)
Height overall	3·49 m (11 ft 5½ in)
Tailplane span	5·18 m (17 ft 0 in)
Wheel track	5·48 m (17 ft 11½ in)
Wheelbase	3·19 m (10 ft 5½ in)
Propeller diameter	1·94 m (6 ft 4½ in)

Passenger door (standard):

Height	1·27 m (4 ft 2 in)
Width	0·61 m (2 ft 0 in)
Cargo door (optional): Height	1·26 m (4 ft 1½ in)
Width	1·05 m (3 ft 5¼ in)

Nose baggage doors (each):

Height	0·51 m (1 ft 8 in)
Width	0·80 m (2 ft 7½ in)

Nacelle baggage doors (each):

Length	0·61 m (2 ft 0 in)
Width	0·62 m (2 ft 0½ in)

DIMENSIONS, INTERNAL:

Cabin:
Length	4·83 m (15 ft 10 in)
Max width	1·42 m (4 ft 8 in)
Max height	1·30 m (4 ft 3 in)
Volume	6·30 m³ (222·4 cu ft)

AREAS:

Wings, gross	20·98 m² (225·8 sq ft)
Fin	2·46 m² (26·50 sq ft)
Rudder, incl tab	1·84 m² (19·85 sq ft)
Tailplane	4·02 m² (43·32 sq ft)
Elevators, incl tab	1·64 m² (17·63 sq ft)

WEIGHTS AND LOADINGS:

Weight empty:
Businessliner	1,848 kg (4,074 lb)
Utililiner	1,860 kg (4,102 lb)
Businessliner II	1,914 kg (4,220 lb)
Utililiner II	1,924 kg (4,241 lb)
Businessliner III	1,962 kg (4,325 lb)
Max T-O and landing weight	3,107 kg (6,850 lb)
Max ramp weight	3,123 kg (6,885 lb)
Max zero-fuel weight	2,955 kg (6,515 lb)
Max wing loading	148·1 kg/m² (30·3 lb/sq ft)
Max power loading	6·42 kg/kW (10·5 lb/hp)

PERFORMANCE (at max T-O weight, except speeds are those at mid-cruise weight):

Never-exceed speed
231 knots (428 km/h; 266 mph) CAS

Max level speed at 4,875 m (16,000 ft)
231 knots (428 km/h; 266 mph)

Max cruising speed, 72% power:
at 6,100 m (20,000 ft) 213 knots (394 km/h; 245 mph)
at 3,050 m (10,000 ft) 194 knots (359 km/h; 223 mph)

Econ cruising speed:
at 6,100 m (20,000 ft) 166 knots (307 km/h; 191 mph)
at 3,050 m (10,000 ft) 142 knots (264 km/h; 164 mph)

Stalling speed, flaps up, power off
78 knots (145 km/h; 90 mph) CAS

Stalling speed, flaps down, power off
68 knots (126 km/h; 78 mph) CAS

Max rate of climb at S/L   442 m (1,450 ft)/min

Rate of climb at S/L, one engine out
92 m (301 ft)/min

Service ceiling	8,200 m (26,900 ft)
Service ceiling, one engine out	4,510 m (14,800 ft)
T-O run	537 m (1,763 ft)
T-O to 15 m (50 ft)	669 m (2,195 ft)
Landing from 15 m (50 ft)	757 m (2,485 ft)
Landing run	322 m (1,055 ft)

Range, recommended lean mixture, allowances for start, taxi, T-O, climb, descent and 45 min reserves at selected cruise power:

72% power at 6,100 m (20,000 ft) with 272 kg (600 lb) usable fuel   362 nm (671 km; 417 miles)
72% power at 6,100 m (20,000 ft) with 561 kg (1,236 lb) usable fuel   983 nm (1,822 km; 1,132 miles)
72% power at 3,050 m (10,000 ft) with 272 kg (600 lb) usable fuel   349 nm (647 km; 402 miles)
72% power at 3,050 m (10,000 ft) with 561 kg (1,236 lb) usable fuel   915 nm (1,695 km; 1,053 miles)
Econ cruising power at 6,100 m (20,000 ft) with 272 kg (600 lb) usable fuel 459 nm (850 km; 528 miles)
Econ cruising power at 6,100 m (20,000 ft) with 561 kg (1,236 lb) usable fuel
        1,233 nm (2,285 km; 1,420 miles)
Econ cruising power at 3,050 m (10,000 ft) with 272 kg (600 lb) usable fuel 499 nm (924 km; 574 miles)
Econ cruising power at 3,050 m (10,000 ft) with 561 kg (1,236 lb) usable fuel
        1,273 nm (2,359 km; 1,466 miles)

CESSNA MODEL 414A CHANCELLOR

Cessna introduced the pressurised twin-engined Model 414 on 10 December 1969 as a 'step-up' aircraft for owners of Cessna or other light unpressurised twins. It combined the basic fuselage and tail unit of the Model 421 with the wing of the Model 402 and had 231 kW (310 hp) turbocharged Continental engines.

It was replaced in 1978 by the similar but much improved Model 414A Chancellor. Major changes included a new bonded 'wet' wing of increased span, extended nose and baggage area, and introduction of an external access door to the tailcone.

Three versions of the Chancellor are available for 1980, as follows:

Model 414A Chancellor. Standard version, as described in detail.

Model 414A Chancellor II. As Model 414A above, but with the following avionics and equipment as standard: dual Series 400 nav/com, with ARC, VOR/ILS and VOR/LOC; Series 400 ADF, DME, transponder, glideslope, marker beacon; marker beacon audio muting switch; 400B Nav-O-Matic autopilot; basic avionics kit, cooling kit, audio system, and all essential antennae; economy mixture indicator, flight hour recorder, co-pilot's blind-flying instrumentation, emergency locator transmitter, cabin pressure control system, cabin hand fire extinguisher, starboard landing light, taxi light, high-intensity strobe light, external power socket, nosewheel fender and static dischargers.

Model 414A Chancellor III. As standard Model 414A, with standard equipment of 414A II plus cabin air-conditioning system and 100A alternators, and an all-weather avionics package which includes dual Series 1000 com, 1000 nav with HSI, 1000 nav with ARC, dual 1000 glideslope, 1000 ADF, RMI, Series 800 DME, RNAV, transponder, encoding altimeter and altitude alerter; 800B IFCS; Series 400 marker beacon; AA-100 radio altimeter; Bendix RDR-160 weather radar; Series 1000 audio panel, basic avionics kit, cooling kit, and all essential antennae.

The Model 414A for 1980 introduces the same standard and optional improvements as detailed for the Model 402C, plus a new control wheel, and a new 35-month or 1,400-h engine repair or replacement warranty.

A total of 513 of the original Model 414s were built before introduction of the more advanced Model 414A, and a combined total of 796 Model 414/414As had been delivered by 1 January 1980.

TYPE: Six/eight-seat pressurised light transport.
WINGS: Cantilever low-wing monoplane. Wing section NACA 23018 (modified) at aircraft centreline, NACA 23015 (modified) at centre-section/outer wing junction, NACA 23009 (modified) at tip. Dihedral 5° on outer panels. Incidence 2°30' at root, —0°30' at tip. All-metal two-spar structure of light alloy with stamped ribs and surface skins reinforced with spanwise stringers. Outer wing panels of bonded construction. All-metal ailerons and electrically-actuated split flaps. Trim tab in port aileron. Optional pneumatic de-icing system.
FUSELAGE: Conventional all-metal semi-monocoque structure, with fail-safe construction in the pressurised section.
TAIL UNIT: Cantilever all-metal structure, with sweptback vertical surfaces. Fixed-incidence tailplane. Trim tabs in rudder and starboard elevator. Optional pneumatic de-icing system.
LANDING GEAR: Hydraulically-retractable tricycle type, main units retracting inward, nosewheel unit aft. Emergency extension by means of a 138 bar (2,000 lb/sq in) rechargeable nitrogen bottle. Oleo-pneumatic shock-absorbers. Steerable nosewheel. Main-wheel tyres size 6·50-10 (8-ply), nosewheel tyre size 6·00-6 (6-ply). Goodyear single-disc hydraulic brakes. Parking brakes.

POWER PLANT: Two 231 kW (310 hp) Continental TSIO-520-NB flat-six turbocharged engines, each driving a McCauley 3AF32C93M/82NC-5·5 three-blade constant-speed fully-feathering metal propeller. Propeller synchrophasers standard; unfeathering pressure accumulator and electrical blade de-icing system optional. Fuel system with max usable capacity of 808 litres (213 US gallons). Oil capacity 24·6 litres (6·5 US gallons).
ACCOMMODATION: Two seats side by side in pilot's compartment. Optional curtain, or solid divider with curtain, to separate pilot's compartment from main cabin. Standard seating arrangement for four forward-facing passenger seats. Optional arrangements provide for front passenger seats to face aft and forward-facing seventh and eighth seats. Individual consoles each include reading light and ventilator. Optional items include executive writing desk, tables, hat shelf, stereo equipment, vertically-adjustable pilot's and co-pilot's seats, refreshment and Thermos units, fore and aft cabin dividers, electric shaver converter, all-leather seats, passenger instrument console (clock, true airspeed indicator and altimeter) and intercom. Door is two-piece type with built-in airstairs in bottom portion, on port side of cabin at rear. Plug-type emergency escape hatch on starboard side of cabin. Double-pane cabin windows. Foul-weather windows for pilot and co-pilot, on each side of fuselage. Windscreen defroster standard, electrical or alcohol windscreen de-icing optional. Baggage accommodated in nose compartment with external access doors, capacity 159 kg (350 lb), two wing lockers, capacity 54·5 kg (120 lb) each, and in rear cabin area, capacity 226 kg (500 lb). Total baggage capacity 494 kg (1,090 lb). External access door to tailcone on starboard side.
SYSTEMS: Cabin pressurisation system, max differential 0·34 bars (5·0 lb/sq in), maintains sea level cabin conditions to an altitude of 3,350 m (11,000 ft), and a 3,050 m (10,000 ft) cabin altitude to a height of 8,075 m (26,500 ft). Electrical system powered by two engine-driven 28V 50A alternators. 24V 25Ah battery. 28V 100A alternators optional, standard on 414A III version. Hydraulic system for operation of landing gear and brakes. Vacuum system for blind-flying instrumentation and optional wing and tail unit de-icing system. Oxygen system of 3·25 m³ (115 cu ft) capacity, or emergency oxygen system of 0·31 m³ (11·0 cu ft) capacity optional. Air-conditioning system optional, standard on 414A III.
AVIONICS AND EQUIPMENT: The various versions of the Model 414A have avionics as detailed in the model listings, plus radio telephone with cockpit control. Optional avionics available for the basic 414A include those detailed for the 414A II/III, and alternative items from the Cessna Series 400, 800 and 1000 range are available for all versions. Standard equipment includes blind-flying instrumentation, quartz crystal clock, outside air temperature gauge, sensitive altimeter, control locks, dual controls, sun visors, alternator failure lights, aircraft systems monitoring device, heater overheat warning light, heated pitot and stall warning transmitter, stall warning device, door 'Not locked' warning light, armrests, cabin air ventilators, window curtains, super soundproofing, instrument post lights, aft cabin light, courtesy lights, reading lights, navigation light detectors, retractable landing light, navigation lights, rotating beacon, full-flow oil filters, non-congealing oil coolers, quick-drain fuel valves, heated fuel vents, towbar, and overall paint scheme. Equipment detailed as standard for the Model 414A II/III is available optionally for the Model 414A. Other optional items for all versions include angle of attack indicator, digital clock, digital fuel flow gauge with computer, instantaneous rate of climb indicator, true airspeed indicator, rudder pedal lock, electric elevator trim, flight deck/cabin divider or curtain, table, refreshment centre, tinted windows, 7th and 8th seats, 'Fasten seat belt' and 'Oxygen' signs, toilet with privacy curtain, internal corrosion proofing, ventilation fan, 'total flood' cabin fire extinguisher, 8-track stereo installation, timer for courtesy lights, ice detection lights, fuselage ice impact panels, dual pitot system, radome nose, and engine fire detection and extinguishing system.

DIMENSIONS, EXTERNAL:

Wing span	13·45 m (44 ft 1½ in)
Wing chord at root	1·77 m (5 ft 9¾ in)
Wing chord at tip	1·05 m (3 ft 5½ in)
Length overall	11·09 m (36 ft 4½ in)
Height overall	3·49 m (11 ft 5½ in)
Tailplane span	5·18 m (17 ft 0 in)
Wheel track	5·47 m (17 ft 11¾ in)
Wheelbase	3·18 m (10 ft 5¼ in)

Cessna Model 414A Chancellor light transport with turbocharged engines

Cessna Model 414A Chancellor six/eight-seat pressurised light transport *(Pilot Press)*

Propeller diameter	1·94 m (6 ft 4½ in)
Passenger door: Height	1·30 m (4 ft 3¼ in)
Width	0·63 m (2 ft 0¾ in)
Height to sill	1·21 m (3 ft 11½ in)

DIMENSIONS, INTERNAL:

Cabin: Length	4·42 m (14 ft 6 in)
Max width	1·40 m (4 ft 7 in)
Max height	1·29 m (4 ft 3 in)
Volume	6·11 m³ (215·6 cu ft)

AREAS:

Wings, gross	20·98 m² (225·8 sq ft)
Fin	2·37 m² (25·53 sq ft)
Rudder, incl tab	1·46 m² (15·72 sq ft)
Tailplane	4·15 m² (44·62 sq ft)
Elevators, incl tab	1·49 m² (16·08 sq ft)

WEIGHTS AND LOADINGS:

Weight empty: 414A	1,976 kg (4,356 lb)
414A II	2,053 kg (4,526 lb)
414A III	2,160 kg (4,763 lb)
Max T-O and landing weight	3,062 kg (6,750 lb)
Max ramp weight	3,078 kg (6,785 lb)
Max zero-fuel weight	2,955 kg (6,515 lb)
Max wing loading	145·94 kg/m² (29·89 lb/sq ft)
Max power loading	6·63 kg/kW (10·89 lb/hp)

PERFORMANCE (at max T-O weight, except speeds are those at mid-cruise weight):

Never-exceed speed	232 knots (430 km/h; 267 mph) CAS
Max level speed at 6,100 m (20,000 ft)	235 knots (436 km/h; 271 mph)
Cruising speed, 74·8% power at 7,470 m (24,500 ft)	224 knots (415 km/h; 258 mph)
Cruising speed, 74·8% power at 3,050 m (10,000 ft)	193 knots (357 km/h; 222 mph)
Econ cruising speed at 7,620 m (25,000 ft)	183 knots (339 km/h; 211 mph)
Econ cruising speed at 3,050 m (10,000 ft)	143 knots (265 km/h; 165 mph)

Stalling speed, flaps up, power off:	
All versions	82 knots (152 km/h; 95 mph) CAS
Stalling speed, flaps down, power off:	
All versions	72 knots (133 km/h; 83 mph) CAS
Max rate of climb at S/L	463 m (1,520 ft)/min
Rate of climb at S/L, one engine out	88 m (290 ft)/min
Service ceiling	9,390 m (30,800 ft)
Service ceiling, one engine out	6,050 m (19,850 ft)
T-O run	666 m (2,185 ft)
T-O to 15 m (50 ft)	791 m (2,595 ft)
Landing from 15 m (50 ft) at max landing weight	729 m (2,393 ft)
Landing run at max landing weight	309 m (1,013 ft)

Range, recommended lean mixture, with allowances for start, taxi, T-O, climb, descent and 45 min reserves at selected cruise power:

74·8% power at 7,470 m (24,500 ft) with 272 kg (600 lb) usable fuel	404 nm (748 km; 465 miles)
74·8% power at 7,470 m (24,500 ft) with 560·5 kg (1,236 lb) usable fuel	1,099 nm (2,036 km; 1,265 miles)
74·8% power at 3,050 m (10,000 ft) with 272 kg (600 lb) usable fuel	382 nm (708 km; 440 miles)
74·8% power at 3,050 m (10,000 ft) with 560·5 kg (1,236 lb) usable fuel	984 nm (1,823 km; 1,133 miles)
Econ cruising power at 7,620 m (25,000 ft) with 272 kg (600 lb) usable fuel	482 nm (893 km; 555 miles)
Econ cruising power at 7,620 m (25,000 ft) with 560·5 kg (1,236 lb) usable fuel	1,293 nm (2,396 km; 1,489 miles)
Econ cruising power at 3,050 m (10,000 ft) with 272 kg (600 lb) usable fuel	532 nm (986 km; 613 miles)
Econ cruising power at 3,050 m (10,000 ft) with 560·5 kg (1,236 lb) usable fuel	1,327 nm (2,459 km; 1,528 miles)

CESSNA MODEL 421

On 28 October 1965, Cessna announced a pressurised twin-engined business aircraft designated Model 421, the prototype of which had flown for the first time on 14 October 1965. FAA type approval was received on 1 May 1967 and deliveries began in the same month.

Two developed versions of the Model 421 were produced subsequently as the 421B Golden Eagle and 421B Executive Commuter, remaining in production until replaced by the Model 421C in 1976.

Three versions of the Model 421C Golden Eagle were available for 1980, as follows:

Model 421C Golden Eagle. Standard version, as described in detail.

Model 421C Golden Eagle II. As Model 421C above, but with the following avionics and equipment as standard: dual Series 400 nav/com, one with VOR/ILS, the other with VOR/LOC, ADF, transponder, DME, glideslope, marker beacon, 400B Nav-O-Matic autopilot, basic avionics and avionics cooling kits, associated antennae, audio system, marker beacon audio muting switch, and slaved directional gyro; co-pilot's blind-flying instrumentation, propeller synchrophaser, economy mixture indicator, flight hour recorder, emergency locator beacon,

cabin pressure control system, cabin hand fire extinguisher, starboard landing light, taxi light, high intensity strobe lights, external power socket, 100A alternators, static dischargers and nosewheel fender.

Model 421C Golden Eagle III. As standard Model 421C, with standard equipment of 421C II, plus cabin air-conditioning system and 100A alternators, and an all-weather avionics package which includes dual Series 1000 com and glideslope, Series 1000 nav with HSI, nav with ARC, ADF, RMI and audio panel; Series 800 DME, RNAV, transponder, encoding altimeter and altitude alerter; 800B IFCS; Series 400 marker beacon; AA-100 radio altimeter; RDR-160 weather radar; basic avionics and cooling kits, and all associated antennae.

The 1980 versions of the Golden Eagle introduce as standard the improvements detailed for the Model 402C, plus new trailing-link main landing gear, an increase in engine TBO from 1,200 to 1,600 h, a similarly expanded engine warranty, new control wheel, and a new dry fuel flow gauge. New options are as for the Model 402C, plus an electrically-heated windscreen, McCauley propeller synchrophaser, and a solid aft cabin divider for use with the optional toilet.

A total of 1,615 Model 421s had been delivered by 1 January 1980.

The description which follows applies to the Model 421C Golden Eagle:

TYPE: Six/eight-seat pressurised light transport.

WINGS, FUSELAGE, TAIL UNIT: As for Model 414A.

LANDING GEAR: Hydraulically-retractable tricycle type, main units retracting inward, nosewheel unit aft. Emergency extension by means of a 138 bar (2,000 lb/sq in) rechargeable nitrogen bottle. Oleo-pneumatic shock-absorbers. Main units of articulated (trailing-link) type. Steerable nosewheel. Main-wheel tyres size 6·50-10 (8-ply), nosewheel tyre 6·00-6 (6-ply). Goodyear single-disc hydraulic brakes. Parking brake.

POWER PLANT: Two 280 kW (375 hp) Continental GTSIO-520-L flat-six geared and turbocharged engines, each driving a McCauley three-blade fully-feathering constant-speed metal propeller. McCauley propeller synchrophaser optional. Standard total fuel capacity is 808 litres (213 US gallons), of which 780 litres (206 US gallons) are usable, contained in 'wet' wing. Optional wing locker tanks provide a maximum usable capacity of 991 litres (262 US gallons). Oil capacity 24·6 litres (6·5 US gallons).

ACCOMMODATION: Generally the same as for Model 414A;

seats have tapered backs and headrests. The nose compartment can contain a total of 272 kg (600 lb) of baggage and avionics, and two wing lockers an additional 91 kg (200 lb) each, plus 226 kg (500 lb) in the rear cabin area, making a total capacity of 680 kg (1,500 lb). Dual-setting electrically-heated windscreen optional.

SYSTEMS, AVIONICS AND EQUIPMENT: Generally as for Model 414A. Hydraulic system for landing gear operation supplied by dual engine-driven pumps, pressure 103·5 bars (1,500 lb/sq in). Rechargeable nitrogen bottle for emergency extension of landing gear, pressure 138 bars (2,000 lb/sq in).

DIMENSIONS, EXTERNAL:

Wing span	12·53 m (41 ft 1½ in)
Wing chord at root	1·77 m (5 ft 9¾ in)
Wing chord at tip	1·14 m (3 ft 8½ in)
Length overall	11·09 m (36 ft 4½ in)
Height overall	3·94 m (12 ft 11 in)
Tailplane span	5·18 m (17 ft 0 in)
Wheel track	5·28 m (17 ft 4 in)
Wheelbase	3·20 m (10 ft 6 in)
Propeller diameter	2·29 m (7 ft 6 in)

AREA:

Wings, gross	19·97 m² (215 sq ft)

WEIGHTS AND LOADINGS:

Weight empty:	
421C Golden Eagle	2,097 kg (4,623 lb)
421C II Golden Eagle	2,183 kg (4,814 lb)
421C III Golden Eagle	2,278 kg (5,022 lb)
Max T-O weight	3,379 kg (7,450 lb)
Max ramp weight	3,402 kg (7,500 lb)
Max zero-fuel weight	3,054 kg (6,733 lb)
Max landing weight	3,266 kg (7,200 lb)
Max wing loading	169·4 kg/m² (34·7 lb/sq in)
Max power loading	6·03 kg/kW (9·9 lb/hp)

PERFORMANCE (at max T-O weight, except speeds are those at mid-cruise weight):

Never-exceed speed	238 knots (441 km/h; 274 mph) CAS
Max level speed at 6,100 m (20,000 ft)	258 knots (478 km/h; 297 mph)
Max cruising speed, 73·5% power at 7,620 m (25,000 ft)	241 knots (447 km/h; 278 mph)
Max cruising speed, 73·5% power at 3,050 m (10,000 ft)	208 knots (386 km/h; 240 mph)
Econ cruising speed at 7,620 m (25,000 ft)	192 knots (356 km/h; 221 mph)

Photograph and three-view drawing *(Pilot Press)* **of the Cessna Model 421C Golden Eagle pressurised light transport**

Econ cruising speed at 3,050 m (10,000 ft)
153 knots (283 km/h; 176 mph)
Stalling speed, flaps up, power off:
All versions   83 knots (154 km/h; 96 mph) CAS
Stalling speed, flaps down, power off:
All versions   74 knots (137 km/h; 85 mph) CAS
Max rate of climb at S/L   591 m (1,940 ft)/min
Rate of climb at S/L, one engine out
107 m (350 ft)/min
Service ceiling   9,205 m (30,200 ft)
Service ceiling, one engine out   4,540 m (14,900 ft)
T-O run   544 m (1,786 ft)
T-O to 15 m (50 ft)   708 m (2,323 ft)
Landing from 15 m (50 ft)   699 m (2,293 ft)
Landing run   219 m (720 ft)
Range, recommended lean mixture, with allowances for start, taxi, T-O, climb, descent and 45 min reserves at selected cruise power:
73·5% power at 7,620 m (25,000 ft) with 561 kg (1,236 lb) usable fuel
882 nm (1,633 km; 1,015 miles)
73·5% power at 7,620 m (25,000 ft) with 713 kg (1,572 lb) usable fuel
1,197 nm (2,218 km; 1,378 miles)
73·5% power at 3,050 m (10,000 ft) with 561 kg (1,236 lb) usable fuel
790 nm (1,464 km; 910 miles)
73·5% power at 3,050 m (10,000 ft) with 713 kg (1,572 lb) usable fuel
1,060 nm (1,963 km; 1,220 miles)
Econ cruising power at 7,620 m (25,000 ft) with 561 kg (1,236 lb) usable fuel
1,088 nm (2,016 km; 1,253 miles)
Econ cruising power at 7,620 m (25,000 ft) with 713 kg (1,572 lb) usable fuel
1,483 nm (2,748 km; 1,708 miles)
Econ cruising power at 3,050 m (10,000 ft) with 561 kg (1,236 lb) usable fuel
1,107 nm (2,052 km; 1,275 miles)
Econ cruising power at 3,050 m (10,000 ft) with 713 kg (1,572 lb) usable fuel
1,485 nm (2,752 km; 1,710 miles)

CESSNA MODEL 425 CORSAIR

Cessna introduced for 1980 a twin-turboprop business aircraft known as the Model 425 Corsair, which is based on the airframe of the Model 421 Golden Eagle. Design began on 1 November 1977, and construction of a prototype was initiated three months later, on 30 January 1978. This flew for the first time on 12 September 1978, and construction of a pre-production example was started during 1979. Initial deliveries of production aircraft were scheduled to be made almost immediately after FAA certification, which had been gained by mid-1980.

TYPE: Six/eight-seat pressurised light transport.
WINGS: Cantilever low-wing monoplane. Wing section NACA 23018-63 (modified) at root, NACA 23009-63 (modified) at tip. Dihedral 5° on outer panels. Incidence 2° 30' at root, −0° 30' at tip. All-metal two-spar structure of light alloy, with stamped ribs and surface skins reinforced with spanwise stringers. Outer wing panels of bonded construction. All-metal ailerons and electrically-operated trailing-edge split flaps. Trim tab in port aileron. Optional pneumatic de-icing of wing leading-edges.
FUSELAGE: Conventional all-metal semi-monocoque structure, with fail-safe construction in the pressurised section.
TAIL UNIT: Conventional all-metal cantilever structure, with sweptback vertical surfaces. Tailplane has dihedral of 12°. Trim tab in starboard elevator, with dual heavy-duty actuator. Trim tab in rudder. Optional pneumatic de-icing of fin and tailplane leading-edges.
LANDING GEAR: Hydraulically-retractable tricycle type, main units retracting inward, nosewheel aft. Oleo-pneumatic shock-absorbers, with main units of articulated (trailing-link) type. Steerable nosewheel. Single wheel on each unit. Main-wheel tyres size 6·50-10, 8-ply rating, pressure 4·83 bars (70 lb/sq in). Nosewheel tyre size 6·00-6, 6-ply rating, pressure 2·42 bars (35 lb/sq in).
POWER PLANT: Two Pratt & Whitney Aircraft of Canada PT6A-112 turboprop engines, flat rated to 335·5 kW (450 shp), each driving a Hartzell wide-chord three-blade constant-speed fully-feathering and reversible-pitch metal propeller. Fuel contained in integral tanks in outer wing panels, nacelle cells, and inboard collector tanks, with combined capacity of 1,411 litres (372·8 US gallons), of which 1,385 litres (366 US gallons) are usable. Refuelling point above each engine nacelle. Oil capacity 19·75 litres (5·25 US gallons). Engine inlet ducts have a separator mechanism to prevent ingestion of water. Propeller de-icing and synchrophaser standard. Engine fire detection system standard.
ACCOMMODATION: Two seats side by side in pilot's compartment, with dual controls. Optional curtain, or solid divider with curtain, to separate pilot's compartment from main cabin. Standard seating provides for four passengers, but optional arrangements have the front passenger seats facing aft and forward-facing seventh and eighth seats. Optional equipment includes storage drawers, refreshment centre, tables, toilet, radio tele-

Cessna Model 425 Corsair, a new six/eight-seat twin-turboprop pressurised transport

Cessna Corsair (two Pratt & Whitney Aircraft of Canada PT6A-112 turboprop engines) (*Michael A. Badrocke*)

phone, stereo system, and aft cabin divider. Door is of two-piece type, with built-in airstairs in bottom portion, on port side of cabin at rear. Plug-type emergency escape hatch overwing on starboard side of cabin. Foul weather windows on each side of fuselage for pilot and co-pilot. Baggage accommodated in nose with external access doors, capacity 272 kg (600 lb), and in rear of cabin area, capacity 227 kg (500 lb). Total baggage capacity 499 kg (1,100 lb). Accommodation is pressurised, heated and air-conditioned.
SYSTEMS: Freon air-conditioning system of 17,500 BTU capacity, plus engine bleed air and electric boost heating. Pressurisation system with max differential of 0·35 bars (5·0 lb/sq in) provides a 3,050 m (10,000 ft) cabin altitude to 8,075 m (26,500 ft). Electrical system includes a 28V 250A starter/generator on the starboard engine and a 40Ah nickel-cadmium battery. Hydraulic system for operation of landing gear and brakes. Vacuum system for blind-flying instrumentation and optional wing and tail unit de-icing. Oxygen system standard.
AVIONICS AND EQUIPMENT: Standard avionics include Cessna Series 400 dual nav/coms, dual glideslope, ADF, DME, marker beacon, transponder, and encoding altimeter; Series 1000 autopilot with 3 in HSI, and yaw damper, audio panel, basic avionics kit, avionics cooling kit, and all associated antennae. Optional avionics include Cessna Series 1000 equipment or Collins Pro Line. Standard equipment includes flight hour recorder; co-pilot's blind-flying instrumentation; cabin pressure control system; emergency locator transmitter; cabin fire extinguisher; starboard landing light; navigation, taxi, and strobe lights; external power socket, nose-wheel fender, and static wicks.

DIMENSIONS, EXTERNAL:
Wing span   13·45 m (44 ft 1½ in)
Wing chord at root   1·77 m (5 ft 9¾ in)
Wing chord at tip   1·05 m (3 ft 5½ in)
Wing aspect ratio   8·65
Length overall   10·93 m (35 ft 10¼ in)
Height overall   3·84 m (12 ft 7¼ in)
Tailplane span   5·82 m (19 ft 1 in)
Wheel Track   5·30 m (17 ft 4½ in)
Wheelbase   3·20 m (10 ft 6 in)
Propeller diameter   2·37 m (7 ft 9½ in)
Propeller ground clearance   0·23 m (9¼ in)
Passenger door: Height   1·30 m (4 ft 3¼ in)
Width   0·63 m (2 ft 8 in)
Height to sill   1·21 m (3 ft 11½ in)
DIMENSIONS, INTERNAL:
Cabin: Length   4·42 m (14 ft 6 in)
Max width   1·40 m (4 ft 7 in)
Max height   1·29 m (4 ft 3 in)
Volume   6·11 m³ (215·6 cu ft)
Nose baggage compartment volume 0·93 m³ (33 cu ft)
AREAS:
Wings, gross   20·90 m² (224·98 sq ft)
Fin   2·37 m² (25·53 sq ft)
Rudder (incl tab)   1·46 m² (15·72 sq ft)
Horizontal tail surfaces (total)   5·76 m² (61·99 sq ft)
WEIGHTS AND LOADINGS:
Weight empty, equipped   2,209 kg (4,870 lb)
Max fuel weight   1,115 kg (2,459 lb)
Max T-O weight   3,720 kg (8,200 lb)
Max ramp weight   3,753 kg (8,275 lb)
Max zero-fuel weight   3,057 kg (6,740 lb)
Max landing weight   3,629 kg (8,000 lb)
Max wing loading   178·0 kg/m² (36·45 lb/sq ft)
Max power loading   5·54 kg/kW (9·11 lb/shp)
PERFORMANCE (at max T-O weight, except where indicated):
Never-exceed speed
Mach 0·52   (229 knots; 424 km/h; 263 mph) CAS
Max cruising speed at 5,400 m (17,700 ft) at AUW of 3,175 kg (7,000 lb) 264 knots (489 km/h; 304 mph)
Stalling speed, flaps and landing gear up, engines idling   88 knots (163 km/h; 102 mph) CAS
Stalling speed, flaps and landing gear down, engines idling   79 knots (147 km/h; 91 mph) CAS
Max rate of climb at S/L   618 m (2,027 ft)/min
Rate of climb at S/L, one engine out
132 m (434 ft)/min
Service ceiling   10,575 m (34,700 ft)
Service ceiling, one engine out   5,640 m (18,500 ft)
T-O run   624 m (2,047 ft)
T-O to 15 m (50 ft)   714 m (2,341 ft)
Landing from 15 m (50 ft)   654 m (2,145 ft)
Landing run   290 m (952 ft)

Range with max fuel at max cruising power, allowances for start, taxi, T-O, climb to cruise altitude, descent, and 45 min reserves at max cruise power:

at 6,100 m (20,000 ft)

1,020 nm (1,889 km; 1,173 miles)

at 9,145 m (30,000 ft)

1,406 nm (2,604 km; 1,618 miles)

Range with max fuel at max range power, allowances as above, and 45 min reserves at max range power:

at 6,100 m (20,000 ft)

1,370 nm (2,537 km; 1,576 miles)

at 9,145 m (30,000 ft)

1,646 nm (3,048 km; 1,894 miles)

CESSNA TITAN

On 16 July 1975 Cessna Aircraft Company announced that it was developing a new twin-engined business/commuter/cargo aircraft, designated Model 404 Titan. The model number was deleted subsequently, and the aircraft is known currently as the Cessna Titan. It was designed to carry a nominal 1,588 kg (3,500 lb) useful load out of a 771 m (2,530 ft) airstrip. A prototype flew for the first time on 26 February 1975, and a total of 241 had been delivered by 1 January 1980.

The Titan offers an increase of more than 30 per cent in ton-miles per gallon by comparison with the Cessna 402. Its cabin, which is almost 5·79 m (19 ft 0 in) long, is designed for rapid conversion to satisfy cargo, commuter and executive transport roles.

The Cessna Titan is available in seven versions for 1980, as follows:

Titan Ambassador. Standard version, configured and equipped for passenger carrying, as described in detail.

Titan Ambassador II. As standard version, but with the following avionics and equipment: dual Series 300 nav/com with VOR/ILS and VOR/LOC; Series 300 ADF; Series 400 transponder, glideslope, marker beacon; 400B Nav-O-Matic autopilot; basic avionics kit, marker beacon audio muting switch, audio system, avionics cooling, and all associated antennae; economy mixture indicator, flight hour recorder, dual controls, emergency locator beacon, cabin fire extinguisher, starboard landing light, taxi light, external power socket, static dischargers, and nosewheel fender.

Titan Ambassador III. As Titan Ambassador, with standard equipment of Ambassador II plus heavy-duty brakes and 100A alternators, and an avionics package which includes Series 400 nav/com with HSI; 400 nav/com with ARC; dual 400 glideslope; 400 ADF, DME, marker beacon, RNAV, transponder; Series 800 encoding altimeter and altitude alert; Series 1000 RMI; 400B IFCS; Bendix RDR-160 weather radar; yaw damper, basic avionics kit, audio system, avionics cooling, and all associated antennae.

Titan Courier. Standard utility version for passenger/cargo role.

Titan Courier II. As standard Courier, but with the avionics and equipment detailed for the Ambassador II.

Titan Freighter. Cargo version with specially designed cabin walls and ceiling of impact resistant polycarbonate material and floor stressed to withstand loading of 976 kg/m² (200 lb/sq ft). Cargo handling facilities include the retention of floor tracks to provide tiedown attachment points, floor pallets to provide durable flooring flush with the tracks, five high-capacity cargo retaining nets. Cargo door 1·26 m (4 ft 1½ in) high and 1·24 m (4 ft 1 in) wide replaces normal cabin door on port side, and crew door is provided on port side over wing.

Titan Freighter II. As Titan Freighter, but with avionics and equipment detailed for Ambassador II.

The 1980 versions of the Titan introduce a number of improvements as standard, including redesigned wingtips that give a 0·10 m (4 in) increase in span, better fuel system inspection facilities, redesigned upper cabin door extender, relocation of the tail navigation light, rearrangement of the IFR instrument layout, and new interior and exterior styling. A new engine repair or replacement warranty gives cover over 1,200 h or 30 months. New options include a McCauley propeller synchrophaser, stereo system, a gas spring actuator for the optional crew door or lower cabin door, and improvements to the air-conditioning system.

TYPE: Two/ten-seat passenger/executive/cargo transport.

WINGS: Cantilever low-wing monoplane. Wing section NACA 23018 at root, NACA 23012 at tip. Dihedral 3° 30′ on wing centre-section, 4° 55′ on outer panels. Incidence 2° at root, −1° at construction tip. All-metal three-spar centre-section structure to meet FAR 23 fail-safe requirements: two-spar structure for outer wing panels. Hydraulically-operated Fowler-type trailing-edge flaps of light alloy construction. Plain ailerons of light alloy construction. Trim tab in port aileron. Pneumatic de-icing system optional.

FUSELAGE: All-metal semi-monocoque structure.

TAIL UNIT: Cantilever structure of light alloy with swept surfaces. Fixed-incidence tailplane, with dihedral of 12°. Trim tab in rudder and each elevator. Electrical operation of trim tabs, and pneumatic de-icing system, optional.

LANDING GEAR: Hydraulically-retractable tricycle type with single wheel on each unit. Main units retract inward into wing, nosewheel aft. Emergency extension by means of a 138 bar (2,000 lb/sq in) rechargeable nitrogen bottle. Cessna oleo-pneumatic shock-absorbers. All legs of articulated (trailing-link) type. Cleveland main wheels with tyres size 22 × 7·75-10, pressure 4·83 bars (70 lb/sq in). Cleveland nosewheel with tyre size 6·00-6, pressure 3·45 bars (50 lb/sq in). Cleveland single-disc hydraulic brakes. Heavy duty brakes optional, standard on Ambassador III. Parking brake.

POWER PLANT: Two 280 kW (375 hp) Continental GTSIO-520-M flat-six engines, each driving a McCauley three-blade constant-speed fully-feathering metal propeller. Integral fuel tanks in wings, with combined usable capacity of 1,287 litres (340 US gallons). Oil capacity 26·5 litres (7 US gallons). Manifold pressure relief valves to prevent overboosting are standard. Propeller synchrophaser, automatic unfeathering system and electrical de-icing system optional.

ACCOMMODATION: Two seats side by side for pilot and co-pilot. Titan Courier has six individual seats and a two-passenger bench seat as standard; Titan Ambassador as Courier, except bench seat is optional. Passenger seats are 'Enviro-form' moulded honeycomb with glassfibre reinforcement. Passenger reading lights standard for Ambassador, optional for Courier. Door with built-in airstair on port side of fuselage, aft of wing. Emergency escape hatch on starboard side of cabin. Storm windows for pilot and co-pilot. Tinted cabin windows. Cargo door and crew access door optional for Courier, standard for Freighter. Baggage area at rear of cabin, capacity 227 kg (500 lb). Nose baggage compartment, with optional carpeting, can accommodate articles up to 1·96 m (6 ft 5 in) in length and has capacity of 159 kg (350 lb), accessible from each side. Avionics/baggage compartment in nose, separate from above baggage compartment and accessible through an 'over the top' 180° cam-lock door, has a capacity of 113 kg (250 lb); side access door optional. Wing lockers, at rear of each engine nacelle, each have capacity of 91 kg (200 lb). If no avionics carried in forward nose compartment, total baggage capacity is 680 kg (1,500 lb). Dual controls optional, standard on Titan II versions. Cabin heated and ventilated; air-conditioning optional.

Windscreen defrosting standard. Electrical anti-icing of pilot's window, or alcohol anti-icing of pilot's and co-pilot's windows, optional.

SYSTEMS: Electrical system powered by two 28V 50A alternators; 100A alternators optional, standard on III versions. Battery, 24V 25Ah, can be sited optionally in nose baggage compartment. Hydraulic system for landing gear and flap operation, and for wheel brakes. Vacuum system provided by two engine-driven pumps. Oxygen system, capacity 1·25 m³ (44 cu ft) or 3·25 m³ (115 cu ft), optional. Heating and ventilation system standard, with 45,000 BTU gasoline heater. Air-conditioning system optional.

AVIONICS AND EQUIPMENT: The various versions of the Titan have avionics as detailed in the model listings. Optional avionics available for the basic Titan versions include those detailed for the II and III versions, and alternative items from the Cessna Series 400, 800 and 1000 are available for all versions. Standard equipment includes blind-flying instrumentation, electric clock, outside air temperature gauge, sensitive altimeter, alternator failure lights, cabin door 'Not locked' warning light, heater overheat warning light, navigation light detectors, stall warning device, armrests, pilot and co-pilot safety belt system, control locks, sun visors, cabin speaker, adjustable air ventilators, shoulder restraint system, super soundproofing, courtesy lights, variable-intensity instrument post lights and floodlights, retractable landing light, navigation lights, three-light strobe system, towbar, and all-over polyurethane paint. Optional equipment for all versions includes GMT clock, high-efficiency exhaust gas temperature gauges, instantaneous rate of climb indicator, true airspeed indicator, digital fuel flow gauge with computer, dual heated static source, 'total flood' cabin fire extinguisher, stereo system, courtesy light timer, ice detection light, and anti-icing kit; items detailed as standard for II and III versions are also available as required.

DIMENSIONS, EXTERNAL:

Wing span	14·23 m (46 ft 8¼ in)
Wing chord at root	1·78 m (5 ft 10 in)
Wing chord at tip	1·22 m (4 ft 0 in)
Wing aspect ratio	9·0
Length overall	12·04 m (39 ft 6¼ in)
Height overall	4·04 m (13 ft 3 in)
Tailplane span	5·82 m (19 ft 1 in)
Wheel track	4·29 m (14 ft 1 in)
Wheelbase	3·82 m (12 ft 6½ in)
Propeller diameter	2·29 m (7 ft 6 in)
Passenger door (port): Height	1·28 m (4 ft 2½ in)
Width	0·61 m (2 ft 0 in)
Height to sill	1·28 m (4 ft 2½ in)
Cargo door (optional, port; standard Freighter):	
Height	1·28 m (4 ft 2½ in)
Width	1·24 m (4 ft 1 in)
Height to sill	1·28 m (4 ft 2½ in)
Nose baggage doors (each):	
Height	0·41 m (1 ft 4 in)
Width	0·86 m (2 ft 9¾ in)
Nacelle baggage doors (each):	
Length	0·62 m (2 ft 0¼ in)
Width	0·64 m (2 ft 1 in)

DIMENSIONS, INTERNAL:

Cabin: Length	5·72 m (18 ft 9 in)
Max width	1·42 m (4 ft 8 in)
Max height	1·31 m (4 ft 3¼ in)
Volume	8·97 m³ (316·6 cu ft)

AREAS:

Wings, gross	22·48 m² (242 sq ft)
Fin	2·54 m² (27·33 sq ft)
Rudder, incl tab	1·50 m² (16·15 sq ft)
Tailplane	4·21 m² (45·31 sq ft)
Elevators, incl tab	1·68 m² (18·07 sq ft)

WEIGHTS AND LOADINGS:

Weight empty: Ambassador	2,184 kg (4,816 lb)
Ambassador II	2,246 kg (4,953 lb)
Ambassador III	2,298 kg (5,067 lb)
Courier	2,197 kg (4,844 lb)
Courier II	2,259 kg (4,981 lb)
Freighter	2,125 kg (4,685 lb)
Freighter II	2,187 kg (4,822 lb)
Max T-O weight	3,810 kg (8,400 lb)
Max ramp weight	3,833 kg (8,450 lb)
Max zero-fuel and landing weight	3,674 kg (8,100 lb)
Max wing loading	169·5 kg/m² (34·71 lb/sq ft)
Max power loading	6·8 kg/kW (11·2 lb/hp)

PERFORMANCE (at max T-O weight unless otherwise indicated, except speeds are those at mid-cruise weight):

Never-exceed speed

238 knots (441 km/h; 274 mph) CAS

Max level speed at 4,875 m (16,000 ft)

232 knots (430 km/h; 267 mph)

Max cruising speed, 74·5% power at 6,100 m (20,000 ft)

217 knots (402 km/h; 250 mph)

Max cruising speed, 75·5% power at 3,050 m (10,000 ft)

199 knots (369 km/h; 229 mph)

Econ cruising speed at 6,100 m (20,000 ft)

163 knots (302 km/h; 188 mph)

Econ cruising speed at 3,050 m (10,000 ft)

140 knots (259 km/h; 161 mph)

Cessna Titan business/commuter/cargo transport

Stalling speed, all versions:
 flaps up, power off
  83 knots (154 km/h; 96 mph) CAS
 flaps down, power off, at max landing weight
  70 knots (130 km/h; 81 mph) CAS
Max rate of climb at S/L 480 m (1,575 ft)/min
Rate of climb at S/L, one engine out
  70 m (230 ft)/min
Service ceiling 7,925 m (26,000 ft)
Service ceiling, one engine out 3,080 m (10,100 ft)
T-O run 545 m (1,788 ft)
T-O to 15 m (50 ft) 721 m (2,367 ft)
Landing from 15 m (50 ft) at max landing weight
  649 m (2,130 ft)
Landing run at max landing weight 335 m (1,100 ft)
Range, recommended lean mixture, allowances for
 start, taxi, T-O, climb, descent, and 45 min reserves at
 selected cruise power:
 74·5% power at 6,100 m (20,000 ft) with 454 kg
  (1,000 lb) usable fuel
  584 nm (1,081 km; 672 miles)
 74·5% power at 6,100 m (20,000 ft) with 936 kg
  (2,064 lb) usable fuel
  1,466 nm (2,717 km; 1,688 miles)
 75·5% power at 3,050 m (10,000 ft) with 454 kg
  (1,000 lb) usable fuel
  553 nm (1,025 km; 637 miles)
 75·5% power at 3,050 m (10,000 ft) with 936 kg
  (2,064 lb) usable fuel
  1,350 nm (2,501 km; 1,554 miles)
 Econ cruising power at 6,100 m (20,000 ft) with 454
  kg (1,000 lb) usable fuel
  726 nm (1,345 km; 836 miles)
 Econ cruising power at 6,100 m (20,000 ft) with 936
  kg (2,064 lb) usable fuel
  1,840 nm (3,410 km; 2,119 miles)
 Econ cruising power at 3,050 m (10,000 ft) with 454
  kg (1,000 lb) usable fuel
  756 nm (1,400 km; 870 miles)
 Econ cruising power at 3,050 m (10,000 ft) with 936
  kg (2,064 lb) usable fuel
  1,837 nm (3,404 km; 2,115 miles)

Cessna Conquest (two Garrett-AiResearch TPE331-8-401S/402S turboprop engines)

Cessna Conquest five/eleven-seat pressurised, turboprop-powered executive transport *(Pilot Press)*

CESSNA CONQUEST

Cessna announced on 15 November 1974 that it was developing a twin-turboprop business aircraft designated Model 441, with initial deliveries scheduled for 1977. This was designed to slot into the market gap between existing twin piston-engined aircraft and turbofan-powered business aircraft.

Now marketed as the Cessna Conquest, this aircraft is powered by Garrett-AiResearch TPE331-8-401 turboprop engines, which have been developed specially to meet the high-altitude high-speed requirements set by Cessna for this aircraft. Its high performance stems in part from use of a new high aspect ratio bonded wing, and from the high-strength trailing-link-type hydraulically retractable tricycle landing gear.

Production aircraft beginning with construction number 116 introduced as standard an automatic engine torque and temperature limiting system, propeller synchrophaser, fuselage ice protection plates, pneumatic actuator for cabin upper door, new low-pressure fuel boost pumps, and fuel pressure switch. New options include a Freon air-conditioning system, wingtip recognition lights, and Bendix RDR-1100 colour radar.

The prototype of the Conquest flew for the first time on 26 August 1975 and 115 aircraft had been delivered by 1 January 1980.

TYPE: Five/eleven-seat pressurised executive transport.

WINGS: As Cessna Titan, except wing span and area increased by addition of wingtip extensions.

FUSELAGE: All-metal semi-monocoque structure of light alloy.

TAIL UNIT: Cantilever structure with sweptback vertical surfaces. Dihedral 12° on horizontal surfaces. Large tab in each elevator and rudder.

LANDING GEAR: As Cessna Titan.

POWER PLANT: Two Garrett-AiResearch TPE 331-8-401S/402S turboprop engines, each flat rated at 474 kW (635·5 shp) to 4,875 m (16,000 ft). Hartzell Type HC-B3TN-5E/T10178B-11 constant-speed fully-feathering and reversible-pitch three-blade propellers. Total fuel capacity 1,823 litres (481·5 US gallons), of which 1,798 litres (475 US gallons) are usable. Refuelling point on upper surface of each wing. Oil capacity 14·2 litres (3·75 US gallons).

ACCOMMODATION: Seats for four to ten persons, and pilot, in pressurised and air-conditioned cabin. Various optional seating arrangements. Door aft of wing on port side, with upward-hinged top portion and downward-hinged lower portion with integral airstairs. Emergency exit over wing on starboard side. Baggage door on each side of nose. Max baggage capacity 680 kg (1,500 lb). Optional items include aft cabin divider, refreshment centre, toilet, writing tables and stereo system.

SYSTEMS: Pressurisation system max differential 0·43 bars (6·3 lb/sq in). Freon air-conditioning systems of 8,000 BTU or 16,000 BTU capacity optional. Hydraulic system for operation of flaps, landing gear and brakes, pressure 103·5 bars (1,500 lb/sq in). Emergency extension of landing gear by means of 138 bar (2,000 lb/sq in)

rechargeable gas bottle. Electrical power supplied by two 28V 200A starter/generators; two 24V 22Ah nickel-cadmium batteries housed in nose compartment. Electronic fuel control system.

AVIONICS: Standard avionics include dual Cessna 1038A com, dual 1048A nav, dual 1043A glideslope, 1046A ADF, 402A marker beacon, 876A DME, 859A transponder, RMI, 400 encoding altimeter, Bendix RDR-160 weather radar, basic avionics kit. Collins avionics package and Bendix RDR-1100 colour radar optional.

DIMENSIONS, EXTERNAL:

Wing span, over tip-lights	15·04 m (49 ft 4 in)
Wing chord at root	1·78 m (5 ft 10 in)
Wing chord at tip	1·22 m (4 ft 0 in)
Wing aspect ratio	9·6
Length overall	11·89 m (39 ft 0¼ in)
Height overall	4·01 m (13 ft 2 in)
Tailplane span	5·81 m (19 ft 1 in)
Wheel track	4·28 m (14 ft 0¾ in)
Wheelbase	3·81 m (12 ft 5⅞ in)
Propeller diameter	2·29 m (7 ft 6 in)

DIMENSIONS, INTERNAL:

Cabin: Length	5·71 m (18 ft 9 in)
Max width	1·41 m (4 ft 7½ in)
Max height	1·29 m (4 ft 3 in)

AREAS:

Wings, gross	23·56 m² (253·6 sq ft)
Ailerons (total)	1·37 m² (14·74 sq ft)
Trailing-edge flaps (total)	3·90 m² (42·00 sq ft)
Fin	2·54 m² (27·33 sq ft)
Rudder (incl tab)	1·50 m² (16·15 sq ft)
Tailplane	4·21 m² (45·31 sq ft)
Elevators (incl tabs)	1·68 m² (18·07 sq ft)

WEIGHTS AND LOADINGS:

Weight empty	2,570 kg (5,666 lb)
Max usable fuel	1,444 kg (3,183 lb)
Max ramp weight	4,502 kg (9,925 lb)
Max T-O weight	4,468 kg (9,850 lb)
Max landing weight	4,246 kg (9,360 lb)
Max zero-fuel weight	3,855 kg (8,500 lb)
Max wing loading	189·6 kg/m² (38·8 lb/sq ft)
Max power loading	4·79 kg/kW (7·88 lb/shp)

PERFORMANCE (at max T-O weight unless otherwise indicated, except speeds are those at mid-cruise weight of 3,788 kg; 8,350 lb):
Never-exceed speed
 Mach 0·55 (243 knots; 450 km/h; 280 mph) CAS
Max level speed at 4,875 m (16,000 ft)
  295 knots (547 km/h; 340 mph)
Max cruising speed at 7,315 m (24,000 ft)
  293 knots (543 km/h; 337 mph)

Stalling speed, gear and flaps up, engines idling
  90 knots (167 km/h; 104 mph) CAS
Stalling speed, gear and flaps down, engines idling
  76 knots (141 km/h; 87·5 mph) CAS
Stalling speed, gear and flaps down, power off, at max
 landing weight 75 knots (139 km/h; 86·5 mph) CAS
Max rate of climb at S/L 742 m (2,435 ft)/min
Rate of climb at S/L, one engine out
  218 m (715 ft)/min
Service ceiling 11,275 m (37,000 ft)
Service ceiling, one engine out 6,515 m (21,380 ft)
Max certificated operating altitude
  10,670 m (35,000 ft)
T-O run 544 m (1,785 ft)
T-O to 15 m (50 ft) 751 m (2,465 ft)
Landing from 15 m (50 ft) at max landing weight
  572 m (1,875 ft)
Landing run 334 m (1,095 ft)
Range, at max T-O weight with 1,444 kg (3,183 lb) fuel,
 at max cruising power, allowances for engine start,
 taxi, T-O, climb, descent and 45 min reserves at max
 cruise power:
 at 5,180 m (17,000 ft)
  1,199 nm (2,220 km; 1,379 miles)
 at 7,620 m (25,000 ft)
  1,571 nm (2,909 km; 1,807 miles)
 at 10,060 m (33,000 ft)
  2,063 nm (3,820 km; 2,374 miles)
Range, at max T-O weight and at max range power,
 allowances as above:
 at 5,180 m (17,000 ft)
  1,471 nm (2,724 km; 1,692 miles)
 at 7,620 m (25,000 ft)
  1,816 nm (3,363 km; 2,090 miles)
 at 10,060 m (33,000 ft)
  2,212 nm (4,096 km; 2,545 miles)

CESSNA CITATION I

On 7 October 1968 Cessna announced that it was developing an eight-seat pressurised executive turbofan aircraft named Fanjet 500, which would be able to operate from most airfields used by light and medium twin-engined aircraft.

After the first flight of the prototype, on 15 September 1969, the aircraft's name was changed to Citation. Subsequently, the gross weight was increased for the first time, and several other changes were made. These included a lengthened front fuselage, movement of the engine nacelles further aft, larger vertical tail, and resiting of, and introduction of dihedral on, the tailplane.

On 1 July 1971 Cessna announced that the first production Citation 0001 (N502CC) had made its first flight.

Final FAA certification under FAR Part 25 was awarded on 9 September 1971. Certification in other countries includes a West German LBA type certificate issued on 21 June 1972, French SGAC type certificate issued on 27 March 1974 and UK type certificate issued on 30 August 1974. The Citation has also satisfied the requirements for registration in Australia, Austria, Belgium, Canada, Denmark, Japan, Italy, the Netherlands, Spain, Sweden, Switzerland, Yugoslavia and Zambia.

The latest increase in take-off gross weight, to a maximum of 5,375 kg (11,850 lb), and the use of optional Rohr Industries thrust reversers, received FAA certification in February 1976. The improved Citation I became available in December 1976, with a wing of increased span and JT15D-1A turbofan engines. It superseded the earlier model on the production line from c/n 350 onward and was certificated on 15 December 1976. The first Citation I was delivered on 21 December 1976. Two versions are currently available:

Citation I. Basic version, as described in detail.

Citation I/SP Model 501. Basically the same as the Citation I, but certificated to FAR 23 for single-pilot operation. Type Certification granted on 7 January 1977, first aircraft delivered on 25 January 1977.

A total of 179 Citation Is, of both models, had been delivered by 1 January 1980.

TYPE: Seven/nine-seat twin-turbofan executive transport.

WINGS: Cantilever low-wing monoplane without sweepback. Wing section at c/l NACA 23014 (modified), at wing station 247·95 NACA 23012. Incidence 2° 30′ at c/l, −0° 30′ at wing station 247·95. Dihedral 4°. All-metal fail-safe structure with two primary spars, an auxiliary spar, three fuselage attachment points and conventional ribs and stringers. Manually-operated ailerons, with manual trim on port aileron. Electrically-operated single-slotted trailing-edge flaps. Hydraulically-operated aerodynamic speed brakes.

FUSELAGE: All-metal pressurised structure of circular section. Fail-safe design, providing multiple load paths.

TAIL UNIT: Cantilever all-metal structure. Horizontal surfaces have dihedral of 9°. Large dorsal fin and smaller ventral fin. Manually-operated control surfaces. Electrical elevator trim with manual override; manual rudder trim.

LANDING GEAR: Hydraulically-retractable tricycle type with single wheel on each unit. Main units retract inward into the wing, nose gear forward into fuselage nose. Free-fall and pneumatic emergency extension systems. Goodyear main wheels and tyres of 559 mm (22 in) diameter, pressure 6·21 bars (90 lb/sq in) on first 70 production aircraft; 71st and subsequent production aircraft have 22 in diameter main-wheel tyres, pressure 6·90 bars (100 lb/sq in). Steerable nosewheel with Goodyear wheel and tyre of 457 mm (18 in) diameter, pressure 8·27 bars (120 lb/sq in). Goodyear hydraulic brakes. Parking brake and pneumatic emergency brake system. Anti-skid system optional.

POWER PLANT: Two Pratt & Whitney JT15D-1A turbofan engines, each rated at 9·77 kN (2,200 lb st) for take-off, mounted in pod on each side of rear fuselage. Rohr thrust reversers optional. Integral tanks in wings, with combined capacity of 2,135 litres (564 US gallons) usable fuel.

ACCOMMODATION: Crew of two on separate flight deck. Fully-carpeted main cabin equipped with two individual forward-facing seats aft, one single forward-facing seat centre port, one single aft-facing seat centre starboard and a fifth aft-facing corner lounge chair at front of cabin on starboard side, all with headrests. Refreshment unit at front of cabin. Toilet compartment and main baggage area at rear of cabin. Second baggage area in nose. Total baggage capacity 454 kg (1,000 lb). Cabin is pressurised, heated and air-conditioned. Individual reading lights and air inlets for each passenger. Dropout constant-flow oxygen system for emergency use. Plug-type door with integral airstair at front on port side and one emergency exit on starboard side. Doors on each side of nose baggage compartment. Tinted windows, each with curtains. Optional layouts for crew of two and six or seven passengers, with executive table, flush toilet replacing standard toilet, and choice of interior trims. Birdproof windscreen with de-fog system, anti-icing, and standby alcohol de-icing.

SYSTEMS: Pressurisation system supplied with engine bleed air, max pressure differential 0·59 bars (8·5 lb/sq in). Hydraulic system, pressure 103·5 bars (1,500 lb/sq in), with two pumps to operate landing gear and speed brakes. Electrical system supplied by two 400A 28V DC starter/generators, with two 300VA inverters and 24V 39Ah nickel-cadmium battery. Oxygen system of 0·62 m³ (22 cu ft) capacity includes two crew demand masks and five dropout constant-flow masks for passengers. High-capacity oxygen system optional.

AVIONICS AND EQUIPMENT: Standard Category II avionics package on aircraft subsequent to c/n 275 comprises Sperry SPZ 500 flight control system with choice of single or double-cue command bars, including Sperry 500 autopilot, Sperry altimeter with altitude alerting and reporting functions, complete vertical navigation capability, air data computer, Sperry Model 600 (port)/Model 044 (starboard) horizontal situation indi-

cator, Sperry ADI Model 300 or Model 600 command and control computer and autopilot servos, Bendix RDR 1200 (RDR 1100 subsequent to c/n 349, and Collins WXR-250C subsequent to c/n 550) continuous vision weather radar, two Collins VHF-20A com transceivers, two Collins VIR-30A nav receivers, Collins TDR-90 transponder, Collins DME-40, two Collins 332-C10 radio magnetic indicators, and ARC-846A ADF (Collins ADF-60 subsequent to c/n 525). Provision for advanced instrumentation and avionics to customer's specification. Standard equipment includes blind-flying instrumentation, generator load ammeters, standby magnetic compass, control locks, storm window, battery temperature and low fuel level warning lights, high Mach/airspeed warning, stall warning device, baggage tiedown kit, cabin fire extinguisher, individual life vests, 'No smoking, fasten seat belt' sign, internally lighted instruments, instrument standby lights, map light, entry light, tailcone compartment light, emergency exit lights, strobe lights, landing light, navigation lights, storm lights, taxi light, wing ice light, automatic engine start system, engine fire warning and extinguishing system, emergency battery pack, external power socket, inlet anti-icing, and surface de-icing system. Optional items include angle of attack indicator, radio telephone, cockpit voice recorder, flight data recorder, ground proximity warning system, emergency locator transmitter, navigation chart case, flush toilets, refreshment cabinets, storage drawers, tables, engine fan synchroniser, anti-collision beacon recognition lights, gravel runway kit, and drag chute.

DIMENSIONS, EXTERNAL:

Wing span	14·35 m (47 ft 1 in)
Wing aspect ratio	6·6
Length overall	13·26 m (43 ft 6 in)
Height overall	4·37 m (14 ft 4 in)
Tailplane span	5·74 m (18 ft 10 in)
Wheel track	3·84 m (12 ft 7 in)
Wheelbase	4·78 m (15 ft 8¼ in)
Cabin door (port): Height	1·29 m (4 ft 2¾ in)
Width	0·60 m (1 ft 11½ in)
Emergency exit (starboard):	
Height	0·95 m (3 ft 1¼ in)
Width	0·56 m (1 ft 10 in)

DIMENSIONS, INTERNAL:

Cabin:

Length, front to rear bulkhead	5·33 m (17 ft 6 in)
Max width	1·50 m (4 ft 11 in)
Max height	1·32 m (4 ft 4 in)
Baggage space: Cabin	1·10 m³ (39 cu ft)
Nose	0·45 m³ (16 cu ft)

AREAS:

Wings, gross	25·9 m² (278·5 sq ft)
Horizontal tail surfaces	6·56 m² (70·6 sq ft)
Vertical tail surfaces	4·73 m² (50·9 sq ft)

WEIGHTS (from aircraft c/n 525 onward):

Weight empty (incl avionics)	2,974 kg (6,557 lb)
Max fuel weight	1,715 kg (3,780 lb)
Max T-O weight	5,375 kg (11,850 lb)
Max ramp weight	5,443 kg (12,000 lb)
Max landing weight	5,148 kg (11,350 lb)
Max zero-fuel weight	3,810 kg (8,400 lb)
Optional max zero-fuel weight	4,309 kg (9,500 lb)

PERFORMANCE (at max T-O weight, except where indicated):

Max operating speed	Mach 0·70
Cruising speed at average cruising weight	352 knots (652 km/h; 405 mph)
Stalling speed at max landing weight	82 knots (152 km/h; 94·5 mph) CAS
Max rate of climb at S/L	817 m (2,680 ft)/min
Rate of climb at S/L, one engine out	244 m (800 ft)/min
Max certificated altitude	12,495 m (41,000 ft)
Service ceiling, one engine out	6,400 m (21,000 ft)
T-O to 15 m (50 ft)	751 m (2,463 ft)
Landing run at max landing weight	692 m (2,270 ft)

Cessna Citation I seven/nine-seat twin-turbofan executive transport

Balanced field length:

at S/L, ISA	893 m (2,930 ft)
at 1,525 m (5,000 ft), 27°C (80°F)	180 m (5,900 ft)
Range with 6 passengers, 45 min reserves	1,326 nm (2,454 km; 1,525 miles)

CESSNA CITATION II

First announced on 14 September 1976, this version of the Citation introduced several new features, including a fuselage lengthened by 1·14 m (3 ft 9 in), an increased-span high aspect ratio wing, increased fuel and baggage capacity, and the installation of Pratt & Whitney Aircraft of Canada JT15D-4 turbofan engines. The prototype (N550CC) flew for the first time on 31 January 1977, and certification was received in late March 1978; deliveries began immediately afterwards and a total of 117 had been delivered by 1 January 1980.

In addition to the standard six/ten-passenger Model 550 Citation II, which is certificated for a crew of two, the Model 551 Citation II/SP is available for single-pilot operation, with up to 10 passengers, at a max T-O weight of 5,670 kg (12,500 lb).

In October 1977, the US Customs Service ordered a special-purpose Citation II, fitted with government-furnished radar and sensing equipment. Follow-on orders are expected.

The description of the Citation I applies basically to the Citation II, except as follows:

POWER PLANT: Two Pratt & Whitney Aircraft of Canada JT15D-4 turbofan engines, each rated at 11·12 kN (2,500 lb st) for take-off, mounted in pod on each side of rear fuselage. Integral fuel tanks in wings, with usable capacity of 2,808 litres (742 US gallons).

ACCOMMODATION: As for Citation I, except seating for 6-10 passengers in main cabin, with toilet in six/eight-seat versions, and increased baggage capacity of up to 522 kg (1,150 lb).

DIMENSIONS, EXTERNAL:

Wing span	15·75 m (51 ft 8 in)
Wing aspect ratio	8·3
Length overall	14·38 m (47 ft 2 in)
Height overall	4·50 m (14 ft 9 in)
Tailplane span	5·74 m (18 ft 10 in)
Wheel track	5·36 m (17 ft 7 in)
Wheelbase	5·54 m (18 ft 2 in)

DIMENSIONS, INTERNAL:

Cabin: Length, front to rear bulkhead

	6·38 m (20 ft 11 in)
Max width	1·50 m (4 ft 11 in)
Max height	1·45 m (4 ft 9 in)
Baggage capacity	1·84 m³ (65 cu ft)

WEIGHTS (A: Citation II; B: Citation II/SP):

Weight empty (incl avionics):	
A, B	3,257 kg (7,181 lb)
Max fuel weight:	
A, B	2,272 kg (5,009 lb)
Max T-O weight:	
A	6,033 kg (13,300 lb)
B	5,670 kg (12,500 lb)
Max ramp weight:	
A	6,123 kg (13,500 lb)
B	5,760 kg (12,700 lb)
Max zero-fuel weight (standard):	
A, B	4,309 kg (9,500 lb)
Max zero-fuel weight (optional):	
A, B	4,989 kg (11,000 lb)
Max landing weight:	
A	5,760 kg (12,700 lb)
B	5,443 kg (12,000 lb)

PERFORMANCE (at max T-O weight except where indicated):

Max operating speed:	
A, B	Mach 0·705
Cruising speed at average cruising weight:	
A	385 knots (713 km/h; 443 mph)
B	387 knots (718 km/h; 446 mph)

The eight/twelve-seat Cessna Citation II executive transport *(Austin J. Brown)*

Stalling speed at max landing weight:
A	82 knots (152 km/h; 94·5 mph) CAS	
B	80 knots (149 km/h; 92·5 mph) CAS	

Max rate of climb at S/L:
A	1,027 m (3,370 ft)/min
B	1,105 m (3,625 ft)/min

Rate of climb at S/L, one engine out:
A	322 m (1,055 ft)/min
B	357 m (1,170 ft)/min

Max certificated altitude:
A, B	13,105 m (43,000 ft)

Service ceiling, one engine out:
A	7,680 m (25,200 ft)
B	8,290 m (27,200 ft)

T-O to 15 m (50 ft):
A	727 m (2,385 ft)
B	639 m (2,095 ft)

Balanced field length (FAR Pt 25):
A	912 m (2,990 ft)
B	808 m (2,650 ft)

Landing run at max landing weight:
A	692 m (2,270 ft)
B	674 m (2,210 ft)

Range with six passengers and 45 min reserves:
A	1,710 nm (3,169 km; 1,969 miles)
B	1,469 nm (2,721 km; 1,691 miles)

CESSNA CITATION III

While retaining some general similarity to earlier members of the Citation family, the Citation III is a very different aeroplane. The original design underwent major refinement during 1978. In particular, a T-tail was introduced, and the basic Citation III will now be supplemented by an extended-range version with an added fuel tank in the rear fuselage.

First flight of the first prototype (N650CC) was made on 30 May 1979. The second prototype flew for the first time on 2 May 1980. Deliveries are scheduled to begin in the late Autumn of 1982.

In September 1979 Cessna announced an increase to 8,845 kg (19,500 lb) in the maximum take-off weight of the Citation III. This allows greater payload/range flexibility. In addition, both the standard and extended-range versions now have the same maximum take-off gross weight.

TYPE: Twin-turbofan 10/15-seat long-range executive transport.

WINGS: Cantilever low-wing monoplane. NASA-developed supercritical section. Sweepback at quarter-chord 25°. Conventional two-spar structure of light alloy, utilising bonded and riveted construction. Anti-icing of wing leading-edges. Hydraulically-actuated trailing-edge flaps and spoilers.

FUSELAGE: Conventional semi-monocoque light alloy structure of circular cross-section. Fail-safe in pressurised area.

TAIL UNIT: Cantilever T-tail structure of light alloy, with swept horizontal and vertical surfaces. Anti-icing of tailplane leading-edges.

LANDING GEAR: Hydraulically-retractable tricycle type. Twin wheels on each main unit, single wheel on hydraulically-steerable nose unit. Oleo-pneumatic shock-absorbers. Hydraulic anti-skid braking system with pneumatic backup.

POWER PLANT: Two Garrett-AiResearch TFE 731-3B-100S turbofan engines, each rated at 16·24 kN (3,650 lb st) for take-off, mounted in pod on each side of rear fuselage. Hydraulically-operated thrust reversers optional. Two independent fuel systems, with integral tanks in each wing; max usable capacity 2,826 kg (6,230 lb). Additional fuel cell available optionally, behind aft fuselage bulkhead, providing max usable capacity of 3,647 kg (8,041 lb). Single-point pressure refuelling. Fuel heaters optional. Engine intake anti-icing system.

ACCOMMODATION: Crew of two on separate flight deck. Eight to thirteen passengers. Standard interior has six individual seats, with toilet at rear of cabin. Storage in fuselage nose for crew baggage. Main baggage space in tailcone. Airstair door forward of wing on port side. Overwing emergency escape hatch on starboard side. Cabin is pressurised, heated and air-conditioned. Extended-range option provides a fuel cell aft of the cabin's rear pressure bulkhead, reducing baggage space by 0·40 m³ (14 cu ft). Windscreen anti-icing.

SYSTEMS: Environmental control system, with separate control of flight deck and cabin conditions. Direct engine bleed pressurisation system, with nominal pressure differential of 0·66 bars (9·5 lb/sq in), provides 2,440 m (8,000 ft) cabin altitude to max certificated altitude. Dual parallel electrical buses. Hydraulic system of 207 bars (3,000 lb/sq in) for operation of flaps, spoilers, brakes, landing gear, nosewheel steering, and optional thrust reversers, with backup system to provide emergency power. Oxygen systems for crew and passengers.

AVIONICS: Standard avionics package provides full Category 2 capability, and includes a Sperry SPZ-650A automatic flight control system, digital central air data computer, vertical navigation (VNAV) system with dual waypoints, AA-215 radio altimeter, dual C-14 slaved compass system and VG-14A vertical gyro; dual nav/com and RMI, transponder, DME and weather radar. A wide range of optional avionics is available to customer's requirements.

DIMENSIONS, EXTERNAL:
Wing span	16·26 m (53 ft 4¼ in)
Wing aspect ratio	8·94
Length overall	16·90 m (55 ft 5½ in)
Height overall	5·27 m (17 ft 3½ in)
Tailplane span	5·60 m (18 ft 4½ in)
Wheel track	2·86 m (9 ft 4½ in)
Wheelbase	6·48 m (21 ft 3 in)

DIMENSIONS, INTERNAL:
Cabin:
Length, front to rear bulkhead	7·01 m (23 ft 0 in)
Length, aft of cockpit divider	5·66 m (18 ft 7 in)
Max width	1·73 m (5 ft 8 in)
Max height	1·78 m (5 ft 10 in)
Baggage capacity (aft)	2·10 m³ (74 cu ft)
Crew baggage compartment (nose)	0·28 m³ (10 cu ft)

AREA:
Wings, gross	29·00 m² (312 sq ft)

WEIGHTS (estimated; A: basic aircraft; B: with extended range option):
Weight empty: A		4,529 kg (9,985 lb)
B		4,569 kg (10,074 lb)
Max fuel: A		2,826 kg (6,230 lb)
B		3,647 kg (8,041 lb)
Max T-O weight: A, B		8,845 kg (19,500 lb)
Max ramp weight: A, B		8,936 kg (19,700 lb)
Max zero-fuel weight: A, B		5,987 kg (13,200 lb)
Max landing weight: A, B		7,484 kg (16,500 lb)

PERFORMANCE (estimated, at max T-O weight of 8,845 kg; 19,500 lb, unless stated otherwise):
Max level speed at 10,060 m (33,000 ft) at average cruise weight of 6,395 kg (14,100 lb):
469 knots (869 km/h; 540 mph)
Max cruising speed at average cruise weight of 6,214 kg (13,700 lb):
at 10,060 m (33,000 ft)	
	469 knots (869 km/h; 540 mph)
at 12,500 m (41,000 ft)	
	Mach 0·8 (459 knots; 850 km/h; 528 mph)
at 13,715 m (45,000 ft)	
	Mach 0·77 (442 knots; 818 km/h; 509 mph)
at 14,325 m (47,000 ft)	
	420 knots (779 km/h; 484 mph)
at 14,935 m (49,000 ft)	
	384 knots (711 km/h; 442 mph)

Stalling speed, flaps and gear down, at max landing weight	90 knots (167 km/h; 104 mph) CAS
Max rate of climb at S/L	1,365 m (4,475 ft)/min
Rate of climb at S/L, one engine out	408 m (1,340 ft)/min
Time to 12,500 m (41,000 ft)	21 min
Certificated ceiling	15,545 m (51,000 ft)
Ceiling, one engine out	8,780 m (28,800 ft)
FAA T-O field length at S/L	1,375 m (4,510 ft)
Landing distance at max landing weight	844 m (2,770 ft)

Range, with two crew and four passengers, standard fuel, allowances for T-O, climb, descent and 45 min reserves
2,375 nm (4,401 km; 2,735 miles)
Range, two crew and six passengers, with rear-fuselage fuel tank, at T-O weight of 8,845 kg (19,500 lb), allowances as above
3,000 nm (5,555 km; 3,450 miles)
Range, two crew and ten passengers, with rear-fuselage fuel tank, at T-O weight of 8,845 kg (19,500 lb), allowances as above
2,600 nm (4,818 km; 2,994 miles)

Prototype Cessna Citation III ten/fifteen-seat executive transport

COLEMILL
COLEMILL ENTERPRISES INC
PO Box 60627, Cornelia Fort Air Park, Nashville, Tennessee 37206
Telephone: (615) 262 0456

Colemill Enterprises is a company which specialises in performance improvement conversions of light twin-engined aircraft. Its most recent programme led to certification of a re-engined version of the Piper Navajo, to which it has given the name Panther Navajo. Representing the company's first conversion of a 'cabin-class' aircraft, the Navajo was selected because, with more than 2,000 in service worldwide, there was a considerable market potential. Testing of the prototype showed that a significant improvement in performance had been achieved and since that time Panthers have set nine world records in the FAI's Classes C1d and C1e, six for declared distance flights, and three for time to height.

COLEMILL PANTHER NAVAJO

Colemill's conversion of the Navajo involves more than a new engine installation. In addition to the power plant change, there are redesigned nacelles, additional continuous-running fuel pumps, a digital fuel totaliser, heavy-duty brakes, and wingtip-mounted landing lights. Conversion normally takes 10-14 days, and by early February 1980 some 70 aircraft had been modified, with output continuing at two per month alongside similar work being carried out on Beech and Cessna aircraft. The basic description of the Navajo, which can be found under the Piper entry in this edition, applies also to the Panther Navajo, except as follows:

WINGS: As for Piper Navajo except for new wingtips with marked under camber, which increase wing span and area.

LANDING GEAR: As for Piper Navajo except for the introduction of Cleveland four-spot heavy-duty disc brakes.

POWER PLANT: Two 261 kW (350 hp) Avco Lycoming TIO-540-J2BD turbocharged engines, each driving a Hartzell four-blade constant-speed fully-feathering metal propeller with 'Q' tips. Pressurised magnetos, Woodward propeller governors, synchrophasers, and unfeathering accumulators standard. Fuel system as for basic Navajo, except for the addition of continuous-running electrically-operated fuel pumps.

EQUIPMENT: Generally as for standard Navajo, but existing fuel-flow gauges are replaced by a Hoskins CFS 2000 fuel management computer giving digital readout of fuel remaining/fuel consumed. Supplemental wingtip landing lights can be operated independently of the standard nosewheel-mounted landing light, prior to lowering of landing gear.

DIMENSIONS, EXTERNAL: As for Piper Navajo except:
Wing span   13·00 m (42 ft 8 in)

LOADING: As for Piper Navajo except:
Max power loading   5·65 kg/kW (9·3 lb/hp)

PERFORMANCE (at max T-O weight):
Max level speed   269 knots (498 km/h; 309 mph)
Max cruising speed, 75% power at optimum altitude
    248 knots (459 km/h; 285 mph)
Cruising speed, 65% power at 7,300 m (24,000 ft)
    235 knots (435 km/h; 270 mph)
Cruising speed, 65% power at 3,650 m (12,000 ft)
    206 knots (381 km/h; 237 mph)
Max rate of climb at S/L   610 m (2,000 ft)/min
Rate of climb at S/L, one engine out
    122 m (400 ft)/min
Short field T-O run   229 m (750 ft)
T-O to 15 m (50 ft)   458 m (1,500 ft)
Landing from 15 m (50 ft)   427 m (1,400 ft)

COLEMILL PANTHER NAVAJO WITH WINGLETS

Colemill Enterprises has completed and flown a version of the Panther Navajo fitted with winglets. The prototype, which was a standard 1972 Piper Navajo, has been refurbished completely. In addition to improvements detailed for the Panther Navajo, and incorporation of winglets, it has its baggage area reduced by 0·28 m² (3 sq ft) to make possible a ten-seat interior with new lightweight seats.

The winglets improve stability in the lower-speed flight zone, down to stalling speed, and also provide cruising speed increases of 4-9 knots (8-16 km/h; 5-10 mph) at altitudes between 4,000 and 7,600 m (13,000 and 25,000 ft), at engine power settings between 45% and 65% of maximum power. This new version is, therefore, able to match the cruising speed of the standard Panther Navajo (without winglets) at power settings which offer greater fuel economy.

The flight test programme to gain a Supplementary Type Certificate was being flown during 1980, and it was anticipated that FAA approval of this conversion would be gained before the end of the year.

Colemill Panther Navajo with starboard propeller feathered (*Flight International*)

Colemill's latest Panther Navajo conversion, with winglets (*Howard Levy*)

COLEMILL EXECUTIVE 600

The Executive 600 is a Cessna 310, of Model G to U series, re-engined by Colemill to have two 224 kW (300 hp) Continental IO-520-E flat-six engines, each driving a McCauley three-blade propeller. Dimensions are unchanged; empty weight is increased by about 14 kg (30 lb); other data are as follows:

WEIGHT:
Max T-O weight   2,358 kg (5,200 lb)
PERFORMANCE (at max T-O weight):
Max cruising speed (75% power)
    205 knots (379 km/h; 236 mph)
Cruising speed (65% power)
    195 knots (361 km/h; 224 mph)
Stalling speed, wheels and flaps down
    64 knots (119 km/h; 74 mph)
Max rate of climb at S/L   762 m (2,500 ft)/min
Service ceiling   5,940 m (19,500 ft)
T-O to 15 m (50 ft)   518 m (1,700 ft)
Landing from 15 m (50 ft)   unchanged
Range with max fuel, 45 min reserves
    1,050 nm (1,944 km; 1,208 miles)

COLEMILL CENTURY 600

The Century 600 is a Cessna 320 re-engined by Colemill to have two 224 kW (300 hp) Continental IO-520-E flat-six engines, each driving a McCauley three-blade propeller. Dimensions are unchanged; empty weight is increased by about 14 kg (30 lb); other data are as follows:

WEIGHT:
Max T-O weight   2,404 kg (5,300 lb)
PERFORMANCE (at max T-O weight):
Max cruising speed (75% power)
    202 knots (374 km/h; 232 mph)

Cruising speed (65% power)
    192 knots (355 km/h; 221 mph)
Stalling speed, wheels and flaps down
    64 knots (119 km/h; 74 mph)
Max rate of climb at S/L   777 m (2,550 ft)/min
Service ceiling   5,940 m (19,500 ft)
T-O to 15 m (50 ft)   518 m (1,700 ft)
Landing from 15 m (50 ft)   unchanged
Range with max fuel, 45 min reserves
    1,060 nm (1,963 km; 1,220 miles)

COLEMILL PRESIDENT 600

The President 600 is a Beechcraft B55 Baron re-engined by Colemill to have two 224 kW (300 hp) Continental IO-520-E flat-six engines, each driving a three-blade propeller. Dimensions are unchanged; empty weight is increased by about 14 kg (30 lb); other data are as follows:

WEIGHT:
Max T-O weight   2,313 kg (5,100 lb)
PERFORMANCE (at max T-O weight):
Max cruising speed (75% power)
    203 knots (376 km/h; 233 mph)
Cruising speed (65% power)
    193 knots (357 km/h; 222 mph)
Stalling speed, wheels and flaps down
    66 knots (123 km/h; 76 mph)
Max rate of climb at S/L   823 m (2,700 ft)/min
Service ceiling   5,940 m (19,500 ft)
T-O to 15 m (50 ft)   497 m (1,631 ft)
Landing from 15 m (50 ft)   unchanged
Range with max fuel, 45 min reserves
    1,050 nm (1,944 km; 1,208 miles)

COMPOSITE AIRCRAFT CORPORATION

c/o DIETRICK SALES AND SERVICE

523 Ridgeview Drive, Florence, Kentucky 41042
Telephone: (606) 371 7247
PRESIDENT: Gerald P. Dietrick
CHIEF ENGINEER: George A. Alther

Mr Gerald P. Dietrick, the owner of Dietrick Sales and Service, has acquired the type certificate, the plant to manufacture non-woven unidirectional glassfibre fabric, moulds and engineering data, for construction of the Windecker Eagle 1, designed and developed from 1959 by Drs L. J. and F. M. Windecker. He has acquired also two of the five production Eagle 1s built by Windecker Industries Inc, and has an exclusive lease on a third aircraft. With these aircraft he is currently developing minor modifications before putting the Eagle back into production. It is planned to build 250 aircraft over a three-year

period, with initial deliveries scheduled for 1982; a company named Composite Aircraft Corporation has been registered for this purpose.

The five production Eagle 1s built by Windecker Industries had accumulated in excess of 8,000 flight hours by mid-January 1978. Details of the development of these aircraft can be found under the Windecker Industries entry in the 1974-75 *Jane's.*

In early 1979, aircraft N4198G was equipped with an autopilot, additional fuel tankage and navigation equipment, prior to being flown nonstop from Gander, Newfoundland, to Paris to participate in the 1979 Paris Air Show. This resulted in the Dietrick/Eagle combination setting two new world speed records in the FAI's Class C1d, with a flight which originated from Cincinnati, Ohio. The total distance covered was 3,622 nm (6,708 km; 4,168 miles), and the FAI accredited speeds were Cincinnati-Paris 164·21 knots (304·12 km/h; 188·97 mph), and New York-Paris 168·85 knots (312·72 km/h; 194·31 mph). Mr

Dietrick flew N4198G to the Hanover Air Show in 1980, and designed and installed an 817·5 litre (216 US gallon) fuel tank in the cabin to make possible a non-stop flight from Cincinnati to Munich at a record speed of 161·68 knots (299·44 km/h; 186·06 mph). At the termination of that flight, N4198G had logged total flight hours exceeding 2,800. Its T-O weight at Cincinnati was 2,250 kg (4,960 lb).

DIETRICK/WINDECKER EAGLE

TYPE: Four-seat cabin monoplane.
WINGS: Cantilever low-wing monoplane. NACA 64₂415 wing section. Dihedral 4° 30'. Incidence 2° 30'. No sweepback. Fail-safe structure of GRP. Frise-type ailerons of GRP with pilot-controlled bungee trimming. Plain trailing-edge flaps constructed of GRP.
FUSELAGE: Fail-safe monocoque structure of GRP.
TAIL UNIT: Conventional cantilever structure of GRP. Fixed-incidence tailplane. Trim tabs on starboard

elevator and rudder. Electrically actuated elevator trim optional.

LANDING GEAR: Retractable tricycle type with single wheel on each unit. Electro-hydraulic retraction, main wheels inward, nosewheel rearward. Main wheels faired by landing gear doors when retracted. Nosewheel door functions as a cowl flap when the gear is retracted. Windecker oleo-pneumatic shock-absorbers. Cleveland 6·00-6 main wheels, 5·00-5 nosewheel; all tyre pressures 3·09 bars (45 lb/sq in). Cleveland hydraulic disc brakes. Parking brake.

POWER PLANT: One 212·5 kW (285 hp) Continental IO-520-C flat-six engine, driving a McCauley two-blade constant-speed propeller. Fuel capacity 318 litres (84 US gallons), in two 159 litre (42 US gallon) integral wing tanks. Refuelling point outboard on upper surface of each wing. Oil capacity 11·5 litres (3 US gallons).

ACCOMMODATION: Four persons in pairs in enclosed cabin. Forward-hinged door on each side of cabin. Compartment aft of rear seats for 54 kg (120 lb) baggage with external access door on port side; hatshelf on bulkhead at rear of cabin. Cabin ventilated and heated by ram air over exhaust. Windscreen defrosting standard.

SYSTEMS: Hydraulic system, pressure 103·5 bars (1,500 lb/sq in), for landing gear. Vacuum system for instruments. 12V 70A alternator. 12V 35Ah battery. Four-outlet oxygen system optional.

AVIONICS AND EQUIPMENT: Standard avionics comprise one Narco MK-16 VHF, one Narco VOA-40 VOR/LOC converter-indicator and an antennae package which includes VOR, communications, ADF sense, transponder, DME, glideslope and marker beacon antennae, headset, microphone and all wiring harnesses. Optional avionics include the Brittain B5 autopilot, and a wide range of Narco units, available singly or as a complete package. Standard equipment includes full blind-flying instrumentation; 8-day clock; outside air temperature gauge; fully-reclining track-mounted seats with seat belt, headrest, fresh-air outlet, and map or magazine storage pocket for each seat; floor console between front seats for map and pencil storage; openable port side storm window; ultraviolet absorbent windscreen; shoulder harness for front seats; alternate static source; stall warning device; baggage net and attachments; soundproofing; tinted cabin windows; dome, radio, and map lights, and instrument panel floodlights; anti-collision beacons; landing, navigation, and taxi lights; external power socket; handholds; jack pads; retractable steps; towbar; and choice of four interior and exterior trims, the latter with polyurethane paint finish. Optional equipment includes control wheel

Dietrick/Windecker Eagle four-seat cabin monoplane of GRP construction, at 1979 Paris Air Show
(Brian M. Service)

mounted chronograph; heated pitot; heated stall warning transmitter; cabin fire extinguisher; cargo tiedown kit; instrument post lights; reading lights for rear seats; white strobe lights; engine primer; engine winterisation kit; and glider tow provisions.

DIMENSIONS, EXTERNAL:
Wing span	9·75 m (32 ft 0 in)
Wing chord, constant	1·68 m (5 ft 6 in)
Wing aspect ratio	5·82
Length overall	8·69 m (28 ft 6 in)
Height overall	2·90 m (9 ft 6 in)
Tailplane span	3·42 m (11 ft 3 in)
Wheel track	2·13 m (7 ft 0 in)
Wheelbase	1·98 m (6 ft 6 in)
Propeller diameter	2·13 m (7 ft 0 in)
Propeller ground clearance	0·28 m (11 in)
Cabin doors: Height	0·89 m (2 ft 11 in)
Width	0·97 m (3 ft 2 in)
Height to sill	0·40 m (1 ft 4 in)
Baggage door (port side):	
Height	0·60 m (1 ft 11½ in)
Width	0·39 m (1 ft 3½ in)

DIMENSIONS, INTERNAL:
Cabin: Length	3·30 m (10 ft 10 in)
Max width	1·28 m (4 ft 2⅜ in)
Max height	1·07 m (3 ft 6 in)

AREAS:
Wings, gross	15·51 m² (167 sq ft)
Ailerons (total)	1·42 m² (15·28 sq ft)
Trailing-edge flaps (total)	1·50 m² (16·1 sq ft)
Fin	0·93 m² (9·97 sq ft)
Rudder	0·59 m² (6·31 sq ft)

Tailplane	1·70 m² (18·3 sq ft)
Elevators, incl tab	1·48 m² (15·97 sq ft)

WEIGHTS AND LOADINGS:
Weight empty	975 kg (2,150 lb)
Max T-O and landing weight	1,542 kg (3,400 lb)
Max wing loading	94·7 kg/m² (19·3 lb/sq ft)
Max power loading	7·26 kg/kW (11·9 lb/hp)

PERFORMANCE (at max T-O weight):
Max level speed at S/L
more than 182 knots (338 km/h; 210 mph)
Cruising speed, 75% power at 2,135 m (7,000 ft)
177 knots (328 km/h; 204 mph)
Cruising speed, 65% power at 3,660 m (12,000 ft)
175 knots (325 km/h; 202 mph)
Stalling speed, flaps and landing gear up, power off
61·5 knots (114 km/h; 71 mph)
Stalling speed, flaps and landing gear down, power off
57·5 knots (106 km/h; 66 mph)
Max rate of climb at S/L 372 m (1,220 ft)/min
Service ceiling 5,485 m (18,000 ft)
T-O run 261 m (855 ft)
T-O to 15 m (50 ft) 515 m (1,690 ft)
Range with max fuel at 3,050 m (10,000 ft), 45 min
reserves 1,068 nm (1,979 km; 1,230 miles)

DIETRICK/WINDECKER EAGLE II

During the 1980 Hanover Air Show, Mr G. P. Dietrick announced that a new version of the Eagle was being studied by Composite Aircraft Corporation. Known as the Eagle II, it would be powered by an Allison 250-B17C turboprop engine, derated to 268 kW (360 shp). This is calculated to make possible a max cruising speed of more than 216 knots (400 km/h; 248 mph).

CONTINENTAL COPTERS
CONTINENTAL COPTERS INC

PO Box 18284, Cardinal Road, Fort Worth, Texas 76118
Telephone: (817) 281 2330
Telex: 758-426
PRESIDENT: John L. Scott

Continental Copters has developed and is producing a series of specialised single-seat agricultural conversions of various versions of the Bell Model 47 helicopter, under the name El Tomcat. Design work on the original conversion began in 1959 and the prototype El Tomcat Mk II flew in April of that year, receiving an FAA Supplemental Type Certificate shortly afterwards. Improved Mk III, IIIA, IIIB and IIIC versions followed, and current conversions embrace the Mk V and VI versions.

The Mk V of 1968 was succeeded subsequently by the Mk V-A, based on the Model 47G-2, with a 194 kW (260 hp) Avco Lycoming VO-435-A1F engine and a 24V electrical system; and the Mk V-B, with a 198 kW (265 hp) Avco Lycoming VO-435-B1A and 24V electrical system. Subsequently, production of both the Mk IIIC and Mk V-B was terminated in favour of the Mk V-A.

Next came the El Tomcat Mk VI, based on the Bell Model 47G-3B with turbocharged engine. Variants are the Mks VI-A and VI-B.

By the beginning of 1980 the company had delivered more than 80 Tomcats. These are in service with customers in the USA, Panama, Portugal, Puerto Rico, Switzerland and Turkey.

In addition, Continental Copters has for some years been producing passenger helicopters conforming to the Bell 47G and G-2 types. These are assembled from spare and/or surplus parts and are listed in the FAA Helicopter Specification H-1. Other helicopters, not included in this list, have been delivered to Latin America.

CONTINENTAL COPTERS JC-1 JET-CAT

In early 1975 the company began work on modifications to develop a special-purpose agricultural aircraft from the airframe of the Bell JetRanger. However, this was deferred in 1977 so that the company could concentrate on conversion of a Bell Model 204 (military UH-1) into a new type of single-seat agricultural aircraft. Work on the JetRanger project was resumed in late 1977, and in early 1978 the prototype, designated provisionally JC-1 Jet-Cat, began load testing. Intended both for agricultural and utility operations, provision is made for the use of a cargo

Continental Copters El Tomcat Mk V-A with current 3-piece centre frame

hook. The single-place cabin is similar in configuration to that of El Tomcat.

CONTINENTAL COPTERS EL TOMCAT Mk V-A

Each version of the El Tomcat is basically a Bell Model 47G-2 helicopter which has been converted into a specialised single-seat agricultural aircraft. Payload is increased by deletion of unnecessary structure and equipment. In particular, the original cabin is replaced by a simple functional cab for the pilot. This was improved during 1974 by the development of a strengthened 'cage' for the pilot, consisting of a rigid forward frame to the cockpit, constructed from 254 mm (1 in) square steel tube. Additionally, a wire deflector installation has been developed for this aircraft, consisting of a steel tube above and below the nose, mounted on the aircraft centreline. This would deflect any wires or cables to sharpened jaws mounted on the steel tubes.

Power plant consists of a 194 kW (260 hp) Avco Lycoming VO-435-A1F engine. Standard Bell Model 47D-1 fuel system with a capacity of 109 litres (29 US gallons). Oil capacity 11 litres (3 US gallons). A 24V electrical system is standard.

In the current El Tomcat Mk V-A, which was awarded a full Type Certificate by the FAA in May 1973, the windscreen has been further reduced in area and moved closer to the pilot compared with earlier versions: in addition, the new strengthened forward frame serves as the windscreen mounting. The glassfibre nose has been modified to ensure easy accessibility to all instruments, the battery and other equipment. It provides a flush mounting for two 600W landing lights which are controllable in elevation by the pilot during flight, landing-light switches being mounted on the collective stick, immediately below the throttle. The cabin roof is of glassfibre, lower than on earlier versions of El Tomcat, and incorporates wraparound side windows for rear-quarter view. An FAA-approved folding jump-seat has been developed to permit carriage of a flagman to distant work sites when large fields are being sprayed. Standard equipment includes pilot's shoulder harness.

Improvements introduced more recently include a three-piece centre frame to simplify air transit, repair and engine replacement; wider nose to provide more foot space for pilot; modified pilot's seat; raised and separated shoulder straps; and use of high compression pistons in the Avco Lycoming VO-435 engine.

El Tomcat has a revised control system. The collective control has been altered to conform to standard collective geometry, but Continental retains ball bearings in the collective jack shaft, instead of brass bushings, to provide smoother operation. A Harley Davidson throttle control is fitted. The flying controls are hydraulically-boosted.

The chemical hoppers take the form of two streamlined blister tanks which fit flush against the sides of the fuselage immediately aft of the cabin. A fan-driven pump is mounted adjacent to each tank, aft of the spraybar supports. A filtered ventilation system for the cockpit minimises toxic spray ingress during spraying operations. Types of spraygear fitted include Bell Agmaster, Simplex Lo-Profile and special designs developed by customers.

Apart from the changes noted, the basic structural description of the standard Bell Model 47 (which can be found under the Agusta entry in the Italian section of the 1976-77 *Jane's*) applies also to El Tomcat.

DIMENSIONS: As for standard Bell Model 47G-2
WEIGHTS:
Weight empty, less specialised equipment
623 kg (1,375 lb)
Max T-O weight   1,111 kg (2,450 lb)
PERFORMANCE:
As for standard Bell Model 47G-2 except:
Range (with fuel reserves for 30 min)
86 nm (160 km; 100 miles)

CONTINENTAL COPTERS
EL TOMCAT Mk VI-B

The original El Tomcat Mk VI was a conversion of the Bell Model 47G-3B, with a turbocharged Avco Lycoming TVO-435 engine, developing 201 kW (270 hp), and Bell 47-110-250-23 main rotor blades. The increased length of these blades made it necessary to extend the basic Mk V-A centre frame both fore and aft. The extension aft (as on

later production Bell 47s) was needed to provide adequate clearance between main and tail rotor blades, and extension forward to compensate for the resulting rearward movement of the CG.

As in the Mk V-A, the battery was accommodated in the nose of the cab. In addition, the engine oil tank was placed in the nose; an airscoop on top of and an outlet on the bottom of the nose were installed to allow ram air to carry away the heat radiated by the tank. The standard El Tomcat in-flight-adjustable landing lights were installed.

Only this prototype of the El Tomcat Mk VI was completed; it was supplied to an operator in the Rocky Mountain area for spraying operations at high altitude. FAA certification was not obtained prior to delivery.

The prototype was claimed to be very stable, and flight tests demonstrated its ability to hover directly into the wind with the pilot's hands and feet off the controls.

A prototype of the Mk VI-B, which has a component similarity to the Bell Model 47G-5, was subsequently completed and flown, and was awarded an FAA Supplemental Type Certificate in the Standard category; this is now the production version. The FAA required installation of a compass and altimeter to meet certification standards, and Continental Copters anticipated that instrument panel and windscreen changes would be required on subsequent aircraft to facilitate installation of these instruments. This has been catered for when carrying out the pilot's 'cage' modification as described for the Mk V-A. A new instrument panel, to bring engine speed and airspeed indicators closer to the pilot's line of vision and reduce reflections, was introduced for 1978: this has resulted in a changed fuselage nose with improved streamlining. Mk VI El Tomcats also have the three-piece centre frame of the Mk V-A.

The hydraulic reservoir/regulator unit for the Simplex Lo-Profile sprayer system fitted to the Mk VI-B has been

Modified nose of current El Tomcat Mk VI-B

mounted forward on the port side of the centre frame instead of in the usual rear position. This enables the pilot to see the hydraulic pressure gauge easily and also offsets the normal aft CG condition of the El Tomcat.

Empty weight of the El Tomcat Mk VI-B is 674 kg (1,487 lb) and max T-O weight 1,293 kg (2,850 lb). Maximum permissible speed has been limited to 61 knots (113 km/h; 70 mph) to minimise the airspeed calibration test. In other respects the flight envelope of the Mk VI-B is identical to that of the Bell 47G-5. Three examples of the Mk VI-B have been exported to Portugal.

Conversion kits for the Mk VI-B installation are available, and Continental Copters states that by using the data gained from this programme Supplemental Type Certification of conversions of Bell Model 47G-2A, -2B and -4 helicopters can be carried out with a minimum of FAA testing.

A Mk VI-C prototype with VO-435-A1F engine, which has high-compression pistons, and with the oil tank relocated in the nose, between instruments and battery, has received FAA approval.

EAGLE
EAGLE AIRCRAFT COMPANY
PO Box 4127, 1755 Westgate Drive, Suite 200, Boise, Idaho 83704
Telephone: (208) 375 7500
PRESIDENT: Dwain Griggs
GENERAL MANAGER: Wayne Mittleider
CHIEF DESIGNER: Dean Wilson
SALES MANAGER: Chet Bowers

EAGLE AIRCRAFT EAGLE DW-1

Eagle Aircraft Company is marketing a new agricultural aircraft, with large-span narrow-chord wings based on advanced glider technology, to which it has given the name Eagle. Other innovations include spraybooms built on to the trailing-edge of the lower wings, spoilers for roll control mounted outboard on each lower wing, and a charcoal filtered cockpit ventilation system, as well as a choice of two power plants.

The prototype flew originally with a Continental radial engine, as illustrated in the 1979-80 *Jane's*. This was replaced subsequently by an Avco Lycoming IO-540 flat-six engine, which was expected to become standard on production Eagles by the end of 1980.

The company announced on 7 June 1979 the signature of an agreement with Bellanca Aircraft Corporation to manufacture the Eagle on its behalf, and built a 2,954 m² (31,800 sq ft) factory adjacent to Bellanca's Alexandria, Minnesota, plant in which the aircraft is being produced. First aircraft delivered, to Precissi Flying Service of Lodi, California, in June 1980, was the radial-engined N8800R.

TYPE: Single-seat agricultural aircraft.
WINGS: Wire-braced single-bay biplane, with N-type interplane and centre-section struts. Narrow-chord wooden wings of advanced design, with spraybooms built on to the trailing-edges of the lower wings. Spoilers, each with booster tab, in upper surface of outboard section of each lower wing. Conventional ailerons with booster tabs on upper wings. Dacron fabric covering, with butyrate dope and polyurethane finish.
FUSELAGE: Conventional welded steel tube structure; rear part covered by Dacron fabric, and the remainder by quickly-removable side panels.
TAIL UNIT: Conventional wire-braced structure, with Dacron fabric covering, butyrate dope and polyurethane finish. Booster tab in elevator and rudder. Trim tab in elevator. Wire deflector cable between tip of fin and centre-section of upper wing.
LANDING GEAR: Non-retractable tailwheel type. Two side Vs and half-axles. Rubber-in-compression shockabsorbers. Cleveland main wheels and high-flotation tyres size 7·50-10. Cleveland hydraulically operated disc brakes. Parking brake. Wire cutter on leading-edge of each main gear V.
POWER PLANT: Alternative power plants include one 164 kW (220 hp) Gulf Coast conversion of the Continental W-670-6N radial engine, driving a Hartzell two-blade

Eagle Aircraft Eagle agricultural aircraft (Avco Lycoming IO-540 engine)

adjustable-pitch propeller; or a 224 kW (300 hp) Avco Lycoming IO-540-M1A5D flat-six engine, driving a Hartzell three-blade constant-speed propeller. Gravity-feed fuel tank in centre-section of upper wing, capacity 157·5 litres (41·6 US gallons). Wingtip fuel tanks for upper wing optional, with combined capacity of 106 litres (28 US gallons). Maximum fuel capacity 263·5 litres (69·6 US gallons). Refuelling point on top surface of upper wing.
ACCOMMODATION: Pilot only, beneath one-piece quick-release transparent canopy which is sealed against ingress of toxic chemicals. Canopy can be hinged to port or starboard by single lever, or can be removed entirely for open-cockpit flight. Pilot's seat has shoulder harness with inertia reel. Cockpit ventilated by ram air passed through charcoal filters. Chemical hopper, capacity 946 litres (250 US gallons) in front fuselage, with lightweight bottom loading valve. Baggage compartment for pilot, with external access door.
SYSTEMS: 24V electrical system powered by 28V 70A alternator. Hydraulic system for brakes only.
EQUIPMENT: Standard equipment includes sensitive altimeter, pilot's headrest, adjustable rudder pedals, stall warning device, windscreen cleaning access windows, stainless steel control cables, quick oil-drains, handholds on aft fuselage, tiedown rings, and complete wet dispersal system with 15·5 m (51 ft 0 in) boom. Internal and external polyurethane anti-corrosion protection. Optional items include air-conditioning and heating systems, dry dispersal system, and a night operations package which includes avionics, emergency

locator transmitter, instrument panel lights, overhead floodlights; beacon, navigation, landing, taxi, strobe and hopper lights, and a heavy-duty battery.
DIMENSIONS, EXTERNAL (A: 220 hp; and B: 300 hp engine):
Wing span: both versions   16·76 m (55 ft 0 in)
Wing aspect ratio   15
Length overall: A   7·92 m (26 ft 0 in)
B   8·38 m (27 ft 6 in)
Height overall: both versions   3·23 m (10 ft 7 in)
AREA:
Wings, gross   35·86 m² (386 sq ft)
WEIGHTS AND LOADINGS:
Weight empty: A   1,156 kg (2,549 lb)
B   1,053 kg (2,322 lb)
Max T-O weight: both versions   2,449 kg (5,400 lb)
Max wing loading, Restricted category:
both versions   68·3 kg/m² (14·0 lb/sq ft)
Max power loading, Restricted category:
A   14·93 kg/kW (24·5 lb/hp)
B   10·95 kg/kW (18·0 lb/hp)
PERFORMANCE (at max T-O weight, Restricted category):
Max working speed:
A   83 knots (153 km/h; 95 mph)
B   104 knots (193 km/h; 120 mph)
Min working speed:
both versions   56·5 knots (105 km/h; 65 mph)
Stalling speed, power off:
both versions   48 knots (88·5 km/h; 55 mph)
Stalling speed, power on:
both versions   44 knots (82 km/h; 51 mph)

ECTOR
ECTOR AIRCRAFT COMPANY
414 East Hillmont Road, Odessa, Texas 79762
Telephone: (915) 362 1841
PRESIDENT: Alvin H. Parker

ECTOR L-19 MOUNTAINEER and SUPER MOUNTAINEER

The Ector Aircraft Company has in production a civil version of the Cessna L-19 Bird Dog (last described in the

1964-65 *Jane's*), to which it has given the name Mountaineer. This is available in two models:

Mountaineer. Standard model, with 159 kW (213 hp) Continental O-470-11 engine and fixed-pitch propeller.

Continental O-470-11-13 (cruising speed increased to 108 knots; 201 km/h; 125 mph at 55% power) or O-470-11-13-15 engine and constant-speed propeller (104 knots; 193 km/h; 120 mph at 57% power) optional.

Super Mountaineer. More powerful version with a 179 kW (240 hp) Avco Lycoming O-540-A4B5 engine, driving a Hartzell Type HC-C2YK-1B two-blade constant-speed metal propeller, and with additional equipment as standard. In 1978 Ector obtained a Supplementary Type Certificate for the Super Mountaineer at a maximum T-O weight of 1,270 kg (2,800 lb), and delivered an aircraft for operation at this weight.

Generally similar to the original Cessna L-19, Ector's Mountaineers are rebuilt completely from new off-the-shelf or serviceable components. The entire airframe is corrosion-proofed with zinc chromate before assembly; mounting brackets for floats are built into the basic airframe; and all four side windows can be opened in flight. The rear seat is removable to permit the carriage of cargo.

More than 30 Mountaineers have been produced for service with various organisations as glider tugs and for patrol and general-purpose duties. Others are flown as sporting aircraft.

TYPE: Two-seat lightweight cabin monoplane.

WINGS: Braced high-wing monoplane. Single streamline-section bracing strut each side. Wing section NACA 2412. Dihedral 2° 8'. Incidence 1° 30' at root, −1° 30' at tip. All-metal single-spar structure, with metal skin. Frise-type all-metal ailerons. Fowler all-metal trailing-edge flaps. No tabs.

FUSELAGE: Conventional all-metal semi-monocoque structure.

TAIL UNIT: Cantilever all-metal structure. Trim tab in elevator. Small auxiliary fins are attached to tailplane tips of floatplane version.

LANDING GEAR: Non-retractable tailwheel type. Cantilever spring steel main legs. Goodyear main wheels with tyres size 6·00-6. Scott steerable tailwheel. Single-disc hydraulic brakes. Floats, skis or tandem landing gear for rough terrain optional.

POWER PLANT: One Continental or Avco Lycoming flat-six engine as detailed in model listings, driving a two-blade fixed-pitch or constant-speed propeller. One fuel tank in each wing root, total capacity 151·4 litres (40 US gallons). Optionally, fuel cells in each wing with a total capacity of 246 litres (65 US gallons). Refuelling points on wing upper surface. Oil capacity 9·4 litres (2·5 US gallons).

Ector Super Mountaineer, a civil version of the Cessna L-19 Bird Dog

ACCOMMODATION: Two seats in tandem in enclosed cabin with 360° field of vision. Door on starboard side. All four cabin side windows can be opened fully. Six skylights in roof. Space for baggage behind rear seats. With rear seat removed, 0·85 m³ (30 cu ft) of space is available for freight. Cabin heated and ventilated.

SYSTEMS: Hydraulic system for brakes only. Electrical system powered by 24V 50A engine-driven generator. Super Mountaineer has a 12V electrical system.

AVIONICS AND EQUIPMENT: Radio equipment available to customer's requirements. Navigation and landing lights, and heated pitot, standard. Stall warning indicator, Hobbs hour meter and Whelen three-light strobe system standard on Super Mountaineer. External power socket and wing racks optional.

DIMENSIONS, EXTERNAL:
Wing span	10·97 m (36 ft 0 in)
Wing chord at root	1·63 m (5 ft 4 in)
Wing chord at tip	1·09 m (3 ft 7 in)
Wing aspect ratio	7·35
Length overall	7·86 m (25 ft 9½ in)
Height overall	2·29 m (7 ft 6 in)
Tailplane span	3·21 m (10 ft 6½ in)
Propeller diameter	2·29 m (7 ft 6 in)
Propeller ground clearance	0·23 m (9 in)

Door: Height	0·64 m (2 ft 1 in)
Width	0·81 m (2 ft 8 in)
Height to sill	1·12 m (3 ft 8 in)

WEIGHTS (A: Mountaineer with O-470-11 engine and fixed-pitch propeller; B: Super Mountaineer):
Weight empty, equipped:	A	658 kg (1,450 lb)
	B	673 kg (1,483 lb)
Max T-O weight:	A	1,043 kg (2,300 lb)
	B	1,270 kg (2,800 lb)

PERFORMANCE (at max T-O weight):
Max level speed at S/L:		
	A	87 knots (161 km/h; 100 mph) TAS
	B	112 knots (208 km/h; 129 mph) IAS
Max cruising speed: B at 2,135 m (7,000 ft)		
		139 knots (257 km/h; 160 mph) TAS
Econ cruising speed: B at 2,895 m (9,500 ft)		
		109 knots (201 km/h; 125 mph) IAS
Stalling speed, flaps down:		
	B	45·5 knots (84 km/h; 52 mph)
Max rate of climb at S/L:	A	366 m (1,200 ft)/min
	B	549 m (1,800 ft)/min
Service ceiling:	A	6,980 m (22,900 ft)
T-O run:	A	122 m (400 ft)
Landing run:	A	98 m (320 ft)
Range with max fuel, no reserves:		
	A	651 nm (1,207 km; 750 miles)

EMAIR

EMAIR (a division of Emroth Co)

Hangar 38, Industrial Airpark, Harlingen, Texas 78550
Telephone: (512) 425 6363
PRESIDENT: George A. Roth

The development history of the original Emair MA-1, of which 25 were built before production ended in January 1976, can be found in earlier editions of *Jane's*. Flight testing of the more powerful MA-1B Diablo 1200 began in August 1975, and this version received FAA Type Approval in May 1976. By early 1980, a total of 48 Diablo 1200s had been delivered.

EMAIR MA-1B DIABLO 1200

The Diablo 1200 was designed specifically for agricultural use. For ease of maintenance and repair the fuselage comprises four bolt-together sections, covered by removable glassfibre side panels. Greater than average gap and stagger of the biplane wings improves pilot view and ensures easy access to the hopper; the wide-track main landing gear ensures adequate stability for operations from rough fields. The cockpit is fully enclosed, and sealed against the entry of dust and sprays.

The hopper, which forms an integral part of the front fuselage, has two outlets on which are mounted liquid-tight gates or doors. For granular dispersal the gates are controlled by a cockpit lever, the distribution of the granules being effected by a low-drag wing-type spreader mounted in the slipstream beneath the aircraft. For the distribution of liquids the gates remain closed, serving only as an emergency jettison device. Dispersal is accomplished by an easily-removable wind-driven spraypump, supplying spraybooms mounted in a low-drag area at the trailing-edge of each lower wing. A cockpit-controlled stop valve is located between the hopper and spraypump.

The Diablo 1200 has an 895 kW (1,200 hp) Wright R-1820 engine, derated to 671 kW (900 hp). This is claimed to make it the most powerful agricultural aircraft in current production in the west, and permits the carriage of very heavy payloads, especially under high-altitude conditions and from short or muddy fields. The geared engine drives a slow-turning, large-diameter propeller with broad blades, resulting in good propulsive efficiency and low noise levels.

TYPE: Single-seat agricultural biplane.

WINGS: Strut-braced biplane with forward-staggered wings of unequal span. NACA 4412 (modified) wing section. Dihedral 1° 30' on upper wing, 3° on lower wings. Incidence 4° 30' on upper wing, 4° on lower wings. No sweepback. Stagger 31°. Upper wing carried on streamline steel tube struts. Conventional two-spar structure. Centre-section of upper wing is of aluminium construction. Outer panels of top wing, and both lower wing panels, have spruce laminated spars and ribs, with duralumin channel-section compression struts and steel tie-rod internal bracing, and fabric covering. Ailerons, of aluminium construction with fabric covering, on both upper and lower wings, linked by struts. No trim tabs or slats. Butt fittings and inboard compression members of lower wings are stainless steel. Glassfibre wingtips.

FUSELAGE: Rectangular welded chrome-molybdenum steel tube framework in four separate bolt-together sections, with glassfibre side panels.

TAIL UNIT: Conventional single fin and rudder, of welded chrome-molybdenum steel tube with fabric covering. Wire-braced fixed-incidence tailplane and fin. Trim tab in each elevator. Trim/balance tab in rudder.

LANDING GEAR: Non-retractable tailwheel type. Oleo-pneumatic shock-absorbers on main and nosewheel units. Main legs enclosed in streamlined glassfibre fairings. Main-wheel tyres size 29 × 11·00-10. Steerable tailwheel, with tyre size 12·5 × 4·5, becomes free-swivelling when rudder is at near full deflection. Cleveland single-disc hydraulic main-wheel brakes. Parking brakes.

POWER PLANT: One 895 kW (1,200 hp) Wright R-1820 radial engine, derated to 671 kW (900 hp) and driving a Hamilton Standard Hydromatic three-blade constant-speed metal propeller. Fuel tank in upper wing centre-section, capacity 408 litres (108 US gallons). Refuelling point above upper wing. Max oil capacity 75·7 litres (20 US gallons).

ACCOMMODATION: Pilot only, on adjustable seat. Fully enclosed, sealed and ventilated cockpit in centre of fuselage, with reinforced overturn structure aft of cockpit. Sliding side-screens of cockpit canopy retract into cockpit wall; overhead section of canopy hinges to either port or starboard.

SYSTEMS: Hydraulic system for brakes only. Electrical system supplied by 24V engine-driven alternator and 24V 25Ah battery.

OPERATIONAL EQUIPMENT: Between the cockpit and the engine is mounted a glassfibre hopper for dust or liquid, with a capacity of 1·80 m³ (63·5 cu ft) or 1,798 litres (475 US gallons). It is built around the fuselage tubing, which in this area is of stainless steel to resist chemical corrosion. A window in the rear wall of the hopper allows in-flight inspection of the contents, and sight gauges are provided on each side of the hopper.

DIMENSIONS, EXTERNAL:
Wing span (upper)	12·70 m (41 ft 8 in)
Wing span (lower)	10·67 m (35 ft 0 in)

Emair MA-1B Diablo 1200 heavy-duty agricultural aircraft

Wing chord (both, constant)	1·60 m (5 ft 3 in)	Width	0·46 m (1 ft 6 in)	Max wing loading	102·53 kg/m² (21·0 lb/sq ft)	
Wing aspect ratio (upper)	7·9	AREAS:		Max power loading	5·68 kg/kW (9·33 lb/hp)	
Wing aspect ratio (lower)	6·7	Wings, gross	37·16 m² (400 sq ft)	PERFORMANCE (at certificated T-O weight):		
Wing stagger	1·19 m (3 ft 11 in)	Ailerons (total)	5·13 m² (55·2 sq ft)	Never-exceed speed		
Wing gap	1·98 m (6 ft 6 in)	Fin	0·29 m² (3·14 sq ft)		128 knots (238 km/h; 148 mph) CAS	
Length overall (tail up)	9·14 m (30 ft 0 in)	Rudder	1·10 m² (11·83 sq ft)	Max cruising and manoeuvring speed		
Height overall (tail down)	3·58 m (11 ft 9 in)	Tailplane	1·97 m² (21·16 sq ft)		102 knots (188 km/h; 117 mph) CAS	
Propeller diameter	3·05 m (10 ft 0 in)	Elevators, incl tabs	1·31 m² (14·14 sq ft)	Stalling speed, power off		
Propeller ground clearance (tail up)	0·25 m (10 in)	WEIGHTS AND LOADINGS:			54 knots (100 km/h; 62 mph)	
Tailplane span	3·81 m (12 ft 6 in)	Weight empty	1,928 kg (4,250 lb)	Stalling speed, power on		
Wheel track	2·59 m (8 ft 6 in)	Hopper load	1,360 kg (3,000 lb)		46 knots (85·5 km/h; 53 mph)	
Wheelbase	6·71 m (22 ft 0 in)	Certificated T-O and landing weight		Max rate of climb at S/L	518 m (1,700 ft)/min	
Hopper opening, above fuselage:			2,834 kg (6,250 lb)	Min ground turning radius	9·14 m (30 ft)	
Length	0·61 m (2 ft 0 in)	Max T-O weight (CAM.8)	3,810 kg (8,400 lb)			

ENSTROM
THE ENSTROM HELICOPTER CORPORATION

HEAD OFFICE AND WORKS: PO Box 277, Twin County Airport, Menominee, Michigan 49858
Telephone: (906) 863 9971
Telex: 26-3451
CHAIRMAN OF THE BOARD: John M. Ferris
PRESIDENT: Herbert Moseley
SENIOR VICE-PRESIDENT: Paul L. Shultz
EXECUTIVE VICE-PRESIDENT: J. F. Hansen
VICE-PRESIDENTS:
   D. E. Brandt (Engineering)
   Robert Kroll (Quality Control)
   Curt Larsen (Finance)

In its original form, as the R. J. Enstrom Corporation, this company began in 1959 to develop an experimental light helicopter built by Rudolph J. Enstrom, which flew for the first time on 12 November 1960. There followed a design and development programme on a new helicopter, designated F-28, and this flew for the first time in May 1962. A limited number of F-28s were built, and were followed by the improved Model F-28A in 1968.

The company was acquired by the Purex Corporation in October 1968 and was operated for a time as part of the Pacific Airmotive Aerospace group. Under this ownership, a turbocharged F-28B version was developed, as well as a Model T-28 turbine-powered version.

The activities of this group ended in February 1970; but in January 1971 the Purex shares were acquired by F. Lee Bailey, and manufacture of the F-28A was resumed. In January 1980 these shares were purchased by Bravo Investments BV, of the Netherlands, which company is now the owner of Enstrom. A total of 667 Enstrom helicopters had been built by 1 February 1980.

ENSTROM MODELS F-28 and 280

Production of the basic Model F-28A and the Model 280 Shark ended during 1978; details of these can be found in the 1978-79 *Jane's*. They were replaced by turbocharged versions of both models, under the designations F-28C and 280C respectively. These received FAA certification on 8 December 1975.

Models available in 1980 were as follows:

F-28C. Basic version, with Avco Lycoming HIO-360 engine and turbocharger.

F-28C-2. As F-28C, but with one-piece windscreen and centre instrument console.

Model 280C. Improved version of F-28C, with changed aerodynamic contours; tail stabilising surfaces which include a small dorsal fin, larger ventral fin, and small fixed horizontal surfaces; and increased fuel capacity.

In addition, the following versions are under development:

F-28F Falcon. Utility version of F-28C with wide one-piece windscreen and pedestal type instrument panel for improved view. New detail design to improve accessibility and simplify maintenance. Powered by a 168 kW (225 hp) Avco Lycoming flat-four engine.

Model 280L Hawk. Four-seat version of Model 280C, first flown on 27 December 1978. Described separately.

Model 480 Eagle. Version of the 280L Hawk powered by an Allison 250-C20B turboshaft engine and with accommodation for five persons.

An Enstrom wet or dry dispersal agricultural kit is available for fitment to the F-28C/280C. It comprises two side-mounted hoppers with large quick-fill openings, and spraybooms with a normal span of 9·04 m (29 ft 8 in), but extendable to 11·07 m (36 ft 4 in). A manually operated clutch provides positive control of the centrifugal pump, which has a liquid capacity of 227 litres (60 US gallons)/min. Dry discharge rate is variable from 0 to 272 kg (600 lb)/min. Weight of the entire quickly-removable dispersal system is 48 kg (105 lb). Hopper capacity is 340 litres (90 US gallons) of liquid or 0·5 m³ (17·4 cu ft) of dry chemicals.

The following description applies to the current production versions:

TYPE: Three-seat light helicopter.

ROTOR SYSTEM: Fully-articulated metal three-blade main rotor. Blades are of bonded light alloy construction, each attached to rotor hub by retention pin and drag link. Blade section NACA 0013·5. Two-blade teetering tail rotor, with blades of bonded light alloy construction. Tail rotor on port side. Blades do not fold. No rotor brake.

Enstrom F-28C-2, latest version of the basic F-28 helicopter

Enstrom Model 280C, with an Avco Lycoming HIO-360-E1AD turbocharged engine

Prototype of the Enstrom Model 280L Hawk four-seat light helicopter *(Howard Levy)*

ROTOR DRIVE: Poly V-belt drive system. Right-angle drive reduction gearbox. Main rotor/engine rpm ratio 1 : 7·154; tail rotor/engine rpm ratio 1 : 1·156.

FUSELAGE: Glassfibre and light alloy cab structure, with welded steel tube centre-section. Semi-monocoque aluminium tailcone structure.

LANDING GEAR: Skids carried on Enstrom oleo-pneumatic shock-absorbers. Air Cruiser inflatable floats available optionally.

POWER PLANT: One 153 kW (205 hp) Avco Lycoming HIO-360-E1AD flat-four engine with Rajay 301 E-10-2 turbocharger. Two fuel tanks, each of 75·7 litres (20 US gallons). Total fuel capacity 151·4 litres (40 US gallons). Oil capacity 7·5 litres (2 US gallons).

ACCOMMODATION: Pilot and two passengers, side by side on bench seat; centre place removable. Fully-transparent removable door on each side of cabin. Baggage space aft of engine compartment, with external access door.

Cabin heated and ventilated.

SYSTEMS: Electrical power provided by 12V 70A engine-driven alternator.

AVIONICS AND EQUIPMENT: Nav/com to customer's requirements. Cargo hook, floats, spraygear and litters optional.

DIMENSIONS, EXTERNAL:

Diameter of main rotor	9·75 m (32 ft 0 in)
Diameter of tail rotor	1·42 m (4 ft 8 in)
Distance between rotor centres	5·56 m (18 ft 3 in)
Main rotor blade chord	0·24 m (9½ in)
Length overall	8·94 m (29 ft 4 in)
Height to top of rotor hub	2·79 m (9 ft 2 in)
Skid track	2·36 m (7 ft 9 in)
Cabin doors (each): Height	1·04 m (3 ft 5 in)
Width	0·84 m (2 ft 9 in)
Height to sill	0·64 m (2 ft 1 in)

Baggage door: Height	0·55 m (1 ft 9½ in)
Width	0·39 m (1 ft 3½ in)
Height to sill	0·86 m (2 ft 10 in)

DIMENSIONS, INTERNAL:
Max width of cabin	1·47 m (4 ft 10 in)
Volume of baggage hold	0·20 m³ (7 cu ft)

AREAS:
Main rotor disc	74·69 m² (804 sq ft)
Tail rotor disc	1·58 m² (17·06 sq ft)

WEIGHTS AND LOADINGS (A: F-28C; B: 280C):
Weight empty: A, B	678 kg (1,495 lb)
Max T-O weight:	
A (normal), B	998 kg (2,200 lb)
A (agricultural)	1,179 kg (2,600 lb)
Max landing weight:	
A (agricultural)	1,066 kg (2,350 lb)
Max disc loading: A, B	13·38 kg/m² (2·74 lb/sq ft)
Max power loading: A, B	6·52 kg/kW (10·73 lb/hp)

PERFORMANCE (at max T-O weight, A: F-28C; B: 280C):
Never-exceed speed at S/L:	
A (normal)	97 knots (180 km/h; 112 mph) IAS
A (agricultural)	65 knots (120 km/h; 75 mph)
B	102 knots (188 km/h; 117 mph)
Max cruising speed at S/L:	
A, B	87 knots (161 km/h; 100 mph)
Max rate of climb at S/L:	
A, B	396 m (1,300 ft)/min
Service ceiling: A, B	5,485 m (18,000 ft)
Hovering ceiling IGE: A, B	3,475 m (11,400 ft)
Hovering ceiling OGE: A, B	2,530 m (8,300 ft)
Range with max fuel:	
A, B	205 nm (381 km; 237 miles)

ENSTROM MODEL 280L HAWK

Design of the Model 280L Hawk, a four-seat version of the Model 280C, began in January 1978; construction of two prototypes started in August. The first flight was made on 27 December 1978, and the first production examples, of which more than 60 have been ordered, are scheduled for delivery in April 1982.

The Model 280L is generally similar to the Model 280C, except as follows:

TYPE: Four-seat light helicopter.
ROTOR SYSTEM: As for Model 280C, except for increased-diameter main rotor blades, with sheet metal tabs at tip and mid-span.
ROTOR DRIVE: As Model 280C, except that engine is installed with drive shaft forward.
FUSELAGE: Glassfibre and light alloy cab structure, with welded steel tube and light alloy centre-section. Semi-monocoque tailcone structure of light alloy. Fail-safe construction in major areas.
TAIL UNIT: Fixed horizontal surface of light alloy, with small endplate fins.
LANDING GEAR: As Model 280C.
POWER PLANT: One 168 kW (225 hp) Avco Lycoming HIO-360-F1AD flat-four engine with Rajay turbocharger. Two fuel tanks, one each side of main transmission, with combined capacity of 170 litres (45 US gallons). Refuelling point on each side of fuselage upper surface. Oil capacity 7·5 litres (2 US gallons).
ACCOMMODATION: Individual, adjustable seats for pilot and co-pilot forward, two passengers aft, with baggage hold at rear of cabin. Double doors on each side of cabin. Accommodation is heated and ventilated as standard. Air-conditioning optional.
SYSTEM: Electrical system powered by 12V 70A engine-driven alternator.
AVIONICS AND EQUIPMENT: As for Model 280C.
DIMENSIONS, EXTERNAL:
Diameter of main rotor	10·36 m (34 ft 0 in)
Diameter of tail rotor	1·42 m (4 ft 8 in)
Distance between rotor centres	5·87 m (19 ft 3 in)
Main rotor blade chord	0·24 m (9½ in)
Length overall	9·86 m (32 ft 4 in)
Height overall	2·79 m (9 ft 2 in)
Cabin doors (each): Height	0·97 m (3 ft 2 in)
Width	1·30 m (4 ft 2 in)
Height to sill	0·71 m (2 ft 4 in)
Baggage door: Height	0·48 m (1 ft 7 in)
Width	0·58 m (1 ft 11 in)
Height to sill	0·71 m (2 ft 4 in)

DIMENSIONS, INTERNAL:
Cabin: Length	1·78 m (5 ft 10 in)
Max width	1·47 m (4 ft 10 in)
Max height	1·22 m (4 ft 0 in)
Floor area	2·60 m² (28 sq ft)
Volume	3·06 m³ (108 cu ft)
Volume of baggage hold	0·34 m³ (12 cu ft)

AREAS:
Main rotor disc	84·35 m² (908 sq ft)
Tail rotor disc	1·58 m² (17·06 sq ft)

WEIGHTS AND LOADINGS:
Weight empty, basic	708 kg (1,560 lb)
Max T-O and landing weight	1,179 kg (2,600 lb)
Max disc loading	13·98 kg/m² (2·86 lb/sq ft)
Max power loading	7·02 kg/kW (11·56 lb/hp)

PERFORMANCE (at max T-O weight):
Never-exceed speed	104 knots (193 km/h; 120 mph)
Max level and cruising speed at S/L	95·5 knots (177 km/h; 110 mph)
Max rate of climb at S/L	349 m (1,144 ft)/min
Service ceiling	3,660 m (12,000 ft)
Hovering ceiling IGE	3,110 m (10,200 ft)
Hovering ceiling OGE	1,890 m (6,200 ft)
Range with max fuel at 1,220 m (4,000 ft)	263 nm (488 km; 303 miles)

EXCALIBUR
EXCALIBUR AVIATION COMPANY

PO Box 32007, San Antonio, Texas 78216
Telephone: (512) 927 6201
PRESIDENT: William C. Hickey

Excalibur Aviation is engaged in the production of improved versions of the Beechcraft Queen Air. These modified aircraft, named Queenaire 800 and Queenaire 8800, are being completed at the rate of one per month. The conversion provides improved speed and range, together with reduced operating costs.

EXCALIBUR QUEENAIRE 800 and 8800

The Excalibur modification of Queen Air 65s and 80s includes installation of two 298 kW (400 hp) Avco Lycoming IO-720-A1B eight-cylinder engines, each driving a Hartzell three-blade constant-speed and fully-feathering metal propeller; new engine mountings; new exhaust system; new low-drag engine nacelles; new (or zero-time overhauled and certificated) accessories; and Excalibur fully-enclosed wheel-well doors. Modifications of the Beechcraft Queen Air 65, A65 and 80 of all serial numbers are designated Queenaire 800; similar modifications to the Queen Air A80 and B80 of all serial numbers have the designation Queenaire 8800.

WEIGHTS (A: Queenaire 800; B: Queenaire 8800):
Weight empty, equipped (average):	
A	2,449 kg (5,400 lb)
B	2,631 kg (5,800 lb)
Max T-O weight:	
A	3,628 kg (8,000 lb)
B	3,991 kg (8,800 lb)
Max landing weight:	
A	3,447 kg (7,600 lb)
B	3,792 kg (8,360 lb)

PERFORMANCE (at max T-O weight):
Cruising speed, 75% power:	
A, B at 2,530 m (8,300 ft)	201 knots (372 km/h; 231 mph)
Cruising speed, 65% power:	
A, B at 3,050 m (10,000 ft)	195 knots (362 km/h; 225 mph)
Cruising speed, 45% power at 3,050 m (10,000 ft):	
A, B	172 knots (319 km/h; 198 mph)
Stalling speed, gear and flaps up:	
A	80 knots (148 km/h; 92 mph)
B	86 knots (160 km/h; 99 mph)
Stalling speed, gear and flaps down:	
A	68 knots (126 km/h; 78 mph)
B	70 knots (129 km/h; 80 mph)
Max rate of climb at S/L:	
A	468 m (1,535 ft)/min
B	454 m (1,490 ft)/min
Rate of climb at S/L, one engine out:	
A	110 m (360 ft)/min
B	76 m (250 ft)/min
Service ceiling:	
A	6,005 m (19,700 ft)
B	5,700 m (18,700 ft)
Service ceiling, one engine out:	
A	3,595 m (11,800 ft)
B	3,110 m (10,200 ft)
T-O to 15 m (50 ft):	
A	520 m (1,706 ft)
B	625 m (2,050 ft)
Landing from 15 m (50 ft):	
A	663 m (2,176 ft)
B	747 m (2,450 ft)
Range with max fuel at 3,050 m (10,000 ft), with 113·5 litres (30 US gallons) reserves:	
A	1,322 nm (2,451 km; 1,523 miles)
B	1,547 nm (2,867 km; 1,782 miles)

Typical Excalibur Queenaire 800/8800 conversion (two Avco Lycoming IO-720-A1B engines)

FAIRCHILD INDUSTRIES
FAIRCHILD INDUSTRIES INC

CORPORATE OFFICES: 20301 Century Boulevard, Germantown, Maryland 20767

Telephone: (301) 428 6000
CHAIRMAN OF THE BOARD AND CHIEF EXECUTIVE OFFICER: Edward G. Uhl
PRESIDENT AND CHIEF OPERATING OFFICER: John F. Dealy
EXECUTIVE VICE-PRESIDENT: Charles Collis
SENIOR CORPORATE VICE-PRESIDENTS:
  Emanuel Fthenakis (Chairman & Chief Executive Officer, Fairchild Space & Electronics Company; President, American Satellite Corporation)
  Constantine J. Stathis (President, Swearingen Aviation Corporation; General Manager, Fairchild Aircraft Service Division)
  James R. Wilson (Treasurer & Chief Financial Officer)
CORPORATE VICE-PRESIDENTS:
  George S. Attridge (Comptroller)
  William R. Beckert
  Robert J. Dixon (President, Fairchild Republic Company)
  Harry Dornbrand
  James J. Foody (Aerospace Development)
  Dr Norman Grossman (Chairman, Fairchild Republic Company)
  Richard R. Molleur (General Counsel)
  J. Gilbert Nettleton Jr (Marketing)
  Joseph F. O'Connell (General Manager, Fairchild Burns Company)
  Richard G. Orr (General Manager, Fairchild Stratos Division)
  Dr John W. Townsend Jr (President, Fairchild Space & Electronics Company)
  Robert C. Woods
SECRETARY: John D. Jackson

Fairchild Republic Company
DIVISIONAL OFFICE AND WORKS: Farmingdale, Long Island, New York 11735
CHAIRMAN: Dr Norman Grossman
PRESIDENT: Robert J. Dixon
HAGERSTOWN FACILITY: Hagerstown, Maryland 21740
SITE ADMINISTRATOR: Paul Schmidt

Fairchild Aircraft Service Division
DIVISIONAL OFFICE AND WORKS: PO Drawer 1177, Crestview, Florida 32536
GENERAL MANAGER: Constantine J. Stathis

Fairchild Space and Electronics Company
Germantown, Maryland 20767
PRESIDENT: Dr John W. Townsend Jr

Swearingen Aviation Corporation
San Antonio, Texas 78284
PRESIDENT: Constantine Stathis

Fairchild Stratos Division
Manhattan Beach, California 90266
GENERAL MANAGER: Richard G. Orr

Fairchild Industrial Products Division
Winston-Salem, North Carolina 27105
GENERAL MANAGER: Robert L. Slater

Fairchild Burns Company
Winston-Salem, North Carolina 27105
GENERAL MANAGER: Joseph F. O'Connell

American Satellite Corporation
Germantown, Maryland 20767
PRESIDENT: Emanuel Fthenakis

S. J. Industries Inc
Alexandria, Virginia 22304
PRESIDENT: R. Hugh Steele

Fairchild Industries is a diversified aerospace and communications company which builds military and civilian

aircraft, manufactures spacecraft and aircraft subsystems, industrial and electronic products, and operates a domestic satellite communications system.

The Fairchild Republic Company (see following entry) combines the corporation's military aircraft research, design, manufacture and personnel into one division. Facilities are located at Farmingdale, Long Island, New York; and Hagerstown, Maryland.

Based in Crestview, Florida, Fairchild Aircraft Service Division is involved in aircraft maintenance, repair and modification, as well as production of aircraft components. Current programmes include support equipment and fire-suppression foam for the A-10, components for Swearingen aircraft, and seats for military aircraft.

The Fairchild Space and Electronics Company directs the corporation's efforts in the design, development and manufacture of spacecraft, spacecraft subsystems, telecommunications ground equipment, and avionics systems; details of some of these programmes can be found in the

Spaceflight section. The division also builds avionics systems, including armament control systems for the Fairchild A-10, Grumman F-14A Tomcat, and the Navy's Light Airborne Multi-Purpose System (LAMPS) helicopter; and aircraft data annotation systems.

The Fairchild Stratos Division specialises in the development and manufacture of aerospace and commercial aircraft subsystems, accessories and components. It is now manufacturing valves and the ammonia boiler cooling system for the Space Shuttle, bleed air turbines for Boeing 747 aircraft, aviation cooling packages, and food carts and galleys for commercial aircraft.

Swearingen Aviation Corporation (which see), a wholly owned Fairchild subsidiary, manufactures the Merlin and Metro series of executive, commuter and special-mission aircraft.

Fairchild Burns Company manufactures aircraft passenger seating used by more than 50 airlines worldwide, including the Airest 2000 line of lightweight seats.

FAIRCHILD REPUBLIC COMPANY
DIVISIONAL OFFICE AND WORKS: Farmingdale, Long Island, New York 11735
Telephone: (516) 531 0105
Telex: 96-7735
Founded on 17 February 1931, as the Seversky Aircraft Company, Republic operated as Republic Aviation Corporation from 1939 until September 1965, when it became a division of Fairchild Hiller Corporation, now Fairchild Industries Inc.

Its current work includes manufacture of the A-10 Thunderbolt II aircraft, structural components for the Boeing 747 and 757 airliners, tail fins and rudders for the Grumman F-14 Tomcat, and wings for Swearingen aircraft. It is developing a new transport aircraft jointly with Saab-Scania of Sweden (see International section).

FAIRCHILD REPUBLIC THUNDERBOLT II
USAF designation: A-10A
On 18 December 1970, Fairchild Republic and Northrop were selected as the two companies that were each to build two prototypes for evaluation under the US Air Force's A-X programme, initiated in 1967, for a close-support aircraft. The first Fairchild Republic prototype (71-1369), designated YA-10A, flew for the first time on 10 May 1972. On 18 January 1973 it was announced that the Fairchild A-10A had been selected as the winner. The first of six DT and E aircraft flew on 15 February 1975. Details of them can be found in the 1977-78 *Jane's*.

The first flight by a production A-10A (75-00258) was made on 21 October 1975. Production of a total of 825 aircraft is planned (including the six DT and E aircraft). The 400th production A-10A was due to be delivered in September 1980.

The first combat-ready A-10A wing was the 354th Tactical Fighter Wing, based at Myrtle Beach, South Carolina, to which deliveries began in March 1977. In May 1977 several A-10As were assigned to the 422nd Fighter Weapons Squadron of the 57th Tactical Training Wing at Nellis AFB, Nevada, for operational training and testing purposes. On 15 October 1977 the 356th Tactical Fighter Squadron of 354 TFW became the first combat-ready A-10 squadron.

In August 1977, six A-10As flew to Europe for the first live firing of the aircraft's 30 mm cannon and the anti-armour Maverick air-to-ground missile in the NATO theatre, expending 7·5 tons of conventional 500 lb bombs and 9,000 rounds of 30 mm ammunition during 117 close support sorties.

The first overseas deployment of the A-10 was made on

25 January 1979, with the arrival of 14 Thunderbolt IIs at RAF stations Bentwaters and Woodbridge in the UK, to equip the US Air Force's 81st Tactical Fighter Wing. Six squadrons will eventually be based at the two UK stations.

Deliveries of new production A-10As to four Tactical Fighter Groups of the Air National Guard are also under way, the A-10 being the first first-line aircraft to be assigned to ANG units. Air Force Reserve units also are scheduled to receive A-10As in 1980-81.

A two-seat night/adverse weather attack version of the A-10A is described separately.

TYPE: Single-seat close-support aircraft.

WINGS: Cantilever low-wing monoplane, with wide-chord, deep aerofoil section (NACA 6716 on centre-section and at start of outer panel, NACA 6713 at tip) to provide low wing loading. Incidence −1°. Dihedral 7° on outer panels. Aluminium alloy three-spar structure, consisting of one-piece constant-chord centre-section and tapered outer panels with integrally stiffened skins and drooped (cambered) wingtips. Outer panel leading-edges and cores of trailing-edges are of honeycomb sandwich. Four-point attachment of wings to fuselage, at front and rear spars. Two-segment, three-position trailing-edge slotted flaps, interchangeable right with left. Wide-span ailerons, made up of dual upper and lower surfaces that separate to serve as airbrakes. Flaps, airbrakes and ailerons actuated hydraulically. Ailerons pilot-controlled by servo tab during manual reversion. Small leading-edge slat inboard of each main-wheel fairing. Redundant and armour-protected flight control system.

FUSELAGE: Semi-monocoque structure of aluminium alloy (chiefly 2024 and 7075), with four main longerons, multiple frames, and lap-jointed and riveted skins. Built in front, centre and aft portions. Single-curvature components aft of nose portion, interchangeable right with left. Centre portion incorporates wing box carry-through structure.

TAIL UNIT: Cantilever aluminium alloy structure, with twin fins and interchangeable rudders mounted at the tips of constant-chord tailplane. Interchangeable elevators, each with an electrically-operated trim tab. Rudders and elevators actuated hydraulically. Redundant and armour-protected flight control system.

LANDING GEAR: Menasco retractable tricycle type with single wheel on each unit. All units retract forward, and have provision for emergency gravity extension. Interchangeable main-wheel units retract into non-structural pod fairings attached to the lower surface of the wings. When fully retracted approximately half of each wheel

protrudes from the fairing. Steerable nosewheel is offset to starboard to clear firing barrel of gun. Main wheels size 36 × 11, Type VII; nosewheel size 24 × 7·7-10, Type VII.

POWER PLANT: Two General Electric TF34-GE-100 high bypass ratio turbofan engines, each rated at 40·3 kN (9,065 lb st), enclosed in separate pods, each pylon-mounted to the upper rear fuselage at a point approximately midway between the wing trailing-edges and the tailplane leading-edges. Fuel is contained in two tear-resistant and self-sealing cells in the fuselage, and two smaller, adjacent integral cells in the wing centre-section. Maximum internal fuel capacity 4,853 kg (10,700 lb). All fuel cells are internally filled with reticulated foam, and all fuel systems pipework is contained within the cells except for the feeds to the engines, which have self-sealing covers. Three 2,271 litre (600 US gallon) jettisonable auxiliary tanks can be carried on underwing and fuselage centreline pylons. Provision for in-flight refuelling using universal aerial refuelling receptacle slipway installation (UARRSI).

ACCOMMODATION: Single-seat enclosed cockpit, well forward of wings, with large transparent bubble canopy to provide all-round view. Bulletproof windscreen. Canopy is hinged at rear and opens upward. Douglas ejection seat operable at speeds from 450 knots (834 km/h; 518 mph) down to zero speed at zero height. Entire cockpit area is protected by an armoured 'bath-tub' structure of titanium, capable of withstanding projectiles of up to 23 mm calibre.

SYSTEMS: Redundant control system incorporates two 207 bar (3,000 lb/sq in) primary hydraulic flight control systems, each powered by an engine-driven pump, and a manual backup. Hydraulic systems actuate flaps, flying control surfaces, landing gear, brakes and nosewheel steering. Two independent hydraulic motors, either of which is sufficient to sustain half-rate firing, supply drive for 30 mm gun barrel rotation. Electrical system includes two 30/40kVA 115/200V AC engine-driven generators and a standby battery and inverter. Auxiliary power unit. Environmental control system, using engine bleed air for cockpit pressurisation and air-conditioning, pressurisation of pilot's g suit, windscreen anti-icing and rain clearance, fuel transfer, gun compartment purging, and other services.

AVIONICS AND EQUIPMENT: Head-up display giving air-speed, altitude and dive angle; weapons delivery package with dual reticle optical sight for use in conjunction with underfuselage Pave Penny laser target seeker pod; target penetration aids; associated equipment for Maverick and other missile systems; IFF/SIF (AIMS); UHF/AM; VHF/AM; VHF/FM; Tacan; UHF/ADF; ILS/FDC; X-band transponder; INS; heading and attitude reference system (HARS); radar homing and warning (RHAW); secure voice communications; active or passive electronic countermeasures (ECM); armament control panel; and gun camera. Space provisions for HF/SSB, and other 'growth' avionics and equipment.

ARMAMENT: General Electric GAU-8/A Avenger 30 mm seven-barrel cannon, mounted in nose with 2° depression and offset slightly to port so that as the barrels rotate the firing barrel is always on the aircraft centreline. Gun and handling system for the linkless ammunition are mechanically synchronised and driven by two motors fed from the aircraft's hydraulic system. The single-drum magazine has a capacity of 1,174 rounds, and has a dual firing rate of either 2,100 or 4,200 rds/min. Four stores pylons under each wing (one inboard and three outboard of each main-wheel fairing), and three under fuselage, for max external load of 7,250 kg (16,000 lb). External load with full internal fuel is 6,640 kg (14,638 lb). The centreline pylon and the two flanking fuselage pylons cannot be occupied simultaneously. The centreline pylon has a capacity of 2,268 kg (5,000 lb); the two fuselage outer pylons and two centre-section underwing pylons 1,587 kg (3,500 lb) each; the two innermost outer-wing pylons 1,134 kg (2,500 lb) each; and the four outermost wing pylons 453 kg (1,000 lb) each. These allow carriage of a wide range

Fairchild Republic A-10A Thunderbolt II single-seat twin-engined close-support aircraft *(Pilot Press)*

Fairchild Republic A-10A Thunderbolt II single-seat close-support aircraft

of stores, including twenty-eight 500 lb Mk-82 LDGP or Mk-82 retarded bombs; six 2,000 lb Mk-84 general-purpose bombs; eight BLU-1 or BLU-27/B incendiary bombs; four SUU-25 flare launchers; twenty Rockeye II cluster bombs, sixteen CBU-52/71 dispenser weapons; six AGM-65A Maverick missiles; Mk-82 and Mk-84 laser-guided bombs; Mk-84 electro-optically-guided bombs; two SUU-23 gun pods; ALE-40 chaff/flare system; ALQ-119 ECM pods, or other jammer pods; or up to three drop-tanks.

DIMENSIONS, EXTERNAL:

Wing span	17·53 m (57 ft 6 in)
Wing chord at root	3·04 m (9 ft 11½ in)
Wing chord (mean)	2·73 m (8 ft 11·32 in)
Wing chord at tip	1·99 m (6 ft 6·4 in)
Wing aspect ratio	6·54
Length overall	16·26 m (53 ft 4 in)
Height overall	4·47 m (14 ft 8 in)
Tailplane span	5·74 m (18 ft 10 in)
Wheel track	5·25 m (17 ft 2½ in)
Wheelbase	5·40 m (17 ft 8¾ in)

AREAS:

Wings, gross	47·01 m² (506·0 sq ft)
Ailerons (total, incl tabs)	4·42 m² (47·54 sq ft)
Trailing-edge flaps (total)	7·99 m² (85·99 sq ft)
Leading-edge slats (total)	0·98 m² (10·56 sq ft)
Airbrakes (total)	8·06 m² (86·78 sq ft)
Fins (total)	7·80 m² (83·96 sq ft)
Rudders (total)	2·18 m² (23·50 sq ft)
Tailplane	8·31 m² (89·40 sq ft)
Elevators (total, incl tabs)	2·69 m² (29·00 sq ft)

WEIGHTS AND LOADINGS:

Manufacturer's empty weight	9,761 kg (21,519 lb)
Operating weight empty	11,302 kg (24,918 lb)
*Basic design weight, equipped	14,420 kg (31,790 lb)
**Forward airstrip weight	14,846 kg (32,730 lb)
Internal fuel load	4,853 kg (10,700 lb)
Max external ordnance	7,250 kg (16,000 lb)
Max external ordnance with full internal fuel	6,640 kg (14,638 lb)
Max T-O weight	22,680 kg (50,000 lb)
Max wing loading	457·4 kg/m² (93·68 lb/sq ft)
Max power loading	266·7 kg/kN (2·61 lb/lb st)
Thrust/weight ratio	0·4

*incl six 500 lb bombs, 750 rds of ammunition, and fuel for 300 nm (555 km; 345 miles) with 20 min reserves
**with four Mk-82 bombs and 750 rds

PERFORMANCE: (at max T-O weight except where indicated):

Never-exceed speed	450 knots (834 km/h; 518 mph)
Max level speed	368 knots (681 km/h; 423 mph)
Combat speed at 1,525 m (5,000 ft), with six Mk-82 bombs	387 knots (717 km/h; 446 mph)

Cruising speed at S/L
300 knots (555 km/h; 345 mph)
Cruising speed at 1,525 m (5,000 ft)
336 knots (623 km/h; 387 mph)
Stabilised 45° dive speed below 2,440 m (8,000 ft), AUW of 15,932 kg (35,125 lb)
260 knots (481 km/h; 299 mph)
Max rate of climb at S/L at basic design weight
1,828 m (6,000 ft)/min
T-O distance:

at max T-O weight	1,220 m (4,000 ft)
at forward airstrip weight	433 m (1,420 ft)

Landing distance:

at max T-O weight	610 m (2,000 ft)
at forward airstrip weight	457 m (1,500 ft)

Operational radius, 20 min reserve:
close air support, 1·8 h loiter
250 nm (463 km; 288 miles)
deep strike 540 nm (1,000 km; 620 miles)
Ferry range, headwind of 50 knots (93 km/h; 58 mph)
2,208 nm (4,091 km; 2,542 miles)

FAIRCHILD REPUBLIC NIGHT/ADVERSE WEATHER A-10

The two-seat version of the A-10A Thunderbolt II is intended as a night/adverse weather (N/AW) attack aircraft, with secondary use as a trainer retaining operational capability. The company-funded prototype was converted under a lease agreement from one of the six single-seat DT & E A-10s built for the US Air Force in 1975, and made its first flight as a two-seater from Edwards AFB, California, on 4 May 1979. The Fairchild test programme continued until the end of September 1979, followed by several months of testing by US Air Force pilots at Eglin AFB,

Florida, where more than 100 flying hours had already been logged by the beginning of 1980. If, as a result of this feasibility evaluation, it is decided to procure the N/AW A-10 in quantity, it has been suggested that it could be deployed effectively on a one-to-one basis alongside in-service A-10As. Alternatively, if considered expedient, it would be possible to retrofit single-seat A-10As to N/AW A-10 standard.

The N/AW version of the A-10 carries, in addition to the pilot, a weapons system officer (WSO) in the aft cockpit, who is responsible for ECM, navigation and target or threat acquisition and designation. This enables the pilot to concentrate on control of the aircraft, with a far higher likelihood of success when attacking targets in darkness or adverse weather.

Generally similar to the single-seat A-10A, the N/AW version differs by having a second, aft, cockpit with raised seat to provide the WSO with virtually the same over-the-nose view as the pilot. His cockpit duplicates that of the pilot, except that it has a cathode ray tube (CRT) in lieu of a head-up display. Both ejection seats are of the Aces II type. Other changes include forward extensions of the port and starboard landing gear housings to accommodate radar and FLIR respectively, and taller twin fins to increase their effective area, thus maintaining the same directional stability factor as the single-seat A-10A. In the construction of the N/AW A-10, Fairchild has introduced welded/bonded fuselage panels and graphite composite tailplane leading-edges for test purposes.

To provide the two-seat A-10 with its essential night/adverse weather capability, there are changes to the avionics equipment. New equipment includes a modified version of the Westinghouse WX-50 multimode radar, which is used as a ground moving target indicator, for ground mapping, terrain following/avoidance, and threat detection; a modified version of the Texas Instruments AAR-42 FLIR; Ferranti Type 105 laser rangefinder; Litton LN-39 INS; Honeywell radar altimeter; a changed Kaiser HUD for the pilot and Hartmann CRT for the WSO; and General Electric low-light-level TV (included for comparison with FLIR). The N/AW A-10 retains the Martin Marietta AN/AAS-35 Pave Penny laser target designation pod, which is standard equipment of in-service A-10As. To cater for the power demands of the additional equipment, two 30/40kVA generators are fitted to this aircraft.

The description of the A-10A Thunderbolt II applies also to the N/AW A-10, except as described above. Available specification and performance figures are as follows:

DIMENSIONS, EXTERNAL: As for A-10A except:
Height overall 4·67 m (15 ft 4 in)
AREAS: As for A-10A except:
Fins (total) 10·37 m² (111·6 sq ft)
WEIGHTS:
Operating weight empty 12,986 kg (28,630 lb)
Mission T-O weight, with 4,853 kg (10,700 lb) fuel
21,061 kg (46,433 lb)
PERFORMANCE (at mission T-O weight):

Max level speed	365 knots (676 km/h; 420 mph)
T-O run	945 m (3,100 ft)
Landing run	427 m (1,400 ft)
Mission radius	247 nm (458 km; 284 miles)

Fairchild Republic two-seat night/adverse weather version of the A-10

Cutaway drawing showing disposition of cockpits and equipment in night/adverse weather version of A-10

FOXJET
FOXJET INTERNATIONAL INC (a subsidiary of Fox Industries Inc)

HEAD OFFICE: 6701 West 110th Street, Minneapolis, Minnesota 55438
Telephone: (612) 941 8870 or (612) 944 2255
PRESIDENT: Tony Fox

In the Spring of 1977, details were released of a light-weight four-seat twin-turbofan transport named Foxjet F600 which was expected to operate at 20 per cent of the fuel costs of the most economical business jet then in service. Since that time, the design has undergone considerable development. In particular, the type of Williams Research turbofan now specified to power the Foxjet develops 40 per cent more thrust than the WR19-3 originally chosen. This has made possible a scale-up of the overall dimensions, and the cabin will now accommodate up to six people in comfort.

A new wing, with reduced sweepback and higher aspect ratio, has been designed for the Foxjet by Branson Aircraft Corporation. Known as the Foxjet Super-Flow wing, this can be modified easily to supercritical form when required by future power increase, and is claimed to improve stability and low-speed control. Performance is generally improved by these changes. Fuel cost was claimed to be less than 10 US cents per mile at mid-1978 prices.

The company announced on 26 March 1979 the formation of Foxjet Austral-Asia by four Australian businessmen to sell and lease the Foxjet F600 in that area.

FOXJET F600

The prototype of this lightweight twin-turbofan transport was expected to fly in 1980. Firm orders for 73 aircraft, backed by deposits, were in hand in mid-1978, and Foxjet International envisages eventual manufacture of 44 Foxjet F600s per month. Engine development is expected to uprate the present turbofan to 5·35 kN (1,200 lb st), with a subsequent refanned version rated at 6·24 kN (1,400 lb st).

TYPE: Four/six-seat twin-turbofan transport.
WINGS: Cantilever low-wing monoplane. NACA 65 Series laminar-flow section. Moderate leading-edge sweepback; straight trailing-edge. All-metal fail-safe structure, primarily of light alloy. Electrically-operated modified Fowler type single-slotted light alloy trailing-edge flaps. Manually-operated ailerons. Hydraulically-operated spoilers, forward of flaps, serve also as airbrakes. Trim tab in port aileron. Electrical anti-icing of each wing leading-edge at root; optional pneumatic de-icing boots for remainder of leading-edges.
FUSELAGE: Semi-monocoque light alloy fail-safe structure of circular cross-section. Light alloy honeycomb pressure bulkheads and baggage deck.
TAIL UNIT: Cantilever multi-spar light alloy structure with swept vertical and horizontal surfaces. Variable-incidence tailplane mounted approximately midway up fin. Manually-operated control surfaces, with tab in rudder. Leading-edges fitted with de-icing system.
LANDING GEAR: Hydraulically-retractable tricycle type, manufactured by Wiebel Tool Company, with twin wheels on each unit. Main units retract inward, nose unit aft. Manually-operated emergency hydraulic system. Oleo-pneumatic shock-absorbers. Main wheels have low-pressure tyres size 5·00-5. Hydraulically-steerable nosewheel unit, with water-chine tyres size 11 × 4·00-5. Hydraulic disc brakes on main wheels.
POWER PLANT: Two 3·78 kN (850 lb st) Williams Research WR44-800 turbofan engines, pod-mounted one each side of rear fuselage. Integral wing fuel tanks, total capacity 825 litres (218 US gallons). Engine inlet anti-icing system.
ACCOMMODATION: Pilot and three to five passengers, in pairs. Dual controls optional. Four standard seats have fore and aft, vertical, and recline adjustment. Seat belts for all seats; pilot's also has shoulder harness. Two-piece door (upward-hinged portion, and downward-

Mockup of the Foxjet F600 lightweight transport aircraft (*Erik Simonsen*)

Foxjet F600 four/six-seat twin-turbofan transport (*Pilot Press*)

hinged portion with integral steps) on port side forward of wing. Emergency exit on starboard side. Accommodation air-conditioned and pressurised. Birdproof windscreen with pneumatic system for rain removal, defogging and defrosting. Equipment access door on port side of nose. Baggage hold aft of cabin.
SYSTEMS: Pressurisation system with max differential of 0·59 bars (8·5 lb/sq in), providing a cabin altitude of 2,440 m (8,000 ft) to 12,500 m (41,000 ft). Electrical system. Hydraulic system, with hydraulic backup. Pneumatic system. Oxygen system.
AVIONICS AND EQUIPMENT: Standard avionics include dual nav/com, autopilot/flight director, ADF, DME and transponder. Weather radar optional. Standard equipment includes full blind-flying instrumentation, sun visors, interior lighting, navigation lights, dual landing lights, taxi light, and three strobe lights. Optional equipment includes electrically-powered one-man towing system, stowed on board.

DIMENSIONS, EXTERNAL:

Wing span	9·64 m (31 ft 7½ in)
Wing aspect ratio	8
Length overall	9·70 m (31 ft 10 in)
Height overall	3·12 m (10 ft 2¾ in)
Diameter of centre-fuselage	1·40 m (4 ft 7 in)
Tailplane span	4·06 m (13 ft 4 in)
Door: Width	0·76 m (2 ft 6 in)

DIMENSIONS, INTERNAL:

Cabin: Length	3·66 m (12 ft 0 in)

Baggage space (pilot and 3 passengers)
1·13 m³ (39·8 cu ft)

AREA:

Wings, gross	11·61 m² (125·0 sq ft)

WEIGHTS AND LOADINGS (estimated):

Weight empty	1,092 kg (2,408 lb)
Max T-O weight	2,064 kg (4,550 lb)
Max wing loading	177·8 kg/m² (36·4 lb/sq ft)
Max power loading	273·0 kg/kN (2·68 lb/lb st)

PERFORMANCE (estimated, at max T-O weight):

Max cruising speed at 11,000 m (36,000 ft)	
	356 knots (659 km/h; 410 mph)
Recommended cruising speed at 11,000 m (36,000 ft)	
	286 knots (529 km/h; 329 mph)
Stalling speed, flaps up 85 knots (158 km/h; 98 mph)	
Stalling speed, flaps down	
	74 knots (137 km/h; 85 mph)
Max rate of climb at S/L	1,035 m (3,400 ft)/min
Rate of climb at S/L, one engine out	
	305 m (1,000 ft)/min
Time to 11,000 m (36,000 ft)	22 min
Service ceiling	12,495 m (41,000 ft)
Service ceiling, one engine out	7,620 m (25,000 ft)
T-O run	488 m (1,600 ft)
T-O to 15 m (50 ft)	823 m (2,700 ft)
Landing from 15 m (50 ft)	567 m (1,860 ft)
Landing run	299 m (980 ft)
Range at recommended cruising speed, 45 min reserves	
	955 nm (1,768 km; 1,099 miles)
Max range	1,215 nm (2,253 km; 1,400 miles)

GACC
GULFSTREAM AMERICAN CORPORATION OF CALIFORNIA (a subsidiary of Gulfstream American Corporation)

HEAD OFFICE AND WORKS: 7701 Woodley Avenue, Van Nuys, California 91406
Telephone: (213) 988 9900
Telex: 662461

CHAIRMAN, PRESIDENT AND CHIEF EXECUTIVE OFFICER: · Allen E. Paulson
EXECUTIVE VICE-PRESIDENT: James L. Bradbury
SENIOR VICE-PRESIDENT: Samuel J. Saso (Parts Sales)
VICE-PRESIDENTS:
 Robert H. Cooper (Marketing)
 Alvin C. Davies (Finance)
 Robert Lillibridge (Operations and Engineering)
 Douglas A. Potter (Operations—Miami)
SECRETARY: John P. Innes II

This is the former American Jet Industries Inc, which was renamed following its acquisition of Grumman American Corporation.

At Van Nuys, California, GACC continues to develop the Hustler twin-turbine business aircraft, and to carry out cargo conversions of civil transport aircraft, and is the western support centre for Gulfstream II and III executive transports. In addition, the programme involving retrofit of the new Gulfstream III wing to Gulfstream II aircraft will be carried out by GACC at Van Nuys.

GULFSTREAM AMERICAN CV-880 AIRLIFTER

Current programmes at Gulfstream American's Van Nuys plant include the conversion of ex-airline Convair 880 passenger transports for operation as convertible all-cargo, or cargo/passenger aircraft. Work involved in this conversion includes the installation of a hydraulically-operated freight door in the port side of the fuselage, forward of the wing, measuring 3·66 × 2·07 m (12 ft 0 in × 6 ft 9½ in). New flooring is fabricated from extruded light alloy planking, able to accept a loading of 732·4 kg/m² (150 lb/sq ft), and six cargo tiedown tracks stressed to 9g are installed in the floor. Windows are plugged to save weight, a fireproof glassfibre liner installed throughout the main cabin/cargo hold, and a smoke detection system and 'door open' warning light are installed. Full cabin pressurisation integrity is retained.

The converted aircraft, known as the Airlifter, will carry its maximum payload of 22,725 kg (50,100 lb) over a range of 1,800 nm (3,336 km; 2,073 miles) at a block speed of nearly 400 knots (740 km/h; 460 mph). Maximum range with reduced payload is 3,000 nm (5,555 km; 3,450 miles).

The first two conversions were completed in 1979, and in early 1980 a further 22 CV-880s were in various stages of conversion.

Details of the standard Convair 880 can be found in the 1965-66 *Jane's*; the following details apply specifically to Gulfstream American's Airlifter conversion:

DIMENSION, INTERNAL:
Total cargo volume   180·0 m³ (6,358 cu ft)

WEIGHTS:
Operating weight empty, average
    36,285 kg (80,000 lb)
Max payload   22,725 kg (50,100 lb)
Max T-O weight   83,685 kg (184,500 lb)
Max ramp weight   83,915 kg (185,000 lb)
Max zero-fuel weight   59,420 kg (131,000 lb)
Max landing weight   70,305 kg (155,000 lb)

Prototype Gulfstream American Hustler Model 400 twin-engined business/utility aircraft

GULFSTREAM AMERICAN HUSTLER MODEL 500

The former American Jet Industries announced in 1975 its plans to build a new general aviation aircraft. The design included a pressurised cabin, to permit cruising altitudes of up to 10,670 m (35,000 ft). STOL characteristics were to be provided by the use of a supercritical wing with full-span Fowler trailing-edge flaps, and spoilers, instead of ailerons, for lateral control. Most unusual feature was the power plant, comprising a nose-mounted Pratt & Whitney Aircraft of Canada PT6A turboprop, with a small Williams Research turbofan standby engine mounted in the aft fuselage. Designated Hustler Model 400, details of this aircraft can be found in the 1977-78 *Jane's*. The prototype, registered N400AJ, made its first flight on 11 January 1978 and had accumulated more than 250 hours' flying by mid-1979.

The desirability of obtaining certification of the Hustler as a twin-engined aircraft, coupled with a delay of some two years before the Williams Research standby turbofan would be available, brought the decision to change to a Pratt & Whitney JT15D-1 turbofan in the aft fuselage. This, in turn, made necessary further design changes, including lengthening the fuselage by insertion of a new 0·81 m (2 ft 8 in) section forward of the wing; resiting the cabin entrance door forward, instead of aft, of the wing; the provision of wingtip tanks to augment fuel capacity; and the replacement of spoilers by conventional ailerons, thus requiring the full-span flaps to be reduced to two-thirds span. The redesigned aircraft was designated Hustler 500.

Gulfstream American announced on 20 April 1979 that the Model 500 was to have a Garrett-AiResearch TPE 331-10 turboprop engine installed in lieu of the Pratt & Whitney PT6A-41; the former engine has a single under-fuselage exhaust outlet which will minimise exhaust gas ingestion by the rear engine. The Model 500 was scheduled to fly with this new forward engine in late 1980. A third prototype was built for static proof load testing at the Los Angeles Division of Rockwell International.

The following description applies to the Model 500:

TYPE: Twin-engined business/utility aircraft.

WINGS: Cantilever low/mid-wing monoplane. Supercritical wing section GAW Mod 4. Thickness/chord ratio 12·5%. Dihedral 2°. Incidence 0°. Sweepback at quarter-chord 15°. Conventional light alloy two-spar fail-safe structure with ribs, stringers and chemically-milled skins, flush riveted. Double-slotted hydraulically actuated light alloy Fowler trailing-edge flaps extending over two-thirds span. Conventional ailerons of light alloy construction. B. F. Goodrich pneumatic de-icing boots on wing leading-edges.

FUSELAGE: Semi-monocoque light alloy structure of circular cross-section, with fail-safe construction in the pressurised section extending between the firewall and aft pressure bulkhead. Clamshell type doors beneath rear fuselage for access to aft engine.

TAIL UNIT: Cantilever light alloy structure with swept vertical surfaces. Manually-operated trim tab in rudder. Trim tabs in elevator. B. F. Goodrich pneumatic de-icing boots on fin and tailplane leading-edges. Ventral fin.

LANDING GEAR: Hydraulically-retractable tricycle type. Main units retract inward, nose unit aft. Oleo-pneumatic shock-absorbers. Single B. F. Goodrich wheel and tyre on each unit. Main wheels and tyres size 22 × 9·00, pressure 3·10 bars (45 lb/sq in); nosewheel size 17·50 × 6·00, pressure 2·41 bars (35 lb/sq in). B. F. Goodrich toe-operated hydraulic brakes.

POWER PLANT: One 671 kW (900 shp) Garrett-AiResearch TPE 331-10-501 turboprop engine, driving a Hartzell four-blade metal constant-speed reversible-pitch propeller with Beta control, mounted conventionally in the fuselage nose, and one 9·77 kN (2,200 lb st) Pratt & Whitney Aircraft of Canada JT15D-1 turbofan engine in the rear fuselage. Fuel in integral wing and wingtip tanks with combined capacity of 1,828 litres (483 US gallons). Refuelling point on upper surface of each wingtip tank. Electrical propeller de-icing. Anti-icing of engine air intake by engine bleed air.

ACCOMMODATION: Two crew, and five or seven seats in passenger cabin. Is to be certificated for one-pilot operation, so co-pilot's seat can be occupied by additional passenger. Refreshment centre; private toilet; folding tables. Baggage space at rear of cabin, capacity 91 kg (200 lb). Two-part door on port side, forward of wing, with airstairs in lower section. Removable plug-type emergency exit on starboard side of cabin, between

Proposed configuration of the production Gulfstream American Hustler Model 500 (*Pilot Press*)

aft- and forward-facing seats. Access door to baggage compartment aft of wing on port side. Accommodation heated, ventilated, air-conditioned and pressurised. Electrical windscreen de-icing.

SYSTEMS: AiResearch air cycle heating and cooling with pressurisation at a differential of 0·55 bars (8·0 lb/sq in). Hydraulic system for flaps, landing gear and brakes. Electrical system at 24V DC supplied by starter/generator. Nickel-cadmium storage battery. Oxygen system for emergency use.

AVIONICS AND EQUIPMENT: A range of avionics is available to customer's requirements, including dual nav/com, flight director, autopilot and weather radar. Blind-flying instrumentation standard. Weather radar mounted in nose of starboard wingtip tank; landing light in nose of port wingtip tank.

DIMENSIONS, EXTERNAL:
Wing span	10·49 m (34 ft 5 in)
Wing chord at root	2·03 m (6 ft 8 in)
Length overall	12·57 m (41 ft 3 in)
Height overall	4·03 m (13 ft 2½ in)
Tailplane span	4·67 m (15 ft 4 in)
Wheel track	3·90 m (12 ft 9·6 in)
Wheelbase	4·57 m (15 ft 0 in)
Propeller diameter	2·35 m (7 ft 8½ in)
Passenger door: Height	1·17 m (3 ft 10 in)
Width	0·76 m (2 ft 6 in)
Emergency exit: Height	0·86 m (2 ft 10 in)
Width	0·71 m (2 ft 4 in)
Baggage door: Height	0·76 m (2 ft 6 in)
Width	0·58 m (1 ft 11 in)

DIMENSIONS, INTERNAL:
Cabin, aft of firewall: Length	5·59 m (18 ft 4 in)
Max width	1·27 m (4 ft 2 in)
Max height	1·27 m (4 ft 2 in)
Volume, incl cockpit area	7·36 m³ (260 cu ft)
Baggage compartment	0·85 m³ (30 cu ft)

AREA:
Wings, gross	17·72 m² (190·71 sq ft)

WEIGHTS AND LOADING:
Weight empty	2,463 kg (5,430 lb)
Max T-O weight	4,536 kg (10,000 lb)
Max ramp weight	4,572 kg (10,080 lb)
Max landing weight	4,309 kg (9,500 lb)
Max wing loading	256 kg/m² (52·4 lb/sq ft)

PERFORMANCE (estimated, at max T-O weight, ISA, except where indicated):
Max cruising speed at 7,620 m (25,000 ft)	400 knots (741 km/h; 461 mph)
Normal cruising speed, both engines, at 11,600 m (38,000 ft)	350 knots (648 km/h; 402 mph)
Approach speed at normal landing weight	103 knots (191 km/h; 119 mph)
Rotation speed	95 knots (176 km/h; 109 mph)
Stalling speed at normal landing weight	79 knots (146 km/h; 91 mph)
Max rate of climb at S/L	1,052 m (3,450 ft)/min
Operational ceiling	11,580 m (38,000 ft)
Operational ceiling, fwd engine only	6,705 m (22,000 ft)
Operational ceiling, aft engine only	8,990 m (29,500 ft)
T-O run (15° flap)	471 m (1,545 ft)
T-O to 15 m (50 ft)	532 m (1,745 ft)

Prototype Gulfstream American Peregrine 600 trainer, with side-by-side seating (*Pilot Press*)

Landing from 15 m (50 ft)   640 m (2,100 ft)
Landing from 15 m (50 ft), with propeller reversal
                                         488 m (1,600 ft)
Range with max fuel, max cruising speed at 7,620 m
  (25,000 ft), 45 min reserves
                      1,120 nm (2,075 km; 1,289 miles)
Max range at normal cruising speed, 45 min reserves
                      2,000 nm (3,706 km; 2,303 miles)
Max range, aft engine shut down after 1·2 h at cruising
  altitude, 45 min reserves
                      2,400 nm (4,448 km; 2,764 miles)

GULFSTREAM AMERICAN PEREGRINE 600

On 25 July 1979, Gulfstream American announced its
intention to build a prototype of the Peregrine 600 two-
seat military trainer, based on its Hustler 500 design. The
trainer will differ primarily by deletion of the forward
engine and wingtip tanks of the Hustler. Seating will be
side by side in the prototype, which will be powered by a
single 13·34 kN (3,000 lb st) Pratt & Whitney Aircraft of
Canada JT15D-5 turbofan engine, mounted in the rear
fuselage. Options available for production Peregrines will
include a different power plant, consisting of two Williams
Research WR44 turbofans (each rated at 5·34 kN; 1,200
lb st), and tandem seating, which will involve further

changes to the forward fuselage, transparent cockpit
canopy and windscreen. In most other respects, the
Peregrine 600 will be similar to the Hustler 500.
  The following preliminary specification details have
been made available:

DIMENSIONS, EXTERNAL:
  Wing span   10·49 m (34 ft 5 in)
  Length overall   11·68 m (38 ft 4 in)
  Height overall   4·09 m (13 ft 5 in)
  Tailplane span   4·67 m (15 ft 4 in)
WEIGHTS (estimated, A: JT15D-5; B: Williams Research
  44s):
  Max T-O and landing weight: A   2,812 kg (6,200 lb)
                              B   2,903 kg (6,400 lb)
  Mission weight: A, B   2,383 kg (5,254 lb)
  Normal landing weight: A   1,997 kg (4,402 lb)
                         B   2,124 kg (4,683 lb)
PERFORMANCE (estimated, at max T-O weight unless
  otherwise detailed):
  Max level speed at 6,100 m (20,000 ft):
    A   394 knots (730 km/h; 454 mph)
    B   374 knots (693 km/h; 431 mph)
  Stalling speed, power off:
    A   66 knots (122 km/h; 76 mph)
    B   67 knots (124 km/h; 77 mph)

Max rate of climb at S/L: A   1,585 m (5,200 ft)/min
                          B   1,204 m (3,950 ft)/min
Service ceiling: A   14,630 m (48,000 ft)
                 B   12,620 m (41,400 ft)
T-O run: A   307 m (1,008 ft)
         B   361 m (1,186 ft)
T-O to 15 m (50 ft): A   489 m (1,604 ft)
                     B   592 m (1,943 ft)
Landing from 15 m (50 ft), at max landing weight:
         A   799 m (2,621 ft)
         B   880 m (2,888 ft)
Landing from 15 m (50 ft), at normal landing weight:
         A   639 m (2,095 ft)
         B   814 m (2,670 ft)
Landing run at max landing weight:
         A   442 m (1,450 ft)
         B   473 m (1,552 ft)
Landing run at normal landing weight:
         A   366 m (1,202 ft)
         B   437 m (1,435 ft)
Mission range at 12,190 m (40,000 ft):
  A at 369 knots (683 km/h; 424 mph)
                      1,080 nm (2,001 km; 1,243 miles)
  B at 319 knots (590 km/h; 367 mph)
                      1,315 nm (2,437 km; 1,514 miles)

GATES LEARJET
GATES LEARJET CORPORATION

CORPORATE OFFICES, AIRCRAFT DIVISION: Mid-Continent
  Airport, PO Box 7707, Wichita, Kansas 67277
Telephone: (316) 946 2000
Telex: 417441

MARKETING HEADQUARTERS, TUCSON OPERATIONS: Tucson
  International Airport, PO Box 11186, Tucson, Arizona
  85734
COMBS-GATES FIXED BASE OPERATIONS: Hangar 7, Sta-
  pleton International Airport, Denver, Colorado 80207
JET ELECTRONICS AND TECHNOLOGY INC: 5353 52nd Street,
  Grand Rapids, Michigan 49508
CHAIRMAN OF THE BOARD: Charles C. Gates
PRESIDENT: Harry B. Combs
EXECUTIVE VICE-PRESIDENTS:
  A. J. Brizzolara (J.E.T.)
  R. E. Cloughley (Combs-Gates)
SENIOR VICE-PRESIDENTS:
  B. S. Stillwell (General Manager, Aircraft Division)
  P. F. Lovett (Marketing)
  R. C. Scott (Operations)
VICE-PRESIDENTS:
  G. D. Gilmore (Governmental Marketing)
  A. F. Green (General Manager, Tucson Operations)
  J. R. Greenwood (Corporate Affairs)
  D. J. Grommesh (Engineering & Research)
  R. Hamlin (Manufacturing)
  F. I. Hedlund (International Marketing)
  P. F. Lovett (Domestic Marketing)
  E. C. Mandenberg (Materiel)
  M. F. Mastin (Marketing Programmes)
  D. B. Norton (Product Support)
TREASURER: W. H. Webster
CONTROLLER: A. M. Hain
SECRETARY: R. C. Troll
DIRECTOR, PUBLIC RELATIONS: J. M. Gregory

Founded in 1960 by the late William P. Lear Sr, this
company was known originally as the Swiss American
Aviation Corporation, which was formed to manufacture
a high-speed twin-jet executive aircraft known as the
Learjet 23 (formerly SAAC-23). Most of the tooling for
production of this aircraft was completed in Europe and
then, in 1962, all company activities were relocated at
Wichita, Kansas; shortly afterwards the company became
known as Lear Jet Corporation. In 1967 all of Mr Lear's
interests in the company (approximately 60 per cent) were
acquired by The Gates Rubber Company of Denver, Colorado, and in January 1970 the company name was
changed to Gates Learjet Corporation.
  On 28 October 1975 Gates Learjet announced
improved models of its Learjet 24, 25 and 35/36, then in
production, under the designation Century III series. All
Century III Learjets incorporate a cambered wing and
other changes to reduce stall and approach speeds and
balanced field length. This wing has a new contour, extending from the leading-edge aft to the second wing spar, and,
coupled with other advances including an improved stall
warning/prevention system, improves lateral stability and
handling qualities in higher flight regimes. Performance increases from Century III improvements include
approach speed reductions of 16-18 knots (30-34 km/h;
18·5-21 mph), and increases in cruise range of as much as
seven per cent. Century III improvements are available as
a factory retrofit modification for earlier Learjet 24, 25, 35
and 36 models, and can be completed in approximately
one week.
  From 1 July 1979, all newly-delivered Learjets have
embodied a 'Softflite' handling package to improve stall
characteristics. Available for retrospective fit on earlier
Century III series aircraft, this comprises a full-chord shallow fence on each wing, small devices on the inboard

leading-edge, and two rows of boundary-layer energisers
forward of each aileron, to energise the airflow and delay
the onset of compressibility. Vortex generators are
removed; the stick shaker/pusher is retained but unlikely
to be required.
  During May 1976 a Learjet 36, captained by golf pro-
fessional/pilot Arnold Palmer, established a business jet
round-the-world speed record in an elapsed time of 57 h
25 min 42 s. The flight of 19,960·24 nm (36,989·96 km;
22,984·55 miles) was flown at an average speed of 347·57
knots (644·107 km/h; 400·23 mph).
  In June and September 1977 Gates Learjet gave provisional details of a new family of advanced models, with
wings of increased span provided with supercritical winglets. Designated Learjet 28/29 Longhorn and Learjet
54/55/56 Longhorn, these have subsequently joined the
earlier models in production.
  During 1979 a total of 107 Learjets were delivered (76
to customers in the USA, the balance for export), making
this the 15th consecutive year in which Gates Learjet has
led in cumulative deliveries of business jet aircraft. Of this
total, 34 were Model 24/25s, 67 were Model 35/36s, and 6
were Model 28/29s. The company delivered its 1,000th
Learjet, a Century III Model 35A, on 28 March 1980.
  Learjets are produced at the company's main facility at
Wichita, Kansas. A new completion centre at Tucson,
Arizona, was opened in 1976, and a new Customer Service
Center was opened in 1978. Other fixed-base operations,
under the name of Combs-Gates, are located at Denver,
Colorado; Indianapolis, Indiana; and Palm Springs,
California. A new assembly plant, for production of the
Learjet 54/55/56 Longhorn, was completed at Tucson in
the Spring of 1979.
  In January 1980 employees at the company's Aircraft
Division facilities numbered approximately 4,150. Com-
bined operations employment, including a wholly-owned
subsidiary, Jet Electronics and Technology Inc, totals
5,050. Company facilities now cover almost 140,000 m²
(1·5 million sq ft).

GATES LEARJET 24F

The prototype Lear Jet twin-jet executive transport flew
for the first time on 7 October 1963 and deliveries of
production Learjet 23 aircraft began on 13 October 1964.
After a total of 104 of this version had been delivered, it
was superseded by the Learjet 24, which was certificated
under Federal Air Regulations Part 25 (formerly CAR
4B), as have been all subsequent models produced by the

Gates Learjet 24 Series twin-jet light executive transport *(Pilot Press)*

company. Deliveries of the Learjet 24 began in March
1966, and a total of 80 were built. This was replaced by a
developed version with more powerful engines, known as
the Learjet 24B, which received FAA certification on 17
December 1968, and then by the 24D (see 1975-76
Jane's) and 24E (see 1978-79 *Jane's*).
  The current Learjet 24F, with Century III modifications
(see introductory notes), replaced the Learjet 24D and
24D/A in 1976. These latter aircraft were the first to
feature a tail unit design in which the non-structural bullet
at the junction of the tailplane and fin was deleted. The
'Softflite' handling package (see introductory notes) was
certificated during 1979.
TYPE: Twin-jet light executive transport.
WINGS: Cantilever low-wing monoplane. Wing section
  NACA 64A 109. Dihedral 2° 30'. Incidence 1°. Sweepback 13° at quarter-chord. All-metal eight-spar structure with milled alloy skins. Manually-operated,
  aerodynamically-balanced all-metal ailerons.
  Hydraulically-actuated all-metal single-slotted flaps.
  Hydraulically-actuated all-metal spoilers ahead of flaps.
  Electrically-operated trim tab in port aileron. Balance
  tab in each aileron. Anti-icing by engine bleed air
  ducted into leading-edges.
FUSELAGE: All-metal flush-riveted semi-monocoque fail-
  safe structure.
TAIL UNIT: Cantilever all-metal sweptback structure, with
  electrically-actuated variable-incidence T-tailplane and
  small ventral fin. Conventional manually-operated control surfaces. Electrically-operated trim tab in rudder.
  Electrically-heated de-icing of tailplane leading-edges.
LANDING GEAR: Retractable tricycle type, with twin
  wheels on each main unit and single steerable nosewheel. Hydraulic actuation, with backup pneumatic
  extension. Oleo-pneumatic shock-absorbers. Main
  wheels fitted with Goodyear 18 × 5·50 10-ply tyres,
  pressure 7·93 bars (115 lb/sq in). Nosewheel fitted with
  Goodyear Dual Chine tyre size 18 × 4·40 10-ply rating,
  pressure 7·24 bars (105 lb/sq in).Goodyear multiple-
  disc hydraulic brakes. Pneumatic emergency braking
  system. Parking brakes. Fully-modulated anti-skid
  system.
POWER PLANT: Two General Electric CJ610-8A turbojet
  engines, each rated at 13·1 kN (2,950 lb st), mounted in
  pod on each side of fuselage aft of wings. Fuel in integral
  wing and wingtip tanks, and a bladder-type cell in the
  fuselage, with a total standard fuel capacity of 3,180
  litres (840 US gallons). Oil capacity 3·75 litres (1 US

gallon) per engine. Engine inlet anti-icing by bleed air.

ACCOMMODATION: Two seats side by side on flight deck, with dual controls. Up to six passengers in cabin, with one on inward-facing bench seat on starboard side at front, then two on forward or aft-facing armchairs with centre aisle, and three on forward-facing couch. Toilet and stowage space under front inward-facing seat, which can be screened from remainder of cabin by curtain. Refreshment cabinet opposite this seat. Baggage compartment aft of cabin. With back of rear bench seat folded down, baggage compartment and rear of cabin can be used to carry cargo or stretchers. Table at rear. In full cargo version, the rearward-facing armchair seats are also removed. Two-piece door, with upward-hinged portion and downward-hinged portion with integral steps, on port side of cabin at front. Emergency exit on starboard side. Cargo door optional. Windscreen anti-icing by engine bleed air with liquid methyl alcohol backup.

SYSTEMS: Air-conditioning by Freon R12 vapour cycle system, supplemented by ram-air heat exchanger during pressurised flight. Cabin pressurisation, by engine bleed air, has max differential of 0·65 bars (9·4 lb/sq in). Electrical system powered by dual 400A 30V DC starter/generators with AC power supplied from dual 1,000 VA solid-state inverters. Dual 24V 41Ah lead-acid batteries; nickel-cadmium batteries optional. Emergency battery pack optional. Dual engine-driven hydraulic pumps, each capable of maintaining full system pressure of 103·5 bars (1,500 lb/sq in). Auxiliary electrically-driven hydraulic pump. Pneumatic system at pressure of 124-207 bars (1,800-3,000 lb/sq in) for emergency extension of landing gear and operation of wheel brakes. Engine fire detection and extinguishing system. Oxygen system for emergency use has crew demand masks and passenger dropout masks. Alcohol anti-icing system for radome.

AVIONICS AND EQUIPMENT: Complete nav/com systems, to full airline standard, are available to customer's requirements, comprising Collins, Bendix, Sperry or export equipment. All have Learjet autopilot as standard. A typical standard avionics package for the Learjet 24F includes dual Collins VHF-20A com, dual Collins VIR-30A VOR/ILS, dual marker lamps, dual Avtech audio heads, Collins DME-40, Collins TDR-90 transponder, Bendix RDR-1200 radar, Collins ADF-60 ADF, dual Allen 3137 RMI, Collins FD112V flight director, FC-110 flight control system, Collins/J.E.T. PN-101/5-4000 flight indicator (co-pilot), dual J.E.T. VG-206A vertical gyros, dual J.E.T. DN-101D directional gyros, and IDC electric-encoding altimeter with altitude alerter and static defect correction module. Standard equipment includes birdproof windscreen; dual clocks, control locks, depressurisation warning and engine fire warning lights, Mach warning and Alpha Dot stall warning device, heated pitot tubes and static ports, ice detector, fire axe, cabin fire extinguisher, stereo system; baggage compartment, cabin dome, courtesy, instrument panel flood, reading, anti-collision, landing, navigation, taxi, and strobe lights; and lightning protection system.

DIMENSIONS, EXTERNAL:

Span over tip-tanks	10·84 m (35 ft 7 in)
Wing chord at root	2·74 m (9 ft 0 in)
Wing chord at tip	1·40 m (4 ft 7 in)
Wing aspect ratio	5·01
Length overall	13·18 m (43 ft 3 in)
Length of fuselage	12·50 m (41 ft 0 in)
Height overall	3·73 m (12 ft 3 in)
Tailplane span	4·47 m (14 ft 8 in)
Wheel track (c/l shock-absorbers)	2·51 m (8 ft 3 in)
Wheelbase	4·93 m (16 ft 2 in)
Cabin door: Height	1·57 m (5 ft 2 in)
Standard width	0·61 m (2 ft 0 in)
Optional width	0·91 m (3 ft 0 in)
Emergency exit: Height	0·71 m (2 ft 4 in)
Width	0·48 m (1 ft 7 in)

DIMENSIONS, INTERNAL:

Cabin, between pressure bulkheads:

Length	5·28 m (17 ft 4 in)
Max width	1·50 m (4 ft 11 in)
Max height	1·32 m (4 ft 4 in)
Volume, incl baggage compartment	6·97 m³ (246·0 cu ft)
Baggage compartment	1·13 m³ (40·0 cu ft)

AREAS:

Wings, gross	21·53 m² (231·77 sq ft)
Ailerons (total)	1·08 m² (11·70 sq ft)
Trailing-edge flaps (total)	3·42 m² (36·85 sq ft)
Spoilers	0·66 m² (7·05 sq ft)
Fin	3·47 m² (37·37 sq ft)
Rudder, incl tab	0·67 m² (7·18 sq ft)
Tailplane	5·02 m² (54·00 sq ft)
Elevators	1·31 m² (14·13 sq ft)

WEIGHTS AND LOADINGS:

Weight empty, equipped	3,204 kg (7,064 lb)
Max payload, cargo configuration*	1,134 kg (2,500 lb)
Max fuel weight	2,553 kg (5,628 lb)
Max T-O weight	6,123 kg (13,500 lb)
Max ramp weight	6,259 kg (13,800 lb)

Max wing bending weight	5,171 kg (11,400 lb)
Max landing weight	5,388 kg (11,880 lb)
Max wing loading	284·4 kg/m² (58·25 lb/sq ft)
Max power loading	233·7 kg/kN (2·29 lb/lb st)

Certification pending, January 1980

PERFORMANCE (ISA, at max T-O weight, unless stated otherwise):

Never-exceed speed	Mach 0·81
Max operating speed at 7,620 m (25,000 ft)	475 knots (880 km/h; 547 mph)
Max cruising speed, mid-cruise weight, at 14,325 m (47,000 ft)	451 knots (835 km/h; 519 mph)
Econ cruising speed, mid-cruise weight, at 14,325 m (47,000 ft)	428 knots (793 km/h; 493 mph)
Stalling speed, wheels and flaps up, engines idling	111 knots (206 km/h; 128 mph) IAS
Stalling speed at max landing weight, wheels and flaps down, engines idling	88 knots (162·5 km/h; 101 mph) IAS
Max rate of climb at S/L	2,164 m (7,100 ft)/min
Rate of climb at S/L, one engine out	625 m (2,050 ft)/min
Service ceiling	15,545 m (51,000 ft)
Service ceiling, one engine out	8,230 m (27,000 ft)
Min ground turning radius	10·46 m (34 ft 4 in)
T-O to 9 m (30 ft), FAA balanced field length	1,005 m (3,297 ft)
Landing from 15 m (50 ft) at max landing weight, without thrust reversers	850 m (2,789 ft)
Range with 4 passengers, max fuel and 45 min reserves	1,474 nm (2,731 km; 1,697 miles)

OPERATIONAL NOISE LEVELS (FAR Pt 36):

T-O noise level	85·8 EPNdB
Approach noise level	95·3 EPNdB
Sideline noise level	103·7 EPNdB

GATES LEARJET 25D

First flown on 12 August 1966 as the Learjet 25, this version is 1·27 m (4 ft 2 in) longer than the series 24 aircraft, and will accommodate eight passengers and a crew of two. FAA certification in the air transport category (FAR 25) was obtained on 10 October 1967 and the initial delivery was made in November 1967. British CAA certification was received on 26 June 1974.

The current version has the designation Learjet 25D, and in 1976 this introduced the same Century III improvements as the Learjet 24 series. The 'Softflite' handling package (see introductory notes) has also been standard on this model since 1 July 1979. In addition, 8° flap settings for take-off are approved for this version, improving the high altitude/hot day take-off performance. Factory-installed thrust reversers for the General Electric CJ610-8A turbojet engines are optional.

Two Learjet 25Bs supplied to the Peruvian Air Force in 1974 are each fitted with an underbelly pack containing two Wild RC-10 aerial survey cameras. An accompanying illustration shows a civil-registered Learjet 25C of Cruzeiro do Sul, Brazil, with a similar installation, which leaves the cabin interior quickly convertible for passenger or cargo transport duties.

The description of the Learjet 24F applies also to the Model 25D, except in the following details:

DIMENSIONS, EXTERNAL: As for Learjet 24F except:

Length overall	14·50 m (47 ft 7 in)
Wheelbase	5·84 m (19 ft 2 in)

DIMENSIONS, INTERNAL: As for Learjet 24F except:

Cabin, between pressure bulkheads:

Length	6·27 m (20 ft 7 in)
Volume, incl baggage compartment	8·47 m³ (299 cu ft)

WEIGHTS AND LOADINGS:

Weight empty, equipped	3,470 kg (7,650 lb)
Max payload, cargo configuration*	1,587 kg (3,500 lb)
Max fuel weight	2,766 kg (6,098 lb)
Max T-O weight	6,804 kg (15,000 lb)
Max ramp weight	7,030 kg (15,500 lb)
Max landing weight	6,033 kg (13,300 lb)
Max wing loading	315·9 kg/m² (64·7 lb/sq ft)
Max power loading	259·7 kg/kN (2·54 lb/lb st)

Certification pending, January 1980

PERFORMANCE (at max T-O weight, unless stated otherwise):

As for Learjet 24F, except:

Stalling speed, wheels and flaps up, engines idling, at max landing weight	113 knots (209 km/h; 130 mph) IAS
Stalling speed, wheels and flaps down, engines idling, at max landing weight	97 knots (180 km/h; 111·5 mph) IAS
Max rate of climb at S/L	2,395 m (7,850 ft)/min
Rate of climb at S/L, one engine out	777 m (2,550 ft)/min
Service ceiling, one engine out	9,600 m (31,500 ft)
Min ground turning radius	11·43 m (37 ft 6 in)
T-O to 9 m (30 ft), FAA balanced field length	1,200 m (3,937 ft)
Landing from 15 m (50 ft) at max landing weight	836 m (2,744 ft)
Range with 4 passengers, max fuel and 45 min reserves	1,535 nm (2,844 km; 1,767 miles)

OPERATIONAL NOISE LEVELS (FAR Pt 36):

T-O noise level	90·9 EPNdB
Approach noise level	103·7 EPNdB
Sideline noise level	95·2 EPNdB

GATES LEARJET 28 and 29 LONGHORN

Displayed for the first time at the US National Business Aircraft Association's annual convention on 27-29 September 1977, the prototype of the Learjet 28/29 series was generally similar to the 10-seat Learjet 25D, except that it introduced a wing of much increased span, fitted with supercritical winglets. Combined with a cambered leading-edge, this is claimed to improve climb performance, reduce drag, offer improved high-altitude cruise efficiency, reduce runway requirements and reduce approach speed. The 'Softflite' handling package (see introductory notes) has been standard since 1 July 1979. No wingtip fuel tanks are fitted.

Like the Learjet 25D the 28/29 is powered by two General Electric CJ610-8A turbojet engines, each rated at 13·1 kN (2,950 lb st). Total usable fuel capacity of the Model 28 is 2,657 litres (702 US gallons), and of the Model 29 is 3,035 litres (802 US gallons). The Model 28 will accommodate a crew of two and ten passengers, the Model 29 a crew of two and eight passengers. In other respects the 28/29 are similar to the 25D.

FAA certification of the Learjet 28/29 was received on 30 January 1979, and the first production deliveries were made shortly after.

On 19-20 February 1979, former astronaut Neil A. Armstrong set five new records for jet aircraft in FAI categories C1f (6,000-8,000 kg) and C1e (3,000-6,000 kg). They were for altitude and sustained altitude of 15,584·6 m (51,130 ft) in each category, and climb to 15,000 m (49,213 ft) in 12 min 26·7 s.

DIMENSIONS, EXTERNAL:

Wing span	13·35 m (43 ft 9·5 in)
Length overall	14·51 m (47 ft 7·6 in)
Height overall	3·73 m (12 ft 3·1 in)

Gates Learjet 25C with twin camera installation in specially modified fuselage

DIMENSIONS, INTERNAL:
Cabin, excl flight deck: Length:
28	4·37 m (14 ft 4 in)
29	3·86 m (12 ft 8 in)
Max width	1·49 m (4 ft 11 in)
Max height	1·32 m (4 ft 4 in)
Volume: 28	5·80 m³ (205 cu ft)
29	4·67 m³ (165 cu ft)
Baggage compartment: 28	0·85 m³ (30 cu ft)
29	0·76 m³ (27 cu ft)

AREA:
Wings, gross	24·57 m² (264·5 sq ft)

WEIGHTS AND LOADINGS:
Weight empty: 28	3,750 kg (8,268 lb)
29	3,730 kg (8,224 lb)
Max payload: 28	1,058 kg (2,332 lb)
29	1,078 kg (2,376 lb)
Max fuel weight: 28	2,124 kg (4,684 lb)
29	2,437 kg (5,373 lb)
Max T-O weight	6,804 kg (15,000 lb)
Max ramp weight	7,030 kg (15,500 lb)
Max landing weight	6,486 kg (14,300 lb)
Max wing loading	276·9 kg/m² (56·71 lb/sq ft)
Max power loading	246·52 kg/kN (2·42 lb/lb st)

PERFORMANCE (at max T-O weight, except where indicated):
Never-exceed speed	Mach 0·81
Max level speed at 7,620 m (25,000 ft)	477 knots (883 km/h; 549 mph)
Max cruising speed, mid-cruise weight, at 14,325 m (47,000 ft)	452 knots (836 km/h; 520 mph)
Econ cruising speed, mid-cruise weight, at 15,545 m (51,000 ft)	408 knots (756 km/h; 470 mph)
Stalling speed, flaps and wheels down, engines idling	89 knots (165 km/h; 102·5 mph) IAS
Service ceiling	15,545 m (51,000 ft)
Service ceiling, one engine out	8,840 m (29,000 ft)
T-O to 9 m (30 ft)	927 m (3,040 ft)
Landing distance from 15 m (50 ft) at max landing weight	833 m (2,734 ft)

Range with 4 passengers, max fuel and 45 min reserves:
28	1,230 nm (2,279 km; 1,416 miles)
29	1,478 nm (2,739 km; 1,702 miles)

GATES LEARJET 35A and 36A

Although generally similar in basic configuration to the Learjet 25, the Learjet 35 and 36 are slightly larger in size and powered by turbofan engines. A prototype (known originally as the Learjet Model 26) made its first flight with Garrett-AiResearch TFE731-2 engines on 4 January 1973. The production 35 and 36, announced in May 1973, are almost identical, differing in fuel capacity and accommodation. FAA certification was awarded in July 1974, and customer deliveries began later that year. French and UK certification were gained during 1979.

Century III improvements, the 'Softflite' handling package (see introductory notes) and engine synchronisers are standard for both models; options include high-energy brakes and an Aeronca Inc thrust reverser package, available both as a retrofit kit and on new production aircraft. Improvements introduced as standard on the Learjet 35A for 1980 include an additional window on each side of the cabin.

A special-mission version known as the **Learjet Sea Patrol**, is available, and is described separately.

The description of the Learjet 24F applies also to the Learjet 35A and 36A, except in the following details:

TYPE: Twin-turbofan light executive transport.

WINGS: As for Learjet 24F, except span increased.

FUSELAGE: As for Learjet 24F, except length increased.

TAIL UNIT AND LANDING GEAR: As for Learjet 24F.

POWER PLANT: Two Garrett-AiResearch TFE 731-2-2B turbofan engines, each rated at 15·6 kN (3,500 lb st), mounted in pod on each side of rear fuselage. Fuel in integral wing and wingtip tanks and a fuselage tank, with a combined usable capacity (Learjet 35A) of 3,524 litres (931 US gallons). Learjet 36A has a larger fuselage tank, giving a combined usable total of 4,201 litres (1,110 US gallons). Refuelling point on upper surface of each wingtip tank. Fuel jettison system. Engine nacelle leading-edges anti-iced by engine bleed air.

ACCOMMODATION: Crew of two on flight deck, with dual controls. Up to eight passengers in Learjet 35A; one on inward-facing bench seat on starboard side at front, then two pairs of forward-facing armchairs with centre aisle, and three on forward-facing couch at rear of cabin. Alternative 'midcabin' arrangement, available optionally, places a refreshment area in the middle of the cabin, accessible from fore and aft club seating areas, each for four passengers. Learjet 36A can accommodate up to six passengers, one pair of forward-facing armchairs being removed. Toilet and stowage space under front inward-facing seat which can be screened from remainder of cabin. Refreshment cabinet opposite this seat, aft of passenger door. Baggage compartment with capacity of 226 kg (500 lb) aft of cabin. Two-piece clamshell door at forward end of cabin on port side, with integral steps built into lower half. Emergency exit on starboard side of cabin. Birdproof windscreens.

SYSTEMS: Environmental control system comprises cabin pressurisation, ventilation, heating and cooling. Heating and pressurisation are provided by engine bleed air,

with a maximum pressure differential of 0·65 bars (9·4 lb/sq in), maintaining a cabin altitude of 1,980 m (6,500 ft) to an actual altitude of 13,715 m (45,000 ft). Freon R12 vapour cycle cooling system supplemented by a ram-air heat exchanger. Flight control system includes dual yaw dampers, dual stick pushers, dual stick shakers and Mach trim. Anti-icing system includes distribution of engine bleed air for wing, tailplane and engine nacelle leading-edges and windscreen; electrical heating of pitot heads, stall warning vanes and static ports; and alcohol spray on windscreen and nose radome. Hydraulic system supplied by two engine-driven pumps, each pump capable of maintaining alone the full system pressure of 103·5 bars (1,500 lb/sq in), for operation of landing gear, brakes, flaps and spoilers. Electrically-driven hydraulic pump for emergency operation of all hydraulic services. Pneumatic system of 124 to 207 bars (1,800 to 3,000 lb/sq in) pressure for emergency extension of landing gear and operation of brakes. Electrical system powered by two 30V 400A brushless generators, two 1kVA solid-state inverters to provide AC power, and two 24V 41Ah lead-acid batteries. Oxygen system for emergency use, with crew demand masks and drop-out masks for each passenger.

AVIONICS: A standard avionics package is available, comprising two Collins VHF-20A transceivers, two Collins VIR-30A VOR/ILS receivers, dual marker lamps, dual Avtech audio controls, Collins DME-40 with 339F-12A indicator and readout on pilot's HSI, dual Collins TDR-90 transponders, Bendix RDR-1200B radar, Collins ADF-60 ADF with pre-select control, dual Allen 3137 RMIs, Collins FD-108Y flight director indicator, integrated with Collins FC-200 flight control system for pilot, Collins/J.E.T. PN-101/5-4000 co-pilot's flight indicator, two J.E.T. VG-206A vertical gyros, two J.E.T. DN-101D directional gyros, IDC electric-encoding altimeter with altitude alerter and static defect correction module, IDC barometric altimeter for co-pilot, Collins ALT-50A radio altimeter, J.E.T. PS-823B and AI-804 emergency battery and attitude gyro, IDC electric ROC for pilot, and Gables controls for navs, coms, XPDRs and DME. Alternatively, customers may select avionics to meet specific requirements.

EQUIPMENT: Standard equipment includes dual angle of attack indicators, dual battery temperature gauges, dual clocks, engine synchronisation meter, cabin differential pressure gauge, cabin rate of climb indicator, exhaust gas temperature and turbine temperature gauges, wing

temperature indicator, alternate static source, dual battery overheat warning, depressurisation warning, engine fire warning lights, Mach warning system, dual stall warning systems, fire axe, cabin fire extinguisher, flotation jackets for crew and passengers, soundproofing; baggage compartment, courtesy, instrument panel, flood, map, and reading lights; dual anti-collision, landing, navigation, recognition, strobe, and taxi lights; dual engine fire extinguishing systems with 'systems armed' and fire warning lights, engine synchronisation system, control lock, external power socket, and lightning protection system.

DIMENSIONS, EXTERNAL:
Wing span over tip-tanks	12·04 m (39 ft 6 in)
Wing chord at root	2·74 m (9 ft 0 in)
Wing chord at tip	1·55 m (5 ft 1 in)
Wing aspect ratio	5·74
Length overall	14·83 m (48 ft 8 in)
Height overall	3·73 m (12 ft 3 in)
Tailplane span	4·47 m (14 ft 8 in)
Wheel track	2·51 m (8 ft 3 in)
Passenger door:	
Standard: Height	1·57 m (5 ft 2 in)
Width	0·61 m (2 ft 0 in)
Optional: Height	1·57 m (5 ft 2 in)
Width	0·91 m (3 ft 0 in)
Emergency exit: Height	0·71 m (2 ft 4 in)
Width	0·48 m (1 ft 7 in)

DIMENSIONS, INTERNAL (A: Learjet 35A; B: Learjet 36A):
Cabin: Length, incl flight deck:
A	6·60 m (21 ft 8 in)
B	5·77 m (18 ft 11 in)
Max width	1·50 m (4 ft 11 in)
Max height	1·32 m (4 ft 4 in)
Volume incl flight deck: A	7·99 m³ (282 cu ft)
B	6·49 m³ (229 cu ft)
Baggage compartment: A	1·13 m³ (40 cu ft)
B	0·76 m³ (27 cu ft)

AREA:
Wings, gross	23·53 m² (253·3 sq ft)

WEIGHTS AND LOADINGS (A: Learjet 35A; B: Learjet 36A):
Weight empty, equipped: A	4,132 kg (9,110 lb)
B	4,152 kg (9,154 lb)
Max payload: A	1,810 kg (3,990 lb)
B	1,790 kg (3,946 lb)
Max T-O weight: A	7,711 kg (17,000 lb)
B	8,164 kg (18,000 lb)

Gates Learjet 28/29 Longhorn, with supercritical winglets *(Pilot Press)*

Gates Learjet 28/29 Longhorn, with increased-span wing and supercritical winglets

Gates Learjet 35A ten-seat twin-turbofan light executive transport

Max wing bending weight: A, B 6,123 kg (13,500 lb)
Max landing weight: A, B   6,486 kg (14,300 lb)
Max wing loading: A   327·6 kg/m² (67·1 lb/sq ft)
  B   347·1 kg/m² (71·1 lb/sq ft)
Max power loading: A   247·1 kg/kN (2·43 lb/lb st)
  B   261·7 kg/kN (2·57 lb/lb st)
PERFORMANCE (at max T-O weight, except where indicated otherwise, A: Learjet 35A; B: Learjet 36A):
Never-exceed speed: A, B   Mach 0·83
Max level speed at 7,620 m (25,000 ft):
  A, B   471 knots (872 km/h; 542 mph)
Max cruising speed, mid-cruise weight, at 12,500 m
  (41,000 ft)   459 knots (850 km/h; 528 mph)
Econ cruising speed, mid-cruise weight, at 13,700 m
  (45,000 ft)   418 knots (774 km/h; 481 mph)
Stalling speed, wheels and flaps down, engines idling:
  A, B   96 knots (178 km/h; 111 mph) IAS
Max rate of climb at S/L: A   1,494 m (4,900 ft)/min
  B   1,379 m (4,525 ft)/min
Rate of climb at S/L, one engine out:
  A   457 m (1,500 ft)/min
  B   404 m (1,325 ft)/min
Service ceiling: A, B   13,715 m (45,000 ft)
Service ceiling, one engine out:
  A   7,710 m (25,300 ft)
  B   7,165 m (23,500 ft)
T-O to 9 m (30 ft): A   1,287 m (4,224 ft)
  B   1,458 m (4,784 ft)
Landing from 15 m (50 ft), at max landing weight:
  A, B   879 m (2,884 ft)
Range with 4 passengers, max fuel and 45 min reserves:
  A   2,422 nm (4,488 km; 2,789 miles)
  B   2,857 nm (5,295 km; 3,290 miles)
OPERATIONAL NOISE LEVELS (FAR Pt 36):
T-O noise level: A   83·7 EPNdB
  B   83·6 EPNdB
Approach noise level: A   91·2 EPNdB
  B   91·3 EPNdB
Sideline noise level: A   86·9 EPNdB
  B   87·4 EPNdB

GATES LEARJET SEA PATROL

A prototype of this special missions version of the Learjet was exhibited at the 1979 Paris Air Show, before making a worldwide demonstration tour. This aircraft (N80SM) is a modified Learjet 35A, with a slightly larger cabin than the equally suitable 36A, enabling more observers to be carried during demonstrations.

Equipment available for the Sea Patrol Learjet includes Litton AN/APS-504(V)2 sea surveillance radar, with 360° sweep from the underbelly radome and digital CFAR clutter suppression; low light level TV with video tape and scan conversion; forward-looking infra-red sensors; Daedalus DS-1210 multi-spectral infra-red and ultra-violet line scanner with tape data storage and hard copy printer; mini-computers for data processing, with tape input/output and graphic display capability; ASW sonobuoy drop and detection equipment; a hardpoint under each wing with an Alkan 165B ejector for survival equipment, flares or up to 220 kg (485 lb) of other stores; drop hatch for rescue gear; high-intensity searchlight; reconnaissance, mapping or LOROP cameras; HF, VHF and UHF homers; GNS-500A VLF Omega navigation system; side-looking airborne radar; Bendix RDR 1300B weather radar; and hand held cameras with position information printout.

Items fitted to the demonstrator make it suitable for location and detection of surface vessels, identification of targets, determination of target activities, and storage of permanent video tape and photographic records of target image, with position, time and date. Its performance ranges from a dash capability of 432 knots (800 km/h; 497 mph) to manoeuvring speeds below 118 knots (220 km/h; 136 mph).
PERFORMANCE (Learjet 36A):
Operating speed at 11,275-12,500 m (37,000-41,000 ft)   415 knots (769 km/h; 478 mph)
Operating speed at 4,575-7,620 m (15,000-25,000 ft)   319 knots (590 km/h; 367 mph)
Operating speed, S/L to 610 m (2,000 ft)   250 knots (463 km/h; 288 mph)
Rate of climb at S/L   1,380 m (4,525 ft)/min
Range at high altitude
              2,249 nm (4,168 km; 2,590 miles)

Range at medium altitude
              1,617 nm (2,996 km; 1,862 miles)
Range at low altitude
              1,060 nm (1,964 km; 1,220 miles)

GATES LEARJET 54, 55 and 56 LONGHORN

Gates Learjet announced, at the Paris Air Show in June 1977, the company's decision to develop a new series of wide body business aircraft known as the Learjet 54, 55 and 56. Stemming from exhaustive engineering and marketing studies, these new aircraft will supplement the existing range of Learjets, providing a wide-body 'stand-up' cabin, and having accommodation for a maximum of eleven passengers in the Learjet 54 and 55, and eight passengers in the Learjet 56.

The first of two Learjet 55 prototypes (N551GL) was rolled out on 2 February 1979, and flew for the first time on 19 April 1979; the second prototype (N552GL) flew on 15 November 1979. The first is being used to prove handling and performance characteristics, the second to verify aircraft systems; both are being used to expedite the certification programme. Certification and first deliveries of the 54/55/56 series were scheduled to be made during 1980, following the flight of the first production example on 11 August. By 1 January 1980 the company had received more than 120 firm orders for these aircraft. Production is intended to reach four per month by mid-1981.

TYPE: Twin-turbofan light executive transport.
WINGS: Cantilever low-wing monoplane. Sweepback 13° at quarter-chord. All-metal multi-spar structure with

cavity-milled wing skins. Wing upper surface skin tapers in thickness from wing root to wingtip to save weight. The design incorporates an advanced cambered leading-edge, the 'Softflite' handling package (see introductory notes to Learjet entry) and supercritical winglets. Manually-operated ailerons. Electrically-operated trim tab in port aileron. Hydraulically-operated all-metal single-slotted trailing-edge flaps. Hydraulically-operated all-metal spoilers mounted on wing upper surface just forward of flaps. Anti-icing by engine bleed air ducted into leading-edges.
FUSELAGE: All-metal flush-riveted semi-monocoque fail-safe structure.
TAIL UNIT: Cantilever all-metal sweptback structure, with electrically-actuated variable-incidence T-tailplane. Small ventral fin. Electrically-heated de-icing of tailplane leading-edge.
LANDING GEAR: Hydraulically-retractable tricycle type, with twin wheels on each main unit and single steerable nosewheel. High-pressure pneumatic system for emergency extension. Oleo-pneumatic shock-absorbers. Chined nosewheel tyre. High-energy hydraulic braking system, with pneumatic backup. Fully-modulated anti-skid units.
POWER PLANT: Two Garrett-AiResearch TFE 731-3A turbofan engines, each rated at 16·24 kN (3,650 lb st), mounted in pod on each side of fuselage aft of wing. Fuel in integral wing tanks and a bladder type fuselage tank, with a combined capacity of (Model 54) 3,282 litres (867 US gallons), (Model 55) 3,846 litres (1,016 US gallons), (Model 56) 4,636 litres (1,225 US gallons). Refuelling point on upper surface of each outer wing. Engine nacelle leading-edges and fan hubs anti-iced by engine bleed air.
ACCOMMODATION: Crew of two on flight deck, with dual controls. Models 54 and 55 can seat from six to ten passengers in differing interior layouts, all with an aft toilet, and all but the 10-seat version with a galley cabinet. Model 56 seats six to eight passengers. Baggage space at rear of cabin, and in fuselage nose and tailcone. Two-piece clamshell door at forward end of cabin on port side, with integral steps built into the lower section. Emergency exit on starboard side of cabin.
SYSTEMS: Environmental control system comprises cabin pressurisation, ventilation, heating and cooling. Heating and pressurisation are provided by engine bleed air, with a maximum pressure differential of 0·65 bars (9·4

Gates Learjet 55 Longhorn eight/twelve-seat executive transport *(Pilot Press)*

Gates Learjet 35A Sea Patrol demonstration aircraft

The first and second prototypes of the Gates Learjet 55 Longhorn in flight over Kansas

lb/sq in), maintaining a cabin altitude of 2,440 m (8,000 ft) to an actual altitude of 15,545 m (51,000 ft). Freon vapour-cycle cooling system, supplemented by a ram-air system. Anti-icing system includes distribution of engine bleed air to wing leading-edges, engine nacelle leading-edges and fan hubs, and pilot and co-pilot windscreens; electrical anti-icing of tailplane leading-edge, pitot heads, stall warning vanes and static ports; and alcohol anti-icing of windscreens and radome. Hydraulic system supplied by two engine-driven variable-volume constant-pressure pumps, one on each engine, each capable of maintaining alone the full system pressure of 103·5 bars (1,500 lb/sq in) for operation of landing gear, brakes, flaps and spoilers. Electrically-driven hydraulic pump for emergency operation of all hydraulic services. Pneumatic system of 124 to 207 bars (1,800 to 3,000 lb/sq in) pressure for emergency extension of landing gear and operation of brakes. Electrical system powered by two 28V 400A engine-driven brush-less generators, either of which is capable of maintaining adequate DC power to operate all electrical services; two 1kVA solid-state inverters to provide AC power; and two 24V 40Ah nickel-cadmium batteries. Oxygen system of 1·08 m³ (38 cu ft) capacity, with crew demand masks; dropout mask for each passenger, which is presented automatically if cabin altitude exceeds 4,265 m (14,000 ft).

AVIONICS (provisional): Standard package will comprise dual Collins VIR-30A nav receivers, dual Collins VHF-20A com transceivers, dual Collins TDR-90 transponders, dual Allen 3137 RMIs, dual J.E.T. VG-206D vertical gyros, dual J.E.T. DN-104A directional gyros, Collins DME-40 DME, Collins ADF-60 ADF, Collins ALT-50A radio altimeter, Bendix RDR-1200B weather radar, and fully integrated autopilot/flight director with dual Collins FD-108Y flight indicators integrated with a J.E.T. FC-200 flight control system.

EQUIPMENT: Standard equipment includes six swivel/reclining seats on Models 54 and 55, five on Model 56, galley cabinet, two folding tables, electric flushing toilet, reading lights, air vents, indirect lighting, window shades, refreshment cabinet, entrance step light, cabin fire extinguisher and axe.

DIMENSIONS, EXTERNAL:
Wing span	13·35 m (43 ft 9½ in)
Length overall	16·80 m (55 ft 1¼ in)
Height overall	4·48 m (14 ft 8¼ in)
Wheelbase	2·51 m (8 ft 3 in)

DIMENSIONS, INTERNAL (A: Model 54; B: Model 55; C: Model 56):
Cabin: Length, excl flight deck: A	5·56 m (18 ft 3 in)
B	5·08 m (16 ft 8 in)
C	4·39 m (14 ft 5 in)
Max width	1·80 m (5 ft 11 in)
Max height	1·74 m (5 ft 8½ in)
Volume, incl flight deck: A	14·00 m³ (495 cu ft)
B	13·35 m³ (472 cu ft)
C	12·70 m³ (449 cu ft)

Baggage capacity, total: A		2·24 m³ (79 cu ft)
B		1·70 m³ (60 cu ft)
C		1·41 m³ (50 cu ft)

AREA:
Wings, gross	24·57 m² (264·5 sq ft)

WEIGHTS AND LOADINGS (estimated):
Weight empty: A	4,968 kg (10,954 lb)
B	4,986 kg (10,992 lb)
C	5,043 kg (11,119 lb)
Max payload: A	973·5 kg (2,146 lb)
B	956 kg (2,108 lb)
C	898·5 kg (1,981 lb)
Max fuel weight: A	2,632 kg (5,804 lb)
B	3,086 kg (6,803 lb)
C	3,685 kg (8,125 lb)
Max T-O weight: A	8,391 kg (18,500 lb)
B	8,845 kg (19,500 lb)
C	9,298 kg (20,500 lb)
Max ramp weight: A	8,505 kg (18,750 lb)
B	8,958 kg (19,750 lb)
C	9,412 kg (20,750 lb)
Max zero-fuel weight: A, B, C	6,123 kg (13,500 lb)
Max landing weight: A, B, C	7,257 kg (16,000 lb)
Max wing loading: A	340·8 kg/m² (69·8 lb/sq ft)
B	359·3 kg/m² (73·6 lb/sq ft)
C	378 kg/m² (77·4 lb/sq ft)
Max power loading: A	258·3 kg/kN (2·53 lb/lb st)
B	272·3 kg/kN (2·67 lb/lb st)
C	286·3 kg/kN (2·81 lb/lb st)

PERFORMANCE (estimated, at max T-O weight except where indicated):
Never-exceed speed: A, B, C	Mach 0·81
Max level speed at 9,150 m (30,000 ft): A, B, C	470 knots (871 km/h; 541 mph)
Max cruising speed at 13,700 m (45,000 ft): A, B, C	439 knots (814 km/h; 506 mph)
Econ cruising speed at 14,935 m (49,000 ft): A, B, C	401 knots (743 km/h; 462 mph)
Stalling speed, flaps down, engines idling: A, B, C	98 knots (182 km/h; 113 mph)
Max rate of climb at S/L: A	1,516 m (4,975 ft)/min
B	1,425 m (4,675 ft)/min
Service ceiling: A, B, C	15,545 m (51,000 ft)
T-O to 9 m (30 ft): A	1,234 m (4,050 ft)
B	1,387 m (4,550 ft)
C	1,564 m (5,130 ft)
Landing from 15 m (50 ft) at max landing weight: A, B, C	900 m (2,950 ft)
Range with 4 passengers, max fuel and 45 min reserves: A	2,105 nm (3,900 km; 2,424 miles)
B	2,483 nm (4,600 km; 2,859 miles)
C	3,013 nm (5,581 km; 3,468 miles)

GENERAL DYNAMICS
GENERAL DYNAMICS CORPORATION

HEAD OFFICE: Pierre Laclede Center, St Louis, Missouri 63105
Telephone: (314) 862 2440
CHAIRMAN AND CHIEF EXECUTIVE OFFICER: David S. Lewis
PRESIDENT: O. C. Boileau
EXECUTIVE VICE-PRESIDENTS:
  James M. Beggs (Aerospace)
  Lester Crown
  Guy W. Fiske (Commercial)
  Gorden E. MacDonald (Finance)
  P. Takis Veliotis (Marine)
VICE-PRESIDENTS:
  Richard E. Adams (General Manager, Fort Worth Division)
  Leonard F. Buchanan (General Manager, Convair Division)
  Otto J. Glasser (International, Washington)
  Max Golden (Contracts)
  Lyman C. Josephs (International)
  E. J. LeFevre (Government Relations)
  Edward E. Lynn (General Counsel)
  Warren G. Sullivan (Industrial Relations)
  Wayne Wells (Treasurer)
  Robert H. Widmer (Science and Engineering)

Convair Division:
PO Box 80847, San Diego, California 92138
VICE-PRESIDENTS:
  G. E. Blackshaw (Research Engineering)
  Leonard F. Buchanan (General Manager)
  B. R. Foushee (Programme Director, Aircraft)
  Jay E. Hawley (Contracts and Estimating)
  Ralph S. MacKenzie (Programme Director, Tomahawk)
  J. A. Robertson (Marketing)
  S. C. Wilkinson (Operations)

Fort Worth Division:
PO Box 748, Fort Worth, Texas 76101

VICE-PRESIDENTS:
  Richard E. Adams (General Manager)
  Forrest E. Armstrong (111 Programmes)
  James E. Ashton (Operations)
  P. R. Cowen (Deputy General Manager)
  Edward E. Hatchett (Finance)
  D. R. Kent (F-16 Engineering)
  Julius Y. McClure (Quality Assurance)
  Robert W. McGuffee (Logistics and Support)
  Herbert F. Rogers (Deputy General Manager and F-16 Programme Director)
  Sterling V. Starr (Director, F-16/79 Export Fighter Programme)
  Theodore S. Webb Jr (Research and Engineering)
  D. J. Wheaton (Marketing)

General Dynamics conducts its US aerospace activities at four divisions: Convair Division, with operations at San Diego, California; Fort Worth Division, with operations at Fort Worth, Texas; Pomona Division, at Pomona, California; and Electronics Division, with headquarters in San Diego. Convair Division is responsible for the design, development and production of aircraft structures and of systems for space exploration. Current programmes include development of the Tomahawk sea-launched cruise missile for the US Navy, and the ground-launched version for the US Air Force. Convair is also engaged in work on the air-launched cruise missile programme. Fort Worth Division is engaged in the design, development and production of military aircraft and electronics. Pomona Division is engaged in tactical missile and other ordnance programmes. Electronics Division is a leader in new technology to support the development and production of advanced electronics systems. Major programmes include sophisticated navigation positioning systems, tactical data and command control systems, automatic test equipment for high performance aircraft, and range measuring systems.

Fort Worth is currently responsible for production of the F-16 multi-role fighter; spares, support and modification/update for the F-111 fighter-bomber; and various ground-based radar systems. Convair Division is responsible for production of a major portion of the fuselage for the McDonnell Douglas DC-10 commercial transport aircraft and the KC-10A tanker/cargo aircraft, the

First of four RAAF aircraft converted to RF-111C configuration for a strike/reconnaissance role

mid-fuselage section of the Space Shuttle Orbiter vehicle, the Atlas-Centaur launch vehicle used to boost unmanned spacecraft and satellites, and cruise missiles.

Convair Division also retains detailed tooling for high-usage spares for the Convair-Liner 240/340/440 series of piston-engined transports, and Convair 880 and 990 jet transports, and is manufacturing components for operators of these types.

GENERAL DYNAMICS F-111

Production of this two-seat variable-geometry tactical fighter was completed in 1976, but the various versions described in the 1978-79 and earlier editions of *Jane's* will remain important elements of US Air Force and Royal Australian Air Force strength for many more years, as will Strategic Air Command's FB-111A medium-range bomber variant.

Important avionics update programmes are continuing to maintain the effectiveness of Tactical Air Command F-111s. Details of some of those programmes follow:

F-111A/E. Current planning involves a modernisation programme for the existing AJQ-20A analogue bombing and navigation system, to improve reliability and provide growth capability for modern guided munitions and advanced sensors. New equipment would include an advanced fleetwide common digital computer, the US Air Force Standard INS, and a new controls/display set. A FY 1981 RDT&E go-ahead is projected.

F-111F. Following completion of a successful US Air Force flight test programme, a decision was made to incorporate AN/AVQ-26 Pave Tack/guided weapons capability into all F-111F aircraft. Kit proofing has been completed, and the first production kit was scheduled for delivery in May 1980. General Dynamics is the prime contractor for integration of the system in the F-111s. The major components of the system are the Ford Aerospace Pave Tack pod, General Electric controls and displays, and a Hughes Aircraft data link pod. The Pave Tack pod is carried inside the aircraft's weapon bay on a cradle which rotates 180° in 5 s to expose it for use. Embodying a data link for stand-off delivery, Pave Tack provides a day/night all-weather capability to acquire, track and designate ground targets for laser, infra-red and electro-optically guided weapons, from very low altitudes if necessary.

EF-111A. ECM jamming version. Developed by Grumman, which converted two F-111As to this configuration for evaluation. Details under Grumman entry.

RF-111C. Four of the Royal Australian Air Force's 20 remaining F-111C strike aircraft have been allocated a strike/reconnaissance role. An accompanying illustration shows the first RF-111C, which was modified at Fort Worth. The modified aircraft, and trained crews with modification kits, returned to Australia in late 1979. Royal Australian Air Force personnel began modification of the second aircraft in January 1980, and all four RF-111Cs were due to be operational by late 1980. Reconnaissance equipment includes a Fairchild KA-56E low-altitude panoramic camera, Chicago Aerial KS-87C vertical cameras, Chicago Aerial KA-93A high-altitude panoramic camera, Honeywell AN/AAD-5 infra-red linescan, and Cardion Electronics TV.

FB-111. The 1978-79 *Jane's* contained details of the FB-111H, a projected manned penetration bomber that could be evolved from the FB-111A to meet SAC requirements following cancellation of the Rockwell B-1. A simpler conversion of approximately 150 F-111Ds and FB-111As was proposed in early 1979, under the tentative designations **FB-111B/C**. Apart from an increase in wing span, modifications would be concentrated mainly on the rear fuselage, to house new engines (probably General Electric F101s as developed for the B-1) and additional fuel. GD believes that converted aircraft could be operational by 1984-85.

The following abbreviated description applies to the F-111F, which was described fully in the 1978-79 *Jane's*:
TYPE: Two-seat variable-geometry multi-purpose fighter.

Artist's impression of FB-111B/C, a proposed conversion of existing F-111D and FB-111A aircraft for penetration bombing missions

POWER PLANT: Two Pratt & Whitney TF30-P-100 turbofan engines, each giving 111·5 kN (25,100 lb st) with afterburning. Fuel tanks in wings and fuselage.

ACCOMMODATION: Crew of two side by side in air-conditioned and pressurised cabin. Portion of canopy over each seat is hinged on aircraft centreline and opens upward. Zero-speed, zero-altitude (including underwater) emergency escape module developed by McDonnell Douglas Corpn and utilising a 178 kN (40,000 lb st) Rocket Power Inc rocket motor. Emergency procedure calls for both crew members to remain in capsule cabin section, which is propelled away from aircraft by rocket motor and lowered to ground by parachute. Airbags cushion impact and form flotation gear in water. Entire capsule forms survival shelter.

ARMAMENT: One M61 multi-barrel 20 mm gun plus one B43 bomb, or two B43s, in internal weapon bay. External stores are carried on three attachments under each wing. The two inboard pylons on each side pivot as the wings sweep back, to keep the stores parallel with the fuselage. The outboard pylon on each wing is jettisonable and non-swivelling.

DIMENSIONS, EXTERNAL:

Wing span: spread	19·20 m (63 ft 0 in)
fully swept	9·74 m (31 ft 11·4 in)
Length overall	22·40 m (73 ft 6 in)
Height overall	5·22 m (17 ft 1·4 in)

WEIGHTS:

Weight empty	21,537 kg (47,481 lb)
Max T-O weight	45,359 kg (100,000 lb)

PERFORMANCE:

Max speed at height	Mach 2·5
Max speed at S/L	Mach 1·2
Service ceiling	over 18,000 m (59,000 ft)
T-O and landing run	under 915 m (3,000 ft)
Range with max internal fuel	over 2,540 nm (4,707 km; 2,925 miles)

GENERAL DYNAMICS F-16 FIGHTING FALCON
USAF designations: F-16A and F-16B

The F-16 had its origin in the US Air Force's Lightweight Fighter (LWF) prototype programme, in 1972. The history of this programme and a description of the YF-16 prototypes can be found in the 1978-79 and 1977-78 editions of *Jane's* respectively.

The first of two YF-16 prototypes (72-01567) made its official first flight on 2 February 1974. A level speed of Mach 2 at 12,200 m (40,000 ft) was attained on 11 March 1974. The second YF-16 (72-01568) flew for the first time on 9 May 1974. During subsequent weapon trials, this aircraft extended the planned operational capability of the design by completing successfully the initial launch of Sparrow missiles on 6 October 1977 and of a Sky Flash missile in November 1978. Also in 1978, the F-16 prototype, fitted with a Martin Marietta ATLIS II (Automatic Tracking Laser Illumination System) pod, became the first single-seat fighter to hit ground targets with GBU-10 and GBU-16 laser-guided bombs, without assistance from air/ground locators.

On 13 January 1975 the Secretary of the US Air Force announced that the F-16 had been selected for full-scale engineering development. The original YF-16 requirement for an air superiority day fighter was expanded, to give equal emphasis to the air-to-surface role, including provision of radar and all-weather navigation capabilities. The manufacture of eight pre-production aircraft, comprising six single-seat **F-16As** and two two-seat **F-16Bs**, began in July 1975. The first development F-16A made its first flight on 8 December 1976, and the first F-16B on 8 August 1977. The last of the eight development aircraft was the second two-seater, which made its first flight in June 1978. Meanwhile, the US Air Force had indicated its intention to procure a total of 1,388 F-16s, including 204 two-seaters. The name Fighting Falcon was adopted in 1980.

On 7 June 1975 a joint announcement by the four NATO countries of Belgium, Denmark, the Netherlands and Norway confirmed their selection of the F-16 to replace F-104s in current service. The initial order was for 348 aircraft (Belgium 116, the Netherlands 58, Norway 72), of which 58 will be two-seaters. Under co-production agreements, final assembly lines for these aircraft have been established in Belgium and the Netherlands. About 30 European companies are producing F-16 components, avionics and equipment. The Royal Netherlands Air Force was in 1980 seeking its government's approval to increase its initial order by 111 aircraft.

On 27 October 1976, the government of Iran announced its decision to acquire 160 F-16s, but these were cancelled in January 1979. In August 1977, Israel announced plans to acquire a minimum of 75 F-16s (including eight two-seaters), and the first of these was handed over on 31 January 1980.

The first production F-16A (78-0001) flew for the first time on 7 August 1978, and was delivered formally to the US Air Force ten days later. By the end of 1979, the US Air Force had accepted 35 F-16As and 30 F-16Bs. The first F-16 to enter operational service was delivered to the US Air Force's 388th Tactical Fighter Wing on 6 January 1979. The first F-16 assigned to the 56th Tactical Fighter Wing, MacDill AFB, Florida, was delivered during October 1979. Three squadrons of F-16s are expected to join the 50th TFW with the US Air Forces Europe from mid-1981, at Hahn AFB in West Germany.

The first F-16 for Europe was delivered to the Belgian Air Force on 26 January 1979. The Royal Netherlands Air Force received its first two F-16s on 6 June 1979, and initial deliveries to the air forces of Denmark and Norway were made in January 1980. Deliveries to all six air forces totalled more than 100 by 1 March 1980. From early 1982, the Egyptian Air Force is to receive 40 F-16s.

The following description applies to the F-16A and F-16B, as indicated:

TYPE: Single-seat lightweight air combat fighter (F-16A) and two-seat fighter/trainer (F-16B).

WINGS: Cantilever mid-wing monoplane, of blended wing/body design and cropped-delta planform. The blended wing/body concept is achieved by flaring the wing/body intersection, thus not only providing lift from the body at high angles of attack but also giving less wetted area and increased internal fuel volume. In addition, thickening of the wing root gives a more rigid structure, with a weight saving of some 113 kg (250 lb). Basic wing is of NACA 64A-204 section, with 40° sweepback on leading-edges. Structure is mainly of aluminium alloy, with 11 spars, 5 ribs and single upper and lower skins, and is attached to fuselage by machined aluminium fittings. Variable wing camber is achieved by the use of leading-edge manoeuvring flaps that are programmed automatically as a function of Mach number and angle of attack. The increased wing camber maintains effective lift coefficients at high angles of attack. These flaps are one-piece bonded aluminium honeycomb sandwich structures, actuated by a Garrett-AiResearch drive system using rotary actuators. The trailing-edges carry large flaperons (flaps/ailerons), which are interchangeable left with right and are actuated by National Water Lift integrated servo-actuators. The maximum rate of flaperon movement is 80°/s.

FUSELAGE: Semi-monocoque all-metal structure of frames and longerons, built in three main modules: forward (to just aft of cockpit), centre and aft. Nose radome built by

General Dynamics F-16A Fighting Falcon multi-role fighter in USAF service

General Dynamics F-16B two-seat fighter/trainer

Brunswick Corporation. Highly-swept vortex control strakes along the fuselage forebody increase lift and improve directional stability at high angles of attack.

TAIL UNIT: Cantilever structure with sweptback surfaces. Fin is multi-spar multi-rib aluminium structure with graphite-epoxy skins, aluminium tip. and glassfibre dorsal fin and root fairing. Interchangeable all-moving tailplane halves, constructed of graphite-epoxy composite laminate skins with full-depth bonded aluminium honeycomb sandwich core, titanium spar, steel leading-edge caps and aluminium tips. Ventral fins are bonded aluminium honeycomb core with aluminium skins. Split speed-brake inboard of rear portion of each horizontal tail surface to each side of nozzle, each deflecting 60° from the closed position. National Water Lift servo-actuators for rudder and tailplane.

LANDING GEAR: Menasco hydraulically-retractable type, nose unit retracting aft and main units forward into fuselage. Nosewheel is located aft of intake, to reduce the risk of foreign objects being thrown into the engine during ground operation, and rotates 90° during retraction to lie horizontally under engine air intake duct. Oleo-pneumatic struts on all units. Goodyear main wheels and brakes; B. F. Goodrich main-wheel tyres, size 25·5 × 8-14. Steerable nosewheel with B. F. Goodrich tyre, size 18 × 5·5-8. All but two main unit components interchangeable. Brake-by-wire system on main gear, with Goodyear anti-skid units. Runway arrester hook under rear fuselage.

POWER PLANT: One Pratt & Whitney F100-PW-200 turbofan engine, rated at approx 111·2 kN (25,000 lb st) with afterburning, mounted within the rear fuselage. Fixed-geometry intake, with boundary layer splitter plate, beneath fuselage. A variable-geometry intake can be fitted later, without difficulty, if desirable to improve high-speed performance. The underfuselage intake position was chosen because here the airflow suffers least disturbance throughout the entire range of aircraft manoeuvres, and because it eliminates the problem of gun gas ingestion. Standard fuel contained in wing and five fuselage cells which function as two tanks; internal fuel weight is 3,162 kg (6,972 lb) in F-16A, and approx 17% less in F-16B. In-flight refuelling receptacle in top of centre-fuselage, aft of cockpit. Auxiliary fuel can be carried in drop-tanks on underwing and underfuselage hardpoints.

ACCOMMODATION: Pilot only in F-16A, in air-conditioned cockpit. McDonnell Douglas Aces II zero-zero ejection seat. Texstar transparent bubble canopy, made of polycarbonate, an advanced plastics material. The windscreen and forward canopy are an integral unit without a forward bow-frame, and are separated from the aft canopy by a simple support structure which serves also as the break-point where the forward section pivots upward and aft to give access to the cockpit. A redundant safety-lock feature prevents canopy loss. Windscreen/canopy design provides 360° all-round view, 195° fore and aft, 40° down over the side, and 15° down over the nose. Supersonic drag penalty is considered to be more than offset by the improved rearward view afforded to the pilot. To enable the pilot to sustain high-g forces, and for pilot comfort, the seat is inclined 30° aft and the heel-line is raised. In normal operation the canopy is pivoted upward and aft by electrical power; the pilot is also able to unlatch the canopy manually and open it with a backup handcrank. Emergency jettison is provided by explosive unlatching devices and two forward-mounted rockets. A limited-displacement, force-sensing control stick is provided on the right hand console, with a suitable armrest, to provide precise control inputs during combat manoeuvres. The F-16B has two cockpits arranged in tandem and equipped with all controls, displays, instruments, avionics and life-support systems required to perform both training and combat missions. The layout of the F-16B second station is essentially the same as that of the F-16A, and is fully systems-operational. A single-enclosure polycarbonate transparency, made in two pieces and spliced aft of the forward seat with a metal bow-frame and lateral support member, provides outstanding view from both cockpits.

SYSTEMS: Regenerative bootstrap air-cycle environmental control system by United Technologies' Hamilton Standard Division, using engine bleed air, for pressurisation and cooling. Two separate and independent hydraulic systems supply power for operation of the primary flight control surfaces and the utility functions. Electrical system powered by engine-driven Westinghouse 40kVA and Lear Siegler 5kVA generators and ground control units, with Sundstrand constant-speed drive. Four dedicated, sealed-cell batteries provide transient electrical power protection for the fly-by-wire flight control system. Application of the control configured vehicle (CCV) principle of relaxed static stability produces a significant reduction in trim drag, especially at high load factors and supersonic speeds. The aircraft centre of gravity is allowed to move aft, reducing both the tail drag and the change in drag on the wing due to changes in lift required to balance the down-load on the tail. Relaxed static stability imposes a requirement for a highly-reliable, full-time-operating, stability augmentation system, including reliable electronic, electrical and hydraulic provisions. The signal paths in this quad-redundant system are used to control the aircraft, replacing the usual mechanical linkages. Direct electrical control is employed from pilot controls to surface actuators. An onboard Sundstrand/Solar jet fuel starter is provided for engine self-start capability. Hamilton Standard turbine compressor, and Sundstrand accessory drive gearbox. Simmonds fuel measuring system. Garrett-AiResearch emergency power unit automatically drives a standby generator and pump to provide uninterrupted electrical and hydraulic power for control in the event of the engine or primary power systems becoming inoperative.

AVIONICS AND EQUIPMENT: Westinghouse pulse-Doppler range and angle track radar, with planar array in nose. The radar has a lookdown range, in ground clutter, of 20-30 nm (37-56 km; 23-35 miles), and a lookup range of 25-40 nm (46-74 km; 29-46 miles). Forward avionics bay, immediately forward of cockpit, contains radar, air data equipment, inertial navigation system and flight control computer; rear avionics bay contains ILS, Tacan and IFF. A Dalmo Victor ALR-69 radar warning system, with AEL antennae, is installed. Communications equipment includes Magnavox AN/ARC-164 UHF transceiver; provisions for a Magnavox KY-58 secure voice system; Collins AN/ARC-186 VHF AM/FM transceiver; government furnished AN/AIC-18/25 intercom; and Novatronics interference blanker. Sperry Flight Systems central air data computer. Singer-Kearfott modified SKN-2400 inertial navigation system; Collins AN/ARN-108 ILS; Collins AN/ARN-118

Tacan; Teledyne Electronics AN/APX-101 air-to-ground IFF transponder with a government furnished IFF control; government furnished National Security Agency KIT-1A/TSEC cryptographic equipment; Lear Siegler stick force sensors; Marconi Avionics electronic head-up display set; a government-furnished horizontal situation indicator; Teledyne Avionics angle of attack transmitter; Gull Airborne angle of attack indicator; Clifton Precision attitude director indicator; Delco fire control computer; Photo-Sonics gun camera; Kaiser radar electro-optical display. Landing/taxying light on each main landing gear strut.

ARMAMENT: General Electric M61A-1 20 mm multi-barrel cannon in the port-side wing/body fairing, equipped with a General Electric ammunition handling system and a 'snapshoot' gunsight (part of the head-up display system) and 500 rounds of ammunition. There is a mounting for an infra-red air-to-air missile at each wingtip, one underfuselage hardpoint and six underwing hardpoints for the carriage of additional stores. The underfuselage station is stressed for a load of up to 1,000 kg (2,200 lb), the two inboard underwing stations for 1,587 kg (3,500 lb) each, the two centre underwing stations for 1,134 kg (2,500 lb) each, all at 5·5g; the two outboard underwing stations and the two wingtip stations 113 kg (250 lb) each, all at 9·0g. Total possible external weapon load, with reduced internal fuel, is 6,894 kg (15,200 lb), and a total load of approximately 5,443 kg (12,000 lb) can be carried with full internal fuel. Typical stores loads can include two wingtip-mounted AIM-9J/L Sidewinders, with up to four more on the outer underwing stations; Sargent-Fletcher 1,400 litre (370 US gallon; 308 Imp gallon) drop-tanks on the inboard underwing stations; a 1,136 litre (300 US gallon; 250 Imp gallon) drop-tank on the underfuselage station; a Martin Marietta Pave Penny laser tracker pod along the starboard side of the nacelle; and single or cluster bombs, air-to-surface missiles, or flare pods, on the four inner underwing stations. Stores can be launched from Aircraft Hydro-Forming MAU-12C/A bomb ejector racks, Hughes LAU-88 launchers, or Orgen triple or multiple ejector racks. Westinghouse AN/ALQ-119 and AN/ALQ-131 ECM (jammer) pods can be carried on the centreline and two underwing stations. Modified Tracor ALE-40 internal pyrotechnic/chaff dispensers have been specified. Weapon delivery capabilities include air-to-air combat with gun and Sidewinder missiles, and air-to-ground attack with gun, rockets, conventional bombs, special weapons, laser-guided and electro-optical weapons. Weapons already launched successfully from F-16s include radar-guided Sparrow and Sky Flash air-to-air missiles and TV-guided Maverick air-to-surface missiles.

DIMENSIONS, EXTERNAL:

Wing span over missile launchers	9·45 m (31 ft 0 in)
Wing span over missiles	10·01 m (32 ft 10 in)
Wing aspect ratio	3·0
Length overall, excl probe	14·52 m (47 ft 7·7 in)
Height overall	5·01 m (16 ft 5·2 in)
Tailplane span	5·495 m (18 ft 0·34 in)
Wheel track	2·36 m (7 ft 9 in)
Wheelbase	4·00 m (13 ft 1·44 in)

AREA:

Wings, gross	27·87 m² (300·0 sq ft)

WEIGHTS AND LOADINGS:

Weight empty:

F-16A	6,866 kg (15,137 lb)
F-16B	7,157 kg (15,778 lb)

General Dynamics F-16A Fighting Falcon, with additional side view (top) of F-16B (*Pilot Press*)

Internal fuel load: F-16A   3,162 kg (6,972 lb)
  F-16B   2,624 kg (5,785 lb)
Max external load   6,894 kg (15,200 lb)
Structural design gross weight (9·0g) with full internal
  fuel   10,205 kg (22,500 lb)
Max symmetrical design load factor with full inter-
  nal fuel at 10,205 kg (22,500 lb) gross weight:
  F-16A/B   9·0
Max T-O weight:
  F-16A, air-to-air, no external tanks
     10,594 kg (23,357 lb)
  F-16B, air-to-air, no external tanks
     10,348 kg (22,814 lb)
  F-16A/B with external load 16,057 kg (35,400 lb)
Wing loading:
  at 10,070 kg (22,200 lb) AUW
     361 kg/m² (74 lb/sq ft)
  at 14,968 kg (33,000 lb) AUW
     537 kg/m² (110 lb/sq ft)
Thrust/weight ratio ('clean')   1·1 to 1
PERFORMANCE (F-16A):
Max level speed at 12,200 m (40,000 ft)
     above Mach 2·0
Service ceiling   more than 15,240 m (50,000 ft)
Radius of action
     more than 500 nm (925 km; 575 miles)
Ferry range, with drop-tanks
     more than 2,100 nm (3,890 km; 2,415 miles)

GENERAL DYNAMICS F-16/79

This aircraft is essentially an F-16 tactical fighter powered by a General Electric J79 afterburning turbojet
engine, for export to nations to which the supply of F100
turbofans might be embargoed by the US government. A
prototype F-16/79 is being produced as a private venture
by General Dynamics, which leased back from the US Air
Force the second F-16B development aircraft for conversion. First flight is scheduled for 1981.

Replacement of the 111·2 kN (25,000 lb st) F100-PW-
200 by the 80·1 kN (18,000 lb st) J79-GE-17X will offer a
considerable reduction in aircraft cost. The basic air combat effectiveness of the F-16 will be retained, with an
increase of some 590 kg (1,300 lb) in the aircraft's empty
weight. Changes will include internal modification of the
engine air intake, to reduce airflow and increase pressure
recovery, and lengthening of the rear fuselage fairing,
increasing the length of the fuselage (but not overall
length) by 0·45 m (1 ft 5½ in).

WEIGHTS (single-seat):
Weight empty   7,333 kg (16,165 lb)
Internal fuel load   3,162 kg (6,972 lb)
Max external load   6,894 kg (15,200 lb)
Normal max T-O weight   11,189 kg (24,668 lb)
Max T-O weight   16,057 kg (35,400 lb)

GENERAL DYNAMICS AFTI-16 PROGRAMME

In December 1978, the US Air Force selected the F-16
as a testbed with which to explore promising new fighter
aircraft technologies, under the Advanced Fighter Technology Integration (AFTI-16) programme directed by the
Air Force Systems Command's Flight Dynamics Laboratory at Wright-Patterson AFB, Ohio. General Dynamics
was awarded a $34·3 million prime contract, under which
it will modify an F-16A returned to the company by the
US Air Force on 6 March 1980.

Changes visible in the accompanying artist's impression
of the modified AFTI-16 testbed include the addition of
two large manoeuvring canards for direct force control,
under the engine air intake duct, and a dorsal fairing to
house flight test equipment. Systems to be developed and
evaluated when flight testing begins at Edwards AFB,
California, in July 1981, will include triplex digital fly-
by-wire flight controls, advanced displays, system management computers, and integrated flight and weapons fire
controls. Information generated by the programme will be
made available generally to the US aircraft industry for
application to the design of future fighter aircraft.

Artist's impression of the AFTI-16 technology testbed aircraft produced by modifying an F-16A

GREAT LAKES
GREAT LAKES AIRCRAFT COMPANY

HEAD OFFICE AND WORKS: Drawer A, Eastman, Georgia
31023
Telephone: (912) 374 5535
SALES DIRECTOR: Richard Ivey

Following its acquisition by Mr R. Dean Franklin, Great
Lakes Aircraft Company was relocated from Enid,
Oklahoma, and Wichita, Kansas, to Eastman, Georgia.
The Great Lakes Sport Trainer Model 2T-1A-2 is again in
production, at the Eastman plant, from where deliveries
began in March 1980. A complete parts department is
being built up for customer service.

GREAT LAKES SPORT TRAINER MODEL 2T-1A-2

The Great Lakes Sport Trainer was produced with Cirrus and Menasco engines by the original Great Lakes
Company, founded on 2 January 1929.

Certification of the Model 2T-1A-1 with 104 kW (140
hp) Avco Lycoming engine was obtained in May 1973,
and delivery of production aircraft began in October 1973,
but production of this version (described in the 1977-78
Jane's) has ended. Current production model is the
2T-1A-2 with 134 kW (180 hp) engine, constant-speed
propeller, inverted fuel and oil systems, ailerons on both
upper and lower wings, and with manifold pressure and
fuel flow gauges as standard. Approved aerobatic manoeuvres are spins, chandelles, lazy eights, loops, barrel
rolls, primary rolls, point rolls, slow rolls, snap rolls,
Cuban 8s, hammerhead turns, Immelmann turns and split
'S'.

A total of 137 examples of the Great Lakes Sport
Trainer were built at Enid and Wichita after production
resumed in 1973. Production, at a projected rate of one
aircraft every seven working days, is now centred at Eastman, Georgia.
TYPE: Two-seat sporting biplane.
WINGS: Braced biplane, with N-type interplane struts,
wire bracing and N-type centre-section support struts.
Dual streamline-section landing and flying wires. Wing
section M-12. No dihedral on upper wing, 2° on lower
wings. Sweepback on upper wing 9° 13'. Composite
structure, with Douglas fir spars, metal ribs and overall
fabric covering. Ailerons on upper and lower wings. No
flaps or tabs.

Great Lakes Sport Trainer Model 2T-1A-2 (Avco Lycoming AEIO-360-B1G6 engine)

FUSELAGE: Welded chrome-molybdenum steel tube. Warren girder structure, with fabric covering.
TAIL UNIT: Wire-braced welded chrome-molybdenum
steel tube structure, fabric-covered. Tailplane incidence
manually adjustable from both cockpits. No controllable tabs.
LANDING GEAR: Non-retractable type, with steerable Scott
tailwheel. Divided main legs with spring-oleo shock-
absorbers standard. Main wheels size 6·00-6 with hydraulic disc brakes. Parking brake. Size 7·00-6 tyres
optional. Leg fairings and wheel fairings standard.
POWER PLANT: One 134 kW (180 hp) Avco Lycoming
AEIO-360-B1G6 flat-four engine, driving a Hartzell
two-blade constant-speed metal propeller type HC-
C2YK-4F/FC7666A-2 with spinner. Fully inverted fuel
system with 98·5 litre (26 US gallon) centre-section

tank in upper wing, and 5·3 litre (1·4 US gallon)
inverted header tank. Refuelling point in upper wing
surface. Fully inverted oil system.
ACCOMMODATION: Two seats in tandem in open cockpits.
Dual controls, with adjustable rudder pedals, standard.
Compass, airspeed indicator, altimeter and engine
speed indicator standard in rear cockpit, optional for
front cockpit. Cockpit heating standard. Baggage compartment aft of rear cockpit, capacity 18 kg (40 lb),
optional.
SYSTEMS: Engine-driven generator and sealed storage battery for electrical supply to navigation lights, two rotating beacons, and rear cockpit instrument lights, standard. Hydraulic system for brakes only.
AVIONICS AND EQUIPMENT: Emergency locator transmitter
standard. Edo-Aire Mitchell 551 transceiver, intercom,

and Edo-Aire Mitchell RT-553 with or without auto omni, optional. Standard equipment includes map case, seat belts and shoulder harness, cockpit lights, navigation lights, two omni-flash beacons, and a choice of four paint trims. Optional equipment includes turn and bank indicator, rate of climb indicator, cylinder head temperature gauge and accelerometer for rear cockpit, glider tow hitch, Hobbs meter, and cockpit covers.

DIMENSIONS, EXTERNAL:

Wing span	8·13 m (26 ft 8 in)
Length overall	6·45 m (21 ft 2 in)
Height overall	2·34 m (7 ft 8 in)
Wheel track	1·78 m (5 ft 10 in)

AREAS:

Wings, gross	17·43 m² (187·6 sq ft)

Ailerons (total)	2·70 m² (29·10 sq ft)
Fin	0·55 m² (5·87 sq ft)
Rudder	0·63 m² (6·81 sq ft)
Tailplane	1·43 m² (15·44 sq ft)
Elevators	0·99 m² (10·68 sq ft)

WEIGHTS AND LOADINGS:

Weight empty	558 kg (1,230 lb)
Max T-O and landing weight	816 kg (1,800 lb)
Max wing loading	47·0 kg/m² (9·63 lb/sq ft)
Max power loading	6·09 kg/kW (10·0 lb/hp)

PERFORMANCE (at max T-O weight):

Max level speed at S/L		
	114 knots (210 km/h; 131 mph)	
Max level speed at 3,050 m (10,000 ft)		
	108 knots (201 km/h; 125 mph)	

Max cruising speed	102 knots (190 km/h; 118 mph)
Approach speed	65 knots (121 km/h; 75 mph)
Stalling speed	50 knots (92 km/h; 57 mph)
Max rate of climb at S/L	350 m (1,150 ft)/min
Service ceiling	5,180 m (17,000 ft)
T-O run	145 m (475 ft)
T-O to 15 m (50 ft)	252 m (825 ft)
Landing from 15 m (50 ft)	252 m (825 ft)
Landing run	122 m (400 ft)
Range with max fuel, no reserves	
	260 nm (482 km; 300 miles)
Endurance with max fuel (75% power)	2 h 51 min
g limits	+5·38; −4

GRUMMAN
GRUMMAN CORPORATION

HEAD OFFICE: 1111 Stewart Avenue, Bethpage, New York 11714

Telephone: (516) 575 0574

CHAIRMAN OF THE BOARD AND CHIEF EXECUTIVE OFFICER: John C. Bierwirth

PRESIDENT AND CHIEF OPERATING OFFICER: Joseph G. Gavin Jr

VICE-CHAIRMAN OF THE BOARD: John F. Carr

VICE-PRESIDENTS:
Nat P.Busi (Controller)
John J. Carroll (Community Affairs)
Robert G. Freese (Treasurer)
Thomas L. Genovese (General Counsel)
Weyman B. Jones (Public Affairs)
Rolf J. Larson (Development)
Ross S. Mickey (International Affairs)

SECRETARY: Robert W. Bradshaw

GRUMMAN AEROSPACE CORPORATION
Entry follows

GRUMMAN ALLIED INDUSTRIES INC

HEAD OFFICE AND WORKS: 445 Broad Hollow Road, Melville, New York 11747

Telephone: (516) 454 8400

CHAIRMAN OF THE BOARD: Robert G. Freese
PRESIDENT: Robert W. Somerville

GRUMMAN DATA SYSTEMS CORPORATION

HEAD OFFICE AND WORKS: Bethpage, New York 11714

Telephone: (516) 575 0574

CHAIRMAN OF THE BOARD: John F. Carr
PRESIDENT: Robert A. Nafis

GRUMMAN ENERGY SYSTEMS INC

HEAD OFFICE AND WORKS: Bethpage, New York 11714

Telephone: (516) 575 0574

CHAIRMAN OF THE BOARD AND PRESIDENT: Ronald B. Peterson

GRUMMAN INTERNATIONAL INC

HEAD OFFICE: Bethpage, New York 11714

Telephone: (516) 575 1101

PRESIDENT: Michael Pelehach

The Grumman Aircraft Engineering Corporation was incorporated on 6 December 1929. Important changes in the corporate structure of the company were announced in 1969, resulting in the formation of Grumman Corporation, a small holding company, with Grumman Aerospace Corporation, Grumman Allied Industries Inc and Grumman Data Systems Corporation. A new organisation known as Grumman Ecosystems Corporation (now Grumman Energy Systems Inc) was brought into operation in January 1971, and on 2 January 1973 a merger took place with American Aviation Corporation of Cleveland, Ohio, to create Grumman American Aviation Corporation as a new subsidiary of Grumman Corporation. In 1978, Grumman Corporation's major holding in Grumman American Aviation was purchased by AJI, which renamed the latter company Gulfstream American Corporation (which see).

GRUMMAN AEROSPACE CORPORATION

HEAD OFFICE AND WORKS: South Oyster Bay Road, Bethpage, New York 11714

Telephone: (516) 575 0574

CHAIRMAN OF THE BOARD AND PRESIDENT: George M. Skurla

EXECUTIVE VICE-PRESIDENT: John O'Brien (Operations)

SENIOR VICE-PRESIDENTS:
Lawrence M. Mead Jr (Departmental Operations)
Gordon H. Ochenrider (Washington Operations)
Peter B. Oram (Aircraft Programmes)
Carl A. Paladino (Treasurer)
Philip S. Vassallo (Corporate Procurement Operations)

VICE-PRESIDENTS:
Alexander D. Alexandrovich (Asst to Executive Vice-President Operations)
John M. Buxton (President, Grumman Houston Corporation)
Renso L. Caporali (Development)
Edward Dalva (Stuart Operations)
Fred W. Haise Jr (Space Programmes)
Thomas J. Kane Jr (Business Development)
Thomas J. Kelly (Engineering)
Frank J. Messina (Manufacturing)
Robert C. Miller (Presidential Asst for Corporate Development)
Robert J. Myers (Resources)
William M. Zarkowsky (Milledgeville Operations)

SECRETARY AND GENERAL COUNSEL: Raphael Mur

Current products of this subsidiary of Grumman Corporation include versions of the A-6 Intruder, EA-6B Prowler, E-2C Hawkeye and F-14 Tomcat for the US Navy, and a tactical jamming version of the General Dynamics F-111, designated EF-111A, for the US Air Force. The Milledgeville plant manufactures wing skins and glassfibre wingtips for the Fairchild A-10A Thunderbolt II attack aircraft. A contract for Grumman Aerospace to build major components for the Sikorsky CH-53E heavy-lift helicopter was announced in the Spring of 1978. Grumman later received a contract from the Boeing Company to manufacture the wing centre-section of the Model 767 civil transport.

In 1979, the Corporation received a $3 million contract from the US Defense Advanced Research Projects Agency to proceed with design and wind tunnel testing of forward-swept wing (FSW) models. Advantages claimed for the FSW aircraft include reduced fuel consumption and greater manoeuvrability at supersonic speeds; greater flexibility in fuselage design; and reductions in aircraft cost, size and weight. Subject to satisfactory results from wind tunnel testing, DARPA may order a small manned FSW technology demonstrator.

GRUMMAN/RESORTS INTERNATIONAL G-111 ALBATROSS

Grumman's Stuart, Florida, facility has completed the modification of an HU-16 Albatross amphibian to 28-passenger commuter configuration on behalf of Chalks International Airlines, a division of Resorts International. The first stage involved the inspection and replacement of

parts to produce the equivalent of a zero-time airframe, followed by modernisation of the flight deck, and the provision of passenger cabin doors and a 28-seat interior. At the same time, the Wright R-1820-82A engines were removed and overhauled, and new fire detection and autofeathering systems installed, together with mufflers to bring noise levels down to FAR Pt 36 standards. During inspection, Grumman found that a rear spar capstrip of 7075-T6 light alloy had suffered deterioration, and it was replaced by a titanium capstrip. Subsequent conversions will have all four capstrips replaced by titanium to give the airframe an unlimited service life. Grumman modifications have included conversion of the port main passenger door to open outward, and the lower portion now mounts a drop-down ladder.

Interior and avionics design and installation were carried out by Jet Executive International of Fort Lauderdale, Florida. Twenty-eight non-reclinable seats are provided at 81 cm (32 in) pitch, with facilities for a flight attendant, and there is provision for a toilet at the rear of the cabin. New lightweight avionics include two Collins VHF-20A com, two VIR-30 nav, ADF-30 ADF, and RCA Weather Scout 2 radar. Equipment removed included the autopilot, JATO and drop fuel tank provisions.

The prototype conversion, of a UF-2 Albatross, flew for the first time on 13 February 1979. FAA certification was received on 29 April 1980, and a second G-111 was scheduled to fly shortly afterwards. At that time, Resorts International planned to have at least 13 more HU-16s similarly converted, and Grumman had purchased 36 others for civil conversion. Grumman believes that there is a potential market for conversions of approximately 200 Albatross aircraft which remain in worldwide use, and was planning in Autumn 1980 to transfer the programme to a former Fairchild Industries factory at St Augustine, Florida. A turboprop-powered version was then also under consideration.

Details of the HU-16 Albatross last appeared in the 1964-65 *Jane's*, and apply generally to this conversion, except as noted above and in the changed specification details which follow:

Grumman/Resorts International commuter conversion of the Albatross military amphibian

DIMENSIONS, INTERNAL:

Cabin: Length	7·96 m (26 ft 1¼ in)
Max height	1·93 m (6 ft 4 in)
Max width	2·26 m (7 ft 4¾ in)
Floor area	13·47 m² (145 sq ft)
Baggage compartment	7·93 m³ (280 cu ft)

WEIGHTS:

Operating weight empty	10,432 kg (23,000 lb)
Max fuel weight	2,920 kg (6,438 lb)
Max T-O weight	14,288 kg (31,500 lb)
Max landing weight	14,061 kg (31,000 lb)

PERFORMANCE (provisional):

Cruising speed	130 knots (241 km/h; 150 mph)
T-O to 15 m (50 ft), water	1,387 m (4,550 ft)
T-O to 15 m (50 ft), land	1,707 m (5,600 ft)
Landing from 15 m (50 ft), land	640 m (2,100 ft)
Landing from 15 m (50 ft), water	579 m (1,900 ft)
Max range	1,042 nm (1,930 km; 1,200 miles)

GRUMMAN HAWKEYE
USN designation: E-2

The E-2 Hawkeye was evolved as a carrier-borne early-warning aircraft, but is suitable also for land-based operations from unimproved fields. The prototype flew for the first time on 21 October 1960, since when the following versions have been built:

E-2A (formerly W2F-1). Initial production version. First flight on 19 April 1961, and first delivery to US Navy on 19 January 1964. Total of 62 built, including three prototypes.

E-2B. Prototype flew for the first time on 20 February 1969. Differs from E-2A by having a Litton Industries L-304 microelectronic general-purpose computer and reliability improvements. A retrofit programme, completed in December 1971, updated all operational E-2As to E-2B standard.

E-2C. First of two E-2C prototypes flew on 20 January 1971. Production began in mid-1971 and the first flight of a production aircraft was made on 23 September 1972. Firm orders from the US Navy cover 79 aircraft, of which 56 had been delivered by the beginning of 1980. Procurement of 22 more is planned by the end of 1986. Israel has four; and in Summer 1979 Japan released funds for four aircraft for delivery in 1982 and 1983. Japan has a requirement for additional E-2C aircraft in the future. The French Air Force conducted an operational evaluation of the 58th production E-2C, from the CEAM, Mont-de-Marsan, in mid-1980.

The E-2C first entered service, with airborne early-warning squadron VAW-123 at NAS Norfolk, Va, in November 1973, and went to sea on board the USS *Saratoga* in late 1974. Nine other squadrons have since received E-2C aircraft, and two **TE-2C** training aircraft are also in service.

The Hawkeye can maintain patrol on naval task force defence perimeters in all weathers, at an operating height of about 9,150 m (30,000 ft), and can detect and assess any threat from approaching high-Mach-number enemy aircraft over ranges approaching 260 nm (480 km; 300 miles). The radar is capable of detecting airborne targets anywhere in a three million cubic mile surveillance envelope. Improvements compared with earlier radars provide increased reliability and easier maintenance. It also monitors movement of enemy ships and land vehicles, enabling each E-2C to track, automatically and simultaneously, more than 250 targets and to control more than 30 airborne intercepts. A Randtron Systems AN/APA-171 antenna system is housed in a 7·32 m (24 ft) diameter saucer-shaped rotodome mounted above the rear fuselage of the aircraft, which revolves in flight at 6 rpm, and can be lowered 0·64 m (1 ft 10¼ in) to facilitate aircraft stowage on board ship. The Yagi type radar arrays within the rotodome are interfaced to the onboard avionic systems, providing radar sum and difference signals plus IFF.

The AN/APS-125 search radar can detect targets as small as a cruise missile at ranges in excess of 100 nm (185 km; 115 miles). The AN/ALR-59 passive detection system (PDS) alerts operators to the presence of electronic emitters at distances up to twice the detection range of the radar system, thus expanding significantly the surveillance capability of the E-2C. Functions of these and other key elements of the E-2C's avionics systems were described more fully in the 1979-80 *Jane's*.

The following details apply to the E-2C Hawkeye:

TYPE: Airborne early-warning aircraft.

WINGS: Cantilever high-wing monoplane of all-metal construction. Centre-section is a structural box consisting of three beams, ribs and machined skins. Hinged leading-edge is non-structural and provides access to flying and engine controls. The outer panels fold rearward about skewed-axis hinge fittings mounted on the rear beams, to stow parallel with the rear fuselage on each side. Folding is done through a double-acting hydraulic cylinder. Trailing-edges of outer panels and part of centre-section consist of long-span ailerons and hydraulically-actuated Fowler flaps. When flaps are lowered, ailerons are drooped automatically. All control surfaces of E-2C are power-operated and incorporate devices to produce artificial feel forces. Automatic flight control system (AFCS) can be assigned sole control of the system hydraulic actuators, or AFCS signals can be superimposed on the pilot's mechanical inputs for stability augmentation. Pneumatically-inflated rubber de-icing boots on leading-edges.

FUSELAGE: Conventional all-metal semi-monocoque structure.

TAIL UNIT: Cantilever structure, with four fins and three double-hinged rudders. Tailplane dihedral 11°. Portions of tail unit made of glassfibre to reduce radar reflection. Power control and artificial feel systems as for ailerons. Pneumatically-inflated rubber de-icing boots on all leading-edges.

LANDING GEAR: Hydraulically-retractable tricycle type. Pneumatic emergency extension. Steerable nosewheel unit retracts rearward. Main wheels retract forward, and rotate to lie flat in bottom of nacelles. Twin wheels on nose unit only. Oleo-pneumatic shock-absorbers. Main wheel tyres size 36 × 11 Type VII 24-ply, pressure 17·93 bars (260 lb/sq in) on ship, 14·48 bars (210 lb/sq in) ashore. Hydraulic brakes. Hydraulically-operated retractable tailskid. A-frame arrester hook under tail.

POWER PLANT: Two 3,661 kW (4,910 shp) Allison T56-A-425 turboprop engines, driving Hamilton Standard type 54460-1 four-blade fully-feathering reversible-pitch constant-speed propellers. These have foam-filled blades which have a steel spar and glassfibre shell which cause minimum interference to the radar equipment. Spinners and blades incorporate electrical anti-icers. Provision for auxiliary fuel tanks in outer wings, and for addition of flight refuelling capability.

ACCOMMODATION: Normal crew of five on flight deck and in ATDS compartment in main cabin, consisting of pilot, co-pilot, combat information centre officer, air control officer and radar operator. Provision for additional operator for long-endurance missions with auxiliary fuel. Downward-hinged doors, with built-in steps, on port side of centre-fuselage.

AVIONICS: AN/APA-171 rotodome (radar and IFF antennae), AN/APS-125 advanced radar processing system (ARPS) with overland/overwater detection capability, RT-988/A IFF interrogator with Hazeltine OL-76/AP IFF detector processor, Litton AN/ALR-59 passive detection system, Hazeltine AN/APA-172 control indicator group, Litton OL-77/ASQ computer programmer

Grumman E-2C Hawkeye twin-turboprop airborne early-warning aircraft *(Pilot Press)*

Grumman E-2C Hawkeye airborne early-warning aircraft from USS *Constellation*

(L-304), ARC-158 UHF data link, ARQ-34 HF data link, ASM-440 in-flight performance monitor, ARC-51A UHF com, ARQ-34 HF com, AIC-14A intercom, Litton AN/ASN-92 (LN-15C) CAINS carrier aircraft inertial navigation system, Conrac Corporation CP-1085/AS air data computer, APN-153 (V) Doppler, ASN-50 heading and attitude reference system, ARN-52 (V) Tacan, ARA-50 UHF ADF, ASW-25B ACLS and APN-171 (V) radar altimeter.

DIMENSIONS, EXTERNAL:

Wing span	24·56 m (80 ft 7 in)
Length overall	17·55 m (57 ft 7 in)
Height overall	5·59 m (18 ft 4 in)
Diameter of rotodome	7·32 m (24 ft 0 in)
Propeller diameter	4·11 m (13 ft 6 in)

AREA:

Wings, gross	65·03 m² (700 sq ft)

WEIGHTS (A: current E-2C; B: with auxiliary fuel):

Weight empty: A		17,241 kg (38,009 lb)
B		17,504 kg (38,589 lb)
Max fuel (internal): A		5,624 kg (12,400 lb)
B		8,981 kg (19,800 lb)
Max T-O weight: A		23,541 kg (51,900 lb)
B		27,161 kg (59,880 lb)

PERFORMANCE (at max T-O weight. A: current E-2C; B: with auxiliary fuel):

Max level speed:		
A, B		325 knots (602 km/h; 374 mph)
Cruising speed (ferry):		
A		269 knots (499 km/h; 310 mph)
B		270 knots (500 km/h; 310 mph)
Approach speed:		
A, B		100 knots (185 km/h; 115 mph)
Stalling speed (landing configuration):		
A		74 knots (138 km/h; 85·5 mph)
Service ceiling: A		9,390 m (30,800 ft)
B		8,840 m (29,000 ft)
T-O run: A		580 m (1,900 ft)
B		884 m (2,900 ft)
T-O to 15 m (50 ft): A		793 m (2,600 ft)
B		1,128 m (3,700 ft)
Ferry range: A	1,394 nm	(2,583 km; 1,605 miles)
B	2,170 nm	(4,018 km; 2,497 miles)
Time on station, 175 nm (320 km; 200 miles) from base:		
A		4 h
B		over 6 h
Endurance with max fuel: A		6 h 6 min
B		9 h 18 min

GRUMMAN INTRUDER

USN designations: A-6, EA-6 and KA-6

The basic A-6A (originally A2F-1) Intruder was con-

ceived as a carrier-borne low-level attack bomber equipped specifically to deliver nuclear or conventional weapons on targets completely obscured by weather or darkness. It currently equips 17 operational US Navy/Marine Corps squadrons, and three readiness training squadrons.

Competition for the original A-6 contract was conducted from May to December 1957, Grumman's contender being selected on 31 December 1957. Seven variants of the basic design have been built, of which the A-6A, A-6B and A-6C (described in 1978-79 *Jane's*) are no longer operational. The current versions are as follows:

EA-6A. First flown in prototype form in 1963, this version retains partial strike capability, but is equipped primarily to support strike aircraft and ground forces by suppressing enemy electronic activity and obtaining tactical electronic intelligence within a combat area. Elements of the A-6A's bombing/navigation system are deleted and the EA-6A carries more than 30 different antennae to detect, locate, classify, record and jam enemy radiation. Externally-evident features include a radome at the top of the tail-fin, and attachment points under the wings and fuselage for ECM pods, fuel tanks and/or weapons. A total of 27 EA-6As were built for the US Marine Corps, including six A-6As modified into EA-6As.

EA-6B Prowler. Advanced electronics development of the EA-6A, described separately.

KA-6D Intruder. An A-6A was modified into a prototype flight refuelling tanker, with hose and reel in the rear fuselage, and flew for the first time on 23 May 1966. The KA-6D production model is fitted with Tacan and can transfer more than 9,500 kg (21,000 lb) of fuel immediately after take-off or 6,800 kg (15,000 lb) at a distance of 250 nm (463 km; 288 miles) from its carrier base. In addition, the KA-6D could act as a control aircraft for air-sea rescue operations or as a day bomber. A total of 62 A-6As were modified to KA-6D configuration.

A-6E Intruder. An advanced conversion of the A-6A with multi-mode radar and an IBM computer similar to that first tested in the EA-6B. First flight of an A-6E was made on 27 February 1970. First squadron deployment was made in September 1972, and the A-6E was approved officially for service use in December 1972. It was planned to acquire a total of 318 A-6Es. Procurement is being completed with 18 ordered in FY 1979-80, bringing to more than 600 the number of A-6s delivered by Grumman.

An **A-6E/TRAM** (target recognition and attack multisensor) version of the A-6E flew for the first time in October 1974. TRAM adds an undernose precision-stabilised turret, with a sensor package, containing both infra-red and laser equipment, to a full-system Intruder,

Grumman A-6E/TRAM, with additional side views of EA-6A (centre) and EA-6B (bottom) *(Pilot Press)*

Grumman A-6E/TRAM aircraft of the US Navy's VA-65 Tiger Squadron from Oceana NAS, Virginia

updates the inertial navigation system with AN/ASN-92 CAINS, provides a new communications-navigation-identification (CNI) system and automatic carrier landing capability. The sensor package is integrated with the multi-mode radar, providing the capability of detecting, identifying and attacking a wide range of targets (as well as viewing the terrain) under adverse weather conditions, and with an improved degree of accuracy, using either conventional or laser-guided weapons. The bombardier/navigator of the A-6E operates the TRAM system by first acquiring the target on his radar screen. He then switches to the FLIR (forward-looking infra-red) system, using an optical zoom to enlarge the target's image. After identifying and selecting his targets, the bombardier uses a laser designator to mark the target with a laser spot, on which his own laser-guided weapons, or those from another aircraft, will home. Using TRAM's laser spot detector, the A-6E can also acquire a target that is being illuminated from another aircraft, or designated by a forward air controller on the ground. Delivery of fully provisioned TRAM aircraft began in February 1979, and the first carrier deployment of the A-6E/TRAM was completed successfully in May 1980.

Intruder training is carried out using Grumman TC-4C (modified Gulfstream I) aircraft, eight of which are in US Navy/US Marine Corps service. Grumman updated all eight to A-6E/TRAM standard during 1978-80.

The following description applies to the standard A-6E:

TYPE: Two-seat carrier-based attack bomber.

WINGS: Cantilever mid-wing monoplane, with 25° sweep-back at quarter-chord. All-metal structure. Hydraulically-operated almost-full-span leading-edge and trailing-edge flaps, with inset spoilers (flaperons) of same span as flaps forward of trailing-edge flaps. Trailing-edge of each wingtip, outboard of flap, splits to form speed-brakes which project above and below wing when extended. Two short fences above each wing. Outer panels fold upward and inward.

FUSELAGE: Conventional all-metal semi-monocoque structure. Bottom is recessed between engines to carry semi-exposed store.

TAIL UNIT: Cantilever all-metal structure. All-moving tailplane, without separate elevators. Electronic antenna in rear part of fin, immediately above rudder.

LANDING GEAR: Hydraulically-retractable tricycle type. Twin-wheel nose unit retracts rearward. Single-wheel main units retract forward and inward into air intake fairings. A-frame arrester hook under rear fuselage.

POWER PLANT: Two 41·4 kN (9,300 lb st) Pratt & Whitney J52-P-8A turbojet engines. Max internal fuel 7,230 kg (15,940 lb), 9,028 litres (2,385 US gallons). Provision for up to four external fuel tanks under wings, each of 1,136 litres (300 US gallons) capacity. Removable flight refuelling probe projects upward immediately forward of windscreen.

ACCOMMODATION: Crew of two on Martin-Baker Mk GRU7 ejection seats, which can be reclined to reduce fatigue during low-level operations. Bombardier/navigator slightly behind and below pilot to starboard. Hydraulically-operated rearward-sliding canopy.

SYSTEMS: Garrett-AiResearch environmental control system for cockpit and avionics bay. Dual hydraulic systems for operation of flight controls, leading-edge and trailing-edge flaps, wingtip speedbrakes, landing gear brakes and cockpit canopy. One electrically-driven hydraulic pump provides restricted flight capability by supplying the tailplane and rudder actuators only. Electrical system powered by two Garrett-AiResearch constant-speed drive starters that combine engine starting and electrical power generation, each delivering 30kVA. A Garrett-AiResearch ram-air turbine, mounted so that it can be projected into the airstream above the port wing-root, provides in-flight emergency electrical power for essential equipment.

AVIONICS AND EQUIPMENT: Development of the A-6E began with the substitution of a single simultaneous multi-mode navigation and attack radar, developed by the Norden Division of UAC for the two earlier radar systems in the A-6A. Following the concepts of the EA-6B, the IBM Corporation and Fairchild Camera and Instrument Corporation have supplied a new attack and navigation computer system and an interfacing data converter. Conrac Corporation has designed an armament control unit and RCA has developed a video tape recorder for post-strike assessment of attacks.

The Norden Division's AN/APQ-148 multi-mode radar provides simultaneous ground mapping; identification, tracking, and rangefinding of fixed or moving targets; and terrain-clearance or terrain-following manoeuvres. It can also detect, locate and track radar beacons used by forward air controllers when providing close support for ground forces. The APQ-148 has mechanical scanning in azimuth and utilises a newly-developed avionics system for simultaneous vertical scanning. There are two cockpit displays, one for the pilot and one for the bombardier/navigator, and terrain data is also presented on a vertical display indicator ahead of the pilot.

IBM's AN/ASQ-133 solid-state digital computer is coupled to the A-6E's radar, inertial and Doppler navigational equipment, communications and automatic flight control system. As mission data is measured in flight by onboard aerodynamic and electronic sensors, the computer compares the data with the programmed information, computes any differences, and provides corrective data that can be used to alter the parameters of the mission.

Fairchild Camera and Instrument Corporation's signal data converter accepts analogue input data from up to sixty sensors, and converts that information to a digital output that is fed into the computer of the navigation and attack system.

Conrac Corporation's armament control unit (ACU) for the A-6E provides in a single unit all the inputs and outputs necessary to select and release the Intruder's weapons. The master arming switch has a 'practice' position that allows the ACU to be cycled up to the point of firing command.

The multi-mode AN/AVA-1 display developed by Kaiser Aerospace and Electronics Corporation serves as a primary flight aid for navigation, approach, landing and weapons delivery. The basic vertical display indicator (VDI) is a 0·20 m (8 in) cathode-ray tube which shows a synthetic landscape, sky, and electronically-generated command flight path that move to simulate the motion of these features as they would be seen by the pilot through the windscreen of the aircraft. Symbols are superimposed to augment the basic attitude data, and for attack a second set of superimposed information provides a target symbol, steering symbol, and release and pull-up markers. A solid-state radar data scan converter can provide on the same display an apparent real-world perspective of terrain, ten shades of grey defining terrain elevation at ten different segmented contour intervals up to 8·7 nm (16 km; 10 miles) ahead of the aircraft. This makes it possible for the pilot to fly the Intruder in either a terrain-following or terrain-avoidance mode at low altitude. Flight path and attack symbols can be superimposed over the terrain elevation data on the VDI, enabling the pilot to make his attack while avoiding or following terrain in the target area. Kaiser has also developed a micromesh filter to prevent 'washout' of the data displayed on the VDI in sunlight conditions. Naval pilots use the VDI as a primary flight instrument, for precise steering in navigation, and for weapons cues, progress, and status information during an attack. For carrier landing the unit is used as a flight director and, linked to the APQ-148 radar, it presents steering information, allowing the pilot to select a descent angle for the final approach.

ARMAMENT: Five weapon attachment points, each with a 1,633 kg (3,600 lb) capacity (max external stores load 8,165 kg; 18,000 lb). Typical weapon loads are thirty 500 lb bombs in clusters of six, or three 2,000 lb general purpose bombs plus two 1,135 litre (300 US gallon) drop-tanks.

DIMENSIONS, EXTERNAL:

Wing span	16·15 m (53 ft 0 in)
Wing mean aerodynamic chord	
	3·32 m (10 ft 10¾ in)
Width folded	7·72 m (25 ft 4 in)
Length overall	16·69 m (54 ft 9 in)
Height overall	4·93 m (16 ft 2 in)
Tailplane span	6·21 m (20 ft 4½ in)

Grumman EA-6B Prowler of Squadron VAQ-134 landing on the USS *Enterprise*

Wheel track	3·32 m (10 ft 10½ in)

AREAS:

Wings, gross	49·1 m² (528·9 sq ft)
Flaperons (total)	3·81 m² (41·0 sq ft)
Trailing-edge flaps (total)	9·66 m² (104·0 sq ft)
Leading-edge slats (total)	4·63 m² (49·8 sq ft)
Fin	5·85 m² (62·93 sq ft)
Rudder	1·52 m² (16·32 sq ft)

WEIGHTS AND LOADING:

Weight empty	11,675 kg (25,740 lb)
Fuel load: internal	7,230 kg (15,940 lb)
external (four tanks)	3,638 kg (8,020 lb)
Max external load	8,165 kg (18,000 lb)

Max T-O weight:

catapult	26,580 kg (58,600 lb)
field	27,397 kg (60,400 lb)
Max zero-fuel weight	20,166 kg (44,460 lb)

Max landing weight:

carrier	16,329 kg (36,000 lb)
field	20,411 kg (45,000 lb)
Max wing loading	557·6 kg/m² (114·2 lb/sq ft)

PERFORMANCE (no stores):

Never-exceed speed	689 knots (1,276 km/h; 793 mph)
Max level speed at S/L	562 knots (1,041 km/h; 647 mph)
Cruising speed at optimum altitude	413 knots (765 km/h; 475 mph)
Stalling speed, flaps up	121 knots (225 km/h; 140 mph)
Stalling speed, flaps down	83 knots (154 km/h; 96 mph)
Max rate of climb at S/L	2,865 m (9,400 ft)/min
Rate of climb at S/L, one engine out	930 m (3,050 ft)/min
Service ceiling	14,415 m (47,300 ft)
Service ceiling, one engine out	10,210 m (33,500 ft)
Min T-O run	549 m (1,800 ft)
T-O run to 15 m (50 ft)	762 m (2,500 ft)
Landing from 15 m (50 ft)	646 m (2,120 ft)
Min landing run	463 m (1,520 ft)
Combat range with max external fuel	2,966 nm (5,496 km; 3,415 miles)
Range with max payload	794 nm (1,471 km; 914 miles)
Ferry range	2,530 nm (4,688 km; 2,913 miles)

GRUMMAN EA-6B PROWLER

The EA-6B is an advanced electronics development of the EA-6A for which Grumman received a prototype design and development contract in the Autumn of 1966. Except for a 1·37 m (4 ft 6 in) longer nose section and large fin pod, the external configuration of this version is the same as that of the basic A-6A.

The longer nose section provides accommodation for a total crew of four, the two additional crewmen being necessary to operate the more advanced ECM equipment. This comprises high-powered electronic jammers and modern computer-directed receivers, which provided the US Navy with its first aircraft designed and built specifically for tactical electronic warfare. The prototype EA-6B flew for the first time on 25 May 1968; deliveries of production aircraft began in January 1971.

The FY 1969 defence budget allocated $139 million for the initial purchase of eight EA-6Bs, and the total programme is expected to cover the supply of 102 aircraft (including the four pre-production and one R and D aircraft), to equip Navy and Marine Corps squadrons.

An ICAP (Increased Capability) version of the EA-6B, which increases substantially the jamming efficiency of the aircraft, has been developed. Current production aircraft are delivered with ICAP as standard, and the first 21 production EA-6Bs have been modified by Grumman to ICAP configuration. Modifications include an expanded onboard tactical jamming system with eight frequency bands, reduced response time, and a new multi-format display. In addition, an automatic carrier landing system (ACLS) to permit carrier recovery in zero-zero weather, a new defensive electronic countermeasures system (DECM) and new communications-navigation-identification (CNI) equipment are installed. Another advanced version, ICAP-2, is under development; the prototype made its first flight on 24 June 1980.

Ten US Navy squadrons (VAQ-129, 130, 131, 132, 133, 134, 135, 136, 137 and 138) were equipped with the Prowler in mid-1977. The first detachment of US Marine Corps Prowler squadron VMAQ-2 began training on the EA-6B in September 1977 at NAS Whidbey Island, Washington, and the detachment deployed in late 1978. Two additional detachments have since completed training, and at least one is deployed at all times.

Under a $4·8 million contract awarded in 1978, Norden Systems is to supply for the EA-6B an advanced navigation radar system designated AN/APS-130. The contract calls for one prototype and three pre-production systems before the start of full production. This is expected to run to approximately 100 systems.

The description of the standard A-6E Intruder applies also to the EA-6B, except as follows:

TYPE: Four-seat carrier- or land-based advanced ECM aircraft.

WINGS: As for A-6E, but reinforced to cater for increased gross weight, fatigue life and 5·5g load factor.

FUSELAGE: As for A-6E, but reinforcement of underfuselage structure in areas of arrester hook and landing gear attachments, and lengthened by 1·37 m (4 ft 6 in).

TAIL UNIT: As for A-6E, except for provision of a large fin-tip pod to house ECM equipment.

LANDING GEAR: As for A-6E, except for reinforcement of attachments, A-frame arrester hook, and upgrading of structure to cater for increased gross weight.

POWER PLANT: Two 50 kN (11,200 lb st) Pratt & Whitney J52-P-408 turbojet engines, each rated at 49·8 kN (11,200 lb st).

ACCOMMODATION: Crew of four under two separate upward-opening canopies. The two additional crewmen are ECM Officers to operate the ALQ-99 equipment from the rear cockpit. Either ECMO can independently detect, assign, adjust and monitor the jammers. The ECMO in the starboard front seat is responsible for communications, navigation, defensive ECM and chaff dispensing.

SYSTEMS: Generally as for A-6E.

AVIONICS: ALQ-99 advanced electronic countermeasures (ECM) to enable the EA-6B to fulfil a tactical electronic warfare role. Five integrally powered pods, with a total of 10 jamming transmitters, can be carried. Each pod covers one of eight frequency bands. Sensitive surveillance receivers in the fin-tip pod for long-range detection of radars; emitter information is fed to a central digital computer that processes the signals for display and recording. Detection, identification, direction-finding and jammer-set-on sequence can be performed automatically or with manual assistance from crew.

DIMENSIONS, EXTERNAL:

As for A-6E, except:

Width folded	7·87 m (25 ft 10 in)
Length overall	18·24 m (59 ft 10 in)
Height overall	4·95 m (16 ft 3 in)
Wheelbase	5·23 m (17 ft 2 in)

AREAS:

As for A-6E

WEIGHTS AND LOADING:

Weight empty	14,588 kg (32,162 lb)
Internal fuel load	6,995 kg (15,422 lb)
Max external fuel load	4,547 kg (10,025 lb)
T-O weight in stand-off jamming configuration	24,703 kg (54,461 lb)
T-O weight in ferry range configuration	27,492 kg (60,610 lb)
Max T-O weight, catapult or field	29,483 kg (65,000 lb)
Max zero-fuel weight	17,708 kg (39,039 lb)
Max landing weight, carrier or field	20,638 kg (45,500 lb)
Max wing loading	600·5 kg/m² (123 lb/sq ft)

PERFORMANCE (A: no stores; B: 5 ECM pods):

Never-exceed speed	710 knots (1,315 km/h; 817 mph)

Max level speed at S/L:

A	566 knots (1,048 km/h; 651 mph)
B	533 knots (987 km/h; 613 mph)

Cruising speed at optimum altitude:

A	418 knots (774 km/h; 481 mph)
B	420 knots (777 km/h; 483 mph)

Stalling speed, flaps up, max power:

A	124 knots (230 km/h; 143 mph)

Stalling speed, flaps down, max power:

A	84 knots (156 km/h; 97 mph)

Max rate of climb at S/L:

A	3,932 m (12,900 ft)/min	
B		3,057 m (10,030 ft)/min

Rate of climb at S/L, one engine out:

A	1,189 m (3,900 ft)/min

Service ceiling:

A	13,565 m (44,500 ft)
B	12,500 m (41,000 ft)

Service ceiling, one engine out:

A	8,930 m (29,300 ft)

T-O to 15 m (50 ft):

A	869 m (2,850 ft)
B	1,065 m (3,495 ft)

Landing from 15 m (50 ft): A	823 m (2,700 ft)

Landing run:

A	579 m (1,900 ft)
B	655 m (2,150 ft)

Combat range with max external fuel:

A	2,085 nm (3,861 km; 2,399 miles)

Range with max payload, 5% reserves plus 20 min at S/L:

A	955 nm (1,769 km; 1,099 miles)

GRUMMAN TOMCAT

USN designation: F-14

Grumman announced on 15 January 1969 that it had been selected as winner of the design competition for a carrier-based fighter for the US Navy. Known as the VFX during the competitive phase of the programme, this aircraft was later designated F-14. First flight of the F-14A Tomcat prototype took place on 21 December 1970. It was lost in a non-fatal accident, and flight testing was resumed on 24 May 1971 with the second aircraft.

The F-14 is designed to fulfil three primary missions. The first of these, fighter sweep/escort, involves clearing contested airspace of enemy fighters and protecting the strike force, with support from early-warning aircraft, surface ships and communications networks to co-ordinate penetration and escape. Second mission is to defend carrier task forces via Combat Air Patrol (CAP) and Deck Launched Intercept (DLI) operations. Third role is secondary attack of tactical targets on the ground, supported by electronic countermeasures and fighter escort. It has also been reported that in tests with targets simulating anti-ship missiles, Phoenix-armed F-14s have proved effective against high, fast, relatively small radar cross-section threats such as the Soviet AS-4/6 air-to-surface missiles.

The configuration of the F-14 is unique, with variable-geometry wings, small foreplanes (glove vanes) which are extended automatically at supersonic speeds to control centre-of-pressure shift, manoeuvring slats and flaps to create a lower effective wing loading, and twin outward-canted fins and rudders. Optimum sweep of the wing is controlled automatically by a Mach sweep programmer, which relates sweep to Mach number and altitude.

Under the initial contracts, Grumman was required to provide the US Navy with a mockup of the F-14A in May 1969, and to build 12 research and development aircraft. Subsequently, the US Navy ordered an initial series of 26 production F-14As, and is expected to acquire a total of 521 Tomcats, including the 12 development aircraft. Carrier trials were started in June 1972, and initial deployment with the fleet began in October 1972. Replacement Training Squadron (RTS) VF-124 at Miramar NAS, San Diego, California, was responsible for working up ground and air crews for the new aircraft, and the first two operational squadrons, VF-1 and VF-2, were serving on board the USS *Enterprise* in the Western Pacific in September 1974. Replacement Training Squadron VF-101 was established in July 1977 to train ground and flight crews for deployment from NAS Oceana, Virginia. A total of 344

Grumman F-14A Tomcat carrier-based multi-mission fighter *(Pilot Press)*

Grumman F-14A Tomcat with tactical air reconnaissance pod system (TARPS)

Northrop TCS under nose of an F-14

F-14As had been delivered by 1 January 1980, and 42 more were scheduled for delivery during 1980.

In mid-1979 the US Navy awarded a $4 million contract to the Northrop Corporation to manufacture pre-production television camera sets (TCSs) for installation on F-14s. Developed by Northrop's Electro-Mechanical Division, the TCS is a closed-circuit TV system, offering both wide-angle (acquisition) and telescopic (identification) fields of view. Mounted beneath the nose of the F-14, the TCS automatically searches for, acquires and locks on to distant targets, displaying them on monitors for the pilot and flight officer. By allowing early identification of targets, the system permits crews of high-speed aircraft to make combat decisions earlier than was possible previously.

The Naval Air Test Center at Patuxent River, Maryland, conducted test and evaluation of a 798 kg (1,760 lb) reconnaissance pod for the F-14 in 1979, and 49 F-14s are being fitted with this pod in 1980-81. Designated **TARPS** (Tactical Air Reconnaissance Pod System), it is mounted 0·38 m (1 ft 3 in) off the centreline of the F-14's underfuselage, in the tunnel between the two engine nacelles. It has four main compartments: the nose carries a CAI KS-87B frame camera for either forward oblique or vertical photographs; the second contains a Fairchild KA-99 low/medium-altitude horizon-to-horizon panoramic camera; the third has a Honeywell AN/AAD-5 infra-red reconnaissance set; and the fourth is an equipment bay containing the ground check maintenance panel and a sensor control data display set.

Without the TARPS pod installed, the F-14 retains its full weapon system capability. The F-14/TARPS aircraft will fulfil an important tactical reconnaissance role pending the evolution of new photo-reconnaissance aircraft.

The Imperial Iranian Air Force ordered 80 F-14As, all of which had been delivered by the end of 1978; first flight by one of these aircraft was made on 5 December 1975, and the first three aircraft were ferried to Khatami AFB, Isfahan, in January 1976. Iranian F-14As retain the Phoenix weapon system, but have slightly different ECM equipment from US Navy aircraft.

TYPE: Two-seat carrier-based multi-role fighter.

WINGS: Variable-geometry mid-wing monoplane, with 20° of leading-edge sweep in the fully-forward position and 68° when fully swept. Oversweep position of 75° for carrier stowage. Wing position is programmed automatically for optimum performance throughout the flight regime, but manual override is provided. A short movable wing outer panel, needing only a comparatively light pivot structure, results from the wide fuselage and fixed centre-section 'glove', with pivot points 2·72 m (8 ft 11 in) from the centreline of the airframe. The inboard wing sections, adjacent to the fuselage, arc upward slightly to minimise cross-sectional area and wave-drag, and consist basically of a one-piece electron beam-welded titanium assembly, 6·70 m (22 ft) in span, made from Ti-6A1-4V titanium alloy. Small canard surfaces, known as glove vanes, swing out from the leading-edge of the fixed portion of the wing, to a maximum of 15° in relation to the leading-edge, as sweep of outer panels is increased. Spoilers on upper surfaces of wing. Stabilisation in pitch, provided by the canard surfaces, leaves the differential tailplane free to perform its primary control function. Trailing-edge control surfaces extend over almost entire span. Leading-edge slats.

FUSELAGE: The centre-fuselage section is a simple, fuel-carrying box structure; forward fuselage section comprises cockpit and nose. The aft section has a tapered aerofoil shape to minimise drag, with a fuel dump pipe projecting from the rear. Speed brakes located on the upper and lower surfaces, between the bases of the vertical tail fins.

TAIL UNIT: Twin vertical fins, mounted at the rear of each engine nacelle. Outward-canted ventral fin under each nacelle. The all-flying horizontal surfaces have skins of boron-epoxy composite material.

LANDING GEAR: Retractable tricycle type. Twin-wheel nose unit and single-wheel main units retract forward and upward. Existing beryllium brakes to be replaced with Goodyear lightweight carbon brakes from Spring 1981. Arrester hook under rear fuselage, housed in small ventral fairing. Nose-tow catapult attachment on nose unit.

ENGINE INTAKES: Straight two-dimensional external compression inlets. A double-hinged ramp extends down from the top of each intake, and these are programmed to provide the correct airflow to the engines automatically under all flight conditions. Each intake is canted slightly away from the fuselage, from which it is separated by some 0·25 m (10 in) to allow sufficient clearance for the turbulent fuselage boundary layer to pass between fuselage and intake without causing turbulence within the intake. Engine inlet ducts and aft nacelle structures are manufactured by Rohr Corporation. The inlet duct, constructed largely of aluminium honeycomb, is about 4·27 m (14 ft) long, while the aft nacelle structure, of bonded aluminium honeycomb and conventional aluminium, is about 4·88 m (16 ft) in length.

POWER PLANT: Two Pratt & Whitney TF30-P-412A turbofan engines of 93 kN (20,900 lb st) with afterburning, mounted in ducts which open to provide 180° access for ease of maintenance. Garrett-AiResearch ATS200-50 air-turbine starter. An external auxiliary fuel tank can be carried beneath each intake trunk.

ACCOMMODATION: Pilot and naval flight officer seated in tandem on Martin-Baker GRU-7A rocket-assisted zero-zero ejection seats, under a one-piece bubble canopy, hinged at the rear and offering all-round view.

AVIONICS: Hughes AN/AWG-9 weapons control system, with ability to track 24 enemy targets and attack six of them simultaneously at varied altitudes and distances. Kaiser Aerospace AN/AVG-12 vertical and head-up display system.

ARMAMENT: One General Electric M61A-1 Vulcan 20 mm gun mounted in the port side of forward fuselage. Four Sparrow air-to-air missiles mounted partially submerged in the underfuselage, or four Phoenix missiles carried on special pallets which attach to the bottom of the fuselage. Two wing pylons, one under each fixed wing section, can carry four Sidewinder missiles or two additional Sparrow or Phoenix missiles with two Sidewinders. Various combinations of missiles and bombs to a max external weapon load of 6,577 kg (14,500 lb). ECM equipment includes Goodyear AN/ALE-39 chaff and flare dispensers, with integral jammers.

DIMENSIONS, EXTERNAL:

Wing span: unswept	19·45 m (64 ft 1½ in)
swept	11·65 m (38 ft 2½ in)
overswept	10·15 m (33 ft 3½ in)
Wing aspect ratio	7·28
Length overall	18·89 m (61 ft 11·9 in)
Height overall	4·88 m (16 ft 0 in)
Tailplane span	9·97 m (32 ft 8½ in)
Distance between fin tips	3·25 m (10 ft 8 in)
Wheel track	5·00 m (16 ft 5 in)
Wheelbase	7·02 m (23 ft 0½ in)

AREAS:

Wings, gross	52·49 m² (565·0 sq ft)
Horizontal tail surfaces (total)	13·01 m² (140·0 sq ft)
Vertical tail surfaces (total)	10·96 m² (118·0 sq ft)

WEIGHTS:

Weight empty	17,830 kg (39,310 lb)
Fuel (usable): internal	7,348 kg (16,200 lb)
external	1,724 kg (3,800 lb)
Normal T-O weight	26,553 kg (58,539 lb)
Max useful load (overload)	8,255 kg (18,200 lb)
T-O weight with 4 Sparrow	26,718 kg (58,904 lb)
T-O weight with 6 Phoenix	31,656 kg (69,790 lb)
Max T-O weight	33,724 kg (74,348 lb)
Design landing weight	23,510 kg (51,830 lb)

PERFORMANCE:

Max design speed	Mach 2·4
Max cruising speed	
400-550 knots (741-1,019 km/h; 460-633 mph)	
Landing speed	120 knots (222 km/h; 138 mph)
Service ceiling	above 15,240 m (50,000 ft)
Min T-O distance	214 m (700 ft)
Min T-O distance at 26,533 kg (58,495 lb) AUW	366 m (1,200 ft)
Min landing distance	488 m (1,600 ft)

GRUMMAN (GENERAL DYNAMICS) EF-111A

The programme to convert General Dynamics F-111As into EF-111A electronic warfare prototypes, and to evaluate their ability to provide ECM jamming coverage for air attack forces, was initiated in 1972-73. Operational deployment of the F-111A in Southeast Asia, from March 1968, had revealed shortcomings, despite special preparation under the Harvest Reaper programme to provide these aircraft with advanced ECM equipment that would facilitate penetration of enemy airspace. Subsequent enquiry revealed that many factors contributed to the limited success of the F-111A in Southeast Asia; lack of adequate and effective ECM jamming was responsible for many of its problems, as well as those of all other types of combat aircraft in that theatre of operations.

Because of the growing potential of Soviet-built air defence systems, which stretch across Eastern Europe, NATO anti-invasion forces must have the capability of suppressing literally thousands of radar 'eyes', able to locate precisely the route and speed of counter-attacking air strikes. In addition, updated SAM systems and new interceptors with sophisticated ECM equipment are being introduced regularly by the Soviet Union, providing its armed forces with a now-acknowledged lead in electronic warfare, both ground and airborne.

Senior US Air Force officials consider that utilisation of the EF-111 as a tactical jamming system, in combination with the E-3 AWACS, is vital to help offset this Soviet lead. Because of its vast masking power, the EF-111 is essential to provide cover for air-to-ground operations along the forward lines, and for support of penetrating allied strike forces. Should some future circumstances make it necessary to launch a counter-strike against Soviet penetration of NATO territory, EF-111s operating on the friendly side of the FEBA (forward edge of the battle area) could blind the other side's electronic 'eyes', making it possible for NATO strike forces to attack the armoured spearhead, as well as resupply areas, reserves and SAM installations 17-35 nm (32-64 km; 20-40 miles) behind the opposing lines, with something less than half the anticipated losses that could be expected without use of the EF-111s' jamming systems.

Three basic modes of deployment are foreseen for the EF-111: standoff, penetration, and close air support. In the standoff role, jamming aircraft would operate within their own airspace, at the FEBA. Out of range of the enemy's ground-based weapons, orbiting EF-111s would use their jamming systems to screen the routes of friendly strike aircraft. In the penetration role, the EF-111s would accompany strike aircraft to high-priority targets, their Mach 2 capability making them ideal escort aircraft for such a task. The close air support requirement calls for EF-111 escorts to neutralise anti-air radars while the strike force delivers its attack on enemy armour.

Design study contracts were awarded to General Dynamics and Grumman by the US Air Force in 1974, and in January 1975 it was announced that Grumman had been awarded an $85·9 million contract to convert two existing F-111As to EF-111A prototype configuration. Basic equipment of these prototypes comprises the Raytheon AN/ALQ-99E tactical jamming system, comprising ten transmitters, five exciters and one RF calibrator per aircraft. In addition, each has a modified AN/ALQ-137 Self Protection System, and a modified AN/ALR-62 Terminal Threat Warning System. The ALQ-99E jammers are mounted in the weapons bay, with their antennae covered by a 4·9 m (16 ft) long canoe-shape radome. The fin-tip pod, similar in shape to that of the EA-6B Prowler, houses the receiver system and antennae. Total weight of the new equipment is about three tons.

The two-man crew of an EF-111 comprises a pilot and an electronic warfare officer (EWO). All tactical jamming functions are managed by the EWO who can, through computer management, handle a tactical electronic warfare workload which required previously several operators and more equipment. In addition, the automated system of the EF-111 has exceptional capability for locating, identifying, and assigning jammers to enemy emitters over a wide range of frequencies.

The first flight of an aerodynamic prototype was made on 10 March 1977, and the complete system was flown for the first time on 17 May 1977, on the second prototype. Subsequent Grumman flight testing of the jamming system involved 84 flights totalling 215 flight hours, completed by the two aircraft during a period of 3½ months. US Air Force flight testing involved 78 flights totalling 258 flight hours during a six-month test programme. The US Air Force tests verified various mission operational concepts, flight formations, and the jammer's electromagnetic compatibility with other strike aircraft. These latter tests dispelled an earlier concern that the friendly strike force, as well as enemy threats, might be jammed by the powerful signals emanating from the EF-111. Structural flight tests under all operating conditions demonstrated an 'infinite' life for all modified areas of the aircraft's structure, and flying qualities were considered virtually identical to those of the F-111 strike aircraft.

US Air Force plans envisage the conversion of 42 F-111Fs as ECM jamming aircraft. The production contract for the first six was signed in April 1979; deliveries are due to begin in July 1981 to the 366th Tactical Fighter Wing at Home AFB, Idaho.

The description of the F-111A in the 1976-77 *Jane's* applies also to the EF-111A, except for the following additional or amended details:

TYPE: ECM tactical jamming aircraft.

WINGS: As detailed for F-111A. Wing section NACA 64A210.68 modified at pivot point, NACA 64A209.80 with modified leading-edge at tip. Dihedral, at 16° sweep, 1°. Incidence, at 16° sweep, 1° at root, −3° at tip.

POWER PLANT: As detailed for F-111A. Fuel capacity 19,010 litres (5,022 US gallons). Oil capacity 30·3 litres (8 US gallons).

AVIONICS: AN/ALQ-99E tactical jamming system; AN/ARC-109 UHF command, AN/AJQ-20A INS, AN/APQ-160 attack radar, AN/APN-167 radar altimeter, AN/APQ-110 terrain-following radar, AN/ARN-58 ILS, AN/ARC-112 HF transceiver, AN/AIC-25 intercom, AN/APX-64 IFF(AIMS), AN/ARN-52 Tacan, AN/ARA-50 UHF/DF, AN/ALQ-137 (modified) SPS, AN/ALR-62 (modified) TTWS, AN/ALR-23 CMRS, and AN/ALE-28 CMDS.

ARMAMENT: None.

DIMENSIONS, EXTERNAL:
Wing span, spread   19·20 m (63 ft 0 in)
Wing span, fully swept   9·74 m (31 ft 11·4 in)
Wing mean aerodynamic chord   2·76 m (9 ft 0 in)
Wing aspect ratio (16° sweep)   7·56
Length overall   23·51 m (77 ft 1·6 in)

Grumman (General Dynamics) EF-111A electronic warfare aircraft *(Pilot Press)*

One of two Grumman-modified EF-111A prototypes being prepared for anechoic chamber testing of its AN/ALQ-99E tactical jamming system *(Howard Levy)*

Height overall	6·10 m (20 ft 0 in)	B	496 knots (919 km/h; 571 mph)
Wheel track	3·19 m (10 ft 0·4 in)	C	438 knots (811 km/h; 504 mph)
Wheelbase	7·44 m (24 ft 4·8 in)	Stalling speed, power off:	
AREA:		A, B, C	135·1 knots (250·4 km/h; 155·6 mph)
Wings, gross (16° sweep)	48·77 m² (525 sq ft)	Rate of climb at S/L, intermediate power:	
WEIGHTS:		A, B, C	1,095 m (3,592 ft)/min
Weight empty (estimated)	24,230 kg (53,418 lb)	Rate of climb at S/L, one engine out, with afterburning:	
Design T-O weight	33,000 kg (72,750 lb)	A, B, C	986 m (3,234 ft)/min
Combat T-O weight	28,000 kg (61,729 lb)	Service ceiling with afterburning, at combat weight:	
Max T-O weight	39,680 kg (87,478 lb)	A	16,670 m (54,700 ft)
Max landing weight	36,287 kg (80,000 lb)	B	15,450 m (50,700 ft)
PERFORMANCE (estimated for typical mission, A: basic standoff; B: penetration; C: close air support. At max T-O weight unless detailed otherwise):		C	16,185 m (53,100 ft)
		T-O run: A, B, C	991 m (3,250 ft)
Max combat speed at combat T-O weight:		T-O to 15 m (50 ft): A, B, C	1,250 m (4,100 ft)
A, B, C	1,007 knots (1,865 km/h; 1,160 mph)	Landing from 15 m (50 ft):	
Average speed, outbound:		A, C, at 26,623 kg (58,693 lb)	853 m (2,800 ft)
A	450 knots (834 km/h; 518 mph)	B, at 32,863 kg (72,451 lb)	1,245 m (4,085 ft)
B	496 knots (919 km/h; 571 mph)	Landing run:	
C	448 knots (830 km/h; 516 mph)	A, C, at 26,623 kg (58,693 lb)	539 m (1,770 ft)
Average speed over combat area:		B, at 32,863 kg (72,451 lb)	759 m (2,490 ft)
A	321 knots (595 km/h; 370 mph)	Combat radius, with reserves:	
B	336 knots (623 km/h; 387 mph)	A	200 nm (370 km; 230 miles)
C	318 knots (589 km/h; 366 mph)	B	250 nm (463 km; 287 miles)
Average speed, inbound:		C	897 nm (1,661 km; 1,032 miles)
A	436 knots (808 km/h; 502 mph)	Ferry range	2,157 nm (3,998 km; 2,484 miles)

GULFSTREAM AMERICAN
GULFSTREAM AMERICAN CORPORATION

HEAD OFFICE AND WORKS: PO Box 2206, Savannah, Georgia 31402
Telephone: (912) 964 3281
Telex: 804 705 Gulfjet Sav
CHAIRMAN, PRESIDENT AND CHIEF EXECUTIVE OFFICER: Allen E. Paulson
EXECUTIVE VICE-PRESIDENT: Alan B. Lemlein
SENIOR VICE-PRESIDENTS:
James L. Bradbury (Finance, and Chief Financial Officer)
Charles G. Vogeley (Commercial Jet Aircraft Marketing)
VICE-PRESIDENTS:
Charles N. Coppi (Engineering)
Albert H. Glenn (General Manager, Savannah Operations)
Richard Kemper (Quality Control; New Products)

TREASURER: J. Lamont Crosby
SECRETARY AND GENERAL COUNSEL: John P. Innes

On 1 September 1978 it was annbunced that American Jet Industries had purchased the 80% holding in Grumman American Aviation Corporation held by Grumman Corporation, and had made a cash offer to the holders of the remaining 20% stock. The company is now known as Gulfstream American Corporation. Under the terms of the transfer of ownership, Grumman is continuing to develop the Gulfstream III executive jet transport under contract with Gulfstream American. It was to receive a royalty on all sales made after 31 December 1979.

Gulfstream American is currently producing the Gulfstream I Commuter and Gulfstream III; is responsible for manufacture and marketing of the Grumman-designed Super Ag-Cat and the turbine-powered Turbo Ag-Cat D; and is continuing development of the Hustler 500 designed by the former American Jet Industries, now known as GACC (Gulfstream American Corporation of California, which see).

GULFSTREAM AMERICAN GAC 159-C
GULFSTREAM I COMMUTER

During the first half of 1979, Gulfstream American conducted marketing and engineering studies to determine the feasibility of putting into production a 32/38-seat commuter version of the twin-turboprop G-159 Gulfstream I, which Grumman Corporation designed as a 19-seat executive aircraft and marketed from 1958 to 1969. A total of 200 Gulfstream Is had been built when production was then terminated in favour of the twin-turbofan Gulfstream II. Gulfstream American acquired the tooling and fixtures for Gulfstream I production when it purchased the former Grumman American Aviation Corporation in September 1978.

Design changes introduced on the new Gulfstream American Commuter include lengthening the fuselage by 3·25 m (10 ft 8 in) to accommodate a maximum of 38 passengers, with room for a toilet and carry-on baggage compartment at the front of the cabin, and a baggage compartment at the rear. The Commuter introduces rectangular cabin windows, and a reshaped nose and wraparound windscreen of the type designed for the Gulfstream III.

As a first stage, Gulfstream American lengthened the fuselage of an existing Gulfstream I during the Summer of 1979, for flight testing and demonstration. This aircraft (N5400C), which flew for the first time in its modified form on 25 October 1979, retains its original Rolls-Royce Dart turboprop engines; but General Electric CT64 and Avco Lycoming T55 turboprops are under consideration as alternatives for future production Gulfstream Commuters. Two GAC 159-C Commuters were due for delivery to Air North by the end of 1980.

Details of the original Grumman G-159 Gulfstream I can be found in the 1968-69 *Jane's*; all available information on the Gulfstream American Commuter follows:

TYPE: Twin-turboprop commuter transport.

WINGS: Cantilever low-wing monoplane. Thickness/chord ratio 10%. Dihedral 6° 30′. Incidence 3° at root. Sweepback at quarter-chord 4° 15′. Conventional structure of light alloy. Light alloy ailerons and trailing-edge flaps. Trim tab in port aileron. Pneumatic de-icing boots on leading-edges.

FUSELAGE: Conventional semi-monocoque structure of light alloy, with fail-safe construction in the pressurised section between fore and aft pressure bulkheads.

TAIL UNIT: Cantilever structure of light alloy. Trim tab in rudder and each elevator. Pneumatic de-icing boots on leading-edges of fin and tailplane.

LANDING GEAR: Hydraulically-retractable tricycle type, with twin wheels on each unit. Steerable nosewheels. All units retract forward. Oleo-pneumatic shock-absorbers. Single-disc brakes. Decelostat anti-skid unit in each brake.

POWER PLANT: Two 1,648 kW (2,210 ehp) Rolls-Royce Dart Mk 529-8 turboprop engines, each driving a Dowty Rotol four-blade constant-speed metal propeller. One fuel tank and one water/methanol tank in each wing. Total usable fuel capacity 5,867 litres (1,550 US gallons); total water/methanol capacity 166 litres (44 US gallons). Refuelling points on wing upper surface. Oil capacity 26·5 litres (7 US gallons).

ACCOMMODATION: Crew of three, comprising pilot, co-pilot and flight attendant. Cabin provides maximum seating for 38 passengers, three-abreast at 74 cm (29 in) pitch, with a toilet and compartment for carry-on baggage at the forward end of the cabin, plus an additional baggage compartment aft. Door with built-in airstair at forward end of cabin on port side. Two emergency exits on starboard side. Accommodation air-conditioned, heated and pressurised. Windscreen wipers standard.

SYSTEMS: Pressurisation system max differential 0·45 bars (6·55 lb/sq in). Single hydraulic system, pressure 103·5 bars (1,500 lb/sq in), for operation of landing gear, brakes, nosewheel steering, trailing-edge flaps, door, airstairs, and windscreen wipers. Pneumatic system, pressure 134·5 bars (1,950 lb/sq in), for emergency extension of landing gear. Electrical system includes two DC generators, two AC alternators and two storage batteries. Oxygen system for emergency use. Engine bleed air used for anti-icing and de-icing systems.

AVIONICS AND EQUIPMENT: A wide range of optional items is available to customer's requirements.

DIMENSIONS, EXTERNAL

Wing span	23·88 m (78 ft 4 in)
Wing chord at root	3·40 m (11 ft 2 in)
Wing chord at tip	1·35 m (4 ft 5 in)
Wing aspect ratio	10
Length overall	22·66 m (74 ft 4 in)
Diameter of fuselage	2·39 m (7 ft 10 in)
Height overall	7·06 m (23 ft 2 in)
Tailplane span	7·77 m (25 ft 6 in)
Wheel track	7·37 m (24 ft 2 in)
Propeller diameter	3·51 m (11 ft 6 in)
Propeller ground clearance	0·48 m (1 ft 7 in)
Distance between propeller centres	
	7·37 m (24 ft 2 in)
Passenger door (fwd, port):	
Height	1·57 m (5 ft 2 in)
Width	0·91 m (3 ft 0 in)
Baggage door (aft, stbd):	
Height	0·71 m (2 ft 4 in)
Width	0·89 m (2 ft 11 in)

DIMENSIONS, INTERNAL:

Cabin (cockpit divider to aft baggage compartment, incl toilet and galley)	
Length	13·21 m (43 ft 4 in)
Max width	2·24 m (7 ft 4 in)
Max height	1·85 m (6 ft 1 in)
Volume	42·76 m³ (1,510 cu ft)
Baggage hold, aft	4·08 m³ (144 cu ft)
Baggage hold, fwd	max 1·95 m³ (69 cu ft)

AREAS:

Wings, gross	56·7 m² (610·3 sq ft)
Ailerons (total)	3·44 m² (37·0 sq ft)
Trailing-edge flaps (total)	10·33 m² (111·2 sq ft)
Fin	10·88 m² (117·1 sq ft)
Rudder (incl tab)	2·67 m² (28·7 sq ft)
Tailplane	12·63 m² (136·0 sq ft)
Elevators (incl tabs)	1·63 m² (17·5 sq ft)

Prototype of the Gulfstream American GAC 159-C Commuter version of the Gulfstream I

WEIGHTS AND LOADINGS:

Max payload (passengers)	3,447 kg (7,600 lb)
Max payload (cargo)	3,719 kg (8,200 lb)
Max fuel weight	4,744 kg (10,460 lb)
Max T-O weight	16,329 kg (36,000 lb)
Max ramp weight	16,420 kg (36,200 lb)
Max zero-fuel weight	14,628 kg (32,250 lb)
Max landing weight	10,818 kg (23,850 lb)
Max wing loading	288·1 kg/m² (59 lb/sq ft)
Max power loading	4·95 kg/kW (8·14 lb/ehp)

PERFORMANCE (at max T-O weight):

Never-exceed speed	342 knots (634 km/h; 394 mph)
Max cruising speed	300 knots (555 km/h; 345 mph)
Stalling speed, flaps down, power off	
	87 knots (161 km/h; 100 mph)
Max rate of climb at S/L	655 m (2,150 ft)/min
Rate of climb at S/L, one engine out	
	183 m (600 ft)/min
Service ceiling	9,266 m (30,400 ft)
Service ceiling, one engine out	4,267 m (14,000 ft)
T-O to 15 m (50 ft)	1,438 m (4,720 ft)
Landing from 15 m (50 ft)	1,384 m (4,540 ft)
Range with max fuel, no reserves	
	1,750 nm (3,243 km; 2,015 miles)
Range with max payload, IFR reserves	
	520 nm (964 km; 599 miles)

GULFSTREAM AMERICAN GULFSTREAM II
US Coast Guard designation: VC-11A

The decision to start production of this twin-turbofan executive transport was announced by Grumman on 17 May 1965. The first production Gulfstream II (no prototype was built) flew for the first time on 2 October 1966. FAA certification was gained on 19 October 1967, and the first production aircraft was delivered to National Distillers & Chemical Corporation on 6 December 1967.

A total of 256 Gulfstream IIs had been completed by 1 January 1980, by which time production had ended. Details of the Gulfstream II can be found in the 1979-80 *Jane's*.

GULFSTREAM AMERICAN GULFSTREAM III

Grumman (now Gulfstream) American announced the resumption of the Gulfstream III programme in the Spring of 1978. It differs from the Gulfstream II primarily in having redesigned wings, with 'winglets' at the tips, a lengthened fuselage, and increased fuel capacity combined with an increase of some 18% in fuel economy and efficiency.

A prototype (N300GA), converted from a production-line Gulfstream II (c/n 249), was rolled out on 21 September 1979, and made its first flight on 2 December 1979. The second Gulfstream III (N901GA; c/n 252) followed on 24 December 1979. It was hoped to deliver 18 production aircraft in 1980, and a further 25 in 1981.

Customers include the Royal Danish Air Force, which will use three (with options on five more) for fishing surveillance, search and rescue and personnel transport duties. This special-purpose maritime version is described separately.

The prototype Gulfstream III flew nonstop from Savannah, Georgia, to Hanover, West Germany, in April 1980, to participate in the Hanover Air Show. The 3,967·37 nm (7,347·58 km; 4,565·57 mile) flight, at an average speed of 449·00 knots (831·54 km/h; 516·70 mph), set a class C1k record for distance in a straight line and a speed record over this recognised course. On the return journey, the aircraft set further course records from Geneva, Switzerland, to Boston, New York and Washington, USA. It also set, on 3 May 1980, a class C1k record of 15,849·6 m (52,000 ft) for sustained altitude in horizontal flight.

The following details refer to the standard Gulfstream III transport:

TYPE: Twin-turbofan executive transport.

WINGS: Cantilever low-wing monoplane of light alloy construction. Dihedral 3°. Incidence 3° 30′ at wing station 50, 1° 30′ at wing station 145, and −0° 30′ at wing station 414. Sweepback 27° 40′ at quarter-chord. By comparison with Gulfstream II, wing has extended-chord leading-edges (0·76 m; 2 ft 6 in at root, 0·13 m; 5 in at tip). NASA (Whitcomb) wingtip winglets. One-piece single-slotted Fowler-type trailing-edge flaps. Spoilers forward of flaps assist in lateral control and can be extended for use as airbrakes. All control surfaces actuated hydraulically. Trim tab in port aileron. Anti-icing by engine bleed air.

FUSELAGE: Conventional semi-monocoque structure of light alloy. Glassfibre nosecone hinged for access.

TAIL UNIT: Cantilever T-tail structure of light alloy, with swept horizontal and vertical surfaces. Trim tab in rudder and each elevator. Powered controls.

LANDING GEAR: Retractable tricycle type, with twin wheels on each unit. Inward-retracting main units; steerable nose unit retracts forward. Main-wheel tyres size 34 × 9·25-16, pressure 10·34 bars (150 lb/sq in). Nosewheel tyres size 21 × 7·25-10, pressure 6·55 bars (95 lb/sq in). Goodyear aircooled carbon brakes, with Goodyear fully-modulating anti-skid units.

POWER PLANT: Two Rolls-Royce Spey Mk 511-8 turbofan engines, each 50·7 kN (11,400 lb st), mounted in pod on each side of rear fuselage. Rohr target-type thrust reverser forms aft part of each nacelle when in stowed position. All fuel in integral tanks in wings, with total capacity of 16,656 litres (4,400 US gallons).

ACCOMMODATION: Crew of two or three. Standard seating for 19 passengers in pressurised and air-conditioned cabin. Large baggage compartment at rear of cabin, capacity 907 kg (2,000 lb). Integral airstair door at front of cabin on port side. Electrically-heated wraparound windscreen.

Gulfstream American Gulfstream III executive transport aircraft (*Pilot Press*)

Gulfstream American Gulfstream III twin-turbofan executive transport aircraft

SYSTEMS: Cabin pressurisation system with max differential of 0·65 bars (9·45 lb/sq in). Two independent hydraulic systems, each 103·5 bars (1,500 lb/sq in). All flying controls hydraulically powered, with manual reversion. APU in tail compartment. Basic 28V DC electrical system, using two 300A generators and four 200A transformer-rectifiers. Two 20kVA alternators provide AC power for secondary and auxiliary systems. Third (APU-driven) 20kVA alternator for on-ground power. Three 2·5kVA inverters, powered by the transformer-rectifiers, provide 400Hz fixed-frequency power. Two 24V batteries.

AVIONICS AND EQUIPMENT: Standard avionics include three Collins VHF com; two Collins VIR-31B VHF nav; two Collins ADF-60A; two Collins transponders; two Collins DME-40; cockpit voice recorders, Sperry SPZ-800 automatic flight guidance and control system; and Collins WXR-250A, or WXR-300; Bendix RDR-1200; or RCA Primus 40 WXD, or Primus 400 weather radar.

DIMENSIONS, EXTERNAL:

Wing span	23·72 m (77 ft 10 in)
Wing area, gross	86·83 m² (934·6 sq ft)
Length overall	25·32 m (83 ft 1 in)
Fuselage length	22·66 m (74 ft 4 in)
Height overall	7·43 m (24 ft 4½ in)
Passenger door (fwd, port):	
Height	1·57 m (5 ft 2 in)
Width	0·91 m (3 ft 0 in)
Baggage door (aft):	
Height	0·72 m (2 ft 4½ in)
Width	0·91 m (2 ft 11¾ in)

DIMENSIONS, INTERNAL:

Cabin: Length	12·60 m (41 ft 4 in)
Width	2·24 m (7 ft 4 in)
Height	1·85 m (6 ft 1 in)
Volume	42·53 m³ (1,502 cu ft)

Aft baggage compartment volume 4·44 m³ (157 cu ft)

WEIGHTS (estimated):

Manufacturer's bare weight	14,742 kg (32,500 lb)
Typical operating weight empty	17,372 kg (38,300 lb)
Max fuel load	12,655 kg (27,900 lb)
Typical payload	726 kg (1,600 lb)
Max T-O weight	30,935 kg (68,200 lb)
Max ramp weight	31,162 kg (68,700 lb)
Max zero-fuel weight	19,050 kg (42,000 lb)
Max landing weight	26,535 kg (58,500 lb)

PERFORMANCE (estimated):

Max cruising speed	Mach 0·85
Long-range cruising speed	Mach 0·775
Approach speed	136 knots (252 km/h; 156 mph)
Stalling speed at max landing weight	105 knots (195 km/h; 121 mph)
Max operating altitude	13,720 m (45,000 ft)
FAA T-O field length	1,783 m (5,850 ft)
FAA landing distance	1,040 m (3,400 ft)

Range with 726 kg (1,600 lb) payload at long-range cruising speed, IFR reserves
3,760 nm (6,968 km; 4,330 miles)
Max range (VFR), 30 min reserves
4,205 nm (7,792 km; 4,842 miles)

GULFSTREAM AMERICAN GULFSTREAM III (MARITIME VERSION)

The special needs posed by the Royal Danish Air Force's fishery patrols, covering some 160,000 nm² (549,500 km²; 212,155 sq miles) around Greenland, and 85,000 nm² (291,912 km²; 112,708 sq miles) around the Faröe Islands, had to take into consideration that, in the event of bad weather prohibiting a landing at either of these places, an 800 nm (1,482 km; 921 mile) flight to an alternate landing field might be necessary. In addition to this primary role, the chosen aircraft was required to be suitable for airdrop, medevac, SAR, tactical air transport, and other special duties. The RDAF has ordered three Gulfstream IIIs (with options on five more) to replace

eight Douglas C-47s currently in use, and to supplement the activities of three Lockheed C-130s. The first is scheduled for delivery to the RDAF's No. 721 Squadron in November 1981, the second in the following month, and the third in March 1982. It is anticipated that one will be operated from Sondrestrom AB, Greenland, the other two from Vaerloese, near Copenhagen.

In the primary role, for fishery patrol, the RDAF will operate the Gulfstream III with a crew of seven, comprising pilot, co-pilot, flight engineer, navigator, observer, photographer and radio operator. The radio operator's station is on the port side of the cabin, immediately aft of the door, and equipment will include dual HF and dual VHF/UHF com. This equipment is removable easily, and the seat can be turned 90° to port, so that the position may be used alternatively by an observer. A purpose-built observer's position is provided on the starboard side, directly opposite the radio operator's station. The standard Gulfstream III windows are retained, as adequate field of view is provided without recourse to special-purpose drag-inducing bubble windows. Aft of the radio operator's position, and also on the port side of the cabin, is the navigator's station. This is equipped with the master console for the Texas Instruments AN/APS-127 sea surveillance radar, dual control display units for the Litton 72R INS, a VHF navigation system, and basic flight instrumentation including rate of climb and airspeed indicators. Provision has been made for later installation of a VHF/Omega nav system if this is considered necessary.

The RDAF Gulfstream III has some structural differences to provide the essential multi-role capability. These include a 1·60 × 2·11 m (63 × 83 in) cargo door on the starboard side of the fuselage, forward of the wing; a cargo roller conveyor system in the aft cabin floor; an overhead cable system for the attachment of drop load parachute lanyards; and a flare launcher system in the aft fuselage, on the port side just aft of the wing trailing-edge. This last feature will permit the launch of a variety of pyrotechnic and/or signalling devices, including parachute flares as large as the LAU-2B. The existing 0·72 × 0·91 m (28·5 × 35·75 in) baggage door on the port side of the fuselage, aft of the wing, is to be used for the airdrop of emergency supplies and/or survival equipment, and a hydraulically-actuated air deflector will be mounted just forward of this door, opening automatically whenever the airdrop door is opened. It has not proved necessary to change the size of this baggage door, since the largest airdrop load for deployment by the RDAF will not exceed 0·60 × 0·60 × 0·90 m (23·5 × 23·5 × 35·4 in). The installation of AN/APS-127 radar antenna in the fuselage nose represents little more than an alternative to the weather radar, but substitution of the radar display for the weather radar display in the instrument panel has necessitated some movement of the surrounding instruments and the inclusion of four sub-panels below the main pilot and co-pilot panels. Standby airspeed, altitude and attitude indicators have been installed on the glareshield panel, and other non-standard instrumentation includes duplicated Sperry AD650 Series attitude and RD650 horizontal situation indicators, SPZ-800 autopilot, and a Teledyne angle of attack indicator.

Performance figures will be very similar to those of the commercial Gulfstream III: max cargo weight will be 2,064 kg (4,551 lb) with reduced fuel load, or 848 kg (1,870 lb) with max fuel load. With a crew of three, max fuel, max ramp weight of 31,162 kg (68,700 lb), payload of 726 kg (1,600 lb) and NBAA VFR reserves, RDAF Gulfstream IIIs will have an estimated range of 4,205 nm (7,459 km; 4,635 miles) at a cruising speed of Mach 0·775.

GULFSTREAM AMERICAN AA-5A, CHEETAH, AA-5B, TIGER, GA-7 and COUGAR

In mid-1980, Gulfstream American was negotiating sale of the AA-5B and Tiger production facilities, but was

continuing to sell and support its range of light aircraft, of which full details can be found in the 1979-80 *Jane's*.

GULFSTREAM AMERICAN SUPER AG-CAT

The prototype of the original Ag-Cat agricultural biplane flew for the first time on 27 May 1957. Series production was entrusted to Schweizer, under subcontract from Grumman. First deliveries were made in 1959, and more than 2,300 Ag-Cats (including 2,250 of the A and B models) had been built by 1 January 1980. Manufacturing then switched progressively from Elmira, NY, to Gulfstream American's plant at Savannah, and the final Elmira-built Ag-Cat was scheduled to fly in May 1980.

Four versions of the current Super Ag-Cat were available in 1980:

Super Ag-Cat B/450. Basic version, powered by a 335·5 kW (450 hp) Pratt & Whitney R-985 nine-cylinder radial aircooled engine, driving a Hamilton Standard two-blade constant-speed metal propeller with type 2D30 hub and AG-100-2 blades.

Super Ag-Cat B/525. As Super Ag-Cat B/450, but with 391·5 kW (525 hp) Continental/Page R-975 nine-cylinder radial aircooled engine, driving a Hamilton Standard two-blade constant-speed metal propeller with type 2D30 hub and AG-100 blades.

Super Ag-Cat C/600. As Super Ag-Cat B/450, but with 447·5 kW (600 hp) Pratt & Whitney R-1340 nine-cylinder radial aircooled engine, driving a Hamilton Standard two-blade constant-speed metal propeller with Type 12D40 hub and AG-100 blades. Larger-capacity hopper.

Turbo Ag-Cat D. As Super Ag-Cat C/600 generally, but with a Pratt & Whitney Aircraft of Canada PT6A-15AG turboprop engine. Described separately.

In addition, Gulfstream American sent to the 1979 Paris Air Show an example converted to carry a second pilot in an open cockpit in place of the hopper. Intended for pilot training, this aircraft is shown in an accompanying illustration.

TYPE: Single-seat agricultural biplane.

WINGS: Single-bay staggered biplane. NACA 4412 (modified) wing section. Dihedral 3°. Incidence 6°. Aluminium alloy (6061-T6) two-spar structure with 6061-T6 skins on entire top surface, around leading-edge and back to front spar on undersurface. Remainder of undersurface fabric-covered. Each D leading-edge is made of five separate sections to facilitate replacement if damaged. Glassfibre wingtips. N-type interplane struts. Ailerons of light alloy construction, with fabric covering, on all four wings. Ground-adjustable tab in both ailerons of lower wing. No flaps.

FUSELAGE: Welded 4130 chrome-molybdenum steel tube structure, covered with duralumin sheet. Removable side panels.

TAIL UNIT: Welded 4130 chrome-molybdenum steel tube structure, covered with fabric and wire-braced. Cable deflector wire from tip of fin to top of cockpit canopy. Controllable trim tab in port elevator. Ground-adjustable tabs on rudder and starboard elevator.

LANDING GEAR: Non-retractable tailwheel type. Cantilever spring steel legs. Cleveland wheels with tyres size 8·50-10 6-ply, pressure 2·42 bars (35 lb/sq in), on the Super Ag-Cat B; size 29 × 11-10 10-ply rated at the same pressure on the Super Ag-Cat C. Steerable tailwheel with tyre size 12·4-4·5, pressure 3·45 bars (50 lb/sq in). Cleveland heavy duty aircooled disc brakes. Parking brake.

POWER PLANT: One Pratt & Whitney or Continental/Page nine-cylinder aircooled radial engine with Hamilton Standard constant-speed propeller, as detailed in model listings. Fuel tank in upper centre-section with standard usable capacity of 174 litres (46 US gallons). Optional tanks, installed in wings on one or both sides of centre-section, are available for total usable capacities of 241 or 302 litres (64 or 80 US gallons) on the Super Ag-Cat B; 302 litres (80 US gallons) standard on Super Ag-Cat C. Single-point refuelling on upper surface of upper wing centre-section. Oil capacity 32·2 litres (8·5 US gallons).

ACCOMMODATION: Single seat beneath enclosed cockpit canopy. Reinforced fairing aft of cockpit for turnover protection. Canopy side panels open outward and down, canopy top upward and to starboard, to provide access. Baggage compartment. Cockpit pressurised against dust ingress and ventilated by ram air. Air-conditioning optional. Safety-padded instrument panel. Air-conditioning by J.B. Systems optional.

SYSTEMS: Hydraulic system for brakes only. Optional electrical system with 24V alternator, navigation lights and/or strobe lights, external power socket, and electric engine starter.

EQUIPMENT: Radio installation optional. Standard equipment includes control column lock, instrument glareshield, seat belt and shoulder harness, tinted windscreen, stall warning light, refuelling steps and assist handles, tiedown rings, and urethane paint external yellow finish.

AGRICULTURAL EQUIPMENT: Forward of cockpit, over CG, is a 1·13 m³ (40 cu ft) glassfibre hopper, capacity (Super Ag-Cat B) 1,136 litres (300 US gallons) of agricultural chemicals (dry or liquid) with distributor beneath fuselage. Low-volume, ULV or high-volume spray system, with leading- or trailing-edge booms. Super Ag-Cat C has 1,893 litre (500 US gallon) capacity hopper. Spray or dust distribution systems available. Emergency dump system for hopper load; can be used also for waterbomber operations.

DIMENSIONS, EXTERNAL (A: B/450; B: B/525; C: C/600):
Wing span: A, B, C   12·88 m (42 ft 3 in)
Wing chord (constant): A, B, C   1·47 m (4 ft 10 in)
Wing aspect ratio, upper wing: A, B, C   8·74
Biplane, effective mean: A, B, C   5·46
Length overall: A, B   7·90 m (25 ft 11 in)
       C   9·14 m (30 ft 0 in)
Height overall: A, B   3·35 m (11 ft 0 in)
       C   3·48 m (11 ft 5 in)
Tailplane span: A, B, C   3·96 m (13 ft 0 in)
Wheel track: A, B   2·44 m (8 ft 0 in)
       C   2·54 m (8 ft 4 in)
Wheelbase: A, B   5·59 m (18 ft 4 in)
       C   6·96 m (22 ft 10 in)
Propeller diameter (max):
       A, B, C   2·74 m (9 ft 0 in)
Propeller ground clearance: A, B   0·27 m (10·8 in)
       C   0·47 m (1 ft 6·7 in)
AREAS:
Wings, gross: A, B, C   36·42 m² (392 sq ft)
Ailerons (total): A, B, C   2·93 m² (31·5 sq ft)
Fin: A, B   1·67 m² (17·97 sq ft)
       C   0·84 m² (9·0 sq ft)
Rudder: A, B, C   1·12 m² (12·0 sq ft)
Tailplane: A, B, C   2·12 m² (22·8 sq ft)
Elevators: A, B, C   2·06 m² (22·2 sq ft)
WEIGHTS AND LOADINGS:
Weight empty equipped, spray version:
       A   1,404 kg (3,095 lb)
       B   1,424 kg (3,140 lb)
       C   1,746 kg (3,850 lb)
Weight empty equipped, duster version:
       A   1,315 kg (2,900 lb)
       B   1,338 kg (2,950 lb)
       C   1,692 kg (3,730 lb)
Max T-O weight (CAM.8):
       A, B   2,755 kg (6,075 lb)
       C (by formula)   3,855 kg (8,500 lb)
       C (recommended)   3,629 kg (8,000 lb)
Max wing loading: A, B   75·68 kg/m² (15·50 lb/sq ft)
       C   99·65 kg/m² (20·41 lb/sq ft)
Max power loading: A   8·21 kg/kW (13·5 lb/hp)
       B   7·04 kg/kW (11·75 lb/hp)
       C   8·11 kg/kW (13·33 lb/hp)
PERFORMANCE (at CAM.8 T-O weight):
Never-exceed speed:
       A, B, C   128 knots (237 km/h; 147 mph)
Max cruising speed, 75% power at 1,525 m (5,000 ft):
       A, B   102 knots (188 km/h; 117 mph)
Econ cruising speed, 50% power at 1,525 m (5,000 ft):
       A, B   85 knots (158 km/h; 98 mph)
Stalling speed, power off:
       A, B   52 knots (96 km/h; 60 mph) CAS
       C   60 knots (111 km/h; 69 mph) CAS
Max rate of climb at S/L: A   323 m (1,060 ft)/min
       B   411 m (1,350 ft)/min
T-O run: A   178 m (585 ft)
       B   165 m (540 ft)
       C   329 m (1,080 ft)
T-O to 15 m (50 ft): A   332 m (1,090 ft)
       B   305 m (1,000 ft)
       C   634 m (2,080 ft)
Landing from 15 m (50 ft): A, B   351 m (1,150 ft)
       C   363 m (1,190 ft)
Landing run: A, B   172 m (565 ft)
       C   180 m (590 ft)
Range with max standard fuel at 50% power:
       A, B   216 nm (401 km; 249 miles)

Three-view drawing of the Gulfstream American Super Ag-Cat B *(Pilot Press)*

GULFSTREAM AMERICAN MODEL G-164D TURBO AG-CAT D

This turboprop-powered version of the Ag-Cat is generally similar to the Super Ag-Cat C/600, but has a Pratt & Whitney Aircraft of Canada PT6A turboprop engine. It is available in three versions, as follows:

Turbo Ag-Cat D/T. With 507 kW (680 shp) PT6A-15 engine and 1,893 litre (500 US gallon) hopper/tank.

Turbo Ag-Cat D/ST. As D/T, but with 559 kW (750 shp) PT6A-34 engine.

Turbo Ag-Cat D/SST. As D/T, but with 634 kW (850 shp) PT6A-41 engine.

Gulfstream American began construction of a prototype in February 1978, and this flew for the first time on 19 July 1978. Construction of the first pre-production aircraft began in September 1978 and FAA certification under CAM 8 was received in early 1979, with production deliveries beginning shortly after.

The description of the Super Ag-Cat applies also to the Turbo Ag-Cat D except as follows:

WINGS AND FUSELAGE: As Super Ag-Cat.

TAIL UNIT: As for Super Ag-Cat, except ground-adjustable trim tab on rudder only.

LANDING GEAR: Non-retractable tailwheel type. Cantilever spring steel main-gear legs. Main-wheel tyres size 29 × 11-10, pressure 2·42 bars (35 lb/sq in). Steerable tailwheel with tyre size 12·5-4·5, pressure 3·80 bars (55 lb/sq in). Cleveland heavy-duty aircooled disc brakes. Parking brake.

POWER PLANT: One 507 kW (680 shp) Pratt & Whitney Aircraft of Canada PT6A-15AG turboprop engine,

driving a Hartzell HC-B3TN-3D/T10282A+4 constant-speed fully-feathering reversible-pitch three-blade metal propeller with Beta control and spinner. Optional power plants as detailed in model listings. Fuel contained in upper centre-section and two wing tanks, with combined capacity of 302 litres (80 US gallons). Single-point refuelling on top surface of upper wing centre-section. Oil capacity 8·7 lires (2·3 US gallons).

ACCOMMODATION: As for Super Ag-Cat, except no optional air-conditioning system.

SYSTEMS: Hydraulic system for brakes only. Electrical system standard, with 24V 250A starter/generator and two 12V 85Ah batteries.

EQUIPMENT: Standard equipment includes sensitive altimeter, adjustable seat with seat belt and shoulder harness, control column lock, adjustable rudder pedals, tinted windscreen, stall warning light, engine oil chip detector with warning light, internal corrosion proofing, stainless steel control cables, external yellow urethane paint scheme. Optional equipment includes stall warning horn, navigation lights, strobe/navigation light system, and external power socket.

AGRICULTURAL EQUIPMENT: This equipment, which includes a variety of options, is generally similar to that described for Super Ag-Cat.

DIMENSIONS, EXTERNAL: As for Super Ag-Cat C, except;
Length overall   10·46 m (34 ft 4 in)
Propeller diameter   2·71 m (8 ft 10½ in)
DIMENSION, INTERNAL:
Max width   0·81 m (2 ft 8 in)

An open front cockpit identifies the pilot training version of the Super Ag-Cat *(Brian M. Service)*

Gulfstream American Turbo Ag-Cat D turboprop-powered agricultural aircraft *(J. M. G. Gradidge)*

Max height	1·37 m (4 ft 6 in)	Max T-O weight (CAM.8): A, B	3,856 kg (8,500 lb)	Stalling speed at usual landing weight	
		Max wing loading	105·9 kg/m² (21·68 lb/sq ft)		49 knots (90 km/h; 56 mph)
		Max power loading	9·85 kg/kW (16·19 lb/shp)	T-O run	223 m (730 ft)

AREAS: As for Super Ag-Cat C

WEIGHTS AND LOADINGS (A: liquid dispersal; B: dust dispersal):

Weight empty, equipped: A	1,565 kg (3,450 lb)	PERFORMANCE (D/T version with PT6A-15AG engine):		T-O to 15 m (50 ft)	411 m (1,350 ft)
B	1,520 kg (3,350 lb)	Max level speed	135 knots (249 km/h; 155 mph)	Landing from 15 m (50 ft) fully loaded	
Max payload (CAM.8): A	2,291 kg (5,050 lb)	Typical working speed			509 m (1,670 ft)
B	2,336 kg (5,150 lb)		82·5-117 knots (153-217 km/h; 95-135 mph)	Landing from 15 m (50 ft) at usual landing weight	
Design T-O weight	2,857 kg (6,300 lb)	Stalling speed at AUW of 2,857 kg (6,300 lb)			411 m (1,350 ft)
			60 knots (110 km/h; 69 mph)	Landing run, fully loaded	259 m (850 ft)
				Landing run at usual landing weight	150 m (490 ft)

HAMILTON
HAMILTON AVIATION

HEAD OFFICE: PO Box 11746, Tucson, Arizona 85734
Telephone: (602) 294 3481
PRESIDENT: Gordon B. Hamilton
VICE-PRESIDENT: Gordon D. Hamilton
CHIEF ENGINEER: Clayton C. Hamilton

Hamilton Aviation, which is engaged primarily in the procurement and overhaul of various types of military aircraft for foreign governments, is also building and marketing two Westwind turboprop conversions of the Beech Model 18 (last described in the 1969-70 *Jane's*).

HAMILTON WESTWIND III

The prototype Westwind III passenger/cargo aircraft flew for the first time in 1963 and FAA certification under CAR Part 3 was awarded in 1964. Passenger seats can be removed easily to make the whole cabin space available for cargo.

The Westwind III can have agricultural or military applications.

TYPE: Utility passenger/cargo commuter airliner.

WINGS, FUSELAGE, TAIL UNIT: As for Beech Model 18.

LANDING GEAR: Electrically-retractable tailwheel type. Oleo-pneumatic shock-absorbers on all units. Main wheels retract aft. Main-wheel tyre pressure 4·14 bars (60 lb/sq in). Tailwheel tyre pressure 5·52 bars (80 lb/sq in). Goodyear single-disc multi-puck hydraulic brakes. Main wheels fully enclosed by doors when retracted.

POWER PLANT: Two 432 kW (579 ehp) Pratt & Whitney Aircraft of Canada PT6A-20 turboprop engines standard. Optional power plants include two 533 kW (715 ehp) (derated to 470 kW; 630 ehp) PT6A-27s, two 533 kW (715 ehp) (derated to 470 kW; 630 ehp) PT6A-28s or two 455 kW (610 ehp) Avco Lycoming LTP 101s. Hartzell three-blade fully-feathering constant-speed metal propellers. Standard fuel capacity 1,544 litres (408 US gallons), contained in outer wing, inner wing and centre-section tanks. Optional total fuel in larger-capacity tanks 2,801 litres (740 US gallons). Refuelling points on wing upper surface. Engine air intakes have an inertial separator system, including foreign object and hail bypass and heating of the leading-edges by engine bleed air.

ACCOMMODATION: Pilot and co-pilot on flight deck, with cabin seating eight passengers. Door on port side, aft of wing, with built-in airstair, can be replaced by larger cargo door. Separate door to flight deck, on port side of fuselage, is optional. Emergency exit (push-out type) on starboard side of cabin. Passenger seating quickly removable for conversion to all-cargo role. Baggage or cargo space aft of cabin and in extended fuselage nose. Cabin is heated by bleed air, and can be cooled by a bleed air converter. Windscreen de-icing standard.

SYSTEMS: Cabin cooling by Garrett-AiResearch engine bleed air converter. Cabin heater manufactured by Hamilton Aviation. Pneumatic system, for flight instruments and wing and tail unit de-icing, supplied by engine bleed air. Electrical system powered by two 200A starter/generators and nickel-cadmium battery. Oxygen system optional.

AVIONICS AND EQUIPMENT: Radio com/nav and radar to customer's requirements. Blind-flying instrumentation standard.

ARMAMENT: Optional armament for military versions includes a cargo pod containing two General Electric Miniguns, and hardpoints on the wings for the carriage of bombs or rockets.

DIMENSIONS, EXTERNAL:

Wing span	14·02 m (46 ft 0 in)
Wing chord at root	4·19 m (13 ft 9 in)
Wing chord at tip	1·07 m (3 ft 6 in)

Hamilton Westwind III conversion of the Beech Model 18 (two PT6A-27 derated turboprop engines)

Wing aspect ratio	6·5
Length overall	10·85 m (35 ft 7¼ in)
Tailplane span	4·56 m (14 ft 11½ in)
Passenger door (port, aft): Height	1·22 m (4 ft 0 in)
Width	0·56 m (1 ft 10 in)
Height to sill	0·79 m (2 ft 7 in)
Cargo door (port, aft, optional):	
Max height (forward edge)	1·52 m (4 ft 11¾ in)
Min height (rear edge)	1·19 m (3 ft 11 in)
Width	1·47 m (4 ft 9¾ in)
Height to sill	0·79 m (2 ft 7 in)
Emergency exit (stbd): Height	0·64 m (2 ft 1 in)
Width	0·48 m (1 ft 7 in)

DIMENSIONS, INTERNAL:

Cabin (bare cargo configuration):	
Length	4·57 m (15 ft 0 in)
Max width	1·32 m (4 ft 4 in)
Max height	1·55 m (5 ft 1 in)
Floor area	7·80 m² (84 sq ft)
Baggage/cargo hold (aft cabin)	0·85 m³ (30 cu ft)
Baggage/cargo hold (fuselage nose)	1·53 m³ (54 cu ft)

AREAS:

Wings, gross	30·32 m² (326·4 sq ft)
Ailerons (total)	2·47 m² (26·6 sq ft)
Trailing-edge flaps (total)	3·49 m² (37·6 sq ft)
Fins (total)	3·03 m² (32·6 sq ft)
Rudders (total)	3·21 m² (34·56 sq ft)
Tailplane	6·08 m² (65·4 sq ft)
Elevator	2·53 m² (27·22 sq ft)

WEIGHTS AND LOADINGS:

Weight empty	2,495 kg (5,500 lb)
Max payload	1,814 kg (4,000 lb)
Max T-O weight	5,094 kg (11,230 lb)
Max zero-fuel weight	4,854 kg (10,700 lb)

Max landing weight	4,763 kg (10,500 lb)
Max wing loading	167·9 kg/m² (34·4 lb/sq ft)
Max power loading	5·90 kg/kW (19·4 lb/ehp)

PERFORMANCE (at max T-O weight. A: PT6A-20 engines; B: PT6A-27s):

Max level speed at 3,660 m (12,000 ft):	
A	234 knots (435 km/h; 270 mph)
B	269 knots (499 km/h; 310 mph)
Max cruising speed at 3,660 m (12,000 ft):	
A	217 knots (402 km/h; 250 mph)
B	252 knots (467 km/h; 290 mph)
Econ cruising speed at 3,050 m (10,000 ft):	
A	204 knots (378 km/h; 235 mph)
B	234 knots (435 km/h; 270 mph)
Max rate of climb at S/L: A	549 m (1,800 ft)/min
B	823 m (2,700 ft)/min
Rate of climb at S/L, one engine out:	
A	183 m (600 ft)/min
B	335 m (1,100 ft)/min
Service ceiling: A	7,315 m (24,000 ft)
B	8,535 m (28,000 ft)
Service ceiling, one engine out:	
A	2,745 m (9,000 ft)
B	3,960 m (13,000 ft)
T-O run: A	549 m (1,800 ft)
B	366 m (1,200 ft)
T-O to 15 m (50 ft): A	1,005 m (3,300 ft)
B	731 m (2,400 ft)
Landing from 15 m (50 ft): A, B	549 m (1,800 ft)
Landing run: A, B	366 m (1,200 ft)
Range with max optional fuel:	
A	3,240 nm (6,004 km; 3,731 miles)
Range with max payload:	
A	810 nm (1,501 km; 933 miles)

HAMILTON WESTWIND II STD

The Westwind II STD is a 'stretched' version of the Beech 18, providing accommodation for a maximum of 17 passengers. Otherwise it is generally similar to the Westwind III except that a tricycle landing gear is available optionally. The Westwind II STD is intended primarily as a commuter airliner, but is convertible for freight carrying or military uses.

The description of the Westwind III applies also to the Westwind II STD, except as follows:

LANDING GEAR: Retractable tricycle type optional.

POWER PLANT: Two 626 kW (840 ehp) Pratt & Whitney Aircraft of Canada PT6A-34 turboprop engines, derated to 470 kW (630 ehp), are standard, each driving a

Hamilton Westwind II STD of Connie Kalitta Services, with newly-added ventral fin *(Austin J. Brown)*

Hartzell constant-speed fully-feathering reversible-pitch propeller. Two 579 kW (776 ehp) Garrett-AiResearch TPE331-6-251 turboprop engines, derated to 470 kW (630 ehp), available optionally.

ACCOMMODATION: Pilot and co-pilot or passenger on flight deck, with seating in main cabin for a maximum of 17 passengers. Two emergency exits on starboard side of fuselage.

DIMENSIONS, EXTERNAL: As for Westwind III, except:
Length overall (standard)   13·72 m (45 ft 0 in)
Length overall (tricycle landing gear)
                                            13·46 m (44 ft 2 in)
DIMENSIONS, INTERNAL: As for Westwind III, except:
Cabin: Length   6·10 m (20 ft 0 in)
WEIGHTS AND LOADING (estimated):
Weight empty   2,712 kg (6,000 lb)
Max payload   2,041 kg (4,500 lb)

Max T-O weight	5,667 kg (12,495 lb)	
Max zero-fuel weight	5,217 kg (11,500 lb)	
Max landing weight	5,217 kg (11,500 lb)	
Max wing loading	186·9 kg/m² (38·3 lb/sq ft)	

PERFORMANCE (at max T-O weight):
Max level speed at 4,265 m (14,000 ft)
                              278 knots (515 km/h; 320 mph)
Max cruising speed at 3,660 m (12,000 ft)
                              261 knots (483 km/h; 300 mph)
Econ cruising speed at 6,705 m (22,000 ft)
                              234 knots (435 km/h; 270 mph)
Stalling speed, flaps up
                               87 knots (161 km/h; 100 mph)
Stalling speed, flaps down
                               74 knots (137 km/h; 85 mph)
Max rate of climb at S/L   945 m (3,100 ft)/min

Rate of climb at S/L, one engine out
                                             274 m (900 ft)/min
Service ceiling   9,755 m (32,000 ft)
Service ceiling, one engine out   5,485 m (18,000 ft)
T-O run   427 m (1,400 ft)
T-O to 15 m (50 ft)   1,036 m (3,400 ft)
Landing from 15 m (50 ft):
  without propeller reversal   671 m (2,200 ft)
  with propeller reversal   335 m (1,100 ft)
Range with max optional fuel
                          3,240 nm (6,004 km; 3,731 miles)
Range with max payload
                            810 nm (1,501 km; 933 miles)

HAMILTON WESTWIND IV

This conversion of the Beech Model 18 is no longer available. Details can be found in the 1979-80 *Jane's*.

HAMMER-HUNT
ROBERT H. HAMMER and RICHARD HUNT

Mr Hammer, an engineer with Boeing, and Mr. Hunt, a test pilot, designed, built and flew from Paine Field, Everett, Washington, a lightweight high-altitude reconnaissance aircraft known as the HH-1 Zipper. It was intended as a lower-cost substitute for the Lockheed U-2s which have operated civilian missions on behalf of US government agencies such as the Agriculture Department, Bureau of Land Management and US Geological Survey.

HAMMER-HUNT HH-1 ZIPPER

The Zipper, which flew for the first time in July 1979, originated as a preliminary concept by Mr Hunt, who subsequently formed a partnership with Mr Hammer. It embodied a number of components bought from surplus stocks, including the wings of a Teledyne Ryan reconnaissance RPV and its General Electric turbojet.

On 15 August 1979, the Zipper crashed into Puget Sound, near Mukilteo, Washington, after Mr Hunt reported that he was in a spin at about 4,250 m (14,000 ft). Mr Hunt lost his life in the accident.

TYPE: Two-seat high-altitude reconnaissance aircraft.
WINGS: Cantilever low-wing monoplane, built originally for a Teledyne Ryan RPV.
FUSELAGE: Semi-monocoque structure of basically circular section.
TAIL UNIT: Cantilever V tail. Small ventral fin.
LANDING GEAR: Retractable nosewheel and main unit in tandem on aircraft centreline. Small non-retractable balancer wheel under each wing at about mid-span (to be retractable on later aircraft).
POWER PLANT: One 12·7 kN (2,850 lb st) General Electric J85-17 turbojet engine, produced by removing afterburner from a surplus J85-5 and pod-mounted above

Hammer-Hunt HH-1 Zipper two-seat high-altitude reconnaissance aircraft

centre-fuselage. Provision for a slipper fuel tank to be mounted on leading-edge of each wing.
ACCOMMODATION: Two seats in tandem in pressurised cockpit, with dual controls, under a long constant-section canopy. Max pressure differential 0·38 bars (5·5 lb/sq in).
EQUIPMENT: Equipment bays in nose and in fuselage aft of wings, for avionics and cameras. Provision for removing rear seat to make room for a large camera on a stabilised mounting.

WEIGHT (estimated for production aircraft):
Max T-O weight   1,450 kg (3,200 lb)

PERFORMANCE (estimated):
Max level speed at operating height   Mach 0·9
Max rate of climb at S/L   4,570 m (15,000 ft)/min
Service ceiling   18,275 m (60,000 ft)
Endurance with internal fuel, 45 min reserves   1 h
Endurance with added slipper tanks, 45 min reserves
                                                  2h 30 min

HAWK
HAWK INDUSTRIES

Yucca Valley, California
PRESIDENT: Ernest Hauk

Hawk Industries is a company specialising in equipment for oil and water well-drilling, and fencing. Having experienced difficulties in transporting its products, the company's President designed a freight-carrying aircraft that might overcome both the slowness of road transport and the high cost, and loading/unloading difficulties, of conventional aircraft. He named his project the GafHawk 125, signifying general aviation freighter. It is intended to have STOL capability, and to be certificated initially at a gross weight of 5,670 kg (12,500 lb) under FAR Pt 23, although it would be capable of operating at a max T-O weight of 6,577 kg (14,500 lb).

HAWK MINIHAWK

The GafHawk concept was tested initially in the form of a radio-controlled scale model. Hawk Industries next constructed one of the largest privately-owned wind tunnels to test the wing design, before rebuilding a Piper Tri-Pacer light aircraft as a small-scale flying testbed. This made its initial flight in 1978.

Known as the MiniHawk, the modified Tri-Pacer is fitted with a 54% scale GafHawk wing, tail assembly and landing gear. The fuselage has also been modified to a representative configuration, but not to scale. Two years of flight testing have shown that the 'rollerons' designed for the GafHawk are as effective during the landing approach, with flaps down, as had been hoped, and that spin recovery can be achieved simply, by working the rollerons against the direction of rotation.

HAWK GAFHAWK

Features considered of prime importance in design of the GafHawk included STOL capability for operation into and from small unprepared strips, a turboprop power plant for economic operations, a square-section fuselage for maximum utilisation of internal capacity, under-tail loading of bulk cargo at truckbed height, and a single engine for economy and for ease of certification and single-pilot operation. Construction of the prototype was under way in 1980, with the first flight scheduled to take place before the end of the year.

The following details apply to the prototype, known as the GafHawk 125. Production aircraft are intended to have a more powerful (1,119 kW; 1,500 shp) PT6A-65 turboprop engine.

TYPE: Single-engined turboprop freighter.

Hawk MiniHawk, a Piper Tri-Pacer converted to evaluate characteristics of the GafHawk 125 *(Henry Artof)*

Full-size mockup of the Hawk GafHawk 125 *(Henry Artof)*

WINGS: Strut-braced shoulder-wing monoplane, with single bracing strut and short auxiliary strut on each side. NASA GAW-1 section, modified by use of a leading-edge cuff. No dihedral. Thickness/chord ratio 17%. Constant-chord structure of light alloy, made up of a leading-edge tubular spar, a box spar, a further tubular spar aft of the box, a total of 78 one-piece ribs, and light alloy skins. Full-span trailing-edge flaps of similar construction. Half-span spoiler/aileron ('rolleron') hinged to top surface within slot between wing and flap in outer half of each wing, operating differentially through a range of 60° up and 10° down.

FUSELAGE: Basic rectangular structure of welded square-section steel tubing, covered with non-structural corrugated skins. These are attached to the hermetically-sealed square tubing by clips, to facilitate the replacement of damaged sections.

TAIL UNIT: Cantilever structure of light alloy. Construction similar to that of wings, but with only fore and aft tubular spars in fin and tailplane. Horn-balanced rudder and one-piece elevator. Dorsal fin.

LANDING GEAR: Non-retractable tricycle type, with single nosewheel, and twin wheels on main units.

POWER PLANT: Prototype has one 875 kW (1,173 shp) Pratt & Whitney Aircraft of Canada PT6A-45B turbo-prop engine, driving a Hartzell five-blade reversible-pitch low-speed propeller with spinner. Fuel tank, capacity 1,363 litres (360 US gallons), mounted above forward fuselage, directly over the wing, and providing gravity feed to engine. Refuelling point on upper surface of tank.

ACCOMMODATION: Pilot only on flight deck, with door on port side forward of wing. Cabin door on side aft of wing, and main cargo loading ramp/door in undersurface of upswept aft fuselage. Main cabin volume augmented by usable space under flight deck.

AVIONICS: Nav/com radios standard.

DIMENSIONS, EXTERNAL:
Wing span	21·77 m (71 ft 5 in)
Wing chord (constant)	2·11 m (6 ft 11 in)
Wing area, gross	45·7 m² (491·9 sq ft)
Length overall	14·30 m (46 ft 11 in)
Height overall	5·49 m (18 ft 0 in)
Tailplane span	7·01 m (23 ft 0 in)
Wheel track (c/l outer tyres)	3·38 m (11 ft 1 in)
Wheelbase	4·39 m (14 ft 5 in)

Propeller diameter	2·82 m (9 ft 3 in)

DIMENSIONS, INTERNAL:
Cabin: Length at floor level, excl flight deck	4·72 m (15 ft 6 in)
Max width	1·88 m (6 ft 2 in)
Max height	1·88 m (6 ft 2 in)
Volume	20·22 m³ (714 cu ft)

WEIGHTS (estimated):
Weight empty	2,835 kg (6,250 lb)
Max T-O weight (initial certification)	5,670 kg (12,500 lb)

PERFORMANCE (prototype, estimated, at max T-O weight):
Max level speed at 3,050 m (10,000 ft)	152 knots (282 km/h; 175 mph)
Econ cruising speed (55% power) at 3,050 m (10,000 ft)	126 knots (233 km/h; 145 mph)
Stalling speed, flaps down	44 knots (82 km/h; 51 mph)
Max rate of climb at S/L	290 m (950 ft)/min
Service ceiling	5,485 m (18,000 ft)
T-O run	189 m (620 ft)
T-O to 15 m (50 ft)	344 m (1,130 ft)
Landing from 15 m (50 ft)	296 m (970 ft)
Landing run	131 m (430 ft)

HILLER

HILLER AVIATION INC

2075 West Scranton Avenue, Porterville, California 93257
Telephone: (209) 781 8000
Telex: 682454
PRESIDENT: Edwin L. Trupe

Hiller Aviation, formed in January 1973, acquired from Fairchild Industries the design rights, production tooling and spares of the Hiller 12E piston-engined light helicopter. Initially, the company provided product support for UH-12 helicopters in service throughout the world, a total then estimated as being in excess of 2,200 aircraft. Service and repair facilities were added as a first move to expand the company's business. It was then decided to begin the manufacture of new aircraft from existing components, incorporating all modifications approved for the type since closure of the production line in the late 1960s.

It was decided also to develop a turbine-powered version of the UH-12, and in conjunction with Soloy Conversions of Chehalis, Washington, the company has developed such an aircraft. Its power plant is suitable not only for new production aircraft, but for retrospective installation in existing UH-12s.

HILLER/FAIRCHILD FH1100

Hiller Aviation announced in April 1980 that it had concluded an agreement with Fairchild Industries to purchase all rights in the Fairchild FH1100 five-passenger light turbine helicopter, last described in the 1973-74 *Jane's*. Hiller is undertaking a three-year programme to increase the engine power and useful load of the FH1100 prior to marketing the aircraft.

HILLER AVIATION UH-12

Following the development of a turbine power plant for the UH-12, the following versions are available:

UH-12E. Basic model, with three-abreast accommodation for a pilot and two passengers.

UH-12E4. Four-seat version of UH-12E, with accommodation for the pilot on a single adjustable seat forward and three passengers side by side on a rear bench seat. Space for cargo in tailboom. An 'L-Cabin' version is available optionally, with wider cabin door for improved access.

UH-12ET. Turbine-powered version of the UH-12E, with the same three-seat accommodation. Power plant as for UH-12E4T.

UH-12E4T. Turbine-powered version with four-seat cabin configuration as in the UH-12E4. Power plant comprises one 313 kW (420 shp) Allison 250-C20B turboshaft engine, derated to 224 kW (301 shp). Certification achieved by Soloy Conversions in January 1976.

The description which follows applies generally to all versions, except as indicated:

TYPE: Three-seat or four-seat utility helicopter.

ROTOR SYSTEM: Two-blade main rotor mounted universally on driveshaft, with small servo rotor; the latter is connected directly to the pilot's cyclic control stick, through a universally-mounted transfer bearing and simple linkage. Movement of the control stick introduces positive or negative pitch changes to the servo rotor paddles. The resulting aerodynamic forces tilt the rotor head and produce cyclic pitch changes to the rotor blades. Main rotor blades are of bonded stainless steel (since April 1978), with aluminium honeycomb core, and wedge tips. Thickness/chord ratio 12%. Blades are interchangeable individually and are bolted to forks which are retained at the rotor head by tension-torsion bars. Blades do not fold. Rotor brake optional. Two-blade tail rotor of light alloy construction, mounted on port side of tailboom.

ROTOR DRIVE: Mechanical drive through two-stage planetary main transmission. Bevel gear drive to auxiliaries. Tail rotor gearbox (and fan gearbox on piston-engined versions). Main rotor/engine rpm ratio 1 : 8·66

Hiller UH-12E three-seat utility helicopter

Hiller UH-12ET, with an Allison 250-C20B turboshaft engine

on piston-engined versions, 1:16·2 on turbine-powered versions. Tail rotor/engine rpm ratio 1 : 1·44 on piston-engined versions, 1:2·52 on turbine-powered versions.

FUSELAGE: Light alloy fully-stressed semi-monocoque platform structure supporting the non-stressed cabin enclosure, engine mounting and landing gear. Tailboom of beaded light alloy sheet with no internal stiffeners.

TAIL UNIT: Horizontal stabiliser on starboard side of tailboom of three-seat versions, with steel tube spar, light alloy ribs and skin. Incidence ground-adjustable. Inverted V stabilising surfaces forward of tail rotor on four-seat versions.

LANDING GEAR: Wide-track light alloy tube skids carried on spring steel cross members. Ground handling wheels standard. Optional 'zip-on' pontoons can be attached above the skids to permit water or land operations, but require alternative extended landing gear.

POWER PLANT: (UH-12E/E4), one 253·5 kW (340 hp) Avco Lycoming VO-540-C2A flat-six engine, installed vertically and derated to 227·5 kW (305 hp). (UH-12ET/E4T), one turboshaft engine as detailed in model listing, mounted diagonally aft of rotor pylon. Single bladder fuel cell, capacity 174 litres (46 US gallons), mounted in lower portion of rear fuselage, beneath engine. Two optional 72 litre (19 US gallon) auxiliary fuel tanks, mounted in fuselage on each side of engine. Oil capacity 12·5 litres (3·3 US gallons) on piston-engined versions.

ACCOMMODATION: Three persons side by side on bench seat; or pilot on single forward seat and three passengers side by side on bench seat. Seat belts for all occupants; provision for shoulder harness. Dual controls optional. Forward-hinged door on each side, with sliding window. Baggage compartment immediately aft of engine. Heater/defroster optional.

SYSTEM: Electrical system includes a 72A alternator, nickel-cadmium battery, and battery temperature monitor.

AVIONICS AND EQUIPMENT: A range of optional avionics is available. Standard equipment includes engine hour meter, edge-lighted instrument panel, outside air temperature gauge, eight-day clock, electrically-controlled trim system, tinted glazing, standard or extended landing gear legs, cargo hook hardpoint, external power socket, and polyurethane paint finish. Optional equipment includes Mason cyclic control grip, fire extinguisher, first aid kit, night lighting equipment, strobe lights, 454 kg (1,000 lb) capacity quick-release cargo hook, twin heavy-duty cargo racks, agricultural spray equipment, loudspeaker/siren, searchlight, tropical doors and twin litters.

DIMENSIONS, EXTERNAL:

Diameter of main rotor	10·80 m (35 ft 5 in)
Main rotor blade chord (constant)	0·33 m (1 ft 1 in)
Diameter of tail rotor	1·68 m (5 ft 6 in)
Distance between rotor centres	6·17 m (20 ft 3 in)
Length overall, rotors turning	12·41 m (40 ft 8½ in)
Length of fuselage: 3-seater	8·69 m (28 ft 6 in)
4-seater	9·08 m (29 ft 9½ in)
Height to top of rotor hub	3·08 m (10 ft 1¼ in)

Skid track	2·29 m (7 ft 6 in)
Cabin doors (standard, each):	
Height	1·13 m (3 ft 8½ in)
Max width	0·81 m (2 ft 8 in)
Height to sill	0·58 m (1 ft 11 in)
Cabin doors (L-cabin, each):	
As above except:	
Max width	0·99 m (3 ft 3 in)

DIMENSIONS, INTERNAL:

Cabin: Length (3-seater)	1·52 m (5 ft 0 in)
Max width	1·50 m (4 ft 11 in)
Max height	1·35 m (4 ft 5 in)
Floor area (3-seater)	1·16 m² (12·5 sq ft)

AREAS:

Tail rotor blades (each)	0·094 m² (1·01 sq ft)
Main rotor disc	91·97 m² (990 sq ft)
Tail rotor disc	2·57 m² (27·7 sq ft)

WEIGHTS AND LOADINGS (A: UH-12E; B: UH-12E4; C: UH-12ET/E4T):

Weight empty: A	798 kg (1,759 lb)
B	833 kg (1,836 lb)
C	748·5 kg (1,650 lb)
Max T-O weight:	
All versions	1,406 kg (3,100 lb)
Max disc loading:	
All versions	15·28 kg/m² (3·13 lb/sq ft)
Max power loading:	
A, B	6·18 kg/kW (10·16 lb/hp)
C	6·28 kg/kW (10·30 lb/shp)

PERFORMANCE (at max T-O weight):

Never-exceed and max level speed:		
A, C	83 knots	(154 km/h; 96 mph)
B	82·5 knots	(153 km/h; 95 mph)
Cruising speed:		
All versions	78 knots	(145 km/h; 90 mph)
Max rate of climb at S/L: A		393 m (1,290 ft)/min
B		303 m (993 ft)/min
C		520 m (1,706 ft)/min
Vertical rate of climb at S/L:		
A, B		225 m (740 ft)/min
C		446 m (1,463 ft)/min
Hovering ceiling IGE:		
A, B		3,170 m (10,400 ft)
C		3,660 m (12,000 ft)
Hovering ceiling OGE:		
A, B		2,070 m (6,800 ft)
C		2,135 m (7,000 ft)
Service ceiling:		
A, B		4,570 m (15,000 ft)
C		3,660 m (12,000 ft)
Range, no reserves:		
A, B, with standard fuel		
		187 nm (346 km; 215 miles)
C, with auxiliary fuel		
		305 nm (565 km; 351 miles)
Endurance, no reserves:		
A, B, with standard fuel		2 h 42 min
C with auxiliary fuel		3 h 32·5 min

HUGHES

HUGHES HELICOPTERS (Division of Summa Corporation)

HEAD OFFICE AND WORKS: Culver City, California 90230
Telephone: (213) 390 4451
Telex: 67-222
PRESIDENT AND CHIEF EXECUTIVE OFFICER:
J. G. Real
VICE-PRESIDENTS:
W. J. Blackburn (Manufacturing Operations)
R. E. Brix (Ordnance)
M. F. Gerardis (Finance and Administration)
J. N. Kerr (Advanced Attack Helicopter Programme)
C. D. Perry (Marketing)
C. E. Schaaf (Legal)
L. P. Sonsini (Product Assurance and Flight Operations)
F. C. Strible (Commercial Helicopters)
PUBLIC RELATIONS MANAGER: Anthony J. Longo

Following reorganisation of Hughes Tool Company as the Summa Corporation, its former Aircraft Division became known as Hughes Helicopters. Its current products are described in this entry. Research activities include work on composite rotor blades and tailbooms, metal insulation and IR suppression systems, and chain gun and lockless ordnance systems for air or ground applications.

Kawasaki Heavy Industries Ltd in Japan (which see) has assembled Model 369HM helicopters, this being the designation of the uprated version of the Hughes OH-6 available to foreign military customers. Other licence manufacture is undertaken by RACA in Argentina, Kawasaki in Japan, KAL in the Republic of Korea and BredaNardi in Italy.

HUGHES MODEL 300C

This is a developed version of the Model 300 (1976-77 *Jane's*), with improvements to allow a 45% increase in payload. The prototype made its first flight in August 1969, followed by the first production model in December 1969. FAA certification was received in May 1970. More than 550 Model 300Cs had been delivered by 1 January 1980.

The Model 300C is also manufactured in Italy by BredaNardi (which see).

A specially equipped 300C is available for police patrol. Known as the **Sky Knight**, it has as standard equipment safety mesh seats with inertia-reel shoulder harness, ballistic glassfibre armour beneath each seat, a high-power public address/siren system, a high-intensity controllable searchlight system, an integrated communications system based on the King KY 195 VHF transceiver, a heavy-duty 28V 100A electrical system, cabin heater, night lights with strobe beacons, cabin utility light, external power socket, fire extinguisher, first aid kit and map case.

Following the research that produced a modified version of the OH-6A known as 'The Quiet One', Hughes used similar techniques to develop and obtain full FAA certification of a quiet version of the Model 300, and this has the designation Model **300CQ**. In this configuration, emission of audible sound is 75 per cent less than with earlier models, and the necessary modifications can be retrofitted to existing 300Cs. Max T-O weight of the 300CQ for quiet operation is 873 kg (1,925 lb), with a useful load of 397 kg (875 lb), and there is little change in range and endurance by comparison with the standard Model 300C.

TYPE: Two- or three-seat light helicopter.

Hughes Model 300C two/three-seat light helicopter equipped for agricultural spraying duties

ROTOR SYSTEM: Fully-articulated metal three-blade main rotor. Blades are of bonded construction, with constant-section extruded aluminium spar, wraparound skin and a trailing-edge section. Blade section NACA 0015. Tracking tabs on blades at three-quarters radius. Electric cyclic trim. Two-blade teetering tail rotor, each blade comprising a steel tube spar with glassfibre skin. Limited blade folding. No rotor brake.

ROTOR DRIVE: Combination V-belt/pulley and reduction gear drive system. Main rotor and tail rotor gearbox have spiral bevel right-angle drive. Main rotor/engine rpm ratio 1 : 6·8. Tail rotor/engine rpm ratio 0·97 : 1.

FUSELAGE: Welded steel tube structure, with light alloy and Plexiglas cabin and one-piece light alloy tube tailboom.

TAIL UNIT: Horizontal and vertical fixed stabilising surfaces, made of light alloy ribs and skins.

LANDING GEAR: Skids carried on Hughes oleo-pneumatic shock-absorbers. Two cast magnesium ground handling wheels with 0·25 m (10 in) balloon tyres, pressure 4·14-5·17 bars (60-75 lb/sq in). Available optionally on floats made of polyurethane coated nylon fabric, 4·70 m (15 ft 5 in) long and with a total installed weight of 27·2 kg (60 lb).

POWER PLANT: One 142 kW (190 hp) Avco Lycoming HIO-360-D1A flat-four engine, mounted horizontally below seats. Aluminium fuel tank, capacity 103·5 litres (30 US gallons) mounted externally aft of cockpit. Crash-resistant fuel tank optional. Provision for aluminium auxiliary fuel tank, capacity 72 litres (19 US gallons), mounted opposite standard tank. Oil capacity 9·5 litres (2·5 US gallons).

ACCOMMODATION: Three persons seated side by side on sculptured and cushioned bench seat, in Plexiglas-enclosed cabin. Carpet and tinted canopy standard.

Door on each side. Dual controls optional. Baggage capacity 45 kg (100 lb). Exhaust muff, or gasoline, heating and ventilation kits available.

SYSTEMS: Standard electrical system includes 28V 70A alternator, battery, starter and external power receptacle; 28V 100A alternator optional.

AVIONICS AND EQUIPMENT: Optional avionics include Collins VHF-251 or Bertea ML360 com transceiver and headsets. Standard equipment includes mapcase, first aid kit, fire extinguisher, engine hour meter, and main rotor blade tiedown kit. Optional equipment includes amphibious floats, litter kits, cargo racks with combined capacity of 91 kg (200 lb), external load sling of 408 kg (900 lb) capacity, agricultural spray or dry powder dispersion kits, 72 litre (19 US gallon) auxiliary fuel tank, night flying kit, dual controls, all-weather cover, heavy-duty skid plates, single or dual exhaust mufflers, door lock, dual oil coolers, tinted glass for cabin windows, gasoline or exhaust manifold cabin heating.

DIMENSIONS, EXTERNAL:

Diameter of main rotor	8·18 m (26 ft 10 in)
Main rotor blade chord	0·171 m (6¾ in)
Diameter of tail rotor	1·30 m (4 ft 3 in)
Length overall, rotor blades fore and aft	
	9·40 m (30 ft 10 in)
Height over rotor hub	2·67 m (8 ft 9 in)
Width, rotor partially folded	2·44 m (8 ft 0 in)
Skid track	1·98 m (6 ft 6 in)
Passenger doors (each): Height	1·09 m (3 ft 7 in)
Width	0·97 m (3 ft 2 in)
Height to sill	0·91 m (3 ft 0 in)

AREAS:

Main rotor blades (each)	0·70 m² (7·55 sq ft)
Tail rotor blades (each)	0·08 m² (0·86 sq ft)
Main rotor disc	52·5 m² (565·5 sq ft)

Tail rotor disc	1·32 m² (14·2 sq ft)
Fin	0·26 m² (2·8 sq ft)
Horizontal stabiliser	0·32 m² (3·44 sq ft)

WEIGHTS AND LOADINGS (A: 300C; B: 300CQ):

Weight empty	476 kg (1,050 lb)
Max T-O weight: A	930 kg (2,050 lb)
B	921 kg (2,030 lb)
Max disc loading: A	17·67 kg/m² (3·62 lb/sq ft)
B	17·48 kg/m² (3·58 lb/sq ft)

PERFORMANCE (at max T-O weight, ISA. A: 300C; B: 300CQ normal operation; C: 300CQ quiet operation at AUW of 873 kg; 1,925 lb):

Never-exceed speed:
| A, B, C | 91 knots (169 km/h; 105 mph) |

Max cruising speed at S/L:
| A, B | 78 knots (145 km/h; 90 mph) |

Max level speed at S/L:
| C | 61 knots (113 km/h; 70 mph) |

Max cruising speed at 1,220 m (4,000 ft):
| A | 82 knots (153 km/h; 95 mph) |
| B | 78 knots (145 km/h; 90 mph) |

Max level speed at 1,220 m (4,000 ft):
| C | 62·5 knots (116 km/h; 72 mph) |

Speed for max range, at 1,220 m (4,000 ft):
| A, B | 67 knots (124 km/h; 77 mph) |

Max rate of climb at S/L: A | 229 m (750 ft)/min
| C | 113 m (370 ft)/min |

Service ceiling: A | 3,110 m (10,200 ft)
| B | 3,050 m (10,000 ft) |
| C | 2,440 m (8,000 ft) |

Hovering ceiling IGE: A | 1,830 m (6,000 ft)
| B | 1,220 m (4,000 ft) |

Hovering ceiling OGE: A | 823 m (2,700 ft)

Range at 1,220 m (4,000 ft), 2 min warm-up, max fuel, no reserves | 200 nm (370 km; 230 miles)

HUGHES MODEL 500, 500C and 500M

These are the commercial and foreign military counterparts of the OH-6A military helicopter last described in the 1977-78 *Jane's*. Full-scale production began in November 1968. The following versions have been announced:

Model 500. Basic commercial version, as described in detail.

Model 500C. As Model 500, except for installation of 298 kW (400 shp) engine for improved hot-day/altitude performance.

Model 500D and **500 MD Defender.** Commercial and foreign military versions respectively, with five-blade main rotor and Allison 250-C20B engine; described separately.

Model 500M. Uprated version of OH-6A, available to foreign military customers. First deliveries to Colombian Air Force in April 1968. Now in service also in Japan, Argentina, Denmark, Spain, Mexico and the Philippines. The Model 500Ms delivered to the Spanish Navy for ASW duties have an AN/ASQ-81 magnetic anomaly detector installed on the starboard side of the fuselage, and can carry two Mk 44 torpedoes beneath the fuselage. Control boxes for the MAD equipment are mounted on the instrument panel and centre pedestal, and special instrumentation includes a 6 in attitude indicator and radar altimeter.

Licence manufacture of the Model 500 Series is undertaken by RACA in Argentina, Kawasaki in Japan and BredaNardi in Italy (which see).

The following description applies to the basic commercial Model 500:

TYPE: Turbine-powered light helicopter.

ROTOR SYSTEM: Four-blade fully-articulated main rotor, with blades attached to laminated strap retention system by means of folding quick-disconnect pins. Each blade consists of an extruded aluminium spar hot-bonded to one-piece wraparound aluminium skin. Trim tab outboard on each blade. Main rotor blades can be folded. Two-blade tail rotor, each blade comprising a swaged steel tube spar and glassfibre skin covering. No rotor brake.

ROTOR DRIVE: Three sets of bevel gears, three drive-shafts and one overrunning clutch. Main rotor/engine rpm ratio 1 : 12·806. Tail rotor/engine rpm ratio 1 : 1·987.

FUSELAGE: Aluminium semi-monocoque structure of pod and boom type. Clamshell doors at rear of pod give access to engine and accessories.

TAIL UNIT: Fixed fin, horizontal stabiliser and ventral fin.

LANDING GEAR: Tubular skids carried on Hughes single-acting shock-absorbers.

POWER PLANT: The 236·5 kW (317 shp) Allison Model 250-C18A turbine engine (civil version of the T63-A-5A), installed in the 500 and 500M, is derated to 207 kW (278 shp) for T-O and has a max continuous rating of 181 kW (243 shp). The Model 500C is powered by a 298 kW (400 shp) Allison Model 250-C20 turboshaft engine; this also is derated to 207 kW (278 shp) for T-O and has a max continuous rating of 181 kW (243 shp). The Models 500 and 500C have a fuel capacity of 242 litres (64 US gallons); Model 500M has a capacity of 227 litres (60 US gallons). A crashworthy auxiliary tank of 132·5 litres (35 US gallons) is available optionally.

ACCOMMODATION (500/500C): Pilot and four passengers or equivalent freight. Optional accommodation for

seven with litter kit in use or with four in passenger compartment.

EQUIPMENT (500/500C): Optional equipment includes shatterproof glass, heating system, radios and intercom, attitude and directional gyros, rate of climb indicator, inertia reels and shoulder harnesses for pilot and co-pilot, fire extinguisher, dual controls, cargo hook, hoist, auxiliary fuel system, heated pitot tube, extended landing gear, blade storage rack, litter kit, emergency inflatable floats, inflated utility floats, rotor brake, seating for four in passenger compartment, and first aid kit. Standard equipment includes engine hour meter, navigation lights, clock and ground handling wheels.

DIMENSIONS, EXTERNAL:
Diameter of main rotor	8·03 m (26 ft 4 in)
Main rotor blade chord	0·171 m (6¾ in)
Diameter of tail rotor	1·30 m (4 ft 3 in)
Distance between rotor centres	4·58 m (15 ft 0¼ in)
Length overall, rotors fore and aft	9·24 m (30 ft 3¾ in)
Length of fuselage	7·01 m (23 ft 0 in)
Height to top of rotor hub	2·48 m (8 ft 1½ in)
Skid track	2·06 m (6 ft 9 in)
Cabin doors (fwd, each): Height	1·19 m (3 ft 11 in)
Width	0·89 m (2 ft 11 in)
Cargo compartment doors (each):	
Height	1·04 m (3 ft 5 in)
Width	0·88 m (2 ft 10½ in)
Height to sill	0·57 m (1 ft 10½ in)

DIMENSIONS, INTERNAL:
Cabin: Length	2·44 m (8 ft 0 in)
Max width	1·37 m (4 ft 6 in)
Max height	1·31 m (4 ft 3½ in)

AREAS:
Main rotor blades (each)	0·69 m² (7·41 sq ft)
Tail rotor blades (each)	0·079 m² (0·85 sq ft)
Main rotor disc	50·60 m² (544·63 sq ft)
Tail rotor disc	1·32 m² (14·19 sq ft)
Fin	0·52 m² (5·65 sq ft)
Horizontal stabiliser	0·72 m² (7·70 sq ft)

WEIGHTS:
Weight empty: 500	493 kg (1,088 lb)
500C	501 kg (1,105 lb)
500M	512 kg (1,130 lb)
Max normal T-O weight	1,157 kg (2,550 lb)
Max overload T-O weight	1,360 kg (3,000 lb)

PERFORMANCE (at max T-O weight):
Max level speed at 305 m (1,000 ft):
| 500, 500M | 132 knots (244 km/h; 152 mph) |
Max cruising speed at S/L:
| 500C | 125 knots (232 km/h; 144 mph) |
Max cruising speed at 1,220 m (4,000 ft):
| 500C | 126 knots (233 km/h; 145 mph) |
Cruising speed for max range at S/L:
| 500, 500M | 117 knots (217 km/h; 135 mph) |
| 500C | 124 knots (230 km/h; 143 mph) |
Max rate of climb at S/L:
| 500, 500C, 500M | 518 m (1,700 ft)/min |
Service ceiling: 500, 500M | 4,390 m (14,400 ft)
| 500C | 4,420 m (14,500 ft) |
Hovering ceiling IGE:
| 500, 500M | 2,500 m (8,200 ft) |
| 500C | 3,960 m (13,000 ft) |
Hovering ceiling OGE:
| 500, 500M | 1,615 m (5,300 ft) |
| 500C | 2,040 m (6,700 ft) |
Range at 1,220 m (4,000 ft):
| 500 | 327 nm (606 km; 377 miles) |
| 500M | 318 nm (589 km; 366 miles) |
Range at 1,220 m (4,000 ft), 2 min warm-up with max fuel, no reserves:
| 500C | 325 nm (603 km; 375 miles) |

Hughes Model 500D one/seven-seat commercial helicopter (*Brian M. Service*)

HUGHES MODEL 500D

Announced in February 1975, the Model 500D is similar in size and general appearance to the Hughes Model 500C. It differs in having a 313 kW (420 shp) Allison 250-C20B engine, plus the modifications applied to 'The Quiet One' OH-6A and which were developed and test-flown extensively on that aircraft. These include a five-blade main rotor, four-blade tail rotor, and engine exhaust muffler; sound blanketing of the complete power plant assembly, including the engine air intake; and reshaping of the tips of the main rotor blades. It introduced also a small T tail which gives greater flight stability in both high and low speed regimes, as well as better handling characteristics in abnormal manoeuvres. Construction of the prototype and its first flight took place in August 1974, and the first flight of a production aircraft was made on 9 October 1975.

Two versions are available:

Model 500D. Basic commercial version, of which description follows. Awarded FAA production certification on 8 December 1976, and deliveries began immediately. By February 1977 more than 250 had been ordered, and production was at the rate of 15 per month.

Model 500MD Defender. Multi-role military version of the Model 500D, available to military customers. Described separately.

TYPE: Turbine-powered light commercial helicopter.

ROTOR SYSTEM: Generally the same as for Model 500C, except five-blade main rotor and two-blade teetering tail rotor with light alloy blades. Rotor brake optional.

ROTOR DRIVE: Generally the same as for Model 500C, but entire drive train strengthened to give longer service life. Main rotor/engine rpm ratio 0·0794; tail rotor/engine rpm ratio 0·5111.

FUSELAGE: As for Model 500C.

TAIL UNIT: T tail, with horizontal stabiliser at tip of narrow-chord sweptback fin. Small auxiliary fin at tip of tailplane on each side. Narrow-chord sweptback ventral fin with integral tailskid to protect tail rotor in taildown attitude near ground.

LANDING GEAR: Tubular skids carried on Hughes oleo-pneumatic shock-absorbers. Utility floats, snow skis and emergency inflatable floats optional.

POWER PLANT: One 313 kW (420 shp) Allison 250-C20B turboshaft engine. Two interconnected bladder fuel tanks with combined usable capacity of 240 litres (63·4 US gallons). Self-sealing fuel tank optional. Refuelling point on starboard side of fuselage. Auxiliary fuel system with 132 litre (35 US gallon) crashworthy internal fuel tank, or two external glassfibre fuel cells with combined capacity of 167 litres (44 US gallons) optional. Oil capacity 5·7 litres (1·5 US gallons).

ACCOMMODATION: Forward bench seat for pilot and two passengers, with two or four passengers, or two litter patients and two medical attendants, in aft portion of cabin. Baggage space, capacity 0·31 m³ (11 cu ft), under and behind rear seat in five-seat form. Clear space for 1·19 m³ (42 cu ft) of cargo or baggage with only three front seats in place. Two doors on each side.

SYSTEM: Electrical system includes a 150A engine-driven generator and a nickel-cadmium battery.

AVIONICS AND EQUIPMENT: Optional avionics include dual King KY 195 com, KX 175 nav/com, KR 85 ADF, and KT 76 transponder; dual Collins VHF-251 com, VHF-251/351 nav/com, IND-350 nav indicator, ADF-650 ADF, and TDR-950 transponder; SunAir ASB 125; intercom system, headsets, microphones; public address system; stereo tape system; and flight management computer system. Standard equipment includes outside

The final production example of 12 Hughes 500MD/ASW aircraft for the Taiwanese Navy *(Howard Levy)*

Hughes 500MD Defender II, with Martin Marietta mast-mounted sight, underfuselage 30 mm chain gun, Stinger missile pod and other new features

air temperature gauge, 8-day clock, engine hour meter, five sets inertia-reel shoulder harness, cargo tiedown fittings, fire extinguisher, first aid kit, passenger steps, external power socket, landing light, skid-tip position light, anti-collision strobe lights, cockpit utility light, aft cabin light, and instrument lights. Optional equipment includes dual controls, blind-flying instrumentation, electric hoist, cargo hook, external baggage pods, cargo racks, underfuselage cargo pod, nylon mesh seats, dual-strap shoulder harnesses, and heating/demisting system.

DIMENSIONS, EXTERNAL: As for Model 500C, except:

Diameter of main rotor	8·08 m (26 ft 6 in)
Distance between rotor centres	4·62 m (15 ft 2 in)
Length overall, rotors fore and aft	9·30 m (30 ft 6 in)
Height to top of rotor hub	2·59 m (8 ft 6 in)
Cabin doors (each): Height	1·16 m (3 ft 9½ in)
Width	0·76 m (2 ft 6 in)
Height to sill	0·76 m (2 ft 6 in)

DIMENSIONS, INTERNAL:
As for Model 500C, except:

Max width	1·31 m (4 ft 3½ in)
Max height	1·52 m (5 ft 0 in)

AREAS:

Main rotor blades (each)	0·69 m² (7·43 sq ft)
Tail rotor blades (each)	0·09 m² (0·94 sq ft)
Main rotor disc	50·89 m² (547·81 sq ft)
Tail rotor disc	1·32 m² (14·19 sq ft)
Fin	0·56 m² (6·05 sq ft)
Tailplane	0·61 m² (6·52 sq ft)

WEIGHTS AND LOADINGS:

Weight empty	598 kg (1,320 lb)
Fuel load	181 kg (400 lb)
Max T-O and landing weight	1,360 kg (3,000 lb)
Max disc loading	26·76 kg/m² (5·48 lb/sq ft)
Max power loading	4·35 kg/kW (7·14 lb/shp)

PERFORMANCE (at max T-O weight, ISA):

Never-exceed speed	152 knots (282 km/h; 175 mph)
Max cruising speed at S/L	139 knots (258 km/h; 160 mph)
Max cruising speed at 1,525 m (5,000 ft)	135 knots (249 km/h; 155 mph)
Econ cruising speed at S/L	130 knots (241 km/h; 150 mph)
Econ cruising speed at 1,525 m (5,000 ft)	126 knots (233 km/h; 145 mph)
Max rate of climb at S/L	579 m (1,900 ft)/min
Service ceiling	4,570 m (15,000 ft)

Hovering ceiling IGE: ISA	2,590 m (8,500 ft)
ISA + 20°C	1,830 m (6,000 ft)
Hovering ceiling OGE: ISA	2,285 m (7,500 ft)
ISA + 20°C	1,370 m (4,500 ft)

Range, 2 min warm-up, standard fuel, no reserves:

at S/L	260 nm (482 km; 300 miles)
at 1,525 m (5,000 ft)	287 nm (531 km; 330 miles)

HUGHES MODEL 500MD DEFENDER

Structurally the military Defender is generally similar to the commercial Model 500M. It differs in having as standard or optional equipment self-sealing fuel cells, engine inlet particle separator, armour protection, Hughes 'Black Hole Ocarina' infra-red suppressor, and provisions for the carriage and deployment of a variety of weapons, including TOW missiles. Its diverse capabilities include training, command and control, scout, light attack, ASW, troop lift, and logistical support duties. It can carry up to seven people, including the pilot; or, in ambulance configuration, two stretcher patients with attendants in addition to a flight crew of two.

The versions now available or proposed are identified as follows:

500 MD Standard Scout. Basic military version, able to carry a variety of alternative weapons, including fourteen 2·75 in rockets and either a 7·62 mm Minigun with 2,000 rounds of ammunition, a 40 mm grenade launcher, a 7·62 mm chain gun with 2,000 rounds of ammunition, or a 30 mm chain gun with 600 rounds of ammunition.

500 MD/TOW. Anti-tank version armed with four TOW air-to-ground missiles. The TOW installation comprises four weapon pods, mounted two each side on a tubular mount carried through the lower aft fuselage, a stabilised telescopic sight mounted on the port side of the nose, sight control and arm rest for the gunner, and a steering indicator for the pilot.

500MD Quiet Advanced Scout. Basically similar to Standard Scout, but with added quietening kit and Martin Marietta mast-mounted sight. Quietening kit features a slower-turning four-blade tail rotor, which imposes no reduction of performance. The sight, mounted on a unique static mast 61 cm (2 ft) above the main rotor, includes a multiple field of view silicon vidicon TV lens, a laser rangefinder/designator and a high-accuracy stabilisation system, with future night vision capability. This enables the crew to hover behind cover, and use the small sight as a periscope to scan a large area out to a range of 3,000 m (9,840 ft). If employed to spot enemy armour, it is envisaged that Scouts would call in TOW Defenders to attack the targets.

500MD/ASW. Version for anti-submarine warfare and surface search missions, with two crew, search radar on nose, AN/ASQ-81 towed MAD, smoke marker launchers, hauldown gear, emergency 'popout' floats and armament of two Mk 44 or Mk 46 homing torpedoes. Max T-O weight 1,610 kg (3,550 lb). Can remain on station for 1 h 48 min when operated at a typical ASW mission radius of 22-87 nm (40-160 km; 25-100 miles) from ship or shore base. Using its radar, 500MD/ASW could locate enemy destroyers and gunboats up to 150 nm (275 km; 172 miles) from its base-ship during a two-hour patrol.

500 MD Defender II. Multi-mission version, introduced in Summer of 1980; available for delivery within two years. Five-blade main rotor standard; four-blade 'quiet' tail rotor optional. Other options include Martin Marietta mast-mounted sight (MMS), Hughes 30 mm chain gun (with firing rate reduced to 350 rds/min), Hughes 'Black Hole' infra-red suppression system, pod containing two Stinger air-to-air missiles, pilot's night vision sensor, radar warning system, and an advanced avionics/mission equipment package.

Standard lightweight avionics equipment (SLAE) as developed for the OH-6A has been adapted for the 500MD with minimal changes. This equipment comprises AN/ARC-164 UHF/AM, AN/ARC-115 UHF/AM, AN/ARC-114 VHF/FM, ARN-89 ADF, APX-72 IFF transponder, AN/ASN-43 directional gyro, ID-1351 heading and bearing indicator, and C-6533/ARC intercom.

The Model 500MD is the subject of a building programme in the Republic of Korea (which see). By early 1980 a total of more than 75 Korean-assembled Scouts and 25 TOW-equipped Defenders had been delivered, with the local content progressing from assembly to full manufacture. Production was then continuing, with the likelihood of a further order for 150 to follow. Israel has ordered 30 of the TOW version, and Kenya is to receive 32 Defenders, of which 15 will be equipped to fire TOW missiles. Deliveries to the Taiwanese Navy of 12 Defenders, equipped with search radar and torpedoes, began in May 1979.

HUGHES MODEL 77
US Army designation: AH-64

The Model 77 was designed by Hughes to meet the US Army's requirement for an Advanced Attack Helicopter (AAH) capable of undertaking a full day/night/adverse weather anti-armour mission, and of fighting, surviving and 'living with' troops in a front-line environment. Two flight test prototypes were built, for competitive evaluation against Bell's YAH-63, and these made their initial flights on 30 September and 22 November 1975. A ground test vehicle was also completed. The Hughes contract covered, in addition, development of the XM-230 chain gun for installation in the Model 77 prototypes, which have the US Army designation YAH-64.

Selection of the YAH-64 was announced on 10 December 1976. This was followed by Phase 2 of the programme, which involved fitting the prototypes with advanced avionics, electro-optical equipment and weapon fire control systems, for further evaluation; continued development of the airframe; and the manufacture of three more aircraft.

These are identified as AVO.1 to AVO.3. In June 1979 the first was being used by the US Army for continuing evaluation. AVO.3 was transferred to the Army's Yuma Proving Ground, Arizona, on 4 June, equipped with the Northrop TADS/PNVS. AVO.2, with the Martin Marietta TADS/PNVS, followed at the end of the same month. Company R & D with these two aircraft was

Hughes 500MD Defender with TOW missile launchers *(Pilot Press)*

expected to continue until the end of the year, with Army testing to follow in 1980 and to be completed in August 1981.

Three additional development aircraft, designated AVO.4 to AVO.6, were flying by the Spring of 1980, described as total systems aircraft.

Teledyne Ryan is responsible for the YAH-64 fuselage, wings, engine nacelles, avionics bays, canopy and tail unit. Martin Marietta and Northrop are developing competitive equipment to fulfil the TADS (Target Acquisition and Designation Sight) and PNVS (Pilot's Night Vision Sensor) tasks in the production AH-64. The former system includes direct-view optics, forward-looking infra-red, TV, laser designator/rangefinder, and a laser tracker. The PNVS consists of an advanced FLIR installation.

In early 1978 the two Phase 2 helicopters began a new series of tests to evaluate planned design modifications known as Mod 1. These included swept tips on the main rotor blades; a Hughes-developed 'Black Hole' IR suppressor for each engine exhaust; a redesigned T tail; and a 76 mm (3 in) increase in tail rotor diameter. A Mod 2 programme, started later in that year, introduced final airframe improvements, as well as all mission equipment including armament, fire control and nav/com systems. These included cockpit windows of modified shape, with single-curvature side panels; and extending aft, to a point below the wing leading-edges, the fuselage side fairings over the forward avionics bay. The two prototype helicopters then completed a programme to confirm the airworthiness of the Mod 2 airframe changes and initial tests of the weapon system, including the Hellfire missile, 2·75 in rocket, 30 mm chain gun, and the fire control system. By mid-June 1979 five ballistic Hellfire missiles had been fired, without guidance system. The first fully-guided launch of a Hellfire was made successfully on 18 September 1979 at the Yuma, Arizona, proving grounds. Target for the laser-guided system was designated from the ground, and a direct hit was made. Northrop TADS/PNVS was installed and functional in the launch YAH-64, but was not used. Approximately one month later the first test firing was made with the Northrop TADS/PNVS providing illumination of the target. Other systems which were fully integrated and flight tested during 1979 included the Litton LR-80 HARS, and the Singer-Kearfott Doppler navigation system.

The 56-month AAH development contract period is due to end in August 1981, and a production decision is expected to be announced in December 1981. This means that initial delivery of production aircraft is unlikely before December 1983, with entry into service in 1984. The US Army's current stated requirement is for 536 AAHs.

The following description applies to the YAH-64 prototypes, except where indicated:

TYPE: Prototype armed helicopter.

ROTOR SYSTEM: Four-blade fully-articulated main rotor and four-blade tail rotor, with blades manufactured by Tool Research and Engineering Corpn (Advanced Structures Division). Main rotor blades are of high-camber aerofoil section and broad chord. Each blade has five stainless steel spars lined with structural glassfibre tubes, a laminated stainless steel skin and a composite aft section, bonded together. Blades are attached to hub by a laminated strap retention system similar to that of the OH-6A, and are fitted with elastomeric lead/lag dampers and offset flapping hinges. Four-blade tail rotor comprises two sets of two blades, mounted on port side of pylon/fin support structure at optimum quiet setting of approx 60°/120° to each other. Rotor mast similar to that of OH-6A, with driveshaft turning within a hollow, fixed outer shaft. Entire system capable of flight in negative g conditions.

ROTOR DRIVE: Transmission to main rotor via Litton (Precision Gear Division) engine nose gearboxes, and to tail rotor via Aircraft Gear Corpn grease-lubricated intermediate and tail rotor gearboxes, with Bendix driveshafts and couplings. Garrett-AiResearch cooling fan for tail rotor gearbox. Redundant flight control system for both rotors. Selected dynamic components constructed of 70/49 aluminium and electro-slag remelt (ESR) steel; critical parts of transmission (eg, bearings) have ESR collars for protection against hits by 12·7 mm or 23 mm ammunition. Rotor/engine rpm ratios approx 66·7 for main rotor, approx 14·3 for tail rotor.

WINGS: Cantilever mid-wing monoplane, of low aspect ratio, aft of cockpit. Trailing-edge flaps deploy automatically as function of control attitude and airspeed (max deflection 20°), and can be deflected 45° upward to offload wings in an emergency autorotative landing. Wings are removable, and attach to sides of cabin for transport and storage. Two hardpoints beneath each wing for the carriage of mixed ordnance.

FUSELAGE: Conventional semi-monocoque aluminium structure, built by Teledyne Ryan Aeronautical. Designed to survive hits by 12·7 mm and 23 mm ammunition.

TAIL UNIT: Hinged and foldable pylon structure with tail rotor mounted on port side. Low-mounted all-flying tailplane (replacing earlier fixed T tail).

LANDING GEAR: Menasco tailwheel type, with single wheel on each unit. Main legs fold rearward to reduce overall

Hughes YAH-64 armed helicopter prototype equipped with Northrop TADS/PNVS

Hughes AH-64 tandem two-seat advanced attack helicopter *(Pilot Press)*

height for storage and transportation. Fully-castoring, self-centering tailwheel. Main-wheel tyres size 22 × 8; tailwheel tyre size 13 × 5. Hydraulic brakes.

POWER PLANT: Two 1,145 kW (1,536 shp) General Electric T700-GE-700 turboshaft engines, derated for normal operations to provide reserve power for combat emergencies. Engines mounted one on each side of fuselage, above wings. Two crashproof fuel cells, combined capacity 1,366 litres (361 US gallons).

ACCOMMODATION: Crew of two in tandem, co-pilot/gunner in front and pilot aft on 483 mm (19 in) elevated seat. Large, shaped transparent cockpit enclosure for optimum field of view. Lightweight boron armour shields in cockpit floor and sides. Cockpits separated by armour plating and a transparent plastics blast shield offering protection against 23 mm high-explosive and armour-piercing rounds.

SYSTEMS AND EQUIPMENT: Large avionics bay adjacent to gunner's position, in lower fuselage. Parker-Bertea hydraulic control system, with hydraulic actuators ballistic tolerant to direct 12·7 mm hits. In the event of hydraulic control system failure, the system adjusts to secondary fly-by-wire control. Bendix electrical power system, with two fully-redundant engine-driven generators and standby DC battery. Sperry Flight Systems automatic stabilisation equipment. Litton LR-80 strapdown heading and attitude reference system (HARS). Singer-Kearfott lightweight Doppler navigation system. Garrett-AiResearch totally integrated pneumatic system includes a shaft-driven compressor, air turbine starters, pneumatic valves, temperature control unit and environmental control unit. Garrett-AiResearch also supplies the GTP 36-55(C) APU. Sperry Flight Systems all-raster symbol generator is under development to process TV data from IR and other sensors, superimpose symbology and distribute the combination to CRT and helmet-mounted displays in the aircraft. BITE fault detection/location system. Hughes Black Hole IR suppression system, with no moving parts, to protect the aircraft from heat-seeking missiles. This eliminates an engine bay cooling fan, by operating from engine exhaust gas through ejector nozzles to lower the gas plume and metal temperatures.

ARMAMENT AND OPERATIONAL EQUIPMENT: Flexible armament consists of a Hughes-developed XM230E1 30 mm chain gun, mounted in an underfuselage turret

between the main-wheel legs, and having a normal rate of fire of 800 rds/min of Honeywell TP, HE and HEDP ammunition. Ammunition max load is 1,200 rds, and is interoperable with NATO Aden/DEFA rounds. Turret designed to collapse into fuselage between pilots in the event of a crash-landing. Four underwing hardpoints, on which can be carried up to sixteen Hellfire anti-tank missiles; or up to seventy-six 2·75 in folding-fin rockets in their launchers; or a combination of Hellfire missiles and rockets. CPG stabilised sight in forward fuselage, ahead of cockpit, incorporates day and night (FLIR: forward-looking infra-red) sighting equipment, laser ranger and target designator, and laser tracker equipment. Co-pilot/gunner has primary responsibility for firing guns and missiles, but pilot can override his controls to fire gun or launch missiles. Pilot's night vision sensor (PNVS) in extreme tip of nose. Integrated Helmet And Display Sighting System (IHADSS) by Honeywell Avionics Division, used by both crew members, will enhance speed and flexibility of target acquisition. Forward bay includes avionics for stabilised sight, missiles and fire control computer provided by Teledyne Systems Inc.

DIMENSIONS, EXTERNAL:

Diameter of main rotor	14·63 m (48 ft 0 in)
Diameter of tail rotor	2·54 m (8 ft 4 in)
Main rotor blade chord	0·53 m (1 ft 9 in)
Length of fuselage	15·06 m (49 ft 5 in)
Length overall, rotors turning	17·60 m (57 ft 9 in)
Wing span	4·98 m (16 ft 4 in)
Height to top of rotor hub	3·83 m (12 ft 6⅞ in)
Tailplane span	3·15 m (10 ft 4 in)
Wheel track	2·03 m (6 ft 8 in)

AREA:

Main rotor disc	168·06 m² (1,809 sq ft)

WEIGHTS:

Weight empty	4,657 kg (10,268 lb)
Primary mission gross weight	6,271 kg (13,825 lb)
Structural design gross weight	6,650 kg (14,660 lb)
Max T-O weight	8,006 kg (17,650 lb)

PERFORMANCE (at 6,316 kg; 13,925 lb AUW, ISA except where indicated):

Never-exceed speed	204 knots (378 km/h; 235 mph)
Max level speed	167 knots (309 km/h; 192 mph)
Max cruising speed	158 knots (293 km/h; 182 mph)
Max vertical rate of climb at S/L	
	878 m (2,880 ft)/min

Max vertical rate of climb at 1,220 m (4,000 ft) at 35°C	259 m (850 ft)/min
Service ceiling	6,250 m (20,500 ft)
Service ceiling, one engine out	3,505 m (11,500 ft)
Hovering ceiling IGE	4,633 m (15,200 ft)

Hovering ceiling OGE	3,780 m (12,400 ft)
Max range, internal fuel 330 nm (611 km; 380 miles)	
Ferry range, max internal and external fuel, still air	974 nm (1,804 km; 1,121 miles)
Endurance at 1,220 m (4,000 ft) at 35°C	1 h 50 min
Max endurance, internal fuel	3 h 23 min

ICX

ICX AVIATION INC

1101 Connecticut Avenue NW, Washington, DC 20036
Telephone: (202) 857 1162
Telex: 82-4446 ICX Group Wsh
PRESIDENT AND CHAIRMAN: Dale P. Lewis
VICE-PRESIDENTS:
Mary M. Anderson (Government Relations)
Charles P. Collins (Administration)
Len Cormier (Engineering)
Pina Schneider (Technology Transfer)
Richard B. Stockton (Finance)
Paul H. Zorger (Product Assurance/Safety)

This company announced in December 1979 the conclusion of an agreement with Aviaexport of the USSR for exclusive world rights to manufacture and market an ICX derivative of the Yakovlev Yak-40 three-turbofan light transport aircraft. ICX has negotiated for a production facility at Wheatfield, New York, and has allocated the name X-Avia and designation LC-3 to the new aircraft. Production of the Yak-40 in the USSR was scheduled to end in early 1980.

ICX AVIATION X-AVIA LC-3

ICX Aviation began adapting the design of the Yak-40 for production in the USA in December 1975. Modification of a Soviet-built Yak-40, to be used as a demonstrator aircraft, was scheduled to begin in mid-1980, with the first flight of a pre-production prototype planned for 1981. It is intended to develop three versions:

LC-3A. Basic version to accommodate a crew of three and 30 passengers.

LC-3B. Version with high-density seating to accommodate a maximum of 40 passengers.

LC-3C An all-cargo version, able to carry a load of up to 4,536 kg (10,000 lb).

TYPE: Three-turbofan short-range transport.

WINGS: Cantilever low-wing monoplane. Dihedral 5° 30'. Incidence 3°. No sweepback. Light alloy structure with main spar, fore and aft auxiliary spars, ribs and stringers, covered with skin of varying thickness for which chemical milling is utilised. Wing made in two sections, joined at aircraft centreline. Manually-operated ailerons, each in two sections. Trim in port aileron. Hydraulically-actuated Fowler-type trailing-edge flaps, in three sections on each wing. De-icing of wing leading-edges by engine bleed air.

FUSELAGE: Semi-monocoque fail-safe light alloy structure of frames, longerons, stringers and skins.

TAIL UNIT: Conventional cantilever T-tail of light alloy. Variable-incidence tailplane. Trim tab in rudder. Anti-icing system being redesigned for US manufacture.

LANDING GEAR: Hydraulically-retractable tricycle type with single wheel on each unit. Main units retract inward, nose unit forward. Hydraulically-steerable nosewheel. Main-wheel tyres size 1,120 × 450 mm; nosewheel tyre size 720 × 310 mm. Brakes and anti-skid units being redesigned for US manufacture. Preliminary design study being made for optional amphibious floatplane version.

POWER PLANT: Three Garrett-AiResearch TFE 731-3 turbofan engines, each rated at 16·5 kN (3,700 lb st). Centre engine has S-duct air intake and thrust reversal. Outboard engines are mounted in pod on each side of rear fuselage. Fuel in integral wing tanks with combined capacity of 4,000 kg (8,818 lb). Single-point pressure refuelling and overwing gravity refuelling points.

ACCOMMODATION: Pilot and co-pilot side by side on flight deck. Cabin will accommodate 30 or 40 passengers and a cabin attendant in alternative layouts. Cargo version proposed with 2·18 m wide × 1·66 m high (7 ft 1¾ in × 5 ft 5¼ in) cargo door. Main door with airstairs in underfuselage, beneath centre engine air intake. Service door/emergency exit at forward end of cabin on port side. Two emergency exits overwing; one above flight deck. Baggage compartments at forward end of cabin on starboard side, and aft end of cabin on port side. Galley and toilet at aft end of cabin on starboard side. Accommodation is pressurised, air-conditioned, heated and ventilated.

SYSTEMS: Garrett-AiResearch pressurisation system, air-conditioning and APU. Hydraulic, pneumatic, electrical, oxygen and de-icing systems being redesigned for US manufacture.

AVIONICS AND EQUIPMENT: Collins communications transceiver and navigation receiver. Blind-flying instrumentation standard. Sperry Flight Systems flight director and SPZ-600 autopilot.

ICX Aviation X-Avia LC-3, a re-engined version of the Soviet Yak-40 light transport (*Pilot Press*)

DIMENSIONS, EXTERNAL:

Wing span	25·00 m (82 ft 0¼ in)
Wing chord at root	3·80 m (12 ft 5½ in)
Wing chord at tip	1·55 m (5 ft 1 in)
Wing aspect ratio	8·9
Length overall	20·36 m (66 ft 9½ in)
Diameter of fuselage	2·40 m (7 ft 10½ in)
Height overall	6·50 m (21 ft 4 in)
Tailplane span	7·50 m (24 ft 7¼ in)
Wheel track	4·52 m (14 ft 10 in)
Wheelbase	7·47 m (24 ft 6 in)
Service door (fwd, port):	
Height	1·20 m (3 ft 11¼ in)
Width	0·55 m (1 ft 9½ in)

DIMENSIONS, INTERNAL (LC-3A version):

Cabin, excl flight deck, incl toilet, baggage storage and galley: Length	10·11 m (33 ft 2 in)
Max width	2·24 m (7 ft 4¼ in)
Max height	1·85 m (6 ft 0¾ in)
Floor area	17·4 m² (187·3 sq ft)
Volume	33·88 m³ (1,196 cu ft)

AREAS:

Wings, gross	70·00 m² (753·50 sq ft)
Ailerons (total)	3·70 m² (39·83 sq ft)
Trailing-edge flaps (total)	16·50 m² (177·61 sq ft)
Fin	10·48 m² (112·81 sq ft)
Rudder (incl tab)	2·64 m² (28·42 sq ft)
Tailplane	13·03 m² (140·26 sq ft)
Elevators	4·91 m² (52·85 sq ft)

WEIGHTS AND LOADINGS (estimated):

Max T-O weight	17,463 kg (38,500 lb)
Max ramp weight	17,531 kg (38,650 lb)
Max zero-fuel weight	13,460 kg (29,674 lb)
Max landing weight	15,000 kg (33,069 lb)
Max wing loading	249·4 kg/m² (51·09 lb/sq ft)
Max power loading	352·8 kg/kN (3·47 lb/lb st)

PERFORMANCE (estimated, at max T-O weight):

Never-exceed speed	Mach 0·6
Max level speed at 9,145 m (30,000 ft)	354 knots (657 km/h; 408 mph)
Max cruising speed at 10,970 m (36,000 ft)	315 knots (584 km/h; 363 mph)
Econ cruising speed at 10,970 m (36,000 ft)	300 knots (555 km/h; 345 mph)
Stalling speed, flaps up, power off	98 knots (182 km/h; 113 mph)
Stalling speed, flaps down, power off	84 knots (156 km/h; 97 mph)
Max rate of climb at S/L	914 m (3,000 ft)/min
Max rate of climb at S/L, one engine out	427 m (1,400 ft)/min
Service ceiling	12,190 m (40,000 ft)
Service ceiling, one engine out	7,620 m (25,000 ft)
Range with 3,400 kg (7,500 lb) cargo payload	868 nm (1,609 km; 1,000 miles)
Range with 4,536 kg (10,000 lb) cargo payload	521 nm (965 km; 600 miles)

ISHAM

ISHAM AIRCRAFT

PO Box 12172, Mid Continent Airport, Wichita, Kansas 67277
Telephone: (316) 755 0713
PRESIDENT: Brad E. Isham

ISHAM (PIPER) PA-28 CHEROKEE and (CESSNA) R172K SKYHAWK CONVERSIONS

Isham AirCraft is marketing, with FAA approval, modification kits for various models of the Piper Cherokee which are designed to improve the aircraft's performance and handling during approach and landing. They are also claimed to make slight improvements in take-off distance, rate of climb and cruising speeds.

Kits are available for the Piper PA-28-140, -150, -160 and -180, to provide light alloy wing and tailplane extensions, Hoerner-type wingtips, dorsal fins of ABS plastics,

Piper PA-28R-180 Cherokee with Isham AirCraft wing and fin modifications

and a third window on each side. The third-window kit is available also for the Piper PA-28-235. A kit to provide the retractable-gear Piper PA-28R-180 and -200 with wing extensions, Hoerner wingtips and dorsal fin can be

obtained from Isham AirCraft, as well as a kit to re-rate the Continental IO-360-K power plant of the Cessna R172K from 145 kW (195 hp) to 157 kW (210 hp) at take-off.

Performance and specification details of aircraft to which these kits have been applied are given in the accompanying table.

Dimensions/Performance	PA-28-140 PA-28-150	PA-28-180	PA-28R-180 PA-28R-200	R172K	Units
Wing span	9·81 (32·2)	9·81 (32·2)	9·81 (32·2)	N/C	m (ft)
Tailplane span	3·91 (12·83)	3·91 (12·83)	N/C	N/C	m (ft)
Wing area	15·7 (169)	15·7 (169)	15·7 (169)	N/C	m² (sq ft)
Max wing loading	62·1 (12·72)	69·3 (14·2)	72·2 (14·79)	N/A	kg/m² (lb/sq ft)
Max level speed	124 (230; 143)	135 (249; 155)	150 (278; 173)	N/A	knots (km/h; mph)
Max cruising speed (75% power)	119 (220; 137)	127 (235; 146)	143 (266; 165)	N/A	knots (km/h; mph)
Stalling speed	N/C	N/C	N/C	N/A	knots (km/h; mph)
Max rate of climb at S/L	247 (810)	274 (900)	302 (990)	351 (1,150)	m (ft)/min
T-O to 15 m (50 ft)	472 (1,547)	450 (1,477)	477 (1,565)	302 (990)	m (ft)
Landing from 15 m (50 ft)	N/C	N/C	N/C	N/A	m (ft)
Range, max fuel	687 (1,273; 791)	643 (1,191; 740)	757 (1,403; 872)	N/A	nm (km; miles)
Reduction in sink rate	27	26·4	27	N/A	%

Figures quoted are for S/L ISA at max T-O weight.
N/A: not available. N/C: no change.

JETCRAFTERS
JETCRAFTERS INCORPORATED

PO Box 32622, San Antonio, Texas 78216
Telephone: (512) 657 2700
PRESIDENT: E. J. Swearingen
VICE-PRESIDENTS:
  E. A. Banks
  G. M. Loudermilk
Well-known as the designer of the Merlin and Metro twin-turboprop executive transports, 'Ed' J. Swearingen established Jetcrafters Inc to initiate a modification programme to enhance the performance and operating economy of the Beechcraft King Air 90 models.

The company's facility at San Antonio is also manufacturing engine nacelles for AiResearch Aviation Company's 731 JetStar conversions, and sheet metal assemblies for Learjet and Falcon Jet aircraft.

JETCRAFTERS TAURUS MODIFICATION

Any model of the Beechcraft King Air 90 series is suitable for incorporation of the Jetcrafters Taurus modification. This involves replacing the existing engines with Pratt & Whitney Aircraft of Canada PT6A-135 turboprop engines, each flat rated at 522 kW (700 shp); modification of the existing engine nacelles to reduce their height and cross-sectional area; provision of new cowls, engine air inlets, inertial water/ice separators, a new low-profile exhaust system to reduce drag and increase thrust, new oil cooler airflow control system, and a new integral nacelle fuel tank with full lightning strike protection; removal of the existing engine-driven cabin supercharger and provision of a new flow control system to provide dual

Jetcrafters Taurus modification of a Beechcraft Model 90 King Air

bleed air pressurisation; and the supply of new engine torque indicators.

After embodiment of the Taurus modification, the King Air 90, A90, B90, C90 and E90 are redesignated respectively Taurus 90, A90, B90, C90 and E90.

Brief details of performance improvements follow:
PERFORMANCE (A: Taurus 90; B: A90; C: B90; D: C90; and E: E90):
Max cruising speed at optimum altitude:
  A, B, C, D, E   278 knots (515 km/h; 320 mph)
Stalling speed, flaps down:
  A, B, C, D, E   69 knots (127 km/h; 79 mph)

Max rate of climb at S/L: A	913 m (2,995 ft)/min
B	884 m (2,900 ft)/min
C, D	852 m (2,795 ft)/min
E	814 m (2,670 ft)/min
Service ceiling: A, B, C, D, E	11,430 m (37,500 ft)
T-O to 15 m (50 ft): A, B	625 m (2,050 ft)
C	533 m (1,750 ft)
D	689 m (2,261 ft)
E	617 m (2,024 ft)
Landing from 15 m (50 ft): A, B	716 m (2,350 ft)
C, D	613 m (2,010 ft)
E	643 m (2,110 ft)

KAMAN
KAMAN AEROSPACE CORPORATION
(a subsidiary of Kaman Corporation)

HEAD OFFICE: Old Windsor Road, Bloomfield, Connecticut 06002
Telephone: (203) 242 4461
PRESIDENT AND CHIEF EXECUTIVE: Fred L. Smith
VICE-PRESIDENTS:
  Wayne D. Hudson (Manufacturing)
  Eamon N. Kelly (Contracts)
  Walter R. Kozlow (Operations)
  Cornelia V. Lynn (Personnel)
  Donald W. Robinson (Marketing and Planning)
  Llewellyn C. Schuler (Engineering)
SECRETARY: J. S. Murtha
MANAGER, WASHINGTON OPERATIONS: Owen F. Polleys
The original Kaman Aircraft Corporation was founded in 1945 by Mr Charles H. Kaman, who continues as President and Chairman of the Board of Kaman Corporation. Its initial programme was to develop and test a novel servo-flap control system for helicopter rotors, and the Kaman K-125 of 1947 was the first in a series of 'synchropter' designs with intermeshing contra-rotating rotors and the servo-flap control system. The later H-2 Seasprite naval helicopter utilises the servo-flap control system on a conventional single main rotor.

Kaman Aerospace operates two plants in Connecticut, located at Bloomfield and Moosup. Its capabilities include major production work in the fields of airframe structures, sheet metal, glassfibre, composites, and reinforced honeycomb bonding. It is also a leading company in the field of helicopter dynamics, research and development, and in the application of new materials and technology.

Kaman Circulation Control Rotor (CCR) on NHH-2D flight test helicopter

Kamatics Corporation, a subsidiary of Kaman Aerospace Corporation, produces bearings and couplings for a variety of aerospace applications.

In research and development, Kaman Aerospace is working on several advanced concepts. One of the most promising programmes is the development of a Circulation Control Rotor (CCR) technology demonstrator aircraft for the Naval Air Systems Command. In this concept

a thin jet of air is ejected from a slot near the trailing-edge of each rotor blade, inducing a circulation which results in lift augmentation. Since conventional cyclic pitch is eliminated, the rotor hub and controls are simplified considerably. Full-scale whirl tests and wind tunnel tests were completed successfully in early 1978, and flight tests on a Kaman NHH-2D helicopter began in September 1979.

Several other R & D programmes are under sponsorship of the US Army Research and Technology Laboratories, Applied Technology Laboratory, Fort Eustis, Virginia. They include a controllable twist rotor (CTR); dynamic anti-resonant vibration isolator; composite rotor hub; repairable/expendable main rotor blade concept; new concepts in structural dynamic testing; maintainability of major helicopter components; elastic pitch beam tail rotor; and new design, fabrication and inspection techniques for helicopter structures. Kaman modified the CTR hardware to incorporate a multicyclic flap system at the request of NASA's Ames Research Center, Moffett Field, California, and testing in the 12 × 24 m (40 × 80 ft) wind tunnel has been completed. Flight testing of the CTR on NASA's Sikorsky-built Rotor Systems Research Aircraft (RSRA) is scheduled for 1983.

For the Office of Naval Research, Kaman is developing and testing the Ship Tethered Aerial Platform (STAPL), a ship-towed drone autogyro (see RPVs and Targets section). Low-altitude flight testing was completed during 1979.

In addition to its R & D programmes related directly to aerospace technology, Kaman is involved in new wind energy programmes. Among these are a composite rotor blade for a 91·44 m (300 ft) diameter wind turbine; development of a smaller wind turbine rated at 40 kW; and a set of composite blades for NASA's 60·96 m (200 ft) diameter MOD-1 wind turbine.

Kaman Aerospace is engaged in several major airframe programmes as a subcontractor, including the construction of flaps, slats, spoilers and cove doors for the US Navy's F-14 Tomcat fighter; engine access, tailpipe, and landing gear doors for the US Navy's A-6E and EA-6B attack aircraft; various detail parts and tools on the US Air Force's A-10A Thunderbolt II close support aircraft; components of the external fuel tank and solid rocket boosters of NASA's Space Shuttle programme; acoustic structural components for jet engines; and structural components for various business and commercial aircraft, including the Boeing Model 767.

Kaman Aerospace is also the supplier of bonded components for the C-130, B-52 and UH-1 aircraft for Army and Air Force government agencies. Kaman designed and since mid-1977 has been producing a new all-composite rotor blade for the Bell AH-1 HueyCobra in service with the US Army, funded by the Army. The first AH-1 fitted with the new blades made its first flight on 26 July 1976. Improved performance, life and operational features have been demonstrated.

Kaman Sciences Corporation, with headquarters at Colorado Springs, Colorado, is engaged in nuclear research, weapons studies, advanced aerodynamics, computer programming and time sharing, neutron generators, advanced materials, measuring devices, systems analysis and solar energy. Kaman's general aviation subsidiaries comprise AirKaman Inc, a fixed-base operator at Bradley International Airport, Windsor Locks, Connecticut; Air Kaman of Omaha, Nebraska, and AirKaman of Jacksonville, Florida, all of which provide sales and service of light and twin-engined business aircraft, repairs, fuel sales, charter service, flight training and airline services.

At the beginning of 1980 total corporate employment was 3,730, of whom 1,150 were engaged in aerospace activities.

KAMAN SEASPRITE
US Navy designations: UH-2 (formerly HU2K-1), HH-2 and SH-2

The prototype Seasprite flew for the first time on 2 July 1959, and many versions (described in previous editions of Jane's) were produced subsequently for the US Navy.

From 1967, all of the original UH-2A/B Seasprites were converted progressively to UH-2C twin-engined configuration, with two 932 kW (1,250 shp) General Electric T58-GE-8B turboshaft engines in place of the former single T58. They have since undergone further modification, under the US Navy's important Mk 1 LAMPS (Light Airborne Multi-Purpose System) programme, to provide helicopters for ASW (anti-submarine warfare) and ASST (anti-ship surveillance and targeting) operations.

The following versions remained available in early 1980:

HH-2D. Two aircraft, without LAMPS modifications, assigned to coast and geodetic survey work.

NHH-2D. Test aircraft assigned to the circulation control rotor (CCR) programme.

SH-2D. LAMPS version, for ASW, ASST and a utility role. The first of 20 SH-2Ds, modified from HH-2D unarmed search and rescue helicopters, made its first flight on 16 March 1971; details of the modifications can be found in the 1979-80 and earlier editions of Jane's.

As the LAMPS helicopters became operational, the Navy organised squadrons to provide detachments to fleet units and to train additional personnel to operate and maintain them.

SH-2F. Deliveries of this further-developed Mk I LAMPS version began in May 1973 and the first unit became operational with squadron HSL-33, deployed to the Pacific, on 11 September 1973. A total of 88 SH-2Fs has been delivered. The earlier SH-2Ds and HH-2Ds are being uprated to SH-2F configuration, this programme being scheduled for completion in March 1982.

Kaman SH-2F LAMPS Mk 1 ASW helicopter, showing sensors and stores

Kaman SH-2F Seasprite Light Airborne Multi-Purpose System (LAMPS) Mk 1 helicopter (Pilot Press)

Other features of the SH-2F include increased-strength landing gear; a shortened wheelbase by relocation of the tailwheel; and T58-GE-8F engines. In early 1980 improvements were being made to the LN-66HP radar, tactical navigation system, ESM, sonobuoys and data link. In January-February 1973 Kaman flight-tested the prototype for flight qualification to a maximum gross weight of 6,033 kg (13,300 lb), which is 227 kg (500 lb) more than the current SH-2F. This could be utilised as increased payload, or in the form of additional fuel in larger auxiliary tanks to provide extended range and endurance in a new production version of the SH-2. US Navy tests have proved the SH-2 suitable for dipping sonar operations, air-to-surface missile firing, and equipment with various guns and rockets.

There are currently eight HSL LAMPS squadrons. Operational deployment began on 7 December 1971. By January 1980, 160 LAMPS SH-2D/F detachments had been deployed (not simultaneously) on long cruises, primarily in the Mediterranean and Pacific, on the following ship classes: FFG-7, DD-963, FFG-1, FF-1052, FF-1040, CGN-11, CG-25 and CG-26. The new DD-963 and FFG-7 classes are designed to operate with two LAMPS helicopters per ship.

The following details apply to the SH-2F version of the Seasprite:

TYPE: Naval anti-submarine warfare and anti-ship missile defence helicopter, with secondary capability for search and rescue, observation and utility missions.

ROTOR SYSTEM: Four-blade main and tail rotors. Kaman '101' main rotor utilises titanium hub and retention assemblies, reducing the number of control elements by two-thirds, and offering increased life for the entire rotor system. Blades of aluminium and glassfibre construction, with servo-flap controls. Blades folded manually. Main rotor rpm 287.

FUSELAGE AND TAIL UNIT: All-metal semi-monocoque structure, with flotation hull housing main fuel tanks. Nose split on centreline, to fold rearward on each side to reduce stowage space required. Fixed horizontal stabiliser on tail rotor pylon.

LANDING GEAR: Tailwheel type, with forward-retracting twin main wheels and non-retractable tailwheel. Liquid spring shock-absorbers in main-gear legs; oleopneumatic shock-absorber in tailwheel unit; which is fully-castoring for taxying but locked fore and aft for T-O and landing. Main wheels have 8-ply tubeless tyres size 17·5 × 6·25-11, pressure 17·25 bars (250 lb/sq in); tailwheel 10-ply tubeless tyre size 5·00-5, pressure 11·04 bars (160 lb/sq in).

POWER PLANT: Two 1,007 kW (1,350 shp) General Electric T58-GE-8F turboshaft engines, mounted on each side of rotor pylon structure. Normal fuel capacity of 1,499 litres (396 US gallons), including external auxiliary tanks with a capacity of 454·6 litres (120 US gallons).

ACCOMMODATION: Crew of three, consisting of pilot, copilot and sensor operator. One passenger or litter patient with LAMPS equipment installed; four passengers or two litters with sonobuoy launcher removed. Provision for transportation of internal or external cargo.

AVIONICS AND EQUIPMENT: Include Canadian Marconi LN-66HP surveillance radar; ASQ-81 magnetic anomaly detector; ALR-54 passive radiation detection receivers (being replaced by ALR-66); SSQ-41 passive and SSQ-47 active sonobuoys (being replaced by DIFAR and DICASS); smoke markers; one or two torpedoes; PT-429 plotting board system (being replaced by Teledyne Systems ASN-123 tactical navigation system with computer and CRT display); APN-182 Doppler radar; and AYK-2 analogue navigation computer. Cargo hook for external loads, capacity 1,814 kg (4,000 lb). Rescue hoist, capacity 272 kg (600 lb).

DIMENSIONS, EXTERNAL:

Diameter of main rotor	13·41 m (44 ft 0 in)
Main rotor blade chord	0·55 m (21·6 in)
Diameter of tail rotor	2·49 m (8 ft 2 in)
Tail rotor blade chord	0·236 m (9·3 in)
Length overall (rotors turning)	16·03 m (52 ft 7 in)
Length overall, nose and blades folded	11·68 m (38 ft 4 in)
Height overall (rotors turning)	4·72 m (15 ft 6 in)
Height to top of rotor head	4·14 m (13 ft 7 in)
Stabiliser span	2·97 m (9 ft 9 in)
Wheel track (outer wheels)	3·30 m (10 ft 10 in)
Wheelbase	5·11 m (16 ft 9 in)

WEIGHTS:

Weight empty	3,193 kg (7,040 lb)
*Normal T-O weight	5,805 kg (12,800 lb)

Although not yet certificated for a T-O gross weight of 6,033 kg (13,300 lb), all testing has been accomplished at that weight

PERFORMANCE (at normal T-O weight, except where indicated):

Max level speed at S/L	143 knots (265 km/h; 165 mph)
Normal cruising speed	130 knots (241 km/h; 150 mph)
Max rate of climb at S/L	744 m (2,440 ft)/min
Service ceiling	6,860 m (22,500 ft)
Hovering ceiling IGE	5,670 m (18,600 ft)
Hovering ceiling OGE	4,695 m (15,400 ft)
Normal range with max fuel	367 nm (679 km; 422 miles)

LAKE
LAKE AIRCRAFT DIVISION OF CONSOLIDATED AERONAUTICS INC

EXECUTIVE OFFICES: PO Box 399, Tomball, Texas 77375
SALES OFFICES: David Hooks Memorial Airport, Tomball, Texas 77375
Telephone: (713) 376 5421
Telex: 76-2054 Lake Air Hou
PRESIDENT: Thomas Habif
EXECUTIVE VICE-PRESIDENT: Armand Rivard
VICE-PRESIDENT: Laurin Darrell (Marketing)
SECRETARY: B. A. Sigsbee
TREASURER: Herbert P. Lindblad

In 1962 Consolidated Aeronautics merged with Lake Aircraft Corporation of Sandford, Maine, as a result of which it operates Lake Aircraft as a division.

It is continuing production of the LA-4 amphibian, which Lake Aircraft developed from the original Colonial C-2 Skimmer IV after purchasing manufacturing rights from Colonial Aircraft Corporation in October 1959.

LAKE LA-4-200 BUCCANEER

Design of the original C-1 Skimmer was started in August 1946. Construction of the prototype began in January 1947 and it flew for the first time in May 1948. Versions of the Lake LA-4 developed from the improved C-2 Skimmer IV have included the LA-4, LA-4A, LA-4P, LA-4S and LA-4T, as described in previous editions of *Jane's*.

The LA-4-200 current production version, described here, received FAA certification in 1970.

LA-4 c/n 1000 was completed on 1 January 1980.

TYPE: Single-engined four-seat amphibian.

WINGS: Cantilever shoulder-wing monoplane with tapered wing panels attached directly to sides of hull. Wing section NACA 4415 at root, NACA 4409 at tip. Dihedral 5° 30′. Incidence 3° 15′. Structure consists of duralumin leading- and trailing-edge torsion boxes separated by a single duralumin main spar. All-metal ailerons and hydraulically-operated slotted flaps over 80% of span. Ground-adjustable trim tabs on ailerons. Wing balancer floats are light alloy monocoque structures.

HULL: Single-step all-metal structure, with double-sealed boat hull. Alodined and zinc chromated inside and out against corrosion, with polyurethane paint exterior finish.

TAIL UNIT: Cantilever all-metal structure. Outboard elevator section separate from inboard section and actuated hydraulically for trimming. Retractable water rudder in base of aerodynamic rudder.

LANDING GEAR: Hydraulically-retractable tricycle type. Consolidated oleo-pneumatic shock-absorbers on main gear, which retracts inward into wings. Long-stroke nosewheel oleo retracts forward. Gerdes main wheels with Goodyear tyres, size 6·00-6, pressure 2·41 bars (35 lb/sq in). Gerdes nosewheel with Goodyear tyre size 5·00-5, pressure 1·38 bars (20 lb/sq in). Gerdes disc brakes. Parking brake. Nosewheel is free to swivel 30° each side.

POWER PLANT: One 149 kW (200 hp) Lycoming IO-360-A1B flat-four engine, mounted on pylon above hull and driving a Hartzell two-blade constant-speed metal

Lake LA-4-200 Buccaneer four-seat light amphibian (Avco Lycoming IO-360-A1B flat-four engine)

pusher propeller. Rajay turbocharger, and Q-tip propeller, optional. US Rubber DL10 fuel tank in hull, capacity 151 litres (40 US gallons). Refuelling point above hull. Auxiliary fuel in stabilising floats, 28·4 litres (7·5 US gallons) each, optional. Total fuel capacity with optional tanks 208 litres (55 US gallons). Oil capacity 7·5 litres (2 US gallons).

ACCOMMODATION: Enclosed cabin seating pilot and three passengers. Front and rear seats removable. Front seats have inertia reel shoulder harness as standard. Dual controls standard; dual brakes for co-pilot optional. Entry through two forward-hinged windscreen sections. Baggage compartment, capacity 90·5 kg (200 lb), aft of cabin. Dual windscreen defroster system.

SYSTEMS: Vacuum system for flight instruments. Hydraulic system, pressure 86·2 bars (1,250 lb/sq in), for flaps, horizontal trim and landing gear actuation; handpump provided for emergency operation. Engine-driven 12V 60A alternator and 12V 30Ah battery. Stewart Warner 20,000 BTU heater optional.

AVIONICS AND EQUIPMENT: Basic avionics installation includes com and nav antennae, cabin speaker, microphone and circuit breakers. An extensive range of avionics by Collins, King and Narco, and autopilots by Brittain and Edo-Aire Mitchell, are available to customers' requirements. Standard equipment includes full blind-flying instrumentation, electric clock, manifold pressure gauge, outside air temperature gauge, recording tachometer, stall warning device, control locks, instrument panel lighting, carpeted floor, four fresh air vents, tinted glass for all windows, map pocket on front seats, baggage tiedown straps, landing and taxi lights, navigation lights, strobe light, heated pitot, fuselage nose bumper, paddle, cleat, line, full-flow oil filter, quick fuel drains, and inboard and outboard tiedown rings. Optional equipment includes hour meter, true airspeed indicator, shoulder harness for rear seats, alternate static source, manual/automatic bilge pump, cabin fire extinguisher, and external metallic paint finish.

DIMENSIONS, EXTERNAL:

Wing span	11·58 m (38 ft 0 in)
Wing chord, mean	1·35 m (4 ft 5·1 in)
Wing aspect ratio	8·67
Length overall	7·60 m (24 ft 11 in)
Height overall	2·84 m (9 ft 4 in)
Tailplane span	3·05 m (10 ft 0 in)
Wheel track	3·40 m (11 ft 2 in)
Wheelbase	2·69 m (8 ft 10 in)
Propeller diameter	1·88 m (6 ft 2 in)

DIMENSIONS, INTERNAL:

Cabin: Length	1·57 m (5 ft 2 in)
Max width	1·05 m (3 ft 5½ in)
Max height	1·32 m (3 ft 11½ in)
Floor area	approx 1·53 m² (16·5 sq ft)
Volume	approx 1·70 m³ (60·0 cu ft)
Baggage hold	0·24 m³ (8·5 cu ft)

AREAS:

Wings, gross	15·8 m² (170 sq ft)
Ailerons (total)	1·16 m² (12·5 sq ft)
Trailing-edge flaps (total)	2·28 m² (24·5 sq ft)
Fin	1·25 m² (13·5 sq ft)
Rudder	0·79 m² (8·5 sq ft)
Tailplane	1·45 m² (15·6 sq ft)
Elevators	0·78 m² (8·4 sq ft)

WEIGHTS AND LOADINGS:

Weight empty, equipped	705 kg (1,555 lb)
Max T-O and landing weight	1,220 kg (2,690 lb)
Max wing loading	74·2 kg/m² (15·2 lb/sq ft)
Max power loading	8·19 kg/kW (13·45 lb/hp)

PERFORMANCE (at max T-O weight):

Max level speed at S/L	126·5 knots (235 km/h; 146 mph)
Max cruising speed, 75% power at 2,440 m (8,000 ft)	130 knots (241 km/h; 150 mph)
Stalling speed	39 knots (72·5 km/h; 45 mph)
Max rate of climb at S/L	366 m (1,200 ft)/min
Service ceiling	4,480 m (14,700 ft)
T-O run on land	183 m (600 ft)
T-O run on water	335 m (1,100 ft)
Landing run on land	145 m (475 ft)
Alighting run on water	183 m (600 ft)
Range with max fuel, at normal cruising speed, with reserves	564 nm (1,046 km; 650 miles)
Max range with max fuel, with reserves	716 nm (1,327 km; 825 miles)

LAS
LOCKHEED AIRCRAFT SERVICE COMPANY
(Division of Lockheed Corporation)

HEAD OFFICE AND WORKS: Ontario International Airport, Ontario, California 91761
Telephone: (714) 988 2411
BASE: Luke Air Force Base, Arizona
SPECIAL DEVICES DIVISION: Ontario, California
LOCKHEED CENTER FOR MARINE RESEARCH: Carlsbad, California
JETPLAN AVIATION SERVICES: Los Gatos, California
PRESIDENT: Edward J. Shockley
EXECUTIVE VICE-PRESIDENTS:
M. H. Greene (Administration)
C. M. Schnepp (Operations)

VICE-PRESIDENTS:
C. W. Boyles (ATC Systems)
K. E. Neudoerffer (Operations)
I. S. Price (Marketing and New Business Development)
D. C. Shea (Operations)
DIRECTOR OF PUBLIC RELATIONS: John R. Dailey

Lockheed Aircraft Service Company is claimed to be the world's largest independent aircraft maintenance and modification company. It has designed and installed major modifications for such aircraft as the Boeing KC-135 and 707; Douglas DC-8; and Lockheed C-130, C-141, L-188 Electra, C-121, L-1649, L-1011 and P-3. In particular, LAS delivered 41 Electras in a cargo configuration; details of this conversion can be found in the 1970-71 *Jane's*. It

has also designed and installed interiors for various transport aircraft.

LAS has diversified into many other fields, including aircraft maintenance training devices, aircraft maintenance recording systems and airborne integrated data systems, marine anti-corrosion systems, aircraft ground support equipment and water pollution monitoring. In addition, LAS and three other US companies were awarded a contract in November 1975 to construct a modern maintenance and manufacturing base for the Hellenic Aerospace Industry (HAI, which see) at Tanagra, some 60 km (37 miles) from Athens. It was dedicated officially on 18 December 1979, and will provide airlines operating in the Mediterranean area with a base for contract maintenance and manufacturing facilities; it will also offer depot level maintenance for the Greek Air Force and state services.

In 1974 LAS began delivery of its Model 280 maintenance recorder, which records 50 h of flight data on an easily accessible cassette. Another LAS development is JETPLAN, a computerised flight planning and worldwide weather service for airlines and corporate jet operations, which has been available on a worldwide basis since 1971.

LOCKHEED C-130 and L-1011 CONVERSIONS

LAS specialises in complex aircraft modifications of all types, both of military aircraft such as the C-130 Hercules, and of commercial transports like the L-1011 TriStar. C-130 work included conversion of an HC-130H to DC-130H drone launch configuration for the US Air Force; and installation and flight testing of an in-flight refuelling system for the C-130, as described briefly in the 1978-79 *Jane's*.

In 1979 LAS delivered to the US Air Force the first C-130E modified to EC-130E configuration. Major exterior modifications added large blade antennae forward of the fin and beneath each wing; three trailing-wire antennae in bullet-shaped canisters; one beneath each wing and another under the tail unit; and two smaller horizontal blade antennae, on each side of the rear fuselage: all can be seen clearly in the accompanying illustration. The air-conditioning system has also been uprated to dissipate heat generated by the onboard electrical equip-

Lockheed EC-130E, modified by LAS for airborne battlefield command and control

ment, with heat exchanger pods located under each wing, above each main landing gear fairing. Lockheed EC-130Es have replaced EC-121s in US Air Force service.

In late 1979, LAS began a modification programme to convert to full passenger configuration the L-1011-500 TriStar testbed aircraft which was used in the type certification programme. It was scheduled for delivery by mid-1980.

LEARAVIA
LEARAVIA CORPORATION

HEAD OFFICE: PO Box 60000, Stead Airport, Reno, Nevada 89506
Telephone: (702) 972 0711
Telex: 35 4463
CHAIRMAN: Moya Olsen Lear
PRESIDENT: Samuel H. Auld
EXECUTIVE VICE-PRESIDENT: Milton Weilenmann
VICE-PRESIDENTS:
  J. S. Lewis (Sales)
  W. W. Surley (Operations)
  R. R. Tracy (Advanced Projects)

LEARAVIA LEAR FAN MODEL 2100

The last aeroplane designed by Mr William P. Lear Sr, before his death on 14 May 1978, was a small twin-turbine business aircraft of advanced design, known originally as the Futura. Since that time it has undergone considerable modification and is known now as the Lear Fan Model 2100.

Of extremely clean appearance, the Model 2100 is built largely of graphite/epoxy composite materials, with other components made of boron, glassfibre, Kevlar and various resins. Design of this aircraft began in June 1977, and construction of the first prototype started in November 1978. First flight was scheduled for October 1980; certification is expected by May 1982, with deliveries beginning in the following month. Orders for the Lear Fan 2100 totalled approx 125 by mid-1980.

Engineering, research and development of the Lear Fan 2100 is the responsibility of Lear Fan Corporation (US), at Reno; production aircraft are to be built at Aldergrove, Northern Ireland, by the newly-formed Lear Fan Ltd (see UK section).

TYPE: Twin-turbine business aircraft.
WINGS: Cantilever low-wing monoplane. Thickness/chord ratio 13·5%. Dihedral 4°. Incidence 1° 30′. No sweepback. Three-spar bonded stressed-skin fail-safe structure of advanced graphite/epoxy composite materials. Hydraulically-actuated plain trailing-edge flaps, and manually-operated ailerons, of graphite/epoxy composites. Trim tab in port aileron. Pneumatic de-icing boots on leading-edges.
FUSELAGE: Semi-monocoque fail-safe pressurised structure of graphite/epoxy composites, comprising frames and longerons bonded to the outer skin.
TAIL UNIT: Cantilever Y-shaped structure of graphite/epoxy composites, comprising single-spar V-tail and two-spar underfin, the latter stressed to withstand ground impact. Manually-operated elevators with trim tab in V-tail, and rudder with trim tab on underfin. Pneumatic de-icing boots on V-tail and fin leading-edges.
LANDING GEAR: Hydraulically-retractable tricycle type with single wheel on each unit; main units retract inward, nosewheel forward. Emergency extension by free fall, with pneumatic bottle backup. Nosewheel steering from rudder pedals. Oleo-pneumatic shock-absorbers. Main wheels have Goodrich tubeless tyres size 7·00-8, 8-ply rating. Nosewheel has Goodrich tyre size 6·00-6, 4-ply rating. Goodrich hydraulically actuated brakes, with optional anti-skid system.
POWER PLANT: Two 634 kW (850 shp) Pratt & Whitney Aircraft of Canada PT6B-35F turboshaft engines, each flat-rated to 485 kW (650 shp), mounted in rear of fuselage and driving, via extension shafts and a combining/reduction gearbox with separate clutches, a Hartzell

Learavia Lear Fan Model 2100 twin-turbine business aircraft (*Pilot Press*)

four-blade constant-speed and reversible-pitch slow-turning pusher propeller constructed of Kevlar composite. Fuel in integral wing tanks with a usable capacity of 946 litres (250 US gallons). Refuelling points on wing upper surface.
ACCOMMODATION: Standard accommodation for a crew of two and six passengers, or crew of two with seven passengers, both layouts with refreshment cabinet and toilet. Alternative two crew/eight passenger high-density arrangement, which retains a toilet facility, or all-cargo version with crew of two. Seat tracks on each side of cabin simplify changes of interior layout, or removal of seats for use in a cargo role. Special optional ambulance version can accommodate two stretcher cases, each with attendant, and has biomedical facilities, therapeutic oxygen and toilet. Clamshell type door, with integral airstairs in lower half, on port side of cabin, forward of wing. Emergency exit on starboard side. Baggage space at rear of cabin, accessible in flight. Entire accommodation pressurised and air-conditioned. Windscreen defrosting and anti-icing.
SYSTEMS: Cabin pressurisation by engine bleed air, with max pressure differential of 0·59 bars (8·6 lb/sq in), can maintain a 2,440 m (8,000 ft) cabin altitude to max certificated altitude. Freon vapour-cycle cooling system. Electrical system powered by two 28V 200A starter/generators, with two 125VA 115V 400Hz solid-state inverters, and 24V nickel-cadmium battery. Hydraulic system of 103·5 bars (1,500 lb/sq in) pressure, provided by two engine-driven hydraulic pumps, either of which is capable of maintaining full system function for operation of trailing-edge flaps and landing gear. Oxygen system of 0·62 m³ (22 cu ft) capacity for emergency use by crew and passengers. Anti-icing system includes pneumatic de-icing of wing and tail unit leading-edges, and electrical or bleed air anti-icing of engine inlets, pitot tubes, propeller leading-edges, static ports, and windscreen.
AVIONICS AND EQUIPMENT: Standard avionics by Collins

include dual VIR-351 VHF nav receivers, dual VHF-251 VHF com transceivers, dual GLS-350 glideslope receivers,* TDR-950 ATC transponder,* ANS-352 area nav, ADF-650 ADF, AMR-350 marker beacon receiver/audio panel, WXR-250 weather radar, IND-351C VOR/ILS indicator and DME-451 DME; plus Sperry C14-D compass system, VG-14D attitude gyro, SPZ-650L AFCS with flight director,* radar altimeter and digital air data computer;* TBD angle of attack system and emergency locator transmitter. Items marked with an asterisk will be optional after first 50 aircraft. Other optional avionics include Collins HF-200 HF com and WXR-300 colour radar; Global Nav GNS-500A VLF/Omega; Sperry air data command display, co-pilot flight director system, and SAT/TAS indicator; TBD RMI/converter, and co-pilot slaved compass system and HSI. Standard equipment includes angle of attack indicator, encoding altimeter, Mach/airspeed indicators, vertical speed indicators, blind-flying instrumentation for co-pilot, cabin pressure indicator, crew seats with lapstraps and shoulder harness, chart/map holders, lap belts for all cabin seats, baggage net or straps, carpeted floor, 'fasten seat belt—no smoking' sign, cabin fluorescent lighting, passenger reading lights, map and instrument panel lights, navigation lights, landing lights, strobe lights, engine fire detection and fire extinguishing systems.

DIMENSIONS, EXTERNAL:

Wing span	11·9 m (39 ft 4 in)
Wing aspect ratio	9·5
Length overall	12·07 m (39 ft 7 in)
Height overall	3·51 m (11 ft 6 in)
Wheel track	3·56 m (11 ft 8 in)
Wheelbase	4·90 m (16 ft 0¾ in)
Propeller diameter	2·29 m (7 ft 6 in)
Passenger door (port, fwd):	
Height	1·36 m (4 ft 5½ in)
Width	0·79 m (2 ft 7¼ in)
Height to sill	0·38 m (1 ft 3 in)

Emergency exit (stbd, fwd):	
Height	0·66 m (2 ft 2 in)
Width	0·48 m (1 ft 7 in)

DIMENSIONS, INTERNAL:
Cabin: Length, fwd to aft pressure bulkhead
5·54 m (18 ft 2 in)
Max width 1·47 m (4 ft 10 in)
Max height 1·42 m (4 ft 8 in)
Volume 6·63 m³ (234 cu ft)
Baggage compartment volume 1·19m³ (42 cu ft)
AREA:
Wings, gross 15·13 m² (162·9 sq ft)
WEIGHTS AND LOADINGS (estimated):
Weight empty 1,656 kg (3,650 lb)
Max fuel weight 771 kg (1,700 lb)
Max T-O weight 3,266 kg (7,200 lb)

Max ramp weight 3,288 kg (7,250 lb)
Max zero-fuel weight 2,676 kg (5,900 lb)
Max landing weight 3,107 kg (6,850 lb)
Max wing loading 215·9 kg/m² (44·2 lb/sq ft)
Max power loading 3·65 kg/kW (6 lb/shp)
PERFORMANCE (estimated, at max T-O weight, unless indicated):
Max level speed at 9,450 m (31,000 ft)
over 347 knots (643 km/h; 400 mph)
Max cruising speed at 9,145 m (30,000 ft)
347 knots (643 km/h; 400 mph)
Econ cruising speed at 12,495 m (41,000 ft)
304 knots (563 km/h; 350 mph)
Stalling speed, flaps down, power off
78 knots (145 km/h; 90 mph)
Max rate of climb at S/L 1,082 m (3,550 ft)/min

Rate of climb at S/L, one engine out
579 m (1,900 ft)/min
Service ceiling 12,500 m (41,000 ft)
Service ceiling, one engine out 8,840 m (29,000 ft)
T-O run 762 m (2,500 ft)
Balanced field length 823 m (2,700 ft)
Balanced field length at 2,722 kg (6,000 lb) AUW
579 m (1,900 ft)
Landing from 15 m (50 ft), at max landing weight
701 m (2,300 ft)
Range at max cruising speed with max payload and max fuel, 45 min reserves
1,415 nm (2,620 km; 1,630 miles)
Range at econ cruising speed with max payload and max fuel, 45 min reserves
2,000 nm (3,700 km; 2,300 miles)

LOCKHEED
LOCKHEED CORPORATION

HEAD OFFICE: Burbank, California 91520
Telephone: (213) 847 6121
CHAIRMAN OF THE BOARD AND CHIEF EXECUTIVE OFFICER:
Roy A. Anderson
PRESIDENT AND CHIEF OPERATING OFFICER: Lawrence O. Kitchen

DIRECTORS:
Roy A. Anderson
Michael Berberian
Edward W. Carter
Joseph P. Downer
Gilbert R. Ellis
Houston I. Flournoy
John T. Gurash
Willis M. Hawkins
Jack K. Horton
Clarence L. Johnson
Laurence O. Kitchen
Joseph R. Rensch
Leslie N. Shaw
John E. Swearingen
Fred M. Vinson Jr

GROUP VICE-PRESIDENT:
G. Graham Whipple (Lockheed Shipbuilding and Construction Co; Lockheed Air Terminal; Lockheed Electronics Co; Lockheed Engineering and Management Services Co)

CORPORATE SENIOR VICE-PRESIDENTS:
Jack J. Catton (Business Development)
John E. Cavanagh (General Counsel)
Dr Edgar M. Cortright (President, Lockheed-California Co)
Robert A. Fuhrman (President, Lockheed Missiles and Space Co)
Vincent N. Marafino (Finance)
Robert B. Ormsby (President, Lockheed-Georgia Co)
William R. Wilson (Strategic Planning)

CORPORATE VICE-PRESIDENTS:
Harold L. Brownman (President, Lockheed Electronics Co)
F. A. Cleveland (Engineering)
R. F. Conley (International Marketing)
Richard K. Cook (Washington Area)
James Everington (Industrial Relations)
W. Paul Frech (Operations)
Melvin H. Greene (Executive Vice-President, Administration, Lockheed Aircraft Service Co)
R. Richard Heppe (General Manager, Operations)
H. Potter Kerfoot (General Manager, Advanced Systems Division, Lockheed Missiles and Space Co)
Alexander H. Lorch (Executive Vice-President, Lockheed-Georgia Co)
Robert R. McKirahan (Treasurer)
Robert H. Northcutt (Controller)

Frederick C. E. Oder (General Manager, Space Systems Division, Lockheed Missiles and Space Co)
Thomas J. O'Hara (Contracts and Pricing)
William D. Perreault (Corporate Communications)
James W. Plummer (Executive Vice-President, Lockheed Missiles and Space Co)
Ben R. Rich (General Manager and Advanced Development Projects, Lockheed-California Co)
James J. Ryan (Secretary and Assistant General Counsel)
Charles M. Schnepp (Executive Vice-President, Operations, Lockheed Aircraft Service Co)
Edward J. Shockley (President, Lockheed Aircraft Service Co)
David M. Simmons (President, Lockheed Air Terminal)
Lawrence A. Smith (President, Lockheed Shipbuilding and Construction Co)
Derald A. Stuart (General Manager, Missile Systems Division, Lockheed Missiles and Space Co)
Richard W. Taylor (Executive Vice-President, Lockheed-California Co)
Joseph G. Twomey (Chief Counsel)

DIVISIONS:
Lockheed-California Company:
Burbank, California 91520
PRESIDENT: Dr Edgar M. Cortright
Lockheed-Georgia Company:
Marietta, Georgia 30063
PRESIDENT: Robert B. Ormsby
Lockheed Aircraft Service Company:
Ontario, California 91761
PRESIDENT: Edward J. Shockley
SUBSIDIARIES:
LOCKHEED AIR TERMINAL INC: Burbank, California 91505
PRESIDENT: David M. Simmons
LOCKHEED ELECTRONICS COMPANY INC: Plainfield, New Jersey 07061
PRESIDENT: Harold L. Brownman
LOCKHEED MISSILES AND SPACE COMPANY INC: Sunnyvale, California 94086
PRESIDENT: Robert A. Fuhrman
LOCKHEED SHIPBUILDING AND CONSTRUCTION COMPANY: Seattle, Washington 98134
PRESIDENT: Lawrence A. Smith
MURDOCK MACHINE & ENGINEERING CO OF TEXAS: Irving, Texas 75060
PRESIDENT: Paul R. Holmes
LOCKHEED ENGINEERING AND MANAGEMENT SERVICES COMPANY INC: Houston, Texas 77058
PRESIDENT: R. B. Young

LOCKHEED FINANCE CORPORATION: Burbank, California 91520
PRESIDENT: James T. West

Built by the brothers Allan and Malcolm Lockheed, the first Lockheed aircraft, a tractor seaplane, first flew in 1913. Three years later the brothers established a company at Santa Barbara, California, to manufacture a twin-engined flying-boat, two seaplanes for the Navy and a small sport biplane that was a forerunner of the true streamlined aeroplane. Lockheed Aircraft Co, formed in 1926, moved to Burbank, California, in 1928 and was reorganised as Lockheed Aircraft Corporation in 1932.

On 30 November 1943, the Vega Aircraft Corporation, which had been formed in 1937 as an affiliate and in 1941 became a wholly-owned subsidiary of the Lockheed Aircraft Corporation, was absorbed and the name Vega abandoned. In September 1977 the title Lockheed Aircraft Corporation was changed to Lockheed Corporation, to reflect the company's diversified activities.

Lockheed's aircraft and missile activities are now handled by three separate companies, which were evolved from the former California, Georgia and Missiles and Space Divisions in the Summer of 1961.

The current products of the Lockheed-California and Lockheed-Georgia companies are described hereafter under the individual company headings.

Lockheed has diversified into many fields of industry since 1959. Following the acquisition of Stavid Engineering Inc, it combined this company and its own Electronics and Avionics Division into Lockheed Electronics Company Inc. Effective in January 1980, certain activities of this company were transferred to a new subsidiary, Lockheed Engineering and Management Services Company Inc.

Lockheed Air Terminal Inc (LAT), a wholly-owned subsidiary, is operating and maintaining during a two-year transitional period the Hollywood-Burbank Airport, which now belongs to the cities of Burbank, Glendale and Pasadena, and provides fuelling and related services at 25 other locations in 11 states, the territory of Guam, and Panama. Lockheed Aircraft Service Co (LAS) designs and manufactures products for the aerospace and marine industries, and carries out aviation maintenance, modification and management services in the USA and other nations. Much of its work outside the USA is done under subcontract for Lockheed Aircraft International AG, a separate subsidiary based in Geneva, Switzerland.

Since April 1959 Lockheed has also had an interest in shipbuilding and heavy construction, following its purchase of the Puget Sound Bridge and Dry Dock Company (now Lockheed Shipbuilding and Construction Co).

LOCKHEED-CALIFORNIA COMPANY
Burbank, California 91520
Lockheed-California has responsibility for production of the land-based P-3 Orion, CP-140 Aurora, developed from the P-3, L-1011 TriStar three-turbofan transport, and a new high-altitude tactical surveillance and reconnaissance aircraft designated TR-1. This is a variant of the U-2R, which may itself go back into production to meet the US Air Force's PLSS programme requirements.

LOCKHEED F-104 STARFIGHTER
The Starfighter continues in production, under licence, by Aeritalia of Italy (which see).

LOCKHEED 'PROJECT STEALTH'
In the so-called 'Skunk Works' at Burbank, Lockheed-California is reported to have built, under a DARPA-funded contract from the USAF's Flight Dynamics Laboratory, a single-seat reconnaissance/strike aircraft, of which a primary feature is low radar, infra-red and optical signatures. The aircraft is said to be powered by two 53·4 kN (12,000 lb st) turbojet engines, and is believed to have flown for the first time in 1977.

LOCKHEED U-2 and TR-1
Development of the U-2 began in the Spring of 1954 to meet a joint CIA/US Air Force requirement for a high-altitude strategic reconnaissance and special-purpose

research aircraft. It took place in the Lockheed 'Skunk Works' at Burbank, California, where, after acceptance of the design in late 1954, two prototypes were hand-built in great secrecy by a small team of engineers. The aircraft's true purpose was cloaked under the US Air Force U-for-Utility designation U-2, and the first flight, by Lockheed test pilot Tony LeVier, took place on or about 1 August 1955 at Watertown Strip in the Nevada desert.

The configuration of the U-2 is basically that of a powered sailplane, which explains its unusual 'bicycle' landing gear, combined with underwing balancer units which provide stability during take-off and are then jettisoned. Range can, if necessary, be extended by shutting off the engine and gliding. Because of its configuration the U-2 requires unusually precise handling during take-off and landing—particularly the latter, since there is an extremely small margin between approach speed and stalling speed. After touchdown, the aircraft comes to rest on one of the down-turned wingtips, which serve as landing skids.

Initial quantities of 48 single-seat and five two-seat U-2s were ordered in FY 1956, but after about 30 of these had been completed the increasing weight of special equipment which the aircraft was required to carry had degraded performance to such an extent that a more powerful engine became necessary, and this was installed from 1959 onwards. At the same time a substantial increase in fuel capacity made possible a considerably

greater range. In FY 1968 the U-2 was put back into production for a period, to replace some of the two dozen or more aircraft lost over hostile territory or in accidents. The production line was again reopened in 1980 to manufacture a new, tactical reconnaissance version, to be known as the TR-1.

In view of the continuing classified nature of much of its work, it is not possible to confirm officially many details concerning the U-2; but some information on its deployment, and on the versions built and subsequent conversions, can be found in the 1979-80 *Jane's*. Most recently built was the U-2R, and available details of this and the TR-1/ER-2 follow:

U-2R. Additional batch of 12 single-seat aircraft, ordered for strategic reconnaissance in FY 1968, by which time approx half of original U-2s had been lost through various causes. Serial numbers 68-10329 to 68-10340. Originally designated WU-2C. Bulged intakes, as on U-2C, but longer nose and fuselage, without dorsal spine fairing: increased wing span and internal fuel capacity: rear fuselage slightly bulged on top, just forward of fin; mainwheel unit further aft, tailwheel unit further forward, than on earlier models. Non-US bases have included Mildenhall, England. The U-2R has been selected as the preferred airborne relay vehicle for the Lockheed PLSS (Precision Location Strike System), intended to locate and identify enemy radar emitters, and to direct strike aircraft against them.

TR-1. Tactical reconnaissance version, described officially by the Department of Defense as "to be equipped with a variety of electronic sensors to provide continuously available, day or night, high-altitude all-weather stand-off surveillance of the battle area in direct support of the US and Allied ground and air forces during peace, crises, and war situations". Tooling for the U-2 has been kept in store at the USAF-owned Plant 42 at Palmdale, California, and the FY 1979 defence budget included $10·2 million to reopen the production line in FY 1980. The TR-1 will have the same basic airframe as the U-2R, still with the J75-P-13 engine, but with the significant addition of an 'advanced synthetic aperture' radar system (ASARS) in the form of a UPD-X side-looking airborne radar (SLAR) and modern electronic countermeasures (ECM). Seen as a replacement for the now-abandoned Compass Cope RPV (see 1977-78 *Jane's*), the TR-1 is intended primarily for use in Europe, where its SLAR will provide the capability to 'see' approximately 30 nm (55 km; 35 miles) into hostile territory without the need to overfly an actual or potential battle area. A further funding of $44·2 million was made under the FY 1980 budget, and a contract covering the construction of three aircraft was received on 16 November 1979. These will be single-seat **TR-1As,** two of which are for service with the US Air Force. The third aircraft is to be modified for use by NASA as an Earth resources research aircraft, with the designation **ER-2.** An additional 23 TR-1s are planned for service with the US Air Force, of which two will be **TR-1B** two-seat trainers. A proposed funding of $128·8 million in FY 1981 will purchase four TR-1s; eight more will be requested in FY 1982. The first TR-1A was scheduled to fly in 1980, and the USAF plans to begin pilot training at Beale AFB, California, in August 1981, following delivery of the first of five aircraft for the reconnaissance training squadron in June of that year.

The following description applies primarily to the single-seat U-2R, but is applicable generally to the TR-1A:

TYPE: High-altitude reconnaissance and research aircraft.

WINGS: Cantilever mid-wing monoplane, with wingtips turned down 90° for use as skids during landing. All-metal structure. Trailing-edge flaps occupy approx 60% of each half-span, with ailerons outboard. Small tubular fairing between each flap and aileron, projecting slightly aft of the trailing-edge. Small plate-type spoiler forward of outer portion of each flap. Some aircraft fitted with trim tab on each aileron.

FUSELAGE: All-metal semi-monocoque structure of circular cross-section, with thin-gauge skin. Fineness ratio approx 10:1. Forward-opening door-type airbrake on each side of fuselage aft of wings, used mainly as a landing aid. Large airscoop fairing beneath rear of wing root: generally on starboard side, but sometimes on port side and sometimes on both. Since about 1974 some aircraft have had a modified tailpipe, to reduce the infra-red signature from the engine.

TAIL UNIT: Cantilever all-metal structure. Trim tab on rudder and in each elevator.

LANDING GEAR: Retractable bicycle type, with twin main wheels and twin small tailwheels in tandem, each unit retracting forward into fuselage. Balancer units under outer wings, each with twin small wheels, are jettisoned on take-off. Tailwheels and underwing wheels have solid tyres; castoring tailwheel unit aids manoeuvring on ground. Brakes on main wheels. Braking parachute in container under rudder.

POWER PLANT: One 75·6 kN (17,000 lb st) Pratt & Whitney J75-P-13 turbojet engine. Normal internal fuel capacity approx 4,448 litres (1,175 US gallons). Provision for two 397·5 litre (105 US gallon) non-jettisonable auxiliary slipper tanks on wing leading-edges.

ACCOMMODATION: Pilot only in TR-1A/ER-2, on ejection seat. Rearward-sliding transparent canopy, protected internally against ultra-violet radiation. Accommodation is not pressurised. Rearview periscope on most aircraft (positions vary).

AVIONICS AND EQUIPMENT: Typical standard avionics can include Magnavox ARC-34 UHF com, Tacan, ILS, Lear A-10 autopilot, Bendix ARN-6 ADF, MA-1 compass, and (for night flying) astro-compass. Equipment includes one vertical and two lateral cameras for training flights, or up to five 70 mm cameras (U-2) or side-looking airborne radar (TR-1) for operational missions. Panoramic camera(s), usually Model 73B or Perkin-Elmer Model 501, with ventral periscopic sight.

DIMENSIONS, EXTERNAL:
Wing span	31·39 m (103 ft 0 in)
Wing aspect ratio	approx 10·2
Length overall	19·20 m (63 ft 0 in)
Height overall	4·88 m (16 ft 0 in)

WEIGHTS:
Fuel and equipment payload:
U-2R	approx 5,443 kg (12,000 lb)

Max T-O weight with slipper tanks:
U-2R	13,154 kg (29,000 lb)

Lockheed U-2R high-altitude reconnaissance aircraft, of which another view is shown below

PERFORMANCE (estimated for TR-1):
Max level speed: TR-1 at 18,290 m (60,000 ft)	373 knots (692 km/h; 430 mph)
Operational ceiling: TR-1	27,430 m (90,000 ft)
Max range: TR-1 more than 2,605 nm (4,830 km; 3,000 miles)	
Max endurance: U-2R, TR-1	12 h

LOCKHEED MODEL 185/285 ORION
US Navy designation: P-3
CAF designation: CP-140 Aurora

In 1958 Lockheed won a US Navy competition for an 'off-the-shelf' ASW aircraft with a developed version of its Electra four-turboprop commercial transport. An aerodynamic prototype flew for the first time on 19 August 1958. A second aircraft, designated YP-3A (formerly YP3V-1), with full avionics, flew on 25 November 1959.

Details of the P-3A initial production version (retired from operational use by active-duty USN patrol squadrons on 13 November 1978) and WP-3A can be found in the 1978-79 *Jane's*. Subsequent production versions are as follows:

P-3B. Follow-on production version with 3,661 kW (4,910 ehp) Allison T56-A-14 turboprop engines, which do not need water-alcohol injection. US Navy contracts covered 124 P-3Bs. In addition, five P-3Bs were delivered to the Royal New Zealand Air Force in 1966, ten to the Royal Australian Air Force during 1968 and five to Norway in the Spring of 1969. USN P-3Bs were modified retrospectively to carry Bullpup missiles. Others became **EP-3Bs.** The US Navy and Lear Siegler developed in 1976 a modification kit for retrofitting to P-3B aircraft. This includes a 32K Rom computer, ASN-84 inertial navigation system, Omega, ASA-66 displays and ASN-124 navigation controller, together with the necessary controls and equipment to integrate the new and existing systems. Kits have been made available for the above installation.

New Zealand's five P-3Bs are currently undergoing modernisation by Boeing Aerospace, involving upgrading of their data handling and display systems, radar, infra-red detection system, and INS. It is planned to upgrade the ASW equipment in a subsequent programme.

P-3C. Advanced version with the A-NEW system of sensors and control equipment, built around a Univac digital computer that integrates all ASW information and permits retrieval, display and transmission of tactical data in order to eliminate routine log-keeping functions. This increases crew effectiveness by allowing them sufficient time to consider all tactical data and devise the best action to resolve problems. First flight of this version was made on 18 September 1968 and the P-3C entered service in 1969. A total of 143 of this version had been delivered to the US Navy by early 1978.

All of those delivered from January 1975 have been to **P-3C Update** standard, with new avionics and electronics software developed to enhance the effectiveness of the aircraft. Equipment includes a magnetic drum that gives a sevenfold increase in computer memory capacity, a new versatile computer language, Omega navigation system, improved acoustic processing sensitivity, a tactical display for two of the sensor stations, and an improved magnetic tape transport. A prototype with this equipment was handed over to the US Navy on 29 April 1974.

Ten Update P-3Cs were delivered to the Royal Australian Air Force in 1978-79 for service with No. 10 Squadron. Japan has ordered 45 P-3Cs, of which four will be assembled and 38 licence-built in Japan by Kawasaki (which see).

The US Navy and Lockheed began in 1976 a further P-3C avionics improvement programme known as **Update II.** This added an infra-red detection system (IRDS) and a sonobuoy reference system (SRS). The Harpoon missile and control system are included in

Lockheed P-3C Orion four-turboprop anti-submarine aircraft *(Pilot Press)*

long-range flight directions; glideslope indicator; on-top position indicator; two ARC-161 HF transceivers; two ARC-143 UHF transceivers; ARC-101 VHF receiver/transmitter; AGC-6 teletype and high-speed printer; HF and UHF secure communication units; ACQ-5 data link communication set and AIC-22 interphone set; APX-72 IFF transponder and APX-76 SIF interrogator. Electronic computer-controlled display equipment includes ASA-70 tactical display; ASA-66 pilot's display; ASA-70 radar display and two auxiliary readout (computer-stored data) displays. ASW equipment includes two ARR-72 sono receivers; two AQA-7 DIFAR sonobuoy indicator sets; hyperbolic fix unit; acoustic source signal generator; time code generator and AQH-4(V) sonar tape recorder; ASQ-81 magnetic anomaly detector; ASA-64 submarine anomaly detector; ASA-65 magnetic compensator; ALQ-78 electronic countermeasures set; APS-115 radar set (360° coverage); ASA-69 radar scan converter; KA-74 forward computer-assisted camera; KB-18A automatic strike assessment camera with horizon-to-horizon coverage; RO-308 bathythermograph recorder. Additional equipment includes APN-141(V) radar altimeter; two APQ-107 radar altimeter warning systems; A/A24G-9 true airspeed computer and ASW-31 automatic flight control system. P-3Cs delivered from 1975 have the avionics/electronics package updated by addition of an extra 393K memory drum and fourth logic unit, Omega navigation, new magnetic tape transport, and an ASA-66 tactical display for the sonar operators. To accommodate the new systems a new operational software computer programme will be written in CMS-2 language. Marconi AQS-901 acoustic signal processing and display system in RAAF P-3Cs.

ARMAMENT: Bomb bay, 2·03 m wide, 0·88 m deep and 3·91 m long (80 in × 34·5 in × 154 in), forward of wing, can accommodate a 2,000 lb MK 25/39/55/56 mine, three 1,000 lb MK 36/52 mines, three MK 57 depth bombs, eight MK 54 depth bombs, eight MK 43/44/46 torpedoes or a combination of two MK 101 nuclear depth bombs and four MK 43/44/46 torpedoes. Ten underwing pylons for stores: two under centre-section each side can carry torpedoes or 2,000 lb mines; three under outer wing each side can carry respectively (inboard to outboard) a torpedo or 2,000 lb mine (or searchlight on starboard wing), a torpedo or 1,000 lb mine or rockets singly or in pods; a torpedo or 500 lb mine or rockets singly or in pods. Torpedoes can be carried underwing only for ferrying; mines can be carried and released. Search stores, such as sonobuoys and sound signals, are launched from inside cabin area in the P-3A/B. In the P-3C sonobuoys are loaded and launched externally and internally. Max total weapon load includes six 2,000 lb mines under wings and a 3,290 kg (7,252 lb) internal load made up of two MK 101 depth bombs, four MK 44 torpedoes, pyrotechnic pistol and 12 signals, 87 sonobuoys, 100 MK 50 underwater sound signals (P-3A/B), 18 MK 3A marine markers (P-3A/B), 42 MK 7 marine markers, two B.T. buoys, and two MK 5 parachute flares. Sonobuoys are ejected from P-3C aircraft with explosive cartridge actuating devices (CAD), eliminating the need for a pneumatic system. Australian P-3Cs use BARRA sonobuoys.

DIMENSIONS, EXTERNAL:

Wing span	30·37 m (99 ft 8 in)
Wing chord at root	5·77 m (18 ft 11 in)
Wing chord at tip	2·31 m (7 ft 7 in)
Wing aspect ratio	7·5
Length overall	35·61 m (116 ft 10 in)
Height overall	10·29 m (33 ft 8½ in)
Fuselage diameter	3·45 m (11 ft 4 in)

Update II, which was incorporated into production aircraft from August 1977. The first Update II P-3C was delivered to the Naval Air Development Center in that same month. The Royal Netherlands Navy has ordered 13 Update II P-3Cs. The first is scheduled for delivery in late 1981.

Update III, of which development began in February 1978, involves mainly ASW avionics, including a new acoustic processor to analyse signals picked up from the sea, a new sonobuoy receiver which replaces DIFAR, an improved APU, and environmental controls to cater for increased heat from the avionics and to further improve crew comfort. A prototype Update III P-3C is scheduled for delivery to the US Navy for test and evaluation in April 1983, with full production to start in April 1984.

Two of the eight international records for turboprop aircraft set up in a P-3C by Cdr Donald H. Lilienthal, in early 1971, had not been beaten by mid-1980. They were a speed of 434·97 knots (806·10 km/h; 500·89 mph) over a 15/25 km course; and a time-to-height record, to 12,000 m in 19 min 42·24 s.

RP-3D. One P-3C was reconfigured during manufacture for a five-year mission to map the Earth's magnetic field, under Project Magnet, controlled by the US Naval Oceanographic Office. Crew of 17. Range increased to more than 5,000 nm (9,265 km; 5,755 miles) by installation of 4,545 litre (1,200 US gallon) fuel tank in weapons bay. Details of other changes in 1977-78 *Jane's*. Operated by US Navy's Oceanographic Development Squadron 8 (VXN-8) based at the Naval Air Test Center, Patuxent River, Maryland. On 4 November 1972, Cdr Philip R. Hite used it to set up an international closed-circuit distance record for turboprop aircraft, covering 5,451·97 nm (10,103·51 km; 6,278·03 miles).

WP-3D. Two aircraft equipped as airborne research centres, ordered by the US National Oceanic and Atmospheric Administration. Equipped to carry out atmospheric research and weather modification experiments. Pitot static boom on port wingtip; gust probe on fuselage; C-band range heading indicator (RHI) dish antenna in belly radome; and X-band antenna in radome at tail. These aircraft became operational during the Summer of 1976.

EP-3E. Ten P-3As and two EP-3Bs were converted to EP-3E configuration to replace Lockheed EC-121s in service with VQ-1 and VQ-2 squadrons. Identified by large canoe-shaped radars on upper and lower surfaces of fuselage and ventral radome forward of wing.

P-3F. Six aircraft, similar to the US Navy's P-3Cs, for the Imperial Iranian Air Force. Used initially for long-range surface surveillance and subsequently also for ASW missions. Delivery completed in January 1975.

CP-140 Aurora. Version for Canadian Armed Forces. Described separately.

By mid-1980 Lockheed-California had delivered more than 500 P-3s of all versions. The following data refer to the P-3C, but are generally applicable to other versions, except for the details noted.

TYPE: Four-turboprop ASW aircraft.

WINGS: Cantilever low-wing monoplane. Wing section NACA 0014 (modified) at root, NACA 0012 (modified) at tip. Dihedral 6°. Incidence 3° at root, 0° 30′ at tip. Fail-safe box beam structure of extruded integrally-stiffened aluminium alloy. Lockheed-Fowler trailing-edge flaps. Hydraulically-boosted aluminium ailerons. Anti-icing by engine bleed air ducted into leading-edges.

FUSELAGE: Conventional aluminium alloy semi-monocoque fail-safe structure.

TAIL UNIT: Cantilever aluminium alloy structure with dihedral tailplane and dorsal fin. Fixed-incidence tailplane. Hydraulically-boosted rudder and elevators. Leading-edges of fin and tailplane have electric anti-icing system.

LANDING GEAR: Hydraulically-retractable tricycle type,

with twin wheels on each unit. All units retract forward, main wheels into inner engine nacelles. Oleo-pneumatic shock-absorbers. Main wheels have size 40-14 type VII 26-ply tubeless tyres. Nosewheels have size 28-7·7 type VII tubeless tyres. Hydraulic brakes. No anti-skid units.

POWER PLANT: Four 3,661 kW (4,910 ehp) Allison T56-A-14 turboprop engines, each driving a Hamilton Standard 54H60 four-blade constant-speed propeller. Fuel in one tank in fuselage and four wing integral tanks, with total usable capacity of 34,826 litres (9,200 US gallons). Four overwing gravity fuelling points and central pressure refuelling point. Oil capacity (min usable) 111 litres (29·4 US gallons) in four tanks. Electrically de-iced propeller spinners.

ACCOMMODATION: Normal ten-man crew. Flight deck has wide-vision windows, and circular windows for observers are provided fore and aft in the main cabin, each bulged to give 180° view. Main cabin is fitted out as a five-man tactical compartment containing advanced electronic, magnetic and sonic detection equipment, an all-electric galley and large crew rest area.

SYSTEMS: Air-conditioning and pressurisation system supplied by two engine-driven compressors. Pressure differential 0·37 bars (5·4 lb/sq in). Hydraulic system, pressure 207 bars (3,000 lb/sq in), for flaps, control surface boosters, landing gear actuation, brakes and bomb bay doors. Pneumatic system, pressure 207/83 bars (3,000/1,200 lb/sq in), for ASW store launchers (P-3A/B only). Electrical system utilises three 60kVA generators for 120/208V 400Hz AC supply. 24V DC supply. Integral APU with 60kVA generator for ground air-conditioning, electrical supply and engine starting.

AVIONICS AND EQUIPMENT: The ASQ-114 general-purpose digital computer is the heart of the P-3C system. Together with the AYA-8 data processing equipment and computer-controlled display systems, it permits rapid analysis and utilisation of electronic, magnetic and sonic data. Nav/com system comprises two ASN-84 inertial navigation systems, with latitude and longitude indicators; APN-187 Doppler; ARN-81 Loran A and C; ARN-84 Tacan; two ARN-87 VOR receivers; ARN-32 marker beacon receiver; ARN-83 LF-ADF; ARA-50 UHF direction finder; AJN-15 flight director indicator for tactical directions; HSI for

Lockheed P-3C Orion in Update II configuration

Tailplane span	13·06 m (42 ft 10 in)
Wheel track (c/l shock-absorbers)	9·50 m (31 ft 2 in)
Wheelbase	9·07 m (29 ft 9 in)
Propeller diameter	4·11 m (13 ft 6 in)
Cabin door: Height	1·83 m (6 ft 0 in)
Width	0·69 m (2 ft 3 in)

DIMENSIONS, INTERNAL:
Cabin, excl flight deck and electrical load centre:

Length	21·06 m (69 ft 1 in)
Max width	3·30 m (10 ft 10 in)
Max height	2·29 m (7 ft 6 in)
Floor area	61·13 m² (658 sq ft)
Volume	120·6 m³ (4,260 cu ft)

AREAS:

Wings, gross	120·77 m² (1,300 sq ft)
Ailerons (total)	8·36 m² (90 sq ft)
Trailing-edge flaps (total)	19·32 m² (208 sq ft)
Fin, incl dorsal fin	10·78 m² (116 sq ft)
Rudder, incl tab	5·57 m² (60 sq ft)
Tailplane	22·39 m² (241 sq ft)
Elevators, incl tabs	7·53 m² (81 sq ft)

WEIGHTS (P-3B/C):

Weight empty	27,890 kg (61,491 lb)
Max expendable load	9,071 kg (20,000 lb)
Max normal T-O weight	61,235 kg (135,000 lb)
Max permissible weight	64,410 kg (142,000 lb)
Design zero-fuel weight	35,017 kg (77,200 lb)
Max landing weight	47,119 kg (103,880 lb)

PERFORMANCE (P-3B/C, at max T-O weight, except where indicated otherwise):
Max level speed at 4,570 m (15,000 ft) at AUW of 47,625 kg (105,000 lb)
411 knots (761 km/h; 473 mph)
Econ cruising speed at 7,620 m (25,000 ft) at AUW of 49,895 kg (110,000 lb)
328 knots (608 km/h; 378 mph)
Patrol speed at 457 m (1,500 ft) at AUW of 49,895 kg (110,000 lb) 206 knots (381 km/h; 237 mph)
Stalling speed, flaps up
133 knots (248 km/h; 154 mph)
Stalling speed, flaps down
112 knots (208 km/h; 129 mph)
Max rate of climb at 457 m (1,500 ft)
594 m (1,950 ft)/min
Service ceiling 8,625 m (28,300 ft)
Service ceiling, one engine out 5,790 m (19,000 ft)
T-O run 1,290 m (4,240 ft)
T-O to 15 m (50 ft) 1,673 m (5,490 ft)
Landing from 15 m (50 ft) at design landing weight
845 m (2,770 ft)
Max mission radius (no time on station) at 61,235 kg (135,000 lb) 2,070 nm (3,835 km; 2,383 miles)
Mission radius (3 h on station at 457 m; 1,500 ft)
1,346 nm (2,494 km; 1,550 miles)

LOCKHEED AURORA

Canadian Armed Forces designation: CP-140

The purchase of 18 special variants of the Lockheed P-3 Orion maritime patrol aircraft for the Canadian Armed Forces, to replace CP-107 Argus maritime reconnaissance aircraft, was announced on 21 July 1976. Designated CP-140 Aurora, each of these aircraft combines the P-3 Orion airframe, power plant and basic aircraft systems with the avionics systems and data processing capability of the US Navy's carrier-based Lockheed S-3A Viking. It is able to perform missions involving a range of more than 4,000 nm (7,400 km; 4,600 miles), or flights of up to 17 hours' duration, and is being deployed initially for ASW duties; national sovereignty patrols; shipping, fisheries and Arctic surveillance; ice reconnaissance; and search and rescue. By the addition of a weapons bay sensors canister at a later date, the CP-140 will be able to undertake additional civilian tasks such as resources location, pollution control and aerial survey.

The first CP-140 (CAF serial number 140104) completed a successful first flight on 22 March 1979, and was handed over to the CAF on 29 May 1980. All 18 are due to be delivered by March 1981, and will be based at Greenwood, Nova Scotia, and Comox, British Columbia.

The cabin interior has been changed extensively to meet Canadian requirements: immediately aft of the flight deck are an observer's station on the port side and crew rest bunks on the starboard side. Moving aft, the tactical compartment comes next, with accommodation for the tactical navigator (TACNAV), navigator/communicator (NAV-COM), two acoustic sensor operators (ASO), and two non-acoustic sensor operators (NASO), all on the port side. Aft of the tactical compartment is the search stores and camera bay, with two more observer stations, one on each side. At the rear of the cabin are a galley, on the port side, a dinette area, and an airborne maintenance station on the starboard side. A toilet is located on the port side of the cabin, immediately aft of the forward observer's position.

On the flight deck, an ASA-82 multi-purpose display (MPD) provides the pilots with a real-time presentation of the tactical situation and sensor information; directions from the TACNAV and NAVCOM are fed through the computer for display on both the MPD and the flight director indicators (FDIs). Cues and alerts, indicating required sequences of action, are displayed on the periphery of the MPD.

An AJN-15 flight director system supplies attitude, heading and fly-to-point references. For long-range navigation, data from the horizontal situation indicator are normally adequate. For precise, close-in tactical manoeuvring the FDI is used, and the automatic flight control system includes full-time attitude control and proportional control-wheel steering.

The three observer stations each have a fully-swivelling seat and are provided with intercom. Each of the observation windows gives full hemispherical view, and there are power and storage provisions for a hand-held camera. Each position is provided with isolation curtains, to screen observer and window from cabin lighting during night visual search. A fourth station can be made available on the starboard side, by removal of the crew rest bunks.

The TACNAV has a console which includes an ASA-82 MPD, an ASQ-147 keyset and trackball, and armament controls. With his keyset the TACNAV can control, via the computer, the sonobuoy reference system (SRS), and can call up and display FLIR and other radar data on his MPD. The NAVCOM also has an ASA-82 and ASQ-147, plus HF, VHF (FM) and UHF transceivers; inertial, VLF (Omega) and Doppler navigation sets; LF and UHF ADF, and VHF homer; a high-speed teleprinter and teletype keyboard; provisions for tactical satellite communications (TACSATCOM); data link; control of reconnaissance photography; provisions for control of survey photography; and provisions for secure communications. The NAVCOM's MPD and keyset serve as a backup for the TACNAV in the event of equipment failure.

The two ASOs share a dual console and each has an ASA-82 MPD and ASQ-147 keyset and trackball. They share also an ASA-82 auxiliary readout unit (ARU), a time code generator, and an AN/ASH-27 28-track tape recorder. Their MPDs can display acoustic data or the tactical plot, but the ARU is a dedicated acoustic display. The acoustic functions of receiving, processing, display and recording are controlled by the keysets through the computer.

The two NASOs also have a dual console, each with an ASA-82 MPD and ASQ-147 keyset and trackball, the keysets being used to control radar, electronic support measures (ESM) and FLIR through the computer. Principal controls shared by these two operators, or available to only one of them, include ASQ-501 MAD, OA-5150/ASQ(FACS II) MAD compensator, video tape recorder, SIF and provisions for SLAR.

The heart of the entire control system is a Univac AN/AYK-10 navigation/tactical computer. Its two central processors function independently; both have co-ordinated access to a core memory of 65,536 words. There is growth capacity for an additional 32,000 words, and space has been allocated for a 127,000-word auxiliary memory in the acoustic system processor for the computer.

The search stores and camera bay has stowage for 'A' size sonobuoys, large and small marine markers, Signals

Underwater Sound (SUS) and flares. Intercom controls and an ordnance status panel are provided for the ordnance crew member. The computer-controlled electrically-fired cartridge-actuated A-size launchers can all be operated with the aircraft pressurised. They comprise 36 underfloor launchers, loadable only on the ground, and three which can be loaded from the cabin with the aircraft pressurised or unpressurised. A C-size chute, just aft of the three cabin launch tubes, allows free-fall launch (with the aircraft unpressurised) of flares, small marine markers, SUS and mail, and airdrops to remote ships or stations.

A KA-107A day/night reconnaissance camera is installed beneath the floor in this area, and is accessible in flight through a floor hatch. The illuminator for night reconnaissance photography is located beneath the floor of the in-flight maintenance station. This position has a bench with 28V DC and 115V 400Hz AC power outlets, and there are provisions for a microfiche reader.

Aircraft operational support equipment for the CP-140 includes the ground-based data interpretation and analysis centre (DIAC), and a ground support computer complex (GSCC). The former provides operational support for the operating squadrons; the latter provides technical support for the operational software, and maintains software configuration records.

The aircraft's weapon bay, which has a maximum capacity of 2,177 kg (4,800 lb) on eight stations, can accommodate and drop the Canadian SKAD/BR search and rescue kit, as well as a variety of ordnance. There are ten underwing hardpoints, with an individual capacity ranging from 277 kg (611 lb) to 1,111 kg (2,450 lb).

Canadair Ltd is manufacturing forward and aft radomes, rear fuselage sections, centre and outer wing sections, and main electrical load centres, both for the Aurora and for Lockheed-built P-3Cs.

TYPE: Four-turboprop long-range ASW and maritime patrol aircraft.

WINGS: As P-3C, with ailerons operated by dual hydraulic boosters, supplied from two independent hydraulic systems.

FUSELAGE: As for P-3C.

TAIL UNIT: As P-3C, with rudder and elevators each operated by dual hydraulic boosters, supplied from two independent hydraulic systems. Trim tabs in elevators and rudder.

LANDING GEAR: Hydraulically-retractable tricycle type with twin wheels on each unit. All units retract forward, main wheels into inner engine nacelles. Oleo-pneumatic shock-absorbers. All units can free-fall to the down and locked position in emergency. Hydraulically-powered steerable nose unit, controlled by handwheel on the pilot's side console. Hydraulically-operated dual segmented-disc brakes. Pneumatic emergency braking system.

POWER PLANT: Four 3,661 kW (4,910 ehp) Allison T56-A-14 turboprop engines, each driving a four-blade metal constant-speed fully-feathering and reversible propeller. Fuel in one fuselage and four wing integral tanks, with total usable capacity of 34,826 litres (9,200 US gallons). Single-point pressure refuelling, and four overwing gravity refuelling points, are provided. Fuel dump system. Propeller blade cuffs and spinners de-iced by electrical heating.

ACCOMMODATION: Normal eleven-man crew, with seating for five additional passengers. Dual controls standard. Flight deck has wide-vision windows, and circular windows for up to four observers are provided in the main cabin, each bulged to give 180° visibility. Main cabin fitted out as detailed in introductory paragraphs. Door on port side, aft of wing. Overwing emergency exit on each side of cabin; others in side and ceiling of flight deck. De-fogging and anti-icing of windscreens by electrical heating; windscreens have mechanical wipers, a washing system for the removal of salt deposits, and a rain-repellent spray system. Stowage for clothing, life jackets and parachute harness. Four floor tie-down areas, combined baggage/cargo capacity 442 kg (975 lb).

The first CP-140 Aurora version of the Lockheed Orion for the Canadian Armed Forces, bearing a US civil registration during its early test flying

SYSTEMS: Air-conditioning and pressurisation system supplied by two engine-driven compressors, maintaining cabin temperatures between 15·6°C and 26·7°C (60°F and 80°F), and a cabin altitude of 2,440 m (8,000 ft) to a height of 9,145 m (30,000 ft). Two independent hydraulic systems, each at a pressure of 207 bars (3,000 lb/sq in) are powered by three interchangeable electrically-driven pumps, any two of which can maintain full hydraulic services. Pneumatic system at pressure of 207 bars (3,000 lb/sq in) for emergency braking. Electrical system of 120/208V 400Hz AC supplied by three 60/90kVA engine-driven generators, any one of which can maintain full normal load. DC power supplied by three 200A 24V transformer-rectifiers and one 31Ah storage battery. APU drives a 60/90kVA generator and provides power and bleed air for ground air-conditioning, weapons bay heating and engine starting; it can also provide emergency electrical power in flight. Oxygen system for crew of three on flight deck with 3·5 hour capacity. Individual portable chemical oxygen generators for emergency use by all crew members. Automatic flight control system (AFCS) with dual-channel fail-safe autopilot; includes tactical and airways nav modes and proportional control wheel steering.

AVIONICS AND EQUIPMENT: Univac AN/AYK-10 navigation/tactical computer; digital magnetic tape units; teleprinter; display generator units; APS-116 search radar; OR-89/AA (modified) FLIR; video recorder for FLIR imagery; ARS-2 sonobuoy reference system; OL-82 (modified) acoustics data processor; RD-348, ASQ-147 and ASA-82 displays; LN-33 inertial navigation system; APN-208 Doppler; ARN-115 Omega; Tacan; revised airways/approach nav aids; dual VOR/ILS; communications sets comprising HF, UHF, VHF (AM), VHF guard receiver, VHF(FM); HF SIMOPS filters; RCVR homing; USH 502 crash position indicator/flight data recorder; ASW-31 AFCS; ALR-47 ESM; AN/ASH-27 28-track tape recorder; ASQ-501 MAD; OA-5150/ASQ (FACSII) MAD compensator; SLAR provisions; IFF; data link: airborne radiation thermometer (ART) provisions; and time coding generator. Equipment includes KA-107A day/night reconnaissance camera and night illuminator; provisions for civil sensors canister; galley with refrigerator and sink; white edge lighting for all console-mounted control panels; white cabin lighting; reading lights at all crew positions; white overhead lights; and aisle lights.

PERFORMANCE (with mission payload of 2,540 kg; 5,600 lb except where stated otherwise):

Max transit speed at optimum altitude
395 knots (732 km/h; 455 mph)
Max level speed below cruise ceiling
375 knots (695 km/h; 432 mph)
FAR balanced field length 2,408 m (7,900 ft)
T-O to 15 m (50 ft) 1,829 m (6,000 ft)
Landing from 15 m (50 ft) at 51,714 kg (114,000 lb)
landing weight 975 m (3,200 ft)
Ferry range 4,500 nm (8,339 km; 5,182 miles)
Endurance on station at 1,000 nm (1,853 km; 1,151 miles) radius 8 h 12 min

LOCKHEED VIKING

US Navy designation: S-3A

Development of the S-3A Viking anti-submarine aircraft (1978-79 *Jane's*) was carried out by Lockheed in partnership with Vought Systems Division of LTV and Univac Federal Systems Division of Sperry Rand. Vought designed and built the wing, engine pods, tail unit and landing gear, and Univac was responsible for the digital computer. Lockheed built the fuselage, integrated the avionics, and was responsible for final assembly at Burbank, California, from where the first prototype flew on 21 January 1972.

Production of 187 S-3As for the US Navy ended in mid-1978. All tooling has been placed in storage at Burbank pending a US Navy decision on further orders, and in early 1980 demonstrator versions of the US-3A (COD) and KS-3 (tanker) were being evaluated by the Navy. No production decision had then been made.

LOCKHEED L-1011 (MODEL 385) TRISTAR

In January 1966, Lockheed-California began a study of future requirements in the short/medium-haul airliner market. The design which emerged, known as the L-1011 (Lockheed Model 385 TriStar), was influenced by the published requirements of American Airlines, which specified optimum payload/range performance over the Chicago-Los Angeles route, coupled with an ability to take off from comparatively short runways with full payload.

The original design centred around a twin-turbofan configuration. Discussions which followed with American domestic carriers led to the eventual selection of a three-engined configuration, and the Rolls-Royce RB.211 high bypass ratio turbofan was chosen as power plant.

In June 1968 the L-1011 TriStar moved to the production design stage. Construction of the first aircraft began in March 1969, and this was rolled out in September 1970. The first flight was made on 16 November 1970. On 22 December 1971 class II provisional Type Certification was received, permitting delivery of aircraft to customers for route proving and demonstration purposes.

Top to bottom: Lockheed KS-3 (tanker), US-3A (COD) and S-3A Viking

The original version of the TriStar is now known as the L-1011-1. Three other versions were available in early 1980, the L-1011-100/-200/-500, which entered service respectively in 1975, 1977, and 1979. Details of current production versions, and available information on proposed new versions, follow:

L-1011-1. Basic TriStar, as described in detail. Initial delivery of the L-1011-1, to Eastern Air Lines for crew training, made on 6 April 1972, followed by a similar delivery to TWA. FAA certification was granted in the same month and the first passenger service with the TriStar was flown by Eastern on 15 April. Scheduled services began eleven days later.

L-1011-100. Longer-range version, with RB.211-22B engines (each 187 kN; 42,000 lb st). Outward configuration identical with that of L-1011-1. Max T-O weight of 211,375 kg (466,000 lb) with additional 8,165 kg (18,000 lb) of fuel in new centre-section tanks. Ordered by Cathay Pacific, Gulf Air, Saudi Arabian Airlines, and TWA.

L-1011-200. Longer-range version, with improved take-off and climb performance, offering particular benefits to operators serving 'hot or high' areas. Outward configuration identical with that of L-1011-1. Powered by RB.211-524 engines (each 213·5 kN; 48,000 lb st). Max T-O weight 211,375 kg (466,000 lb). First flight of TriStar testbed with RB.211-524 (one only) made on 10 April

1976. L-1011-200 certificated by FAA on 26 April 1977. Ordered by British Airways, Delta Air Lines, Gulf Air, Saudi Arabian Airlines, and Trans Carib Air.

L-1011-500. Extended-range version, with a max T-O weight of 224,980 kg (496,000 lb) and max fuel capacity of 96,160 kg (212,000 lb) through added centre-section tankage. Fuselage is shortened by 4·11 m (13 ft 6 in); most other external dimensions are the same as for L-1011-1. Three RB.211-524B or B4 engines (each 222·4 kN; 50,000 lb st). Galley located on main deck. Forward cargo hold accommodates 12 LD-3 containers or four pallets each measuring 2·24 m × 3·17 m (88 in × 125 in). Centre hold takes 7 LD-3 containers. In a mixed class configuration, with 24 first class passengers in six-abreast seating and 222 economy passengers in nine-abreast seating, the aircraft carries 246 passengers. Max accommodation for 330 passengers. Ordered by AeroPeru, Air Canada, Air Lanka, British Airways, BWIA, Delta Air Lines, LTU (West Germany), PanAm and TAP/Air Portugal. New fuselage/centre engine fairing, installed first on the -500, may be adopted as standard for all TriStar models. Flight testing of this version began in October 1978, and -500s entered service with British Airways on 7 May 1979.

In November 1979, flight testing began of the first production L-1011-500 fitted with a 1·37 m (4 ft 6 in) extension to each wingtip. This was made possible by the intro-

Lockheed L-1011-500 TriStar extended-range wide-bodied transport, with added side view (bottom) and scrap view of wingtip of L-1011-100 *(Pilot Press)*

Lockheed L-1011-500 TriStar of Pan Am with wing-span extension, active controls, and Rolls-Royce RB.211-524B3 engines (later to be upgraded to -524B4)

duction of automatically activated ailerons, and test results to early 1980 had shown a fuel efficiency improvement of 3 per cent. Extended wingtips and active controls of this kind were being introduced on Delta, Pan Am, LTU and Air Canada -500s during 1980-81 and will also be standard on TAP aircraft. Pan Am-500s will also pioneer in airline service the automatic brakes and digital autopilot which have been flown on the Advanced TriStar, and will introduce a catalytic ozone converter.

Advanced TriStar. The original TriStar prototype (N1011) continues in use by Lockheed, under the name Advanced TriStar, to test and develop new ideas and systems that are under consideration for inclusion in future versions of this aircraft. It is powered by three 222·4 kN (50,000 lb st) Rolls-Royce RB.211-524 turbofan engines. Its equipment includes automatic brakes, automatic take-off thrust control, a flight management system, extended wingtips, active aileron control, Autoland, direct lift control, all-moving tailplane, a new digital autopilot, and an area navigation system with moving map display.

Automatic brakes operating in conjunction with anti-skid units ensure that braking is optimum at all times, in relation to load, speed and weather conditions. Automatic take-off thrust control allows the pilot to use reduced take-off power settings, and to operate from shorter field lengths than would be normal for such settings. With the throttles set to provide the requisite take-off power, in relation to field length, altitude and aircraft gross weight, failure of an engine during take-off would be offset by automatic advance of the remaining two engines to rated take-off thrust, or to a pre-set emergency power rating limit, thus minimising any time lag that might be experienced due to slow crew response.

Each wing of the Advanced TriStar has been extended at the tip by 1·37 m (4 ft 6 in), resulting in a significant reduction of induced drag, and producing fuel savings in the order of 3 per cent. However, the added span generates an increased wing lift increment which would be unacceptable under certain manoeuvre or gust loads. This required the introduction of an active control system, to provide automatic aileron deflection to offset such loads, thus eliminating the need for wing structural redesign.

In mid-1980 Lockheed had built for structure testing a TriStar fin made of advanced composite materials. Weighing 106 kg (235 lb) less than the standard metal fin, a similar fin may be flown eventually on the Advanced TriStar.

By 8 April 1980, Lockheed had delivered 174 L-1011 TriStars to AeroPeru, Air Canada, All Nippon Airways, British Airways, Cathay Pacific Airways, Court Line, Delta Air Lines, Eastern Air Lines, Gulf Air, Lufttransport Unternehmen, Pacific Southwest Airlines, Saudi Arabian Airlines and Trans World Airlines. Sales totalled 236, with options on 76 more, by the same date.

The description which follows applies to the L-1011-1 TriStar in its initial operational form, except where indicated. The basic structural details apply to all current production derivatives.

TYPE: Three-turbofan commercial transport.

WINGS: Cantilever low-wing monoplane. Special Lockheed aerofoil sections. Dihedral at trailing-edge 7° 31′ on inner wings, 5° 30′ outboard. Sweepback at quarter-chord 35°. The wing consists of a centre-section, passing through the lower fuselage, and an outer wing panel on each side. It is of conventional fail-safe construction, with aluminium alloy surfaces, ribs and spars, and integral fuel tanks. Hydraulically-powered aluminium alloy ailerons of conventional two-spar box construction, with aluminium alloy honeycomb trailing-edge, in inboard and outboard sections on each wing, operate in conjunction with flight spoilers. The low-speed ailerons extend from approximately 80% of semi-span to within 0·25 m (10 in) of the wingtips, the high-speed ailerons

extend from approximately WBL 387 to WBL 480 on each wing. Double-slotted Fowler trailing-edge flaps, constructed of aluminium alloy and aluminium alloy honeycomb. Each flap segment consists of a honeycomb trailing-edge, a front spar, ribs, skin panels, carriages, and tracks mounted on the forward segment to provide for extension and rotation of the aft segment. A sheet metal vane surface, actuated by a linkage system during flap rotation, forms the forward section of the extended flap. Four aluminium alloy leading-edge slats outboard of engine pylon on each wing. Each segment is mounted to two roller-supported tracks and extends in a circular motion down and forward for take-off and landing. Three leading-edge slats inboard of engine pylon on each wing, made of aluminium alloy honeycomb and sheet metal fairings. Six spoilers on the upper surface of each wing, two inboard and four outboard of the inboard aileron, constructed from bonded aluminium alloy tapered honeycomb. No trim tabs. Flight controls fully powered. Each control surface system is controlled by a multiple redundant servo actuator system that is powered by four independent and separate hydraulic sources. Thermal de-icing of outboard wing leading-edge slats by engine bleed air.

FUSELAGE: Semi-monocoque structure of aluminium alloy. Constant cross-sectional diameter of 5·97 m (19 ft 7 in) for most of the length. Bonding utilised in skin joints, for attaching skin-doublers at joints and around openings to improve fatigue life. Skins and stringers supported by frames spaced at 0·51 m (20 in) intervals, with fail-safe straps midway between frames. These frames, with the exception of main frames and door-edge members, are 0·076 m (3 in) deep at the sides of the cabin, increasing progressively to a depth of 0·15 m (6 in) at the top of the fuselage and below the floor. Fuselage length reduced on L-1011-500.

TAIL UNIT: Conventional cantilever structure, consisting of variable-incidence horizontal tailplane-elevator assembly and vertical fin and rudder. Primary loads of the fin are carried by a conventional box-beam structure, with ribs spaced at approx 0·51 m (20 in) centres. The rudder comprises forward and aft spars, glassfibre trailing-edges, hinge and actuator backup ribs, sheet metal formers, box surface panels and leading-edge fairings. Elevators are of similar construction. Truss members for the tailplane centre-section are built up from forged and extruded sections. Outboard of the centre-section, construction is similar to that of the fin box-beam, leading- and trailing-edges, except that the surface structure is integrally stiffened. The elevators are linked mechanically to the tailplane actuation gear, to modify its camber and improve its effectiveness. No trim tabs. Controls are fully powered, the hydraulic servo actuators receiving power from four independent hydraulic sources, under control of electronic flight control system. Control feel is provided, with the force gradient scheduled as a function of flight condition. No de-icing equipment.

LANDING GEAR: Menasco hydraulically-retractable tricycle type. Twin-wheel units in tandem on each main gear; twin wheels on nose gear, which is steerable 65° on each side. Nosewheels retract forward into fuselage. Main wheels retract inward into fuselage wheel-wells. Oleo-pneumatic shock-absorbers on all units. Goodrich forged aluminium alloy wheels of split construction. Main wheels have tubeless tyres size 50 × 20-20, Type VIII, pressure 10·34-11·38 bars (150-165 lb/sq in) for short- to medium-range operational weights, 12·41 bars (180 lb/sq in) for max-range weight. Nosewheels have tubeless tyres size 36 × 11-16, Type VII, pressure 12·76 bars (185 lb/sq in). Hydraulically-operated brakes, controlled by the rudder pedals. Anti-skid units, with individual wheel skid and modulated control, installed in the normal and alternative braking systems.

POWER PLANT (L-1011-1): Three Rolls-Royce RB.211-22B turbofan engines, each rated at 187 kN (42,000 lb st). Two engines mounted in pods on pylons under the wings, the third mounted in the rear fuselage at the base of the fin. Engine bleed air is used to anti-ice the engine inlet lips. Two integral fuel tanks in each wing; inboard tank capacity 30,581 litres (8,079 US gallons), outboard tank capacity 14,489 litres (3,828 US gallons). Total fuel capacity 90,140 litres (23,814 US gallons). Pressure refuelling points in wing leading-edges. Oil capacity approx 34 litres (9 US gallons) per engine. A detachable pylon can be fitted between the starboard engine nacelle and fuselage to permit carriage of a replacement engine for another TriStar. Alternative power plants for -100, -200 and -500 detailed under model listings. These four models each have provision for additional centre-section tankage, raising total fuel capacity to 100,317 litres (26,502 US gallons) in -100 and -200, and 119,774 litres (31,642 US gallons) in -500.

ACCOMMODATION: Crew of 13. First class and coach mixed accommodation for 256 passengers, with a maximum of 400 in all-economy configuration. Alternative intermediate seating capacities are provided by using eight seat-tracks which permit 6, 8, 9 or 10-abreast seating, with two full-length aisles. Underfloor galley. Seven lavatories are provided, two forward and five aft. Three Type A passenger doors of the upward-opening plug type on each side of the fuselage, one pair immediately aft of flight deck, one pair forward of wing, one pair aft of wing. Two Type I emergency exit doors, one each side of fuselage, at rear of cabin, replaced by two Type A doors for 10-abreast seating. Baggage and freight compartments beneath the floor able to accommodate 16 containers, totalling 71·58 m³ (2,528 cu ft), and 19·8 m³ (700 cu ft) bulk cargo (19 containers and 14·2 m³; 500 cu ft in -500).

SYSTEMS: Air-conditioning and pressurisation system, using engine bleed air or APU air combined with air-cycle refrigeration. Pressurisation system maintains equivalent of 2,440 m (8,000 ft) conditions to 12,800 m (42,000 ft). Normal cabin pressure differential 0·58 bars (8·44 lb/sq in). Four independent 207 bar (3,000 lb/sq in) hydraulic systems provide power for primary flight control surfaces, normal brake power, landing gear retraction and nosewheel steering. Electrical system includes four 120/208V 400Hz alternators, one on each engine and one driven by the APU, which is sited in the aft fuselage. APU provides ground and in-flight power, to an altitude of 9,145 m (30,000 ft), producing both shaft and pneumatic power for utilisation by the electrical, environmental control and hydraulic systems. Integral electric heaters to anti-ice windscreens, pitot masts and total temperature probes.

AVIONICS AND EQUIPMENT: Standard equipment includes two ARINC 546 VHF communication transceivers, two ARINC 547 VHF navigation systems, two ARINC 568 interrogator units, an ARINC 564 weather radar system, two ARINC 572 air traffic control transponders, partial provision for a dual collision system, three vertical gyros, and full blind-flying instrumentation. Space is provided for installation of two ARINC 533A HF transceivers and a dual SATCOM system.

DIMENSIONS, EXTERNAL:

Wing span	47·34 m (155 ft 4 in)
Wing chord at root	10·46 m (34 ft 4 in)
Wing chord at tip	3·12 m (10 ft 3 in)
Wing aspect ratio	6·95
Length overall:	
-1, -100, -200	54·17 m (177 ft 8½ in)
-500	50·05 m (164 ft 2½ in)
Height overall	16·87 m (55 ft 4 in)
Tailplane span	21·82 m (71 ft 7 in)

Wheel track	10·97 m (36 ft 0 in)
Wheelbase: -1, -100, -200	21·34 m (70 ft 0 in)
-500	19·71 m (64 ft 8 in)
Passenger doors (each): Height	1·93 m (6 ft 4 in)
Width	1·07 m (3 ft 6 in)
Height to sill	4·60 m (15 ft 1 in)
Emergency passenger doors (each):	
Height	1·52 m (5 ft 0 in)
Width	0·61 m (2 ft 0 in)
Height to sill	4·60 m (15 ft 1 in)
Baggage and freight compartment doors (forward and	
centre): Height	1·73 m (5 ft 8 in)
Width	1·78 m (5 ft 10 in)
Height to sill	2·72 m (8 ft 11 in)
Baggage and freight compartment doors (aft):	
Height	1·22 m (4 ft 0 in)
Width	1·12 m (3 ft 8 in)
Height to sill	2·92 m (9 ft 7 in)

DIMENSIONS, INTERNAL:

Cabin, excl flight deck and underfloor galley:	
Length	41·43 m (135 ft 11 in)
Max width	5·77 m (18 ft 11 in)
Max height	2·41 m (7 ft 11 in)
Floor area: -1, -100, -200	215·5 m² (2,320 sq ft)
-500	192·6 m² (2,073 sq ft)
Volume	453 m³ (16,000 cu ft)
Baggage/cargo holds, bulk capacity:	
-1, -100, -200	110·4 m³ (3,900 cu ft)
-500	118·9 m³ (4,200 cu ft)

AREAS:

Wings, gross	320·0 m² (3,456 sq ft)
Ailerons (total)	14·86 m² (160 sq ft)
Trailing-edge flaps (total)	49·80 m² (536 sq ft)
Leading-edge slats (total):	
inboard slats	11·52 m² (124 sq ft)
outboard slats	21·93 m² (236 sq ft)

Spoilers (total)	19·88 m² (214 sq ft)
Fin	51·10 m² (550 sq ft)
Rudder	11·89 m² (128 sq ft)
Tailplane	119·10 m² (1,282 sq ft)

WEIGHTS:

Operating weight empty:	
-1	109,045 kg (240,400 lb)
-100	110,720 kg (244,100 lb)
-200	111,495 kg (245,800 lb)
-500	109,298 kg (240,963 lb)
Max payload: -1	38,373 kg (84,600 lb)
-100	34,427 kg (75,900 lb)
-200	33,020 kg (72,800 lb)
-500	44,015 kg (97,037 lb)
Max T-O weight: -1	195,045 kg (430,000 lb)
-100	211,375 kg (466,000 lb)
-200	216,363 kg (477,000 lb)
-500	224,980 kg (496,000 lb)
Max zero-fuel weight: -1	147,417 kg (325,000 lb)
-100, -200	145,150 kg (320,000 lb)
-500	153,315 kg (338,000 lb)
Max landing weight: -1	162,385 kg (358,000 lb)
-100, -200, -500	166,920 kg (368,000 lb)

PERFORMANCE (A: L-1011-1 at max T-O weight of 195,045 kg: 430,000 lb; B and C: L-1011-100 and L-1011-200 respectively at max T-O weight of 211,375 kg: 466,000 lb; D: L-1011-500 at max T-O weight of 224,980 kg: 496,000 lb, except where indicated):

Never-exceed speed, all versions	
Mach 0·95 (435 knots; 806 km/h; 501 mph) CAS	
Max cruising speed, mid-cruise weight at 9,145 m	
(30,000 ft): A	520 knots (964 km/h; 599 mph)
B	515 knots (954 km/h; 593 mph)
C	530 knots (982 km/h; 610 mph)
D	525 knots (973 km/h; 605 mph)

Econ cruising speed, mid-cruise weight at 10,670 m	
(35,000 ft): A, B	480 knots (890 km/h; 553 mph)
C, D	485 knots (899 km/h; 558 mph)
Stalling speed at max landing weight, flaps and gear up:	
A	148 knots (274 km/h; 170 mph)
B, C, D	151 knots (280 km/h; 174 mph)
Stalling speed at max landing weight, flaps and gear	
down: A	108 knots (200 km/h; 124 mph)
B, C	109 knots (202 km/h; 126 mph)
D	111 knots (206 km/h; 128 mph)
Max rate of climb at S/L: A	856 m (2,810 ft)/min
B	765 m (2,510 ft)/min
C	847 m (2,780 ft)/min
D	777 m (2,550 ft)/min
Service ceiling, all versions	12,800 m (42,000 ft)
FAR T-O field length: A	2,426 m (7,960 ft)
B	3,243 m (10,640 ft)
C	2,460 m (8,070 ft)
D	2,975 m (9,760 ft)
FAR landing field length, at max landing weight:	
A	1,734 m (5,690 ft)
B, C	1,768 m (5,800 ft)
D	1,957 m (6,420 ft)
Range with max passengers and baggage, international	
reserves: A	2,870 nm (5,319 km; 3,305 miles)
B	3,660 nm (6,783 km; 4,215 miles)
C	3,680 nm (6,820 km; 4,238 miles)
D	5,209 nm (9,653 km; 5,998 miles)
Range with max fuel, international reserves:	
A	4,360 nm (8,080 km; 5,021 miles)
B	4,820 nm (8,932 km; 5,550 miles)
C	4,880 nm (9,044 km; 5,619 miles)
D	6,150 nm (11,397 km; 7,082 miles)

OPERATIONAL NOISE LEVELS (FAR Pt 36):

T-O	97 EPNdB
Approach	103 EPNdB
Sideline	95 EPNdB

LOCKHEED-GEORGIA COMPANY

86 South Cobb Drive, Marietta, Georgia 30063

Lockheed-Georgia's main building at Marietta is one of the world's largest aircraft production plants under a single roof. Aircraft in current production on its assembly lines are the C-130 Hercules turboprop transport and its commercial counterpart, the L 100. Major modification programmes are under way on USAF C-141 StarLifter and C-5 Galaxy transports. Studies include an 'all-electric' aircraft, without hydraulic or pneumatic systems, which would offer economies in construction, operating and maintenance costs, and reduced fuel consumption, by comparison with conventional designs.

Lockheed-Georgia had a total of approximately 11,000 employees at the beginning of 1980.

LOCKHEED MODEL 382 HERCULES

US Air Force designations: C-130, AC-130, DC-130, HC-130, JC-130, MC-130, RC-130 and WC-130
US Navy designations: C-130, DC-130, EC-130 and LC-130
US Marine Corps designation: KC-130
US Coast Guard designation: HC-130
Canadian Armed Forces designation: CC-130
RAF designations: Hercules C.Mk 1, W.Mk 2 and C.Mk 3

The C-130 was designed to a specification issued by the US Air Force Tactical Air Command in 1951. Lockheed was awarded its first production contract for the C-130A in September 1952, and a total of 461 C-130As and C-130Bs was manufactured. Details of these basic versions and of many variants for special duties can be found in the 1967-68 and 1975-76 Jane's. Later military versions of the C-130 are as follows:

C-130E (Lockheed Model 382-44). Extended-range development of C-130B, with four 3,020 kW (4,050 ehp) T56-A-7 turboprop engines and two 5,145 litre (1,360 US gallon) underwing fuel tanks. Deliveries began in April 1962, and by February 1975 the planned production of a total of 503 C-130Es had been completed. Details of the basic C-130E can be found in the 1973-74 Jane's.

EC-130E. Eight aircraft modified for USAF to carry the USC-15 Airborne Battlefield Command and Control Center. Large blade antennae added above dorsal fin and under each outer wing. Smaller antennae include horizontal blade on each side of rear fuselage. Bullet-shape canisters outboard of each underwing antenna and at extreme tail of aircraft house trailing wire antennae which extend several hundred feet behind the EC-130E in flight. Aircraft, numbered 621791, 621809, 621818, 621825, 621832, 621836, 621857 and 621862, operated by 7th Airborne Command and Control Squadron (TAC) from Keesler AFB, Mississippi.

MC-130E. Version of C-130E modified for USAF Special Operations such as covert infiltration and exfiltration at very low altitudes at night, using special avionics for terrain masking, navigation and airdrops, under codename Combat Talon.

EC-130G. Redesignation of four C-130Gs acquired by US Navy. Equipped with VLF radio to relay emergency action messages to Fleet Ballistic Missile submarines anywhere in the world.

Lockheed C-130E Hercules four-turboprop medium/long-range combat transport (Pilot Press)

C-130H. Similar to earlier Hercules models except for more powerful engines: T56-A-15 turboprops rated at 3,661 kW (4,910 ehp) for take-off, but limited to 3,362 kW (4,508 ehp). Deliveries to USAF began in April 1975.

C-130H-MP. Maritime patrol, search and rescue version, based on C-130H. Crew of eight (pilot, co-pilot, flight engineer, navigator and four observers). Max T-O weight 70,310 kg (155,000 lb). Max payload 21,500 kg (47,400 lb). Four 3,362 kW (4,509 ehp) engines. Standard equipment includes sea search radar, computerised area navigation system, cameras with inbuilt illumination. Optional equipment includes searchlights, ramp pallet incorporating aft observer station, scanner seats, observer doors and windows, slide-in modules containing crew rest facilities, lavatory and galley, flare launcher, airdrop rescue kit. Special corrosion protection. Search time 2 h 30 min at radius of 1,800 nm (3,334 km; 2,071 miles); 16 h at radius of 200 nm (370 km; 230 miles). One ordered for Japan Maritime Safety Agency and three for Royal Malaysian Air Force.

C-130H-30. 'Stretched' version, with structural changes similar to those of RAF Hercules C.Mk 3 (see C-130K paragraph). Five ordered for Indonesian Air Force.

HC-130H. Extended-range version for Aerospace Rescue and Recovery Service of the US Air Force for aerial recovery of personnel or equipment and other duties. The US Coast Guard subsequently ordered seven. Total of 66 delivered, of which the first one flew on 8 December 1964. Details in 1979-80 Jane's. Four modified as **JHC-130H** with added equipment for aerial recovery of re-entering space capsules. One modified by LAS to **DC-130H.**

KC-130H. A tanker version of the C-130H, very similar to the KC-130R. Exported to Argentina (2), Brazil (2),

Lockheed C-130H Hercules of the Egyptian Air Force (Antonio Camarasa)

Israel (2), Saudi Arabia (6) and Spain (3). One more ordered by Spain in 1980, plus tanker kits for installation in five C-130H aircraft of Spanish Air Force.

C-130K. This is basically a C-130H, modified to meet requirements of the Royal Air Force. Much of the avionics and instrumentation is of UK manufacture. Sixty-six delivered as **Hercules C. Mk 1**, of which the first flew on 19 October 1966. One modified by Marshall of Cambridge (Engineering) Ltd in the UK for use by the RAF Meteorological Research Flight, under the designation **Hercules W. Mk 2**. Thirty of the others are each being lengthened by 4·58 m (15 ft 0 in), equivalent to commercial L 100-30 standard, during 1978-82. This will increase payload capacity to seven cargo pallets instead of five, or 128 troops instead of 92, or 92 fully-equipped paratroops instead of 64, or 93 stretcher patients (and six attendants) instead of 70. The first aircraft was modified at Lockheed-Georgia in 1979; the remaining 29 are being lengthened by Marshall of Cambridge (which see). After modification, these aircraft are redesignated **Hercules C. Mk 3**.

HC-130N. Search and rescue version for recovery of aircrew and retrieval of space capsules after re-entry, using advanced direction-finding equipment. Fifteen delivered to US Air Force.

HC-130P. Twenty HC-130Hs modified to have capability of refuelling helicopters in flight, and for mid-air retrieval of parachute-borne payloads. Details in 1979-80 *Jane's*.

EC-130Q. Fifteen aircraft similar to EC-130G but with improved equipment and crew accommodation, for US Navy command communications (TACAMO) duties.

KC-130R. Tanker version of C-130H: 14 built for US Marine Corps. Major changes from earlier KC-130F include engines of 3,362 kW (4,508 ehp), increased T-O and landing weights, pylon-mounted fuel tanks to provide additional 10,296 litres (2,720 US gallons) of fuel, and removable 13,627 litre (3,600 US gallon) fuel tank in cargo compartment.

LC-130R. Basically a C-130H with wheel-ski gear for US Navy. Four converted, for service in the Antarctic. Two more acquired by National Science Foundation, for use in the Antarctic. Details in 1979-80 *Jane's*.

During 1980, a USAF C-130E from Pope AFB was fitted with two light alloy and glassfibre strakes, each 2·13 m (7 ft) long, 0·50 m (1 ft 8 in) deep and 0·10 m (4 in) thick, on the undersurface of the rear fuselage. Flight testing showed that the resulting drag reduction offered fuel savings of more than 3 per cent. Evaluation is continuing.

Commercial versions of the Hercules are described separately.

The C-130 is able to deliver single loads of up to 11,340 kg (25,000 lb) by the ground proximity extraction method. This involves making a flypast 1·2-1·5 m (4-5 ft) above the ground with the rear loading ramp open. The aircraft trails a hook which is attached by cable to the palletised cargo. The hook engages a steel cable on the ground and the cargo is extracted from the aircraft and brought to a stop on the ground in about 30 m (100 ft) by an energy absorption system manufactured by All American Engineering of Wilmington, Delaware. An alternative extraction technique involves deploying a 6·70 m (22 ft) ribbon parachute to drag the pallet from the cabin. Loads of up to 22,680 kg (50,000 lb) have been delivered by this method.

By January 1980 firm orders for all versions of the C-130 totalled 1,592 for 46 nations. This total comprised 1,011 C-130s for the US services, 478 for foreign military operators, and 78 commercial Hercules. The 1,500th Hercules, a C-130H for the Sudan Air Force, was delivered on 13 March 1978. Production rate for 1980 was set at three aircraft per month.

The following details refer specifically to the C-130H, except where indicated otherwise:

TYPE: Medium/long-range combat transport.

WINGS: Cantilever high-wing monoplane. Wing section NACA 64A318 at root, NACA 64A412 at tip. Dihedral 2° 30'. Incidence 3° at root, 0° at tip. Sweepback at quarter-chord 0°. All-metal two-spar stressed-skin structure, with integrally-stiffened tapered machined skin panels up to 14·63 m (48 ft 0 in) long. Conventional aluminium alloy ailerons have tandem-piston hydraulic boost, operated by either of two independent hydraulic systems. Lockheed-Fowler aluminium alloy trailing-edge flaps. Trim tabs in ailerons. Leading-edges anti-iced by engine bleed air.

FUSELAGE: Semi-monocoque structure of aluminium and magnesium alloys.

TAIL UNIT: Cantilever all-metal stressed-skin structure. Fixed-incidence tailplane. Trim tabs in elevators and rudder. Elevator tabs use AC electrical power as primary source and DC as emergency source. Control surfaces have tandem-piston hydraulic boost. Hot-air anti-icing of tailplane leading-edge, by engine bleed air.

LANDING GEAR: Hydraulically-retractable tricycle type. Each main unit has two wheels in tandem, retracting into fairings built on to the sides of the fuselage. Nose unit has twin wheels and is steerable through 60° each side of centre. Oleo shock-absorbers. Main-wheel tyres size 56 × 20-20, pressure 5·52 bars (80 lb/sq in). Nose-wheel tyres size 39 × 13-16, pressure 4·14 bars (60 lb/sq in). Goodyear aircooled hydraulic brakes with anti-skid units. Retractable combination wheel-skis available.

POWER PLANT: Four 3,362 kW (4,508 ehp) Allison T56-A-15 turboprop engines, each driving a Hamilton Standard type 54H60 four-blade constant-speed fully-feathering reversible-pitch propeller. Eight Aerojet-General 15KS-1000 JATO units (each 4·45 kN; 1,000 lb st for 15 sec) can be carried. Fuel in six integral tanks in wings, with total capacity of 26,344 litres (6,960 US gallons) and two underwing pylon tanks, each with capacity of 5,146 litres (1,360 US gallons). Total capacity 36,636 litres (9,680 US gallons). Single pressure refuelling point in starboard wheel well. Overwing gravity fuelling. Oil capacity 182 litres (48 US gallons).

ACCOMMODATION: Crew of four on flight deck, comprising pilot, co-pilot, navigator and systems manager. Provision for fifth man to supervise loading. Sleeping quarters for relief crew, and galley. Flight deck and main cabin pressurised and air-conditioned. Standard complements are as follows: troops (max) 92, paratroops (max) 64, litters 74 and 2 attendants. As a cargo carrier, loads can include heavy equipment such as a 12,080 kg (26,640 lb) type F.6 refuelling trailer or a 155 mm howitzer and its high-speed tractor. Up to six preloaded pallets of freight can be carried. Hydraulically-operated main loading door and ramp at rear of cabin. Paratroop door on each side aft of landing gear fairing.

SYSTEMS: Air-conditioning and pressurisation system max pressure differential 0·52 bars (7·5 lb/sq in). Two independent hydraulic systems, pressure 207 bars (3,000 lb/sq in). Electrical system supplied by four 40kVA AC generators, plus one 40kVA auxiliary generator driven by APU. Current production aircraft incorporate many systems and component design changes for increased reliability. There are differences between the installed components for US government and export versions.

DIMENSIONS, EXTERNAL:

Wing span	40·41 m (132 ft 7 in)
Wing chord at root	4·88 m (16 ft 0 in)
Wing chord, mean	4·16 m (13 ft 8½ in)
Wing aspect ratio	10·09

Length overall:	
all except HC-130H	29·79 m (97 ft 9 in)
Height overall	11·66 m (38 ft 3 in)
Tailplane span	16·05 m (52 ft 8 in)
Wheel track	4·35 m (14 ft 3 in)
Wheelbase	9·77 m (32 ft 0¾ in)
Propeller diameter	4·11 m (13 ft 6 in)
Main cargo door (rear of cabin):	
Height	2·77 m (9 ft 1 in)
Width	3·05 m (10 ft 0 in)
Height to sill	1·03 m (3 ft 5 in)
Paratroop doors (each): Height	1·83 m (6 ft 0 in)
Width	0·91 m (3 ft 0 in)
Height to sill	1·03 m (3 ft 5 in)

DIMENSIONS, INTERNAL:

Cabin, excl flight deck:	
Length without ramp	12·60 m (41 ft 5 in)
Length with ramp	15·73 m (51 ft 8½ in)
Max width	3·13 m (10 ft 3 in)
Max height	2·81 m (9 ft 2¾ in)
Floor area, excl ramp	39·5 m² (425 sq ft)
Volume, incl ramp	127·4 m³ (4,500 cu ft)

AREAS:

Wings, gross	162·12 m² (1,745 sq ft)
Ailerons (total)	10·22 m² (110 sq ft)
Trailing-edge flaps (total)	31·77 m² (342 sq ft)
Fin	20·90 m² (225 sq ft)
Rudder, incl tab	6·97 m² (75 sq ft)
Tailplane	35·40 m² (381 sq ft)
Elevators, incl tabs	14·40 m² (155 sq ft)

WEIGHTS AND LOADINGS:

Operating weight empty	34,397 kg (75,832 lb)
Max payload	19,645 kg (43,310 lb)
Max normal T-O weight	70,310 kg (155,000 lb)
Max overload T-O weight	79,380 kg (175,000 lb)
Max landing weight	79,380 kg (175,000 lb)
Max zero-fuel weight, 2·5 g	54,040 kg (119,142 lb)
Max wing loading	434·5 kg/m² (89 lb/sq ft)
Max power loading	5·23 kg/kW (8·6 lb/ehp)

PERFORMANCE (at max T-O weight, unless indicated otherwise):

Max cruising speed	335 knots (621 km/h; 386 mph)
Econ cruising speed	300 knots (556 km/h; 345 mph)
Stalling speed	100 knots (185 km/h; 115 mph)
Max rate of climb at S/L	579 m (1,900 ft)/min
Service ceiling at 58,970 kg (130,000 lb) AUW	10,060 m (33,000 ft)
Service ceiling, one engine out, at 58,970 kg (130,000 lb) AUW	8,075 m (26,500 ft)
Min ground turning radius	19·2 m (63 ft)

Runway LCN at 70,310 kg (155,000 lb) AUW:

asphalt	37
concrete	42
T-O run	1,091 m (3,580 ft)
T-O to 15 m (50 ft)	1,573 m (5,160 ft)
Landing from 15 m (50 ft) at 45,360 kg (100,000 lb) AUW	823 m (2,700 ft)
Landing from 15 m (50 ft) at max landing weight	1,509 m (4,950 ft)
Landing run at max landing weight	732 m (2,400 ft)

Range with max payload, with 5% reserves and allowance for 30 min at S/L
  2,160 nm (4,002 km; 2,487 miles)

Range with max fuel, incl external tanks, 9,070 kg (20,000 lb) payload and reserves of 5% initial fuel plus 30 min at S/L 4,000 nm (7,412 km; 4,606 miles)

LOCKHEED L 100 SERIES COMMERCIAL HERCULES

Details of initial versions of the commercial Hercules have appeared in previous editions of *Jane's;* current models are as follows:

Lockheed L 100-30 Hercules commercial transport in service with Safair Freighters of South Africa

L 100-20 (Model 382E). Certificated on 4 October 1968, this 'stretched' version of the Hercules has a 2·54 m (100 in) fuselage extension. A 1·52 m (60 in) fuselage plug is inserted aft of the forward crew door and a 1·02 m (40 in) plug aft of the paratroop doors. Allison 501-D22A engines. Operators have included Alaska International Air, Delta Air Lines, Saturn Airways and Southern Air Transport in the USA; Pacific Western Airlines in Canada; SATCO in Peru; Safair Freighters in the Republic of South Africa; the Kuwait Air Force (2); the Peruvian Air Force (5); Philippine Aerotransport; the Philippine Air Force (4); and the Republic of Gabon (2).

L 100-30 (Model 382G). Generally similar to the L 100-20, but with the fuselage extended a further 2·03 m (80 in). Rear cargo windows and provision for JATO eliminated; paratroop doors optional. Saturn Airways was the first operator of this model, with services beginning in December 1970. Alaska International Air, Pelita Air Service (Indonesia), PEMEX (Mexico), Safair Freighters, the Republic of Gabon, the Republic of Uganda, the Bolivian and Indonesian Air Forces, SCIBE and Southern Air are among those who have operated the L 100-30.

A total of 78 commercial Hercules (all versions) had been delivered by January 1980. Details given for the C-130H apply also to the L 100-20 and L 100-30, except as follows:

TYPE: Medium/long-range transport.

LANDING GEAR: As for C-130H, except main-wheel tyre pressure 3·24-7·38 bars (47-107 lb/sq in) and nose-wheel tyre pressure 4·14 bars (60 lb/sq in).

POWER PLANT: Four 3,362 kW (4,508 ehp) Allison 501-D22A turboprop engines.

DIMENSIONS, EXTERNAL:

Length overall: L 100-20	32·33 m (106 ft 1 in)
L 100-30	34·37 m (112 ft 9 in)
Wheelbase: L 100-20	11·30 m (37 ft 1 in)
L 100-30	12·32 m (40 ft 5 in)
Crew door (integral steps):	
Height	1·14 m (3 ft 9 in)
Width	0·76 m (2 ft 6 in)
Height to sill	1·04 m (3 ft 5 in)

DIMENSIONS, INTERNAL:

Cabin, excl flight deck:	
Length: L 100-20	15·04 m (49 ft 4 in)
L 100-30	17·07 m (56 ft 0 in)
Max height	2·74 m (9 ft 0 in)
Floor area, excl ramp:	
L 100-20	46·36 m² (499 sq ft)
L 100-30	52·30 m² (563 sq ft)
Floor area, ramp	9·57 m² (103 sq ft)
Volume, incl ramp:	
L 100-20	150·28 m³ (5,307 cu ft)
L 100-30	171·5 m³ (6,057 cu ft)

WEIGHTS AND LOADINGS:

Operating weight empty:	
L 100-20	32,934 kg (72,607 lb)
L 100-30	33,194 kg (73,181 lb)
Max payload: L 100-20	21,497 kg (47,393 lb)
L 100-30	23,505 kg (51,819 lb)
Max ramp weight	70,670 kg (155,800 lb)
Max T-O weight	70,308 kg (155,000 lb)
Max landing weight:	
L 100-20	58,970 kg (130,000 lb)
L 100-30	61,235 kg (135,000 lb)
Max zero-fuel weight:	
L 100-20	54,430 kg (120,000 lb)
L 100-30	56,700 kg (125,000 lb)
Max wing loading	433·5 kg/m² (88·8 lb/sq ft)
Max power loading	5·23 kg/kW (8·6 lb/ehp)

PERFORMANCE (at max T-O weight):

Max cruising speed at 6,100 m (20,000 ft) at 54,430 kg (120,000 lb) AUW	
	314 knots (581 km/h; 361 mph)
Landing speed:	
L 100-20	126 knots (233 km/h; 145 mph)
L 100-30	128 knots (237 km/h; 147 mph)
Max rate of climb at S/L	579 m (1,900 ft)/min
Min ground turning radius: L 100-20	26·8 m (88 ft)
L 100-30	27·5 m (90 ft)

Runway LCN: asphalt	37
concrete	42
FAR T-O field length	1,830 m (6,000 ft)
FAR landing field length, at max landing weight:	
L 100-20	1,450 m (4,760 ft)
L 100-30	1,472 m (4,830 ft)
Range with max payload, 45 min reserves:	
L 100-20	2,100 nm (3,889 km; 2,417 miles)
L 100-30	1,742 nm (3,226 km; 2,005 miles)
Range with zero payload, 45 min reserves:	
L 100-20	4,250 nm (7,871 km; 4,891 miles)
L 100-30	4,200 nm (7,778 km; 4,833 miles)

OPERATIONAL NOISE LEVELS (FAR Pt 36):

T-O	98·4 EPNdB
Approach	99·1 EPNdB
Sideline	93·9 EPNdB

LOCKHEED MODEL L 100-50 HERCULES REGIONAL AIRFREIGHTER

Lockheed-Georgia was working in early 1980 on a new high-capacity version of the L 100 commercial Hercules, for operation over short to medium ranges. Extra capacity results from lengthening the basic L 100 airframe by 11·18 m (36 ft 8 in), with a 6·10 m (20 ft 0 in) plug forward of the wing, and one of 5·08 m (16 ft 8 in) aft of the wing. This would provide a cargo compartment length of 26·54 m (87 ft 1 in) including the ramp, and a bulk volume capacity of 225·1 m³ (7,948 cu ft).

This new version of the commercial Hercules would be able to carry most common unit load devices, and would be suitable for interline operation with wide-body freighters. Loading and unloading would be carried out via a 2·90 × 2·74 m (9 ft 6 in × 9 ft 0 in) forward side cargo door, and the cargo compartment would be able to accommodate nine 2·44 × 3·18 × 2·62 m (96 × 125 × 103 in) pallets, or ten 2·24 × 3·18 × 2·62 m (88 × 125 × 103 in) pallets plus an additional pallet on the ramp, providing a total palletised volume of 193·4 m³ (6,830 cu ft) and 192·3 m³ (6,790 cu ft) respectively.

Aircraft weights being contemplated would ensure that the aircraft met FAR Pt 36 Stage III noise standards, and are estimated as follows:

Operating weight empty	38,634 kg (85,175 lb)
Max payload	30,316 kg (66,835 lb)
Max T-O weight	79,378 kg (175,000 lb)
Max ramp weight	79,886 kg (176,120 lb)
Max zero-fuel weight	68,950 kg (152,010 lb)
Max landing weight	74,842 kg (165,000 lb)

LOCKHEED L 400 TWIN HERCULES

On 8 January 1980, Lockheed Corporation announced that it had begun design and development of this twin-turboprop transport, the first example of which was scheduled to fly in the Spring of 1982. Anticipated launch orders were not confirmed, and the company decided later in the same year to delay any firm commitment to build the L 400 Twin Hercules until 1981-82.

Details of the project can be found in the 1979-80 *Jane's*.

LOCKHEED MODEL 1329-25 JETSTAR II

Production of the JetStar II began in the Spring of 1975, and the first aircraft flew on 18 August 1976. FAA certification was granted on 14 December 1976. By January 1980, a total of 40 JetStar IIs had been built by Lockheed-Georgia. Production has now been suspended, and it is unlikely that Lockheed will resume manufacture. However, Garrett-AiResearch will continue to offer its re-engining scheme to convert early JetStars to TFE731 turbofan power. The first AiResearch Aviation Company 731 JetStar conversion flew for the first time on 10 July 1974, and the first production conversion on 18 March 1976.

Details of the JetStar II can be found in the 1978-79 and 1979-80 *Jane's*.

LOCKHEED C-141B STARLIFTER

Operational experience with the Lockheed C-141A StarLifter by the USAF's Military Airlift Command showed that on many occasions the cargo compartment was physically packed to capacity without the aircraft's maximum payload capability being reached. Parametric studies carried out by Lockheed showed that lengthening the fuselage by 7·11 m (23 ft 4 in) would provide an optimum relationship between modification cost and payload improvement, while at the same time allowing the existing wings, landing gear and power plant to be retained.

Under USAF contract, Lockheed-Georgia began work on the conversion of a C-141 in 1976. Designated YC-141B, this prototype was rolled out on 8 January 1977 and made its first flight on 24 March. The fuselage had been lengthened by the insertion of a 4·06 m (13 ft 4 in) plug immediately forward of the wing, and by a similar 3·05 m (10 ft 0 in) plug immediately aft of the wing. These two plug sections are designed so that the lengthened aircraft retains the same operational features and mission versatility as the C-141A. As a result of this modification, the

Lockheed C-141B lengthened version of the StarLifter logistics transport (*Pilot Press*)

Lockheed C-141B 'stretched' StarLifter about to refuel in flight from a Boeing KC-135A over Edwards AFB, California

floor area of the cargo compartment is increased by 22·26 m² (239·6 sq ft), and its volume by 61·48 m³ (2,171 cu ft). Thirteen standard 463L cargo pallets can be accommodated in the C-141B StarLifter, instead of the ten carried by an unmodified C-141A. The four 93·4 kN (21,000 lb st) Pratt & Whitney TF33-P-7 turbofan engines are unchanged.

To satisfy another proven requirement, for flight refuelling capability, a Universal Aerial Refuelling Receptacle Slipway Installation (UARRSI) has been incorporated in the upper surface of the forward fuselage, just aft of the flight deck.

The first production C-141B was delivered to the USAF on 4 December 1979, ahead of schedule and below projected cost. Lockheed planned to deliver 80 C-141B conversions during 1980, and is due to complete the modification of all of Military Airlift Command's 271 StarLifters by mid-1982.

DIMENSIONS, EXTERNAL:

Wing span	48·74 m (159 ft 11 in)
Length overall	51·29 m (168 ft 3½ in)
Height overall	11·96 m (39 ft 3 in)

DIMENSIONS, INTERNAL:

Cargo compartment: Length	28·44 m (93 ft 3½ in)
Max height	2·77 m (9 ft 1 in)
Max width	3·11 m (10 ft 2½ in)
Usable cargo volume	322·71 m³ (11,399 cu ft)

WEIGHTS:

Operating weight (MAC)	67,186 kg (148,120 lb)
Max payload (2·5g)	32,025 kg (70,605 lb)
Max payload (2·25g)	41,222 kg (90,880 lb)
Max T-O weight (2·5g)	146,555 kg (323,100 lb)
Max T-O weight (2·25g)	155,580 kg (343,000 lb)
Emergency war planning T-O weight	156,445 kg (344,900 lb)
Max zero-fuel weight (2·5g)	99,210 kg (218,725 lb)
Max zero-fuel weight (2·25g)	108,410 kg (239,000 lb)
Max landing weight	155,580 kg (343,000 lb)

PERFORMANCE (at max 2·5g T-O weight, except where indicated):

Max cruising speed	492 knots (910 km/h; 566 mph)
Long-range cruising speed	430 knots (796 km/h; 495 mph)
Max rate of climb at S/L	890 m (2,920 ft)/min
T-O to 15 m (50 ft)	1,768 m (5,800 ft)
Landing from 15 m (50 ft) at normal landing weight	1,128 m (3,700 ft)
Range with max payload	2,550 nm (4,725 km; 2,935 miles)
Ferry range	5,550 nm (10,280 km; 6,390 miles)

LOCKHEED C-5 GALAXY

USAF designation: C-5A

In early 1978 Lockheed received a $24·3 million USAF contract to manufacture two new sets of wings for the C-5A, of a design intended to reduce stress and increase service life to 30,000 h. Apart from the moving surfaces, these wings are of virtually new design, using 7175-T73511 aluminium alloy for greater strength and increased resistance to corrosion. One set was for ground testing, and one for flight trials, which began in the Summer of 1980. If these tests proved successful it was planned to fit similar new wings to the 77 Galaxies still in operational service with the USAF, between 1982 and 1987. A $68 million contract to begin production of the wings was received by Lockheed in August 1980.

Full structural and specification details of the C-5A can be found in the 1975-76 *Jane's*. An abbreviated entry, with illustrations, appeared in the 1978-79 edition.

MARSH
MARSH AVIATION COMPANY

5060 East Falcon Drive, Mesa, Arizona 85205
Telephone: (602) 832 3770
Telex: 165 028
VICE-PRESIDENT: William G. Walker Jr

MARSH/ROCKWELL S2R-T TURBO THRUSH

Marsh Aviation Company has converted the piston-engined Rockwell Thrush Commander to turbine power by the installation of a Garrett-AiResearch TPE331-1-101 turboprop engine. Derated to 447 kW (600 shp) for this conversion, the full 580 kW (778 shp) output of the TPE331 is available in emergency. This engine drives a Hartzell constant-speed fully-feathering and reversible-pitch propeller. Single-cycle air-conditioning and cockpit heating provided by engine bleed air, and agricultural spraypump is also operated by bleed air. The empty weight of the Turbo Thrush is 227 kg (500 lb) less than that of the Rockwell Thrush Commander, providing increased payload capability and improved speed and performance. For agricultural operators working in remote areas the TPE331 installation has the advantage that ordinary automotive diesel fuel can be used if jet fuel is not available.

Standard fuel capacity of the Turbo Thrush is 401 litres (106 US gallons). Standard hopper capacity is 1·50 m³ (53 cu ft) or 1,514 litres (400 US gallons). A larger hopper is available optionally, capacity 1·89 m³ (66·8 cu ft) or 1,892·5 litres (500 US gallons).

Following more than 600 h of flight by two prototypes, an FAA Supplemental Type Certificate was issued. The first production conversion was handed over in September 1976. Orders for the Turbo Thrush totalled 61 by 1 January 1980, of which 52 had been delivered to operators in Africa, Europe, Mexico, the Middle East and the USA.

DIMENSIONS, EXTERNAL: As for Thrush Commander except:

Length overall	9·27 m (30 ft 5 in)

WEIGHTS AND LOADINGS: As for Thrush Commander except:

Weight empty	1,633 kg (3,600 lb)
Typical operating weight (CAR Pt 8)	4,173 kg (9,200 lb)

PERFORMANCE (at 2,721 kg; 6,000 lb T-O weight, except where indicated):

Never-exceed speed

	138 knots (256 km/h; 159 mph) IAS
Max level speed at 4,420 m (14,500 ft)	178 knots (330 km/h; 205 mph)
Econ cruising speed at 4,420 m (14,500 ft)	139 knots (257 km/h; 160 mph)
Cruising speed, 50% power	127 knots (235 km/h; 146 mph)
Working speed, 50% power	108·5 knots (201 km/h; 125 mph)

Marsh Turbo Thrush, a turbine-engined conversion of the Rockwell International Thrush Commander

Stalling speed, flaps up	41·5 knots (77 km/h; 48 mph)
Stalling speed, flaps down	38 knots (71 km/h; 44 mph)
Stalling speed, flaps up at normal landing weight	39 knots (72·5 km/h; 45 mph)
Stalling speed, flaps down at normal landing weight	37 knots (69 km/h; 43 mph)
Max rate of climb at S/L	915 m (3,000 ft)/min
Service ceiling	7,620 m (25,000 ft)
T-O run	183 m (600 ft)
Landing run	91 m (300 ft)
Range with max payload	278 nm (515 km; 320 miles)
Ferry range, at 60% power	521 nm (966 km; 600 miles)

MARSH/GULFSTREAM AMERICAN G-164 C-T TURBO CAT

Marsh Aviation has developed a turbine engine conversion for the Grumman/Gulfstream American G-164 Super Ag-Cat C, replacing the original Pratt & Whitney R-1340 piston engine with a 580 kW (778 shp) Garrett-AiResearch TPE331-1-101 turboprop. In this application the engine is derated to 447 kW (600 shp), and drives a Hartzell constant-speed fully-feathering and reversible-pitch propeller. This engine installation in the Marsh/Gulfstream Turbo Cat is approved for unlimited operation on automotive diesel fuel, as well as on all jet fuels, and for limited operation on 80/87/100 octane aviation gasoline.

Features of the Turbo Cat, which has an empty weight 263 kg (580 lb) below that of the standard G-164 Super Ag-Cat C, include automatic start sequencing, automatic fuel nozzle purging, engine inlet and fuel filter anti-icing, improved reliability and performance, and increased payload. Options available include air-conditioning, single-point refuelling, and hydraulic spray systems.

By 1 January 1980 the prototype had completed more than 100 h of flight testing, and certification was expected during the following month. At that time Marsh Aviation had received orders for four conversions, and deliveries were scheduled to begin immediately certification had been received. The description of the Gulfstream American Super Ag-Cat C in this edition applies also to the Marsh Turbo Cat conversion, except as follows:

DIMENSIONS, EXTERNAL:

Length overall	9·60 m (31 ft 6 in)

WEIGHTS:

Weight empty	1,424 kg (3,140 lb)
Typical operating weight (CAR Pt 8)	4,082 kg (9,000 lb)

PERFORMANCE (at max T-O weight, except where indicated):

Never-exceed speed

	121 knots (223 km/h; 139 mph) IAS
Cruising speed at 4,420 m (14,500 ft)	139 knots (257 km/h; 160 mph) TAS
Stalling speed	57 knots (106 km/h; 66 mph) IAS
Max rate of climb at S/L	914 m (3,000 ft)/min
T-O run	183 m (600 ft)
Landing run at max landing weight	91 m (300 ft)

MARSH/BEECHCRAFT T-34 TURBO MENTOR

In early 1980 Marsh Aviation was involved in the development of a turboprop conversion of the Beechcraft T-34A/B Mentor two-seat primary trainer (last described in the 1960-61 *Jane's*). This has involved replacement of the original 168 kW (225 hp) Continental O-470 piston engine that powered these aircraft, by a 580 kW (778 shp) Garrett-AiResearch TPE331-1 turboprop engine, flat rated to 335 kW (450 shp), and driving a Hartzell constant-speed fully-feathering and reversible-pitch propeller.

It is intended to market the Marsh Turbo Mentor as a low-cost, high-performance military trainer that will provide greatly improved performance and aerobatic capability by comparison with the piston-engined Beechcraft T-34A/B. The prototype conversion was flown for the first time in December 1979. It was anticipated that first deliveries of converted aircraft could be made in late 1980 or early 1981.

DIMENSIONS, EXTERNAL:

Wing span	10·00 m (32 ft 9½ in)
Length overall	8·05 m (26 ft 5 in)
Height overall	2·98 m (9 ft 9½ in)

Marsh Turbo Cat, a turbine-engined conversion of the Gulfstream American Super Ag-Cat C

WEIGHTS:
Weight empty	1,088 kg (2,400 lb)
Max T-O weight	1,497 kg (3,300 lb)

PERFORMANCE:
Never-exceed speed
    243 knots (450 km/h; 280 mph) IAS
Cruising speed at 7,010 m (23,000 ft)
    305 knots (565 km/h; 350 mph) TAS
Normal operating speed
    219 knots (406 km/h; 252 mph) IAS
Stalling speed, flaps and landing gear up
    56 knots (104 km/h; 64·5 mph) IAS
Stalling speed, flaps and landing gear down
    47 knots (88 km/h;; 54·5 mph) IAS

Max rate of climb at S/L	762 m (2,500 ft)/min
Service ceiling	7,620 m (25,000 ft)
T-O and landing run	91 m (300 ft)
Range	912 nm (1,690 km; 1,050 miles)

Prototype of the Marsh Turbo Mentor, a turboprop conversion of the Beechcraft T-34A/T-34B

MAULE
MAULE AIRCRAFT CORPORATION

HEAD OFFICE AND WORKS: Spence Air Base, Moultrie, Georgia 31768
Telephone: (912) 985 2045
PRESIDENT: B. D. Maule
VICE-PRESIDENT: Mrs B. D. (June) Maule (Treasurer)
SALES MANAGER: Brenda Corbin

This company was formed to manufacture the Maule M-4 four-seat light aircraft, production of which ended in 1975. It transferred to new facilities in Moultrie, Georgia, in September 1968, and is now concentrating on production of the uprated M-5 Lunar Rocket.

The company has also designed auxiliary fuel transfer tanks for installation in the outboard wing bays of M-4 and M-5 aircraft. Providing a total usable additional fuel capacity of 87 litres (23 US gallons), these tanks offer owners of the M-4 or M-5 a minimum-payload range of 650 nm (1,200 km; 750 miles). FAA approval of the modification was given on 31 October 1973.

MAULE M-5 LUNAR ROCKET

Developed from the M-4 Strata-Rocket, the M-5 Lunar Rocket series has a 30 per cent increase in flap area and enlarged tail surfaces to improve short-field performance and rate of climb. Two prototypes were built originally. First to fly, on 1 November 1971, was the M-5-220C prototype, powered by a 164 kW (220 hp) Franklin 6A-350-C1 engine. Manufacture of this version has since been discontinued as the Franklin engine is no longer in production in the USA.

Versions available currently are as follows:
M-5-180C. With 134 kW (180 hp) Avco Lycoming O-360-C1F flat-four engine, driving a Hartzell two-blade constant-speed metal propeller. Prototype first flown on 18 May 1978.

M-5-210C. Basic model with 156·5 kW (210 hp) Continental IO-360-D flat-six engine, driving a McCauley two-blade constant-speed metal propeller. Second prototype Lunar Rocket, flown on 16 October 1973, was of this version; FAA certification awarded on 28 December 1973.

M-5-210TC. Cargo version with 156·5 kW (210 hp) Avco Lycoming TO-360-C1A6D flat-four turbocharged engine, driving a Hartzell two-blade constant-speed metal propeller. Prototype first flown on 9 August 1978.

M-5-235C. Version with the more powerful 175 kW (235 hp) Avco Lycoming O-540-J1A5D flat-six engine, driving a larger-diameter Hartzell two-blade constant-speed metal propeller. Certification programme completed on 6 April 1976.

Maule Patroller. Civil patrol version of Lunar Rocket (any power plant), with any or all of the following modifications: Plexiglas-covered doors for improved view; port side rear observation window; 3·5 million candlepower belly-mounted manually-controlled searchlight; 100/200W siren and public address system; 28V electrical system; specialised radios to customer's requirements.

The M-5-210C/M-5-235C is a STOL aircraft, the 'C' in its designation implying that it has double aft doors on the starboard side to facilitate the loading of cargo.
TYPE: Four-seat light aircraft.
WINGS: Braced high-wing monoplane. Streamline-section Vee bracing strut each side. USA 35B (modified) wing section. Dihedral 1°. Incidence 0° 30′. All-metal two-spar structure with metal covering and glassfibre tips. All-metal ailerons and two-position flaps. Ailerons linked with rudder tab, so that aircraft can be controlled in flight by using only the control wheel in the cockpit. Cambered wingtips standard.
FUSELAGE: Welded 4130 steel tube structure. Covered with glassfibre, except for metal doors and aluminium skin around cabin.
TAIL UNIT: Braced steel tube structure with glassfibre covering. Trim tab in port elevator. Servo tab in rudder linked to aileron movement. Starboard rudder trim via spring to starboard rudder pedal.
LANDING GEAR: Non-retractable tailwheel type. Maule oleo-pneumatic shock-absorbers on main units. Maule

Maule M-5 Lunar Rocket with optional float landing gear

steerable tailwheel. Cleveland main wheels with Goodyear or McCreary tyres size 17 × 6·00-6, pressure 1·79 bars (26 lb/sq in). Tailwheel tyre size 8 × 3·50-4, pressure 1·03-1·38 bars (15-20 lb/sq in). Cleveland hydraulic disc brakes. Parking brake. Oversize tyres, size 20 × 8·50-6 (pressure 1·24 bars; 18 lb/sq in), and fairings aft of main wheels optional. Provisions for fitting optional Edo Model 248B2440, Pee Kay Model 2300 or Aqua Model 2400 floats, or Federal skis Model C2200H or C3000H.
POWER PLANT: One flat-four or flat-six engine, driving a constant-speed propeller, as detailed in model listings. Two fuel tanks in wings with total usable capacity of 151 litres (40 US gallons). Optional auxiliary fuel tanks in outer wings, each with usable capacity of 43·5 litres (11·5 US gallons). Maximum usable fuel capacity 238 litres (63 US gallons). Refuelling points on wing upper surface. Oil capacity: M-5-210C 9·5 litres (2·5 US gallons); M-5-235C 11·5 litres (3 US gallons).
ACCOMMODATION: Pilot and three passengers on two front bucket seats and rear bench seat, or optional quickly-removed rear sling seat. One door on port side of fuselage, hinged at front edge and opening forward. Three doors on starboard side of fuselage, the forward and centre doors hinged at the front edge, the rear baggage door hinged at the rear edge. The centre and aft doors can be opened together to provide an opening 1·24 m (4 ft 1 in) wide to facilitate loading of bulky cargo. Accommodation heated and ventilated.
SYSTEMS: Hydraulic system for brakes only. Electrical system powered by 60A engine-driven alternator. 28V electrical system optional.
AVIONICS AND EQUIPMENT: A wide range of Collins Micro Line, King, Genave and Narco communication and navigation equipment is available to customer's requirements. Blind-flying instrumentation, autopilot, wing levelling system and automatic glideslope optional.

DIMENSIONS, EXTERNAL:
Wing span	9·40 m (30 ft 10 in)
Wing chord, constant	1·60 m (5 ft 3 in)
Wing aspect ratio	5·71
Length overall:	
M-5-180C, M-5-210C	6·93 m (22 ft 9 in)
M-5-210TC	7·26 m (23 ft 10 in)
M-5-235C	7·16 m (23 ft 6 in)
Height overall	1·89 m (6 ft 2½ in)
Tailplane span	3·28 m (10 ft 9 in)
Wheel track	1·83 m (6 ft 0 in)
Wheelbase	4·82 m (15 ft 10 in)
Propeller diameter: M-5-210C	1·88 m (6 ft 2 in)
M-5-235C	1·98 m (6 ft 6 in)
Cabin doors (fwd, each): Height	0·84 m (2 ft 9 in)
Width	0·76 m (2 ft 6 in)
Height to sill	0·94 m (3 ft 1 in)
Cabin door (centre, stbd):	
Height	0·75 m (2 ft 5½ in)
Width	0·69 m (2 ft 3 in)
Height to sill	0·76 m (2 ft 6 in)

Baggage door (aft, stbd): Height	0·58 m (1 ft 11 in)
Width	0·56 m (1 ft 10 in)
Height to sill	0·61 m (2 ft 0 in)

AREAS:
Wings, gross	14·67 m² (157·9 sq ft)
Ailerons (total)	1·19 m² (12·8 sq ft)
Trailing-edge flaps (total)	1·75 m² (18·8 sq ft)
Fin	1·22 m² (13·14 sq ft)
Rudder, incl tab	0·54 m² (5·83 sq ft)
Tailplane	1·32 m² (14·2 sq ft)
Elevators, incl tab	1·58 m² (17·0 sq ft)

WEIGHTS AND LOADINGS (A: M-5-180C; B: M-5-210C; C: M-5-210TC; D: M-5-235C):
Basic operating weight: B	601 kg (1,325 lb)
Weight empty: A	601 kg (1,325 lb)
B	612 kg (1,350 lb)
C, D	635 kg (1,400 lb)
Max T-O and landing weight:	
All versions	1,043 kg (2,300 lb)
Max wing loading: All versions	71·3 kg/m² (14·6 lb/sq ft)
Max power loading: A	7·78 kg/kW (12·78 lb/hp)
B, C	6·66 kg/kW (10·95 lb/hp)
D	5·96 kg/kW (9·79 lb/hp)

PERFORMANCE (at max T-O weight. A: M-5-180C; B: M-5-210C; C: M-5-210TC; D: M-5-235C):
Never-exceed speed:	
B, D	156 knots (290 km/h; 180 mph)
Max level speed at optimum altitude:	
A	117 knots (217 km/h; 135 mph)
B	137 knots (254 km/h; 158 mph)
C	165 knots (306 km/h; 190 mph)
D	149 knots (277 km/h; 172 mph)
Max cruising speed at optimum altitude:	
A	110 knots (204 km/h; 127 mph)
B	137 knots (254 km/h; 158 mph)
C	148 knots (274 km/h; 170 mph)
D	149 knots (277 km/h; 172 mph)
Econ cruising speed, 65% power at 2,440 m (8,000 ft):	
A	106 knots (196 km/h; 122 mph)
B	130 knots (241 km/h; 150 mph) CAS
C	135 knots (251 km/h; 156 mph)
D	139 knots (257 km/h; 160 mph) CAS
Stalling speed, flaps up:	
B	53 knots (98 km/h; 61 mph)
Stalling speed, flaps down:	
B	49 knots (90 km/h; 56 mph)
Max rate of climb at S/L: A	229 m (750 ft)/min
B	380 m (1,250 ft)/min
C, D	411 m (1,350 ft)/min
Service ceiling: A	4,570 m (15,000 ft)
B	5,485 m (18,000 ft)
C	7,620 m (25,000 ft)
D	6,100 m (20,000 ft)
T-O and landing run: B, D	122 m (400 ft)
T-O to and landing from 15 m (50 ft):	
B, D	183 m (600 ft)

Range with max standard fuel:		Range with max fuel, 30 min reserves:	
A	426 nm (789 km; 490 miles)	A	651 nm (1,207 km; 750 miles)
B	521 nm (966 km; 600 miles)	B	760 nm (1,408 km; 875 miles)
C	391 nm (724 km; 450 miles)	C	625 nm (1,159 km; 720 miles)
D	478 nm (885 km; 550 miles)	D	695 nm (1,287 km; 800 miles)

MBB
MBB HELICOPTER CORPORATION (a subsidiary of Messerschmitt-Bölkow-Blohm GmbH)

HEAD OFFICE: Weston Way, PO Box 514, West Chester, Pennsylvania 19380
Telephone: (215) 431 4150
Telex: 902041
PRESIDENT: C. W. Moore
DIRECTOR OF MARKETING: Samuel E. Rocray

Messerschmitt-Bölkow-Blohm of West Germany (which see) established this subsidiary company in the USA, in early 1979, to take over marketing and product support of the company's family of twin-turbine helicopters in North America and Mexico. These functions had been carried out since 1972 by Boeing Vertol, which maintained continuity of product support during the Summer of 1979 while the new company's 1,393 m² (15,000 sq ft) spares administration and maintenance training centre, which is near the West Chester head office, was being readied for operation.

This facility has been fully operational since September 1979 and, in addition to marketing the BO 105 CBS, which is the equivalent of the version which Boeing Vertol sold as the Executaire, MBB Helicopter Corporation will market and support the entire range of MBB helicopters. This will apply also to the 8/10-seat multi-purpose BK 117 helicopter, being developed jointly by MBB and Kawasaki of Japan (see International section), which is scheduled for certification in mid-1981.

MCDONNELL DOUGLAS
MCDONNELL DOUGLAS CORPORATION

HEAD OFFICE AND WORKS: Box 516, St Louis, Missouri 63166
Telephone: (314) 232 0232
Telex: 44-857

DIRECTORS:
John C. Brizendine
George H. Capps
William H. Danforth
Donald W. Douglas Jr
George S. Graff
Robert L. Johnson
Edwin S. Jones
Robert C. Little
Donald S. Macdonald
James S. McDonnell III
John F. McDonnell
Sanford N. McDonnell (President)
James T. McMillan
William R. Orthwein Jr
John T. Sant
PRESIDENT AND CHIEF EXECUTIVE OFFICER: Sanford N. McDonnell
CORPORATE EXECUTIVE VICE-PRESIDENT: John F. McDonnell
CORPORATE OFFICERS:
Harold D. Altis (Vice-President, Engineering and Research)
David C. Arnold (Vice-President)
Alvin L. Boyd (Vice-President)
Erwin F. Branahl (Vice-President)
John C. Brizendine (Vice-President)
Jerry G. Brown (Vice-President, Treasurer)
John E. Crosthwait (Vice-President, Far East)
Richard J. Davis (Vice-President, External Relations)

Walter E. Diggs Jr (Secretary and Counsel)
Charles M. Forsyth (Vice-President)
George S. Graff (Vice-President)
Gordon M. Graham (Vice-President, Washington)
Robert L. Harmon (Vice-President)
Robert L. Johnson (Vice-President)
Warren E. Kraemer (Vice-President, Europe)
Robert C. Little (Vice-President, Operations and Marketing)
James H. MacDonald (Vice-President, Personnel)
James S. McDonnell III (Vice-President, Marketing)
James T. McMillan (Vice-President)
Donald Malvern (Vice-President)
William R. Orthwein Jr (Vice-President)
A. Joseph Quackenbush (Vice-President)
Albert J. Redway Jr (Vice-President, Eastern Region)
John T. Sant (Vice-President and General Counsel)
Stanley J. Sheinbein (Asst Treasurer)
Harry I. Sieferman (Tax Officer)
Albert H. Smith Jr (Vice-President, Contracts, and Controller)
John W. Walbran (Asst General Counsel)
STAFF OFFICERS:
R. Joseph Alagna (Vice-President, Material)
Donald P. Ames (Vice-President, McDonnell Douglas Research Laboratories)
Charles A. Gaskill (Vice-President, Properties and Facilities)
Arthur W. Hyland (Vice-President, Accounting)
Leo I. Mirowitz (Vice-President, Corporate Diversification)
William E. Schowengerdt (Vice-President, Auditing)
Howard C. Todt (Vice-President, Quality Assurance)
Michael Witunski (Vice-President)

McDonnell Douglas Research Laboratories
Box 516, St Louis, Missouri 63166
STAFF VICE-PRESIDENT: Dr Donald P. Ames

McDonnell Douglas Corporation was formed on 28 April 1967, by the merger of the former Douglas Aircraft Company Inc and McDonnell Company. It encompasses both of the original companies and their subsidiaries.

Major operating components of McDonnell Douglas Corporation, are as follows:

Douglas Aircraft Company
See pages 385-90 of this section
McDonnell Douglas Astronautics Company
See Air-launched Missiles and Spaceflight sections
McDonnell Aircraft Company
See following entry
McDonnell Douglas Automation Company
Box 516, St Louis, Missouri 63166
CHAIRMAN: William R. Orthwein Jr
PRESIDENT: A. Joseph Quackenbush
McDonnell Douglas Electronics Company
St Charles, Missouri
PRESIDENT: David C. Arnold
McDonnell Douglas—Tulsa
Tulsa, Oklahoma
VICE-PRESIDENT AND GENERAL MANAGER:
Robert C. Lindstrom

Subsidiaries:
Subsidiaries of McDonnell Douglas Corporation include McDonnell Douglas Canada Ltd, Malton, Ontario; McDonnell Douglas (Japan) Ltd, Tokyo; MDC Realty Company, Long Beach, California; McDonnell Douglas Finance Corporation, Long Beach, California; Microdata Corporation, Irvine, California; and Vitek Systems Inc.

At 1 July 1980, McDonnell Douglas employed a total of 84,427 people, working in 73 communities in 30 states, the District of Columbia, Kwajalein in the Pacific Ocean, and twelve foreign nations. Total office, engineering, laboratory and manufacturing floor area was 2,486,727 m² (26,766,914 sq ft).

MCDONNELL AIRCRAFT COMPANY (A Division of McDonnell Douglas Corporation)

HEADQUARTERS: Box 516, St Louis, Missouri 63166
Telephone: (314) 232 0232
PRESIDENT: George S. Graff
EXECUTIVE VICE-PRESIDENT: Donald Malvern
VICE-PRESIDENTS:
Aksel R. Andersen (Avionics Engineering)
Robert C. Bartz (Material)
William J. Blatz (Engineering Technology)
Alvin L. Boyd (Fiscal Management)
Chester V. Braun (General Manager F-15)
John J. Burns (Advanced Engineering)
Denver D. Clark (Marketing)
Paul T. Homsher (F-15 Saudi Arabian Operations)
Robert H. Koenig (Controller)
Edward B. Kuhlmann (Quality Assurance)
Richard A. Noyes (Aircraft Engineering)
Herbert Perlmutter (Manufacturing)
Madison L. Ramey (Engineering)
William S. Ross (Flight and Laboratory Development)
John N. Schuler (Contracts and Pricing)
Vernon E. Teig (Product Support)
Joseph C. Waldner (General Manager F-18)
Darrell F. Waters (Personnel, East)

Development and production at St Louis continues to be concentrated on versions of the F-15 Eagle air superiority fighter, AV-8B Advanced Harrier and F-18 Hornet naval strike fighter.

MCDONNELL DOUGLAS PHANTOM II
US Navy and USAF designations: F-4 and RF-4

The Phantom II was developed initially as a twin-engined two-seat long-range all-weather fleet air defence fighter for service with the US Navy. A letter of intent to order two prototypes was issued on 18 October 1954, at which time the aircraft was designated AH-1. The designation was changed to F4H-1 on 23 June 1955, with change of mission to missile fighter, and the prototype F4H-1 flew for the first time on 27 May 1958. The first production Phantom II was delivered to US Navy Squadron VF-121 on 29 December 1960. Trials in a ground attack role led to USAF orders, and the basic USN and USAF versions became the F-4B and F-4C respectively. Many other variants appeared subsequently, and details of these have been given in earlier editions of *Jane's*.

The most recent updating programmes have covered the conversion of 116 F-4E aircraft to operational F-4G (Advanced Wild Weasel) configuration, and modification of F-4Js to F-4S standard, as follows:

F-4G (Advanced Wild Weasel). The USAF's Wild Weasel programme is concerned with the suppression of hostile weapon radar guidance systems. The provision of airborne equipment able to fulfil such a role, and modification of the necessary aircraft to create an effective force for deployment against such targets, had first priority in tactical Air Force planning in the Spring of 1975. In the interests of force standardisation and airframe life, the F-4E Phantom (see 1979-80 *Jane's*) was selected for modification to fulfil the Advanced Wild Weasel role, technical studies of the F-4D and F-4E having shown the latter aircraft to be easier to modify. External changes include the addition of a torpedo-shape fairing to the top of the tail fin to carry APR-38 antennae; removal of the M61A-1 gun system and its replacement by a chin pod containing APR-38 subsystems (receiver, homing and warning computer, computer interface system); and the addition of other APR-38 antennae, of which there are 56 in all on the fin-tip and fin sides, along the upper surface of the fuselage, and elsewhere. The new chin pod is of laminated glassfibre construction, and there are new fairing doors in place of the gun muzzle fairings. Internal modifications consist of a number of added and revised systems, chief of which is the McDonnell Douglas AN/APR-38 radar homing and warning system (RHAWS) itself. Changes have been made to the LCOSS (lead-computing optical sight system) amplifier in the upper equipment bay, and the computer interface system (CIS) installations in the front and rear cockpits; suitable cockpit displays have been provided. Additional equipment is installed in the compartment vacated by the ammunition for the M61 gun, and there is provision for further electronics packages if required. The gun purge scoop and entire gun hydraulic system of the F-4E are removed; pitot-static system drains are relocated in the chin pod; and a 7·5 cm (3 in) extension is added to the pitot-static nose boom. The radar cooling duct is modified, to provide open ducting for the APR-38 components on the equipment shelves in the nose. All gun control and APR-36/37 wiring in the F-4E is replaced by new wiring and co-axial cables for the APR-38 system in the radome, nose, inboard wing panels, and forward/centre/aft fuselage locations. New wiring uses F-15 assembly techniques and materials, and additional wiring provides interface with new weapons launchers. The Advanced Wild Weasel F-4G is cleared for operation with AGM-45 Shrike, AGM-78 Standard ARM, and AGM-65 Maverick (including IIR: imaging infra-red version) air-to-surface missiles. Use of the IIR Maverick greatly enhances night and adverse weather capability. Testing with AGM-88 HARM is under way. For self-defence, AIM-7F Sparrow and/or AIM-9L Sidewinder air-to-air missiles can also be carried.

A digital computer receives, processes and displays emitter information to the crew in the form of CRT presentations, digital readouts, advisory/warning lights, and aural tones. Computerised information is also provided to the weapon system for use in munition delivery, and to various instruments used by the crew to perform delivery manoeuvres. This frees both the pilot and the electronics warfare officer (EWO) of many of the analytical and manual duties once required, presents them with an accurate view of the enemy's defence environment, and allows them an unprecedented flexibility in seeking out and destroying those defences. The AN/APR-38 beam receivers (23 cm; 9 in arrays) which obtain range and azimuth information are located on the front and each side of the chin pod, and on the vertical fin looking aft. The range and azimuth information for all ground threats received is displayed on the plan position indicator (PPI), which is one of three scopes in the rear cockpit. There is a repeater PPI in the front cockpit. Priorities are assigned to the top 15 targets by the computer. Threats are indicated by letter and number symbols. A triangle is placed around the highest-priority threat, which is determined by the computer classification table. If desired, the EWO may override and designate a threat for the Weasel to work: this threat is designated by a diamond around the symbol. The homing and warning computer (HAWC) is one of the most important parts of the system. It can be re-programmed to include new or changed threats. The optical sight, which has been modified, indicates the radar emitter position with its red reticle. Ground track of the aircraft in azimuth is indicated by a green cross caged in elevation to the radar boresight of the aircraft. The Weasel pilot can bomb 'blind' by positioning the green cross over the reticle, depressing the bomb button, and starting a recovery. The selected store will release automatically at the correct point. The mission recorder provides the capability to play back the mission on the ground for training and study purposes.

Although the Advanced Wild Weasel F-4G aircraft would be able to operate independently in a hunter/killer role, their main utilisation is likely to be as a component of a strike force, where they would detect, identify, locate and warn of hostile electromagnetic emitters, and deploy against them suitable weapons for their suppression or destruction.

The USAF sought funding in FY 1976 for the Advanced Wild Weasel concept, in order to provide an expansion in memory capability of the airborne processor and to extend coverage of low-frequency emissions. The programme provided for the first F-4G operational kit installation in the Spring of 1976 and the second in the Autumn of that year, followed by 15 installations in 1977, 60 in 1978, and 39 in 1979, to provide a force of 116 aircraft (96 for combat units, 20 for training and testing). The first F-4G was delivered on 28 April 1978, and the type entered service with the 35th Tactical Fighter Wing (39th Tactical Fighter Squadron, for training) at George AFB, California, in October 1978. The first two F-4Gs of 24 for the 81st TFS, USAFE, at Spangdahlem, Federal Republic of Germany, were delivered in the Spring of 1979.

F-4J. Development of F-4B for US Navy and Marine Corps, primarily as interceptor but with full ground attack capability. Powered by J79-GE-10 turbojets. Fitted initially with 16½° drooping ailerons and slotted tailplane, to reduce approach speed in spite of increased landing weight; Westinghouse AN/AWG-10 X-band pulse-Doppler fire-control system; Lear Siegler AJB-7 bombing system; and 30 kVA generators. First flight of a production F-4J was made on 27 May 1966; production of 522 examples was completed in January 1972. Before the end of the war in Viet-Nam, production F-4Js underwent a series of retrofit programmes, aimed chiefly at improving the aircraft's electronic warfare equipment. Under a programme named Shoehorn, the F-4J was equipped with an AN/APR-25 warning receiver, AN/APR-27 missile launch warning system, and an AN/ALQ-100 jamming system. Also incorporated at this time was an update of the AN/APX-76 IFF system, known as AIMS (Air traffic control radar beacon IFF Mk XII System). In 1971, the APR-25 and -27 were replaced by improved AN/ALR-45 and AN/ALR-50 warning receivers, which provided better threat response and displayed a letter/number readout instead of coded vectors. During 1973-74, an I-band AN/ALQ-126 jamming system replaced the earlier ALQ-100. In 1979 the Applied Technology Inc AN/APR-43 Compass Sail/Clockwise warning receiver and the AN/ALQ-162 Clockwise jamming system were being considered for installation in the F-4J, the former to replace the ALR-50, the latter as a complement to the ALQ-126. Other avionics in the F-4J included originally an RT-793 UHF com transceiver and AN/APR-69 UHF auxiliary receiver, replaced later by two Collins AN/ARC-159. It is planned to replace the latter, in the early 1980s, with Collins AN/ARC-182 VHF (AM/FM) and UHF (AM/FM) sets. Similarly, the earlier AN/ARN-86 Tacan was scheduled to be replaced from 1980 by new Collins AN/ARN-118 system. These new com/nav installations will permit relocation of the AN/APX-76 in a position more accessible for maintenance and overhaul. The original AN/APN-141 radar altimeter has been replaced by a Honeywell AN/APN-194 system.

F-4N. Number updated from F-4B was 227, one more than stated in 1979-80 *Jane's*.

F-4S. The US Navy plans to modify up to 265 F-4Js, possibly more, under this designation. Changes include replacement of the original wing leading-edge flaps by highly-cambered, bulbous-nosed leading-edge slats; addition of an inboard leading-edge flap (similar to that on the F/RF-4B); and structural strengthening, including the fitting of steel fatigue straps under the lower skins of the inboard wing panels, at the main spar. Outer wing panels are of entirely new construction. Internally, the aircraft is completely rewired, using lightweight Kapton wiring; and

McDonnell Douglas F-4G Advanced Wild Weasel. AN/APR-38 9 in beam receivers are visible in nose and sides of chin pod and on the fin-tip, facing aft

has an improved Westinghouse AN/AWG-10A digital weapon control system. Modifications are undertaken jointly by McDonnell Douglas and the Naval Air Rework Facility at North Island, California. Deliveries began, with aircraft serial number 155565, to the Naval Air Test Center at Patuxent River, Maryland, on 11 May 1978.

A total of 5,057 completed Phantoms had been delivered from St Louis when production ended on 26 October 1979. This total included 2,597 for the US Air Force, 1,264 for the US Navy/Marine Corps, and 1,196 for foreign customers. In addition, 11 Phantoms were supplied in kit form to Japan for assembly by Mitsubishi, which built a further 127 under licence in that country, bringing total Phantom production to 5,195. McDonnell Douglas also completed, but did not assemble, 16 RF-4Es ordered by Iran before the change of government in that country in 1979. Instructions from the US government for the disposal of these 16 aircraft were still awaited in mid-1980.

A full description of the Phantom airframe and systems can be found in the 1978-79 *Jane's*. The following shortened description applies to the F-4E:

TYPE: Twin-engined two-seat all-weather fighter.

POWER PLANT: Two General Electric J79-GE-17A turbojet engines (each 79·6 kN; 17,900 lb st with afterburning). Integral fuel tankage in wings, between front and main spars, and in seven fuselage tanks, with total capacity of 7,022 litres (1,855 US gallons). Provision for one 2,270 litre (600 US gallon) external tank under fuselage and two 1,400 litre (370 US gallon) underwing tanks. Equipment for probe-and-drogue and 'buddy tank' flight refuelling, with retractable probe in starboard side of fuselage.

ACCOMMODATION: Crew of two in tandem on Martin-Baker Mk H7 ejection seats, under individual rearward-hinged canopies. Optional dual controls.

AVIONICS AND EQUIPMENT: As listed in 1979-80 *Jane's*.

ARMAMENT: Four Falcon, Sparrow, Sidewinder, Shrike or Walleye missiles, or two Bullpup missiles, on four semi-submerged mountings under fuselage and four underwing mountings. Provision for carrying alternative loads of up to about 7,250 kg (16,000 lb) of nuclear or conventional bombs and stores on seven attachments under wings and fuselage. Stores which can be carried include B-28, -43, -57, -61 nuclear bombs; M117, M118, M129, MC-1, Mk 36, Mk 81, Mk 82, Mk 83 and Mk 84 bombs; MLU-10 land mine; BLU-1, -27, -52 and -76 fire bombs; cluster bombs; practice bombs; flares; rocket packs; ECM pods; gun pods; spray tanks; tow targets; Pave Knife pod; and AAVS IV camera pod. One M61A-1 nose-mounted gun.

DIMENSIONS, EXTERNAL:
Wing span	11·77 m (38 ft 7½ in)
Width, wings folded	8·41 m (27 ft 7 in)
Wing area, gross	49·2 m² (530 sq ft)
Length overall	19·20 m (63 ft 0 in)
Height overall	5·02 m (16 ft 5½ in)
Wheel track	5·45 m (17 ft 10½ in)

WEIGHTS AND LOADINGS:
Weight empty	13,757 kg (30,328 lb)
Weight empty, basic mission	14,448 kg (31,853 lb)
Combat T-O weight	18,818 kg (41,487 lb)
Max T-O weight	28,030 kg (61,795 lb)
Max landing weight	20,865 kg (46,000 lb)
Max wing loading	569·2 kg/m² (116·59 lb/sq ft)
Max power loading	176·1 kg/kN (1·73 lb/lb st)

PERFORMANCE (A at 24,410 kg: 53,814 lb; B at 24,572 kg: 54,171 lb; C at 25,397 kg: 55,991 lb; D at 27,954 kg: 61,629 lb; and E at 28,030 kg: 61,795 lb T-O weight, except where indicated):
Max level speed with external stores		over Mach 2

Average speed:
A, B	504 knots (934 km/h; 580 mph)
C	506 knots (938 km/h; 583 mph)
D	502 knots (930 km/h; 578 mph)
E	496 knots (919 km/h; 571 mph)

Stalling speed, approach power with BLC:
A	148 knots (273·5 km/h; 170 mph)
B	148·5 knots (275 km/h; 171 mph)
C	151 knots (280 km/h; 174 mph)
D	158·4 knots (294 km/h; 182·5 mph)
E	158·6 knots (294·5 km/h; 183 mph)

Max rate of climb at S/L: A	2,847 m (9,340 ft)/min
B	2,816 m (9,240 ft)/min
C	2,621 m (8,600 ft)/min
D	2,003 m (6,570 ft)/min
E	1,881 m (6,170 ft)/min
Service ceiling (supersonic)	16,580 m (54,400 ft)
T-O run: A	969 m (3,180 ft)
B	985 m (3,230 ft)
C	1,064 m (3,490 ft)
D	1,329 m (4,360 ft)
E	1,338 m (4,390 ft)

Landing run (A at landing weight of 16,706 kg: 36,831 lb; B and C at 15,937 kg: 35,134 lb; D at 17,155 kg: 37,821 lb; and E at 17,211 kg: 37,944 lb):
A	1,122 m (3,680 ft)
B, C	1,073 m (3,520 ft)
D	1,146 m (3,760 ft)
E	1,152 m (3,780 ft)

Landing run, with parabrake: A 927 m (3,040 ft)
B, C	887 m (2,910 ft)
D	948 m (3,110 ft)
E	951 m (3,120 ft)

Combat radius:
Area intercept	683 nm (1,266 km; 786 miles)
Defensive counter-air	429 nm (795 km; 494 miles)
Interdiction	618 nm (1,145 km; 712 miles)
Ferry range	1,718 nm (3,184 km; 1,978 miles)

MCDONNELL DOUGLAS F-15 EAGLE

The USAF requested development funding for a new air superiority fighter in 1965, and in due course design proposals were sought from three airframe manufacturers: Fairchild Hiller Corporation, McDonnell Douglas Corporation, and North American Rockwell Corporation. On 23 December 1969 it was announced that McDonnell Douglas had been selected as prime airframe contractor. The contract called for the design and manufacture of 20 aircraft for development testing, these to comprise 18 single-seat **F-15As** and two **TF-15A** two-seat trainers, with production scheduled at a rate of one aircraft every other month.

First flight of the F-15A was made on 27 July 1972, and the first flight of a two-seat TF-15A trainer, designated subsequently **F-15B**, on 7 July 1973.

A production go-ahead for the first 30 operational aircraft (FY 1973 funds) was announced on 1 March 1973. The FY 1974 Defense Procurement Bill authorised production of 62 aircraft, and the Defense Procurement Bills for FY 1975, 1976/7T, 1977, 1978 and 1979 authorised further production of 72, 135, 108, 97 and 78 aircraft respectively. The FY 1973-74 production contracts included 13 of the two-seat F-15B version; one of these (the 21st Eagle built) was the first Eagle delivered to the USAF, on 14 November 1974. Structural weight of the F-15B is approx 363 kg (800 lb) more than that of the single-seater. Eagles delivered from mid-1979 are to **F-15C** and **F-15D** standard, which provides for an additional 907 kg (2,000 lb) of internal fuel, and the ability to carry FAST Packs (see later paragraphs). Beginning in mid-1980 the APG-63 radar of these aircraft will be equipped with programmable signal processors, providing for future software changes and increased computer capability. F-15C and F-15D aircraft delivered prior to the availability of the programmable signal processor and expanded computer will be retrofitted subsequently to bring them up to standard.

The first F-15C (78-468) flew for the first time on 26 February 1979.

By 1 April 1980 a total of 526 Eagles had been delivered, and were in operational service with the 57th TTW at Nellis AFB, Nevada, the 58th TTW at Luke AFB, Arizona, the 1st TFW at Langley AFB, Virginia, the 36th TFW at Bitburg, West Germany, the 49th TFW at Holloman AFB, New Mexico, the 33rd TFW at Eglin AFB, Florida, and the 32nd Tactical Fighter Squadron based at Soesterburg in the Netherlands. It is planned to procure a total of 749 for the USAF by 1983, including the 20 R & D models. Twenty-five were delivered under an initial contract from the Israeli Air Force, and 60 have been ordered by Saudi Arabia, of which deliveries are due to begin in January 1982. The JASDF plans to purchase 92 **F-15Js** and eight **TF-15Js**, of which all except eight will be licence-built in Japan, with Mitsubishi as the prime contractor. The first (US-built) F-15J was handed over on 15

July 1980. The FY 1980 Japanese defence budget approved the purchase of the first 34 aircraft for the JASDF.

Designed specifically as an air superiority fighter, the F-15A Eagle has proved equally suitable for air-to-ground missions without degradation of its primary role. It is able to carry a variety of air-to-air and air-to-ground weapons (see Addenda).

A large increase in the normal ferry range of a 'clean' F-15 can be achieved by the use of two low-drag fuel pallets known as FAST Packs (Fuel And Sensor Tactical Packs) developed specially for the F-15 by McDonnell Aircraft Company. Each FAST Pack contains approximately 3,228 litres (114 cu ft) of usable volume, which can accommodate 2,268 kg (5,000 lb) of JP-4 fuel. It attaches to the side of either the port or starboard engine air intake trunk (being made in handed pairs), is designed to the same load factors and airspeed limits as the basic aircraft, and can be removed in 15 minutes. FAST Packs can accommodate avionics such as reconnaissance sensors, radar detection and jamming equipment, a laser designator, low-light-level TV system, and reconnaissance cameras, in addition to fuel. All external stores stations remain available with the pallets in use. AIM-7F missiles and air-to-ground weapons can be attached to the corners of the FAST Packs.

The programmable signal processor for the F-15C/D will enable changes to be incorporated in the radar earlier and more cheaply. An updated radar data processor will be fitted which will increase memory capability from 24K to 96K. These added features will enable the radar to operate in a high-resolution rate assessment mode which can identify clustered targets individually. The PEP-2000 (Production Eagle Package-2,000 lb; 907 kg of additional fuel) expands the fighter's combat endurance considerably, and includes attachment points and fuel plumbing to accommodate FAST Packs.

Minor changes have been made to tyres, wheels and brakes to allow for an increased maximum T-O weight, which could be as high as 30,844 kg (68,000 lb) with full internal fuel, FAST Packs and external tanks. Landing gear and fuel system changes have added about 227 kg (500 lb) to the aircraft's dry weight.

Under a programme dubbed 'Streak Eagle', the F-15 demonstrated its climb capability by capturing eight time-to-height records, between 16 January and 1 February 1975. These records were listed in the 1979-80 *Jane's*; six of them remained unbeaten in mid-1980.

The following description applies to the F-15A:

TYPE: Single-seat twin-turbofan air superiority fighter, with secondary attack role.

WINGS: Cantilever shoulder-wing monoplane. Leading-edge swept back at 45°.

FUSELAGE: All-metal semi-monocoque structure.

TAIL UNIT: Cantilever structure with twin fins and rudders. All-moving horizontal tail surfaces outboard of fins, with extended chord on outer leading-edges. Rudder servo actuators by Ronson Hydraulic Units Corporation. Actuators for horizontal surfaces by National Water Lift Company. Boost and pitch compensator for control stick by Moog Inc, Controls Division.

Fully-armed McDonnell Douglas F-15A Eagles on patrol duties in Europe *(USAF)*

LANDING GEAR: Hydraulically-retractable tricycle type, with single wheel on each unit. Nose and main landing gear by Cleveland Pneumatic Tool Company. Wheels and carbon brake assemblies by Goodyear Tire and Rubber Company. Main and nosewheel tyres by B. F. Goodrich Company. Wheel braking skid control system by Hydro-Aire Division of Crane Company. All units retract forward.

POWER PLANT: Two Pratt & Whitney F100-PW-100 turbofan engines of approximately 111·2 kN (25,000 lb st). Internal fuel load 5,260 kg (11,600 lb). Fuel tanks by Goodyear Aviation Products Division. Fuel gauge system by Simmonds Precision Products Inc. FAST Pack conformal fuel pallets attached to side of engine air intakes, beneath wing, can be removed within 15 min. Each has usable volume of 3·23 m³ (114 cu ft) and can contain 2,268 kg (5,000 lb) of JP-4 fuel.

ENGINE INTAKES: Straight two-dimensional external compression inlets, on each side of the fuselage. Air inlet controllers by Hamilton Standard. Air inlet actuators by National Water Lift Company.

ACCOMMODATION: Pilot only, on Aces II ejection seat developed by Douglas. Stretched acrylic canopy and windscreen. Windscreen anti-icing valve by Dynasciences Corporation.

SYSTEMS: Electric power generating system by Lear Siegler Power Equipment Division; transformer-rectifiers by Electro Development Corporation; 40/50kVA generator constant-speed drive units by Sundstrand Corporation, Aviation Division. Three independent hydraulic systems (each 207 bars; 3,000 lb/sq in) powered by Abex engine-driven pumps; modular hydraulic packages by Hydraulic Research and Manufacturing Company. The oxygen system includes a liquid oxygen indicator by Simmonds Precision Products Inc. Air-

conditioning system by AiResearch Manufacturing Company. Automatic flight control system by General Electric, Aircraft Equipment Division. Auxiliary power unit for engine starting, and for the provision of electric or hydraulic power on the ground independently of the main engines, supplied by AiResearch Manufacturing Company.

AVIONICS: Lightweight APG-63 pulse-Doppler radar developed by Hughes Aircraft Company provides long-range detection and tracking of small high-speed targets operating at all altitudes down to treetop level, and feeds accurate tracking information to the airborne central computer to ensure effective launch of the aircraft's missiles or the firing of its internal gun. For close-in dogfights, the radar automatically acquires the target on a head-up display. International Business Machines, Electronic Systems Center, is subcontractor for the central computer, and McDonnell Douglas Electronics Company for the head-up display. This latter unit projects all essential flight information in the form of symbols on to a combining glass positioned above the instrument panel at pilot's eye level. The display presents the pilot with all the information required to intercept and destroy an enemy aircraft without need for him to remove his eyes from the target. The display also provides navigation and other steering control information under all flight conditions. A transponder for the IFF system, developed by Teledyne Electronics Company, informs ground stations and other suitably equipped aircraft that the F-15 is a friendly aircraft. It also supplies data on the F-15's range, azimuth, altitude and identification to air traffic controllers. The F-15 carries an AN/APX-76 interrogator receiver-transmitter, built by Hazeltine Corporation, to inform the pilot if an aircraft seen visually or on radar is friendly. A reply evaluator for the IFF system, which operates with the AN/APX-76, was developed by Litton Systems Inc, Van Nuys. A vertical situation display set, that uses a cathode-ray tube to present radar, electro-optical identification and attitude director indicator formats to the pilot, has been developed by Sperry Rand Corporation, Sperry Flight Systems Division. This permits inputs received from the aircraft's sensors and the central computer to be visible to the pilot under any light conditions. This company has also developed an air data computer for the F-15, as well as an attitude and heading reference set to provide information on the aircraft's pitch, roll and magnetic heading that is fed to cockpit displays. This latter unit also serves as a backup to the inertial navigation set developed by Litton Guidance and Control Systems Division. This provides the basic navigation data and is the aircraft's primary attitude reference, enabling the F-15 to navigate anywhere in the world. In addition to giving the aircraft's position at all times, the inertial navigation system provides pitch, roll, heading, acceleration and speed information.

Other specialised equipment for flight control, naviation and communications includes a micro-miniaturised Tacan system by Collins Radio Company; a horizontal situation indicator to present aircraft navigation information on a symbolic pictorial display, by Collins Radio Company, which is also responsible for the ADF and ILS receivers. Magnavox provides the UHF transceiver and UHF auxiliary transceiver. The communications sets have cryptographic capability. Dorne and Margolin Aviation Products is responsible for the glideslope localiser antenna, and Teledyne Avionics Company for angle of attack sensors. An internal countermeasures set, designated AN/ALQ-135, which provides automatic jamming of enemy radar signals, is supplied by Northrop's Defense Systems Division; radar warning systems by Loral Electronic Systems; and an electronic warfare warning set by Magnavox.

EQUIPMENT: Tachometer, fuel and oil indicators by Bendix

McDonnell Douglas F-15A Eagle twin-turbofan air superiority fighter *(Pilot Press)*

McDonnell Douglas F-15B Eagle two-seat trainer, fitted with FAST Packs

Corporation, Flight and Engine Instrument Division. Feel trim actuators by Plessey Airborne Corporation.

ARMAMENT: Provision for carriage and launch of a variety of air-to-air weapons over short and medium ranges, including four AIM-9L Sidewinders, four AIM-7F Sparrows, and a 20 mm M61A-1 six-barrel gun with 940 rounds of ammunition. A lead-computing gyro has been developed by the General Electric Co. To keep the pilot informed of the status of his weapons and provide for their management, an armament control set has been developed by Dynamic Controls Corporation. Five weapon stations allow for the carriage of up to 7,257 kg (16,000 lb) of bombs, rockets or additional ECM equipment.

DIMENSIONS, EXTERNAL:

Wing span	13·05 m (42 ft 9¾ in)
Length overall	19·43 m (63 ft 9 in)
Height overall	5·63 m (18 ft 5½ in)
Tailplane span	8·61 m (28 ft 3 in)
Wheel track	2·75 m (9 ft 0¼ in)
Wheelbase	5·42 m (17 ft 9½ in)

AREA:

Wings, gross	56·5 m² (608 sq ft)

WEIGHTS (A: F-15A; B: F-15C):

T-O weight (interceptor, full internal fuel and 4 Sparrows): A	18,824 kg (41,500 lb)
B	20,185 kg (44,500 lb)
T-O weight (incl three 2,271 litre; 600 US gallon droptanks): A	24,675 kg (54,400 lb)
B	26,035 kg (57,400 lb)
Max T-O weight: A	25,401 kg (56,000 lb)
B	30,845 kg (68,000 lb)

PERFORMANCE:

Max level speed	more than Mach 2·5 (800 knots; 1,482 km/h; 921 mph CAS)
Approach speed	125 knots (232 km/h; 144 mph) CAS
T-O run (interceptor)	274 m (900 ft)
Landing run (interceptor), without braking parachute	762 m (2,500 ft)
Absolute ceiling	30,500 m (100,000 ft)
Ferry range: without FAST Pack	more than 2,500 nm (4,631 km; 2,878 miles)
with FAST Pack	more than 3,000 nm (5,560 km; 3,450 miles)
g limits	+9·0; −3·0

AV-8B ADVANCED HARRIER

In late 1973 and early 1974 the British and US governments received for approval various proposals for an advanced version of the BAe (HS) Harrier (see UK section). Subsequent to this came the announcement, on 15 May 1975, of the first British order for Sea Harrier FRS. Mk 1s for the Royal Navy.

Two months before the announcement of this order, the British Secretary of State for Defence, Mr Roy Mason, had stated that there was "not enough common ground on the Advanced Harrier for us to join in the programme with the US", and development studies for a US version have therefore been continued primarily by McDonnell Douglas to meet requirements of the US Navy and Marine Corps.

Essentially, the objective of the Advanced Harrier programme is to evolve a version which, without too much of a departure from the existing Harrier airframe, would virtually double the aircraft's weapons payload/combat radius.

The USMC has stated a requirement for 336 Advanced Harriers, and initially McDonnell Douglas modified two AV-8As as prototype YAV-8Bs. The first of these flew for the first time on 9 November 1978, and the second in February 1979. Prototype demonstration was completed in Summer 1979, in 185 test flights totalling 173 flying hours, during which the two aircraft met or exceeded all performance requirements specified by the Marine Corps and Naval Air Systems Command. The second prototype was lost during its 106th flight, on 15 November 1979.

Aim of the AV-8B is to achieve the improved performance capability required of the original AV-16A proposal by aerodynamic means, while retaining the same basic F402-RR-404 (Pegasus 11) engine, thus saving the cost of developing the Pegasus 15 engine that was originally considered necessary for the advanced version.

Aerodynamic changes include use of a supercritical wing; the addition of under-gun-pod strakes and a movable flap panel forward of the pods, to increase lift for vertical take-off; the use of larger wing trailing-edge flaps and drooped ailerons; and redesigned engine air intakes. The landing gear is strengthened to cater for the higher operating weights and greater external stores loads made possible by these changes.

Four full-scale development aircraft are to be built next, contingent on further action by Congress and passage of the 1981 Defense Department budget; the first of these is scheduled to fly in October 1981, with Navy BIS (Bureau of Inspection and Survey) trials following in Spring 1983. The operational date planned for the AV-8B is mid-1985, should production be approved. McDonnell Douglas would be prime contractor for the airframe, with British Aerospace as subcontractor; prime engine contractor

McDonnell Douglas YAV-8B Advanced Harrier, armed with five 500 lb bombs and two Sidewinder missiles, with which it can take off vertically

Production configuration of AV-8B Advanced Harrier, under development by McDonnell Douglas for the US Marine Corps *(Pilot Press)*

would be Rolls-Royce, with Pratt & Whitney as subcontractor.

The following description applies to the proposed production AV-8B:

TYPE: Single-seat V/STOL combat aircraft.

WINGS: Cantilever shoulder-wing monoplane, of broadly similar planform to Harrier/AV-8A but of supercritical section, approx 20% greater in span and 14% greater in area. Thickness/chord ratio 11·5% at root, 7·5% at tip. 10° less sweepback on leading-edges, and non-swept inboard trailing-edges. Composite construction, making extensive use of graphite epoxy in the main multispar torsion box, ribs, skins, outrigger fairings and wingtips. Trailing-edge single-slotted flaps, of substantially greater chord than those of AV-8A, with flap slot closure doors. Drooping ailerons, also of graphite epoxy construction.

FUSELAGE: Generally similar to AV-8A, but longer. New forward fuselage, with raised cockpit, constructed from graphite epoxy composite material, and additional lift-augmenting surfaces. These comprise a fixed strake on each of the two underfuselage gun packs, and a retractable forward flap just aft of the nosewheel unit. During VTOL modes the 'box' formed by the ventral strakes and the lowered nose flap augment lift by trapping the cushion of air bounced off the ground by the engine exhaust. This additional lift allows the AV-8B to take off vertically at a gross weight equal to its maximum hovering gross weight.

TAIL UNIT: Taller fin than that of AV-8A, resembling that of UK Sea Harrier. New tailplane planform, with constant sweep on leading-edges and reduced sweep on trailing-edges.

LANDING GEAR: Main landing gear strengthened to cater for higher operating weights. Dowty Rotol/Cleveland outrigger wheels, moved inboard to approx mid-span beneath each wing between flaps and ailerons, and with fairings deleted on production AV-8B.

POWER PLANT: One Rolls-Royce Pegasus (F402-RR-404) vectored-thrust turbofan engine rated at 95·64 kN (21,500 lb st). Engine air intakes redesigned, with elliptical lip shape and disposal of single row of suction relief doors. Increased fuel tankage available in wings, raising total internal fuel capacity (fuselage and wing tanks) from approx 2,268 kg (5,000 lb) in the AV-8A to 3,402 kg (7,500 lb) in the AV-8B. Each of the four inner underwing stations capable of carrying an

auxiliary fuel tank. Probe for in-flight refuelling.

ACCOMMODATION: Pilot only, on ejection seat, in pressurised, heated and air-conditioned cockpit. In production configuration the cockpit is raised by comparison with the AV-8B prototype, and has a redesigned windscreen and canopy to provide a better all-round view.

AVIONICS AND EQUIPMENT: Improved attitude and heading reference system, AN/ARN-84 Tacan, AN/ARC-159 UHF, AN/APX-100 IFF, visual landing aids, inertial navigation system, dual combining glass head-up display, and CRT multi-purpose display. Marconi Avionics self-contained pitch and roll autostabilisation computer, with built-in rate gyroscopes and added electronic package to interface with forward reaction control nozzle. Garrett-AiResearch air data computer.

ARMAMENT AND OPERATIONAL EQUIPMENT: Twin underfuselage gun/ammunition packs, each mounting a US 25 mm cannon or a 30 mm Aden gun. Single 454 kg (1,000 lb) stores point on fuselage centreline, between gun packs. Three stores stations under each wing, the inner one capable of carrying a 907 kg (2,000 lb) store, the centre one 454 kg (1,000 lb), and the outer one 286 kg (630 lb). The four inner wing stations are 'wet', permitting the carriage of auxiliary fuel tanks. Including fuel, stores, weapons and ammunition, and water injection for the engine, the maximum useful load for vertical take-off is approximately 3,175 kg (7,000 lb), and for short take-off nearly 7,710 kg (17,000 lb). Typical weapons include Mk 82 Snakeye bombs, and laser or electro-optical guided weapons. Main weapon delivery by Angle Rate Bombing System (ARBS), comprising a dual-mode (TV and laser) target seeker linked to a Marconi head-up display via an IBM digital computer. Passive ECM equipment.

DIMENSIONS, EXTERNAL:

Wing span	approx 9·25 m (30 ft 4 in)
Length overall	14·12 m (46 ft 4 in)
Height overall	3·56 m (11 ft 8 in)

AREA:

Wings, gross	21·37 m² (230 sq ft)

WEIGHTS:

Basic operating weight empty	5,783 kg (12,750 lb)
Max fuel, internal and external	7,180 kg (15,829 lb)
Max T-O weight: STO	13,494 kg (29,750 lb)
VTO	8,913 kg (19,650 lb)
Design landing weight	8,799 kg (19,400 lb)

PERFORMANCE (estimated):
Operational radius with external loads shown:
short T-O (305 m; 1,000 ft), twelve Mk 82 Snakeye bombs, internal fuel, 1 h loiter
more than 150 nm (278 km; 172 miles)
short T-O (305 m; 1,000 ft), seven Mk 82 Snakeye bombs, external fuel tanks, no loiter
more than 650 nm (1,204 km; 748 miles)
Unrefuelled ferry range
2,600 nm (4,825 km; 3,000 miles)

BRITISH AEROSPACE/McDONNELL DOUGLAS AV-8C HARRIER

The AV-8C is an updated conversion of the basic AV-8A Harrier that was produced by British Aerospace for the US Marine Corps. All 61 existing AV-8As are to be updated to the improved standard; the first conversions were made by McDonnell Douglas, the remainder will be carried out by the Marine Corps at Cherry Point, North Carolina. Details of the AV-8C can be found in the British Aerospace entry in the UK section.

MCDONNELL DOUGLAS F/A-18 HORNET

In the Spring of 1974 the US Department of Defense accepted a proposal from the US Navy to study a low-cost lightweight multi-mission fighter, then identified as the VFAX. In June 1974 the USN approached the US aircraft industry to submit critiques and comments on such an aircraft. Six companies responded, including McDonnell Aircraft Company; but in August of that year Congress terminated the VFAX concept, directing instead that the Navy should investigate versions of the General Dynamics YF-16 and Northrop YF-17 lightweight fighter prototypes then under evaluation for the USAF.

McDonnell Douglas made a study of the configuration of these two aircraft and concluded that Northrop's contender could be redesigned at minimum cost to meet the Navy's requirements. It then teamed with Northrop to propose a derivative of the YF-17 to meet the Navy's requirement, with McDonnell Douglas as the prime contractor. Identified as the Navy Air Combat Fighter (NACF), this received the designation F-18 Hornet when selected for further development, and the following production versions are now proposed:

F-18A. Basic single-seat escort fighter/interdictor to replace F-4.

TF-18A. Tandem two-seat version of F-18A for training, with combat capability. Fuel capacity reduced by under 6 per cent.

CF-18A. Version for Canadian Armed Forces, which plan to purchase 137. Selection announced on 10 April 1980.

A-18. Single-seat attack version to replace A-4, A-7 and AV-8A. The A-18 is identical to the F-18 except that FLIR and a laser tracker, which are being developed as part of the Hornet programme, will take the place of fuselage-mounted Sparrows for attack missions.

On 22 January 1976 it was announced that full-scale development had been initiated by the US Navy, with initial funding of $16 million. Total cost of the development programme was expected to be about $1·4 billion, including the production of 11 YF-18s for the flight test programme.

The first Hornet (160775) was rolled out on 13 September 1978, and made its first flight on 18 November 1978; the second flew on 12 March 1979, and all 11 development aircraft were flying by March 1980, including two TF-18A two-seat combat-capable trainers. The first batch of nine production Hornets was authorised in FY 1979, followed by 25 in FY 1980 and 60 in FY 1981. In the fourth quarter of 1979, a Hornet became the first modern jet aircraft to complete initial sea trials within one year of its first flight, and the first production aircraft was delivered to the US Navy for operational evaluation in May 1980. The first development squadron was scheduled to form at NAS Lemoore, California, in the Autumn of 1980. The F-18 is due to become operational with the US Navy in 1982.

The Hornet airframe differs from that of the YF-17

McDonnell Douglas TF-18A, a combat-capable two-seat training version of the Hornet

McDonnell Douglas F-18A Hornet development aircraft in operational finish, using three shades of grey and low-profile markings

prototype by having increased wing area, a wider and longer fuselage to provide greater internal fuel capacity, an enlarged nose to accommodate the 0·71 m (28 in) radar dish to meet the Navy's search range requirement of over 30 nm (56 km; 35 miles), and strengthening of the airframe structure to cater for the increased loads caused by catapult launches and arrested landings. Approximately 2,000 kg (4,400 lb) of additional fuel is carried to meet Navy mission range requirements.

Ease of maintenance was given careful consideration in formulation of the F-18's design. An engine change can be effected within approx 20 min, and radar equipment is track-mounted so that it can be rolled out for maintenance. Electronics equipment is housed behind quick-release doors at chest height, and the windscreen is hinged to permit easy access behind the instrument panel. A built-in test panel mounted within the nosewheel well pinpoints system failures, and when the indicated access door is opened the assembly which has failed 'flags' confirmation that it needs repair or replacement. Groundcrew have access to a 'go, no go' panel for rapid pre-flight check; this confirms levels of essential liquids, such as engine oil, hydraulic fluid, radar coolant, APU oil and oxygen. Safety features include self-sealing fuel tanks and fuel lines, fire suppressant foam within the fuel tanks, built-in fire extinguishers, filler foam in the fuselage for fire suppression, and a system which detects hydraulic fluid leaks and then isolates the relative section.

Conventional instrumentation has almost disappeared from the cockpit, replaced by three cathode ray tubes and an information control panel directly in front of the pilot. A head-up display is fitted and, so that the pilot will not be distracted by having to move his hands to different controls, every critical switch for air-to-air and air-to-surface engagements is either in the throttle in his left hand, or on the control stick in his right hand. During air-to-air combat the Hughes AN/APG-65 radar can track multiple targets, displaying up to eight target tracks while retaining

up to ten in its memory. A raid assessment mode enables the pilot to discriminate between closely spaced targets. The radar information is displayed on a clutter-free scope in either lookup or lookdown attitude; it provides also range-while-search capability, long-range search and track, and several modes for close-in combat. Doppler beam sharpening (DBS) achieves greater resolution of radar signal returns during air-to-surface mapping.

McDonnell Douglas is prime contractor for the Hornet, with the centre of activities at St Louis, Missouri. Northrop builds the centre and aft fuselage, which is delivered totally assembled to McDonnell Douglas. Assembly is completed at St Louis and flight testing is carried out at NATC Patuxent River, Maryland.

A total of 1,377 Hornets, including the 11 development aircraft, is planned for construction by the end of the 1980s, for the US Navy and Marine Corps. More than 150 of those built will be two-seat trainers.

The following information applies specifically to the single-seat F-18/A-18:

TYPE: Single-seat carrier-based naval strike fighter.
WINGS: Cantilever mid-wing monoplane. Moderate-sweep multi-spar structure, primarily of light alloy and graphite/epoxy. Boundary layer control achieved by wing-root slots. Full-span leading-edge manoeuvring flaps have a maximum extension angle of 30°. Single-slotted trailing-edge flaps, actuated by Bertea hydraulic cylinders, deploy to a maximum of 45°. Ailerons, with Hydraulic Research actuators, can be drooped to 45°, providing the advantages of full-span flaps for low approach speeds. Leading- and trailing-edge flaps are computer programmed to deflect for optimum lift and drag in both manoeuvring and cruise conditions. Notched sections on outer wing leading-edge to enhance aileron effectiveness. Wing-root leading-edge extensions (LEX) permit flight at angles of attack exceeding 60°. Wings fold, by means of AiResearch mechanical drive, at the inboard end of each aileron.
FUSELAGE: Semi-monocoque basic structure, primarily of light alloy, with graphite/epoxy used for access doors/panels. Titanium firewall between engines. Air-brake in upper surface of fuselage between tail fins. Pressurised cockpit section of fail-safe construction. Arrester hook for carrier landings under rear fuselage.
TAIL UNIT: Cantilever structure with swept vertical and horizontal surfaces. Twin outward-canted fins and rudders, mounted forward of all-moving horizontal surfaces (stabilators), which are actuated collectively and differentially by National Water Lift servo-cylinder hydraulic units for pitch and roll control.
LANDING GEAR: Retractable tricycle type, manufactured by Cleveland, with twin-wheel nose and single-wheel main units. Nose unit retracts forward, main wheels aft, turning 90° to stow horizontally inside the lower surface of the engine air ducts. Bendix wheels and brakes. Ozone nosewheel steering unit. Nose unit towbar for catapult launch.
POWER PLANT: Two General Electric F404-GE-400 low bypass turbofan engines, each producing approx 71·2 kN (16,000 lb thrust). Self-sealing fuel feed tanks and

McDonnell Douglas F-18A Hornet, with additional side view (top) of the TF-18A training version *(Pilot Press)*

fuel lines; foam in wing tanks and fuselage voids. Internal fuel load approx 4,990 kg (11,000 lb); provision for up to three 1,192 litre (315 US gallon) external tanks, increasing total fuel capacity to more than 7,257 kg (16,000 lb). Simmonds fuel gauging system. Fixed-ramp air intakes.

ACCOMMODATION: Pilot only, on Martin-Baker US10S ejection seat in pressurised, heated and air-conditioned cockpit. Upward-opening two-part canopy, both sections hinged individually.

SYSTEMS: Two completely separate hydraulic systems. Quadruplex digital fly-by-wire flight control system, with direct electrical backup to all surfaces, and direct mechanical backup to stabilators. Garrett-AiResearch air-conditioning system. GEC electrical power system. Oxygen system. Fire detection and extinguishing systems.

AVIONICS AND EQUIPMENT: Will include an automatic carrier landing system (ACLS) for all-weather carrier operations; a Hughes AN/APG-65 multi-mode digital air-to-air and air-to-ground tracking radar, with air-to-air modes which include Velocity Search (VS), Range While Search (RWS), Track While Scan (TWS), which can track ten targets and display eight to the pilot, and Raid Assessment Mode (RAM). Itek ALR-67

radar warning receiver; General Electric quadruple-redundant flight control system with two AYK-14 digital computers; Litton inertial navigation system; Kaiser multi-purpose cockpit display, including head-up display and three CRTs; Conrac communications system control; Normalair-Garrett digital data recorder for Bendix maintenance recording system; Smiths standby altimeter; and Kearflex standby airspeed indicator, standby vertical speed indicator, and cockpit pressure altimeter. Garrett-AiResearch APU for engine starting and ground pneumatic, electrical and hydraulic power.

ARMAMENT: Nine external weapon stations with a combined capacity of 7,710 kg (17,000 lb) of mixed ordnance at high g. These comprise two wingtip stations for AIM-9 Sidewinder air-to-air missiles; two outboard wing stations for an assortment of air-to-ground or air-to-air weapons, including AIM-7 Sparrows; two inboard wing stations for external fuel tanks or air-to-ground weapons; two nacelle fuselage stations for Sparrows or Martin Marietta AN/ASQ-173 laser spot tracker/strike camera (LST/SCAM) and Ford FLIR pods; and a centreline fuselage station for external fuel or weapons. An M61 20 mm six-barrel gun, with 570 rounds, is mounted in the nose and will have a McDonnell Douglas director gunsight, with a conventional sight as backup.

DIMENSIONS, EXTERNAL:

Wing span	11·43 m (37 ft 6 in)
Wing span over missiles	12·31 m (40 ft 4¾ in)
Width, wings folded	8·38 m (27 ft 6 in)
Length overall	17·07 m (56 ft 0 in)
Height overall	4·66 m (15 ft 3½ in)
Tailplane span	6·58 m (21 ft 7¼ in)
Wheel track	3·11 m (10 ft 2½ in)
Wheelbase	5·42 m (17 ft 9½ in)

AREA:

Wings, gross	37·16 m² (400 sq ft)

WEIGHTS:

Fighter mission T-O weight	15,234 kg (33,585 lb)
Attack mission T-O weight	21,319 kg (47,000 lb)

PERFORMANCE (estimated):

Max level speed	more than Mach 1·8
Max speed, intermediate power	more than Mach 1·0
Approach speed	130 knots (240 km/h; 150 mph)
Combat ceiling	approx 15,240 m (50,000 ft)
T-O run	less than 305 m (1,000 ft)
Combat radius, fighter mission	more than 400 nm (740 km; 460 miles)
Combat radius, attack mission	550 nm (1,019 km; 633 miles)
Ferry range, unrefuelled	more than 2,000 nm (3,706 km; 2,303 miles)

DOUGLAS AIRCRAFT COMPANY (a Division of McDonnell Douglas Corporation)

HEADQUARTERS: 3855 Lakewood Boulevard, Long Beach, California 90846
Telephone: (213) 593 5511
PRESIDENT: John C. Brizendine
EXECUTIVE VICE-PRESIDENTS:
 Walter F. Burke
 Charles M. Forsyth
SENIOR VICE/PRESIDENTS:
 Charles Conrad Jr (Marketing)
 Edward Curtis (Fiscal Management)
 William T. Gross (Operations)
VICE-PRESIDENTS:
 Ray E. Bates (Advanced Programmes)
 Harold Bayer (Product Support)
 Richard A. Bibee (Contracts and Pricing)
 Jerald D. Burns (Commercial Contracts)
 Larry S. Dickenson (Commercial Sales, Europe, Africa and Middle East)
 Eugene F. Dubil (Engineering)
 N. Douglas Ingebretsen (Personnel, West)
 Robert C. P. Jackson (Plans)
 Ray J. Kleinberg (Operations)
 Donald J. Krokus (Commercial Sales, Pacific and Asia)
 Marvin D. Marks (General Manager, CX Programme)
 Victor R. Saliture (Manufacturing)
 John W. Stillwell (Quality Assurance)
 Howell L. Walker (Commercial Sales, the Americas)
 Lupton A. Wilkinson Jr (Manufacturing PRC Programme)
 William R. Worrell (Material)
CHIEF COUNSEL: John H. Carroll
DIRECTOR, EXTERNAL RELATIONS: Raymond L. Towne
 The Douglas Aircraft Company operates plants at Long Beach, Palmdale and Torrance, California.

MCDONNELL DOUGLAS DC-8 FREIGHTER CONVERSION

Under a programme launched at Tulsa works in February 1976, McDonnell Douglas is modifying DC-8 passenger transports into specialised freighters at a current rate of up to nine aircraft per year. First to be converted were two DC-8-43 series airliners, which were also re-engined with Pratt & Whitney JT3D turbofans, under contract from Frederick B. Ayer and Associates. Subsequent orders for a total of eight conversions have been received from Intercontinental Airways, International Air Leases Inc, International Air Service, Overseas National Airways and Transmeridian Air Cargo.

Modification includes removal of passenger installations and fitting a production freighter seven-track floor, and a 2·16 m × 3·56 m (85 × 140 in) main deck cargo door. Cabin windows are replaced by metal plugs, and a cargo loading system is installed. Conversion to turbofan power is optional for turbojet models.

MCDONNELL DOUGLAS DC-8 SERIES 71, 72 and 73

A brief paragraph in the 1979-80 *Jane's* gave preliminary details of the company's plans to re-engine DC-8 Srs 61, 62 and 63 aircraft with General Electric/SNECMA CFM56 or Pratt & Whitney JT8D-209 turbofan engines, under the respective designations of DC-8 Srs 71, 72 and 73. Since that time, engineering design for the DC-8/CFM56 conversion has continued, and was scheduled for completion in May 1980. The first modification will be that of a DC-8 Srs 61, and FAA certification of the resulting Srs 71 is anticipated by the end of 1981. By that date a DC-8 Srs 63 will also have been converted to the new power plant, and certification of this Srs 73 is programmed for April 1982. It is intended to carry out similar conversions to Srs 61F/61CF, 62F/62CF, and 63F/63CF Jet

Artist's impression of the McDonnell Douglas DC-8 Srs 73, a version of the DC-8 Srs 63 re-engined with CFM56 turbofans

Traders. At the beginning of February 1980, the company had received 56 firm orders and 44 options for conversions.

Douglas states that Srs 71, 72 and 73 aircraft with CFM56-2-1C engines are expected to be the quietest large four-engined transports when they enter service, offering airport communities a true noise reduction in the order of 70 per cent. This means that these aircraft will not only be able to meet the requirements of FAR Pt 36-7 and -8, but will offer protection against future, more stringent regulations.

This considerable reduction in environmental noise pollution is gained without loss of aircraft performance. On the contrary, Douglas claims that the DC-8 Super Seventy series with CFM56 engines will offer improved performance, including reduced take-off run, increased range, and fuel savings over a 3,000 nm (5,560 km; 3,455 mile) route of as much as 7,711 kg (17,000 lb), 3,855 kg (8,500 lb), and 4,990 kg (11,000 lb) for the DC-8 Srs 71, 72 and 73 respectively.

Only limited specification estimates for these conversions were available in early 1980, as follows:

WEIGHTS AND LOADINGS (estimated. A: Srs 71; B: Srs 72; C: Srs 73; D: Srs 71F Jet Trader; E: Srs 72F; and F: Srs 73F):

Operating weight empty: A	73,800 kg	(162,700 lb)
B	69,220 kg	(152,600 lb)
C	75,115 kg	(165,600 lb)
Max payload: A, C	30,240 kg	(66,665 lb)
B	19,315 kg	(42,580 lb)
Fuel weight: A	71,093 kg	(156,733 lb)
B	70,734 kg	(155,942 lb)
C	73,773 kg	(162,642 lb)
Max T-O weight: A, D	147,415 kg	(325,000 lb)
B, E	151,955 kg	(335,000 lb)
C	158,755 kg	(350,000 lb)
F	161,025 kg	(355,000 lb)
Max zero-fuel weight: A	101,605 kg	(224,000 lb)
B	88,450 kg	(195,000 lb)
C	104,325 kg	(230,000 lb)
Max landing weight: A, B	108,860 kg	(240,000 lb)
C	111,115 kg	(245,000 lb)
D, E	117,025 kg	(258,000 lb)
F	124,740 kg	(275,000 lb)
Max wing loading:		
A, D	550·2 kg/m²	(112·69 lb/sq ft)
B, E	558·8 kg/m²	(114·45 lb/sq ft)
C	583·8 kg/m²	(119·58 lb/sq ft)
F	592·1 kg/m²	(121·28 lb/sq ft)

PERFORMANCE (estimated, at max T-O weight with CFM56-2-1C engines):
Max level speed, all versions
 521 knots (965 km/h; 600 mph)
Cruising speed, all versions Mach 0·80

MCDONNELL DOUGLAS DC-9
USAF designations: C-9A and VC-9C
US Navy designation: C-9B

Design study data on the DC-9, then known as the Douglas Model 2086, were released in 1962. Preliminary design work began during that year. Fabrication was started on 26 July 1963 and assembly of the first airframe began on 6 March 1964. It flew for the first time on 25 February 1965 and five DC-9s were flying by the end of June 1965. These were of the basic version, known as the DC-9 Series 10, of which production has ended; details can be found in the 1978-79 *Jane's*. Other variants are as follows:

Series 20. For operation in hot climate/high-altitude conditions, combining long-span wings of Series 30 with short fuselage of original Series 10. Up to 90 passengers. Two 64·5 kN (14,500 lb st) JT8D-9 turbofans. The Series 20 flew for the first time on 18 September 1968, and was certificated on 11 December 1968. The first Series 20 was delivered to SAS on the same day and entered commercial service on 23 January 1969. Described in 1977-78 *Jane's*.

Series 30. Developed version, initially with 62·3 kN (14,000 lb st) JT8D-7s, increased wing span, longer fuselage accommodating up to 105 passengers (normal) or 119 (with reduced facilities), and new high-lift devices including full-span leading-edge slats and double-slotted flaps. First Srs 30 flew for first time on 1 August 1966. First delivery, to Eastern Air Lines, was made on 27 January 1967 and scheduled services began on 1 February 1967. Engine options available include JT8D-9 of 64·5 kN (14,500 lb st); JT8D-11 of 66·7 kN (15,000 lb st); JT8D-15 of 69 kN (15,500 lb st); and JT8D-17 of 71·2 kN (16,000 lb st). Newer engines have sound-treated nacelles that comply with FAA FAR Pt 36 noise regulations.

Series 40. As Series 30, but with 64·5 kN (14,500 lb st) JT8D-9, 69 kN (15,500 lb st) JT8D-15 or 71·2 kN (16,000 lb st) JT8D-17 turbofans, increased fuel capacity, longer fuselage accommodating up to 132 passengers, and greater AUW. First flight was made on 28 November 1967 and FAA certification was received on 27 February 1968. The first Series 40 was delivered to SAS on 29 February 1968 and entered commercial service with that airline on 12 March 1968.

Series 50. 'Stretched' short/medium-range development of the Series 30, announced on 5 July 1973. High-density seating for up to 139 passengers made possible by a 4·34 m (14 ft 3 in) fuselage extension. A 'new look' interior features enclosed overhead racks for carry-on baggage, sculptured wall panels, acoustically-treated ceiling panels and indirect lighting. Available with either Pratt & Whitney JT8D-15 or -17 turbofan engines, rated at 69 kN (15,500 lb st) and 71·2 kN (16,000 lb st) respectively, and embodying sound-absorption materials as developed for the engines and nacelles of the DC-10, the Series 50 meets FAR Pt 36 noise requirements. The engines are smokeless and have thrust reversers rotated 17° from the vertical to reduce the possibility of exhaust gas ingestion. The landing gear is fitted with an improved anti-skid braking system. First flight of a Series 50 was made on 17 December 1974. First deliveries were made to Swissair, with whom it entered service in August 1975.

Super 80. Increased capacity short/medium-range version of the DC-9, with accommodation for a maximum of 172 passengers. Described separately.

Current versions are offered in passenger, cargo (**DC-9F**), convertible (**DC-9CF**) or passenger-cargo (**DC-9RC**) configurations. The cargo and convertible models have a main cabin cargo door measuring 3·45 m (11 ft 4 in) wide and 2·06 m (6 ft 9 in) high. An executive transport version is also offered, with increased fuel, enabling up to 15 persons to be carried nonstop over 2,865 nm (5,300 km; 3,300 mile) transcontinental or transocean stages. First delivery of an all-cargo model, a DC-9 Srs 30F, was made to Alitalia on 13 May 1968. This model has 122·1 m³ (4,313 cu ft) of cargo space in main cabin, plus the underfloor hold, enabling it to carry eight full cargo pallets and two half-pallets with total weight of nearly 18,144 kg (40,000 lb).

There are also three military versions of the DC-9, as follows:

C-9A Nightingale. Aeromedical airlift transport, based on DC-9 Srs 30; 21 delivered to USAF between 1968-73. Details in 1977-78 *Jane's*.

C-9B Skytrain II. Fleet logistic support transport, of which 17 were ordered by the USN and two by Kuwait. Described in 1979-80 and earlier editions of *Jane's*.

VC-9C. Three DC-9-30 type aircraft with special configuration, delivered in 1975 to the USAF for service in the Special Air Missions Wing based at Andrews AFB, Maryland.

Orders for the DC-9 totalled 1,061 (with conditional orders and options for 34 others), including military versions, by 1 July 1980. A total of 944 DC-9s (including 21 C-9As, 17 C-9Bs and 3 VC-9Cs) had been delivered by 1 July 1980.

In June 1966, the FAA certificated three Category 2 all-weather landing systems for the DC-9, comprising the Collins FD-108 flight director system, Sperry AD-200 flight director system, and coupled approach utilising the Sperry SP-50A autopilot.

The following structural details apply to the DC-9 Series 30:

TYPE: Twin-turbofan short/medium-range airliner.
WINGS: Cantilever low-wing monoplane. Mean thickness/chord ratio 11·0%. Dihedral 3°. Sweepback 24° 30′ at quarter-chord. All-metal construction, with three spars inboard, two spars outboard and spanwise stringers riveted to skin. Glassfibre trailing-edges on wings, ailerons and flaps. Manually-controlled aileron on each wing. Wing-mounted speed brakes. Full-span leading-edge slats (also on Srs 20/40/50). Hydraulically-actuated double-slotted trailing-edge flaps over 67% of semi-span. Single boundary-layer fence (vortillon) under each wing. Detachable wingtips. Thermal anti-icing of leading-edges.
FUSELAGE: Conventional all-metal semi-monocoque structure.
TAIL UNIT: Cantilever all-metal structure with electrically-actuated variable-incidence T-tailplane. Manually-controlled elevators with servo tabs. Hydraulically-controlled rudder with manual override. Glassfibre trailing-edges on control surfaces.
LANDING GEAR: Retractable tricycle type of Menasco manufacture, with steerable nosewheel. Hydraulic retraction, nose unit forward, main units inward. Twin Goodyear wheels on each unit. Main-wheel tyres size 40 × 14. Nosewheel tyres size 26 × 6·60. Goodyear brakes. Hydro-Aire Hytrol anti-skid units.
POWER PLANT: Two Pratt & Whitney JT8D turbofan engines (details given under individual model listings), pod-mounted on each side of rear fuselage. Engines fitted with 40% target-type thrust reversers for ground operation only. Standard fuel capacity 13,937 litres (3,682 US gallons), also in Srs 10 and 20; 16,122 litres (4,259 US gallons) in Srs 40; and up to 19,074 litres (5,039 US gallons) in Srs 50. In Srs 30, 40 and 50 aircraft an additional 8,517 litres (2,250 US gallons) can be stored in auxiliary tanks.
ACCOMMODATION: Crew of two on flight deck, plus cabin attendants. Normal accommodation in main cabin is for 105 passengers, with seating for maximum of 119 with reduced facilities. Fully pressurised and air-conditioned. Toilets at rear of cabin. Provision for galley. Passenger door at front of cabin on port side, with electrically-operated built-in airstairs. Optional ventral stairway. Servicing and emergency exit door opposite on starboard side. Underfloor freight and baggage holds, with forward and rear doors on starboard side.
DIMENSIONS, EXTERNAL:
Wing span: Srs 30, 40, 50   28·47 m (93 ft 5 in)
Wing aspect ratio: Srs 30, 40, 50   8·71
Length overall: Srs 30   36·37 m (119 ft 3½ in)
    Srs 40   38·28 m (125 ft 7¼ in)
    Srs 50   40·72 m (133 ft 7¼ in)
Height overall: Srs 30   8·38 m (27 ft 6 in)
    Srs 40, 50   8·53 m (28 ft 0 in)

Tailplane span:
Srs 30, 40, 50   11·23 m (36 ft 10¼ in)
Wheel track: Srs 30, 40, 50   5·03 m (16 ft 6 in)
Wheelbase: Srs 30   16·22 m (53 ft 2½ in)
    Srs 40   17·10 m (56 ft 1¼ in)
    Srs 50   18·56 m (60 ft 11 in)
Passenger door (port, fwd):
    Height   1·83 m (6 ft 0 in)
    Width   0·85 m (2 ft 9½ in)
    Height to sill   2·13 m (7 ft 2 in)
Servicing door (stbd, fwd): Height   1·22 m (4 ft 0 in)
    Width   0·69 m (2 ft 3 in)
    Height to sill   2·18 m (7 ft 2 in)
Freight and baggage hold doors:
    Height   1·27 m (4 ft 2 in)
    Width: fwd   1·35 m (4 ft 5 in)
    rear   0·91 m (3 ft 0 in)
    Height to sill   1·07 m (3 ft 6 in)
DIMENSIONS, INTERNAL:
Cabin: Max width   3·07 m (10 ft 1 in)
    Floor width   2·87 m (9 ft 5 in)
    Max height   2·06 m (6 ft 9 in)
Freight hold (underfloor):
    Srs 30   25·3 m³ (895 cu ft)
    Srs 40   28·9 m³ (1,019 cu ft)
    Srs 50   33·24 m³ (1,174 cu ft)
AREAS:
Wings, gross:
    Srs 30, 40, 50   92·97 m² (1,000·7 sq ft)
Ailerons (total): All versions   3·53 m² (38·0 sq ft)
Trailing-edge flaps (total):
    All versions   19·58 m² (210·8 sq ft)
Leading-edge slats (total):
    Srs 50   11·22 m² (120·8 sq ft)
Spoilers (total): All versions   3·22 m² (34·7 sq ft)
Fin: All versions   14·96 m² (161·0 sq ft)
Rudder: All versions   6·07 m² (65·3 sq ft)
Tailplane: All versions   25·60 m² (275·6 sq ft)
Elevators, incl tabs: All versions
    9·83 m² (105·8 sq ft)
WEIGHTS:
Manufacturer's empty weight:
    Srs 30   25,940 kg (57,190 lb)
    Srs 40   26,612 kg (58,670 lb)
    Srs 50   28,068 kg (61,880 lb)
Max space-limited payload:
    Srs 30   14,118 kg (31,125 lb)
    Srs 40   15,610 kg (34,415 lb)
Max weight-limited payload:
    Srs 30   12,743 kg (28,094 lb)
    Srs 40   14,363 kg (31,665 lb)
    Srs 50   15,617 kg (34,430 lb)
Max T-O weight:
    Srs 30, 40, 50   54,885 kg (121,000 lb)
Max ramp weight:
    Srs 30, 40, 50   55,338 kg (122,000 lb)
Max zero-fuel weight:
    Srs 30, 40, 50   44,678 kg (98,500 lb)
Max landing weight:
    Srs 30, 40, 50   49,895 kg (110,000 lb)
PERFORMANCE (at max T-O weight, except where indicated):
Never-exceed speed:
    Srs 50   537 knots (995 km/h; 618 mph)
Max level speed:
    All versions   500 knots (926 km/h; 575 mph)
Max cruising speed at 7,620 m (25,000 ft):
    Srs 30   490 knots (907 km/h; 564 mph)
    Srs 40, 50   485 knots (898 km/h; 558 mph)
Average long-range cruising speed at 9,145-10,675 m (30,000-35,000 ft) 443 knots (821 km/h; 510 mph)
Max rate of climb at S/L:
    Srs 30   885 m (2,900 ft)/min
    Srs 40   865 m (2,850 ft)/min
    Srs 50   792 m (2,600 ft)/min

FAA T-O field length: Srs 30   1,685 m (5,530 ft)
    Srs 40   2,088 m (6,850 ft)
FAA landing field length: Srs 30   1,425 m (4,680 ft)
    Srs 40   1,440 m (4,720 ft)
    Srs 50   1,485 m (4,880 ft)
Range at Mach 0·8, with reserves for 200 nm (370 km; 230 mile) flight to alternate and 60 min hold at 3,050 m (10,000 ft):
    Srs 30 at 9,150 m (30,000 ft) with 64 passengers and baggage   1,160 nm (2,148 km; 1,335 miles)
    Srs 40 at 7,620 m (25,000 ft) with 70 passengers and baggage   930 nm (1,723 km; 1,071 miles)
Range at long-range cruising speed at 9,150 m (30,000 ft), reserves for 200 nm (370 km; 230 mile) flight to alternate and 45 min continued cruise at 9,150 m (30,000 ft):
    Srs 30 with 80 passengers and baggage   1,670 nm (3,095 km; 1,923 miles)
    Srs 40 with 87 passengers and baggage   1,555 nm (2,880 km; 1,790 miles)
    Srs 50 with 97 passengers and baggage   1,795 nm (3,326 km; 2,067 miles)
Ferry range, reserves as above:
    Srs 30   1,980 nm (3,669 km; 2,280 miles)
    Srs 40   1,850 nm (3,428 km; 2,130 miles)
    Srs 50   2,185 nm (4,049 km; 2,516 miles)

MCDONNELL DOUGLAS DC-9 SUPER 80

The McDonnell Douglas DC-9 Super 80 was developed specifically to meet the needs of operators on short/medium-range routes who require an aircraft of increased capacity, and the basic design has been modified to offer improved economy in operation, reduced fuel consumption, and far quieter engines. The following versions have been announced to date:

DC-9 Super 81. Basic version, powered by two Pratt & Whitney JT8D-209 turbofan engines. Certificated at a max T-O weight of 63,500 kg (140,000 lb).

DC-9 Super 82. Announced on 16 April 1979, with Pratt & Whitney JT8D-217 turbofan engines, each rated at 89 kN (20,000 lb st), and with an emergency thrust reserve of 3·78 kN (850 lb st). It is planned to certificate this version at a max T-O weight of 66,680 kg (147,000 lb). Otherwise generally similar to Super 81, with same fuel capacity and max landing weight.

DC-9 Super 83. Proposed European charter version, with a max T-O weight of 68,945 kg (152,000 lb).

DC-9 Super 80SF. Proposed short-field version, with the fuselage length and capacity of the DC-9 Srs 40, but with the new wings and more powerful engines of the Super 80 Series.

The new wings are increased in span by the insertion of wing root plugs and by a 0·61 m (2 ft 0 in) extension on each tip, giving a gross area 28% greater than that of the DC-9 Srs 50. The fuselage of the Super 81 is extended in length by insertion of a 3·86 m (12 ft 8 in) plug forward of the wing, and a 0·48 m (1 ft 7 in) segment aft of the wing. The cabin has 'wide look' decor, with large enclosed overhead baggage compartments, acoustic ceiling and soft fluorescent lighting.

Basic power plant of the DC-9 Super 81 comprises two Pratt & Whitney JT8D-209 turbofan engines, each with an emergency thrust reserve which becomes available automatically in an engine-out situation. Refanned with a larger-diameter single-stage fan, this version of the JT8D engine has a bypass ratio of 1·68, by comparison with 1·00 of earlier versions, resulting in a lower specific fuel consumption and reduced noise emission. In addition, sound suppression materials applied to the inlet, fan duct and tailpipe duct of each nacelle, plus a cold/hot-stream exhaust mixer, reduce engine noise to levels below the requirements of FAR Pt 36 Stage 3, and also satisfy the more stringent requirements of ICAO CAN 5 established for new aircraft designs. Standard fuel capacity is increased by 5,754 litres (1,520 US gallons) as a result of the larger wing.

McDonnell Douglas DC-9 Super 80 'stretched' version of this twin-turbofan transport *(Pilot Press)*

Third McDonnell Douglas DC-9 Super 80 to fly, in the insignia of Austrian Airlines

The DC-9 Super 82 proposal, with the more powerful Pratt & Whitney JT8D-217 turbofan engines, is regarded as being particularly suitable for operation from 'hot and high' airports. The higher thrust available would make possible an increased payload and range when operating from standard airports. At an airport such as Denver, Colorado, which is 1,525 m (5,000 ft) above sea level, the Super 82 would be able to take off with 155 passengers and their baggage, and have a nonstop range of approximately 1,300 nm (2,409 km; 1,497 miles).

Systems improvements in the Super 80s include a new digital electronics integrated flight guidance and control system; a 'dial-a-flap' system to permit more accurate selection of flap angle for optimum take-off and landing performance; flow-through cooling of the aircraft's avionics compartment; a larger-capacity APU; a new recirculating system for ventilation air; and an advanced digital fuel quantity gauging system.

The first DC-9 Super 81 made a first flight of 2 h 50 min on 18 October 1979. The second and third prototypes (N1002G and N1002W) flew on 6 December 1979 and 29 February 1980 respectively. FAA certification was granted on 26 August 1980.

First order for the Super 80 series had been placed by Swissair, for 15 Super 81 aircraft, in October 1977. This airline was first to take delivery of a Super 81, on 12 September 1980, and started to operate the aircraft on its London-Zurich route from 5 October. First order (of three aircraft) for the Super 82 was placed by Aeromexico in September 1979. By 12 September 1980 firm orders totalled 87 aircraft, plus conditional firm orders and options for 28 more, to serve with 12 customers.

The following description applies to the Super 81, but except for the power plant applies generally also to the Super 82:

TYPE: Twin-turbofan short/medium-range airliner.

WINGS: Cantilever low-wing monoplane. Mean thickness/chord ratio 11·0%. Dihedral 3°. Incidence 1° 15'. Sweepback at quarter-chord 24° 30'. All-metal construction, with three spars inboard, two spars outboard and spanwise stringers riveted to skin. Glassfibre trailing-edges on wings, ailerons and flaps. Manually-controlled aileron on each wing. Wing-mounted speed brakes. Full-span leading-edge slats. Hydraulically-actuated double-slotted trailing-edge flaps over 67% of semi-span. Single boundary-layer fence (vortillon) under each wing. Three spoilers per wing; two outboard segments act as flight and ground spoilers, inboard segment is ground spoiler only. Detachable wingtips. Thermal anti-icing of leading-edges.

FUSELAGE: All-metal semi-monocoque fail-safe structure of heat-treated light alloy. Majority of cabin floor constructed of balsa or Nomex core composite. Engine pylons built by Calcor, fuselage panels by Aeritalia.

TAIL UNIT: Cantilever all-metal structure with electrically-actuated variable-incidence T tailplane. Manually-controlled elevators with servo tabs. Hydraulically-controlled rudder with manual override. Glassfibre trailing-edges on control surfaces.

LANDING GEAR: Retractable tricycle type of Cleveland Pneumatic manufacture, with steerable nosewheels. Hydraulic retraction, nose unit forward, main units inward. Twin Goodyear wheels and tyres on each unit. Main-wheel tyres size 44·5 × 16·5-20, pressure 11·38 bars (165 lb/sq in). Nosewheel tyres size 26 × 6·6-14, pressure 10·34 bars (150 lb/sq in). Goodyear disc brakes. Hydro-Aire Mk IIIA anti-skid units. Douglas ram-air brake cooling.

POWER PLANT (Super 81): Two Pratt & Whitney JT8D-209 turbofan engines, pod-mounted on each side of rear fuselage, and each rated at 82·3 kN (18,500 lb st), with emergency thrust reserve of 3·3 kN (750 lb st). Standard fuel capacity 21,876 litres (5,779 US gallons). Pressure refuelling point in starboard wing leading-edge. Overwing gravity refuelling points.

ACCOMMODATION: Crew of two on flight deck, plus cabin attendants. Standard accommodation in main cabin is for 12 first class and 125 coach class passengers, but optional arrangements provide a maximum capacity of 172 passengers. Fully pressurised and air-conditioned. Toilets at rear of cabin. Provision for galley. Passenger door at front of cabin on port side, with electrically-operated built-in airstairs. Servicing and emergency exit doors at starboard forward end and aft port end of cabin. Three cargo doors for underfloor holds on starboard side. Overwing emergency exits, two each side. Optional ventral stairway.

SYSTEMS: Garrett-AiResearch dual air cycle air-conditioning and pressurisation system utilising engine bleed air, max differential 0·54 bars (7·77 lb/sq in). Two separate 207 bar (3,000 lb/sq in) hydraulic systems for operation of spoilers, flaps, slats, rudder, landing gear, nosewheel steering, brakes, rotated thrust reversers and ventral stairway. Pneumatic system, for air-conditioning/pressurisation, engine starting and ice protection, utilises 8th or 13th stage engine bleed air and/or APU. Electrical system includes three 40kVA 120/208V three-phase 400Hz alternators, two engine-driven, one driven by APU. Oxygen system of diluter-demand type for crew on flight deck; continuous-flow type with automatic mask presentation for cabin passengers. Anti-icing of wing and engine inlets, and de-icing of tailplane, by engine bleed air. Electrical de-icing of windscreen. APU provides pneumatic and electrical power on ground, and electrical power in flight.

AVIONICS AND EQUIPMENT: All-digital avionics, including dual Sperry integrated flight systems; Sperry Cat IIIA autoland; autopilot and stability augmentation system; speed command with digital autothrottles; rat/thrust rating indicator system; dual air data systems; automatic reserve thrust; tune ADF system; and weather radar display. Sundstrand head-up display.

DIMENSIONS, EXTERNAL:
Wing span	32·87 m (107 ft 10 in)
Wing chord at root	7·05 m (23 ft 1½ in)
Wing chord at tip	1·10 m (3 ft 7½ in)
Wing aspect ratio	9·62
Length overall	45·06 m (147 ft 10 in)
Length of fuselage	41·30 m (135 ft 6 in)
Height overall	9·04 m (29 ft 8 in)
Tailplane span	12·24 m (40 ft 2 in)
Wheel track	5·08 m (16 ft 8 in)
Wheelbase	22·07 m (72 ft 5 in)
Passenger door (port, fwd):	
Height	1·83 m (6 ft 0 in)
Width	0·86 m (2 ft 10 in)
Height to sill	2·24 m (7 ft 4 in)
Servicing door (stbd, fwd): Height	1·22 m (4 ft 0 in)
Width	0·69 m (2 ft 3 in)
Height to sill	2·24 m (7 ft 4 in)
Servicing door (port, rear): Height	1·52 m (5 ft 0 in)
Width	0·69 m (2 ft 3 in)
Height to sill	2·67 m (8 ft 9 in)
Freight and baggage hold doors:	
Height	1·27 m (4 ft 2 in)
Width	1·35 m (4 ft 5 in)
Height to sill: fwd	1·17 m (3 ft 10 in)
centre	1·30 m (4 ft 3 in)
aft	1·52 m (5 ft 0 in)
Emergency exits (overwing, port and stbd):	
Height	0·91 m (3 ft 0 in)
Width	0·51 m (1 ft 8 in)

DIMENSIONS, INTERNAL:
Cabin, excl flight deck, incl toilets:	
Length	30·78 m (101 ft 0 in)
Max width	3·07 m (10 ft 1 in)
Max height	2·06 m (6 ft 9 in)
Floor area	89·65 m² (965 sq ft)
Volume	191·9 m³ (6,778 cu ft)
Freight holds (underfloor):	
fwd	13·14 m³ (464 cu ft)
centre	9·80 m³ (346 cu ft)
aft	12·54 m³ (443 cu ft)

AREAS:
Wings, gross	118·8 m² (1,279 sq ft)
Ailerons (total)	3·53 m² (38·0 sq ft)
Fin	14·96 m² (161·0 sq ft)
Rudder	6·07 m² (65·3 sq ft)
Tailplane	29·17 m² (314·0 sq ft)

WEIGHTS AND LOADINGS (A: Super 81; B: Super 82):
Weight empty: A		36,177 kg (79,757 lb)
B		36,534 kg (80,543 lb)
Fuel load: A, B		17,748 kg (39,128 lb)
Max T-O weight: A		63,500 kg (140,000 lb)
B		66,680 kg (147,000 lb)
Max zero-fuel weight: A, B		53,524 kg (118,000 lb)
Max landing weight: A, B		58,060 kg (128,000 lb)
Max wing loading: A	534·6 kg/m²	(109·5 lb/sq ft)
B	561·0 kg/m²	(114·9 lb/sq ft)
Max power loading: A	385·8 kg/kN	(3·78 lb/lb st)
B	374·6 kg/kN	(3·68 lb/lb st)

PERFORMANCE (at max T-O weight):
Max level speed:		
A, B	500 knots	(927 km/h; 576 mph)
Max cruising speed: A, B		Mach 0·80
Normal cruising speed: A, B		Mach 0·76
Landing speed:		
A, B	124 knots	(230 km/h; 143 mph)
FAA T-O field length: A		2,192 m (7,190 ft)
B		2,176 m (7,140 ft)
FAA landing field length: A, B		1,286 m (4,220 ft)
Range with max fuel:		
A		2,657 nm (4,925 km; 3,060 miles)
B		2,596 nm (4,812 km; 2,990 miles)

OPERATIONAL NOISE LEVELS (FAR Pt 36):
T-O	90·4 EPNdB
Sideline	94·6 EPNdB
Approach	93·3 EPNdB

MCDONNELL DOUGLAS DC-10

The DC-10 was developed by McDonnell Douglas as an all-purpose commercial transport able to operate economically over ranges from 260 nm to 5,300 nm (480 to 9,815 km; 300 to 6,100 miles), according to Series, and able to carry 270 mixed class passengers, or a maximum of 380 passengers in an all-economy configuration.

There are five basic production versions, as follows:

Series 10. Initial version, powered by three General Electric CF6-6D or -6D1 turbofan engines, each rated at 178 kN (40,000 lb st) or 182·4 kN (41,000 lb st) respectively. Intended for service on domestic routes of 260-3,125 nm (480-5,795 km; 300-3,600 miles). First ordered, by American Airlines, on 19 February 1968. First flight 29 August 1970. Type certificated by FAA on 29 July 1971.

First scheduled passenger flight 5 August 1971, by American Airlines.

Series 15. Basically as Series 10, but with General Electric CF6-50C2F engines, each rated at 233·5 kN (52,500 lb st). Two each ordered by Aeromexico and Mexicana in Summer 1979, for delivery in 1981. Three more ordered subsequently by Mexicana.

Series 30. Extended-range version for inter-continental operations, powered by three General Electric CF6-50A or -50C turbofan engines, each rated at 218 kN (49,000 lb st) and 227 kN (51,000 lb st) respectively. Later versions have CF6-50C1 or C2 engines rated at 233·5 kN (52,500 lb st). Increased fuel capacity. Wing span increased by 3·05 m (10 ft 0 in). Landing gear supplemented by additional dual-wheel unit, mounted on the fuselage centreline between the four-wheel bogie main units. First flight 21 June 1972. FAA certification granted 21 November 1972, simultaneously with first deliveries of production aircraft to KLM and Swissair.

Series 30ER. Developed version of Series 30, with range extended still further by installing a 5,792 litre (1,530 US gallon) auxiliary fuel tank in rear of cargo compartment, giving total capacity of 144,224 litres (38,100 US gallons) and increasing range by up to 695 nm (1,287 km; 800 miles). More powerful (240·2 kN; 54,000 lb st) CF6-50-C2B engines; max T-O weight 263,085 kg (580,000 lb); max range 5,730 nm (10,620 km; 6,600 miles). First order (for two) placed by Swissair in July 1980, plus kits to convert two of its existing DC-10s to Srs 30ER configuration.

Series 40. Extended-range version for intercontinental operations, powered by three Pratt & Whitney turbofan

McDonnell Douglas DC-10 Series 30 in the insignia of Ariana Afghan Airlines, the national airline of Afghanistan

engines. Twenty-two early models, built for Northwest Orient Airlines, had JT9D-20 turbofans, each rated at 220 kN (49,400 lb st) with water injection. First flight of Series 40 (known originally as Series 20) was on 28 February 1972; FAA certification received 20 October 1972. Later versions, built for Japan Air Lines, equipped with JT9D-59A turbofans, each rated at 236 kN (53,000 lb st). First flight of a Series 40 with this latter power plant was on 25 July 1975.

There are also convertible cargo versions designated Model **10CF** and **30CF**, of which the latter is described separately. On 19 December 1977 the USAF announced selection of the DC-10 Srs 30CF as its **Advanced Tanker/ Cargo Aircraft (ATCA)**, and this version also is described separately (see entry for KC-10A Extender).

Under consideration for possible future production are domestic and intercontinental versions with fuselages lengthened by 7·92 to 12·19 m (26 to 40 ft) compared with current series. The largest of the new models would accommodate a total of 395 passengers in mixed first class/coach seating, with improved seat/mile costs and reduced fuel consumption per seat. Winglets were due to be flight tested on a DC-10 before the end of 1980.

DC-10 subassemblies and components are brought together at Long Beach for final assembly. Certain major subassemblies are produced at other divisions of McDonnell Douglas, and Convair Division of General Dynamics Corporation at San Diego, California, is subcontractor for the fuselage, being responsible for five sections totalling 39·01 m (128 ft).

By 1 July 1980, McDonnell Douglas had received firm orders for 358 DC-10s, plus conditional orders and options on 32 more, making a total of 390, of which 324 had been delivered. At that date, 46 airlines, plus the USAF, had ordered DC-10s: the worldwide fleet had then carried 252 million passengers and had amassed more than 1,749 million nm (3,241 million km; 2,014 million miles) of flying.

TYPE: Three-turbofan commercial transport.

WINGS: Cantilever low-wing monoplane of all-metal fail-safe construction. Several different wing sections of Douglas design are used between wing root and tip. Thickness/chord ratio varies from slightly more than 12·2% at root to less than 8·4% at tip. Dihedral 5° 14·4' inboard, 3° 1·8' outboard. Incidence ranges from positive at wing root to negative at tip. Sweepback at quarter-chord 35°. All-metal inboard and outboard ailerons, the former used conventionally, the latter only when the leading-edge slats are extended. Double-slotted all-metal trailing-edge flaps mounted on external hinges, with an inboard and outboard flap panel on each wing. Five all-metal spoiler panels on each wing, at the rear edge of the fixed wing structure, forward of the flaps. All spoilers operate in unison as lateral control, speed brake and ground spoilers. Full-span three-position all-metal leading-edge slats. Ailerons are powered by hydraulic actuators manufactured by Bertea Corporation, spoilers by hydraulic actuators manufactured by Parker-Hannifin Corporation. Each aileron is powered by either of two hydraulic systems; each spoiler is powered by a single system. All leading-edge slat segments outboard of the engines are anti-iced with engine bleed air.

FUSELAGE: Aluminium alloy semi-monocoque fail-safe structure of circular cross-section. Except for auxiliary areas the entire fuselage is pressurised.

TAIL UNIT: Cantilever all-metal structure. Variable-incidence tailplane, actuated by Vickers hydraulic motors. Longitudinal and directional controls are fully powered and comprise inboard and outboard elevators, each segment powered by a Bertea tandem actuator; upper and lower rudder each powered by a Bertea actuator. Rudder standby power supplied by two transfer motor pumps manufactured by Abex Corporation.

LANDING GEAR (Srs 10): Hydraulically-retractable tricycle type, with gravity free-fall for emergency extension. Nosewheel unit retracts forward, main units inward into fuselage. Twin-wheel steerable nose unit. Main gear comprises two four-wheel bogies. Oleo-pneumatic shock-absorbers on all units. Goodyear nosewheels and tyres size 37 × 14-14, pressure 11·03 bars (160 lb/sq in). Goodyear main wheels and tyres size 50 × 20-20, pressure 11·72 bars (170 lb/sq in). Goodyear disc brakes and anti-skid system, with individual wheel control.

LANDING GEAR (Srs 30 and 40): These versions have an additional dual-wheel main unit mounted on the fuselage centreline between the four-wheel bogie units, and this retracts forward. Goodyear nosewheels and tyres size 40 × 15·5-16, pressure 12·41 bars (180 lb/sq in). Four-wheel bogie main units and centreline unit have Goodyear wheels and tyres size 52 × 20·5-23. The former have a pressure of 11·38 bars (165 lb/sq in), the latter 9·65 bars (140 lb/sq in). Otherwise as Srs 10.

POWER PLANT: Three turbofan engines (details under Series descriptions), two of which are mounted on underwing pylons, the third above the rear fuselage at the base of the fin. All engines are fitted with thrust reversers for ground operation. Engine air inlets have load-carrying acoustically-treated panels for noise attenuation, and each engine fan case and fan exhaust is similarly treated. Three integral wing fuel tanks with a total capacity of approximately 82,142 litres (21,700 US gallons). Four standard pressure refuelling adapters, two in each wing outboard of the engine pylons. Series 30 and 40 aircraft have four integral wing fuel tanks and an auxiliary tank in the wing centre-section with a connected structural compartment fitted with a bladder cell, giving increased total capacity of approximately 138,165 litres (36,500 US gallons). Oil capacity, Series 10 and 30: 34·1 litres (9 usable US gallons); Series 40: 56·8 litres (15 usable US gallons).

ACCOMMODATION: Crew of three (pilot, first officer, flight engineer), with seating for two observers, plus cabin attendants. Standard seating for 255 or 270 in mixed class versions, with a maximum of 380 passengers in an economy class arrangement. Two aisles run the length of the cabin, which is separated into sections by cloakroom dividers. In the first class section, with three pairs of reclining seats abreast, the aisles are 0·78 m (2 ft 7 in) wide. In the coach class section, four pairs of seats, with a table between the centre pairs, also have two aisles, these being 0·51 m (1 ft 8 in) wide. One pair of seats is

exchanged for a three-seat unit in the nine-abreast high-density layout. Up to nine lavatories located throughout the passenger cabin. Cloakrooms of standard and elevating type distributed throughout the cabin. Cabin windows, 0·28 × 0·41 m (11 in × 16 in), are spaced at 0·51 m (20 in) centres. Overhead stowage modules, fully enclosed and providing stowage for passengers' personal effects, are located on the sidewalls and extend the full length of the cabin. Optional centreline overhead baggage racks available. Eight passenger doors, four on each side, open by sliding inward and upward into the above-ceiling area. Containerised or bulk cargo compartments located immediately forward and aft of the wing, with outward-opening doors on the starboard side. A bulk cargo compartment is located in the lower aft section of the fuselage, with its door on the port side. Entire accommodation is fully air-conditioned, with five separate control zones for the standard below-floor galley configuration. Series 30 and 40 aircraft have an optional main cabin galley to replace the lower galley, and in this configuration there are four separate control zones for the air-conditioning. The lower-deck galley is provided with five to eight high-temperature ovens, and with refrigerators, storage space for linen, china and other accessories. Serving carts are taken to cabin level by two electric elevators, to a buffet service centre, from where stewardesses serve passengers. To permit quick turnround at terminals, without interference to passenger movement in the main cabin, the kitchen is provisioned through the cargo doors at ground level.

SYSTEMS: Three parallel continuously-operating and completely separate hydraulic systems supply the fully-powered flight controls and wheel brakes. Normally, one of the systems supplies power for landing gear actuation. Two reversible motor pumps, each sized to deliver power from one of the other two systems for standby operation of landing gear, can also power any other hydraulically operated unit. Each hydraulic system is powered by two identical engine-driven pumps, capable of delivering a total of 265 litres (70 US gallons)/min at 207 bars (3,000 lb/sq in) at take-off. All three hydraulic systems are applied to each primary control axis in a manner which ensures maximum control effectiveness in the event of single or dual hydraulic system failures. A Garrett-AiResearch TSCP-700-4 APU provides ground electrical and pneumatic power,

McDonnell Douglas DC-10 Series 30 high-capacity three-engined transport (*Pilot Press*)

including main engine starting, and auxiliary electrical power in flight.

AVIONICS AND EQUIPMENT: A dual fail-operative landing system is installed to meet Category IIIA weather minima. Digital air data computer meeting ARINC 576 requirements on Srs 10. Triple inertial navigation system meeting ARINC 561 requirements on Srs 30 and 40, with optional dual area navigation system capability.

DIMENSIONS, EXTERNAL:

Wing span: Series 10, 15	47·34 m (155 ft 4 in)
Series 30, 40	50·41 m (165 ft 4·4 in)
Wing chord at root	10·71 m (35 ft 1·8 in)
Wing chord at tip: Series 10	3·21 m (10 ft 6½ in)
Series 30, 40	2·73 m (8 ft 11½ in)
Wing aspect ratio: Series 10	6·8
Series 30, 40	7·5
Length overall: Series 10	55·30 m (181 ft 5 in)
Series 15, 30, 40	55·50 m (182 ft 1 in)
Length of fuselage	51·97 m (170 ft 6 in)
Height overall	17·70 m (58 ft 1 in)
Tailplane span	21·69 m (71 ft 2 in)
Wheel track	10·67 m (35 ft 0 in)
Wheelbase: Series 10, 40	22·07 m (72 ft 5 in)
Series 30	22·05 m (72 ft 4 in)

DIMENSIONS, INTERNAL:

Cabin: Length, from aft bulkhead of flight deck to aft cabin bulkhead approx 41·45 m (136 ft 0 in)

Max width	5·72 m (18 ft 9 in)
Height (basic)	2·41 m (7 ft 11 in)

Series 10, 30, 40 in lower-galley configuration:
Forward baggage and/or freight hold (forward of wing):
Containerised volume	27·2 m³ (960 cu ft)
Bulk volume	37·9 m³ (1,339 cu ft)

Centre baggage and/or freight hold (aft of wing):
Containerised volume	36·2 m³ (1,280 cu ft)
Bulk volume	43·9 m³ (1,552 cu ft)

Aft hold:
Bulk volume	22·8 m³ (805 cu ft)

Series 30, 40 in upper-galley configuration:
Forward baggage and/or freight hold (forward of wing):
Containerised volume	72·5 m³ (2,560 cu ft)
Bulk volume	86·2 m³ (3,045 cu ft)

Centre baggage and/or freight hold (aft of wing):
Containerised volume	45·3 m³ (1,600 cu ft)
Bulk volume	54·8 m³ (1,935 cu ft)

Aft hold:
Bulk volume	14·4 m³ (510 cu ft)

AREAS:

Wings, gross: Series 10	358·7 m² (3,861 sq ft)
Series 30, 40	367·7 m² (3,958 sq ft)
Ailerons, inboard (total)	7·68 m² (82·7 sq ft)
Ailerons, outboard (total)	9·76 m² (105·1 sq ft)
Trailing-edge flaps (total)	62·1 m² (668·2 sq ft)
Leading-edge slats (total):	
Series 10	42·05 m² (452·6 sq ft)
Series 30, 40	43·84 m² (471·9 sq ft)
Spoilers (total)	12·73 m² (137·0 sq ft)
Fin	45·92 m² (494·29 sq ft)
Rudders (total)	10·29 m² (110·71 sq ft)
Tailplane	96·6 m² (1,040·2 sq ft)
Elevators (total)	27·7 m² (298·1 sq ft)

WEIGHTS AND LOADINGS:

Basic weight empty:
Series 10	111,086 kg (244,903 lb)
Series 15	111,832 kg (246,547 lb)
Series 30	121,198 kg (267,197 lb)
Series 40	122,951 kg (271,062 lb)

Max payload:
Series 10	44,678 kg (98,500 lb)
Series 30	48,330 kg (106,550 lb)
Series 40	46,243 kg (101,950 lb)

Max T-O weight:
Series 10, 15	206,384 kg (455,000 lb)
Series 30	259,450 kg (572,000 lb)
Series 40 (-20 engines)	251,744 kg (555,000 lb)
Series 40 (-59A engines)	259,450 kg (572,000 lb)

Max ramp weight:
Series 10	207,745 kg (458,000 lb)
Series 30	260,815 kg (575,000 lb)
Series 40 (-20 engines)	253,105 kg (558,000 lb)
Series 40 (-59A engines)	260,815 kg (575,000 lb)

Max zero-fuel weight:
Series 10	151,953 kg (335,000 lb)
Series 30, 40	166,922 kg (368,000 lb)

Max landing weight:
Series 10, 15	164,880 kg (363,500 lb)
Series 30, 40	182,798 kg (403,000 lb)

Max wing loading:
Series 10, 15	575·4 kg/m² (117·8 lb/sq ft)
Series 30	705·6 kg/m² (144·5 lb/sq ft)
Series 40 (-20 engines)	684·6 kg/m² (140·2 lb/sq ft)
Series 40 (-59A engines)	705·6 kg/m² (144·5 lb/sq ft)

PERFORMANCE (at max T-O weight unless specified):

Never-exceed speed Mach 0·95
Max level speed at 7,620 m (25,000 ft)
Mach 0·88 (530 knots; 982 km/h; 610 mph)

Max cruising speed at 9,145 m (30,000 ft):
Series 10 (-6D engines)	499 knots (925 km/h; 575 mph)
Series 10 (-6D1 engines)	501 knots (928 km/h; 577 mph)
Series 30	490 knots (908 km/h; 564 mph)
Series 40 (-20 engines)	489 knots (906 km/h; 563 mph)
Series 40 (-59A engines)	498 knots (922 km/h; 573 mph)

Normal cruising speed, all versions Mach 0·82
T-O speed (V₂):
Series 10 (-6D engines)	181 knots (335 km/h; 208 mph)
Series 10 (-6D1 engines)	175 knots (325 km/h; 202 mph)
Series 30 (-50C engines)	189 knots (351 km/h; 218 mph)
Series 40 (-20 engines)	187 knots (346 km/h; 215 mph)
Series 40 (-59A engines)	178 knots (330 km/h; 205 mph)

Landing speed (with full load of passengers and baggage):
Series 10	128·5 knots (238 km/h; 148 mph)
Series 15	129 knots (240 km/h; 149 mph)
Series 30, 40	138 knots (256 km/h; 159 mph)

Max rate of climb at S/L:
Series 10 (-6D engines)	817 m (2,680 ft)/min
Series 10 (-6D1 engines)	838 m (2,750 ft)/min
Series 30	884 m (2,900 ft)/min
Series 40 (-20 engines)	829 m (2,720 ft)/min
Series 40 (-59A engines)	762 m (2,500 ft)/min

Service ceiling:
Series 10 (-6D engines) at 192,775 kg (425,000 lb) AUW 10,605 m (34,800 ft)
Series 10 (-6D1 engines) at 192,775 kg (425,000 lb) AUW 10,730 m (35,200 ft)
Series 30 at 249,475 kg (550,000 lb) AUW 10,180 m (33,400 ft)
Series 40 (-20 engines) at 242,670 kg (535,000 lb) AUW 9,660 m (31,700 ft)
Series 40 (-59A engines) at 254,010 kg (560,000 lb) AUW 9,965 m (32,700 ft)

En-route climb altitude, one engine out:
Series 10 at 195,045 kg (430,000 lb) AUW 4,145 m (13,600 ft)
Series 30 at 251,744 kg (555,000 lb) AUW 4,360 m (14,300 ft)
Series 40 (-20 engines) at 247,205 kg (545,000 lb) AUW 3,565 m (11,700 ft)
Series 40 (-59A engines) at 254,010 kg (560,000 lb) AUW 5,135 m (16,850 ft)

FAA T-O field length:
Series 10 (-6D1 engines)	3,200 m (10,500 ft)
Series 15 (-50C2F engines)	2,285 m (7,500 ft)
Series 30 (-50C2 engines)	3,170 m (10,400 ft)
Series 40 (-59A engines)	3,135 m (10,280 ft)

FAA landing field length:
Series 10	1,585 m (5,200 ft)
Series 15	1,600 m (5,250 ft)
Series 30, 40	1,630 m (5,350 ft)

Range with max fuel, no payload:
Series 10	5,514 nm (10,220 km; 6,350 miles)
Series 15	5,466 nm (10,130 km; 6,295 miles)
Series 30	6,504 nm (12,055 km; 7,490 miles)
Series 40	6,305 nm (11,685 km; 7,260 miles)

Range with max payload at max zero-fuel weight:
Series 10	2,350 nm (4,355 km; 2,706 miles)
Series 30	4,000 nm (7,413 km; 4,606 miles)
Series 40 (-20 engines)	3,500 nm (6,485 km; 4,030 miles)
Series 40 (-59A engines)	4,050 nm (7,505 km; 4,663 miles)

MCDONNELL DOUGLAS DC-10 SERIES 30CF

The Series 30CF is a convertible freighter version of the McDonnell Douglas DC-10 transport. Generally similar to the basic DC-10 Series 30 and 40, it is designed for easy conversion to either passenger or cargo configuration. Its payload can consist of 380 passengers and baggage or 64,860 kg (143,000 lb) of cargo over full intercontinental range; or up to 70,626 kg (155,700 lb) of cargo on domestic transcontinental routes.

The first Series 30CF was powered by three General Electric CF6-50A turbofans. It flew for the first time on 28 February 1973 and initial deliveries were made to Overseas National Airways and Trans International Airlines on 17 April 1973. In June 1977, Overseas National Airways took delivery of two of the later DC-10 Srs 30CFs, powered by General Electric CF6-50C1 engines rated at 233·5 kN (52,500 lb st).

In the passenger configuration, interior layout is generally similar to that of the DC-10, but the Series 30CF was designed to permit overnight conversion to an all-cargo configuration. This entails removal of seats, overhead baggage racks, forward food service centre, cloakrooms and carpeting from the main cabin, and installation of freight loading tracks and rollers, a cargo tiedown system and restraint nets. Coffee service fixtures and lavatories in the aft cabin may also be removed but are retained normally for regular cargo flights.

The cargo loading system for the Series 30CF is based on that in use in the DC-8 Super Sixty Series freighters. A two-channel network of roller conveyors, adjustable guide rails and pallet restraint fittings is installed in the seat tracks in the cabin floor by use of simple stud and locking pin devices. A 2·59 m high × 3·56 m wide (8 ft 6 in × 11 ft 8 in) cargo door in the side of the fuselage swings upward and allows easy loading of bulky freight.

A total of 30 standard 2·24 m × 2·74 m (7 ft 4 in × 9 ft) cargo pallets, or 22 larger pallets measuring 2·24 m × 3·18 m (7 ft 4 in × 10 ft 5 in) or 2·44 m × 3·05 m (8 ft × 10 ft), can be accommodated in the main cabin. The Series 30CF with upstairs galleys also has 132·2 m³ (4,670 cu ft) of cargo space in the two lower cargo compartments for bulk freight, or for 26 half-size containers, or for five full-size pallets and 16 half-size containers.

A DC-10 Series 30CF delivered to Sabena Belgian World Airlines in 1973 is certificated for carrying combination loads of freight and passengers in the main cabin. Other DC-10 series aircraft are also offered in convertible versions. Continental Air Lines is operating the DC-10 Series 10CF. More than 30 CF models had been ordered by 1 January 1980.

While weight and performance figures are generally similar to those of the DC-10 Series 30, the differing figures which follow should be noted for the Series 30CF:

WEIGHTS:
Weight empty	108,385 kg (238,948 lb)
Max landing weight	190,962 kg (421,000 lb)

PERFORMANCE:
Landing speed at max landing weight
148·5 knots (275 km/h; 171 mph)
FAA T-O field length at max T-O weight
3,170 m (10,400 ft)
FAA landing field length at max landing weight
1,868 m (6,130 ft)
Max range with max cargo
3,581 nm (6,637 km; 4,124 miles)

MCDONNELL DOUGLAS EXTENDER
US Air Force designation: KC-10A

The USAF announced on 19 December 1977 that, following evaluation of the Boeing 747 and McDonnell Douglas DC-10 to meet its requirement for an Advanced Tanker/Cargo Aircraft (ATCA), the DC-10 ATCA was selected to fulfil this role. Subsequently, the aircraft was designated KC-10A and named Extender.

A force of KC-10As will greatly enhance the ability of the USAF to deploy combat aircraft, men and supplies on a global scale. This point was emphasised in a USAF submission to Congress in which the spokesman commented that 40 Boeing KC-135 tankers and a number of cargo aircraft would be needed to fuel an F-4 fighter squadron and carry its personnel and equipment from the USA to the Middle East. Just 17 of the proposed KC-10As could fulfil the same task, more economically and efficiently. USAF Military Airlift Command's (MAC) need for support by such aircraft was highlighted during the 1973 Arab-Israeli war, when many countries denied landing rights to MAC aircraft. From these circumstances came the decision to develop an ATCA to support the strategic airlift fleet, under the operational control of the USAF Strategic Air Command.

The initial $28 million contract awarded to McDonnell Douglas covered the funding for initial production planning, engineering and tooling. A second $429,000 contract was for initial planning of a logistics support programme covering the entire KC-10A military tanker fleet.

On 20 November 1978, the USAF authorised McDonnell Douglas to begin production of the KC-10A. This FY 1979 contract called for an expenditure of $148 million by the USAF, for the acquisition of two KC-10As, and in payment of the balance of the non-recurring engineering costs. In addition, under a separate $15·6 million contract, McDonnell Douglas was authorised to purchase the initial spare parts and support equipment for the KC-10A system. Four additional KC-10As were ordered by the USAF in November 1979, under the FY 1980 budget; six were requested in FY 1981. Quantities of KC-10As to be procured over subsequent years will be determined by available funding, but it is anticipated that at least 20 KC-10As may be procured eventually by the USAF. The first KC-10A (USAF serial number 79-0433) made its first flight on 12 July 1980 and was scheduled for delivery to Barksdale AFB, Louisiana, for operation by SAC, in early 1981.

The commercial DC-10 Series 30CF convertible freighter, the basic airframe chosen for conversion to the ATCA role, is currently certificated for operation at a max T-O weight of 267,620 kg (590,000 lb).

The modifications necessary to convert the DC-10-30CF to the ATCA configuration include the installation of fuel cells in the lower fuselage compartment; the provision of a boom operator station, an aerial refuelling boom, a refuelling receptacle, an improved cargo handling system, and some military avionics systems. Various seating layouts are available in the forward area to permit the transport of a fighter squadron's essential support personnel. Seven bladder fuel cells are installed in the lower fuselage compartments, three forward and four aft of the

Three-view drawing (*Pilot Press*) **and photograph of the McDonnell Douglas KC-10A Extender advanced tanker/cargo aircraft for the US Air Force**

wing, mounted within framework that restrains and supports the cells. These contain a total of 53,297 kg (117,500 lb) of fuel, equivalent to approx 68,420 litres (18,075 US gallons), and are interconnected with the aircraft's basic fuel system, comprising 108,211 kg (238,565 lb). All can then be used for extended range, or fuel from the lower deck cells and the aircraft's basic fuel system can be used for in-flight refuelling. The KC-10A is designed to deliver 90,718 kg (200,000 lb) of fuel to a receiver 1,910 nm (3,540 km; 2,200 miles) from its home base.

The aerial refuelling operator's station, with access from the upper main deck, is sited in the lower aft fuselage and can accommodate the boom operator, an instructor and an observer, although only the boom operator is needed for a refuelling mission. The station has a rear window and a periscope observation system to give a wide field of view, and is pressurised and air-conditioned. The advanced aerial refuelling boom, which is the production version of a boom developed and tested in prototype form by McDonnell Douglas, provides greater capability than the type installed in the KC-135; in particular, it has a greater transfer flow rate, being rated at 5,678 litres (1,500 US gallons)/min. The boom operator 'flies' it by means of a digital fly-by-wire control system supplied by Sperry Flight Systems. A hose/reel unit for probe and drogue refuelling is also installed, so that the KC-10A can service USN, USMC, and NATO aircraft, as well as older types of fighter still serving with Reserve and ANG units.

The provision of a refuelling receptacle, above the flight deck of the KC-10A, allows greater flexibility on long-range cargo or refuelling operations, extending the range beyond the nominal 6,000 nm (11,112 km; 6,905 miles) with a 45,400 kg (100,000 lb) payload. The improved cargo handling system, by comparison with the basic DC-10-30CF, includes an increased floor area covered by omni-directional rollers, power rollers, and a portable winch to move cargo fore and aft.

Changes to the avionics are concerned chiefly with the deletion of equipment intended specifically for commercial operations, and the addition of UHF and secure com systems, Tacan, IFF, beacon transponder and a radar beacon mode.

The description of the DC-10 Series 30CF applies to the KC-10A, except as follows:

TYPE: Military flight refuelling/cargo aircraft.
WINGS, FUSELAGE, TAIL UNIT: As for DC-10-30CF,

except for omission of most upper-deck cabin windows and lower-deck cargo doors.
LANDING GEAR: As for DC-10-30CF, except Goodyear nosewheels and tyres size 40 × 15·5-16, pressure 13·10 bars (190 lb/sq in). Four-wheel bogie main units and centreline unit have Goodyear wheels and tyres size 52 × 20·5-23. The former have a pressure of 13·79 bars (200 lb/sq in), the latter 10·69 bars (155 lb/sq in). Goodyear disc brakes and anti-skid system, with individual wheel control.
POWER PLANT: Three 233·53 kN (52,500 lb st) General Electric CF6-50C2 turbofan engines. Basic aircraft fuel system comprises three integral main wing fuel tanks, and an integral auxiliary tank in the wing centre-section with a connected structural compartment fitted with a bladder cell, giving a total capacity of approximately 132,331 litres (34,958 US gallons). Oil capacity 34·1 litres (9 US gallons).
ACCOMMODATION: Three crew on flight deck. Various seating arrangements for a limited number of essential support personnel at forward end of main cabin. Aerial refuelling station, with accommodation for boom operator, instructor and a student observer at aft end of lower fuselage compartment. Five passenger doors on main deck. A 2·59 m × 3·56 m (8 ft 6 in × 11 ft 8 in) cargo door on the port side of the fuselage permits

loading of standard USAF 463L pallets, bulk cargo or wheeled vehicles. Maximum capacity for 25 pallets with access from both sides of the compartment, or 27 pallets with a single aisle on the starboard side.
SYSTEMS: As for DC-10-30CF.
AVIONICS AND EQUIPMENT: Include some additional military avionics, comprising navigation, communication, Tacan, IFF transponder, and modified commercial weather radar. Seven Goodyear Aerospace rubberised fabric fuel cells mounted in the lower fuselage compartments, with combined capacity of 53,446 kg (117,829 lb) fuel, equivalent to approx 68,610 litres (18,125 US gallons), which are interconnected into the aircraft's basic fuel system. Flight refuelling boom mounted under rear fuselage, plus hose/reel unit for probe and drogue refuelling. Director lights to guide receiver. Flight refuelling receptacle mounted on fuselage upper surface above flight deck.
DIMENSIONS, EXTERNAL: As for DC-10-30CF except:
Length overall 55·35 m (181 ft 7 in)
Height overall 17·70 m (58 ft 1 in)
Wheel track 10·57 m (34 ft 8 in)
AREAS: As for DC-10-30CF
WEIGHTS AND LOADING (estimated):
Operating weight empty:
tanker 108,973 kg (240,245 lb)
cargo 110,890 kg (244,471 lb)
Max cargo payload 76,897 kg (169,529 lb)
Design max T-O weight 267,620 kg (590,000 lb)
Max wing loading 727·8 kg/m² (149·06 lb/sq ft)
PERFORMANCE (estimated):
Critical field length 3,353 m (11,000 ft)
Max range with max cargo
3,797 nm (7,032 km; 4,370 miles)
Max ferry range, unrefuelled
9,993 nm (18,507 km; 11,500 miles)

MCDONNELL DOUGLAS SKYHAWK
US Navy designation: A-4

Construction of the XA-4A (originally XA4D-1) prototype Skyhawk began in September 1953, and the first flight of this aircraft took place on 22 June 1954.

Production of the A-4 ended on 27 February 1979, when the US Navy took delivery of the final aircraft off the assembly line, an A-4M for the US Marine Corps. Delivered to Marine Attack Squadron VMA-331, it was the 2,960th Skyhawk manufactured by McDonnell Douglas in 26 years of continuous production. The total was made up of 2,405 attack aircraft and 555 trainers, as follows:

XA4D-1	1	TA-4G	2
YA4D-1	19	A-4H	90
A4D-1 (A-4A)	146	TA-4H	10
A4D-2 (A-4B)	542	TA-4J	291
A4D-2N (A-4C)	638	A-4K	10
YA4D-5 (YA-4E)	2	TA-4K	4
A4D-5 (A-4E)	494	A-4KU	30
A-4F	146	TA-4KU	6
TA-4F	242	A-4M	162
A-4G	8	A-4N	117

In mid-1980 the Indonesian Air Force had begun to receive the first of 14 A-4Es and two TA-4Hs purchased from Israel. In mid-1981 the Royal Malaysian Air Force is due to receive the first 22 of a total of 88 surplus US Navy A-4Cs and A-4Ls.

Details of Skyhawk variants can be found in earlier editions of *Jane's*. A version that entered service during the past year is as follows:

OA-4M. Forward air control version for US Marine Corps, converted from TA-4F. Total of 23 being converted by Naval Air Rework Facility at Pensacola, Florida. Avionics and weapons capability similar to those of A-4M. First OA-4M (154294) began flight testing at NATC Patuxent River in July 1978, prior to entry into service with H & MS 32 at Cherry Point, North Carolina, in late 1979.

McDonnell Douglas OA-4M Skyhawk, a two-seat FAC version for service with the US Marine Corps

McKINNON—*See Canadian section*

MEYERS
MEYERS AIRCRAFT MANUFACTURING COM-PANY (a division of Branson Aircraft Corporation)

HEAD OFFICE: 4275 Broadway, Denver, Colorado 80216

Telephone: (303) 825 3529
PRESIDENT: Carl F. Branson

Meyers Aircraft Manufacturing Company was formed to manufacture the Meyers 200D four-seat light monoplane. Designed and produced originally by the Meyers Aircraft Company of Tecumseh, Michigan, the prototype Model 200 flew for the first time on 8 September 1953. It was produced subsequently by Aero Commander's Albany Division.

No recent information has been received from the Meyers company, but details of the Meyers 200D can be found in the 1979-80 *Jane's.*

MID-CONTINENT
MID-CONTINENT AIRCRAFT CORPORATION

Drawer L, Hayti, Missouri 63851
Telephone: (314) 359 0500
Telex: 447183
PRESIDENT: Richard Reade

MID-CONTINENT KING CAT

Mid-Continent Aircraft Corporation, an operator and distributor of Gulfstream American/Grumman Ag-Cats, has obtained an FAA Supplementary Type Certificate for an Ag-Cat re-engined with an 895 kW (1,200 hp) Wright R-1820-202A radial engine, driving a three-blade metal propeller. The engineering work for this STC was carried out by Serv-Aero Engineering Inc (which see). After modification, the aircraft is known as a King Cat.

Based on the airframe of the Super Ag-Cat C, which has a hopper accommodating 1,893 litres (500 US gallons) of spray or 1,814 kg (4,000 lb) of dry chemicals, the King Cat offers improved high-altitude/high-temperature performance. It is available as a conversion of a new Super Ag-Cat C, or a kit is obtainable for installation by the customer or his maintenance organisation. Options which are available include Serv-O ailerons and increased fuel capacity of 431·5 litres (114 US gallons).
PERFORMANCE (at max T-O weight):
Working speed
    87-113 knots (161-209 km/h; 100-130 mph)

Mid-Continent King Cat, a Wright-engined conversion of the Grumman Super Ag-Cat C *(Howard Levy)*

Ferry speed   117 knots (217 km/h; 135 mph)
T-O run, 32°C   less than 365 m (1,200 ft)

MITSUBISHI
MITSUBISHI AIRCRAFT INTERNATIONAL INC

HEAD OFFICE: Park Central III, 12700 Park Central Drive, Suite 1310, PO Box 57, Dallas, Texas 75251
Telephone: (214) 387 5600
Telex: 73 2575
PRESIDENT: Takaaki Yamada
WORKS: PO Box 3848, San Angelo, Texas 76901
Telephone: (915) 944 1511
Telex: 73 9438

This wholly-owned subsidiary of Mitsubishi Heavy Industries Ltd of Japan (which see) was established at San Angelo, Texas, in 1965 to undertake final assembly and flight testing of the MU-2 twin-turboprop STOL multipurpose transport aircraft designed by the parent company. The head office of the company was moved to Dallas in 1977.

Mitsubishi Aircraft International is now responsible also for the new Diamond I business jet designed by the parent company.

MITSUBISHI MU-2

Details of early history and production of the MU-2 appear in the Japanese section of this and earlier editions of *Jane's*. By 1 January 1980, total orders for all versions had reached 623, including 574 for export and 49 for Japanese customers. The two current versions are:

Marquise. Basically similar to MU-2N (1978-79 *Jane's*), but with Garrett-AiResearch TPE331-10-501M turboprop engines, four-blade propellers and increased fuel capacity. Manufacturer's designation MU-2B-60. First flown 13 September 1977. Certificated 2 March 1978. Total of 31 delivered by 1 January 1980.

Solitaire. Basically similar to MU-2P (1978-79 *Jane's*), but with Garrett-AiResearch TPE331-10-501M turboprop engines, rated in this installation at 495·5 kW (665 shp) each. Propeller and fuel capacity details as for Marquise. Manufacturer's designation MU-2B-40. First flown 28 October 1977. Certificated 2 March 1978. Total of 25 delivered by 1 January 1980.

Wing, fuselage and tail unit components for the Marquise and Solitaire are manufactured in Japan by the parent company and shipped to the USA. At the San Angelo factory, they go on to a production line where American-built components (which include engines, propellers, tyres, brakes, avionics and interior furnishing) are installed. Examples of the MU-2 produced at San Angelo are in service in Africa, Australia, Canada, Europe, Mexico, the Middle East, South America and the USA.
TYPE: Twin-turboprop business aircraft.
WINGS: Cantilever high-wing monoplane. Wing section NACA 64A415 at root, NACA 63A212 (modified) at tip. No dihedral. Incidence 2°. Washout 3°. Sweepback 0° 21′ at quarter-chord. One-piece two-spar all-metal structure with chemically milled skins of 2024 and 7075 aluminium alloy. Spoilers for lateral control, between rear spar and flaps. Electrically-actuated full-span double-slotted Fowler-type flaps of aluminium alloy and plastics construction. Outboard flap section each side incorporates trim aileron. All primary controls manually-operated. Pneumatic de-icing rubber boots.

Mitsubishi Solitaire business transport (two Garrett-AiResearch TPE331 turboprop engines)

Mitsubishi Marquise twin-turboprop multi-purpose transport *(Pilot Press)*

FUSELAGE: Circular-section aluminium alloy semi-monocoque structure.
TAIL UNIT: Cantilever structure of aluminium alloy, except for top of fin, which is of reinforced plastics. Small auxiliary fin beneath each side of rear fuselage on Marquise. Trim tab in rudder and each elevator.

Pneumatic de-icing rubber boots.
LANDING GEAR (Marquise): Retractable tricycle type, with single wheel on each main unit and twin-wheel steerable nose unit. All wheels retract electrically, nosewheel forward, main wheels upward into fairings on fuselage sides. Manual backup system provided. Oleo-

pneumatic shock-absorbers. Main-wheel tyres Type III, size 8·50-10 (10-ply). Nosewheel tyres Type III, size 5·00-5 (6-ply). Tyre pressure 2·76-4·34 bars (40-63 lb/sq in) on main units, 3·79 bars (55 lb/sq in) on nose unit. Goodrich double-disc hydraulic brakes. No anti-skid units or brake cooling.

LANDING GEAR (Solitaire): Retractable tricycle type, with single wheel on each main unit and twin-wheel steerable nose unit. All wheels retract rearward electrically. Manual backup system provided. Oleo-pneumatic shock-absorbers. Main-wheel tyres Type III 8·50-10 (10-ply). Nosewheel tyres Type III 5·00-5 (6-ply). Main-wheel tyre pressure 2·76-4·34 bars (40-63 lb/sq in), nosewheel tyre pressure 3·79 bars (55 lb/sq in). Goodrich double-disc hydraulic brakes. No anti-skid units or brake cooling.

POWER PLANT (Marquise): Two Garrett AiResearch TPE 331-10-501M turboprop engines, each rated at 533 kW (715 shp) and driving a Hartzell HC-B4TN-5DL/LT10282B-5·3R four-blade fully-feathering constant-speed reversible-pitch propeller. Fuel in five integral wing tanks, total usable capacity 844 litres (223 US gallons; 185·7 Imp gallons) and two fixed wingtip tanks with total usable capacity of 682 litres (180 US gallons; 150 Imp gallons). Max total usable fuel capacity of 1,526 litres (403 US gallons; 335·7 Imp gallons). Oil capacity 11·8 litres (3·1 US gallons; 2·6 Imp gallons).

POWER PLANT (Solitaire): Two Garrett AiResearch TPE 331-10-501M turboprop engines, each rated at 495·9 kW (665 shp). Propeller, fuel and oil details as for Marquise.

ACCOMMODATION (Marquise): Seats for pilot and co-pilot or passenger on flight deck. Seating in pressurised main cabin for seven to nine persons. Separate compartment at rear of cabin provides coat locker, toilet and baggage compartment. Door at rear of cabin on port side with built-in steps. Emergency exit door under wing on starboard side.

ACCOMMODATION (Solitaire): Seats for pilot and co-pilot or passenger on flight deck. Standard seating for six or seven passengers in pressurised main cabin. Pressurised baggage compartment over main-wheel bays, capacity 100 kg (220 lb). Baggage compartments aft of main-wheel bays, capacity 70 kg (154 lb); port compartment of Solitaire pressurised, others non-pressurised. Space for coats and small baggage at rear of cabin. Door under wing on port side. Emergency exit door opposite main door.

SYSTEMS: Garrett-AiResearch pressurisation and Hamilton Standard air-conditioning systems, using engine bleed air. Differential 0·41 bars (6·0 lb/sq in). Hydraulic braking system. 28V DC primary electrical system, supplemented by 115V AC system (two static inverters) for instruments and avionics. DC power supplied by two 30V 200A starter/generators and two 24V 40Ah nickel-cadmium batteries. Scott automatic flow pressure-type oxygen system, with outlet for each seat. Rubber-boot pneumatic de-icing of wing and tail leading-edges; hot-air anti-icing of engine air intakes; heated windscreens; electrically heated propellers and oil cooler inlets.

AVIONICS AND EQUIPMENT: Blind-flying instrumentation standard. Radio and radar to customers' requirements. Standard avionics include VOR/LOC, glideslope, ADF and marker beacon receivers; ATC transponder; DME; VHF or other communications systems; Sperry SPZ-500 integrated autopilot/flight director system; VG-14A vertical gyro; dual C-14 compass systems; and weather radar.

DIMENSIONS, EXTERNAL:

Wing span over tip-tanks	11·94 m (39 ft 2 in)
Wing chord (mean)	1·54 m (5 ft 1 in)
Wing aspect ratio	7·71
Length overall: Marquise	12·02 m (39 ft 5 in)
Solitaire	10·13 m (33 ft 3 in)
Length of fuselage: Marquise	11·84 m (38 ft 10 in)
Solitaire	9·98 m (32 ft 9 in)
Fuselage: Max diameter	1·65 m (5 ft 5 in)
Height overall: Marquise	4·17 m (13 ft 8 in)
Solitaire	3·94 m (12 ft 11 in)
Tailplane span	4·80 m (15 ft 9 in)
Wheel track: Marquise	2·40 m (7 ft 11 in)
Solitaire	2·36 m (7 ft 9 in)
Wheelbase: Marquise	4·40 m (14 ft 5 in)
Solitaire	4·52 m (14 ft 10 in)
Propeller diameter	2·48 m (8 ft 2 in)
Distance between propeller centres	4·50 m (14 ft 9 in)
Propeller ground clearance:	
Marquise	0·66 m (2 ft 2 in)
Solitaire	0·53 m (1 ft 9 in)
Cabin door: Height	1·17 m (3 ft 10 in)
Width	0·74 m (2 ft 5 in)
Height to sill: Marquise	0·38 m (1 ft 3 in)
Solitaire	0·51 m (1 ft 8 in)
Emergency exit door: Height	0·71 m (2 ft 4 in)
Width	0·69 m (2 ft 3 in)

DIMENSIONS, INTERNAL:

Cabin, incl flight deck and baggage compartment:

Length: Marquise	6·76 m (22 ft 2 in)
Solitaire	4·88 m (16 ft 0 in)
Max width	1·47 m (4 ft 10 in)
Max height	1·30 m (4 ft 3 in)
Volume: Marquise (usable)	9·83 m³ (347 cu ft)
Solitaire (total)	6·94 m³ (245 cu ft)
Baggage volume (total):	
Marquise	1·95 m³ (69·0 cu ft)
Solitaire	1·22 m³ (43·0 cu ft)

AREAS (both versions):

Wings, gross	16·55 m² (178 sq ft)
Flaps (total)	3·90 m² (42·00 sq ft)
Spoilers (total)	0·54 m² (5·82 sq ft)
Fin: Marquise	2·85 m² (30·70 sq ft)
Solitaire	2·77 m² (29·80 sq ft)
Rudder, incl tab	1·17 m² (12·60 sq ft)
Tailplane	4·01 m² (43·30 sq ft)
Elevators, incl tabs	1·40 m² (15·00 sq ft)

WEIGHTS AND LOADINGS:

Weight empty, equipped:	
Marquise	3,470 kg (7,650 lb)
Solitaire	3,180 kg (7,010 lb)
Max payload: Marquise	1,043 kg (2,300 lb)
Solitaire	1,220 kg (2,690 lb)
Max ramp weight: Marquise	5,270 kg (11,625 lb)
Solitaire	4,770 kg (10,520 lb)
Max T-O weight: Marquise	5,250 kg (11,575 lb)
Solitaire	4,750 kg (10,470 lb)
Max landing weight: Marquise	5,000 kg (11,025 lb)
Solitaire	4,515 kg (9,955 lb)
Max zero-fuel weight: Marquise	4,513 kg (9,950 lb)
Solitaire	4,400 kg (9,700 lb)
Max wing loading: Marquise	317·4 kg/m² (65·0 lb/sq ft)
Solitaire	287·9 kg/m² (59·0 lb/sq ft)
Max power loading: Marquise	5·30 kg/kW (8·70 lb/shp)
Solitaire	4·79 kg/kW (7·87 lb/shp)

PERFORMANCE (at max T-O weight, except where indicated):

Max operating speed (both, all weights)
　　Mach 0·57 (250 knots; 463 km/h; 288 mph) CAS

Max cruising speed:
　Marquise at 4,880 m (16,000 ft)
　　　　308 knots (571 km/h; 355 mph)
　Solitaire at 6,100 m (20,000 ft)
　　　　321 knots (595 km/h; 370 mph)

Econ cruising speed at 6,100 m (20,000 ft):
　Marquise　295 knots (547 km/h; 340 mph)
　Solitaire　313 knots (579 km/h; 360 mph)

Stalling speed, power off, flaps up:
　Marquise, AUW of 4,626 kg (10,200 lb)
　　　　100 knots (185 km/h; 115 mph)
　Solitaire, AUW of 4,173 kg (9,200 lb)
　　　　97 knots (180 km/h; 112 mph)

Stalling speed, power off, flaps down:
　Marquise, AUW of 4,626 kg (10,200 lb)
　　　　76 knots (141 km/h; 87·5 mph)
　Solitaire, AUW of 4,173 kg (9,200 lb)
　　　　73 knots (135 km/h; 84 mph)

Max rate of climb at S/L:
　Marquise　670 m (2,200 ft)/min
　Solitaire　716 m (2,350 ft)/min

Rate of climb at S/L, one engine out:
　Marquise　125 m (410 ft)/min
　Solitaire　145 m (475 ft)/min

Service ceiling: Marquise　8,960 m (29,400 ft)
　Solitaire　10,210 m (33,500 ft)

Service ceiling, one engine out:
　Marquise　4,510 m (14,800 ft)
　Solitaire　5,150 m (16,900 ft)

Min ground turning radius:
　Marquise (port)　32·61 m (107 ft 0 in)
　Marquise (stbd)　35·81 m (117 ft 6 in)
　Solitaire (port)　31·39 m (103 ft 0 in)
　Solitaire (stbd)　35·61 m (116 ft 10 in)

T-O run: Marquise	556 m (1,825 ft)
Solitaire	472 m (1,550 ft)
T-O to 15 m (50 ft): Marquise	660 m (2,170 ft)
Solitaire	550 m (1,800 ft)
Landing from 15 m (50 ft):	
Marquise	671 m (2,200 ft)
Solitaire	594 m (1,950 ft)
Landing run at max landing weight:	
Marquise	402 m (1,320 ft)
Solitaire	357 m (1,170 ft)
Range with max fuel at 9,450 m (31,000 ft), 45 min reserves:	
Marquise	1,395 nm (2,584 km; 1,606 miles)
Solitaire	1,600 nm (2,964 km; 1,842 miles)

MITSUBISHI DIAMOND I

Mitsubishi Heavy Industries Ltd had already completed a prototype of this twin-turbofan business aircraft (known in Japan as the MU-300) before releasing very brief details of it in the Summer of 1978. When this prototype (c/n 001) made its first flight on 29 August 1978, it was known only that it had two Pratt & Whitney Aircraft of Canada JT15D-4 turbofan engines, and that the major design objectives included low operating noise levels, a high standard of cabin comfort, fuel economy, and a high degree of reliability and maintainability.

By 3 December 1978 the first MU-300 had made 60 flights, totalling 117 hours. A second prototype (c/n 002) made its first flight on 13 December 1978.

Mitsubishi took the step of seeking US certification first, with domestic certification by the JCAB to follow later; the aircraft will be certificated in the Transport category of FAR Pt 25, for IFR operation in known icing conditions. The two prototypes, which by then had accumulated more than 350 hours' flying in Japan, were shipped in the Summer of 1979 to the USA, where they were reassembled by Mitsubishi Aircraft International (MAI) at San Angelo, Texas. First flight in the United States was made on 10 August 1979 by the second prototype, now registered N81DM. This is being used as the systems and equipment test aircraft in the FAA certification programme, while the first prototype undertakes general performance and handling trials. Certification was scheduled for December 1980.

The next four aircraft are Japanese-built production Diamond Is, and were due to be dispatched to San Angelo for reassembly by the Autumn of 1980. From the seventh aircraft onward, Mitsubishi (Japan) will deliver the aircraft in the form of major subassemblies to MAI, and the latter will be responsible for their assembly, installation of engines and avionics, furnishing, and flight test.

By August 1980, MAI had received orders for 97 Diamond Is, approx 80 of these being from US customers, one of whom had ordered 12 aircraft. Customer deliveries are expected to begin in early 1981, in which year it is planned to deliver more than 40 Diamond airframes to San Angelo. The delivery rate will rise in 1982 to six Diamonds per month, depending upon the number then on order.

The following description applies to the prototypes:

TYPE: Twin-turbofan business aircraft.

WINGS: Cantilever low-wing monoplane. Mitsubishi computer-designed wing sections: thickness/chord ratio 13·2% at root, 11·3% at tip. Dihedral from roots. Incidence 3° at root. Washout 6° 30'. Sweepback 20° at quarter-chord. Wings are basically of aluminium alloy construction, and built in three parts: a centre-section and two outer panels. Each wing has two primary box-beam spars, forming an integral fuel tank. Narrow-chord Fowler-type flaps over most of trailing-edges, actuated hydraulically and having double-slotted inboard and single-slotted outboard segments.

Mitsubishi Diamond I twin-turbofan business aircraft (*Pilot Press*)

Second prototype Mitsubishi Diamond I (two Pratt & Whitney Aircraft of Canada JT15D-4 turbofan engines)

Immediately forward of flaps are long-span narrow-chord spoilers, for roll control; these also serve as air-brakes, and can be used as lift dumpers to assist braking on touchdown. Outboard of each outer trailing-edge flap is a small, short-span aileron for roll trim. Leading-edges are anti-iced by hot air.

FUSELAGE: Pressurised, fail-safe fatigue-resistant semi-monocoque structure, of oval cross-section with flattened cabin floor. Construction is mainly of aluminium alloy, using multiple load paths, bonded doublers and small skin panels in the principal load-bearing members. Built in three main portions: forward (including flight deck), centre and rear.

TAIL UNIT: Cantilever T tail, with sweepback on all surfaces; construction generally similar to that of wings. Curved dorsal fin, plus small underfin. A small horizontal strake is fitted on each side of rear fuselage, abreast of main fin, to assist airflow control. Trim tab in base of rudder. Small yaw-damping control surface above rudder. Variable-incidence tailplane, with elevators.

LANDING GEAR: Sumitomo retractable tricycle type, with single wheel and oleo-pneumatic shock-absorber on each unit. Hydraulic actuation, controlled electrically. Emergency free-fall extension. Nosewheel, which is steerable by rudder pedals, retracts forward; main wheels retract inward into fuselage. Goodyear wheels, with Goodrich tyres, on all units. Goodyear brakes.

POWER PLANT: Two Pratt & Whitney Aircraft of Canada JT15D-4 turbofan engines, mounted in pod on each side of rear fuselage, each rated at 11·1 kN (2,500 lb st) for T-O and 10·4 kN (2,345 lb st) for max cruise. Aircraft is designed with capability to accept more powerful engines later, if required. Fuel in two 1,018 litre (224 Imp gallon; 269 US gallon) integral tanks in wings, plus a

further 469 litres (103 Imp gallons; 124 US gallons) in aft tanks in fuselage. Total fuel capacity 2,505 litres (551 Imp gallons; 662 US gallons), of which 2,445 litres (538 Imp gallons; 646 US gallons) are usable. Fully-automatic fuel feed system. Refuelling points in upper surface of each wing and on starboard side of fuselage at rear.

ACCOMMODATION: Crew of two on flight deck. Standard layout seats seven passengers in pressurised cabin, with toilet and baggage compartment (capacity 295 kg; 650 lb) at rear. Crew/passenger door forward of wing on port side. Emergency exit forward of wing on starboard side.

SYSTEMS: Pressurisation system, with max differential of 0·62 bars (9·0 lb/sq in). Backup pressurisation system, using engine bleed air, for use in emergency. Hydraulic system, pressure 103·5 bars (1,500 lb/sq in), for actuation of flaps, landing gear and other services. All systems are, wherever possible, of modular conception: for example, entire hydraulic installation can be removed as a single unit. Stick shaker as backup stall warning device.

AVIONICS: Standard avionics include Sperry SPZ-900 integrated flight control system, with pilot's flight director, encoding altimeter, dual nav/com and audio systems, ADF, DME, ATC transponder, twin compasses and RMIs, and RCA colour weather radar.

DIMENSIONS, EXTERNAL:

Wing span	13·23 m (43 ft 5 in)
Wing aspect ratio	7·54
Length overall	14·73 m (48 ft 4 in)
Fuselage: Length	13·16 m (43 ft 2 in)
Max width	1·68 m (5 ft 6 in)
Max height	1·85 m (6 ft 1 in)

Height overall	4·19 m (13 ft 9 in)
Tailplane span	5·00 m (16 ft 5 in)
Wheel track	2·84 m (9 ft 4 in)
Wheelbase	5·86 m (19 ft 3 in)
Crew/passenger door: Height	1·27 m (4 ft 2 in)
Width	0·71 m (2 ft 4 in)

DIMENSIONS, INTERNAL:

Cabin: Max length, incl flight deck	6·37 m (20 ft 11 in)
Length, excl flight deck	4·77 m (15 ft 8 in)
Max width	1·50 m (4 ft 11 in)
Max height	1·47 m (4 ft 10 in)
Volume: incl flight deck	11·33 m³ (400 cu ft)
excl flight deck	8·64 m³ (305 cu ft)
Baggage compartment volume	1·4 m³ (50 cu ft)

AREA:

Wings, net	22·43 m² (241·4 sq ft)

WEIGHTS AND LOADINGS:

Weight empty, equipped	3,764 kg (8,300 lb)
Basic operating weight empty	3,945 kg (8,700 lb)
Max fuel	1,964 kg (4,330 lb)
Max payload	458 kg (1,010 lb)
Max T-O weight	6,395 kg (14,100 lb)
Max zero-fuel weight	4,798 kg (10,580 lb)
Max wing loading	285 kg/m² (58·4 lb/sq ft)
Max power loading	288 kg/kN (2·82 lb/lb st)

PERFORMANCE (estimated):

Max operating Mach number (MMO) above 7,925 m (26,000 ft)	Mach 0·78
Max operating speed (VMO) between 4,875 m (16,000 ft) and 7,925 m (26,000 ft)	320 knots (593 km/h; 368 mph)
Max level speed at 9,145 m (30,000 ft)	434 knots (805 km/h; 500 mph)
Typical speed at 11,890 m (39,000 ft)	410 knots (760 km/h; 472 mph)
Long-range speed at 11,890 m (39,000 ft)	375 knots (695 km/h; 432 mph)
Stalling speed at AUW of 4,672 kg (10,300 lb)	77 knots (143 km/h; 89 mph)
Max rate of climb at S/L, ISA	914 m (3,000 ft)/min
Rate of climb at S/L, ISA, one engine out	247 m (810 ft)/min
Max operating altitude	12,500 m (41,000 ft)
FAA T-O field length, ISA, zero wind	1,250 m (4,100 ft)
FAA landing field length, ISA, zero wind	823 m (2,700 ft)
Range with four passengers at econ cruising speed, ISA, zero wind:	
NBAA IFR reserves	1,252 nm (2,317 km; 1,440 miles)
NBAA VFR reserves	1,565 nm (2,896 km; 1,800 miles)

MOONEY
MOONEY AIRCRAFT CORPORATION
(Subsidiary of Republic Steel Corporation)

HEAD OFFICE AND WORKS: PO Box 72, Kerrville, Texas 78028
Telephone: (512) 896 6000
PRESIDENT: T. J. Smith
VICE-PRESIDENTS:
  Don K. Cox (Marketing)
  L. P. Lopresti (Engineering)
  Vendal D. Giacinto (Finance)

The original Mooney Aircraft Inc was formed in June 1948, in Wichita, Kansas, from where the single-seat Model M-18 Mooney Mite was produced until 1952. The company transferred to Kerrville, Texas, in 1953 and completed a merger with Alon Inc of McPherson, Kansas, in October 1967. Subsequently, in late 1969, Butler Aviation International acquired 100 per cent stock ownership of Mooney Aircraft, the company name being changed to Aerostar Aircraft Corporation on 1 July 1970. Production of Aerostar aircraft was suspended in early 1972. On 4 October 1973 came news that the Republic Steel Corporation of Cleveland, Ohio, had assumed control of the company, once again named Mooney Aircraft.

MOONEY RANGER

The prototype Ranger (known initially as Mooney Mark 21) flew on 23 September 1961 and the first production model on 7 November 1961. More than 2,000 were built before production ended in 1979; details can be found in the 1979-80 *Jane's*.

MOONEY 201 (M20J)

The Mooney 201, a faster development of the now discontinued Executive (last described in the 1977-78 *Jane's*), first flew in June 1976 and received FAA certification in September 1976. A total of 940 had been produced by 1 January 1980.

TYPE: Four-seat cabin monoplane.
WINGS: Cantilever low-wing monoplane. Wing section NACA 63₂-215 at root, NACA 64₁-412 at tip. Dihedral 5° 30'. Incidence 2° 30' at root, 1° at tip. Sweepforward

2° 29'. Light alloy structure with flush-riveted stretch-formed wraparound skins. Full-span main spar; rear spar terminates at mid-span of flaps. Sealed-gap differentially-operated light alloy ailerons. Electrically-operated single-slotted light alloy flaps over 70% of trailing-edge. No tabs.

FUSELAGE: Composite all-metal structure. Cabin section is of welded 4130 chrome-molybdenum steel tube with sheet light alloy covering. Rear section is of semi-monocoque construction, with sheet light alloy bulkheads and skin and extruded alloy stringers.

TAIL UNIT: Cantilever light alloy structure, with variable-incidence tailplane. All surfaces covered with wraparound metal skin.

LANDING GEAR: Electrically-retractable levered-suspension tricycle type. Nosewheel retracts rearward,

main units inward into wings. Rubber disc shock-absorbers on main units. Delco hydraulic shock-absorber on nose unit. Cleveland main wheels, size 6·00-6, and steerable nosewheel, size 5·00-5. Tyre pressure: main wheels 2·07 bars (30 lb/sq in), nosewheel 3·38 bars (49 lb/sq in). Cleveland hydraulic single-disc brakes on main wheels. Parking brakes.

POWER PLANT: One 149 kW (200 hp) Avco Lycoming IO-360-A3B6D flat-four engine, driving a McCauley two-blade constant-speed metal propeller. Two integral fuel tanks in wings, with combined usable capacity of 242 litres (64 US gallons). Refuelling points in wing upper surface. Oil capacity 7·5 litres (2 US gallons).

ACCOMMODATION: Cabin accommodates four in two individual front seats and one side-by-side rear bench seat; front seats have reclining backs. Dual controls standard.

Mooney 201 four-seat cabin monoplane (Avco Lycoming IO-360-A3B6D engine)

Standard rudder pedals optionally removable to allow more leg room for passenger. Overhead ventilation system. Cabin heating and cooling system, with adjustable outlets and illuminated control. One-piece wraparound windscreen. Tinted Plexiglas windows. Starboard front seat removable for freight stowage. Single door on starboard side. Compartment for 54 kg (120 lb) baggage behind cabin, with access from cabin or through door on starboard side. Windscreen defrosting system standard.

SYSTEMS: Hydraulic system for brakes only. Electrical system includes 60A alternator, 12V 35Ah battery, voltage regulator and warning light, together with protective circuit breakers.

AVIONICS AND EQUIPMENT: An extensive range of optional avionics by Bendix, Collins, Edo-Aire Mitchell and King, and RCA WeatherScout weather radar, are available to customer's requirements. Standard equipment includes sensitive altimeter, instrument panel glareshield, sun visors, shoulder harness, annunciator lights, cabin lights, landing light, navigation lights, taxi light, full-flow oil filter, quick oil drain, zinc chromate anti-corrosion treatment, and streamlined propeller spinner. An optional operational package includes blind-flying instrumentation, electric clock, exhaust gas temperature gauge, outside air temperature gauge, turn co-ordinator, microphone jacks, emergency locator transmitter, alternate static source, heated pitot, wingtip strobe lights, com and nav antennae, and cabin speaker. Other optional equipment includes encoding altimeter, knots-only airspeed indicator, hour meter, de luxe control wheel with map light and microphone button, dual brakes, headrests, all-leather interior furnishing, cabin fire extinguisher, rotating beacon and external power socket.

DIMENSIONS, EXTERNAL:
Wing span	10·67 m (35 ft 0 in)
Wing chord, mean	1·50 m (4 ft 11¼ in)
Length overall	7·52 m (24 ft 8 in)
Height overall	2·54 m (8 ft 4 in)
Wheel track	2·76 m (9 ft 0¾ in)
Wheelbase	1·82 m (5 ft 11½ in)
Propeller diameter	1·88 m (6 ft 2 in)
Propeller ground clearance	0·24 m (9½ in)

DIMENSIONS, INTERNAL:
Cabin: Length	2·90 m (9 ft 6 in)
Max width	1·10 m (3 ft 7½ in)
Max height	1·13 m (3 ft 8½ in)
Baggage compartment	0·48 m³ (17 cu ft)

WEIGHTS AND LOADINGS:
Weight empty	743 kg (1,640 lb)
Max T-O and landing weight	1,243 kg (2,740 lb)
Max wing loading	80·07 kg/m² (16·4 lb/sq ft)
Max power loading	8·34 kg/kW (13·7 lb/hp)

PERFORMANCE (at max T-O weight):
Never-exceed speed	196 knots (364 km/h; 226 mph)
Max level speed at S/L	175 knots (325 km/h; 202 mph)
Max cruising speed, 75% power at 2,470 m (8,100 ft)	169 knots (314 km/h; 195 mph)
Econ cruising speed, 55% power at 2,470 m (8,100 ft)	145 knots (269 km/h; 167 mph)
Stalling speed, flaps up	63 knots (117 km/h; 72·5 mph) IAS
Stalling speed, flaps down	55 knots (102 km/h; 63·5 mph) IAS
Max rate of climb at S/L	314 m (1,030 ft)/min
Service ceiling	5,730 m (18,800 ft)
T-O to 15 m (50 ft)	463 m (1,517 ft)
Landing from 15 m (50 ft)	491 m (1,610 ft)
Landing run	235 m (770 ft)
Range, 75% power, no reserves	974 nm (1,804 km; 1,121 miles)

TURBO MOONEY 231 (M20K)

Mooney began the design of this turbocharged version of the 201 in May 1976. Construction of the prototype began in the following month, and the first flight was recorded in October 1976. Certification in the Normal category was awarded by the FAA on 16 November 1978. Generally similar to the 201, the Turbo Mooney 231

differs mainly in having a turbocharged engine and increased wing span. A total of 288 had been built by 1 January 1980.

TYPE: Four-seat cabin monoplane.

WINGS: Cantilever low-wing monoplane. Wing section NACA 63₂-215 at root, NACA 64₁-412 at tip. Dihedral 5° 30'. Incidence 2° 30'. No sweepback. Conventional structure of light alloy. Plain ailerons and trailing-edge flaps of light alloy construction. No tabs.

FUSELAGE AND TAIL UNIT: As for 201.

LANDING GEAR: Electrically-retractable tricycle type. Nosewheel retracts rearward, main units inward into wings. All wheels faired by doors when retracted. Shock-absorption of nosewheel and main-wheel units by Lord rubber discs. Cleveland wheels, with main-wheel tyres size 6·00-6 6-ply, pressure 2·90 bars (42 lb/sq in). Nosewheel tyre size 5·00-5 6-ply, pressure 3·38 bars (49 lb/sq in). Cleveland hydraulic brakes on main wheels. Parking brake.

POWER PLANT: One 156·5 kW (210 hp) Continental TSIO-360-GB flat-six turbocharged engine, driving a McCauley constant-speed metal propeller. Goodrich propeller de-icing optional. Two integral fuel tanks in inner wings, with combined capacity of 303 litres (80 US gallons), of which 272·5 litres (72 US gallons) are usable. Refuelling points in upper surface of the inboard section of each wing. Oil capacity 7·5 litres (2 US gallons).

ACCOMMODATION: Cabin accommodates four on two individual front seats and a rear bench seat. Cabin door on starboard side. Baggage space aft of rear seat, accessible from cabin and via baggage door on starboard side. Accommodation heated and ventilated.

SYSTEMS: Hydraulic system for brakes only. Electrical system powered by a 64A engine-driven alternator. Oxygen system.

AVIONICS: Nav/coms by Bendix, Collins and King, autopilot, flight director, RNAV and RCA Weather-Scout weather radar optional.

DIMENSIONS, EXTERNAL:
Wing span	11·00 m (36 ft 1 in)
Wing aspect ratio	7·448
Length overall	7·75 m (25 ft 5 in)
Height overall	2·51 m (8 ft 3 in)
Tailplane span	3·58 m (11 ft 9 in)
Wheel track	2·76 m (9 ft 0¾ in)
Wheelbase	1·82 m (5 ft 11½ in)
Propeller diameter	1·88 m (6 ft 2 in)
Propeller ground clearance	0·24 m (9½ in)
Cabin door (stbd, over wing):	
Height	1·13 m (3 ft 8½ in)
Width	0·74 m (2 ft 5 in)
Baggage door (stbd, aft):	
Height	0·52 m (1 ft 8½ in)
Width	0·43 m (1 ft 5 in)
Height to sill	1·17 m (3 ft 10 in)

DIMENSIONS, INTERNAL:
Cabin: Length	2·90 m (9 ft 6 in)
Max width	1·10 m (3 ft 7½ in)
Max height	1·13 m (3 ft 8½ in)
Baggage compartment	0·48 m³ (17 cu ft)

AREAS:
Wings, gross	16·24 m² (174·8 sq ft)
Ailerons (total)	1·06 m² (11·4 sq ft)
Trailing-edge flaps (total)	1·66 m² (17·9 sq ft)
Fin	0·72 m² (7·7 sq ft)
Tailplane	1·99 m² (21·42 sq ft)
Elevators	1·21 m² (13·0 sq ft)

WEIGHTS AND LOADINGS:
Weight empty	816 kg (1,800 lb)
Max T-O and landing weight	1,315 kg (2,900 lb)
Max zero-fuel weight	1,119 kg (2,468 lb)
Max wing loading	80·97 kg/m² (16·6 lb/sq ft)
Max power loading	8·4 kg/kW (13·8 lb/hp)

PERFORMANCE (at max T-O weight):
Never-exceed speed	195 knots (362 km/h; 225 mph)
Max level speed	182 knots (338 km/h; 210 mph)
Max cruising speed, 75% power at 5,485 m (18,000 ft)	174 knots (322 km/h; 200 mph)
Econ cruising speed, 55% power at 7,315 m (24,000 ft)	162 knots (301 km/h; 187 mph)
Stalling speed, flaps down, idling power	57 knots (106 km/h; 66 mph)
Max rate of climb at S/L	329 m (1,080 ft)/min
Certificated ceiling	7,315 m (24,000 ft)
T-O to 15 m (50 ft)	628 m (2,060 ft)
Landing from 15 m (50 ft)	695 m (2,280 ft)
Landing run	350 m (1,147 ft)
Range with max fuel, 55% power, no reserves	1,182 nm (2,190 km; 1,361 miles)

MOONEY M-30

Mooney Aircraft announced at the 1980 US Reading Air Show that the company had designed and planned to build a new six-seat pressurised aircraft designated M-30. Of cantilever low-wing configuration, it features a wing of advanced aerodynamic section, with two top-surface spoilers on each wing to supplement roll control, and Fowler-type trailing-edge flaps over 90% of the wing span. Entry to the cabin will be by means of a door with integral airstairs. Power plant will consist of one 261 kW (350 hp) Avco Lycoming turbocharged engine in the TIO-540 series; fuel capacity will be 380 litres (100 US gallons). Systems and equipment will include pressurisation (differential 0·32 bars; 4·7 lb/sq in), providing a 3,050 m (10,000 ft) cabin altitude to a height of 7,620 m (25,000 ft), anti-icing equipment, weather radar, and advanced avionics for communications and navigation. First flight of a prototype M-30 is planned for 1982, with certificated production aircraft to be available in 1985.

PERFORMANCE (estimated):
Max level speed	243-259 knots (450-480 km/h; 280-298 mph)
Cruising speed	210-235 knots (390-435 km/h; 242-270 mph)
Stalling speed	52-56·5 knots (96-104 km/h; 60-65 mph)
Range at 75% power	990 nm (1,840 km; 1,140 miles)
Range at 65% power	1,120 nm (2,080 km; 1,290 miles)

Turbo Mooney 231, a turbocharged version of the Mooney 201 four-seat cabin monoplane

NASA
NATIONAL AERONAUTICS AND SPACE ADMINISTRATION

HEADQUARTERS: 400 Maryland Avenue SW, Washington, DC 20546

Telephone: (202) 755 2320

NASA has several research programmes of general aviation interest, including an augmentor wing jet STOL research aircraft, digital fly-by-wire techniques, continuing evaluation of the supercritical wing, conversion of a Lockheed JetStar to fulfil a General Purpose Airborne Simulator role, implementation of a Terminal Configured Vehicle programme, testing of a Quiet Short-haul Research Aircraft (QSRA), and development and testing of the Space Shuttle Orbiter.

NASA/BOEING QSRA

Under a $21 million contract, Boeing carried out for NASA the conversion of a DHC C-8A Buffalo into a

Quiet Short-Haul Research Aircraft (QSRA). This aircraft is being used to develop the technology for quiet short-haul commercial airliners of the future, with short take-off and landing capabilities, as well as to explore the operating procedures of such aircraft in the airport terminal environment. Additionally, the QSRA provides NASA with an alternative powered-lift system for comparison with that of the NASA/DITC C-8A augmentor wing jet STOL research aircraft (see 1978-79 *Jane's*).

Boeing was responsible for construction of the new wing; new engine nacelles to provide for upper surface blowing (USB) of the inboard Coanda flaps; cross-ducting to supply boundary layer control (BLC) air to the wing leading-edge and ailerons; construction of a new tail, similar in configuration to that of the original; and the installation of new instrumentation. The noise shielding inherent in the upper surface blowing concept, combined with the high climb and descent angles which stem from the advanced techniques being explored, was expected to

result in a 90 EPNdB 'footprint' area of only three-tenths of a square mile (0·78 km²). This means that the noise level would be unobtrusive even at small, secondary airports.

The first flight of the QSRA aircraft took place on 6 July 1978; subsequently, it was flown in a series of tests from Boeing's Seattle facility, during which Boeing and NASA research pilots demonstrated steady-state flight at speeds of 50-190 knots (93-352 km/h; 58-219 mph), shutdown and restart of all four engines in flight, three-engine take-off and landing, a rate of climb of 1,067 m (3,500 ft)/min, operation at altitudes up to 4,570 m (15,000 ft), and high-performance T-O with a run of only 247 m (810 ft). In August 1978 the QSRA was delivered to Ames Research Center, at Moffett Field, California, for 'proof of concept' flight testing. The aircraft was being used for advanced flight research in early 1980, to be followed by a series of flight experiment activities. The latter included a series of simulated and actual deck landings on the USS *Kitty Hawk*, to evaluate the application of this form of

NASA/Boeing Quiet Short-haul Research Aircraft (four Avco Lycoming YF102 turbofan engines)

powered-lift system to carrier aircraft.

A detailed description of the QSRA appeared in the 1977-78 *Jane's*; important amendments to this description can be found in the 1979-80 edition.

NASA SHUTTLE TRAINING AIRCRAFT

To help train astronauts for Space Shuttle Orbiter landings, NASA acquired two Gulfstream American Gulfstream II twin-jet executive aircraft which had been specially modified for this role. Details of these aircraft can be found in the 1979-80 *Jane's*.

NASA AD-1 OBLIQUE-WING AIRCRAFT

On 20 February 1978, NASA announced the award of a $218,000 fixed-price contract to Ames Industrial Corporation of Bohemia, New York, for the construction of a small research aircraft to explore in piloted flight the viability of the pivoting-wing, or oblique-wing, concept that had emanated from NASA's Dryden Flight Research Center at Edwards, California.

Detail design of the aircraft, designated AD-1 (Ames/Dryden-1), was performed for NASA by Mr Burt Rutan, who was responsible for the well-known Vari-Viggen and VariEze designs for homebuilders. For operation at low speeds, and during take-off and landing, its wing is intended to be positioned conventionally. For flight at higher speeds, the wing is pivoted to form an oblique angle of up to 60° with the fore-and-aft centreline of the fuselage, reducing drag and promising increased speed and range for no increase in fuel consumption.

The AD-1 (N805NA) was delivered to Dryden Center in March 1979, and first flown on 21 December 1979. After eight flights with the wing in conventional configuration, during which the flight envelope was extended to 3,660 m (12,000 ft) altitude and maximum speed of 173 knots (322 km/h; 200 mph), the initial flight with the wing skewed was made in the first week of February 1980. The pivoting operation took place at an altitude of 3,810 m (12,500 ft), the wing being canted in stages of 5° to a maximum of 15°, with the starboard wing 15° forward and the port wing 15° aft of standard configuration. At each 5° stage of sweep, flutter control inputs were induced over a speed range of 110-150 knots (204-278 km/h; 127-173 mph) to determine flight characteristics. These procedures were repeated at a height of 2,285 m (7,500 ft) before the aircraft landed. Testing continued at this modest 15° angle through February and March 1980. NASA's programme called for the slew to be increased by increments of 15° up to the maximum of 60°, with at least two flights being made at each setting. No significant change in flight and control characteristics was anticipated until the wing setting exceeded 45°, the angle first adopted during the 14th flight of the AD-1 at the end of May 1980.

Type: Oblique-wing research aircraft.

Wings: Pivoting cantilever high-wing monoplane, with wing constructed in one piece. Thickness/chord ratio 12%. No dihedral. Incidence 2° at root, 0° at tip. No sweepback. Composite structure, based on a foam core with glassfibre/epoxy laminate covering. Conventional manually-operated ailerons of similar construction. No trailing-edge flaps. Electrically-operated trim tab in starboard aileron.

Fuselage: Composite semi-monocoque structure, utilising foam core with glassfibre/epoxy laminate covering for bulkheads and skin.

Tail Unit: Conventional tail unit, with cantilever fixed-incidence tailplane. Fixed surfaces and control surfaces constructed on a foam core with glassfibre/epoxy laminate covering. Electrically-operated trim tab in port elevator. All controls manually operated.

Landing Gear: Non-retractable tricycle type, with glassfibre/epoxy laminate cantilever struts manufactured by Jiran Glider Repairs. Single wheel on each unit. Cleveland 127 mm (5 in) main wheels and tyres, pressure 6·56 bars (95 lb/sq in). Nosewheel tyre pressure 3·11 bars (45 lb/sq in). Cleveland brakes.

Power Plant: Two 0·98 kN (220 lb st) Ames Industrial Corporation TRS 18-046 turbojet engines, mounted on short mid-set stub wings on each side of fuselage, with their intakes just aft of the leading-edge of the pivoting wing. Two fuel tanks in fuselage; total capacity approx 303 litres (80 US gallons). Refuelling points on fuselage upper surface, one forward and one aft of the wing. Oil capacity 1·44 litres (0·38 US gallons).

Accommodation: Pilot only, beneath transparent cockpit canopy hinged on starboard side. Accommodation ventilated.

Systems: Electrical system powered by two 600W engine-driven DC generators; 28V SAFT nickel-cadmium battery. Scott Executive Mk II oxygen system.

Dimensions, external:
Wing span	9·75 m (32 ft 0 in)
Wing chord at root	1·31 m (4 ft 3·4 in)
Wing chord at tip	0·47 m (1 ft 6·4 in)
Length overall, incl nose probe	11·68 m (38 ft 4 in)
Width, wing skewed	4·93 m (16 ft 2 in)
Height overall	1·98 m (6 ft 6 in)
Tailplane span	2·44 m (8 ft 0 in)
Wheel track	0·99 m (3 ft 3 in)
Wheelbase	4·27 m (14 ft 0 in)

Dimensions, internal:
Cockpit: Length	1·52 m (5 ft 0 in)
Max width	0·57 m (1 ft 10·3 in)
Max height	0·84 m (2 ft 9 in)

Areas:
Wings, gross	8·64 m² (93 sq ft)
Vertical tail surfaces (total)	1·29 m² (13·9 sq ft)
Horizontal tail surfaces (total)	2·46 m² (26·5 sq ft)

NASA/Ames AD-1 (two Ames Industrial Corporation TRS 18 turbojets) *(Pilot Press)*

NASA/Ames AD-1 oblique-wing research aircraft, with wing unskewed in early test flight and at full 60° on ground *(Howard Levy)*

WEIGHT:
Max T-O weight   907 kg (2,000 lb)
PERFORMANCE (demonstrated by January 1980):
Max level speed   173 knots (322 km/h; 200 mph)
Service ceiling   3,660 m (12,000 ft)

NASA TERMINAL CONFIGURED VEHICLE

The Terminal Configured Vehicle (TCV) programme was established to conduct research, and to develop and evaluate aircraft and flight management technology, that will benefit conventional take-off and landing operations in the terminal area.

The objectives and programme elements are:
1. To improve terminal area capacity and efficiency by:
   Systems and procedures for ATC evolution.
   Systems and procedures for runway capacity.
   Profiles and procedures for fuel conservation.
2. To improve approach and landing capability in adverse weather using:
   Human factor elements for effective flight management.
   Systems and information to minimise wind-shear hazard.
   Airborne sensors for weather penetration.
3. To reduce noise impact through:
   Development of profiles and configuration for noise reduction.

The research programme involves analyses, simulation and flight studies with a modified Boeing 737 aircraft, provided with highly flexible display and control equipment, and an aft flight deck for research purposes. A series of development and demonstration activities is being conducted to evolve practical systems and to solicit and encourage acceptance by flight crews and the airlines.

A Boeing 737-100 was obtained and a second (aft) flight deck and an array of computers and monitors were installed in the passenger cabin. The aircraft is designed to be flown from the forward flight deck with the conventional controls, and from the aft flight deck using a fly-by-wire, triple-redundant digital computer system. From the aft flight deck, the aircraft can be flown with advanced electronic displays and pilot selectable automatic navigation, guidance and control systems in simulated Cat III operations. Safety is assured through monitoring, and by takeover capability of the forward flight deck crew.

NASA AGRICULTURAL AIRCRAFT

NASA is undertaking studies, using an Ayres Thrush Commander 800, to improve the aerodynamics and application equipment and techniques of future agricultural aircraft.

NASA ELECTRICALLY-POWERED LIGHT AIRCRAFT

In collaboration with the Jet Propulsion Laboratory, NASA's Dryden Research Center is studying a possible future electrically-powered light aircraft which will derive its power from a ground-transmitted microwave beam. A Schweizer SGS 1-26E sailplane was to be modified to flight test the concept.

NASA AIRCRAFT NOISE MONITORING PROGRAMME

NASA's Ames Research Center was in 1977-78 modifying a Lockheed YO-3A to act as a flying platform for equipment designed to monitor noise made by other aircraft. No further news of this programme has been received.

NATURAL LAMINAR FLOW AIRCRAFT

In April 1979 it was reported that NASA had been gathering performance data on General Dynamics F-111 aircraft, prior to carrying out natural laminar flow testing of an F-111 at Dryden Flight Research Center in the late Summer of 1979. Study proved that it would be possible to fly the aircraft without flaps at safe take-off and landing speeds, which is essential for the flight tests which are to be made.

Cutaway model of NASA's TCV Boeing 737, showing internal layout

Boeing KC-135 fitted with NASA winglets, to evaluate their fuel-saving potential

Under the joint NASA/USAF programme, the wings of the F-111 are to be fitted with aerofoil shapes known as 'gloves', to determine the effect on cruise efficiency. Wind tunnel tests have already shown that the selected 'glove' maintains a favourable pressure gradient over most of the wing chord. It is suggested that if the airflow over the 'gloves' is predominantly laminar, turbulence will be reduced, thus increasing cruise efficiency and at the same time reducing fuel consumption.

NASA/USAF KC-135 WINGLET TESTS

In February 1978 a US Air Force KC-135 cargo/tanker aircraft was delivered to NASA's Dryden Flight Research Center, where it was modified by the installation of NASA winglets and is being test flown to evaluate the fuel-saving potential of these supplementary aerofoil surfaces. They are expected to improve overall performance by some 8%. According to the US Air Force's Flight Dynamics Laboratory, this could represent annual fuel savings of about 140 million litres (37 million US gallons) for the KC-135 fleet, as well as improving take-off performance and slightly improving fuel offload capability.

Under a US Air Force contract worth approximately $3 million, The Boeing Company constructed the winglets. Each has a chord of 0·61 m (2 ft 0 in) at the tip, 1·83 m (6 ft 0 in) at the base, and is 2·74 m (9 ft 0 in) in length. Constructed of light alloy, they weigh approximately 68 kg (150 lb) each. Boeing installed them on outer wing panels. These outer panels with winglets were then installed on the KC-135 by NASA personnel at Dryden, where the modified aircraft flew for the first time on 24 July 1979. It is possible to make adjustments to the incidence and cant angle of the winglets between flights, so that the optimum setting can be established.

Data from the fully instrumented KC-135 will be compared with data that was gathered from flight testing prior to installation of the winglets, allowing a direct comparison to be made.

The winglet concept was developed in wind tunnels at NASA's Langley Research Center by Dr Richard T. Whitcomb, who was also responsible for the NASA supercritical wing.

GOSSAMER ALBATROSS

NASA has sponsored a short-term flight research programme with Gossamer Albatross No. 2, under a $65,000 contract awarded to Dr Paul MacCready's AeroVironment Inc. Initial 'power plant' was to be Bryan Allen, who flew the first Gossamer Albatross across the English Channel on 12 June 1979. It was planned, however, to replace muscle-drive subsequently by a small battery-powered electric motor that would provide a steady-state output, although the pilot would remain in control of the aircraft. The primary objective of NASA's test programme, conducted at the Dryden Flight Research Center, was to study the unusual aerodynamic performance, stability and control characteristics of large, but very lightly loaded and slow flying aircraft. Such data is required for the design of future aircraft intended for extremely low-speed flight at any altitude, and particularly for low-power flight in the very low air densities at altitudes up to 30,480 m (100,000 ft). The data may also help scientists to assess the feasibility of low-speed flight within very low density atmospheres, such as that which surrounds the planet Mars.

Gossamer Albatross No. 2 being flown at NASA's Dryden Flight Research Center

NORTHROP
NORTHROP CORPORATION

CORPORATE OFFICE: 1800 Century Park East, Century City, Los Angeles, California 90067

Telephone: (213) 553 6262
CHAIRMAN OF THE BOARD AND CHIEF EXECUTIVE OFFICER:
Thomas V. Jones
VICE-CHAIRMAN OF THE BOARD: Richard W. Millar

PRESIDENT AND CHIEF OPERATING OFFICER, AND GROUP EXECUTIVE, COMMUNICATIONS AND ELECTRONICS:
Dr Thomas O. Paine

SENIOR VICE-PRESIDENTS AND GROUP EXECUTIVES:
   Frank W. Lynch (Tactical Systems Group)
   Ross F. Miller (Aircraft Group)
   Frederick Stevens (Construction Group)
SENIOR VICE-PRESIDENTS:
   William M. Elliott (General Counsel, and Secretary)
   Welko E. Gasich (Advanced Projects)
   Donald A. Hicks (Marketing and Technology)
   James V. Holcombe (Asst to Chief Executive Officer
      for Government Relations)
   James D. Willson (Finance)
DIVISION VICE-PRESIDENTS:
   David N. Ferguson (Electronics)
   George H. Hage (Electro-Mechanical)
   Kent Kresa (Ventura)
   F. J. Manzella (Aircraft Services)
   Ross F. Miller (Aircraft)
   Wallace C. Solberg (Defense Systems)
   Joseph Yamron (Precision Products)
SUBSIDIARY PRESIDENTS:
   Frank Caramelli (Page Communications Engineers Inc)
   L. Kaufold (Wilcox Electric Inc)
   D. A. McInnis (Northrop Services Inc)
   James E. Ware (Northrop Architectural Systems Inc)
OTHER VICE-PRESIDENTS:
   J. R. Alison (Customer Relations)
   C. H. Bernstein (Asst to Chief Executive Officer for
      Analysis)
   J. B. Campbell (Controller)
   William J. Chalmers (Manager, Northrop Research and
      Technology Center)
   W. B. Dennis (Forward Planning)
   Stanley Ebner (Manager, Eastern Regional Office)
   William A. Fifer (Senior Corporate Executive, Saudi
      Arabia)
   C. R. Gates (Northrop International, and F-5G)
   D. G. Head (President, George A. Fuller Company)
   R. P. Jackson (Programme Management)
   J. C. Jones (Asst to Chief Executive Officer for
      Aeronautical Systems)
   D. L. Lewis (Business Analysis)
   T. A. McDougall (International Business Operations)
   John J. Richardson (Industrial Relations)

   Keith L. Robinett (Manager, Northrop Data Proces-
      sing)
   Donald D. Warner (Material, Facilities and Services)
   Robert B. Watts Jr (Asst General Counsel)
   G. Ronald Wenninger (Advanced Systems)
CORPORATE TREASURER: Richard B. Lohrer
ASST TO CHAIRMAN—COMMUNITY RELATIONS: W. H.
   Habblett
EXECUTIVE ASST TO CHAIRMAN: W. H. Gurnee
DIRECTOR OF PUBLIC AFFAIRS—EUROPE: J. K. Corfield
DIRECTOR OF INFORMATION: A. W. Cantafio

This company was formed in 1939 by John K. Northrop and others to undertake the design and manufacture of military aircraft. During the second World War it built 1,131 aircraft of its own design and was engaged in extensive subcontract work. It also devoted considerable attention to the design and construction of aircraft of the 'Flying Wing' type.

Although continuing its activities in the design, development and production of aircraft, missiles and target drone systems, Northrop has broadened its scope of operation to include electronics, space technology, communications, construction, support services and commercial products. To reflect this changing character of its business, the company changed its name from Northrop Aircraft Inc to Northrop Corporation in 1959.

In October 1976 Northrop established an Aircraft Group, comprising its existing Aircraft Division and a new organisation, the Aircraft Services Division, to give greater attention to aircraft design, development and production, as well as to programmes of training, support and service. The company had established previously an Electronics and Communications Group, and a Construction Group. The company established a Tactical Systems Group in January 1978, comprising the Electro-Mechanical and Ventura Divisions, and Northrop Services Inc (a subsidiary). A corporate office of advanced projects was established in May 1979.

Divisions of Northrop now include Aircraft Division, specialising in the research, development, production and sale of military aircraft, commercial airframe assemblies and subassemblies; Aircraft Services Division, engaged

primarily in worldwide total air base systems support, requirement analysis and planning, programme management, facilities development and maintenance, training, logistics, aircraft maintenance and overhaul, and base operation; Electronics Division, which handles the company's activities in electronics research, development, and manufacturing of navigation and guidance systems; Electro-Mechanical Division, which handles advanced missile programmes, electro-optical systems for target identification and target designation; Defense Systems Division, designer and manufacturer of electronics countermeasures systems, including the internal countermeasures set (ICS) for the US Air Force's F-15 Eagle; Precision Products Division, a leading supplier of precision gyroscopes and related guidance and control systems for communication and weather satellites, in key missile programmes, and on aircraft, submarines and ships; Ventura Division, designer and manufacturer of remotely piloted vehicles, target systems for anti-aircraft gunnery, surface-to-air and air-to-air missile crew training and weapons system evaluation, recoverable and expendable target aircraft, operation, maintenance and target range support services, torpedo modification kits, and mobile underwater targets; and George A. Fuller Company, a leading construction and construction-management company.

Northrop's communications activities are handled by two subsidiaries: Wilcox Electric Inc of Kansas City, Missouri, designers and producers of a wide range of ground-based navigation equipment, and Page Communications Engineers, Vienna, Virginia, which designs, engineers, installs and maintains total communications systems.

To further expand its research and development work, Northrop has divided its Research and Technology Center into three organisations: the Corporate Laboratories, Laser System Laboratories and Laser Technology Laboratories. Current programmes include research and development in such fields as information sciences, electronic devices and materials, nuclear radiation effects, high-energy laser development and laser systems applications.

The number of employees of Northrop Corporation totalled about 28,800 on 1 January 1980.

NORTHROP CORPORATION AIRCRAFT GROUP

3901 West Broadway, Hawthorne, California 90250
Telephone: (213) 970 2000
SENIOR VICE-PRESIDENT AND GROUP EXECUTIVE:
   Ross F. Miller
CORPORATE VICE-PRESIDENT: R. P. Jackson (Manager,
   F-18 Programme)
SENIOR VICE-PRESIDENT: M. G. Gonzalez (Business Oper-
   ations)
VICE-PRESIDENTS:
   R. A. Graham (Marketing)
   M. Kuska (General Manager Aircraft Programmes)
   J. Mannion (Public Affairs)
   G. S. Shackelford (Contracts and Pricing)
   S. R. Smith (Iran Operations)
   R. S. Taylor (Finance)
   Robert W. Young (Administration)
ASSTS TO V-P FINANCE:
   W. G. Niemann
   S. Zitter
Aircraft Division:
CORPORATE VICE-PRESIDENT AND GENERAL MANAGER:
   Ross F. Miller
VICE-PRESIDENTS:
   C. W. Benson (Materiel)
   R. D. Lovell (Manufacturing)
   J. L. McCoy (Product Support)
   B. T. Moser (Production Operations)
   Thomas R. Rooney (Technical)
Aircraft Services Division:
CORPORATE VICE-PRESIDENT AND GENERAL MANAGER:
   F. J. Manzella
VICE-PRESIDENTS:
   H. B. Gunther (Construction Operations)
   L. J. Hunt Jr (Manager, Saudi Arabia Programme)
   R. H. Madeira (Support Services)
   Current production at Northrop's Aircraft Division is centred on the F-5E Tiger II fighter, F-5F two-seat fighter/trainer, F/A-18 Hornet multi-mission fighter, and major Boeing 747 subcontract work, which includes the main fuselage section and the extra-large side-loading cargo door. The company was also engaged in 1980 in the development of an advanced version of the F-5E, to which the designation F-5G has been allocated.
   Northrop's share of work on development and production of the US Navy's F/A-18 Hornet multi-mission fighter is proceeding on schedule. Northrop builds the centre and aft fuselage and the twin vertical tails of the Navy version of the Hornet. The company is responsible also for integration of all internal systems such as the environmental control system and auxiliary power system. McDonnell Douglas (which see) is prime contractor to the US Navy for the carrier-based Hornet, with Northrop responsible for about 40 per cent of production. The Navy has stated a requirement for 1,366 operational Hornets, to replace its

existing A-7 and F-4 aircraft. Northrop's land-based version of the F-18 is known as the F-18L. As prime contractor for the land-based F-18, Northrop would carry out approximately 60 per cent of its production, McDonnell Douglas 40 per cent. Both carrier- and land-based versions use the same General Electric engines, and they are 80-90 per cent identical in high-usage spare parts. Design modifications to convert the carrier-designed F-18 airframe for land-based operation are intended to simplify it, and reduce the cost.
   On 11 October 1979, Northrop announced the receipt of a $12·4 million contract from the US Air Force to design technology for highly loaded primary wing and fuselage structures, and to build and test graphite composite airframe components. Under the contract Northrop will build more than 800 test items, ranging from small components to 2·54 × 4·06 m (8 ft 4 in × 13 ft 4 in) structures. Each will be subjected to tests designed to prove material and structural integrity under a wide range of atmospheric conditions. The primary purpose of the five-year programme is to develop more cost-effective methods of testing airframe parts made from graphite composite.
   In addition to its main factory at Hawthorne, the Aircraft Division has facilities at El Segundo, Carson, Torrance, Palmdale and Edwards Air Force Base, California. The 176,500 m² (1·9 million sq ft) facility at El Segundo, purchased in December 1978, now houses what are regarded as the most modern tactical fighter production lines in the USA, and has made it possible to double the machine tool capacity at Hawthorne.

NORTHROP TIGER II
USAF designations: F-5E and F-5F
   The F-5E was selected in November 1970 by the US government as the winner of a competition to determine the single-seat International Fighter Aircraft (IFA) which

Northrop F-5E Tiger II for service with the Indonesian Air Force

was to succeed Northrop's F-5A. The two-seat F-5F was developed subsequently.
   The F-5E design places particular emphasis on manoeuvrability rather than high speed, notably by the incorporation of manoeuvring flaps, based on the design of a similar system for the Netherlands Air Force's NF-5A/Bs. Full-span leading-edge flaps work in conjunction with conventional trailing-edge flaps, and are operated by a control on the pilot's throttle quadrant.
   Wing loading on the F-5E is maintained at approximately the same value as on the F-5A, as the result of an increase in wing area to 17·30 m² (186 sq ft). This is due principally to the widened fuselage, which also increases wing span. The tapered wing leading-edge extension, between the inboard leading-edge and fuselage, was modified to enhance airflow over the wing at high angles of attack.
   The F-5E incorporates other features developed for the Canadian, Dutch and Norwegian F-5s. These include two-position nosewheel gear, which increases wing angle of attack on the ground by 3° 22′ and which, in conjunction with the more powerful engines, has improved F-5E take-off performance some 30% by comparison with earlier F-5s. Arrester gear permits operation from short runways. It is qualified to carry two 1,040 litre (275 US gallon) underwing fuel tanks, in addition to the centreline 1,040 litre (275 US gallon) tank, and up to seven 500 lb MK-82 bombs, following the addition of a Multiple Ejector Rack (MER) on the centreline stores station.
   The first F-5E was rolled out on 23 June 1972, and made its first flight on 11 August 1972. USAF Tactical Air Command, with assistance from Air Training Command, was assigned responsibility for training pilots and technicians of user countries. First deliveries of the F-5E, to the US Air Force's 425th Tactical Fighter Squadron, were made in the Spring of 1973. Twenty aircraft had been supplied for the US Air Force training programme by the

Northrop F-5E Tiger II single-seat twin-jet tactical fighter aircraft *(Pilot Press)*

end of September 1973, and deliveries to foreign countries began in late 1973. The 1,000th F-5E/F was delivered to the Republic of Korea in August 1979, and production continues at an average rate of about five per month. Customers to date include the US Air Force (112 F-5Es), US Navy (10 F-5Es and 3 F-5Fs), Brazil, Chile, Republic of China, Iran, Jordan, Kenya, South Korea, Malaysia, Saudi Arabia, Singapore, Sudan, Switzerland, Thailand and the Yemen Arab Republic.

In addition to their use as tactical fighters, F-5Es are operated by the US Air Force and US Navy in the 'aggressor' role, to simulate 'enemy' aircraft at major air combat training schools in the USA, England and the Philippines.

Details of the current production versions of the Tiger II are as follows:

F-5E. Standard production version, to which the detailed description applies. In production also, under licence, by AIDC in Taiwan (which see). Can be fitted with an R-843A/ARN-58 localiser receiver and a reconnaissance nose containing four KS-121A 70 mm framing cameras and related equipment. Intended for low/medium-altitude photo-reconnaissance, the nose is similar to that of the RF-5A. New 'shark' profile nose developed for the F-5G (which see) is to be introduced on standard production F-5E and F-5F.

To extend the range of armament options, an F-5E completed a technology flying demonstration with a 30 mm underbelly gun pod developed by General Electric. More than 800 rounds of 30 mm GAU-8 type ammunition were fired on US Air Force test ranges at Edwards AFB, California.

The F-5Es for the Royal Saudi Air Force (RSAF) have a Litton LN-33 inertial navigation system, capable of accuracy exceeding 1·5 nm (2·7 km; 1·7 miles) CEP per flight hour, which provides attitude reference, range and bearing to ten pre-set destinations, as well as true ground track steering. The system is self-aligning in 10 min in the gyro compass mode, and can be aligned in 3 min to a stored heading. In-flight refuelling capability is also provided. F-5Es of the Brazilian Air Force have a large dorsal fin to accommodate an ADF antenna.

F-5F. Tandem two-seat version of F-5E, with fuselage lengthened by 1·08 m (3 ft 6½ in). Fire control system retained, enabling aircraft to be used for both training and combat duties, but one M-39 gun deleted. Development approved by US Air Force in early 1974. First flight was made on 25 September 1974. Two F-5Fs completed flight test and qualification in early 1976. Total of 118 ordered; deliveries began in the Summer of 1976.

On 31 March 1978, Northrop announced receipt of US government approval for a company-funded development and flight demonstration programme of an **RF-5E** specialised reconnaissance version of the F-5E. This has a modified forward fuselage with quick-change capabilities to accommodate a wide variety of reconnaissance equipment. Both day and night photo missions were demonstrated during the subsequent test programme. Modification of a production F-5E made possible the first flight of the RF-5E prototype in January 1979, and a brief description of this aircraft is given separately.

The following details refer to the F-5E, but are generally applicable to the F-5F also, except for details noted under model listings.

TYPE: Single-seat light tactical fighter.

WINGS: Cantilever low-wing monoplane. Wing section NACA 65A004·8 (modified). No dihedral. No incidence. Sweepback at quarter-chord 24°. Multi-spar light alloy structure with heavy plate machined skins. Hydraulically-powered sealed-gap ailerons at approximately mid-span. Electrically-operated light alloy single-slotted trailing-edge flaps inboard of ailerons. Electrically-operated leading-edge manoeuvring flaps. No de-icing system.

FUSELAGE: Light alloy semi-monocoque basic structure, with steel, magnesium and titanium used in certain areas. Two hydraulically-actuated airbrakes of magnesium alloy construction, mounted on underside of fuselage forward of main-wheel wells. Avionics bay and cockpit pressurised; fail-safe structure in pressurised sections.

TAIL UNIT: Cantilever all-metal structure, with hydraulically-powered rudder and one-piece all-moving tailplane. Tailplane incidence varied by hydraulic actuators. No trim tabs. Dual hydraulic actuators of Northrop design for control of rudder and tailplane.

LANDING GEAR: Hydraulically-retractable tricycle type, main units retracting inward into fuselage, nosewheel forward. Oleo-pneumatic struts of Northrop design on all units. Two-position extending nose unit increases static angle of attack by 3° 22′ to reduce T-O distance, and is shortened automatically during the retraction cycle. Gravity-operated emergency extension. Main wheels and tyres size 24 × 8·00-13, pressure 14·48 bars (210 lb/sq in). Steerable nose unit with wheel and tyre size 18 × 6·50-8, pressure 8·27 bars (120 lb/sq in). All-metal multiple-disc brakes of Northrop design.

POWER PLANT: Two General Electric J85-GE-21A turbojet engines, each rated at 22·24 kN (5,000 lb st) with afterburning. Two independent fuel systems, one for each engine. Fuel for starboard engine supplied from two rubber-impregnated bladder-type nylon fabric cells, comprising a centre-fuselage cell of 803 litre (212 US gallon) capacity, and an aft-fuselage cell of 640 litre (169 US gallon) capacity. Port engine supplied from a forward fuselage cell of 1,120 litre (296 US gallon) capacity. Total fuel capacity 2,563 litres (677 US gallons). No fuel is carried in the wings. Fuel crossfeed system allows fuel from either or both cell systems to be fed to either or both engines. Auxiliary jettisonable fuel tanks of 568 or 1,040 litres (150 or 275 US gallons) can be carried on the fuselage centreline pylon and the inboard underwing pylons. Single refuelling point on lower fuselage for fuselage fuel cell and external tank installation. Provision for in-flight refuelling by means of a detachable probe. Oil capacity 4·5 litres (1·2 US gallons) per engine.

ENGINE INTAKES: Intakes are supplemented with auxiliary air inlet doors for use during T-O and low-speed flight, to improve compressor face pressure recovery and to decrease distortion. Each door consists of a set of six pivot-mounted louvres in removable panels on each side of the fuselage. The doors are actuated by the pilot at T-O, and controlled automatically in flight by Mach sensor switches, and are maintained in the open position at airspeeds below Mach 0·35-0·4.

ACCOMMODATION: Pilot only in pressurised, heated and air-conditioned cockpit, on rocket-powered ejection seat. Upward-opening canopy, hinged at rear.

SYSTEMS: Cockpit and avionics bay pressurised, heated and air-conditioned by engine bleed air, maximum pressure differential 0·34 bars (5 lb/sq in). Hydraulic power supplied by two independent systems at a pressure of 207 bars (3,000 lb/sq in). Flight control system provides power solely for operation of primary flight control surfaces. Utility system provides hydraulic backup power for the primary flight control surfaces and operating power for the landing gear, landing gear doors, airbrakes, wheel brakes, nosewheel steering, gun bay purge doors, gun gas deflectors and stability augmentation system. Electrical power supplied by two 13/15kVA 115/200V three-phase 320-480Hz non-paralleled engine-driven alternators. Each alternator has the capacity to accept full aircraft power load via an

automatic transfer function. 250VA 115V 400Hz single-phase solid-state static inverter provides secondary AC source for engine starting. Two 33A 26-32V transformer-rectifiers and a 24V 11Ah nickel-cadmium battery provide DC power. Liquid oxygen system with capacity of 5 litres.

AVIONICS AND EQUIPMENT (F-5E): AN/ARC-164 UHF command radio, 3,500-channel with 50kHz spacing. Emerson Electric AN/APQ-159 lightweight micro-miniature X-band pulse radar for air-to-air search and range tracking; target information, at a range of up to 20 nm (37 km; 23 miles), is displayed on a 0·13 m (5 in) DVST in cockpit. AN/ARA-50 UHF ADF; AN/AIC-18 intercom system; AN/APX-101 IFF/SIF system; AN/ARN-118 Tacan; attitude and heading reference system; angle of attack system; and central air data computer. Full blind-flying instrumentation. Optional avionics include LN-33 inertial navigation system; AN/ARN-108 instrument landing system; CPU-129/A flight director computer; VHF; VOR/ILS with DME; LF ADF; CRT with scan converter for radar or electro-optical weapon (AGM-65 Maverick); and radar warning receiver.

AVIONICS AND EQUIPMENT (F-5F): AN/ARC-164 UHF/AM command radio, AN/AIC-18 or -25 interphone set, AN/APX-101 IFF/SIF transponder, TS1843/APX transponder test set, AN/ARN-118 Tacan, AN/APQ-159 fire control radar, AN/ASG-29 lead computing optical sight, and AN/ARA-50 UHF/DF. Optional equipment includes photo-reconnaissance nose; in-flight refuelling system; pylon jettison conversion kits; anti-skid brakes; and chaff/flare countermeasures package.

ARMAMENT (F-5E): Two AIM-9 Sidewinder missiles on wingtip launchers. Two M-39A2 20 mm cannon mounted in fuselage nose, with 280 rounds per gun. Up to 3,175 kg (7,000 lb) of mixed ordnance can be carried on one underfuselage and four underwing stations, including M129 leaflet bombs; MK-82 GP and Snakeye 500 lb bombs; MK-36 destructors; MK-84 2,000 lb bomb; BLU-1, -27 or -32 U or F napalm; LAU-68 (7) 2·75 in rockets; LAU-3 (19) 2·75 in rockets; CBU-24, 49, -52 or -58 cluster bomb units; SUU-20 bomb and rocket packs; SUU-25 flare dispensers; TDU-10 tow targets (Dart); and RMU-10 reel (Dart). Lead-computing optical gunsight uses inputs from airborne radar for air-to-air missiles and cannon, and provides a roll-stabilised manually-depressible reticle aiming reference for air-to-ground delivery. A 'snapshoot' capability is included for attack on violently manoeuvring and fleeting targets. The gunsight incorporates also a detachable 16 mm reticle camera with 15 m (50 ft) film magazine. Optional ordnance capability includes the AGM-65 Maverick; centreline multiple ejector rack; and laser guided bombs.

ARMAMENT (F-5F): Two AIM-9J Sidewinder missiles on wingtip launchers. One M-39 20 mm cannon in port side of nose with 140 rounds. Underfuselage and underwing stores as detailed for the F-5E. Optional ordnance includes a laser designator in the rear cockpit.

DIMENSIONS, EXTERNAL:
Wing span	8·13 m (26 ft 8 in)
Span over missiles	8·53 m (27 ft 11⅞ in)
Wing chord at root	3·57 m (11 ft 8⅝ in)
Wing chord at tip	0·68 m (2 ft 2⅞ in)
Wing aspect ratio	3·82
Length overall (incl nose-probe):	
F-5E	14·68 m (48 ft 2 in)
F-5F	15·72 m (51 ft 7 in)
Height overall: F-5E	4·06 m (13 ft 4 in)
F-5F	4·01 m (13 ft 1¾ in)
Tailplane span	4·31 m (14 ft 1½ in)
Wheel track	3·80 m (12 ft 5½ in)
Wheelbase	5·17 m (16 ft 11½ in)

AREAS:
Wings, gross	17·3 m² (186 sq ft)
Ailerons (total)	0·86 m² (9·24 sq ft)
Trailing-edge flaps (total)	1·95 m² (21·0 sq ft)
Leading-edge flaps (total)	1·14 m² (12·3 sq ft)
Fin	3·85 m² (41·42 sq ft)
Rudder	0·57 m² (6·10 sq ft)
Tailplane	5·48 m² (59·0 sq ft)

Northrop F-5F tandem two-seat fighter-trainer, armed with wingtip-mounted Sidewinder missiles

WEIGHTS AND LOADINGS:

Weight empty: F-5E	4,392 kg (9,683 lb)	
F-5F	4,793 kg (10,567 lb)	
Max T-O weight: F-5E	11,193 kg (24,676 lb)	
F-5F	11,442 kg (25,225 lb)	
Max landing weight: F-5F	11,406 kg (25,147 lb)	
Max zero-fuel weight: F-5E	7,953 kg (17,534 lb)	
Max wing loading: F-5E	649·4 kg/m² (133 lb/sq ft)	
Max power loading: F-5E	251·6 kg/kN (2·5 lb/lb st)	

PERFORMANCE (F-5E at combat weight of 6,055 kg; 13,350 lb, F-5F at combat weight of 6,375 kg; 14,055 lb, unless stated otherwise):

Never-exceed speed
710 knots (1,314 km/h; 817 mph) EAS

Max level speed:

F-5E at 10,975 m (36,000 ft)	Mach 1·63
F-5F at 11,000 m (36,090 ft)	Mach 1·55

Max cruising speed:

F-5E at 10,975 m (36,000 ft)	Mach 0·98
Econ cruising speed	Mach 0·80

Stalling speed, flaps down, power off:

F-5E	124 knots (230 km/h; 143 mph)
F-5F	136 knots (253 km/h; 157 mph)

Max rate of climb at S/L:

F-5E	10,516 m (34,500 ft)/min
F-5F	10,030 m (32,900 ft)/min
Service ceiling: F-5E	15,790 m (51,800 ft)
F-5F	15,484 m (50,800 ft)

Service ceiling, one engine out:

F-5E	over 12,495 m (41,000 ft)
F-5F	12,285 m (40,300 ft)

T-O run:

F-5E at 7,053 kg (15,550 lb)	610 m (2,000 ft)
F-5F at 7,371 kg (16,250 lb)	701 m (2,300 ft)

T-O run at max T-O weight:

F-5E	1,737 m (5,700 ft)
F-5F	1,829 m (6,000 ft)

T-O to 15 m (50 ft):

F-5E at 7,053 kg (15,550 lb)	884 m (2,900 ft)
F-5F at 7,371 kg (16,250 lb)	975 m (3,200 ft)

Landing from 15 m (50 ft):

F-5E at 5,230 kg (11,530 lb), without brake chute
1,417 m (4,650 ft)

F-5F at 5,554 kg (12,245 lb), without brake chute
1,524 m (5,000 ft)

Landing run with brake chute:

F-5E at 5,230 kg (11,530 lb)	762 m (2,500 ft)
F-5F at 5,554 kg (12,245 lb)	792 m (2,600 ft)

Range, F-5E:

with max fuel and reserves for 20 min max endurance
at S/L: tanks retained
1,340 nm (2,483 km; 1,543 miles)
tanks dropped
1,545 nm (2,863 km; 1,779 miles)

Combat radius, F-5E:
with max fuel, two Sidewinder missiles, allowances as above and 5 min combat with max afterburning power at 4,570 m (15,000 ft)
570 nm (1,056 km; 656 miles)
with 2,358 kg (5,200 lb) ordnance load, two Sidewinder missiles, max fuel, allowances as above and 5 min combat at military power at S/L, lo-lo-lo mission
120 nm (222 km; 138 miles)
with max fuel, two Sidewinder missiles and two 530 lb bombs, allowances as above and 5 min combat at military power at S/L, hi-lo-hi mission
480 nm (890 km; 553 miles)

Range, F-5F:
ferry range with max fuel, allowances comprising 5 min at normal thrust, 1 min at max thrust, 20 min loiter at S/L, plus reserve of 5% of initial fuel: crew of two 1,270 nm (2,353 km; 1,462 miles)

Combat radius, F-5F:
with max internal fuel, and allowances comprising 2 min at normal thrust, 1 min at max thrust, 5 min max thrust for combat at 4,570 m (15,000 ft), 20 min loiter at S/L, plus reserve of 5% of initial fuel
520 nm (964 km; 599 miles)
with max fuel, two Sidewinder missiles and two 530 lb bombs, allowances as above, and 5 min combat at military power at S/L, hi-lo-hi mission
450 nm (834 km; 518 miles)

NORTHROP RF-5E

Northrop's RF-5E prototype made its international debut at the 1979 Paris Air Show, following a flight from Edwards AFB, California. First flown in January 1979, this prototype had completed more than 60 test and demonstration flights by the beginning of June 1979, during which missions had been flown at heights between 61 m (200 ft) and 14,325 m (47,000 ft), by day and night, at speeds of up to 600 knots (1,112 km/h; 691 mph).

Basically similar to the F-5E Tiger II, the RF-5E differs by having a modified forward fuselage, and specialised equipment to enable it to fulfil a highly efficient reconnaissance role. The modified forward fuselage extends the overall length by 0·20 m (8 in), and provides 0·74 m³ (26 cu ft) of space to accommodate reconnaissance equipment. To allow maximum flexibility for differing reconnaissance roles, Northrop decided to group the various combinations of proposed cameras/sensors on portable

Close-up of sensor windows beneath the forward fuselage of Northrop's RF-5E reconnaissance aircraft

pallets, any one of which could be loaded easily and quickly into this forward fuselage compartment. In addition to the selected pallet, a KS-87B oblique frame camera is mounted in a forward nose compartment and provided with lenses of 6 in and 12 in focal length.

Four pallets have been developed to date for the RF-5E, the first comprising a KA-95 medium/high-altitude panoramic camera, KA-56E low-altitude panoramic camera, and an RS-702 infra-red linescanner. Pallet 2 also has the KA-56E panoramic camera, with a KA-93 panoramic camera for horizon-to-horizon coverage at heights of 3,050-15,240 m (10,000-50,000 ft). Pallet 3 is configured for long-range oblique photo (LOROP) missions, and carries a single LOROP camera of 48 in or 66 in focal length. Pallet 4 provides night reconnaissance capability, equipped with a KA-98 covert laser linescanner and an RS-702 infra-red linescanner. Optionally available for use with Pallet 4 is a special nosecone accommodating the AN/APQ-146 terrain-following radar system which equips B-1 and F-111 aircraft.

The pilot has available advanced nav/com systems to complement the reconnaissance equipment, plus a video viewfinder system which enables him to view the terrain below the aircraft on a cathode ray tube (CRT) display in the cockpit. Using this system, the pilot can monitor and correct his line-of-flight during mapping runs, and can also update the INS when passing over recognisable terrain features. In addition, there is an integrated sensor control system (ISCS), which handles many operations automatically, thus reducing the pilot's workload. The ISCS takes inputs from the radar altimeter and INS to compute the angular velocity (V/H) for the terrain passing below the aircraft. V/H signals and the camera cycle rates are directed to individual cameras, with the appropriate scaling factor required for that particular sensor. The ISCS can cater for a wide variety of additional growth sensors.

The RF-5E retains the external stores stations of the

F-5E, permitting the carriage of up to three external fuel tanks (each 1,040 litres; 275 US gallons) for maximum range and speed performance. It has essentially the same performance and armament capabilities as the F-5E tactical fighter, and on all missions is able to carry one M-39 20 mm gun with 280 rounds, plus two AIM-9 missiles.

Pilots of four nations had made flights in the RF-5E by the time it was shown at the 1979 Paris Air Show, and many of the 27 nations now flying F-5s had expressed their interest in evaluating the RF-5E.

PERFORMANCE:

Mission radius (A, with one external fuel tank and two AIM-9s; B, with three external fuel tanks and two AIM-9s):

low altitude throughout:

A	250 nm (463 km; 287 miles)
B	365 nm (676 km; 420 miles)
hi-lo-hi: A	410 nm (759 km; 471 miles)
B	560 nm (1,037 km; 644 miles)
hi-lo-lo-hi: A	365 nm (676 km; 420 miles)
B	520 nm (963 km; 598 miles)

high altitude throughout:

A	495 nm (916 km; 569 miles)
B	630 nm (1,166 km; 725 miles)

NORTHROP F-5G

Latest addition to Northrop's family of lightweight tactical fighters, this export fighter has evolved from company studies which began more than three years ago. These showed that modification of the F-5E to have a single 71·17 kN (16,000 lb st) General Electric F404-GE-400 low bypass turbofan engine, with variable-geometry nozzle, in place of the two standard General Electric J85 turbojets, would result in a combat aircraft with much-improved performance at reasonable cost. This was one of the criteria which led to the definition of 'intermediate

Northrop F-5G intermediate export fighter (General Electric F404-GE-400 turbofan engine) *(Pilot Press)*

fighter' for the F-5G, being regarded by the US government as an aircraft "whose cost and performance characteristics would generally lie between the current export fighter, the F-5E, and fighter aircraft now in production for US forces, such as the F-16."

Although generally similar in appearance, and with much the same avionics and weapon systems as the F-5E, the new aircraft will have significant performance improvements, resulting from a 60 per cent increase in available thrust from the changed power plant. Low-speed wind tunnel testing of the F-5G has demonstrated that it retains the handling characteristics of the F-5E, and high-speed wind tunnel testing was scheduled to follow. Economies in purchase and operation will result from the interchangeability of many F-5E components, the ability to use existing F-5E support and training systems for the F-5G, and improved reliability and reduced maintenance associated with the General Electric F404 engine.

Following Presidential approval of the intermediate export fighter concept in January 1980, Northrop announced on 24 March 1980 the company's intention to engage an additional 200 employees to work on the project, thus doubling by the end of 1980 the number involved originally in the development of this aircraft.

AIRFRAME: Enlarged air intakes, to accommodate increased mass flow of F404 engine, are extended forward slightly and also allow greater boundary layer gap between intakes and fuselage. Wing inboard leading-edge strakes extended forward to cater for new intake leading-edge position. Fuselage lengthened by insertion of 12·7 cm (5 in) plug aft of cockpit, and has less area-rule 'waisting' than F-5E. Slimmer rear fuselage than F-5E, with twin underfuselage 'step' fairings running aft from approx wing mid-chord position. 'Banjo' frame around rear of engine provides mounting for fin. Graphite composite skins on rear fuselage and tail unit. More streamlined brake 'chute fairing. Nose has flatter top surface, to improve stability at high angles of attack. Otherwise generally similar to F-5E. Existing choice of single-seat, two-seat and reconnaissance noses retained.

DIMENSIONS, EXTERNAL:
Wing span over missiles	8·13 m (26 ft 8 in)
Wing area, gross	17·28 m² (186 sq ft)
Length overall	14·78 m (48 ft 6 in)
Height overall	4·52 m (14 ft 10 in)

WEIGHTS:
Weight empty	5,089 kg (11,220 lb)
Max internal fuel	2,014 kg (4,440 lb)
Max external weapons	3,175 kg (7,000 lb)
T-O weight 'clean'	7,761 kg (17,110 lb)
Max T-O weight	11,857 kg (26,140 lb)

PERFORMANCE (estimated):
Max level speed at height	Mach 2·1
Max rate of climb at S/L	15,331 m (50,300 ft)/min
Time to 12,190 m (40,000 ft)	2 min 18 s
Service ceiling	16,765 m (55,000 ft)
T-O run (S/L, ISA)	442 m (1,450 ft)

Operational radius:
combat air patrol, two Sidewinders and three 1,041 litre (275 US gallon) drop-tanks, 77 min patrol and 20 min reserves at S/L
300 nm (555 km; 345 miles)
hi-lo-hi interdiction, with above load plus seven Mk 82 bombs, allowances for 5 min combat and 20 min reserves at S/L 360 nm (667 km; 414 miles)

Mockup of two-seat version of F/A-18L at 1979 Paris Air Show

Prototype for the Northrop F-18L takes off at Edwards AFB on a Spanish Air Force evaluation flight

NORTHROP F/A-18L

The F/A-18L is a multi-role land-based version of the US Navy's F/A-18 Hornet carrier-suitable combat aircraft, for which McDonnell Douglas (which see) is prime contractor. Both aircraft are derivatives of the YF-17 twin-engined fighter prototypes, which represented Northrop's submission in the US Air Force's Lightweight Fighter (LWF) prototype programme. In the case of the F/A-18 Hornet production programme, Northrop's share of the work is approximately 40 per cent, that of McDonnell Douglas approximately 60 per cent. The percentages are reversed in the F/A-18L programme, for which Northrop is prime contractor.

The land-based F/A-18L and carrier-suitable F/A-18 Hornet are about 80-90 per cent common in high-value/high-usage spare parts, with the same General Electric F404 engines. The F/A-18L is, however, considerably lighter in terms of empty weight as a result of the deletion of specifically-naval equipment and requirements, such as the heavy-duty landing gear and arrester hook needed for deck operations. This makes it possible for the land-based version to carry up to 9,000 kg (19,840 lb) of stores on 11 weapon stations.

A two-seat version of the F/A-18L is also available, and would be capable of both transitional training and full tactical employment.

The description and dimensions given for the F/A-18 Hornet apply generally to the F/A-18L.

PERFORMANCE (estimated, F-18L in basic air-to-air interception configuration):
Max level speed, with afterburning	in Mach 2 class
Max level speed, without afterburning, with two Sidewinders	above Mach 1
Approach speed	115 knots (213 km/h; 132 mph)
Stalling speed at air-to-air landing weight	92 knots (171 km/h; 106 mph)
Max rate of climb at S/L (50% fuel, two Sidewinders)	more than 18,290 m (60,000 ft)/min

T-O run (two Sidewinders):
with afterburning	275 m (900 ft)
without afterburning	396 m (1,300 ft)

T-O run (7,257 kg; 16,000 lb external load), with afterburning 670 m (2,200 ft)
Landing run (without brake chute)	518 m (1,700 ft)

Combat radius more than 700 nm (1,295 km; 805 miles)
Ferry range more than 2,500 nm (4,630 km; 2,875 miles)
g limit (60% fuel) +9

OMAC
OMAC INC

Stead Airport, PO Box 60250, Reno, Nevada 89506
Telephone: (702) 972 3273
PRESIDENT: Carl Parise
VICE-PRESIDENT: Larry Heuberger

This relatively new company has been founded by Larry Heuberger and industrialist Carl Parise. Larry Heuberger was William Lear's project engineer in the early days of the Learjet 23 and 24, and chief engineer on the Lear Star 600. OMAC's aim is to develop a new low-cost high-performance and economical six/eight-seat turboprop-powered business aircraft of canard configuration. A full-size mockup was exhibited at the NBAA display at Atlanta, Georgia, in September 1979. A prototype was scheduled for rollout in mid-Summer 1980, with type certification and initial deliveries following in early 1981. All components and assemblies for production aircraft will be contracted out, leaving OMAC responsible for final assembly and flight testing.

OMAC I

TYPE: Lightweight business aircraft.

WINGS: Cantilever high-wing monoplane, with 45° swept inboard leading-edge and 10° swept constant-chord outer wing panels. Aerofoil section NACA 64₁-212 (Mod B). Dihedral 1° 30'. Conventional two-spar structure of light alloy, with H-section extruded front spar. Hydraulically-operated half-span trailing-edge plain flaps. Half-span cable-actuated ailerons. Trim tab in port aileron. Winglets fitted at wingtips, each carrying a rudder with 25° of outward movement.

Model of OMAC I lightweight turboprop-powered business aircraft *(Howard Levy)*

FUSELAGE: Conventional light alloy semi-monocoque pressurised structure.

FOREPLANE: Low-set constant-chord cantilever monoplane. Aerofoil section NACA 54₁-212 (Mod B). Conventional two-spar light alloy structure. Both spars of extruded H section. Full-span elevator each side. Trim tab in each elevator, electrically and manually actuated, and spring-interlocked with flaps for automatic trimming.

LANDING GEAR: Hydraulically-retractable tricycle type. Steerable nosewheel retracts forward. Oleo-pneumatic shock-absorber with shimmy damper on nosewheel.

Main units have tubular spring steel legs. Nosewheel tyre size 6·00-6. Main wheels have heavy-duty tyres size 17·5-6·25 × 6. Heavy-duty brakes.

POWER PLANT: One 522 kW (700 shp) Avco Lycoming LTP 101-700A-A1 turboprop engine, driving a three-blade reversible-pitch metal pusher propeller, with 'Q' tips and Beta control. Fuel in wing leading-edge and aft-fuselage main feed tank, with combined capacity of 1,090 litres (288 US gallons). Refuelling points on wing upper surface.

ACCOMMODATION: Three alternative layouts for a pilot and one, six or seven passengers. Two forward-facing seats for pilot and co-pilot/passenger, with two or three individual reclining and swivelling seats, and three-seat bench at rear of cabin. Baggage compartment aft of rear seats, with space for toilet with privacy curtain. Split-type airstair door on port side. Emergency exit on starboard side.

SYSTEMS: Max cabin pressure differential 0·38 bars (5·5 lb/sq in). Hydraulic system with electrically-powered pump for operation of flaps, landing gear and brakes. Electrical system. Oxygen system.

AVIONICS: Bendix BX 2000 and RDR 160 radar standard.

DIMENSIONS, EXTERNAL:

Wing span	10·67 m (35 ft 0 in)
Foreplane span	4·06 m (13 ft 4 in)
Length overall	8·99 m (29 ft 6 in)
Height overall	3·35 m (11 ft 0 in)
Wheel track	2·59 m (8 ft 6 in)
Wheelbase	4·69 m (15 ft 4¾ in)
Propeller diameter	2·29 m (7 ft 6 in)

DIMENSIONS, INTERNAL:

Cabin: Length	4·52 m (14 ft 10 in)
Max height	1·37 m (4 ft 6 in)
Max width	1·42 m (4 ft 8 in)

PERFORMANCE (estimated, at max T-O weight):

Max cruising speed at 6,100 m (20,000 ft)	257 knots (476 km/h; 296 mph)
Econ cruising speed at 9,145 m (30,000 ft)	217 knots (402 km/h; 250 mph)
Range with max fuel, 1 h hold	2,345 nm (4,345 km; 2,700 miles)

OMNIONICS

Meritt Island, Florida

In 1965, Omnionics began development of an all-glassfibre amphibian for commuter and business transport operation. This has evolved as the Dolphinair, of which available details follow:

OMNIONICS DOLPHINAIR

The general configuration of this unique transport amphibian is shown in the accompanying photograph of a model displayed in 1979. The sweptback high-mounted wings carry at each wingtip a large fixed float/fuel tank, with an aerofoil, similar to a large NASA winglet, mounted on the upper surface. Outboard of this is a smaller winglet at the tip of a wing extension which can retract into or extend from the main wing structure, to give a variable span and area. Wing section will be a 12% NACA aerofoil.

The Dolphinair is to be powered by two Garrett-AiResearch ATF3 turbofan engines (each 22·7 kN; 5,100 lb st), each pod-mounted above the side of the rear fuselage. The cabin is nearly 7·3 m (24 ft) long, with a max headroom and width of 1·83 m (6 ft), to accommodate up to 12 passengers in executive layout or 20 commuters.

In mid-1979, moulds were being made for construction of Kevlar, carbon fibre and glassfibre airframe components. The prototype Dolphinair is expected to be completed in mid-1981, and to fly for the first time at the beginning of 1982.

DIMENSIONS, EXTERNAL:

Wing span: extensions out	24·38 m (80 ft 0 in)
extensions in	13·56 m (44 ft 6 in)

Model of the Omnionics Dolphinair variable-span amphibian *(Howard Levy)*

Wing aspect ratio: extensions out	11·3
extensions in	4·5

WEIGHT:

Max T-O weight	11,340 kg (25,000 lb)

PERFORMANCE (estimated):

Max cruising speed	Mach 0·85
Approach speed	90 knots (167 km/h; 104 mph)
Max rate of climb at S/L	2,750 m (9,000 ft)/min
Service ceiling	18,275 m (60,000 ft)
Service ceiling, one engine out	9,150 m (30,000 ft)
Landing run, ashore	610 m (2,000 ft)
Range with max fuel, 45 min reserves	3,000 nm (5,550 km; 3,450 miles)

PIASECKI
PIASECKI AIRCRAFT CORPORATION

HEAD OFFICE AND WORKS: Island Road, International Airport, Philadelphia, Pennsylvania 19153
Telephone: (215) 365 2222
DIRECTORS:
Virgil Kauffman
Donald N. Meyers
Arthur J. Kania
J. Mecallef
F. N. Piasecki
PRESIDENT: Frank N. Piasecki
VICE-PRESIDENT: Donald N. Meyers (Engineering)
SECRETARY: Arthur J. Kania
INDUSTRIAL ENGINEERING: K. R. Meenen

The Piasecki Aircraft Corporation was formed in 1955 by Mr Frank Piasecki, who was formerly Chairman of the Board and President of the Piasecki Helicopter Corporation (now the Boeing Vertol Company).

PIASECKI HELI-STAT

A Heli-Stat is a hybrid VTOL vehicle which links the envelope of a lighter-than-air craft with current-technology helicopters, the aerostat providing static lift to support approximately the full empty weight of the entire assembly. The helicopters furnish the lift to support the payload, as well as providing propulsion and control, with adequate control forces to enable the Heli-Stat to hover with precision, a characteristic with which conventional airships cannot comply.

Details of an early Heli-Stat project can be found in the 1977-78 *Jane's*. By 1979 Piasecki had started engineering work on a prototype, designated **Model 97-34J** and named **Logger**, and has since received a contract from the US Navy to design, build and fly this vehicle for use by the US Forest Service. It is intended to demonstrate the advantages of such a vehicle for tasks such as the economic transportation of otherwise inaccessible timber over distances of up to 8·7 nm (16 km; 10 miles).

FUSELAGE: Frame structure of light alloy and composite materials to provide mountings for four Sikorsky SH-34J helicopters, on outriggers which will provide adequate clearance for their rotors and ensure that they are not blanketed by the aerostat envelope. In addition, this structure serves as the basic framework on which the cargo hold is built.

TAIL UNIT: Comprises light alloy frame with fabric covering, and mounts a composite control surface which serves the dual roles of rudder and elevator.

LANDING GEAR: Four non-retractable units, each with twin wheels, are mounted one at each corner of the basic fuselage frame.

POWER PLANT: Basically four Sikorsky SH-34J helicopters without landing gear, each powered by a 1,137 kW (1,525 hp) Wright R-1820-84A radial aircooled engine, and each driving the conventional rotor system of the SH-34J, last described in the 1970-71 *Jane's*. Total combined fuel capacity 4,640 litres (1,226 US gallons).

ACCOMMODATION: Crew of four, comprising a master pilot in the port aft helicopter, and a flight engineer in each of the other helicopters. Controls of the four helicopters linked by a fly-by-wire system.

SYSTEMS: Duplicated hydraulic system in each helicopter, pressure 103·5 bars (1,500 lb/sq in), for operation of rotor controls. Electrical system includes four 28V 400A engine-driven DC generators, and eight 115V 400Hz AC inverters in the helicopters.

EQUIPMENT: Includes full blind-flying instrumentation.

DIMENSIONS, ENVELOPE:

Length overall	74·07 m (243 ft 0 in)
Max diameter	26·06 m (85 ft 6 in)

DIMENSIONS, EXTERNAL:

Width overall, rotors turning	60·05 m (197 ft 0 in)
Width overall, rotor blades folded	45·72 m (150 ft 0 in)
Wheel track	24·17 m (79 ft 3½ in)
Wheelbase	13·41 m (44 ft 0 in)

DIMENSION, INTERNAL:
Freight hold will accept two containers, each 2·44 × 2·44 × 12·19 m (8 × 8 × 40 ft)

Volume (total)	145·0 m³ (5,120 cu ft)

AREA:

Rotor discs (total)	915·3 m² (9,852 sq ft)

WEIGHTS (estimated):

Weight empty	24,895 kg (54,885 lb)
Max payload	23,586 kg (52,000 lb)
Max fuel load	4,646 kg (10,244 lb)
Max hovering weight	50,469 kg (111,265 lb)
Max landing weight	30,267 kg (66,729 lb)

Artist's impression of a Heli-Stat hauling timber

PERFORMANCE (estimated, at max T-O weight):

Max level speed at S/L	71 knots (132 km/h; 82 mph)
Max cruising speed at S/L	61 knots (113 km/h; 70 mph)
Max rate of climb at S/L	290 m (950 ft)/min
Ballonet ceiling	3,810 m (12,500 ft)
Range with max fuel, 10% reserves	1,784 nm (3,307 km; 2,055 miles)
Range with max payload, 10% reserves	43 nm (80 km; 50 miles)

PIPER

PIPER AIRCRAFT CORPORATION (Subsidiary of Bangor Punta Corporation)

HEAD OFFICE AND WORKS: Lock Haven, Pennsylvania 17745
Telephone: (717) 748 6711
Telex: 841425

OTHER WORKS:
Vero Beach, Florida 32960
Lakeland, Florida 33801
Piper, Pennsylvania 16845
Renovo, Pennsylvania 17764
Santa Maria, California 93454

BOARD OF DIRECTORS:
Max E. Bleck
Stephen Galle
Thomas W. Gillespie
J. Lynn Helms
Sheldon Kaplan
Alfred J. Koontz Jr (Finance)
Jonathan Lushing
Dudley C. Phillips (General Counsel)
James E. Stewart
David H. Street
David W. Wallace

PRESIDENT AND CHIEF EXECUTIVE OFFICER: Max E. Bleck
CHAIRMAN OF THE BOARD: J. Lynn Helms
EXECUTIVE VICE-PRESIDENT:
Robert D. Dickerson
SENIOR VICE-PRESIDENTS:
Thomas W. Gillespie Jr (Marketing and Sales)
Alfred J. Koontz Jr (Finance)
Dudley C. Phillips (General Counsel)
GROUP VICE-PRESIDENTS:
Vincent J. Montuoro (Vero Beach and Santa Maria Divisions)
Harry M. Graham (Lakeland and Lock Haven Divisions)
VICE-PRESIDENTS:
Marion J. Dees Jr (Engineering)
Findley A. Estlick (Plant Facilities & Foreign Assembly Operations)
C. Raymond Johnson (Sales)
CONTROLLER: Jack J. Cattoni
SECRETARY: Morgan C. Brown III
TREASURER: John R. Leeson
ADMINISTRATOR, CORPORATE COMMUNICATIONS:
John W. Alter

In April 1976, Piper produced its 100,000th aircraft, a twin-turboprop Cheyenne.

Vero Beach is responsible for the experimental development of Piper aircraft and also houses one of the company's Plastics Divisions. Lock Haven also has R & D facilities for aircraft built at Lock Haven.

Piper operates also four other plants. The first two are at Piper, Pennsylvania, where sheet metal parts are formed, and Renovo, Pennsylvania, which makes plastics components; the third is at Lakeland, Florida, where PA-31 aircraft are in production; the fourth, at Santa Maria, California, is the former Ted Smith Aerostar Corporation, which Piper acquired in 1978.

Optional equipment on several current models includes a choice of four automatic flight systems, details of which have been given in earlier editions of *Jane's*.

In 1971, 1974 and 1977 respectively, Piper announced agreements with Chincul SA (which see) for the manufacture of a broad range of Piper products in Argentina; with EMBRAER (which see) for the development, production and marketing of Piper aircraft in Brazil; and with PZL Mielec (which see) of Poland to assemble, manufacture and distribute the Piper Seneca II light twin-engined aircraft in that country.

PIPER (PA-18-150) SUPER CUB

The original PA-18 with 67 kW (90 hp) Continental C90-12F engine received FAA Type Approval on 18 November 1949. The PA-18-150, PA-18A-150 agricultural aircraft and PA-18S and PA-18AS seaplanes were all approved on 1 October 1954.

The current international height record in Class C1b (aircraft with T-O weight of 500-1,000 kg) is held by Miss C. Bayley of the USA, who climbed to a height of 9,206 m (30,203 ft) in a Super Cub with 93·2 kW (125 hp) Lycoming engine, on 4 January 1951.

Five factory-installed avionics packages are available optionally for the Super Cub, comprising nav/coms and associated equipment by Collins, Edo-Aire Mitchell, King and Narco. Optional items available from the same manufacturers, plus United, include altitude reporting/digitisers, encoding altimeters, and transponders.

More than 40,000 examples of the PA-18 Cub and its predecessors have been delivered.

TYPE: Two-seat light cabin monoplane.
WINGS: Braced high-wing monoplane, with steel tube V bracing struts each side. Wing section USA 35B. Thickness/chord ratio 12%. Dihedral 1°. No incidence at mean aerodynamic chord. Total washout of 3° 18'.

Aluminium spars and ribs, aluminium sheet leading-edge and aileron false spar, wingtip bow of ash, with Dacron covering overall and fire-resistant Duraclad plastic finish. Plain ailerons and trailing-edge flaps of light alloy construction.
FUSELAGE: Rectangular welded steel tube structure covered with Dacron. Fire-resistant Duraclad plastic finish.
TAIL UNIT: Wire-braced structure of welded steel tubes and channels, covered with Dacron. Fire-resistant Duraclad plastic finish. Tailplane incidence variable for trimming. Balanced rudder and elevators.
LANDING GEAR: Non-retractable tailwheel type. Two side Vs and half axles hinged to bottom of fuselage. Rubber cord shock-absorption. Main-wheel tyres size 6·00-6 four-ply, with 7·00-6 six-ply, or 8·00-6 four-ply, optional. Steerable leaf-spring tailwheel. Dual expanding brakes. Parking brake.
POWER PLANT: One 112 kW (150 hp) Avco Lycoming O-320 flat-four engine, driving a Sensenich two-blade fixed-pitch metal propeller with spinner. Steel tube engine mounting is hinged at firewall, allowing it to be swung to port for access to rear of engine. One 68 litre (18 US gallon) metal fuel tank in each wing. Total fuel capacity 136 litres (36 US gallons), of which 135·5 litres (35·8 US gallons) are usable. Refuelling points on top of wing.
ACCOMMODATION: Enclosed cabin seating two in tandem with dual controls. Adjustable front seat. Rear seat quickly removable for cargo carrying. Inertia-reel shoulder harness and seat belts standard for front and rear seats. Heater and adjustable cool-air vent. Downward-hinged door on starboard side, and upward-hinged window above, can be opened in flight. Sliding windows on port side. Baggage compartments aft of rear seat, capacity 22 kg (50 lb).
SYSTEMS: Electrical system, comprising 14V 60A alternator, 12V 35Ah battery, optional. Vacuum system for gyro driven instruments optional.
AVIONICS AND EQUIPMENT: In addition to the optional factory-installed avionics packages mentioned, Edo-Aire Mitchell, King, Narco and United avionics items are available optionally. Standard equipment includes a recording tachometer, sensitive altimeter, provisions for emergency locator transmitter, stall warning device, seat belts and shoulder safety belts, engine quick oil drain, and tiedown rings. Optional equipment includes blind-flying instrumentation, clock, vertical speed indicator, outside air temperature gauge, emergency locator transmitter, control locks, cabin fire extinguisher, internal corrosion proofing, stainless steel control cables, dome light, instrument panel lights, landing light, navigation lights, strobe light, metallising and polyurethane finish for steel components, and glider tow hook.

DIMENSIONS, EXTERNAL:
Wing span	10·73 m (35 ft 2½ in)
Wing chord (constant)	1·60 m (5 ft 3 in)
Wing aspect ratio	7
Length overall	6·88 m (22 ft 7 in)
Height overall	2·04 m (6 ft 8½ in)
Tailplane span	3·20 m (10 ft 6 in)
Wheel track	1·84 m (6 ft 0½ in)
Propeller diameter	1·88 m (6 ft 2 in)

DIMENSION, INTERNAL:
Baggage compartment	0·51 m³ (18 cu ft)

AREAS:
Wings, gross	16·58 m² (178·5 sq ft)
Ailerons (total)	1·75 m² (18·80 sq ft)
Trailing-edge flaps (total)	1·07 m² (11·50 sq ft)
Fin	0·43 m² (4·66 sq ft)
Rudder	0·63 m² (6·76 sq ft)
Tailplane	1·40 m² (15·10 sq ft)
Elevators	1·09 m² (11·70 sq ft)

WEIGHTS AND LOADINGS (N: Normal category; R: Restricted, agricultural, category):
Weight empty: N, R	446 kg (983 lb)
Max T-O and landing weight: N	794 kg (1,750 lb)
R	939 kg (2,070 lb)
Max wing loading: N	48·8 kg/m² (10·0 lb/sq ft)
R	56·64 kg/m² (11·6 lb/sq ft)
Max power loading: N	7·09 kg/kW (11·6 lb/hp)
R	8·38 kg/kW (13·8 lb/hp)

PERFORMANCE (at max T-O weight: N: Normal category; R: Restricted, agricultural, category):
Never-exceed speed:	
N, R	132 knots (246 km/h; 153 mph)
Max level speed: N	113 knots (209 km/h; 130 mph)
Max cruising speed, 75% power at 1,525 m (5,000 ft):	
N	100 knots (185 km/h; 115 mph)
R	91 knots (169 km/h; 105 mph)
Stalling speed, flaps down:	
N	37 knots (69 km/h; 43 mph)
R	39 knots (73 km/h; 45 mph)
Max rate of climb at S/L: N	293 m (960 ft)/min
R	232 m (760 ft)/min
Service ceiling: N	5,795 m (19,000 ft)
R	5,180 m (17,000 ft)
Absolute ceiling: N	6,492 m (21,300 ft)
T-O run: N	61 m (200 ft)
R	92 m (300 ft)
T-O to 15 m (50 ft): N	153 m (500 ft)
R	290 m (950 ft)
Landing from 15 m (50 ft): N	270 m (885 ft)
R	267 m (875 ft)
Landing run: N	107 m (350 ft)
R	125 m (410 ft)
Range with max fuel and max payload, 75% power at optimum altitude: N	400 nm (741 km; 460 miles)
R	312 nm (580 km; 360 miles)

PIPER (PA-23-250) AZTEC F

The 1980 version of the Aztec, designated Model F, has a number of improvements as standard. These include a new pitch control configuration to reduce control forces, redesigned seats, and a wider range of colours and fabrics for interior finish. The Aztec is available in basic form and in several optional configurations, as follows:

Custom Aztec. As basic model, described in detail, with addition of true airspeed indicator, alternate instrument static source and window curtains; adding 1·4 kg (3 lb) to basic empty weight.

Sportsman Aztec. As Custom model, with addition of external power socket; adding 4·5 kg (10 lb) to basic empty weight.

Professional Aztec. As Sportsman model, with addition of electrically heated windscreen panel, electrical propeller de-icing, pneumatic de-icing boots on wings and tail, and wing ice inspection light; adding 23·6 kg (52·1 lb) to basic empty weight.

Turbo Aztec. Turbocharged version, described separately.

Each of the above versions can be fitted with one of eight factory-installed avionics packages, including nav/coms, ADF, DME, glideslope and marker beacon receivers, transponder, autopilot, and associated equipment by Bendix, Collins, Edo-Aire Mitchell, King, Narco, Piper and SunAir.

The Aztec received FAA Type Approval as a five-seat aircraft on 18 September 1959, and with six seats on 15 December 1961.

The prototype of a floatplane version of the Aztec was produced as a joint project by Melridge Aviation of Vancouver, Washington, and Jobmaster Company Inc of Seattle. Fitted with Edo 4930 floats, this aircraft can take off from calm water in 20 seconds at max T-O weight of 2,360 kg (5,200 lb). Useful load is 816 kg (1,800 lb), permitting a six-passenger load with 455 litres (120 US gallons) of fuel. To simplify docking and loading from either side, a door was designed for installation on the port side, by the pilot's seat, and is part of the kit offered by Melridge Aviation to permit conversion in the field.

TYPE: Six-seat twin-engined executive transport.

Piper Super Cub two-seat light cabin monoplane (Avco Lycoming O-320 engine)

WINGS: Cantilever low-wing monoplane. Wing section USA 35-B (modified). Thickness/chord ratio 14%. Dihedral 5°. Incidence 0° at root, −1° 12′ at mean chord. All-metal stressed-skin structure, with heavy stepped-down main spar, front and rear auxiliary spars, ribs, stringers and detachable wingtips. Plain all-metal ailerons and hydraulically-actuated flaps. Optional Goodrich de-icing system.

FUSELAGE: Basic aluminium semi-monocoque structure with welded steel tube truss around cabin. Bob weight in nose to provide more balanced control forces in pitch.

TAIL UNIT: Cantilever all-metal structure with swept fin and all-moving horizontal surfaces which interconnect mechanically with the flap system to avoid need for pitch re-trim when flaps are lowered. Trim tab in rudder. Geared anti-servo tab in horizontal surfaces. Optional Goodrich de-icing system.

LANDING GEAR: Retractable tricycle type. Hydraulic retraction, with CO_2 emergency extension system. Nosewheel retracts rearward, main wheels forward. Wheel doors enclose landing gear fully when retracted. Electrol oleo shock-absorber struts. Cleveland main wheels, size 6·00-6, with size 7·00-6 8-ply tyres. Cleveland steerable nosewheel, size 6·00-6, with 6·00-6 4-ply tyre. Hydraulic disc brakes. Parking brake.

POWER PLANT: Two 186·5 kW (250 hp) Avco Lycoming IO-540-C4B5 flat-six engines, each driving a Hartzell HC-E2YK-2RB two-blade constant-speed fully-feathering metal propeller. Two rubber fuel cells in each wing with NACA type anti-icing non-siphoning vents. Total standard fuel capacity 544 litres (144 US gallons); 519 litres (137·2 US gallons) usable. Refuelling points above wings. Two internal wingtip fuel tanks optional, with total capacity of 151 litres (40 US gallons). Oil capacity 22·7 litres (6 US gallons). Propeller synchroniser and electrical de-icing system optional.

ACCOMMODATION: Six persons on two pairs of adjustable individual seats and rear bench seat. Shoulder harnesses for pilot's and co-pilot's seat; seat belts for all seats. Dual controls standard. Individual seat lights and controllable overhead ventilation. 35,000 BTU heater with four adjustable cool/warm air outlets and two windscreen defrosters. Heated windscreen optional. Double pane windows. Passenger step. Door at front of cabin on starboard side. Emergency exit at rear on port side. Centre and rear seats removable to provide space for stretcher, survey camera or up to 725 kg (1,600 lb) of freight. Rear cabin bulkhead removable for stretcher and cargo loading via rear baggage door. Baggage compartments at rear of cabin and in nose, with tiedown fittings, each with capacity of 68 kg (150 lb). Baggage doors on starboard side; rear one enlarged on current aircraft, for stretcher loading. Armrests, cabin dome light, individual reading lights, coat hooks, complete soundproofing and two sun visors. Seat headrests and leather upholstery optional.

SYSTEMS: Hydraulic system with dual engine-driven pumps, pressure 79 bars (1,150 lb/sq in), for landing gear and flaps. Two 70A 28V alternators. 24V 17Ah battery. 28V 25Ah battery optional. Oxygen system, with 3·23 m³ (114 cu ft) bottle and six outlets, optional.

AVIONICS AND EQUIPMENT: Optional avionics, in addition to items included in factory-installed packages, include automatic flight system/flight directors, encoding altimeters, radar and radio altimeters, radio telephone, RNAV, and weather radar. Standard equipment includes full blind-flying instrumentation with 3 in pictorial rate of turn indicator; artificial horizon and directional gyro; clock; dual recording tachometers/hour meters; outside air temperature gauge; sensitive altimeter; dual vacuum gauges; cabin and baggage door locks; nosewheel safety mirror; heated pitot head; door-ajar indicator lights; stall warning device; baggage compartment, cabin dome, instrument, map, reading, anti-collision, landing, navigation and taxi lights; quick oil drains; jack pads; tiedown rings; towbar; and a choice of exterior trims. Optional items as mentioned under model listings, plus co-pilot's blind-flying instrumentation and toe-brakes, exhaust gas temperature gauge, emergency locator transmitter, inertia reel shoulder safety belts for rear seats, cabin fire extinguisher, tinted windows, leather upholstery, instrument panel coloured light, strobe tail light, propeller ice protection shields, and zinc chromate treatment of aluminium parts.

DIMENSIONS, EXTERNAL:

Wing span	11·37 m (37 ft 3¾ in)
Wing chord (constant)	1·70 m (5 ft 7 in)
Wing aspect ratio	6·8
Length overall	9·52 m (31 ft 2⅝ in)
Height overall	3·07 m (10 ft 1 in)
Tailplane span	3·81 m (12 ft 6 in)
Wheel track	3·45 m (11 ft 4 in)
Wheelbase	2·29 m (7 ft 6 in)
Propeller diameter	1·96 m (6 ft 5 in)
Cabin door: Height	0·97 m (3 ft 2 in)
Width	0·84 m (2 ft 9 in)
Baggage compartment door (front):	
Height	0·49 m (1 ft 7½ in)
Width	0·77 m (2 ft 6½ in)
Baggage compartment door (rear):	
Height	0·76 m (2 ft 6 in)
Width	0·79 m (2 ft 7 in)

Piper Aztec F six-seat twin-engined executive transport

DIMENSIONS, INTERNAL:

Cabin: Length	2·59 m (8 ft 6 in)
Max width	1·14 m (3 ft 9 in)
Max height	1·28 m (4 ft 2½ in)
Baggage compartments: front	0·49 m³ (17·4 cu ft)
rear	0·65 m³ (23·0 cu ft)
Max cargo space, incl baggage compartments	
	3·45 m³ (122 cu ft)

AREAS:

Wings, gross	19·23 m² (207·0 sq ft)
Ailerons (total)	0·77 m² (8·38 sq ft)
Trailing-edge flaps (total)	1·54 m² (16·60 sq ft)
Fin	1·37 m² (14·80 sq ft)
Rudder	0·96 m² (10·30 sq ft)
Horizontal surfaces (total)	3·70 m² (39·80 sq ft)

WEIGHTS AND LOADINGS:

Weight empty	1,444 kg (3,183 lb)
Max T-O and ramp weight	2,360 kg (5,200 lb)
Max landing weight	2,241 kg (4,940 lb)
Max wing loading	122·7 kg/m² (25·12 lb/sq ft)
Max power loading	6·33 kg/kW (10·4 lb/hp)

PERFORMANCE (at max T-O weight):

Never-exceed speed	240 knots (446 km/h; 277 mph)
Max level speed	187 knots (346 km/h; 215 mph)
Normal cruising speed at 1,175 m (3,850 ft)	
	179 knots (332 km/h; 206 mph)
Intermediate cruising speed at 1,830 m (6,000 ft)	
	176 knots (327 km/h; 203 mph)
Econ cruising speed at 1,905 m (6,250 ft)	
	170 knots (315 km/h; 196 mph)
Long-range cruising speed at 3,290 m (10,800 ft)	
	162 knots (301 km/h; 187 mph)
Stalling speed, power off, flaps up	
	61 knots (113 km/h; 70 mph)
Stalling speed, power off, flaps down	
	54·5 knots (101 km/h; 63 mph)
Max rate of climb at S/L	426 m (1,400 ft)/min
Rate of climb at S/L, one engine out	
	72 m (235 ft)/min
Service ceiling	5,365 m (17,600 ft)
Service ceiling, one engine out	1,465 m (4,800 ft)
T-O run, normal	302 m (990 ft)
T-O run, short-field	288 m (945 ft)
T-O to 15 m (50 ft), normal	604 m (1,980 ft)
T-O to 15 m (50 ft), short-field	517 m (1,695 ft)
Landing from 15 m (50 ft), normal	483 m (1,585 ft)
Landing from 15 m (50 ft), short run	399 m (1,310 ft)
Landing run, normal	232 m (760 ft)
Landing run, short-field	204 m (670 ft)

Range with standard max fuel, allowances for start, taxi, T-O, climb, and 45 min reserves at long-range cruise power:

Intermediate cruise power
790 nm (1,464 km; 910 miles)
Econ cruise power 830 nm (1,538 km; 956 miles)
Long-range cruise power at 2,135 m (7,000 ft)
985 nm (1,825 km; 1,134 miles)

Range with optional max fuel, allowances as above:
Intermediate cruise power
1,060 nm (1,963 km; 1,220 miles)
Econ cruise power
1,110 nm (2,055 km; 1,277 miles)
Long-range cruise power at 2,135 m (7,000 ft)
1,320 nm (2,444 km; 1,519 miles)

PIPER (PA-23T-250) TURBO AZTEC F

The Turbo Aztec F is identical in every way with the Aztec F, except that it has 186·5 kW (250 hp) Avco Lycoming TIO-540-C1A engines, fitted with the Garrett-AiResearch turbocharging system. These specially modified engines allow a turbo cruise setting at 2,400 rpm, providing a constant manifold pressure from sea level to 6,705 m (22,000 ft), and result in considerably improved performance.

Standard equipment includes a density controller to prevent inadvertent overboost of the engines at full throttle, and a differential pressure controller to provide constant manifold pressure during cruising flight. An oxygen system with 3·23 m³ (114 cu ft) bottle and six outlets is optional.

WEIGHTS AND LOADINGS:
As for Aztec F, except:
Weight empty (standard)   1,507 kg (3,322 lb)

PERFORMANCE (at max T-O weight):
As for Aztec F, except:
Max level speed at 5,640 m (18,500 ft)
220 knots (407 km/h; 253 mph)
Turbo cruising speed at 6,705 m (22,000 ft)
215 knots (399 km/h; 248 mph)
Intermediate cruising speed at 7,315 m (24,000 ft)
208 knots (384 km/h; 239 mph)
Econ cruising speed at 7,315 m (24,000 ft)
193 knots (357 km/h; 222 mph)
Long-range cruising speed at 6,100 m (20,000 ft)
174 knots (322 km/h; 200 mph)
Max rate of climb at S/L   448 m (1,470 ft)/min
Rate of climb at S/L, one engine out
68 m (225 ft)/min
Service ceiling   over 7,315 m (24,000 ft)
Service ceiling, one engine out   4,055 m (13,300 ft)
Range with standard max fuel, allowances for start, taxi, T-O, climb, and 45 min reserves at long-range cruise power:
Turbo cruising speed
695 nm (1,287 km; 800 miles)
Intermediate cruising speed
740 nm (1,371 km; 852 miles)
Econ cruising speed
780 nm (1,445 km; 898 miles)
Long-range cruising speed
835 nm (1,548 km; 962 miles)
Range with optional max fuel, allowances as above:
Turbo cruising speed
947 nm (1,753 km; 1,089 miles)
Intermediate cruising speed
1,020 nm (1,889 km; 1,173 miles)
Econ cruising speed
1,075 nm (1,990 km; 1,237 miles)
Long-range cruising speed
1,145 nm (2,120 km; 1,317 miles)

PIPER (PA-25-235) PAWNEE D

The current version of the Pawnee D is available with five optional factory-installed avionics packages comprising nav/coms and associated equipment by Collins, Edo-Aire Mitchell, King and Narco.

TYPE: Single-seat agricultural monoplane.

WINGS: Braced low-wing monoplane. Streamlined V bracing struts on each side of fuselage, with additional short support struts. Wing section USA 35B (modified). Thickness/chord ratio 12%. Dihedral 7°. Incidence 1° 18′ at mean aerodynamic chord. Wings are of fabric-covered aluminium construction, with fire-resistant Duraclad plastic finish. Trailing-edge flaps and ailerons of light alloy construction. No trim tabs.

FUSELAGE: Basically rectangular-section welded steel tube structure, with fabric covering and Duraclad plastic finish, except for removable metal underskin and removable metal top of rear fuselage. Glassfibre engine cowling.

TAIL UNIT: Wire-braced steel tube structure with fabric covering and Duraclad plastic finish. Fixed-incidence tailplane. Balanced rudder and elevators. No trim tabs. Cable from top of cockpit to top of rudder to deflect wires and cables.

LANDING GEAR: Non-retractable tailwheel type. Bungee rubber shock-absorbers. Main gear has two side Vs and half-axles hinged to centreline of underside of fuselage.

Cleveland 40-84A main wheels, with 8·00-6 4-ply tyres. Cleveland type 30-41 toe-actuated hydraulic brakes. Parking brake. Wire-cutters on leading-edge of each side V. Scott 200 mm (8 in) steerable tailwheel.

POWER PLANT: One 175 kW (235 hp) (derated) Avco Lycoming O-540 flat-six engine, driving a McCauley Type 1A200/FA84 two-blade fixed-pitch metal propeller with spinner. Fuel tank in each wing, with combined capacity of 145·7 litres (38·5 US gallons), of which 136 litres (36 US gallons) are usable. Oil capacity 11·5 litres (3 US gallons).

ACCOMMODATION: Pilot on adjustable seat in specially-strengthened enclosed cockpit, with steel tube overturn structure. Heavy-duty safety belt and shoulder harness with inertia reel. Wire-cutter mounted on centre of windscreen. Combined window and door on each side, hinged at bottom. Window assemblies jettisonable for emergency exit; quick-release hinge pins in side windows. Cabin is heated and ventilated. Adjustable cool air vents. Utility compartment under seat.

SYSTEMS: Electrical system includes a 14V 60A alternator, 12V 35Ah battery and a battery charging diode. Hydraulic system for brakes only.

AVIONICS AND EQUIPMENT: Optional avionics, additional to items included in factory-installed packages, add a transponder by each manufacturer. Standard equipment includes a non-corrosive hopper/tank, installed forward of cockpit and approximately on CG, volume of which is 0·59 m³ (21 cu ft) or 568 litres (150 US gallons), with capacity for 544 kg (1,200 lb) of dust; quick-change boom brackets, and quick dump valve; recording tachometer; sensitive altimeter; under-seat storage; low-fuel quantity warning light; provisions for emergency locator transmitter; engine bay fire extinguisher; full-flow oil filter; quick-drain oil sump; top-deck loading door; and tiedown rings. Optional high and low volume dispersal systems for wet or dry applications with associated equipment, side loading nozzle for liquid chemicals, electric turn and bank indicator, control lock, multi-directional inertia reel shoulder harness, emergency locator transmitter, hand held fire extinguisher, rotating beacon, landing light and navigation lights.

DIMENSIONS, EXTERNAL:

Wing span	11·02 m (36 ft 2 in)
Wing chord (constant)	1·60 m (5 ft 3 in)
Wing aspect ratio	7·15
Length overall	7·53 m (24 ft 8½ in)
Height overall	2·21 m (7 ft 3 in)
Tailplane span	2·90 m (9 ft 6 in)
Wheel track	2·13 m (7 ft 0 in)
Wheelbase	5·52 m (18 ft 1¼ in)
Propeller diameter	2·13 m (7 ft 0 in)

AREAS:

Wings, gross	17·0 m² (183 sq ft)
Ailerons (total)	1·78 m² (19·2 sq ft)
Trailing-edge flaps (total)	0·78 m² (8·4 sq ft)
Fin	0·35 m² (3·8 sq ft)
Rudder	0·64 m² (6·9 sq ft)
Tailplane	1·21 m² (13·0 sq ft)
Elevators	1·27 m² (13·7 sq ft)

WEIGHTS AND LOADINGS:

Weight empty:	
no dispersal equipment	726 kg (1,599 lb)
duster	746 kg (1,645 lb)
sprayer	749 kg (1,652 lb)
Max T-O and landing weight	1,315 kg (2,900 lb)
Max wing loading	77·15 kg/m² (15·8 lb/sq ft)
Max power loading	7·51 kg/kW (12·3 lb/hp)

PERFORMANCE (at max T-O weight, except where indicated):

Never-exceed speed	135 knots (251 km/h; 156 mph)
Max level speed at S/L:	
no dispersal equipment	
	108 knots (200 km/h; 124 mph)
duster	96 knots (177 km/h; 110 mph)
sprayer	102 knots (188 km/h; 117 mph)

Piper Pawnee D agricultural aircraft (Avco Lycoming O-540 flat-six engine)

Max cruising speed (75% power):	
no dispersal equipment	
	99 knots (183 km/h; 114 mph)
duster	87 knots (161 km/h; 100 mph)
sprayer	91 knots (169 km/h; 105 mph)
Stalling speed, flaps down	
	53 knots (98 km/h; 61 mph)
Stalling speed at normal landing weight of 771 kg (1,700 lb)	40 knots (74 km/h; 46 mph)
Max rate of climb at S/L:	
no dispersal equipment	213 m (700 ft)/min
duster	152 m (500 ft)/min
sprayer	192 m (630 ft)/min
T-O run: no dispersal equipment	239 m (785 ft)
duster	291 m (956 ft)
sprayer	244 m (800 ft)
T-O to 15 m (50 ft):	
no dispersal equipment	411 m (1,350 ft)
duster	448 m (1,470 ft)
sprayer	418 m (1,370 ft)
Max landing run	259 m (850 ft)
Range (75% power) with max fuel:	
no dispersal equipment	
	251 nm (467 km; 290 miles)
duster	221 nm (410 km; 255 miles)
sprayer	234 nm (434 km; 270 miles)

PIPER (PA-28-161) WARRIOR II

Design of the Warrior began in June 1972, an important feature being replacement of the earlier constant-chord wings of the Cherokee series by a longer-span wing with tapered outer panels. As a result of its introduction the Warrior, which at that time was essentially the same 112 kW (150 hp) engine as the discontinued Cherokee Cruiser, was certificated at a maximum T-O weight 79 kg (175 lb) greater. First flight of a prototype was made on 17 October 1972, and FAA certification of the original Model PA-28-151 was granted on 9 August 1973.

The current PA-28-161 Warrior II version, first flown on 27 August 1976, has a 119 kW (160 hp) engine which operates on 100 octane low-lead fuel.

Two groups of optional equipment are available for the current Warrior II as basic packages:

Custom. Includes blind-flying instrumentation with 3 in gyros; clock; outside air temperature gauge; rate of climb and true airspeed indicators; instrument panel white backlighting; overhead red spotlight; cabin dome, radio dimming, navigation, landing and taxi lights; rotating beacon; assist strap; aircraft step; engine primer system; quick oil drain; wheel fairings; and towbar; adding 19·7 kg (43·4 lb) to basic empty weight.

Executive. As Custom package less rotating beacon, plus pilot's vertically-adjustable seat, sun visors, alternate static source, heated pitot, emergency locator transmitter, strobe lights, external power socket, and 35Ah battery; adding 33·4 kg (73·7 lb) to basic empty weight.

In addition, eight optional avionics groups are available

for factory installation in the Warrior II, these including nav/coms, ADF, autopilot, glideslope and marker beacon receivers, and transponders by Collins, King, Narco and Piper: there is also an extensive range of optional avionics by these manufacturers, plus Bendix.

TYPE: Four-seat cabin monoplane.

WINGS: Cantilever low-wing monoplane. Wing section NACA 65₂-415 on inboard panels; outboard leading-edge incorporates modification No. 5 of NACA TN 2228. Dihedral 7°. Incidence 2° at root, −1° at tip. Sweepback at quarter-chord 5°. Light alloy single-spar structure with glassfibre wingtips. Plain ailerons of light alloy construction. Four-position manually-actuated trailing-edge flaps constructed of light alloy with ribbed skins.

FUSELAGE: Light alloy semi-monocoque structure with glassfibre nose cowl and tailcone.

TAIL UNIT: Cantilever structure of light alloy, except for glassfibre tips on fin and tailplane. Fin and rudder have ribbed light alloy skins. One-piece all-moving tailplane, with combined anti-servo and trim tab. Rudder trimmable, but no trim tab in rudder.

LANDING GEAR: Non-retractable tricycle type. Steerable nosewheel. Piper oleo-pneumatic shock-absorbers; single wheel on each unit. Cleveland wheels with 4-ply tyres size 6·00-6 on main units, pressure 1·65 bars (24 lb/sq in). Cleveland nosewheel and 4-ply tyre size 5·00-5, pressure 1·65 bars (24 lb/sq in). Cleveland disc brakes. Parking brake. Glassfibre wheel fairings optional.

POWER PLANT: One 119 kW (160 hp) Avco Lycoming O-320-D3G flat-four engine, driving a Sensenich two-blade fixed-pitch metal propeller type 74DM6-0-60. Fuel in two wing tanks, with total capacity of 189 litres (50 US gallons), of which 181·5 litres (48 US gallons) are usable. Refuelling point on upper surface of each wing. Oil capacity 7·5 litres (2 US gallons).

ACCOMMODATION: Four persons in pairs in enclosed cabin. Individual adjustable front seats, bench type rear seat. Shoulder harnesses with inertia reel on two front seats. Dual controls and brakes standard. Large door on starboard side. Baggage compartment and hatshelf at rear of cabin, with volume of 0·68 m³ (24 cu ft) and capacity of 90 kg (200 lb). External access door on starboard side. Heating, ventilation and windscreen defrosting standard.

SYSTEMS: Hydraulic system for brakes only. Electrical system powered by 14V 60A engine-driven alternator. 12V 25Ah battery standard, 12V 35Ah battery optional. Vacuum system for optional blind-flying instrumentation is available, complete with vacuum gauge, regulator, filter, and annunciator light. Piper Aire air-conditioning system optional.

AVIONICS AND EQUIPMENT: Collins, King and Narco avionics in eight optional groups, or an extensive range of King, Narco, Bendix and Piper avionics. Standard equipment includes recording tachometer, sensitive altimeter, armrests, map pockets, pilot's storm window, stall warning device, carpeted floor, soundproofing, full-flow oil filter, tiedown rings and fuel tank quick drains. Optional equipment, in addition to that listed under Custom and Executive packages, includes encoding altimeter, engine hour recorder, outside air temperature gauge, pilot and co-pilot headrests, cabin fire extinguisher, inertia reel shoulder safety belts for rear seats, floor and/or overhead ventilation with booster fan, stainless steel control cables, tinted windows, and zinc chromate paint for aluminium parts.

DIMENSIONS, EXTERNAL:

Wing span	10·67 m (35 ft 0 in)
Wing chord at root	1·60 m (5 ft 3 in)
Wing chord at tip	1·07 m (3 ft 6¼ in)
Wing aspect ratio	7·24
Length overall	7·25 m (23 ft 9½ in)
Height overall	2·22 m (7 ft 3½ in)
Tailplane span	3·96 m (12 ft 11¾ in)
Wheel track	3·05 m (10 ft 0 in)
Wheelbase	2·03 m (6 ft 8 in)
Propeller diameter	1·88 m (6 ft 2 in)
Propeller ground clearance	0·21 m (8¼ in)

Piper Warrior II four-seat cabin monoplane

Piper Warrior II (Avco Lycoming O-320-D3G engine) *(Pilot Press)*

Cabin door: Height	0·89 m (2 ft 11 in)
Width	0·91 m (3 ft 0 in)
Baggage door: Height	0·51 m (1 ft 8 in)
Max width	0·56 m (1 ft 10 in)
Height to sill	0·71 m (2 ft 4 in)

DIMENSIONS, INTERNAL:
Cabin: Length (instrument panel to rear bulkhead)

	2·46 m (8 ft 1 in)
Max width	1·05 m (3 ft 5½ in)
Max height	1·24 m (4 ft 1 in)
Floor area	2·28 m² (24·5 sq ft)
Volume (incl baggage area)	3·00 m³ (106·0 cu ft)

AREAS:

Wings, gross	15·8 m² (170 sq ft)
Ailerons (total)	1·23 m² (13·2 sq ft)
Trailing-edge flaps (total)	1·36 m² (14·6 sq ft)
Fin	0·69 m² (7·4 sq ft)
Rudder	0·38 m² (4·1 sq ft)
Tailplane, incl tab	2·46 m² (26·5 sq ft)

WEIGHTS AND LOADINGS:

Weight empty, standard	608 kg (1,340 lb)
Max T-O and landing weight	1,054 kg (2,325 lb)
Max wing loading	66·74 kg/m² (13·67 lb/sq ft)
Max power loading	8·86 kg/kW (14·53 lb/hp)

PERFORMANCE (at max T-O weight):
Never-exceed speed 153 knots (282 km/h; 176 mph)
*Max level speed at S/L

126 knots (233 km/h; 145 mph)
*Best power cruising speed, 75% power at 2,745 m
(9,000 ft)   127 knots (235 km/h; 146 mph)
*Best power cruising speed, 65% power at 3,810 m
(12,500 ft)   118 knots (219 km/h; 136 mph)
*Best power cruising speed, 55% power at 3,810 m
(12,500 ft)   107 knots (198 km/h; 123 mph)
*Best econ cruising speed, 75% power at 2,745 m (9,000
ft)   122 knots (225 km/h; 140 mph)
*Best econ cruising speed, 65% power at 3,810 m
(12,500 ft)   116 knots (215 km/h; 134 mph)
*Best econ cruising speed, 55% power at 3,810 m
(12,500 ft)   103 knots (191 km/h; 119 mph)
Stalling speed, flaps up
56 knots (104 km/h; 65 mph) CAS
Stalling speed, flaps down
50 knots (93 km/h; 57·5 mph) CAS

Max rate of climb at S/L	216 m (710 ft)/min
Service ceiling	4,265 m (14,000 ft)
Absolute ceiling	4,600 m (15,100 ft)
T-O run	297 m (975 ft)
T-O to 15 m (50 ft)	454 m (1,490 ft)
Landing from 15 m (50 ft)	340 m (1,115 ft)
Landing run	181 m (595 ft)

*Range with max fuel, with allowances for taxi, T-O,
climb, and descent, and 45 min reserves at max range
power:
at best power settings:
75% power at 2,745 m (9,000 ft)
525 nm (972 km; 604 miles)
65% power at 3,810 m (12,500 ft)
553 nm (1,025 km; 637 miles)
55% power at 3,810 m (12,500 ft)
565 nm (1,047 km; 651 miles)
at best econ power settings:
75% power at 2,745 m (9,000 ft)
590 nm (1,092 km; 679 miles)
65% power at 3,810 m (12,500 ft)
633 nm (1,173 km; 729 miles)
55% power at 3,810 m (12,500 ft)
640 nm (1,186 km; 737 miles)
*With optional wheel fairings

PIPER (PA-28-181) ARCHER II

On 9 October 1972 Piper introduced the Cherokee
Challenger as successor to the Cherokee 180. In 1974 this
was superseded by the Cherokee Archer, with the same
basic airframe and power plant, but with many additional
equipment and avionics options. In 1976 this aircraft was
redesignated PA-28-181 Cherokee Archer II, and in 1978
introduced the tapered wings of the Warrior II.

The Archer II can be fitted with generally similar
optional Custom and Executive equipment packages, as
well as the eight optional avionics packages, which are
available for the Warrior II. The equipment packages vary
as follows:

Custom. As for Warrior II, except for deletion of towbar and engine primer system.

Executive. As for Warrior II, plus exhaust gas temperature gauge, rotating beacon and strobe lights for wings
only, and deletion of sun visors, towbar and engine primer
system.

TYPE: Four-seat cabin monoplane.
WINGS: Cantilever low-wing monoplane. Wing section
NACA 65₂-415 on inboard panels; outboard leading-
edge has modification No. 5 of NACA TN 2228.
Dihedral 7°. Incidence 2° at root, −1° at tip. Sweepback
at quarter-chord 5°. Light alloy single-spar structure
with glassfibre wingtips. Plain ailerons of light alloy
construction. Trailing-edge flaps constructed of light
alloy with ribbed skins.
FUSELAGE: Aluminium alloy semi-monocoque structure.
Glassfibre engine cowling.
TAIL UNIT: Cantilever structure of aluminium alloy,
except for glassfibre tips on fin and tailplane. Fin and
rudder have corrugated metal skin. One-piece all-
moving horizontal surface with combined anti-servo
and trim tab. Trim tab in rudder.
LANDING GEAR: Non-retractable tricycle type. Steerable
nosewheel. Piper oleo-pneumatic shock-absorbers.
Cleveland wheels and Schenuit tyres, size 6·00-6, 4-ply
rating, on all three wheels. Cleveland high capacity disc
brakes. Parking brake. Wheel speed fairings optional.
POWER PLANT: One 134 kW (180 hp) Avco Lycoming
O-360-A4M flat-four engine, driving a Sensenich two-
blade fixed-pitch metal propeller with spinner. Fuel in
two tanks in wing leading-edges, with total capacity of
189 litres (50 US gallons), of which 181·5 litres (48 US
gallons) are usable. Oil capacity 7·5 litres (2 US gallons).

ACCOMMODATION: Four persons in pairs in enclosed cabin.
Individual adjustable front seats, with dual controls;
individual rear seats. Large door on starboard side.
Baggage compartment aft of cabin, with volume of 0·68
m³ (24 cu ft) and capacity of 90 kg (200 lb); door on
starboard side. Hatshelf. Rear seats removable to provide 1·25 m³ (44 cu ft) cargo space. Accommodation
heated and ventilated. Windscreen defrosting.
SYSTEMS: Optional Piper Aire air-conditioning system.
Electrical system includes 60A alternator and 12V
25Ah battery. 35Ah battery optional. Hydraulic system
for brakes only. Vacuum system optional.
AVIONICS AND EQUIPMENT: As for Warrior II, except that
options include an exhaust gas temperature gauge, sun
visors and towbar.
DIMENSIONS, EXTERNAL AND INTERNAL:
As for Warrior II, except:

Tailplane span	3·92 m (12 ft 10½ in)
Wheelbase	2·00 m (6 ft 7 in)
Propeller diameter	1·93 m (6 ft 4 in)

AREAS: As for Warrior II
WEIGHTS AND LOADINGS:

Weight empty, equipped (standard)	643 kg (1,418 lb)
Max T-O and landing weight	1,156 kg (2,550 lb)
Max wing loading	73·2 kg/m² (15·0 lb/sq ft)
Max power loading	8·63 kg/kW (14·17 lb/hp)

PERFORMANCE (at max T-O weight):
Never-exceed speed
148 knots (275 km/h; 171 mph) CAS
*Max level speed at S/L
128 knots (237 km/h; 147 mph)
*Best power cruising speed, 75% power at 2,440 m
(8,000 ft)   129 knots (239 km/h; 148·5 mph)
*Best power cruising speed, 65% power at 3,660 m
(12,000 ft)   125 knots (231 km/h; 144 mph)
*Best power cruising speed, 55% power at 3,810 m
(12,500 ft)   111 knots (206 km/h; 128 mph)
*Best econ cruising speed, 75% power at 2,440 m (8,000
ft)   126 knots (233 km/h; 145 mph)
*Best econ cruising speed, 65% power at 3,660 m
(12,000 ft)   122 knots (225 km/h; 140 mph)
*Best econ cruising speed, 55% power at 3,810 m
(12,500 ft)   107 knots (198 km/h; 123 mph)
Stalling speed, flaps up
59 knots (109 km/h; 68 mph) CAS
Stalling speed, flaps down
53 knots (98 km/h; 61 mph) CAS

Max rate of climb at S/L	224 m (735 ft)/min
Service ceiling	4,570 m (15,000 ft)
Absolute ceiling	4,800 m (15,750 ft)
T-O run	265 m (870 ft)
T-O to 15 m (50 ft)	495 m (1,625 ft)
Landing from 15 m (50 ft)	427 m (1,400 ft)
Landing run	285 m (935 ft)

*Range with max fuel, allowances for taxi, T-O, climb
and descent, and 45 min reserves at max range power:
at best power settings:
75% power at 2,440 m (8,000 ft)
520 nm (964 km; 599 miles)
65% power at 3,660 m (12,000 ft)
565 nm (1,048 km; 651 miles)
55% power at 3,810 m (12,500 ft)
580 nm (1,075 km; 668 miles)
at best econ power settings:
75% power at 2,440 m (8,000 ft)
600 nm (1,112 km; 691 miles)
65% power at 3,660 m (12,000 ft)
645 nm (1,196 km; 743 miles)
55% power at 3,810 m (12,500 ft)
670 nm (1,242 km; 772 miles)
*With optional wheel fairings

PIPER (PA-28RT-201) ARROW IV

The Piper Arrow derives from the Cherokee Arrow II,
which was generally similar to the Cherokee Archer II but
had a retractable landing gear, more powerful engine, and

Piper Archer II, which has the tapered wings introduced on the Warrior

the untapered wing of the 1975 PA-28-180 Archer. In 1977, Piper updated this model by fitting long-span tapered wings identical with those of the Archer II, but with increased fuel capacity, giving improved performance. The 1978 version of this aircraft was named Arrow III, the prototype of which flew for the first time on 16 September 1975, followed by the first production aircraft on 7 January 1977. Piper designation was PA-28R-201. The Turbo Arrow III differed by having a turbocharged engine, mounted in a streamline cowling, and the first production example of this version flew on 1 December 1976.

In 1979 Piper introduced an improved model with an all-moving T tailplane, and two version are available currently:

Arrow IV. Basic model, as described; Piper designation **PA-28RT-201.**

Turbo Arrow IV. As Arrow IV, but power plant comprises one 149 kW (200 hp) Continental TSIO-360-F flat-six turbocharged engine, mounted in a streamline cowling, and driving a Hartzell constant-speed metal propeller with spinner. A three-blade propeller is optional. Piper designation **PA-28RT-201T.**

Two groups of optional equipment are available for the Arrow IV as recommended packages:

Custom. Includes blind-flying instrumentation with 3 in gyros; electric clock; outside air temperature gauge; rate of climb and true airspeed indicators; vacuum system for gyro instruments; a basic lighting package comprising instrument panel white backlighting with overhead red lighting, cabin dome and radio dimming lights; landing, navigation, taxi and wing strobe lights; assist strap; and entrance step; adding 13·0 kg (28·7 lb) to aircraft basic weight.

Executive. As Custom package, plus alternate static source; heated pitot; landing gear sensor; emergency locator transmitter; pilot's vertically adjustable seat; 35Ah battery; and external power socket; adding 22·1 kg (48·7 lb) to aircraft basic weight.

In addition to the above equipment, the avionics packages which are available for the Warrior II are also available optionally for the Arrow IV.

The tricycle landing gear of both versions is retracted hydraulically, with an electrically-operated pump supplying the hydraulic pressure. In addition to the usual 'gear up' warning horn and red light, both Arrow IVs have an automatic extension system which drops the landing gear automatically if power is reduced and airspeed drops below 91 knots (169 km/h; 105 mph). The sensing system consists of a small probe mounted on the port side of the fuselage. Being located in the propeller slipstream, it can differentiate between a climb with power on and an approach to land with power reduced. A free-fall emergency extension system is also fitted. An 'anti-retraction' system guards against premature retraction of the landing gear below an airspeed of 74 knots (137 km/h; 85 mph) at take-off, or accidental retraction on the ground. There is also a manual override lever by which the pilot can hold the landing gear retracted as airspeed falls below 91 knots (169 km/h; 105 mph).

The description of the Archer II applies also to the Arrow IV, except for the following details:

TAIL UNIT: Cantilever T tail of light alloy construction. All-moving tailplane with trim tab. Rudder trim.

LANDING GEAR: Retractable tricycle type, with single wheel on each unit. Hydraulic retraction, main units inward into wings, nose unit rearward. Free-fall emergency extension system. All units fitted with oleo-pneumatic shock-absorbers. Main wheels and tyres size 6·00-6, 6-ply rating. Nosewheel and tyre size 5·00-5, 4-ply rating. High-capacity dual hydraulic disc brakes and parking brake.

POWER PLANT: Arrow IV has one 149 kW (200 hp) Avco Lycoming IO-360-C1C6 flat-four engine, driving a Hartzell HC-C2YK-1/F7666A-2R two-blade constant-speed metal propeller with spinner. Turbo Arrow IV as detailed in model listing. Both versions have fuel tanks in wing leading-edges with total capacity of 291 litres (77 US gallons), of which 273 litres (72 US gallons) are usable. Oil capacity 7·5 litres (2 US gallons).

AVIONICS AND EQUIPMENT: Optional avionics and standard equipment generally as detailed for Warrior II, plus cylinder head temperature gauge, exhaust gas temperature gauge, 65A electric generator, dual range electric auxiliary fuel pump, all standard on Turbo Arrow IV. Optional equipment as listed in Custom and Executive paragraphs and for Archer II and Warrior II, plus cold weather start kit for Turbo Arrow IV.

DIMENSIONS, EXTERNAL:

Wing span	10·80 m (35 ft 5 in)
Wing chord at root	1·60 m (5 ft 3 in)
Wing chord at tip	1·07 m (3 ft 6¼ in)
Length overall: Arrow IV	8·23 m (27 ft 0 in)
Turbo Arrow IV	8·33 m (27 ft 3¾ in)
Height overall	2·52 m (8 ft 3¼ in)
Tailplane span	3·30 m (10 ft 10 in)
Wheel track	3·19 m (10 ft 5½ in)
Wheelbase	2·39 m (7 ft 10¼ in)
Propeller diameter: Arrow IV	1·88 m (6 ft 2 in)
Turbo Arrow IV	1·93 m (6 ft 4 in)

Piper Turbo Arrow IV retractable-gear four-seat cabin monoplane with T tail

Cabin door (stbd): Width		0·91 m (3 ft 0 in)
Height		0·89 m (2 ft 11 in)
Baggage door (stbd): Width		0·56 m (1 ft 10 in)
Height		0·51 m (1 ft 8 in)

DIMENSIONS, INTERNAL:

Cabin:		
Length, panel to rear bulkhead		2·41 m (7 ft 11 in)
Max width		1·05 m (3 ft 5½ in)
Max height		1·24 m (4 ft 1 in)
Volume (incl baggage area)		3·00 m³ (106 cu ft)

AREA:

Wings, gross	15·79 m² (170 sq ft)

WEIGHTS AND LOADINGS (A: Arrow IV; B: Turbo Arrow IV):

Weight empty: A		744 kg (1,641 lb)
B		766 kg (1,690 lb)
Max T-O weight: A		1,247 kg (2,750 lb)
B		1,315 kg (2,900 lb)
Max wing loading: A	79·0 kg/m² (16·18 lb/sq ft)	
B	83·29 kg/m² (17·06 lb/sq ft)	
Max power loading: A	8·37 kg/kW (13·75 lb/hp)	
B	8·83 kg/kW (14·5 lb/hp)	

PERFORMANCE (at max T-O weight):

Never-exceed speed		186 knots (344 km/h; 214 mph) CAS
Max level speed:		
A at S/L	152 knots (282 km/h; 175 mph)	
B at 4,265 m (14,000 ft)		
	178 knots (330 km/h; 205 mph)	
Best power cruising speed, 75% power at optimum		
altitude: A	143 knots (265 km/h; 165 mph)	
B	172 knots (319 km/h; 198 mph)	
Best power cruising speed, 65% power at optimum		
altitude: A	138 knots (256 km/h; 159 mph)	
B	167 knots (309 km/h; 192 mph)	
Best power cruising speed, 55% power at optimum		
altitude: A	131 knots (243 km/h; 151 mph)	
B	158 knots (293 km/h; 182 mph)	
Best econ cruising speed, 75% power at optimum		
altitude: A	139 knots (257 km/h; 160 mph)	
B	167 knots (309 km/h; 192 mph)	
Best econ cruising speed, 65% power at optimum		
altitude: A	133 knots (246 km/h; 153 mph)	
B	164 knots (304 km/h; 189 mph)	
Best econ cruising speed, 55% power at optimum		
altitude: A	122 knots (226 km/h; 140 mph)	
B	154 knots (285 km/h; 177 mph)	
Stalling speed, flaps up:		
A	59 knots (109 km/h; 68 mph) CAS	
B	63 knots (117 km/h; 72 mph) CAS	
Stalling speed, flaps down:		
A	55 knots (102 km/h; 63·5 mph) CAS	
B	58 knots (107·5 km/h; 67 mph) CAS	
Max rate of climb at S/L: A	253 m (831 ft)/min	
B	287 m (940 ft)/min	
Service ceiling: A	5,180 m (17,000 ft)	
*B	6,100 m (20,000 ft)	
Absolute ceiling: A	5,610 m (18,400 ft)	
*B	6,100 m (20,000 ft)	
T-O run: A	312 m (1,025 ft)	
B	338 m (1,110 ft)	
T-O to 15 m (50 ft): A	488 m (1,600 ft)	
B	494 m (1,620 ft)	
Landing from 15 m (50 ft): A	465 m (1,525 ft)	
B	474 m (1,555 ft)	
Landing run: A	188 m (615 ft)	
B	197 m (645 ft)	

Range with max fuel, allowances for taxi, T-O, climb and descent, and 45 min reserves at max range power:

at best power settings:		
75% power:		
A		720 nm (1,334 km; 829 miles)
B		695 nm (1,287 km; 800 miles)
65% power:		
A		770 nm (1,427 km; 887 miles)
B		725 nm (1,343 km; 835 miles)
55% power:		
A		795 nm (1,473 km; 915 miles)
B		775 nm (1,435 km; 892 miles)
at best econ power settings:		
75% power:		
A		810 nm (1,502 km; 933 miles)
B		790 nm (1,465 km; 910 miles)
65% power:		
A		845 nm (1,566 km; 973 miles)
B		830 nm (1,539 km; 956 miles)
55% power:		
A		875 nm (1,622 km; 1,008 miles)
B		900 nm (1,667 km; 1,036 miles)

*Max approved operating altitude

PIPER (PA-28-236) DAKOTA

Piper introduced in 1978 an addition to the Warrior, Archer, Arrow line known as the PA-28-236 Dakota, which differs primarily by having a 175 kW (235 hp) Avco Lycoming engine to provide increased performance, and increased capacity fuel tanks to cater for this power plant. Like the related aircraft mentioned earlier, it is available with a variety of optional factory-installed avionics packages, and also two Operational Groups as follows:

Custom. As detailed for Warrior II, but with deletion of engine primer system, quick oil drain and towbar; adding 20·1 kg (44·4 lb) to basic empty weight.

Executive. As detailed for Warrior II, but with deletion of sun visors, engine primer system, quick oil drain and towbar; plus a tail-mounted rotating beacon instead of strobe light; adding 31·6 kg (69·7 lb) to basic empty weight.

The description of the Archer II applies also to the Dakota, except as follows:

POWER PLANT: One 175 kW (235 hp) Avco Lycoming O-540-J3A5D flat-six engine, driving a Hartzell two-blade constant-speed metal propeller with spinner. Two integral fuel tanks in each wing, with a total capacity of 291 litres (77 US gallons), of which 273 litres (72 US gallons) are usable. Refuelling points on upper surface of each wing. Oil capacity 11·5 litres (3 US gallons).

AVIONICS AND EQUIPMENT: A variety of optional factory-installed avionics packages is available, as well as a wide range of other avionics equipment to customer's requirements. Standard equipment as for Warrior II, plus quick oil drain valve. Optional equipment includes items provided in the Custom and Executive packages, plus engine hour recorder, exhaust gas temperature gauge, outside air temperature gauge, co-pilot's vertically adjustable seat, cabin fire extinguisher, de luxe interior, shoulder safety belts with inertia reel for rear seats, super soundproofing, overhead air vents, Piper Aire air-conditioning, stainless steel control cables, tinted windows, ventilation fan, and zinc chromate treatment of aluminium parts.

DIMENSIONS, EXTERNAL AND INTERNAL: As for Archer II except:

Length overall	7·54 m (24 ft 8¾ in)
Height overall	2·18 m (7 ft 2 in)
Wheelbase	1·98 m (6 ft 6 in)

WEIGHTS AND LOADINGS:

Weight empty	727 kg (1,602 lb)
Max T-O weight	1,361 kg (3,000 lb)
Max wing loading	85·93 kg/m² (17·6 lb/sq ft)
Max power loading	7·78 kg/kW (12·8 lb/hp)

PERFORMANCE (at max T-O weight):

Max level speed at S/L	148 knots (274 km/h; 170 mph)
Best power cruising speed, 75% power at optimum altitude	144 knots (267 km/h; 166 mph)
Best power cruising speed, 65% power at optimum altitude	138 knots (256 km/h; 159 mph)
Best power cruising speed, 55% power at optimum altitude	130 knots (241 km/h; 150 mph)
Best econ cruising speed, 75% power at optimum altitude	141 knots (261 km/h; 162 mph)
Best econ cruising speed, 65% power at optimum altitude	137 knots (253 km/h; 157 mph)
Best econ cruising speed, 55% power at optimum altitude	129 knots (239 km/h; 148 mph)
Stalling speed, flaps up	63 knots (117 km/h; 72·5 mph) CAS

Stalling speed, flaps down
           56 knots (104 km/h; 64·5 mph) CAS
Max rate of climb at S/L   338 m (1,110 ft)/min
Service ceiling   5,335 m (17,500 ft)
Absolute ceiling   5,945 m (19,500 ft)
T-O run   270 m (886 ft)
T-O to 15 m (50 ft)   371 m (1,216 ft)
Landing from 15 m (50 ft) 430 m (1,410 ft)
Landing run   284 m (932 ft)
Range with max fuel, allowances for taxi, T-O, climb, cruise, descent, and 45 min reserves at max range power:
  at best power settings at optimum altitude:
    75% power   650 nm (1,205 km; 748 miles)
    65% power   710 nm (1,315 km; 817 miles)
    55% power   755 nm (1,399 km; 869 miles)
  at best econ power settings at optimum altitude:
    75% power   710 nm (1,315 km; 817 miles)
    65% power   765 nm (1,418 km; 881 miles)
    55% power   810 nm (1,501 km; 933 miles)

PIPER (PA-28-201T) TURBO DAKOTA

Piper introduced in 1979 a low-cost four-seat turbocharged aircraft with fixed landing gear. The company claimed it to be the first aircraft to enter production in this specific class. Although named Turbo Dakota, it has the company designation PA-28-201T which links it more directly with the Arrow than with the PA-28-236 Dakota.

The Turbo Dakota is available with a wide variety of optional avionics to meet customer's requirements, as well as a number of optional factory-installed avionics packages. Two groups of optional equipment are also available for the Turbo Dakota as basic packages:

Custom. As described for Dakota.
Executive. As described for Dakota.
TYPE: Four-seat cabin monoplane.
WINGS, FUSELAGE AND TAIL UNIT: Generally as for Arrow IV.
LANDING GEAR: Non-retractable tricycle type with single wheel on each unit. Piper oleo-pneumatic shock-absorbers. Main-wheel tyres size 6·00-6, 6-ply rating. Steerable nosewheel with tyre size 5·00-5, 6-ply rating. High capacity disc brakes. Parking brake.
POWER PLANT: One 149 kW (200 hp) Continental TSIO-360-FB flat-six turbocharged engine, driving a two-blade constant-speed metal propeller with spinner. Two fuel tanks in wings, with combined capacity of 291 litres (77 US gallons), of which 273 litres (72 US gallons) are usable. Refuelling point on upper surface of each wing. Oil capacity 7·5 litres (2 US gallons).
ACCOMMODATION: As described for Archer II.
SYSTEMS: Electrical system includes 14V 65A alternator and 12V 25Ah battery. 12V 35Ah battery optional. Hydraulic system for brakes only. Air-conditioning system, vacuum system and oxygen system optional.
AVIONICS AND EQUIPMENT: A number of factory-installed avionics packages and a wide range of additional avionics items are available to customer's requirements. Standard equipment as for Dakota, plus fuel flow/manifold pressure gauge, cylinder head and exhaust gas temperature gauges, dual range auxiliary fuel pump, and electric engine priming system. Optional equipment generally as for Dakota, plus engine cold weather starting kit.
DIMENSIONS, EXTERNAL: As for Arrow IV, except:
Length overall   7·62 m (25 ft 0¼ in)
Height overall   2·32 m (7 ft 7¼ in)
Tailplane span   3·92 m (12 ft 10½ in)
Wheel track   3·05 m (10 ft 0 in)
Wheelbase   2·22 m (7 ft 3½ in)
Propeller diameter   1·88 m (6 ft 2 in)
DIMENSIONS, INTERNAL: As for Arrow IV, except:
Cabin:
  Length, panel to rear bulkhead 2·46 m (8 ft 1 in)
AREA:
Wings, gross   15·79 m² (170 sq ft)

Piper Turbo Dakota, a low-cost turbocharged aircraft with fixed landing gear

WEIGHTS AND LOADINGS:
Weight empty   716 kg (1,579 lb)
Max T-O weight   1,315 kg (2,900 lb)
Max wing loading   83·3 kg/m² (17·06 lb/sq ft)
Max power loading   8·83 kg/kW (14·5 lb/hp)
PERFORMANCE (at max T-O weight):
Max level speed at 4,570 m (15,000 ft)
          162 knots (300 km/h; 186 mph)
Best power cruising speed at optimum altitude:
  75% power   156 knots (290 km/h; 180 mph)
  65% power   151 knots (280 km/h; 174 mph)
  55% power   142 knots (264 km/h; 164 mph)
Best econ cruising speed at optimum altitude:
  75% power   154 knots (285 km/h; 177 mph)
  65% power   148 knots (274 km/h; 170 mph)
  55% power   139 knots (257 km/h; 160 mph)
Stalling speed, flaps up
          65 knots (121 km/h; 75 mph) CAS
Stalling speed, flaps down
          58 knots (108 km/h; 67 mph) CAS
Max rate of climb at S/L   275 m (902 ft)/min
*Service ceiling   6,100 m (20,000 ft)
T-O run   294 m (963 ft)
T-O to 15 m (50 ft)   427 m (1,402 ft)
Landing from 15 m (50 ft) 517 m (1,697 ft)
Landing run   262 m (861 ft)
Range at optimum altitude with max fuel, allowances for taxi, T-O, climb, descent, and 45 min reserves at max range power:
At best power settings:
  75% power   633 nm (1,173 km; 729 miles)
  65% power   660 nm (1,223 km; 760 miles)
  55% power   690 nm (1,279 km; 795 miles)
At best econ power settings:
  75% power   729 nm (1,350 km; 839 miles)
  65% power   766 nm (1,419 km; 882 miles)
  55% power   795 nm (1,473 km; 915 miles)
*Max certificated altitude

PIPER (PA-32-301) SARATOGA

On 17 December 1979, Piper announced that it had begun production of a new family of six/seven-seat single-engined aircraft known as Saratogas, to replace the PA-32 SIX 300 and T-tail Lance series (all described in 1979-80 *Jane's*). All Saratogas have a common airframe, with a conventional low-mounted tailplane and a semi-tapered wing of longer span than the wing of the aircraft they supersede.

Four versions of the Saratoga are available:
PA-32-301 Saratoga. Basic version, as described in detail.
PA-32-301T Turbo Saratoga. As Saratoga, but

power plant comprises one 224 kW (300 hp) Avco Lycoming TIO-540-S1AD flat-six turbocharged engine, driving a Hartzell two-blade constant-speed metal propeller. Three-blade propeller optional. Additional standard equipment for the Turbo Saratoga includes cylinder head and exhaust gas temperature gauges, engine overboost warning light, and manually controlled cowl flap.
PA-32R-301 Saratoga SP. Retractable landing gear version of the Saratoga, described separately.
PA-32R-301T Turbo Saratoga SP. Retractable landing gear version of the Turbo Saratoga, described separately.

These aircraft are available with a variety of optional factory-installed avionics packages, and also two Operational Groups as follows:
Custom. Includes blind-flying instrumentation with 3 in attitude and directional gyros; electric clock; outside air temperature gauge; rate of climb and true airspeed indicators; basic lighting package which comprises avionics dimming, instrument panel white backlighting and overhead red lighting; cabin dome, map and reading lights; landing, navigation, taxi and wing strobe lights; rotating beacon; waterfall switch panel; assist straps; entrance step; wheel fairings; vacuum system with vacuum gauge, regulator, filter and warning lights; 35Ah battery; and quick oil drain; adding 20·1 kg (44·5 lb) to basic empty weight.
Executive. As Custom package, plus alternate static source; emergency locator transmitter; heated pitot; pilot's vertically adjustable seat; courtesy lighting package comprising forward baggage compartment light, and forward and aft cabin door lights; and external power socket; adding 30·8 kg (68·0 lb) to basic empty weight.
TYPE: Six/seven-seat cabin monoplane.
WINGS: Cantilever low-wing monoplane. Light alloy single-spar structure with glassfibre wingtips. Plain ailerons of light alloy construction. Manually-operated four-position trailing-edge flaps of light alloy construction with ribbed skins.
FUSELAGE: Conventional semi-monocoque structure of light alloy. Glassfibre engine cowling.
TAIL UNIT: Cantilever structure of light alloy, except for glassfibre tips on fin and tailplane. Fin and rudder have ribbed metal skins. One-piece all-moving horizontal surface with combined anti-servo and trim tab. Trimmable rudder.
LANDING GEAR: Non-retractable tricycle type. Steerable nosewheel. Piper oleo-pneumatic shock-absorbers. Single wheel on each unit. Main-wheel tyres size 6·00-6, 8-ply rating. Nosewheel tyre size 5·00-5, 6-ply rating. Nosewheel tyre size 6·00-6 optional. High-capacity disc brakes. Parking brake. Wheel fairings optional. Heavy-duty brakes and tyres optional.
POWER PLANT: One 224 kW (300 hp) Avco Lycoming IO-540-K1G5D flat-six engine, driving a Hartzell two-blade constant-speed metal propeller with spinner. Three-blade propeller optional. Turbo Saratoga as detailed in model listings. Two fuel tanks in each wing with combined capacity of 405 litres (107 US gallons), of which 386 litres (102 US gallons) are usable. Refuelling points on wing upper surface. Oil capacity 11·5 litres (3 US gallons).
ACCOMMODATION: Enclosed cabin, seating six people in pairs. Seventh seat, between two centre seats, optional. Dual controls and toe brakes standard. Two forward-hinged doors, one on starboard side forward, overwing; one on port side at aft end of cabin. Space for 45 kg (100 lb) baggage at rear of cabin, with external baggage/utility door on port side. Additional baggage space, capacity 45 kg (100 lb), between engine fireproof bulkhead and instrument panel, with external access door on starboard side. Pilot's storm window. Sun visors. Accommodation heated and ventilated. Windscreen defroster standard.
SYSTEMS: Piper Aire air-conditioning, vacuum and oxygen systems optional. Hydraulic system for brakes only. Electrical system includes a 14V 60A engine-driven

Piper's new PA-32-301 Saratoga six/seven-seat cabin monoplane

alternator, and 12V 25Ah battery. 35Ah battery optional.

AVIONICS AND EQUIPMENT: A wide range of avionics is available to customer's requirements, including weather radar with internal wing-mounted antenna. Standard equipment includes recording tachometer, sensitive altimeter, fore and aft adjustable pilot and co-pilot seats with shoulder and safety belts and inertia reels, armrests, map pockets, glove compartment, stall warning device, provisions for emergency locator transmitter, alternator failure and low oil pressure warning lights, full-flow oil filter, fuel quick drains, oil quick drain, jack pads, stowable towbar, and tiedown rings. Optional equipment includes items detailed in Custom and Executive packages, plus encoding altimeter; engine hour recorder; de luxe interior groups including headrests, window curtains, club seating arrangement, refreshment console; shoulder safety belts with inertia reels for passenger seats; tinted windows; stainless steel control cables; ventilation fan; super soundproofing; and zinc chromate treatment of aluminium parts.

DIMENSIONS, EXTERNAL:

Wing span	11·02 m (36 ft 2 in)
Length overall	8·59 m (28 ft 2 in)
Height overall	2·49 m (8 ft 2 in)
Tailplane span	3·94 m (12 ft 11 in)
Wheel track	3·23 m (10 ft 7 in)
Wheelbase	2·34 m (7 ft 8 in)
Cabin door (fwd, stbd): Height	0·89 m (2 ft 11 in)
Width	0·91 m (3 ft 0 in)
Cabin door (rear, port): Height	0·84 m (2 ft 9 in)
Width	0·74 m (2 ft 5 in)
Baggage door (fwd): Height	0·46 m (1 ft 6 in)
Width	0·61 m (2 ft 0 in)
Baggage/utility door (aft): Height	0·71 m (2 ft 4 in)
Width	0·51 m (1 ft 8 in)

DIMENSIONS, INTERNAL:

Cabin: Length (instrument panel to rear bulkhead)	3·18 m (10 ft 5 in)
Max width	1·24 m (4 ft 1 in)
Max height	1·24 m (4 ft 1 in)
Volume (incl aft baggage area)	5·53 m³ (195·3 cu ft)
Baggage compartment volume:	
forward	0·20 m³ (7·0 cu ft)
aft	0·49 m³ (17·3 cu ft)

AREA:

Wings, gross	16·2 m² (174·5 sq ft)

WEIGHTS AND LOADINGS (A: Saratoga; B: Turbo Saratoga):

Weight empty: A	871 kg (1,920 lb)
B	907 kg (2,000 lb)
Max T-O weight:	
A, B	1,633 kg (3,600 lb)
Max ramp weight: A	1,640 kg (3,615 lb)
B	1,641 kg (3,617 lb)
Max wing loading: A, B	100·6 kg/m² (20·6 lb/sq ft)
Max power loading: A, B	7·30 kg/kW (12·0 lb/hp)

PERFORMANCE (at max T-O weight, except where indicated. A: Saratoga/two-blade propeller; B: Turbo Saratoga/two-blade propeller; C: Saratoga/three-blade propeller; D: Turbo Saratoga/three-blade propeller):

Max level speed at optimum altitude:

A	152 knots (282 km/h; 175 mph)
B	178 knots (330 km/h; 205 mph)
D	182 knots (337 km/h; 210 mph)

Best power cruising speed at optimum altitude:

at 75% power: A	150 knots (278 km/h; 173 mph)
B	165 knots (306 km/h; 190 mph)
at 65% power: A	146 knots (270 km/h; 168 mph)
B	154 knots (285 km/h; 177 mph)
at 55% power: A	136 knots (252 km/h; 156·5 mph)
B	139 knots (258 km/h; 160 mph)

Best econ cruising speed at optimum altitude:

at 75% power: A	148 knots (274 km/h; 170 mph)
B	160 knots (296 km/h; 184 mph)
at 65% power: A	144 knots (267 km/h; 166 mph)
B	148 knots (274 km/h; 170 mph)
at 55% power: A	133 knots (246 km/h; 153 mph)
B	132 knots (245 km/h; 152 mph)

Stalling speed, flaps up:

A	66 knots (122 km/h; 76 mph) CAS
B	67 knots (125 km/h; 77·5 mph) CAS

Stalling speed, flaps down:

A, B	60 knots (111 km/h; 69 mph) CAS

Max rate of climb at S/L: A	302 m (990 ft)/min
B	328 m (1,075 ft)/min
Service ceiling: A	4,300 m (14,100 ft)
*B	6,100 m (20,000 ft)
Absolute ceiling: A	4,845 m (15,900 ft)
*B	6,100 m (20,000 ft)
T-O run: A	361 m (1,183 ft)
B	338 m (1,110 ft)
C	309 m (1,013 ft)
D	293 m (960 ft)
T-O to 15 m (50 ft): A	536 m (1,759 ft)
B	485 m (1,590 ft)
C	479 m (1,573 ft)
D	433 m (1,420 ft)
Landing from 15 m (50 ft), standard brakes:	
A	491 m (1,612 ft)
B	518 m (1,700 ft)

Piper PA-32-301 Saratoga (Avco Lycoming IO-540-K1G5D engine) *(Michael A. Badrocke)*

Piper PA-32R-301T Turbo Saratoga SP, a turbocharged version of the Saratoga with retractable landing gear

Landing from 15 m (50 ft), heavy-duty brakes:	
A	466 m (1,530 ft)
B	500 m (1,640 ft)
Landing run, standard brakes: A	223 m (732 ft)
B	274 m (900 ft)
Landing run, heavy-duty brakes:	
A, B	198 m (650 ft)

Range with max fuel, allowances for taxi, T-O, climb, descent, and 45 min reserves at max range power:

Best power settings at optimum altitude:

75% power: A	745 nm (1,381 km; 858 miles)
B	684 nm (1,267 km; 788 miles)
65% power: A	805 nm (1,492 km; 927 miles)
B	730 nm (1,352 km; 841 miles)
55% power: A	849 nm (1,573 km; 978 miles)
B	772 nm (1,430 km; 889 miles)

Best econ power settings at optimum altitude:

75% power: A	823 nm (1,525 km; 948 miles)
B	780 nm (1,445 km; 898 miles)
65% power: A	911 nm (1,688 km; 1,049 miles)
B	845 nm (1,566 km; 973 miles)
55% power: A	960 nm (1,778 km; 1,105 miles)
B	860 nm (1,593 km; 990 miles)

*Max certificated altitude

PIPER (PA-32RT-300) LANCE II and (PA-32RT-300T) TURBO LANCE II

Production of these six/seven-seat versions of the Cherokee family has now ended. They have been replaced by retractable landing gear versions of the Saratoga, of which details follow.

PIPER (PA-32R-301) SARATOGA SP

This is the designation of the retractable landing gear model of the new Piper Saratoga, of which two versions were introduced for 1980.

PA-32R-301 Saratoga SP. Basic version, similar to the PA-32-301 Saratoga but with retractable landing gear and new options as described.

PA-32R-301T Turbo Saratoga SP. As Saratoga SP, but with turbocharged power plant and additional standard equipment as detailed for the Turbo Saratoga. New options available for this version include a de-icing package, and a built-in oxygen system.

Both models are available with a variety of optional factory-installed avionics packages, including a King flight director, and with Custom and Executive Operational Groups.

Custom. As detailed for Saratoga/Turbo Saratoga, but with deletion of wheel speed fairings, rotating beacon and quick oil drain; adding 10 kg (22·0 lb) to basic empty weight.

Executive. As detailed for Saratoga/Turbo Saratoga, but with deletion of wheel speed fairings and quick oil drain. A heated landing gear sensor is included, the entire package adding 22·4 kg (49·4 lb) to basic empty weight.

De-Icing Group. Available for Turbo Saratoga SP, includes pneumatic de-icing boots for wing and tail unit leading-edges, electrical propeller de-icing, electrically heated pilot's windscreen plate, ice inspection light, and illuminated outside air temperature gauge.

The description of the Saratoga/Turbo Saratoga applies also to the retractable landing gear versions except as follows.

WINGS: As for Saratoga, except wing leading-edge pneumatic de-icing boots available optionally for Turbo Saratoga SP.

TAIL UNIT: As for Saratoga, except fin and tailplane leading-edge pneumatic de-icing boots available optionally for Turbo Saratoga SP.

LANDING GEAR: Hydraulically-retractable tricycle type with single wheel on each unit. Main units retract inward, nosewheel aft. Integrated automatic system which extends the landing gear at 102 knots (189 km/h; 117 mph), unless overridden by pilot. Emergency free-fall extension system. Piper oleo-pneumatic shock-absorbers. Main-wheel tyres size 6·00-6, 8-ply rating. Nosewheel tyre size 5·00-5, 6-ply rating. High-capacity disc brakes. Parking brake. Heavy-duty tyres and brakes optional.

POWER PLANT: As for Saratoga/Turbo Saratoga, except propeller de-icing optional for Turbo Saratoga SP.

ACCOMMODATION: As for Saratoga, but electrically heated pilot's windscreen plate optional for Turbo Saratoga SP.

SYSTEMS: As for Saratoga, but electrically-driven hydraulic pump for landing gear actuation; built-in oxygen system of 1·78 m³ (63 cu ft) capacity and 95A alternator available optionally for Turbo Saratoga SP.

AVIONICS AND EQUIPMENT: Generally as for Saratoga/Turbo Saratoga, except as amended by details in this entry.

DIMENSIONS, EXTERNAL: As for Saratoga, except:

Length overall: Saratoga SP	8·64 m	(28 ft 4 in)
Turbo Saratoga SP	8·84 m	(29 ft 0 in)
Height overall	2·90 m	(9 ft 6 in)
Wheel track	3·38 m	(11 ft 1 in)
Wheelbase	2·41 m	(7 ft 11 in)

AREA:

Wings, gross	16·56 m²	(178·3 sq ft)

WEIGHTS AND LOADINGS (A: Saratoga SP; B: Turbo Saratoga SP):
As for Saratoga/Turbo Saratoga, except:

Weight empty: A	901 kg	(1,986 lb)
B	940 kg	(2,073 lb)
Max wing loading: A, B 98·6 kg/m² (20·19 lb/sq ft)		

PERFORMANCE (at max T-O weight, except where indicated. A: Saratoga SP/two-blade propeller; B: Turbo Saratoga SP/two-blade propeller; C: Saratoga SP/three-blade propeller; D: Turbo Saratoga SP/three-blade propeller):

Max level speed at optimum altitude:

A	164 knots	(304 km/h; 189 mph)
B	191 knots	(354 km/h; 220 mph)
D	195 knots	(361 km/h; 225 mph)

Best power cruising speed at optimum altitude:

at 75% power: A	159 knots	(295 km/h; 183 mph)
B	177 knots	(328 km/h; 204 mph)
at 65% power: A	153 knots	(283 km/h; 176 mph)
B	166 knots	(307 km/h; 191 mph)
at 55% power: A	144 knots	(267 km/h; 166 mph)
B	152 knots	(282 km/h; 175 mph)

Best econ cruising speed at optimum altitude:

at 75% power: A	157 knots	(291 km/h; 181 mph)
B	171 knots	(317 km/h; 197 mph)
at 65% power: A	151 knots	(280 km/h; 174 mph)
B	160 knots	(296 km/h; 184 mph)
at 55% power: A	141 knots	(261 km/h; 162 mph)
B	145 knots	(269 km/h; 167 mph)

Stalling speeds, flaps up:

A	65 knots	(121 km/h; 75 mph) CAS
B	63 knots	(118 km/h; 72·5 mph) CAS

Stalling speed, flaps down:

A	59 knots	(110 km/h; 68 mph) CAS
B	60 knots	(111 km/h; 69 mph) CAS

Max rate of climb at S/L: A	308 m	(1,010 ft)/min
B	341 m	(1,120 ft)/min
Service ceiling: A	5,090 m	(16,700 ft)
*B	6,100 m	(20,000 ft)
Absolute ceiling: A	5,595 m	(18,350 ft)
*B	6,100 m	(20,000 ft)

T-O run, and T-O to 15 m (50 ft):
As for Saratoga and Turbo Saratoga

Landing from 15 m (50 ft), standard brakes:

A	491 m	(1,612 ft)
B	500 m	(1,640 ft)

Landing run, standard brakes:

A	223 m	(732 ft)
B	198 m	(650 ft)

Range with max fuel, allowances for taxi, T-O, climb, descent, and 45 min reserves at max range power:
Best power settings at optimum altitude:

75% power: A	784 nm	(1,453 km; 903 miles)
B	730 nm	(1,353 km; 840 miles)
65% power: A	828 nm	(1,533 km; 953 miles)
B	790 nm	(1,465 km; 910 miles)
55% power: A	869 nm	(1,611 km; 1,001 miles)
B	843 nm	(1,562 km; 971 miles)

Best econ power settings at optimum altitude:

75% power: A	865 nm	(1,603 km; 996 miles)
B	844 nm	(1,564 km; 972 miles)
65% power: A	937 nm	(1,736 km; 1,079 miles)
B	920 nm	(1,704 km; 1,059 miles)
55% power: A	983 nm	(1,821 km; 1,132 miles)
B	950 nm	(1,760 km; 1,094 miles)

*Max certificated altitude

PIPER (PA-31) NAVAJO

On 30 September 1964 Piper flew the first of what it described as a new series of larger executive aircraft for corporate and commuter airline service. Named Navajo, it was then available with normally-aspirated or turbo-charged engines, the latter being known as the Turbo Navajo. Subsequently, three additional versions were introduced, the Navajo C/R, the Pressurised Navajo and Navajo Chieftain. The Pressurised Navajo has been discontinued but details can be found in the 1977-78 *Jane's*. The Navajo C/R and Chieftain are described separately.

Six optional factory-installed avionics packages are available for the Navajo, including nav/coms, ADF, AFCS, DME, glideslope and marker beacon receivers, transponder, and associated equipment by Bendix, Collins, King and Piper. There are, in addition, two optional equipment groups, as follows:

Co-pilot Flight Instrument Group. Includes blind-flying instrumentation with 3 in attitude and directional gyros, clock, rate of climb indicator, sensitive altimeter, true airspeed indicator, heated pitot, alternate static source, and individual rheostat controlled lighting. Group available with electrical or vacuum gyros, adding 5·6 kg (12·4 lb) or 5·9 kg (12·9 lb) respectively to basic empty weight.

De-icing Group. Pneumatic de-icing boot installation for wing and tail unit leading-edges; electrical propeller de-icing; ice inspection light; and electrical windscreen de-icing and windscreen wiper port side; adding 27·1 kg (59·8 lb) to basic empty weight.

Improvements in the 1980 version of the Navajo include refinements to the cabin, and new interior and exterior finishes. Re-certification for flight into known icing conditions, to newer, more stringent standards, applies to aircraft equipped with the optional De-icing Group.

TYPE: Six/eight-seat corporate and commuter airline transport.

WINGS: Cantilever low-wing monoplane. Wing section NACA 63₂415 at root, NACA 63₁212 at tip. 1° aerodynamic twist. 2° 30′ geometric twist. All-metal structure, with heavy stepped-down main spar, front and rear spars, lateral stringers, ribs and stressed skin. Wings spliced on centreline with heavy steel plates. Flush riveted forward of main spar. Wing-root leading-edge extended forward between nacelle and fuselage. Glassfibre wingtips. Balanced ailerons are interconnected with rudder. Trim tab in starboard aileron. Electrically-operated flaps. Pneumatic de-icing boots optional.

FUSELAGE: Conventional all-metal semi-monocoque structure.

TAIL UNIT: Cantilever all-metal structure, with sweptback vertical surfaces. Variable-incidence tailplane. Trim tabs in rudder and starboard elevator. Optional pneumatic de-icing boots.

LANDING GEAR: Hydraulically-actuated retractable tricycle type, with single wheel on each unit. Manual hydraulic emergency extension. Main wheels and tyres size 6·50-10, eight-ply rating, pressure 4·14 bars (60 lb/sq in). Steerable nosewheel and tyre size 6·00-6, six-ply rating, pressure 2·90 bars (42 lb/sq in). Toe-controlled hydraulic disc brakes. Heavy duty brakes and toe-operated brakes for co-pilot optional. Parking brake. Main-wheel doors close when gear is fully extended.

POWER PLANT: Two 231 kW (310 hp) Avco Lycoming TIO-540-A2C flat-six turbocharged engines. Hartzell three-blade constant-speed fully-feathering metal propellers with spinners. Propeller de-icing, and synchrophaser, optional. Four rubber fuel cells in wings; inboard cells each contain 212 litres (56 US gallons),

outboard cells 151·5 litres (40 US gallons) each. Total fuel capacity 727 litres (192 US gallons), of which 709 litres (187·3 US gallons) are usable. Fuel cells equipped with NACA-type anti-icing non-siphoning fuel vents. Oil capacity 22·7 litres (6 US gallons). Two-piece glassfibre engine nacelles.

ACCOMMODATION: Six individual seats, with headrests and armrests, in pairs with centre aisle. Seventh and eighth seats optional. Dual controls standard. 'No smoking, fasten seat belt' sign. Thermostatically-controlled Janitrol 35,000 BTU combustion heater, windscreen defrosters and fresh air system standard. Double-glazed windows. Electrical de-icing and windscreen wiper for port side of windscreen optional. 'Dutch' door at rear of cabin on port side. Top half hinges upward; lower half hinges down and has built-in steps. Pilot's and co-pilot's storm windows. Sun visors. Super soundproofing. Divider curtain between cabin and flight deck. Window curtains. Emergency exit. Baggage compartments in nose, capacity 68 kg (150 lb), and in rear of cabin, capacity 91 kg (200 lb). Cargo door and cockpit door optional.

SYSTEMS: Hydraulic system utilises two engine-driven pumps. 24V electrical system supplied by two engine-driven 28V 70A alternators and 24V 17Ah battery; 25Ah battery optional. External power socket standard. Oxygen system of 3·25 m³ (115 cu ft) capacity optional.

AVIONICS AND EQUIPMENT: In addition to the optional factory-installed avionics packages, there is a wide range of alternative options by Aeronetics, Bendix, Collins, King, Piper, RCA and SunAir. These include encoding altimeter, HF transceiver, radar altimeter, radio altimeter, radio telephone, RNAV, VNAV, and weather radar. Standard equipment includes pilot's blind-flying instrumentation; clock; dual exhaust gas temperature gauges; flight hour recorder; dual manifold pressure gauges; outside air temperature gauge; rate of climb indicator; sensitive altimeter; true airspeed indicator; fully-adjustable pilot and co-pilot seats with shoulder safety belts and inertia reels; headrests; folding armrests; alternate static source; heated pitot; alternator and pneumatic failure, door ajar, and heater overheat warning lights; stall warning device; corrosion proofing; cabin dome, courtesy, instrument panel, map, reading, landing, navigation, strobe and taxi lights; external power socket; tiedown rings; and stowable towbar. Optional equipment includes items covered by the Operational Groups as detailed, plus a wide range of cabin equipment including storage cabinets and drawers, tables, seventh and eighth seats, seventh seat with combined toilet and privacy curtain, fore and aft cabin dividers, auxiliary cabin heater, cabin fire extinguisher, tinted windows, thermos unit and refreshment centre, emergency locator transmitter, ground and in-flight recognition lights, and fuselage ice protection shields.

DIMENSIONS, EXTERNAL:

Wing span	12·40 m	(40 ft 8 in)
Length overall	9·94 m	(32 ft 7½ in)
Height overall	3·96 m	(13 ft 0 in)
Tailplane span	5·52 m	(18 ft 1½ in)
Wheel track	4·19 m	(13 ft 9 in)
Wheelbase	2·64 m	(8 ft 8 in)
Propeller diameter	2·03 m	(6 ft 8 in)
Distance between propeller centres	3·86 m	(12 ft 8 in)
Cabin door (port, aft): Height	1·14 m	(3 ft 9 in)
Width	0·70 m	(2 ft 3½ in)
Utility door (port, aft): Height	1·14 m	(3 ft 9 in)
Width	0·43 m	(1 ft 5 in)
Baggage door (port, fwd): Height	0·64 m	(2 ft 1 in)
Width	0·71 m	(2 ft 4 in)

Piper Navajo six/eight-seat light transport, basic version of the Navajo series

DIMENSIONS, INTERNAL:
Cabin: Length   3·33 m (10 ft 11 in)
       Max width   1·27 m (4 ft 2 in)
       Max height   1·31 m (4 ft 3½ in)
Baggage compartments: Nose   0·40 m³ (14 cu ft)
       Aft   0·62 m³ (22 cu ft)
AREA:
Wings, gross   21·3 m² (229 sq ft)
WEIGHTS AND LOADINGS:
Weight empty   1,816 kg (4,003 lb)
Max T-O and landing weight   2,948 kg (6,500 lb)
Max ramp weight   2,965 kg (6,536 lb)
Max zero-fuel weight   2,812 kg (6,200 lb)
Max wing loading   138·7 kg/m² (28·4 lb/sq ft)
Max power loading   6·38 kg/kW (10·5 lb/hp)
PERFORMANCE (at max T-O weight, except where indicated):
Max level speed at average cruise weight
                        227 knots (420 km/h; 261 mph)
Cruising speed at average cruise weight:
  75% power at 6,705 m (22,000 ft)
                        215 knots (399 km/h; 248 mph)
  75% power at 3,660 m (12,000 ft)
                        196 knots (363 km/h; 226 mph)
  65% power at 7,320 m (24,000 ft)
                        204 knots (378 km/h; 235 mph)
  65% power at 3,660 m (12,000 ft)
                        185 knots (343 km/h; 213 mph)
  55% power at 7,320 m (24,000 ft)
                        186 knots (344 km/h; 214 mph)
  55% power at 3,660 m (12,000 ft)
                        171 knots (317 km/h; 197 mph)
Stalling speed, flaps down
                        70 knots (130 km/h; 81 mph) IAS
Max rate of climb at S/L   372 m (1,220 ft)/min
Rate of climb at S/L, one engine out
                                    75 m (245 ft)/min
Service ceiling   8,015 m (26,300 ft)
Service ceiling, one engine out   4,635 m (15,200 ft)
Normal T-O run   319 m (1,045 ft)
Normal T-O to 15 m (50 ft)   639 m (2,095 ft)
*Normal landing from 15 m (50 ft) at max landing
  weight   554 m (1,818 ft)
*Short-field landing from 15 m (50 ft) 464 m (1,521 ft)
*Normal landing run   276 m (906 ft)
*Short-field landing run   274 m (900 ft)
Range with max fuel, allowances for start, taxi, T-O,
  climb, and 45 min reserves at long-range cruise
  power:
  75% power at 6,100 m (20,000 ft)
                        1,005 nm (1,862 km; 1,157 miles)
  75% power at 3,660 m (12,000 ft)
                        995 nm (1,844 km; 1,146 miles)
  65% power at 6,100 m (20,000 ft)
                        1,055 nm (1,955 km; 1,215 miles)
  65% power at 3,660 m (12,000 ft)
                        1,050 nm (1,945 km; 1,209 miles)
  55% power at 6,100 m (20,000 ft)
                        1,065 nm (1,973 km; 1,226 miles)
  55% power at 3,660 m (12,000 ft)
                        1,065 nm (1,973 km; 1,226 miles)
*With optional heavy duty brakes

PIPER (PA-31-325) NAVAJO C/R

Identical to the PA-31 Navajo except for having counter-rotating engines and nacelle baggage compartments as introduced on the Navajo Chieftain in 1972. The Navajo C/R is available in the same optional versions, and with the same optional avionics and operational package options, as the Navajo.
POWER PLANT: One 242·5 kW (325 hp) Avco Lycoming LTIO-540-F2BD and one 242·5 kW (325 hp) Avco Lycoming TIO-540-F2BD flat-six turbocharged counter-rotating engines.
WEIGHTS AND LOADINGS: As for Navajo, except:
Weight empty   1,859 kg (4,099 lb)
Max ramp weight   2,966 kg (6,540 lb)
PERFORMANCE (at max T-O weight, except where indicated):
Max level speed at average cruise weight
                        228 knots (422 km/h; 262 mph)
Cruising speed at average cruise weight:
  75% power at 6,100 m (20,000 ft)
                        220 knots (407 km/h; 253 mph)
  75% power at 3,660 m (12,000 ft)
                        202 knots (375 km/h; 233 mph)
  65% power at 6,100 m (20,000 ft)
                        208 knots (386 km/h; 240 mph)
  65% power at 3,660 m (12,000 ft)
                        190 knots (352 km/h; 219 mph)
  55% power at 4,875 m (16,000 ft)
                        180 knots (333 km/h; 207 mph)
  55% power at 3,660 m (12,000 ft)
                        175 knots (325 km/h; 202 mph)
Stalling speed, flaps down
                        70 knots (130 km/h; 81 mph) IAS
Max rate of climb at S/L   366 m (1,200 ft)/min
Rate of climb at S/L, one engine out
                                    78 m (255 ft)/min
Service ceiling   8,045 m (26,400 ft)
Service ceiling, one engine out   4,665 m (15,300 ft)

Normal T-O run   302 m (990 ft)
Normal T-O to 15 m (50 ft)   634 m (2,080 ft)
*Normal landing from 15 m (50 ft)   554 m (1,818 ft)
*Short-field landing from 15 m (50 ft) 464 m (1,521 ft)
*Normal landing run   276 m (906 ft)
*Short-field landing run   274 m (900 ft)
Range with max fuel, allowances for start, taxi, T-O,
  climb, and 45 min reserves at long-range cruise
  power:
  75% power at 6,100 m (20,000 ft)
                        940 nm (1,741 km; 1,082 miles)
  75% power at 3,660 m (12,000 ft)
                        910 nm (1,687 km; 1,048 miles)
  65% power at 6,100 m (20,000 ft)
                        1,000 nm (1,854 km; 1,152 miles)
  65% power at 3,660 m (12,000 ft)
                        970 nm (1,798 km; 1,117 miles)
  55% power at 4,875 m (16,000 ft)
                        1,040 nm (1,928 km; 1,198 miles)
  55% power at 3,660 m (12,000 ft)
                        1,025 nm (1,899 km; 1,180 miles)
*With optional heavy duty brakes

PIPER (PA-31-350) CHIEFTAIN

First announced on 11 September 1972, the PA-31-350 Chieftain is a lengthened version of the Navajo, with the fuselage extended by 0·61 m (2 ft 0 in) and with 261 kW (350 hp) counter-rotating turbocharged engines.

The main cabin floor is designed to carry heavy concentrated loads of up to 976 kg/m² (200 lb/sq ft) and, in addition to the 6·14 m³ (217 cu ft) of cargo space in the main cabin, 91 kg (200 lb) of cargo or baggage can be carried in the forward nose compartment, and 68 kg (150 lb) in the rear of each engine nacelle.

Two optional interior groups of equipment are available, depending upon the proposed use of the aircraft:
Standard Interior Group. Comprises six adjustable seats. Passenger seats in club arrangement with headrests, folding armrests, seat belts, oxygen mask stowage beneath each seat, and magazine storage pockets on each seat back. 'No smoking/Fasten seat belt' sign. Pull-curtain cockpit divider. Choice of seven interior colour schemes.
Commuter Interior Group. Comprises ten forward-facing seats. Eight adjustable and reclining passenger seats with oxygen mask stowage and magazine storage as above. 'No smoking/Fasten seat belt' sign. Pull-curtain cockpit divider. Adds 39·5 kg (87 lb) to basic empty weight.

Operational groups, comprising Co-pilot Instrument Group and De-icing Group, and avionics groups as for the Navajo, are available for the Chieftain, as well as a wide range of optional avionics.

The description of the Navajo applies also to the Chieftain, except as follows:
FUSELAGE: As for Navajo, except length increased by 0·61 m (2 ft 0 in).
POWER PLANT: Two 261 kW (350 hp) Avco Lycoming flat-six turbocharged engines, one TIO-540-J2BD and one LTIO-540-J2BD, each driving a Hartzell three-blade constant-speed fully-feathering metal propeller. Four rubber fuel cells in wings; inboard cells each contain 212 litres (56 US gallons), outboard cells each 151·5 litres (40 US gallons). Total fuel capacity 727 litres (192 US gallons), of which 689 litres (182 US gallons) are usable. Oil capacity 22·7 litres (6 US gallons).
ACCOMMODATION: Pilot and co-pilot on individually adjustable and reclining seats. Dual controls standard. Interior seating and equipment as detailed in optional interior groups. Cabin heated by thermostatically-controlled Janitrol 50,000 BTU combustion heater. Piper Aire 16,000 BTU air-conditioning system optional. Baggage/cargo compartments in nose and aft fuselage, capacity of each 91 kg (200 lb), and in the rear of each engine nacelle, each 68 kg (150 lb).
AVIONICS AND EQUIPMENT: A wide range of optional avionics is available, including a flight director system integrated with autopilot and weather radar. Standard and optional equipment is generally similar to that available for the Navajo. Also available optionally for all interior groups is a cargo kit which includes cargo barriers, tiedown rings and net, eight seat-track tiedown rings, four plug-in tiedown rings, and four tiedown straps.
DIMENSIONS, EXTERNAL:
Wing span   12·40 m (40 ft 8 in)
Length overall   10·55 m (34 ft 7½ in)
Height overall   3·96 m (13 ft 0 in)
Tailplane span   5·52 m (18 ft 1½ in)
Wheel track   4·19 m (13 ft 9 in)
Wheelbase   3·24 m (10 ft 7½ in)
Propeller diameter   2·03 m (6 ft 8 in)
Distance between propeller centres   3·86 m (12 ft 8 in)
DIMENSIONS, INTERNAL:
Cabin: Length   3·84 m (12 ft 7 in)
       Width   1·27 m (4 ft 2 in)
       Height   1·31 m (4 ft 3½ in)
Baggage/cargo compartments:
       Nose   0·40 m³ (14 cu ft)
       Aft   0·62 m³ (22 cu ft)
       Engine nacelles (each)   0·37 m³ (13·25 cu ft)
AREA:
Wings, gross   21·3 m² (229 sq ft)

Photograph and three-view drawing (*Pilot Press*) **of the Piper Chieftain six/ten-seat executive/commuter/cargo aircraft**

WEIGHTS AND LOADINGS:

Weight empty (standard)	1,915 kg (4,221 lb)
Max T-O and landing weight	3,175 kg (7,000 lb)
Max ramp weight	3,196 kg (7,045 lb)
Max wing loading	149·4 kg/m² (30·6 lb/sq ft)
Max power loading	6·08 kg/kW (10·0 lb/hp)

PERFORMANCE (at max T-O weight, except where indicated):

Max level speed at average cruise weight
231 knots (428 km/h; 266 mph)
Cruising speed at average cruise weight:
75% power at 6,100 m (20,000 ft)
221 knots (409 km/h; 254 mph)
75% power at 3,660 m (12,000 ft)
205 knots (380 km/h; 236 mph)
65% power at 6,100 m (20,000 ft)
210 knots (389 km/h; 242 mph)
65% power at 3,660 m (12,000 ft)
191 knots (354 km/h; 220 mph)
55% power at 4,570 m (15,000 ft)
177 knots (328 km/h; 204 mph)
55% power at 3,660 m (12,000 ft)
173 knots (320 km/h; 199 mph)
Stalling speed, flaps up 80 knots (148 km/h; 92 mph)
Stalling speed, flaps down
74 knots (137 km/h; 85 mph)
Max rate of climb at S/L 341 m (1,120 ft)/min
Rate of climb at S/L, one engine out
70 m (230 ft)/min
Service ceiling 8,290 m (27,200 ft)
Service ceiling, one engine out 4,175 m (13,700 ft)
Normal T-O run 415 m (1,360 ft)
Normal T-O to 15 m (50 ft) 747 m (2,450 ft)
Normal landing from 15 m (50 ft) 573 m (1,880 ft)
Short-field landing from 15 m (50 ft) 491 m (1,610 ft)
Normal landing run 319 m (1,045 ft)
Short-field landing run 297 m (975 ft)
Accelerate/stop distance 640 m (2,100 ft)
Range with max fuel, allowances for start, taxi, T-O, climb, and 45 min reserves at long-range cruise power:
75% power at 6,100 m (20,000 ft)
885 nm (1,640 km; 1,019 miles)
75% power at 3,660 m (12,000 ft)
855 nm (1,585 km; 985 miles)
65% power at 6,100 m (20,000 ft)
925 nm (1,714 km; 1,065 miles)
65% power at 3,660 m (12,000 ft)
900 nm (1,667 km; 1,036 miles)
55% power at 4,570 m (15,000 ft)
950 nm (1,761 km; 1,094 miles)
55% power at 3,660 m (12,000 ft)
950 nm (1,761 km; 1,094 miles)

PIPER (PA-31T-1) CHEYENNE I

Introduced in 1978, the Cheyenne I is a low-cost version of the established Cheyenne PA-31T, which has been redesignated Cheyenne II, and which is described separately. It differs primarily by having less powerful engines. It is available with the optional Standard and Executive interiors, De-icing Group and Co-pilot Flight Group as detailed for the Cheyenne II. Also available optionally are three factory-installed avionics packages which include nav/coms, ADF, AFCS, DME, glideslope and marker beacon receivers, transponder, weather radar, and associated equipment by Bendix, Collins, King and Piper. Additional optional avionics items by Aeronetics, Smith and SunAir as well as the above manufacturers, include altitude alerter, encoding altimeter, radio telephone, radio altimeter, radar altimeter, and RNAV.

FAA certification was received on 23 March 1978, and deliveries began at the end of April 1978. The 500th Cheyenne delivered, in August 1980, was a Cheyenne I.

The 1980 version of the Cheyenne I introduces a number of improvements as standard, including a new

windscreen of 20% greater area, a digital clock, refinements to the overhead control panel, and fore and aft adjustable and reclining rearward-facing seats. New options include factory-installed engine wash rings, and a radome erosion guard.

The description of the Cheyenne II applies also to the Cheyenne I, except as follows:

LANDING GEAR: As Cheyenne II except: Cleveland Type 40-106 main wheels, with 6·50 × 10 10-ply tyres, pressure 5·52 bars (80 lb/sq in). Cleveland Type 40-120A nosewheel, with 17·5 × 6·25 10-ply tyre, pressure 5·52 bars (80 lb/sq in). Cleveland Type 30-106 brakes.

POWER PLANT: Two 372·6 kW (500 shp) Pratt & Whitney Aircraft of Canada PT6A-11 turboprop engines, each driving a Hartzell Type HC-BTN-3B three-blade constant-speed reversible-pitch and fully-feathering metal propeller. Each wing has three interconnected fuel cells, with total capacity of 1,166 litres (308 US gallons), of which 1,136 litres (300 US gallons) are usable. Optional wingtip tanks, each of 113·5 litres (30 US gallons) capacity, plus installational plumbing, provide a maximum total usable capacity of 1,446 litres (382 US gallons). Refuelling points on top of engine nacelles and on upper surface of each tip-tank. Oil capacity 24·6 litres (6·5 US gallons).

DIMENSIONS, EXTERNAL: As for Cheyenne II, except:

Wing span	12·40 m (40 ft 8 in)
Wing chord at root	2·61 m (8 ft 6¾ in)
Wing chord at tip	0·97 m (3 ft 2 in)
Wing aspect ratio	7·37
Passenger door (port, aft):	
Height to sill	0·97 m (3 ft 2 in)
Baggage door (port, fwd):	
Width	0·53 m (1 ft 9 in)

DIMENSIONS, INTERNAL: As for Cheyenne II, except:

Cabin (excl flight deck): Length	2·57 m (8 ft 5 in)
Max width	1·27 m (4 ft 2 in)
Max height	1·31 m (4 ft 3½ in)

AREAS: As for Cheyenne II, except:

Fin	1·37 m² (14·72 sq ft)
Rudder, incl tab	1·20 m² (12·88 sq ft)

WEIGHTS AND LOADINGS:

Weight empty	2,224 kg (4,904 lb)
Max T-O and landing weight	3,946 kg (8,700 lb)
Max ramp weight	3,969 kg (8,750 lb)
Max zero-fuel weight	3,266 kg (7,200 lb)
Max wing loading	185·5 kg/m² (38·0 lb/sq ft)
Max power loading	5·30 kg/kW (8·7 lb/shp)

PERFORMANCE (at max T-O weight and without optional wingtip tanks installed, unless specified otherwise):

Cruising speed, max cruise power, average cruise weight of 3,400 kg (7,500 lb), at:
3,660 m (12,000 ft) 249 knots (461 km/h; 287 mph)
4,875 m (16,000 ft) 248 knots (460 km/h; 286 mph)
6,100 m (20,000 ft) 244 knots (452 km/h; 281 mph)
7,620 m (25,000 ft) 236 knots (437 km/h; 272 mph)
Stalling speed, wheels and flaps up, engines idling
84 knots (156 km/h; 97 mph) IAS
Stalling speed, wheels and flaps down, engines idling
72 knots (133 km/h; 83 mph) IAS
Rotation speed 89 knots (167 km/h; 104 mph)
Approach speed 101 knots (187 km/h; 116 mph)
Max rate of climb at S/L 533 m (1,750 ft)/min
Rate of climb at S/L, one engine out:
without tip-tanks 126 m (413 ft)/min
with tip-tanks 134 m (440 ft)/min
Service ceiling 8,595 m (28,200 ft)
Service ceiling, one engine out:
without tip-tanks 3,810 m (12,500 ft)
with tip-tanks 4,190 m (13,750 ft)
T-O run 436 m (1,429 ft)
T-O to 15 m (50 ft) 745 m (2,444 ft)
Landing from 15 m (50 ft) 678 m (2,223 ft)
Landing from 15 m (50 ft) with propeller reversal
473 m (1,553 ft)

Landing run 472 m (1,549 ft)
Landing run with propeller reversal 272 m (893 ft)
Accelerate/stop distance 1,016 m (3,334 ft)
Range with standard fuel, allowances for start, taxi, T-O, climb, descent, and 45 min reserves at max range cruising power:
Max cruising power at:
3,660 m (12,000 ft)
715 nm (1,325 km; 823 miles)
4,875 m (16,000 ft)
780 nm (1,445 km; 897 miles)
6,100 m (20,000 ft)
850 nm (1,575 km; 978 miles)
7,620 m (25,000 ft)
940 nm (1,742 km; 1,081 miles)
Max range power at:
3,660 m (12,000 ft)
775 nm (1,435 km; 892 miles)
4,875 m (16,000 ft)
845 nm (1,565 km; 972 miles)
6,100 m (20,000 ft)
910 nm (1,685 km; 1,047 miles)
7,620 m (25,000 ft)
980 nm (1,815 km; 1,128 miles)
Range with max optional fuel, allowances as above:
Max cruising power at:
3,660 m (12,000 ft)
955 nm (1,770 km; 1,100 miles)
4,875 m (16,000 ft)
1,040 nm (1,927 km; 1,198 miles)
6,100 m (20,000 ft)
1,130 nm (2,094 km; 1,301 miles)
7,620 m (25,000 ft)
1,260 nm (2,335 km; 1,451 miles)
Max range power at:
3,660 m (12,000 ft)
1,040 nm (1,927 km; 1,198 miles)
4,875 m (16,000 ft)
1,135 nm (2,102 km; 1,306 miles)
6,100 m (20,000 ft)
1,220 nm (2,260 km; 1,404 miles)
7,620 m (25,000 ft)
1,330 nm (2,463 km; 1,530 miles)

PIPER (PA-31T) CHEYENNE II

Design of the PA-31T began at the end of 1965. First flight of the prototype was made on 20 August 1969, and FAA certification was granted on 3 May 1972. The first production aircraft flew for the first time on 22 October 1973. Following the introduction of the low-cost Cheyenne I and 6/11-seat Cheyenne III, both of which are described separately, the original version was redesignated Cheyenne II.

It is available with Standard and Executive interior options and two operational group options as follows:

Standard. Six individual seats in pairs, with headrests and armrests. Pilot/co-pilot seats four-way adjustable with shoulder harness and inertia reels; third and fourth cabin seats aft facing; and all cabin seats with seat belts; window curtains and wall to wall carpet. Rear cabin divider with clothes bar and baggage security net. Forward cabin divider curtain. 'No smoking/Fasten seat belt' sign. Oxygen outlets and masks at each seat position. Options available include a cabin instrumentation panel comprising digital readouts of altitude, outside air temperature, time, and true airspeed; pneumatic door extender; forward cabin combination unit; storage cabinets; folding tables; aft cabin combination unit, which includes side-facing seventh seat/toilet; seventh and eighth seats; tinted cabin windows; cabin fire extinguisher; stereo system; and all-leather seat covering.

Executive. Six individual seats, comprising two crew seats and four reclining chairs in the Standard arrangement. Other standard equipment as described, plus forward cabin combination unit which includes cabin dividers and curtain, electrically-heated Thermos unit, cup dispenser, storage for ice, beverages and manuals; two folding tables; pneumatic door extender and aft cabin combination unit which includes side-facing seventh seat/toilet, cabin divider with mirror, privacy curtain, refreshment centre; AC power outlet for electric razor; and baggage security net. Options are the same as for the Standard interior, unless included in the Executive package. Adds 55·3 kg (121·9 lb) to basic empty weight.

De-icing Group. Pneumatic de-icing boots for wing and tail unit leading-edges, and wing ice inspection light; adding 17·9 kg (39·4 lb) to basic empty weight.

Co-pilot Flight Group. Airspeed and rate of climb indicator, altimeter, electric turn rate indicator, attitude and directional gyros, clock, heated pitot, static system with alternate source, co-pilot's toe-brakes and windscreen wiper; adding 8·9 kg (19·7 lb) to basic empty weight.

In addition to the six/eight-seat passenger versions of the Cheyenne II, as described, Piper has developed a special multi-purpose model known as the **Maritime Surveillance Cheyenne II.** The prototype (N431PC), shown in an accompanying illustration, has a radar pod under the port wing. It can, however, be equipped for a wide range of

Piper Cheyenne I pressurised six/eight-seat cabin monoplane, with optional wingtip tanks

Piper Cheyenne II (two P&WC PT6A-28 turboprop engines) equipped as maritime patrol demonstrator

Original version of the Piper Cheyenne pressurised six/eight-seat cabin monoplane which is now designated Cheyenne II *(Pilot Press)*

special missions, including photo mapping, airways calibration, geological survey, rainmaking and hail suppression. A quick-change interior is standard, permitting conversion for corporate use in 30 min.

The 1980 versions of the Cheyenne II introduce the new standard and optional improvements as detailed for the Cheyenne I.

TYPE: Six/eight-seat cabin monoplane.

WINGS: Cantilever low-wing monoplane. Wing section NACA 63₂A415 at root, NACA 63₁A212 at tip. Dihedral 5°. Incidence 1° 30' at root, −1° at tip. Sweepback 0° at 30% chord. Three-spar structure of 2024ST light alloy. Balanced ailerons and single-slotted trailing-edge flaps of 2024ST light alloy. Trim tab in starboard aileron. Pneumatic de-icing boots on wing leading-edges optional.

FUSELAGE: Semi-monocoque structure of 2024ST light alloy, with fail-safe structure in the pressurised areas.

TAIL UNIT: Cantilever structure of 2024ST light alloy with sweptback vertical surfaces. Fixed-incidence tailplane. Trim tabs in elevators and rudder. Pneumatic de-icing of fin and tailplane leading-edges optional.

LANDING GEAR: Hydraulically-retractable tricycle type with single wheel on each unit, main units retracting inward and nosewheel aft. Nosewheel safety mirror. Piper oleo-pneumatic shock-absorbers. Main wheels and tyres size 6·50-10, 10-ply rating. Steerable nosewheel with Type VII tyre size 18 × 4·4, 6-ply rating. Goodyear disc-type hydraulic brakes. Parking brake.

POWER PLANT: Two 462 kW (620 ehp) Pratt & Whitney Aircraft of Canada PT6A-28 turboprop engines, each driving a Hartzell three-blade constant-speed reversible-pitch fully-feathering metal propeller type HC-BTN-3B. Propeller synchrophasers optional. Each wing has three interconnected fuel cells and a tip-tank, giving total fuel capacity of 1,476 litres (390 US gallons), of which 1,446 litres (382 US gallons) are usable. Refuelling points in engine nacelles and on upper surface of each tip-tank. NACA type anti-icing non-siphoning fuel tank vents with flame arresters. Oil capacity 24·6 litres (6·5 US gallons). Electrically heated air intake anti-icing boot, air intake ice deflection and air bypass doors. Electrical propeller de-icing.

ACCOMMODATION: Pilot and co-pilot on two individual adjustable seats. Dual controls standard. Pilot's storm window. Heated windscreen and windscreen wiper for pilot, optional for co-pilot. Cabin seating for four to six passengers on individual seats. Door with built-in airstair on port side, which has seven locking pins and inflatable pressurisation seal. Dual-pane windows. Emergency exit window on starboard side. Cabin heated and air-conditioned. Forward and aft cabin dividers. A wide range of options for cabin includes folding tables, beverage dispensers, pneumatic door extender, storage cabinets and tinted windows. Baggage compartments in nose, capacity 136 kg (300 lb), and

rear of cabin, capacity 91 kg (200 lb). External access door to nose compartment.

SYSTEMS: Air-conditioning and pressurisation, with pressure differential of 0·38 bars (5·5 lb/sq in). Freon-type air-conditioner of 23,000 BTU capacity. Janitrol combustion heater of 35,000 BTU capacity with automatic windscreen defroster. Hydraulic system supplied by dual engine-driven pumps for landing gear retraction and brakes. Pneumatic system and vacuum system provided by engine bleed air. Electrical system supplied by two 28V 200A starter/generators and 24V 43Ah nickel-cadmium battery. External power socket standard. Oxygen system of 1·37 m³ (48·3 cu ft) capacity. De-icing system comprises electric anti-icing boots for air intakes, heated pitot and electric propeller de-icing. Fire detection system with six sensors; engine fire extinguishing system optional.

AVIONICS: Six optional factory-installed avionics packages are available, these including nav/coms, ADF, AFCS, DME, glideslope and marker beacon receivers, RNAV, transponder, and weather radar by Bendix, Collins, King and Piper. Options include alternatives to or duplication of the above equipment, plus altitude alerter, encoding altimeter, radar altimeter, radio altimeter, radio telephone, global navigation system, and HF transceivers by manufacturers which include the above, plus Aeronetics, RCA, Smith, Sperry and SunAir.

EQUIPMENT: Installed standard equipment is extensive, and optional items include flight instrument group, toe brakes, heated windscreen and windscreen wiper for co-pilot, emergency locator transmitter, wing and tail pneumatic de-icing boots, engine fire extinguisher system, emergency electrical power supply system, fuselage ice protection plates, ice inspection lights and propeller synchrophasers.

DIMENSIONS, EXTERNAL:

Wing span over tip-tanks	13·01 m (42 ft 8¼ in)
Length overall	10·57 m (34 ft 8 in)
Height overall	3·89 m (12 ft 9 in)
Tailplane span	6·05 m (19 ft 10 in)
Wheel track	4·19 m (13 ft 9 in)
Wheelbase	2·64 m (8 ft 8 in)
Propeller diameter	2·36 m (7 ft 9 in)
Distance between propeller centres	3·85 m (12 ft 7½ in)
Propeller ground clearance	0·27 m (10½ in)
Passenger door (port, aft):	
Height	1·17 m (3 ft 10 in)
Width	0·71 m (2 ft 4 in)
Height to sill	0·94 m (3 ft 1 in)
Baggage door (fwd): Height	0·53 m (1 ft 9 in)
Width	0·66 m (2 ft 2 in)
Height to sill	1·10 m (3 ft 7½ in)
Emergency exit (stbd, fwd):	
Height	0·64 m (2 ft 1 in)
Width	0·48 m (1 ft 7 in)

DIMENSIONS, INTERNAL:

Cabin: Length, incl flight deck	4·90 m (16 ft 1 in)
Length, excl flight deck	2·57 m (8 ft 5 in)
Max width	1·27 m (4 ft 2 in)
Max height	1·31 m (4 ft 3½ in)
Floor area	4·37 m² (47 sq ft)
Volume	6·29 m³ (222 cu ft)
Forward baggage compartment	0·57 m³ (20 cu ft)
Aft baggage compartment	0·62 m³ (22 cu ft)

AREAS:

Wings, gross	21·3 m² (229 sq ft)
Ailerons (total)	1·21 m² (13 sq ft)
Trailing-edge flaps (total)	3·12 m² (33·6 sq ft)
Fin	1·48 m² (15·9 sq ft)
Rudder, incl tab	0·98 m² (10·6 sq ft)
Tailplane	3·92 m² (42·2 sq ft)
Elevators, incl tab	2·63 m² (28·3 sq ft)

WEIGHTS AND LOADINGS:

Weight empty, standard, equipped	2,259 kg (4,980 lb)
Max T-O and landing weight	4,082 kg (9,000 lb)
Max ramp weight	4,105 kg (9,050 lb)
Max zero-fuel weight	3,265 kg (7,200 lb)
Max wing loading	191·9 kg/m² (39·3 lb/sq ft)
Max power loading	4·42 kg/kW (7·26 lb/ehp)

PERFORMANCE (at max T-O weight, unless specified otherwise):

Cruising speed, max cruise power, average cruise weight of 3,493 kg (7,700 lb) at:

3,350 m (11,000 ft)	283 knots (524 km/h; 325 mph)
4,875 m (16,000 ft)	277 knots (513 km/h; 318 mph)
6,400 m (21,000 ft)	268 knots (496 km/h; 308 mph)
8,840 m (29,000 ft)	250 knots (463 km/h; 287 mph)

Stalling speed, wheels and flaps up, engines idling	86 knots (159 km/h; 99 mph) IAS
Stalling speed, wheels and flaps down, engines idling	75 knots (139 km/h; 96 mph) IAS
Rotation speed	91 knots (167 km/h; 105 mph) IAS
Approach speed	98 knots (182 km/h; 113 mph)
Max rate of climb at S/L	826 m (2,710 ft)/min
Rate of climb at S/L, one engine out	201 m (660 ft)/min
Service ceiling	9,630 m (31,600 ft)
Service ceiling, one engine out	4,450 m (14,600 ft)
T-O run	430 m (1,410 ft)
T-O to 15 m (50 ft)	604 m (1,980 ft)
Landing from 15 m (50 ft)	756 m (2,480 ft)
Landing from 15 m (50 ft) with propeller reversal	567 m (1,860 ft)
Landing run	436 m (1,430 ft)
Landing run with propeller reversal	291 m (955 ft)
Accelerate/stop distance	1,006 m (3,300 ft)

Range with max fuel at max cruise power, with allowances for start, taxi, T-O, climb, descent, and 45 min reserves at long-range cruise power at:

3,660 m (12,000 ft)	905 nm (1,676 km; 1,041 miles)
4,875 m (16,000 ft)	1,020 nm (1,889 km; 1,173 miles)
6,400 m (21,000 ft)	1,155 nm (2,139 km; 1,329 miles)
8,840 m (29,000 ft)	1,380 nm (2,555 km; 1,588 miles)

Range at max range power, fuel and allowances as above, at:

3,660 m (12,000 ft)	1,090 nm (2,018 km; 1,254 miles)
4,875 m (16,000 ft)	1,195 nm (2,213 km; 1,375 miles)
6,400 m (21,000 ft)	1,330 nm (2,463 km; 1,530 miles)
8,840 m (29,000 ft)	1,510 nm (2,796 km; 1,737 miles)

PIPER (PA-42) CHEYENNE III

Piper announced on 26 September 1977 the introduction of a third member of the Cheyenne family of twin-turboprop aircraft. Designated Cheyenne III, it differs from the I and II by having increased wing span, a lengthened fuselage, a T tail and more powerful PT6A-41 engines. The production prototype flew for the first time on 18 May 1979; FAA certification was gained in early 1980, and deliveries of production aircraft began on 30 June 1980.

The Cheyenne III is available with Standard and Executive interior options, and Co-pilot Flight Groups, as detailed for the Cheyenne II. Full de-icing equipment is standard.

TYPE: Six/eleven-seat corporate and commuter airline transport.

WINGS: Cantilever low-wing monoplane. Wing section NACA 63₂A415, modified, at root, NACA 63₁A212 at tip. Dihedral 5°. Incidence 1° 30'. No sweepback. Three-spar fail-safe structure of light alloy. Ailerons and trailing-edge flaps as for Cheyenne II. B.F. Goodrich pneumatic de-icing boots for wing leading-edges are standard.

FUSELAGE: Conventional semi-monocoque structure of light alloy, with fail-safe structure in the pressurised areas.

TAIL UNIT: Cantilever T tail of light alloy construction,

with sweptback vertical surfaces. Fixed-incidence tail-plane. Elevators and rudder of light alloy. Servo tab in rudder; anti-servo tab in elevator. Goodrich de-icing equipment standard for leading-edges of tailplane and fin.

LANDING GEAR: Hydraulically-retractable tricycle type with single wheel on each unit. Main units retract inward, nosewheel aft. Manually-operated hydraulic system for emergency extension. Piper oleo-pneumatic shock-absorbers. Cleveland main wheels with tyres size 6·50-10 12-ply Type III, pressure 6·90 bars (100 lb/sq in). Cleveland steerable nosewheel with tyre size 17·5 × 6·25, 10-ply rating Type III, pressure 4·83 bars (70 lb/sq in). Cleveland hydraulically-operated disc brakes. Parking brake.

POWER PLANT: Two Pratt & Whitney Aircraft of Canada PT6A-41 turboprop engines, each flat rated to 537 kW (720 shp) and driving a Hartzell three-blade constant-speed feathering and reversible-pitch metal propeller with Q-tips. Automatic propeller feathering system and synchrophaser optional. Each wing has three interconnected fuel cells and a tip-tank, with a combined total capacity of 1,514 litres (400 US gallons), of which 1,476 litres (390 US gallons) are usable. Optional fuel tanks in each engine nacelle, capacity 284 litres (75 US gallons), to provide total usable capacity of 2,044 litres (540 US gallons). Refuelling points on upper surface of each tip-tank and engine nacelle. Oil capacity 24·6 litres (6·5 US gallons). Electrical intake anti-icing and propeller de-icing.

ACCOMMODATION: Pilot and co-pilot on two individual adjustable seats. To be certificated for single-pilot operation. Dual controls standard. Pilot's storm window. Cabin seats up to nine passengers in individual reclinable seats. Door with built-in airstair on port side, with seven locking pins and inflatable pressurisation seal. Emergency exit window on starboard side. Forward and aft cabin dividers. A wide range of options for cabin furnishing. Baggage compartments in nose and aft cabin, each with capacity of 136 kg (300 lb). When aircraft is operated without engine nacelle fuel tank option, an additional 136 kg (300 lb) of baggage can be accommodated in each nacelle locker to give a maximum total baggage capacity of 544 kg (1,200 lb). Accommodation is pressurised, heated and air-conditioned. Pilot's windscreen heated; provisions for heating co-pilot windscreen. Pilot and co-pilot windscreen wipers standard.

SYSTEMS: Garrett-AiResearch pressurisation system with max differential of 0·43 bars (6·3 lb/sq in), maintaining a cabin altitude of 3,050 m (10,000 ft) to a height of 10,060 m (33,000 ft). Environmental control system, combining the functions of heater, air-conditioner, and dehumidifier. Hydraulic system supplied by dual engine-driven pumps. Pneumatic system and vacuum system supplied by engine bleed air. Electrical system includes two 28V 250A engine-driven generators and 24V 43Ah storage battery. Oxygen system of 0·62 m³ (22 cu ft) capacity with ten outlets. De-icing system includes pneumatic wing and tailplane de-icing boots, electrical anti-icing of engine air intakes, heated pitots, electrical propeller de-icing, and windscreen heating.

AVIONICS AND EQUIPMENT: Generally as for Cheyenne II, including King 300 and Collins AP-106 autopilot/flight directors.

DIMENSIONS, EXTERNAL:As for Cheyenne II, except:

Wing span over tip-tanks	14·53 m (47 ft 8⅛ in)
Wing chord at root	3·12 m (10 ft 3 in)
Wing chord at tip	0·97 m (3 ft 2 in)
Wing aspect ratio	7·82
Length overall	12·23 m (43 ft 4¾ in)
Height overall	4·50 m (14 ft 9 in)
Tailplane span	6·65 m (21 ft 10 in)
Wheel track	5·72 m (18 ft 9 in)
Wheelbase	3·23 m (10 ft 7¼ in)
Propeller diameter	2·41 m (7 ft 11 in)
Distance between propeller centres	
	5·38 m (17 ft 8 in)

DIMENSIONS, INTERNAL:

Cabin (incl flight deck and aft baggage area):	
Length	6·99 m (22 ft 11 in)
Max width	1·30 m (4 ft 3 in)
Max height	1·35 m (4 ft 5 in)
Volume	approx 9·91 m³ (350 cu ft)
Nose baggage compartment	0·46 m³ (16·25 cu ft)
Aft baggage compartment	0·88 m³ (31 cu ft)
Nacelle baggage locker (two, each)	
	0·41 m³ (14·5 cu ft)

AREAS:

Wings, gross	27·22 m² (293 sq ft)
Ailerons (total)	1·25 m² (13·5 sq ft)
Trailing-edge flaps (total)	3·98 m² (42·8 sq ft)
Fin	2·17 m² (23·36 sq ft)
Rudder, incl tab	1·88 m² (20·2 sq ft)
Tailplane	3·48 m² (37·5 sq ft)
Elevators, incl tab	2·26 m² (24·3 sq ft)

WEIGHTS AND LOADINGS:

Basic weight empty	2,830 kg (6,240 lb)
Max T-O weight	4,990 kg (11,000 lb)
Max ramp weight	5,025 kg (11,080 lb)
Max zero-fuel weight	4,422 kg (9,750 lb)

Photograph and three-view drawing *(Michael A. Badrocke)* of Piper's T-tailed Cheyenne III

Max landing weight	4,685 kg (10,330 lb)
Max wing loading	183·29 kg/m² (37·54 lb/sq ft)
Max power loading	4·65 kg/kW (7·64 lb/shp)

PERFORMANCE (at max T-O weight, except where indicated):

Max level speed at average cruise weight of 4,218 kg (9,300 lb)   292 knots (541 km/h; 336 mph)

Cruising speed at max cruise power, at average cruise weight of 4,218 kg (9,300 lb):

at 6,100 m (21,000 ft)	
	289 knots (536 km/h; 333 mph)
at 7,620 m (25,000 ft)	
	283 knots (524 km/h; 326 mph)
at 9,145 m (30,000 ft)	
	275 knots (509 km/h; 316 mph)
at 10,060 m (33,000 ft)	
	270 knots (501 km/h; 311 mph)

Stalling speed:

flaps and gear up, power off   95 knots (176 km/h; 109 mph) CAS

flaps and gear down, power off   83 knots (155 km/h; 96 mph) CAS

Rotation speed	98 knots (182 km/h; 113 mph) CAS
Approach speed	
	104 knots (193 km/h; 120 mph) CAS
Max rate of climb at S/L	732 m (2,400 ft)/min
Rate of climb at S/L, one engine out	
	172 m (565 ft)/min
Service ceiling	10,000 m (32,800 ft)
Service ceiling, one engine out	4,435 m (14,550 ft)
T-O run	533 m (1,750 ft)
T-O to 15 m (50 ft)	722 m (2,369 ft)
Landing from 15 m (50 ft)	860 m (2,820 ft)
Landing from 15 m (50 ft) with propeller reversal	
	713 m (2,340 ft)
Landing run	532 m (1,745 ft)
Landing run with propeller reversal	382 m (1,255 ft)

Accelerate/stop distance	1,128 m (3,700 ft)

Range, with max usable fuel, allowances for taxi, T-O, climb, descent, and 45 min reserves at max range power:

Max cruising power at:

6,100 m (20,000 ft)	
	1,302 nm (2,411 km; 1,498 miles)
7,620 m (25,000 ft)	
	1,326 nm (2,455 km; 1,526 miles)
9,145 m (30,000 ft)	
	1,785 nm (3,306 km; 2,054 miles)
10,060 m (33,000 ft)	
	1,985 nm (3,676 km; 2,284 miles)

Max range power at:

6,100 m (20,000 ft)	
	1,597 nm (2,957 km; 1,837 miles)
7,620 m (25,000 ft)	
	1,798 nm (3,330 km; 2 069 miles)
9,145 m (30,000 ft)	
	1,964 nm (3,637 km; 2,260 miles)
10,060 m (33,000 ft)	
	2,040 nm (3,778 km; 2,347 miles)

PIPER (PA-34-200T) SENECA II

On 23 September 1971, Piper announced a twin-engined light aircraft which had the company designation PA-34 and, following Piper tradition, the Indian name Seneca. Built at Piper's Vero Beach, Florida, factory, the aircraft was redesignated Seneca II from 1975.

The Seneca II has counter-rotating (C/R) engine and propeller installations. The retractable landing gear is operated by an electro-hydraulic system and includes an emergency extension system which allows the wheels to free-fall into the down and locked position. A dual-vane stall warning system provides warning by horn well in advance of the stall in either 'clean' or gear/flaps-down configuration.

The 1980 Seneca II introduced a number of new options, including a built-in oxygen system, a de-icing equipment package, and advanced avionics.

It was announced on 3 January 1977 that Piper had signed an agreement with Pezetel, the Polish foreign trade organisation, enabling PZL Mielec to assemble, manufacture and distribute the Seneca II in Eastern Europe. These aircraft (several hundred are involved in the agreement) are powered by 164 kW (220 hp) PZL-Franklin engines and are named **M-20 Mewa** (Gull).

The following optional operational groups are available:

Custom. Comprising an instrument package which includes blind-flying instrumentation with 3 in attitude and directional gyros, electric clock, outside air temperature gauge, rate of climb indicator, true airspeed indicator, and dual engine-driven pressure pumps; a lighting package which includes instrument panel white lighting and overhead red lighting, avionics dimming, cabin dome, map, reading, waterfall switch panel, landing, navigation, taxi, and wing strobe lights; heated pitot and stall warning device; assist straps; and towbar; adding 16·6 kg (36·5 lb) to basic empty weight.

Executive. As Custom group, plus pilot's vertically adjustable seat, shoulder and safety belts with inertia reels for rear seats, tinted windows, emergency locator transmitter, baggage compartment and entrance door lights, external power socket, and quick oil drain valves; adding 23 kg (50·6 lb) to basic empty weight.

De-icing Group. Comprising pneumatic de-icing boots for wing and tail unit leading-edges, electrical propeller de-icing, luminous outside air temperature gauge, ice inspection light, and electrical windscreen de-icing plate; adding 24·5 kg (54·1 lb) to basic empty weight.

TYPE: Six/seven-seat twin-engined light aircraft.

WINGS: Cantilever low-wing monoplane. Dihedral 7°. Single-spar wings, Frise ailerons, and wide-span manually-operated slotted flaps, of light alloy construction. Glassfibre wingtips. Pneumatic de-icing boots for wing leading-edges optional.

FUSELAGE: Light alloy semi-monocoque structure.

TAIL UNIT: Cantilever structure of light alloy. One-piece all-moving horizontal surface with combined anti-balance and trim tab. Anti-servo tab in rudder. Pneumatic de-icing boots for fin and tailplane leading-edges optional.

LANDING GEAR: Hydraulically-retractable tricycle type. Main units retract inward, nose unit forward. Oleo-pneumatic shock-absorbers. Steerable nosewheel. Emergency free-fall extension system. Main-wheel tyre size 6·00-6, 8-ply rating; nosewheel tyre size 6·00-6, 6-ply rating. Nosewheel safety mirror. High-capacity disc brakes. Parking brake. Heavy-duty tyres and brakes optional.

POWER PLANT: Two 149 kW (200 hp) Continental TSIO-360-E flat-six turbocharged counter-rotating engines, driving Hartzell two-blade constant-speed fully-feathering metal propellers. Three-blade propellers, propeller de-icing, and propeller synchrophasers optional. Fuel in two tanks in wings, with a total capacity of 371 litres (98 US gallons) of which 352 litres (93 US gallons) are usable. Optional 57 litre (15 US gallon) auxiliary tank in each wing to provide a max capacity of 485 litres (128 US gallons) of which 466 litres (123 US gallons) are usable. Oil capacity 7·5 litres (2 US gallons). Glassfibre engine cowlings.

ACCOMMODATION: Enclosed cabin, seating six people in pairs on individual seats with 0·25 m (10 in) centre aisle. Optional seventh seat between two centre seats. Dual controls standard. Pilot's storm window. Two forward-hinged doors, one on starboard side at front, the other on port side at rear. Large optional door adjacent to rear cabin door provides an extra-wide opening for loading bulky items. Passenger seats removable easily to provide different seating/baggage/cargo combinations. Space for 45 kg (100 lb) baggage at rear of cabin, and for 45 kg (100 lb) in nose compartment with external access door on port side. Cabin heated and ventilated. Windscreen defrosters standard. Electrically de-iced windscreen for pilot, and ice inspection light, optional.

SYSTEMS: Electro-hydraulic system for landing gear retraction. Electrical system powered by two 14V 65A alternators. 12V 35Ah battery. Oxygen system with six outlets, or built-in oxygen system of 1·78 m³ (63 cu ft), optional. Dual engine-driven vacuum pumps for flight instruments optional. Piper Aire air-conditioning system of 14,500 BTU capacity optional. Janitrol 45,000 BTU combustion heater standard.

AVIONICS AND EQUIPMENT: Seven optional factory-installed packages of avionics are available, these including nav/coms, ADF, autopilot, DME, glideslope and marker beacon receivers, and transponder, by Collins, King, Narco and Piper. Options include alternatives to or duplication of the above equipment, plus autopilot/flight director systems, encoding altimeter, HF transceiver, RNAV, radio altimeter, and weather radar, by manufacturers which include the above, plus Bendix, Bonzer, SunAir and United. Standard equipment includes two cylinder head and two exhaust gas temperature gauges, two manifold pressure gauges, two recording tachometers, and sensitive altimeter. Pilot and co-pilot's seats are fore and aft adjustable and reclining, and have shoulder and safety belts with inertia reels, and armrests; pilot's storm window, sun visors, stall warning device, provisions for emergency locator transmitter, carpeted floor, soundproofing, jack pads, and tiedown rings. Items in operational groups are available optionally, plus co-pilot's blind-flying instrumentation, cabin fire extinguisher, headrests, window curtains, tables, refreshment console, shoulder safety belts with inertia reels for passenger seats, tinted windows, ventilation fan, stainless steel control cables, towbar, and zinc chromate finish for aluminium parts.

DIMENSIONS, EXTERNAL:

Wing span	11·85 m (38 ft 10¾ in)
Length overall	8·72 m (28 ft 7½ in)
Height overall	3·02 m (9 ft 10¾ in)
Tailplane span	4·14 m (13 ft 6¾ in)
Wheel track	3·38 m (11 ft 1 in)
Wheelbase	2·13 m (7 ft 0 in)
Propeller diameter	1·93 m (6 ft 4 in)
Distance between propeller centres	3·80 m (12 ft 5½ in)
Cabin door (stbd, fwd): Height	0·89 m (2 ft 11 in)
Width	0·91 m (3 ft 0 in)
Cabin door (port, aft): Height	0·84 m (2 ft 9 in)
Width	0·74 m (2 ft 5 in)
Baggage door (stbd, aft): Height	0·51 m (1 ft 8 in)
Width	0·71 m (2 ft 4 in)
Baggage door (port, fwd): Height	0·46 m (1 ft 6 in)
Width	0·61 m (2 ft 0 in)

DIMENSIONS, INTERNAL:

Cabin (incl flight deck):	
Length	3·17 m (10 ft 5 in)
Max width and height	1·24 m (4 ft 1 in)
Volume	5·53 m³ (195·3 cu ft)
Forward baggage compartment	0·43 m³ (15·3 cu ft)
Aft baggage compartment	0·49 m³ (17·3 cu ft)

AREA:

Wings, gross	19·39 m² (208·7 sq ft)

WEIGHTS AND LOADINGS:

Weight empty	1,289 kg (2,841 lb)
Max T-O weight	2,073 kg (4,570 lb)
Max landing weight	1,969 kg (4,342 lb)
Max wing loading	107·4 kg/m² (22 lb/sq ft)
Max power loading	6·96 kg/kW (11·4 lb/hp)

PERFORMANCE (at max T-O weight, except where indicated):

Max level speed at 3,660 m (12,000 ft)
195 knots (361 km/h; 225 mph)
Cruising speed:
75% power at 6,100 m (20,000 ft)
190 knots (352 km/h; 219 mph)
75% power at 3,050 m (10,000 ft)
178 knots (330 km/h; 205 mph)
65% power at 7,315 m (24,000 ft)
181 knots (335 km/h; 208 mph)
65% power at 3,050 m (10,000 ft)
166 knots (308 km/h; 191 mph)
55% power at 7,620 m (25,000 ft)
165 knots (306 km/h; 190 mph)
55% power at 3,050 m (10,000 ft)
154 knots (285 km/h; 177 mph)
Stalling speed, flaps up
66 knots (122 km/h; 76 mph) CAS
Stalling speed, flaps down
61 knots (113 km/h; 70 mph) CAS
Max rate of climb at S/L   408 m (1,340 ft)/min
Rate of climb at S/L, one engine out
69 m (225 ft)/min
Certificated operating ceiling   7,620 m (25,000 ft)
Service ceiling, one engine out   4,080 m (13,400 ft)
T-O run   274 m (900 ft)
T-O to 15 m (50 ft)   378 m (1,240 ft)
Landing from 15 m (50 ft)   637 m (2,090 ft)
*Landing from 15 m (50 ft)   567 m (1,860 ft)
Landing run   421 m (1,380 ft)
*Landing run   320 m (1,050 ft)
Accelerate/stop distance   768 m (2,520 ft)
*Accelerate/stop distance   690 m (2,264 ft)
Range with standard fuel, allowances for taxi, T-O, climb, descent, and 45 min reserves at long-range cruise power:
75% power at 6,100 m (20,000 ft)
555 nm (1,028 km; 639 miles)
65% power at 6,550 m (21,500 ft)
590 nm (1,092 km; 679 miles)
55% power at 6,100 m (20,000 ft)
620 nm (1,148 km; 714 miles)
Range with max optional fuel, allowances as above:
75% power at 6,100 m (20,000 ft)
800 nm (1,482 km; 921 miles)
65% power at 6,550 m (21,500 ft)
855 nm (1,583 km; 985 miles)
55% power at 6,100 m (20,000 ft)
885 nm (1,639 km; 1,019 miles)
*With optional heavy duty brakes

PIPER (PA-36) BRAVE

On 9 October 1972 Piper Aircraft Corporation released details of a new agricultural aircraft named the Pawnee Brave, with a more powerful engine than the PA-25 Pawnee D and larger, with increased capacity for either liquid or dry chemicals.

The basic configuration seats the pilot well aft. The long nose is designed to collapse progressively in an emergency. The fuselage is a welded truss structure of chrome-molybdenum steel, which is graded in strength to provide high energy absorption and progressive collapse. A sturdy overturn pylon is an integral part of the fuselage structure. The wing is of conventional cantilever construction, with laminated spars to provide structural redundancy. The wing leading-edges each comprise two glassfibre sections, reinforced by a foam insert beam running spanwise. Normal impacts are absorbed by the leading-edge, more serious contacts by ribs designed to collapse with minimal impact transference to the basic wing structure.

The pilot is located in an isolated cockpit capsule which keeps him well clear of main structural members. The floor is 0·30 m (1 ft 0 in) above the lower longerons, and a cockpit width of 0·97 m (3 ft 2 in) allows for substantial deformation of the fuselage structure without hazard to the pilot. The seat is attached to the overturn pylon, and is articulated to allow the pilot's position to change with fuselage deformation. The cockpit capsule is sealed to prevent the ingress of toxic chemicals; and all protrusions, knobs and levers which might cause injury are eliminated. The instrument panel is equipped with a large energy-absorbing crash roll.

The cockpit capsule is ventilated via an airscoop in the top of the canopy, which filters the incoming air before discharge through two adjustable diffusers. A heating system is standard, and the inflow of ventilating and/or heated air has the effect of pressurising the cockpit, further discouraging any inflow of toxic fumes or chemicals. For 1980 an improved 'pressure air' system was introduced.

The fuel tanks, located in the wing roots, are filled with reticulated polyurethane foam to serve both as a fire suppressant and as a constant baffle to reduce fuel surge. Fire-resistant fuel pipes are wire-reinforced at potential rupture points.

Two hopper sizes are available. The larger hopper has a maximum dry chemicals capacity of 862 kg (1,900 lb), and is compatible with applicators designed to spread chemicals at rates of up to 181 kg (400 lb) per acre.

Spray equipment for the Brave can dispense up to 863 litres (228 US gallons) per minute, which is the equivalent of 64 litres (17 US gallons) per acre at 117 knots (217 km/h; 135 mph) and with a 15·25 m (50 ft) swath width. The spray equipment consists of a quickly-removable pylon-mounted wind-driven spraypump, and spraybooms located just aft of the wing trailing-edges. This location reduces drag and allows the pilot to make visual checks of their operation.

All parts of the Brave's airframe are treated to prevent corrosion damage, with extensive use of polyurethane coating, selection of stainless steel for cables and other moving components in vulnerable areas, and internal oiling of lower truss sections. The design eliminates dust traps and inaccessible areas, and fuselage covering is

Piper Seneca II, powered by two Continental TSIO-360-E turbocharged counter-rotating engines

spaced away from the frame to permit thorough hosing down. To facilitate washing, inspection and maintenance, the plastics side panels and entire belly covering are attached by quick-release fasteners.

Two versions of the Brave are available:

Brave 300. Basic version, equipped with one 224 kW (300 hp) Avco Lycoming IO-540-K1G5 flat-six engine, driving a Hartzell HC-C2YK-1BF two-blade constant-speed metal propeller. Three-blade propeller optional.

Brave 375. Introduced in 1978: basically as Brave 300, but equipped with 279·5 kW (375 hp) Avco Lycoming IO-720-D1CD flat-eight engine, driving a Hartzell three-blade constant-speed metal propeller, and with the 862 kg (1,900 lb) hopper as standard. FAA certification in Normal and Restricted categories was awarded on 4 October 1977.

The following description applies to both versions of the Brave:

TYPE: Single-seat agricultural aircraft.

WINGS: Cantilever low-wing monoplane. Wing section NACA 63₃-618. Dihedral 6°. Incidence 2° 30′ at root, 0° 30′ at tip. Conventional two-spar metal structure. Light alloy laminated spars with two-bolt main spar attachment to fuselage structure. Light alloy covering, except for detachable leading-edges of glassfibre, reinforced by foam inserts, and glassfibre wingtips. Conventional ailerons and trailing-edge flaps. Landing lights in wing leading-edges.

FUSELAGE: Welded chrome-molybdenum steel tube structure. Removable metal underskin and removable side panels of plastics material. Glassfibre engine cowling.

TAIL UNIT: Cantilever all-metal structure. Tailplane has glassfibre tips. Tab on rudder and in each elevator. Cable from top of cockpit structure to tip of fin to deflect cables.

LANDING GEAR: Non-retractable tailwheel type. Interchangeable cantilever spring steel main-gear struts, with wire-cutters on leading-edges. Cleveland main wheels type 40-101 with tyres size 8·50-10, 6-ply rating, pressure 1·93-2·21 bars (28-32 lb/sq in). Scott steerable tailwheel type 3450-21 with tyre of 0·25 m (10 in) diameter, pressure 2·41-3·10 bars (35-45 lb/sq in). Cleveland type 30-67B hydraulic brakes. Parking brake.

POWER PLANT: One engine as detailed in model listings. Three-blade constant-speed propeller optional for Brave 300. One fuel tank in each wing root, capacity 170·3 litres (45 US gallons). Total fuel capacity for both versions 337 litres (89 US gallons), of which 325·5 litres (86 US gallons) are usable. Refuelling point on upper surface of each wing. Fuel tanks filled with reticulated polyurethane safety foam (Safom). Oil capacity of Brave 300, 11·5 litres (3 US gallons); Brave 375, 16·1 litres (4·25 US gallons).

ACCOMMODATION: Pilot only, on adjustable seat in an isolated cockpit capsule, with steel tube overturn structure. Seat, equipped with double shoulder harness and inertia reel, is attached to overturn structure. Wire-cutter mounted in centre of windscreen. Combined window and door on each side, hinged at bottom. Cockpit capsule is ventilated and can be heated optionally.

SYSTEMS: Electrical system of Brave 300 supplied by 28V 70A alternator, with 24V 17Ah battery. Brave 375 has 28V 70A alternator with two 12V 25Ah batteries in series. Hydraulic system for brakes only.

AVIONICS: The optional factory-installed avionics packages available for the Pawnee D can be obtained also for the Brave, as well as a range of transponders.

EQUIPMENT: Standard on Brave 300 is a non-corrosive hopper/tank of translucent GRP, installed forward of cockpit and approximately on CG, of 0·85 m³ (30 cu ft) capacity, containing 852 litres (225 US gallons). Hopper/tank of 1·08 m³ (38 cu ft) capacity, containing 1,041 litres (275 US gallons) optional for Brave 300, standard for Brave 375. The latter has a maximum capacity for dry chemicals of 862 kg (1,900 lb). Venturi-type dry material spreaders of either stainless steel or aluminium available, including a basic design capable of application rates of 2·3 to 91 kg (5 to 200 lb) per acre. Spray system comprises an easily-removable wind-driven spraypump and 38 mm (1½ in) diameter spraybooms equipped with 60 nozzles. Other optional equipment includes 8-day clock; turn co-ordinator; emergency locator transmitter; landing and taxi lights; navigation, instrument panel and anti-collision lights; cockpit fire extinguisher; and heater.

DIMENSIONS, EXTERNAL:
Wing span	11·82 m (38 ft 9½ in)
Wing chord at root	2·03 m (6 ft 8 in)
Wing chord at tip	1·75 m (5 ft 9 in)
Wing aspect ratio	6·66
Length overall: Brave 300	8·17 m (26 ft 9½ in)
Brave 375	8·38 m (27 ft 6 in)
Height overall	2·29 m (7 ft 6 in)
Tailplane span	4·01 m (13 ft 1¾ in)
Wheel track	2·65 m (8 ft 8⅜ in)
Wheelbase: Brave 300	6·22 m (20 ft 4¾ in)
Brave 375	5·91 m (19 ft 4¾ in)
Propeller diameter: Brave 300	2·41 m (7 ft 11 in)
Brave 375	2·18 m (7 ft 2 in)

Chincul Argentinian-built example of the Piper Brave 300 agricultural aircraft

Propeller ground clearance:
Brave 300	0·25 m (10 in)
Brave 375	0·23 m (9 in)

Access doors:
Both versions: Height	0·76 m (2 ft 6 in)
Width	0·71 m (2 ft 4 in)
Height to sill	1·57 m (5 ft 2 in)

Hopper loading door, Brave 375:
Length	1·27 m (4 ft 2 in)
Width	0·48 m (1 ft 7 in)

DIMENSIONS, INTERNAL:
Cockpit: Max width	0·97 m (3 ft 2 in)
Max height	1·32 m (4 ft 4 in)

AREAS:
Wings, gross	20·96 m² (225·65 sq ft)
Ailerons (total)	2·01 m² (21·6 sq ft)
Trailing-edge flaps (total)	2·32 m² (25·0 sq ft)
Fin	0·95 m² (10·2 sq ft)
Rudder	0·90 m² (9·7 sq ft)
Tailplane	2·11 m² (22·67 sq ft)
Elevators (incl tabs)	1·92 m² (20·66 sq ft)

WEIGHTS AND LOADINGS (A: Brave 300; B: Brave 375):

Weight empty: No dispersal equipment:
A	997 kg (2,198 lb)
B	1,118 kg (2,465 lb)
Sprayer: A	1,050 kg (2,314 lb)
B	1,154 kg (2,544 lb)
Duster: A	1,048 kg (2,310 lb)
B	1,152 kg (2,540 lb)

Max T-O weight, Normal category:
A, B	1,769 kg (3,900 lb)

Max T-O weight, Restricted category:
A	1,996 kg (4,400 lb)
B	2,177 kg (4,800 lb)

Max landing weight, Normal and Restricted categories:
A, B	1,769 kg (3,900 lb)

Max wing loading, Normal category:
A, B	84·4 kg/m² (17·3 lb/sq ft)

Max wing loading, Restricted category:
A	95·2 kg/m² (19·5 lb/sq ft)
B	103·9 kg/m² (21·3 lb/sq ft)

Max power loading, Normal category:
A	7·90 kg/kW (13·0 lb/hp)
B	6·33 kg/kW (10·4 lb/hp)

Max power loading, Restricted category:
A	8·91 kg/kW (14·7 lb/hp)
B	7·79 kg/kW (12·8 lb/hp)

PERFORMANCE (at Normal category max T-O weight, no dispersal equipment installed; A: Brave 300; B: Brave 375):

Max level speed at optimum altitude:
A	129 knots (238 km/h; 148 mph)
B	139 knots (257 km/h; 160 mph)

Cruising speed, best power mixture:
A, 75% power at 1,675 m (5,500 ft)	123 knots (228 km/h; 142 mph)
B, 75% power at 1,705 m (5,600 ft)	129 knots (240 km/h; 149 mph)
A, 65% power at 2,835 m (9,300 ft)	120 knots (222 km/h; 138 mph)
B, 65% power at 2,895 m (9,500 ft)	126 knots (233 km/h; 145 mph)
A, 55% power at 3,415 m (11,200 ft)	109 knots (203 km/h; 126 mph)
B, 55% power at 4,265 m (14,000 ft)	119 knots (220 km/h; 137 mph)

Cruising speed, best econ mixture:
A, 75% power at 1,675 m (5,500 ft)	123 knots (228 km/h; 142 mph)
B, 75% power at 1,705 m (5,600 ft)	128 knots (236 km/h; 147 mph)
A, 65% power at 2,835 m (9,300 ft)	118 knots (219 km/h; 136 mph)
B, 65% power at 2,895 m (9,500 ft)	124 knots (230 km/h; 143 mph)
A, 55% power at 3,415 m (11,200 ft)	108 knots (199 km/h; 124 mph)
B, 55% power at 4,265 m (14,000 ft)	117 knots (217 km/h; 135 mph)

Stalling speed, flaps up:
A, B	62·5 knots (116 km/h; 72 mph) CAS

Stalling speed, flaps down:
A	54 knots (100 km/h; 62 mph) CAS
B	57·5 knots (107 km/h; 66 mph) CAS

Max rate of climb at S/L: A 235 m (770 ft)/min
B	321 m (1,051 ft)/min

T-O run: A 293 m (960 ft)
B	218 m (715 ft)

T-O to 15 m (50 ft): A 465 m (1,525 ft)
B	368 m (1,208 ft)

Landing from 15 m (50 ft): A 503 m (1,650 ft)
B	564 m (1,850 ft)

Landing run: A 213 m (700 ft)
B	226 m (740 ft)

Range with max fuel, best econ mixture, with allowances for start, taxi, T-O climb, descent and 45 min reserves:
A	75% power at 1,675 m (5,500 ft)	556 nm (1,030 km; 640 miles)
B	75% power at 1,705 m (5,600 ft)	465 nm (861 km; 535 miles)
A	65% power at 2,835 m (9,300 ft)	586 nm (1,086 km; 675 miles)
B	65% power at 2,895 m (9,500 ft)	495 nm (917 km; 570 miles)
A	55% power at 3,415 m (11,200 ft)	612 nm (1,135 km; 705 miles)
B	55% power at 4,265 m (14,000 ft)	525 nm (974 km; 605 miles)

PERFORMANCE (at Restricted category max T-O weight, except where indicated. A: Brave 300 sprayer; B: Brave 300 duster; C: Brave 375 sprayer; D: Brave 375 duster):

Max speed at optimum altitude:
A	109 knots (203 km/h; 126 mph)
B	103 knots (191 km/h; 119 mph)
C	123 knots (229 km/h; 142 mph)
D	119 knots (220 km/h; 137 mph)

Cruising speed, best power mixture:
A 75% power at 1,675 m (5,500 ft)	102 knots (190 km/h; 118 mph)
A 65% power at 1,675 m (5,500 ft)	89 knots (166 km/h; 103 mph)
B 75% power at 1,675 m (5,500 ft)	94 knots (174 km/h; 108 mph)
C 75% power at 1,310 m (4,300 ft)	118 knots (219 km/h; 136 mph)
D 75% power at 1,310 m (4,300 ft)	113 knots (209 km/h; 130 mph)

Max rate of climb at S/L: A 114 m (375 ft)/min
B	97 m (320 ft)/min
C	168 m (550 ft)/min
D	116 m (380 ft)/min

T-O run: A 411 m (1,350 ft)
B	448 m (1,470 ft)
C, D	367 m (1,203 ft)

T-O to 15 m (50 ft): A 637 m (2,090 ft)
B	678 m (2,225 ft)
C, D	608 m (1,994 ft)

Landing from 15 m (50 ft), at Restricted category max landing weight: A 448 m (1,470 ft)
B	450 m (1,475 ft)
C, D	439 m (1,440 ft)

Landing run, at Restricted category max landing weight: A 232 m (760 ft)
B	216 m (710 ft)
C, D	140 m (460 ft)

Range with max fuel, cruising at best power mixture, allowances for start, taxi, T-O, climb, descent and 45 min reserves at 45% power:
A (75% power)	399 nm (740 km; 460 miles)
A (65% power)	391 nm (724 km; 450 miles)
B (75% power)	360 nm (668 km; 415 miles)
C (75% power)	392 nm (727 km; 452 miles)
D (75% power)	372 nm (689 km; 428 miles)

PIPER (PA-38-112) TOMAHAWK

Piper introduced a completely new trainer in 1978, under the name of Tomahawk. It provides side-by-side seating in a roomy cabin with all-round view, has a T-tail and wide-track landing gear, and is available with an optional factory-installed Special Training Package or an optional factory-installed avionics package in lieu:

Special Training Package. Comprises advanced instrument package, true airspeed indicator, sun visors, tinted windscreen and side windows, dual toe-operated brakes, night lighting, entrance steps each side, towbar, and avionics including King KX 170B 720-channel transceiver with 200-channel nav, King KI 208 indicator with VOR/LOC converter, Telex 66T microphone, Telex headset, and Poly Planar cabin speaker; adding 21·3 kg (47·0 lb) to basic empty weight.

Group KS-1-38. Comprising King KX 170B 720-channel com transceiver and 200-channel nav receiver, King KI 208 VOR/LOC indicator with VOR/LOC converter, Telex 66T microphone, Telex headset, and Poly Planar cabin speaker; adding 5·3 kg (11·7 lb) to basic empty weight.

The STP and avionics packages include all associated antennae.

FAA certification of the Tomahawk was granted on 20 December 1977, and the 1,000th production example was delivered in November 1978.

The 1980 versions of the Tomahawk introduced several improvements as standard, including redesign of flap manual operation mechanism, improved door latch, and provision of external visual fuel gauging and a winterisation kit.

TYPE: Two-seat trainer/utility aircraft.

WINGS: Cantilever low-wing monoplane. NASA GAW-1 aerofoil section. Thickness/chord ratio 17%. Dihedral 5°. Incidence 2° at root, 0° at tip. No sweepback. Conventional structure of light alloy with plastics wingtips. Plain ailerons of light alloy construction. Manually-operated plain trailing-edge flaps of light alloy construction. No trim tabs.

FUSELAGE: Conventional semi-monocoque structure, primarily of light alloy, but with some components of steel or plastics. High strength roll-over structure.

TAIL UNIT: Cantilever T tail of light alloy construction, with plastics fin and tailplane tips. Fixed-incidence tailplane. Spring-loaded elevator trim. Ground-adjustable trim tab on rudder.

LANDING GEAR: Non-retractable tricycle type. Main wheels carried on interchangeable cantilever steel leaf springs. Nose unit has Piper oleo-pneumatic shock-absorber. Cleveland main wheels Type 40-78B and nosewheel Type 40-77B, all fitted with 5·00-5 4-ply tyres and tubes, pressure 1·79 bars (26 lb/sq in). Wheels and tyres size 6·00-6 optional. Cleveland Type 30-9 hand-operated brakes. Dual toe-operated brakes optional. Parking brake.

POWER PLANT: One 83·5 kW (112 hp) Avco Lycoming O-235-L2C flat-four engine, driving a Sensenich two-blade fixed-pitch metal propeller with spinner. One integral fuel tank in each wing, total capacity 121 litres (32 US gallons), of which 113·5 litres (30 US gallons) are usable. Refuelling point in upper surface of each wing. Oil capacity 5·7 litres (1·5 US gallons).

ACCOMMODATION: Enclosed cabin seating two, side by side, with dual controls standard. High strength roll-over support structure in cabin area. Door on each side. Fore, aft, and vertically adjustable seats with safety belts and shoulder harnesses. Baggage space, capacity 45·4 kg (100 lb), behind seats. Accommodation heated and ventilated. Sun visors, tinted windscreen and side windows optional. Windscreen defroster standard.

SYSTEM: Electrical system includes a 14V 60A alternator and 12V 25Ah battery. Hydraulic system for brakes only. Vacuum system optional.

AVIONICS AND EQUIPMENT: Optional avionics, in addition to those detailed in the STP and KS-1-38 packages, include second nav/com, ADF, encoding altimeter, glideslope and marker beacon receiver, and transponder. Standard equipment includes instrument panel glareshield, recording tachometer, sensitive altimeter, fore/aft/vertically-adjustable pilot/co-pilot seats with safety belts and shoulder harness, dual controls, alternate static source, stall warning device, baggage tiedown straps, carpeted floor, soundproofing, engine priming system, full-flow oil filter, oil quick drain valve, tiedown rings, and winterisation kit. Optional equipment includes attitude and directional gyros, electric clock, flight hour recorder, outside air temperature gauge, true airspeed indicator, turn co-ordinator, vertical speed indicator, sun visors, tinted windscreen and windows, emergency locator transmitter, heated pitot, cabin fire extinguisher, corrosion proofing, stainless steel control cables, external power socket, and static wicks.

Photograph and three-view drawing *(Pilot Press)* **of the Piper Tomahawk two-seat trainer/utility aircraft**

DIMENSIONS, EXTERNAL:	
Wing span	10·36 m (34 ft 0 in)
Wing chord, constant	1·12 m (3 ft 8 in)
Wing aspect ratio	9·27
Length overall	7·04 m (23 ft 1¼ in)
Height overall	2·76 m (9 ft 0¾ in)
Tailplane span	3·20 m (10 ft 6 in)
Wheel track	3·05 m (10 ft 0 in)
Wheelbase	1·45 m (4 ft 9 in)
Propeller diameter	1·83 m (6 ft 0 in)
Propeller ground clearance	0·18 m (7 in)
Doors (port and stbd, each):	
Height	0·74 m (2 ft 5 in)
Width	0·58 m (1 ft 11 in)
Height to sill	1·02 m (3 ft 4 in)
DIMENSIONS, INTERNAL:	
Cabin, from instrument panel to rear bulkhead:	
Length	1·74 m (5 ft 8½ in)
Max width	1·07 m (3 ft 6 in)
Max height	1·28 m (4 ft 2½ in)
Baggage space	0·57 m³ (20 cu ft)
AREAS:	
Wings, gross	11·59 m² (124·7 sq ft)
Ailerons (total)	1·02 m² (11·0 sq ft)
Trailing-edge flaps (total)	1·01 m² (10·9 sq ft)
Vertical tail surfaces (total)	1·42 m² (15·3 sq ft)
Horizontal tail surfaces (total)	2·03 m² (21·9 sq ft)
WEIGHTS AND LOADINGS:	
Weight empty	502 kg (1,108 lb)
Max T-O and landing weight	757 kg (1,670 lb)
Max wing loading	65·42 kg/m² (13·4 lb/sq ft)
Max power loading	9·07 kg/kW (14·9 lb/hp)
PERFORMANCE (at max T-O weight):	
Never-exceed speed	
	138 knots (256 km/h; 159 mph) IAS
Max level speed at S/L	
	109 knots (202 km/h; 126 mph)
Max cruising speed, 75% power at 2,165 m (7,100 ft)	
	108 knots (200 km/h; 124 mph)

Cruising speed, 65% power at 3,200 m (10,500 ft)
100 knots (185 km/h; 115 mph)
Stalling speed, flaps up
52 knots (96 km/h; 60 mph) IAS
Stalling speed, flaps down
49 knots (91 km/h; 56·5 mph) IAS

Max rate of climb at S/L	219 m (718 ft)/min
Service ceiling	3,960 m (13,000 ft)
Absolute ceiling	4,265 m (14,000 ft)
T-O run	250 m (820 ft)
T-O to 15 m (50 ft)	445 m (1,460 ft)
Landing from 15 m (50 ft)	471 m (1,544 ft)
Landing run	215 m (707 ft)

Range with max fuel, allowances for taxi, T-O, climb, descent, with 45 min reserves at 55% power:
75% power at 2,165 m (7,100 ft)
452 nm (838 km; 520 miles)
65% power at 3,200 m (10,500 ft)
468 nm (867 km; 539 miles)

PIPER PA-40 ARAPAHO

An accompanying illustration is the first to show this Piper light twin, with retractable landing gear. Only two prototypes and one production Arapaho were built. This last aircraft was sold to a private owner and was still flying in mid-1980.

PIPER (PA-44-180) SEMINOLE

The Seminole lightweight twin-engined four-seat cabin monoplane was announced by Piper on 21 February 1978. Features of this economically-priced aircraft (first flown in prototype form in May 1976) are the T tail for improved controllability and stability, counter-rotating engines, a new fuel drain sump system with only two drain valves for the entire system, and a one-piece glassfibre nosecone to give easy access to the landing gear mechanism, combustion heater, battery and landing light. Improvements introduced for 1980 include an increased-capacity ventilation fan and an avionics master switch. New options include a wider range of avionics and a dual-needle tachometer.

Two optional equipment packages are available for the Seminole:

Custom. Comprising blind-flying instrumentation including 3 in attitude and directional gyros, electric clock, outside air temperature gauge, rate of climb indicator, and true airspeed indicator; avionics dimming, and instrument panel white and overhead red lighting; map, cabin dome, waterfall switch panel, landing, navigation, taxi, and wing strobe lights; assist strap; entrance step; vacuum system with dual engine-driven pumps; and quick oil drains; adding 15·7 kg (34·6 lb) to basic empty weight.

Executive. As Custom group, plus exhaust gas temperature gauge, emergency locator transmitter, heated pitot and stall warning transmitter, pilot's vertically adjustable seat, and external power socket; adding 22·4 kg (49·3 lb) to basic empty weight.

TYPE: Twin-engined lightweight four-seat cabin monoplane.

The Piper PA-40 Arapaho, of which only three examples were built *(John Langston)*

WINGS: Cantilever low-wing monoplane. Conventional structure of light alloy. Plain ailerons and manually-operated four-position trailing-edge flaps of light alloy construction.

FUSELAGE: Conventional semi-monocoque structure, primarily of light alloy.

TAIL UNIT: Cantilever T tail of light alloy construction. All-moving tailplane with full-span tab. Rudder anti-servo tab.

LANDING GEAR: Hydraulically-retractable tricycle type. Free-fall emergency extension system. Piper oleo-pneumatic shock-absorbers. Main-wheel tyres size 6·00-6, 8-ply, with tubes. Steerable nosewheel with 5·00-5, 6-ply tyre and tube. Nosewheel safety mirror. Dual toe-operated high-capacity disc brakes. Parking brake. Heavy-duty brakes and tyres optional.

POWER PLANT: Two 134 kW (180 hp) Avco Lycoming flat-four counter-rotating engines (one O-360-E1AD and one LO-360-E1AD), each driving a Hartzell two-blade constant-speed fully-feathering metal propeller with spinner. Three-blade propellers and propeller synchrophasers optional. One bladder-type fuel tank in each engine nacelle, with total capacity of 416 litres (110 US gallons), of which 409 litres (108 US gallons) are usable. Refuelling point on upper surface of each nacelle. Oil capacity 11·5 litres (3 US gallons).

ACCOMMODATION: Cabin seats four in two pairs of individual seats. Pilot and co-pilot seats horizontally adjustable, and fitted with seat belts and shoulder harness, with inertia reels. Dual controls standard. Rear seats have safety belts and are reclinable. Cabin door on starboard side. Emergency exit window on port side. Pilot's storm window. Baggage compartment at rear of cabin, capacity 91 kg (200 lb). Accommodation heated and ventilated. Windscreen defrosters.

SYSTEMS: Hydraulic system for landing gear actuation and brakes. Electrical system includes two engine-driven 14V 60A alternators and 12V 35Ah battery. Janitrol combustion heater of 45,000 BTU capacity. Vacuum system optional.

AVIONICS AND EQUIPMENT: A wide range of optional avionics is available to customer's requirements, including eight factory-installed avionics packages based on dual nav/com, ADF, DME, encoding altimeter, glide-slope and marker beacon receivers, HSI, RNAV, radar altimeter and transponder, by manufacturers which include Collins, King, Narco and Piper. Standard equipment includes two cylinder head temperature and two manifold pressure gauges, two recording tachometers, sensitive altimeter, pilot and co-pilot's seats with fore/aft/recline adjustment and inertia reel shoulder and safety belts, map pockets, pilot's storm window, sun visors, armrests, alternate static source, alternator failure warning light, stall warning device, provisions for emergency locator transmitter, soundproofing, fuel tank quick drains, full flow oil filters, manually-controlled cowl flaps, engine priming system, jack pads, tiedown rings and stowable towbar. Optional equipment includes engine hour recorders, pilot and co-pilot's vertically-adjustable seats, cabin fire extinguisher, headrests, shoulder safety belts with inertia reels for aft seats, stainless steel control cables, tinted windows, ventilation fan, window curtains, and zinc chromate treatment of aluminium parts.

DIMENSIONS, EXTERNAL:

Wing span	11·75 m (38 ft 6⅝ in)
Length overall	8·41 m (27 ft 7¼ in)
Height overall	2·59 m (8 ft 6 in)
Wheel track	3·37 m (11 ft 0¾ in)
Wheelbase	2·56 m (8 ft 4¾ in)
Propeller diameter	1·88 m (6 ft 2 in)
Cabin door (stbd): Width	0·91 m (3 ft 0 in)
Height	0·89 m (2 ft 11 in)
Baggage door: Width	0·56 m (1 ft 10 in)
Height	0·51 m (1 ft 8 in)

Piper Seminole lightweight twin-engined four-seat cabin monoplane *(Pilot Press)*

DIMENSIONS, INTERNAL:
Cabin, instrument panel to rear bulkhead:

Length	2·46 m (8 ft 1 in)
Max width	1·05 m (3 ft 5½ in)
Max height	1·245 m (4 ft 1 in)
Volume	3·00 m³ (106 cu ft)

AREA:

Wings, gross	16·72 m² (180 sq ft)

WEIGHTS AND LOADINGS:

Weight empty	1,070 kg (2,360 lb)
Max T-O weight	1,723 kg (3,800 lb)
Max wing loading	103·1 kg/m² (21·11 lb/sq ft)
Max power loading	6·43 kg/kW (10·55 lb/hp)

PERFORMANCE (at max T-O weight, except where indicated):

Max level speed at S/L
168 knots (311 km/h; 193 mph)
Cruising speed at average cruise weight of 1,360 kg (3,000 lb), best power settings:
75% power at 2,440 m (8,000 ft)
166 knots (308 km/h; 191 mph)
65% power at 3,630 m (11,900 ft)
162 knots (300 km/h; 187 mph)
55% power at 4,875 m (16,000 ft)
153 knots (284 km/h; 176 mph)
Cruising speed at average cruise weight of 1,360 kg (3,000 lb), best econ power settings:
75% power at 2,135 m (7,000 ft)
161 knots (298 km/h; 185 mph)
65% power at 3,260 m (10,700 ft)
157 knots (291 km/h; 181 mph)
55% power at 4,420 m (14,500 ft)
149 knots (276 km/h; 171 mph)
Stalling speed, flaps up
64 knots (119 km/h; 74 mph) CAS
Stalling speed, flaps down
59 knots (109 km/h; 68 mph) CAS
Max rate of climb at S/L   408 m (1,340 ft)/min
Rate of climb at S/L, one engine out
66 m (217 ft)/min
Service ceiling   5,210 m (17,100 ft)
Service ceiling, one engine out   1,250 m (4,100 ft)
Absolute ceiling   5,670 m (18,600 ft)
Absolute ceiling, one engine out   1,600 m (5,250 ft)
T-O run   268 m (880 ft)
T-O to 15 m (50 ft)   427 m (1,400 ft)
Landing from 15 m (50 ft)   363 m (1,190 ft)

Landing run   117 m (383 ft)
Accelerate/stop distance, with heavy-duty brakes
631 m (2,070 ft)
Range with max fuel at best power settings, allowances for taxi, T-O, climb, descent, and 45 min reserves at max range power:
75% power at 2,135 m (7,000 ft)
690 nm (1,278 km; 794 miles)
65% power at 3,260 m (10,700 ft)
725 nm (1,343 km; 834 miles)
55% power at 4,420 m (14,500 ft)
730 nm (1,352 km; 840 miles)
Range with max fuel at econ power settings, allowances as above:
75% power at 2,135 m (7,000 ft)
790 nm (1,463 km; 909 miles)
65% power at 3,260 m (10,700 ft)
850 nm (1,574 km; 978 miles)
55% power at 4,420 m (14,500 ft)
880 nm (1,630 km; 1,012 miles)

PIPER (PA-44-180T) TURBO SEMINOLE

Piper announced on 24 April 1980 the introduction of a turbocharged version of the twin-engined four-seat Seminole, from which it differs in its power plant and related equipment. It also includes provisions for a built-in optional oxygen system, to permit high-altitude operation.

The description of the PA-44-180 Seminole applies also to the Turbo Seminole, except as follows. The new model is available with optional Custom and Executive equipment packages: the former is as described for the Seminole, but the latter comprises the following:

Executive. As for Custom package, with the addition of a pilot's vertically adjustable seat in lieu of standard type, an emergency locator transmitter, heated pitot and stall warning transmitter, and an external power socket. The complete Executive package adds 22·3 kg (49·3 lb) to basic empty weight.

WINGS, FUSELAGE, TAIL UNIT AND LANDING GEAR: As for Seminole.

POWER PLANT: Two 134 kW (180 hp) Avco Lycoming flat-four counter-rotating (one TO-360-E1 and one LTO-360-E1) turbocharged engines, each driving a Hartzell two-blade constant-speed fully-feathering metal propeller with spinner. Three-blade propellers and propeller synchrophasers optional. Fuel system and capacity as for Seminole.

ACCOMMODATION, SYSTEMS, AVIONICS AND EQUIPMENT: Generally as for Seminole.

DIMENSIONS, EXTERNAL AND INTERNAL, AND AREAS: As for Seminole

WEIGHTS AND LOADINGS:

Weight empty	1,105 kg (2,435 lb)
Max T-O weight	1,780 kg (3,925 lb)
Max ramp weight	1,788 kg (3,943 lb)
Max zero fuel weight	1,723 kg (3,800 lb)
Max wing loading	106·5 kg/m² (21·81 lb/sq ft)
Max power loading	6·64 kg/kW (10·90 lb/hp)

PERFORMANCE (at max T-O weight):

Max level speed at optimum altitude
195 knots (361 km/h; 224 mph)
Max cruising speed, 75% power at optimum altitude
183 knots (339 km/h; 210 mph)
Cruising speed at 3,050 m (10,000 ft)
167 knots (309 km/h; 192 mph)
Stalling speed, flaps and gear up
64 knots (119 km/h; 74 mph)
Stalling speed, flaps and gear down
61 knots (113 km/h; 70 mph)
Max rate of climb at S/L   393 m (1,290 ft)/min
Rate of climb at S/L, one engine out
55 m (180 ft)/min
Service ceiling, certificated   6,100 m (20,000 ft)
Service ceiling, one engine out   3,800 m (12,500 ft)

Piper's new Turbo Seminole with Avco Lycoming turbocharged engines

*T-O run	275 m (900 ft)
*T-O to 15 m (50 ft)	458 m (1,500 ft)
*Landing from 15 m (50 ft)	363 m (1,190 ft)
*Landing run	180 m (590 ft)

Range, with allowances for warm-up, taxi, T-O, climb, and 45 min reserves (GAMA format):
75% power at optimum altitude
785 nm (1,453 km; 903 miles)
65% power at optimum altitude
800 nm (1,481 km; 920 miles)

55% power at optimum altitude
820 nm (1,518 km; 943 miles)

*Short-field operation.

PIPER ENFORCER

Piper completed two prototypes of this turboprop-powered light attack aircraft in the early 1970s, after acquiring the programme from Cavalier Aircraft Corporation (see 1971-72 *Jane's*). The Enforcer is a development of the wartime North American P-51D Mustang, with a 1,890 kW (2,535 shp) Avco Lycoming T55-L-9 engine and extensive armour protection. The first prototype made its initial flight on 29 April 1971, but was lost in a crash three months later. The second aircraft was evaluated in the US Air Force's Pave Coin programme in the same year, but was not selected for production.

The US Air Force will now re-evaluate the Enforcer, and funding for one aircraft is included in the FY 1981 budget requests.

SANTA MARIA DIVISION

2560 Skyway Drive, Santa Maria, California 93454
Telephone: (805) 922 8411
GENERAL MANAGER: Ron W. Smith

On 27 March 1978, Piper Aircraft Corporation and Ted Smith Aerostar Corporation announced jointly the acquisition by Piper of all of the assets and business of Aerostar with effect from 24 March 1978. The existing Aerostar facility became Piper's Santa Maria Division with Ron W. Smith, formerly President of Aerostar, remaining with the Division in the capacity of General Manager. Piper is not only continuing to manufacture the Aerostar 600, 601 and 601P, but has increased production at Santa Maria to satisfy the demand for these aircraft. On 12 April 1978, Piper received the FAA Production Certificate for these three aircraft. The earlier history of Ted Smith Aerostar Corporation can be found under that company's entry in the 1977-78 *Jane's*.

PIPER (PA-60) AEROSTAR 600/601/601P

Design work on this series was started by the Ted Smith Aircraft Company in November 1964 and the first Model 600/601 prototype made its first flight in October 1967. FAA Type Approval of the Model 600 was awarded in March 1968, and of the Model 601 in November 1968.

It is claimed that the Aerostar airframe contains only 50% as many components as are used in other designs of comparable size. Construction involves extensive use of monocoque assemblies, in which unstiffened sections of heavy-gauge skin carry loads. The horizontal and vertical fixed tail surfaces, together with their related control surfaces, are interchangeable.

On 6 August 1975, an Aerostar 601A piloted by Jack F. Chrysler set a Class C1d 2,000 km closed-circuit speed record for piston-engined landplanes of 237·08 knots (439·07 km/h; 272·83 mph).

On 8 November 1977, an Aerostar 601P piloted by Philander Claxton III and Jack Cink recorded a new round-the-world speed record for piston-engined aircraft, completing the 19,974 nm (37,015 km; 23,000 mile) flight in 104 h 5 min, and so beating the previous record of 122 h set by two Australians in a Beechcraft Duke.

Current production versions of the Aerostar comprise:
Model 600A. Powered by two 216 kW (290 hp) Avco Lycoming IO-540-K1J5 flat-six engines. European models designated 600AE.

Model 601B. As Model 600A, but with increased wing span and powered by two 216 kW (290 hp) Avco Lycoming IO-540-S1A5 flat-six turbocharged engines. European models designated 601BE.

Model 601P. As Model 601B, but with higher flow-rate turbochargers to supply bleed air for cabin pressurisation. European models designated 601PE.

The 1980 versions of the Aerostar introduced a number of improvements as standard, including a new fuel gauging system, greater angle deflection of the nosewheel power steering unit, and a new paint scheme. New options include a luminescent outside air temperature gauge, an electrically-heated windscreen de-icing panel, and additional avionics.

An optional group of factory-installed de-icing equipment is available for all three versions, and comprises de-icing boots for wing and tail unit leading-edges, electrically heated propeller boots, alcohol de-icing system or electrically-heated plate for windscreen, and wing ice inspection light; adding 33·5 kg (73·9 lb) to basic empty weight.

TYPE: Twin-engined light transport aircraft.
WINGS: Cantilever mid-wing monoplane. Wing section NACA 64₁A212. Dihedral 2°. Incidence 1°. No sweepback. All-metal structure using heavy gauge skins attached to three spars, several bulkheads and stringers. Entire wing assembly, excluding attachments for ailerons and flaps, contains fewer than 50 detail parts. Ailerons and hydraulically-actuated Fowler-type trailing-edge flaps each comprise a spar, ribs, nose skin and one-piece wraparound light alloy skin aft of spar. No trim tabs. De-icing for wing leading-edges optional.
FUSELAGE: All-metal fail-safe monocoque structure. Skin composed of large segments of light alloy sheet over stringers and frames. Entire fuselage contains fewer than 100 parts, including skin panels. All fuselage assemblies designed basically for pressurisation.
TAIL UNIT: Cantilever all-metal structure, with swept vertical and horizontal surfaces. Both fixed and control surfaces are interchangeable. Electrically-operated trim tab in rudder and each elevator. De-icing boots for fin and tailplane leading-edges optional.

LANDING GEAR: Hydraulically-retractable tricycle type. Main units retract inward, nosewheel forward. Hydraulically-powered nosewheel steering. Hydraulically-operated heavy-duty dual caliper brakes. Parking brake.
POWER PLANT: Two Avco Lycoming engines, as detailed in model listings, each driving a Hartzell three-blade constant-speed and fully-feathering metal propeller with spinner. Fuel in integral wing tanks and fuselage tank with total capacity of 657 litres (173·5 US gallons), of which 626 litres (165·5 US gallons) are usable. Oil capacity 22·7 litres (6 US gallons).
ACCOMMODATION: Cabin seats six people on track-mounted individual reclining seats, in pairs. Dual controls standard. Door on port side by pilot's seat; top half hinges upward, bottom half downward. Emergency escape window at rear of cabin. Tinted windscreen and dual pane tinted cabin windows. Large utility shelf in aft cabin. Baggage compartment, capacity 109 kg (240 lb), aft of cabin, with external access on port side. Individual air vents and reading lights for each seat. Cabin heated/ventilated in 600A/601B, and also pressurised in 601P. Control locks. Windscreen defrosting; alcohol de-icing system, or electrically-heated windscreen plate, optional.
SYSTEMS: Heating/ventilation system includes a Janitrol 35,000 BTU heater. Pressurisation system for Model 601P supplied by engine bleed air; pressure differential 0·29 bars (4·25 lb/sq in). Hydraulic system for landing gear actuation, wheel brakes and flaps, powered by an engine-driven pump, pressure 69 bars (1,000 lb/sq in). Dual pneumatic systems for instrument gyros and optional de-icing boots. Electrical system powered by two 28V 70A engine-driven alternators with failure warning lights. Two 12V 24Ah batteries. External power socket. Models 601B and 601P each have an oxygen system, with individual outlets at each seat, as standard; capacity 601B 3·26 m³ (115 cu ft), 601P 0·31 m³ (11 cu ft).
AVIONICS AND EQUIPMENT: A wide range of optional avionics is available for all three versions of the Aerostar, including nav/coms, ADF, autopilots, DME, encoding altimeter, glideslope and marker beacon receivers, HF transceiver, RNAV, radio altimeter, transponder and weather radar, by manufacturers which include Aeronetics, Aerosonics, Bendix, Bonzer, Collins, King, Piper and SunAir. Standard equipment includes blind-flying instrumentation with 3 in attitude and directional gyros, clock, flight hour meter, dual manifold pressure gauges (601B/P have also dual exhaust temperature gauges), outside air temperature gauge, sensitive altimeter, turn co-ordinator, and vertical speed indicator; control locks; inertia reel shoulder harness for pilot and co-pilot seats; storm windows; sun visors; alternator failure, heater failure, and low fuel warning lights; emergency locator transmitter, heated pitot (601P has also an alternate static source); cabin air ventilators, dual pane tinted windows, carpeted floor, window curtains, super soundproofing; map, instrument panel red and white, reading, landing, navigation, taxi, and strobe lights; full-flow oil filters, jack pads and towbar. An extensive range of optional equipment is also available.

DIMENSIONS, EXTERNAL:	
Wing span: 600A	10·41 m (34 ft 2 in)
601B, 601P	11·18 m (36 ft 8 in)
Wing chord at root	2·18 m (7 ft 2 in)
Wing chord at tip: 600A	0·87 m (2 ft 10⅜ in)
601B, 601P	0·76 m (2 ft 6 in)
Wing aspect ratio: 600A	6·83
601B, 601P	7·55
Length overall	10·61 m (34 ft 9¾ in)
Height overall	3·70 m (12 ft 1½ in)
Tailplane span	4·37 m (14 ft 4 in)
Wheel track	3·11 m (10 ft 2½ in)
Propeller diameter	1·98 m (6 ft 6 in)
Passenger door: Height	1·14 m (3 ft 9 in)
Width	0·71 m (2 ft 4 in)
Baggage compartment door:	
Height	0·61 m (2 ft 0 in)
Width	0·56 m (1 ft 10 in)
DIMENSIONS, INTERNAL:	
Cabin: Length	3·81 m (12 ft 6 in)
Width	1·17 m (3 ft 10 in)
Height	1·22 m (4 ft 0 in)
Baggage space	0·85 m³ (30 cu ft)
AREAS:	
Wings, gross: 600A	15·79 m² (170 sq ft)
601B, 601P	16·54 m² (178 sq ft)
Tailplane	4·20 m² (45·2 sq ft)
WEIGHTS AND LOADINGS:	
Weight empty, equipped: 600A	1,695 kg (3,737 lb)
601B	1,795 kg (3,958 lb)
601P	1,840 kg (4,056 lb)
Max T-O, landing and ramp weight:	
600A	2,495 kg (5,500 lb)
601B, 601P	2,721 kg (6,000 lb)
Max wing loading: 600A	158·2 kg/m² (32·4 lb/sq ft)
601B, 601P	164·5 kg/m² (33·7 lb/sq ft)
Max power loading: 600A	5·77 kg/kW (9·5 lb/hp)
601B, 601P	6·29 kg/kW (10·34 lb/hp)

PERFORMANCE (at max T-O weight, A: 600A; B: 601B; C: 601P):
Cruising speed at average cruise weight:
A   75% power at 2,285 m (7,500 ft)
220 knots (408 km/h; 253 mph)
B, C   75% power at 7,620 m (25,000 ft)
257 knots (476 km/h; 296 mph)
B   75% power at 3,050 m (10,000 ft)
221 knots (410 km/h; 254 mph)
C   75% power at 4,570 m (15,000 ft)
233 knots (431 km/h; 268 mph)
A   65% power at 3,050 m (10,000 ft)
213 knots (394 km/h; 245 mph)
A   65% power at 2,285 m (7,500 ft)
208 knots (385 km/h; 239 mph)
B, C   65% power at 7,620 m (25,000 ft)
238 knots (441 km/h; 274 mph)
B   65% power at 3,050 m (10,000 ft)
208 knots (385 km/h; 239 mph)
C   65% power at 4,570 m (15,000 ft)
218 knots (404 km/h; 251 mph)

Piper Aerostar Model 600A, the basic version of the three Aerostar light transports

A 55% power at 3,050 m (10,000 ft)
   197 knots (365 km/h; 227 mph)

A 55% power at 2,285 m (7,500 ft)
   193 knots (357 km/h; 222 mph)

B, C 55% power at 7,620 m (25,000 ft)
   218 knots (404 km/h; 251 mph)

B 55% power at 3,050 m (10,000 ft)
   192 knots (356 km/h; 221 mph)

C 55% power at 6,100 m (20,000 ft)
   209 knots (388 km/h; 241 mph)

C 55% power at 4,570 m (15,000 ft)
   201 knots (372 km/h; 231 mph)

Stalling speed, flaps down:
| A | 74 knots (137 km/h; 85 mph) IAS |
| B, C | 77 knots (143 km/h; 89 mph) IAS |

Max rate of climb at S/L: A   549 m (1,800 ft)/min
B, C   445 m (1,460 ft)/min

Rate of climb at S/L, one engine out:
| A | 110 m (360 ft)/min |
| B, C | 73 m (240 ft)/min |

Service ceiling: A   6,460 m (21,200 ft)
B   9,145 m (30,000 ft)
C   7,620 m (25,000 ft)

Service ceiling, one engine out:
| A | 1,920 m (6,300 ft) |
| B, C | 2,680 m (8,800 ft) |

T-O run: A   472 m (1,550 ft)
B, C   579 m (1,900 ft)

T-O to 15 m (50 ft): A   594 m (1,950 ft)
B, C   759 m (2,490 ft)

Landing from 15 m (50 ft): A   561 m (1,840 ft)
B, C   619 m (2,030 ft)

Landing run: A   317 m (1,040 ft)
B, C   375 m (1,230 ft)

Range with max fuel, allowances for start, taxi, T-O, climb, and 45 min reserves at long-range cruise power:
A 75% power at 1,830 m (6,000 ft)
   983 nm (1,821 km; 1,132 miles)
A 65% power at 2,745 m (9,000 ft)
   1,079 nm (2,000 km; 1,242 miles)
B, C 65% power at 4,570 m (15,000 ft)
   1,024 nm (1,897 km; 1,179 miles)
B 65% power at 3,050 m (10,000 ft)
   1,056 nm (1,957 km; 1,216 miles)
A 55% power at 3,050 m (10,000 ft)
   1,201 nm (2,225 km; 1,383 miles)
B, C 55% power at 4,570 m (15,000 ft)
   1,173 nm (2,172 km; 1,350 miles)
B 55% power at 3,050 m (10,000 ft)
   1,144 nm (2,120 km; 1,317 miles)
C 55% power at 6,100 m (20,000 ft)
   1,198 nm (2,219 km; 1,379 miles)
C 55% power at 7,620 m (25,000 ft)
   1,101 nm (2,040 km; 1,268 miles)

PITTS
PITTS AEROBATICS

PO Box 547, Afton, Wyoming 83110
Telephone: (307) 886 3151
GENERAL MANAGER: E. H. Andersen Jr

One of the best-known US designers of high-performance sporting aircraft, Mr Curtis Pitts, announced on 1 January 1977 that he had sold the manufacturing, engineering, and sales rights of the Pitts S-1 and S-2 aircraft to Doyle Child of Afton, Wyoming. A new company, Pitts Aerobatics, was formed to continue engineering and sales activities, being based at the same location as Aerotek Inc, which formerly produced the S-2 for Pitts Aviation Enterprises.

Detailed construction drawings for the single-seat S-1 version are available to amateur constructors (see Homebuilts section). For pilots who do not wish to build their own aircraft, Aerotek Inc can supply a ready-to-fly single-seater designated S-1S. The two-seat S-2 is available both as a factory-built aircraft and in kit form, and is produced by Aerotek for Pitts Aerobatics. The single-seat S-2S, of which the first production examples became available in late 1978, is also being marketed in kit form for amateur construction. Production S-2S aircraft are certificated currently in the Experimental-Exhibition category, but it is planned to gain full type certification.

PITTS S-1 SPECIAL

The original single-seat Pitts Special was designed in 1943-44. Construction of a prototype began in 1944 and it flew in September of that year. One of the most successful early models was *Little Stinker*, powered by a 67 kW (90 hp) Continental engine, and built by Mr Pitts in 1947 for Miss Betty Skelton, then an internationally-known aerobatic display pilot. The *Black Beauty* biplane, built by Pitts for Miss Caro Bailey, was of similar design, but powered by a 93 kW (125 hp) Avco Lycoming O-290-D engine.

Since then even more powerful engines have been installed in Pitts Specials built by both the designer and other people, and those versions of the single-seat Special for which drawings are available are designed to take an Avco Lycoming engine of up to 134 kW (180 hp), as noted in the Homebuilts section.

Current versions of the S-1 are as follows:

S-1D. Intended for homebuilders only, with plans available. Generally similar to the S-1S.

S-1E. Intended for homebuilders only; has wings of symmetrical aerofoil section. Plans available.

S-1S. Production aircraft, FAA type certificated and built at rate of 25 aircraft per year. It is available also in kit form, parts, materials and components being produced under an FAA Approved Production Certificate.

There is also an S-1C version, but Pitts can no longer supply plans for its construction.

Details of some of the major successes achieved by US pilots of Pitts Specials in national and international aerobatic competitions, since 1966, have been given in the 1972-73 and later *Jane's*.

The details which follow apply to the S-1S factory-built aircraft with 134 kW (180 hp) engine, but engines of 74·5-134 kW (100-180 hp) can be fitted to the S-1 Special.
TYPE: Single-seat sporting biplane.
WINGS: Braced biplane type, with single faired interplane strut each side and N-type cabane struts. Dual streamline flying and landing wires. Wing section M6. Thickness/chord ratio 12%. Dihedral 0° on upper wing, 3° on lower wings. Incidence 1° 30′ on upper wing, 0° on lower wings. Sweepback at quarter-chord 6° 40′ on upper wing only. Wooden structure, with fabric covering. Frise-type ailerons on both upper and lower wings, of similar construction to wings. No flaps or tabs.
FUSELAGE: Welded steel tube structure, fabric covered.
TAIL UNIT: Wire-braced steel tube structure, fabric-covered. Fixed-incidence tailplane. Trim tab in each elevator.

LANDING GEAR: Non-retractable tailwheel type. Rubber-cord shock-absorption. Cleveland main wheels with 6-ply tyres, size 5·00-5, pressure 2·07 bars (30 lb/sq in). Cleveland hydraulic disc brakes. Steerable tailwheel. Glassfibre fairings on main wheels.
POWER PLANT: One 134 kW (180 hp) Avco Lycoming IO-360-B4A flat-four engine, driving a Sensenich type 76EM8-O-56/62 two-blade fixed-pitch metal propeller. Fuel tank aft of firewall, capacity 75 litres (20 US gallons). Refuelling point on upper surface of fuselage, forward of windscreen. Oil capacity 7·5 litres (2 US gallons). Inverted fuel and oil systems standard.
ACCOMMODATION: Single seat in open cockpit.
DIMENSIONS, EXTERNAL:
Wing span, upper	5·28 m (17 ft 4 in)
Wing chord (constant, both)	0·91 m (3 ft 0 in)
Wing aspect ratio	5·77
Length overall	4·71 m (15 ft 5½ in)
Height overall	1·92 m (6 ft 3½ in)
Tailplane span	1·98 m (6 ft 6 in)
Propeller diameter	1·93 m (6 ft 4 in)
AREA:
Wings, gross	9·15 m² (98·5 sq ft)
WEIGHTS AND LOADING:
Weight empty	326 kg (720 lb)
Max T-O weight	521 kg (1,150 lb)
Max power loading	3·89 kg/kW (6·38 lb/hp)
PERFORMANCE (at max T-O weight):
Never-exceed speed 176 knots (326 km/h; 203 mph)
Max level speed at S/L
   153 knots (283 km/h; 176 mph)
Max cruising speed at S/L
   122 knots (227 km/h; 141 mph)
Stalling speed   54 knots (100 km/h; 62 mph)
Max rate of climb at S/L   792 m (2,600 ft)/min
Service ceiling   6,795 m (22,300 ft)
T-O to 15 m (50 ft)   331 m (1,085 ft)
Range with max fuel, no reserves
   273 nm (507 km; 315 miles)

PITTS S-2A SPECIAL

First flown in 1967, the S-2A is a two-seat version of the Pitts Special. It is similar to the single-seat S-1 in basic configuration and construction, but is slightly larger in overall dimensions, with no attempt at commonality of components. The increased size and power, coupled with aerodynamic changes, give the two-seater improved aerobatic and landing characteristics, and make it extremely stable in rough air conditions. Control

Pitts S-2A Special, a factory-built two-seater with extended canopy covering both cockpits

responses are better than on the S-1. The ailerons are aerodynamically balanced for higher rate of roll at low speeds, and full vertical rolls can be made with ease. The different wing sections used on the S-2A provide inverted performance equal to conventional flight, and facilitate outside loops.

The S-2A is FAA type certificated in the Normal and Aerobatic categories. It is a production aeroplane, not intended for the homebuilder, and plans are not available.

Five S-2As, each fitted with a 149 kW (200 hp) Avco Lycoming engine, were supplied in early 1973 to the British aerobatic display team then financed by the Rothman Tobacco Company. During displays, the front cockpit of each aircraft was covered by a removable panel. Five similar aircraft were supplied to the Carling Black Label aerobatic team operating from Toronto, Canada.

S-2As have been exported to Australia, Brazil, Sweden and Venezuela. In mid-1976, the Peruvian Air Force announced an order for six Pitts Specials, for 'an unspecified training role'.
TYPE: Two-seat aerobatic biplane.
WINGS: Braced biplane type, with single faired interplane strut each side and N-type cabane. Wing section NACA 6400 series on upper wing, 00 series on bottom wings. Two-spar wooden (spruce) structure with fabric covering. Aerodynamically-balanced ailerons on both upper and lower wings. No flaps or tabs.
FUSELAGE: Welded steel tube structure with wooden stringers, covered with Dacron fabric except for metal top-decking.
TAIL UNIT: Wire-braced welded steel tube structure. Fixed surfaces metal-covered, control surfaces fabric-covered. Trim tab in each elevator.
LANDING GEAR: Non-retractable tailwheel type. Rubber-cord shock-absorption. Steerable tailwheel. Fairings on main wheels.
POWER PLANT: One 149 kW (200 hp) Avco Lycoming IO-360-A1A flat-four engine, driving a Hartzell type HC-C2YK-4/C7666A-2 two-blade constant-speed metal propeller with spinner. Fuel tank in fuselage, immediately aft of firewall, capacity 90·5 litres (24 US gallons). Refuelling point on fuselage upper surface forward of front windscreen. Oil capacity 7·5 litres (2 US gallons). Inverted fuel and oil systems standard.
ACCOMMODATION: Two seats in tandem cockpits with dual controls. Rear cockpit can be enclosed by a transparent canopy if required, and an extended one-piece canopy to cover both cockpits is also available. Space for 9 kg (20 lb) baggage aft of rear cockpit when flown in non-aerobatic category.

SYSTEM: Electrical system powered by 12V 40A alternator and non-spill 12V battery.

DIMENSIONS, EXTERNAL:
Wing span, upper	6·10 m (20 ft 0 in)
Wing span, lower	5·79 m (19 ft 0 in)
Wing chord (constant, both)	1·02 m (3 ft 4 in)
Length overall	5·41 m (17 ft 9 in)
Height overall	1·94 m (6 ft 4½ in)

AREA:
Wings, gross	11·6 m² (125 sq ft)

WEIGHTS AND LOADINGS (A: Aerobatic; B: Normal category):
Weight empty: A, B	453 kg (1,000 lb)
Max T-O weight: A	680 kg (1,500 lb)
B	714 kg (1,575 lb)
Max wing loading: A	58·6 kg/m² (12·0 lb/sq ft)
B	61·5 kg/m² (12·6 lb/sq ft)
Max power loading: A	4·56 kg/kW (7·5 lb/hp)
B	5·33 kg/kW (7·87 lb/hp)

PERFORMANCE (at max T-O weight. A: Aerobatic; B: Normal category):
Never-exceed speed:	
A, B	176 knots (326 km/h; 203 mph)
Max level speed at S/L:	
A, B	136 knots (253 km/h; 157 mph)
Max cruising speed at S/L:	
A, B	132 knots (245 km/h; 152 mph)
Stalling speed: A	51 knots (94 km/h; 58 mph)
B	51·5 knots (95 km/h; 59 mph)
Max rate of climb at S/L: A	579 m (1,900 ft)/min
B	549 m (1,800 ft)/min
Service ceiling: A	6,125 m (20,100 ft)
B	4,875 m (16,000 ft)
T-O to 15 m (50 ft): A	351 m (1,150 ft)

Pitts Model S-2S single-seat biplane (Lycoming AEIO-540-D4A5 engine)

Range with max fuel:	
A	297 nm (552 km; 343 miles)

PITTS MODEL S-2S

Pitts Aerobatics began production in late 1978 of this single-seat version of the S-2A. It has a modified forward fuselage to permit the installation of a 194 kW (260 hp) Avco Lycoming AEIO-540-D4A5 flat-six engine, driving a McCauley Type 1A/200 two-blade fixed-pitch metal propeller with spinner. The first flight of the prototype was made on 9 December 1977. Maximum level speed is 157 knots (291 km/h; 181 mph), max rate of climb at S/L 915 m (3,000 ft)/min. The Model S-2S is available either as a factory-built aircraft, or in kit form for amateur construction.

In early 1980 the S-2S was available only with Experimental category certification, but the company intends to obtain FAA type certification.

RAISBECK
THE RAISBECK GROUP

CORPORATE OFFICES AND WORKS: 7777 Perimeter Road S, Seattle, Washington 98108
Telephone: (206) 762 5156
Telex: Aeroamerica 32 0233
PRESIDENT AND BOARD CHAIRMAN: James D. Raisbeck
EXECUTIVE VICE-PRESIDENT—FINANCE:
Dwight D. Christy Jr
SENIOR VICE-PRESIDENT:
R. Kim Frinell (Experimental Operations)
VICE-PRESIDENT:
Thomas P. May (Contract Administration)

The Raisbeck Group was formed in 1974, bringing together many of the team members who had developed and certificated high-lift systems for Boeing, McDonnell Douglas and Robertson Aircraft Corporation. The Group is dedicated to the logical introduction of state-of-the-art technology in business, corporate and commercial jet aircraft. This technology covers the spectrum from low- and high-speed aerodynamics to structures, propulsion and systems. In general, five goals are established by The Raisbeck Group for each programme, aimed at increasing payload, range, cruising speeds, operational flexibility (lower take-off and landing speeds), and operational safety. Heavy emphasis is placed on aerodynamic refinements to reduce cruise drag at normal operating speeds, and to reduce required runway field lengths through an associated reduction in certificated stalling speeds in take-off and landing configurations.

To date, three principal product lines have been introduced: the Mark II System for basic Gates Learjet aircraft in a joint venture with The Dee Howard Company during 1974-75; the Mark Five System for Rockwell Sabreliners, 1976-79; and the Mark IV System for Gates Learjet Century III aircraft, 1979-80. Details of these systems follow:

HOWARD/RAISBECK MARK II SYSTEM

The first programme by The Raisbeck Group involved the Gates Learjet family of aircraft. Work on a 'Mark II System' began in late 1973. Subsequent flight test and development, initially in conjunction with Gates Learjet Corporation and completed later through a joint effort with The Dee Howard Company of San Antonio, Texas, brought to the market an advanced technology high-lift system for Learjet aircraft. This makes the following contribution to the aircraft's performance:

(i) Reduction in T-O and approach speeds of 16-23 knots (30-43 km/h; 18·5-26·5 mph), depending on configuration and the specific model.

(ii) Reduction in the aircraft's cruise drag of measurably significant proportions.

(iii) Certification of the turbojet versions of the Learjet Models 23, 24 and 25 to FAR Part 36 acoustic requirements without the use of sound suppressors or any change to the engine nacelle configuration.

(iv) Elimination of the stick-pusher as a performance-limiting item.

(v) Aircraft has inherent aerodynamic stall-warning characteristics.

Certification of the Mark II System was received by the Howard/Raisbeck joint venture in October 1975, and production of retrofit systems for the Learjet family of aircraft was launched immediately. By mid-1979 more than 260 production Mark II Systems had been delivered for retrofit to existing Learjet 23/24/25 aircraft, and pro-

duction was continuing.

Features of the Mark II System include the installation of full-span supercritical wing leading-edges over the first 5% of wing chord, while retaining the standard Learjet anti-icing system; addition of strakes inboard of the wingtip tanks to enhance aileron response during slow-speed and engine-out operation; removal of vortex generators; provision of new aileron gap seals; extension of the upper surface of the basic wing to cover the existing trailing-edge flap, combined with new flap tracks, to allow a significant increase in aft flap travel prior to downward deflection; addition of stall turbulators on wing leading-edges; provision of a flap-actuated pitch trim system which puts an 'up' pre-load on the elevators automatically as the flaps are deflected; installation of improved angle of attack indicator and new flap position sensor/indicator systems; and resetting of the stick shaker and pusher to conform with enhanced aerodynamic stall characteristics. A new trailing-edge flap preselect system, as part of the Mark II System for all Learjet Model 23, 24 and 25 aircraft, was announced on 18 August 1976 following certification under FAR 25. This allows easy preselection of all flap settings from full up to 10° T-O; 20° T-O, approach and go-around; and full down landing position. Announced subsequently, on 17 January 1977, was the certification of the Teledyne angle of attack system for Model 23 and 24 Learjets.

The new system provides precise stall warning capability, using existing Learjet shaker and pusher equipment which is controlled by a new computer. This also drives flap-position compensated and normalised angle of attack indicators, to provide a lift situation display which is valid for the entire flight regime.

Feature	Sabreliner 40A	Sabreliner 40B Mark Five	Sabreliner 60	Sabreliner 60A Mark Five	Sabreliner 75A	Sabreliner 80A Mark Five
Max ramp weight	8,634 kg (19,035 lb)	9,707 kg (21,400 lb)	9,241 kg (20,372 lb)	10,387 kg (22,900 lb)	10,659 kg (23,500 lb)	11,566 kg (25,500 lb)
Max T-O weight	8,459 kg (18,650 lb)	9,707 kg (21,400 lb)	9,150 kg (20,172 lb)	10,297 kg (22,700 lb)	10,569 kg (23,300 lb)	11,566 kg (25,500 lb)
Design landing weight	7,938 kg (17,500 lb)	9,344 kg (20,600 lb)	7,938 kg (17,500 lb)	9,344 kg (20,600 lb)	9,979 kg (22,000 lb)	9,979 kg (22,000 lb)
Max zero-fuel weight	6,260 kg (13,800 lb)	7,099 kg (15,650 lb)	6,260 kg (13,800 lb)	7,053 kg (15,550 lb)	7,085 kg (15,620 lb)	8,255 kg (18,200 lb)
Flaps up wing area	31·77 m² (342 sq ft)	35·30 m² (380 sq ft)	31·77 m² (342 sq ft)	35·30 m² (380 sq ft)	31·77 m² (342 sq ft)	35·30 m² (380 sq ft)
Flaps down wing area	32·61 m² (351 sq ft)	39·11 m² (421 sq ft)	32·61 m² (351 sq ft)	39·11 m² (421 sq ft)	32·61 m² (351 sq ft)	39·11 m² (421 sq ft)
Wing aspect ratio	5·57	6·70	5·57	6·70	5·57	6·70
T-O flap settings	0°	0°, 10°, 20°	0°	0°, 10°, 20°	0°, 15°	0°, 10°, 20°
Landing flap settings	25°	36°	25°	36°	25°	36°
Wing lift spoilers	None	26% span	None	26% span	None	26% span
Nacelle inlet	Splitters	Clean	Splitters	Clean	—	—
Anti-skid system	On/off	Fully-modulated	On/off	Fully-modulated	Fully-modulated	Fully-modulated

Comparative data for standard Sabreliners and those embodying the Rockwell/Raisbeck Mark Five System

A summary of Howard/Raisbeck Mark II System performance improvements for Gates Learjet aircraft is given in the table at the bottom of this page.

RAISBECK MARK IV SYSTEM

In late 1978 it became necessary to reduce the sensitivity of the Gates Learjet Century III wing to inadvertent ice shapes, principally in the stalling characteristics region. Raisbeck designed, developed and certificated the Mark IV System for Gates Learjet Century III aircraft, the first production delivery following immediately after certification on 4 May 1979. The system includes the installation of two stall fences on the leading-edge of each wing, removal of the wing vortex generators (which brings about a 7-10% reduction in cruise drag, and an additional reduction in stalling speed), introduction of aileron gap seals, and adjustment of the aircraft's stick pusher system to permit certification without the requirement of a stick pusher. Options include a new stall warning and angle of attack system, and a flap preselect system to set the flaps automatically after position selection. Stall characteristics of the Mark IV equipped Century III Learjet are extremely docile, with full aerodynamic buffet and warning from 10 knots (18·5 km/h; 11·5 mph) prior to pitch through. Due to the urgent need to introduce the Mark IV System in the Learjet Century III fleet, associated reductions in take-off and landing speed, and field lengths, were ignored for the first round of installations.

The Model 35A/36A Learjets were the first to be certificated by The Raisbeck Group, and installation of the Mark IV System on these aircraft is carried out by Raisbeck at its Seattle, Washington, facility. The accompanying table (right) gives comparative figures of the basic Learjet 35A/36A Century III, and of the same aircraft with the Mark IV System.

ROCKWELL/RAISBECK MARK FIVE SYSTEM

In a joint venture with Rockwell International Sabreliner Division, the Raisbeck Group designed, developed, and certificated on 15 November 1978 the Mark Five System for the Sabreliner 60.

The Mark Five System for the Sabreliner includes a supercritical wing which increases the span by 1·83 m (6 ft), 100% chord Fowler-type trailing-edge flaps, thermal anti-icing of the wing leading-edge, an additional 590 kg (1,300 lb) of fuel in the wing, hydraulically actuated automatic spoilers on the wings, advanced technology anti-skid braking system, an increase in tailplane and elevator size, and a rebuilding of the aircraft's structure to give many of its elements a 30,000-hour life cycle.

Resulting comparative specifications of the Mark Five Sabreliner Models 40B, 60A and 80A are given in the table on page 420. Not included in this table are other improvements, such as a 0·05 increase in cruise Mach number, higher initial cruise altitude, up to 10% reduction in fuel consumption, and a quieter cabin due to the sweeping of the shock wave at the wing root.

By mid-1979, a total of 90 Mark Five kits had been ordered by Rockwell for its new Sabreliner Model 65. Ten previously-owned Sabreliners had already been retrofitted by Raisbeck at Seattle, and production for the retrofit line was established at 41 per year.

Rockwell Sabreliner 60 used for flight testing the Raisbeck Mark Five System

Feature	Century III Learjet 35A/36A	Mark IV Learjet 35A/36A
Stalling speed at 7,257 kg (16,000 lb): Flaps up	123 knots (228 km/h; 142 mph)	112 knots (207·5 km/h; 129 mph)
Flaps 8° down	111 knots (206 km/h; 128 mph)	106 knots (196 km/h; 122 mph)
Flaps down	100·5 knots (186·5 km/h; 116 mph)	98·5 knots (183 km/h; 113·5 mph)
Initial cruising altitude	Base	+305 m (1,000 ft)
Cruising fuel consumption	Base	−8%

Summary of performance improvements offered by Raisbeck Mark IV System

Raisbeck Mark IV System applied to Gates Learjet Century III Learjet 35A/36A

	LEARJET 23		LEARJET 24B/24D		LEARJET 25/25B/25C	
	Basic Aircraft knots-km/h-mph	Mk II System knots-km/h-mph	Basic Aircraft knots-km/h-mph	Mk II System knots-km/h-mph	Basic Aircraft knots-km/h-mph	Mk II System knots-km/h-mph
T-O speed at max T-O weight, 10° flap	*	119-221-137	*	123-229-142	*	130-241-150
T-O speed at max T-O weight, 20° flap	129-239-149	113-210-130	131-243-151	115-212-132	144-267-166	121-224-139
Minimum control speed (V_MC)	82-152-95	83-154-96	108-200-124	80-148-92	102-188-117	Below stall speed
Normal cruising speed	441-816-507	458-848-527	441-816-507	458-848-527	441-816-507	458-848-527
Long-range cruising speed	405-750-466	430-796-494	405-750-466	430-797-495	408-756-470	434-805-500
Approach speed at max landing weight, flaps down	127-235-146	115-213-133	133-246-153	115-212-132	139-257-160	122-225-140
Approach speed at 120% of empty weight, flaps down	121-224-139	109-202-126	114-211-131	95-175-109	118-219-136	101-187-116
Stalling speed at max T-O weight, flaps up	118-219-136	106-197-122	126-233-145	106-196-122	137-254-158	112-208-129
Stalling speed at max T-O weight, 10° flap	*	101-187-117	*	101-187-116	*	106-196-122
Stalling speed at max T-O weight, 20° flap	104-193-120	95-176-110	109-203-126	94-174-108	118-219-136	99-183-114
Stalling speed at max landing weight, flaps down	96-178-111	90-167-104	100-185-115	85-158-98	107-198-123	91-169-105

NOTE: Figures quoted are indicated airspeeds (IAS) and are stated by Howard/Raisbeck to be typical of the improvements under all operating conditions. *Indicates new capability in this configuration.

Summary of Howard/Raisbeck Mark II System performance improvements for Gates Learjet aircraft

RILEY
RILEY AIRCRAFT CORPORATION

2016 Palomar Airport Road, Carlsbad, California 92008
Telephone: (714) 438 0660
Telex: 69 7936 Riley Jet
PRESIDENT: Jack M. Riley

Mr J. Riley was responsible for the Riley 55 Twin-Navion conversion scheme in 1952 and the Riley Rocket conversion of the Cessna 310 in 1962, as well as for Dove, Heron and Cessna 310/320 conversions known respectively as the Riley Turbo-Exec 400, Turbo Skyliner and Turbostream. His company is marketing currently a Cessna 310/320 conversion known as the Riley Super 310; two Cessna 340 conversions which are designated Riley Super 340 and Riley Rocket 340; a conversion of the Cessna 414 designated Riley Rocket Power 414, and a Cessna 421 conversion designated Riley Turbine Rocket 421.

FAA approved export conversion kits are available for the five aircraft in the current production programme, and assistance is available if required to gain approval by the civil aviation authority in the country to which the kit has been exported.

In early 1980 the company was involved in the certification programme of a second Cessna 421 conversion. Given the name Riley Turbine Eagle 421, it was anticipated that certification would be awarded during Spring 1980.

RILEY SUPER 310

The Super 310 represents a similar conversion to that of the Super 340, the existing power plants in the Cessna 310/320 being replaced by 231 kW (310 hp) Continental TSIO-520-Js. The conversion is FAA approved for the Cessna 310I to 310R, 320B to 320F and T310P to T310R. Installation of the complete kit requires 12 working days.

A description of the current Cessna Model 310 appears under the Cessna entry in this edition. It applies also to the Riley Super 310, except as follows:

POWER PLANT: As described for Riley Super 340.
WEIGHTS AND LOADING: As for the appropriate Cessna 310/320 model except as follows:

Weight empty	increased by 10 kg (22 lb)
Max payload	reduced by 10 kg (22 lb)
Max power loading	5·11 kg/kW (8·4 lb/hp)

PERFORMANCE (at max T-O weight):

Max level speed at 7,315 m (24,000 ft)	270 knots (500 km/h; 311 mph)
Max cruising speed at 7,315 m (24,000 ft)	255 knots (473 km/h; 294 mph)
Max cruising speed at 3,660 m (12,000 ft)	225 knots (417 km/h; 259 mph)
Econ cruising speed at 3,660 m (12,000 ft)	200 knots (370 km/h; 230 mph)
Max rate of climb at S/L	671 m (2,200 ft)/min
Cruise rate of climb at max cruising power	457 m (1,500 ft)/min
Rate of climb at S/L, one engine out	152 m (500 ft)/min
Service ceiling	10,980 m (36,000 ft)
Service ceiling, one engine out	7,315 m (24,000 ft)
T-O run	335 m (1,100 ft)
T-O to 15 m (50 ft)	472 m (1,550 ft)
Landing from 15 m (50 ft)	546 m (1,790 ft)
Range with 757 litres (200 US gallons) fuel, max cruising speed at 7,315 m (24,000 ft), no reserves	1,476 nm (2,735 km; 1,700 miles)
Range with 757 litres (200 US gallons) fuel, econ cruising speed at 7,315 m (24,000 ft), no reserves	1,815 nm (3,363 km; 2,090 miles)

RILEY SUPER 340

The Riley Super 340 differs from the standard Cessna 340 primarily through replacement of the latter's TSIO-520-K engines by TSIO-520-Js. The most important change associated with this new engine installation is the addition of an intercooler which allows a higher power output and also improves specific fuel consumption, critical altitude, engine life and reliability.

The prototype Super 340 received FAA certification in June 1974 and 177 aircraft had been modified by January 1978. The standard Cessna 340A for 1976 was updated in a manner similar to that of the Riley Super 340. Consequently, only Cessna 340 aircraft constructed from 1972 until the last of the 1975 models were completed are suitable for this conversion, which is completed by Riley engineers in five working days.

A description of the current Cessna Model 340A appears under the Cessna entry in this edition. It applies also to the Riley Super 340, except as follows:

POWER PLANT: Two 231 kW (310 hp) Continental TSIO-520-J flat-six turbocharged and intercooled engines, each driving a McCauley three-blade propeller. Engine installation upgraded from Cessna 340 to Cessna 414 configuration. Fuel system as for Cessna 340. Optional aft nacelle fuel tanks, each of 75·7 litres (20 US gallons), provide max optional fuel capacity of 920 litres (243 US gallons) when used in conjunction with the Cessna optional 768 litre (203 US gallon) system.

WEIGHTS AND LOADING:

Weight empty	1,754 kg (3,868 lb)
Max payload	904 kg (1,993 lb)
Max T-O weight	2,710 kg (5,975 lb)
Max power loading	5·87 kg/kW (9·64 lb/hp)

PERFORMANCE (at max T-O weight):

Max level speed at 7,315 m (24,000 ft)	252 knots (467 km/h; 290 mph)
Max cruising speed at 7,315 m (24,000 ft)	234 knots (435 km/h; 270 mph)
Max cruising speed at 5,485 m (18,000 ft)	226 knots (418 km/h; 260 mph)
Max cruising speed at 4,265 m (14,000 ft)	217 knots (402 km/h; 250 mph)
Econ cruising speed at 7,315 m (24,000 ft)	208 knots (386 km/h; 240 mph)
Max rate of climb at S/L	549 m (1,800 ft)/min
Cruise rate of climb at max cruising power	305 m (1,000 ft)/min
Rate of climb at S/L, one engine out	107 m (350 ft)/min
Service ceiling	9,755 m (32,000 ft)
Service ceiling, one engine out	4,875 m (16,000 ft)
T-O run	457 m (1,500 ft)
T-O to 15 m (50 ft)	594 m (1,950 ft)
Landing from 15 m (50 ft)	561 m (1,840 ft)
Landing run	233 m (765 ft)

Riley Rocket 340 conversion of the Cessna Model 340 (Avco Lycoming TIO-540-R engines)

Range with 768 litres (203 US gallons) fuel, max cruising speed at 7,315 m (24,000 ft), no reserves	1,302 nm (2,415 km; 1,500 miles)
Range with 920 litres (243 US gallons) fuel, econ cruising speed at 7,315 m (24,000 ft), no reserves	2,170 nm (4,025 km; 2,500 miles)
Range with pilot, co-pilot, four passengers, 91 kg (200 lb) baggage, fuelled to max T-O weight, econ cruising speed at 7,315 m (24,000 ft), no reserves	868 nm (1,610 km; 1,000 miles)

RILEY ROCKET 340

This Riley conversion of the Cessna 340 is, like the Super 340 conversion, concerned primarily with the installation of a different power plant to improve performance. Thus, the Continental TSIO-520-J engines of the Super 340 are replaced by counter-rotating Avco Lycoming TIO-540-Rs of increased power. These engines feature the latest Garrett-AiResearch turbocharger system, with the wastegate and automatic manifold pressure controller integral with the engine turbocharger. First flight of a Rocket 340 was made in December 1977.

A description of the current Cessna Model 340A appears under the Cessna entry in this edition. It applies to also to the Riley Rocket 340, except as follows:

POWER PLANT: One Avco Lycoming TIO-540-R and one LTIO-540-R flat-six engine, each rated at 254 kW (340 hp) for take-off and driving a Hartzell propeller with spinner. Fuel system as for Riley Super 340. Intake air intercoolers standard.

AVIONICS AND EQUIPMENT: Standard equipment includes a propeller synchrophaser. A range of optional avionics is available to customer's requirements. Optional equipment includes a custom interior, seventh cabin seat, super soundproofing of nose baggage area adjacent to propeller arc, Cleveland heavy-duty wheels and brakes, J.B. Systems electrically-driven air-conditioner, automatic in-line fuel boost pumps, wing and tailplane de-icing boots, and polyurethane exterior paint finish.

WEIGHT AND LOADINGS:

Max T-O weight	2,853 kg (6,290 lb)
Max wing loading	158·7 kg/m² (32·5 lb/sq ft)
Max power loading	5·62 kg/kW (9·25 lb/hp)

PERFORMANCE (at max T-O weight, ISA):

Max cruising speed at 7,315 m (24,000 ft)	261 knots (483 km/h; 300 mph)
Cruising speed, 65% power at 7,315 m (24,000 ft)	240 knots (444 km/h; 276 mph)
Max rate of climb at S/L	655 m (2,150 ft)/min
Rate of climb at S/L, one engine out	152 m (500 ft)/min
Service ceiling	over 9,145 m (30,000 ft)
Service ceiling, one engine out	6,310 m (20,700 ft)
Minimum field length	561 m (1,840 ft)
Max range, 45 min reserves:	
444 kg (978 lb) fuel	960 nm (1,778 km; 1,105 miles)
552 kg (1,218 lb) fuel	1,260 nm (2,335 km; 1,451 miles)

RILEY ROCKET POWER 414

This Riley conversion of the Cessna 414 involves installation of Avco Lycoming IO-720 flat-eight engines to provide improved performance. It moves the empty aircraft CG forward, allowing more flexibility in loading, and introduces also Hartzell automatic propeller synchrophasing, an Aerosonic electronic fuel management system, and heavy-duty Cleveland brakes. The engines are mounted in new glassfibre cowlings which have louvres for engine cooling, making redundant the cowl flaps which were provided originally, and these are removed.

A description of the current Cessna Model 414 appears under the Cessna entry in this edition. It applies also to the Riley Rocket Power 414, except as follows:
POWER PLANT: Two 298 kW (400 hp) Avco Lycoming

Riley Rocket Power 414, a conversion of the Cessna 414 (two Avco Lycoming IO-720 engines)

IO-720 flat-eight engines, each driving a Hartzell four-blade constant-speed metal propeller. Riley intake air intercoolers standard. Fuel system as for Cessna 414, except that an Aerosonic fuel management system is provided. Hartzell automatic propeller synchrophasers standard.

WEIGHT AND LOADINGS:
Max T-O and landing weight 3,096 kg (6,825 lb)
Max wing loading 170·0 kg/m² (34·82 lb/sq ft)
Max power loading 5·19 kg/kW (8·53 lb/hp)
PERFORMANCE (at max T-O weight, ISA):
Max level speed, turbo cruise power:
At 7,315 m (24,000 ft)
  261 knots (483 km/h; 300 mph)
At 3,660 m (12,000 ft)
  217 knots (402 km/h; 250 mph)
Speed at intermediate cruise power:
At 7,315 m (24,000 ft)
  243 knots (451 km/h; 280 mph)
At 3,660 m (12,000 ft)
  200 knots (370 km/h; 230 mph)
Max rate of climb at S/L 686 m (2,250 ft)/min
Rate of climb at S/L, one engine out
  122 m (400 ft)/min
Service ceiling 9,145 m (30,000 ft)
Service ceiling, one engine out 7,620 m (25,000 ft)
Max range, 45 min reserves:
490 kg (1,080 lb) fuel
  771 nm (1,429 km; 888 miles)
653 kg (1,440 lb) fuel
  1,136 nm (2,105 km; 1,308 miles)

RILEY TURBINE ROCKET 421

This Riley conversion of the pressurised Cessna 421 involves installation of Avco Lycoming LTP 101-700 turboprop engines, each rated normally at 522 ekW (700 ehp), but flat rated in this application to approximately 70% of normal T-O power. First flight of a Turbine Rocket 421 was made on 10 January 1978, followed by the first production conversion on 4 June 1978.

The description of the Cessna 421 Golden Eagle which appears under the Cessna entry in this edition applies also to the Riley Turbine Rocket 421, except that the landing gear is equipped with Cleveland 199-76 heavy-duty brakes; each engine drives a Hartzell propeller with Q-tips and Beta propeller reversal; and optional wing fuel tanks

Prototype of Riley's new Turbine Eagle 421, a conversion of the Cessna 421C Golden Eagle

are available to add 363 litres (96 US gallons) to the max total capacity.
WEIGHT AND LOADINGS:
Max T-O weight 3,470 kg (7,650 lb)
Max wing loading 173·7 kg/m² (35·58 lb/sq ft)
Max power loading 4·75 kg/kW (7·81 lb/ehp)
PERFORMANCE (at max T-O weight, ISA):
Max cruising speed at 6,100 m (20,000 ft)
  270 knots (500 km/h; 311 mph)
Max rate of climb at S/L 1,067 m (3,500 ft)/min
Rate of climb at S/L, one engine out
  225 m (737 ft)/min
Service ceiling 9,145 m (30,000 ft)
Service ceiling, one engine out 5,485 m (18,000 ft)
Min landing field length 686 m (2,250 ft)
Landing run with propeller reversal 152 m (500 ft)
Max range 1,301 nm (2,410 km; 1,498 miles)

RILEY TURBINE EAGLE 421

Claimed by Riley Aircraft to be the world's fastest executive turboprop aircraft, this modification unites the Cessna 421C Golden Eagle airframe with Pratt & Whitney Aircraft of Canada PT6A turboprop engines,

mounted in new low-drag nacelles. Each of these engines has more than double the power output of the engine it replaces, yet weighs some 40 per cent less. The prototype Turbine Eagle 421 flew for the first time in late November 1979, at Palomar Airport, and completion of the certification programme was planned for the Spring of 1980.

A description of the current Cessna 421C Golden Eagle appears under the Cessna entry in this edition; it applies also to the Riley Turbine Eagle 421, except as follows:
POWER PLANT: Two Pratt & Whitney Aircraft of Canada PT6A-135 turboprop engines, each flat rated at 580 kW (780 shp), and driving Hartzell three-blade constant-speed metal propellers with Q-tips.
WEIGHT:
Max T-O weight 3,492 kg (7,700 lb)
PERFORMANCE (provisional, at max T-O weight):
Max cruising speed at 8,230 m (27,000 ft)
  318 knots (589 km/h; 366 mph)
Max rate of climb at S/L 1,525 m (5,000 ft)/min
Rate of climb, one engine out 305 m (1,000 ft)/min
Service ceiling, one engine out 7,620 m (25,000 ft)
Range with IFR reserves
  more than 1,156 nm (2,142 km; 1,331 miles)

ROBERTSON
ROBERTSON AIRCRAFT CORPORATION

Snohomish County Airport, Everett, Washington 98204
Telephone: (206) 355 8700
PRESIDENT: Leland R. Lynch
SENIOR VICE-PRESIDENT AND CHIEF PILOT: Henry I. McKay
CHIEF ENGINEER: Sherman Hall
SALES MANAGER: Thomas Raschella
PUBLIC RELATIONS MANAGER: Merle E. Dowd

Robertson Aircraft Corporation was formed by the late Mr James L. Robertson, who had long been a pioneer in the development of STOL aircraft, having been responsible for the Skycraft Skyshark, Wren 460 and STOL modifications to the IMCO CallAir A-9 and B-1. It has designed, built and certificated a series of Hi-Lift advanced technology safety and performance systems for standard single- and twin-engined Beech, Cessna and Piper aircraft.

During 1980, Robertson transferred all its manufacturing, management, sales and engineering departments from its former facilities at Renton Municipal Airport to two buildings at the edge of Paine Field, near Everett. This has permitted expansion of its own manufacturing activities. It has also entered into an agreement with Astec Corporation (which see), to manufacture and install Astec's Eagle modification to Cessna Citation jet aircraft. Astec will continue to market and deliver the modified aircraft.

A new canard-like wing root airflow energiser was certificated on the Cessna 414A in early 1980. The Robertson Hi-Lift system for this aircraft includes also Fowler-type trailing-edge flaps of improved aerofoil section and with longer tracks. A similar programme has adapted the above system for installation on the Cessna 402C and 421C. The wing root airflow energiser consists of a flat plate 0·102 m (4 in) wide which is attached to the fuselage skin forward of each wing. With a length of 0·38 m (1 ft 3 in), each energiser is mounted directly ahead of the wing leading-edge and in line with the wing chord. The addition of this device reduces stalling speed by 6 knots (11 km/h; 7 mph) with flaps up, and by 7 knots (13 km/h; 8 mph) with the flaps extended.

Research contracts with Kansas University and NASA were completed in 1974, covering the design of an Advanced Technology Light Twin (ATLIT). A standard Piper Seneca fuselage was fitted with an experimental wing that had a new aerofoil section and 30% chord full-span Fowler flaps. There were no ailerons and roll control was achieved by the use of upper-surface spoilers. Construction of the aircraft was completed by Piper Aircraft Corporation and the first flight was recorded in late 1974.

Following completion of the ATLIT research programme, Robertson embarked on a project to develop spoilers and full-span flaps suitable for retrofit on the

Beechcraft V35 Bonanza, with Robertson full-span flaps extended, makes approach for short-field landing

Cessna T210 equipped with Robertson high-differential drooped aileron system, and with WeatherScout I radar built into leading-edge of starboard wing

standard Piper Seneca I. FAA certification of the resulting system represented the first approval of spoilers for use on general aviation aircraft manufactured in the USA (see full description under this entry). This

spoiler/full-span flap system has since been certificated for Beech Bonanza V35 series aircraft, and for the Piper PA-32-300 Cherokee SIX.

The most recent Robertson development has provided a

high-differential aileron-droop Hi-Lift system for high-performance single-engined aircraft, such as the Cessna Model 210 Pressurised Centurion.

Robertson holds an FAA Supplementary Type Certificate covering the installation of RCA WeatherScout I radar inside the leading-edge of the starboard wing of a number of aircraft including the Cessna 206F, T206F, TU206G, U206G and 210N series. The truncated 13 × 30 cm (5 × 12 in) antenna is housed inside a leading-edge cutaway, with the receiver/transmitter built integrally at the back of the antenna. The wing structure is reinforced around the cutaway. A reinforced epoxy/glassfibre radome encloses the opening. Total system weight is 10·5 kg (23·1 lb). WeatherScout I is basically weather radar, but provides limited ground-mapping capability.

ROBERTSON / CESSNA and ROBERTSON / PIPER SAFETY and STOL CONVERSIONS

Continuous product improvement has been made on Robertson's line of Hi-Lift systems for Cessna and Piper single-engined and smaller twin-engined aircraft. The Robertson modification, first applied to a Cessna 182, comprises full-span wing leading-edge and trailing-edge high-lift systems which greatly reduce the take-off and landing distances normally required by such aircraft.

The existing ailerons are used as an integral part of the full-span trailing-edge flap system. When the conventional inboard flaps are lowered for take-off or landing, the ailerons droop with them, virtually doubling the wing lift at low speeds. The ailerons retain their differential operation for roll control when drooped.

In addition, the wing is fitted with a full-span distributed-camber leading-edge to provide an optimum spanwise lift distribution for maximum cruise efficiency. The cambered leading-edge also reduces the aerofoil leading-edge pressure peak at high angles of attack, to impart maximum resistance to stall and to provide highly-responsive manoeuvrability at low airspeeds. Some types of Cessna single-engined aircraft built since 1972 include this Robertson leading-edge as a standard production feature.

The full-span flap system, in combination with Robertson's conical-cambered wingtips, dorsal and ventral fins, belly-mounted vortex generators, and flap/elevator automatic trim system, are combined in various models to offer increased performance.

To improve controllability at low speeds, stall fences are provided between flaps and ailerons, and to complete the Hi-Lift modification the aileron gap is sealed with a strip of aluminium sheet or rubberised canvas. These modifications permit safe STOL landings and take-offs by even novice pilots, and cruising speed and range are increased by 2-4%.

Maximum gross weight increases have accompanied the certification of Robertson modifications of twin-engined aircraft such as the Cessna Super Skymaster and Piper Twin Comanche. This is due primarily to their increased climb performance and slower take-off and landing speeds.

Development of a Hi-Lift system for the Cessna 400 series of twin-engined business aircraft entailed complete redesign of the wings from the rear spar aft to allow installation of 100% Fowler flaps and flap-actuated drooping ailerons. This system, in combination with Robertson's automatic pitch trim system and double-hinged rudder, led to FAA-certificated decreases in take-off and landing field lengths of approximately 40%.

In 1974, the FAA certificated the Robertson-equipped Piper Seneca I, with wing upper-surface spoilers for roll control, full-span slotted flaps, cambered wingtips and an anti-servo rudder tab. These modifications allow shorter take-off and landing distances; minimum control speed is reduced by 16%, the best rate of climb speed is lowered by 19%, single-engine service ceiling is raised by 213 m (700 ft) and roll response is increased greatly at all speeds and configurations. A similar modification of the Seneca II was certificated during 1976.

More recent activities have entailed fitting full-span trailing-edge flaps and spoilers for roll control on a Piper Cherokee SIX; and developing a high-differential aileron-droop Hi-Lift system for high-performance

R/STOL Cessna 340 tests Fowler flap extension at altitude

Robertson STOL conversion of the Cessna 414A; the Fowler-type trailing-edge flaps add 13 per cent to wing area. Also visible is the small airflow control device on the fuselage, forward of the wing leading-edge, which reduces stalling speed by 6 knots with flaps up

single-engined aircraft, such as the Cessna Model P210 Pressurised Centurion. In this application a new and improved control mechanism droops both ailerons symmetrically to 15° when the trailing-edge flaps are extended to 20° for take-off. For roll control the ailerons travel up and down in high-ratio differential: thus, with the control wheel fully to starboard, the starboard aileron moves up 42° to act as a spoiler (27° up from its normal faired position); at the same time the port aileron is deflected downward an additional 12° to a total of 27°. Ailerons are also drooped symmetrically by 15° when the trailing-edge flaps are extended to 30° for approach and landing.

Benefits from this advanced Hi-Lift system include a greatly-reduced adverse yaw tendency in turns, and a higher roll rate for more precise control when flaps are down and speed low. Control wheel forces are significantly less than with unmodified aircraft, due to a tailoring of aerodynamic forces on the up-moving aileron and a cross-over cable which minimises friction in the control runs.

Four stall strips, two on each wing, retain the desirable stall characteristics common to all Robertson Hi-Lift systems. For aircraft fitted with wing leading-edge de-icing boots, rubber strips are cemented to the rubber boots; when these are not fitted, aluminium stall strips are riveted to the wing leading-edge. A strip 0·13 m (5 in) long, close to the wing root, initiates an early-warning signal that the aircraft is approaching the stall. A longer strip, mounted further outboard and lower than the first, initiates the stall of the inboard and centre wing sections, while the outboard section and the wingtip are still unaffected by stall conditions. When the aircraft stalls it noses forward and down, under the complete control of ailerons which remain unstalled and effective for roll control.

The Robertson integrated high-lift and safety systems have been designed for easy field maintenance. They are designed to be applicable to almost the entire range of Cessna and Piper aircraft.

Full details of the basic Cessna and Piper airframes are given under the appropriate company headings in this and earlier editions of Jane's, and apply also to the Robertson versions, except for the added Hi-Lift systems as described. Weights and performance details of the entire range of Hi-Lift modifications are given in the accompanying tables. The conversions can be fitted as a retrospective modification to any of the models listed, irrespective of year.

The complete line of Robertson STOL systems is available throughout the world from 23 installation centres and more than 60 dealers.

R/STOL VERSION OF BEECH MODEL

	Weight empty equipped kg (lb)	Weight gross kg (lb)	Max level speed knots (km/h; mph)	Max cruising speed knots (km/h; mph)	Stalling speed, wheels and flaps down knots (km/h; mph)	Max rate of climb at S/L m (ft)/ min	Single-engine rate of climb at S/L m (ft)/ min	Service ceiling m (ft)	T-O run m (ft)	T-O to 15 m (50 ft) m (ft)	Landing from 15 m (50 ft) m (ft)	Landing run m (ft)	Max range** nm (km; miles)
V35B Bonanza	987 (2,176)	1,542 (3,400)	181 (335; 208)	176 (325; 202)	53 (98; 61)	343 (1,125)	—	5,443 (17,858)	B 239 (785)	B 420 (1,377)	B 279 (914)	B 146 (478)	875 (1,620; 1,007)

B: Robertson Normal operation. **With optional long-range tanks fitted.

R/STOL VERSIONS OF CESSNA MODELS

	Weight empty equipped kg (lb)	Weight gross kg (lb)	Max level speed knots (km/h; mph)	Max cruising speed knots (km/h; mph)	Stalling speed, wheels and flaps down knots (km/h; mph)	Max rate of climb at S/L m (ft)/min	Single-engine rate of climb at S/L m (ft)/min	Service ceiling m (ft)	T-O run m (ft)	T-O to 15 m (50 ft) m (ft)	Landing from 15 m (50 ft) m (ft)	Landing run m (ft)	Max range** nm (km; miles)	Min control speed knots (km/h; mph)
Model 150 and Commuter	449 (990)	725 (1,600)	110 (204; 127)	105 (195; 121)	26 (48·3; 30)	213 (700)		3,930 (12,900)	A 129 (422) B 161 (527)	A 248 (815) B 273 (895)	A 193 (632) B 230 (755)	A 90 (295) B 106 (348)	790 (1,464; 910)	
Model 172 and Skyhawk†	572 (1,263)	1,043 (2,300)	126 (233; 145)	118 (219; 136)	28 (51·5; 32)	206 (675)		4,150 (13,600)	A 140 (460) B 175 (575)	A 274 (900) B 302 (990)	A 223 (730) B 267 (875)	A 92 (302) B 109 (356)	738 (1,367; 850)	
Model 172 and Skyhawk floatplane*	646 (1,425)	1,007 (2,220)	97 (180; 112)	94 (174; 108)	28 (51·5; 32)	191 (625)		3,765 (12,350)	A 256 (840) B 320 (1,050)	A 405 (1,330) B 451 (1,480)	A 267 (875) B 296 (970)	A 145 (475) B 171 (560)	477 (885; 550)	
Model 180 Skywagon†	707 (1,560)	1,270 (2,800)	152 (282; 175)	144 (267; 166)	32·2 (60; 37)	364 (1,195)		6,215 (20,400)	A 110 (360) B 137 (450)	A 216 (710) B 239 (785)	A 207 (680) B 254 (835)	A 88 (290) B 104 (342)	1,098 (2,035; 1,265)	
Model 180 Skywagon floatplane	850 (1,875)	1,338 (2,950)	142 (264; 164)	133 (246; 153)	32·2 (60; 37)	332 (1,090)		5,425 (17,800)	A 245 (805) B 307 (1,006)	A 369 (1,210) B 402 (1,320)	A 254 (832) B 308 (1,010)	A 145 (475) B 171 (560)	1,063 (1,971; 1,225)	
Model 182 and Skylane†	725 (1,599)	1,338 (2,950)	150 (278; 173)	143 (266; 165)	33 (62; 38)	288 (945)		5,610 (18,400)	A 131 (430) B 164 (537)	A 248 (815) B 270 (885)	A 237 (777) B 280 (920)	A 99 (325) B 117 (384)	1,050 (1,947; 1,210)	
Model 182 RG	800 (1,764)	1,412 (3,112)	187 (347; 215)	173 (321; 199)	42 (80; 48)	317 (1,040)		6,100 (20,000)	A 133 (435)	A 248 (815)	A 237 (777)	A 119 (389)	1,030 (1,909; 1,186)	
Model 185 Skywagon†	721 (1,590)	1,519 (3,350)	159 (295; 183)	149 (277; 172)	34 (63; 39)	320 (1,050)		5,440 (17,850)	A 114 (375) B 143 (469)	A 233 (763) B 265 (870)	A 230 (755) B 271 (890)	A 95 (310) B 111 (365)	972 (1,802; 1,120)	
Model 185 Skywagon floatplane	866 (1,910)	1,505 (3,320)	149 (277; 172)	140 (259; 161)	34 (63; 39)	311 (1,020)		5,210 (17,100)	A 182 (596) B 227 (745)	A 332 (1,090) B 364 (1,195)	A 265 (870) B 326 (1,070)	A 146 (480) B 173 (566)	903 (1,673; 1,040)	
Model 188 AGwagon 230	836 (1,844)	1,723 (3,800)	124 (230; 143)	116 (214; 133)	38·5 (71; 44)	245 (805)		4,330 (14,200)	A 207 (680) B 259 (850)	A 338 (1,110) B 431 (1,420)	A 186 (610) B 256 (840)	A 94 (308) B 111 (363)	303 (563; 350)	
Model A188 AGwagon 300†	843 (1,859)	1,814 (4,000)	135 (251; 156)	127 (235; 146)	40 (74; 46)	302 (990)		4,905 (16,100)	A 183 (600) B 229 (750)	A 293 (960) B 381 (1,250)	A 186 (610) B 256 (840)	A 94 (308) B 111 (363)	390 (724; 450)	
Model 206 Stationair 6†	785 (1,732)	1,633 (3,600)	155 (288; 179)	148 (274; 170)	36 (66; 41)	296 (970)		4,695 (15,400)	A 147 (482) B 184 (603)	A 302 (990) B 352 (1,155)	A 226 (740) B 270 (885)	A 92 (301) B 108 (355)	916 (1,697; 1,055)	
Model 206 Stationair 6 floatplane	943 (2,080)	1,587 (3,500)	144 (267; 166)	136 (253; 157)	36 (66; 41)	276 (905)		4,450 (14,600)	A 248 (815) B 311 (1,019)	A 454 (1,490) B 486 (1,595)	A 280 (917) B 343 (1,125)	A 148 (485) B 174 (572)	833 (1,544; 960)	
Model T206 Turbo Stationair 6	831 (1,832)	1,633 (3,600)	178 (330; 205)	163 (303; 188)	36 (66; 41)	322 (1,055)		8,260 (27,100)	A 148 (485) B 185 (606)	A 303 (995) B 358 (1,175)	A 226 (740) B 270 (885)	A 92 (301) B 108 (355)	963 (1,786; 1,110)	
Model T206 Turbo Stationair 6 floatplane	979 (2,160)	1,633 (3,600)	164 (304; 189)	148 (274; 170)	36 (66; 41)	311 (1,020)		7,650 (25,100)	A 241 (790) B 301 (987)	A 442 (1,450) B 475 (1,560)	A 283 (928) B 344 (1,130)	A 151 (495) B 178 (584)	911 (1,690; 1,050)	
Model 207 Skywagon and Stationair 7	862 (1,902)	1,723 (3,800)	150 (278; 173)	142 (264; 164)	38·5 (71; 44)	262 (860)		4,205 (13,800)	A 155 (510) B 194 (637)	A 332 (1,090) B 390 (1,280)	A 244 (800) B 298 (975)	A 97 (318) B 114 (375)	829 (1,536; 955)	
Model T207 Turbo Skywagon and Turbo Stationair 7	908 (2,002)	1,723 (3,800)	168 (312; 194)	156 (290; 180)	38·5 (71; 44)	277 (910)		7,650 (25,100)	A 155 (510) B 194 (637)	A 332 (1,090) B 390 (1,280)	A 244 (800) B 298 (975)	A 97 (318) B 114 (375)	812 (1,504; 935)	
Model 210 Centurion II	953 (2,102)	1,723 (3,800)	178 (330; 205)	167 (309; 192)	38·5 (71; 44)	274 (900)		4,905 (16,100)	A 155 (510) B 194 (637)	A 326 (1,070) B 376 (1,232)	A 239 (783) B 293 (960)	A 93 (305) B 110 (360)	1,137 (2,108; 1,310)	
Model T210 Turbo Centurion II	998 (2,202)	1,723 (3,800)	204 (378; 235)	192 (356; 221)	38·5 (71; 44)	293 (960)		9,020 (29,600)	A 160 (525) B 200 (656)	A 328 (1,075) B 401 (1,318)	A 239 (783) B 293 (960)	A 93 (305) B 110 (360)	1,133 (2,100; 1,305)	

A, B, *, **, † see notes under Cessna table on page 426.

CESSNA MODELS—continued

Model	Weight empty equipped kg (lb)	Weight gross kg (lb)	Max level speed knots (km/h; mph)	Max cruising speed knots (km/h; mph)	Stalling speed, wheels and flaps down knots (km/h; mph)	Max rate of climb at S/L m (ft)/min	Single-engine rate of climb at S/L m (ft)/min	Service ceiling m (ft)	T-O run m (ft)	T-O to 15 m (50 ft) m (ft)	Landing from 15 m (50 ft) m (ft)	Landing run m (ft)	Max range** nm (km; miles)	Min control speed knots (km/h; mph)
Model P210 Pressurised Turbo Centurion II	1,008 (2,222)	1,723 (3,800)	204 (378; 235)	192 (356; 221)	49 (91; 57)	293 (960)		9,020 (29,600)	200 (656)	401 (1,318)	293 (960)	110 (360)	1,133 (2,100; 1,305)	
Model P210 Pressurised Centurion	1,064 (2,345)	1,822 (4,016)	206 (381; 237)		55 (102; 63)	283 (930)		7,010 (23,000)	366 (1,200)	607 (1,990)	271 (890)	424 (1,390)	925 (1,714; 1,065)	
Model 310R	1,701 (3,750)	2,495 (5,500)	237 (439; 273)	223 (414; 257)	64 (119; 74)	518 (1,700)	119 (390)	8,350 (27,400)	B 290 (950)	B 448 (1,470)	B 355 (1,165)	B 219 (720)	1,242 (2,301; 1,430)	69 (129; 80) CAS
Model 337 Super Skymaster	1,196 (2,638)	2,100 (4,630)	177 (328; 204)	168 (312; 194)	39 (72·5; 45)	369 (1,210)	99 (325)	6,125 (20,100)	A 130 (428) B 163 (535)	A 265 (870) B 322 (1,055)	A 273 (895) B 323 (1,060)	A 105 (343) B 123 (405)	1,207 (2,236; 1,390)	
Model T337 Turbo Super Skymaster	1,289 (2,843)	2,131 (4,700)	204 (378; 235)	200 (370; 230)	40 (74; 46)	353 (1,160)	93 (305)	9,265 (30,400)	A 136 (445) B 169 (556)	A 280 (920) B 332 (1,088)	A 273 (895) B 323 (1,060)	A 107 (352) B 126 (415)	1,406 (2,607; 1,620)	
Model T337 Pressurised Super Skymaster	1,315 (2,900)	2,132 (4,700)	217 (402; 250)	208 (385; 239)	40 (74; 46)	353 (1,160)	126 (415)	6,100 (20,000)	A 126 (413) B 157 (516)	A 280 (920) B 332 (1,088)	A 273 (895) B 323 (1,060)	A 107 (352) B 126 (415)	1,307 (2,422; 1,505)	
Model 340	1,878 (4,140)	2,717 (5,990)	242 (447; 278)	228 (421; 262)	61 (114; 71)	503 (1,650)	96 (315)	9,085 (29,800)					1,372 (2,542; 1,580)	75 (140; 87) CAS
Model 401	1,673 (3,690)	2,858 (6,300)	226 (420; 261)	208 (386; 240)	65·5 (121; 75)	491 (1,610)	69 (225)	7,980 (26,180)	A 240 (786) B 300 (983)	A 378 (1,240) B 472 (1,550)	A 354 (1,160) B 442 (1,450)	A 155 (510) B 183 (600)	1,263 (2,340; 1,454)	72 (134; 83)
Model 402C	1,849 (4,076)	3,107 (6,850)			65 (121; 75)	442 (1,450)	91 (300)	9,145 (30,000)	329 (1,080)	533 (1,750)	427 (1,400)	259 (850)	1,220 (2,261; 1,405)	74 (137; 85)
Model 411	1,764 (3,890)	2,948 (6,500)	233 (431; 268)	212 (393; 244)	61·5 (114; 71)	579 (1,900)	98 (320)	7,925 (26,000)	A 278 (912) B 347 (1,140)	A 372 (1,220) B 465 (1,525)	A 340 (1,115) B 425 (1,395)	A 183 (600) B 276 (905)	1,303 (2,414; 1,500)	76 (142; 88)
Model 414A	1,975 (4,354)	3,062 (6,750)			65 (121; 75)	480 (1,575)	88 (290)	9,145 (30,000)	329 (1,080)	533 (1,750)	405 (1,330)	238 (780)	1,300 (2,409; 1,497)	73 (135; 84)
Model 421A	1,932 (4,260)	3,102 (6,840)	240 (444; 276)	224 (414; 258)	69 (128; 79)	512 (1,680)	88 (290)	8,230 (27,000)	A 307 (1,008) B 384 (1,260)	A 443 (1,452) B 553 (1,815)	A 419 (1,375) B 524 (1,720)	A 208 (683) B 245 (804)	1,488 (2,756; 1,713)	83 (153; 95)
Model 421B	2,011 (4,435)	3,379 (7,450)	245 (454; 282)	230 (426; 265)	71 (132; 82)	564 (1,850)	93 (305)	9,450 (31,000)	A 313 (1,028) B 365 (1,196)	A 428 (1,403) B 535 (1,754)	A 427 (1,400) B 534 (1,752)	A 134 (440) B 158 (517)	1,490 (2,762; 1,716)	78 (145; 90)
Model 421C	2,173 (4,790)	3,379 (7,450)	256 (475; 295)	240 (444; 276)	71 (132; 82)	591 (1,940)	107 (350)	9,200 (30,200)	B 396 (1,300)	B 558 (1,830)	B 518 (1,700)	B 317 (1,040)	1,487 (2,755; 1,712)	77 (143; 89) CAS

A: Robertson STOL operation. B: Robertson Normal operation. *Available also with engines of increased horsepower. **With optional long-range tanks fitted, if available.
†Leading-edge already installed by Cessna on current models.

R/STOL VERSIONS OF PIPER MODELS

Model	Weight empty equipped kg (lb)	Weight gross kg (lb)	Max level speed knots (km/h; mph)	Max cruising speed knots (km/h; mph)	Stalling speed, wheels and flaps down knots (km/h; mph)	Max rate of climb at S/L m (ft)/min	Single-engine rate of climb at S/L m (ft)/min	Service ceiling m (ft)	T-O run m (ft)	T-O to 15 m (50 ft) m (ft)	Landing from 15 m (50 ft) m (ft)	Landing run m (ft)	Max range** nm (km; miles)	Min control speed knots (km/h; mph)
PA-28-140 Cherokee	558 (1,232)	975 (2,150)	126 (223; 145)	120 (222; 138)	29 (53·2; 33)	206 (675)		4,480 (14,700)	A 171 (560) B 189 (620)	A 354 (1,160) B 404 (1,325)	A 192 (630) B 221 (725)	A 94 (310) B 110 (360)	825 (1,529; 950)	
PA-28-160 Cherokee	576 (1,270)	997 (2,200)	128 (237; 147)	121 (224; 139)	31 (56·5; 35)	216 (710)		4,970 (16,300)	A 152 (500) B 177 (580)	A 341 (1,120) B 390 (1,280)	A 204 (670) B 226 (740)	A 104 (340) B 114 (375)	838 (1,553; 965)	
PA-28-180 Cherokee	638 (1,406)	1,111 (2,450)	129 (238; 148)	122 (227; 141)	36 (66; 41)	221 (725)		4,313 (14,510)	A 165 (540) B 186 (610)	A 351 (1,150) B 399 (1,310)	A 238 (780) B 262 (860)	A 131 (430) B 146 (480)	596 (1,104; 686)	

A: Robertson STOL operation.   B: Robertson Normal operation.
**With optional long-range tanks fitted, if available.

PIPER MODELS—*continued*

	Weight empty equipped kg (lb)	Weight gross kg (lb)	Max level speed knots (km/h; mph)	Max cruising speed knots (km/h; mph)	Stalling speed, wheels and flaps down knots (km/h; mph)	Max rate of climb at S/L m (ft)/min	Single-engine rate of climb at S/L m (ft)/min	Service ceiling m (ft)	T-O run m (ft)	T-O to 15 m (50 ft) m (ft)	Landing from 15 m (50 ft) m (ft)	Landing run m (ft)	Max range** nm (km; miles)	Min control speed knots (km/h; mph)
PA-28R-180 Cherokee Arrow II	611 (1,349)	1,134 (2,500)	149 (275; 171)	142 (262; 163)	35 (64·5; 40)	270 (885)		4,695 (15,400)	A 171 (560) B 195 (640)	A 347 (1,140) B 396 (1,300)	A 259 (850) B 299 (980)	A 145 (475) B 168 (550)	911 (1,690; 1,050)	
PA-28R-200 Cherokee Arrow II	693 (1,528)	1,202 (2,650)	152 (282; 175)	143 (266; 165)	37 (69; 43)	274 (900)		4,570 (15,000)	A 175 (575) B 198 (650)	A 344 (1,130) B 393 (1,290)	A 283 (930) B 319 (1,045)	A 168 (550) B 187 (615)	782 (1,448; 900)	
PA-28-235 Cherokee 235	712 (1,570)	1,361 (3,000)	140 (259; 161)	132 (245; 152)	39 (72; 45)	244 (800)		3,660 (12,000)	A 168 (550) B 191 (625)	A 265 (870) B 302 (990)	A 274 (900) B 312 (1,025)	A 149 (490) B 171 (560)	926 (1,716; 1,066)	
PA-32-260 Cherokee SIX	783 (1,726)	1,542 (3,400)	144 (267; 166)	137 (254; 158)	38 (71; 44)	259 (850)		4,420 (14,500)	A 180 (590) B 238 (780)	A 317 (1,040) B 341 (1,120)	A 247 (810) B 267 (875)	A 155 (510) B 171 (560)	964 (1,786; 1,110)	
PA-32-300 Cherokee SIX	825 (1,819)	1,542 (3,400)	151 (280; 174)	146 (270; 168)	38 (71; 44)	320 (1,050)		4,955 (16,250)	A 171 (560) B 226 (740)	A 299 (980) B 320 (1,050)	A 247 (810) B 267 (875)	A 158 (520) B 168 (550)	921 (1,706; 1,060)	
PA-24-180 Comanche	694 (1,530)	1,157 (2,550)	149 (277; 172)	143 (266; 165)	35 (64; 40)	293 (960)		5,850 (19,200)	A 183 (600) B 302 (990)	A 324 (1,065) B 475 (1,560)	A 262 (860) B 326 (1,070)	A 128 (420) B 149 (490)	868 (1,609; 1,000)	
PA-24-250 Comanche	776 (1,710)	1,315 (2,900)	168 (311; 193)	161 (298; 185)	35·5 (66; 41)	427 (1,400)		6,310 (20,700)	A 187 (615) B 290 (950)	A 296 (970) B 389 (1,275)	A 256 (840) B 347 (1,140)	A 140 (460) B 213 (700)	1,537 (2,848; 1,770)	
PA-24-260 Comanche	812 (1,792)	1,451 (3,200)	174 (322; 200)	164 (304; 189)	36 (66; 41)	410 (1,345)		6,355 (20,850)	A 200 (655) B 302 (990)	A 338 (1,110) B 401 (1,315)	A 268 (880) B 360 (1,180)	A 152 (500) B 226 (740)	1,137 (2,108; 1,310)	
PA-24-260 Turbo Comanche	821 (1,810)	1,451 (3,200)	213 (394; 245)	201 (372; 231)	36 (66; 41)	410 (1,345)		7,620 (25,000)	A 200 (655) B 302 (990)	A 338 (1,110) B 401 (1,315)	A 268 (880) B 360 (1,180)	A 152 (500) B 226 (740)	1,306 (2,422; 1,505)	
PA-24-400 Comanche	966 (2,130)	1,633 (3,600)	196 (364; 226)	189 (351; 218)	39 (72; 45)	506 (1,660)		6,155 (20,200)	A 126 (415) B 168 (550)	A 233 (765) B 271 (890)	A 303 (995) B 379 (1,245)	A 184 (605) B 216 (710)	1,568 (2,905; 1,805)	
PA-30 Twin Comanche*	1,022 (2,253)	1,724 (3,800)	158 (293; 182)	153 (283; 176)	45 (84; 52)	427 (1,400)	79 (260)	6,100 (20,000)	B 206 (675)	B 341 (1,120)	B 355 (1,165)	B 186 (610)	1,481 (2,744; 1,705)	69 (129; 80)
PA-30 Turbo Twin Comanche*	1,088 (2,399)	1,724 (3,800)	213 (394; 245)	197 (365; 227)	45 (84; 52)	427 (1,400)	69 (225)	7,620 (25,000)	B 206 (675)	B 341 (1,120)	B 355 (1,165)	B 186 (610)	1,528 (2,832; 1,760)	69 (129; 80)
PA-39 Twin Comanche C/R*	1,022 (2,253)	1,724 (3,800)	181 (336; 209)	174 (322; 200)	45 (84; 52)	445 (1,460)	79 (260)	6,100 (20,000)	B 206 (675)	B 320 (1,050)	B 355 (1,165)	B 186 (610)	1,468 (2,720; 1,690)	65 (121; 75)
PA-39 Turbo Twin Comanche C/R*	1,088 (2,399)	1,724 (3,800)	212 (393; 244)	197 (365; 227)	45 (84; 52)	427 (1,400)	69 (225)	7,620 (25,000)	B 158 (520)	B 323 (1,060)	B 355 (1,165)	B 189 (620)	1,515 (2,808; 1,745)	65 (121; 75)
PA-23-235 Aztec	1,241 (2,735)	2,177 (4,800)	182 (338; 210)	175 (325; 202)	40 (74; 46)	465 (1,525)	62 (205)	5,515 (18,100)	B 210 (690)	B 331 (1,085)	B 381 (1,250)	B 195 (640)	1,090 (2,020; 1,255)	54 (98; 62)
PA-E23-250 Aztec	1,339 (2,953)	2,266 (4,995)	197 (365; 227)	191 (354; 220)	41 (76; 47)	509 (1,670)	99 (325)	6,615 (21,700)	B 190 (625)	B 315 (1,035)	B 395 (1,295)	B 203 (665)	1,112 (2,060; 1,80)	56 (103; 64)
PA-23-250 Aztec	1,326 (2,925)	2,359 (5,200)	188 (348; 216)	179 (332; 206)	45·5 (84; 52)	491 (1,610)	85 (280)	6,035 (19,800)	B 195 (640)	B 323 (1,060)	B 395 (1,295)	B 203 (665)	916 (1,697; 1,055)	56 (105; 65)
PA-23-250 Turbo Aztec	1,397 (3,080)	2,359 (5,200)	222 (412; 256)	182 (388; 210)	43 (79; 49)	372 (1,220)	64 (210)	9,145 (30,000)	B 195 (640)	B 323 (1,060)	B 395 (1,295)	B 203 (665)	1,050 (1,947; 1,210)	56 (105; 65)
PA-34 Seneca I	1,160 (2,557)	1,905 (4,200)	170 (315; 196)	162 (300; 187)	58 (106; 66)	414 (1,360)	57 (190)	5,730 (18,800)	B 195 (640)	B 320 (1,050)	B 381 (1,250)	B 196 (645)	743 (1,378; 856)	57 (106; 65)
PA-34 Seneca II	1,280 (2,823)	2,073 (4,570)	195 (361; 225)	190 (352; 219)	66 (122; 76)	421 (1,380)	67 (220)	7,620 (25,000)	B 198 (650)	B 332 (1,090)	B 573 (1,880)	B 213 (700)	882 (1,633; 1,015)†	57 (106; 65)

A: Robertson STOL operation.   B: Robertson Normal operation.   *Available also with engines of increased horsepower.
**With optional long-range tanks fitted, if available.   †1,192 (2,207; 1,371) with optional long-range tanks.

ROBINSON
ROBINSON HELICOPTER COMPANY INC

HEAD OFFICE AND WORKS: 24747 Crenshaw Boulevard, Torrance, California 90505
Telephone: (213) 539 0508
CHAIRMAN OF THE BOARD: C. K. LeFiell
PRESIDENT: Franklin D. Robinson
VICE-PRESIDENT: C. K. LeFiell
MARKETING CO-ORDINATOR: Karen L. Walling

Robinson Helicopter Company was formed to design and manufacture a lightweight helicopter which could be competitive in price with current two/four-seat fixed-wing light aircraft. The design of this aircraft, the Robinson R22, began in June 1973 with emphasis on efficiency, low noise emission and minimum maintenance. The first prototype flew for the first time on 28 August 1975, and the second was completed in early 1977. Both were employed in the programme which led to FAA certification on 16 March 1979.

Orders for a total of 805 R22s had been received by 1 May 1980. Deliveries of production helicopters began in

October 1979, and the production rate is scheduled to increase to two R22s per day by mid-1981.

ROBINSON MODEL R22

TYPE: Two-seat lightweight helicopter.

ROTOR SYSTEM: Two-blade main rotor, with a tri-hinged underslung rotor hub to reduce blade flexing, rotor vibration and control force feedback. Main rotor blade section NACA 63-015 (modified). Rigid-in-plane, and free to flap, these blades are of bonded all-metal construction, with a stainless steel spar and leading-edge, light alloy skin and light alloy honeycomb core. One fixed trim tab on main rotor blades. The two-blade tail rotor, mounted on the port side, is of light alloy bonded construction.

ROTOR DRIVE: V-belt drive with sprag-type overrunning clutch. The main and tail gearboxes each utilise spiral bevel gears. Maintenance-free flexible couplings of proprietary manufacture are used in both the main and tail rotor drive systems. Main rotor/engine rpm ratio 1:5. Tail rotor/engine rpm ratio 1·28:1.

FUSELAGE: Welded steel tube and light alloy primary structure for cabin, rotor pylon and engine mounting, with full monocoque tailcone. Cabin skins of light alloy and glassfibre.

TAIL UNIT: Cruciform light alloy structure with fixed horizontal stabiliser and vertical fin. Small spring skid beneath lower half of fin to give protection in a tail-down landing.

LANDING GEAR: Welded steel tube and light alloy skid landing gear, with energy-absorbing crosstubes.

POWER PLANT: One 112 kW (150 hp) Avco Lycoming O-320-A2B flat-four engine (derated to 92·5 kW; 124 hp), mounted in the lower aft section of the main fuselage, and partially exposed to improve cooling and simplify maintenance. Light alloy fuel tank in upper rear section of the fuselage on port side, usable capacity 75·5 litres (20 US gallons). Oil capacity 7·5 litres (2 US gallons).

ACCOMMODATION: Two seats side by side in enclosed cabin. Cyclic control stick mounted between seats, with dual grips on yoke so that aircraft can be flown from either seat. Conventional dual collective and throttle controls mounted at the port side of each seat. Cyclic control pivots to either side to simplify entry and exit. Curved two-panel windscreen. Door, with window, on each side. Baggage space beneath each seat. Cabin heated and ventilated.

SYSTEM: Electrical system powered by 12V DC generator.

AVIONICS AND EQUIPMENT: Optional avionics include a King KY-197 com transceiver, KN-53 nav receiver, KT-76A transponder and KR-87 ADF, or similar avionics by Narco. Standard equipment includes sensitive altimeter, low rpm warning horn, temperature and

Robinson Model R22 two-seat lightweight helicopter (Avco Lycoming O-320-A2B engine)

chip warning lights for main gearbox and chip warning light for tail gearbox, soundproofing, anti-collision light and ground handling wheels. Optional equipment includes cabin heater and lighting package.

DIMENSIONS, EXTERNAL:

Diameter of main rotor	7·67 m (25 ft 2 in)
Diameter of tail rotor	1·07 m (3 ft 6 in)
Main rotor blade chord	0·18 m (7·2 in)
Distance between rotor centres	4·39 m (14 ft 5 in)
Length overall (rotors turning)	8·76 m (28 ft 9 in)
Length of fuselage	6·30 m (20 ft 8 in)
Height overall	2·67 m (8 ft 9 in)
Skid track	1·93 m (6 ft 4 in)

DIMENSION, INTERNAL:

Cabin: Max width	1·12 m (3 ft 8 in)

AREAS:

Main rotor blades (each)	0·70 m² (7·55 sq ft)
Tail rotor blades (each)	0·037 m² (0·40 sq ft)
Main rotor disc	46·21 m² (497·4 sq ft)
Tail rotor disc	0·89 m² (9·63 sq ft)
Fin	0·21 m² (2·28 sq ft)
Stabiliser	0·14 m² (1·53 sq ft)

WEIGHTS AND LOADINGS:

Weight empty	361 kg (796 lb)
Fuel load	54·5 kg (120 lb)
Max T-O and landing weight	590 kg (1,300 lb)
Max zero-fuel weight	535 kg (1,180 lb)
Max disc loading	12·77 kg/m² (2·61 lb/sq ft)
Max power loading	6·38 kg/kW (10·48 lb/hp)

PERFORMANCE (at max T-O weight):

Never-exceed speed	102 knots (190 km/h; 118 mph)
Max level speed	97 knots (180 km/h; 112 mph)
Cruising speed, 65% power at 2,440 m (8,000 ft)	94 knots (174 km/h; 108 mph)
Econ cruising speed	82 knots (153 km/h; 95 mph)
Max rate of climb at S/L	366 m (1,200 ft)/min
Service ceiling	4,265 m (14,000 ft)
Hovering ceiling IGE	1,980 m (6,500 ft)
Hovering ceiling OGE	1,370 m (4,500 ft)
Range with max fuel and max payload, no reserves	208 nm (386 km; 240 miles)
Endurance at 65% power, no reserves	2 h 30 min

ROCKWELL INTERNATIONAL
ROCKWELL INTERNATIONAL CORPORATION

CORPORATE OFFICES: 2230 East Imperial Highway, El Segundo, California 90245

600 Grant Street, Pittsburgh, Pennsylvania 15219

CHAIRMAN OF THE BOARD AND CHIEF EXECUTIVE OFFICER: Robert Anderson

PRESIDENT AND CHIEF OPERATING OFFICER: Donald R. Beall

CORPORATE VICE-PRESIDENTS:
Robert De Palma (Finance and Chief Financial Officer)
J. A. Earley (Corporate Development)
Charles Fazio (General Industries Operations)
Richard W. Foxen (Strategic Management)
Kenneth B. Gay (Purchasing)
George W. Jeffs (President, North American Aerospace Operations)

Samuel Petok (Communications)
A. B. Kight (International)
Edward A. Loeser (Operations)
William L. Neely (Treasurer)
Carl J. Oles (Personnel)
John J. Roscia (General Counsel)
C. E. Ryker (Controller)
W. F. Swanson Jr (Secretary)
Martin D. Walker (President, Automotive Operations)
Donald J. Yockey (Electronics Operations)

North American Aviation Inc, incorporated in Delaware in 1928 and a manufacturer of aircraft of various kinds from 1934, and Rockwell-Standard Corporation of Pittsburgh, Pennsylvania, a manufacturer of automotive components and builder of the Aero Commander line of civilian aircraft, merged on 22 September 1967 to form North American Rockwell Corporation.

During 1971 the Corporation was reorganised into four principal parts: the North American Aerospace Group (formerly the Aerospace and Systems Office); the Industrial Products Group (formerly the Commercial Products Group); the Automotive Group; and the Electronics Group. There is, in addition, a further component known as the Utility and Consumer Products Group. The constitution of the Corporation was changed on 16 February 1973, when North American Rockwell and Rockwell Manufacturing Company merged to become Rockwell International Corporation.

In September 1978, as the culmination of a succession of organisational changes, the company's aerospace activities were consolidated into one organisation, North American Aerospace Operations, comprising the Aircraft Group, the Space Systems Group and the Energy Systems Group.

NORTH AMERICAN AEROSPACE OPERATIONS

EXECUTIVE OFFICES: 2230 East Imperial Highway, El Segundo, California 90245
Telephone: (213) 647 5000
PRESIDENT: George W. Jeffs

Rocketdyne Division
6633 Canoga Avenue, Canoga Park, California 91304
Telephone: (213) 334 4000
PRESIDENT: Norman J. Ryker

AIRCRAFT GROUP
2230 East Imperial Highway, El Segundo, California 90245
Telephone: (213) 647 5000
PRESIDENT: Bastian J. Hello
VICE-PRESIDENT, COMMERCIAL AIRCRAFT:
James J. Edwards

General Aviation Division
5001 North Rockwell Avenue, Bethany, Oklahoma 73008
Telephone: (405) 789 5000
PRESIDENT: Cornell J. Slivinsky

North American Aircraft Division
Los Angeles Plant:
815 Lapham Street, Los Angeles, California 90045
Telephone: (213) 647 1000
Columbus Plant:
4300 East Fifth Avenue, Columbus, Ohio 43216
Telephone: (614) 239 3344
VICE-PRESIDENT: B. Hello (Acting)

Sabreliner Division
6161 Aviation Drive, St Louis, Missouri 63134
Telephone: (314) 731 2260
PRESIDENT: Alan B. Kehlet

Tulsa Division
2000 North Memorial Drive, Tulsa, Oklahoma 74151
Telephone: (918) 835 3111
PRESIDENT: E. H. Ricketts

SPACE SYSTEMS GROUP
EXECUTIVE OFFICES: 12214 Lakewood Boulevard, Downey, California 90241
Telephone: (213) 922 2111
PRESIDENT: George W. Jeffs

Space Transportation System Development and Production Division
12214 Lakewood Boulevard, Downey, California 90241
Telephone: (213) 922 2111
PRESIDENT: Charles H. Feltz

Space Operations and Satellite Systems Division
12214 Lakewood Boulevard, Downey, California 90241
Telephone: (213) 922 2111
VICE-PRESIDENT: William E. Dean

AIRCRAFT GROUP
Latest aircraft products of the Aircraft Group are as follows:

ROCKWELL INTERNATIONAL BUCKEYE
USN Designation: T-2

After a design competition among several leading US manufacturers, what was then North American's Columbus Division was awarded a contract in 1956 to develop and build a jet training aircraft for the US Navy. The first T2J-1 flew on 31 January 1958. Five versions of the aircraft were produced subsequently, and have been described in the 1979-80 and earlier editions of Jane's.

Manufacture of the T-2 Buckeye ended after 609 production aircraft had been built, but tooling was retained in anticipation of additional foreign sales.

ROCKWELL INTERNATIONAL BRONCO
US military designation: OV-10

The development history of the Bronco and a detailed structural description can be found in the 1978-79 and earlier editions of *Jane's*. The type is no longer in production, but tooling remains in place in anticipation of further foreign sales.

The following production versions were built:

OV-10A. Initial production version, first flown on 6 August 1967. Used by US Marine Corps for light armed reconnaissance, helicopter escort and forward air control duties, and by US Air Force in the forward air control role, and for limited quick-response ground support pending the arrival of tactical fighters. Total of 271 built; six transferred to Royal Moroccan Air Force.

OV-10B. Generally similar to the OV-10A; six supplied to Federal German government for target towing.

OV-10B(Z). Structurally similar to OV-10B. Provision for General Electric J85-GE-4 turbojet of 13·12 kN (2,950 lb st) to be mounted above wing, to increase performance for target towing. Twelve delivered to Federal German government.

OV-10C. Version of OV-10A for Royal Thai Air Force; 32 delivered.

OV-10D. In 1974, Rockwell received a US Navy contract to establish and test a production OV-10D configuration. This led to delivery of 17 US Marine Corps OV-10As to Rockwell's Columbus Aircraft Division, beginning in the Spring of 1978, for conversion to the Night Observation Surveillance (NOS) role. In addition to the NOS systems and the retention of basic OV-10A fuselage stores and external fuel capability, the OV-10D NOS has uprated (775·5 kW; 1,040 shp) engines, wing pylons capable of carrying rocket pods, flare pods, free-fall stores and 378 litre (100 US gallon) external fuel tanks when extended radius/loiter time is required. A Texas Instruments FLIR sensor and laser target designator are installed in a rotating ball turret in the nose. The sensor turret can be linked to a turret-mounted General Electric M-97 20 mm cannon, mounted beneath the fuselage, in lieu of normal operation with standard OV-10A armament sponsons and centreline station.

OV-10E. Version of OV-10A for Venezuelan Air Force. Sixteen delivered.

OV-10F. Version of OV-10A for Indonesia. Sixteen delivered.

The following abbreviated description applies to the standard OV-10A, except where stated:

TYPE: Two-seat multi-purpose counter-insurgency aircraft.

POWER PLANT: Two 533 kW (715 ehp) Garrett-AiResearch T76-G-416/417 turboprop engines, each driving a Hamilton Standard three-blade constant-speed reversible-pitch and fully-feathering metal propeller. (OV-10D has 775·5 kW; 1,040 shp T76-G-420/421 engines, each driving a similar Hamilton Standard propeller but with glassfibre blades.) Five self-sealing bladder-type fuel tanks in wings, with combined capacity of 954 litres (252 US gallons). Gravity refuelling point above each tank on wing upper surface. Provision for carrying one 568 litre (150 US gallon) drop-tank on underfuselage pylon; OV-10D also has provisions for carrying one 378 litre (100 US gallon) drop-tank on each wing pylon. Oil capacity 11·5 litres (3 US gallons).

ACCOMMODATION: Crew of two in tandem, on LW-3B zero-zero ejection seats, under canopy with two large upward-opening transparent door panels on each side. Dual controls optional. Cargo compartment aft of rear seat, with rear-loading door at end of fuselage pod. Rear seat removable to provide increased space for up to 1,452 kg (3,200 lb) of freight, or for carriage of five paratroops, or two stretcher patients and attendant.

SYSTEMS: Heating and ventilation system combines engine bleed air and cold ram air to provide temperature controlled conditions. Engine bleed air is used also for windscreen defrosting and to supply crew's anti-g suits. Hydraulic system of intermittent-duty type powered by an electrically-driven hydraulic pump at a pressure of 103·5 bars (1,500 lb/sq in), for actuation of trailing-edge flaps, landing gear and nosewheel steering. Wheel brakes, which have two independent manually-driven brake units, are fed directly from the hydraulic system reservoir. Electrical system powered by two 30V 300A starter/generators and two 24V 22Ah nickel-cadmium batteries. (OV-10D has two 30V 400A starter/generators and two 24V 30Ah aircooled batteries.) AC power derived from two 750VA inverters which supply 115V at 400Hz three-phase; single-phase AC of 115V or 26V at 400Hz can be tapped from the bus system. (An additional 3,000VA inverter is installed in the OV-10D.) External power sockets for engine starting and utility services; the latter can be used to provide 28V DC to other aircraft for engine starting or servicing. Demand-regulated oxygen system supplied from two 0·008 m³ (0·3 cu ft) oxygen cylinders at a pressure of 124 bars (1,800 lb/sq in). Independent fire warning system for each engine, comprising control unit, sensing elements, and warning lights. US Air Force aircraft (only) have an electrically-fired fire extinguishing system installed in each engine nacelle. No pneumatic system.

Rockwell International OV-10D, with production-configuration Night Observation Surveillance (NOS) equipment

AVIONICS: US Air Force OV-10As are equipped with AN/AIC-18 intercom; AN/ARC-51BX UHF, Wilcox 807A VHF, dual FM-622A VHF, and HF-103 HF com radios; nav system includes AN/ASN-75 compass, AN/ARN-52(V) Tacan, AN/ARA-50 UHF-ADF, AN/ARN-83 LF-ADF, 51R-6 VOR, and 51V-4A ILS glideslope; identification system includes AN/APX-64(V) IFF/SIF, and SST-181-X radar beacon. US Marine Corps aircraft are equipped with AN/AIC-18 intercom; AN/ARC-51AX VHF, AN/ARC-54 VHF, and AN/ARC-120 HF com radios; nav system includes AN/ASN-75 compass, AN/APN-171 radar altimeter, AN/ARN-52(V) Tacan, and AN/ARA-50 UHF-ADF; AN/APX-64(V) IFF/SIF for identification. (OV-10D NOS aircraft have a FLIR sensor system package, comprising FLIR, a laser target designator, and an automatic video tracker.)

ARMAMENT: Four weapon attachment points, each with capacity of 272 kg (600 lb), under short sponsons extending from bottom of fuselage on each side, under wings. Fifth attachment point, capacity 544 kg (1,200 lb) under centre fuselage. Two 7·62 mm M-60C machine-guns, each with 500 rounds of ammunition, carried in each sponson. USMC OV-10A has provision also for carrying one AIM-9D Sidewinder missile under each wing. Stores which can be carried on the underfuselage and sponson stations include Mk 81, 82 and 83 GP bombs, Mk 81 and 82 GP (Snakeye) bombs; Mk 77 Mod 2 and Mod 4 fire bombs; LAU-3/A, LAU-10/A, LAU-32/A, LAU-59/A, LAU-60/A, LAU-61/A, LAU-68/A and LAU-69/A rocket packages; SUU-11A/A (7·62 mm Minigun), Mk 4 Mod 0 (20 mm), and GPU-2/A (20 mm) gun pods; SUU-40/A and SUU-44/A with Mk 24 and Mk 45 flares; Mk 12 Mod 0 (Podeye) smoke tank; Mk 86A/A37B-3 MBR with Mk 76 and Mk 106 practice bombs; CBU-55/B cluster bomb. Max weapon load on fuselage stations 1,633 kg (3,600 lb). (OV-10D aircraft have wing pylons with stores capacity of 272 kg; 600 lb each, which can carry CBU-55/B cluster bombs; LAU-10/A, LAU-68/A and LAU-69/A rocket packages; SUU-40/A and SUU-44/A with Mk 24 and Mk 45 flares. In lieu of sponsons and fuselage centreline load, the OV-10D can accommodate a 20 mm gun turret kit installed on centreline station hardpoint.)

DIMENSIONS, EXTERNAL:
Wing span	12·19 m (40 ft 0 in)
Length overall	12·67 m (41 ft 7 in)
Height overall	4·62 m (15 ft 2 in)
Tailplane span	4·45 m (14 ft 7 in)
Wheel track	4·52 m (14 ft 10 in)
Wheelbase	3·56 m (11 ft 8 in)
Propeller diameter	2·59 m (8 ft 6 in)
Rear loading door: Height	0·99 m (3 ft 3 in)
Width	0·76 m (2 ft 6 in)

AREA:
Wings, gross	27·03 m² (291 sq ft)

WEIGHTS AND LOADING:
Weight empty	3,127 kg (6,893 lb)
Normal T-O weight	4,494 kg (9,908 lb)
Overload T-O weight	6,552 kg (14,444 lb)
Max wing loading	242·4 kg/m² (49·6 lb/sq ft)

PERFORMANCE (OV-10A/C/E/F at weights stated):
Max level speed at S/L, without weapons	244 knots (452 km/h; 281 mph)
Max rate of climb at S/L at max T-O weight	790 m (2,600 ft)/min
T-O run at normal T-O weight	226 m (740 ft)
T-O to 15 m (50 ft):	
at normal T-O weight	341 m (1,120 ft)
at max T-O weight	853 m (2,800 ft)
Landing from 15 m (50 ft) at normal T-O weight	372 m (1,220 ft)
Landing run:	
at normal T-O weight	226 m (740 ft)
at max T-O weight	381 m (1,250 ft)
Combat radius with max weapon load, no loiter	198 nm (367 km; 228 miles)
Ferry range with auxiliary fuel	1,200 nm (2,224 km; 1,382 miles)

ROCKWELL INTERNATIONAL B-1

The B-1 was the outcome of a succession of defence studies, begun in 1962 and leading to the AMSA (Advanced Manned Strategic Aircraft) requirement of 1965, for a low-altitude penetration bomber to replace the Boeing B-52s of USAF Strategic Air Command by 1980. It was to be the third and most flexible component of the US Triad defence system, comprising also land-based and submarine-launched ballistic missiles.

To meet the B-1 requirement, the Department of Defense issued RFPs (Requests For Proposals) to the US aerospace industry on 3 November 1969, and from three airframe and two engine finalists it awarded research, development, test and evaluation contracts on 5 June 1970 to North American Rockwell's Los Angeles Division for the airframe and to the General Electric Company for the F101 turbofan engine. The original cost-plus-incentive contracts were for five flying prototypes, two structural test airframes and 40 engines; in January 1971, in which month the essential design of the B-1 was frozen, these quantities were reduced to three flight test aircraft, one ground test aircraft and 27 engines. Procurement of a fourth flight test aircraft, as a pre-production prototype, was approved under the FY 1976 budget. The US Air Force hoped to order 244 B-1s, including prototypes, to replace B-52s now in service.

The B-1 prototypes were assembled in US Air Force facilities known as Plant 42 at Palmdale, California. Assembly of the first aircraft began in late 1972; this aircraft (74-0158) made its first flight, at Palmdale, on 23 December 1974. This occasion was also the first flight of the YF101 engine. The third B-1, used as a testbed for the avionics systems, made its first flight on 1 April 1976, and was followed by the first flight of the second B-1 on 14 June 1976. The second aircraft had been used for proof loads testing; these tests occupied approximately eight months during 1975, after which No. 2 was converted to a flight test aircraft. By 1 January 1979 the three aircraft involved in the test programme had accumulated a total of over 1,200 hours in more than 200 test missions.

The fourth B-1 (76-0174) flew for the first time on 14 February 1979, and represents an operational configuration, with both offensive and defensive avionics systems

Fourth Rockwell International B-1 strategic bomber, with its wings in the fully-swept position

installed. The first prototype, devoted to evaluating aircraft stability and control, performance and flutter limits, completed its test programme in 1978 and has been placed in storage. The second prototype, used for air-loads testing and engine/inlet evaluation, completed its testing during 1979 and has been stored in flyable condition.

The third prototype has been modified by the addition of an advanced ECM system, and with a Doppler beam sharpening modification to the forward-looking attack radar. Continued testing of the third and fourth B-1s has been concentrated on defensive system performance and advanced ECM development. Testing is being carried out against simulated enemy threats, defence systems, and against US surrogate threats. Results of the B-1 test programme are expected to contribute greatly to validation and definition of design requirements for any future manned penetration bomber.

In 1978, B-1 derivative designs were included in US Department of Defense studies to evaluate various types of aircraft as cruise missile carriers. In November 1979, as a result of these studies, Rockwell was requested by the US Air Force to submit a proposal for the initial planning and design effort associated with flight demonstration of a prototype B-1 derivative aircraft. Identified as a strategic ALCM launcher (SAL), it will be produced by modification of the third B-1 prototype. This work was authorised in January 1980, and began shortly after, with a planned first flight in late 1981.

A full description of the B-1 can be found in the 1977-78 *Jane's*.

DIMENSIONS, EXTERNAL:
Wing span: fully spread   41·67 m (136 ft 8½ in)
    fully swept   23·84 m (78 ft 2½ in)
Wing area, gross   approx 181·2 m² (1,950 sq ft)
Length overall: incl nose probe 45·78 m (150 ft 2½ in)
    excl nose probe   44·70 m (146 ft 8 in)
Height overall   10·24 m (33 ft 7¼ in)
Wheel track (c/l of shock-absorbers)
                            4·42 m (14 ft 6 in)
Wheelbase   17·53 m (57 ft 6 in)
WEIGHTS:
Design max T-O weight   179,170 kg (395,000 lb)
Max landing weight   approx 158,755 kg (350,000 lb)

Rockwell International XFV-12A prototype during tethered testing in the hover mode

PERFORMANCE (estimated, with VG inlets):
Max level speed at 15,240 m (50,000 ft)
                            approx Mach 2·2
    (1,260 knots; 2,335 km/h; 1,451 mph)
Max level speed at 152 m (500 ft)
    approx 650 knots (1,205 km/h; 750 mph)
Cruising speed at 15,240 m (50,000 ft)
    Mach 0·85 (562 knots; 1,042 km/h; 648 mph)
Max range without refuelling   Intercontinental

ROCKWELL INTERNATIONAL XFV-12A

The US Navy initiated the XFV-12A V/STOL Fighter/Attack Technology Prototype programme to develop the capability of V/STOL operation from comparatively small carrier decks that would have neither catapult nor arrester gear.

The single-seat prototype aircraft, roughly the size of a McDonnell Douglas A-4 Skyhawk, employs an augmentor-wing concept with forward canard and aft semi-delta wings, and is powered by a single, special version of the Pratt & Whitney F401-PW-400 advanced-technology turbofan engine.

Funding limitations continue to constrain severely the progress of this programme, a full description of which can be found in the 1979-80 *Jane's*.

POWER PLANT: One modified Pratt & Whitney F401-PW-400 afterburning turbofan engine in the 133·4 kN (30,000 lb) thrust class. Fuel in two fuselage bladder tanks, capacity 1,590 litres (420 US gallons), and integral wing tanks, capacity 1,173 litres (310 US gallons). Total fuel capacity 2,763 litres (730 US gallons).

DIMENSIONS, EXTERNAL:
Wing span   8·69 m (28 ft 6¼ in)
Wing area, gross   27·2 m² (293 sq ft)
Canard surfaces span   3·69 m (12 ft 1¼ in)
Canard surface area, gross 7·72 m² (83·05 sq ft)
Length overall   13·39 m (43 ft 11 in)
Height overall   3·15 m (10 ft 4 in)
Wheel track   7·34 m (24 ft 1 in)
Wheelbase   7·62 m (25 ft 0 in)

WEIGHTS (estimated):
Basic operating weight   6,259 kg (13,800 lb)
Max vertical T-O weight   8,845 kg (19,500 lb)
Max short-field T-O weight 11,000 kg (24,250 lb)

PERFORMANCE (estimated, at max T-O weight):
Max level speed   in excess of Mach 2
T-O run at 11,000 kg (24,250 lb)   91 m (300 ft)

SABRELINER DIVISION

EXECUTIVE OFFICES: 6161 Aviation Drive, St Louis, Missouri 63134
Telephone: (314) 731 2260
Telex: 44-7227
PRESIDENT: Alan B. Kehlet
EXECUTIVES:
    E. J. Brandreth Jr (Vice-President, Marketing and Customer Service)
    C. Castillo (Manager, Public Relations)
    D. Denison (Manager, Pre-Owned Aircraft Sales)
    H. L. Humble (Manager, Western Regional Sales)
    A. J. Marcus (Manager, Marketing Services)
    J. Medeiros (Manager, Sales Administration)
    P. Picciano (Manager, Customer Support)
    R. H. Reid (Vice-President, Finance, and Controller)
    T. Reilly (Manager, Eastern Regional Sales)
    F. Smith (Director, US Government Sales)
    P. Wickham (Chief Engineer)
    Carl G. Ziegler (Manager, International Sales)

On 4 March 1977 Rockwell International announced the intention to consolidate Sabreliner activities in St Louis, Missouri. Structures and components continue to be manufactured in Los Angeles and are shipped to Perryville Municipal Airport, Missouri, for final assembly and flight test.

Delivery of the 500th Sabreliner, a Model 75A, was made in July 1977. Production of this version, and of the Sabreliner 60, was completed in Spring 1979, since when manufacture has concentrated on the Sabreliner 65.

ROCKWELL SABRELINER 65

Construction of a prototype of Rockwell's Sabreliner 65, which has the company Model number NA-265-65, began in January 1977, and this aircraft made its first flight on 29 June 1977. Construction of a pre-production aircraft began in December 1977, and this entered the certification programme in February 1979. Certification was gained on 28 November 1979, and deliveries of production aircraft began during the following month.

On a demonstration flight from San Francisco to Paris, via Boston, a Sabreliner 65 piloted by Bill Hallock and Jud Brandreth of Rockwell's Sabreliner Division set seven world records for speed over recognised courses in FAI Class C1g. These include San Francisco to Boston, a distance of 2,342 nm (4,337 km; 2,695 miles), at 464·90 knots

(860·99 km/h; 535·00 mph); and from Boston to Paris, 3,052 nm (5,652 km; 3,512 miles), at 449·47 knots (832·42 km/h; 517·24 mph).

TYPE: Twin-turbofan business transport.

WINGS: Cantilever low-wing monoplane. Supercritical wing with dihedral. Incidence 1·68° at root, —4·64° at tip. Sweepback at quarter-chord 32·79°. Integrally stiffened milled skin light alloy structure. Conventional ailerons with single spar and ribbed skins of light alloy. Electrically-operated Fowler-type trailing-edge flaps of light alloy construction. Hydraulically-operated spoilers of light alloy construction, two on upper surface of each wing, forward of flaps, are operable in flight and on the ground. Electrically-operated trim tab in port aileron. Anti-icing of wing leading-edges by engine bleed air.

FUSELAGE: Conventional semi-monocoque safe-life structure of light alloy.

TAIL UNIT: Cantilever structure of light alloy. Electrically-operated variable-incidence tailplane. Electrically-operated trim tab in rudder.

LANDING GEAR: Hydraulically-retractable tricycle type, with single wheel on each main unit and twin nosewheels. Main units retract outward, nose unit forward; all wheels enclosed by fairings when retracted. Oleo-pneumatic shock-absorbers on all units. Main wheels have tyres size 26 × 6·75, 16-ply rating, pressure 17·86 bars (259 lb/sq in). Nosewheel tyres size 18 × 4·4 Type VII, 10-ply rating, pressure 5·17 bars (75 lb/sq in). Nose unit steerable. Hydraulically-operated disc brakes. Parking brake. Electrically-controlled hydraulically-actuated fully-modulating anti-skid units.

POWER PLANT: Two Garrett-AiResearch TFE731-3-1D turbofan engines, each 16·46 kN (3,700 lb st), mounted in pod on each side of rear fuselage. Hydraulically-actuated target-type thrust reversers. Integral fuel tanks in wings, with capacity of 4,063 litres (1,073·4 US gallons), one aft fuselage bladder tank, capacity 606 litres (160·2 US gallons), and one forward fuselage bladder tank, beneath cabin floor, with capacity of 213 litres (56·3 US gallons), providing total fuel capacity of 4,882 litres (1,289·9 US gallons). Single-point refuelling standard. Gravity refuelling points on wing upper surface, and on starboard side of fuselage, above engine.

ACCOMMODATION: Crew of two and eight passengers in pressurised and air-conditioned cabin with a variety of seating layouts, all with galley, toilet and baggage compartment. Dual controls standard. Bottom-hinged downward-opening door with built-in airstairs forward of wing on port side. Overwing emergency exit on each side of cabin, FAA Type IV, removable from inside or outside. Baggage compartment at forward end of cabin on starboard side; baggage space in aft toilet compartment; total baggage capacity 247 kg (545 lb).

SYSTEMS: Air-conditioning and pressurisation by engine bleed air, max differential 0·61 bars (8·8 lb/sq in) to provide cabin altitude of 2,440 m (8,000 ft) to a height of 13,715 m (45,000 ft); separate ducting and temperature controls for cabin and flight deck. Hydraulic system supplied by a single electrically-driven pump, pressure 207 bars (3,000 lb/sq in). Auxiliary hydraulic accumulator for emergency use provides through separate lines a limited number of cycles for anti-skid units, wheel brakes, nosewheel steering and spoilers. Electrical system includes two 400A engine-driven generators.

Pre-production Rockwell Sabreliner 65, with supercritical wing and other aerodynamic improvements

Oxygen system comprising one 2·10 m³ (74 cu ft) cylinder in aft cabin, with quick-donning crew masks and automatic dropout masks for passengers. Anti-icing of wing leading-edges and engine air intakes by engine bleed air; electrical de-icing of pitots, stall-warning vanes and windscreens. APU optional for air-conditioning and electrical/hydraulic power on the ground and for electrical/hydraulic power when airborne.

AVIONICS: Include dual Collins VHF com, dual VHF nav with VOR/ILS, dual FD 109 flight directors, APS-80 autopilot, WXR-250 weather radar, DME-40, ADF-60A, TRD-90 transponder, and dual MC-103 compasses. Full blind-flying instrumentation is standard.

DIMENSIONS, EXTERNAL:

Wing span	15·37 m (50 ft 5⅛ in)
Length overall	14·30 m (46 ft 11 in)
Height overall	4·88 m (16 ft 0 in)
Tailplane span	5·91 m (19 ft 4⅝ in)
Wheel track	2·20 m (7 ft 2½ in)
Wheelbase	4·85 m (15 ft 10¾ in)
Cabin door (port, fwd): Height	1·19 m (3 ft 11 in)
Width	0·71 m (2 ft 4 in)
Emergency exits (port, stbd, each):	
Height	0·66 m (2 ft 2 in)
Width	0·51 m (1 ft 8 in)

DIMENSIONS, INTERNAL:

Cabin (excl flight deck): Length	5·79 m (19 ft 0 in)
Max width	1·60 m (5 ft 3 in)
Max height	1·60 m (5 ft 3 in)
Volume	13·59 m³ (480 cu ft)
Baggage compartments (fore and aft):	
Volume	1·22 m³ (43 cu ft)

AREAS:

Wings, gross	35·30 m² (380 sq ft)
Ailerons (total)	1·53 m² (16·42 sq ft)
Trailing-edge flaps (total)	3·87 m² (41·67 sq ft)
Spoilers (total)	1·11 m² (11·92 sq ft)
Fin	3·86 m² (41·58 sq ft)
Rudder, incl tab	0·83 m² (8·95 sq ft)
Tailplane	8·37 m² (90·08 sq ft)
Elevators	1·80 m² (19·43 sq ft)

WEIGHTS AND LOADINGS:

Weight empty, basic (incl 2 crew)	6,420 kg (14,154 lb)
Max T-O weight	10,886 kg (24,000 lb)
Max zero-fuel weight	7,371 kg (16,250 lb)
Max landing weight	9,868 kg (21,755 lb)
Max wing loading	308·4 kg/m² (63·2 lb/sq ft)
Max power loading	330·7 kg/kN (3·24 lb/lb st)

PERFORMANCE: (at max T-O weight, unless specified otherwise):

Max operating speed	Mach 0·83 IAS
High-speed cruise	Mach 0·81
Recommended cruising speed	Mach 0·77
Long-range cruising speed	Mach 0·73
Stalling speed, flaps up	115 knots (212 km/h; 132 mph) IAS
Stalling speed, full flap, operating weight empty, plus 4 passengers and reserve fuel	82 knots (152 km/h; 95 mph) IAS
Max rate of climb at S/L	1,051 m (3,450 ft)/min
Rate of climb at S/L, one engine out	272 m (893 ft)/min
Service ceiling	13,715 m (45,000 ft)
Service ceiling, one engine out	6,100 m (20,000 ft)
FAA T-O field length	1,797 m (5,895 ft)
FAA landing field length	1,020 m (3,345 ft)
Range with 907 kg; 2,000 lb payload, NBAA VFR reserves	2,413 nm (4,469 km; 2,777 miles)
Range with max fuel, NBAA VFR reserves	2,800 nm (5,185 km; 3,222 miles)

GENERAL AVIATION DIVISION

EXECUTIVE OFFICES: 5001 North Rockwell Avenue, Bethany, Oklahoma 73008
Telephone: (405) 789 5000
Telex: 747193
PRESIDENT: Cornell J. Slivinsky
VICE-PRESIDENT, OPERATIONS: Harvey O. Nay
EXECUTIVES:
  Alvin F. Balaban (Manager, Communications)
  Suresh Chandra (Director, Quality Assurance)
  J. Cobb (Director, Industrial Relations)
  Herbert B. Franck (Manager, Multi-engine Sales)
  Gary Glancy (Manager, Single-engine Sales)
  Kenneth L. Hale (Director, Engineering)
  Bill M. Humes (Director, Operations)
  C. J. Slivinsky (Acting Director, Marketing)

Rockwell International's General Aviation Division is a part of North American Aerospace Operations, and incorporates the Corporation's manufacturing, marketing and servicing of general aviation aircraft. It manufactures and markets Rockwell Commander turboprop and piston-engined multi-engine aircraft.

ROCKWELL ALPINE COMMANDER and GRAN TURISMO COMMANDER

During the past year, Rockwell has terminated its production of single-engined personal and business aircraft. Details of the Alpine Commander and Gran Turismo Commander can be found in the 1979-80 Jane's.

ROCKWELL SHRIKE COMMANDER 500S

The Rockwell Shrike Commander is a twin-engined aircraft designed for the businessman-pilot and certificated for Utility category operation.

Rockwell Shrike Commander 500S twin-engined light transport aircraft

TYPE: Twin-engined light transport.

WINGS: Cantilever high-wing monoplane. Wing section NACA 23012 (modified). Dihedral 4°. Incidence 3° at root, −3° 30′ at tip. All-metal two-spar flush-riveted structure. Frise statically-balanced all-metal ailerons. Hydraulically-operated all-metal slotted flaps. Ground-adjustable tab in starboard aileron. Pneumatic de-icing boots optional.

FUSELAGE: All-metal semi-monocoque structure with flush-riveted skin.

TAIL UNIT: Cantilever all-metal structure with 10° dihedral on tailplane. Trim tabs in each elevator and rudder. Pneumatic de-icing boots optional.

LANDING GEAR: Retractable tricycle type, with single wheel on each unit. All wheels retract rearward hydraulically, main wheels turning through 90° to stow horizontally in nacelles. Oleo-pneumatic shock-absorbers. Hydraulically-steerable nosewheel. Goodyear main wheels with 8-ply tyres size 25·65 × 8·70-10, pressure 3·79 bars (55 lb/sq in). Nosewheel with 6-ply tyre size

17·5 × 6·30-6, pressure 2·90 bars (42 lb/sq in). Goodyear aircooled hydraulic disc brakes.

POWER PLANT: Two 216 kW (290 hp) Avco Lycoming IO-540-E1B5 flat-six engines, each driving a Hartzell HC-C3YR-2/C8468-6R three-blade constant-speed fully-feathering metal propeller. Electrically-adjustable engine cowl flaps. Bag-type fuel tanks in wings, with usable capacity of 590 litres (156 US gallons). Overwing refuelling. Oil capacity 22·7 litres (6 US gallons) total. Electrically-heated fuel vents; propeller synchrophasers, propeller unfeathering pump, and propeller anti-icing boots, optional.

ACCOMMODATION: Four individual seats: two in front with inertia-reel and shoulder harness, and two at rear. Dual controls. Curtains divide pilot's compartment from cabin. Swivel-mounted fresh air vents above each seat, window curtains, emergency exit, announcement signs, adjustable heating and fresh air ventilation ports at cabin floor level, double-glazed windows in cabin and a hatbox shelf in aft cabin bulkhead are standard. Optional seating layouts for up to seven persons, some with rear bench seat for three. Optional refreshment cabinet for hot and cold drinks. Forward-opening passenger door under wing on port side. Forward-opening door by pilot's seat at front of cabin on port side. All equipment can be removed to permit cabin to be used for freight carrying. Compartment for 227 kg (500 lb) baggage aft of cabin, with outside door. Windscreen wiper and alcohol de-icing system for port side optional.

SYSTEMS: Hydraulic system, pressure 86 bars (1,250 lb/sq in), for landing gear, flaps, brakes and nosewheel steering. Electrical hydraulic pump emergency system for brakes. Electrical system includes two 70A alternators and two 35 Ah batteries. 100A alternators optional. Vacuum system for flight instruments, with two engine-driven vacuum pumps, and filters. Janitrol cabin heater of 35,000 BTU capacity. Oxygen system of 1·37 m³ (48·3 cu ft) or 2·74 m³ (96·6 cu ft) capacity optional.

AVIONICS AND EQUIPMENT: A wide range of optional avionics is available in package form for factory installation, or as individual items. Standard equipment includes full blind-flying instrumentation; clock; alternate static source; stall warning device; vacuum system failure warning lights; instrument lights; reading lights; anti-collision, landing and position lights; and external power socket. Optional equipment includes advanced instruments and co-pilot's blind-flying instrumentation, pilot's and co-pilot's vertically-adjustable seats, two relief tubes, co-pilot's storm window, sun visors, emergency locator transmitter, heated pitot and stall warning transmitter, cabin fire extinguisher, combined seat/toilet with privacy curtain, extra seat tracks, stereo system, storage drawers, table, tinted windows, rotating beacon, strobe lights, wing ice lights, fuselage ice shields, and static discharge wicks.

DIMENSIONS, EXTERNAL:
Wing span	14·95 m (49 ft 0½ in)
Wing chord at root	2·54 m (8 ft 4 in)
Wing chord at tip	0·65 m (2 ft 1½ in)
Wing aspect ratio	9·45
Length overall	11·22 m (36 ft 9¾ in)
Height overall	4·42 m (14 ft 6 in)
Tailplane span	5·10 m (16 ft 9 in)
Wheel track	3·95 m (12 ft 11 in)
Wheelbase	4·26 m (13 ft 11¾ in)
Propeller diameter	2·03 m (6 ft 8 in)
Crew door (fwd): Height	1·17 m (3 ft 10 in)
Width	0·58 m (1 ft 11 in)
Passenger door (aft): Height	1·14 m (3 ft 9 in)
Width	0·71 m (2 ft 4 in)
Baggage door: Height	0·60 m (1 ft 11½ in)
Width	0·48 m (1 ft 7 in)

DIMENSIONS, INTERNAL:
Cabin: Length	3·24 m (10 ft 7½ in)
Max width	1·32 m (4 ft 4 in)
Max height	1·35 m (4 ft 5 in)
Volume	5·01 m³ (177 cu ft)
Baggage hold	0·91 m³ (32 cu ft)

AREAS:
Wings, gross	23·69 m² (255 sq ft)
Ailerons (total)	1·90 m² (20·52 sq ft)
Trailing-edge flaps (total)	1·97 m² (21·20 sq ft)
Fin	2·23 m² (24·00 sq ft)
Rudder, incl tab	1·43 m² (15·40 sq ft)
Tailplane	3·07 m² (33·06 sq ft)
Elevators, incl tabs	1·91 m² (20·54 sq ft)

WEIGHTS AND LOADINGS:
Weight empty, equipped	2,102 kg (4,635 lb)
Max T-O and landing weight	3,062 kg (6,750 lb)
Max wing loading	129·2 kg/m² (26·47 lb/sq ft)
Max power loading	7·09 kg/kW (11·64 lb/hp)

PERFORMANCE (at max T-O weight):
Max cruising speed at S/L	187 knots (346 km/h; 215 mph)
Max cruising speed (75% power) at 2,745 m (9,000 ft)	176 knots (326 km/h; 203 mph)
Stalling speed, flaps and landing gear up	68 knots (126 km/h; 78 mph) CAS
Stalling speed, flaps and landing gear down	59 knots (109 km/h; 68 mph) CAS
Min single-engine control speed	65·5 knots (121 km/h; 75 mph)

Max rate of climb at S/L	408 m (1,340 ft)/min
Rate of climb at S/L, one engine out	81 m (266 ft)/min
Service ceiling	5,915 m (19,400 ft)
Service ceiling, one engine out	1,980 m (6,500 ft)
Min ground turning radius	11·63 m (38 ft 2 in)
T-O to 15 m (50 ft)	584 m (1,915 ft)
Landing from 15 m (50 ft)	681 m (2,235 ft)
Range with standard fuel at 2,745 m (9,000 ft) at 178 knots (330 km/h; 205 mph), 45 min reserves	693 nm (1,282 km; 797 miles)
Range, conditions as above, no reserves	824 nm (1,525 km; 948 miles)
Absolute range, standard fuel, at 4,570 m (15,000 ft) at 45% power and cruising speed of 118 knots (262 km/h; 163 mph), 45 min reserves	1,033 nm (1,915 km; 1,190 miles)

ROCKWELL COMMANDER 700 and 710

In December 1979, Rockwell decided to terminate the agreement with Fuji of Japan under which the two companies had developed jointly the Commander 700 and were planning to market also the more powerful Commander 710. When the joint programme ended, Rockwell had completed 30 Commander 700s, of which 17 had been delivered to customers in the USA and 8 to other operators.

Fuji (which see) now has worldwide manufacturing rights in the FA-300 (Japanese designation of the Commander 700), with worldwide product support from Rockwell's General Aviation Division.

ROCKWELL JETPROP COMMANDER 840

The Rockwell Jetprop Commander 840 is a pressurised transport aircraft, powered by two Garrett-AiResearch turboprop engines, which was developed from the Turbo Commander 690C. This latter aircraft was described in the 1979-80 *Jane's*.

The Jetprop Commander 840 differs from the Turbo Commander 690C in having a wing of increased span, with twist in the outer panels, shallow winglets above the tips, and increased fuel capacity. In addition, Dowty Rotol 'supercritical' propellers are provided for the Garrett-AiResearch turboprop engines. It was certificated on 7 September 1979; first deliveries of production aircraft followed shortly afterwards.

TYPE: Twin engined light transport

WINGS: Cantilever high-wing monoplane. Wing section NACA 23012 modified. Dihedral 4°. Incidence 3° at root, 0° 31' at tip. All-metal two-spar flush-riveted structure. Shallow winglet above each wingtip. Frise statically-balanced all-metal ailerons. Hydraulically-operated all-metal flaps. Electrically-operated trim tab in starboard aileron. Pneumatic de-icing boots standard.

FUSELAGE: All-metal semi-monocoque structure with flush-riveted skin.

TAIL UNIT: Cantilever all-metal structure with 10° dihedral on fixed-incidence tailplane. Trim tabs in each elevator and rudder. Electrically-actuated elevator trim when Collins or King autopilot installed, with Collins, King or Rockwell actuators. Pneumatic de-icing boots standard.

LANDING GEAR: Retractable tricycle type, with single wheel on each unit. All wheels retract rearward hydraulically, main wheels turning through 90° to stow horizontally in nacelles. Ozone Aircraft Systems oleo-pneumatic shock-absorbers. Hydraulically-steerable nosewheel. Goodyear main wheels with tyres size 25·65 × 8·70-10, pressure 5·04 bars (73 lb/sq in). Nosewheel tyre size 17·5 × 6·30-6, pressure 2·21 bars (32 lb/sq in). Goodyear aircooled multi-disc hydraulic brakes.

POWER PLANT: Two 626 kW (840 shp) Garrett-AiResearch TPE331-5-254K turboprop engines, each flat rated at 522 kW (700 shp), and each driving a Dowty Rotol (C)R306/3-82-F/7-(C)VP2926 three-blade 'supercritical' constant-speed fully-feathering and reversible-pitch propeller. Two combination bladder and integral tanks, with total usable capacity of 1,609 litres (425 US gallons). Refuelling points on upper surface of each wing. Oil capacity 11·5 litres (3 US gallons). Manually controlled oil temperature control doors. Electrical propeller de-icing.

ACCOMMODATION: Standard seating for pilot and six passengers, on two adjustable seats on flight deck, two forward-facing single seats and a three-place forward-facing bench seat in main cabin. Dual controls and co-pilot's instrumentation standard. A variety of optional seating layouts offer accommodation for a pilot and up to 10 passengers. Cabin pressurised, heated and air-conditioned. Forward-hinged outward-opening cabin door on port side, with retractable cabin step. Plug-type pull-in emergency exit on starboard side of fuselage. Baggage compartment of 1·98 m³ (70 cu ft) with 272 kg (600 lb) capacity aft of rear pressure bulkhead with external access door on port side of fuselage. Electrical windscreen anti-icing.

SYSTEMS: Sundstrand bleed air air-conditioning and pressurisation system, with max differential of 0·37 bars (5·4 lb/sq in), and normal differential of 0·36 bars (5·2 lb/sq in). Single hydraulic system with two engine-driven

pumps, an emergency reservoir and an electrically-operated auxiliary pump; normal pressure between 62 and 74 bars (900 and 1,075 lb/sq in), with pressure relief valve set at 86 bars (1,250 lb/sq in), ±3·5 bars (50 lb/sq in); for operation of landing gear, brakes, nosewheel steering and trailing-edge flaps. Electrical system includes two 30V 300A starter/generators, and two 24V lead-acid batteries. Scott emergency oxygen system of 0·6 m³ (22 cu ft) capacity, with constant-flow outlets at each passenger position, and diluter-demand systems at crew stations. Pneumatic system using engine bleed air, for operation of wing and tail unit de-icing boots, cabin door seal, environmental control unit, and optional co-pilot's gyro horizon.

AVIONICS AND EQUIPMENT: Optional avionics include a variety of radio equipment by Collins and King; weather radar by Bendix, Collins and RCA; and autopilot/flight director systems by Collins and King. Standard equipment includes heated pitot, static source, and stall warning transmitter. Blind-flying instrumentation optional.

DIMENSIONS, EXTERNAL:
Wing span	15·89 m (52 ft 1½ in)
Wing chord at root	2·64 m (8 ft 7¾ in)
Wing aspect ratio	9.772
Length overall	13·10 m (42 ft 11¾ in)
Height overall	4·55 m (14 ft 11½ in)
Tailplane span	6·03 m (19 ft 9¼ in)
Wheel track	4·70 m (15 ft 5 in)
Wheelbase	5·38 m (17 ft 7¾ in)
Propeller diameter	2·69 m (8 ft 10 in)
Propeller ground clearance	0·32 m (1 ft 0¾ in)
Distance between propeller centres	5·36 m (17 ft 7 in)
Cabin door: Height	1·19 m (3 ft 11 in)
Width	0·67 m (2 ft 2½ in)
Height to sill	0·47 m (1 ft 6½ in)
Baggage door: Height	0·79 m (2 ft 7¼ in)
Width	0·50 m (1 ft 7¾ in)
Height to sill	0·52 m (1 ft 8½ in)
Emergency exit: Height	0·47 m (1 ft 6½ in)
Width	0·66 m (2 ft 2¼ in)

DIMENSIONS, INTERNAL:
Cabin: Length	4·34 m (14 ft 3 in)
Max width	1·25 m (4 ft 1¼ in)
Max height	1·36 m (4 ft 5⅝ in)
Floor area (incl flight deck)	5·41 m² (58·19 sq ft)
Baggage hold volume	1·98 m³ (70 cu ft)

AREAS:
Wings, gross	25·95 m² (279·35 sq ft)
Ailerons (total)	1·90 m² (20·52 sq ft)
Trailing-edge flaps (total)	1·93 m² (20·80 sq ft)
Fin	2·52 m² (27·15 sq ft)
Rudder (incl tab)	1·59 m² (17·12 sq ft)
Tailplane	2·59 m² (27·83 sq ft)
Elevators (incl tab)	1·91 m² (20·54 sq ft)

WEIGHTS AND LOADINGS:
Weight empty, standard	2,776 kg (6,120 lb)
Max usable fuel weight	1,292 kg (2,848 lb)
Max T-O weight	4,683 kg (10,325 lb)
Max ramp weight	4,706 kg (10,375 lb)
Max zero-fuel weight	3,839 kg (8,463 lb)
Max landing weight	4,389 kg (9,675 lb)
Max wing loading	180·5 kg/m² (36·96 lb/sq ft)
Max power loading	4·49 kg/kW (7·38 lb/shp)

PERFORMANCE (at max T-O weight, except where indicated):
Never-exceed speed	Mach 0·52 (243 knots; 450 km/h; 280 mph CAS)
Max level speed at 3,660 m (12,000 ft)	290 knots (537 km/h; 333 mph)
Max cruising speed at 5,485 m (18,000 ft)	287 knots (531 km/h; 330 mph)
Econ cruising speed at 9,450 m (31,000 ft)	234 knots (433 km/h; 269 mph)
Stalling speed, flaps up	77 knots (143 km/h; 89 mph) CAS
Stalling speed, flaps down	75 knots (139 km/h; 87 mph) CAS
Max rate of climb at S/L	860 m (2,824 ft)/min
Rate of climb at S/L, one engine out	305 m (1,002 ft)/min
Service ceiling, certificated	9,450 m (31,000 ft)
Service ceiling, one engine out	6,400 m (21,000 ft)
T-O run	392 m (1,285 ft)
T-O to 15 m (50 ft)	559 m (1,833 ft)
Landing from 15 m (50 ft), no propeller reversal	711 m (2,332 ft)
Landing run, no propeller reversal	472 m (1,549 ft)
Range with max fuel, allowances of 23 kg (50 lb) fuel for start and taxi, plus 45 min reserves at holding power	1,779 nm (3,294 km; 2,047 miles)
Range with max payload, allowances as above	1,080 nm (2,000 km; 1,243 miles)

ROCKWELL JETPROP COMMANDER 980

The Jetprop Commander 980 differs from the 840 version primarily by having more powerful (730 kW; 980 shp) Garrett-AiResearch turboprop engines. It was certificated in November 1979, and initial deliveries of production aircraft were scheduled in early 1980.

The description of the Jetprop Commander 840 applies also to this version, except as detailed:

POWER PLANT: As for Jetprop Commander 840, except

two 730 kW (980 shp) Garrett-AiResearch TPE331-10-501K turboprop engines, each flat rated at 533 kW (715 shp).

ACCOMMODATION: As for Jetprop Commander 840, except standard seating for pilot and seven passengers, on two adjustable seats on flight deck, a side-facing combined seat/toilet with privacy curtain aft of the co-pilot's seat, two aft-facing single seats, and a three-place forward-facing bench seat in main cabin.

DIMENSIONS, EXTERNAL: As for Jetprop Commander 840, except:

Baggage door: Width	0·63 m (2 ft 1 in)

WEIGHTS AND LOADINGS: As for Jetprop Commander 840, except:

Weight empty, standard	3,049 kg (6,721 lb)
Max power loading	4·39 kg/kW (7·22 lb/shp)

PERFORMANCE (at max T-O weight, except where indicated):

As for Jetprop Commander 840 except:

Max level speed at 5,485 m (18,000 ft)	306 knots (566 km/h; 352 mph)
Max cruising speed at 6,700 m (22,000 ft)	315 knots (583 km/h; 362 mph)
Econ cruising speed at 9,450 m (31,000 ft)	300 knots (555 km/h; 345 mph)
Max rate of climb at S/L	846 m (2,777 ft)/min
Rate of climb at S/L, one engine out	299 m (982 ft)/min
Service ceiling, certificated	9,450 m (31,000 ft)
Service ceiling, one engine out	7,560 m (24,800 ft)

Rockwell Jetprop Commander 980 (two Garrett-AiResearch TPE331-10-501K turboprops)

T-O run	396 m (1,299 ft)
T-O to 15 m (50 ft)	565 m (1,854 ft)
Landing from 15 m (50 ft), no propeller reversal	704 m (2,310 ft)
Landing run	466 m (1,527 ft)
Range with max fuel	1,800 nm (3,333 km; 2,071 miles)

Range with max payload	1,247 nm (2,309 km; 1,435 miles)

ROCKWELL JETPROP COMMANDER 1000

This derivative of the Jetprop Commander 980 was undergoing flight testing in mid-1980. Brief details can be found in the Addenda.

SCENIC
SCENIC AVIATION SERVICES

241 East Reno Avenue, Las Vegas, Nevada 89119
Telephone: (702) 739 5611
Telex: 684476

PRESIDENT: Karl A. Fahr

Scenic Air Lines acquired from American Jet Industries of Van Nuys, California, in early 1977, all engineering and manufacturing rights for the turboprop conversions of

Cessna Model 402 and 414 aircraft designed by AJI. A description of the Turbo Star Pressurised 414 appeared in the 1977-78 *Jane's*; details of the Turbo Star 402 can be found in the 1979-80 *Jane's*.

SCHAPEL
SCHAPEL AIRCRAFT COMPANY

PO Box 60039, Reno, Nevada 89506
Telephone: (702) 972 8937
PRESIDENT: Rodney E. Schapel

SCHAPEL S-525 SUPER SWAT

Believing that present-day agricultural aircraft designs are many years behind their potential, having regard to current technological advances in aerodynamics and structural materials, Schapel Aircraft Company began studies in 1977 which it was hoped would lead to the design of an advanced agricultural aircraft. By the Spring of 1979, wind tunnel testing of a model had been completed successfully. Construction of a prototype began in July 1979, and this aircraft was scheduled to make its first flight in October 1980.

Known as the S-525 Super Swat, the aircraft is of conventional configuration and is constructed primarily of composites.

TYPE: Advanced-design agricultural aircraft.

WINGS: Cantilever shoulder-wing monoplane. Aerofoil section NASA (Whitcomb) GAW-1. Thickness/chord ratio 17%. Dihedral 1° 30′. Incidence 3°. No sweepback. Fail-safe plate stringer structure of carbon fibre/epoxy. Slot-lip ailerons of glassfibre, Kevlar 49 (R) and honeycomb/epoxy sandwich. Full-span electrically-actuated Fowler-type trailing-edge flaps of similar construction. Trim tab in starboard aileron.

FUSELAGE: Welded steel tube structure, with skins of composite materials. Tailbooms of carbon fibre/epoxy construction.

TAIL UNIT: Twin endplate fins with rudders, mounted on tailbooms, with fixed-incidence tailplane between, forming a rigid box structure. One-piece elevator. Construction of glassfibre, Kevlar 49 (R) and honeycomb/epoxy sandwich. Trim tabs in elevator and rudders.

LANDING GEAR: Non-retractable tricycle type, with single wheel on each unit. Main wheels carried on cantilever units. Shock-absorption by rubber in compression. Cleveland main wheels with tyres of 685 mm (27·00 in) diameter. Nosewheel tyre 585 mm (23·00 in) diameter. Cleveland brakes.

POWER PLANT: One 507 kW (680 shp) Pratt & Whitney Aircraft of Canada PT6A-15AG turboprop engine, driving a Hartzell constant-speed three-blade metal pusher propeller. Fuel in two wing tanks with combined capacity of 378·5 litres (100 US gallons). Single-point pressure refuelling in side of fuselage. Gravity refuelling point on upper surface of each wing.

ACCOMMODATION: Single seat for pilot. Cockpit canopy hinged at top, and openable upward on each side. Accommodation heated, ventilated and air-conditioned.

SYSTEMS: Air-conditioning and electrical systems.

Schapel S-525 Super Swat (P&WC PT6A-15AG turboprop engine) *(Michael A. Badrocke)*

EQUIPMENT: Hopper in fuselage for liquid spray or dry chemicals, volume 2·04 m³ (72 cu ft), capacity 1,987 litres (525 US gallons). Liquids are sprayed from a full-span manifold with more than 100 nozzles. Dry chemicals can be dispensed by means of an applicator spanning 16·5 m (54 ft 0 in). Standard equipment includes an Agrinautics hydraulic drive and control system which will allow the Super Swat to dispense a swath of liquid chemicals 30 per cent greater than that of any US agricultural aircraft in current use. In the case of dry chemicals, the standard applicator will provide a swath up to 24·4 m (80 ft 0 in) wide. The hopper is mounted within the fuselage nacelle, aft of the pilot; this places it close to the aircraft's CG, and minimises the effects of varying chemical loads. Liquid can be dispensed at a rate of 30·6 litres/hectare (20 US gallons/acre), and dry chemicals at 73·4 kg/hectare (400 lb/acre).

DIMENSIONS, EXTERNAL:

Wing span	16·46 m (54 ft 0 in)
Wing aspect ratio	10·33
Length overall	9·66 m (31 ft 8½ in)
Height overall	3·26 m (10 ft 8½ in)
Tailplane span	3·66 m (12 ft 0 in)
Wheel track	2·44 m (8 ft 0 in)
Wheelbase	2·96 m (9 ft 8½ in)
Propeller diameter	2·44 m (8 ft 0 in)

Propeller ground clearance	0·15 m (6 in)

AREA:

Wings, gross	26·48 m² (285 sq ft)

WEIGHTS AND LOADINGS (estimated):

Weight empty	1,270 kg (2,800 lb)
Max T-O and landing weight	3,629 kg (8,000 lb)
Max zero-fuel weight	3,342 kg (7,367 lb)
Max wing loading	126·2 kg/m² (28·07 lb/sq ft)
Max power loading	6·59 kg/kW (11·76 lb/shp)

PERFORMANCE (estimated, at max T-O weight):

Never-exceed speed	250 knots (463 km/h; 288 mph)
Max level speed at S/L	177 knots (328 km/h; 204 mph)
Cruising speed at 7,620 m (25,000 ft)	175 knots (324 km/h; 202 mph)
Stalling speed, flaps up	74·9 knots (139 km/h; 86 mph)
Stalling speed, flaps down	50·4 knots (93 km/h; 58 mph)
Max rate of climb at S/L	503 m (1,650 ft)/min
Service ceiling	7,620 m (25,000 ft)
T-O run	238 m (780 ft)
T-O to 15 m (50 ft)	511 m (1,677 ft)
Landing from 15 m (50 ft)	233 m (765 ft)
Landing run	140 m (460 ft)
Range with max fuel, no payload	890 nm (1,649 km; 1,025 miles)

SEAPLANES
SEAPLANES INC
PO Box 2164, Pearson Air Park, Vancouver, Washington 98661
Telephone: (206) 694 6287
PRESIDENT: L. W. Soukup

Seaplanes Inc is carrying out STOL and/or performance improvements to a variety of lightplanes manufactured by Cessna, Maule, Piper, Stinson and Waco. Performance increases result largely from replacing the original power plant by a Franklin engine of increased power, but the company has also designed a STOL kit for installation on Cessna 170B, 172 and 175 aircraft. This includes a stall fence, leading-edge cuff and aileron gap seals, which improve take-off and landing performance by approx 7 per cent.

Power plant replacements involve removal of the existing engine from Cessna 170B, 172 and 175, and Stinson 108 aircraft, and the installation of a 164 kW (220 hp) Franklin flat-six engine. The 186 kW (250 hp) turbocharged Franklin can also be installed in the Cessna 172, 175 and Stinson 108, and this power plant is used also for installation in the Maule M-5 Lunar Rocket in lieu of a 157 kW (210 hp) Continental or 164 kW (220 hp) Franklin engine. Conversion of the Piper Cherokee and Waco Vela to use a 164 kW (220 hp) and 186 kW (250 hp) Franklin engine respectively was under way in 1980.

Performance figures for Seaplanes' conversions certificated by early 1980 are given in the table.

	Max level speed knots (km/h; mph)	Max cruising speed at 2,135 m (7,000 ft) knots (km/h; mph)	Max rate of climb at S/L m (ft)/min	Service ceiling m (ft)	T-O run m (ft)	Range nm (km; miles)
Cessna 170B	A 148 (274; 170)	A 137 (254; 158)	A 457 (1,500)	A 5,485 (18,000)	A 91 (300)	A 434 (804; 500)
Cessna 172	A 145 (269; 167) B 148 (274; 170)*	A 135 (251; 156) B 148+ (274; 170)	A 427 (1,400) B 549 (1,800)	A 5,485 (18,000) B 9,145 (30,000)	A 91 (300) B 84 (275)	A 521 (966; 600) B 521 (966; 600)
Cessna 175	A 145 (269; 167) B 148 (274; 170)*	A 135 (251; 156) B 148+ (274; 170)	A 427 (1,400) B 549 (1,800)	A 5,485 (18,000) B 9,145 (30,000)	A 91 (300) B 84 (275)	A 521 (966; 600) B 521 (966; 600)
Stinson 108	A 139 (258; 160) B 139 (258; 160)*	A 131 (243; 151) B 139 (258; 160)	A 488 (1,600) B 579 (1,900)	A 5,485 (18,000) B 9,145 (30,000)	A 91 (300) B 84 (275)	A 521 (966; 600) B 521 (966; 600)
Maule M-5	B 152 (282; 175)	B 142 (263; 164)	B 549 (1,800)	B 9,145 (30,000)	B 84 (275)	B 564 (1,045; 650)

A: 164 kW (220 hp) Franklin 6A-350-C2 normally aspirated engine
B: 186 kW (250 hp) Franklin 6AS-350-A1 turbocharged engine
* max certificated speed

Seaplanes Inc modification of Cessna 170B with Franklin 6A-350-C2 engine

SERV-AERO
SERV-AERO ENGINEERING INC
Municipal Airport, Salinas, California 93901
Telephone: (408) 422 7866/7
PRESIDENT: Floyd N. Perry

Serv-Aero Engineering is involved in programmes to re-engine standard types of agricultural aircraft which are powered by Pratt & Whitney radial engines. The R-1340 radial, in particular, has been out of production since the mid-fifties, and spare parts for this engine have become difficult to obtain.

THRUSH COMMANDER/R-1820
This conversion of the Thrush Commander involves removal of the Pratt & Whitney R-1340 or Wright R-1300 and its replacement by an 895 kW (1,200 hp) Wright R-1820-71 radial piston engine, driving a slow-turning large-diameter three-blade Hamilton Standard propeller. A Supplemental Type Certificate covering this airframe/engine combination was received on 8 October 1977, followed subsequently by Parts Manufacturing Approval covering the production of conversion kits.

It is reported that this engine installation provides a 396 m (1,300 ft) T-O run with full hopper (1,476-1,514 litres; 390-400 US gallons) at S/L in zero-wind ISA conditions. Working speed is 117-126 knots (217-233 km/h; 135-145 mph), resulting in a lower fuel consumption per acre worked. The slower-turning, quieter propeller permits operators to work closer to inhabited areas without creating noise problems.

By mid-1980, some operators of Thrush Commanders

Thrush Commander with R-1820 engine and Serv-Aero's fuselage fairing and spring tailwheel modification

with R-1820 engine had logged nearly 2,000 flying hours on individual aircraft, as a result of which they claimed an increase of 35-45 per cent in productivity with no increase in fuel consumption compared with that of the formerly-installed R-1340 engine.

Serv-Aero has FAA approval for a 3·05 m (10 ft) diameter propeller on the 3:2 geared version of the R-1820. In mid-1980, it was engaged in flight testing to achieve approval for a similar propeller on the quieter and smoother 16:9 series geared engines.

SERV-AERO/AYRES THRUSH MODIFICATION
This FAA-approved modification to the Ayres Thrush involves addition of a streamlined top fuselage fairing and a spring-type tailwheel leg. The fairing adds considerably to the airspeed and smooths airflow over the tail unit. By smoothing the aircraft's taxying, the new tailwheel leg reduces maintenance time, by reducing shock loads imposed on the fuselage structure, and improves directional stability on the ground. This modification is approved also for the Turbo-Thrush.

SIKORSKY
SIKORSKY AIRCRAFT, DIVISION OF UNITED TECHNOLOGIES CORPORATION
HEAD OFFICE AND WORKS: Stratford, Connecticut 06602
Telephone: (203) 378 6361
OTHER WORKS: South Avenue, Bridgeport, Connecticut; Sikorsky Memorial Airport, Stratford, Connecticut; and Development Flight Test Center, West Palm Beach, Florida
PRESIDENT AND CHIEF EXECUTIVE OFFICER: Gerald J. Tobias
EXECUTIVE VICE-PRESIDENT AND CHIEF OPERATING OFFICER: Robert F. Daniell
EXECUTIVE VICE-PRESIDENT: Fred W. Carroll (Operations)
SENIOR VICE-PRESIDENTS:
　John R. Graham (Finance and Administration)
　William F. Paul (Engineering & Development)
　Robert J. Torok (Production Programmes)

VICE-PRESIDENTS:
　John P. Balaguer (Bridgeport/Florida Manufacturing)
　Eugene Buckley (Stratford Manufacturing)
　J. Colin Green (Planning and Services)
　Willard E. Lewis (Finance)
　Philip Locke (Contracts and Counsel)
　Porter D. Lyke (Personnel and Industrial Relations)
　Wayne B. Parker (Government Relations)
　Allan K. Poole (Product Support—Government Programmes)
　David O. Smith (Marketing and Customer Service)
　Harvey I. White (Material)
　Robert Zincone (Engineering)
DIVISIONAL AUDITOR: H. W. Engstrom
DIRECTOR OF PUBLIC RELATIONS: Robert G. H. Carroll III
Founded on 5 March 1923 by the late Igor I. Sikorsky as the Sikorsky Aero Engineering Corporation, this company has been a division of United Technologies since

1929. Its main plant at Stratford, which has 120,775 m² (1,300,000 sq ft) of working space, produces the S-61 twin-turbine amphibious military transport helicopter and its ASW counterparts, and the S-65 series of large multipurpose military transports. It houses also the production line for the US Army's twin-turbine UH-60A Black Hawk helicopter. The Bridgeport facility, which has 55,740 m² (600,000 sq ft) of working space, houses the production line for the S-76 twin-turbine commercial helicopter, and is used for detail fabrication, overhaul and repair. The Development Flight Test Center is in Florida.

Sikorsky is involved currently in a number of important development programmes, including the three-engined CH-53E heavy transport helicopter for the US Navy and Marine Corps. Its ABC (advancing blade concept) helicopter, the S-69, has successfully completed flight tests in its pure helicopter configuration and is now undergoing tests using auxiliary propulsion for flight at speeds up to 300 knots (556 km/h; 345 mph). Also under development are two high-speed multi-purpose research helicopters for NASA and the US Army, known as Rotor Systems Research Aircraft (RSRA).

Sikorsky licensees include Westland of Great Britain, Agusta of Italy, Aérospatiale of France, VFW in West Germany, Mitsubishi of Japan, and Pratt & Whitney Aircraft of Canada Ltd.

SIKORSKY S-61A and S-61B

US military designations: SH-3 Sea King, HH-3A, VH-3

CAF designation: CH-124

The first version of the S-61 ordered into production was the SH-3A (originally HSS-2) Sea King amphibious anti-submarine helicopter, of which the prototype flew for the first time on 11 March 1959. Deliveries to the US Navy began in September 1961. On 11 March 1979, Sikorsky drew attention to the 20th anniversary of the prototype's first flight, since when more than 900 military S-61s had accumulated over 3 million flight hours, and 130 commercial S-61s had logged a total of more than 815,000 hours.

The S-61 series includes the following military and commercial variants:

SH-3A Sea King. Initial anti-submarine version for the US Navy, powered by 932 kW (1,250 shp) General Electric T58-GE-8B turboshaft engines. A total of 255 were produced by Sikorsky. Also standard equipment in the Japan Maritime Self-Defence Force (see entry for Mitsubishi, which also converted two SH-3As to S-61A standard for use during Antarctic expeditions).

CH-124. Designation of 41 aircraft, similar to SH-3A, for the Canadian Armed Forces. First of these was delivered in May 1963: fifth and subsequent aircraft were assembled by United Aircraft of Canada Ltd. Originally designated CHSS-2.

S-61A. Amphibious transport, generally similar to the US Navy's SH-3A. Accommodates 26 troops, 15 litters, cargo, or 12 passengers in VIP configuration. Rolls-Royce Gnome H.1200 turboshafts available as alternative to standard General Electric T58 engines. Nine delivered to Royal Danish Air Force for long-range air/sea rescue duties, with additional fuel tankage. One delivered to Construction Helicopters.

S-61A-4 Nuri. Thirty-eight delivered to Royal Malaysian Air Force, each with 31 seats, rescue hoists and auxiliary fuel tanks as standard equipment. Used for troop transport, cargo carrying and rescue.

HH-3A. Variant of SH-3A, for search and rescue duties with US Navy. HH-3A conversion kits were supplied to the Navy's overhaul and repair base at Quonset Point, Rhode Island, where 12 conversions were carried out. Changes included installation of two electrically-powered Minigun turrets behind the sponsons, T58-GE-8F turbine engines, a high-speed refuelling and fuel dumping system, a high-speed rescue hoist, modified electronics package, external auxiliary fuel tanks and complete armour installation. The SH-3A's sonar well is covered and a reinforced cabin floor substituted.

SH-3D Sea King. Standard anti-submarine helicopter of the US Navy, with T58-GE-10 engines and more fuel than SH-3A. First SH-3D, delivered in June 1966, was one of 10 for the Spanish Navy, which later ordered 12 more. Four were delivered to the Brazilian Navy and 72 to the US Navy. Versions with Rolls-Royce Gnome turboshaft engines and British anti-submarine equipment are manufactured by Westland Helicopters Ltd (which see).

Sikorsky SH-3H twin-engined multi-purpose amphibious helicopter *(Pilot Press)*

SH-3Ds are also manufactured under licence by Agusta in Italy.

S-61D-4. Four for Argentinian Navy, similar to SH-3D.

VH-3D. Eleven delivered to replace VH-3As of US Executive Flight Detachment.

SH-3G. US Navy conversion of 105 SH-3As into utility helicopters, by removing anti-submarine warfare equipment. Six equipped with Minigun pods for search and rescue missions in combat conditions.

SH-3H. Multi-purpose version of SH-3G with T58-GE-10 engines. US Navy contracts, awarded from 1971, called for conversion of 163 existing aircraft by 1980, to increase fleet helicopter capability against submarines and low-flying enemy missiles. New ASW equipment includes lightweight sonar, active and passive sonobuoys, and magnetic anomaly detection equipment. Electronic surveillance measurement (ESM) equipment enables the SH-3H to make an important contribution to the missile defence of the fleet.

S-61L. Non-amphibious civil transport with longer fuselage than S-61A/B. Described in 1979-80 *Jane's*.

S-61N. Amphibious counterpart of S-61L; described in 1979-80 *Jane's*.

S-61R. Development of S-61B for transport duties with US Air Force, under the designations **CH-3C** and **E.** Described separately.

By mid-1980, more than 750 examples of the S-61 (all models) had been built by Sikorsky, and more than 350 by the company's foreign licensees.

The following details apply to the SH-3D Sea King, but are generally applicable to other versions except for accommodation and equipment:

TYPE: Twin-engined amphibious all-weather anti-submarine helicopter.

ROTOR SYSTEM: Five-blade main and tail rotors. All-metal fully-articulated oil-lubricated main rotor. Flanged cuffs on blades bolted to matching flanges on all-steel rotor head. Main rotor blades are interchangeable and are provided with an automatic powered folding system. Rotor brake standard. All-metal tail rotor.

ROTOR DRIVE: Both engines drive through freewheel units and rotor brake to main gearbox. Steel drive-shafts. Tail rotor shaft-driven through intermediate and tail gearboxes. Accessories driven by power take-off on tail

rotor shaft. Additional freewheel units between accessories and port engine, and between accessories and tail rotor shaft. Main rotor/engine rpm ratio 1 : 93·43. Tail rotor/engine rpm ratio 1 : 16·7.

FUSELAGE: Boat hull of all-metal semi-monocoque construction. Single step. Tail section folds to reduce stowage requirements.

TAIL SURFACE: Fixed stabiliser on starboard side of tail section.

LANDING GEAR: Amphibious. Land gear consists of two twin-wheel main units, which are retracted rearward hydraulically into stabilising floats, and non-retractable tailwheel. Oleo-pneumatic shock-absorbers. Goodyear main wheels and tubeless tyres size 6·50-10 type III, pressure 4·83 bars (70 lb)sq in). Goodyear tailwheel and tyre size 6·00-6. Goodyear hydraulic disc brakes. Boat hull and pop-out flotation bags in stabilising floats permit emergency operation from water.

POWER PLANT: Two 1,044 kW (1,400 shp) General Electric T58-GE-10 turboshaft engines. Three bladder-type fuel tanks in hull; forward tank 1,314 litres (347 US gallons), centre tank 530 litres (140 US gallons), rear tank 1,336 litres (353 US gallons). Total fuel capacity 3,180 litres (840 US gallons). Refuelling point on port side of fuselage. Oil capacity 26·5 litres (7 US gallons).

ACCOMMODATION: Pilot and co-pilot on flight deck, two sonar operators in main cabin. Dual controls. Crew door at rear of flight deck on port side. Large loading door at rear of cabin on starboard side.

SYSTEMS: Primary and auxiliary hydraulic systems, pressure 103·5 bars (1,500 lb/sq in), for flying controls. Utility hydraulic system, pressure 207 bars (3,000 lb/sq in), for landing gear, winches and blade folding. Pneumatic system, pressure 207 bars (3,000 lb/sq in), for blow-down emergency landing gear extension. Electrical system includes one 300A DC generator, two 20kVA 115A AC generators and 24V 22Ah battery. APU optional.

AVIONICS AND EQUIPMENT: Bendix AQS-13 sonar with 180° search beam width. Hamilton Standard autostabilisation equipment. Automatic transition into hover. Sonar coupler holds altitude automatically in conjunction with Teledyne APN-130 Doppler radar (Litton AN/APS-503 in CH-124) and radar altimeter. Provision for 272 kg (600 lb) capacity rescue hoist and

Sikorsky SH-3H multi-purpose helicopter for ASW and fleet missile defence

3,630 kg (8,000 lb) capacity automatic touchdown-release low-response cargo sling for external loads.

ARMAMENT: Provision for 381 kg (840 lb) of weapons, including homing torpedoes.

DIMENSIONS, EXTERNAL:

Diameter of main rotor	18·90 m (62 ft 0 in)
Main rotor blade chord	0·46 m (1 ft 6¼ in)
Diameter of tail rotor	3·23 m (10 ft 7 in)
Distance between rotor centres	11·10 m (36 ft 5 in)
Length overall	22·15 m (72 ft 8 in)
Length of fuselage	16·69 m (54 ft 9 in)
Length, tail pylon folded	14·40 m (47 ft 3 in)
Width, rotors folded	4·98 m (16 ft 4 in)
Height to top of rotor hub	4·72 m (15 ft 6 in)
Height overall	5·13 m (16 ft 10 in)
Wheel track	3·96 m (13 ft 0 in)
Wheelbase	7·18 m (23 ft 6½ in)
Crew door (fwd, port): Height	1·68 m (5 ft 6 in)
Width	0·91 m (3 ft 0 in)
Height to sill	1·14 m (3 ft 9 in)
Main cabin door (stbd): Height	1·52 m (5 ft 0 in)
Width	1·73 m (5 ft 8 in)
Height to sill	1·14 m (3 ft 9 in)

DIMENSIONS, INTERNAL (S-61A):

Cabin: Length	7·60 m (24 ft 11 in)
Max width	1·98 m (6 ft 6 in)
Max height	1·92 m (6 ft 3½ in)
Floor area	15·1 m² (162 sq ft)
Volume	28·9 m³ (1,020 cu ft)

AREAS:

Main rotor blades (each)	4·14 m² (44·54 sq ft)
Tail rotor blades (each)	0·22 m² (2·38 sq ft)
Main rotor disc	280·5 m² (3,019 sq ft)
Tail rotor disc	8·20 m² (88·30 sq ft)
Stabiliser	1·86 m² (20·00 sq ft)

WEIGHTS:

Weight empty: S-61A	4,428 kg (9,763 lb)
S-61B	5,382 kg (11,865 lb)
Normal T-O weight: S-61A	9,300 kg (20,500 lb)
SH-3A (ASW)	8,185 kg (18,044 lb)
SH-3D (ASW)	8,449 kg (18,626 lb)
Max T-O weight: S-61A	9,750 kg (21,500 lb)
S-61B	9,300 kg (20,500 lb)
SH-3H	9,525 kg (21,000 lb)

PERFORMANCE (at 9,300 kg; 20,500 lb AUW):

Max level speed	144 knots (267 km/h; 166 mph)
Cruising speed for max range	
	118 knots (219 km/h; 136 mph)
Max rate of climb at S/L	670 m (2,200 ft)/min
Service ceiling	4,480 m (14,700 ft)
Hovering ceiling IGE	3,200 m (10,500 ft)
Hovering ceiling OGE	2,500 m (8,200 ft)
Range with max fuel, 10% reserves	
	542 nm (1,005 km; 625 miles)

SIKORSKY S-61L and S-61N

Production of these commercial versions of the S-61 ended on 19 June 1980, when the last S-61N was delivered to Siller Brothers Inc of California, for use in support of logging activities. During 19 years of production, 13 S-61Ls and 123 S-61Ns were built. Details of these aircraft can be found in the 1979-80 *Jane's*.

SIKORSKY S-61R

US military designations: CH-3 and HH-3 Jolly Green Giant

Although based on the SH-3A, this amphibious transport helicopter introduced many important design changes. They include provision of a hydraulically-operated rear ramp for straight-in loading of wheeled vehicles, a 907 kg (2,000 lb) capacity winch for internal cargo handling, retractable tricycle-type landing gear, pressurised rotor blades for quick and easy inspection, gas-turbine auxiliary power supply for independent field operations, self-lubricating main and tail rotors, and built-in equipment for the removal and replacement of all major components in remote areas.

The first S-61R flew on 17 June 1963, followed by the first CH-3C a few weeks later. FAA Type Approval was received on 30 December 1963, and the first delivery of an operational CH-3C was made on the same day, for drone recovery duties at Tyndall AFB, Florida. Subsequent deliveries made to USAF Aerospace Defense Command, Air Training Command, Tactical Air Command, Strategic Air Command and Aerospace Rescue and Recovery Service.

Production by Sikorsky has ended, but S-61R variants continue to be available from Agusta in Italy (which see).

There were four Sikorsky-built versions, as follows:

CH-3C. Two 969·5 kW (1,300 shp) T58-GE-1 turboshaft engines. After a total of 41 had been built for the US Air Force, production was switched to the CH-3E. All aircraft delivered as CH-3Cs were modified to CH-3E standard.

CH-3E. Designation applicable since February 1966, following introduction of uprated engines (1,118 kW; 1,500 shp T58-GE-5s). A total of 42 were built as new aircraft to this standard.

HH-3E. For US Air Force Aerospace Rescue and Recovery Service. Additional equipment comprises armour, self-sealing fuel tanks, retractable flight refuelling probe, defensive armament and rescue hoist. Two 1,118

kW (1,500 shp) T58-GE-5 turboshafts. A total of 50 HH-3Es were converted from CH-3Es, and are known as **Jolly Green Giants.**

HH-3F. Similar to HH-3E, for US Coast Guard, which gave them the name **Pelican.** Advanced electronic equipment for search and rescue duties. No armour plate, armament or self-sealing tanks. First order announced in August 1965. Deliveries began in 1968 and 40 were built.

The following details apply to the CH-3E:

TYPE: Twin-engined amphibious transport helicopter.

ROTOR SYSTEM: Five-blade fully-articulated main rotor of all-metal construction. Flanged cuffs on blades bolted to matching flanges on rotor head. Control by rotating and stationary swashplates. Blades do not fold. Rotor brake standard. Conventional tail rotor with five aluminium blades.

ROTOR DRIVE: Twin turbines drive through freewheeling units and rotor brake to main gearbox. Steel drive-shafts. Tail rotor shaft-driven through intermediate gearbox and tail gearbox. Main rotor/engine rpm ratio 1 : 93·43. Tail rotor/engine rpm ratio 1 : 16·7.

FUSELAGE: All-metal semi-monocoque structure of pod and boom type. Cabin of basic square section.

TAIL SURFACE: Horizontal stabiliser on starboard side of tail rotor pylon.

LANDING GEAR: Hydraulically-retractable tricycle type, with twin wheels on each unit. Main wheels retract forward into sponsons, each of which provides 2,176 kg (4,797 lb) of buoyancy and, with boat hull, permits amphibious operation. Oleo-pneumatic shock-absorbers. All wheels and tyres tubeless Type III rib, size 22·1 × 6·50-10, manufactured by Goodyear. Tyre pressure 6·55 bars (95 lb/sq in). Goodyear hydraulic disc brakes.

POWER PLANT: Two 1,118 kW (1,500 shp) General Electric T58-GE-5 turboshaft engines, mounted side by side above cabin, immediately forward of main transmission. Fuel in two bladder-type tanks beneath cabin floor; forward tank capacity 1,204 litres (318 US gallons), rear tank capacity 1,226 litres (324 US gallons). Total fuel capacity 2,430 litres (642 US gallons). Refuelling point on port side of fuselage. Total oil capacity 26·5 litres (7 US gallons).

ACCOMMODATION: Crew of two side by side on flight deck, with dual controls. Provision for flight engineer or attendant. Normal accommodation for 25 fully-equipped troops. Alternative arrangements for 30 troops, 15 stretchers or 2,270 kg (5,000 lb) of cargo. Jettisonable sliding door on starboard side at front of cabin. Internal door between cabin and flight deck. Hydraulically-operated rear loading ramp for vehicles, in two hinged sections, giving opening with minimum width of 1·73 m (5 ft 8 in) and headroom of up to 2·21 m (7 ft 3 in).

SYSTEMS: Primary and auxiliary hydraulic systems, pressure 103·5 bars (1,500 lb/sq in), for flying control servos. Utility hydraulic system, pressure 207 bars (3,000 lb/sq in), for landing gear, rear ramp and winches. Pneumatic system, pressure 207 bars (3,000 lb/sq in), for emergency blow-down landing gear extension. Electrical system includes 24V 22Ah battery, two 20kVA 115V AC generators and one 300A DC generator. APU standard.

DIMENSIONS, EXTERNAL:

Diameter of main rotor	18·90 m (62 ft 0 in)
Main rotor blade chord	0·46 m (1 ft 6¼ in)
Diameter of tail rotor	3·15 m (10 ft 4 in)
Distance between rotor centres	11·22 m (36 ft 10 in)

Length overall	22·25 m (73 ft 0 in)
Length of fuselage	17·45 m (57 ft 3 in)
Width over landing gear	4·82 m (15 ft 10 in)
Height to top of rotor hub	4·90 m (16 ft 1 in)
Height overall	5·51 m (18 ft 1 in)
Wheel track	4·06 m (13 ft 4 in)
Wheelbase	5·21 m (17 ft 1 in)
Cabin door (fwd, stbd): Height	1·65 m (5 ft 4¾ in)
Width	1·22 m (4 ft 0 in)
Height to sill	1·27 m (4 ft 2 in)
Rear ramp: Length	4·29 m (14 ft 1 in)
Width	1·85 m (6 ft 1 in)

DIMENSIONS, INTERNAL:

Cabin (excl flight deck):	
Length	7·89 m (25 ft 10½ in)
Max width	1·98 m (6 ft 6 in)
Max height	1·91 m (6 ft 3 in)
Floor area	approx 15·61 m² (168 sq ft)
Volume	approx 29·73 m³ (1,050 cu ft)

AREAS:

Main rotor blades (each)	3·71 m² (39·9 sq ft)
Tail rotor blades (each)	0·22 m² (2·35 sq ft)
Main rotor disc	280·5 m² (3,019 sq ft)
Tail rotor disc	7·80 m² (83·9 sq ft)
Stabiliser	2·51 m² (27·0 sq ft)

WEIGHTS:

Weight empty	6,010 kg (13,255 lb)
Normal T-O weight	9,635 kg (21,247 lb)
Max T-O weight	10,000 kg (22,050 lb)

PERFORMANCE (at normal T-O weight):

Max level speed at S/L	
	141 knots (261 km/h; 162 mph)
Cruising speed for max range	
	125 knots (232 km/h; 144 mph)
Max rate of climb at S/L	400 m (1,310 ft)/min
Service ceiling	3,385 m (11,100 ft)
Hovering ceiling IGE	1,250 m (4,100 ft)
Min ground turning radius	11·29 m (37 ft 0½ in)
Runway LCN at max T-O weight	approx 4·75
Range with max fuel, 10% reserves	
	404 nm (748 km; 465 miles)

SIKORSKY S-65A

US Navy designation: CH-53A Sea Stallion
US Air Force designations: HH-53B/C/H
US Marine Corps designations: CH-53A/D

Although no longer in production, this large twin-turboshaft helicopter continues in first-line service in the several versions described in the 1978-79 *Jane's*.

Eight HH-53Cs are being modified to HH-53H standard for night and adverse weather search and rescue operations under the US Air Force's Pave Low 3 programme, following evaluation of a prototype conversion which flew for the first time in June 1975. The work is being done at the US Naval Air Rework Facility (NARF), Naval Air Station, Pensacola, Florida, on behalf of Military Airlift Command's Aerospace Rescue and Recovery Service.

The **Pave Low 3 HH-53H** has a stabilised Texas Instruments FLIR (forward-looking infra-red) installation mounted below the refuelling boom; a Litton inertial navigation system; a Canadian Marconi Doppler navigation system; an IBM computer; Systems Research symbol generator; and Texas Instruments terrain following/avoidance radar in an offset (to port) 'thimble' fairing on the nose.

The US Air Force accepted the first production Pave Low 3 HH-53H at Pensacola on 13 March 1979. All eight

Sikorsky HH-53H modified under the USAF's Pave Low 3 programme

Sikorsky CH-53E heavy-lift helicopter (three General Electric T64-GE-415 turboshaft engines)

conversions were scheduled for completion by Spring 1980.

SIKORSKY CH-53E
US Navy designation: CH-53E Super Stallion

The Sikorsky S-65 was chosen in 1973 for development with three engines to provide the US Navy and Marine Corps with a heavy-duty multi-purpose helicopter. Other changes to increase performance included installation of a new seven-blade main rotor of increased diameter, with blades of titanium/glassfibre construction, and an uprated transmission of 9,798 kW (13,140 shp) capacity to cater for future development.

Development was initiated by the award of a $1·7 million US Navy cost-plus-fixed-fee contract; in May 1973 Sikorsky announced that construction of two prototypes, designated YCH-53E, was to begin, with the first flight scheduled for April 1974. Bettering this by a month, the first YCH-53E made a successful half-hour flight on 1 March 1974. It was lost subsequently in an accident on the ground, but the programme was resumed on 24 January 1975 with the second YCH-53E. This aircraft flew subsequently at an AUW of 33,793 kg (74,500 lb), the highest gross weight achieved by any helicopter outside the USSR. It was used for preliminary evaluation and testing under Phase I of the development programme. Phase II covered the construction of a static test vehicle and two pre-production prototypes, the first of which flew on 8 December 1975. In February 1978 Sikorsky was awarded a contract to begin full-scale production, with initial approval for six aircraft. The first two of these were in final assembly in mid-1980. A further 14 were ordered in FY 1979 and 15 in FY 1980, with 14 requested in the FY 1981 budget. The eventual production total may exceed 100.

The US Navy plans to use the CH-53E for vertical onboard delivery operations, to support mobile construction battalions, and for the removal of battle-damaged aircraft from carrier decks. In amphibious operations, it would be able to airlift 93 per cent of a US Marine division's combat items, and would be able to retrieve 98 per cent of the Marine Corps' tactical aircraft without disassembly. Features include extended-range fuel tanks, in-flight refuelling capability, an onboard all-weather navigation system, and an advanced dual digital automatic flight control system. It is anticipated that CH-53Es will begin to join the US fleet during the first half of 1981.

The CH-53E is the largest helicopter capable of full operation from the Navy's existing and planned ships, requiring only 10 per cent more deck space than the twin-turbine H-53. It offers double the lift of the latter aircraft with an increase of only 50 per cent in engine power.

TYPE: Triple-turbine heavy-duty multi-purpose helicopter.

ROTOR SYSTEM AND TRANSMISSION: Seven-blade main rotor with blades of titanium/glassfibre construction. Titanium and steel main rotor head. Main rotor blades fold. Four-blade tail rotor mounted on pylon canted 20° to port. Rotor transmission, manufactured by Indiana Gear Works, is rated at 9,798 kW (13,140 shp) for 10 min, 8,628 kW (11,570 shp) for 30 min. Tail rotor pylon folds on starboard side of fuselage.

FUSELAGE: Conventional semi-monocoque structure of light alloy, steel and titanium.

TAIL SURFACE: Initial fixed tailplane on undersurface of fuselage, superseded successively by single high-mounted stabiliser on starboard side and lightweight gull-wing type.

LANDING GEAR: Retractable tricycle type, with twin wheels on each unit. Main units retract into rear of sponsons on each side of fuselage.

POWER PLANT: Three General Electric T64-GE-415 turboshaft engines, each with a max rating of 3,266 kW (4,380 shp) for 10 min, intermediate rating of 3,091 kW (4,145 shp) for 30 min and max continuous power rating of 2,756 kW (3,696 shp).

ACCOMMODATION: Crew of three. Main cabin will accommodate up to 55 troops in a high-density seating arrangement.

DIMENSIONS, EXTERNAL:
Main rotor diameter	24·08 m (79 ft 0 in)
Tail rotor diameter	6·10 m (20 ft 0 in)
Length overall, rotors turning	30·20 m (99 ft 1 in)
Length, rotor and tail pylon folded	18·44 m (60 ft 6 in)
Length of fuselage	22·35 m (73 ft 4 in)
Width of fuselage	2·69 m (8 ft 10 in)
Width, rotor and tail pylon folded	8·41 m (27 ft 7 in)
Height overall, tail rotor turning	8·66 m (28 ft 5 in)
Height, rotor and tail pylon folded	5·74 m (18 ft 10 in)
Wheel track (c/l of shock-struts)	3·96 m (13 ft 0 in)
Wheelbase	8·31 m (27 ft 3 in)

DIMENSIONS, INTERNAL:
Cabin: Length	9·14 m (30 ft 0 in)
Max width	2·29 m (7 ft 6 in)
Max height	2·01 m (6 ft 6 in)

WEIGHTS:
Weight empty	14,913 kg (32,878 lb)
Internal payload (100 nm; 185 km; 115 miles radius)	13,607 kg (30,000 lb)
External payload (50 nm; 92·5 km; 57·5 miles radius)	14,515 kg (32,000 lb)
Max T-O weight	33,339 kg (73,500 lb)

PERFORMANCE (ISA, at T-O weight of 25,400 kg; 56,000 lb):
Max level speed at S/L	170 knots (315 km/h; 196 mph)
Cruising speed at S/L	150 knots (278 km/h; 173 mph)
Max rate of climb at S/L	838 m (2,750 ft)/min
Service ceiling, at max continuous power	5,640 m (18,500 ft)
Hovering ceiling IGE, at max power	3,520 m (11,550 ft)
Hovering ceiling OGE, at max power	2,895 m (9,500 ft)
Range, at optimum cruise condition for best range	1,120 nm (2,075 km; 1,290 miles)

SIKORSKY S-69
US Army designation: XH-59A

On 7 February 1972 Sikorsky announced that the company was designing and building a research aircraft, designated S-69, to flight test the Advancing Blade Concept (ABC) rotor system, under a US Army contract. Subsequently, the value of the contract was increased to cover detail design changes and the construction of two demonstrator aircraft under the Army designation XH-59A. The first aircraft (21941) made its first flight on 26 July 1973.

The ABC rotor system, consisting of two coaxial counter-rotating rigid rotors, takes advantage of the aerodynamic lift potential of the advancing blades. At high speed, the retreating blades are unloaded, the majority of the load being carried on the advancing sides of both rotors, and the usual penalties of retreating blade stall are eliminated. This removes the need for a wing to supplement the rotor to provide speed and agility, even at high density altitude. Another advantage of the concept is the elimination of a conventional anti-torque tail rotor and its drive system.

Details of the results of early flight trials can be found in the 1979-80 *Jane's*, together with a full description of the S-69. Installation of the J60-P-3A turbojets on the second aircraft was carried out during 1978, and low-speed testing with these auxiliary engines was completed before the end of that year. The high-speed and load factor test programme was completed in May 1980 at United Technologies Division's Development Flight Test Center near West Palm Beach, Florida. On 21 April 1980 the S-69 attained a speed of 238 knots (441 km/h; 274 mph) in level flight. Its maximum design speed is 300 knots (555 km/h; 345 mph) at a 2g load factor. A new US Army/Navy contract, effective from 1 June 1980, called for expansion of the altitude and CG flight envelopes, plus further investigation of general performance. This phase of flight testing began in August 1980 and was scheduled to continue for 11 months.

Under NASA contract, the first S-69 is being rebuilt and modified as a full-scale wind-tunnel vehicle for testing in NASA's 40 × 80 ft tunnel at Moffett Field, California.

TYPE: Two-seat research helicopter.

POWER PLANT: One 1,360 kW (1,825 shp) Pratt & Whitney Aircraft of Canada PT6T-3 Turbo Twin Pac mounted within the fuselage, and two Pratt & Whitney J60-P-3A turbojet engines (each 13·35 kN; 3,000 lb st) in pod on each side of the fuselage.

DIMENSIONS, EXTERNAL:
Diameter of rotors (each)	10·97 m (36 ft 0 in)
Mean rotor blade chord	0·44 m (1 ft 5¼ in)
Length overall, rotors fore and aft	12·62 m (41 ft 5 in)
Length of fuselage	12·42 m (40 ft 9 in)
Fuselage: Max diameter	1·85 m (6 ft 1 in)
Height over fins	3·12 m (10 ft 3 in)
Height overall	3·94 m (12 ft 11 in)
Height over fins	3·94 m (12 ft 11 in)
Tailplane span	4·72 m (15 ft 6 in)
Wheel track	2·44 m (8 ft 0 in)

WEIGHTS AND LOADINGS (A, PT6T-3 only; B, with J60 engines):
Design max T-O weight: A		4,082 kg (9,000 lb)
B		5,035 kg (11,100 lb)
Max disc loading: A		42·9 kg/m² (8·8 lb/sq ft)
B		53·2 kg/m² (10·9 lb/sq ft)

PERFORMANCE:
Max diving speed: A		196 knots (363 km/h; 225 mph)
Max level speed at S/L:		
A		160 knots (296 km/h; 184 mph)
B		280 knots (518 km/h; 322 mph)
Hovering ceiling IGE: A		2,042 m (6,700 ft)
B		183 m (600 ft)
g limits: A		+2·5
B		+2·0

SIKORSKY S-70
US Army designations: UH-60A and EH-60A/B Black Hawk

At the end of August 1972, the US Army selected Sikorsky and Boeing Vertol as competitors to build three

Sikorsky S-69 (XH-59A) prototype for evaluation of the ABC rotor system

prototypes each, plus one ground test vehicle, of their submissions for the Utility Tactical Transport Aircraft System (UTTAS) requirement. Sikorsky's $61 million contract called for flight trials to begin in November 1974, but the first YUH-60A flew on 17 October 1974, six weeks ahead of schedule. The second prototype flew on 21 January 1975, followed by the third on 28 February 1975. Fly-off evaluation against Boeing Vertol's YUH-61A prototypes began in early 1976 and occupied a period of seven months. On 23 December 1976 Sikorsky's design was declared the winner, and it was subsequently named Black Hawk.

Designed to carry 11 fully-equipped troops plus a crew of three, the UH-60A has a large cabin which enables it to be used without modification for medical evacuation, reconnaissance, command and control purposes or troop resupply. For external lift missions its cargo hook has a capacity of up to 3,630 kg (8,000 lb). Design is compact, so that the helicopter itself can be airlifted over long ranges. One can be accommodated in a C-130, two in a C-141 and six in a C-5A.

The UH-60A is intended to serve as the US Army's primary combat assault helicopter, and the Army plans to procure a total of 1,107 by the mid-eighties. The basic production contract awarded to Sikorsky, plus options exercised by mid-1980, covered the construction of 255 aircraft during the first four years of production, which began in the Autumn of 1977. The first flight of a production aircraft was made in October 1978, and Black Hawks were delivered for pilot training to the US Army Aviation Center, Fort Rucker, Alabama, in April 1979. The first delivery of production aircraft to an operational unit was made on 19 June 1979, when four Black Hawks were handed over to the 101st Airborne Division at Fort Campbell, Kentucky. They were used initially by this unit in an extensive Force Development Test and Experimentation (FDTE) programme under field conditions. Later, planned deployment of Black Hawks began to jungle areas of Panama, to desert regions in the southwest USA, and to the Arctic, for testing under a wide variety of temperatures and conditions. A total of 74 Black Hawks had been delivered by 31 August 1980.

In tests carried out during early 1979, the Black Hawk demonstrated its ability to sustain heavy landing impacts without damage. In a series of such tests, the helicopter sustained drop rates of 3·5 m (11·5 ft)/s at a forward speed of 63 knots (117 km/h; 73 mph) and gross weight of 7,632 kg (16,825 lb). Another aircraft, flown under artificial icing conditions, confirmed that safe flight can be made in moderate icing conditions by use of a specially developed de-icing kit.

Two special variants of the Black Hawk have been announced, as follows:

EH-60A. ECM variant, designed to intercept and jam enemy communications. US Army requested $14·5 million in FY 1980 and $2·3 million in FY 1981, to begin the integration of Quick Fix II equipment into the Black Hawk.

EH-60B. Eight prototypes being produced under a $36·6 million US Army contract, announced in September 1979, for SOTAS (Stand-Off Target Acquisition System) missions. Each will be equipped with a rotating underbelly antenna and a data terminal in the main cabin, to detect the movement of enemy forces on the battlefield and relay the information to a ground station. Electronics packages to be supplied by Motorola. First prototype, modified from a production UH-60A, was nearing completion in September 1980. Army plans envisage eventual production of 75-100 SOTAS helicopters.

The following description applies to the UH-60A:

TYPE: Twin-turbine combat assault squad transport.

ROTOR SYSTEM: Four-blade main rotor. Sikorsky SC-1095 blade section, with thickness/chord ratio of 9·5%. Middle section has leading-edge droop and trailing-edge tab to overcome vortex impingement from preceding blade in cruising flight. Blade twist 18°. Blade tip swept back

Production example of the Sikorsky UH-60A Black Hawk combat assault helicopter

Sikorsky UH-60A Black Hawk combat assault helicopter *(Pilot Press)*

20°. Each blade consists of an oval titanium spar, Nomex honeycomb core, graphite trailing-edge and root, covered with glassfibre, and with plastics leading-edge counterweight and titanium leading-edge sheath. Blades are tolerant to small arms damage, and are pressurised and equipped with gauges providing fail-safe confirmation of blade structural integrity. Electrically-heated de-icing mat in leading-edge of each blade. C/R Industries elastomeric rotor hub bearings require no lubrication, reducing hub maintenance by 60%. Bifilar self-tuning vibration absorbers on rotor head. Manual blade folding. Canting of tail rotor (20° to port) increases vertical lift and allows greater CG travel. 'Cross beam' four-blade tail rotor of composite materials, eliminating all rotor head bearings.

ROTOR DRIVE: Conventional transmission system with both turbines driving through freewheeling units to main gearbox. This is of modular construction to simplify maintenance. Transmission can operate for 30 min following total oil loss. Intermediate and tail rotor gearboxes oil lubricated.

FUSELAGE: Conventional semi-monocoque light alloy crashworthy structure.

TAIL UNIT: Pylon structure with port-canted tail rotor mounted on starboard side. Large variable-incidence tailplane has a control system which senses airspeed, collective-lever position, pitch-attitude rate and lateral acceleration. Tailplane is set at about +34° incidence in

the hover, and −6° for autorotation. Tailplane moved by dual electric actuators, with manual backup.

LANDING GEAR: Non-retractable tailwheel type with single wheel on each unit. Energy-absorbing main gear with a tailwheel which gives protection for the tail rotor in taxying over rough terrain or during a high-flare landing. Axle assembly and main gear shock-absorbers by General Mechatronics.

POWER PLANT: Two 1,151 kW (1,560 shp) General Electric T700-GE-700 advanced technology turboshaft engines; combined transmission rating 2,109 kW (2,828 shp). Two crashworthy, bulletproof fuel tanks, with combined capacity of 1,340 litres (354 US gallons), aft of cabin.

ACCOMMODATION: Pilot and co-pilot on armour protected seats. Main cabin area open to cockpit to provide good communication with flight crew and forward view for squad commander. Accommodation for 11 troops and crew of three. Eight troop seats can be removed and replaced by four litters for medevac missions, or to make room for internal cargo. Cabin heated and ventilated. External cargo hook, having a 3,630 kg (8,000 lb) lift capability. Large aft-sliding door on each side of fuselage for rapid entry and exit. Electrical windscreen de-icing.

SYSTEMS: Solar T-62T-40-1 APU; AiResearch engine start system; Bendix 30/40kVA and 20/30kVA electric power generators; 17Ah nickel-cadmium battery. Engine fire extinguishing system.

AVIONICS: Include VHF/AM, VHF/FM and UHF/AM com, Singer Doppler, LF/ADF, AN/APR-39 radar warning receiver, SIF/IFF, and TSEC/KY-28 secure speech.

ARMAMENT AND OPERATIONAL EQUIPMENT: Provision for one or two M-60 side-firing machine-guns in forward area of cabin, infra-red jamming flares and XM-130 chaff dispenser.

DIMENSIONS, EXTERNAL:

Main rotor diameter	16·36 m (53 ft 8 in)
Main rotor blade chord	0·53 m (1 ft 8¾ in)
Tail rotor diameter	3·35 m (11 ft 0 in)
Length overall (rotors turning)	19·76 m (64 ft 10 in)
Length, rotors and tail pylon folded	12·60 m (41 ft 4 in)
Fuselage length	15·26 m (50 ft 0¾ in)
Fuselage width	2·36 m (7 ft 9 in)
Fuselage depth	1·75 m (5 ft 9 in)
Height overall, tail rotor turning	5·13 m (16 ft 10 in)
Height to top of rotor hub	3·76 m (12 ft 4 in)
Height in air-transportable configuration	2·67 m (8 ft 9 in)
Tailplane span	4·38 m (14 ft 4½ in)
Wheel track	2·705 m (8 ft 10½ in)

Artist's impression of the EH-60A communications jamming version of the Black Hawk

Artist's impression of Sikorsky EH-60B SOTAS variant of the Black Hawk

Wheelbase	8·83 m (28 ft 11¾ in)
Cabin doors (each): Height	1·37 m (4 ft 6 in)
Width	1·75 m (5 ft 9 in)

DIMENSION, INTERNAL:

Cabin: Volume	10·90 m³ (385 cu ft)

AREAS:

Main rotor blades (each)	4·34 m² (46·70 sq ft)
Tail rotor blades (each)	0·41 m² (4·45 sq ft)
Main rotor disc	210·05 m² (2,261 sq ft)
Tail rotor disc	8·83 m² (95·0 sq ft)

WEIGHTS:

Weight empty	4,819 kg (10,624 lb)
Mission T-O weight	7,375 kg (16,260 lb)
Max alternative T-O weight	9,185 kg (20,250 lb)

PERFORMANCE (at mission T-O weight, except where indicated):

Never-exceed speed	195 knots (361 km/h; 224 mph)
Max level speed at S/L	160 knots (296 km/h; 184 mph)
Max level speed at max T-O weight	158 knots (293 km/h; 182 mph)
Max cruising speed at 1,220 m (4,000 ft)	145 knots (269 km/h; 167 mph)
Single-engine cruising speed	105 knots (195 km/h; 121 mph)
Vertical rate of climb at S/L	over 137 m (450 ft)/min
Service ceiling	5,790 m (19,000 ft)
Hovering ceiling IGE (35°C)	2,895 m (9,500 ft)
Hovering ceiling OGE: ISA	3,170 m (10,400 ft)
35°C	1,705 m (5,600 ft)
Range at max T-O weight, 30 min reserves	324 nm (600 km; 373 miles)
Endurance	2 h 18 min

SIKORSKY S-70L
US Navy designation: SH-60B Seahawk

The S-70L, since designated SH-60B Seahawk, was Sikorsky's submission for the US Navy's LAMPS (Light Airborne Multi-Purpose System) Mk III competition, and was selected as the winner in September 1977 in preference to Boeing Vertol's Model 237.

Detail design of the Seahawk was initiated by a US Navy award to Sikorsky of a $2·7 million sustaining engineering contract. At the same time, General Electric was given a $547,000 contract for further development of the T700 advanced turboshaft engine to provide increased power and improved corrosion resistance, while a $17·9 million contract went to IBM Federal Systems to continue development of the avionics essential for the SH-60B to fulfil the LAMPS Mk III role. On 28 February 1978, it was announced that the US Department of Defense had authorised full-scale development of the SH-60B, and had awarded Sikorsky a $109·3 million contract for the development, manufacture and flight testing of five prototypes, plus a further airframe for ground testing.

Earlier, Sikorsky had updated the original UH-60A Black Hawk mockup to SH-60B configuration, and this was formally reviewed just prior to announcement of the contract award. In July and August 1978, this mockup was used for shipboard compatibility trials on board the frigate USS *Oliver Hazard Perry* (FFG-7) and the Spruance class destroyer USS *Arthur W. Radford* (DD-968).

In February 1979, the main transmission of the SH-60B completed qualification testing, during which it was run at up to 2,685 kW (3,600 shp). This is 447 kW (600 shp) in excess of the Navy's mission performance specification. On 29 March 1979 it was announced that final assembly of the first Seahawk prototype (US Navy serial number 161169) had begun, and the first flight was made on 12 December 1979. The remaining four prototypes were flown on 11 February, 17 March, 26 April and 14 July 1980.

The US Navy has indicated a requirement for 204 of these helicopters for deployment on board Spruance class ASW destroyers, Aegis-equipped guided missile destroyers, and guided missile frigates in the class of the FFG-7 USS *Oliver Hazard Perry*. In addition to the LAMPS Mk III primary missions of anti-submarine warfare (ASW) and anti-ship surveillance and targeting (ASST), the Seahawk is required also to perform secondary missions which include search and rescue (SAR), medical evacuation (Medevac) and vertical replenishment (Vertrep). It is intended for operational deployment in 1984.

Generally similar to the UH-60A Black Hawk, the Seahawk differs in the modifications necessary for shipboard compatibility and in the provision of avionics and equipment suitable for the naval mission. The former includes a rotor brake, automatic blade folding, folding tailplane and tail rotor pylon, a simplified short-wheelbase landing gear, sliding cabin door, and the introduction of recovery assist, secure and traversing (RAST) equipment for rapid hauldown of the helicopter on to a small deck in rough sea conditions, hovering in-flight refuelling capability, and buoyancy features. Modifications necessary for the mission requirement include the provision of a sensor operator's station, rescue hoist, chin-mounted pods for ESM equipment, pylons for two Mk 46 torpedoes or auxiliary fuel tanks, a pylon on the starboard side to carry MAD equipment, a sonobuoy launcher on the port side, an increased capacity fuel system, and deletion of armour for the pilot's and co-pilot's seats.

TYPE: Twin-turbine ASW/ASST helicopter.

ROTOR SYSTEM: As for UH-60A, except that main rotor blades can be folded by electrical power, and a rotor brake is provided.

ROTOR DRIVE: As for UH-60A.

FUSELAGE: As for UH-60A, except for inclusion of flotation bags and sealing of tailboom to provide buoyancy.

TAIL UNIT: As for UH-60A, except that the pylon structure can be folded to port pneumatically, eliminating the necessity to fold the tail rotor, and the tailplane folds upward.

LANDING GEAR: Non-retractable tailwheel type, with single wheels on main units and twin wheels on tail unit. Wheelbase shortened by 46·6%. Landing gear structure is less complex since the SH-60B's vertical impact requirement is 71·5% below that of the UH-60A. Main-wheel tyres size 26 × 10·0-11; tailwheel tyres size 17·5 × 6·00-6. Multiple disc brakes.

POWER PLANT: Two 1,260 kW (1,690 shp) General Electric T700-GE-401 advanced technology turboshaft engines. Crash-resistant twin-cell fuel system in rear fuselage with total capacity of 2,241 litres (592 US gallons). Lower one-third of fuel cells is self-sealing. Single-point refuelling connection on port side. Hovering in-flight refuelling capability. Two auxiliary fuel tanks can be carried on fuselage pylons.

ACCOMMODATION: Pilot and co-pilot/ATO in cockpit, sensor operator in specially-equipped station. Sliding door with jettisonable window on starboard side. Accommodation is heated, ventilated and air-conditioned.

SYSTEMS: Generally as for UH-60A.

Sikorsky SH-60B Seahawk twin-turbine ASW/ASST helicopter *(Pilot Press)*

First prototype Sikorsky SH-60B Seahawk, developed to meet the US Navy's LAMPS Mk III requirement

Sikorsky S-76 general-purpose commercial helicopter in service with Bristow Helicopters

AVIONICS AND EQUIPMENT: Avionics include Collins AN/ARC-159 UHF and AN/ARC-174 HF com, Hazeltine AN/APX-76A active IFF, IBM AN/UYS-1 acoustic processor, Raytheon AN/ALQ-142 ESM, Teledyne Ryan AN/APN-217 Doppler, Texas Instruments AN/ASQ-81 MAD and AN/APS-124 search radar. Equipment includes a 25 tube pneumatic launcher for sonobuoys, and a rescue hoist for SAR operations.

ARMAMENT: Includes two Mk 46 torpedoes.

DIMENSIONS, EXTERNAL: As UH-60A except:
Length overall (rotors and tail pylon folded)
  12·51 m (41 ft 0½ in)
Width (rotors folded) 4·37 m (14 ft 4 in)
Height to top of rotor hub 3·63 m (11 ft 11 in)
Height overall, tail rotor turning
  5·23 m (17 ft 2 in)
Height overall (pylon folded) 4·01 m (13 ft 2 in)
Tailplane span 4·37 m (14 ft 4 in)
Wheel track 2·79 m (9 ft 2 in)
Wheelbase 4·83 m (15 ft 10 in)

AREAS: As UH-60A

WEIGHTS (estimated. A, ASW mission; B, ASST mission):
Weight empty, equipped: A, B 6,191 kg (13,648 lb)
Desired mission T-O weight: A 8,983 kg (19,804 lb)
B 8,148 kg (17,963 lb)
Max T-O weight: A 9,908 kg (21,844 lb)
B 9,926 kg (21,884 lb)

PERFORMANCE (estimated, at mission T-O weight):
Max cruising speed at 1,525 m (5,000 ft), tropical conditions: A 135 knots (249 km/h; 155 mph)
Vertical rate of climb at S/L:
A 319 m (1,045 ft)/min
Rate of climb at S/L, one engine out:
A, B 198 m (650 ft)/min

SIKORSKY S-72 (RSRA)

Two S-72s were developed and built in 1973-78, for long-term use by NASA and the US Army as multi-configuration rotor systems research aircraft (RSRA). Full details can be found in the 1979-80 *Jane's*.

SIKORSKY S-76

Sikorsky Aircraft announced on 19 January 1975 the company's decision to build a new 12-passenger twin-turbine commercial helicopter, as the first stage of a programme intended to give the company a bigger share of the civil aircraft market. The go-ahead for prototype construction followed a period of market research during which firm contracts were signed with numerous commercial operators, both in the USA and abroad.

Construction of four prototypes began in May 1976, and the first flight was made, by the No. 2 aircraft (N762SA), on 13 March 1977. Second prototype to fly, in late April 1977, was the No. 3 aircraft, and a further prototype was flown about a month later.

Designated Sikorsky S-76, the design conforms with FAR Part 29 Category A IFR. By designing and building to this standard, Sikorsky has produced a rugged and reliable civil helicopter, and one which can be taken 'off the shelf' to satisfy a wide variety of air transport missions.

The S-76 benefits from the design, research and development work carried out on the dynamic system of Sikorsky's UH-60A Black Hawk. The main rotor, for example, is a scaled-down version of that developed for the UH-60A. The power plant consists of two Allison 250-C30 turboshaft engines, a growth version of the current production Model 250-C20 which powers a number of important helicopters.

By 24 September 1980, a total of 418 S-76s had been ordered by 101 operators, half of them for offshore duties. Initial deliveries of fully certificated IFR production aircraft were made to Air Logistics of Lafayette, Louisiana, on 27 February 1979, and a total of 37 entered service during that year. Deliveries totalled 81 by the end of August 1980.

TYPE: Twin-turbine general-purpose all-weather helicopter.

Sikorsky S-76 eight/twelve-passenger commercial transport helicopter *(Pilot Press)*

ROTOR SYSTEM: Four-blade main rotor. Each blade consists of a titanium spar, titanium leading-edge cover, nickel leading-edge abrasion strip, and glassfibre/nylon honeycomb trailing-edge. Blades have swept tips (30° on leading-edges, 10° on trailing-edges). Elastomeric rotor hub bearings which need no lubrication. Bifilar vibration absorbers on rotor head. Cross-beam four-blade tail rotor of composite materials. Rotor brake optional.

ROTOR DRIVE: Conventional transmission system, with both turbines driving through freewheeling units to main gearbox. Intermediate and tail rotor gearboxes are oil lubricated.

FUSELAGE: Composite structure, comprising glassfibre nose, light alloy honeycomb cabin, semi-monocoque light alloy tailcone and Kevlar fairings.

TAIL UNIT: Pylon structure with tail rotor on port side. All-moving tailplane, which serves also to protect passengers or ground crew from contact with tail rotor.

LANDING GEAR: Hydraulically-retractable tricycle type, with single wheel on each unit. Nosewheel retracts aft, main units inward into rear fuselage; all three units are enclosed by wheel doors when retracted. Main-wheel tyres size 14·5 × 5·5-6, nosewheel tyre size 13 × 5·00-4. Hydraulic brakes; hydraulic main-wheel parking brake.

POWER PLANT: Two 485 kW (650 shp) Allison 250-C30 turboshaft engines, mounted above the cabin aft of the main rotor shaft. Standard fuel system has a capacity of 1,060 litres (280 US gallons). Extended range fuel tanks and closed circuit refuelling optional.

ACCOMMODATION: Pilot and co-pilot plus a maximum of 12 passengers. In this configuration passengers are seated on three four-abreast rows of seats, floor-mounted at a pitch of 79 cm (31 in). A number of executive layouts are available, including a four-passenger 'Office-in-the-Sky' configuration. Executive versions will have luxurious interior trim, full carpeting, special soundproofing, radio-telephone, and co-ordinated furniture. Dual controls optional. Two large doors on each side of fuselage, hinged at their forward edges; sliding doors are available optionally. Baggage hold aft of cabin, with external access door on each side of the fuselage. Cabin heated and ventilated. Windscreen demisting and dual windscreen wipers. Windscreen heating optional. Optional external cargo hook with capacity of 1,814 kg (4,000 lb).

SYSTEMS: Hydraulic system at pressure of 207 bars (3,000 lb/sq in) supplied by two pumps driven from main gear-box. Electrical system comprises one Lucas 7·5kVA gearbox-driven generator, two 200A starter/generators, one 115V 600VA 400Hz static inverter and 24V 17Ah nickel-cadmium battery. Engine fire detection and extinguishing system.

AVIONICS AND EQUIPMENT: Standard equipment includes provision for dual controls; cabin fire extinguishers; cockpit, cabin, instrument, navigation and anti-collision lights; landing light; external power socket; first aid kit; and utility soundproofing. VHF com transceiver and intercom system standard. Optional equipment includes air-conditioning, cargo hook, rescue hoist, emergency flotation gear, engine air particle separators, full IFR instrumentation, litter installation and stability augmentation system. Wide range of optional avionics available, according to configuration, including VHF receivers, transponder, compass system, weather radar, flight director system, radar altimeter, ADF, DME, VLF nav system and ELT and sonic transmitters.

DIMENSIONS, EXTERNAL:
Diameter of main rotor 13·41 m (44 ft 0 in)
Main rotor blade chord 0·39 m (1 ft 3½ in)
Diameter of tail rotor 2·44 m (8 ft 0 in)
Tail rotor blade chord 0·16 m (6½ in)
Length overall, rotors turning 16·00 m (52 ft 6 in)
Height overall, tail rotor turning
  4·41 m (14 ft 5¾ in)
Tail rotor ground clearance 1·97 m (6 ft 5¾ in)
Tailplane span 2·95 m (9 ft 8 in)
Length of fuselage 13·22 m (43 ft 4½ in)
Width of fuselage 2·13 m (7 ft 0 in)
Depth of fuselage 1·83 m (6 ft 0 in)
Wheel track 2·44 m (8 ft 0 in)
Wheelbase 5·00 m (16 ft 5 in)

DIMENSIONS, INTERNAL:
Cabin: Length 2·46 m (8 ft 1 in)
  Max width 1·93 m (6 ft 4 in)
  Max height 1·35 m (4 ft 5 in)
  Floor area 4·18 m² (45 sq ft)
  Volume 5·78 m³ (204 cu ft)
Baggage compartment volume 1·08 m³ (38 cu ft)

AREAS:
Main rotor disc 116·77 m² (1,257 sq ft)
Tail rotor disc 4·67 m² (50·27 sq ft)
Tailplane 2·00 m² (21·5 sq ft)

WEIGHTS AND LOADING:
Weight empty, standard equipment
  2,483 kg (5,475 lb)

Max T-O weight	4,536 kg (10,000 lb)		Cruising speed for max range:	

Max T-O weight   4,536 kg (10,000 lb)
Max disc loading   38·9 kg/m² (7·96 lb/sq ft)
PERFORMANCE (A: at gross weight of 4,536 kg; 10,000 lb.
B: at gross weight of 3,810 kg; 8,400 lb):
Max cruising speed:
A   145 knots (269 km/h; 167 mph)
B   155 knots (286 km/h; 178 mph)

Cruising speed for max range:
A   125 knots (232 km/h; 144 mph)
Max rate of climb at S/L   411 m (1,350 ft)/min
Service ceiling: A   4,570 m (15,000 ft)
Service ceiling, one engine out:
A   1,890 m (6,200 ft)
B   3,445 m (11,300 ft)

Hovering ceiling IGE: A   1,890 m (6,200 ft)
B   3,415 m (11,200 ft)
Range with 12 passengers, standard fuel, 30 min
reserves   404 nm (748 km; 465 miles)
Range with 8 passengers, auxiliary fuel and offshore
equipment   600 nm (1,112 km; 691 miles)

SKY SPORTS
SKY SPORTS INTERNATIONAL
PO Box 507, 394 Somers Road (Route 83), Ellington,
Connecticut 06029

Following a flying accident in his ultralight Voyager on
10 October 1979, Mr Klaus Hill (designer of the Hill
Hummer, which see) died from his injuries. Subsequently,
Gemini International Inc of Reno, Nevada, and Sky
Sports Inc, of Ellington, Connecticut, acquired the rights
to continue development and manufacture of a production
version of Klaus Hill's last design, the ultralight powered
Humbug. A new company, Sky Sports International, was
formed by the two companies to develop, manufacture
and market this aircraft in completed and individually
test-flown form.

SKY SPORTS HUMBUG
Although the Sky Sports version of the Humbug is very
similar to Klaus Hill's design, the landing gear has been
improved to make it more suitable for operation from
grass fields, the twin power plant has been changed from
pusher to tractor configuration, and the wing design has
been modified to incorporate a form of aileron. This has
been made possible by introducing a universal joint into
one of the wing battens (ribs) on each side. The 'aileron'
consists of a warping portion of the outboard trailing-edge
of each wing which, linked to an Ercoupe-like two-control
system, allows 'ailerons' and rudders to be operated by a
single control to produce smooth co-ordinated turns. The
Humbug is foot launchable and, under FAA regulations
current in 1980, can be flown without being licensed, and
by an unlicensed pilot.
TYPE: Single-seat ultralight powered aircraft.
WINGS: Wire-braced high-wing monoplane. Wings similar
to those of a flexwing, with a leading-edge tubular spar,
a similar spar at approx 70% chord, and a wire-in-
tension trailing-edge. The tubular spars fit into sockets
of wingtip tubes, and the wing is tensioned by spring
compression tubes between the tubular spars. Light
alloy tubular ribs are contained within pockets sewn into
the wing fabric. Small portion of outboard trailing-edge
of each wing can be warped to act as an aileron. Wings
braced by landing wires running from triangular kingpost above fuselage structure, and by flying wires

attached to fuselage.
FUSELAGE: Rectangular base frame of light alloy tube, to
carry landing gear and support pilot's sling seat. Light
alloy tube pyramid structure above base frame supports
forward end of wing mounting, kingpost and power
plant.
TAIL UNIT: V tail of lightweight tube with fabric covering,
carried on twin light alloy tube tailboom and further
tubes from each wing rear spar. Movable surfaces of V
tail serve as both rudders and elevators.
LANDING GEAR: Fixed tricycle type. Small non-steerable
nosewheel; larger-diameter plastic-spoked minibike
main wheels. Small castoring wheel beneath tail unit.
Float landing gear under test.

POWER PLANT: Two Gemini modified chain-saw two-
stroke engines, mounted one each side of the pilot on
the aft vertical fuselage tubes, and each driving a two-
blade fixed-pitch propeller. Because of their proximity
to the pilot, propeller blade guards are fitted.
ACCOMMODATION: Pilot only, in open adjustable-tension
sling seat.
DIMENSION, EXTERNAL:
Wing span   10·52 m (34 ft 6 in)
WEIGHT:
Weight empty   54 kg (120 lb)
PERFORMANCE:
Cruising speed   approx 26 knots (48 km/h; 30 mph)
Landing speed   approx 22 knots (40 km/h; 25 mph)

Sky Sports Humbug
ultralight aircraft in
floatplane form

SMITH
MIKE SMITH AIRCRAFT INC
PO Box 430, Johnson, Kansas 67855
Telephone: (316) 492 6254

SMITH SUPER INTERCEPTOR
As a first step towards the development of a
turboprop-powered four/six-seat light aircraft, which has
since materialised as the Lightning, Mr Mike Smith
decided in 1978 to design and build a two-seat lightplane
with a turboprop power plant, to evaluate the speed and
economics of an aircraft in this class. Named Super Interceptor, this aircraft was completed and flown but, at an
early stage of flight testing, the failure of a fuel control unit
caused an off-airport forced landing which resulted in
substantial damage. The performance demonstrated by
that time was sufficiently impressive for Mr Smith to proceed with design and construction of the turboprop-
powered Lightning.

All available details of the Super Interceptor follow:
TYPE: Two-seat turboprop-powered lightplane.
WINGS: Cantilever low-wing monoplane, primarily of
conventional light alloy construction. Plain ailerons.
FUSELAGE: Semi-monocoque structure, primarily of light
alloy.
TAIL UNIT: Conventional cantilever structure, primarily of
light alloy.
LANDING GEAR: Retractable tricycle type, with single
wheel on each unit.
POWER PLANT: One 559 kW (750 shp) Pratt & Whitney
Aircraft of Canada PT6A-34 turboprop engine, driving
a four-blade constant-speed propeller with spinner and
Beta control.
ACCOMMODATION: Two seats side by side in enclosed cabin,
with an aft-sliding transparent canopy.
DIMENSIONS, EXTERNAL:
Wing span   7·32 m (24 ft 0 in)
Length overall   7·01 m (23 ft 0 in)
Height overall   2·44 m (8 ft 0 in)
WEIGHTS:
Weight empty   726 kg (1,600 lb)
Max T-O weight   998 kg (2,200 lb)
PERFORMANCE (designed):
Max level speed   382 knots (708 km/h; 440 mph)
Max rate of climb at S/L   2,743 m (9,000 ft)/min

SMITH LIGHTNING MODEL 400
Mike Smith Aircraft has designed and is building the
prototype of an advanced technology aircraft which has
been given the name Lightning Model 400. Design began
in July 1979, and construction of the prototype started in
January 1980. It was planned that the first flight would be
made in December 1980, with certification under FAA Part
23 anticipated by the Spring of 1982. A second prototype
is to be built.
TYPE: Six-seat cabin monoplane.
WINGS: Cantilever mid-wing monoplane. Supercritical
GST wing section of 12% thickness/chord ratio.
Dihedral 1° 48'. Incidence 3° 12'. Sweepback at
quarter-chord 7°. Conventional structure of light alloy.
Plain trailing-edge flaps. Plain ailerons, hinged at lower
surface and designed to droop with flaps. Servo tab on
each aileron. Anti-icing of wing leading-edges by engine
bleed air.
FUSELAGE: Semi-monocoque fail-safe structure of
light alloy. Cabin area and part of baggage compartment pressurised.
TAIL UNIT: Cantilever structure of light alloy, comprising
fixed-incidence tailplane and endplate fins and rudders.

Servo tabs on elevators. Anti-icing of tailplane
leading-edges by engine bleed air.
LANDING GEAR: Hydraulically-retractable tricycle type,
with single wheel on each unit. Nosewheel retracts forward, main units aft. Cleveland brakes and brake cooling system.
POWER PLANT: One 633 kW (850 shp) Pratt & Whitney
Aircraft of Canada PT6A-42 turboprop engine
mounted in the aft fuselage, and driving a Hartzell
three-blade constant-speed metal pusher propeller with
spinner. One 227 litre (60 US gallon) fuel tank in each
wing and one 113·5 litre (30 US gallon) fuselage tank,
providing a total capacity of 567·5 litres (150 US gallons).
ACCOMMODATION: Pilot and five passengers in enclosed
cabin, which is pressurised, heated and air-conditioned.
Door of two-piece clamshell type on port side, forward
of wing, with airstairs built into lower portion. Baggage
compartments at rear of cabin and in nose.
SYSTEMS: Details not finalised. Air-conditioning and pressurisation system, with max differential of 0·59 bars (8·5
lb/sq in). Hydraulic system for landing gear operation.
Electrical, oxygen and anti-icing systems.
EQUIPMENT: Blind-flying instrumentation is standard.

Mike Smith Super Interceptor (Pratt & Whitney Aircraft of Canada PT6A-34 turboprop) *(Howard Levy)*

DIMENSIONS, EXTERNAL:

Wing span	9·04 m (29 ft 8 in)
Wing chord at root	1·42 m (4 ft 8 in)
Wing chord at tip	0·76 m (2 ft 5¾ in)
Wing aspect ratio	8·00
Length overall	9·51 m (31 ft 2½ in)
Height overall	2·98 m (9 ft 9½ in)
Tailplane span	3·48 m (11 ft 5 in)
Wheel track	2·29 m (7 ft 6 in)
Wheelbase	3·57 m (11 ft 8½ in)
Propeller diameter	2·29 m (7 ft 6 in)
Propeller ground clearance	0·68 m (2 ft 3 in)
Passenger door: Height	1·22 m (4 ft 0 in)
Width	0·61 m (2 ft 0 in)
Height to sill	0·92 m (3 ft 0 in)

DIMENSIONS, INTERNAL:

Cabin: Max width	1·33 m (4 ft 4½ in)
Max height	1·26 m (4 ft 1½ in)
Volume	3·96 m³ (140 cu ft)
Baggage compartments: aft	0·41 m³ (14·4 cu ft)
nose	0·42 m³ (14·8 cu ft)

AREAS:

Wings, gross	10·22 m² (110 sq ft)
Vertical tail surfaces (total)	0·94 m² (10·15 sq ft)
Horizontal tail surfaces (total)	2·94 m² (31·7 sq ft)

WEIGHTS AND LOADINGS (estimated):

Weight empty	1,086 kg (2,394 lb)
Max fuel	459 kg (1,011 lb)
Max T-O and landing weight	1,905 kg (4,200 lb)
Max zero-fuel weight	1,446 kg (3,189 lb)
Max wing loading	186·4 kg/m² (38·18 lb/sq ft)
Max power loading	3·01 kg/kW (4·94 lb/shp)

PERFORMANCE (estimated, at max T-O weight):

Max level speed at 7,620 m (25,000 ft)	400 knots (741 km/h; 460 mph)
Max cruising speed at 12,200 m (40,000 ft)	380 knots (703 km/h; 437 mph)

Smith Lightning Model 400 (one P&WC PT6A-42 turboprop engine) *(Michael A. Badrocke)*

Econ cruising speed at 12,200 m (40,000 ft)		Service ceiling	12,200 m (40,000 ft)
	280 knots (518 km/h; 322 mph)	T-O to 15 m (50 ft)	443 m (1,451 ft)
Stalling speed, flaps and gear up		Landing from 15 m (50 ft)	695 m (2,281 ft)
	91·8 knots (170 km/h; 105 mph)	Range with max fuel	2,700 nm (5,000 km; 3,107 miles)
Stalling speed, flaps and gear down		Range with max payload	
	78 knots (145 km/h; 90 mph)		2,100 nm (3,890 km; 2,416 miles)
Max rate of climb at S/L	1,615 m (5,300 ft)/min		

SPITFIRE
SPITFIRE HELICOPTER COMPANY LTD
PO Box 61, Media, Pennsylvania 19063
Telephone: (215) 565 2986
Telex: 831750
PRESIDENT: John J. Fetsko

Spitfire Helicopter Company began in January 1975 the design of a new lightweight helicopter known as the Spitfire Mark I. Evolved from the basic design of the Enstrom F-28A, this has a turbine power plant instead of the Avco Lycoming piston engine of the original aircraft. The drive from the turbine passes via a reduction gear, instead of through multiple V belts, showing a weight saving of 91 kg (200 lb), as well as freeing space which can be utilised for additional cargo or auxiliary fuel. Construction of the prototype began in January 1976, and of pre-production aircraft in February 1977.

The company has designed and built the prototype of an improved four-seat version designated Spitfire Mark II. It has also projected a completely new four-seat helicopter with a 224 kW (300 hp) Avco Lycoming piston engine and stub wings, designated Spitfire Mark III; a Mark IIIA which differs by having a turboshaft engine; and an advanced version of the same design with stub wings of increased span and area, to be powered by twin Allison turboshafts. In this latter version, which has the designation Spitfire Mk IV, reversible ducted fans, mounted at the tip of each stub wing, will replace the tail rotor for torque control.

On 12 August 1978, Spitfire concluded an agreement with the Polish aircraft marketing organisation Pezetel, under which Spitfire received limited rights to distribute the WSK-PZL Swidnik (Mil) Mi-2 twin-turbine helicopter in Western markets. Spitfire's main interest is in the latest version of the Mi-2 with an Allison power plant, which it will market as the Taurus (see Polish section).

SPITFIRE MARK I
TYPE: Three-seat turbine-powered light helicopter.
ROTOR SYSTEM: Fully-articulated metal three-blade main

Spitfire Mark I, a three-seat turbine-powered development of the Enstrom F-28A

rotor. Blades of bonded light alloy construction, each attached to rotor hub by retention pin and drag link. Blade section NACA 00135. Two-blade teetering tail rotor, with blades of bonded light alloy construction. Blades do not fold. Rotor brake optional.
ROTOR DRIVE: Shaft drive to both main and tail rotors through reduction gear. Main rotor/engine rpm ratio 1 : 18·2. Tail rotor/engine rpm ratio 1 : 2·54.
FUSELAGE: Glassfibre and light alloy cab structure, with welded steel tube centre-section. Semi-monocoque light alloy tailcone structure.
LANDING GEAR: Skids, carried on oleo-pneumatic shock-absorbers. Ground handling wheels available.
POWER PLANT: One 313 kW (420 shp) Allison 250-C20B turboshaft engine, derated to 179 kW (240 shp) for

take-off. Total standard fuel capacity 265 litres (70 US gallons).
ACCOMMODATION: Pilot and two passengers, side by side on bench seat. Fully-transparent removable door on each side of cabin. Baggage compartment of 0·57 m³ (20 cu ft) capacity forward of engine compartment, with external access door on each side of fuselage. Helicopter can be operated with these doors removed to permit loading of outsize cargo. Cabin heated and ventilated.
SYSTEM: Electrical system is supplied by a 28V DC engine-driven generator and 24V nickel-cadmium battery.
AVIONICS AND EQUIPMENT: Various nav/com systems available to customer's requirements. IFR provisions. Cargo hook and litters optional. It is intended to make available survey and agricultural equipment.

DIMENSIONS, EXTERNAL:

Diameter of main rotor	9·75 m (32 ft 0 in)
Diameter of tail rotor	1·42 m (4 ft 8 in)
Distance between rotor centres	5·56 m (18 ft 3 in)
Main rotor blade chord	0·241 m (9½ in)
Length of fuselage	8·96 m (29 ft 4¾ in)
Height overall	2·79 m (9 ft 2 in)
Skid track	2·36 m (7 ft 9 in)
Cabin doors (each): Height	1·09 m (3 ft 7 in)
Width	1·02 m (3 ft 4 in)
Height to sill	0·61 m (2 ft 0 in)

AREAS:

Main rotor blades (each)	2·22 m² (23·94 sq ft)
Main rotor disc	74·69 m² (804 sq ft)
Tail rotor disc	1·59 m² (17·1 sq ft)

WEIGHTS AND LOADINGS:

Weight empty	567 kg (1,250 lb)
Max T-O weight	1,066 kg (2,350 lb)
Max disc loading	14·27 kg/m² (2·92 lb/sq ft)
Max power loading	5·95 kg/kW (9·79 lb/shp)

Prototype of the further-developed four-seat Spitfire Mark II

PERFORMANCE (at max T-O weight):
Never-exceed speed   112 knots (208 km/h; 129 mph)
Max level speed   112 knots (208 km/h; 129 mph)
Cruising speed   95·5 knots (177 km/h; 110 mph)
Max rate of climb at S/L   472 m (1,550 ft)/min
Service ceiling   4,570 m (15,000 ft)
Hovering ceiling IGE   4,085 m (13,400 ft)
Hovering ceiling OGE   2,440 m (8,000 ft)
Range with max fuel   267 nm (495 km; 308 miles)
Endurance with max fuel   4 h

SPITFIRE MARK II

Information available indicates that the Mark II version of the Spitfire helicopter is generally similar to the production Mark I, except that more power is available at take-off from the derated Allison turboshaft engine, and that fuselage dimensions have been increased to provide room for an additional seat.

The description of the Spitfire Mark I applies also to the Mark II, except as follows:

TYPE: Four-seat turbine-powered light helicopter.

ACCOMMODATION: Pilot at front and three passengers side by side on rear bench seat. Cabin door on starboard side of fuselage. Baggage space in fuselage, aft of cabin, with external access door on each side; baggage volume 0·57 m³ (20 cu ft). Cabin heated and ventilated.

DIMENSIONS, EXTERNAL: As for Spitfire Mk I, except:
Length of fuselage   9·30 m (30 ft 6 in)
WEIGHTS AND LOADING (estimated):
Weight empty   601 kg (1,325 lb)
Max T-O weight   1,134 kg (2,500 lb)
Max disc loading   13·96 kg/m² (3·11 lb/sq ft)
PERFORMANCE (estimated, at max T-O weight):
Max level speed   117 knots (217 km/h; 135 mph)
Cruising speed   104 knots (193 km/h; 120 mph)
Max rate of climb at S/L   472 m (1,550 ft)/min
Service ceiling   4,570 m (15,000 ft)
Hovering ceiling IGE   4,085 m (13,400 ft)
Hovering ceiling OGE   2,440 m (8,000 ft)
Range with max fuel   267 nm (495 km; 308 miles)
Max endurance   4 h

Artist's impression of the Spitfire Mark IV four/five-seat commercial helicopter

SPITFIRE MARK IV

An accompanying illustration shows the four/five-seat Spitfire Mark IV, of which first details were given by Spitfire Helicopter Company at the Helicopter Association of America's 1979 convention in Las Vegas. The aircraft would be powered by two 313 kW (420 shp) Allison 250-C20B turboshaft engines, driving both the four-blade fully-articulated glassfibre rotor and a pair of reversible ducted fans, mounted at the tips of stub-wings and dispensing with the need for a tail rotor for torque control. Max fuel capacity is 455 litres (120 US gallons).

DIMENSIONS, EXTERNAL:
Diameter of main rotor   10·15 m (33 ft 3½ in)
Length overall   10·91 m (35 ft 9½ in)
Length of fuselage   9·15 m (30 ft 0 in)
Height overall   2·44 m (8 ft 0 in)
WEIGHTS:
Weight empty   1,044 kg (2,300 lb)
Max T-O weight   1,995 kg (4,400 lb)
PERFORMANCE (estimated, at max T-O weight):
Never-exceed speed   187 knots (346 km/h; 215 mph)
Max cruising speed   175 knots (323 km/h; 201 mph)
Max rate of climb at S/L   670 m (2,200 ft)/min
Service ceiling   5,180 m (17,000 ft)
Range with max fuel   418 nm (775 km; 482 miles)
Endurance with max fuel   4 h

SUMMIT
SUMMIT AVIATION INC
Middletown, Delaware 19709

Telephone: (302) 834 5400
Telex: 83-5499

MILITARY DIRECTOR: Patrick J. Foley

SUMMIT SENTRY O2-337

Summit Aviation is producing for sale to military customers a version of the Cessna Model T337 which is suitable for a wide range of missions. These include forward air control, helicopter escort, light air-to-ground attack, convoy protection, maritime patrol, six-seat personnel carrier, light cargo transport, aerial photography, psychological warfare and airborne discharge. Special configurations are available for VIP transport, medevac, and high-altitude missions. In all configurations day or night capability can be provided.

Summit's modifications, to fit this aircraft for the specific role required by the customer, begin with the purchase of a new Model T337, as described under the Cessna entry in this edition. Power plant of this version comprises two 168 kW (225 hp) Continental TSIO-360 turbocharged flat-six engines.

With four standard NATO MALL-4A pylons mounted beneath the wings, each able to carry a max load of 159 kg (350 lb), the Summit Sentry can carry weapons which include SUU-11A/A 7·62 mm gun pods; FFV UNI 12·75 mm gun pods; LAU-32A/A, 32B/A, 59A, 68A and 68B/A rocket launchers; CBU-14, SUU-14/A containers

Summit Sentry O2-337, a multi-role military version of the Cessna Model T337

and bombs, LUU-1B, 5B, and Mod 6 Mk 3 markers; Mk 24 flares; ADSID; and a combined search radar and speaker system.

Summit Aviation has received an order for the supply of six Sentry O2-337s for service with the Royal Thai Navy Air Arm, and delivery of these was in progress in the early Summer of 1980. Other reported operators include the air forces of Haiti, Honduras, Nicaragua and Senegal.

Available specification and performance details are as follows:

WEIGHTS:
Weight empty, approx   1,433 kg (3,160 lb)
Max T-O weight   2,359 kg (5,200 lb)
Max landing weight   2,200 kg (4,850 lb)
PERFORMANCE (at max T-O weight):
Max level speed at S/L 163 knots (302 km/h; 188 mph)

Max level speed at 3,050 m (10,000 ft)
                     179 knots (332 km/h; 206 mph)
Max cruising speed at S/L
                     150 knots (278 km/h; 173 mph)
Max cruising speed at 1,525 m (5,000 ft)
                     155 knots (287 km/h; 178 mph)
Max cruising speed at 3,050 m (10,000 ft)
                     165 knots (306 km/h; 190 mph)
Max rate of climb at S/L   335 m (1,100 ft)/min
Service ceiling   8,690 m (28,500 ft)
T-O run   164 m (538 ft)
Landing run   137 m (449 ft)
Range, at 75% power with 560 litres (148 US gallons)
  usable fuel   955 nm (1,770 km; 1,100 miles)
Max range, long-range cruise power, fuel as above
                     1,175 nm (2,177 km; 1,353 miles)

SWEARINGEN
SWEARINGEN AVIATION CORPORATION
(a subsidiary of Fairchild Industries)
PO Box 32486, San Antonio, Texas 78284
Telephone: (512) 824 9421
Telex: 767-315
CHAIRMAN: E. J. Swearingen
PRESIDENT: W. Daniel Heidt
VICE-PRESIDENTS:
R. D. Busey (Treasurer)
Don Howard (Operations)
R. E. McKelvey (Engineering)
Salvatore J. Mira (Contracts)
Richard N. Robinson (Marketing)

As detailed in earlier editions of *Jane's*, this company has been a wholly-owned subsidiary of Fairchild Industries since 1979.

Swearingen has been engaged in the manufacture of the Merlin series of twin-turboprop pressurised executive transport aircraft and the Metro airliner since 1966. A total of 426 Merlins and Metros of all models had been delivered throughout the world by January 1980. Production was then at a rate of seven aircraft per month. This

rate is to be increased to 12 a month, and the company's manufacturing facilities are being expanded by about 50 per cent to permit this.

SWEARINGEN MODEL SA-226TC METRO II

The Metro II is a 19/20-passenger all-weather pressurised, air-conditioned airliner, certificated under Special Federal Air Regulation 23. The standard aircraft has an easily convertible passenger/cargo interior with special kits available for conversion to an executive interior, air ambulance with up to 10 litters, hospital equipped for on-board emergency operations, and single or dual camera photographic configuration. An all-cargo configuration is available, with 286 kg (630 lb) additional payload and without windows and passenger amenities.

The Metro II differs from the earlier Metro (1974-75 *Jane's*) by the introduction of larger windows and major systems and flight deck improvements.

A total of 128 Metros/Metro IIs had been delivered by 1 January 1980. Total number in service or on order was then more than 180, for 23 airlines in the USA and 13 in Canada, Australia, Europe, the Middle East and South America.

TYPE: Twin-turboprop 19/20-passenger commuter airliner.

WINGS: Cantilever low-wing monoplane. Wing section NACA 65_2A215 at root, NACA 64_4A415 at tip. Dihedral 5°. Incidence 1° at root, −1° at tip. Sweepback at quarter-chord 0·9°. All-metal two-spar semi-monocoque fail-safe structure of aluminium alloy. Hydraulically-operated double-slotted trailing-edge flaps. Manually-controlled trim tab in port aileron. Goodrich pneumatic de-icing boots on wing leading-edges, with automatic bleed air cycling system.

FUSELAGE: All-metal cylindrical semi-monocoque fail-safe structure of aluminium alloy, flush-riveted throughout. Glassfibre honeycomb nose-cap can accommodate a 0·45 m (18 in) weather radar antenna.

TAIL UNIT: Cantilever all-metal structure with sweptback surfaces and dorsal fin. Small ventral fin. Electrically-adjustable variable-incidence tailplane. Manually-controlled rudder trim. Goodrich pneumatic de-icing boots on tailplane leading-edges, with automatic bleed air cycling system.

LANDING GEAR: Retractable tricycle type with twin wheels on each unit. Hydraulic retraction, with dual actuators

Swearingen Metro II 19/20-passenger airliner in service with Austrian Air Service *(Prof Johannes Zopp)*

on each unit. All wheels retract forward, main gear into engine nacelles, nosewheels into fuselage. Ozone Aircraft Systems oleo-pneumatic shock-absorber struts. Nosewheel steerable. Free-fall emergency extension system, with backup of hand-operated hydraulic pump. Goodrich main wheels and tyres, size 18 × 5·50, type VII, pressure 6·90 bars (100 lb/sq in). Jay-Em nosewheels and Goodyear tyres, size 16 × 4·40, type VII, pressure 5·86 bars (85 lb/sq in). Low-pressure tyres optional. Goodrich self-adjusting hydraulically-operated disc brakes. Heavy duty brakes and anti-skid system optional.

POWER PLANT: Two 626 kW (840 shp) dry/701 kW (940 shp) wet Garrett-AiResearch TPE331-3UW-304G turboprop engines with automatic emergency water-methanol system, each driving a Hartzell three-blade fully-feathering and reversible propeller with automatic synchronisation. Integral fuel tank in each wing, each with a usable capacity of 1,226 litres (324 US gallons). Total usable fuel capacity 2,452 litres (648 US gallons). Refuelling point on each outer wing panel. Oil capacity 15·1 litres (4 US gallons). Engine inlet de-icing by bleed air. Oil cooler inlet anti-icing by hot oil. Electrical propeller de-icing. Automatic fuel heating system to prevent filter icing. Flush-mounted fuel vents. Single-point rapid drain provisions. Optional JATO (single 1·56 kN; 350 lb st rocket) and continuous alcohol and water injection for 'hot and high' operations.

ACCOMMODATION: Crew of two on flight deck, separated from passenger/cargo area by arm-level curtain. Dual controls standard. Bulkhead between cabin and flight deck optional. Standard accommodation for 19-20 passengers seated two abreast, on each side of centre aisle. Double pane windows. 'No Smoking' and 'Fasten seat belt' signs. Stowing fold-up seats for rapid conversion to cargo or mixed passenger/cargo configuration. Movable bulkhead between passenger and cargo sections. Snap-in carpeting. Self-stowing aisle filler. Tiedown fittings for cargo at 0·76 m (30 in) spacing. Integral-step passenger door on port side of fuselage, immediately aft of flight deck. Large cargo loading door on port side of fuselage at rear of cabin, hinged at top. Three window emergency exits, one on the port, two on the starboard side. Forward baggage compartment in nose, capacity 1·27 m³ (45 cu ft). Pressurised rear cargo compartment in passenger version, capacity 3·85 m³ (136 cu ft). Cabin air-conditioned and pressurised. Electrical windscreen de-icing. Windscreen wipers.

SYSTEMS: Garrett-AiResearch automatic cabin pressure control system maintains a differential of 0·48 bars (7·0 lb/sq in). Engine bleed air heating, dual air-cycle cooling system, with automatic temperature control. Air blower system for on-ground ventilation. Independent hydraulic system for brakes. Dual engine-driven hydraulic pumps, using fire-resistant MIL-H-83282 hydraulic fluid, provide 138 bars (2,000 lb/sq in) to operate flaps and landing gear. Electrical system supplied by two 300A 28V DC starter/generators. Fail-safe system with overload and over-voltage protection. Redundant circuits for essential systems. Two 250VA solid-state inverters supply 115V and 26V AC. Two 25Ah nickel-cadmium batteries for main services. One small nickel-cadmium battery for utility lights only. Engine fire detection system standard. Engine fire extinguisher systems optional. Oxygen system of 1·39 m³ (49 cu ft) capacity with flush outlets at each seat; system with capacity of 3·26 m³ (115 cu ft) optional. Stall avoidance system comprising angle indicator, visual and aural warning and stick pusher.

AVIONICS AND EQUIPMENT: Two flight deck and four cabin speakers standard; provisions for installation of

remotely-mounted or panel-mounted avionics, customer-furnished antennae, weather radar and autopilot. Standard equipment includes pilot and co-pilot foot warmers; internally-operated control locks, individual reading lights and air vents for each passenger; heated pitot; heated static sources; baggage compartment, cargo compartment, entrance, map and instrument panel, ice inspection, retractable landing, navigation, rotating beacon and taxi lights; automatic engine-start cycle; external power socket; and static wicks.

DIMENSIONS, EXTERNAL:

Wing span	14·10 m (46 ft 3 in)
Wing chord at root	2·62 m (8 ft 7 in)
Wing chord at tip	1·04 m (3 ft 5 in)
Wing aspect ratio	7·71
Length overall	18·10 m (59 ft 4¾ in)
Height overall	5·12 m (16 ft 9¾ in)
Tailplane span	4·61 m (15 ft 1½ in)
Wheel track	4·57 m (15 ft 0 in)
Wheelbase	5·83 m (19 ft 1½ in)
Propeller diameter	2·59 m (8 ft 6 in)
Propeller ground clearance	0·254 m (10 in)
Passenger door (fwd): Height	1·35 m (4 ft 5 in)
Width	0·64 m (2 ft 1 in)
Cargo door (aft): Height	1·30 m (4 ft 3¼ in)
Width	1·35 m (4 ft 5 in)
Height to sill	1·30 m (4 ft 3¼ in)

DIMENSIONS, INTERNAL:

Cabin, excl flight deck and aft cargo compartment:

Length	7·75 m (25 ft 5 in)
Max width	1·57 m (5 ft 2 in)
Max height (aisle)	1·45 m (4 ft 9 in)
Floor area	13·01 m² (140 sq ft)
Volume	13·88 m³ (490 cu ft)

Aft cargo compartment (pressurised):

Length	2·34 m (7 ft 8 in)
Max width	1·57 m (5 ft 2 in)
Max height	1·32 m (4 ft 4 in)
Volume	3·85 m³ (136 cu ft)

Nose cargo compartment (unpressurised):

Length	1·75 m (5 ft 9 in)
Volume	1·27 m³ (45 cu ft)

AREAS:

Wings, gross	25·78 m² (277·50 sq ft)

Swearingen Metro II nineteen/twenty-passenger commuter airliner *(Pilot Press)*

Ailerons (total)	1·31 m² (14·12 sq ft)
Trailing-edge flaps (total)	3·78 m² (40·66 sq ft)
Fin	5·20 m² (56·00 sq ft)
Rudder, incl tab	1·80 m² (19·38 sq ft)
Tailplane	7·06 m² (75·97 sq ft)
Elevators	1·98 m² (21·27 sq ft)

WEIGHTS AND LOADINGS:

Weight empty	3,379 kg (7,450 lb)
Max T-O and landing weight	5,670 kg (12,500 lb)
Max ramp weight	5,715 kg (12,600 lb)
Max wing loading	219·7 kg/m² (45·0 lb/sq ft)
Max power loading	4·04 kg/kW (6·65 lb/shp)

PERFORMANCE (at max T-O weight except where indicated):

Max cruising speed at 3,050 m (10,000 ft), at 5,445 kg (12,000 lb) AUW 255 knots (473 km/h; 294 mph)

Long range cruising speed at 6,100 m (20,000 ft), at 5,445 kg (12,000 lb) AUW
242 knots (449 km/h; 279 mph)

Max speed, flaps and wheels down
153 knots (283 km/h; 176 mph)

Stalling speed, flaps and wheels up
97 knots (180 km/h; 112 mph)

Stalling speed, flaps and wheels down
86 knots (160 km/h; 99 mph)

Max rate of climb at S/L 732 m (2,400 ft)/min

Rate of climb at S/L, one engine out
198 m (650 ft)/min

Service ceiling at 5,445 kg (12,000 lb)
8,230 m (27,000 ft)

Service ceiling at 5,445 kg (12,000 lb), one engine out
4,480 m (14,700 ft)

T-O to 15 m (50 ft) 799 m (2,620 ft)

Landing from 15 m (50 ft) 1,082 m (3,550 ft)

Range at max cruising speed, with 19 passengers and 45 min reserves 187 nm (346 km; 215 miles)

Range at max cruising speed, with 15 passengers and 45 min reserves 595 nm (1,102 km; 685 miles)

Max ferry range (allowance for taxi, T-O, climb, cruise, descent and 45 min reserves)
2,132 nm (3,952 km; 2,456 miles)

SWEARINGEN METRO IIA

On 23 June 1980, it was announced that this version of the Metro had become the first aircraft to be certificated by the FAA under the provisions of new Special Federal Aviation Regulation (SFAR) 41, for operation at gross weights in excess of 5,670 kg (12,500 lb).

Following the incorporation of numerous additional safety provisions, which met or exceed SFAR 41 requirements, the Metro IIA was approved initially for operation at a max T-O weight of 5,942 kg (13,100 lb). Increase to 6,000 kg (13,230 lb) was anticipated before the end of 1980, and deliveries of the Metro IIA will begin in early 1981.

SWEARINGEN MERLIN IIIB

The original Merlin III received FAA certification on 27 July 1970, and was described in the 1974-75 *Jane's*. The later Merlin IIIA was described in the 1977-78 edition. A total of 92 of these models was delivered.

The Merlin IIIB, which received FAA Type Approval on 3 November 1978, has interior and exterior refinements and uprated engines. Exterior improvements include reshaped wing root/fuselage fairings, new tailplane leading-edge contours, new rudder bias system, and large-diameter four-blade propellers fitted with a noise-reducing synchrophaser system. Internally, cabin comfort is improved by movable seating and a new environmental control system. Significant performance improvements were announced in September 1979, as a result of further test flying, together with an increase in max landing weight.

Delivery of the first Merlin IIIB was made on 1 December 1978. The first example exported to Europe (D-IBBB) set a class C1e distance record of 3,277·63 km (6,070·18 km; 3,771·83 miles), during delivery, from Teterboro, New Jersey, to Cologne-Bonn Airport, West Germany, on 5-6 January 1979.

TYPE: Eight/eleven-seat twin-turboprop executive transport.

WINGS: As for Metro II, but with improved wing root/fuselage fairings.

FUSELAGE: As Metro II, except that nose-cap will accommodate a 0·38 m (15 in) weather radar antenna.

TAIL UNIT: As for Metro II.

LANDING GEAR: As for Metro II.

POWER PLANT: Two 671 kW (900 shp) Garrett-AiResearch TPE331-10U-501G turboprop engines, each driving a Hartzell four-blade fully-feathering and reversible-pitch metal propeller fitted with synchrophaser. Continuous alcohol/water injection system optional. Fuel system and engine inlet de-icing as for Metro II.

ACCOMMODATION: Crew of two on flight deck, with dual controls. Bulkhead with sliding door divides flight deck from cabin. Standard accommodation for six to nine passengers with seats disposed on each side of a central aisle. Rapid relocation of seats and couches is made possible by continuous tracks recessed into floor, permitting layout to be varied according to mission. Large 360° rotating chairs, with retracting arms and reclining backs, are optional; these chairs track laterally and fore and aft. Passenger door at rear of cabin on port side, with integral airstair. Emergency exit on starboard side of cabin.

SYSTEMS: Electronic temperature control system. Dual, totally redundant cooling/heating systems. Cabin pressure differential 0·48 bars (7·0 lb/sq in). Conrac stall avoidance system, with nose-mounted stall vane. Otherwise generally similar to Metro II except that automatic water-methanol system is not standard.

DIMENSIONS, EXTERNAL AND AREAS As Metro II except:
Length overall	12·85 m (42 ft 1·9 in)
Wheelbase	3·23 m (10 ft 7 in)
Propeller diameter	2·69 m (8 ft 10 in)
Propeller ground clearance	0·305 m (1 ft 0 in)

DIMENSIONS, INTERNAL:
Length, incl flight deck and rear utility section	6·93 m (22 ft 9 in)
Passenger cabin: Length, incl rear utility section	5·31 m (17 ft 5 in)
Width	1·57 m (5 ft 2 in)
Height	1·45 m (4 ft 9 in)
Volume, incl rear utility section	9·09 m³ (321 cu ft)
Baggage volume (total)	2·97 m³ (105 cu ft)

WEIGHTS AND LOADINGS:
Weight empty, equipped	3,538 kg (7,800 lb)
Fuel load	1,969 kg (4,342 lb)

Swearingen Merlin IIIB eight/eleven-seat twin-turboprop executive transport

Max T-O weight	5,670 kg (12,500 lb)
Max ramp weight	5,715 kg (12,600 lb)
Max zero-fuel weight	4,535 kg (10,000 lb)
Max landing weight	5,670 kg (12,500 lb)
Max wing loading	219·7 kg/m² (45·0 lb/sq ft)
Max power loading	4·22 kg/kW (6·94 lb/shp)

PERFORMANCE (at max T-O weight except where indicated):
Max cruising speed at 3,660 m (12,000 ft), and at AUW of 4,535 kg (10,000 lb)
309 knots (571 km/h; 355 mph)
Stalling speed, flaps and wheels up
103 knots (191 km/h; 119 mph) IAS
Stalling speed, flaps and wheels down
89 knots (164 km/h; 102 mph) IAS
Max rate of climb at S/L	847 m (2,780 ft)/min
Service ceiling	9,570 m (31,400 ft)
Max operating altitude	9,450 m (31,000 ft)
T-O to 15 m (50 ft) at S/L, ISA	905 m (2,970 ft)
Landing from 15 m (50 ft) at S/L, ISA 987 m (3,240 ft)
Range with max fuel at econ cruising speed, IFR reserves 2,468 nm (4,574 km; 2,842 miles)

SWEARINGEN MERLIN IVA

The Merlin IVA is a corporate version of the Metro II commuter airliner, to which it is generally similar. It differs principally in its internal configuration, which provides accommodation for 12 to 15 passengers, with a private toilet and a baggage volume of 4·05 m³ (143 cu ft). Initial deliveries of the earlier Merlin IV (1974-75 *Jane's*) were made in 1970, following FAA certification on 23 September that year. A total of 57 Merlin IV/IVAs had been delivered by 1 January 1980.

The description of the Metro applies also to the Merlin IVA, except for some variation in the systems. In particular, usable fuel capacity is 2,096 litres (554 US gallons).

A **Merlin SM** maritime surveillance version is also available.

DIMENSIONS, EXTERNAL: As for Metro II
DIMENSIONS, INTERNAL:
Cabin, excl flight deck and aft baggage compartment: Length	7·75 m (25 ft 5 in)
Baggage compartment: Length	2·34 m (7 ft 8 in)
Volume	4·05 m³ (143 cu ft)

AREAS: As for Metro II
WEIGHTS AND LOADINGS:
Weight empty, equipped	3,719 kg (8,200 lb)
Max T-O, landing and zero-fuel weight	5,670 kg (12,500 lb)
Max ramp weight	5,715 kg (12,600 lb)
Max wing loading	219·7 kg/m² (45·0 lb/sq ft)
Max power loading	4·53 kg/kW (7·44 lb/shp)

PERFORMANCE (at max T-O weight): As for Metro II except:
Max cruising speed at 4,875 m (16,000 ft)
269 knots (499 km/h; 310 mph)
Econ cruising speed at 8,535 m (28,000 ft)
240 knots (444 km/h; 276 mph)
Range with max fuel at max cruising speed, 45 min reserves 1,367 nm (2,534 km; 1,575 miles)
Ferry range with max fuel at econ cruising speed, 45 min reserves 1,819 nm (3,371 km; 2,095 miles)

SWEARINGEN MERLIN SM MARITIME SURVEILLANCE AIRCRAFT

Swearingen announced on 6 August 1979 the availability of a new multi-mission aircraft, configured specifically for maritime surveillance, which has been developed from the Metro II commuter airliner. FAA certification in the Restricted category for operation of the Metro II or Merlin IVA as special mission aircraft, at a max T-O weight of 6,350 kg (14,000 lb), was announced as long ago as 9 March 1978, and since that time the company has been developing this maritime surveillance version. Its basic structure is generally similar to that of the Metro II, but is readily identifiable externally by the addition of a rotatable searchlight in the fuselage nose, a blister radome housing the search radar antenna beneath the centre fuselage, and a large bubble window for an observer mounted on the starboard side of the rear fuselage.

The pressurised cabin of this aircraft provides ample accommodation for a crew of seven and all avionics/surveillance equipment essential for the maritime mission, but is designed also for quick conversion to passenger, cargo or other roles. All special mission equipment can be removed or exchanged when the aircraft is used for other applications.

The basic description of the Metro II applies also to this aircraft, except as follows:

TYPE: Twin-turboprop multi-mission aircraft.

WINGS: As for Metro II.

FUSELAGE: As for Metro II, except rotatable searchlight mounted in nose.

TAIL UNIT, LANDING GEAR, POWER PLANT: As for Metro II.

ACCOMMODATION: Crew of seven, comprising pilot and co-pilot; navigator/flight co-ordinator, seated on starboard side of cabin, just forward of the wing; two observers, one on starboard side adjacent to bubble window, one at camera position on fuselage centreline, slightly forward of first observer; and two relief crew on port side, one seated overwing and one just aft of the wing. Dual controls standard. Navigator's console on port side, forward of wing. Scanner console and other avionics equipment on starboard side, aft of wing. Camera installation on fuselage centreline. Toilet compartment at rear of cabin on starboard side. Integral-step passenger door on port side of fuselage, immediately aft of pilot's position. Large outward-opening cargo door on port side of fuselage at rear of cabin, hinged at top, and with inward opening drop door forming the centre of cargo door. Two emergency exits overwing, one on each side. Cabin air-conditioned and pressurised. Electrical windscreen de-icing. Windscreen wipers.

SYSTEMS: Generally as for Metro II.

AVIONICS: Includes Litton AN/APS-504 (V) search radar, with 1·07 × 0·46 m (3 ft 6 in × 1 ft 6 in) flat-plate antenna; Bendix M²S modular multiband scanner, or Daedalus DS-1220 infra-red scanner; thermal reference unit, signal processing unit, power supply, and stabilising gyro for M²S system, or film recorder, scanner control, tape machine, and power supply for DS-1220 system; Decca ground speed and drift meter; Decca TANS computer display; Decca 72 Doppler; Collins VHF 20-B transceiver; Collins 718U-5 HF transceiver; Collins ARC-159-V-1 UHF transceiver; Global Navigation Inc GNS-500A-VLF/Omega navigation system, or Litton LTN-72 INS; ground stabilisation interface unit; control and display unit for VLF/Omega or INS; azimuth/range indicator; and radar control unit.

EQUIPMENT: Includes Wild NF-2 or Zeiss NT-2 navigation sight; Zeiss RMKA 8·5/23 camera, or Wild RC-10 camera, with 0·61 × 0·61 m (2 ft × 2 ft) optical glass; Agiflite hand-held camera; Locator Model B or Radiation Corporation rotatable searchlight; and 15-man droppable liferaft.

DIMENSIONS, AREAS: As for Metro II.

WEIGHT:
Max T-O weight	6,350 kg (14,000 lb)

Swearingen Merlin IVA, a corporate version of the Metro II commuter airliner

PERFORMANCE (at max T-O weight):
Max cruising speed, at AUW of 5,443 kg (12,000 lb) at 3,050 m (10,000 ft)
248 knots (460 km/h; 286 mph)

Low-altitude loiter speed, AUW of 5,443 kg (12,000 lb) at 610 m (2,000 ft)
139 knots (257 km/h; 160 mph)
Range with max fuel 1,758 nm (3,257 km; 2,024 miles)

TAYLORCRAFT
TAYLORCRAFT AVIATION CORPORATION

14600 Commerce Avenue NE, Alliance, Ohio 44601
Telephone: (216) 823 6675
PRESIDENT: Dorothy A. Feris

Taylorcraft Aviation Corporation, which was re-formed on 1 April 1968 primarily to provide product support, has in production a two-seat trainer/sporting aircraft designated Model F-19 Sportsman 100. Design originated in August 1967, based on the well-known Taylorcraft Model B of second World War origin; construction of pre-production and production aircraft started in 1973.

In early 1980, the Model F-19 (see 1979-80 *Jane's*) had been taken out of production, and the company was involved in the certification of a higher-powered version designated F-21. It was anticipated that certification would be gained by mid-1980.

TAYLORCRAFT MODEL F-21

TYPE: Two-seat trainer/sporting aircraft.
WINGS: Braced high-wing monoplane with Vee bracing struts each side. Wing section NACA 23012. Dihedral 1°. Composite structure with spruce spars, stamped metal ribs and fabric covering. Plain wide-span ailerons of similar construction. No flaps. No trim tabs.
FUSELAGE: Welded structure of 4130 steel tube with fabric covering.
TAIL UNIT: Wire-braced welded steel tube structure with fabric covering. Trim tab in port elevator.
LANDING GEAR: Non-retractable tailwheel type. Two side Vees and half-axles. Main wheels fitted with 6·00-6 4-ply tyres; swivelling tailwheel has pneumatic tyre of 20 cm (8 in) diameter. Cleveland hydraulic brakes. Parking brake. Wheel fairings optional. No approval for floats or skis.
POWER PLANT: One 85·75 kW (115 hp) Avco Lycoming O-235-L2C flat-four engine, driving a Sensenich 72-0-50 two-blade fixed-pitch metal propeller with spinner. One fuel tank in each wing, with combined capacity of 45·4 litres (12 US gallons), and one fuel tank in fuselage, immediately aft of firewall, with capacity of 45·4 litres (12 US gallons). Total fuel capacity 90·8 litres (24 US gallons). Oil capacity 5·7 litres (1·5 US gallons).

Taylorcraft Model F-19 Sportsman 100, now superseded by the higher-powered Model F-21

ACCOMMODATION: Two seats, with shoulder harnesses, side by side in enclosed cabin. Dual controls standard. Carpeted floor. Metal door each side with sliding windows. Baggage compartment aft of seats, capacity 32·7 kg (72 lb). Cargo tiedown straps standard. Accommodation heated and ventilated.
SYSTEM: Electrical system powered by 12V 60A engine-driven alternator, with 12V storage battery. Wiring provisions for landing and anti-collision light. Engine-driven vacuum pump when optional blind-flying instrumentation installed.
AVIONICS AND EQUIPMENT: Optional avionics include Genave Alpha 200B com transceiver, King KX 145 com transceiver, KR 86 ADF and KT 76 transponder, EBC-102A emergency locator transmitter, microphone, headsets, speakers and com antenna. Standard equipment includes recording tachometer, sensitive altimeter, glove compartment, wiring provisions for anti-collision and landing lights, navigation lights, and tiedown rings. Optional equipment includes full blind-flying instrumentation with vacuum systems; rate of climb indicator; electric clock; cockpit, anti-collision, and landing lights; and choice of Grade A or Dacron covering.
DIMENSIONS, EXTERNAL:
Wing span 10·97 m (36 ft 0 in)

Wing chord (constant)	1·60 m (5 ft 3 in)
Length overall	6·74 m (22 ft 1¼ in)
Height overall	1·98 m (6 ft 6 in)
Tailplane span	3·05 m (10 ft 0 in)
Wheel track	1·83 m (6 ft 0 in)

AREAS:

Wings, gross	17·07 m² (183·71 sq ft)
Ailerons (total)	1·86 m² (20·0 sq ft)
Fin	0·34 m² (3·7 sq ft)
Rudder	0·59 m² (6·3 sq ft)
Tailplane	1·21 m² (13·0 sq ft)
Elevators, incl tab	0·99 m² (10·66 sq ft)

WEIGHTS AND LOADINGS:

Weight empty	449 kg (990 lb)
Max T-O weight	680 kg (1,500 lb)
Max wing loading	39·9 kg/m² (8·17 lb/sq ft)
Max power loading	7·93 kg/kW (13·04 lb/hp)

PERFORMANCE (at max T-O weight, provisional):

Cruising speed	108-113 knots (201-209 km/h; 125-130 mph)
Stalling speed	37·5 knots (69·5 km/h; 43 mph)
Max rate of climb at S/L	267 m (875 ft)/min
Service ceiling	5,485 m (18,000 ft)
T-O run	91 m (300 ft)
T-O to, and landing from, 15 m (50 ft)	107 m (350 ft)
Range with max fuel	317 nm (587 km; 365 miles)

TEXAS HELICOPTER
TEXAS HELICOPTER CORPORATION

1336 South Irving Heights Drive, Irving, Texas 75060
Telephone: (214) 445 0926
Telex: 73-2272
PRESIDENT: Gifton McCreary
CHIEF ENGINEER: Wallace Widtman

TEXAS HELICOPTER WASP

Texas Helicopter has developed a high-performance agricultural/utility helicopter which is based on the Bell 47G. Early examples of this aircraft, which has the name Wasp, have a refurbished engine, transmission and tail rotor gearbox. It is planned, however, to use all-new components in the construction of later production aircraft. A lightweight spray system has been developed by the company for the Wasp, which is available in three versions:

Wasp. Two single-seat versions, based on the military OH-13E (company designation **M74**) and OH-13H (**M74A**), which received FAA certification on 3 May 1976 and 31 August 1977 respectively. Many of those which have been converted are employed on agricultural work. Other uses include transport, fish spotting and law enforcement.

Wasp II. Under the company designation **M79S**, Texas Helicopters completed the design of a tandem two-seat conversion of the military TH-13T. Conversion of a prototype began in March 1978, and this flew for the first time on 6 January 1979. Initial delivery of production conversions scheduled for mid-1980.

The description which follows applies to all three versions, as detailed:
TYPE: Lightweight general utility helicopter.
ROTOR SYSTEM: Two-blade semi-rigid main rotor, with interchangeable blades of all-metal construction on Wasp M74A and Wasp II; wooden blades standard for Wasp M74. Blades attached to hub by grips. M74A available without main rotor stabilisation bar, offering weight saving of 11·3 kg (25 lb). Conventional swashplate assembly for cyclic-pitch and collective-pitch control. Blades do not fold. Brake on main rotor optional. Two-blade all-metal tail rotor assembly, with blades of light alloy honeycomb. Tracking tabs on main rotor blades.
ROTOR DRIVE: Through centrifugal clutch and two-stage planetary transmission. Steel shaft drive to tail rotor with 90° gearbox at aft end of tailboom. Main rotor/engine rpm ratio M74: 0·111; M74A/M79S: 0·06.

Texas Helicopter Corporation M74A Wasp single-seat conversion of a Bell OH-13H

FUSELAGE: In three sections: centre, rear fuselage and cabin. Centre section is a welded 4130 steel tube structure to carry the engine and cabin. Rear section is also a steel tube structure of 4130 steel, triangular in cross-section, and serves as a support for the tail rotor drive shaft.
TAIL UNIT: All versions have a small ventral fin constructed of light alloy honeycomb sandwich. Both versions of Wasp have very small fixed horizontal surfaces at forward end of ventral fin. Wasp II has an all-moving tailplane. Trim tab on elevator.
LANDING GEAR: Tubular fixed skid type. Shock-absorption by flexing of cross tubes. Two small ground handling wheels standard. Float kit optional.
POWER PLANT (Wasp M74): One 149 kW (200 hp) Avco Lycoming TVO-435-AIE vertically-mounted flat-six engine. One fuel tank aft of engine with capacity of 110 litres (29 US gallons). Refuelling point at each side of tank. Oil capacity 7·6 litres (2 US gallons).

POWER PLANT (Wasp M74A, Wasp II): One Avco Lycoming TVO-435 vertically-mounted flat-six engine, with max T-O rating of 179 kW (240 hp) for 2 min on Wasp M74A, and of 201 kW (270 hp) for 5 min on Wasp II. Wasp M74A fuel capacity as M74; Wasp II has two stub-wing type fuel tanks above the fuselage at the base of the rotor mast, with a total capacity of 284 litres (75 US gallons). Refuelling point at top of each tank. Oil capacity as for Wasp M74.
ACCOMMODATION: Both versions of Wasp seat a pilot only, with door on each side. Wasp II seats pilot and passenger in tandem, with two doors on starboard side. Dual controls for Wasp II optional. Safety belt and shoulder harness. Tinted Plexiglas bubble and doors, with sliding windows. Cabin of all three versions ventilated; heating optional.
SYSTEMS: Hydraulic system, with manual backup, for operation of flight controls. Electrical system supplied by 28V 50A alternator, with 24V battery. 200A alternator optional for Wasp II.

AVIONICS AND EQUIPMENT: Radio optional on Wasp II only. Blind-flying instrumentation standard only on Wasp II. Special equipment available includes Ag King Model 500B spray system, cargo sling kit, night flying kit, external cargo racks, fire extinguisher, first aid kit, and 8-day clock.

DIMENSIONS, EXTERNAL (A: Wasp M74; B: Wasp M74A; C: Wasp II):

Diameter of main rotor:

A, B	10·70 m (35 ft 1¼ in)
C	11·31 m (37 ft 1¼ in)
Diameter of tail rotor: A, B, C	1·73 m (5 ft 8¼ in)
Main rotor blade chord: A, B, C	0·28 m (11 in)

Length overall, excl main rotor:

A, B	9·59 m (31 ft 5½ in)
C	10·97 m (36 ft 0 in)

Height to top of rotor hub:

A, B, C	2·84 m (9 ft 3¾ in)
Skid track	2·29 m (7 ft 6 in)

DIMENSIONS, INTERNAL:

Cabin: Length: A, B 1·40 m (4 ft 7 in)
          C   2·74 m (9 ft 0 in)

Max width: A, B	0·66 m (2 ft 2 in)
C	0·74 m (2 ft 5 in)
Max height: A, B, C	1·35 m (4 ft 5 in)

AREAS:

Main rotor blades (each): A, B	1·65 m² (17·71 sq ft)
C	1·73 m² (18·63 sq ft)
Tail rotor blades (each): A, B, C	0·11 m² (1·2 sq ft)
Main rotor disc: A, B	90·02 m² (969 sq ft)
C	100·69 m² (1083·87 sq ft)
Tail rotor disc: A, B, C	2·35 m² (25·31 sq ft)
Ventral fin: A, B, C	0·36 m² (3·86 sq ft)

Horizontal tail surfaces (total):

A, B	0·19 m² (2 sq ft)
Tailplane: C	0·42 m² (4·5 sq ft)

WEIGHTS AND LOADINGS:

Weight empty: A, B	649 kg (1,430 lb)
C	780 kg (1,720 lb)
Max T-O weight: A	1,111 kg (2,450 lb)
B	1,247 kg (2,750 lb)
C	1,451 kg (3,200 lb)

Max disc loading: A	12·34 kg/m² (2·53 lb/sq ft)
B	13·85 kg/m² (2·84 lb/sq ft)
C	14·41 kg/m² (2·95 lb/sq ft)
Max power loading: A	7·46 kg/kW (12·25 lb/hp)
B	6·97 kg/kW (11·46 lb/hp)
C	7·22 kg/kW (11·85 lb/hp)

PERFORMANCE (at max T-O weight):

Never-exceed speed:

A, B	87 knots (161 km/h; 100 mph)
C	92 knots (170 km/h; 106 mph)

Max level speed:

A, B	87 knots (161 km/h; 100 mph)
C	92 knots (170 km/h; 106 mph)

Max cruising speed:

A, B	74 knots (137 km/h; 85 mph)
C	85 knots (158 km/h; 98 mph)

Econ cruising speed:

A, B, C	69·5 knots (129 km/h; 80 mph)

Range with max fuel, no reserves:

A, B	130 nm (241 km; 150 miles)
C	260 nm (482 km; 300 miles)

Texas Helicopter Corporation M79S Wasp II with newly-developed stub-wing fuel tanks

Twin Cat agricultural aircraft, a twin-engined conversion of the Grumman/Gulfstream American Ag-Cat *(Howard Levy)*

TRI TURBO
TRI TURBO CORPORATION

PO Box 217, Hangar No. 3, Camarillo Airport, Camarillo, California 93010
Telephone: (805) 484 4394 and 482 5576

This company was responsible for the Tri Turbo-3 conversion of the DC-3, produced originally for Specialized Aircraft Co and described in the 1979-80 *Jane's*.

Some doubt exists concerning the continuation of this programme, following the death of Mr Jack M. Conroy,

Tri Turbo's President, in December 1979, coupled with reports that the FAA considered the Tri-Turbo conversion too big a change to be covered by a Supplemental Type Certificate.

TWIN CAT
TWIN CAT CORPORATION

1225 Wildcat Drive, Daytona Beach, Florida 32014
Telephone: (904) 255 0471
EXECUTIVES: Sam Goldman
G. Thomas Peterson

Twin Cat Corporation was formed in 1979 to market kits for the conversion of the Gulfstream American Ag-Cat to twin-engine configuration. The project was initiated by Mr Sam Goldman, President of Chesapeake Airways, who some years ago originated the Turbo Albatross conversion of the Grumman SA-16 amphibian built by Conroy Corporation. His associate in Twin Cat Corporation is Mr G. Thomas Peterson, owner and operator of the airport at Plains, Georgia, and a former chief test pilot at the General Aviation Division of Rockwell International.

TWIN CAT (GULFSTREAM AMERICAN) TWIN CAT

Re-engining of the Grumman/Gulfstream American G-164A Ag-Cat was initiated originally to overcome the scarcity of Pratt & Whitney R-1340 radial aircooled engines which power the single-engined version. A twin-engined layout was chosen to provide an additional safety factor. At first, it was planned to use a pair of Continental IO-520 or Tiara horizontally-opposed engines, but further study led to selection of the Avco Lycoming TIO-540 turbocharged flat-six as being a more convenient choice. In addition to its ready availability, and a TBO of 2,000 h compared with 1,000 h for the R-1340, the TIO-540-A2, which powers the prototype conversion, delivers its full 231 kW (310 hp) at altitudes of up to 4,570 m (15,000 ft) and in temperatures as high as 38°C (100°F). Its critical altitude is 5,485 m (18,000 ft), compared with only 1,070 m (3,500 ft) for the R-1340. Fuel consumption of the Twin Cat, which in 'production' kit form utilises the TIO-540-J version of this engine, is virtually the same as that of the single-engined version.

Design of the conversion was undertaken by two independent engineering consultants, with assistance from Gulfstream American Corporation. Basically, it consists of removing the single R-1340 engine of the standard Ag-Cat, replacing this with a glassfibre nosecone fairing.

Mounting of the two Lycoming engines is essentially simple, requiring no cutting or welding. They are close-mounted against the sides of the forward fuselage, on a platform which is bolted to the main longerons; this limits the asymmetry when flying with one engine inoperative. Each engine is canted slightly outward and downward, which is claimed to improve the airflow over the wings, thereby improving stall performance by some 10·5 knots (19·5 km/h; 12 mph) compared with the single-engined Ag-Cat. The twin slipstreams also aid the dispersal of chemical. At reduced T-O weight, the Twin Cat can take off on one engine, from a standing start. Using both engines, take-off distances and rates of climb are approximately 20 per cent better than those of the standard Ag-Cat.

Empty weight of the Twin Cat is about the same as that of the Ag-Cat, the extra weight of the twin-engine installation being offset by deleting the 24·5 kg (54 lb) counterweight in the rear fuselage of the single-engined version. On the Twin Cat prototype (N8761H), which flew for the first time in 1979, the nose compartment remained empty, but the conversion kit provides for an 85 US gallon tank to be accommodated in this position, counterbalanced by a 40 US gallon tank in the rear fuselage. These tanks can be used to carry either fuel or agricultural chemicals.

Type approval for the single-engined Ag-Cat has been extended to the Twin Cat by the issue of an FAA Supplemental Type Certificate under CAM Pt 8. Most of the test flying for the STC was done by former Lockheed test pilot Herman ('Fish') Salmon, and the Twin Cat was also evaluated by several experienced agricultural pilots. FAA approval was based on minimum criteria which included the ability to take off, from a 610 m (2,000 ft) runway over a 15 m (50 ft) obstacle, at a speed of 52 knots (97 km/h; 60 mph) and a maximum gross weight of 2,948 kg (6,500 lb); to accelerate to 70 knots (129 km/h; 80 mph) after unstick, throttle-stop the port engine, dump load, wait 3 s before feathering the propeller, clear the obstacle, and land either straight ahead or circle for landing. The STC permits operation of the Twin Cat at normal and maximum take-off weights of 2,041 kg (4,500 lb) and 2,948 kg (6,500 lb) respectively, at the pilot's discretion. A quick-dump facility allows the load to be jettisoned in 1½ s in an emergency, to reduce gross weight from 6,500 lb to 4,500 lb.

Conversion kits became available from Twin Cat Corporation in early 1980.

TYPE: Twin-engined agricultural biplane.
WINGS: As for Ag-Cat.
FUSELAGE: As for Ag-Cat, except for replacement of single nose-mounted engine by a glassfibre nosecone, and mountings for twin-engine power plant.
TAIL UNIT AND LANDING GEAR: As for Ag-Cat.
POWER PLANT: Two 268·5 kW (360 hp) Avco Lycoming TIO-540-J flat-six turbocharged engines, derated to 231 kW (310 hp) and close-mounted on each side of forward fuselage. Each engine drives a Hartzell HC-E3YR-2A/C8468-6R three-blade fully-feathering propeller. Provision for fuel tank of 322 litres (71 Imp gallons; 85 US gallons) capacity in nose compartment, and second tank of 151·5 litres (33 Imp gallons; 40 US gallons) in rear fuselage aft of cockpit.
ACCOMMODATION, SYSTEMS AND EQUIPMENT: As for Ag-Cat, except for effect of twin-engine installation on forward/downward view from cockpit. Additional fuel tanks can be used instead for chemicals.
DIMENSIONS, EXTERNAL: As for Ag-Cat, except for length overall and:

Propeller diameter	2·13 m (7 ft 0 in)
Propeller ground clearance (tail up)	0·46 m (1 ft 6 in)

WEIGHTS:

Weight empty	1,588 kg (3,500 lb)
Normal T-O weight	2,041 kg (4,500 lb)
Max T-O weight	2,948 kg (6,500 lb)

PERFORMANCE (at normal T-O weight):

Max cruising speed at 4,270 m (14,000 ft)
          130 knots (241 km/h; 150 mph)
Operating speed 91 knots (169 km/h; 105 mph)

Stalling speed:

in 30° turn	54 knots (100 km/h; 62 mph)
power off	49 knots (91 km/h; 56 mph)
power on	43 knots (79 km/h; 49 mph)

Climbing speed, one engine out
          65 knots (121 km/h; 75 mph)

Rate of climb:

at S/L, two engines	488 m (1,600 ft)/min
at S/L, one engine out	122 m (400 ft)/min
at 1,525 m (5,000 ft), one engine out	
	46 m (150 ft)/min

UNIVAIR
UNIVAIR AIRCRAFT CORPORATION

HEAD OFFICE AND WORKS: Route 3, PO Box 59, Aurora,
Colorado 80011
Telephone: (303) 364 7661
CHAIRMAN OF THE BOARD: Veda Dyer Williams
PRESIDENT: Stephen E. Dyer
VICE-PRESIDENTS:
F. A. King (Sales)
Robert M. Williams (Production)
SECRETARY: Janice M. Dyer

Univair Aircraft Corporation, founded in 1946, is a
company specialising in the manufacture of propellers and
components for light aircraft. It holds 19 Type Certificates
and 12 Supplemental Type Certificates, drawings, production tooling and rights to manufacture aircraft which
include the Globe and Temco Swift Models GC-1A and
GC-1B; the Ercoupe, Alon, Forney and Mooney M-10
Cadet series; and the Stinson 108. Details of these aircraft
have appeared in earlier editions of *Jane's*, under their
original manufacturers. The company also holds 224 Parts
Manufacture Approvals (PMAs), covering 444 items for
various models of classic or older aircraft. Wing lift struts
for fabric-wing Cessna 120 and 140 aircraft are but a
single example of the parts being manufactured for older
designs by such companies as Aeronca, Cessna, Lus-
combe, Navion, Piper and Taylorcraft.

Propellers produced by Univair under Type Certificate
include Flottorp wooden fixed-pitch, Flottorp variable-
pitch (of Beech-Roby design), Flottorp F1 fixed-pitch and
F12 constant-speed metal, Flottorp F200 and Aeromatic
220 automatic propellers.

Univair rebuilt a Piper J3 Cub and re-engined it with a
Continental O-200. Certification tests were completed in
1977 and the company was awarded a multiple Supplemental Type Certificate by the FAA for O-200 engine
installations in clipped-wing J3 Cubs. Either an Aeromatic
automatically adjustable propeller, or a McCauley fixed-
pitch metal propeller, can be used with this STC.

The company has built to order an updated version of
the Stinson 108, which has the designation Univair Stinson
108-5.

UNIVAIR STINSON 108-5

Design of Univair's version of the Stinson 108 began in
November 1962, and the first flight of the prototype was
made on 21 April 1964; FAA certification was granted
almost three months later, on 14 July. Subject to availability of 134 kW (180 hp) Franklin engines, Univair
markets a kit to convert the earlier Stinson Model 108-3 to
Univair Stinson standard.

TYPE: Four-seat cabin monoplane.
WINGS: Braced high-wing monoplane, with light alloy V
bracing struts each side. Wing section NACA 4412.
Dihedral 2° 30′. Incidence 1° 31′ at root, 0° 7′ at tip. No
sweepback. Constant-chord two-spar structure of light
alloy with fabric covering. Plain ailerons of light alloy
and fabric covering, with a fixed slot forward of each
aileron. Plain trailing-edge flaps of light alloy stressed-
skin construction. Ground-adjustable tab on each
aileron.
FUSELAGE: Welded steel tube structure, with fabric covering.

Univair Stinson 108-5 four-seat cabin monoplane (Franklin 6A-335-B1 engine)

TAIL UNIT: Cantilever all-metal structure of light alloy.
Fixed-incidence tailplane with horn-balanced elevators.
Servo tab in port elevator. Horn-balanced rudder with
servo tab.
LANDING GEAR: Non-retractable tailwheel type. Cantilever main units with spring/hydraulic shock-
absorbers. Cleveland main wheels with tyres size 7·00-
6, pressure 1·38 bars (20 lb/sq in). Maule P8 steerable
tailwheel, with tyre-size 2·80 × 2·50-4, pressure 1·72
bars (25 lb/sq in). Cleveland hydraulic shoe or disc
brakes.
POWER PLANT: One 134 kW (180 hp) Franklin 6A-335-B1
flat-six engine, driving a McCauley two-blade
constant-speed metal propeller type 2A31C21/84S
with spinner. One fuel tank in each wing; total capacity
189·3 litres (50 US gallons). Refuelling point on
inboard upper surface of each wing. Oil capacity 8·5
litres (2·25 US gallons).
ACCOMMODATION: Standard seating for four in two pairs,
with rear seats easily removable to accommodate cargo
or extra baggage. Door, with window, on each side of
cabin. Accommodation heated and ventilated. Space
for 45 kg (100 lb) baggage, with external access door.
SYSTEMS: Electrical system powered by 12V DC engine-
driven generator, with storage battery. Scott Mark II
oxygen system.
AVIONICS AND EQUIPMENT: Narco Mark 12 VHF nav/com
with VOR. Blind-flying instrumentation standard.

DIMENSIONS, EXTERNAL:
Wing span	10·34 m (33 ft 11 in)
Wing chord, constant	1·45 m (4 ft 9 in)
Wing aspect ratio	6·8
Length overall	7·67 m (25 ft 2 in)
Height overall	2·29 m (7 ft 6 in)
Tailplane span	3·40 m (11 ft 2 in)
Wheel track	2·16 m (7 ft 1 in)
Wheelbase	5·66 m (18 ft 7 in)
Propeller diameter	1·93 m (6 ft 4 in)
Propeller ground clearance	0·23 m (9·14 in)

DIMENSIONS, INTERNAL:
Passenger doors (each): Height		1·22 m (4 ft 0 in)
Width		0·76 m (2 ft 6 in)
Height to sill		0·81 m (2 ft 8 in)
Baggage door: Height		0·61 m (2 ft 0 in)
Width		0·56 m (1 ft 10 in)
Height to sill		0·99 m (3 ft 3 in)

DIMENSIONS, INTERNAL:
Cabin: Length	1·75 m (5 ft 9 in)
Max width	0·97 m (3 ft 2 in)
Max height	1·42 m (4 ft 8 in)

AREAS:
Wings, gross	14·4 m² (155 sq ft)
Ailerons (total)	1·675 m² (18·02 sq ft)
Trailing-edge flaps (total)	1·14 m² (12·22 sq ft)
Fin	1·33 m² (14·28 sq ft)
Rudder, incl tab	0·63 m² (6·78 sq ft)
Tailplane	1·36 m² (14·66 sq ft)
Elevators, incl tab	1·60 m² (17·24 sq ft)

WEIGHTS AND LOADINGS:
Weight empty, equipped	590 kg (1,300 lb)
Max T-O and landing weight	1,088 kg (2,400 lb)
Max wing loading	75·7 kg/m² (15·5 lb/sq ft)
Max power loading	8·12 kg/kW (13·3 lb/hp)

PERFORMANCE (at max T-O weight):
Never-exceed speed	147 knots (273 km/h; 170 mph)
Max level speed at S/L	132 knots (245 km/h; 152 mph)
Max cruising speed, 75% power at 1,525 m (5,000 ft)	117 knots (217 km/h; 135 mph)
Econ cruising speed at 2,285 m (7,500 ft)	115 knots (212 km/h; 132 mph)
Stalling speed, flaps up	56·5 knots (105 km/h; 65 mph)
Stalling speed, flaps down	53 knots (98·5 km/h; 61 mph)
Max rate of climb at S/L	305 m (1,000 ft)/min
Service ceiling	5,790 m (19,000 ft)
T-O run	122 m (400 ft)
T-O to 15 m (50 ft)	213 m (700 ft)
Landing from 15 m (50 ft)	198 m (650 ft)
Landing run	91·5 m (300 ft)
Range with max payload, 45 min reserves	412 nm (764 km; 475 miles)

UTC
UNITED TECHNOLOGIES CORPORATION

HEAD OFFICE: United Technologies Building, Hartford,
Connecticut 06101
Telephone: (203) 728 7000
BOARD OF DIRECTORS:
Robert J. Carlson
Hubert Faure
T. Mitchell Ford
Harry J. Gray
Alexander M. Haig Jr
Melvin C. Holm
Paul W. O'Malley
Walter F. Probst
Peter L. Scott
William Simon
Darwin E. Smith
Richard S. Smith
William I. Spencer
Robert L. Sproull
Alfred W. Van Sinderen
Jacqueline Grennan Wexler
CORPORATE OFFICERS:
Harry J. Gray (Chairman, Chief Executive Officer)
Alexander M. Haig Jr (President, Chief Operating
Officer)

Robert J. Carlson (Executive V-P, Power; President,
Pratt & Whitney Aircraft Group)
Peter L. Scott (Executive V-P, Electronics)
Raymond D'Argenio (Senior V-P, Communications)
Stillman B. Brown (Senior V-P, Chief Financial Officer)
Hubert Faure (Chairman, Otis Group)
Richard F. Gamble (Group V-P, Controls Group)
Melvin C. Holm (Chairman, Carrier Group)
Wesley A. Kuhrt (Senior V-P, Technology)
Edward W. Large (Senior V-P, General Counsel)
Clark MacGregor (Senior V-P, External Affairs)
Sidney F. McKenna (Senior V-P, Human Resources
and Organisation)
Paul W. O'Malley (Group V-P)
Edward J. Rapetti (Group V-P, Automotive Group)
Rolf D. Bibow (V-P)
Joseph A. Biernat (V-P, Treasurer)
Robert B. Burgess (President, International Support
Systems)
Robert L. Cole (V-P)
William J. Evans (V-P)
Russell G. Meyerand Jr (V-P, Research and Develop-
ment)
Nathaniel B. Morse (V-P, Industrial Relations)
Francis L. Murphy (V-P, Public Relations and Com-
munications)

Donald Nigro (V-P, Manufacturing)
Charles B. Preston (V-P, Controller)
Dale W. Van Winkle (V-P)
Ralph A. Weller (V-P)
George E. Williams (V-P)
Hugh E. Witt (V-P, Government Liaison)
Martin R. Lewis Jr (Secretary)
DIVISIONS AND SUBSIDIARIES:
Pratt & Whitney Aircraft Group (see Engines section,
Canada and USA):
Commercial Products Division
Government Products Division
Manufacturing Division
Pratt & Whitney Aircraft of Canada Ltd (see Engines
section)
Carrier Group
Otis Group
Essex Group
Sikorsky Aircraft (see this section)
Hamilton Standard
Power Systems
Norden Systems
Chemical Systems (see Engines section)
Mostek Corporation
United Technologies Metal Products Inc
United Technologies Research Center

VARGA
VARGA AIRCRAFT CORPORATION

12250 East Queen Creek Road, Chandler, Arizona 85224
Telephone: (602) 963 4914
PRESIDENT: George Varga Jr
GENERAL MANAGER: George Varga III

Varga Aircraft Corporation purchased from Shinn
Engineering Inc in 1965 the full manufacturing rights,
tooling and spare parts inventory for the Shinn Model
2150A, and put it into production as the Model 2150A
Kachina. The design had originated in the plywood Morrisey Nifty of 1957, built by a former Douglas Aircraft

chief test pilot. Ten examples of an improved all-metal
version, designated Morrisey Model 2150, were produced
by Morrisey Aviation Inc, and this version was described
in the 1959-60 *Jane's*. Production rights were then
acquired by Shinn Engineering Inc, which put into production the further improved Shinn Model 2150A, with

changes to the engine installation, landing gear and interior arrangement. This version was certificated by the FAA on 31 July 1961 and was last described in the 1964-65 *Jane's*. The Varga Kachina is basically the same as the Shinn 2150A.

VARGA MODEL 2150A KACHINA

The current production Kachina is described. In Summer 1980 Varga was engaged in certificating a new version with a 134 kW (180 hp) engine, and a conversion kit for tailwheel-type landing gear.

TYPE: Two-seat lightweight sporting/training aircraft.

WINGS: Cantilever low-wing monoplane. Wing section NACA 43015. Dihedral 7°. Incidence 3°. No sweepback. Conventional two-spar stressed-skin structure of light alloy. Plain ailerons and two-position trailing-edge flaps of light alloy construction. Ground-adjustable trim tab in starboard aileron. Glassfibre wingtips.

FUSELAGE: Forward fuselage of welded 4130 steel tube with light alloy covering. Semi-monocoque light alloy structure aft of cockpit. Nose cowl and tailcone of glassfibre.

TAIL UNIT: Cantilever structure of light alloy. Fixed-incidence tailplane. Fin and tailplane have glassfibre tips. Ground-adjustable trim tab on rudder.

LANDING GEAR: Non-retractable tricycle type. Oleo-pneumatic shock-absorbers on all units. Main units attached directly to rear spar of wing. Steerable nose-wheel. Main wheel tyre pressure 1·66 bars (24 lb/sq in). Nosewheel tyre pressure 1·52 bars (22 lb/sq in). Cleveland hydraulic disc brakes. Parking brake.

POWER PLANT: One 112 kW (150 hp) Avco Lycoming O-320-A2C flat-four engine, driving a Sensenich two-blade fixed-pitch metal propeller type M74DM. Fuel tank in each wing, total capacity 132·5 litres (35 US gallons). Refuelling points in upper surface of wings. Oil capacity 7·5 litres (2 US gallons).

ACCOMMODATION: Two seats in tandem under sideways-opening cockpit canopy, hinged on starboard side. Tinted windscreen and windows. Rear window of canopy completes 360° unrestricted view. Dual controls standard. Baggage space aft of rear seat, capacity 22·7 kg (50 lb). Utility shelf. Accommodation heated and ventilated.

SYSTEMS: Electrical system powered by 60A engine-driven alternator and 12V 25Ah battery. Hydraulic system for brakes only.

Varga Model 2150A Kachina two-seat sporting/training aircraft *(Ian MacFarlane)*

AVIONICS AND EQUIPMENT: Optional avionics equipment by Edo-Aire, King and Narco. Standard equipment includes sensitive altimeter, recording tachometer, stall warning device, carpet, soundproofing, navigation lights, landing light in nose cowl, electric starter, quick gascolator drain, and tiedown rings.

DIMENSIONS, EXTERNAL:

Wing span	9·14 m (30 ft 0 in)
Wing chord at root	1·52 m (5 ft 0 in)
Wing chord at tip	1·14 m (3 ft 9 in)
Length overall	6·45 m (21 ft 2 in)
Height overall	2·13 m (7 ft 0 in)
Tailplane span	2·79 m (9 ft 2 in)
Propeller diameter	1·88 m (6 ft 2 in)

AREAS:

Wings, gross	13·38 m² (144 sq ft)
Ailerons (total, incl tab)	2·60 m² (28 sq ft)
Trailing-edge flaps (total)	2·42 m² (26 sq ft)
Fin	0·33 m² (3·6 sq ft)
Rudder (incl tab)	0·53 m² (5·7 sq ft)
Tailplane	1·34 m² (14·4 sq ft)
Elevators	0·62 m² (6·7 sq ft)

WEIGHTS AND LOADINGS:

Weight empty	510 kg (1,125 lb)
Max T-O weight, Utility category	712 kg (1,570 lb)
Max T-O weight, Normal category	824 kg (1,817 lb)
Max wing loading	61·6 kg/m² (12·6 lb/sq ft)
Max power loading	7·36 kg/kW (12·1 lb/hp)

PERFORMANCE (at max T-O weight):

Never-exceed speed	147·5 knots (273 km/h; 170 mph)
Max level speed at S/L	128 knots (238 km/h; 148 mph)
Cruising speed, 75% power at optimum altitude	117 knots (217 km/h; 135 mph)
Cruising speed, 65% power at optimum altitude	110 knots (204 km/h; 127 mph)
Stalling speed, flaps up	49·5 knots (92 km/h; 57 mph)
Stalling speed, flaps down	45 knots (84 km/h; 52 mph)
Max rate of climb at S/L	442 m (1,450 ft)/min
Service ceiling	6,705 m (22,000 ft)
T-O to 15 m (50 ft)	134 m (440 ft)
Landing from 15 m (50 ft)	137 m (450 ft)
Range with max fuel	455 nm (845 km; 525 miles)

VOLPAR
VOLPAR INC

HEAD OFFICE AND WORKS: 7929 Hayvenhurst Avenue, Van Nuys, California 91406
Telephone: (213) 787 4393 and 873 5599
Telex: 65-1419
PRESIDENT: William E. Lindsey
EXECUTIVE VICE-PRESIDENT: Frank V. Nixon Jr
VICE-PRESIDENTS:
  Albert B. Seed (Operations)
  Kevin Kuniyoshi (Maintenance)
CHIEF ENGINEER: James Roberts

Volpar International Corporation

HEAD OFFICE: 7929 Hayvenhurst Avenue, Van Nuys, California 91406
Telephone: (213) 785 7461
PRESIDENT: Daniel W. Bowles
EXECUTIVE VICE-PRESIDENT: Ernest Taub

Volpar Inc was formed in 1960 by Volitan Aviation Inc, a modification and repair company, and Paragon Tool, Die and Engineering, an established manufacturer of turbine engine components and other precision machined parts. Its original purpose was to design, develop and manufacture tricycle landing gear kits for the Beech Model 18, while Volitan was to install the kits. In 1968, however, Volitan was merged into Volpar, which continued all of the aviation activities. The Volpar landing gear kit was certificated in 1960, becoming original equipment on new Beech aircraft.

As a follow-up to this modification, Volpar produces kits to convert the Model 18 to turboprop power, using Garrett-AiResearch TPE331 engines. The basic converted aircraft is known as the Turbo 18. After wide acceptance of this, Volpar introduced a 'stretched' version known as the Turboliner, and then the Turboliner II which is approved under SFAR 23 for commuter airline operation.

Using the nacelles that were developed for the Turbo 18 and Turboliner, Volpar next produced an engine installation which it markets under the name of Packaged Power. This is available with any of the Garrett-AiResearch TPE331 series of turboprop engines, with either over-engine or under-engine air intake as required by the particular installation. Packaged Power units have been fitted to such aircraft as the Beechcraft Model 18, de Havilland Dove, Grumman Goose and de Havilland Beaver. It is understood that they are being considered for installation in several aircraft currently in the development stage.

In February 1976 Volpar, in conjunction with Century Aircraft Corporation of Amarillo, Texas, became engaged in the installation of Garrett-AiResearch

TPE331-3U-303 turboprop engines in Handley Page H.P.137 Jetstream aircraft. Other programmes have included modification of Cessna Model 402B and 421C aircraft to accept Wild camera systems and navigational sights, under contract to foreign governments.

Volpar International Corporation was formed in 1979 to act as the sales agent for all of Volpar's domestic and international programmes and products.

VOLPAR (BEECHCRAFT) MODEL 18

The basic Volpar modification converts the Beechcraft Model 18 to a tricycle landing gear configuration, offering substantially lower approach speeds, greatly improved braking and easier ground handling. Cruising speed is improved, as all three wheels retract completely in flight. Futhermore, the aircraft can be kept in hangars with a lower roof clearance, since the overall height is reduced to 2·79 m (9 ft 2 in).

The Volpar kit, which passed all FAA static tests for a maximum landing weight of 4,433 kg (9,772 lb), utilises basic components of the existing main landing gear. The new nose gear is connected to the existing retraction system, where the tailwheel connection was removed. The complete modification can be made without removing the wings or stripping any of the wing skin. All cockpit controls and emergency procedures are unchanged, including the instrument panel wheel position indicator. Existing airstair doors can be retained with only minor modification.

Basically, the modification moves the main landing gear 1·22 m (4 ft 0 in) aft of the original position, attaching it to a welded tube truss that increases the torsional strength of the centre wing structure by 60 per cent in landing configuration. The nose assembly is completely new and includes a streamlined nose fairing which adds 0·67 m (2 ft 2½ in) to the fuselage length. Space inside the fairing can be used for additional equipment, including a weather radar dish of up to 0·305 m (12 in) diameter.

All three wheels are of aluminium and can be fitted with either Goodrich or Goodyear tubed or tubeless tyres, size 8·50-10, ten-ply rating. Main-wheel tyre pressure 4·48 bars (65 lb/sq in), nosewheel tyre pressure 3·10 bars (45 lb/sq in). Shock-absorption is provided by hydraulic oleo struts of Volpar manufacture. Goodrich multiple disc brakes. All three wheels retract forward in less than eight seconds. On the ground the cabin floor is only 1·07 m (3 ft 6 in) off the ground at the door. Wheelbase is 2·62 m (8 ft 7 in). The aircraft will turn on a 1·22 m (4 ft) radius for the inside wheel and a centering device is incorporated on the shimmy damper for take-off and landing.

The current Mk IV Volpar conversion incorporates Goodrich nine-piston full-circle brakes with twice the braking energy and three times the service life of the two-piston type fitted formerly. The new brakes fit on the original gear and are obtainable from either Volpar or Goodrich.

More than 400 sets of Volpar tri-gear have been delivered.

Volpar 'Packaged Power' units, embodying Garrett-AiResearch TPE331-2U-203 engines, in a Grumman Goose

Volpar Turbo 18 conversion of the Beechcraft Model 18, operated by the Environmental Protection Agency of the US government

VOLPAR (BEECHCRAFT) TURBO 18

The Volpar Turbo 18 is a Beechcraft Model 18 fitted with the Volpar Mk IV tricycle landing gear and re-engined with two 526 kW (705 ehp) Garrett-AiResearch TPE331-1-101B turboprop engines, flat rated to 451 kW (605 ehp). The wing planform is changed, by extending forward the entire leading-edge inboard of each engine nacelle and carrying the new leading-edge line past the nacelle, so increasing the chord and sweepback to a point outboard of the nacelle. The rectangular wingtip panels of the standard Super 18 are replaced by smaller tips which decrease the wing span and maintain the normal leading-edge sweep to the tip.

Installation of TPE331 engines and Hartzell HC-B3TN-5 three-blade reversible-pitch propellers reduces the empty weight, permitting an increase in fuel or payload. Internal fuel capacity is increased by 379 litres (100 US gallons) by installing new integral tanks in the leading-edge immediately outboard of each engine nacelle. These become the main tanks, each delivering fuel directly to the adjacent engine. They increase the maximum fuel capacity to 2,385 litres (630 US gallons), with a normal capacity of 1,159 litres (306 US gallons).

Air-conditioning and heating installations are available, using engine bleed air. A large cargo door, 1·57 m (5 ft 2 in) wide, with a max height of 1·09 m (3 ft 7 in), can be provided, incorporating the existing airstair door.

The detailed description of the Turboliner (which follows), applies also to the Turbo 18, except that the Turbo 18 does not have the 'stretched' fuselage.

FAA Supplemental Type Approval of the Turbo 18 was received on 17 February 1966. Two aircraft were delivered to the US Environmental Protection Agency in 1966, and production of conversion kits was initiated. Customers include Air Asia of Taiwan, which converted 15 C-45H aircraft for the US government. These aircraft were acquired in 1977 by Ciba Pilatus Aerial Spraying Co Ltd of Switzerland.

In April 1977, Volpar received FAA Supplemental Type Approval to increase the max T-O weight of the Turbo 18 from 4,666 kg (10,286 lb) to 5,216 kg (11,500 lb). The required modification includes strengthening of the centre wing structure and replacement of some landing gear components, involving an increase of only 13·6 kg (30 lb) in the aircraft's structural weight.

DIMENSIONS, EXTERNAL:

Wing span	14·02 m (46 ft 0 in)
Length overall	11·40 m (37 ft 5 in)
Height overall	2·92 m (9 ft 7 in)
Wheelbase	2·62 m (8 ft 7 in)

DIMENSIONS, INTERNAL:
Cabin, excl flight deck:

Length	3·87 m (12 ft 8½ in)
Max width	1·32 m (4 ft 4 in)
Max height	1·68 m (5 ft 6 in)
Volume	7·36 m³ (260 cu ft)

WEIGHTS AND LOADINGS (A: basic Turbo 18; B Turbo 18 with Volpar increased gross weight conversion):

Weight empty, basic: A	2,495 kg (5,500 lb)
B	2,508 kg (5,530 lb)
Max payload: A	2,171 kg (4,786 lb)
B	2,708 kg (5,970 lb)
Max T-O weight: A	4,666 kg (10,286 lb)
B	5,216 kg (11,500 lb)
Max zero-fuel weight: A	4,082 kg (9,000 lb)
Max landing weight: A	4,433 kg (9,772 lb)
Max wing loading: A	134·3 kg/m² (27·51 lb/sq ft)
B	150·2 kg/m² (30·76 lb/sq ft)
Max power loading: A	5·17 kg/kW (8·50 lb/ehp)
B	5·78 kg/kW (9·50 lb/ehp)

PERFORMANCE (A, at max T-O weight):

Max cruising speed at 3,050 m (10,000 ft)
243 knots (451 km/h; 280 mph)
Econ cruising speed at 3,050 m (10,000 ft)
222 knots (412 km/h; 256 mph)
Stalling speed, wheels and flaps up, power off
80 knots (148 km/h; 92 mph)
Stalling speed, wheels and flaps down, power off
77 knots (142 km/h; 88 mph)

Max rate of climb at S/L	521 m (1,710 ft)/min
Service ceiling	7,925 m (26,000 ft)
Service ceiling, one engine out	4,265 m (14,000 ft)
T-O run	507 m (1,665 ft)
T-O to 15 m (50 ft)	725 m (2,380 ft)
Landing from 15 m (50 ft)	642 m (2,107 ft)
Landing run with reverse thrust	265 m (870 ft)

Range with max fuel at 222 knots (412 km/h; 256 mph), 45 min reserves 1,884 nm (3,492 km; 2,170 miles)
Range with max payload, 45 min reserves
400 nm (741 km; 461 miles)

VOLPAR (BEECHCRAFT) TURBOLINER

This is a 15-passenger version of the Volpar (Beechcraft) Turbo 18, with lengthened fuselage, intended for the third-level airline market. Design was started in August 1966 and construction of the prototype began in December 1966. This aircraft flew for the first time on 12 April 1967 and FAA certification was granted on 29 March 1968, the Turboliner being approved for operation at a gross weight of 5,216 kg (11,500 lb).

By the beginning of 1980 about 27 Turboliners had been delivered and were in service with small airlines throughout the world. In March 1970 a Turboliner (N353V), on a delivery flight from Los Angeles to Singapore, set six official international speed records. It carried on board during the flight all necessary spares for one year's normal operation, together with a 1,515 litre (400 US gallon) ferry tank in the fuselage, and was in operation with a commuter airline two days after arrival in Singapore.

TYPE: Twin-turboprop light transport aircraft.

WINGS: Cantilever low-wing monoplane. Wing section NACA 63-015 at station 28·0, NACA 23014 at station 144·5, NACA 23012 at station 260·4. Dihedral 6°. Incidence 5° 20′ at root, 1° at tip. Sweepback 16° 21′ on inner wings, 8° 23′ on outer panels. Steel truss centre-section spar; remainder of structure aluminium semi-monocoque. Plain differential ailerons and plain trailing-edge flaps of conventional aluminium construction. Trim tab in port aileron. Optional Goodrich pneumatic de-icing boots on leading-edges.

FUSELAGE: Conventional aluminium semi-monocoque structure.

TAIL UNIT: Cantilever aluminium semi-monocoque structure with twin endplate fins and rudders. Fixed-incidence tailplane. Trim tabs in rudder and elevators. Optional Goodrich pneumatic de-icing boots on leading-edges.

LANDING GEAR: Volpar electrically-retractable tricycle type. All units retract forward, main wheels into engine nacelles. Volpar hydraulic shock-absorbers. All three wheels size 8·50-10 with Goodrich or Goodyear tubeless or tube-type tyres. Main-wheel tyre pressure 5·52 bars (80 lb/sq in); nosewheel tyre pressure 3·10 bars (45 lb/sq in). Goodrich multiple-disc brakes.

POWER PLANT: Two 526 kW (705 ehp) Garrett-AiResearch TPE 331-1-101B turboprop engines, each driving a Hartzell HC-B3TN-5 three-blade reversible-pitch propeller with T10176H blades. Four to eight fuel tanks in wings, including new integral main tanks in wing leading-edges outboard of nacelles. Normal fuel capacity 1,159 litres (306 US gallons); max capacity 2,385 litres (630 US gallons). Refuelling points in upper surface of wings. Total oil capacity 11·5 litres (3 US gallons).

ACCOMMODATION: Crew of two and up to 15 passengers. Downward-hinged airstair door on port side at rear of cabin. Optional double-door for freight loading. Seats

Volpar 'Asterix' series VLR Turboliner II long-range maritime reconaissance aircraft operated by Société Interthon

removable to enable aircraft to be used for freight-carrying. Heating and air-conditioning optional. Baggage space aft of cabin and in each wing.

SYSTEMS: Hydraulic system for brakes only. Electrical supply from two 200A starter/generators and two 24V batteries, for landing gear and flap operation, propeller anti-icing, landing lights, radio and lighting.

AVIONICS AND EQUIPMENT: Blind-flying instrumentation, radio and radar to customer's specification.

DIMENSIONS, EXTERNAL:

Wing span	14·02 m (46 ft 0 in)
Wing chord at root	4·15 m (13 ft 7·36 in)
Wing chord at tip	1·14 m (3 ft 8·94 in)
Wing aspect ratio	5·67
Length overall	13·47 m (44 ft 2½ in)
Height overall	2·92 m (9 ft 7 in)
Tailplane span	4·57 m (15 ft 0 in)
Wheel track	3·94 m (12 ft 11 in)
Wheelbase	3·84 m (12 ft 7 in)
Propeller diameter	
	2·46 to 2·57 m (8 ft 0⅜ in to 8 ft 5⅜ in)
Passenger door: Height	1·22 m (4 ft 0 in)
Width	0·69 m (2 ft 3 in)
Height to sill	1·07 m (3 ft 6 in)

DIMENSIONS, INTERNAL:

Cabin, excl flight deck: Length	5·94 m (19 ft 6 in)
Max width	1·32 m (4 ft 4 in)
Max height	1·68 m (5 ft 6 in)
Floor area	7·43 m² (80 sq ft)
Volume	11·16 m³ (394 cu ft)
Freight hold (aft of cabin) volume	0·65 m³ (23 cu ft)
Freight holds (wings) volume (total)	
	0·91 m³ (32 cu ft)

AREAS:

Wings, gross	34·75 m² (374 sq ft)
Ailerons (total)	2·47 m² (26·6 sq ft)
Trailing-edge flaps (total)	2·62 m² (28·2 sq ft)
Fins (total)	1·51 m² (16·3 sq ft)
Rudders (total)	16·05 m² (17·28 sq ft)
Tailplane	35·49 m² (38·2 sq ft)
Elevators, incl tab	25·28 m² (27·22 sq ft)

WEIGHTS AND LOADINGS:

Weight empty: Cargo version	2,676 kg (5,900 lb)
Airliner	2,993 kg (6,600 lb)
Max T-O weight	5,216 kg (11,500 lb)
Max zero-fuel weight	4,762 kg (10,500 lb)
Max landing weight	4,989 kg (11,000 lb)
Max wing loading	150·1 kg/m² (30·75 lb/sq ft)
Max power loading	4·96 kg/kW (8·15 lb/ehp)

PERFORMANCE (at max T-O weight):

Max level and cruising speed at 3,050 m (10,000 ft)	
	243 knots (451 km/h; 280 mph)
Econ cruising speed at 3,050 m (10,000 ft)	
	222 knots (412 km/h; 256 mph)
Stalling speed, wheels and flaps up, power off	
	84 knots (154·5 km/h; 96 mph)
Stalling speed, wheels and flaps down, power off	
	80 knots (148·5 km/h; 92 mph)
Max rate of climb at S/L	463 m (1,520 ft)/min
Service ceiling	7,315 m (24,000 ft)
Service ceiling, one engine out	3,960 m (13,000 ft)
T-O run	570 m (1,870 ft)
T-O to 15 m (50 ft)	989 m (3,245 ft)
Landing from 15 m (50 ft)	762 m (2,500 ft)
Landing run	317 m (1,040 ft)
Range with max fuel, 45 min reserves	
	1,802 nm (3,340 km; 2,076 miles)
Range with max payload, min reserves	
	300 nm (556 km; 346 miles)

VOLPAR (BEECHCRAFT) TURBOLINER II

The Turboliner II is basically a Turboliner modified to meet the requirements of SFAR 23. The prototype was completed in February 1970 and received certification in July 1970. Dimensions and performance are the same as those given for the Turboliner.

Recent conversions incorporate a number of improvements, including battery temperature indicators, a fail-safe Hydro-Aire Hytrol anti-skid braking system, installation of a 38,000 BTU Janitrol heater in the nose for ground heating of cockpit and engine nacelles, and modification to the standard Volpar side-opening cargo door. This now incorporates an inward-opening door 0·66 m (2 ft 2 in) in width and with a minimum height of 1·16 m (3 ft 9½ in), which may be opened in flight to permit the airdrop of firefighting personnel or cargo. During 1974 Volpar, in conjunction with Sierracin Manufacturing Company, developed electrically heated windscreens for

the Turboliner II. Complete installation kits are available also for other Volpar conversions.

During 1977 Volpar developed and delivered a specially modified long-range Turboliner II to Société Interthon of Port Peche, France. This aircraft is identified as the 'Asterix' series VLR Turboliner, and is designed for long-range maritime reconnaissance. It can carry a complement of observers, offshore nav/com systems, proprietary marine search equipment and ocean survival gear. The standard 'Asterix' aircraft has 2,385 litres (630 US gallons) of fuel in wing tanks, plus 757 litres (200 US gallons) in two removable cabin fuel tanks; total capacity 3,142 litres (830 US gallons), providing an endurance of almost 12 h and range of 2,200 nm (4,076 km; 2,533 miles) with reserves. Special bubble-type windows are provided for both pilots; other equipment includes an inward/outward-opening cargo door for airdrops to surface vessels, lavatory, navigation tables, refreshment console, and provisions for camera and special search equipment. Certification by the FAA and French DGAC was awarded in December 1977.

VOLPAR (BEECHCRAFT) T-34V TURBOTRAINER

This programme (see 1979-80 *Jane's*) is no longer active.

VOLPAR (CENTURY) JETSTREAM III

In 1976 Volpar was engaged by Century Aircraft Corporation of Amarillo, Texas, to re-engine the Handley Page H.P.137 Jetstream with Garrett-AiResearch TPE-331-3U-303 turboprop engines. Flight testing of the prototype conversion began in August 1976, and FAR certification under FAR 23 for Part 135 operation was awarded in June 1977.

Known as the Century Jetstream III, this aircraft was offered in both executive and 18-passenger commuter configurations. Conversions included four for Air Illinois and two for Air US of Denver, Colorado. It is likely that this completed the programme, as there appear to be no more Jetstreams available for conversion.

Details of this conversion can be found in the 1979-80 *Jane's*.

VOUGHT

VOUGHT CORPORATION (a subsidiary of THE LTV CORPORATION)

HEAD OFFICE: PO Box 225907, Dallas, Texas 75265
Telephone: (214) 266 2011
PRESIDENT AND CHIEF EXECUTIVE OFFICER: R. L. Kirk
SENIOR VICE-PRESIDENTS:
R. S. Buzard
E. F. Cvetko (Operations)
R. N. Parker (Research and Engineering)
B. M. Smith
J. J. Welch Jr
VICE-PRESIDENTS:
D. P. Appleby (Materials)
K. R. Chapman (Planning)
Michael Collins (Field Operations)
Felix Fenter (Research & Advanced Technology)
H. M. Fish (International)
D. R. Hagler (General Counsel)
P. W. Hare (Miniature Systems)
W. R. Kiefer (Manufacturing)
G. F. Montry (Finance)
F. W. Randall (Subcontracts)
W. L. Shepard (Strategic Defense)
C. E. Snyder (Human Resources)
J. P. Woolnough (MLRS Programme Development)
DIRECTOR, CORPORATE COMMUNICATIONS: Beal Box

The former Chance Vought Aircraft Inc, founded in 1917 and a leading producer of aircraft for the US Navy throughout its history, became the Chance Vought Corporation on 31 December 1960. On 31 August 1961, Chance Vought Corporation merged with Ling-Temco Electronics Inc, to form a combined company known as Ling-Temco-Vought Inc (now The LTV Corporation).

After a succession of reorganisations, what is now known as Vought Corporation took over responsibility for all LTV's aircraft and space activities, aerospace support and training equipment from 1 January 1976, including current construction of Boeing 747 tail assemblies, McDonnell Douglas DC-10 tailplanes and elevators, and Lockheed C-130 control surfaces.

On 23 February 1979 the company announced receipt of a multi-million dollar contract from The Boeing Company covering the construction of up to 300 complete tailplane assemblies for the Boeing Model 767. Initial delivery was scheduled for November 1980, with continuing production until June 1985 of six to nine units per month. On 11 October 1979 the company contracted also to build the complete tail unit for the Boeing 757, including the aft fuselage section

Vought has in production the A-7E attack aircraft and TA-7C two-seat trainer for the US Navy and is providing five TA-7H two-seat trainers for the Hellenic Air Force. In addition, Congress has appropriated FY 1979 and FY

Vought TA-7C tandem two-seat trainer of US Navy Squadron VA-122

1980 funds for procurement of 12 A-7K two-seat trainers for the US Air National Guard. Other current products include the Scout launch vehicle for NASA; components for manned and unmanned space vehicles; advanced missile, guidance, control and environmental systems; Airtrans automatic transit systems; and advanced thermal protection systems.

In December 1974, Vought's Low Volume RamJet (LVRJ) propulsion system test vehicle made a successful first flight, covering a distance of more than 30 nm (56 km; 35 miles) and attaining a speed in excess of 1,259 knots (2,334 km/h; 1,450 mph). In four subsequent flights, extending into 1976, the vehicle demonstrated speeds well above 1,476 knots (2,736 km/h; 1,700 mph) and a range of more than 87 nm (161 km; 100 miles). Air-launched from a US Navy A-7 Corsair II, the flight test vehicle is 4·57 m (15 ft) long and 0·38 m (1 ft 3 in) in diameter. It can be scaled up or down for air-to-air, surface-to-air or surface-to-surface applications. Development is continuing as part of the US Navy's Supersonic Tactical Missile programme, and on 21 April 1979 an integral rocket/ramjet vehicle, featuring lower-cost propulsion system components and elements of a guidance system, was test flown with equal success.

Vought is also one of two finalists to develop a Multiple Launch Rocket System for the US Army and NATO allies.

VOUGHT CORSAIR II

US military designation: A-7

On 11 February 1964 the US Navy named the former LTV Aerospace Corporation winner of a design competition for a single-seat carrier-based light attack aircraft. The requirement was for a subsonic aircraft able to carry a greater load of non-nuclear weapons than the A-4E Skyhawk. To keep costs to a minimum and speed delivery

it had been stipulated by the Navy that the new aircraft should be based on an existing design; the LTV design study was based, therefore, on the F-8 Crusader. An initial contract to develop and build three aircraft, under the designation A-7A, was awarded on 19 March 1964; first flight was made on 27 September 1965.

Since that time several versions of the A-7 have been evolved as Corsair IIs, for the US Navy, the US Air Force and the Hellenic Air Force. Details of the A-7A, A-7B, A-7C and A-7D can be found in the 1979-80 and earlier editions of *Jane's*. The most recent versions are:

TA-7C. Sixty A-7Bs and A-7Cs are being converted into tandem two-seat trainers, with operational capability, under this designation. The first of them (154477) flew for the first time on 17 December 1976. Flight refuelling capability, gun and weapon pylons are retained, and TA-7Cs have the modern navigation/weapons delivery system used in the A-7E. Powered by non-afterburning 59·6 kN (13,400 lb st) Pratt & Whitney TF30-P-408 engine. Entered service with VA-122 and VA-174 in 1978.

A-7E. Developed version for the US Navy equipped as a light attack/close air support/interdiction aircraft. All except first 67 aircraft (since redesignated A-7C) powered by Allison TF41-A-2 (Spey) non-afterburning turbofan engine, which provides 66·8 kN (15,000 lb st). First flight 25 November 1968; deliveries began 14 July 1969. The A-7E entered combat service in Southeast Asia with Attack Squadrons 146 and 147 in May 1970, and equipped 26 Navy Squadrons in 1980. Production continues at a rate of about one a month.

In early 1977 production began of an **A-7E FLIR** version, called formerly TRAM (target recognition and attack multi-sensor system). This has a 327 kg (720 lb) pod under the starboard wing to house equipment which includes a Texas Instruments FLIR gimballed sensor, and a Marconi raster-HUD cockpit display, to provide improved night capability. Deliveries of new-production FLIR-equipped A-7Es to the Navy began on 15 September 1978. By the beginning of 1980, orders covered the production of 36 FLIR pods and 62 FLIR aircraft provisions. Plans call for eventual delivery of 179 pods and 349 FLIR installations.

A-7H. Land-based version of A-7E, retaining the folding wings. First A-7H flew for first time on 6 May 1975. Total of 60 delivered to the Hellenic Air Force. In service with Nos. 338, 340 and 345 Squadrons.

TA-7H. Two-seat version for the Hellenic Air Force, with an Allison TF41-A-400 engine. Configuration similar to TA-7C, but no in-flight refuelling capability. First TA-7H flew for first time on 4 March 1980. Five ordered; first two handed over in early July 1980.

A-7K. Two-seat version of the US Air Force's A-7D. Congress appropriated funds in FY 1979 for the first 12 of a planned procurement of 42 for service with the US Air National Guard from 1981. Funds for 12 more were included in FY 1980 appropriations. Basically two-seat trainers, these aircraft will retain combat capability. They are preceded by a prototype, being converted from an A-7D.

A-7P. Designation of 20 refurbished A-7As to be supplied to Portuguese Air Force from 1981. Refitted with TF30-P-408 engines and A-7E-standard avionics.

Orders for all versions totalled 1,539 by 1 January 1980, of which more than 1,500 had been delivered by mid-1980.

The following description, which applies in particular to the A-7E, is generally applicable to other versions of the A-7 except as detailed under the individual model listings:

TYPE: Subsonic single-seat tactical fighter.

WINGS: Cantilever high-wing monoplane. Wing section NACA 65A007. Anhedral 5°. Incidence −1°. Wing sweepback at quarter-chord 35°. Outer wing sections fold upward for carrier parking, and in the A-7H to allow best utilisation of revetments at combat airfields. All-metal multi-spar structure with integrally-stiffened aluminium alloy upper and lower skins. Plain sealed inset aluminium ailerons, outboard of wing fold, are actuated by fully-triplicated hydraulic system. Leading-edge flaps. Large single-slotted trailing-edge flaps. Spoiler above each wing forward of flaps.

FUSELAGE: All-metal semi-monocoque structure. Large door-type ventral speed-brake under centre-fuselage.

TAIL UNIT: Large vertical fin and rudder, swept back 44·28° at quarter-chord. One-piece all-moving tailplane, swept back 45° at quarter-chord and set at dihedral angle of 5° 25′. Tailplane is operated by triplicated hydraulic systems, and the rudder powered by two systems.

LANDING GEAR: Hydraulically-retractable tricycle type, with single wheel on each main unit and twin-wheel nose unit. Main wheels retract forward into fuselage, nosewheels aft. Main wheels and tyres size 28 × 9-12; nosewheels and tyres size 22 × 5·50. Nose gear launch bar for carrier catapulting. Sting-type arrester hook under rear fuselage for carrier landings, emergency landings or aborted take-offs. Anti-skid brake system.

POWER PLANT: One Allison TF41-A-2 (Rolls-Royce Spey) non-afterburning turbofan engine, rated at 66·7 kN (15,000 lb st). The A-7E has a pneumatic starter requiring ground air supply; A-7H, TA-7H and A-7K engines have self-start capability through the medium of battery-powered electric motor that actuates a small gas turbine engine (jet fuel starter) which, in turn, starts the main engine through the gearbox. The engine has self-contained ignition for start/airstart, automatic relight and selective ignition. Integral fuel tanks in wings and additional fuselage tanks. Maximum internal fuel 5,678 litres (1,500 US gallons). Maximum external fuel 4,542 litres (1,200 US gallons). The A-7E and A-7H have the

Vought A-7D tactical fighter version of the Corsair II for the USAF (*Pilot Press*)

Vought A-7E Corsair II close air support/interdiction aircraft of the US Navy

fuselage sump tank filled with polyurethane fire-suppressing foam. Some fuselage tanks and fuel lines self-sealing. Flight refuelling capability of A-7E provided by a probe and drogue system; A-7K has boom receptacle above fuselage on port side in line with wing leading-edge. The A-7H and TA-7H do not have an air refuelling capability. Boron carbide (HFC) engine armour.

ACCOMMODATION: Pilot on McDonnell Douglas Escapac rocket-powered ejection system, complete with US Navy life support system on the A-7E/H. Escape system provides a fully-inflated parachute three seconds after sequence initiation; positive seat/man separation and stabilisation of the ejected seat and pilot. Boron carbide (HFC) cockpit armour.

SYSTEMS: Triple-redundant hydraulic system for flight controls; double-redundant system for flaps, brakes and landing gear retraction. Liquid oxygen system. An air-conditioning unit using engine bleed air provides pressurisation and cooling for the cockpit and cooling for certain avionics components. Automatic flight control system provides control-stick steering, altitude hold,

heading hold, heading pre-select and attitude hold, which is coupled for automatic carrier landings. Ram-air turbine provides hydraulic pressure and electrical power down to airspeeds below those used in normal landing approaches.

AVIONICS AND EQUIPMENT: The navigation/weapon delivery system is the heart of the A-7E/H light attack aircraft. It performs continuously the computations needed for greatly increased delivery accuracy, and for manoeuvering freedom during navigation to a target and the attack, weapon release, pull up, and safe return phases of the mission. The system not only provides the pilot with a number of options during navigation and weapon delivery, but also relieves him of much of his workload. The AN/ASN-91(V) navigation/weapon delivery computer is the primary element of the system, in constant 'conversation' with basic electronic sensors, and computes and displays continuously present position, using computed position and stored data to calculate navigation and weapon delivery solutions, and monitors the reliability of data inputs and outputs. An AN/ASN-90(V) inertial measurement set is the basic three-axis reference system for navigation and weapon delivery. AN/APN-190(V) Doppler measures groundspeed and drift angle. AN/APQ-126(V) forward-looking radar provides the pilot with ten modes of operation: air-to-ground ranging; terrain following; terrain avoidance; ground mapping, shaped beam; ground mapping, pencil beam; beacon; cross-scan terrain avoidance; cross-scan ground mapping; pencil; TV; and SIDS. An AN/AVQ-7(V) HUD receives and displays computed attack, navigation and landing data from the tactical computer; aircraft performance data from flight sensors: and discrete signals from various aircraft systems. CP-953A/AJQ air data computer is a solid-state servomechanical analogue computer which measures and computes continuously required altitude and airspeed information. The Armament Station Control unit integrates and controls the weapon release system; it supplies electrical signals to arm and release or jettison external stores; controls and fires the Vulcan cannon; furnishes store-type information to the tactical computer; supplies weapon status information to the pilot; determines weapon release according to priority of stations; and determines compatibility of selected release mode with the stores on selected stations. Standard aeronautical charts reproduced on 35 mm film in full colour are stored in an AN/ASN-99 Projected Map

Artist's impression of the Vought A-7K, a two-seat version of the A-7D

Display Set which, as a subsystem of the tactical computer, provides a continuous display of the aircraft's geographical position. Other avionics include AN/ASN-54 approach power compensator; AN/ASW-30 AFCS; ARA-63 ACLS; dual AN/ARC-159 UHF com; AN/ARN-84 Tacan; AN/APX-72 IFF transponder; AN/AN-154 radar beacon; AN/ASW-25 data link; AN/ARA-50 ADF; and AN/AIC-25 audio system. ECM equipment includes ALR-45/50 internal homing and warning systems; ALQ-126 active ECM; chaff/flare dispensers; and external pod-mounted systems compatible with the aircraft's internal sytems.

ARMAMENT: A wide range of stores, to a total weight of more than 6,805 kg (15,000 lb), can be carried on six underwing pylons and two fuselage weapon stations, the latter suitable for Sidewinder air-to-air missiles. Two outboard pylons on each wing can each accommodate a load of 1,587 kg (3,500 lb). Inboard pylon on each wing can carry 1,134 kg (2,500 lb). Two fuselage weapon stations, one on each side, can each carry load of 227 kg (500 lb). Weapons carried include air-to-air and air-to-ground (anti-tank and anti-radar missiles); electro-optical (TV) and laser guided weapons; general-purpose bombs; bomblet dispensers; rockets; gun pods; and auxiliary fuel tanks. In addition, an M61A-1 Vulcan 20 mm cannon is mounted in the port side of the fuselage. This has 1,000-round ammunition storage and selected firing rates of 4,000 or 6,000 rds/min. Strike camera in lower rear fuselage for damage assessment.

DIMENSIONS, EXTERNAL:

Wing span	11·80 m (38 ft 9 in)
Width, wings folded	7·24 m (23 ft 9 in)
Wing chord at root	4·72 m (15 ft 6 in)
Wing chord at tip	1·18 m (3 ft 10¼ in)
Wing aspect ratio	4
Length overall	14·06 m (46 ft 1½ in)
Height overall	4·90 m (16 ft 0¾ in)
Tailplane span	5·52 m (18 ft 1½ in)
Wheel track	2·90 m (9 ft 6 in)

AREAS:

Wings, gross	34·83 m² (375 sq ft)
Ailerons (total)	1·85 m² (19·94 sq ft)
Trailing-edge flaps (total)	4·04 m² (43·48 sq ft)
Leading-edge flaps (total)	3·46 m² (37·24 sq ft)
Spoiler	0·43 m² (4·60 sq ft)
Deflector	0·32 m² (3·44 sq ft)
Fin	10·70 m² (115·20 sq ft)
Rudder	1·40 m² (15·04 sq ft)
Horizontal tail surfaces	5·22 m² (56·19 sq ft)
Speed-brake	2·32 m² (25·00 sq ft)

WEIGHTS:

Weight empty	8,668 kg (19,111 lb)
Max T-O weight	19,050 kg (42,000 lb)

PERFORMANCE:

Max level speed at S/L
600 knots (1,112 km/h; 691 mph)
Max level speed at 1,525 m (5,000 ft):
with 12 Mk 82 bombs
562 knots (1,040 km/h; 646 mph)
after dropping bombs
595 knots (1,102 km/h; 685 mph)
Sustained manoeuvring performance at 1,525 m (5,000 ft), at AUW of 13,047 kg (28,765 lb) with 6 pylons and 2 Sidewinder missiles
1,770 m (5,800 ft) turning radius at 4g and
500 knots (925 km/h; 575 mph)
T-O run at max T-O weight   1,830 m (6,000 ft)
Ferry range:
max internal fuel
1,981 nm (3,671 km; 2,281 miles)
max internal and external fuel
2,485 nm (4,604 km; 2,861 miles)

VOUGHT CORSAIR II₂
US military designation: YA-7E

Under a project funded partially by the company, and by modification of the first production Spey-engined A-7E, furnished by the US Navy, Vought designed and built the prototype of a two-seat version of the A-7 Corsair II. Envisaged as an advanced trainer, or as a new operational configuration for tactical duties such as electronic countermeasures, it was known originally as the Vought Project V-519, and later as the YA-7H, but was then given the designation YA-7E to avoid confusion with the single-seat A-7H and two-seat TA-7H ordered by the Hellenic Air Force.

Details of the YA-7E, which made its first flight on 29 August 1972, can be found in the 1979-80 Jane's. The TA-7C Corsair II trainers undergoing conversion from A-7B/C are similar in configuration to the YA-7E, as is the new production A-7K.

WEATHERLY
WEATHERLY AVIATION COMPANY INC

2304 San Felipe Road, Hollister, California 95023
Telephone: (408) 637 5534
PRESIDENT: John C. Weatherly

Weatherly Aviation developed in the early 1960s a conversion of the Fairchild M-62 for service in an agricultural role, and a total of 19 of the resulting Weatherly WM-62Cs was produced by the Autumn of 1965. Most of these were powered by Continental W670 radial engines, but a few had Pratt & Whitney R-985s. On the basis of this conversion programme, a somewhat larger aircraft, designated Model 201, was developed subsequently and remained in production in several successive versions until late 1979, when construction of the Model 201C ended after more than 100 examples of all versions had been built. A description of the Model 201C can be found in the 1979-80 Jane's.

Weatherly developed for it small sweptback vanes which can be attached to, or removed easily from, each wingtip. These have two primary functions: to increase the effective swath width; and to reduce the amount of spray materials lost from the swath area. With the vanes installed the swath width is increased by 1·80 to 2·75 m (6 to 9 ft), but because of reduced outboard airflow the vanes are not used when dispersing dust or other solid material. Normal flight characteristics are not impaired with the vanes installed. Take-off run is reduced by a few feet, and cruising speed is increased approximately 1·7 knots (3·2 km/h; 2 mph), due to a reduction in induced drag.

WEATHERLY MODEL 620

For 1980 Weatherly introduced two new versions of a slightly larger, sturdier, and faster aircraft than the Model 201C, which has the designation Weatherly Model 620. Both are available with the optional small sweptback wingtip vanes which were developed for the Model 201. These can be folded back beneath the wing for hangar storage.

Two versions of the Model 620 are available:

Model 620. Basic version, with a 336 kW (450 hp) Pratt & Whitney R-985 radial engine, and with a 1,268 litre (335 US gallon) hopper for liquid or dry chemicals.

Model 620TP. Version with a 373 kW (500 shp) Pratt & Whitney Aircraft of Canada PT6A-11AG turboprop engine, and a 1,287 litre (340 US gallon) hopper.

Few details are available except that these two versions are basically the same from the engine firewall aft; it is believed that in most constructional details they are similar to the Model 201C.

DIMENSIONS, EXTERNAL:

Wing span	12·50 m (41 ft 0 in)
Wing span, with optional wingtip vanes	14·33 m (47 ft 0 in)

WEIGHTS (A: Model 620; B: Model 620TP):

Weight empty, with spray system:

A	1,270 kg (2,800 lb)
B	1,134 kg (2,500 lb)

Weatherly Model 620, with Pratt & Whitney R-985 piston-engine and wingtip vanes

The turboprop Weatherly Model 620TP, also fitted with wingtip vanes

Design T-O weight: A, B		1,814 kg (4,000 lb)
Max T-O weight (Restricted category):		
A		2,495 kg (5,500 lb)
B		2,449 kg (5,400 lb)

PERFORMANCE (at design T-O weight):

Stalling speed: A, B	50·4 knots (93·3 km/h; 58 mph)
Endurance: A	2 h 30 min
B	2 h 0 min

WING
WING AIRCRAFT COMPANY

HEAD OFFICE: 2925 Columbia Street, Torrance, California 90503
Telephone: (213) 533 0714
PRESIDENT: George S. Wing

CHIEF ENGINEER: Glenn Errington

Wing Aircraft Company was incorporated on 27 June 1966, when it became completely separated from its parent company, Hi-Shear Corporation. In 1971 the company's twin-engined Derringer was exhibited at the Paris Air Show, just prior to the start of planned production, but for several reasons this did not proceed, and no further progress was made until 1978. Mr George Wing then resigned from Chairmanship of Hi-Shear Corporation to concentrate on production of the Derringer, and it is reported that those aircraft which were in various stages of assembly when operations ceased in 1971 were first completed. New production then started, with delivery of 120 Derringers envisaged during 1980.

WING D-1 DERRINGER

Named after the well-known American compact pocket pistol, the twin-engined high-performance Derringer utilises manufacturing techniques that were new to the lightplane industry at the time of its inception. Butt-jointed, flush-riveted, chemically-milled and stretch-formed skins are used throughout the airframe. This simplifies the achievement of a flush surface finish and provides integral stiffness, since the skins are left thicker at the points where additional strength is needed. Assembly is simplified as, for example, each wing has a single stretch-formed chemically-milled skin that acts also as an integral fuel tank.

Design began originally in June 1960; the prototype flew for the first time on 1 May 1962, powered by two 86 kW (115 hp) engines. Used to prove the design concept, it was retired after logging more than 300 flying hours. The second aircraft, with 112 kW (150 hp) engines, was redesigned to production standards and flew for the first time on 19 November 1964, but was lost subsequently during flight testing. A third aircraft was used for static structural testing, and the fourth, with 119 kW (160 hp) engines, flew on 25 August 1965. FAA type certification under CAR Part 3 was gained on 20 December 1966.

TYPE: Two-seat twin-engined light aircraft.
WINGS: Cantilever low-wing monoplane. Wing section NACA 65$_2$-415. Dihedral 6°. Incidence 1°. All-metal two-spar structure of light alloy, except for glassfibre wingtips. Plain ailerons of light alloy with piano-type hinges. Electrically-actuated slotted trailing-edge flaps of similar construction. Ground-adjustable trim tab on each aileron. Bungee-type trim control.
FUSELAGE: All-metal semi-monocoque light alloy structure, except for glassfibre nose.
TAIL UNIT: Cantilever structure of light alloy with swept vertical surfaces. Tailplane has variable incidence. Electrically-operated rudder and elevator trim tabs.
LANDING GEAR: Electrically-retractable tricycle type with single wheel on each unit. Nosewheel retracts forward, main units upward into nacelles. Oleo-pneumatic shock-absorbers. Steerable nosewheel has tubeless tyre size 5·00-5, pressure 2·41 bars (35 lb/sq in); main wheels have low-profile tyres size 6·00-6, pressure 2·76 bars (40 lb/sq in). Cleveland single-disc hydraulic brakes.
POWER PLANT: Two 119 kW (160 hp) Avco Lycoming IO-320-B1C flat-four engines, each driving a Hartzell two-blade constant-speed and fully-feathering metal propeller with spinner. Engine nacelles of glassfibre construction. Integral fuel tank in the leading-edge of each outer wing, with combined capacity of 333 litres (88 US gallons). Refuelling point at each wingtip. Oil capacity 15 litres (4 US gallons).
ACCOMMODATION: Two seats side by side under large upward-hinged canopy with opaque top. Tinted windscreen and windows. Dual controls standard. Baggage compartment with capacity of 113 kg (250 lb). Accommodation is heated and ventilated.

Wing D-1 Derringer two-seat twin-engined light aircraft (*J. M. G. Gradidge*)

SYSTEMS: Electrical system includes two 60A alternators and a 12V 35Ah storage battery. Vacuum system for flight instruments only. Hydraulic system for brakes only. Oxygen system optional.
AVIONICS AND EQUIPMENT: Standard avionics include two 360-channel nav/coms; two VORs, one with glideslope indicator; ADF; three-light marker beacon receiver; related antennae, audio amplifier, cabin speaker, microphone and headset. Optional avionics include autopilot, DME and transponder. Standard equipment includes full IFR instrumentation; exhaust gas and outside air temperature gauges; turn co-ordinator; map pockets; pilot's storm window; heated pitot; stall warning device; instrument lights; anti-collision, landing and navigation lights; corrosion proofing; external power socket; and towbar. Optional equipment includes shoulder harness, and propeller unfeathering accumulators.

DIMENSIONS, EXTERNAL:
Wing span	8·89 m (29 ft 2 in)
Wing chord, constant	1·27 m (4 ft 2 in)
Wing aspect ratio	7
Length overall	7·01 m (23 ft 0 in)
Height overall	2·44 m (8 ft 0 in)
Tailplane span	3·30 m (10 ft 10 in)
Wheel track	3·30 m (10 ft 10 in)
Wheelbase	1·64 m (5 ft 4½ in)
Propeller diameter	1·68 m (5 ft 6 in)
Propeller ground clearance	0·20 m (8 in)

DIMENSIONS, INTERNAL:
Cabin: Length	2·54 m (8 ft 4 in)
Max width	1·12 m (3 ft 8 in)
Max height	1·22 m (4 ft 0 in)
Floor area	1·11 m² (12 sq ft)
Volume	1·59 m³ (56 cu ft)
Baggage hold, volume	0·62 m³ (22 cu ft)

AREAS:
Wings, gross	11·24 m² (121 sq ft)
Ailerons (total)	0·74 m² (8·00 sq ft)
Flaps (total)	1·11 m² (12·00 sq ft)
Fin	1·08 m² (11·65 sq ft)
Rudder, incl tab	0·48 m² (5·18 sq ft)
Tailplane	1·72 m² (18·56 sq ft)
Elevators, incl tabs	1·07 m² (11·51 sq ft)

WEIGHTS AND LOADINGS:
Weight empty	939 kg (2,070 lb)
Max T-O weight	1,383 kg (3,050 lb)
Max landing weight	1,315 kg (2,900 lb)
Max wing loading	123 kg/m² (25·2 lb/sq ft)
Max power loading	5·81 kg/kW (9·5 lb/hp)

PERFORMANCE (at max T-O weight):
Max level speed at S/L	201 knots (373 km/h; 232 mph)
Max cruising speed, 75% power at 3,050 m (10,000 ft)	190 knots (352 km/h; 219 mph)
Cruising speed, 65% power at 3,960 m (13,000 ft)	184 knots (341 km/h; 212 mph)
Approach speed	82·5 knots (153 km/h; 95 mph)
Stalling speed, flaps and gear up	69·5 knots (129 km/h; 80 mph)
Stalling speed, flaps and gear down	63 knots (116 km/h; 72 mph)
Max rate of climb at S/L	518 m (1,700 ft)/min
Rate of climb at S/L, one engine out	127 m (418 ft)/min
Service ceiling	5,975 m (19,600 ft)
Service ceiling, one engine out	2,440 m (8,000 ft)
T-O run	280 m (920 ft)
T-O to 15 m (50 ft)	360 m (1,180 ft)
Landing from 15 m (50 ft)	640 m (2,100 ft)
Landing run	378 m (1,240 ft)
Range with max fuel, 65% power at 3,050 m (10,000 ft), no reserves	1,007 nm (1,866 km; 1,160 miles)

YUGOSLAVIA

SOKO
SOKO VAZDUHOPLOVNA INDUSTRIJA, RO VAZDUHOPLOVSTVO

79000 Mostar
Telephone: 22-121, 25-120, 33-831, 35-244, 35-541, 37-943
Telex: 46-180, 46-181
DIRECTOR, AIRCRAFT DIVISION: Dr Krsto Draca
DIRECTOR, AIRCRAFT FACTORY: Zijo Kreso, BSc
DIRECTOR, MARKETING: Novica Djurica, BSc
DIRECTOR, RESEARCH AND DEVELOPMENT: Dipl Ing Milenko Pjescić

Founded in 1951, this company manufactures aircraft of its own design and is participating, with Romania, in developing and producing the Orao strike aircraft described under the SOKO/CNIAR heading in the International section.

Soko is also building under licence the Aérospatiale/Westland Gazelle helicopter, on behalf of the Yugoslav government.

SOKO G2-A GALEB (SEAGULL)

Design of the Galeb was started in 1957. Construction of two prototypes began in 1959 and the first of these flew for the first time in May 1961. Production began in 1963 and has continued since that time, to fulfil Yugoslav and export orders. First overseas operator was the Zambian Air Force, in early 1971.

There are two production versions of the Galeb:

G2-A. Standard version for Yugoslav Air Force. Progressive design improvements included optional cockpit air-conditioning system. Production completed.

G-2A-E. Export version, with updated equipment. First flown in late 1974. Series production began in 1975, reportedly for the Libyan Arab Air Force, and will continue until the end of 1980 or mid-1981 to meet current commitments.

Soko G2-A Galeb two-seat basic training aircraft (Rolls-Royce Viper 11 turbojet engine)

TYPE: Two-seat armed jet basic trainer, designed for load factors of +8g and −4g.
WINGS: Cantilever low-wing monoplane. Wing section NACA 64A213·5 at root, NACA 64A212·0 at tip. Dihedral 1° 30'. No incidence. Sweepback at quarter-chord 4° 19'. Conventional light alloy two-spar stressed-skin structure, consisting of a centre-section, integral with the fuselage, and two outer panels which can be removed easily. Manually-operated light alloy ailerons. Trim tab on port aileron. Hydraulically-actuated Fowler flaps. No de-icing system.
FUSELAGE: Light alloy semi-monocoque structure in two portions, joined together by four bolts at frame aft of wing trailing-edge. Rear portion removable for engine

servicing. Two hydraulically-actuated door-type air-brakes under centre-fuselage.

TAIL UNIT: Cantilever light alloy stressed-skin structure. Fixed-incidence tailplane. Rudder and elevators statically and dynamically balanced and manually operated. Manually-operated trim tab in each elevator. VHF radio aerial forms tip of fin.

LANDING GEAR: Hydraulically-retractable tricycle type, with single wheel on each unit. Nosewheel retracts forward, main units inward into wings. Oleo-pneumatic shock-absorbers manufactured by Prva Petoletka of Trstenik. Dunlop main wheels and tyres size 23 × 7·25-10, pressure 4·41 bars (64 lb/sq in). Dunlop nosewheel and tyre size 6·50-5·5 TC, pressure 3·43 bars (49·8 lb/sq in). Prva Petoletka hydraulic differential disc brakes, toe-operated from both cockpits.

POWER PLANT: One Rolls-Royce Viper 11 Mk 22-6 turbojet engine, rated at 11·12 kN (2,500 lb st). Two flexible fuel tanks aft of cockpits, with total capacity of 780 kg (1,720 lb). Two jettisonable wingtip tanks, each with capacity of 170 kg (375 lb). Refuelling point on upper part of fuselage aft of cockpits. Fuel system designed to permit up to 15 seconds of inverted flight. Oil capacity 6·25 litres (1·4 Imp gallons).

ACCOMMODATION: Crew of two in tandem on HSA (Folland) Type 1-B fully-automatic lightweight ejection seats. Separate sideways-hinged (to starboard) jettisonable canopy over each cockpit. Cockpit air-conditioning to special order only.

SYSTEMS: Hydraulic system, pressure 58·5-69 bars (850-1,000 lb/sq in), for landing gear, airbrakes and flaps. Separate system for wheel brakes. Pneumatic system for armament cocking. Electrical system includes 6kW 24V generator, 24V battery, and inverter to provide 115V 400Hz AC supply for instruments. G2-A has low-pressure oxygen system, capacity 1,450 litres. G-2A-E has high-pressure oxygen system.

AVIONICS AND EQUIPMENT (G2-A): Blind-flying instrumentation, Marconi radio compass (licence-built by Rudi Cajavec), intercom and STR-9Z1 VHF radio transceiver standard. Standard electrical equipment includes navigation lights, 250W landing lamp in nose, and 50W taxying lamp on nose landing gear. Camera, with focal length of 178 mm (7 in) and 125-exposure magazine, can be fitted in fuselage, under rear cockpit floor. Flares can be carried on the underwing bomb racks for night photography. Target towing hook under centre-fuselage.

AVIONICS AND EQUIPMENT (G-2A-E): Full IFR instrumentation. Electronique Aérospatiale (EAS) Type TVU-740 VHF/UHF com radio transceiver, Marconi AD 370B radio compass, EAS RNA-720 VOR/LOC and ILS, Iskra 75R4 marker beacon receiver, and intercom. Vinten Type 360/140A camera with 3 in automatic exposure-control lens. Otherwise as G2-A.

ARMAMENT: All production aircraft have two 0·50 in machine-guns in nose (with 80 rds/gun); and underwing pylons for two 50 kg or 100 kg bombs and four 57 mm rockets or two 127 mm rockets; or clusters of small bombs and expendable bomblet containers of up to 150 kg (330 lb) weight (300 kg; 660 lb total).

DIMENSIONS, EXTERNAL:

Wing span	10·47 m (34 ft 4½ in)
Wing span over tip-tanks	11·62 m (38 ft 1½ in)
Wing chord at root	2·36 m (7 ft 9 in)
Wing chord at tip	1·40 m (4 ft 7 in)
Wing aspect ratio	5·55
Length overall	10·34 m (33 ft 11 in)
Height overall	3·28 m (10 ft 9 in)
Tailplane span	4·27 m (14 ft 0 in)
Wheel track	3·89 m (12 ft 9 in)
Wheelbase	3·59 m (11 ft 9½ in)

AREAS:

Wings, gross	19·43 m² (209·14 sq ft)
Ailerons (total)	2·36 m² (25·40 sq ft)
Trailing-edge flaps (total)	2·02 m² (21·75 sq ft)
Airbrake	0·34 m² (3·66 sq ft)
Fin	1·34 m² (14·42 sq ft)
Rudder, incl tab	0·56 m² (6·03 sq ft)
Tailplane	3·66 m² (39·40 sq ft)
Elevators, incl tabs	0·83 m² (8·93 sq ft)

WEIGHTS:

Weight empty, equipped	2,620 kg (5,775 lb)
Max T-O weight:	
Fully-aerobatic trainer ('clean')	3,374 kg (7,438 lb)
Basic trainer (no tip-tanks)	3,488 kg (7,690 lb)
Navigational trainer (with tip-tanks)	3,828 kg (8,439 lb)
Weapons trainer	3,988 kg (8,792 lb)
Strike version	4,300 kg (9,480 lb)

PERFORMANCE (at normal T-O weight):

Max level speed at S/L	408 knots (756 km/h; 470 mph)
Max level speed at 6,200 m (20,350 ft)	438 knots (812 km/h; 505 mph)
Max cruising speed at 6,000 m (19,680 ft)	394 knots (730 km/h; 453 mph)
Stalling speed: flaps and airbrakes down	85 knots (158 km/h; 98 mph)
flaps and airbrakes up	97 knots (180 km/h; 112 mph)
Max rate of climb at S/L	1,370 m (4,500 ft)/min
Time to 3,000 m (9,840 ft)	2·4 min
Time to 6,000 m (19,680 ft)	5·5 min
Time to 9,000 m (29,520 ft)	10·2 min
Service ceiling	12,000 m (39,375 ft)
T-O run on grass	490 m (1,610 ft)
T-O to 15 m (50 ft)	640 m (2,100 ft)
Landing from 15 m (50 ft)	710 m (2,330 ft)
Landing run on grass	400 m (1,310 ft)
Max range at 9,000 m (29,520 ft), with tip-tanks full	669 nm (1,240 km; 770 miles)
Max endurance at 7,000 m (23,000 ft)	2 h 30 min

SOKO JASTREB (HAWK)

Production of all single-seat attack, reconnaissance and two-seat trainer versions of the Jastreb has been completed. Details of these aircraft can be found in the 1979-80 *Jane's*.

UTVA
FABRIKA AVIONA UTVA

HEAD OFFICE AND WORKS: Ul Utve Zlatokrile 9, 26000 Pancevo
Telephone: 013 44 755
Telex: 131-16
GENERAL MANAGER: Dipl Ecc Marko Saranović
MANAGER OF AIRCRAFT DIVISION:
Dipl Ing Vladimir Nikolić
MANAGER OF AIRCRAFT DEVELOPMENT:
Dipl Ing Dragoslav Dimić

UTVA-75

The UTVA-75 is a side-by-side two-seat training, glider towing and utility lightplane, which was projected, designed and built in partnership by UTVA-Pancevo, Prva Petoletka-Trstenik, Vazduhoplovnotehnicki Institut and Institut Masinskog Fakulteta of Belgrade. Design was started in 1974. Construction of two prototypes was undertaken in 1975; the first of these flew for the first time on 20 May 1976 and the second on 18 December 1976. Series production began immediately and is continuing.

TYPE: Two-seat light aircraft.

WINGS: Cantilever low-wing monoplane, with short-span centre-section and two constant-chord outer panels. Wing section NACA 65₂415. Dihedral 0° on centre-section, 6° on outer panels. Conventional all-metal structure. Ailerons and flaps along entire trailing-edge of outer panels, except for tips. Flettner trim tab on each aileron.

FUSELAGE: Conventional all-metal semi-monocoque structure.

TAIL UNIT: Cantilever all-metal structure, with sweptback vertical surfaces. Fluted skin on fin and rudder. Elevator and rudder horn-balanced. Trim tab in elevator. Flettner trim tab on rudder.

LANDING GEAR: Non-retractable tricycle type, with single wheel on each unit, and small tail bumper. Prva Petoletka-Trstenik oleo-pneumatic shock-absorbers. Dunlop tyres, size 6·00-6 on main wheels, 5·00-5 on nosewheel. Prva Petoletka-Trstenik hydraulic brakes.

POWER PLANT: One 134 kW (180 hp) Avco Lycoming IO-360-B1F flat-four engine, driving a Hartzell HC-C2YK-1BF/F7666A two-blade metal variable-pitch propeller. Two integral fuel tanks in wings, total capacity 160 litres (35 Imp gallons). Provision for carrying two 100 litre (22 Imp gallon) drop-tanks under wings, raising max total capacity to 360 litres (79 Imp gallons). Oil capacity 10 litres (2·2 Imp gallons).

ACCOMMODATION: Two seats side-by-side in enclosed cabin, with large upward-opening canopy door over each seat, hinged on centreline. Dual stick-type controls standard. Cabin heated and ventilated.

SYSTEMS: Dual hydraulic systems. 12V electrical system, with 35Ah battery, navigation lights, rotating beacon and landing lights as standard equipment.

AVIONICS AND EQUIPMENT: King KY 195B radio optional. Standard equipment includes radio compass.

ARMAMENT AND MILITARY EQUIPMENT: Standard fittings for light weapon loads underwing.

DIMENSIONS, EXTERNAL:

Wing span	9·73 m (31 ft 11 in)
Wing chord (constant)	1·55 m (5 ft 1 in)
Length overall	7·11 m (23 ft 4 in)
Height overall	3·15 m (10 ft 4 in)
Tailplane span	3·80 m (12 ft 5½ in)
Wheel track	2·58 m (8 ft 5½ in)
Wheelbase	1·99 m (6 ft 6¼ in)
Propeller diameter	1·93 m (6 ft 4 in)
Propeller ground clearance	0·295 m (11¾ in)

AREA:

Wings, gross	14·63 m² (157·5 sq ft)

WEIGHTS:

Weight empty, equipped	650 kg (1,433 lb)
Max T-O weight	960 kg (2,116 lb)

PERFORMANCE (at max T-O weight):

Max level speed	118 knots (220 km/h; 136 mph)
Econ cruising speed	89 knots (165 km/h; 102 mph)
Stalling speed, engine idling:	
flaps up	51·5 knots (95 km/h; 59 mph)
25° flap	43 knots (80 km/h; 50 mph)
Max rate of climb at S/L	270 m (885 ft)/min
Service ceiling	4,500 m (14,760 ft)
T-O run	125 m (410 ft)
T-O to 15 m (50 ft)	250 m (820 ft)
Landing from 15 m (50 ft)	350 m (1,150 ft)
Range with drop-tanks, no reserves	1,078 nm (2,000 km; 1,242 miles)

UTVA-75 two-seat training and utility aircraft (Avco Lycoming IO-360-B1F engine)

Publisher's note

The following sections were passed for press before the main aircraft section, enabling this most important section to be updated to the last possible moment. The allocation of a starting point for the homebuilt aircraft section before the completion of the aircraft section accounts for the gap in the sequence of page numbers between 455 and 465.

HOMEBUILT AIRCRAFT
(including man-powered and racing aircraft)

AUSTRALIA

CORBY
JOHN C. CORBY

86 Eton Street, Sutherland, NSW 2232

Mr Corby, a consultant aero engineer, has designed and is marketing plans for a single-seat wooden ultra-light aircraft known as the Starlet. By early 1980 at least nine Starlets had been completed and a further 40 were known to be under construction in Australia, Tasmania and New Zealand, including a metal version.

CORBY CJ-1 STARLET

The first Starlet (VH-ULV) was built by a group of about ten members of the Latrobe Valley division of the Australian Ultra Light Aircraft Association. Mr Erle Jones (Secretary and former President of the ULAA, Latrobe Valley Aero Club) was responsible for test flying the completed aircraft, with Mr John Brown acting as instructor in building techniques. Details of this aircraft were given in the 1974-75 *Jane's*.

The following description applies to the standard Starlet, as built to current plans:

TYPE: Single-seat ultra-light homebuilt aircraft.

WINGS: Cantilever low-wing monoplane of wooden construction. Wing section NACA 43012A. Dihedral 6°. Incidence 2° 30' at root, −1° at tip. Laminated main spar of solid spruce, subspars of spruce, built-up girder-type ribs and D-shaped nose section. Plywood covering from leading-edge to main spar, remainder fabric covered. Provision for dismantling into two equal halves. Ailerons, of spruce with birch plywood covering, deflect 15° up and down.

FUSELAGE: Plywood-covered spruce structure.

TAIL UNIT: Cantilever type, of similar construction to wings. Fixed-incidence tailplane. Plywood-covered fixed surfaces; fabric-covered rudder and elevators. Elevators deflect 30° up, 20° down; rudder deflects 25° to left and right.

LANDING GEAR: Non-retractable two-wheel type standard. Separate spring steel leaf-type shock-absorbing main legs, attached directly to fuselage via a solid spruce/ash beam which also serves as the wing leading-edge attachment member. Wheels, tyres and brakes of customer's choice, subject to main wheels of 89 mm (3½ in) minimum diameter with 4·00-4 tyres and Olympic go-kart hubs. Sturmey Archer cycle drum/shoe brakes may be used. Leaf-spring tailskid, or tailwheel at customer's option. Wheel fairings optional.

POWER PLANT: Any suitable engine of up to 56 kW (75 hp) and 72 kg (160 lb) weight, driving a two-blade propeller. Fuel tank, capacity 36-45 litres (8-10 Imp gallons), aft of engine firewall. Oil capacity 2·25 kg (5 lb).

ACCOMMODATION: Single seat. Sliding canopy optional. Baggage locker behind seat.

DIMENSIONS, EXTERNAL:
Wing span	5·64 m (18 ft 6 in)
Wing chord at root	1·32 m (4 ft 4 in)
Wing area, gross	6·36 m² (68·50 sq ft)
Length overall	4·50 m (14 ft 9 in)
Fuselage: Max width	0·55 m (1 ft 9¾ in)
Height overall	1·47 m (4 ft 10 in)
Tailplane span	1·98 m (6 ft 6 in)
Wheel track	1·37 m (4 ft 6 in)
Propeller diameter	1·37 m (4 ft 6 in)

WEIGHTS:
Weight empty	183-190 kg (405-420 lb)
Max T-O weight (semi-aerobatic)	295 kg (650 lb)

PERFORMANCE (prototype, with 36·5 kW; 49 hp engine, at 295 kg; 650 lb AUW):
Never-exceed speed	138 knots (255 km/h; 159 mph) IAS
Max level speed	117 knots (217 km/h; 135 mph)
Max cruising speed	107 knots (198 km/h; 123 mph)
Stalling speed, power off:	42 knots (79 km/h; 49 mph)
	30 knots (57 km/h; 35 mph) IAS
Typical rate of climb at S/L	213-259 m (700-850 ft)/min
Service ceiling	4,420 m (14,500 ft)
T-O to, and landing from, 15 m (50 ft)	305-335 m (1,000-1,100 ft)
g limits	±4·5

KIMBERLEY
GARY KIMBERLEY

255 Woniora Road, Blakehurst, New South Wales 2221
Telephone: (02) 546 4143

KIMBERLEY SKY-RIDER

Mr Gary Kimberley has designed and built a 'minimum' aircraft known as the Sky-Rider. Conforming to Australian Department of Transport Air Navigation Order 95.10, which covers powered hang gliders and ultralight aircraft, it is a single-seat monoplane powered by a 9 kW (12 hp) modified McCulloch two-stroke engine. Construction is of wire-braced aluminium tubing, with Dacron covering on the wings and tail unit. Conventional control surfaces are fitted. The Sky-Rider can be dismantled for transportation on the roof of a car and for stowage. Plans are available to amateur constructors.

TYPE: Single-seat ultralight aircraft.

DIMENSIONS, EXTERNAL:
Wing span	9·75 m (32 ft 0 in)
Wing chord: at root	1·52 m (5 ft 0 in)
at tip	1·22 m (4 ft 0 in)
Length overall	5·49 m (18 ft 0 in)
Height overall	2·39 m (7 ft 10 in)

WEIGHTS:
Weight empty	95·25 kg (210 lb)
Max T-O weight	181·4 kg (400 lb)

PERFORMANCE:
Max level speed	43·5 knots (80·5 km/h; 50 mph)
Cruising speed	35 knots (64·5 km/h; 40 mph)
Stalling speed, flaps up	20 knots (37 km/h; 23 mph)
Stalling speed, flaps down	17·5 knots (32 km/h; 20 mph)
Stalling speed IGE	16 knots (29 km/h; 18 mph)
Max rate of climb at S/L	46 m (150 ft)/min
Service ceiling (official limit)	91 m (300 ft)
T-O run	75 m (246 ft)
Landing run	50 m (164 ft)
Endurance	45 min

TODHUNTER
R. W. TODHUNTER

5 Leemon Street, Condell Park, NSW 2200

In 1963, Mr Reg Todhunter began the design of a man-powered aircraft named the Skycycle. His brother shared in its construction, which required approximately 4,000 man-hours of work over a six-year period, beginning in 1970. Following an accident during testing in January 1977, which broke the port wing, the original upper-surface spoiler system was replaced by a new system for lateral and yaw control.

In its new form, the Skycycle made six short flights under tow, between January and March 1979, the greatest distance covered being about 91 m (300 ft). The new wingtips performed well, and yaw control was improved, but elevator control still caused problems and the aircraft was again badly damaged in an accident. It was being rebuilt in early 1980, but will probably be used as a testbed for solar-powered flight research, if funding can be arranged.

A detailed description of the Skycycle can be found in the 1979-80 *Jane's*. Mr Todhunter is now developing an ultralight powered sailplane known as the T-5 Blue Wren.

AUSTRIA

WESTERMAYER
OSKAR WESTERMAYER

A-2161 Poysbrunn, Hauptstrasse 11
Telephone: 02554 405

Herr Westermayer, who manufactures rotor blades for small aircraft, has built four single-seat rotorcraft, of which brief details follow:

WESTERMAYER WE 01

Completed in 1969, the WE 01 (OE-AXW) is similar in general configuration to the Bensen B-8M. It is powered by a 48·5 kW (65 hp) 1,800 cc Volkswagen engine and has a two-blade teetering rotor, made originally of wood but now fitted with Gfk blades.

DIMENSIONS, EXTERNAL:
Rotor diameter	6·90 m (22 ft 7½ in)
Length of fuselage	3·10 m (10 ft 2 in)
Height overall	2·00 m (6 ft 6¾ in)

WEIGHTS:
Weight empty	155 kg (342 lb)
Max T-O weight	270 kg (595 lb)

PERFORMANCE:
Max level speed	65 knots (120 km/h; 75 mph)
Cruising speed	48 knots (90 km/h; 56 mph)
Max rate of climb at S/L	120-180 m (393-590 ft)/min
T-O run	100 m (328 ft)
Range with max fuel	86 nm (160 km; 99 miles)

WESTERMAYER WE 02

Testbed for a new Gfk rotor, with teetering hub and automatic pitch change from pre-rotation to flight pitch.

WESTERMAYER WE 03

More refined rotorcraft (OE-AXB, illustrated in 1979-80 *Jane's*) used to flight test various early forms of the rotor head used on the WE 04. Powered by 2,600 cc Volkswagen engine.

WESTERMAYER WE 04

Similar to the WE 03 in general configuration, the WE 04 (OE-AXR) represents the fully-developed Westermayer single-seat rotorcraft. It was flown for the first time in early 1980, and embodies a number of design features new to aircraft in this category, including all-glassfibre rotor blades and a patented helicopter-type rotor head that provides cyclic and collective pitch to the blades, offering improved stability and safety. The blades are pre-spun to 500 rpm prior to take-off and pitched to +7° for flight.

The blades, built by Mr. Westermayer, are made from Gevetex Glasrovings and cloth, with a Rohacell 31 foam core, bonded with CIBA epoxy resin in heated aluminium moulds. Blade section is NACA 8H-12.

The fuselage is made of metal, with Gfk covering on the cabin and a side-hinged (to starboard) one-piece canopy/windscreen. A non-retractable tricycle landing gear is fitted, with steerable nosewheel and a small bumper

Corby Starlet single-seat homebuilt aircraft

Kimberley Sky-Rider ultralight aircraft

wheel at the rear of the tailboom. The horizontal tail surfaces are fixed, but there is a large rudder with a ground-adjustable tab on its trailing-edge. All tail surfaces are wooden-covered.

Power plant is a 52·2 kW (70 hp) 2,600 cc Volkswagen engine, driving a two-blade wooden fixed-pitch pusher propeller. Normal autorotative rotor rpm in cruising flight is 380-400.

The WE 04 will be certificated to FAR Pt 27, and plans will be made available to amateur constructors.

DIMENSIONS, EXTERNAL:
Rotor diameter	7·40 m (24 ft 3½ in)
Rotor blade chord, constant	18 cm (7·09 in)
Length of fuselage	3·92 m (12 ft 10½ in)
Height overall	2·20 m (7 ft 2½ in)
Propeller diameter	1·38 m (4 ft 6½ in)

WEIGHTS:
Weight empty	230 kg (507 lb)
Max T-O weight	340 kg (750 lb)

PERFORMANCE:
Max level speed	81 knots (150 km/h; 93 mph)
Cruising speed	65 knots (120 km/h; 75 mph)
Max rate of climb at S/L	300 m (985 ft)/min
T-O run	10 m (33 ft)
Range with max fuel	135 nm (250 km; 155 miles)

CANADA

FLETCHER
DAN & RICHARD FLETCHER
Apt 3112, 30 Exeter Road, Ajax, Ontario L1F 2J6

FLETCHER BUSHBIRD
Few details are available concerning the Bushbird (C-GRYF) which flew for the first time in 1979. Designed and constructed by Dan and Richard Fletcher, it is a three-seat strut-braced high-wing monoplane, powered by one 112 kW (150 hp) Avco Lycoming O-320 engine. It is to be flight tested also as a floatplane. Of all-metal construction, it took approximately ten years to build. Maximum take-off weight is said to be 1,066 kg (2,350 lb).

JONES
DANIEL G. JONES
Grosse Isle, Manitoba

JONES D-1
Designed and constructed by Daniel Jones, the D-1 (CF-UOZ) is a small single-seat biplane, powered by a 67 kW (90 hp) Continental engine. Large fairings cover the main wheels of the tailwheel-type landing gear. Wing span is reported to be 5·74 m (18 ft 10 in) and range 260 nm (480 km; 300 miles) at a cruising speed of 91 knots (169 km/h; 105 mph).

MACFAM
MACFAM WORLD TRADERS
4623 Fortune Road SE, Calgary, Alberta T2A 2A7
Telephone: (403) 272 3658

Macfam (formerly K & S Aircraft) is continuing to sell to amateur constructors plans for its popular SA 102·5 Cavalier, SA 103 and SA 104 Cavalier, and the SA 105 Super Cavalier with retractable landing gear. However, priority has shifted away from the SA 102·5, due to the ready availability of larger engines and the roomier cockpits and increased baggage capacity of the later models.

Each of the SA 103/104/105 models is available in **BCD** (bubble canopy with doors) and **BSC** (bubble sliding canopy) forms. BCD/BSC aircraft retain the original windshield, but have the turtledeck aft of the seats lowered, giving improved rearward visibility and necessitating revision of the tail fin curve.

MACFAM SA 102·5 CAVALIER
TYPE: Two-seat or '2+2' light aircraft.
WINGS: Cantilever low-wing monoplane. Wing section NACA 23015 at root, NACA 23012 at tip. Dihedral 6°. Incidence 3° 30' at root, washed out to 1° at tip. No sweepback at quarter-chord. Single wooden box-spar, plywood leading-edge, and auxiliary rear spar to carry aileron and flap loads. Diagonal I-section drag spar between front and rear spar in each wing. Entire centre-section is plywood-covered and contoured to serve as cabin seat. Outer panels covered with Dacron synthetic fabric, finished with a polyurethane compound. Single-slotted Frise-type ailerons of spruce and plywood. Cable-operated split flaps of spruce and birch ply. Optional plans available for building wing in three pieces and for electrical actuation of flaps.
FUSELAGE: Truss-type structure, with four main longerons, of spruce and birch plywood construction. Cockpit canopy and doors of moulded glassfibre, rear part of top-decking fabric-covered.
TAIL UNIT: Cantilever structure, with sweptback vertical surfaces. All-wood construction, with Dacron covering. Fixed-incidence tailplane. Elevators operated by pushrods. Trim tab in starboard elevator.
LANDING GEAR: Non-retractable tricycle type. All units have spring steel legs of Macfam design. Wheel size 5·00-5, tyre pressure 2·75 bars (40 lb/sq in), on all

units. For rough-field operation, 6·00-6 main wheels with low-profile tyres are used optionally. Expanding-shoe brakes, operated hydraulically by dual toe-controls. Glassfibre wheel fairings. Alternative 680 kg (1,500 lb) capacity floats or ski landing gear optional.
POWER PLANT: Wide choice of four-cylinder engines available, including 63·5, 67 or 74·5 kW (85, 90 or 100 hp) Continental, 93-97 kW (125-130 hp) Franklin Sport 4A, 80·5 or 86 kW (108 or 115 hp) Avco Lycoming O-235, or 93 or 101 kW (125 or 135 hp) Avco Lycoming O-290. Choice of wood or metal, fixed-pitch or variable-pitch propellers, with diameters from 1·68 m (5 ft 6 in) to 1·83 m (6 ft 0 in). Whichever engine is used, an extension shaft 7·6 to 12·7 cm (3 to 5 in) long is fitted between the propeller and the crankshaft, permitting the use of more streamlined cowling panels and a reduction in the compression of airflow between the propeller and engine. All fuel in permanent wingtip tanks, with choice of two sizes: 64 or 75 litres (17 or 20 US gallons) each. Oil capacity 5·7-6·8 litres (1·5-1·8 US gallons), according to engine fitted.
ACCOMMODATION: Side-by-side seating for pilot and one adult passenger, with optional rear jump-seat for two small children in what would normally be the baggage area. Without this rear seat, up to 56 kg (125 lb) of baggage can be carried, depending upon engine and equipment installations. Forward-opening door on each side of heated and ventilated cabin.
AVIONICS AND EQUIPMENT: Standard nav/com equipment, including 1 or 2 VHF sets. ADF and transponder optional.
DIMENSIONS, EXTERNAL:
Wing span over tip-tanks	8·33 m (27 ft 4 in)
Width, outer wing panels folded	3·63 m (11 ft 11 in)
Wing area, gross	10·96 m² (118·0 sq ft)
Wing aspect ratio	6·25
Length overall	6·71 m (22 ft 0 in)
Height overall	2·23 m (7 ft 4 in)
Wheelbase	1·37 m (4 ft 6 in)
Propeller diameter	see under 'Power Plant'

WEIGHTS AND LOADINGS:
Basic operating weight empty	408 kg (900 lb)
Max T-O weight	680 kg (1,500 lb)
Max wing loading	2·60 kg/m² (12·7 lb/sq ft)
Max power loading (63·5 kW; 85 hp engine)	10·73 kg/kW (17·6 lb/hp)

PERFORMANCE (at max T-O weight, 93 kW; 125 hp Avco Lycoming engine):
Never-exceed speed	199 knots (370 km/h; 230 mph)
Max level speed at 2,135 m (7,000 ft)	160 knots (297 km/h; 185 mph)
Max cruising speed	143 knots (265 km/h; 165 mph)
Econ cruising speed	134 knots (249 km/h; 155 mph)
Stalling speed, flaps up	43·5 knots (81 km/h; 50 mph) IAS
Stalling speed, flaps down	35 knots (65 km/h; 40 mph) IAS
Max rate of climb at S/L	over 518 m (1,700 ft)/min
Service ceiling	4,875 m (16,000 ft)
T-O run	107 m (350 ft)
T-O to 15 m (50 ft)	305 m (1,000 ft)
Landing from 15 m (50 ft)	396 m (1,300 ft)
Landing run	183 m (600 ft)
Max range, no reserves	720 nm (1,335 km; 830 miles)

MACFAM SA 103 CAVALIER
This aircraft combines a simplified version of the SA 105 airframe with a non-retractable tailwheel type landing gear. It provides a roomier cabin than the SA 102·5, for improved passenger comfort and increased baggage space, and allows use of the plentiful engines in the 93-134 kW (125-180 hp) category that are currently available, including the Javelin listed under the SA 105 entry.

Available in standard, BCD or BSC form (see introductory notes).

MACFAM SA 104 CAVALIER
The SA 104 differs from the SA 103 in having a non-retractable tricycle landing gear similar to that of the SA 102·5.

Available in standard, BCD or BSC form (see introductory notes).

MACFAM SA 105 SUPER CAVALIER
Although similar in general configuration to the SA 102·5, the SA 105 is an entirely new design, with only the ailerons and wingtip tanks interchangeable between the two types. Overall dimensions are slightly greater, offering improved comfort and more baggage space; and a retractable tricycle landing gear is standard.

The size of the elevator trim tab has been increased in 1980; the plans have also been improved and simplified.

Westermayer WE 04 light rotorcraft

Westermayer WE 01 single- seat rotorcraft

Westermayer WE 02, testbed for a new Gfk rotor

Fletcher Bushbird three-seat light monoplane *(Neil A. Macdougall)*

Macfam SA 105 Super Cavalier built by Mr Hank Q. Johnson

Macfam SA 102·5 Cavalier owned by Mr M. Johnson

First example to fly was the aircraft shown in the accompanying illustration (N17HJ), built by Mr Hank Q. Johnson of Memphis, Tennessee. This is powered by a 149 kW (200 hp) Avco Lycoming IO-360 flat-four engine in a Gulfstream American Traveler cowling, without a propeller extension, which compromises its appearance and performance by comparison with the basic Macfam design. Max cruising speed is 191 knots (354 km/h; 220 mph) at 2,135 m (7,000 ft) with a constant-speed propeller; econ cruising speed is 156-165 knots (289-305 km/h; 180-190 mph); and max rate of climb at S/L 760 m (2,500 ft)/min.

The following description applies to the standard SA 105 built to Macfam plans:

TYPE: Two-seat all-wood light aircraft.

WINGS: Cantilever low-wing monoplane. Wing section NACA 23015 at root, NACA 23010 at tip. Dihedral at chord line 6° from roots. Washout 2° 30′ between ribs 0 and 5. All-wood structure of Sitka spruce spars, fir/mahogany marine ply ribs, and leading-edge skin of Finnish birch plywood. Fabric covering aft of main spar, except for plywood walkways at roots, and tips. Ailerons of similar construction to wings. Split type mechanically-actuated (electric or hydraulic actuation optional) flap system has been developed, effectively changing the wing aerofoil section from 230 series to 23 (sailplane) series. These flaps operate at 15°, 30° and 45°, and can be set at negative angles of up to 12° for cruising flight to increase cruising speed. Glassfibre canted wingtip tanks, which have similar effect to winglets, and increase wing area, aspect ratio and lift.

FUSELAGE: Truss structure, with four longerons, of Sitka spruce and Finnish birch plywood. Cockpit roof, side window/door frames and engine cowling of glassfibre. Rear fuselage and rear part of top-decking fabric covered.

TAIL UNIT: Cantilever wood structure, with sweptback vertical surfaces. Fin and tailplane plywood covered; control surfaces fabric covered. Trim tab in starboard elevator.

LANDING GEAR: Retractable tricycle type, with mechanical (optionally electric or hydraulic) actuation. Main units retract inward into wing roots, nosewheel rearward. Spring steel legs. All three wheels size 5·00-5. Brakes on main wheels, toe-operated from port seat.

POWER PLANT: One Avco Lycoming, Franklin or similar flat-four engine, with propeller extension shaft. Recommended are 112-119 kW (150-160 hp) Avco Lycoming O-320/IO-320, driving a variable-pitch or constant-speed propeller. Min recommended power plant is 93 kW (125 hp) Franklin 4A-235 or Avco Lycoming O-290/O-290-D2/O-290-G driving a fixed-pitch propeller. Max recommended is 149 kW (200 hp) Avco Lycoming O-360/IO-360. Other suitable engines include the Javelin Aircraft 2,300 cc turbocharged Ford conversion with ground-adjustable wooden propeller. Normal capacity of wingtip tanks 127 litres (28 Imp gallons). Optional sump tanks (with engines over 112 kW; 150 hp) raise total capacity to 152·75 litres (33·6 Imp gallons).

ACCOMMODATION: Two seats side by side in enclosed cabin. Dual controls. Forward-hinged window/door on each side in standard form. Available also in BCD or BSC form (see introductory notes). Baggage space aft of seats, capacity up to 172 kg (379 lb).

DIMENSIONS, EXTERNAL:
Wing span over tip-tanks	8·31 m (27 ft 3⅜ in)
Wing area, gross, flaps 0°	10·87 m² (117 sq ft)
Length overall	7·25 m (23 ft 9½ in)
Wheel track	2·58 m (8 ft 5½ in)
Wheelbase	1·33 m (4 ft 4¼ in)
Propeller diameter	1·83 m (6 ft 0 in)

WEIGHTS:
Weight empty	431-454 kg (950-1,000 lb)
Max T-O weight (dependent on engine)	up to 885 kg (1,950 lb)

PERFORMANCE (estimated, at AUW of 816 kg; 1,800 lb. A = 93 kW; 125 hp. B = 112 kW; 150 hp. C = 134 kW; 180 hp):

Never-exceed speed 200 knots (370 km/h; 230 mph)
Cruising speed:
A	143-148 knots (265-273 km/h; 165-170 mph)
B	152-156 knots (281-289 km/h; 175-180 mph)
C	165-174 knots (305-322 km/h; 190-200 mph)

Stalling speed, flaps 0°
52-61 knots (96·5-105 km/h; 60-65 mph) IAS
Stalling speed, flaps down 15°
48-52 knots (89-96·5 km/h; 55-60 mph) IAS
Max rate of climb at S/L: A 183-213 m (600-700 ft)/min
B	274-305 m (900-1,000 ft)/min
C	365-488 m (1,200-1,600 ft)/min

T-O run: A 274 m (900 ft)
B	244 m (800 ft)
C	183 m (600 ft)

JEAN ST-GERMAIN
CENTRE DE RECHERCHES JEAN ST-GERMAIN INC
924 St-Pierre, Drummondville, PQ
Telephone: (819) 477 1221

DESIGNER: Jean Saint-Germain
GENERAL MANAGER: Gilbert Lapointe

JEAN ST-GERMAIN RAZ-MUT
The Raz-Mut was designed by Jean Saint-Germain as an easy-to-build and easy-to-fly ultra-light aircraft, suitable for home construction, for sport flying by amateurs, and for a variety of utility applications including agricultural spraying and survey work. Design of the aircraft was started in May 1976 and the original prototype, built at Mr Saint-Germain's research centre, flew for the first time on 24 October 1976, powered by a 33 kW (44 hp) Kohler

K-440-2AS-M aircooled two-stroke engine. It proved to be underpowered, and the third Raz-Mut, demonstrated at the 1977 EAA Fly-in at Oshkosh and shown in the accompanying illustration, has a 1,700 cc Volkswagen engine. Also at the Fly-in was a then-unflown version with the alternative McCulloch MC-431 engine. Both embodied a number of aerodynamic refinements compared with the first Raz-Mut, including a drooped wing leading-edge, upper-surface fences and wide fairings over the wing bracing struts.

Kit production began in December 1976; by Spring 1979 about 100 sets of plans and/or kits had been sold, and several amateur-built Raz-Muts were flying in Canada. The first example built in Europe, by M Jean-Pierre Marie, was nearing completion at Mantes at that time.

The basic kit contains all raw materials and components needed to build the Raz-Mut, including the engine and propeller but excluding instruments, battery and seat cushion. A more expensive kit offers the materials and components in pre-finished state, so that only a simple tool kit is required to complete the aircraft. As an alternative, building and servicing instructions, and a list of materials, are available to those who are willing to purchase their own materials and perform all the machining and other work.

TYPE: Single-seat ultra-light aircraft.
WINGS: Strut-braced high-wing monoplane, with single wide aerofoil-section bracing strut each side. Modified NACA 4400 wing section. Thickness/chord ratio 13%. Constant chord. Some dihedral. Plain aileron and three-position flap form entire trailing-edge of each wing. Entire wing and control surfaces of aluminium, including covering. Shallow fence above each wing between aileron and flap. Endplates standard.
FUSELAGE: Open structure of square-section aluminium tube, bolted together.
TAIL UNIT: All-moving horizontal surface with ground-adjustable tab at centre of trailing-edge. Small fin and large-area horn-balanced rudder with ground adjustable tab. All control surfaces cable-actuated. Entire structure of aluminium with fabric covering.
LANDING GEAR: Non-retractable tricycle type. Brake on nosewheel. Small tail bumper wheel in rear end of keel member. Skis and floats optional.
POWER PLANT: One 52 kW (70 hp) 1,700 cc Volkswagen flat-four four-stroke or 53·5 kW (72 hp) McCulloch MC-431 flat-four two-stroke engine, driving a two-blade fixed-pitch wooden pusher propeller through multiple belts. Fuel tank, capacity 23 litres (6 US gal-

lons), aft of seat. Provision for second, similar, tank. Manual or electric engine starting.
ACCOMMODATION: Pilot only, on open seat. Glassfibre cabin enclosure optional.

DIMENSIONS, EXTERNAL:
Wing span	7·01 m (23 ft 0 in)
Wing area, gross	8·55 m² (92 sq ft)
Wing chord, constant	1·22 m (4 ft 0 in)
Length overall	5·58 m (18 ft 3½ in)
Height overall	1·77 m (5 ft 9½ in)
Propeller diameter	1·09 m (3 ft 7 in)

WEIGHTS (VW engine):
Weight empty	204 kg (450 lb)
Max T-O weight	363 kg (800 lb)

PERFORMANCE (VW engine):
Max level speed	74 knots (136 km/h; 85 mph)
Max cruising speed	61 knots (112 km/h; 70 mph)
Landing speed	39 knots (73 km/h; 45 mph)
Max rate of climb at S/L	198 m (650 ft)/min
Service ceiling	2,745 m (9,000 ft)
T-O run	61 m (200 ft)
Landing run	54 m (175 ft)
Range with standard fuel	130 nm (240 km; 150 miles)

REPLICA PLANS
REPLICA PLANS
PO Box 94248, Richmond, BC V6Y 2A6

The SE-5A replica was designed to be an easy-to-build and inexpensive 85 per cent scale representation of the famous first World War fighter, although exact reproduction was waived in favour of making the aircraft simple to construct, using modern and more readily available materials.

Design of the aircraft began in 1969, in which year construction of the first prototype also started. The SE-5A prototypes were designed for Continental engines ranging from 48·5 to 74·5 kW (65-100 hp), but larger engines can be installed to the individual homebuilder's preference. The first prototype flew for the first time in 1970 and certification has been granted by the FAA in the Experimental (homebuilt) category.

Plans are available to amateur builders, and more than 300 sets had been sold by early 1980.

REPLICA PLANS SE-5A REPLICA
TYPE: Single-seat sporting biplane.
WINGS: Braced biplane wings of Clark CYH section.

Dihedral 3°. Incidence 3°. Ailerons on lower wings only. Centre-section of upper wing houses a small tank which can be used as an auxiliary fuel tank or smoke tank, or can be left out at building stage. The centre-section is carried on four spruce cabane struts and is braced with stainless steel cables and turnbuckles. Spruce interplane struts, with 4130 steel end fittings. Stainless steel flying, landing and incidence wires. Wing ribs of mahogany plywood, with cap strips; spruce spars. From the front spar forward, the leading-edge is covered with glassfibre or aluminium. Wings are fabric-covered.
FUSELAGE: Ply-skinned box structure, with fabric-covered turtledeck and aluminium-covered forward top decking. Dummy Vickers machine-gun in housing on port side of fuselage, and gunsights on decking forward of windscreen.
TAIL UNIT: Tail surfaces built on spruce spars, with structure similar to that of wings except for drag bracing. Pushrod-operated elevators. Cable-operated rudder, with a horn for tailwheel steering.
LANDING GEAR: Non-retractable tailwheel type. Bungee cord shock-absorption. Converted motorcycle wheels on main units, size 3·25-16. Size 6·00-2 tailwheel.

Mechanical brakes.
POWER PLANT: Various engines can be installed. Performance figures quoted relate to aircraft with 63·5 kW (85 hp) Continental C85 flat-four engine, driving a two-blade fixed-pitch wooden propeller. Fuel capacity 72 litres (19 US gallons). Oil capacity 3·8 litres (1 US gallon).
ACCOMMODATION: Single seat in open cockpit.

DIMENSIONS, EXTERNAL:
Wing span	6·96 m (22 ft 10 in)
Wing chord, constant	1·27 m (4 ft 2 in)
Wing area, gross	13·01 m² (140 sq ft)
Height overall	2·18 m (7 ft 2 in)
Wheel track	1·52 m (5 ft 0 in)
Propeller diameter	1·83 m (6 ft 0 in)

WEIGHTS:
Weight empty	358 kg (790 lb)
Max T-O weight	499 kg (1,100 lb)

PERFORMANCE:
Max level speed at S/L	78 knots (145 km/h; 90 mph)
Max cruising speed	74 knots (137 km/h; 85 mph)
Stalling speed	30·5 knots (57 km/h; 35 mph)
Max rate of climb at S/L	152 m (500 ft)/min

WESTERN
WESTERN AIRCRAFT SUPPLIES
623 Markerville Road NE, Calgary, Alberta T2E 5X1
Telephone: (403) 276 3087
DIRECTOR: Jean J. Peters

Western Aircraft Supplies markets materials for amateur aircraft constructors, and has sold plans for construction of the RL-3 Monsoon, a two-seat light aircraft originally designed in India. At least 12 sets of plans for the Monsoon and five kits of materials were sold. Details of this aircraft can be found in the 1977-78 *Jane's*.

Western has developed another aircraft, of basic wooden construction, known as the PGK-1 Hirondelle. Plans and wood kits are available to amateur constructors, as well as preformed engine cowlings, windscreens and fuel tanks.

PGK-1 HIRONDELLE
Design of the PGK-1 Hirondelle began in 1969 and construction of a prototype (C-GWYL) started in July 1970. First flight was achieved on 27 June 1976. It is said to be suited for cross-country and recreational flying, and simple enough for first-time constructors to build. All fabric covering is glued in place, rather than stitched.
TYPE: Two-seat light aircraft.
WINGS: Cantilever low-wing monoplane of constant

chord. Wing section NACA 23012. Dihedral 4° from roots. Incidence 4° at root, 2° at tip. No sweepback. Wooden box spar and plank-type auxiliary rear spar. Plywood ribs. Dacron fabric covered, with dope and polyurethane finish. Ailerons of wood and fabric construction. No flaps or tabs.
FUSELAGE: Conventional structure of spruce bulkheads and spruce longerons, plywood covered to rear of cabin, with outer covering of Dacron. Cabin constructed of wood formers with polystyrene foam infill and glassfibre top. Rounded corners of turtledeck formed from foam and glassfibre. Rear fuselage Dacron-covered, with dope and polyurethane finish.
TAIL UNIT: Cantilever structure of capped spars and plywood ribs, all plywood-covered and with outer covering of Dacron. Tab in starboard elevator.
LANDING GEAR: Non-retractable tailwheel type. Tapered spring steel main struts; 5·00-5 tyres on main wheels. Industrial Dynamics brakes. Cessna 150 main-wheel fairings.
POWER PLANT: One 86 kW (115 hp) Avco Lycoming O-235-C1B flat-four engine, driving a Warnke three-blade ground-adjustable propeller. Two glassfibre fuel tanks in leading-edges of wings, each 54·5 litres (12 Imp gallons) capacity. Oil capacity 5·7 litres (1·25 Imp gallons).
ACCOMMODATION: Two seats side by side in enclosed cabin.

Dual controls and heater standard.
SYSTEM: Electrical system includes 12V 20A generator for lights, radio and fuel pump.
AVIONICS: Genave Alpha 200B radio and VOR.

DIMENSIONS, EXTERNAL:
Wing span	7·92 m (26 ft 0 in)
Wing chord, constant	1·40 m (4 ft 7 in)
Wing area, gross	10·96 m² (118 sq ft)
Wing aspect ratio	5·7
Length overall	6·27 m (20 ft 7 in)
Height overall	2·29 m (7 ft 6 in)
Wheel track	2·03 m (6 ft 8 in)
Wheelbase	4·39 m (14 ft 5 in)
Propeller diameter	1·68 m (5 ft 6 in)

WEIGHTS:
Weight empty, equipped	428 kg (944 lb)
Max T-O weight	669 kg (1,475 lb)

PERFORMANCE (at max T-O weight):
Never-exceed speed	160 knots (297 km/h; 185 mph)
Max level speed	123 knots (228 km/h; 142 mph)
Max cruising speed	117 knots (217 km/h; 135 mph)
Stalling speed	52·5 knots (96·5 km/h; 60 mph)
Max rate of climb at S/L	over 305 m (1,000 ft)/min
Service ceiling	3,840 m (12,600 ft)
T-O run	approx 228 m (750 ft)
Endurance, with 45 min reserves	3 h 36 min

ZENAIR
ZENAIR LTD
236 Richmond Street, Richmond Hill, Ontario L4C 3Y8
Telephone: (416) 884 9044
WORKS: 25 King Road, Nobleton, Ontario
Telephone: (416) 859 4556
PRESIDENT AND DESIGNER: Christophe Heintz

M Heintz, a professional aeronautical engineer, participated in the design of several of the aircraft produced by Avions Pierre Robin. While in France, he also designed and built the prototype of a two-seat light aircraft named the Zénith, intended for amateur construction. More than 60 Zéniths are now flying, and others are under construction, including single-seat and three-seat models, as described in this entry. In addition, Mr Heintz' Zenair company is developing the four-seat Zénith-CH 400 for factory production (see main Aircraft section).

In 1974 the Zénith-CH 200 was granted the National

Association of Sport Aircraft Designers (NASAD, USA) 'seal of quality' No. 108. In 1979 the Mono Z-CH 100 and Tri-Z CH 300 were granted NASAD 'seals of quality' Nos. 115 and 116 respectively; the Mono Z-CH 100, Zénith-CH 200 and CH 250, and Tri-Z CH 300 were granted NASAD kit 'seals of quality' Nos. 301, 302 and 303 respectively.

In 1978, EAA President Paul Poberezny presented Christophe Heintz with the Dr August Raspet Memorial Award for making an 'outstanding contribution to the advancement of the design of light aircraft'.

Zenair Ltd has thirteen full-time employees. Subsidiary manufacturing and distributing companies are Zenair Atlanta Inc (Georgia, USA) and Zenair Seattle Inc (Washington, USA).

ZÉNITH-CH 200
Work on the Zénith-CH 200 began in October 1968;

the prototype, registered F-WPZY (later C-FEYC), flew for the first time on 22 March 1970 and was granted French CNRA (homebuilt experimental aircraft) certification. In October 1970 the original wing of NACA 64A315 (modified) section was replaced by one offering improved low-speed characteristics.

Sets of plans and a constructional manual for the Zénith-CH 200 are available to amateur builders, as follows:

French manual and metric measurements from D. Triques, 23 Ave Edouard Belin, Fontaine d'Ouche, F21 Dijon.

German manual and metric measurements from K. Arens, Rollstrasse 26, D 3392 Klausthal Zellerfeld-1.

English manual and drawings to US standards, with Imperial and metric measurements, from Zenair, which offers materials, parts and complete kits for all current Heintz designs. Zenair also designs and manufactures

Jean St-Germain Raz-Mut (1,700 cc Volkswagen engine) *(Howard Levy)*

Replica Plans SE-5A, an 85 per cent scale representation of a first World War fighter *(Tony Swain)*

Prototype PGK-1 Hirondelle two-seat light aircraft

Floatplane version of the Zénith-CH 200 with a modified cockpit canopy (93 kW; 125 hp Avco Lycoming O-290)

Mono Z-CH 100 (41 kW; 55 hp Volkswagen engine)

Tri-Z CH 300 'stretched' version of the CH 200 (112 kW; 150 hp Avco Lycoming O-320)

---

wooden propellers for engines of up to 134 kW (180 hp).

The Zénith-CH 200 is approved by the Australian DCA and the New Zealand airworthiness authorities. Several kits have been exported to these countries, as well as to sixteen other countries, including South Africa, Botswana, Norway, New Guinea, Iceland, Ireland, Belgium, Sweden, the UK and Switzerland.

During the 1976 eight-day EAA Fly-in at Oshkosh, Chris Heintz, assisted by volunteer experienced metal workers, built a Zénith-CH 200 from standard pre-fabricated kit components (as available to the home-builder) and flew it on the last day of the meeting.

The single-seat Mono Z-CH 100 and three-seat Tri-Z-CH 300 are variations of the basic design and are described separately. Several optional items are available for all three aircraft, including tailwheel landing gear, a forward-sliding canopy, dual control column (not on CH 100) and detachable wings.

The following description applies to the standard Zénith-CH 200, of which Zenair was producing five complete kits each month in early 1980:

TYPE: Two-seat all-metal homebuilt light aircraft, with ultimate stress factor of 9g.

WINGS: Cantilever low-wing monoplane. Constant-chord wings, of NACA 64A515 (modified) section. Dihedral 6° from roots. Single-spar aluminium alloy structure, with blind riveted aluminium alloy skin. Hoerner wing-tips. Aluminium alloy piano-hinged ailerons and electrically-actuated plain flaps on trailing-edge.

FUSELAGE: Conventional aluminium alloy stressed-skin structure, of basically rectangular section with rounded top-decking.

TAIL UNIT: Rectangular one-piece all-moving tailplane, with combined trim and anti-servo tabs. Plans show rudder only, with slight sweepback. Conventional fin and rudder can be fitted if desired. Tailplane and rudder are both single-spar structures with ribs and skin of aluminium alloy.

LANDING GEAR: Non-retractable tricycle type, with rubber-block shock-absorbers. Manual locking of steerable nosewheel. All three Cleveland wheels and tyres size 6·00-6. Hydraulically-actuated disc brakes on

main units. Streamlined glassfibre fairings over all three wheels and legs. At least one aircraft is fitted with twin floats in summer and skis in winter.

POWER PLANT: Design suitable for engines from 63·5 kW (85 hp) to 119 kW (160 hp). Fuel tank in fuselage, aft of seats, capacity 90 litres (20 Imp gallons). Optional fuel tanks in wing leading-edges, total capacity 72·5 litres (16 Imp gallons). Refuelling point aft of canopy on port side.

ACCOMMODATION: Side-by-side seating for pilot and one passenger under sideways-opening (to starboard) Plexiglas canopy. Dual controls, with single control column located centrally between seats. Space for 35 kg (77 lb) of baggage aft of seats. Cabin heated and ventilated.

SYSTEMS: 12V battery and generator provide power for engine starting, fuel pump and flap actuation. VHF radio.

DIMENSIONS, EXTERNAL:

Wing span	7·00 m (22 ft 11¾ in)
Wing chord, constant	1·40 m (4 ft 7 in)
Wing area, gross	9·80 m² (105·9 sq ft)
Wing aspect ratio	5
Length overall	6·30 m (20 ft 8 in)
Height overall	1·85 m (6 ft 0¾ in)
Tailplane span	2·30 m (7 ft 6½ in)
Wheel track	2·25 m (7 ft 4½ in)
Wheelbase	1·42 m (4 ft 8 in)
Propeller diameter	1·83 m (6 ft 0 in)

DIMENSION, INTERNAL:

Cabin: Max width	1·01 m (3 ft 3¾ in)

WEIGHTS (with 74·5 kW; 100 hp engine):

Weight empty, equipped	400 kg (881 lb)
Normal T-O and landing weight	650 kg (1,433 lb)
Max T-O weight	680 kg (1,499 lb)

PERFORMANCE (at max T-O weight. A: 74·5 kW; 100 hp engine, B: 112 kW; 150 hp engine):

Max level speed at S/L:

A	126 knots (233 km/h; 145 mph)
B	143 knots (266 km/h; 165 mph)

Cruising speed (75% power) at S/L:

A	110 knots (205 km/h; 127 mph)
B	132 knots (245 km/h; 152 mph)

Cruising speed (75% power) at 2,750 m (9,000 ft):

A	116 knots (215 km/h; 134 mph)
B	135 knots (251 km/h; 156 mph)

Stalling speed, flaps down:

A, B	46 knots (85 km/h; 53 mph)

Max rate of climb at S/L:

A	240 m (787 ft)/min
B	426 m (1,400 ft)/min

Service ceiling:

A	4,600 m (15,100 ft)
B	over 4,875 m (16,000 ft)

Range with max fuel, no reserves (75% power):

A	432 nm (800 km; 497 miles)
B	451 nm (836 km; 520 miles)

ZÉNITH-CH 250

The Zénith-CH 250 is an improved version of the Zénith-CH 200 with two 65 litre (14 Imp gallon) fuel tanks in the wings and an 0·71 m³ (25 cu ft) baggage area. A forward-sliding canopy and rear windows similar to those of the Tri-Z CH 300 are fitted. Recommended engines are in the 93-119 kW (125-160 hp) range. A tailwheel type or float landing gear can be fitted as alternatives to the standard tricycle type. Performance is the same as that of the Zénith-CH 200.

By early 1980, more than 200 sets of plans and fifty kits to construct the Zénith-CH 250 had been sold.

MONO Z-CH 100

The single-seat Mono Z-CH 100 is of generally similar all-metal construction to the two-seat Zénith, but is slightly smaller overall and is designed to be powered by engines in the 37·25 to 74·5 kW (50 to 100 hp) range. The prototype (C-GNYM), which has a Volkswagen engine, made its first flight on 8 May 1975. Like the two-seat Zénith, it is stressed to ± 9g ultimate at normal max T-O weight.

Construction drawings and manual, materials, parts and complete kits to build the Mono Zénith are available from Zenair and 80 sets had been sold by early 1980.

TYPE: Single-seat homebuilt light aircraft.

WINGS: Cantilever low-wing monoplane. Wing section GA(PC) 1. Thickness/chord ratio 15%. Dihedral 6°. Incidence 7° 30′. Single-spar aluminium alloy structure, with aluminium alloy skin, blind riveted. Aluminium alloy piano-hinged ailerons. Wings easily removable.

FUSELAGE: Conventional aluminium alloy stressed-skin structure, of basically rectangular section, with rounded top-decking.

TAIL UNIT: Rectangular one-piece all-moving tailplane, with automatic and controllable trim tab. Single-spar structures, with ribs and skins of aluminium.

LANDING GEAR: Non-retractable tricycle type, with rubber-block shock-absorbers. Tailwheel gear optional. All three Cleveland wheels and tyres size 5·00-5. Hydraulically-actuated disc brakes.

POWER PLANT: One 41 kW (55 hp) 1,700 cc converted Volkswagen motor-car engine in prototype, driving a Zenair wooden propeller. Continental engine optional. Fuel tank in fuselage, capacity 55 litres (12 Imp gallons).

ACCOMMODATION: Single seat under Plexiglas canopy. Baggage compartment aft of seat, capacity 11·3 kg (25 lb).

DIMENSIONS, EXTERNAL:
Wing span	6·71 m (22 ft 0 in)
Wing chord, constant	1·27 m (4 ft 2 in)
Wing area, gross	8·50 m² (91·5 sq ft)
Wing aspect ratio	5·27
Length overall	5·94 m (19 ft 6 in)
Tailplane span	2·26 m (7 ft 5 in)
Wheel track	2·13 m (7 ft 0 in)
Wheelbase	1·27 m (4 ft 2 in)
Propeller diameter	1·47 m (4 ft 10 in)

WEIGHTS:
Weight empty	263 kg (580 lb)
Max T-O weight:	
VW engine	413 kg (910 lb)
74·5 kW; 100 hp engine	444 kg (980 lb)

PERFORMANCE (A: 1,700 cc Volkswagen, B: 48·5 kW; 65 hp, C: 74·5 kW; 100 hp engine):
Max level speed:	
A	103 knots (190 km/h; 118 mph)
B	109 knots (200 km/h; 125 mph)
C	130 knots (240 km/h; 150 mph)
Cruising speed (75% power):	
A	91 knots (170 km/h; 105 mph)
B	97 knots (180 km/h; 112 mph)
C	118 knots (218 km/h; 135 mph)
Stalling speed:	
A, B, C	41 knots (76 km/h; 47 mph)
Max rate of climb at S/L:	
A	200 m (610 ft)/min
B	220 m (720 ft)/min
C	490 m (1,500 ft)/min
Service ceiling: A	3,050 m (10,000 ft)
T-O run: A	183 m (600 ft)
T-O to 15 m (50 ft): A	335 m (1,100 ft)
Landing run: A	152 m (500 ft)
Range with 55 litres (12 Imp gallons) fuel:	
A, B	350 nm (645 km; 400 miles)
C	312 nm (580 km; 360 miles)
Endurance with 55 litres (12 Imp gallons) fuel:	
A, B	4 h 0 min
C	2 h 30 min

TRI-Z CH 300

The three-seat Tri-Z CH 300 is a 'stretched' version of the two-seat CH 200, with a longer fuselage and enlarged cabin, to provide room for a rear bench seat able to carry a third adult, two children or 95 kg (210 lb) of baggage. It has a greater wing span and larger tailplane; a fin and rudder assembly is standard. The ailerons are aerodynamically balanced, and electrically-actuated slotted flaps are fitted. Recommended power is in the 93-134 kW (125-180 hp) range. Fuel is carried in two 65 litre (14 Imp gallon) tanks, one in each wing leading-edge. Extra fuel can be carried in similar tanks installed in the outer wing sections. A forward-sliding canopy is standard. Limiting load factors are ±5·7g ultimate.

The prototype (C-GQTR), built by Harold Allsop of Toronto and powered by a 112 kW (150 hp) Avco Lycoming O-320 engine, made its first flight on 9 July 1977.

Sets of plans and a constructional manual for the Tri-Z CH 300 are available to amateur builders (300 sold by early 1980), as are materials, prefabricated component parts and complete kits.

A Tri-Z CH 300 (C-GOVK) was built by Robin 'Red' Morris, Gerry Boudreau and Doug Holtby in a little over six months, including modifications to the fuel system to provide 773 litres (170 Imp gallons) of fuel in two fuselage and six wing tanks. Max T-O weight of this aircraft is 1,134 kg (2,500 lb), with a 134 hp (180 hp) Avco Lycoming O-360-2F engine, and full IFR equipment. It was flown non-stop by 'Red' Morris from Vancouver International Airport to Halifax International Airport between 1 July and 2 July 1978, covering approximately 2,397 nm (4,440 km; 2,759 miles) in a flying time of 22 h 44 min. This set FAI Class C1c records between Vancouver and North Bay (103·831 knots; 192·295 km/h; 119·487 mph); Vancouver and Winnipeg (109·977 knots; 203·678 km/h; 126·560 mph); and Vancouver and Halifax (105·344 knots; 195·097 km/h; 121·228 mph).

DIMENSIONS, EXTERNAL:
Wing span	8·10 m (26 ft 6¾ in)
Wing chord, constant	1·48 m (4 ft 10½ in)
Wing area, gross	12·00 m² (129·2 sq ft)
Wing aspect ratio	5·48
Length overall	6·85 m (22 ft 5¾ in)
Tailplane span	2·60 m (8 ft 6¼ in)
Wheel track	2·25 m (7 ft 4½ in)
Wheelbase	1·45 m (4 ft 9 in)

WEIGHTS :
Weight empty	498 kg (1,100 lb)
Max T-O weight	840 kg (1,850 lb)

PERFORMANCE (at max T-O weight, with 112 kW; 150 hp engine):
Max level speed	137 knots (254 km/h; 158 mph)
Max cruising speed (75% power)	126 knots (233 km/h; 145 mph)
Stalling speed, flaps down	46 knots (85 km/h; 53 mph)
Max rate of climb at S/L	305 m (1,000 ft)/min
Range at max cruising speed	434 nm (804 km; 500 miles)
Endurance at max cruising speed	3 h 30 min

CH 50 MINI Z

Construction began in February 1978 of the prototype (C-GTZI) of this small single-seat monoplane, and the first flight was made in 1979.

TYPE: Single-seat light aircraft.

WINGS: Cantilever low-wing monoplane. Wing section NACA 4415. Dihedral 6°. Incidence 6°. Single-spar aluminium alloy structure. Elastic-hinged plain ailerons. No flaps. Wings removable.

FUSELAGE: Conventional aluminium alloy stressed-skin structure, of basically rectangular section with rounded top-decking.

TAIL UNIT: One-piece all-moving tailplane, with combined trim and anti-servo tabs. Vertical surfaces comprise rudder only. Tailplane and rudder are single-spar structures with ribs and skin of aluminium alloy.

LANDING GEAR: Non-retractable tailwheel type. Aluminium spring shock-absorption. Main wheels and tyres size 4·10 ×3·50-4. Tyre pressure 1·24 bars (18 lb/sq in).

POWER PLANT: One 18 kW (24 hp) Cuyuna two-cylinder two-stroke engine, driving a Zenair fixed-pitch wooden propeller. Single fuel tank in fuselage, capacity 23 litres (5 Imp gallons). Refuelling point on top of fuselage.

ACCOMMODATION: Single seat in open cockpit. Space for 10 kg (22 lb) of baggage, aft of cockpit.

DIMENSIONS, EXTERNAL:
Wing span	5·70 m (18 ft 8¼ in)
Wing area, gross	6·20 m² (66·74 sq ft)
Wing chord, constant	1·10 m (3 ft 7¼ in)
Wing aspect ratio	5·2
Height overall	approx 1·60 m (5 ft 3 in)
Tailplane span	2·00 m (6 ft 7 in)
Wheel track	3·50 m (11 ft 5¾ in)
Wheelbase	1·35 m (4 ft 5 in)
Propeller diameter	1·16 m (3 ft 10 in)
Propeller ground clearance	0·40 m (1 ft 3¾ in)

WEIGHTS:
Weight empty	137 kg (303 lb)
Max T-O weight	252 kg (555 lb)

PERFORMANCE:
Max level speed at S/L	76·5 knots (142 km/h; 88 mph)
Max cruising speed at S/L	71 knots (132 km/h; 82 mph)
Stalling speed	40 knots (74 km/h; 46 mph)
Max rate of climb at S/L	128 m (420 ft)/min
T-O and landing run	183 m (600 ft)
T-O to, and landing from, 15 m (50 ft)	305 m (1,000 ft)
Range with max fuel	191 nm (354 km; 220 miles)

ACRO Z-CH 150

The prototype of this latest addition to the Zenair range was expected to fly for the first time in May 1980. Plans and kits are available to amateur constructors.

Developed from the Mono Z-CH 100, the Acro Z-CH 150 has a tailwheel landing gear and is intended for aerobatic training and competition flying, with an engine of 74·5-119 kW (100-160 hp) and fuel and oil systems suitable for inverted flight. The airframe has been strengthened to withstand ±19g, and an NACA 0015 symmetrical wing section is employed. The cockpit length has been increased to allow room for a parachute, and the fuselage turtledeck has been lowered to accept a bubble canopy for improved rearward vision during aerobatics. The normal fuel capacity of 55 litres (12 Imp gallons) can be increased to 122 litres (27 Imp gallons) by use of a ferry tank. Other features include a battery-operated radio, quick-release canopy attachment, and five-point pilot's harness.

DIMENSIONS, EXTERNAL:
Wing span	6·17 m (20 ft 3 in)
Wing area, gross	7·83 m² (84·3 sq ft)
Wing aspect ratio	4·85
Wheel track	1·55 m (5 ft 1 in)
Wheelbase	4·32 m (14 ft 2 in)

WEIGHTS:
Weight empty	300 kg (660 lb)
Max T-O weight	522 kg (1,150 lb)

PERFORMANCE (Avco Lycoming O-320 with fixed-pitch propeller, estimated):
Max level speed at S/L	148 knots (273 km/h; 170 mph)
Max cruising speed (75% power at S/L)	135 knots (250 km/h; 155 mph)
Stalling speed	45·5 knots (84 km/h; 52 mph)
Max rate of climb at S/L	518 m (1,700 ft)/min
Range with ferry fuel	456 nm (845 km; 525 miles)

CZECHOSLOVAKIA

SIMŮNEK/KAMARÝT
JAN SIMŮNEK MSc/JAROSLAV KAMARÝT MSc

Rudý Letov Narodni Podnik, Praha 9, Letňany, Beranových 65, Post Code 199 02

SIMŮNEK/KAMARÝT SK-1 TREMPÍK (LITTLE TRAMP)

In 1968, Mr Jan Simůnek began the design of a light aircraft which eventually became the Trempík. In the following year, Mr Jaroslav Kamarýt joined the project to assist with the design and stress calculations. Construction began in Mr Simůnek's apartment in 1969, and continued there until 1975 when the aircraft outgrew the available space. The unfinished airframe was then transferred into the possession of the Rudý Letov company, with the understanding that completion would remain the responsibility of Mr Simůnek and Mr Kamarýt, with assistance from the SSM youth organisation and the Rudý Letov management. First flight of the Trempík was achieved on 19 October 1979, followed by the aircraft's public debut twelve days later. By the end of 1979, the first stages of certification under FAR 23 regulations had been completed.

TYPE: Tandem two-seat light monoplane.

WINGS: Strut-braced high-wing monoplane. Wing section NACA 23012 on constant-chord centre-section; NACA 4412 at wingtip. Washout 2°. Dihedral 1°. Incidence 4° 30′. Two-spar wooden structure, with leading-edge of birch plywood stiffened internally with styrofoam. Remainder of wing fabric covered. Wingtips of GRP; streamline-section bracing struts of steel tubing. Slotted and partially mass-balanced ailerons of wooden construction, fabric covered.

FUSELAGE: Composite structure, comprising welded steel tube forward section and wooden semi-monocoque rear section, made up of spruce longerons, plywood, spruce and pine bulkheads, and beech plywood covering. Side walls reinforced internally with styrofoam slabs.

TAIL UNIT: Conventional structure comprising all-wooden fin integral with fuselage, rudder of duralumin tubing with fabric covering, and all-wooden tailplane and elevator. Horizontal surfaces reinforced with styrofoam slabs. Trim tab on elevator.

LANDING GEAR: Non-retractable tailwheel type. Barum Aero mainwheel tyres size 420 × 152-52; Barum Aero tailwheel tyre size 260 ×85. Type B-2101 A3 mechanical drum brakes. Streamline fairings can be fitted to landing gear legs and wheels.

POWER PLANT: One 56 kW (75 hp) Praga D-1 flat-four engine, driving a two-blade wooden fixed-pitch propeller from a Praga E-117 Air Baby. Two fuel tanks, with total capacity of 60 litres (13·2 Imp gallons), fore and aft of cabin. Refuelling points in forward top decking and on starboard side of fuselage aft of cabin door.

ACCOMMODATION: Two seats in tandem in fully-enclosed cabin. Forward-hinged jettisonable door on starboard side.

AVIONICS: Tesla LS-4/1 sailplane-type radio, battery-powered.

DIMENSIONS, EXTERNAL:
Wing span	9·294 m (30 ft 6 in)
Wing chord: at root	1·50 m (4 ft 11 in)
at tip	1·00 m (3 ft 3¼ in)
Wing area, gross	12·51 m² (134·7 sq ft)
Wing aspect ratio	6·7
Length overall	5·93 m (19 ft 5½ in)

Zenair Acro Z-CH 150 single-seat aerobatic and competition aircraft (*Michael A. Badrocke*)

PIK-21 Super Sytky single-seat racing aircraft (*Roy J. Grainge*)

Nearly completed PIK-21 Super Sytky in December 1979

Simůnek/Kamarýt SK-1 Trempik (Little Tramp) *Oldrich Steklý*

CH 50 Mini Z single-seat light aircraft

Height overall	2·27 m (7 ft 5½ in)	Max payload	175 kg (386 lb)	Cruising speed at S/L	
Tailplane span	2·05 m (6 ft 8¾ in)	Max T-O weight	575 kg (1,267 lb)		86 knots (160 km/h; 99 mph) IAS
Wheel track	1·52 m (4 ft 11¾ in)	PERFORMANCE:		Stalling speed	43 knots (80 km/h; 50 mph) IAS
Wheelbase	4·12 m (13 ft 6¼ in)	Never-exceed speed at S/L		Max rate of climb at S/L	210 m (690 ft)/min
Propeller diameter	1·60 m (5 ft 3 in)		116 knots (215 km/h; 133 mph) IAS	Service ceiling (estimated)	4,400 m (14,425 ft)
WEIGHTS:		Max level speed at S/L		T-O run	150 m (492 ft)
Weight empty	356 kg (785 lb)		97 knots (180 km/h; 112 mph) IAS	Max range (estimated)	324 nm (600 km; 373 miles)

DENMARK

SEREMET
W. VINCENT SEREMET
Godsparken 50, 2670 Greve Strand
Telephone: (01) 90 29 49

Since 1962, Mr W. Vincent Seremet, a Danish engineer and amateur constructor, has designed and built a series of small rotating-wing aircraft of which details have appeared annually in *Jane's*. Two of his latest designs are

the W.S.9 Autogyrocopter and W.S.12 powered parawing, of which illustrations and brief technical details can be found in the 1979-80 *Jane's*.

FINLAND

PIK
POLYTEKNIKKOJEN ILMAILUKERHO
(The Flying Club of the Helsinki University of Technology)
Lepolantie 69D, 00660 Helsinki
PROJECT ENGINEER: Kai Mellén

Mr K. Mellén, an engineer with Finnair, has built, under the auspices of the Polyteknikkojen Ilmailukerho, a Formula V racing aircraft known as the Super Sytky. Design started at the end of 1973, and construction of the prototype began on 15 March 1975.

The Super Sytky was nearly complete in January 1980, requiring only a little work on the engine installation, and exterior painting.

PIK-21 SUPER SYTKY
TYPE: Single-seat racing monoplane.
WINGS: Cantilever constant-chord wooden wings, with no anhedral or dihedral. Wing section NACA 64₂212. Single box spar and truss ribs, plywood covered. Full-

span narrow-chord ailerons of plywood-covered wood construction. No tabs.
FUSELAGE: Conventional semi-monocoque wooden structure, plywood covered.
TAIL UNIT: Cantilever wooden structure, plywood covered. Constant-chord tailplane and elevators. Fin integral with rear fuselage. Ground-adjustable trim tabs in rudder and elevator.
LANDING GEAR: Non-retractable tailwheel type. Steel leaf spring main legs, carrying Azuza wheels, with tyres size 5·00-5. Tapered rod tailspring with 12·7 cm (5 in) tailwheel. Reinforced plastics main-wheel fairings. Azuza mechanical brakes.
POWER PLANT: One 1,600 cc modified Volkswagen motor car engine, producing 37·25 kW (50 hp) at 3,400 rpm and driving a Ray Hegy two-blade wooden fixed-pitch propeller, with large spinner. One fuel tank in fuselage, capacity 40 litres (8·8 Imp gallons). Refuelling point in front of windscreen. Oil capacity 2·5 litres (0·55 Imp gallons).

ACCOMMODATION: Enclosed cabin seating pilot only. One-piece jettisonable windscreen/canopy, hinged on starboard side.

AVIONICS: Radio fitted.

DIMENSIONS, EXTERNAL:
Wing span	5·30 m (17 ft 4¾ in)
Wing area, gross	7·20 m² (77·5 sq ft)
Wing chord, constant	1·37 m (4 ft 6 in)
Wing aspect ratio	3·87
Length overall	5·16 m (16 ft 11¼ in)
Tailplane span	1·70 m (5 ft 7 in)
Wheel track	1·32 m (4 ft 4 in)
Wheelbase	3·93 m (12 ft 10¾ in)
Propeller diameter	1·32 m (4 ft 4 in)

WEIGHTS (estimated):
Weight empty, equipped	200 kg (441 lb)
Max T-O weight	320 kg (705 lb)

PERFORMANCE: No data available.

TERVAMÄKI
JUKKA TERVAMÄKI
Aidasmäentie 16-20E, 00650 Helsinki 65

Mr Tervamäki, Technical Manager of a medical instrument company, first became interested in autogyros in 1956. In 1959 he worked briefly for the Bensen Aircraft

Corporation in the USA. He obtained a Diploma in Aeronautical Engineering at the Helsinki Institute of Technology in 1963, and later served in the helicopter section of the Finnish Air Force. He was for two years project manager and chief designer of the PIK-19 Muhinu glider-towing aircraft. In 1974 he modified a Schleicher ASK 14 powered sailplane to make it capable of taxiing on large airports; and designed the engine installation for the JT-6 prototype powered sailplane, which is in production as the PIK-20E (see Sailplanes section).

Autogyros designed by Mr Tervamäki were completed in 1958 (JT-1), 1965 (JT-2), 1968 (Tervamäki-Eerola ATE-3) and 1972 (JT-5).

TERVAMÄKI JT-5

The JT-5 is a development of the ATE-3, the major visible differences being the use of a triple tail assembly, to improve static and dynamic stability; a fully-enclosed cockpit; improved, low-drag fuselage contours; and extensive use of plastics materials in the basic structure and main components. Other features include an upward-directed exhaust, to reduce engine noise, and a simplified carburettor installation and heating system of Tervamäki design.

The prototype JT-5 (OH-XYS) was flown for the first time on 7 January 1973. It was later sold, together with production rights, tools and moulds, to Sr Vittorio Magni of Italy. In 1979 plans, component parts, materials and complete kits of the Magni-Tervamäki MT-5 were made available to amateur constructors by V.P.M. (see Italy). By early 1980 Mr Tervamäki had sold about 30 sets of plans for the JT-5, and several aircraft were under construction.

The autogyro illustrated was completed in 1975 by Arvo and Hannu Taupila. It is a hybrid of the ATE-3 and JT-5, combining the steel-tube structure, landing gear and rotor head of the former with the cockpit, tail surfaces and rotor blades of the JT-5.

The following details apply to the standard JT-5.

TYPE: Single-seat light autogyro.

ROTOR SYSTEM: Two-blade semi-rigid rotor of glassfibre-reinforced epoxy resin, with polyurethane plastics foam core. Blades, of constant chord and NACA 8-H-12 section, are each attached to hub by two bolts. A lead bar in each blade leading-edge forms the chordwise balance weight. Rotor mast of streamlined SAE 4130 steel tubing. Rotor head is of a compact offset-gimbal type with centrifugal teeter stops and rotor brake installed. There are two spiral springs for trim adjustment, which is effected via the control stick twist-grip handle. Normal rotor rpm is 400, maximum 600. Designed for the JT-5, but not yet fitted, is a modified Cierva-type inclined drag hinge which would allow the blades to move to zero pitch when pre-rotation torque is applied, permitting an increase of 100 rpm in pre-spin speed and, consequently, a shorter take-off.

ROTOR DRIVE: Rotor spin-up by Vee-belt, clutch, 90° gearbox, sliding universal shaft and inertia-operated Bendix drive. Overall reduction ratio 8. Rotor spin-up of 300 rpm can be achieved.

FUSELAGE: Basic structure of welded 4130 steel tubing with a glassfibre/HFB honeycomb sandwich cockpit. All internal cockpit structures of glassfibre-reinforced epoxy resin. One-piece aluminium engine cowling.

TAIL UNIT: Central main fin and rudder, of glassfibre-reinforced epoxy resin, with rigid PVC foam ribs and Courtauld carbon fibre stiffeners. Horizontal tail and auxiliary endplate fins of glassfibre sandwich construction with honeycomb core. Tail assembly attached to fuselage by a single streamlined steel tube. Small tail-wheel beneath base of fin.

LANDING GEAR: Non-retractable tricycle type. Main gear legs consist of 4 × 4 cm (1·6 × 1·6 in) glassfibre-reinforced epoxy resin springs, encased in streamlined fairings of the same material. Cables inside these fairings to main gear drum brakes. Main-wheel tyres size 300 × 100. Compression rubber shock-absorption in nose gear. Nosewheel tyre size 260 × 80. Nosewheel steerable by rudder pedals.

POWER PLANT: One 56 kW (75 hp) 1·7 litre Volkswagen engine, converted for autogyro use by Limbach Motorenbau. No oil cooler, generator or electric starter. Two-blade pusher propeller, of glassfibre-reinforced epoxy. Glassfibre fuel tank, integrally built into fuselage aft of pilot's seat, capacity 50 litres (11 Imp gallons).

ACCOMMODATION: Single seat under sideways-opening Plexiglas canopy. Instrument panel cover and pilot's seat back (the latter also forming a firewall to the engine compartment) open together with the canopy.

EQUIPMENT: Standard equipment and controls are as listed in the 1974-75 Jane's. A 6-channel radio is installed.

DIMENSIONS, EXTERNAL:

Rotor diameter	7·00 m (22 ft 11½ in)
Rotor blade chord (constant, each)	0·18 m (7·1 in)
Length of fuselage	3·50 m (11 ft 5¾ in)
Height overall	2·00 m (6 ft 6¾ in)
Wheel track	1·70 m (5 ft 7 in)
Propeller diameter	1·20 m (3 ft 11¼ in)

AREAS:

Rotor blades (each)	0·63 m² (6·78 sq ft)
Rotor disc	38·50 m² (414·4 sq ft)

WEIGHTS:

Weight empty, equipped	167 kg (368 lb)
Max T-O weight	290 kg (639 lb)

PERFORMANCE (at max T-O weight):

Never-exceed speed 97 knots (180 km/h; 111·5 mph)	
Max level speed at S/L 92 knots (170 km/h; 106 mph)	
Max cruising speed at S/L	81 knots (150 km/h; 93 mph)
Econ cruising speed	70 knots (130 km/h; 81 mph)
Min level speed	19 knots (35 km/h; 22 mph)
Max rate of climb at S/L	180 m (590 ft)/min
Service ceiling	4,000 m (13,125 ft)
T-O run	70 m (230 ft)
T-O to 15 m (50 ft)	120 m (394 ft)
Landing from 15 m (50 ft)	50 m (165 ft)
Landing run	5 m (16 ft)
Range with max fuel, no reserves	189 nm (350 km; 217 miles)

FRANCE

CHAGNES
LÉO CHAGNES
160 avenue de Castres, 31000 Toulouse

CHAGNES MICROSTAR

M Léo Chagnes built at Toulouse this variant of the Rutan VariViggen, the basic version of which is described among the US entries in this section. Generally similar to the standard VariViggen, the Chagnes Microstar differs primarily in its power plant and associated equipment, the usual rear-mounted 112 kW (150 hp) piston engine being replaced by two Microturbo TRS 18-046 turbojets (each 0·898 kN; 202 lb st). Their installation was carried out with the co-operation of Microturbo SA; and because of the light weight of the engines, which are positioned one above the other at the rear of the fuselage, no CG problem was encountered.

Taxi tests of this homebuilt began in February 1979, and the first flight was made by M Chagnes on 20 July 1979. With both seats occupied, and maximum fuel load of 271 litres (60 Imp gallons), the Microstar has a take-off weight below the maximum allowable.

DIMENSIONS, EXTERNAL:

Wing span	7·188 m (23 ft 7 in)
Wing area, gross	13·5 m² (145·3 sq ft)
Span of foreplane	2·825 m (9 ft 3¼ in)
Length overall	6·076 m (19 ft 11¼ in)
Height overall	1·75 m (5 ft 9 in)

WEIGHTS:

Weight empty	545 kg (1,202 lb)
Max T-O weight	889 kg (1,960 lb)

PERFORMANCE (at max T-O weight):

Max level speed	215 knots (400 km/h; 248 mph)
Cruising speed	173 knots (320 km/h; 199 mph)
Stalling speed	46 knots (85 km/h; 53 mph)
Rate of climb at S/L	360 m (1,180 ft)/min
Service ceiling	8,000 m (26,250 ft)
T-O to 15 m (50 ft)	300 m (984 ft)
Landing run	150 m (492 ft)
Endurance	1 h

COLOMBAN
MICHEL COLOMBAN
37bis rue Lakanal, 92500-Rueil-Malmaison
Telephone: 967-88-76

Formerly with the Morane and Potez companies, and now an aerodynamicist with Aérospatiale, M Colomban designed and built a very small and unique twin-engined lightplane named the Cricri. Its construction required some 1,200 hours of work and cost only 5,000 francs (1971-72 prices), including the engines.

M Colomban intended to make plans of the latest MC 12 version of the Cricri available to amateur constructors in 1980.

COLOMBAN MC 12 CRICRI (CRICKET)

The MC 10 prototype of the Cricri was powered by two Rowena 6507J single-cylinder two-stroke engines of 137cc, each giving 6·7 kW (9 hp) and weighing 6·5 kg (14·3 lb). It was claimed to be the smallest twin-engined aeroplane then flying, and the only one able to lift a useful load equivalent to 170 per cent of its own empty weight. Special constructional features permitted assembly or disassembly in only five minutes. Its light weight and small size made it particularly easy to transport on a trailer towed by car and to store in a garage or shed.

The Cricri was flown for the first time on 19 July 1973 by Robert Buisson, a 68-year-old pilot who had already logged 12,000 flying hours. A number of design refinements were made later that year, after which testing was resumed. Within fifteen days the Cricri had logged a total of 13 trouble-free flying hours, including rolls, reversements, 'split S' manoeuvres and inverted flight, made possible by its Tillotson diaphragm carburettor. Flight tests at up to 135 knots (250 km/h; 155 mph) confirmed that no special piloting skills were needed to fly the aircraft.

In particular, the Cricri handled like a single-engined design. This resulted from the fact that the two small engines were mounted close together, and from the carefully-conceived shape of the cockpit canopy which deflected the propeller slipstream over the tail surfaces in such a way that the failure of one engine would produce no dangerous handling problems. If one engine was throttled back fiercely, with hands and feet off the controls, the Cricri was said to do no more than begin a gentle turn.

A number of improved and re-engined Cricris have been built by friends of M Colomban, and one of these (No. 4, built by M Gérard Constant of Dreux) was exhibited in the static park at the 1977 Paris Salon. This aircraft, powered by two 125 cc McCulloch MC-101 single-cylinder two-stroke engines (each 8·9 kW; 12 hp), flew for the first time in July 1978 and performed entirely satisfactorily. Take-off was achieved in 80 m (263 ft), in a time of 7 s, in zero wind, followed by a stabilised climb at a rate of 360 m (1,180 ft)/min. On the other hand, the MC-101 engines were clearly too sophisticated for this application. So, although they proved generally satisfactory, they have been superseded by Valmet SM 160J engines on both M Constant's Cricri and on the version shown on the plans available to amateur constructors. With Valmet engines the Cricri is designated MC 12.

Four MC 12s were expected to be flying during 1980.

TYPE: Twin-engined single-seat ultra-light aircraft, stressed to +10g and −5g.

WINGS: Cantilever low-wing monoplane of constant chord. Laminar-flow aerofoil derived from a Wortmann section. Thickness/chord ratio 21·7%. Dihedral 4° from roots. Incidence 1° at root, −30′ at tip. No sweep. Single-spar box structure. Spar comprises a web riveted to AU4G angle-section booms. Inboard end of spar in each wing is of 'forked-tongue' form, like that of many sailplanes, to permit rapid assembly and disassembly of wings (2 minutes). Closely-spaced Klégécel ribs are bonded fore and aft of the spar. Skin consists of a single sheet of AU4G, bonded to structure under pressure after its leading-edge has been formed. No rear spar. Wing box is closed at each end by a riveted metal rib. Entire trailing-edge is occupied by two-section external flaps of the kind fitted to many wartime Junkers aircraft, operating collectively as high-lift devices and differentially as ailerons. Flaps are spar-less, consisting of a metal monocoque structure, with four metal ribs per section (at each tip and each pivot point), filled with Klégécel over the entire span and over 20% of the chord. Flaps are each actuated via a ball-joint at the root. No controls pass through the wing box, which contains only an AU4G tube as provision for any future installation of fuel tanks on wingtips.

FUSELAGE: Simple metal box structure of AU4G sheet made in two parts to reduce space required for manufacture. Rear portion is of inverted triangular section. Rectangular-section forward portion is riveted together with four angle sections at the corners. Structure is stiffened by Klégécel stringers, bonded in place. AU4G frames riveted in position in line with the attachments for the wings, landing gear, tail unit and engine mountings.

TAIL UNIT: Cantilever T type, with sweptback vertical surfaces and all-moving constant-chord horizontal surface. Construction similar to that of wings. No tabs. Tailplane actuated by control rods, rudder by cables. Tailplane provided with artificial loading by bungee cord.

LANDING GEAR: Non-retractable tricycle type. Nosewheel fitted with bungee shock-absorption and linked to rudder bar for steering. Each main wheel carried on cantilever leg of glassfibre/epoxy laminations. Main-wheel tyres size 210-70, pressure 1·80 bars (28 lb/sq in). Nosewheel tyre size 200-50, pressure 0·80 bars (11·6 lb/sq in). Colomban disc brakes. Provision for fairing on all three wheels.

POWER PLANT: Two modified 160 cc Valmet SM 160J single-cylinder two-stroke engines, each giving 8·9 kW (12 hp) at 6,500 rpm. Tillotson diaphragm carburettors for all-altitude flight. Each engine drives an MCH 700-18 two-blade propeller, made of glassfibre. Plastics fuel tank in fuselage, capacity 20 litres (4·4 Imp gallons). Provision for tank on each wingtip, total capacity 24 litres (5·25 Imp gallons).

ACCOMMODATION: Single seat under large transparent canopy, hinged to open sideways, to starboard. Ventilation through port in side of fuselage. No heating.

The hybrid ATE-3/JT-5 built by Arvo and Hannu Taupila of Kihniö, Finland

Coupé-Aviation JC-01 two-seat lightplane

Microstar built by M Chagnes, with two Microturbo TRS 18-046 turbojet engines

MC 12 Cricri (two Valmet SM 160J engines) built by Gérard Constant of Dreux
(Aviasport; M. Battarel)

DIMENSIONS, EXTERNAL:
Wing span, with or without tip-tanks
                                4·90 m (16 ft 0¾ in)
Wing chord, incl flap (constant) 0·63 m (2 ft 0¾ in)
Wing chord, excl flap (constant) 0·48 m (1 ft 6¾ in)
Wing area, gross   3·10 m² (33·4 sq ft)
Wing aspect ratio   7·75
Length overall   3·91 m (12 ft 10 in)
Height overall   1·20 m (3 ft 11¼ in)
Tailplane span   1·55 m (5 ft 1 in)
Wheel track   1·10 m (3 ft 7¼ in)
Wheelbase   1·15 m (3 ft 9¼ in)
Propeller diameter   0·68 m (2 ft 2¾ in)

Distance between propeller centres
                                0·95 m (3 ft 1½ in)
DIMENSIONS, INTERNAL:
Cabin: Length   1·30 m (4 ft 3¼ in)
    Max width   0·55 m (1 ft 9½ in)
    Max height   0·82 m (2 ft 8¼ in)
WEIGHTS:
Weight empty   70 kg (154 lb)
Max T-O and landing weight   170 kg (375 lb)
PERFORMANCE (estimated, at AUW of 160 kg; 352 lb):
Never-exceed speed 158 knots (293 km/h; 182 mph)
Max level speed   118 knots (220 km/h; 136 mph)
Max cruising speed (75% power)
                    105 knots (195 km/h; 121 mph)

Stalling speed, flaps down
                    42 knots (77 km/h; 48 mph)
Stalling speed, flaps up   50 knots (93 km/h; 58 mph)
Best glide ratio, engines off and T-O configuration, at
    60 knots (110 km/h; 69 mph)   11
Max rate of climb at S/L   336 m (1,100 ft)/min
Rate of climb at S/L, one engine out
                    80 m (262 ft)/min
Service ceiling   4,600 m (15,090 ft)
T-O run   110 m (360 ft)
T-O to 15 m (50 ft)   310 m (1,020 ft)
Landing from 15 m (50 ft)   350 m (1,150 ft)
Landing run   150 m (495 ft)
Range with max fuel   430 nm (800 km; 496 miles)

COUPÉ-AVIATION
COUPÉ-AVIATION
La Trute, Azay-sur-Cher, 37270 Montlouis
Telephone: (47) 55 31 84

M Jacques Coupé has designed and built a two-seat lightplane designated JC-01 (F-PXKV), which was flown for the first time on 16 March 1976. Design emphasis was placed on ensuring that homebuilders would find it easy to construct, and plans are available from Coupé-Aviation. In early 1980 the company had almost completed construction of a derivative of the JC-01. Designated JC-2, it is powered by a 67 kW (90 hp) engine and has tricycle landing gear; its first flight was anticipated during 1980. A number of JC-01s are being built, some powered by modified Volkswagen motor car engines of 1,600 or 1,700 cc.

COUPÉ-AVIATION JC-01
TYPE: Two-seat lightweight sporting aircraft.

WINGS: Cantilever low-wing monoplane of constant chord. Conventional single-spar structure of wood, with lightweight lattice ribs and fabric covering. Leading-edge fixed slot. Slotted ailerons of similar construction to wings.
FUSELAGE: Lattice structure of wood, with wood and fabric covering. The fin is constructed integrally with the fuselage.
TAIL UNIT: Cantilever structure of wood; fin, rudder and elevators fabric-covered. Fixed-incidence tailplane has plywood skin. Manually-operated trim tab in elevator.
LANDING GEAR: Non-retractable tailwheel type. Shock-absorption of main units by rubber in compression, and of tailwheel by coil spring. Main-wheel tyres size 420 × 150. Cable-operated caliper brakes.
POWER PLANT: One 48·5 kW (65 hp) Continental A65-8F flat-four engine, driving a two-blade fixed-pitch wooden propeller with spinner. Fuel tank forward of cockpit, capacity 60 litres (13 Imp gallons).

ACCOMMODATION: Two seats side by side, beneath aft-sliding transparent canopy. Dual controls. Accommodation is heated and ventilated.
DIMENSIONS, EXTERNAL:
Wing span   8·35 m (27 ft 4¾ in)
Wing area, gross   11·69 m² (125·83 sq ft)
Wing aspect ratio   5·95
Length overall   6·40 m (21 ft 0 in)
WEIGHTS:
Weight empty   330 kg (728 lb)
Max T-O weight   580 kg (1,279 lb)
PERFORMANCE (at max T-O weight):
Max level speed   108 knots (200 km/h; 124 mph)
Max cruising speed   81 knots (150 km/h; 93 mph)
Econ cruising speed 76 knots (140 km/h; 87 mph)
T-O speed   27 knots (50 km/h; 31 mph)
Approach speed 37-43 knots (70-80 km/h; 43-50 mph)
Stalling speed   24·5 knots (45 km/h; 28 mph)
T-O run   90 m (295 ft)

CROSES
EMILIEN CROSES
Route de Davayé (Aérodrome), 71000 Charnay les Macon
Telephone: (85) 38 07 31

Since M Emilien Croses began work as a designer/constructor in 1947, he has been responsible for nine different prototypes, all of which have been certificated. Addition of the initial 'B' in the designation of some of these reflects assistance given to M Croses by M R. Bujon, a specialist metal worker. Other assistance is given by MM J. Mottez with stressing and aerodynamics; Alain Croses with aerodynamic studies; and Y. Croses, an engineer specialising in applications of high-strength plastics and glassfibre.

CROSES EAC-3 POUPLUME
As in the familiar Mignet designs, the Pouplume single-seat tandem-wing biplane has a fixed rear wing and a pivoted forward wing which dispenses with the need for ailerons and elevators. A conventional rudder is fitted, with a large tailwheel built into its lower edge.

Construction is conventional, with spruce wing structure and a square-section spruce fuselage covered with okoumé ply. The main landing gear consists of Vespa scooter wheels carried on a wooden cross-member.

The power unit in the prototype (EAC-3-01) is a 7·8 kW (10·5 hp) Moto 232 cc two-stroke motorcycle engine, with chain reduction drive to the propeller shaft. The reduction ratio is 3·5 : 1, giving a propeller speed of 1,300

rpm. Fuel capacity is 10 litres (2·2 Imp gallons).

The EAC-3-01 Pouplume took 600 h to build and flew for the first time in June 1961. This machine was followed, in 1967, by a second prototype (EAC-3-02), with a 20 cm (8 in) longer fuselage. M Croses is offering sets of plans to other constructors, and at least 12 Pouplumes had flown by early 1980. The one shown in the accompanying illustration was built in France by an amateur constructor.

A version known as the Pouplume Sport differs in having a 1500 cc Volkswagen engine and reduced span of 6·40 m (21 ft 0 in). About 55 Pouplume Sports were under construction in early 1980.

The following data apply to the standard Moto-powered Pouplume:

DIMENSIONS, EXTERNAL:
Span of forward wing   7·8 m (25 ft 7 in)
Span of rear wing   7·0 m (23 ft 0 in)
Wing area, gross   16·0 m² (172 sq ft)
Length overall   4·7 m (15 ft 3 in)
Height overall   1·8 m (5 ft 11 in)

WEIGHTS:
Weight empty   110-140 kg (243-310 lb)
Max T-O weight   220-260 kg (485-573 lb)

PERFORMANCE (A: 7·8 kW; 10·5 hp engine. B: 13·4 kW; 18 hp engine):
Max level speed:
A   38 knots (70 km/h; 43·5 mph)
B   65 knots (120 km/h; 75 mph)
Econ cruising speed:
A   27 knots (50 km/h; 31 mph)
B   38 knots (70 km/h; 43·5 mph)
T-O speed:
A   13·5 knots (25 km/h; 15·5 mph)
Landing speed:
A   9·7 knots (18 km/h; 11 mph)
T-O run:
A   60 m (200 ft)
B   40 m (131 ft)
Landing run:
A   24 m (80 ft)
Fuel consumption:
A   4·5 litres (1 Imp gallon)/h

CROSES EC-6 CRIQUET (LOCUST)

This design by Emilien Croses is a development of his earlier EC-1-02 prototype and is a side-by-side two-seater based on the familiar Mignet tandem-wing formula. Construction of the prototype was started in March 1964 and the EC-6-01 flew for the first time on 6 July 1965.

Plans of the wooden version of the Criquet, of which details follow, are available to amateur constructors. At least seven examples were flying by early 1980, with about 60 more under construction.

An all-plastics version, known as the LC-10, was described briefly in the 1977-78 Jane's. Plans of this are not available.

TYPE: Two-seat tandem-wing light aircraft.

WINGS: Forward wing built in one piece and pivoted on two streamlined supports, giving variable incidence between −2° and +12°. Fixed rear (lower) wing. Wing section NACA 23012 (modified). Both wings have two-spar wooden structure, with plywood leading-edge, overall fabric covering and some components of glassfibre. Ailerons optional.

FUSELAGE: Spruce structure, covered with plywood. Glassfibre engine cowling.

TAIL UNIT: Plywood-covered spruce fin and rudder. No tailplane or elevators.

LANDING GEAR: Non-retractable tailwheel type. Main wheels, size 420-150, carried on single cantilever arch structure made from ash wood on a forme and covered with glassfibre. Tailwheel, size 420-150, semi-enclosed in bottom of rudder.

POWER PLANT: One 67 kW (90 hp) Continental flat-four engine, driving a modified SIPA two-blade propeller. Fuel capacity originally 60 litres (13 Imp gallons); planned to be increased to 90 litres (20 Imp gallons).

ACCOMMODATION: Two seats side by side in enclosed cabin. Door on starboard side. Constructors can utilise either the special Mignet type of control system or a conventional system with ailerons and rudder bar.

DIMENSIONS, EXTERNAL:
Span of forward wing   7·80 m (25 ft 7 in)
Span of rear wing   7·00 m (22 ft 11½ in)
Wing chord (constant, each)   1·20 m (3 ft 11¼ in)
Wing area, gross   16·0 m² (172 sq ft)
Length overall   4·65 m (15 ft 3 in)

WEIGHTS:
Weight empty   290 kg (639 lb)
Max T-O weight   550 kg (1,213 lb)

PERFORMANCE (officially certificated, at max T-O weight):
Max level speed at S/L   115 knots (213 km/h; 132 mph)
Max cruising speed   92 knots (170 km/h; 106 mph)
Econ cruising speed   86 knots (160 km/h; 99 mph)
Min flying speed   22 knots (40 km/h; 25 mph)
Will not stall
T-O time (max)   6 s
Climb to 2,000 m (6,560 ft)   6 min 14 s

CROSES EC-8 TOURISME

This three-seat touring aircraft is generally similar to the standard wooden Criquet but has an 'all-terrain' landing gear comprising two tandem pairs of main wheels. At least two EC-8s are flying.

CROSES B-EC-9 PARAS-CARGO

Unique in being a cargo transport for construction and operation by amateurs, the B-EC-9 employs the same Mignet tandem-wing configuration and simple wood construction as earlier Croses designs. Like them, it can be built with conventional three-axis controls or the special two-control system devised by Henri Mignet, with large 'tab' control surfaces on the trailing-edge of the rear wing.

It is intended to certificate the prototype, following tests of the aircraft's suitability as a transport for parachutists. It will be offered to amateur constructors and clubs in the form of both plans and kits of components.

TYPE: Light cargo transport and utility aircraft for amateur construction.

WINGS: Tandem-wing configuration of Mignet type, with forward wing supported, parasol-fashion, at three pivot points. Fixed cantilever aft wing mounted at top of rear fuselage. Both wings have same constant chord, with round and slightly upswept tips. No dihedral. No sweep. Wood structure, with fabric covering aft of main spar. Large inset tab in trailing-edge of each rear wing, but no ailerons, on prototype, which has Mignet two-control system.

FUSELAGE: Large-volume plywood box structure, with unobstructed interior.

TAIL UNIT: Fin, integral with fuselage, and rudder only, of plywood-covered wood construction. No tabs.

LANDING GEAR: Croses 'tous terrains' type. Two pairs of main wheels in tandem, carried on one-piece cantilever arch structure of wood covered with glassfibre. Two forward wheels larger than rear wheels. Large tailwheel semi-enclosed in base of rudder.

POWER PLANT: One 134 kW (180 hp) Avco Lycoming flat-four engine, driving a two-blade fixed-pitch propeller without spinner.

ACCOMMODATION: Crew of two side by side on flight deck, connected by a passage to the square-section main cabin. Accommodation for freight, four parachutists, two stretcher patients and seats for two attendants, or agricultural equipment. Very low floor for easy loading. Large door on port side of cabin opens inward and upward to permit airdropping of parachutists or cargo. Separate forward-hinged crew door on port side of flight deck. Use of a door at the rear of the cabin would permit the carriage of items such as metal tubes, boards or helicopter rotor blades up to 5·50 m (18 ft 0 in) long.

DIMENSIONS, EXTERNAL:
Wing span:
front wing   9·60 m (31 ft 6 in)
rear wing   8·80 m (28 ft 10½ in)
Wing chord, constant   1·60 m (5 ft 3 in)
Wing gap (projected)   0·94 m (3 ft 1 in)
Length overall   7·50 m (24 ft 7¼ in)

DIMENSIONS, INTERNAL:
Cabin: Length   2·60 m (8 ft 6¼ in)
Max width   1·35 m (4 ft 5 in)
Max height   1·45 m (4 ft 9 in)
Usable volume   5 m³ (176 cu ft)

WEIGHTS:
Weight empty   650 kg (1,433 lb)
Max payload   450 kg (992 lb)

PERFORMANCE:
Normal cruising speed 94 knots (175 km/h; 108 mph)
Econ cruising speed   86 knots (160 km/h; 99 mph)
Speed for airdropping   32 knots (60 km/h; 37 mph)
Rate of climb at S/L   240 m (785 ft)/min
T-O run   150 m (490 ft)

DELEMONTEZ-CAUCHY
ALAIN CAUCHY
Aérodrome de Persan-Beaumont, Val d'Oise

Among new amateur-built aircraft which took part in the RSA meeting at Brienne-le-Château in July 1979 was a small two-seater designated DC-1, with a configuration reminiscent of that of the well-known Jodel series of designs. It had been built over a period of 18 months by M Alain Cauchy, with design assistance from M Jean Delemontez, President-Director General of Avions Jodel SA, and had flown for the first time on 6 July 1979.

DELEMONTEZ-CAUCHY DC-1

TYPE: Low-cost two-seat light aircraft.

WINGS: Cantilever low-wing monoplane. Single-spar wing, with wide-span centre-section of constant chord and thickness, and two tapered outer panels set at a coarse dihedral (12°). All-wood structure. Plywood-covered leading-edge forward of spar; fabric covering aft of spar. Fabric-covered wooden ailerons.

FUSELAGE: Plywood-covered wooden structure of basically rectangular section, with rounded top-decking.

TAIL UNIT: Cantilever wood structure. No fin. Tailplane plywood-covered; elevators and rudder fabric-covered.

LANDING GEAR: Non-retractable tailwheel type. Cantilever main legs with rubber-in-compression shock-absorption. Steerable tailwheel.

POWER PLANT: One 1,600 cc converted Volkswagen motorcar engine, driving a two-blade wooden fixed-pitch propeller made by Evra to Delemontez design.

ACCOMMODATION: Two seats side by side in enclosed cabin. Centrally-mounted control column and dual rudder pedals.

DIMENSIONS, EXTERNAL:
Wing span   7·40 m (24 ft 3½ in)
Wing area, gross   9·45 m² (101·7 sq ft)
Length overall   7·40 m (24 ft 3½ in)

DIMENSION, INTERNAL:
Cabin: Max width   1·00 m (3 ft 3¼ in)

WEIGHT:
Weight empty   216 kg (476 lb)

PERFORMANCE (measured on first flight, pilot only):
Max level speed   113 knots (210 km/h; 130 mph)
Max cruising speed (75% power)   86 knots (160 km/h; 99 mph)
Approach speed   43 knots (80 km/h; 50 mph)
Max rate of climb at S/L   240 m (785 ft)/min
T-O run   120 m (394 ft)
Landing run   100 m (328 ft)

DURUBLE
ROLAND DURUBLE
40 rue du Paradis, Les Essarts, 76530 Grand-Couronne
Telephone: 92 20 63

M Roland Duruble, with MM Guy Chanut and Legrand, designed and built a two-seat all-metal light aircraft named the RD-02 Edelweiss, which flew for the first time on 7 July 1962. Full details of this aircraft can be found in the 1972-73 Jane's.

Plans of an enlarged and improved version, known as the RD-03 Edelweiss, are available to other constructors.

DURUBLE RD-03 EDELWEISS

The RD-03 Edelweiss is designed to AIR 2052 (CAR 3) standards, in three versions, as follows:

RD-03A. With 74·5 kW (100 hp) Continental O-200 flat-four engine and fuel capacity of 100 litres (22 Imp gallons) in two wing tanks. Can be fitted with 67 kW (90 hp) engine or 100·5 kW (135 hp) Lycoming O-320 engine. Side-by-side seats for pilot and one passenger (total weight 172 kg; 380 lb) in cabin.

RD-03B. With 100·5 kW (135 hp) Avco Lycoming O-320 or Franklin Sport 4B engine and same fuel capacity as RD-03A. Seating as RD-03A for Utility category operation, or in '2 + 2' arrangement for pilot and three passengers (154 kg; 340 lb on front seats, 110 kg; 240 lb on rear seats) in Normal category.

RD-03C. With 112 kW (150 hp) Avco Lycoming engine and additional wing tanks, increasing total fuel capacity to 150 litres (33 Imp gallons). In Utility two-seat form (as RD-03A) or with seating for a pilot and three passengers (total weight 308 kg; 680 lb) in Normal category.

Plans of the RD-03 have been available since the Autumn of 1970. By early 1980, a total of 48 sets of plans had been sold. Nine Edelweiss are known to be under construction in France, two in Belgium, eleven in Canada and the USA, and one in New Zealand. The first of these, under construction by M. Duruble and M. Gastan, was expected to fly in 1980.

TYPE: Two/four-seat light aircraft.

WINGS: Cantilever low-wing monoplane. Wing section NACA 23000 series. Thickness/chord ratio 18% at root, 12% at tip. Dihedral 6° 5′ from roots. Incidence 3° at root, 0° at tip. No sweepback. All-metal two-spar duralumin structure, with metal slotted trailing-edge flaps and slotted ailerons. No trim tabs.

FUSELAGE: Conventional semi-monocoque duralumin structure.

TAIL UNIT: Cantilever all-metal structure, with sweptback vertical surfaces. Fixed-incidence tailplane. Trim tab in each elevator, one actuated by flap linkage and the other manually.

LANDING GEAR: Retractable tricycle type. Hydraulic retraction, nosewheel rearward, main units inward into wings. Duruble hydro-air shock-absorbers on all three units. Main-wheel tyres size 355 × 150, nosewheel tyre size 330 × 130. Pressure (all tyres) 1·24 bars (18 lb/sq in). Hydraulic disc brakes.

POWER PLANT: One 67, 74·5, 100·5 or 112 kW (90, 100, 135 or 150 hp) flat-four engine (details under individual model listings). Refuelling point above wing.

ACCOMMODATION: Side-by-side seats for two, three or four persons (details under individual model listings) in fully-enclosed cabin.

SYSTEMS: Hydraulic system, pressure 69 bars (1,000 lb/sq in), for flap and landing gear actuation.

AVIONICS AND EQUIPMENT: Radio optional. Blind-flying instrumentation not fitted.

DIMENSIONS, EXTERNAL:
Wing span   8·82 m (28 ft 11¼ in)
Wing chord at root   1·70 m (5 ft 7 in)
Wing chord at tip   0·86 m (2 ft 10 in)
Wing area, gross   11·07 m² (119·2 sq ft)
Wing aspect ratio   7·05
Length overall (RD-03A)   6·875 m (22 ft 6¾ in)
Height overall   2·60 m (8 ft 6¼ in)
Tailplane span   3·05 m (10 ft 0 in)

DIMENSIONS, INTERNAL:
Cabin: Max length   2·44 m (8 ft 0 in)
Max width   1·10 m (3 ft 7¼ in)

Croses EAC-3 Pouplume light aircraft (Moto engine)

Croses EC-6 Criquet built by M Cuesuin of Belfort

Croses B-EC-9 Paras-Cargo light utility/cargo transport *(Geoffrey P. Jones)*

Delemontez-Cauchy DC-1 *(S. A. MacConnacher)*

Duruble RD-03C Edelweiss two/four-seat light aircraft

Gatard AG 02 Poussin No. 19, built by M A. Hézard of Dijon

WEIGHTS (estimated. A: RD-03A; B: RD-03B; C: RD-03C):

Weight empty, equipped:
A	426 kg (940 lb)
B	436 kg (962 lb)
C	443 kg (976 lb)

Max T-O and landing weight:
A (Utility)	689 kg (1,519 lb)
B (Utility)	705 kg (1,554 lb)
B (Normal)	817 kg (1,801 lb)
C (Utility)	731 kg (1,611 lb)
C (Normal)	887 kg (1,955 lb)

PERFORMANCE (estimated, at max T-O weight):
Never-exceed speed:
A (Utility), B (Utility), C (Utility)
170 knots (316 km/h; 196 mph)
B (Normal), C (Normal)
182 knots (339 km/h; 210 mph)
Max level speed at S/L:
A (Utility)　139 knots (257 km/h; 160 mph)

B (Utility)	143 knots (265 km/h; 165 mph)
B (Normal)	141 knots (262 km/h; 163 mph)
C (Utility)	149 knots (277 km/h; 172 mph)
C (Normal)	146 knots (270 km/h; 168 mph)

Max cruising speed at S/L:
A (Utility)	126·5 knots (234 km/h; 145·5 mph)
B (Utility)	129 knots (240 km/h; 149 mph)
B (Normal)	128 knots (238 km/h; 148 mph)
C (Utility)	136 knots (252 km/h; 157 mph)
C (Normal)	133 knots (246 km/h; 153 mph)

Econ cruising speed at S/L:
A (Utility), B (Utility)
121 knots (224 km/h; 139 mph)
B (Normal)	120 knots (222 km/h; 138 mph)
C (Utility)	128 knots (237 km/h; 147·5 mph)
C (Normal)	125 knots (233 km/h; 144·5 mph)

Stalling speed, flaps up:
A (Utility), B (Utility)
50 knots (92 km/h; 57·5 mph)
B (Normal), C (Utility)
56 knots (104 km/h; 65 mph)
C (Normal)　59 knots (109 km/h; 68 mph)

Stalling speed, flaps down:
A (Utility), B (Utility)
43 knots (79 km/h; 49·5 mph)
B (Normal)	48 knots (88 km/h; 55 mph)
C (Utility)	45 knots (83 km/h; 51·5 mph)
C (Normal)	48 knots (89 km/h; 55·5 mph)

Max rate of climb at S/L:
A	198 m (650 ft)/min
B	213 m (700 ft)/min
C	300 m (985 ft)/min

Service ceiling:
A, B	4,570 m (15,000 ft)
C	5,030 m (16,500 ft)

T-O to 15 m (50 ft):
A, B	450 m (1,475 ft)
C	510 m (1,675 ft)

Landing from 15 m (50 ft):
A	500 m (1,640 ft)
B, C	515 m (1,690 ft)

Range with max fuel, 30 min reserves:
A, C	502 nm (930 km; 578 miles)
B	512 nm (950 km; 590 miles)

FAUVEL
CHARLES FAUVEL

M Charles Fauvel, whose unique tailless designs have been described for many years in successive editions of *Jane's*, was killed on 10 September 1979 during a flight between Milan and Nice. His Supercab light aircraft crashed into a hill in bad weather. M Fauvel was aged 75.

GATARD
AVIONS A. GATARD

Villa la Devallée, 17130 Montendres/Royan
Telephone: (46) 49 42 76

M Albert Gatard has developed a control system for aeroplanes which involves the use of a variable-incidence lifting tailplane of large area, and has built a series of aircraft, including the Alouette, Poussin and Pigeon, incorporating his ideas. The Alouette (described in the 1959-60 *Jane's*) was purely experimental, but plans of the Poussin are available to amateur constructors.

Instead of altering the wing angle of attack to increase lift on these aircraft, the pilot lowers full-span slotted aileron/flaps and adjusts the tailplane to maintain pitching equilibrium. In consequence, the aircraft climb with the fuselage datum at no more than 4° to the horizontal, which preserves a good forward view and low body drag.

GATARD STATOPLAN AG 02 POUSSIN (CHICK)

M Gatard built two prototypes of the Poussin, and the detailed description applies to the second of these, which introduced a number of design improvements, in its original form. Flight tests revealed excellent aerobatic qualities and the power plant is modified to permit up to 20 s of inverted flying.

This prototype was extensively flight-tested at the Centre d'Essais en Vol at Istres, and the performance figures quoted are those which were obtained during the tests. As a result of recommendations by the CEV, a 27 kW (36 hp) Rectimo (modified Volkswagen VW 1200) engine is suggested as the most suitable power plant for use by amateur constructors of the Poussin. The second prototype has been re-engined with a 1,200 cc Volkswagen, by M Mathevet of Mollard-Chateauneuf (Loirs), on behalf of M Gatard. Installation of this engine was expected to improve the CG position and make possible a max speed of approx 92 knots (170 km/h; 106 mph), a max cruising speed of approx 83 knots (155 km/h; 96 mph) and a rate of climb at S/L of 210 m (690 ft)/min.

Several Poussins are being built by amateur constructors, and three of these had been completed and flown by March 1979, one (F-PYBS) with a non-standard tricycle landing gear. Another of them is shown in an accompanying illustration.

The plans were refined during 1978-79, and the version of the Poussin now offered for amateur construction is designated **AG 02Sp**. The wingtips are now more rounded, with inset ailerons. The wing structure has been modified to permit an increased max T-O weight of 305 kg (672 lb); and the landing gear has been refined to give an increase of about 5 per cent in cruising speed.

The following details apply to the standard Poussins now flying:

TYPE: Single-seat ultra-light monoplane.
WINGS: Cantilever low-wing monoplane. NACA 23012 wing section. Dihedral 4°. Incidence 3° 30' at root, 2° at tip. Plywood-covered single-spar all-wood structure. Full-span slotted aileron/flaps, each in two sections which are moved together but at different angles (inboard sections up to 35°, outboard up to 20°) to give the effect of increased aerodynamic twist of the complete wing/aileron/flap assemblies. Aileron/flaps are linked with the variable-incidence tailplane.
FUSELAGE: Plywood-covered wood structure. Perforated airbrake, under fuselage, operates automatically when the main aileron/flaps are lowered at large angles, as during landing.
TAIL UNIT: Braced all-wood structure, with variable-incidence all-moving tailplane of NACA 2309 section. Endplates fitted to tailplane to increase vertical fin area and effective tailplane span. No elevators. Rudder trim tab actuated by lateral movement of control column, permitting full control by means of the control column alone in normal flight.
LANDING GEAR: Non-retractable tailwheel type. Cantilever levered-suspension main units with rubber-band shock-absorption. Modified Dunlop brakes. Steerable tailwheel.
POWER PLANT: One 18 kW (24 hp) modified Volkswagen

flat-four engine, driving a Gatard two-blade fixed-pitch wooden propeller. Provision for fitting any alternative engine of up to 30 kW (40 hp) weighing between 50 and 60 kg (110-132 lb). Fuel tank aft of firewall, capacity 30 litres (6·6 Imp gallons). Oil capacity 2 litres (0·45 Imp gallons).
ACCOMMODATION: Single seat under large rearward-sliding transparent canopy. Baggage space aft of seat. Two map pockets.

DIMENSIONS, EXTERNAL:

Wing span	6·40 m (21 ft 0 in)
Wing chord, constant	1·00 m (3 ft 3¼ in)
Wing area, gross	6·15 m² (66·2 sq ft)
Length overall	4·53 m (14 ft 10½ in)
Height overall	1·50 m (4 ft 11 in)
Wheel track	1·50 m (4 ft 11 in)
Wheelbase	3·20 m (10 ft 6 in)

WEIGHTS:

Weight empty	170 kg (375 lb)
Max T-O weight	280 kg (617 lb)

PERFORMANCE (at max T-O weight):

Never-exceed speed	116 knots (216 km/h; 134 mph)
Max cruising speed	77 knots (144 km/h; 89 mph)
Max speed for aerobatics	69 knots (130 km/h; 80 mph)
Stalling speed	35 knots (65 km/h; 40·5 mph)
Max rate of climb at S/L	132 m (435 ft)/min
T-O run	190 m (625 ft)
T-O to 15 m (50 ft)	435 m (1,425 ft)
Landing from 15 m (50 ft)	320 m (1,050 ft)
Landing run	200 m (655 ft)

GATARD STATOPLAN AG 04 PIGEON

The AG 04 Pigeon is a two/three-seat high-wing monoplane, powered by a 67 kW (90 hp) Continental engine. It utilises the same type of control system as its predecessors, except that the Statoplan aileron/flaps are in three sections on each wing. As on the Poussin, they move together but through different angles (successively 45°, 30° and 20°) to give the effect of increased aerodynamic twist of the complete wing/aileron/flap assemblies.

The wings are braced by a single streamline-section strut each side and can be folded by two people in seven or eight minutes, to permit the aircraft to be towed along roads behind M Gatard's 6 cv Peugeot 204 motor car, on its own wheels, at 70 km/h (43 mph). Overall dimensions

under tow are: length 6·00 m (19 ft 8¼ in), width 2·10 m (6 ft 10¾ in) and height 3·00 m (9 ft 10 in).

A non-retractable tailwheel-type landing gear is fitted, with long-stroke rubber-ring shock-absorbers on all three units. Both manual and toe-operated brakes are specified, the former serving also as a parking brake.

The two front seats are adjustable fore and aft and tilt forward to facilitate access to the rear of the cabin. All controls are so mounted that the main cabin area is completely clear, with a suspended control column. Full control is possible in normal flight by means of this control column alone, as on the Poussin. Dual controls are provided for a second pilot, but can be disconnected easily. Entry is via a two-section door on each side; the lower section opens forward, the top section upward under the wing. The top section can be opened to a mid-position for additional ventilation while taxying. An optional door on the starboard side permits loading of a stretcher 1·80 m long by 0·45 m wide (5 ft 11 in by 1 ft 6 in) when the aircraft is used in an ambulance role. The rear seat on this side can be folded down to make room for the stretcher.

Fuel is carried in two completely independent tanks, with capacities of 70 litres (15·4 Imp gallons) and 14 litres (3·08 Imp gallons) respectively. Should the fuel pump fail, a special cock enables the engine to be supplied by gravity feed.

The prototype Pigeon was flying by mid-1976 and had logged 60 flying hours in about 180 flights by March 1979.

DIMENSIONS, EXTERNAL:

Wing span	9·00 m (29 ft 6¼ in)
Wing area, gross	11·75 m² (126·5 sq ft)
Length overall	6·00 m (19 ft 8¼ in)

WEIGHTS:

Weight empty	398 kg (878 lb)
Max T-O weight	715 kg (1,576 lb)

PERFORMANCE:

Max level speed	94 knots (175 km/h; 108 mph)
Max cruising speed, three persons	81 knots (150 km/h; 93 mph)
Stalling speed	35 knots (65 km/h; 41 mph)
Max rate of climb at S/L	210 m (690 ft)/min
T-O run	100 m (328 ft)
T-O to 15 m (50 ft)	280 m (920 ft)
Landing from 15 m (50 ft)	260 m (855 ft)
Landing run	150 m (493 ft)
Range with max fuel	297 nm (550 km; 341 miles)
Range with max payload	243 nm (450 km; 280 miles)

GRINVALDS
JEAN GRINVALDS

65 avenue J. Jaurès, 10150 Pont Ste Marie

Aircraft exhibited at the 1979 Paris Air Show under the auspices of the RSA (Réseau du Sport de l'Air) included the four-seat all-plastics Orion, designed and built by M Grinvalds with the assistance of M Calvel, whose Frelon motor glider is described in this edition. The Orion project had first attracted attention at the 1977 RSA meeting at Brienne-le-Château, where a radio-controlled scale model was demonstrated. The full-scale prototype was not quite complete, lacking its tail-mounted propeller, when shown at Le Bourget and Brienne in the Summer of 1979.

GRINVALDS ORION

The entire airframe of the Orion is made of glassfibre, reinforced locally with carbon fibre and Kevlar.
TYPE: Four-seat all-plastics light aircraft.
WINGS: Cantilever low-wing monoplane, built in one piece tip-to-tip, and installed in housing moulded into undersurface of fuselage. Wing section NACA 43015 at root, NACA 43012 at tip. Dihedral 4° 18' from root. Incidence 2° 18' at root, 0° 18' at tip. Aileron and slotted flap along entire trailing-edge of each wing. No tabs.
FUSELAGE: All-plastics structure of ovoid section, with integral tail fin and wing-root stubs and fillets.

TAIL UNIT: Cantilever T-tail, with fixed tailplane, horn-balanced elevator and inset rudder. Fixed ventral fin. Tab in elevator.
LANDING GEAR: Retractable tricycle type, with single wheel on each unit. Electrical retraction, nosewheel forward, main units inward under fuselage. Manual emergency actuation. Main gear fully enclosed when retracted, by doors attached to legs. All three legs of Wittman cantilever leaf-spring type. Hydraulic disc brakes on main wheels. Tailskid under ventral fin to protect propeller in taildown attitude.
POWER PLANT: Prototype has one Avco Lycoming flat-four engine, of 112-134 kW (150-180 hp), mounted inside rear fuselage and driving a tail-mounted four-blade propeller, with spinner, by means of Aerocar-type shafting. Access to engine via large door on each side, over wing trailing-edge. Cooling air enters via two underbelly scoops; hot air and exhaust gases ejected through ducts on each side of rear fuselage. After initial flight trials, and certification, the prototype is planned to flight test alternative power plants, including Wankel and 112 kW (150 hp) SACMA engines.
ACCOMMODATION: Four persons, in pairs, in enclosed cabin, or three persons, depending on engine power. Upward-opening window/door on each side, forward of wing. Large baggage space at rear of cabin. Dual controls.

DIMENSIONS, EXTERNAL:

Wing span	9·00 m (29 ft 6½ in)
Wing chord at root	1·50 m (4 ft 11 in)
Wing chord at tip	1·00 m (3 ft 3¼ in)
Wing aspect ratio	7·2
Wing area, gross	11·25 m² (121·1 sq ft)
Length overall	6·70 m (21 ft 11¾ in)
Tailplane span	3·30 m (10 ft 10 in)
Wheel track	2·90 m (9 ft 6 in)
Propeller diameter	1·50 m (4 ft 11 in)

DIMENSIONS, INTERNAL:

Cabin: Length	2·30 m (7 ft 6½ in)
Max height	1·10 m (3 ft 7¼ in)
Max width	1·10 m (3 ft 7¼ in)

WEIGHTS (A, 112 kW; 150 hp: B, 134 kW; 180 hp):

Weight empty, equipped: A	535 kg (1,180 lb)
B	550 kg (1,213 lb)
Max T-O weight: A	975 kg (2,150 lb)
B	990 kg (2,183 lb)

PERFORMANCE (estimated, at max T-O weight):

Max level speed, three occupants:	
A	162 knots (300 km/h; 186 mph)
Max level speed, three/four occupants:	
B	173 knots (320 km/h; 199 mph)
Max cruising speed: A	146 knots (270 km/h; 168 mph)
B	156 knots (290 km/h; 180 mph)

JODEL
AVIONS JODEL SA

HEAD OFFICE: 36 Route de Seurre, 21-Beaune
DESIGN OFFICE: 21-Darois
PRESIDENT-DIRECTOR GENERAL: J. Delemontez

The Société des Avions Jodel was formed in March 1946, by MM Jean Delemontez and Edouard Joly, with the former acting as business and technical manager and the latter as test pilot.

Its first activities were concerned with the repair of gliders and light aircraft of the Service d'Aviation Légère et Sportive, on behalf of the State. Simultaneously, the company designed and built the D.9 Bébé Jodel single-seat light monoplane, which made its first flight in January 1948. This aeroplane, which is certificated with various power plants, proved ideal for amateur construction and can be built in as little as 500 man-hours.

As the result of official tests with the D.9, the French authorities placed an order for the development and construction of two prototypes of a two-seat model, the D.11 fitted with a 33·6 kW (45 hp) Salmson, and the D.111 with a 56 kW (75 hp) Minié engine. Subsequent developments

of the D.11 are the D.112 and D.119, which have a 48·5 kW (65 hp) and 67 kW (90 hp) Continental engine respectively. These designs also have been built in large numbers, both commercially and by amateurs.

Avions Jodel now devotes its activities mainly to designing advanced developments of its established types and to acting as a consultant to those building and developing its designs.

JODEL D.9 and D.92 BÉBÉ

The type designation of the Bébé varies according to the type of engine fitted. The original version, with 18·6 kW (25 hp) Poinsard engine, was designated D.9; the D.92 has a modified Volkswagen engine.

The following details refer to all standard versions of the Bébé:
TYPE: Single-seat light monoplane.
WINGS: Cantilever low-wing monoplane. Single-spar one-piece wing with wide-span centre-section of constant chord and thickness and two tapering outer portions set at a coarse dihedral angle (14°). Spar and ribs of spruce and plywood, with fabric covering. Ailerons similar in construction.

FUSELAGE: Rectangular spruce and plywood structure.
TAIL UNIT: Cantilever structure of spruce and plywood, with plywood covering on tailplane and fabric-covered rudder and elevators. No fin.
LANDING GEAR: Non-retractable cantilever main legs with rubber-in-compression springing. Leaf-spring tailskid or tailwheel. Cable brakes.
POWER PLANT: One 18·6 kW (25 hp) Poinsard (D.9) or modified Volkswagen (D.92) flat-four engine, but other engines of 18·5 to 48·5 kW (25 to 65 hp) may be fitted, including the 27 kW (36 hp) Aeronca JAP and Continental A40. Fuel tank in fuselage, capacity 25 litres (5·5 Imp gallons).
ACCOMMODATION: Single seat in open cockpit.
DIMENSIONS, EXTERNAL:

Wing span	7·00 m (22 ft 11 in)
Wing chord (centre-section, constant)	1·40 m (4 ft 7 in)
Wing area, gross	9·0 m² (96·8 sq ft)
Wing aspect ratio	5·45
Length overall	5·45 m (17 ft 10½ in)

Gatard Statoplan AG 04 Pigeon (Geoffrey P. Jones)

Grinvalds Orion awaiting its tail-mounted propeller (J. M. G. Gradidge)

Jodel F.11, a Canadian example of the D.11 built by Mr Anatel Yaremchuk of Vernon, BC (Phil Hanson)

Jodel Bébé single-seat homebuilt aircraft (Roland Eichenberger)

Jurca M.J.2D Tempête built by M Sire of Pons (Michel Bernard)

Prototype M.J.3H Dart, built by Mr Denis Jacobs of Dayton, Ohio

---

WEIGHTS:

Weight empty	190 kg (420 lb)
Max T-O weight	320 kg (705 lb)

PERFORMANCE (30 kW; 40 hp engine, at max T-O weight):

Max level speed at S/L	87 knots (160 km/h; 100 mph)
Cruising speed	74 knots (137 km/h; 85 mph)
Stalling speed	35 knots (65 km/h; 40 mph)
Max rate of climb at S/L	180 m (590 ft)/min
T-O run	110 m (360 ft)
Landing run	100 m (330 ft)
Range with max fuel	217 nm (400 km; 250 miles)

JODEL D.11 and D.119

The original D.11, with 33·5 kW (45 hp) Salmson engine, was the basic model in the series of Jodel two-seaters for amateur and commercial production.

The version for amateur construction with 67 kW (90 hp) Continental engine is designated D.119.

A typical D.11 was built over an eight-year period by Wayne Nelson, an aeronautical engineer of Bountiful, Utah, at a cost of $2,000. The wing is of wood, covered with Dacron, the fuselage and tail unit of wood covered

with glassfibre. Changes from the standard design include the fitting of a fixed tail-fin forward of the rudder, and of cantilever spring main landing gear legs. This D.11 spans 8·23 m (27 ft 0 in), has an empty weight of 340 kg (750 lb) and loaded weight of 562 kg (1,240 lb), and is powered by a 48·5 kW (65 hp) Continental A65-8 flat-four engine. Performance is as follows:

PERFORMANCE:

Max level speed at S/L	93 knots (173 km/h; 108 mph)
Cruising speed	86 knots (161 km/h; 100 mph)
Landing speed	35 knots (64·5 km/h; 40 mph)
Max rate of climb at S/L	152 m (500 ft)/min
Service ceiling	4,875 m (16,000 ft)
T-O run	152 m (500 ft)
Landing run	244 m (800 ft)
Range with max fuel	260 nm (482 km; 300 miles)

JODEL D.112 CLUB

The D.112 is a two-seat dual-control version of the D.9. Except for increased overall dimensions, a wider fuselage and enclosed side-by-side cockpit, the D.112 conforms in

layout and structure to the D.9, but is fitted normally with a 48·5 kW (65 hp) Continental flat-four engine. Fuel capacity is 60 litres (13 Imp gallons).

DIMENSIONS, EXTERNAL:

Wing span	8·2 m (26 ft 10 in)
Wing area, gross	12·72 m² (137 sq ft)
Length overall	6·36 m (20 ft 10 in)
Dihedral on outer wings	19°

WEIGHTS:

Weight empty	270 kg (600 lb)
Max T-O weight	520 kg (1,145 lb)

PERFORMANCE (at max T-O weight):

Max level speed at S/L	102 knots (190 km/h; 118 mph)
Max cruising speed	92 knots (170 km/h; 105·5 mph)
Econ cruising speed	81 knots (150 km/h; 93 mph)
Stalling speed	38 knots (70 km/h; 43 mph)
Max rate of climb at S/L	193 m (632 ft)/min
T-O run	137 m (450 ft)
Landing run	120 m (395 ft)
Range with max fuel	323 nm (600 km; 373 miles)

JURCA
MARCEL JURCA

2, rue des Champs Philippe, 92-La Garenne-Colombes (Seine)

Telephone: 242.9633 and 551.6306

M Marcel Jurca, an ex-military pilot and hydraulics engineer, has designed a series of high-performance light aircraft of which plans are available to amateur constructors.

A prototype of his first design, the M.J.1, was built but did not fly. To gain experience, M Jurca next built a two-seat Jodel light aircraft, with the help of members of the Aéro Club of Courbevoie, and this flew for the first time in 1954.

The same team then built a prototype of M Jurca's second design, the M.J.2 Tempête single-seat light aircraft, incorporating many Jodel components. It proved so successful that sets of plans were offered to amateur constructors and many Tempêtes are now flying or under assembly throughout the world.

M Jurca developed from the Tempête the two-seat M.J.5 Sirocco and the M.J.51 Sperocco, and has produced a further series of designs by scaling down the basic airframes of second World War fighters to two-thirds or three-quarters of the original size.

For the North American market, Jurca plans are available from Mr Ken Heit, 581 Helen Street, Mt Morris, Michigan 48458, USA. Representative for Australia and New Zealand is Mr Steve Rankin, RD 9, Whangarei, New Zealand.

JURCA M.J.2 and M.J.20 TEMPÊTE

The prototype Tempête was flown for the first time, by its designer, on 27 June 1956. It obtained its certificate of airworthiness very quickly, and a total of at least 28 Tempêtes are now flying, with 20 more under construction, in France, Denmark, Luxembourg, Portugal, the UK, the United States and Canada, all amateur built.

The type of engine fitted to a particular aircraft is indicated by a suffix letter in its designation. Suffix letters are

A for the 48·5 kW (65 hp) Continental A65, B for the 56 kW (75 hp) Continental A75, C for the 63·5 kW (85 hp) Continental C85, D for the 67 kW (90 hp) Continental C90-14F, E for the 74·5 kW (100 hp) Continental O-200-A, F for the 78·5 kW (105 hp) Potez 4 E-20, G for the 86 kW (115 hp) Potez 4 E-30, and H for the 93 kW (125 hp) Avco Lycoming.

The standard version is the M.J.2A with A65 engine. The M.J.2D, with 67 kW (90 hp) C90-14F, cruises at 105 knots (195 km/h; 121 mph) and climbs to 1,000 m (3,280 ft) in 3 minutes. It can also perform aerobatics without loss of height. The Tempête built in Portugal is an M.J.2D with 67 kW (90 hp) Continental.

A version known as the **M.J.20** was under construction in Denmark with a 134 kW (180 hp) engine and strengthened airframe. It has been abandoned and its role as a prototype has been taken by a 112 kW (150 hp) Tempête being built in the Rouen area of France by M Yves Chopart.

The Tempête is basically a single-seat aircraft, but the

112 and 134 kW (150 and 180 hp) versions have provision for carrying behind the pilot on cross-country flights a second person weighing not more than 55 kg (121 lb). This is not permitted by the DGAC in France; but a two-seater has already flown in the USA, built by Mr Don Kerkhof of Mankato, Minnesota.

The 112 and 134 kW versions are intended to have an aerobatic capability adequate to compete with the American Pitts Specials in international competitions.

The following details apply generally to all basic single-seat M.J.2 models:

TYPE: Single-seat light monoplane.
WINGS: Cantilever low-wing monoplane. NACA 23012 wing section. Incidence varies according to engine power. The 48·5 kW (65 hp) version has an incidence of 4° at root, 2° at tip. No dihedral. All-wood one-piece single-spar structure with fabric covering. Fabric-covered wooden ailerons.
FUSELAGE: All-wood structure of basic rectangular section, plywood-covered.
TAIL UNIT: Cantilever all-wood structure. Tailplane and fin plywood-covered, elevators and rudder fabric-covered. Trim tab on starboard elevator.
LANDING GEAR: Non-retractable tailwheel type. Jodel D.112 cantilever legs with rubber-in-compression springing. Jodel D.112 wheels and Dunlop 420 × 150 tyres. Jodel D.112 tailskid or tailwheel.
POWER PLANT: One 48·5 kW (65 hp) Continental A65 flat-four engine, driving a Ratier two-blade wooden propeller with ground-adjustable pitch. Provision for fitting 56, 63·5, 67, or 74·5 kW (75, 85, 90 or 100 hp) Continental, 78·5 or 86 kW (105 or 115 hp) Potez or 93 kW (125 hp) Avco Lycoming engine. Jodel engine mounting and cowling. Jodel fuel tank, capacity 60 litres (13·2 Imp gallons), aft of firewall in fuselage.
ACCOMMODATION: Single seat under long rearward-sliding transparent canopy.
DIMENSIONS, EXTERNAL:
Wing span	6·00 m (19 ft 8 in)
Wing chord (basic)	1·40 m (4 ft 7 in)
Wing area, gross	7·98 m² (85·90 sq ft)
Wing aspect ratio	4·5
Length overall	5·855 m (19 ft 2½ in)
Height overall	2·40 m (7 ft 10 in)
Tailplane span	2·50 m (8 ft 2 in)
Wheel track	2·30 m (7 ft 6½ in)

WEIGHTS:
Weight empty	90 kg (639 lb)
Max T-O weight	430 kg (950 lb)

PERFORMANCE (48·5 kW; 65 hp engine):
Max level speed	104 knots (193 km/h; 120 mph)
Cruising speed	89 knots (165 km/h; 102 mph)
Landing speed	43 knots (80 km/h; 50 mph)
Max rate of climb at S/L	170 m (555 ft)/min
Service ceiling	3,500 m (11,500 ft)
T-O run	250 m (820 ft)
Endurance	3 h 20 min

JURCA M.J.3H DART

The M.J.3H Dart is a single-seat all-wood monoplane, with the fuselage of the M.J.2 Tempête and the wings of the M.J.5 Sirocco. The prototype, built by Denis Jacobs of Dayton, Ohio, made its first flight in 1977.
TYPE: Single-seat sporting aircraft.
WINGS: As for M.J.5 Sirocco. Wing section NACA 23012. No dihedral. Incidence 3°. Washout 2° at half-span. Wood construction, including three-position split flaps and ailerons.
FUSELAGE: As for M.J.2 Tempête. All-wooden semi-monocoque structure.
TAIL UNIT: Conventional cantilever all-wooden structure, comprising fin and rudder, tailplane and elevators with trim tab on starboard side.
LANDING GEAR: Retractable tailwheel type. Main wheels retract inward.
POWER PLANT: One 86 kW (115 hp) Avco Lycoming O-235-C1 flat-four engine, driving a two-blade propeller. Fuel tanks in front and rear fuselage, total capacity 75·7 litres (16·6 Imp gallons).
ACCOMMODATION: Single seat under sliding transparent canopy.
DIMENSIONS, EXTERNAL:
Wing span	6·35 m (20 ft 10 in)
Wing chord at tip	1·40 m (4 ft 7 in)
Wing area, gross	9·66 m² (104 sq ft)
Wing aspect ratio	4·25
Length overall	6·248 m (20 ft 6 in)
Tailplane span	2·54 m (8 ft 4 in)
Wheel track	2·44 m (8 ft 0 in)

WEIGHTS:
Weight empty	476 kg (1,050 lb)
Max T-O weight	612 kg (1,350 lb)

PERFORMANCE (48·5 kW; 65 hp engine):
Never-exceed speed	173 knots (322 km/h; 200 mph)
Max level speed at 1,525 m (5,000 ft)	134 knots (248 km/h; 154 mph)
Max cruising speed (75% power) at 1,525 m (5,000 ft)	123 knots (229 km/h; 142 mph)
Econ cruising speed	117 knots (217 km/h; 135 mph)
Stalling speed, landing gear and flaps up	52 knots (97 km/h; 60 mph)

Stalling speed, landing gear and flaps down
	48 knots (88·5 km/h; 55 mph)
Time to 1,000 m (3,280 ft)	3 min 15 s
Service ceiling (estimated)	3,660 m (12,000 ft)
T-O run, 15·5°C	229 m (750 ft)
Landing run	305 m (1,000 ft)
Endurance	2 h 45 min
Load factors	+9g, −4·5g (ultimate)

JURCA M.J.5 SIROCCO

The M.J.5 Sirocco is a tandem two-seat monoplane, developed from the M.J.2 Tempête as a potential club training and touring aircraft. It is fully aerobatic when flown as a two-seater.

The longer-span wings have an extended leading-edge inboard of the fence on each side and a completely new tip shape. A sweptback fin and rudder are standard.

The prototype M.J.5 flew for the first time on 3 August 1962, powered by a 78·5 kW (105 hp) Potez 4 E-20 engine. It was fitted originally with a non-retractable landing gear, but retractable landing gear and a 119·5 kW (160 hp) Avco Lycoming O-320 engine were fitted in 1966, followed by a 134 kW (180 hp) Avco Lycoming engine later. Its fuel capacity is 116 litres (25·5 Imp gallons).

By mid-February 1967, five more Siroccos were flying, one of them factory-built at Nancy. This aircraft, powered by a 74·5 kW (100 hp) Continental engine, concluded tests at Istres in January 1969. The French government then concluded an agreement with Constructions Aéronautiques Lorraines, François et Cie of Nancy, which built an airframe for static tests, in March 1971. These were required in view of the fact that the Sirocco is regarded as a basic trainer suitable for amateur construction; and it was awarded subsequently a certificate of airworthiness in the Utility category. Supplementary tests were conducted at the CEV with another Sirocco, powered by a 100·5 kW (135 hp) Avco Lycoming O-320 engine.

A full C of A, covering Aerobatic requirements and unlimited spinning, is applicable only when a power plant of 112 kW (150 hp) minimum rating is installed.

The version of the Sirocco for amateur construction is generally similar to the factory-built version, with optional retractable landing gear.

At least 40 Siroccos are reported to be flying or under construction by amateurs in France, Canada, West Germany, Switzerland, England and the USA, with various engines.

The type of engine fitted to a particular aircraft is indicated by a suffix letter in its designation. Suffix letters are A for the 67 kW (90 hp) Continental C90-8 or -14F, B for the 74·5 kW (100 hp) Continental O-200-A, C for the 78·5 kW (105 hp) Potez 4 E-20, D for the 86 kW (115 hp) Potez 4 E-30, E for the 78·5 kW (105 hp) Hirth, F for the 93 kW (125 hp) Avco Lycoming, G for the 100·5 kW (135 hp) Regnier, H for the 119·5 kW (160 hp) Avco Lycoming, K for the 134 kW (180 hp) Avco Lycoming and L for the 164 kW (220 hp) Franklin. Addition of the numeral 1 indicates a non-retractable landing gear and the numeral 2 indicates a retractable landing gear. Thus, the designation of the original prototype in its current form is M.J.5K2. The example built at Nancy for certification has a 74·5 kW (100 hp) Continental engine and so is designated M.J.5B1.

Two examples of the M.J.5K, flying in Vichy and Montelimar, France, are each fitted with a 134 kW (180 hp) Avco Lycoming engine and Christen inverted fuel system. Work on two M.J.5L Siroccos, with 164 kW (220 hp) Franklin engine, was started in 1975, in the USA and France, for use in international aerobatic championships.

A Sirocco with 86 kW (115 hp) Avco Lycoming O-235-C2B engine and 1·85 m (6 ft 0¾ in) diameter propeller was constructed by Luftsportgruppe Liebherr-Aero-Technik (LAT) in West Germany. This has a modified rudder of reduced height and greater chord, and a jettisonable, sideways-hinged cockpit canopy, and is intended for certification for aerobatic flying. The details which follow apply to this aircraft, but are generally typical of all versions.

A developed version, known as the M.J.51 Sperocco, is described separately.

DIMENSIONS, EXTERNAL:
Wing span	7·00 m (23 ft 0 in)
Wing area, gross	10·00 m² (107·64 sq ft)
Wing aspect ratio	4·9
Length overall	6·15 m (20 ft 2 in)

Height overall, tail up:
standard model	2·80 m (9 ft 2¼ in)
LAT version	2·60 m (8 ft 6¼ in)
Tailplane span	3·24 m (10 ft 7½ in)
Wheel track	2·80 m (9 ft 2¼ in)

WEIGHTS:
Weight empty	430 kg (947 lb)
Max T-O weight	680 kg (1,499 lb)

PERFORMANCE (at max T-O weight):
Max level speed	127 knots (235 km/h; 146 mph)
Cruising speed	116 knots (215 km/h; 134 mph)
Stalling speed	44 knots (80 km/h; 50 mph)
Climb to 1,000 m (3,280 ft)	4 min
Service ceiling	5,000 m (16,400 ft)
T-O run	250 m (820 ft)

Landing run	200 m (655 ft)
Endurance	4 h 20 min

JURCA M.J.5 SIROCCO (SPORT WING)

A special version of the Sirocco, with 86 kW (115 hp) engine and increased wing span, has been evolved for the New Zealand and Australian market. Known as a 'Sport' wing, the wing of this aircraft embodies one additional rib and inter-rib bay each side. The modification is available in the English-language set of Sirocco plans.

JURCA M.J.51 SPEROCCO

Using knowledge gained from flight experience with the M.J.5 and the Canadian prototype M.J.7, M Jurca evolved, with the assistance of M J. Lecarme, a design incorporating features of each aircraft. It is known as the M.J.51 Sperocco, the name being a contraction of 'Special Sirocco', and is intended for high-performance aerobatic and competition flying. Like other Jurca designs, the M.J.51 is suitable for amateur construction.

The wings, of Habib 64000 748 laminar-flow profile, are essentially those of the M.J.7 Gnatsum. They are without dihedral, and the angle of incidence varies according to the rating of the engine that is installed, as in the Tempête. The fuselage is of completely new design, with a basically triangular cross-section, but is of similar construction to the M.J.5. The tail unit consists of M.J.7 horizontal surfaces with a shorter and wider-chord fin and rudder. Landing gear is of the M.J.5 type and is fully retractable.

Any horizontally-opposed engine of 112-179 kW (150-240 hp) may be installed. Fuel is contained in two wing tanks, each of 55 litres (12 Imp gallons) capacity, and one fuselage tank of 45 or 100 litres (10 or 22 Imp gallons) capacity.

The M.J.51 seats two persons in tandem under a one-piece sliding canopy, the rear seat being 10 cm (3·9 in) higher than the front seat.

The first M.J.51, powered by a 134 kW (180 hp) Avco Lycoming AIO-360 engine, is under construction by M Serge Brilliant at Melun.

DIMENSIONS, EXTERNAL:
Wing span	7·623 m (25 ft 0 in)
Wing area, gross	11·00 m² (118 sq ft)
Length overall	7·24 m (23 ft 9 in)

WEIGHT:
Max T-O weight	730 kg (1,653 lb)

PERFORMANCE (estimated, with 112 kW; 150 hp Lycoming engine):
Max level speed	149 knots (275 km/h; 171 mph)
Max cruising speed (75% power)	135 knots (250 km/h; 155 mph)
Stalling speed	49 knots (90 km/h; 56 mph)
Time to 1,000 m (3,280 ft)	1 min 30 s

JURCA M.J.7 and M.J.77 GNATSUM

The Gnatsum is a scale replica, for amateur construction, of the North American P-51 Mustang single-seat fighter of the second World War. Its name 'Gnatsum' is 'Mustang' reversed.

Initially, M Jurca designed the wings, fuselage, tail surfaces and manually-retractable landing gear. The engine installation was deliberately not designed, to permit constructors to utilise any of the suitable Avco Lycoming, Continental, Ranger or other power plants that are available.

During construction of the M.J.7 prototype in Canada (see below), a number of modifications and improvements were made to the basic design. These were embodied in the drawings, which are available from M Jurca in two forms, as follows:

M.J.7. To two-thirds scale. Prototype (CF-XZI, now N51HR) built in the works of Falconar Aircraft Ltd on the Industrial Airport, Edmonton, Alberta, Canada, and first flown on 31 July 1969. Granted DoT type approval by early 1970. Described under the 'SAL' entry in the Canadian section of the 1973-74 Jane's. The second M.J.7 built in Canada was the one constructed by Captain W. T. Foster, to which the data given at the end of this entry apply. Two other Gnatsums were flown in 1977, under the SAL designation, built by Mr Bill Slater and Mr Ross Grady of the USA. The first example built in the UK, by Mr W. E. Wilks, was illustrated in the 1978-79 Jane's. Plastics fuselage shells for the M.J.7 are available from Boeve Brothers of Holland, Michigan, USA.

M.J.77. To three-quarters scale. Examples under construction by Mr Bob Aughton in Michigan, M Glorieux of Pau, M Piazola of Egletons and M Semenadisse of Hyères, near Toulon, France.

Unlike previous small-scale replicas of this aircraft, the Gnatsum is scaled down precisely. Use of an in-line engine, such as the 134 kW (180 hp) or 149 kW (200 hp) Ranger, permits the fuselage cowling lines to follow closely those of the original. Alternative installation of a 149 kW (200 hp) Avco Lycoming horizontally-opposed aircooled engine requires fairing blisters over the cylinders.

M Jurca's plans provide for alternative plywood-covered semi-monocoque fuselage construction or a square wooden box structure covered with two plastics shells.

Jurca M.J.5EA2 Sirocco, with retractable landing gear *(Geoffrey P. Jones)*

Jurca M.J.7H Gnatsum built in Canada by Capt W. T. Foster, CAF

Jurca M.J.14 Fourtouna single-seat racing aircraft *(Roy J. Grainge)*

Jurca M.J.8 1-Nine-O built by Mr Joseph Kiska of Connecticut

DIMENSIONS, EXTERNAL:
Wing span	7·52 m (24 ft 8¼ in)
Wing area, gross	10·41 m² (112 sq ft)
Length overall	6·55 m (21 ft 6 in)

WEIGHTS (Capt Foster's M.J.7 with 149 kW; 200 hp Ranger engine):
Weight empty	673 kg (1,485 lb)
Max T-O weight	850 kg (1,875 lb)

PERFORMANCE (Capt Foster's M.J.7 with 149 kW; 200 hp Ranger engine):
Max level speed	190 knots (351 km/h; 218 mph)
Cruising speed at 2,135 m (7,000 ft)	175 knots (325 km/h; 202 mph)
Stalling speed (flaps down)	57 knots (106 km/h; 66 mph)
Take-off speed (flaps up)	70-75 knots (131-139 km/h; 81-86·5 mph)
Landing speed (flaps up)	65-70 knots (121-130 km/h; 75-81 mph)
Landing speed (flaps down)	63 knots (117 km/h; 72·5 mph)
Max rate of climb at S/L	305 m (1,000 ft)/min
T-O run	457 m (1,500 ft)
Landing run	610-762 m (2,000-2,500 ft)

JURCA M.J.7S SOLO

Intended as a single-seat advanced trainer, the M.J.7S Solo is basically similiar to the M.J.7 Gnatsum but does not retain the underbelly scoop which the latter inherited from the original P-51 Mustang design. A prototype is under construction by M Duhamel of Strasbourg, with a 134 kW (180 hp) Avco Lycoming AIO-360 flat-four engine.

The wing section of the M.J.7S is quoted as Habib 64-000 748-MJ7-104.

DIMENSIONS, EXTERNAL:
Wing span	7·523 m (24 ft 8½ in)
Wing area, gross	10·8 m² (116·2 sq ft)
Length overall, tail up	6·664 m (21 ft 10 in)
Tailplane span	3·00 m (9 ft 10 in)

JURCA M.J.8 and M.J.80 1-NINE-O

The M.J.8 is a single-seat sporting aircraft which has been designed by M Jurca by scaling down to three-quarters of the original dimensions the airframe of the Focke-Wulf Fw 190 fighter. Its general appearance is shown in the accompanying illustration.

This prototype, built by Mr Ronald Kitchen of Carson City, Nevada, flew for the first time on 30 March 1975. A second example was built by Mr J. Kiska of Norwalk, Connecticut; and Mr Evan Wolfe of California is con-

structing an enlarged M.J.8, in an attempt to produce a full-size 'Fw 190'. This has been designated **M.J.80**.

The M.J.8 prototype has a 216 kW (290 hp) Avco Lycoming IO-540 engine, but the design is suitable for the alternative use of any horizontally-opposed or radial engine in the 74·5-149 kW (100-200 hp) range. The landing gear is retractable.

DIMENSIONS, EXTERNAL (M.J.8):
Wing span	7·87 m (25 ft 10 in)
Wing chord at root	1·70 m (5 ft 7 in)
Wing chord at tip	0·90 m (2 ft 11½ in)
Wing area, gross	10·2 m² (109·8 sq ft)
Length overall	6·63 m (21 ft 9 in)
Tailplane span	2·84 m (9 ft 4 in)

WEIGHTS (M.J.8, 119·5 kW; 160 hp engine):
Weight empty	400 kg (880 lb)
Max T-O weight	626 kg (1,380 lb)

PERFORMANCE (M.J.8, estimated, with 119·5 kW; 160 hp engine):
Max level speed at S/L	139 knots (257 km/h; 160 mph)
Max cruising speed	124 knots (230 km/h; 143 mph)
Stalling speed	49 knots (90 km/h; 56 mph)
Max rate of climb at S/L	503 m (1,650 ft)/min

JURCA M.J.9 ONE-OH-NINE

A prototype three-quarter scale Messerschmitt Bf 109 fighter of the second World War is being constructed by Mr Werner Hohn of Carson City, Nevada. This has been designated M.J.9. A second example is being built by Mr Heyser of Tustin, California.

JURCA M.J.10 SPIT

The M.J.10 is a single-seat, three-quarter scale representation of the Supermarine Spitfire which can also be modified as a two-seater. It is suitable for any horizontally-opposed or in-line engine of 89·5-164 kW (120-220 hp), although some slight variations from the Spitfire's contours are necessary in the former case. Construction is entirely of wood, except for the glassfibre engine cowling and fabric covering on the control surfaces. The single-spar wing is similar in construction to that of the Sirocco. The manually-operated retractable landing gear is fitted with helicoidal spring shock-absorbers.

The basic plans adopted the Spitfire Mk IX as the standard M.J.10 version, but alternative detail plans are available for representing both Merlin- and Griffon-engined models, including the Mks VC and XIV, and for clipped, standard or extended-span wings.

A prototype is under construction by Mr Pendlebury of the Chesterfield Air Touring Group at West Bridgford,

Nottingham, England. Another is being built by Mr Ed Storo of New York, USA.

DIMENSIONS, EXTERNAL:
Wing span:	
standard	8·40 m (27 ft 6¾ in)
clipped	7·46 m (24 ft 5½ in)
Wing area, gross	12·60 m² (135·6 sq ft)
Length overall	7·125 m (23 ft 4½ in)

WEIGHTS (119·5 kW; 160 hp engine):
Weight empty	658 kg (1,450 lb)
Max T-O weight	907 kg (2,000 lb)

PERFORMANCE (estimated, with 119·5 kW; 160 hp engine):
Max level speed at S/L	139 knots (257 km/h; 160 mph)
Cruising speed	124 knots (230 km/h; 143 mph)
Stalling speed	49 knots (90 km/h; 56 mph)
Max rate of climb at S/L	503 m (1,650 ft)/min
T-O run	200 m (660 ft)

JURCA M.J.12 PEE-40

The M.J.12 is a three-quarter scale representation of the Curtiss P-40 single-seat fighter of the second World War. It spans 8·524 m (27 ft 11½ in) and has an overall length (tail up) of 7·62 m (25 ft 0 in).

Two M.J.12s are under construction in the USA, one by Mr Ron Kitchen of Carson City, Nevada, who built the prototype M.J.8.

JURCA M.J.14 FOURTOUNA

Designed in 1971, the M.J.14 Fourtouna (Tempête in Romanian) will be a small single-seat racing aircraft of unorthodox configuration, with a semi-reclining seat for the pilot. Construction of a prototype was undertaken by M Beliard in Coutances, France, and was well advanced in the Spring of 1978. Its general appearance is shown in the accompanying three-view drawing.

The standard tapered wings can be replaced by constant-chord wings of the same span if the aircraft is intended for 'rapid liaison'. Tailplane incidence is adjustable on the ground. The following data apply to the aircraft as illustrated, with a 67 kW (90 hp) Continental C90-8F flat-four engine. Fuel capacity is 70 litres (15·5 Imp gallons).

DIMENSIONS, EXTERNAL:
Wing span	6·00 m (19 ft 8½ in)
Wing area, gross	6·1 m² (65·66 sq ft)
Length overall	5·68 m (18 ft 7½ in)
Tailplane span	2·97 m (9 ft 9 in)

WEIGHTS:
Weight empty	250 kg (550 lb)
Max T-O weight	420 kg (925 lb)

KOENIG
M KOENIG

KOENIG TOM-POUSS

Under the aegis of the RSA, a number of French amateur designer/constructors exhibited their latest products at the 1979 Paris Air Show. One of the completely

new types on display was the Koenig Tom-Pouss side-by-side two-seat light aircraft, which is of epoxy/carbon fibre construction and is powered by a fan-cooled 1,700 cc Volkswagen engine, mounted at the rear of the fuselage pod and driving a pusher propeller. Twin tailbooms carry the inverted-V tail unit, and there is a fixed NASA-type

winglet at each wingtip. Large 'flaperons' on the wing trailing-edges provide high lift augmentation and roll control. Pitch and yaw control are assured by the combined elevator/rudders which can be operated both differentially and collectively. Maximum speed is quoted as 143 knots (265 km/h; 165 mph).

The Koenig Tom-Pouss, of epoxy/carbon fibre construction *(J. M. G. Gradidge)*

Laudray GL-1 *(Geoffrey P. Jones)*

LAUDRAY
GILBERT LAUDRAY
28 rue Remontry, 91560-Crosne

LAUDRAY GL-1
M Laudray has designed and constructed a tandem-wing light aircraft, based presumably on the Croses EC-6 Criquet and designated GL-1. Changes include a new cockpit canopy, two (instead of one) forward wing control rods, and four (instead of two) pivot points. The wheels of the landing gear are enclosed in streamline fairings. No further information is available.

LEDERLIN
FRANÇOIS LEDERLIN
2 rue Charles Peguy, 38-Grenoble

M Lederlin, an architect, designed and built a two-seat light aeroplane based on the familiar Mignet 'Pou-du-Ciel' formula. Although derived from the Mignet HM-380 and designated 380-L, it retains little of the original except for the wing section. First flight was made on 14 September 1965, a restricted C of A being granted in the following month.

Plans of the 380-L, annotated in English and with both English and metric measurements, are available to amateur constructors, and several examples are under construction or already flying.

LEDERLIN 380-L
TYPE: Two-seat amateur-built light aircraft.
WINGS: Tandem-wing biplane. Wing section 3·40-13. Dihedral 3° 30' on outer sections only (both wings). Incidence variable from 0° to 12° (forward wing). Incidence of rear wing 6°. No sweepback. Each wing is made in two parts, bolted together at the centreline. Construction is conventional, with wooden box-spar and trellis ribs, plywood leading-edge and overall fabric covering. The variable-incidence front wing is pivoted on the cabane structure by ball-joints and on the bracing struts (one each side) by cardan-joints. No ailerons or flaps. Long-span tab on trailing-edge of rear wing, controllable in flight.
FUSELAGE: Welded steel tube structure, covered with light alloy to front of cabin and with fabric on rear fuselage, over light spruce formers.
TAIL UNIT: Fin and rudder only. Spruce and ply structure, covered with fabric. Ground-adjustable tab in rudder.
LANDING GEAR: Non-retractable tailwheel type. Cantilever main legs consist of conical spring steel rods, inclined rearward. Fournier main wheels and tyres, size 380 × 150, with mechanical brakes. Large tailwheel, carried on telescopic leg with spring shock-absorber, can be steered by the rudder controls through a linkage engaged by the pilot.
POWER PLANT: One 67 kW (90 hp) Continental C90-14F flat-four engine, driving a McCauley two-blade metal fixed-pitch propeller. Single fuel tank, capacity 85 litres (18·75 Imp gallons). Oil capacity 4·5 litres (1 Imp gallon).
ACCOMMODATION: Two seats side by side in enclosed cabin. Forward-hinged door on each side. Controls comprise a rudder bar for directional control and a stick, suspended from the roof of the cabin and free laterally, to control the incidence of the forward wing. A further lever, suspended from the roof, controls the tab on the rear wing. Baggage space aft of seats.
DIMENSIONS, EXTERNAL:

Wing span:	
forward	7·92 m (26 ft 0 in)
rear	6·00 m (19 ft 8¼ in)
Wing chord (constant, each)	1·30 m (4 ft 3¼ in)
Wing area, gross:	
forward	9·92 m² (106·8 sq ft)
rear	7·43 m² (80·0 sq ft)

Length overall	4·77 m (15 ft 7¾ in)
Height overall	2·08 m (6 ft 10 in)
Wheel track	2·05 m (6 ft 8¾ in)
Wheelbase	3·10 m (10 ft 2 in)
Propeller diameter	1·83 m (6 ft 0 in)
Doors (each): Height	0·90 m (2 ft 11½ in)
Width	0·75 m (2 ft 5½ in)
Height to sill	0·50 m (1 ft 7½ in)
DIMENSIONS, INTERNAL:	
Cabin:	
Max width	1·07 m (3 ft 6 in)
Max height	1·03 m (3 ft 4 in)
Baggage space	0·20 m³ (7 cu ft)
WEIGHTS:	
Weight empty	360 kg (794 lb)
Max T-O weight	600 kg (1,323 lb)
PERFORMANCE (at max T-O weight):	
Never-exceed speed	126 knots (233 km/h; 145 mph)
Max level speed at 305 m (1,000 ft)	109 knots (201 km/h; 125 mph)
Max cruising speed	97 knots (180 km/h; 112 mph)
Econ cruising speed at 610 m (2,000 ft)	87 knots (161 km/h; 100 mph)
Stalling speed, power off	26 knots (49 km/h; 30 mph)
Max rate of climb at S/L	275 m (900 ft)/min
Service ceiling	over 3,660 m (12,000 ft)
T-O run	122 m (400 ft)
Landing run	153 m (500 ft)
Range at econ cruising speed	477 nm (885 km; 550 miles)

LEFEBVRE
ROBERT LEFEBVRE
CES A. Camus, rue Adeline, 76100-Rouen

M Lefebvre has built and flown a small single-seat racing aircraft named the Busard, assisted by pupils of the A. Camus technical school at Rouen. Basis of the design was the MP.204 prototype racer with 56 kW (75 hp) Minié engine, designed by Max Plan and first flown on 5 June 1952. By comparison with the MP.204, the Busard has been lightened, and simplified for construction by amateurs.

LEFEBVRE MP.205 BUSARD
The description below applies to the prototype Busard (F-PTXT) built and flown by M. Lefebvre. This aircraft was powered originally with a 48·5 kW (65 hp) Continental engine and was illustrated in this form in the 1974-75 *Jane's*. After 20 flying hours it was re-engined with a 67 kW (90 hp) Continental and underwent several refinements, including the fitting of main-wheel fairings.

At least fifteen sets of plans have been sold to amateur constructors. One Busard is being built with a 48·5 kW (65 hp) Walter engine, two with versions of the Volkswagen, and the remainder with Continentals.
TYPE: Single-seat amateur-built racing aircraft.
WINGS: Cantilever low-wing monoplane. Wing section NACA 23012. Constant incidence of 1°. Slight dihedral. Conventional single-spar wood structure, covered entirely with plywood. Fabric-covered wooden slotted ailerons, operated by control rods. Fabric-covered wooden slotted three-position trailing-edge flaps.
FUSELAGE: Conventional wooden structure, covered with plywood. Domed plywood decking. Plastics engine cowling, built in top and bottom sections.
TAIL UNIT: Cantilever wood structure. Fixed surfaces plywood-covered; control surfaces fabric-covered. Neither rudder nor elevators are aerodynamically balanced. Flettner tab in starboard elevator. Rudder is cable-operated.
LANDING GEAR: Non-retractable tailwheel type. Cessna-type aluminium leaf-spring cantilever main legs, with plastics wheel fairings. Steerable tailwheel. Brakes on main wheels.
POWER PLANT: One 67 kW (90 hp) Continental flat-four engine, driving a two-blade fixed-pitch propeller. Light alloy fuel tank aft of firewall in fuselage, capacity 40 litres (8·8 Imp gallons).
ACCOMMODATION: Single seat in enclosed cabin, with max width of 0·58 m (1 ft 10¾ in). Sideways-opening canopy, hinged on starboard side. Baggage space aft of seat.
DIMENSIONS, EXTERNAL:

Wing span	6·00 m (19 ft 8¼ in)
Wing chord at root	1·50 m (4 ft 11 in)
Wing chord at tip	0·75 m (2 ft 5½ in)
Wing area, gross	6·00 m² (64·6 sq ft)
Wing aspect ratio	6·00
Length overall:	
Continental	5·35 m (17 ft 6¾ in)
Volkswagen	5·20 m (17 ft 0¾ in)
Height overall	1·50 m (4 ft 11 in)

WEIGHTS (A, 48·5 kW; 65 hp Continental; B, 67 kW; 90 hp Continental):

Weight empty:	
A	233 kg (514 lb)
B	239 kg (527 lb)
Max T-O weight:	
A	339 kg (747 lb)
B	345 kg (760 lb)

PERFORMANCE (A, 48·5 kW; 65 hp Continental; B, 67 kW; 90 hp Continental; C, 1,600 cc Volkswagen):

Max level speed at S/L:	
A	127 knots (235 km/h; 146 mph)
B	156 knots (290 km/h; 180 mph)
C	113 knots (210 km/h; 130 mph)
Landing speed:	
A	43 knots (80 km/h; 50 mph)
Range with max fuel:	
A	242 nm (450 km; 279 miles)

LUCAS
EMILE LUCAS
12 résidence du Château-Estreux, 59990-Saultain

Emile Lucas has built a two-seat light aircraft designated Lucas L5. Design began in 1969, and construction of the prototype was undertaken in the designer's living room. First flight was made on 13 August 1976. Three more L5s are under construction.

LUCAS L5
TYPE: Two-seat light monoplane.
WINGS: Cantilever low-wing monoplane. Dihedral 3°. Incidence 3°. No sweepback. All-metal construction of AU2G and AU4G light alloy, including metal ailerons and two-position flaps. Chord sharply reduced at each wingtip by curved trailing-edge. Leading-edge of each wing extended forward at root to house main landing gear leg when retractable landing gear is fitted. No tabs.
FUSELAGE: Conventional all-metal structure of AU2G and AU4G light alloy.
TAIL UNIT: Cantilever structure of AU4G light alloy. Constant-chord tailplane, with one-piece elevator, horn-balanced at tips. Sweptback fin and horn-balanced rudder. No tabs.
LANDING GEAR: Non-retractable tricycle or mechanically-retractable tailwheel type, both having been fitted to prototype during development. Rubber

Lederlin 380-L two-seat light aircraft (Continental C90-14F engine) *(Peter J. Bish)*

Lefebvre MP.205 Busard (67 kW; 90 hp Continental engine) *(J. M. G. Gradidge)*

Two views of the Lucas L5 prototype, with non-retractable tricycle (left) and retractable tailwheel landing gear respectively

Midgy LD 261 light biplane *(Geoffrey P. Jones)*

PMB-78 Faucon single-seat light aircraft *(S. A. MacConnacher)*

---

shock-absorption. Wheel size 420 × 150 on all three units (both versions). Hydraulic brakes.

POWER PLANT: One 85·75 kW (115 hp) Avco Lycoming O-235 flat-four engine, driving an EVRA two-blade fixed-pitch propeller with spinner. One fuel tank standard in fuselage. Total fuel capacity 75 or 115 litres (16·5 or 25·3 Imp gallons).

ACCOMMODATION: Two seats side by side under transparent canopy. Baggage hold, capacity 30 kg (66 lb).

ELECTRONICS: Jolliet ER400 VHF radio.

DIMENSIONS, EXTERNAL:
Wing span   9·20 m (30 ft 2¼ in)
Wing area, gross   11·90 m² (128·1 sq ft)

Wing aspect ratio	7·2
Length overall	6·30 m (20 ft 8 in)
Height overall	2·10 m (6 ft 10¾ in)
Propeller diameter	1·70 m (5 ft 7 in)
Propeller ground clearance	0·30 m (11¾ in)

WEIGHTS:
Weight empty, equipped   505 kg (1,113 lb)
Max T-O weight   746 kg (1,644 lb)

PERFORMANCE:
Never-exceed speed 161 knots (300 km/h; 186 mph)
Max level speed:
retractable landing gear
                    140 knots (260 km/h; 162 mph)

fixed gear   127 knots (235 km/h; 146 mph)
Max cruising speed:
retractable landing gear
                    129 knots (240 km/h; 149 mph)
fixed gear   108 knots (200 km/h; 124 mph)
Econ cruising speed:
retractable landing gear
                    108 knots (200 km/h; 124 mph)
fixed gear   97 knots (180 km/h; 112 mph)
Max rate of climb at S/L   300 m (985 ft)/min
T-O to 15 m (50 ft)   280 m (920 ft)
Landing from 15 m (50 ft)   380 m (1,245 ft)
Range with max fuel 539 nm (1,000 km; 621 miles)

MIDGY
DENIS BERIN

72 avenue René Panhard, 94320-Thiais

MIDGY LD 261

The Midgy LD 261 (F-PCAN, formerly F-BCAN) is a two-seat cabin biplane. As can be seen from the accompanying illustration, the constant-chord upper wings have considerable dihedral and are braced to the constant-chord lower wings by narrow I-type interplane struts. A tailwheel type landing gear is used, and the otherwise conventional tail unit has added endplate fins. No further information is available.

MILON
PIERRE MILON

10 avenue Guynemer, 19100-Brive

PMB-78 FAUCON (FALCON)

M Pierre Milon, chief mechanic of the Aero-Club de Brive, designed and built under the designation PMB-78 (Pierre Milon-Brive 1978), a single-seat parasol-wing monoplane. Design began in November 1977; the PMB-78 was taxied for the first time in December 1978, and its initial flight was accomplished on 19 January 1979. The airframe embodies major assemblies and components of several aircraft, primarily the Stampe SV-4 and Piper Cub. This course was adopted to provide the club with a new aircraft as quickly and cheaply as possible, and one which could be expected to prove robust and reliable because of its incorporation of well-proven assemblies and components.

TYPE: Single-seat sporting aircraft.

WINGS: Parasol monoplane. Wings supported on wire-braced centre-section struts, and V bracing struts each side. Wings, of wood construction and fabric-covered, were the upper wings of a Stampe SV-4. Plain wide-span ailerons.

FUSELAGE: Basically an SV-4 fuselage, of spruce construction with internal steel bracing wires, which has been stripped, slightly shortened and rebuilt.

TAIL UNIT: Conventional wire-braced structure from a Stampe SV-4.

LANDING GEAR: Non-retractable tailwheel type. Modified main gear of a Piper Cub, comprising two side Vs and half-axles hinged to cabane structure of lower fuselage. Shock-absorption of main units by rubber bungee. SV-4 tailwheel. Main-wheel brakes.

POWER PLANT: One 74·5 kW (100 hp) Rolls-Royce Continental O-200 flat-four engine, driving a two-blade fixed-pitch metal propeller, made by M Milon, with spinner. Fuel tank in wing centre-section.

ACCOMMODATION: Pilot only in open cockpit.

SYSTEM: Electrical system includes engine-driven generator and storage battery.

DIMENSIONS, EXTERNAL:
Wing span   8·40 m (27 ft 6¾ in)
Wing area   9·54 m² (102·7 sq ft)
Tailplane span   2·86 m (9 ft 4½ in)
Wheel track   1·87 m (6 ft 1½ in)
Propeller diameter   1·76 m (5 ft 9¼ in)

WEIGHTS:
Weight empty   390 kg (860 lb)
Max T-O weight   550 kg (1,213 lb)

PERFORMANCE:
Endurance   4 h

PIEL
AVIONS CLAUDE PIEL

104 côte de Beulle, 78580-Maule
Telephone: 478.82.49

M Claude Piel has designed several light aircraft, including the Emeraude, Diamant and Beryl, of which sets of plans are available to amateur constructors. In addition, M Piel granted licence rights for their manufacture by several commercial concerns (see 1977-78 *Jane's*).

The authorised distributor for plans of all Piel designs available to amateur constructors is:

E. Littner, CP 272, Saint Laurent, Montreal, Quebec H4L 4V6, Canada.

PIEL EMERAUDE and SUPER EMERAUDE

There have been several factory-built versions of the Emeraude and Super Emeraude, but the aircraft are no longer being produced in this form. The designs continue to be available for amateur construction, and the following amateur-built versions have flown:

C.P.301. With 67 kW (90 hp) Continental engine.

C.P.304. With 63·4 kW (85 hp) Continental C85-12F engine and wing flaps.

C.P.305. With 86 kW (115 hp) Avco Lycoming engine.

C.P.308. With 56 kW (75 hp) Continental engine.

C.P.320. With Super Emeraude wings and 74·5 kW (100 hp) Continental engine. **C.P.320A** has sweptback fin.

C.P.321. As C.P.320, with 78·5 kW (105 hp) Potez engine.

C.P.323A. With 112 kW (150 hp) Avco Lycoming engine and sweptback fin. **C.P.323AB** has tricycle landing gear.

In addition, Mr Jason Petroelje of Holland, Michigan, brought to the 1979 EAA Fly-in an Emeraude (N78JP) with retractable tailwheel-type landing gear. This is shown in an accompanying illustration.

The Emeraude is one of the types approved by the Popular Flying Association for amateur construction in the United Kingdom.

The following details refer to the basic C.P.301 Emeraude and C.P.320 Super Emeraude, but are generally applicable to all versions:

TYPE: Two-seat light monoplane.

WINGS: Cantilever low-wing monoplane. NACA 23012 wing section. Dihedral 5° 40'. Incidence 4° 10'. Inner half of each wing is rectangular in plan, outer half semi-elliptical. All-wood single-spar structure with fabric covering overall. Slotted ailerons and flaps.

FUSELAGE: Conventional wood structure, covered with fabric.

TAIL UNIT: Cantilever wood structure. Fin integral with fuselage. Single-piece all-wood tailplane. Elevators and rudder fabric-covered. Trim tab in starboard elevator.

LANDING GEAR: Non-retractable tailwheel type. Cantilever main legs have rubber-in-compression springing. Hydraulic brakes.

POWER PLANT (C.P.301): One 67 kW (90 hp) Continental C90-12F flat-four engine. Two-blade fixed-pitch wooden propeller. Fuel tank in fuselage, behind fireproof bulkhead, capacity 80 litres (17·6 Imp gallons). Provision for auxiliary tank, capacity 40 litres (8·8 Imp gallons).

POWER PLANT (C.P.320): One 74·5 kW (100 hp) Continental O-200 flat-four engine, driving a two-blade fixed-pitch wooden propeller. Fuel as for C.P.301.

ACCOMMODATION: Enclosed cockpit seating two side by side with dual controls. Sides of canopy hinge forward for access and exit. Heating and ventilation.

DIMENSIONS, EXTERNAL:

Wing span	8·04 m (26 ft 4½ in)
Wing chord at root	1·50 m (4 ft 11 in)
Wing chord at tip	0·55 m (1 ft 9½ in)
Wing area, gross	10·85 m² (116·7 sq ft)
Wing aspect ratio	5·95
Length overall:	
C.P.301	6·30 m (20 ft 8 in)
C.P.320	6·45 m (21 ft 2 in)
Height overall:	
C.P.301	1·85 m (6 ft 0¾ in)
C.P.320	1·90 m (6 ft 2¾ in)
Wheel track	2·05 m (6 ft 8¾ in)
Propeller diameter:	
C.P.301	1·80 m (5 ft 11 in)
C.P.320	1·78 m (5 ft 10 in)

WEIGHTS:

Weight empty:	
C.P.301	380 kg (838 lb)
C.P.320	410 kg (903 lb)
Max T-O weight:	
C.P.301	650 kg (1,433 lb)
C.P.320	700 kg (1,543 lb)

PERFORMANCE (at max T-O weight):

Never-exceed speed:	
C.P.301	118·5 knots (220 km/h; 136·5 mph)
C.P.320	149 knots (277 km/h; 172 mph)
Max level speed:	
C.P.301	110 knots (205 km/h; 127 mph)
C.P.320	124 knots (230 km/h; 143 mph)
Max cruising speed (75% power) at 1,200 m (3,940 ft):	
C.P.301	108 knots (200 km/h; 124 mph)
C.P.320	119 knots (220 km/h; 137 mph)
Econ cruising speed (65% power) at 1,200 m (3,940 ft):	
C.P.301	101 knots (187 km/h; 116 mph)
C.P.320	110 knots (205 km/h; 127 mph)
Approach speed, flaps down:	
C.P.301, C.P.320	65 knots (120 km/h; 75 mph)
Stalling speed, flaps up:	
C.P.301	51 knots (92 km/h; 58 mph)
C.P.320	53 knots (97 km/h; 61 mph)
Stalling speed, flaps down:	
C.P.301	46 knots (85 km/h; 53 mph)
C.P.320	49 knots (90 km/h; 56 mph)
Max rate of climb at S/L:	
C.P.301	168 m (551 ft)/min
C.P.320	240 m (787 ft)/min

Service ceiling:	
C.P.301	4,000 m (13,125 ft)
C.P.320	4,300 m (14,100 ft)
T-O run:	
C.P.301	250 m (820 ft)
C.P.320	230 m (755 ft)
T-O to 15 m (50 ft):	
C.P.301	440 m (1,443 ft)
C.P.320	400 m (1,312 ft)
Landing from 15 m (50 ft):	
C.P.301	475 m (1,558 ft)
C.P.320	490 m (1,608 ft)
Landing run:	
C.P.301	250 m (820 ft)
C.P.320	260 m (853 ft)
Range at econ cruising speed:	
C.P.301, C.P.320	538 nm (1,000 km; 620 miles)

PIEL C.P.1320

This aircraft combines the general characteristics of the Super Emeraude with the Diamant's three-seat cabin and fuel tanks in the wings. It can be fitted with engines of 112 kW (150 hp) to 149 kW (200 hp) and the prototype, built by Mr Lascoutounas of Blanquefort, near Bordeaux, will have a 119·5 kW (160 hp) Avco Lycoming. Design started in January 1977 and construction of the prototype began in September of the same year. Although plans for amateur construction of the C.P.1320 had not been completed by January 1979, six sets had already been sold and work on several aircraft had been started.

Normal load factors will be +5g and −2·5g. For aerobatics in two-seat form at a T-O weight of 720 kg (1,585 lb), the permissible load factors will be +6g and −3g.

TYPE: Three-seat light monoplane.

WINGS: Cantilever low-wing monoplane. NACA 23012 wing section. Dihedral 3°. Incidence 2°. Conventional all-wood structure. Slotted ailerons and slotted flaps of wood construction.

FUSELAGE: Conventional wooden semi-monocoque structure.

TAIL UNIT: Cantilever wooden structure. Sweptback fin and long dorsal fin integral with fuselage. All-wood constant-chord tailplane and elevator. Tab in elevator trailing-edge.

LANDING GEAR: Tailwheel type. Main units retract inward. Electrical retraction. Non-retractable tailwheel. Drum brakes on main wheels.

POWER PLANT: Prototype has one 119·5 kW (160 hp) Avco Lycoming engine, driving a two-blade Evra wooden fixed-pitch propeller. Single fuel tank in fuselage, capacity 70 litres (15·4 Imp gallons), and two fuel tanks in wings with total capacity of 70 litres (15·4 Imp gallons). Max fuel capacity 140 litres (30·8 Imp gallons).

ACCOMMODATION: Three seats, under rearward-sliding transparent canopy.

DIMENSIONS, EXTERNAL:

Wing span	7·90 m (25 ft 11 in)
Wing area, gross	11·10 m² (119·48 sq ft)
Wing chord, at root	1·64 m (5 ft 4½ in)
Wing chord, at tip	1·14 m (3 ft 9 in)
Wing aspect ratio	5·62
Length overall	6·60 m (21 ft 8 in)
Height overall	1·80 m (5 ft 11 in)
Tailplane span	2·50 m (8 ft 2½ in)
Wheel track	2·20 m (7 ft 2½ in)
Propeller diameter	1·80 m (5 ft 11 in)

WEIGHTS:

Weight empty	470 kg (1,036 lb)
Max T-O weight	800 kg (1,764 lb)

PERFORMANCE:

Never-exceed speed	183 knots (340 km/h; 211 mph)
Max level speed	162 knots (300 km/h; 186 mph)
Max cruising speed (75% power)	
	145 knots (270 km/h; 167 mph)
Econ cruising speed (65% power)	
	132 knots (245 km/h; 152 mph)
Approach speed, flaps down	
	70 knots (130 km/h; 81 mph)
Stalling speed, flaps up	54 knots (100 km/h; 62 mph)
Stalling speed, flaps down	
	51·5 knots (95 km/h; 59 mph)
Max rate of climb at S/L	600 m (1,968 ft)/min
Service ceiling	5,000 m (16,400 ft)
T-O run	200 m (657 ft)
T-O to 15 m (50 ft)	420 m (1,378 ft)
Landing from 15 m (50 ft)	600 m (1,968 ft)
Landing run	300 m (984 ft)
Range with max fuel (65% power)	
	593 nm (1,100 km; 683 miles)

PIEL SUPER DIAMANT

The Super Diamant is essentially a three/four-seat version of the Emeraude. It is fully certificated for commercial production and is available also in plan form for construction by amateurs. By early 1979, 42 sets of plans had been sold. Current versions are as follows:

C.P.604. Prototype (F-PMEC) flown in Summer of 1964, with a 108 kW (145 hp) Continental engine. Current version has swept vertical tail surfaces.

C.P.605. Much-modified four-seat ('2+2') version, with 112 kW (150 hp) Avco Lycoming O-320-E2A engine. Fully certificated for commercial production, as

well as for amateur construction. Details in 1973-74 *Jane's.*

C.P.605B. Version of C.P.605 with retractable tricycle landing gear.

TYPE: Three/four-seat light monoplane.

WINGS: Cantilever low-wing monoplane. Wing section NACA 23012. Dihedral 5° 40'. Incidence 4° 10'. All-wood single-spar structure, made in one piece, with fabric covering. Slotted ailerons and slotted flaps of wood construction, with fabric covering.

FUSELAGE: Wood structure, covered with fabric.

TAIL UNIT: Cantilever wood structure, with sweptback fin and rudder. Fixed surfaces plywood-covered. Control surfaces fabric-covered. Ground-adjustable tab on each elevator.

LANDING GEAR (C.P.604): Non-retractable tailwheel type. Main wheels size 420 × 150. Hydraulic brakes. Wheel fairings. Steerable tailwheel, size 155 × 50.

LANDING GEAR (C.P.605B): Retractable tricycle type. Main wheels retract inward. All three wheels and tyres size 400 × 100.

POWER PLANT: One flat-four engine, driving an EVRA two-blade fixed-pitch wooden propeller. Fuel tank in fuselage, capacity 85 litres (18·7 Imp gallons). Provision for additional tankage to give total capacity of 160 litres (35 Imp gallons). Oil capacity 4 litres (0·9 Imp gallons).

ACCOMMODATION: Four seats ('2+2') in enclosed cabin under large rearward-sliding transparent canopy.

DIMENSIONS, EXTERNAL (C.P.605B):

Wing span	9·20 m (30 ft 2¼ in)
Wing chord at root	1·50 m (4 ft 11 in)
Wing area, gross	13·30 m² (143·2 sq ft)
Wing aspect ratio	6·4
Length overall	7·00 m (22 ft 11¾ in)
Height overall	2·00 m (6 ft 6¾ in)
Wheel track	3·00 m (9 ft 10 in)
Propeller diameter	1·80 m (5 ft 11 in)

WEIGHTS (C.P.605B):

Weight empty	520 kg (1,146 lb)
Max T-O weight	850 kg (1,873 lb)

PERFORMANCE (C.P.605B, at max T-O weight):

Never-exceed speed	151 knots (280 km/h; 174 mph)
Max level speed	141 knots (260 km/h; 162 mph)
Max cruising speed (75% power) at 1,200 m (3,940 ft)	132 knots (245 km/h; 152 mph)
Econ cruising speed (65% power) at 1,200 m (3,940 ft)	124 knots (230 km)h; 143 mph)
Approach speed, flaps down	
	68 knots (125 km/h; 78 mph)
Stalling speed, flaps up	49 knots (90 km/h; 56 mph)
Stalling speed, flaps down	
	45 knots (82 km/h; 51 mph)
Max rate of climb at S/L	330 m (1,082 ft)/min
Service ceiling	5,000 m (16,400 ft)
T-O run	160 m (525 ft)
T-O to 15 m (50 ft)	380 m (1,247 ft)
Landing from 15 m (50 ft)	600 m (1,969 ft)
Landing run	270 m (886 ft)
Range at econ cruising speed	
	620 nm (1,150 km; 714 miles)

PIEL C.P.70, C.P.750 and C.P.751 BERYL

The prototype **C.P.70 Beryl** was displayed publicly for the first time in August 1965. It combines the wing of the C.P.30 Emeraude, virtually unchanged, with a fuselage containing two seats in tandem, and with non-retractable tricycle landing gear. It is powered by a 48·5 kW (65 hp) Continental engine.

Intended for aerobatic flying, the **C.P.750 Beryl** is also similar in general appearance to the Emeraude but has a longer, steel tube fuselage seating two persons in tandem, slightly reduced span, non-retractable tailwheel-type landing gear, 112 kW (150 hp) Avco Lycoming engine and other changes.

The C.P.750 has so far been built principally by amateur constructors in Canada, but may also be built in France through the facilities offered by M Choisel at Abbeville. By early 1980, at least fifteen sets of plans had been sold.

A further variant is the **C.P.751** shown in the accompanying illustration. This aircraft (F-PYHM) was built by M Daniel Poulet and made its first flight at Les Mureaux on 2 March 1980. It introduces several new design features and has a 134 kW (180 hp) Avco Lycoming O-360-A engine.

TYPE: Two-seat aerobatic monoplane.

WINGS: Cantilever low-wing monoplane. Wing section NACA 23012. Dihedral 5° 40'. Incidence 4° 10'. All-wood single-spar structure, made in one piece, with fabric covering. Slotted ailerons and slotted flaps of wood construction with fabric covering.

FUSELAGE: Fabric-covered structure of wood (C.P.70) or welded steel tube (C.P.750).

TAIL UNIT: Cantilever wood structure. Fixed surfaces plywood-covered, control surfaces fabric-covered. Ground-adjustable tab on each elevator.

LANDING GEAR (C.P.70): Non-retractable tricycle type.

LANDING GEAR (C.P.750): Non-retractable tailwheel type. Main wheels size 420 × 150, pressure 1·65 bars (24 lb/sq in). Hydraulic brakes. Wheel fairings. Steerable tailwheel.

POWER PLANT (C.P.70): One 48·5 kW (65 hp) Continental

Piel C.P.1320 three-seat light aircraft *(Michael A. Badrocke)*

Piel C.P.90 Pinocchio single-seat light sporting aircraft *(Pilot Press)*

Piel C.P.500 tandem-wing twin-engined light aircraft *(Roy J. Grainge)*

Piel Super Diamant (112 kW; 150 hp Avco Lycoming engine) built by Mr Eric R. Glew of Agincourt, Ontario, Canada *(Neil A. Macdougall)*

Modified Piel Emeraude, with retractable landing gear *(J. M. G. Gradidge)*

C.P.80 No. 01 single-seat racing aircraft built by M Claude Piel

Piel C.P. 751 Beryl built by M Daniel Poulet *(Wolfgang Wagner)*

C65-8F flat-four engine, driving a two-blade wooden propeller. Fuel tank in fuselage, capacity 70 litres (15·4 Imp gallons).

POWER PLANT (C.P.750): One 112 kW (150 hp) Avco Lycoming O-320-E2A flat-four engine, driving an EVRA two-blade fixed-pitch wooden propeller. Fuel tank in fuselage, capacity 70 litres (15·4 Imp gallons), with provision for two auxiliary tanks in wings to give total capacity of 140 litres (30·75 Imp gallons). Oil capacity 5 litres (1·0 Imp gallon).

ACCOMMODATION: Two seats in tandem under rearward-sliding transparent canopy. Rear seat of C.P.70 is wide enough to accommodate one adult and a child, or two children.

DIMENSIONS, EXTERNAL:

Wing span:	
C.P.70	8·25 m (27 ft 0¾ in)
C.P.750	8·04 m (26 ft 4½ in)
Wing chord at root	1·50 m (4 ft 11 in)
Wing area, gross:	
C.P.70	10·85 m² (116·8 sq ft)
C.P.750	11·00 m² (118 sq ft)
Wing aspect ratio:	
C.P.70	5·95
C.P.750	5·85
Length overall:	
C.P.70	6·45 m (21 ft 2 in)
C.P.750	6·90 m (22 ft 7¾ in)
Height overall:	
C.P.70	1·60 m (5 ft 3 in)
C.P.750	2·10 m (6 ft 10¾ in)
Wheel track:	
C.P.70	2·00 m (6 ft 6¾ in)
C.P.750	2·40 m (7 ft 10½ in)
Propeller diameter	1·80 m (5 ft 11 in)

WEIGHTS:

Weight empty:	
C.P.70	320 kg (705 lb)
C.P.750	480 kg (1,058 lb)
Max T-O weight:	
C.P.70	540 kg (1,190 lb)
C.P.750	760 kg (1,675 lb)

PERFORMANCE (at max T-O weight):

Never-exceed speed:		
C.P.70	118·5 knots	(220 km/h; 136·5 mph)
C.P.750	183 knots	(340 km/h; 211 mph)
Max level speed:		
C.P.70	95 knots	(175 km/h; 109 mph)
C.P.750	151 knots	(280 km/h; 174 mph)
Max cruising speed (75% power) at 1,200 m (3,940 ft):		
C.P.70	84 knots	(156 km/h; 97 mph)
C.P.750	143 knots	(265 km/h; 165 mph)
Econ cruising speed (65% power) at 1,200 m (3,940 ft):		
C.P.70	78 knots	(145 km/h; 90 mph)
C.P.750	135 knots	(250 km/h; 155 mph)
Approach speed, flaps down:		
C.P.70	54 knots	(100 km/h; 62·5 mph)
C.P.750	70 knots	(130 km/h; 81 mph)
Stalling speed, flaps up:		
C.P.70	41 knots	(75 km/h; 47 mph)
C.P.750	54 knots	(100 km/h; 62·5 mph)
Stalling speed, flaps down:		
C.P.70	39 knots	(70 km/h; 44 mph)
C.P.750	52 knots	(95 km/h; 59 mph)
Max rate of climb at S/L:		
C.P.70	120 m	(394 ft)/min
C.P.750	390 m	(1,280 ft)/min
Service ceiling:		
C.P.70	3,000 m	(9,850 ft)
C.P.750	5,200 m	(17,060 ft)

T-O run:	
C.P.70	280 m (919 ft)
C.P.750	190 m (623 ft)
T-O to 15 m (50 ft):	
C.P.70	420 m (1,378 ft)
C.P.750	350 m (1,148 ft)
Landing from 15 m (50 ft):	
C.P.70	280 m (919 ft)
C.P.750	520 m (1,706 ft)
Landing run:	
C.P.70	140 m (459 ft)
C.P.750	280 m (919 ft)
Range at econ cruising speed:	
C.P.70	323 nm (600 km; 372 miles)
C.P.750	593 nm (1,100 km; 683 miles)

PIEL C.P.80

The C.P.80 was designed as a single-seat racing aircraft for amateur construction. The basic version is made of wood, as described; but M Calvel of l'Hospitalet du Larzac adapted the design to enable his C.P.80 Zef to be constructed of laminated plastics. This was the first C.P.80 to fly, followed in July 1974 by the C.P.80 Racer No. 01 (F-PVQF) built by M Claude Piel.

About 61 wooden C.P.80s are under construction by amateurs. The general appearance of the aircraft is shown in the accompanying illustration.

M Piel's prototype has confirmed the accuracy of the estimated weight and performance figures quoted. It has attained a maximum level speed of 162 knots (300 km/h; 186 mph) without main wheel fairings, suggesting an eventual maximum level speed of 172 knots (320 km/h; 199 mph) when these are fitted and development is completed.

TYPE: Single-seat amateur-built racing aircraft.

WINGS: Cantilever low-wing monoplane. Wing section NACA 23012. Dihedral 3°. Incidence 2° (constant). No sweep at quarter-chord. Conventional single-spar wood structure, plywood-covered and with polyester plastics tips. Ailerons mass-balanced and cable-actuated. No flaps or tabs.

FUSELAGE: Conventional plywood-covered wood structure of basic rectangular section, with four longerons, nine frames and domed rear decking. Polyester plastics engine cowling. Steel tube engine mounting attached to fireproof bulkhead.

TAIL UNIT: Cantilever plywood-covered all-wood structure, with vertical surfaces swept back at 50° on leading-edge. All-moving constant-chord horizontal surfaces, with centrally-positioned anti-balance and trim tab, and with mass-balance arm projecting forward inside fuselage. Horn-balanced rudder. Control surfaces cable-operated.

LANDING GEAR: Non-retractable tailwheel type. Main wheels carried on cantilever spring legs of treated AU4SG alloy. Steerable tailwheel carried on steel spring. Hydraulic brakes on main wheels.

POWER PLANT: One 67 kW (90 hp) Continental C90-8F flat-four engine, driving through a short extension shaft a two-blade fixed-pitch wooden propeller. Provision for other engines, including 48·5 kW (65 hp) Continental. Fuel tank of AG-3 alloy, capacity 40 litres (8·8 Imp gallons) aft of firewall, with refuelling point in top-decking.

ACCOMMODATION: Pilot only, in enclosed cockpit, under sideways-hinged transparent canopy.

DIMENSIONS, EXTERNAL:
Wing span	6·00 m (19 ft 8¼ in)
Wing chord at aircraft centreline	1·35 m (4 ft 5¼ in)
Wing chord at tip	0·90 m (2 ft 11½ in)
Wing area, gross	6·20 m² (66·7 sq ft)
Wing aspect ratio	5·8
Length overall	5·30 m (17 ft 4¾ in)
Height overall	1·70 m (5 ft 7 in)
Tailplane span	1·58 m (5 ft 2¼ in)
Wheel track	1·60 m (5 ft 3 in)
Wheelbase	3·50 m (11 ft 5¾ in)
Propeller diameter	1·52 m (5 ft 0 in)

WEIGHTS (67 kW; 90 hp engine):
Weight empty	260 kg (573 lb)
Max T-O weight	380 kg (837 lb)

PERFORMANCE (estimated, with 67 kW; 90 hp engine, at max T-O weight):
Never-exceed speed	205 knots (380 km/h; 236 mph)
Max level speed	167 knots (310 km/h; 193 mph)
Max cruising speed (75% power) at 1,200 m (3,940 ft)	151 knots (280 km/h; 174 mph)
Econ cruising speed (65% power) at 1,200 m (3,940 ft)	129·5 knots (240 km/h; 149 mph)
Approach speed	70 knots (130 km/h; 81 mph)
Stalling speed	51·5 knots (95 km/h; 59 mph)
Max rate of climb at S/L	720 m (2,360 ft)/min
Service ceiling	6,000 m (19,685 ft)
T-O run	200 m (656 ft)
T-O to 15 m (50 ft)	400 m (1,312 ft)
Landing from 15 m (50 ft)	360 m (1,181 ft)
Landing run	200 m (656 ft)
Range at econ cruising speed	243 nm (450 km; 280 miles)

g limits	+8; −6

PIEL C.P.90 PINOCCHIO

The C.P.90 Pinocchio is essentially a smaller, single-seat development of the basic Emeraude, intended for aerobatic and general sporting flying. At least six sets of plans had been sold by early 1980.

WINGS: Cantilever low-wing monoplane, of similar general planform and construction to Emeraude. Dihedral 5° 40'. Incidence 3°. Ailerons only, no flaps.

FUSELAGE: Fabric-covered wooden structure of basically rectangular cross-section with domed decking.

TAIL UNIT: Cantilever fabric-covered wooden structure, similar to that of Emeraude.

LANDING GEAR: Non-retractable tailwheel type. Streamlined leg and wheel fairings on main units.

POWER PLANT: One 74·5 kW (100 hp) Continental O-200 flat-four engine, driving a two-blade wooden propeller. Fuel capacity 60 litres (13·2 Imp gallons).

ACCOMMODATION: Single seat under fully-transparent canopy.

DIMENSIONS, EXTERNAL:
Wing span	7·20 m (23 ft 7½ in)
Wing area, gross	9·65 m² (103·9 sq ft)
Wing aspect ratio	5·4
Length overall	6·00 m (19 ft 8¼ in)
Height overall	1·80 m (5 ft 11 in)
Wheel track	1·60 m (5 ft 3 in)
Propeller diameter	1·80 m (5 ft 11 in)

WEIGHTS:
Weight empty	335 kg (738 lb)
Max T-O weight	460 kg (1,014 lb)

PERFORMANCE (estimated, at max T-O weight):
Never-exceed speed	171 knots (320 km/h; 198 mph)
Max level speed	141 knots (260 km/h; 162 mph)
Max cruising speed (75% power) at 1,200 m (3,940 ft)	132 knots (245 km/h; 152 mph)
Econ cruising speed (65% power) at 1,200 m (3,940 ft)	124 knots (230 km/h; 143 mph)
Approach speed	59 knots (110 km/h; 68 mph)
Stalling speed	41 knots (75 km/h; 47 mph)
Max rate of climb at S/L	480 m (1,575 ft)/min
Service ceiling	6,000 m (19,685 ft)
T-O run	180 m (590 ft)
T-O to 15 m (50 ft)	400 m (1,312 ft)
Landing from 15 m (50 ft)	300 m (984 ft)
Landing run	160 m (525 ft)
Range at econ cruising speed	296 nm (550 km; 341 miles)

PIEL C.P.500

As can be seen in the accompanying illustration, the C.P.500 is a 'push and pull' twin-engined aircraft of staggered tandem-wing configuration. Although this gives it some similarity to the Mignet formula, the wings are fixed, and the pilot's controls conventional.

The strut-braced forward wing has four-section slotted trailing-edge flaps over 75% of the span and 25% of the chord, actuated electrically through 35°. The rear wing carries two elevons, actuated by control rods from 40° up to 35° down; these function differentially for roll control and collectively for pitch control. Endplate fins and rudders on the rear wing provide yaw control. The relative position of the wings is expected to permit steep 'parachute' descents of the kind possible with Mignet designs.

Wing section is NACA 23015. The front wing has a dihedral of 1° 30' and incidence of 2° 30' constant; the rear wing has a constant incidence of 4° 30' but no dihedral.

Construction of the prototype C.P.500 has been started by the Aero Club Jean Bertin. Although it was intended originally to be built of wood, this aircraft is now basically of metal construction, as specified for any future series production of the type. The engine cowlings, wingtips and fairings are of laminated plastics. Two 112/119·5 kW (150/160 hp) Avco Lycoming O-320 flat-four engines are specified, with the rear engine driving its propeller through an extension shaft, 15 cm (5·9 in) long. Fuel tanks in the tips of the forward wing have a combined capacity of 300 litres (66 Imp gallons).

A non-retractable tricycle landing gear is standard, with Wittman-type cantilever steel spring main legs and a steerable nosewheel. Each main wheel is fitted with a hydraulic brake.

Basic accommodation is for two persons side by side in front, with optional dual controls, and three passengers on a rear bench seat. Aft of the rear seat is space for a sixth person or a considerable quantity of baggage.

DIMENSIONS, EXTERNAL:
Wing span:	
front	8·80 m (28 ft 10½ in)
rear	6·43 m (21 ft 1¼ in)
Wing chord (constant):	
front	1·50 m (4 ft 11 in)
rear	1·10 m (3 ft 7¼ in)
Wing area, gross:	
front	13·20 m² (142·1 sq ft)
rear	7·10 m² (76·42 sq ft)
Wing aspect ratio:	
front	5·85
rear	5·88
Wing stagger	0·46 m (1 ft 6 in)
Length overall	6·10 m (20 ft 0 in)
Height overall	2·25 m (7 ft 4½ in)
Fuselage depth (max)	1·56 m (5 ft 1½ in)
Fuselage width (max)	1·40 m (4 ft 7 in)
Wheel track	2·56 m (8 ft 4¾ in)
Wheelbase	2·60 m (8 ft 6¼ in)

WEIGHTS:
Weight empty	866 kg (1,909 lb)
Max T-O weight	1,500 kg (3,307 lb)

PERFORMANCE (estimated):
Max level speed	162 knots (300 km/h; 186 mph)
Max level speed, one engine out	129 knots (240 km/h; 149 mph)
Max cruising speed (75% power)	143 knots (265 km/h; 165 mph)
Max cruising speed, one engine out (75% power)	108 knots (200 km/h; 124 mph)
Stalling speed, flaps down	49 knots (90 km/h; 56 mph)
Max rate of climb at S/L	540 m (1,770 ft)/min
Max rate of climb at S/L, one engine out	180 m (590 ft)/min
Service ceiling	6,800 m (22,300 ft)
Service ceiling, one engine out	3,000 m (9,850 ft)
Range with max fuel	647 nm (1,200 km; 745 miles)

POTTIER
JEAN POTTIER

4 rue de Poissy, 78130 les Mureaux
Telephone: 099 13-85

In addition to the light aircraft and sailplanes that he designed jointly with M Robert Jacquet, during his period as technical director at Société CARMAM, M Pottier is responsible for the purely amateur projects of which details follow.

POTTIER P.50 BOUVREUIL (BULLFINCH)

Designed by M Jean Pottier, the Bouvreuil is a single-seat racing monoplane, intended for construction by amateurs. Construction is entirely of wood, except for the plastics engine cowling and main-wheel fairings.

The Bouvreuil can be fitted with a variety of engines in the 48·5-86 kW (65-115 hp) category. It has also been designed from the start to have either a non-retractable (P.50) or retractable (P.50R) landing gear. Design load factors are ± 10.

The first Bouvreuil to be completed was number 04, built in Switzerland by M Sugnaux of Billens, which flew for the first time on 27 July 1979 and was displayed at the 1979 RSA meeting at Brienne in France. This aircraft (HB-YBF) has a 74·5 kW (100 hp) Continental O-200 engine, slotted flaps and electrically-retractable tailwheel-type landing gear. It differs from plans in having extended and cambered wingtips, and two underwing attachments for camera pods or external fuel tanks. Its load factors for aerobatics are calculated as +12/−7g. Equipment includes VHF radio and VOR. Number 04 has a wing span of 6·48 m (21 ft 3 in), wing area of 7·5 m² (80·7 sq ft), length of 5·25 m (17 ft 2¾ in), height of 1·70 m (5 ft 7 in), empty weight of 360 kg (794 lb) and max T-O weight

of 450 kg (992 lb). Its max rate of climb at S/L is 360 m (1,180 ft)/min.

The French-built 02 has a 48·5 kW (65 hp) Continental and non-retractable landing gear.

TYPE: Single-seat racing monoplane.

WINGS: Cantilever low-wing monoplane. Wing section NACA 23015 at root, NACA 23012 at tip. Dihedral from roots. All-wood structure, with full-span ailerons and flaps. No tabs.

FUSELAGE: Conventional wood semi-monocoque structure, with plastics engine cowling.

TAIL UNIT: Cantilever all-wood structure, with swept vertical surfaces. Trim tab in each elevator.

LANDING GEAR: Alternative retractable or non-retractable tailwheel type. Wheel fairings standard on non-retractable main wheels. Steerable tailwheel. Independent main-wheel brakes.

POWER PLANT: Standard power plant is a 67 kW (90 hp) Continental C90 flat-four engine, driving a two-blade fixed-pitch propeller with spinner. Other engines of 48·5 to 86 kW (65-115 hp) are optional. Fuel capacity 60 litres (13 Imp gallons) for racing, 100 litres (22 Imp gallons) for touring. Provision for carrying one removable auxiliary fuel tank under each wing.

ACCOMMODATION: Single seat in enclosed cabin, under large rearward-sliding transparent canopy.

DIMENSIONS, EXTERNAL:
Wing span	6·20 m (20 ft 4 in)
Wing area, gross	7·50 m² (80·7 sq ft)
Wing aspect ratio	5·10
Length overall	5·65 m (18 ft 6½ in)

WEIGHTS (67 kW; 90 hp engine):
Weight empty	270 kg (595 lb)
Max T-O weight	400 kg (882 lb)

PERFORMANCE (estimated, with 67 kW; 90 hp engine and non-retractable landing gear):
Max level speed	167 knots (310 km/h; 192 mph)
Max cruising speed (75% power)	151 knots (280 km/h; 174 mph)
Min speed	43 knots (80 km/h; 50 mph)

POTTIER P.70S

This small sporting aircraft is derived from the P.70B, designed by M Pottier and built by M Alain Besneux (see 1976-77 *Jane's*). Design of the P.70S was started in January 1974, and by January 1980 twenty-five were being or had been completed by amateur builders, of which six were expected to be in use in 1980. First to fly, in 1977, was No. 23 (F-PYEF), powered by a 30 kW (40 hp) Volkswagen 1,500 cc engine and embodying some design changes, including a tailwheel-type landing gear (illustrated in 1978-79 *Jane's*).

The following details apply to the standard P.70S.

TYPE: Single-seat sporting aircraft.

WINGS: Cantilever mid-wing monoplane. Wing section NACA 4415. No dihedral. Incidence 2°. No sweep. Constant-chord all-metal structure of 2024 alloy, with I-beam main spar and channel-section rear spar. Entire trailing-edge of each wing formed by aileron hinged to upper surface and plain flap hinged to bottom surface. No tabs.

FUSELAGE: All-metal structure of 2024 alloy, built up on five frames.

TAIL UNIT: Cantilever all-metal structure, with sweptback vertical surfaces. Minimal fixed fin. No tabs.

LANDING GEAR: Non-retractable tricycle type. Cantilever main legs.

POWER PLANT: One 30/44·7 kW (40/60 hp) Volkswagen

Pottier P.50R Bouvreuil single-seat racing aircraft *(Roy J. Grainge)*

The prototype Pottier P.80S, constructed at the 1977 Paris Air Show
(Geoffrey P. Jones)

Pottier P.70S with standard tricycle landing gear *(M. J. Hooks)*

Pottier P.110TS three-seat light aircraft *(Michael A. Badrocke)*

converted motor car engine, driving a two-blade fixed-pitch propeller. Single fuel tank in fuselage, aft of firewall, capacity 40 litres (8·75 Imp gallons).

ACCOMMODATION: Pilot only, in enclosed cockpit.

DIMENSIONS, EXTERNAL:
Wing span	5·85 m (19 ft 2¼ in)
Wing chord, constant	1·25 m (4 ft 1¼ in)
Wing area, gross	7·2 m² (77·5 sq ft)
Wing aspect ratio	4·8
Length overall	5·15 m (16 ft 10¾ in)
Height overall	1·60 m (5 ft 3 in)
Tailplane span	2·10 m (6 ft 10¾ in)
Wheel track	1·20 m (3 ft 11¼ in)
Propeller diameter	1·30 m (4 ft 3¼ in)

WEIGHTS:
Weight empty, equipped	215 kg (474 lb)
Max T-O and landing weight	325 kg (716 lb)

PERFORMANCE (A: standard P.70S with 30 kW; 40 hp engine, B: 44·7 kW; 60 hp engine, at max T-O weight, except where indicated):
Never-exceed speed at S/L	
	129 knots (240 km/h; 149 mph)
Max level speed at S/L:	
A	97 knots (180 km/h; 112 mph)
B	116 knots (215 km/h; 133·5 mph)
No. 23	110 knots (205 km/h; 127 mph)
Max cruising speed at S/L:	
A	89 knots (165 km/h; 103 mph)
B	108 knots (200 km/h; 124 mph)
No. 23	100 knots (185 km/h; 115 mph)
Econ cruising speed at S/L:	
A	65 knots (120 km/h; 75 mph)
Stalling speed, flaps down	
	38 knots (70 km/h; 44 mph)
Max rate of climb at S/L:	
A	150 m (490 ft)/min
B	330 m (1,080 ft)/min
Service ceiling: A	4,500 m (14,775 ft)
T-O run: A	350 m (1,150 ft)
B	200 m (657 ft)
Range	215 nm (400 km; 248 miles)
g limit	+9 (ultimate)

POTTIER P.80S

The Pottier P.80S is a small single-seat sporting aircraft derived from the P.70S. Overall dimensions, structures, weights and performance are unchanged, but the P.80S is a low-wing monoplane and has a restyled cockpit hood. The prototype is powered by a 30 kW (40 hp) Rectimo 4 AR 1200 engine, itself a derivative of the Volkswagen motorcar engine, but engines of 30-44·7 kW (40-60 hp) can be fitted. Fuel capacity is 50 litres (11 Imp gallons).

Design of the P.80S began in January 1977 and construction of the prototype (F-PYEB) started in June 1977 at the Paris Air Show. Roll-out was achieved at the Show on 12 June. By early 1980, sixteen more were under construction by amateur builders, three or four of which were expected to fly that year.

POTTIER P.100TS and P.110TS

The P.100TS and P.110TS are small high-wing monoplanes of generally similar configuration, accommodating two and three persons respectively. Two examples of the P.100TS are under construction, but plans are not available to amateur builders at the present time. Both aircraft have an NACA 4415 wing section. The P.100TS can be fitted with Avco Lycoming or Continental engines of 48·5-93 kW (65-125 hp), the P.110TS with Avco Lycoming or Continental engines of 67-112 kW (90-150 hp). Fuel capacity of each aircraft is 90 litres (19·8 Imp gallons). The first P.100TS was expected to fly in the Spring of 1980.

TYPES: Two-seat (P.100TS) and three-seat (P.110TS) light monoplanes.

DIMENSIONS, EXTERNAL (A: P.100TS, B: P.110TS):
Wing span: A	6·70 m (21 ft 11¾ in)
B	7·70 m (25 ft 3 in)
Wing chord, constant	1·35 m (4 ft 5¼ in)
Wing area, gross: A	8·70 m² (93·65 sq ft)
B	10·00 m² (107·64 sq ft)
Wing aspect ratio: A	5·2
B	5·9
Length overall: A	6·50 m (21 ft 4 in)
B	7·00 m (23 ft 0 in)
Height overall: A	2·20 m (7 ft 2½ in)
B	2·25 m (7 ft 4½ in)
Wheel track: A, B	1·70 m (5 ft 7 in)

WEIGHTS (A: P.100TS with 67 kW; 90 hp engine, B: P.110TS):
Weight empty: A	315 kg (694 lb)
B	360 kg (794 lb)
Max baggage: A	33 kg (72·7 lb)
B	46 kg (101·4 lb)
Max T-O weight: A	565 kg (1,245 lb)
B	700 kg (1,543 lb)

PERFORMANCE (A: P.100TS with 93 kW; 125 hp engine, B: P.110TS with 112 kW; 150 hp engine):
Max level speed:	
A	135 knots (250 km/h; 155 mph)
B	143 knots (265 km/h; 165 mph)
Max cruising speed:	
A	127 knots (235 km/h; 146 mph)
B	135 knots (250 km/h; 155 mph)
Stalling speed:	
A, B	43·5 knots (80 km/h; 50 mph)
Max rate of climb at S/L: A	372 m (1,220 ft)/min
B	390 m (1,280 ft)/min
T-O run: A, B	230 m (755 ft)
Range with max fuel:	
A, B	350 nm (650 km; 403 miles)
Endurance, with 45 min reserves:	
A	3 h 30 min
B	3 h
g limits: A, B	+5·7 (ultimate)

POTTIER P.105TS

The Pottier P.105TS is, as its designation suggests, a hybrid of the P.100TS and P.110TS. Power is provided by an Avco Lycoming or Continental engine of 48·5-104·5 kW (65-140 hp). Two P.105TS aircraft were under construction in 1980, but plans are not available to amateur constructors.

TYPE: Two-seat light monoplane.

DIMENSIONS, EXTERNAL:
Wing span	7·70 m (25 ft 3 in)
Wing chord, constant	1·35 m (4 ft 5¼ in)
Wing area, gross	10·00 m² (107·64 sq ft)
Wing aspect ratio	5·9
Length overall	6·50 m (21 ft 4 in)
Height overall	2·20 m (7 ft 2½ in)
Wheel track	1·70 m (5 ft 7 in)

WEIGHTS:
Weight empty	350 kg (772 lb)
Max T-O weight	600 kg (1,323 lb)

PERFORMANCE (A: 48·5 kW; 65 hp engine, B: 104·5 kW; 140 hp engine):
Max level speed:	
A	94·5 knots (175 km/h; 109 mph)
B	135 knots (250 km/h; 155 mph)
Max cruising speed:	
A	86·5 knots (160 km/h; 99·5 mph)
B	129 knots (240 km/h; 149 mph)
Stalling speed	41 knots (75 km/h; 47 mph)
Rate of climb at S/L: A	144 m (472 ft)/min
B	396 m (1,300 ft)/min
T-O run: A	320 m (1,050 ft)
B	180 m (590 ft)
Range with max fuel:	
A, B	351 nm (650 km; 404 miles)
g limit	+5·7 (ultimate)

POTTIER P.170S

The P.170S is a tandem two-seat version of the P.70S. It is of all-metal (AU4G) construction and has a retractable tricycle landing gear. Power is provided by a 37·25-52 kW (50-70 hp) Volkswagen modified motor car engine. Plans are available to amateur constructors, and by early 1980 seven P.170S were being built, one of which was expected to fly in the Summer of 1980.

TYPE: Two-seat sporting aircraft.

DIMENSIONS, EXTERNAL:
Wing span	5·95 m (19 ft 6¼ in)
Wing chord, constant	1·25 m (4 ft 1¼ in)
Wing area, gross	7·40 m² (79·65 sq ft)
Wing aspect ratio	4·8
Length overall	5·70 m (18 ft 8½ in)
Height overall	1·65 m (5 ft 5 in)
Wheel track	1·20 m (3 ft 11¼ in)

WEIGHTS:
Weight empty	230 kg (507 lb)
Max T-O weight	445 kg (981 lb)

PERFORMANCE (A: 37·25 kW; 50 hp engine, B: 52 kW; 70 hp engine):
Max level speed:	
A	94·5 knots (175 km/h; 109 mph)
B	108 knots (200 km/h; 124 mph)

Max cruising speed:
A	84 knots	(155 km/h; 96·5 mph)
B	102·5 knots	(190 km/h; 118 mph)
Stalling speed	41 knots	(75 km/h; 47 mph)
Max rate of climb at S/L: A	150 m	(490 ft)/min
B	300 m	(980 ft)/min
T-O run: A	380 m	(1,250 ft)
B	220 m	(722 ft)
Landing from 15 m (50 ft)	350 m	(1,150 ft)
Range with standard 50 litres (11 Imp gallons) of fuel, 45 min reserves	215 nm	(400 km; 248 miles)
g limit		+6·6 (ultimate)

POTTIER P.180S

The P.180S is a side-by-side two-seat version of the P.80S. It is of all-metal (AU4G) construction and has a non-retractable tricycle landing gear with fairings over the wheels. Power is provided by a 41-67 kW (55-90 hp) Volkswagen modified motor car engine. Plans are available to amateur constructors and by early 1980 twenty P.180S were being built, one or two of which were expected to fly in 1980.

TYPE: Two-seat sporting aircraft.

DIMENSIONS, EXTERNAL:
Wing span	6·50 m	(21 ft 4 in)
Wing chord, constant	1·25 m	(4 ft 1¼ in)
Wing area, gross	7·80 m²	(83·96 sq ft)
Wing aspect ratio		5·3
Length overall	5·35 m	(17 ft 6½ in)
Height overall	1·70 m	(5 ft 7 in)
Wheel track	1·65 m	(5 ft 5 in)

WEIGHTS:
Weight empty	240 kg	(529 lb)
Max T-O weight	470 kg	(1,036 lb)

PERFORMANCE (A: 41 kW; 55 hp engine, B: 67 kW; 90 hp engine):

Max level speed:
A	97 knots	(180 km/h; 112 mph)
B	124 knots	(230 km/h; 143 mph)

Max cruising speed:
A	89 knots	(165 km/h; 102·5 mph)
B	119 knots	(220 km/h; 137 mph)
Stalling speed	41 knots	(75 km/h; 47 mph)
Max rate of climb at S/L: A	168 m	(550 ft)/min
B	330 m	(1,080 ft)/min
T-O run: A	330 m	(1,080 ft)
B	200 m	(656 ft)
Landing from 15 m (50 ft)	350 m	(1,150 ft)
Range	270 nm	(500 km; 310 miles)
g limit		+5·7 (ultimate)

SÉGUIN
M SÉGUIN

SÉGUIN/ADAMS-WILSON HELICOPTER

M Séguin has completed development and construction of a lightweight single-seat helicopter which is based on the configuration of the Adams-Wilson Model 101 Hobby Copter, first flown in the USA in November 1958 and last described in the 1963-64 *Jane's*. By that time some 700 sets of plans had been sold to amateur constructors, and M Séguin managed to acquire one of these original plan sets. Significant design changes to the main and tail rotors have been made; the engine is provided with a cooling fan, and there are a number of minor changes due to the use of alternative materials. The first flight of M Séguin's helicopter was made in early 1980.

TYPE: Single-seat homebuilt light helicopter.

ROTOR SYSTEM: Two-blade main rotor, formed from solid Oregon pine, with a stabilisation bar similar to that of the Bell 47. Blades, of NACA 0012 symmetrical section, and with constant chord, were hand-shaped using a template, and were fabric-covered before painting. Conventional swashplate for control of cyclic and collective pitch. Two-blade teetering tail rotor.

ROTOR DRIVE: Chain drive between engine and gearbox, and via Borg Warner automatic free-wheeling clutch and drive shaft to the rotor head. Tail rotor driven from gearbox by a V belt. Main rotor rpm 390; tail rotor rpm 2,500.

FUSELAGE: Space-frame bolted structure of AV4C-T4 light alloy tube, comprising integral frames to carry the main rotor pylon, tail rotor support, pilot's seat and controls, power plant and landing gear.

LANDING GEAR: Simple tubular skids without shock-absorption.

POWER PLANT: One 39 kW (52 hp) Triumph 650 cc two-cylinder motorcycle engine. Fuel tank mounted within rotor pylon structure. Motorcycle kick starter used conventionally.

ACCOMMODATION: Single glassfibre bucket seat forward of rotor pylon. Pilot's position has been enclosed by a cabin since the aircraft was first completed.

DIMENSIONS:
Main rotor diameter	6·55 m	(21 ft 5¾ in)
Tail rotor diameter	0·92 m	(3 ft 2¼ in)
Length of fuselage	4·60 m	(15 ft 1 in)
Skid track	1·52 m	(4 ft 11¾ in)

WEIGHTS:
Weight empty	155 kg	(342 lb)
Max T-O weight	257 kg	(567 lb)

STARCK
ANDRÉ STARCK

M André Starck, who died on 16 December 1979, first left the ground in a Chanute-type hang glider. He next built a Mignet Pou-du-Ciel, followed by the first of his own designs, the AS-10. This was a tandem two-seat biplane, and led to the AS-20, first flown on 23 October 1942, with the sharply staggered narrow-gap biplane wing arrangement first conceived by an aerodynamicist named Nenadovitch.

Five fairly conventional monoplane designs were next, designated AS-70 Jac, AS-71, AS-57, AS-80 Holiday and AS-90 New-Look. In the AS-27 Starcky (see 1978-79 *Jane's*) and AS-37, described briefly below, M Starck reverted to the narrow-gap staggered biplane formula.

STARCK AS-37

As can be seen in the accompanying illustration, this design by M André Starck embodies the narrow-gap, sharply staggered biplane wing configuration that characterised several of his earlier products. The power plant is also unusual, as the engine is mounted behind the side-by-side two-seat cabin and drives, through timing belts, two pusher propellers mounted in the gap between the wings, on each side. This is claimed to enhance, by means of the propeller slipstream, the slot effect produced by the wing arrangement.

The prototype (F-WYBQ), built by M Rudy Nickel of Romans, flew for the first time on 13 January 1977. It was powered at that time by a 48·5 kW (65 hp) Citroën GS 1220 aircooled four-cylinder engine, with a 1:2 reduction in the belt drive, so that each propeller turned at 2,200 rpm in cruising flight. Wingtip 'curtains', inclined at 45° to join the wingtips, stiffened the overall structure, making dihedral unnecessary on the main wings, and were claimed to improve stall characteristics and lateral control; the ailerons were attached to their trailing-edges. Construction of the aircraft was all-wooden, with spruce structure and acajou ply covering. Disc brakes were fitted to the main wheels of the non-retractable tricycle landing gear. Dual controls were fitted.

In that original form, as the **AS-37A**, M Nickel's aircraft logged 100 flying hours and 300 flights by October 1977. A second AS-37A (F-WXDU) was built and flown by M Léon Knoepfli of Sélestat, also with a GS 1220 engine.

After a short period of flight testing, this was modified to **AS-37B** standard. The wingtip 'curtains' were removed and replaced by wide cantilever interplane struts, some distance inboard from extended wingtips. Conventional ailerons were installed on the upper wings, and flaps on the lower wings. Other changes included replacement of the original main landing gear legs, comprising side Vs and half-axles, with new cantilever legs of laminated glassfibre, with streamline fairings over all three wheels.

Flight trials of the AS-37B soon confirmed its stability in yaw and roll, as well as its manoeuvrability. However, the increase in empty weight, to 451 kg (995 lb), suggested that a more powerful engine might be desirable. Both the AS-37A of M Nickel and AS-37B of M Knoepfli have therefore been re-engined with a 74·5 kW (100 hp) Porsche 2 flat-four engine, with dual electronic ignition on the AS-37A. Other AS-37s, under construction by M Boucher of Saint-Marcellin and M Bourdreux of Cadarache, will have a 67 kW (90 hp) Renault 843-01 engine and a SACMA engine respectively. M Nickel's aircraft is also being tested with three-blade ground-adjustable wooden propellers.

At least 23 sets of plans for the AS-37 had been sold to amateur constructors by early 1980.

The following data apply to the AS-37A as originally flown:

DIMENSIONS, EXTERNAL:
Wing span	6·30 m	(20 ft 8 in)
Wing aspect ratio		3·0
Wing area, gross	13·60 m²	(146·4 sq ft)
Length overall	6·00 m	(19 ft 8 in)
Height overall	1·60 m	(5 ft 3 in)

WEIGHTS:
Weight empty	400 kg	(882 lb)
Max T-O weight	620 kg	(1,366 lb)

PERFORMANCE (estimated):
Max level speed at S/L	100 knots	(185 km/h; 115 mph)
Cruising speed at S/L	91 knots	(170 km/h; 105 mph)
Landing speed	38 knots	(70 km/h; 43·5 mph)
Rate of climb at S/L	210 m	(690 ft)/min
Service ceiling	4,500 m	(14,750 ft)
T-O run	200 m	(655 ft)
Landing run	140 m	(460 ft)
Range with 90 litres (19·75 Imp gallons) fuel	810 nm	(1,500 km; 930 miles)

STARCK SUPER NEW LOOK

This simple, low-cost, single-seat light aircraft had its origin in André Starck's AS-90 New Look, the first example of which was flown on 11 June 1950. At the request of French amateur constructors, he has updated the design, with a strut-braced wing of new section and powered by any one of a variety of modified motorcar engines. A prototype is under construction by M Parent of Cannes.

TYPE: Single-seat ultra-light monoplane.

WINGS: Braced mid-wing monoplane. Single bracing strut each side, from main landing gear struts. Wing section GAW 1. Thickness/chord ratio 17%. Dihedral 3° from roots. Incidence 4°. Sweepback on leading-edge 6°. Constant-chord wood structure, with single plank-like main spar and trellis ribs, fabric-covered. Elliptical aileron articulated under each wingtip trailing-edge. No flaps.

FUSELAGE: Welded tube girder structure, fabric-covered.

TAIL UNIT: Cantilever structure of welded tube, fabric-covered. No tabs.

LANDING GEAR: Non-retractable two-wheel type, with tailskid. Each main wheel carried on a faired, welded tube V and a strut from the wing root.

POWER PLANT: One 24·5 kW (33 hp) Citroën Ami 6 converted motor car engine (alternative engines from Volkswagen and DAF suitable). Provision for 20 kg (44 lb) of fuel.

ACCOMMODATION: Single seat in enclosed cockpit, under sideways hinged fully transparent canopy.

DIMENSIONS, EXTERNAL:
Wing span	8·00 m	(26 ft 3 in)
Wing chord, constant	1·20 m	(3 ft 11¼ in)
Wing aspect ratio		7
Wing area, excl ailerons	8·46 m²	(91·06 sq ft)
Length overall	5·50 m	(18 ft 0½ in)
Height overall	1·40 m	(4 ft 7¼ in)

WEIGHTS:
Weight empty	154 kg	(340 lb)
Max T-O weight	262 kg	(578 lb)

PERFORMANCE (estimated, with Citroën Ami 6 engine):
Max level speed at S/L	81 knots	(150 km/h; 93 mph)
Cruising speed	73 knots	(135 km/h; 84 mph)
Landing speed	27 knots	(50 km/h; 31 mph)
Service ceiling	3,500 m	(11,500 ft)

GERMANY
(FEDERAL REPUBLIC)

BINDER
HELLMUTH BINDER

7000 Stuttgart 61, Weinklinge 24
Telephone: (0711) 424912

BINDER Bi 20

Information was received concerning a four/five-seat homebuilt aircraft of unusual design, known as the Binder Bi 20. It is not known when design of the Bi 20 was started or whether construction of a prototype has begun; but a 1·80 m (5 ft 11 in) span scale model has been flight tested.

Details and a three-view drawing can be found in the 1979-80 *Jane's*.

WALLERKOWSKI
HEINZ WALLERKOWSKI

Rablstrasse 16/8, 8 Munich 80

Telephone: (089) 486678

Heinz Wallerkowski is an airline captain with Hapag Lloyd. He began the design of the Hornisse (D-EBXG) in January 1974; construction of the prototype was initiated one year later, and the first flight took place on 30 June 1978. By the end of October 1979, 80 flying hours had

Starck Super New Look ultralight monoplane (*Michael A. Badrocke*)

Starck AS-37A built by M Rudy Nickel, as originally flown (*Geoffrey P. Jones*)

Starck AS-80 Holiday (*Geoffrey P. Jones*)

Wallerkowski Hornisse single-seat monoplane with new streamlined landing gear and canopy

VPM MT7 two-seat autogyro (*Michael A. Badrocke*)

VPM MT5 single-seat autogyro

been logged, and the flight test programme to FAR Pt 23 had been completed. Captain Wallerkowski is a member of the Oskar-Ursinus-Vereinigung, the German Chapter of the EAA.

WALLERKOWSKI HORNISSE (HORNET)

TYPE: Single-seat monoplane.
WINGS: Cantilever low-wing monoplane. NACA 23012 wing section. Dihedral 3° 30′. Incidence 1°. No sweepback. All-metal (2024-T3) construction, flush-riveted. All-metal Frise-type ailerons and all-metal flaps. No tabs.
FUSELAGE: All-metal semi-monocoque structure, flush-riveted.
TAIL UNIT: Conventional cantilever assembly of all-metal construction. Two-spar tailplane, with only two ribs each side and heavy skin. Flettner-type trim tabs in elevators.
LANDING GEAR: Non-retractable tailwheel type. Cantilever steel-tube main legs, with streamline fairings. Main wheels size 5·00-5. Wheel fairings. Steerable tailwheel. Gerdes hydraulic brakes.
POWER PLANT: One 112 kW (150 hp) Avco Lycoming

O-320-E1C flat-four engine, driving a Hoffmann three-blade ground-adjustable propeller. Two fuel tanks in wings, total capacity 90 litres (20 Imp gallons).
ACCOMMODATION: Single seat under starboard-hinged transparent canopy. Baggage space behind seat.
SYSTEM: 12V battery for engine starting.
DIMENSIONS, EXTERNAL:

Wing span	6·14 m (20 ft 1¾ in)
Wing chord, constant	1·38 m (4 ft 6¼ in)
Wing area, gross	8·4 m² (90·4 sq ft)
Wing aspect ratio	4·45
Length overall	5·80 m (19 ft 1 in)
Height overall	1·60 m (5 ft 3 in)
Tailplane span	2·22 m (7 ft 3½ in)
Wheel track	1·80 m (5 ft 11 in)
Wheelbase	4·70 m (15 ft 5 in)
Propeller diameter	1·55 m (5 ft 1 in)

DIMENSIONS, INTERNAL:

Cockpit: Length	1·20 m (3 ft 11¼ in)
Max width	0·64 m (2 ft 1¼ in)
Max height	1·04 m (3 ft 5 in)

WEIGHTS:

Weight empty	334 kg (736 lb)

Max payload	95 kg (210 lb)
Max T-O weight: normal	510 kg (1,124 lb)
aerobatic	460 kg (1,014 lb)

PERFORMANCE (at max T-O weight):
Never-exceed speed 189 knots (350 km/h; 217 mph)
Max level speed at 2,440 m (8,000 ft)
    188 knots (348 km/h; 216 mph)
Max cruising speed at 2,440 m (8,000 ft)
    173 knots (320 km/h; 199 mph)
Econ cruising speed at 2,440 m (8,000 ft)
    151 knots (280 km/h; 174 mph)
Stalling speed, flaps down, power off
    45 knots (82 km/h; 51 mph)
Stalling speed, flaps up, power off
    48 knots (88 km/h; 55 mph)
Max rate of climb at S/L 561 m (1,840 ft)/min
Service ceiling over 6,100 m (20,000 ft)
T-O run 150 m (490 ft)
T-O to 15 m (50 ft) 300 m (985 ft)
Landing from 15 m (50 ft) 300 m (985 ft)
Landing run 200 m (655 ft)
Range with max fuel, 45 min reserves
    432 nm (800 km; 497 miles)

ITALY

VPM
VPM SnC
Via per Besnate 10, 21040 Jerago (Va)
Telephone: 0331 217328
WORKS MANAGER: Vittorio Magni
TECHNICAL MANAGER: Ing Mario Puppi
SALES MANAGER: Ing Marcello Puppi

Sr Magni has built four small rotorcraft, of which the first and second were, respectively, single- and two-seat gyro-gliders of the Bensen type. The third aircraft was powered by a Volkswagen engine; the fourth had a 44·7 kW (60 hp) Franklin, and was displayed at the 1972 Turin Air Show. It was illustrated and briefly described in the 1973-74 *Jane's*.

Sr Magni has purchased from Mr Jukka Tervamäki of Finland the prototype, and all tooling, moulds and production rights, of the latter's JT-5 single-seat autogyro. In 1979 VPM SnC was established to produce plans, component parts and complete kits for amateur builders of the updated MT5 version of this autogyro. It is also developing a two-seat derivative, as the MT7.

VPM MT5

The description of the Tervamäki JT-5 that appears in the Finnish section of this edition is generally applicable also to the VPM MT5, the main difference being the use of a 1,700 cc Limbach engine to power the MT5. However, the MT5 has slightly greater dimensions, resulting in changes in all-up weight and performance, as follows:

DIMENSIONS, EXTERNAL:

Rotor diameter	7·19 m (23 ft 7 in)
Length of fuselage	3·61 m (11 ft 10 in)
Height overall	1·96 m (6 ft 5 in)

WEIGHTS:

Weight empty	167 kg (368 lb)
Max T-O weight	300 kg (661 lb)

PERFORMANCE:

Max level speed	81 knots (150 km/h; 93 mph)
Max cruising speed	70 knots (130 km/h; 81 mph)
Min level speed	22 knots (40 km/h; 25 mph)
Max rate of climb at S/L	183 m (600 ft)/min
Service ceiling	4,000 m (13,125 ft)
T-O run	80 m (262 ft)

VPM MT7

The MT7, the design of which began in early 1980, is basically an enlarged two-seat version of the MT5. Construction of a prototype was expected to begin at the end of the same year; but no plans or kits are yet available. Design of the airframe, control and rotor systems was entrusted to Mr Jukka Tervamäki of Finland, with VPM concentrating on the engine installation, instrumentation, landing gear and other details. Power plant will be a 112 kW (150 hp) Avco Lycoming O-320 flat-four engine. Design emphasis has been placed on aerodynamic refinement to give the aircraft the best possible cross-country performance at low power settings.

As can be seen from the accompanying drawing, the MT7 is generally similar in configuration to the MT5, the most obvious external differences being the selection of a twin-fin-and-rudder tail unit, with a forward-swept horizontal surface, and a more streamlined landing gear incorporating wheel fairings. Provisional data are as follows:

DIMENSIONS, EXTERNAL:

Rotor diameter	8·70 m (28 ft 6½ in)
Length of fuselage	4·40 m (14 ft 5¼ in)
Width overall, excl rotor	2·10 m (6 ft 10¾ in)
Height overall	2·40 m (7 ft 10½ in)

WEIGHTS:

Weight empty	290 kg (639 lb)
Max T-O weight	480 kg (1,058 lb)

PERFORMANCE (estimated):

Max level speed	95 knots (175 km/h; 109 mph)
Max cruising speed	81 knots (150 km/h; 93 mph)
Max rate of climb at S/L	180 m (590 ft)/min
Range	161 nm (300 km; 186 miles)

JAPAN

ABE
KEICHI ABE
4 Cho-Me, 17-11 Masuura, Kushiro-Shi, Hokkaido

Mr Keichi Abe has designed and is building a light-weight single-seat monoplane known as the Mizzet (Midget) No. III. Design work began in September 1977, and construction of the prototype was started in November of the same year. By early 1980 the aircraft was almost complete, and expected to fly during the year.

ABE MIZZET No. III

TYPE: Single-seat lightweight monoplane.

WINGS: Strut-braced low-wing monoplane. Göttingen 387 wing section. Thickness/chord ratio 15%. Dihedral 3°. Incidence 0°. Constant-chord all-wood structure, with two box-spars, fabric covered. Ailerons, but no flaps.

FUSELAGE: Main structure of 6063T rectangular metal beams and tubes. Plywood and urethane used for sides of cockpit and nose, and to give form to rear fuselage. Fabric covering overall.

TAIL UNIT: Cantilever wooden structure, fabric covered. Constant-chord tailplane, with elevators. Small dorsal fin and large horn-balanced rudder.

LANDING GEAR: Non-retractable tricycle type, relying upon low-pressure tyres for shock-absorption. Main-wheel tyres size 3·40-10, nosewheel tyre size 2·50-4. Brakes fitted.

POWER PLANT: One 30 kW (40 hp) 1,200 cc modified Volkswagen motor car engine, driving a two-blade fixed-pitch wooden propeller. Two glassfibre fuel tanks in wing leading-edge, with total capacity of 10 litres (2·2 Imp gallons). Oil capacity 2·5 litres (0·55 Imp gallons).

ACCOMMODATION: Single seat in open cockpit.

AVIONICS: Battery-powered VHF com radio.

DIMENSIONS, EXTERNAL:

Wing span	7·30 m (23 ft 11½ in)
Wing area, gross	8·75 m² (94·2 sq ft)
Wing chord, constant	1·20 m (3 ft 11¼ in)
Wing aspect ratio	6·3
Length overall	5·26 m (17 ft 3 in)
Height overall	2·05 m (6 ft 8¾ in)
Tailplane span	2·40 m (7 ft 10½ in)
Propeller diameter	1·35 m (4 ft 5 in)

WEIGHTS:

Weight empty	188 kg (414 lb)
Max fuel weight	14·4 kg (31·7 lb)
Max T-O weight	288 kg (635 lb)

PERFORMANCE (estimated):

Never-exceed speed	102 knots (189 km/h; 117 mph)
Max level speed	81 knots (150 km/h; 93 mph)
Max cruising speed	65 knots (120 km/h; 74·5 mph)
Stalling speed	38 knots (70 km/h; 43·5 mph)
Max rate of climb at S/L	366 m (1,200 ft)/min
Service ceiling	3,000 m (9,840 ft)
T-O to 15 m (50 ft)	116 m (381 ft)
Landing from 15 m (50 ft)	205 m (673 ft)
Range with max fuel	113 nm (210 km; 130 miles)

JAPAN AMATEUR BUILT AIRCRAFT LEAGUE
% JAA (Japan Aeronautical Association), 1-18-2 Shimbashi, Minato-ku, Tokyo
Telephone: (03) 502 1203

This new organisation came into being in April 1978, superseding the former Japan Experimental Aircraft Association. Various fixed- and rotating-wing aircraft have been designed and/or built and flown by its members, and several of these have been described and illustrated in recent editions of *Jane's*. Others are examples of US homebuilt types such as the Baby Great Lakes, Flaglor Scooter, Hovey Whing Ding II, Stolp Starduster and Bensen Gyro-Copter as described in the US section.

HAMAO SHIOKARATOMBO

This small single-seat biplane, designed and built by Mr Y. Hamao, is powered by a 112 kW (150 hp) Avco Lycoming O-320 engine.

The Shiokaratombo is of wooden construction, fabric covered, and its general layout can be seen in the accompanying photograph. The wing section is NACA 4218.

DIMENSIONS, EXTERNAL:

Wing span (upper)	6·40 m (21 ft 0 in)
Wing span (lower)	5·60 m (18 ft 4½ in)
Wing chord, mean	0·90 m (2 ft 11½ in)
Wing area, gross	10 m² (107·6 sq ft)
Length overall	5·70 m (18 ft 8¼ in)
Height overall	2·40 m (7 ft 10½ in)
Tailplane span	2·40 m (7 ft 10½ in)
Propeller diameter	1·88 m (6 ft 2 in)

WEIGHTS:

Weight empty	380 kg (838 lb)
Max T-O weight	500 kg (1,102 lb)

PERFORMANCE: No details available

MUKAI
ISAO MUKAI
KO 4, No. 1, Kisho, Utsumi-Machi, Shozu-Gun, Kagawa Prefecture

MUKAI OLIVE No. 2

The Olive No. 2 is Mr Mukai's second aircraft project. Design began in 1972 and the prototype was completed in March of the following year. Taxying trials started in July 1976, followed shortly afterwards by the first flight. At least one other Olive had been constructed by Spring 1979.

TYPE: Single-seat light seaplane.

WINGS: Braced high-wing monoplane. Constant chord. Clark Y wing section. No dihedral on centre-section; slight dihedral on outer wings. Two-spar all-wooden structure, fabric covered, with dope and enamel finish. V main bracing struts. Large-span wooden ailerons. No flaps.

FUSELAGE: Welded metal tube truss structure, fabric covered.

TAIL UNIT: Braced all-wood structure, fabric covered. Horizontal surfaces of constant chord. Ground-adjustable tab on starboard elevator. All-moving vertical tail surface.

LANDING GEAR: Twin floats of all-wooden construction, plywood covered.

POWER PLANT: One 48·5 kW (65 hp) 1,834 cc modified Volkswagen motor car engine, driving a two-blade propeller. One fuel tank, aft of pilot's seat, capacity 50 litres (11 Imp gallons).

ACCOMMODATION: Single seat in enclosed cabin. Upward-hinged door on port side of fuselage. Space for baggage aft of pilot's seat.

DIMENSIONS, EXTERNAL:

Wing span	12·00 m (39 ft 4½ in)
Wing chord, constant	1·40 m (4 ft 7 in)
Wing area, gross	16·80 m² (180·8 sq ft)
Wing aspect ratio	8·6
Length overall	7·30 m (23 ft 11½ in)
Height overall	2·98 m (9 ft 9¼ in)
Tailplane span	3·20 m (10 ft 6 in)
Propeller diameter	1·35 m (4 ft 5 in)

DIMENSIONS, INTERNAL:

Cabin: Length	1·30 m (4 ft 3 in)
Max width	0·80 m (2 ft 7½ in)
Max height	1·00 m (3 ft 3½ in)

WEIGHTS:

Weight empty, incl oil and fuel	295 kg (650 lb)
Max T-O weight	365 kg (805 lb)

PERFORMANCE:

Max level speed at 1,000 m (3,280 ft)	59·5 knots (110 km/h; 68·5 mph)
Max cruising speed	49 knots (90 km/h; 56 mph)
Econ cruising speed	43·5 knots (80 km/h; 50 mph)
Stalling speed	24·5 knots (45 km/h; 28 mph)
Max rate of climb at S/L	150 m (490 ft)/min
T-O run	150 m (490 ft)
T-O to 15 m (50 ft)	300 m (980 ft)
Landing from 15 m (50 ft)	180 m (590 ft)
Range with max fuel	215 nm (400 km; 248 miles)

MUKAI OLIVE SMG III

Latest of Mr Mukai's aircraft is the Olive SMG III flying-boat motor-glider. Design began on 3 May 1978, and construction of the prototype started on 10 October 1978. By early 1979 it was 10% complete, and the first flight was expected to take place in October 1980.

TYPE: Two-seat flying-boat motor-glider.

WINGS: Strut-braced high-wing monoplane. Göttingen 549 wing section. Slight dihedral. Wooden box-spar and ribs, fabric covered. Large-span wooden ailerons. Air-brakes standard.

FUSELAGE: Conventional flying-boat hull. Welded stainless steel tube truss structure, glassfibre-covered on lower surface and Dacron fabric-covered on upper surface.

TAIL UNIT: Braced all-wood structure, fabric covered. High-mounted tailplane. Tab in starboard elevator. Fin integral with fuselage. Horn-balanced rudder, with water-rudder beneath.

LANDING GEAR: Hull, with stabilising floats under wings.

POWER PLANT: One 45 kW (60 hp) modified Volkswagen motor car engine, mounted on struts above wing and driving a two-blade propeller. Two fuel tanks, total capacity 30 litres (6·6 Imp gallons). Oil capacity 2·5 litres (0·55 Imp gallons).

ACCOMMODATION: Two seats in fully enclosed cabin.

DIMENSIONS, EXTERNAL:

Wing span	14·00 m (46 ft 0 in)
Wing area, gross	16·80 m² (180·83 sq ft)
Wing chord, at root	1·40 m (4 ft 7 in)
Wing chord, at tip	0·80 m (2 ft 7½ in)
Wing aspect ratio	11·7
Length overall	7·80 m (25 ft 7 in)
Height overall	2·85 m (9 ft 4¼ in)
Tailplane span	3·20 m (10 ft 6 in)

WEIGHTS:

Weight empty	430 kg (948 lb)
Max T-O weight	575 kg (1,268 lb)

PERFORMANCE (estimated):

Best glide ratio	20
Max level speed	81 knots (150 km/h; 93 mph)
Max cruising speed	54 knots (100 km/h; 62 mph)
Stalling speed	30 knots (55 km/h; 34 mph)
Max rate of climb at S/L	150 m (492 ft)/min
Range with max fuel	215 nm (400 km; 248 miles)

Abe Mizzet No. III (*Michael A. Badrocke*)

Abe Mizzet No. III under construction

Shiokaratombo single-seat biplane designed by Mr Y. Hamao (Avco Lycoming O-320 engine)

Mukai Olive SMG III (*Michael A. Badrocke*)

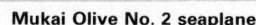

Mukai Olive No. 2 seaplane

Sawano S25X II Tandem Smoothie two-seat homebuilt (*M. Tatahashi*)

NIHON UNIVERSITY
COLLEGE OF SCIENCE AND TECHNOLOGY (DEPARTMENT OF AEROSPACE ENGINEERING), NIHON UNIVERSITY

1-8 Kanda-Surugadai, Chiyoda-ku, Tokyo 101
Telephone: Tokyo (03) 293 3251
Chief Professor: Dr Hidemasa Kimura

Chairman: Dr Renzo Yokoi

Under the leadership of Dr Kimura, students of Nihon University have designed and built several aircraft, including the Okamura N-52 and N-58 Cygnet lightplanes and a STOL lightplane designated N-62, in collaboration with the Itoh company, which built the prototype. The N-62 was put into production by Itoh, as the Eaglet, and was described in the 1968-69 *Jane's*.

This design team has also built a series of successful man-powered aircraft named Linnet, Egret, Stork and Ibis A, all of which have been described fully in previous editions of *Jane's*. A motor-glider, the N-70 Cygnus, was described in the 1974-75 edition; a new motor-glider, known as N-75 Cygnus II, is currently under construction.

SAWANO
SHIRO SAWANO

6-147 Isezaki-cho, Naka-ku, Yokohama, Kanagawa Prefecture
Telephone: (045) 251 2580

SAWANO S25X MR SMOOTHIE

Built by Mr Shiro Sawano, this modified Bowers Fly Baby was described and illustrated in the 1978-79 *Jane's*. Design began in 1967 and construction was started in the following year. By May 1975 the aircraft had been completed, but test flying did not begin until one year later. In 1978 Mr Sawano began modifying Mr Smoothie into a tandem two-seater, with an engine of greater power and a strengthened wing and fuselage. All available details of this conversion follow:

SAWANO S25X II TANDEM SMOOTHIE

Conversion of the original homebuilt Mr Smoothie to tandem two-seat configuration began in August 1978, and it was flown for the first time in this form on 21 October 1979.

Type: Two-seat light aircraft.
Wings: Wire-braced low-wing monoplane. Wing section

Clark Y. Thickness/chord ratio 12%. Pronounced dihedral. Two-spar constant-chord structure, with wooden spars and ribs, and fabric covering. Wings can be folded back alongside fuselage. Plain wooden ailerons, fabric covered.
Fuselage: Conventional wooden structure, with plywood skins.
Tail Unit: Cantilever structure, primarily of wood. Fin has plywood skins, but constant-chord tailplane, elevators and rudder are fabric-covered. Ground-adjustable trim tab on rudder; manually-controlled trim tab in elevator.
Landing Gear: Braced non-retractable tailwheel type. Main wheels carried on side Vs with cross axle. Mainwheel tyres size 450 × 200, pressure 0·48 bars (7 lb/sq in). Tailwheel has solid tyre, size 160 × 60. Honda hydraulic brakes.
Power Plant: One 39·5 kW (53 hp) modified Volkswagen motor car engine of 1,850 cc capacity, driving a two-blade fixed-pitch wooden propeller. Glassfibre fuel tank in fuselage, aft of firewall, capacity 30 litres (6·6 Imp gallons). Refuelling point on upper surface of fuselage, forward of windscreen. Oil capacity 2 litres (0·44 Imp gallons).

Accommodation: Pilot and passenger, seated in tandem, beneath sideways-hinged (to stbd) transparent canopy. Dual controls.
System: Electrical system for engine starting.
Dimensions, external:

Wing span	7·60 m (24 ft 11¼ in)
Wing chord, constant	1·20 m (3 ft 11¼ in)
Wing area, gross	9·12 m² (98·2 sq ft)
Wing aspect ratio	6·3
Length overall	5·72 m (18 ft 9¼ in)
Height overall	2·15 m (7 ft 0¾ in)
Tailplane span	2·10 m (6 ft 10¾ in)
Wheel track	1·27 m (4 ft 2 in)
Wheelbase	4·05 m (13 ft 3½ in)
Propeller diameter	1·43 m (4 ft 8¼ in)

Weights:

Weight empty	307 kg (677 lb)
Max fuel weight	22 kg (48·5 lb)
Max T-O and landing weight	483 kg (1,065 lb)

Performance:
Not yet established, except:
Never-exceed speed (calculated)
81 knots (150 km/h; 93 mph)

YAMATO
SAWAZO YAMATO
1-5-27 Imaike-cho, Sakai-Shi, Osaka Prefecture
Telephone: 0722 38 7510

YAMATO SY MOTOR GLIDER
Design of the SY motor glider began in April 1976 and construction was started in March 1977. Construction was completed by the Summer of 1979 but, due to the fact that the Volkswagen engine is not certificated in Japan for aviation use, Mr Sawazo Yamato was unable to fly this aircraft during 1979. He was hoping that he might be able to test it during 1980.

TYPE: Single-seat ultralight monoplane.
WINGS: Strut-braced parasol monoplane. Rear section of wing rests on raised fuselage turtleback. Wing section NACA 4412. Dihedral 1°. Incidence 3°. All-wood structure, with two spruce box-spars, fabric-covered and dope-finished. Plain half-span ailerons of spruce. V bracing struts. No tabs.
FUSELAGE: Conventional structure with four spruce longerons, 1·5 mm plywood-covered.
TAIL UNIT: Conventional all-wood (spruce) structure, fabric-covered and dope-finished. No tabs.
LANDING GEAR: Non-retractable tailwheel type. Main gear carried on side Vs and half-axles. Main wheels size 340 × 110, with brakes. Piper Cub type bungee shock-absorption.
POWER PLANT: One 30 kW (40 hp) modified Volkswagen 1,600 cc motor car engine, driving a fixed-pitch wooden propeller of home construction. Fuel tank aft of firewall, capacity 20 litres (4·4 Imp gallons). Oil capacity 3 litres (0·66 Imp gallons).
ACCOMMODATION: Single seat in open cockpit.
DIMENSIONS, EXTERNAL:
Wing span   12·22 m (40 ft 1 in)

Wing chord, constant	1·40 m (4 ft 7 in)
Wing area, gross	17·00 m² (183·0 sq ft)
Wing aspect ratio	8·87
Length overall	6·58 m (21 ft 7 in)
Height overall	2·40 m (7 ft 10½ in)
Tailplane span	3·40 m (11 ft 1¾ in)
Wheel track	1·60 m (5 ft 3 in)
Wheelbase	5·30 m (17 ft 4½ in)
Propeller diameter	1·35 m (4 ft 5¼ in)

WEIGHTS:
Weight empty	284 kg (626 lb)
Max T-O weight	349 kg (769 lb)

PERFORMANCE (estimated):
Never-exceed speed	80·5 knots (150 km/h; 93 mph)
Max level speed	57 knots (105 km/h; 66 mph)
Max cruising speed	41 knots (75 km/h; 47 mph)
Stalling speed	29 knots (53 km/h; 33 mph)

NEW ZEALAND

ARDC of NZ
AERONAUTICAL RESEARCH and DEVELOPMENT COMPANY OF NEW ZEALAND LTD
PO Box 11542, Wellington
DIRECTOR: James Lobet
TECHNICAL DIRECTOR: George Jacquemin

The original Ganagobie single-seat light aircraft was designed and built by the brothers William and James Lobet at Lille, France, and made its first flight in 1953, powered by an old Clerget engine. After modification and redesignation as Ganagobie 02 it flew for a further 30 h before being grounded by engine failure in 1954, and later became Ganagobie 2 when fitted with a two-stroke target drone engine.

Construction of a second aircraft, Ganagobie 03, was started in Alberta, Canada, by Mr La Rue Smith and completed by Mr Pierre Descamps. Built of birch plywood, it was somewhat heavier than the first aircraft and was powered by a 26 kW (35 hp) Poinsard engine. Engines fitted to later Ganagobie 03s were a 53·7 kW (72 hp) McCulloch and a 30 kW (40 hp) Continental; this version is also suitable for converted Volkswagen engines of 1,500 cc and above. The 'ultra-light' version, known as the Ganagobie 04, is suitable for 35·8 kW (48 hp) Nelson and other small two-stroke engines. Very light okoumé mahogany, and other weight-saving features, may be used in its construction. Latest version is the Ganagobie 05, of which the prototype is being completed in New Zealand.

Mr Lobet decided to establish the present company in New Zealand for financial reasons, as it had proved difficult to produce kits at a competitive price in Australia, which had been the home of the Ganagobie programme for a number of years.

ARDC of NZ may develop a variety of aeronautical and engineering products, including energy systems using wind and solar power, and expects to market plans and kits for a number of aircraft in addition to the Ganagobies.

GANAGOBIE 05
The Ganagobie 05 is a small, high-wing single-seat aircraft, designed primarily for amateur construction. The basic homebuilt model is all-wooden; but improved production versions are under consideration, either in kit form with a fabric-covered steel tube fuselage and wooden wings and tail, or in factory-built form with all-metal fabric-covered wing and tail control surfaces. The 1979-80 edition of *Jane's* contains a description of the all-wood homebuilt version, of which a prototype (the property of ARDC of NZ) is expected to fly in New Zealand by about 1981.

SOUTH AFRICA

VAN ASWEGEN
C. H. J. VAN ASWEGEN
Box 88, Plettenberg Bay 6600
The 1979-80 *Jane's* contained details of a single-seat light monoplane named the Bergwind that was designed and built by Mr van Aswegen. This has been followed by a new four-seat lightplane named the Vansin.

VAN ASWEGEN VANSIN
Following completion of the Bergwind, Mr van Aswegen began in July 1977 the design of a lightplane named the Vansin. His aim was to evolve a four-seat aircraft of reasonable performance without the use of a high-power engine. As a result, he has had to rely upon producing a very clean aircraft of minimum frontal area and flush-riveted throughout. Construction also began in July 1977 and the Vansin was flown for the first time in May 1979. Later that year it was awarded as a prize as the Best Homebuilt of 1979 by the EAA of South Africa.
TYPE: Four-seat cabin monoplane.
WINGS: Cantilever low-wing monoplane. Wing section NACA 2412 extensively modified. Thickness/chord ratio approximately 12%. Dihedral 7°. Incidence 1°. No sweepback. All-metal two-spar structure. Spars fabricated from 2024-T3 sheet and 7075-T6 extruded light alloy. Flush-riveted skins. Plain piano-hinged ailerons, and electrically-actuated Fowler-type trailing-edge flaps, of light alloy construction. Wingtip fuel tanks.
FUSELAGE: Conventional semi-monocoque structure of light alloy, with flush-riveted skins.
TAIL UNIT: Cantilever structure of light alloy, with flush-riveted skins. Fixed-incidence tailplane. Mechanically-actuated trim tab in elevator.
LANDING GEAR: Non-retractable tailwheel type. Cantilever main landing gear struts of spring steel. Cleveland main wheels, with tyres size 6·00-6. Maule 20 cm (8 in) diameter pneumatic tailwheel. Hydraulic disc brakes. Main-wheel fairings of GRP.
POWER PLANT: One 119 kW (160 hp) Avco Lycoming IO-320-C1A flat-four engine with turbocharger, driving a Hartzell Type HC-EZYL-2A two-blade constant-speed metal propeller with spinner. Two main fuel tanks in wings, each 70 litres (15·4 Imp gallons), and two wingtip tanks, each 50 litres (11 Imp gallons); total fuel capacity 240 litres (52·8 Imp gallons). Refuelling points on upper surface of each wing and each tip-tank. Oil capacity 8 litres (1·75 Imp gallons).
ACCOMMODATION: Pilot and three passengers in enclosed cabin. Upward-opening door on starboard side, hinged on fuselage centreline. Accommodation heated and ventilated.
SYSTEMS: Hydraulic system for brakes only. Electrical system includes engine-driven alternator and 25Ah storage battery, to operate engine starter and trailing-edge flaps.
AVIONICS AND EQUIPMENT: King KY 90 720-channel VHF com, and King ADF. Full IFR instrumentation.
DIMENSIONS, EXTERNAL:
Wing span over tip-tanks	9·22 m (30 ft 3 in)
Wing chord at root	1·80 m (5 ft 10¾ in)

Wing chord at tip	1·16 m (3 ft 9¾ in)
Wing area, gross	14·0 m² (150·7 sq ft)
Wing aspect ratio	6·1
Length overall	7·30 m (23 ft 11½ in)
Height overall	1·90 m (6 ft 2¾ in)
Tailplane span	2·80 m (9 ft 2¼ in)
Wheel track	2·10 m (6 ft 10¾ in)
Propeller diameter	1·80 m (5 ft 10¾ in)

WEIGHTS:
Weight empty, equipped	670 kg (1,477 lb)
Max fuel weight	170 kg (375 lb)
Max T-O weight	1,032 kg (2,275 lb)

PERFORMANCE (at max T-O weight):
Never-exceed speed	187 knots (346 km/h; 215 mph)
Max level speed at S/L	165 knots (306 km/h; 190 mph)
Max cruising speed at S/L	139 knots (257 km/h; 160 mph)
Econ cruising speed at 1,525 m (5,000 ft)	130 knots (241 km/h; 150 mph)
Stalling speed, flaps down, engine idling	42 knots (77 km/h; 48 mph)
Max rate of climb at S/L	244 m (800 ft)/min
Service ceiling	tested to 4,265 m (14,000 ft)
T-O run	220 m (722 ft)
Landing run	300 m (984 ft)
Range with max fuel, 1 h reserves	825 nm (1,529 km; 950 miles)
Range with max payload, 30 min reserves	521 nm (966 km; 600 miles)

SWEDEN

ANDREASSON
BJÖRN ANDREASSON
c/o Saab-Scania, Box 463, S-201 24, Malmö 1
Mr Andreasson has designed eleven different types of light aircraft. Of these, the BA-7 was built in series by AB Malmö Flygindustri as the MFI-9B Trainer/Militrainer and by MBB in West Germany as the BO 208 C Junior (see 1970-71 *Jane's*).

An earlier design, the BA-4 biplane, was modernised by Mr Andreasson for members of the Swedish branch of the Experimental Aircraft Association, and a prototype was built by apprentices of the MFI apprentice school as part of their training programme. To distinguish it from the original BA-4, it is designated BA-4B.

Mr Andreasson's latest design is the BA-11.

ANDREASSON BA-4B
The prototype BA-4B, built by MFI apprentices, was of all-metal construction. The design provides for alternative all-wooden wings.

World manufacturing rights in the BA-4B are held by Mr P. J. C. Phillips of Down House, Cocking, Midhurst, Sussex, and the aircraft has been built in small numbers in the UK by Crosby Aviation Ltd (which see). Plans for homebuilders continue to be available from Mr Andreasson.

About three amateur-built BA-4Bs are flying in Sweden.
TYPE: Single-seat fully-aerobatic light biplane.
WINGS: Braced biplane type, with a single streamline-section interplane strut each side. A streamline-section bracing strut runs from the bottom fuselage longeron on each side to the top of the interplane strut, and an N-type cabane structure supports the centre-section. Incidence, upper wing 3°, lower wings 4°. Stagger 20°. Dihedral, upper wing 2°, lower wings 4°. Alternative all-metal structure or all-wood structure, with solid spars, covered with heavy plywood skin. Pop-riveted ailerons, of simplified sheet metal construction, on lower wings only. No flaps. Provision for fitting detachable plastics wingtips.
FUSELAGE: Sheet metal structure, with external stringers, making extensive use of pop-riveting. Turtledeck either sheet metal or reinforced plastics.
TAIL UNIT: Cantilever structure of pop-riveted sheet metal construction.
LANDING GEAR: Non-retractable tailwheel type. Cantilever spring steel main legs. Main wheels size 5·00-4 or 5·00-5. Hydraulic brakes. Steerable tailwheel carried on leaf spring.
POWER PLANT: Prototype has 74·5 kW (100 hp) Rolls-Royce Continental O-200-A flat-four engine. Provision for other engines, including Volkswagen conversions. Standard fuel tank, capacity 50 litres (11 Imp gallons),

Yamato SY single-seat motor glider

van Aswegen Vansin four-seat cabin monoplane *(Steve Crutchley)*

Andreasson BA-11 tandem two-seat biplane *(Hans Strömberg)*

Andreasson BA-4B single-seat fully-aerobatic homebuilt biplane

Ekström Humlan 2 built by Mr Tommy Nilsson of Björklinge, Sweden

forward of cockpit. Provision for carrying external 'bullet' tank of 50 litres (11 Imp gallons) capacity under fuselage.

ACCOMMODATION: Single seat in open cockpit.

ELECTRONICS AND EQUIPMENT: Provision for battery, VHF radio and IFR instrumentation.

DIMENSIONS, EXTERNAL:

Wing span:
upper	5·34 m (17 ft 7 in)
lower	5·14 m (16 ft 11 in)

Wing chord (upper and lower, constant)
0·80 m (2 ft 7½ in)
Wing area, gross 8·3 m² (90 sq ft)
Wing aspect ratio (upper and lower) 6
Length overall 4·60 m (15 ft 0 in)
Tailplane span 2·00 m (6 ft 6¾ in)

WEIGHT:
Max T-O weight 375 kg (827 lb)

PERFORMANCE (prototype, at max T-O weight):
Max level speed 122 knots (225 km/h; 140 mph)
Max cruising speed 104 knots (193 km/h; 120 mph)

Min flying speed 35 knots (64 km/h; 40 mph)
Max rate of climb at S/L 610 m (2,000 ft)/min
T-O and landing run less than 100 m (330 ft)
Range with standard fuel
152 nm (280 km; 175 miles)

ANDREASSON BA-11

The BA-11 is an all-metal biplane, intended for single-seat aerobatic, two-seat training or competition flying. It is designed generally to FAR Pt 23 Appendix A category A (Aerobatic) requirements, but has enhanced limiting load factors of +9 to −6g as a single-seater, and in excess of +6 to −3g as a two-seater.

TYPE: Two-seat training and competition biplane.

WINGS: Biplane type, braced with dual sets of streamlined tie-rods. Ailerons, of simplified pop-riveted sheet metal construction, on both upper and lower wings. Positive stagger.

FUSELAGE: Metal structure, with one-piece moulded glassfibre turtledeck.

TAIL UNIT: All-metal structure. Control surfaces of similar construction to ailerons.

LANDING GEAR: Non-retractable tailwheel type. Main legs consist of two steel leaf springs attached to bottom of fuselage. Size 5·50-5 main wheels, with hydraulic disc brakes. Tailwheel also uses leaf spring and is steerable.

POWER PLANT: Designed for one 149 kW (200 hp) Avco Lycoming fuel-injection engine, driving a 1·88 m (6 ft 2 in) diameter Hartzell constant-speed propeller. Main fuel tank in upper front fuselage, capacity approx 60 litres (13 Imp gallons). Auxiliary fuel tank, capacity approx 50 litres (11 Imp gallons), in upper wing centre-section.

ACCOMMODATION: Two seats in tandem, each designed to accommodate a back-type parachute. Prototype has enclosed cockpits, but open cockpits are optional. Basic instrumentation only in forward cockpit. Instrument panel of rear cockpit is large enough to accommodate a limited IFR panel in addition to the normal engine instruments. Electrical equipment, including starter, alternator and battery, can be fitted.

DIMENSIONS, WEIGHTS AND PERFORMANCE:
No details received for publication

EKSTRÖM
STAFFAN W. EKSTRÖM
Tivedsvägen 1, S-181 64 Lidingö
Telephone: (08) 766 34 48

EKSTRÖM HUMLAN 2

Mr Ekström began the design of this single-seat autogyro in June 1971. Construction began in April 1972, and it flew for the first time in June 1973. Four more Humlans had been completed and flown in Sweden by early 1980, with others under construction.

The prototype (SE-HXE) was fitted initially with the standard tricycle landing gear, as described. It now has twin floats, each weighing 16 kg (35 lb), as illustrated in the 1978-79 *Jane's*.

TYPE: Single-seat homebuilt autogyro.

ROTOR SYSTEM: Single two-blade semi-rigid rotor, attached to hub by a single bolt. Ztan Zee rotor blades. Rotor brake added 1975.

ROTOR DRIVE: Flexible shaft for rotor spin-up only, via gearbox and two Vee-belts.

FUSELAGE: Cruciform chassis of 6061 T6 square-section aluminium tube, on which is mounted a pod-type nacelle.

TAIL UNIT: Conventional single fin and rudder, and fixed tailplane with dihedral, built of 0·4 mm and 0·8 mm aluminium sheet.

LANDING GEAR: Non-retractable tricycle type, with additional small wheel beneath tail. Rubber shock-absorption on tailwheel only. Go-kart wheels on main and nose units, tyre pressure 0·88 bars (12·8 lb/sq in). Nosewheel is steerable, self-centering, and is fitted with cycle-type brake.

POWER PLANT: One 67 kW (90 hp) McCulloch AF 100-X3 four-cylinder engine, driving a two-blade fixed-pitch pusher propeller. Fuel tank, capacity 32 litres (7 Imp gallons), behind pilot's seat. Fuel is a petrol/oil mixture, with 5% oil.

ACCOMMODATION: Single seat in open cockpit. One-piece curved windscreen. Shoulder harness fitted.

DIMENSIONS, EXTERNAL (wheel landing gear):
Rotor diameter	6·80 m (22 ft 3¾ in)
Length overall	3·42 m (11 ft 2¾ in)
Height overall	1·98 m (6 ft 6 in)
Width over wheels	1·65 m (5 ft 5 in)
Propeller diameter	1·20 m (3 ft 11¼ in)

WEIGHTS (A: wheel landing gear, B: floats):
Weight empty:
A	145 kg (320 lb)
B	182 kg (401 lb)

Normal max T-O weight:
A	260 kg (573 lb)
B	285 kg (628 lb)

Max T-O weight:
A	295 kg (650 lb)

PERFORMANCE (A: wheel landing gear, B: floats, at 260 kg; 573 lb AUW):

Never-exceed speed
A, B	97 knots (180 km/h; 111·5 mph)

Max cruising speed:
A	81 knots (150 km/h; 93 mph)
B	65 knots (120 km/h; 74 mph)

Econ cruising speed:
A	64·5 knots (120 km/h; 74·5 mph)
B	54-59 knots (100-110 km/h; 62-68 mph)

Max rate of climb at S/L:
A	300 m (984 ft)/min
B	180 m (590 ft)/min

T-O run:
A	60 m (197 ft)
B	200 m (656 ft)

T-O to 15 m (50 ft):
A	100 m (328 ft)
B	400 m (1,312 ft)

Landing from 15 m (50 ft), zero wind:
A	30 m (98 ft)

Landing run, zero wind:
A	5 m (16 ft)

Max range, no reserves:
A	97 nm (180 km; 112 miles)
B	75 nm (140 km; 87 miles)

SWITZERLAND

BERGER

BERGER-HELIKOPTER

CH-6573 Magadino TI

Telephone: (092) 64 21 71

DIRECTOR: Hans Berger

Mr Berger has built and flown prototypes of two light helicopters, of which available details follow:

BERGER BX-50A

TYPE: Single-seat light helicopter.

ROTOR SYSTEM: Two-blade main rotor and two-blade tail rotor.

FUSELAGE: All-metal frame of tubular alloy construction. Lower cabin fairing and forward-sliding transparent half-canopy.

TAIL UNIT: Small ventral fin.

LANDING GEAR: Skid-type.

POWER PLANT: One 67 kW (90 hp) Continental C90 flat-four engine. Fuel in one or two tanks mounted aft of pilot.

ACCOMMODATION: Semi-enclosed cockpit for pilot only.

DIMENSIONS, EXTERNAL:
Diameter of main rotor	8·00 m (26 ft 3 in)
Diameter of tail rotor	1·10 m (3 ft 7¼ in)

WEIGHTS:
Weight empty	290 kg (639 lb)
Max T-O weight	410 kg (904 lb)

PERFORMANCE:
Never-exceed speed	75 knots (140 km/h; 87 mph)
Max cruising speed	65 knots (120 km/h; 75 mph)

BERGER BX-110

The BX-110 (HB-YAK) is a two-seat homebuilt light helicopter, powered by a Wankel rotating-piston engine. It flew for the first time on 3 June 1974, and has been awarded a permit for experimental flying by the Swiss Board of Aviation.

TYPE: Two-seat light helicopter.

ROTOR SYSTEM: Three-blade semi-rigid main rotor and two-blade tail rotor. Main rotor blades are of NACA 0012 section, and are foldable. Max pitch of main rotor 12°. Main and tail rotors of alloy construction. No rotor brake.

ROTOR DRIVE: By toothed belt, from specially designed gearbox. Main rotor/engine rpm ratio 0·09 : 1; tail rotor/engine rpm ratio 0·6 : 1.

FUSELAGE: All-metal frame, of square and circular tubular alloy construction. Large 'goldfish bowl' cabin, with framed transparencies.

TAIL UNIT: Half-tailplane on starboard side of tailboom, forward of tail rotor, with approx 45° dihedral.

LANDING GEAR: Original skid-type replaced later by non-retractable tricycle wheeled gear, with main-wheel brakes.

POWER PLANT: One 134 kW (180 hp) Wankel rotating-piston engine. Fuel in two saddle tanks aft of cabin, total capacity 108 litres (23·75 Imp gallons). Refuelling point on top of each tank. Oil capacities: engine 4 litres (0·9 Imp gallons); gearbox 4 litres (0·9 Imp gallons); tail rotor 0·2 litres (0·04 Imp gallons).

ACCOMMODATION: Side-by-side seats for pilot and one passenger in 'goldfish bowl' cabin.

ELECTRICAL SYSTEM: 12V battery.

DIMENSIONS, EXTERNAL:
Diameter of main rotor	7·40 m (24 ft 3¼ in)
Diameter of tail rotor	1·20 m (3 ft 11¼ in)
Distance between rotor centres	4·35 m (14 ft 3¼ in)
Length overall	6·40 m (21 ft 0 in)
Height to top of rotor hub	2·52 m (8 ft 3¼ in)
Wheel track	1·85 m (6 ft 0¾ in)

DIMENSIONS, INTERNAL:
Cabin: Length	1·30 m (4 ft 3¼ in)
Max width	1·25 m (4 ft 1¼ in)
Max height	1·28 m (4 ft 2½ in)

AREAS:
Main rotor disc	43·00 m² (462·85 sq ft)
Tail rotor disc	1·13 m² (12·16 sq ft)

WEIGHTS:
Weight empty	460 kg (1,014 lb)
Max T-O weight	720 kg (1,587 lb)

PERFORMANCE (at max T-O weight):
Never-exceed speed	91 knots (170 km/h; 105 mph)
Max cruising speed	86 knots (160 km/h; 99 mph)
Max rate of climb at S/L	240 m (787 ft)/min

BRÜGGER

MAX BRÜGGER

CH- 1724 Zénauva

Telephone: (037) 33 29 20

Brief details of the Brügger Colibri 1 single-seat ultralight aircraft, which flew for the first time on 30 October 1965, were given in the 1967-68 and 1971-72 *Jane's*.

More recent designs are the Colibri 2 and MB-3, of which details follow:

BRÜGGER MB-2 COLIBRI 2

Mr Brügger began design of the Colibri 2 in January 1966. Construction was started a year later, and the first of two prototypes flew for the first time on 1 May 1970. Plans are available to amateur constructors, and 165 Colibri 2s were under construction or flying in Europe by early 1980.

TYPE: Single-seat light aircraft.

WINGS: Cantilever low-wing monoplane. Wing section NACA 23012. Dihedral from roots. Two-spar constant-chord wings. Wings and ailerons built of spruce with fabric covering. No flaps or tabs.

FUSELAGE: Plywood-covered wooden structure.

TAIL UNIT: Cantilever all-wood structure. Rudder only: no fin. All-moving horizontal surfaces, with Flettner-type elevators.

LANDING GEAR: Non-retractable tailwheel type, with coil spring shock-absorption on main units. Main wheels size 400 × 100, with streamline fairings. Tailwheel mounted on leaf spring. Mechanically-operated disc brakes.

POWER PLANT: One 30 kW (40 hp) 1,600 cc Volkswagen engine (Brügger modification), driving a Brügger two-blade fixed-pitch wooden propeller with plastics-coated blades. Fuel in single fuselage tank, capacity 33 litres (7·25 Imp gallons). Oil capacity 2·5 litres (0·55 Imp gallons).

ACCOMMODATION: Single seat under one-piece moulded transparent canopy, with quarter-lights to rear.

DIMENSIONS, EXTERNAL:
Wing span	6·00 m (19 ft 8¼ in)
Wing chord, constant	1·40 m (4 ft 7 in)
Wing area, gross	8·20 m² (88·25 sq ft)
Length overall	4·80 m (15 ft 9 in)
Height overall	1·60 m (5 ft 3 in)
Tailplane span	2·00 m (6 ft 6¾ in)
Wheel track	1·80 m (5 ft 11 in)
Propeller diameter	1·38 m (4 ft 6⅓ in)

WEIGHTS:
Weight empty	215 kg (474 lb)
Max T-O and landing weight	330 kg (727 lb)

PERFORMANCE (at max T-O weight):
Max speed at 1,000 m (3,280 ft)	97 knots (180 km/h; 111 mph)
Econ cruising speed (70% power) at 1,000 m (3,280 ft)	86 knots (160 km/h; 99 mph)
Stalling speed	32·5 knots (60 km/h; 37·5 mph)
Max rate of climb at S/L	180 m (590 ft)/min
Service ceiling	4,500 m (14,760 ft)
T-O and landing run	200 m (656 ft)
Range with max fuel	270 nm (500 km; 310 miles)

BRÜGGER MB-3

Design of this single-seat all-metal light aircraft (HB-YBB) was started in July 1974. Construction took from February 1975 until December 1976, and it flew for the first time on 19 March 1977. Plans are not available.

Among outstanding features are that the aircraft can be made ready for flight after transportation, or dismantled for transportation after flight, in only three minutes. It can be towed on its own wheels behind a small car.

Major differences by comparison with the all-wood Colibri are the MB-3's pop-riveted metal airframe; dismountable tail surfaces with anti-tabs; and 33·5 kW (45 hp) 1,600 cc Volkswagen engine, driving a two-blade fixed-pitch wooden propeller of Mr Brügger's own manufacture. The single fuselage fuel tank has a capacity of 46 litres (10 Imp gallons). Oil capacity is unchanged at 2·5 litres (0·55 Imp gallons).

DIMENSIONS, EXTERNAL:
Wing span	6·00 m (19 ft 8¼ in)
Wing area, gross	7·20 m² (77·5 sq ft)
Length overall	5·00 m (16 ft 4¾ in)
Height overall	1·56 m (5 ft 1½ in)
Tailplane span	1·91 m (6 ft 3¼ in)
Wheel track	1·57 m (5 ft 2 in)
Propeller diameter	1·36 m (4 ft 5½ in)

WEIGHTS:
Weight empty	236 kg (520 lb)
Max T-O weight	360 kg (793 lb)

PERFORMANCE (at max T-O weight):
Max level speed	108 knots (200 km/h; 124 mph)
Max cruising speed	97 knots (180 km/h; 112 mph)
Stalling speed	38 knots (70 km/h; 43·5 mph)
Max rate of climb at S/L	240 m (785 ft)/min
Service ceiling	4,000 m (13,125 ft)
T-O run	220 m (722 ft)
Landing run	250 m (820 ft)
Range with max fuel	432 nm (800 km; 497 miles)

NEUKOM

ALBERT NEUKOM SEGELFLUGZEUGBAU

Flugplatz Schmerlat, CH-8213 Neuenkirch

Mr Albert Neukom, constructor of the Elfe series of sailplanes (see Sailplanes section of this edition), has designed and built a single-seat sporting aircraft (HB-YAX). First flight was made on 9 September 1976, with Mr Neukom at the controls. Performance proved disappointing with the 31 kW (42 hp) converted Volkswagen motor car engine then installed, and this has since been replaced by a Continental engine, as described:

NEUKOM AN-100

TYPE: Single-seat light sporting monoplane.

WINGS: Cantilever low-wing monoplane. Eppler 441 section. GFK spar, four plywood ribs, and GFK sandwich skin. Plain trailing-edge flaps.

FUSELAGE: Conventional semi-monocoque structure of plywood frames and fir stringers, covered with laminated okoumé plywood and glassfibre.

TAIL UNIT: Cantilever structure of wood and glassfibre. Fin integral with fuselage. Narrow chord rudder. All-moving tailplane.

LANDING GEAR: Non-retractable tailwheel type. Cantilever spring steel main legs. Fairings over main wheels. Brakes on main wheels.

POWER PLANT: One 48·5 kW (65 hp) Continental A65-12F flat-four engine, driving a two-blade wooden propeller. Close cowling over engine. Fuel capacity 72 litres (15·75 Imp gallons), in wing and fuselage tanks.

ACCOMMODATION: Single-seat under rearward-hinging transparent canopy.

DIMENSIONS, EXTERNAL:
Wing span	7·80 m (25 ft 7 in)
Wing area, gross	7·20 m² (77·5 sq ft)
Wing aspect ratio	8·2
Length overall	6·10 m (20 ft 0 in)
Height overall	1·50 m (4 ft 11 in)

WEIGHTS:
Weight empty	280 kg (617 lb)
Max T-O weight	420 kg (926 lb)

PERFORMANCE:
Max level speed	140 knots (260 km/h; 162 mph)
Max cruising speed	119 knots (220 km/h; 137 mph)
Approach speed	65-70 knots (120-130 km/h; 75-81 mph)
Stalling speed	49 knots (90 km/h; 56 mph)
Max rate of climb at S/L	240-300 m (785-985 ft)/min
T-O run	250 m (820 ft)
Range with max fuel	431 nm (800 km; 497 miles)

UNITED KINGDOM

CLUTTON-TABENOR

ERIC CLUTTON

92 Newlands Street, Shelton, Stoke-on-Trent, Staffordshire ST4 2RF

CLUTTON-TABENOR FRED SERIES 2 and SERIES 3

FRED (Flying Runabout Experimental Design) was designed as a powered aircraft that could be flown by any reasonably experienced glider pilot without further training. Other aims were that it should be able to operate from small, rough fields and be roadable.

First flight of the prototype (G-ASZY) was made on 3 November 1963, with a 20 kW (27 hp) 500 cc Triumph 5T motorcycle engine; this was replaced later by a Scott A2S engine, and later still (1966) by a converted American-built Lawrance radial engine from an APU, at which stage the prototype was redesignated **FRED Series 2**.

Another change made after the first flights was replacement of the original bungee-in-tension landing gear shock-absorbers by steel springs.

During 1968 the Lawrance engine was replaced by a 49 kW (66 hp) Volkswagen 1,500 cc engine, modified by the provision of a toothed belt to drive the propeller at half engine speed. Next stage involved another engine change, to a Franklin 4AC-150.

The prototype has now been modified further, to **FRED**

Berger BX-50A single-seat helicopter, with canopy open

Prototype of the all-metal Brügger MB-3 (*Jean-Claude Bersier*)

Neukom AN-100 light sporting monoplane (*Roland Eichenberger*)

First 'plans-built' FRED Series 2, constructed by Mr Richard Yates

Berger BX-110 two-seat helicopter

Brügger MB-2 Colibri 2 single-seat light aircraft

E.C.2 Easy Too, designed by Eric Clutton (*Michael A. Badrocke*)

Series 3 standard, with some dihedral on the wings, a shorter tailplane and increased fuel tankage. FRED Series 3 was complete in January 1980, when only adverse weather conditions were delaying the first flight in its new form.

FRED is described by its builders as being virtually unstallable with power on or off. Wings can be folded by one person unaided, and the tail unit is quickly detachable for easy transportation. Folded and tail-less width of FRED is 1·22 m (4 ft).

Plans for FRED have been available to amateur constructors since February 1970. Approximately 170 sets had been sold by early 1980, when four aircraft were flying, including one in New Zealand. Most are powered by direct-drive 1,600 cc Volkswagen engines.

The FRED Series 2 illustrated was built by Mr Richard Yates in nine months. It has a modified rudder shape, and this restyling is shown on current plans. First flight was made in November 1976. Powered by a 1,600 cc Volkswagen engine, Mr Yates' FRED has a cruising speed of 61·5 knots (114 km/h; 71mph) at 2,900 rpm and can take off to 61 m (200 ft) in 274 m (900 ft). Maximum nose-up attitude, power off, gives 35 knots (64 km/h; 40 mph) with no stall.

The following details apply basically to FRED Series 2 G-ASZY with Franklin engine:

TYPE: Single-seat light aircraft.

WINGS: Wire-braced parasol monoplane. Wing section Göttingen 535. Thickness/chord ratio 17·2%. No dihedral or incidence. 1° washout at tips. Spruce and plywood structure, with torsion-box leading-edge, auxiliary rear spar and drag spar, fabric-covered. Non-differential ailerons. No flaps or trim tabs.

FUSELAGE: Spruce longerons. Plywood covered to rear of cockpit, except for aluminium top decking. Fabric covering on rear fuselage, except for plywood top decking, front portion of which is removable for access to baggage locker.

TAIL UNIT: Cantilever structure of spruce and plywood. No fixed fin. Tailplane incidence adjustable on ground. Pushrod-operated elevators. No tabs.

LANDING GEAR: Non-retractable main wheels and tailskid. Main units sprung with motorcycle rear suspension springs. Industrial truck wheels. Tyre pressure 1·79 bars (26 lb/sq in). No brakes.

POWER PLANT: One 37·25 kW (50 hp) Franklin 4AC-150 engine in prototype, giving performance roughly equivalent to a geared 1,600 cc Volkswagen modified motor car engine, driving a two-blade fixed-pitch propeller. Single fuel tank in centre-section, capacity 34 litres (7·5 Imp gallons). Provision for second centre-section tank. Oil capacity 3·5 litres (0·75 Imp gallons).

ACCOMMODATION: Single seat in open cockpit.

DIMENSIONS, EXTERNAL:

Wing span	6·86 m (22 ft 6 in)
Wing chord, constant	1·52 m (5 ft 0 in)
Wing area, gross	10·22 m² (110 sq ft)
Wing aspect ratio	4·4
Length overall	5·18 m (17 ft 0 in)
Height overall	1·83 m (6 ft 0 in)
Tailplane span	2·74 m (9 ft 0 in)
Wheel track	1·22 m (4 ft 0 in)
Wheelbase	3·20 m (10 ft 6 in)
Propeller diameter	1·83 m (6 ft 0 in)

WEIGHTS:

Weight empty	242 kg (533 lb)
Max T-O weight	350 kg (773 lb)

PERFORMANCE (at max T-O weight):

Max cruising speed	70 knots (130 km/h; 81 mph)
Econ cruising speed	55 knots (101 km/h; 63 mph)
Approach speed	40-45 knots (74-84 km/h; 46-52 mph)
Stalling speed	approx 35 knots (63 km/h; 40 mph)
Range with max fuel	173 nm (320 km; 200 miles)

CLUTTON-TABENOR E.C.2 EASY TOO

The Easy Too design was started in 1969 to utilise a geared Volkswagen power plant developed by Mr Clutton and Mr Tabenor. It is a single-seat all-wooden folding-wing aircraft, plywood-covered with a polyester resin finish, and is stressed for aerobatics. A full centre-section flap is fitted.

Completion of the prototype was delayed by other work, and in 1976-77 the Easy Too underwent some redesign, to enable it to qualify as an entrant for a PFA competition, on the lines of the Light Aeroplane Competitions organised at Lympne in the 1920s. By early 1978, only the wing outer panels were awaiting assembly; but completion has been delayed by repair work on FRED after a heavy landing, by continued propeller research, and by the design of a new featherweight aircraft of which no details are available.

The general appearance of the redesigned Easy Too can be seen in the accompanying three-view drawing. The prototype has a direct-drive 1,600 cc Volkswagen engine, but the aircraft is equally suited to 1,500 cc or larger-bore Volkswagen engines. Fuel capacity is 41 litres (9 Imp gallons).

The decision to use a direct-drive 1,600 cc VW engine meant that the engine mounting had to be lengthened by comparison with the original design (see 1976-77 *Jane's*), altering the aircraft's appearance considerably. The new engine drives a four-blade propeller. A further design change has been the adoption of a mechanically-retractable landing gear in place of the original fixed and trousered type.

The outer wing panels can be folded back by one person, by withdrawing pins and replacing them by an irreversible screwjack arrangement which locks them in position. The ailerons and flaps are coupled automatically. The folding hinge and support are entirely separate from the flying fittings, and the aeroplane can be towed on the road behind a motor car. The wingtips, of glassfibre, are of similar type and size to those fitted to the Druine Turbulent and the Taylor Monoplane. A one-piece sliding cockpit canopy is fitted. It is intended to make plans of the aircraft available after the conclusion of flight testing.

DIMENSIONS, EXTERNAL:

Wing span	7·11 m (23 ft 4 in)
Length overall	5·08 m (16 ft 8 in)
Height overall	1·37 m (4 ft 6 in)

WEIGHTS (estimated):

Weight empty	254 kg (560 lb)
Max T-O weight	363 kg (800 lb)

PERFORMANCE (estimated):

Normal cruising speed	100 knots (185 km/h; 115 mph)
Range with max fuel	347 nm (644 km; 400 miles)

COATES
J. R. COATES

The Spinney, Breachwood Green, Hitchin, Hertfordshire SG4 8PL

Mr Coates designed and built a two-seat light aircraft known as the S.A.II Swalesong, which was described fully in the 1975-76 *Jane's*. Drawings for amateur construction are not available, but a simplified version, the S.A.III, is under development and will be suitable for homebuilding.

COATES S.A.III SWALESONG

This aircraft (G-BAAH) is a development of the S.A.II, and the best features of that aircraft have been maintained. Changes include a fuselage of more rounded form, a simplified wing of constant chord, and a vertical tail unit of reduced height. All control surfaces are mass and aerodynamically balanced.

The prototype S.A.III is being built in all-wood form. Following flight development, some parts may be changed to metal or structural foam, the latter being preferred as it enables weight reductions to be achieved and allows engines like the Volkswagen to be considered as adequate power sources.

First flight was expected to take place in 1980.

TYPE: Two-seat light aircraft.

WINGS: Cantilever low-wing monoplane. Wing section NACA 63415. Dihedral 4°. Incidence 1° 30'. All-wood (spruce) structure with plywood covering, built in three pieces. All-wood slotted ailerons. Slotted all-wood flaps.

FUSELAGE: Semi-monocoque spruce structure with plywood covering.

TAIL UNIT: Cantilever structure, with sweptback vertical surfaces. Tailplane incidence adjustable on ground. One-piece fabric-covered wooden elevator, with tab.

LANDING GEAR: Non-retractable tricycle type. Cantilever light alloy main legs. Steerable nosewheel, with motor car shock-absorber and glassfibre fairing. Size 5·00-5 tyres on main wheels; 130-1300 tyre on nosewheel. Disc brakes.

POWER PLANT: One 63·4-80·5 kW (85-108 hp) Continental or Avco Lycoming flat-four engine, driving a fixed-pitch wooden propeller. Fuel capacity 72·7 litres (16 Imp gallons).

ACCOMMODATION: Two seats side by side in enclosed cockpit, with sliding one-piece hood. Baggage space aft of seats. Cockpit heated and ventilated.

DIMENSIONS, EXTERNAL:

Wing span	7·62 m (25 ft 0 in)
Wing chord, constant	1·37 m (4 ft 6 in)
Wing area, gross	10·41 m² (112 sq ft)

Wing aspect ratio	5·6
Length overall	5·64 m (18 ft 6 in)
Width, wings folded	1·73 m (5 ft 8 in)
Height overall	2·08 m (6 ft 10 in)
Tailplane span	2·44 m (8 ft 0 in)
Wheel track	1·68 m (5 ft 6 in)
Wheelbase	1·30 m (4 ft 3 in)
Propeller diameter	1·63 m (5 ft 4 in)

DIMENSION, INTERNAL:

Cockpit: Max width	1·07 m (3 ft 6 in)

WEIGHTS:

Weight empty	317 kg (700 lb)
Max T-O and landing weight	544 kg (1,200 lb)

PERFORMANCE (estimated):

Never-exceed speed at 305 m (1,000 ft)	165 knots (305 km/h; 190 mph)
Max level speed at 305 m (1,000 ft)	130 knots (241 km/h; 150 mph)
Max cruising speed at 305 m (1,000 ft)	113 knots (209 km/h; 130 mph)
Econ cruising speed at 305 m (1,000 ft)	95·5 knots (177 km/h; 110 mph)
Stalling speed, flaps down	44 knots (81 km/h; 50 mph)
Max rate of climb at S/L	260 m (850 ft)/min

CROSBY
CROSBY AVIATION LTD

Archery House, Leycester Road, Knutsford, Cheshire
Telephone: 0565 4254
DIRECTORS:
John Crosby
P. J. C. Phillips

CROSBY (ANDREASSON) BA-4B

The Andreasson BA-4B single-seat biplane, described in the Swedish section, is available in the UK from Crosby Aviation. Mr P. J. C. Phillips holds the world rights for commercially-manufactured examples of this aircraft, and has vested these rights in Crosby Aviation, of which he is a director. Crosby markets plans and kits for amateur constructors wishing to build their own aircraft, and approximately 50 sets of plans had been sold by early 1980. Plans (only) can also be obtained from the BA-4B's Swedish designer, Mr Björn Andreasson.

Five versions are available from Crosby Aviation; examples of three of these are known to have flown by 1980:

BA-4B. Basic model with 74·5 kW (100 hp) Rolls-Royce Continental O-200-A flat-four engine. Standard fuel capacity 56·3 litres (12·4 Imp gallons). Provision for carrying an external 'bullet' tank of 50 litres (11 Imp gallons) capacity.

Super BA-4B. Structurally identical to BA-4B, but powered by a 97 kW (130 hp) Rolls-Royce Continental O-240-A flat-four engine. The Super BA-4B is able to tow a modern two-seat sailplane to 610 m (2,000 ft) in 4½ minutes.

Super BA-4B Srs 2. Identical to Super BA-4B except for having modified fuel and oil systems for inverted flight; full IFR equipment, including VOR; and an enclosed cockpit.

Prototypes of the remaining variants were still under construction in 1979. One has a 119 kW (160 hp) Avco Lycoming AEIO-320-D1A flat-four engine, on a dynafocal mounting, and Christen inverted fuel and oil systems. The other has a 112 kW (150 hp) Avco Lycoming O-320 engine.

The description of the BA-4B given in the Swedish section applies also to the aircraft produced in the UK, except in the following details:

ELECTRONICS AND EQUIPMENT: Aircraft can be equipped with electric starter for engine, engine-driven alternator, battery, 360-channel VHF com radio, cabin heater, disc brakes, fully-castoring tailwheel, corrosion proofing and g-meter.

DIMENSIONS, EXTERNAL (A: BA-4B; B: Super BA-4B):

Wing span	5·64 m (18 ft 6 in)
Wing area, gross	8·36 m² (90 sq ft)
Length overall:	
A	4·67 m (15 ft 4 in)
B	4·72 m (15 ft 6 in)

WEIGHTS (A: BA-4B; B: Super BA-4B):

Weight empty, basic:	
A	295 kg (650 lb)
B	304 kg (670 lb)
T-O weight, aerobatic	451 kg (996 lb)
Max T-O weight	460 kg (1,014 lb)

PERFORMANCE (at max T-O weight. A: BA-4B; B: Super BA-4B):

Never-exceed speed:	
A, B	161 knots (299 km/h; 186 mph)
Max level speed at S/L:	
A	130 knots (241 km/h; 150 mph)
B	139 knots (257 km/h; 160 mph)
Max cruising speed, 75% power at 2,135 m (7,000 ft):	
A	117 knots (217 km/h; 135 mph)
B	126 knots (233 km/h; 145 mph)
Stalling speed, power off:	
A, B	51 knots (94 km/h; 58 mph)
Stalling speed, power on:	
A, B	39 knots (73 km/h; 45 mph)
Max rate of climb at S/L:	
A	366 m (1,200 ft)/min
B	549 m (1,800 ft)/min
Range, standard fuel, 75% power:	
A	282 nm (523 km; 325 miles)
B	273 nm (507 km; 315 miles)
Range, max optional fuel, 75% power:	
A	529 nm (981 km; 610 miles)
B	521 nm (965 km; 600 miles)

ISAACS
JOHN O. ISAACS

23 Linden Grove, Chandler's Ford, Hampshire SO5 1LE
Telephone: 042 15 60885

Mr Isaacs designed and built a single-seat light aircraft, the airframe of which is basically a ⁷/₁₀th scale wooden version of that of the Hawker Fury fighter of the 1930s. Constructional drawings are available to amateur builders.

He has also designed and built an all-wood scaled-down version of the Supermarine Spitfire single-seat fighter of the second World War.

ISAACS FURY II

Design of the Isaacs Fury was started in January 1961 and construction of the aircraft began in April 1961. It flew for the first time on 30 August 1963, powered by a 48·5 kW (65 hp) Walter Mikron engine (see 1965-66 *Jane's*).

In 1966-67 Mr Isaacs modified the Fury prototype to Mk II standard, by restressing the airframe and installing a 93 kW (125 hp) Avco Lycoming engine, and flew the aircraft in this form in the Summer of 1967. It was acquired subsequently by Mr W. Raper of Wrotham, Kent, who made further refinements, including the addition of blister fairings over the engine cylinders. It has since changed hands again, and is now based at Land's End airfield.

Fury plans have been supplied to amateur constructors in Australia, Canada, Denmark, Finland, West Germany, Jersey, the Netherlands, New Zealand, Norway, the UK, the USA and Yugoslavia. In addition to the prototype, two Furies are flying in the UK, three in New Zealand, one in Canada and two in the USA.

TYPE: Single-seat ultra-light biplane, stressed to 9g for aerobatics.

WINGS: Staggered biplane, with N type interplane strut each side and two N strut assemblies supporting centre-section of top wing above fuselage. Conventional wire bracing. Wing section RAF 28. Thickness/chord ratio 9·75%. Dihedral 1° on top wing, 3° 30' on bottom wings. Incidence 3° 20' on top wing, 3° 50' on bottom wings. Spruce 'plank' spars and Warren girder ribs, with fabric covering. Fabric-covered spruce ailerons on top wing only. No flaps.

FUSELAGE: Spruce structure, covered with birch plywood.

TAIL UNIT: Strut-braced spruce structure of 'plank' spars and girder ribs, fabric-covered. Ground-adjustable tab in port elevator.

LANDING GEAR: Non-retractable type, with tailskid. Cross-axle tied to Vees with rubber-cord shock-absorption. Main wheels consist of WM.2 355 mm (14 in) rims spoked to home-made hubs. Dunlop tyre, size 3·25-14, pressure approx 2·28 bars (33 lb/sq in). Brakes optional.

POWER PLANT (prototype): One 93 kW (125 hp) Avco Lycoming O-290 flat-four engine. Two-blade fixed-pitch propeller. Fuel tank in fuselage, aft of fireproof bulkhead, capacity 45·5 litres (10 Imp gallons) or 54·5 litres (12 Imp gallons).

ACCOMMODATION: Single seat in open cockpit. Small door above top longeron on port side opens downward. Space for light baggage aft of seat. Radio optional.

DIMENSIONS, EXTERNAL:

Wing span:	
upper	6·40 m (21 ft 0 in)
lower	5·54 m (18 ft 2 in)
Wing chord (both, constant)	1·07 m (3 ft 6 in)
Wing area (total)	11·50 m² (123·8 sq ft)
Wing aspect ratio (upper)	6
Length overall	5·87 m (19 ft 3 in)
Height over tail (flying attitude)	2·16 m (7 ft 1 in)
Tailplane span	2·13 m (7 ft 0 in)
Wheel track	1·27 m (4 ft 2 in)

WEIGHTS (93 kW; 125 hp Avco Lycoming):

Weight empty	322 kg (710 lb)
Max permissible T-O weight	450 kg (1,000 lb)

Coates S.A.III Swalesong *(Michael A. Badrocke)*

Partially-completed fuselage of the Coates S.A. III Swalesong
(S. A. MacConnacher)

Crosby (Andreasson) BA-4B (Rolls-Royce Continental O-200-A engine)

Prototype Isaacs Spitfire single-seat light sporting aircraft

Two Isaacs Furies built and flying in New Zealand

Knowles Duet, adapted from Luton Minor

PERFORMANCE (with uncowled 93kW; 125 hp engine):
Max level speed   100 knots (185 km/h; 115 mph)
Stalling speed   33 knots (61 km/h; 38 mph)
Max rate of climb at S/L   488 m (1,600 ft)/min

ISAACS SPITFIRE

Construction of this prototype ⁶/₁₀-scale Spitfire (G-BBJI) began in the Summer of 1969, and it flew for the first time on 5 May 1975. The airframe is stressed to meet the aerobatic requirements of +9g and −4·5g (factored) as laid down in BCAR. Plans for the Isaacs Spitfire are available to homebuilders, and five sets had been supplied by early 1980.
TYPE: Single-seat sporting aircraft.
WINGS: Cantilever low-wing monoplane of semi-elliptical planform. Wing section NACA 2200 series. Thickness/chord ratio 13·2% at root, 6% at tip. Dihedral 6°. Incidence 2° at root, −30′ at tip. Two-spar wing built in

one piece, mainly of spruce, with birch plywood covering, except for ailerons which are fabric-covered.
FUSELAGE: Spruce structure, covered with birch plywood.
TAIL UNIT: Cantilever structure of plywood-covered spruce.
LANDING GEAR: Non-retractable tailwheel type on prototype. Cantilever main legs. Dunlop 5·00-5 tyres, wheels and hydraulic disc brakes.
POWER PLANT: One 74·5 kW (100 hp) Continental O-200 flat-four engine, or alternative engine in same category. Two-blade ground-adjustable Ratier metal propeller. Fuel tank in fuselage, aft of fireproof bulkhead, capacity 45·5 litres (10 Imp gallons).
ACCOMMODATION: Single seat under blister-type transparent canopy. Space for light baggage aft of seat.
DIMENSIONS, EXTERNAL:
Wing span   6·75 m (22 ft 1½ in)

Wing chord at root   1·52 m (5 ft 0 in)
Wing area, gross   8·08 m² (87 sq ft)
Length overall   5·88 m (19 ft 3 in)
Height overall   1·73 m (5 ft 8 in)
Tailplane span   1·92 m (6 ft 3½ in)
Wheel track   1·80 m (5 ft 11 in)
WEIGHTS:
Weight empty   366 kg (805 lb)
Max T-O weight   499 kg (1,100 lb)
PERFORMANCE (at max T-O weight):
Max level speed   130 knots (240 km/h; 150 mph)
Cruising speed   116 knots (215 km/h; 134 mph)
Stalling speed, 'clean'
    45-47 knots (84-87 km/h; 52-54 mph)
Stalling speed, with optional fuselage airbrake extended   41 knots (76 km/h; 47 mph)
Max rate of climb at S/L   336 m (1,100 ft)/min

KNOWLES
GP CAPT A. S. KNOWLES
17 East Meads, Guildford, Surrey GU2 5SW
Telephone: 0483 4242

KNOWLES DUET

The Duet, known originally as the Minor III, is a version of the Luton L.A.4a Minor (see description under PFA heading in this section) with side-by-side seating for two persons, and was developed originally by Gp Capt A. S.

Knowles in association with the former Phoenix Aircraft Ltd. Design began in 1968 and the prototype Duet (registration G-AYTT) flew for the first time on 22 June 1973. A special category C of A was granted on 24 June 1974.
During 1976 shaped wingtips were developed for the Duet, and flight testing with these began in early 1977. The new tips increased the wing span by 0·71 m (2 ft 4 in), and resulted in reduced stalling speed, increased rate of climb and improved gliding angle.
Final plans for the Duet, to allow home construction by

amateurs, are being prepared and at least one other Duet is known to be under construction.
TYPE: Two-seat light aircraft.
WINGS: Strut-braced parasol monoplane. Fabric-covered wooden wings, braced with steel tube struts, as described for L.A.4a.
FUSELAGE: Wood- and fabric-covered wooden structure, as L.A.4a except for widened cockpit.
TAIL UNIT: Cantilever fabric-covered wooden structure, as L.A.4a. Plain tab on elevator.

Replica de Havilland (Airco) D.H.2 fighter (*Leisure Sport*)

Replica Albatros D.Va fighter (*Leisure Sport*)

Replica Fokker Dr.I (*Leisure Sport*)

Replica SPAD XIII fighter (*Leisure Sport*)

LANDING GEAR: Non-retractable tailwheel type, as L.A.4a, with rubber-block shock-absorption. Mainwheel tyres size 6 in × 6 in, pressure 0·83 bars (12 lb/sq in). Goodyear caliper brakes. Solid tailwheel.

POWER PLANT: One 71 kW (95 hp) Continental C90 flat-four engine, driving a two-blade fixed-pitch propeller. Single fuel tank in upper forward fuselage, capacity 63·6 litres (14 Imp gallons). Refuelling point above tank. Oil capacity 4·5 litres (1 Imp gallon).

ACCOMMODATION: Side-by-side seats for two persons, with dual controls, in open cockpit under wing centre-section. Baggage locker aft of seats.

AVIONICS AND EQUIPMENT: Venturi-driven full blind-flying panel. Avionic Systems (Heathrow) Ltd 360-channel VHF radio.

DIMENSIONS, EXTERNAL:
Wing span with new tips	8·89 m (29 ft 2 in)
Wing chord, constant	1·60 m (5 ft 3 in)
Wing aspect ratio with new tips	5·37
Wing area, gross, with new tips	13·75 m² (148·0 sq ft)
Length overall	6·55 m (21 ft 6 in)
Height overall	2·01 m (6 ft 7 in)
Tailplane span	2·44 m (8 ft 0 in)
Wheel track	1·68 m (5 ft 6 in)
Wheelbase	4·50 m (14 ft 9 in)
Propeller diameter	1·75 m (5 ft 9 in)

DIMENSIONS, INTERNAL:
Cockpit: Max width	1·07 m (3 ft 6 in)
Baggage compartment volume	0·06 m³ (2·0 cu ft)

WEIGHTS:
Max payload	170 kg (375 lb)
Max T-O and landing weight	544 kg (1,200 lb)

PERFORMANCE (at max T-O weight):
Never-exceed speed	130 knots (240 km/h; 149 mph)
Max cruising speed at S/L	85 knots (157 km/h; 98 mph)
Econ cruising speed at S/L	70 knots (130 km/h; 81 mph)
Stalling speed	32 knots (60 km/h; 37 mph)
Max rate of climb at S/L	146 m (480 ft)/min
Service ceiling	2,440 m (8,000 ft)
T-O run	128 m (420 ft)
Landing run	110 m (360 ft)
Max range with 9·1 litres (2 Imp gallons) reserve fuel	185 nm (342 km; 213 miles)

LEISURE SPORT

LEISURE SPORT LTD (Member Company of the Ready Mixed Concrete Ltd Group)

Thorpe Park, Staines Lane, Chertsey, Surrey KT16 8PN
Telephone: 09328 62633

Since building and flying a full-size reproduction of the Supermarine S.5 Schneider Trophy seaplane of 1927 (see 1977-78 *Jane's*), Leisure Sport has financed and flown replicas of several first World War fighters, including two Sopwith Camel F.1s (one with 97 kW; 130 hp Clerget and one with 123 kW; 165 hp Warner Scarab engine), a Fokker Dr.I triplane (123 kW; 165 hp Warner Scarab engine), Fokker D.VII (149 kW; 200 hp Ranger engine), Albatros D.Va (149 kW; 200 hp Ranger engine), SPAD XIII (149 kW; 200 hp Avco Lycoming engine) and de Havilland (Airco) D.H.2 (67 kW; 90 hp Pobjoy engine). A Sopwith 1½-Strutter (97 kW; 130 hp Clerget engine) and a Fokker D.VIII (123 kW; 165 hp Warner Scarab engine) were being completed in 1980.

NIPPER

NIPPER KITS AND COMPONENTS LTD

1 Ridgeway Drive, Bromley, Kent BR1 5DG
Telephone: 01-857 7821
DIRECTORS:
D. P. L. Antill (Chairman)
A. F. Ayles
A. S. Pearcey

Complete world-wide rights for the Nipper aircraft were purchased from Belgium in 1966, and the aircraft was marketed in both factory-built form and in the form of several stages of kits for amateur construction.

The former Nipper Aircraft Ltd went into receivership in May 1971. Prior to this Mr D. P. L. Antill, formerly Managing Director of Nipper Aircraft Ltd, acquired all rights in the Nipper aircraft, and on 20 October 1971 formed a new company, Nipper Kits and Components Ltd, to supply spares for existing aircraft and to encourage and support amateur construction of the Nipper. Plans and an advisory service for amateur constructors continue to be available.

Two new Nipper kits were completed in 1979. Options for an unspecified number of kits had been taken out for 1980.

NIPPER Mk III and IIIA

The Mk III Nipper is powered by a 1·5 litre Rollason Ardem engine; when fitted with the 1·6 litre Ardem engine it is known as the Mk IIIA. The Nipper may also be fitted with wingtip fuel tanks which almost double the standard fuel capacity. With these tanks fitted, but empty, the aircraft remains aerobatic. Flutter tests were completed satisfactorily at speeds up to 156 knots (290 km/h; 180 mph).

TYPE: Single-seat ultra-light monoplane.

WINGS: Cantilever mid-wing monoplane. Modified NACA 43012A wing section. Dihedral 5° 30'. Incidence 2°. All-wood one-piece single-spar structure, with plywood-covered leading-edge and overall fabric covering. Wooden ailerons with fabric covering. No flaps. Portion of port wing-root trailing-edge is made of light alloy and hinged, with built-in foot-rest, so that it can be folded down to assist access to cockpit. Wing is quickly removable, to permit aircraft to be towed behind a motor car.

FUSELAGE: Welded steel tube structure. Underfuselage fairing of glassfibre. Rear fuselage fabric-covered.

TAIL UNIT: Braced tailplane and elevators of wood construction. No fin. Rudder of steel tube construction with fabric covering.

LANDING GEAR: Non-retractable tricycle type. Nieman transverse rubber-ring shock-absorbers. Steerable nosewheel. Continental tyres, size 4·00-4, pressure 1·79 bars (26 lb/sq in). Disc brakes.

POWER PLANT: Standard power plant is one 41 kW (55 hp) Rollason Ardem XI flat-four engine, driving a two-blade fixed-pitch wooden propeller with glassfibre spinner. More powerful versions of Ardem engine can be fitted optionally. Fuel tank between engine and cockpit, capacity 34 litres (7·5 Imp gallons). Provision for two 16·5 litre (3·6 Imp gallon) wingtip fuel tanks. Oil capacity 3·5 litres (0·77 Imp gallons).

ACCOMMODATION: Single seat under blown Perspex canopy which hinges sideways to starboard. Small baggage space aft of seat.

AVIONICS: Pye Bantam, Bayside BEI 990P and various other radio installations available.

DIMENSIONS, EXTERNAL:
Wing span (without tip-tanks)	6·00 m (19 ft 8 in)
Wing span (with tip-tanks)	6·25 m (20 ft 6 in)
Wing chord at c/l	1·40 m (4 ft 7¼ in)
Wing chord at tip	1·10 m (3 ft 7¼ in)
Wing area, gross	7·50 m² (80·70 sq ft)

Replica Fokker D.VII *(Leisure Sport)*

Replica Sopwith Camel F.1 (Clerget engine) *(Leisure Sport)*

Nipper Mk III single-seat ultra-light aircraft *(Aly Aviation)*

Druine D31 Turbulent, described under PFA entry *(David Partington)*

Currie Wot (41 kW; 55 hp Avco Lycoming engine), described under PFA entry

Luton L.A.4a Minor, described under PFA entry

Wing aspect ratio		4·8
Length overall		4·56 m (15 ft 0 in)
Height overall		1·91 m (6 ft 3 in)
Tailplane span		2·14 m (7 ft 0 in)
Wheel track		1·40 m (4 ft 7 in)
Wheelbase		1·13 m (3 ft 8 in)
WEIGHTS:		
Weight empty		210 kg (465 lb)
Max T-O weight:		
Aerobatic		310 kg (685 lb)

Normal	340 kg (750 lb)
PERFORMANCE (at max T-O weight):	
Never-exceed speed	126 knots (235 km/h; 146 mph)
Max level speed at S/L:	
without tip-tanks	93 knots (173 km/h; 107 mph)
with tip-tanks	83 knots (155 km/h; 96 mph)
Max cruising speed (75% power) at S/L:	
without tip-tanks	81 knots (150 km/h; 93 mph)
Econ cruising speed at S/L	
	78 knots (145 km/h; 90 mph)

Stalling speed, power off 33 knots (61 km/h; 38 mph)	
Max rate of climb at S/L	198 m (650 ft)/min
Service ceiling	3,660 m (12,000 ft)
T-O run	85 m (280 ft)
T-O to 15 m (50 ft)	338 m (1,110 ft)
Landing from 15 m (50 ft)	457 m (1,500 ft)
Landing run	110 m (360 ft)
Range with max internal fuel, 30 min reserves	
	173 nm (320 km; 200 miles)
Range with tip-tanks	390 nm (720 km; 450 miles)

PFA
POPULAR FLYING ASSOCIATION
Terminal Building, Shoreham Airport, Shoreham-by-Sea, Sussex BN4 5FF
Telephone: 079 17 61616

Following the collapse of Phoenix Aircraft Ltd, the PFA assumed responsibility for marketing plans of the Luton L.A.4a Minor. Other types of which plans are obtainable from the Association include the Isaacs Fury, Evans VP-1 and Pazmany PL-4, described under their designers' names in this section of *Jane's*, and the Currie Wot and Druine Turbulent, described below with the L.A.4a Minor.

CURRIE WOT
This aircraft was designed originally by Mr J. R. Currie in 1937. Two examples were built at Lympne in that year, but were destroyed in a wartime bombing raid. Mr V. H. Bellamy took over the design after the war, at the Hampshire Aeroplane Club, and the first Wot built by members of this club (G-APNT) flew for the first time on 11 September 1958. The second example built at the club (G-APWT) was powered by a 45 kW (60 hp) Walter Mikron flat-four engine. Both aircraft were described in earlier editions of *Jane's*.

Further Wots have since been completed, including G-ARZW with a 48·5 kW (65 hp) Walter Mikron III engine, built by Dr J. H. B. Urmston.

Dr Urmston purchased all rights in the design from Mr Bellamy, and the following details refer to G-ARZW, built to standard plans, as obtainable from the PFA. Data on the versions with Aeronca-JAP and Mikron engines can be found in the 1961-62 *Jane's*.

TYPE: Single-seat fully-aerobatic light biplane.
WINGS: Braced biplane type, with two parallel interplane struts each side and N-type centre-section support struts. Wing section Clark Y. Dihedral (both wings) 3°. No incidence. Conventional spruce and plywood structure, with fabric covering. Fabric-covered ailerons on lower wings only. No flaps.
FUSELAGE: All-wood structure. Plywood-box construction, with overall fabric covering.
TAIL UNIT: Cantilever structure of spruce and plywood, with fabric covering. Fixed-incidence tailplane. Adjustable tab on rudder. Trim tab in port elevator.
LANDING GEAR: Non-retractable two-wheel type. Rubber-cord shock-absorption. Main wheels fitted with Dunlop tyres, size 400 × 8, pressure 1·24 bars (18 lb/sq in). No brakes.
POWER PLANT: One 48·5 kW (65 hp) Walter Mikron III four-cylinder inverted in-line engine, driving a two-blade fixed-pitch wooden propeller. Fuel tank aft of firewall, capacity 54·5 litres (12 Imp gallons). Oil capacity 7 litres (1·5 Imp gallons).
ACCOMMODATION: Single seat in open cockpit.
DIMENSIONS, EXTERNAL:

Wing span (both)	6·73 m (22 ft 1 in)
Wing chord (both), constant	1·07 m (3 ft 6 in)
Wing area, gross	13·0 m² (140 sq ft)
Wing aspect ratio	6·3
Length overall	5·58 m (18 ft 3½ in)
Height overall	2·06 m (6 ft 9 in)
Wheel track	1·38 m (4 ft 6½ in)
WEIGHTS:	
Weight empty	250 kg (550 lb)
Max T-O weight	408 kg (900 lb)

PERFORMANCE (at max T-O weight):

Never-exceed speed	112 knots (209 km/h; 130 mph)
Max level speed at 610 m (2,000 ft)	
	83 knots (153 km/h; 95 mph)
Max cruising speed at 610 m (2,000 ft)	
	78 knots (145 km/h; 90 mph)
Econ cruising speed at 610 m (2,000 ft))	
	69 knots (129 km/h; 80 mph)
Stalling speed	35 knots (65 km/h; 40 mph)
Max rate of climb at S/L	183 m (600 ft)/min
Range with max fuel	208 nm (385 km; 240 miles)

DRUINE D31 TURBULENT
The following data apply to the D31 Turbulent as factory-built in the UK for many years by Rollason Aircraft and Engines Ltd. Rollason's version was generally similar to the standard Druine design. Main differences were that it had wheels of slightly greater size and a tailskid instead of a tailwheel, although a tailwheel was available optionally.

The fitting of optional wheel spats and a sliding canopy increases speed by about 7 knots (13 km/h; 8 mph).
TYPE: Single-seat ultra-light monoplane.
WINGS: Cantilever low-wing monoplane. Wing section NACA 23012. Dihedral 4°. Incidence 3° 40'. All-wood two-spar structure, covered with fabric. Built-in leading-edge slot on outer 45% of half-span. Wooden slotted ailerons with fabric covering. No flaps or tabs.
FUSELAGE: Conventional rectangular four-longeron wood structure with domed decking. Plywood-covered.
TAIL UNIT: Cantilever wooden structure. Fixed surfaces plywood-covered, movable surfaces fabric-covered. No tabs.

LANDING GEAR: Non-retractable tailwheel type (optional tailskid). Compression-spring shock-absorbers. Dunlop or Goodyear main wheels and tyres, size 14 × 3, pressure 1·95 bars (28 lb/sq in). Vespa mechanical brakes. Wheel spats, taxying and parking brakes optional. Skis or floats may be fitted as alternative to wheels.

POWER PLANT: One 33·5 kW (45 hp) Rollason Ardem 4CO2 Mk IV or 41 kW (55 hp) Ardem Mk V flat-four engine, driving a two-blade fixed-pitch wooden propeller. Fuel tank in fuselage forward of cockpit, capacity 39 litres (8·5 Imp gallons). Oil capacity 2·25 litres (0·5 Imp gallons).

ACCOMMODATION: Pilot only, in open cockpit (sliding canopy optional). Baggage locker aft of seat, capacity 11·5 kg (25 lb).

AVIONICS: Provision for lightweight radio.

DIMENSIONS, EXTERNAL:
Wing span	6·58 m (21 ft 7 in)
Wing chord, constant	1·90 m (3 ft 11 in)
Wing area, gross	7·20 m² (77·5 sq ft)
Wing aspect ratio	5·4
Length overall	5·33 m (17 ft 6 in)
Height overall	1·52 m (5 ft 0 in)
Tailplane span	1·98 m (6 ft 6 in)
Wheel track	1·73 m (5 ft 8 in)
Wheel/tailskid base	3·81 m (12 ft 6 in)

WEIGHTS:
Weight empty	179 kg (395 lb)
Max T-O weight	281 kg (620 lb)

PERFORMANCE (with 33·5 kW; 45 hp engine, at max T-O weight):
Never-exceed speed	108 knots (202 km/h; 125 mph)
Max level speed	95 knots (176 km/h; 109 mph)
Max cruising speed	87 knots (161 km/h; 100 mph)
Econ cruising speed	76 knots (141 km/h; 87 mph)
Stalling speed	39 knots (71 km/h; 44 mph)
Max rate of climb at S/L	137 m (450 ft)/min

Service ceiling	2,740 m (9,000 ft)
T-O run from grass	95 m (310 ft)
T-O to 15 m (50 ft) from grass	125 m (410 ft)
Landing from 15 m (50 ft) on grass	98 m (320 ft)
Landing run on grass	52 m (170 ft)
Range with max fuel, normal allowances	
	217 nm (400 km; 250 miles)

LUTON L.A.4a MINOR

The first Luton Minor flew in 1936 and proved entirely suitable for construction and operation by amateur builders and pilots. Examples were built pre-war in England and other parts of the world.

In 1960, the design was modernised and restressed completely to the latest British Airworthiness Requirements, allowing for a power increase to 41 kW (55 hp) and a maximum flying weight of 340 kg (750 lb).

Minors are under construction in many parts of the world, and a considerable number of amateur-built examples have been completed and flown successfully since mid-1962. At least one of them, built in Australia by R. A. Pearman and H. Nash, obtained a full Certificate of Airworthiness.

The following description applies to the aircraft in the form previously marketed by Phoenix.

TYPE: Single-seat light monoplane.

WINGS: Strut-braced parasol monoplane. Wing section RAF 48. No dihedral. Wooden two-spar structure in two halves, attached to the fuselage by tubular centre-section pylons and braced by parallel lift struts of streamline-section steel tubing. Wings removable for ground transport and storage. Leading-edge and tips plywood-covered, remainder fabric-covered. Plain ailerons of wood construction, fabric-covered, hinged directly from rear spar. No flaps.

FUSELAGE: Rectangular all-wood structure. Sides and bottom plywood-covered. Curved decking aft of cockpit fabric-covered.

TAIL UNIT: Cantilever all-wood structure, fabric-covered. Fixed fin. Aerodynamically-balanced rudder.

LANDING GEAR: Non-retractable tailwheel type with divided main legs of tubular steel construction. Rubber disc shock-absorbers. Brakes and wheel fairings optional. Fully-castoring tailwheel.

POWER PLANT: One aircooled engine in the 27·5-41 kW (37-55 hp) range, driving a two-blade fixed-pitch wooden propeller. Fuel tank forward of cockpit, capacity 29·5 litres (6·5 Imp gallons). Provision for additional tanks in wings.

ACCOMMODATION: Single seat in open cockpit. Coupé top optional. Baggage space aft of seat.

DIMENSIONS, EXTERNAL:
Wing span	7·62 m (25 ft 0 in)
Wing chord, constant	1·60 m (5 ft 3 in)
Wing area, gross	11·6 m² (125 sq ft)
Wing aspect ratio	5
Length overall	6·32 m (20 ft 9 in)
Height overall	2·29 m (7 ft 6 in)

WEIGHTS:
Weight empty	177 kg (390 lb)
Max T-O weight	340 kg (750 lb)

PERFORMANCE (27·5 kW; 37 hp Aeronca-JAP J.99 engine, at normal T-O weight):
Max level speed at 450 m (1,500 ft)	
	60 knots (111 km/h; 69 mph)
Normal cruising speed	55 knots (102 km/h; 63 mph)
Stalling speed	25 knots (45 km/h; 28 mph)
Max rate of climb at S/L	76 m (250 ft)/min
T-O run	92 m (300 ft)
Landing run	36·5 m (120 ft)
Range with standard fuel	
	155 nm (290 km; 180 miles)
Range with auxiliary tanks	
	340 nm (645 km; 400 miles)

PRACTAVIA
PRACTAVIA LTD

Wycombe Air Park, Booker, near Marlow, Buckinghamshire

Telephone: 0494 35342

MANAGING DIRECTOR: C. B. Healey

This company was formed to market plans and kits of a two-seat all-metal aerobatic aircraft known as the Sprite, the design of which was initiated by *Pilot* magazine. It also manufactures a light aircraft engine.

PRACTAVIA SPRITE

Initial design work on the Sprite was started by the staff of *Pilot* magazine in early 1968, after consultation with many experienced light aircraft constructors, and a design and development panel was set up to foster the project. Detailed design began in November 1968 and construction of the first Sprite was started in 1969. Mr Brian Healey is project executive, and Mr Lloyd Jenkinson and Mr Peter Sharman, lecturers at Loughborough University, are the designers.

First flight of a Sprite, built by Mr Peter Burril of Snape, Yorkshire, took place on 16 June 1976. Plans and kits are available for amateur construction, and 150 Sprites were reported to be at various stages of completion by January 1980, at which time eight were flying.

TYPE: Two-seat all-metal aerobatic aircraft.

WINGS: Cantilever low-wing monoplane. Wing section NACA 64315. Dihedral 6° on outer panels only. No incidence or sweepback. All-metal structure of aluminium alloy, built in three equal-length sections. Single main spar with light rear spar forming central torsion box. Skins and ribs of L72 alloy, extrusions of L65 alloy and spar caps of L73 alloy. Single-slotted flaps and plain ailerons of L72 alloy extend over full span. No trim tabs. Outer wing panels detachable for transit.

FUSELAGE: All-metal semi-monocoque structure, with no double curvature. Longerons of L65 aluminium alloy, skins and frames of L72 alloy. Sides and top curved to avoid drumming.

TAIL UNIT: Cantilever all-metal structure with swept vertical surfaces, constructed of L72 alloy. Fixed-incidence tailplane. Trim tab in centre of elevator trailing-edge, of one-third span; outer one-third on each side comprises anti-balance tab.

LANDING GEAR: Non-retractable tricycle type standard, although design of wing structure will allow for retractable gear as a future development. Shock-absorption by rubber in compression. Wheels and tyres size 5·00-5. Hydraulic disc brakes.

POWER PLANT: One 97 kW (130 hp) Rolls-Royce Continental O-240-A flat-four engine (now standard), driving a two-blade fixed-pitch propeller. Fuel contained in one fuselage tank, aft of firewall, capacity 54·5 litres (12 Imp gallons), and standard wingtip fuel tanks, capacity 54·5 litres (12 Imp gallons) each. Maximum total capacity 163·5 litres (36 Imp gallons). Oil capacity 4·5 litres (1 Imp gallon)

ACCOMMODATION: Two seats, side by side, in enclosed cockpit, with rearward-sliding transparent canopy. Space for baggage behind seats.

SYSTEMS: Hydraulic system for brakes only. 12V electrical system.

AVIONICS AND EQUIPMENT: Radio, blind-flying instrumentation and special equipment to individual builder's requirements.

DIMENSIONS, EXTERNAL:
Wing span over tip-tanks	8·23 m (27 ft 0 in)
Wing chord, constant	1·22 m (4 ft 0 in)
Wing area, gross	8·92 m² (96 sq ft)
Wing aspect ratio	6
Length overall	6·10 m (20 ft 0 in)
Width, outer wing panels removed	2·44 m (8 ft 0 in)
Height overall	2·51 m (8 ft 3 in)
Tailplane span	2·44 m (8 ft 0 in)
Wheel track	2·29 m (7 ft 6 in)
Wheelbase	1·40 m (4 ft 7 in)

DIMENSION, INTERNAL:
Cabin:
Max width	1·17 m (3 ft 10 in)

WEIGHTS (74·5 kW; 100 hp engine):
Weight empty	385 kg (850 lb)
Max T-O weight	635 kg (1,400 lb)

PERFORMANCE (at max T-O weight with 93 kW; 125 hp engine):
Never-exceed speed	212 knots (394 km/h; 245 mph)
Max cruising speed	120 knots (222 km/h; 138 mph)
Econ cruising speed	111 knots (206 km/h; 128 mph)
Stalling speed, flaps down	48 knots (89 km/h; 55 mph)

PROCTER
PROCTER AIRCRAFT ASSOCIATES LTD

c/o Kinetrol Ltd, Trading Estate, Farnham, Surrey

Telephone: 0252 723688

DIRECTORS:
Alan R. B. Nash, BSc, CEng, MICE, MRAeS
Richard C. Nash, BA (Cantab)
Roy G. Procter, CEng, MRAeS

In early 1978 a controlling interest in this company was obtained by Mr Alan Nash. It remains the intention of Procter Aircraft Associates to exploit the commercial potential of both the single-seat Kittiwake (see 1978-79 *Jane's*) and the two-seat Petrel. However, Mr Nash's main interest is in using the aircraft as the basis for a manufacturing programme rather than in the amateur plans/kits market, although sympathetic to the latter.

PROCTER PETREL

This two-seat light aircraft is based upon the Kittiwake I single-seat lightplane (see 1978-79 *Jane's*), with many components in common, but has increased wing area and has been optimised for glider towing. It has a number of improvements and simplifications to the detail mechanical design, compared with Kittiwake I. Materials used throughout are L72 clad dural and S510 mild steel.

Completion of the company's prototype Petrel is being undertaken by Mr Alan Nash. Another Petrel was built by British Aerospace apprentices at Preston.

At the present time, Mr Nash does not consider tne existing drawings of Petrel to be complete or sufficiently definitive for sale to amateurs.

TYPE: Two-seat light aircraft.

WINGS: Cantilever low-wing monoplane. Wing section NACA 3415. Dihedral 5° on outer panels. No sweepback or washout. All-metal constant-chord structure, built in three sections: centre-section, integral with fuselage, to which outer panels are each attached with three bolts. Single main spar at 30% chord and lightweight auxiliary spar at 66% chord. Multiple ribs, with no spanwise stiffeners. All-metal NACA slotted flaps and ailerons. Flaps are operated manually by pushrod and torque tube; ailerons are mass-balanced and operated by cables.

FUSELAGE: All-metal structure. Four-longeron basic structure, with flat sides and bottom and single-curvature top-decking. Integral wing centre-section forms seat and main landing gear attachment structure.

TAIL UNIT: Cantilever all-metal structure. Fixed-incidence tailplane. Manually-operated tab in starboard elevator. Tab on rudder. Control surfaces mass-balanced and operated by cables.

LANDING GEAR: Non-retractable tricycle type. Nose unit is an oleo-pneumatic strut with Goodyear 5·00-6 wheel, and is steerable from the rudder pedals. Main gear is of cantilever spring type, with Goodyear 6·00-6 wheels and hydraulic disc brakes. Tyre pressure (all) 1·72 bars (25 lb/sq in).

POWER PLANT: One 97 kW (130 hp) Rolls-Royce Continental O-240 flat-four engine, driving a McCauley fixed-pitch two-blade metal propeller. Fuel capacity 73 litres (16 Imp gallons).

ACCOMMODATION: Two persons side by side, on seats with individually adjustable backs. Baggage space aft of seats.

EQUIPMENT: Starter, generator and basic instrumentation. Radio, navigation and other equipment to builder's requirements.

DIMENSIONS, EXTERNAL:
Wing span	9·14 m (30 ft 0 in)
Wing chord, constant	1·38 m (4 ft 6½ in)
Wing area, gross	12·5 m² (135·0 sq ft)
Wing aspect ratio	6·6
Length overall	6·30 m (20 ft 8 in)
Height overall	2·33 m (7 ft 8 in)
Tailplane span	2·79 m (9 ft 2 in)
Wheel track	2·24 m (7 ft 4 in)
Wheelbase	1·52 m (5 ft 0 in)

WEIGHTS:
Weight empty	515·5 kg (1,137 lb)
Max T-O weight	762 kg (1,680 lb)

PERFORMANCE (at max T-O weight: estimated, based on measured performance of Kittiwake I):
Max level speed	113 knots (209 km/h; 130 mph)
Cruising speed	104 knots (193 km/h; 120 mph)
Max rate of climb at S/L	305 m (1,000 ft)/min

Practavia Sprite two-seat aerobatic lightplane (*J. M. G. Gradidge*)

Procter Petrel two-seat light aircraft built by British Aerospace apprentices

Taylor J.T.1 single-seat fully-aerobatic aircraft (*R. Kunert*)

Taylor J.T.2 Titch built by Jim Miller of Missouri

TAYLOR
Mrs JOHN F. TAYLOR
25, Chesterfield Crescent, Leigh-on-Sea, Essex SS9 5PD
Telephone: 0702 521063

The late Mr John Taylor, AMIED, an amateur constructor, designed and built the prototype of a single-seat ultra-light sporting monoplane, designated J.T.1. His object was to produce the airframe for not more than £100 (at 1959 prices). Construction took about 14 months, and it flew for the first time on 4 July 1959.

A second design by Mr Taylor, the J.T.2 Titch, was awarded second prize in the Midget Racer Design Competition organised by Mr Norman Jones of the Rollason company in 1964. A prototype was built and flown successfully, but crashed on 16 May 1967, killing its designer.

Mrs J. F. Taylor is continuing to market plans of both of these aircraft to amateur constructors.

TAYLOR J.T.1 MONOPLANE
Plans of the Taylor monoplane have been sold to amateur constructors in the United Kingdom and about 20 other countries in all parts of the world. More than 70 J.T.1s are known to be flying in the UK, Canada, USA, Australia and New Zealand, including ten completed in these countries during 1978.

Aircraft currently flying or under construction are fitted with a variety of engines, including the 30 kW (40 hp) Aeronca E 113, 48·5 kW (65 hp) Continental A65, 48·5 kW (65 hp) Avco Lycoming, 53·7 kW (72 hp) two-stroke McCulloch and the modified Volkswagen series. Aircraft with the 48·5 kW (65 hp) engines have a 10 cm (4 in) longer nose and 25 cm (10 in) longer rear fuselage to maintain the correct CG position.

TYPE: Single-seat fully-aerobatic ultra-light monoplane.
WINGS: Cantilever low-wing monoplane. Wing section RAF 48. Constant chord. Dihedral on outer panels 4°. Incidence 3°. Wooden two-spar structure, comprising centre-section and outer panels. Plywood and fabric covering. Differential ailerons. Split trailing-edge flaps. No tabs.
FUSELAGE: Conventional plywood-covered structure of four main longerons and curved formers. Centre-section integral with fuselage.
TAIL UNIT: Cantilever fin and fixed-incidence tailplane are plywood-covered wood structures. Elevators and rudder are fabric-covered wood structures.
LANDING GEAR: Non-retractable two-wheel type. Cantilever main legs, with coil spring shock-absorption. Size 5 × 4 (305 mm; 12 in) main wheels, tyre pressure 1·65 bars (24 lb/sq in). Leaf spring tailskid with steerable skid-pad. One example, built by Mr R. Ladd in the US (see 1972-73 *Jane's*), has manually-actuated inward-retracting main gear.

POWER PLANT (prototype): One 28·3 kW (38 hp) JAP two-cylinder engine, driving a modified Flottorp two-blade wooden fixed-pitch propeller. Fuel tank aft of firewall, capacity 27 litres (6 Imp gallons).
ACCOMMODATION: Single seat under transparent Perspex canopy. Aerobatic harness. Small locker aft of seat.
DIMENSIONS, EXTERNAL:

Wing span	6·40 m (21 ft 0 in)
Wing area, gross	7·06 m² (76 sq ft)
Wing aspect ratio	6
Length overall	4·57 m (15 ft 0 in)
Height over tail	1·47 m (4 ft 10 in)
Tailplane span	1·98 m (6 ft 6 in)
Wheel track	1·52 m (5 ft 0 in)

WEIGHTS:

Weight empty	186 kg (410 lb)
Max T-O weight	276 kg (610 lb)

PERFORMANCE:

Never-exceed speed	113 knots (209 km/h; 130 mph)
Max level speed at S/L	91 knots (169 km/h; 105 mph)
Econ cruising speed	78 knots (145 km/h; 90 mph)
Never-exceed speed with flaps down	56 knots (105 km/h; 65 mph)
Stalling speed, flaps up	40 knots (75 km/h; 46 mph)
Stalling speed, flaps down	33 knots (62 km/h; 38 mph)
Max rate of climb at S/L	305 m (1,000 ft)/min
Range	200 nm (370 km; 230 miles)
g limits	+9; −9

TAYLOR J.T.2 TITCH
Construction of the prototype Titch was started in February 1965 and it flew for the first time on 22 January 1967.

Nineteen Titches are known to be flying, including 12 in the USA, two in New Zealand, one in France, one in Rhodesia and three in England; plans have also been supplied to amateur constructors in Alaska, Argentina, Brazil, Iceland, Ireland, Japan, Italy, Kenya, Mexico and Spain.

The Titch illustrated was built by Jim Miller of Missouri, USA. Maximum speed is 139 knots (257 km/h; 160 mph) at 2,700 rpm and cruising speed 122 knots (225 km/h; 140 mph) at 2,600 rpm with a metal propeller. When fitted with a wooden propeller, the rate of climb is stated to be 700 m (2,300 ft)/min. Empty weight is 255 kg (562 lb).

The following description refers to the prototype:
TYPE: Single-seat light monoplane.
WINGS: Cantilever low-wing monoplane. Taylor-modified NACA 23012 wing section. Dihedral 5° on top surface. Incidence 3°. Spruce structure with main box-spar and 'plank' auxiliary spar. Plywood and fabric covering.

Plain manually-operated ply-covered flaps over half-span and fabric-covered differential ailerons.
FUSELAGE: All-wood structure, with four main longerons, four secondary longerons and double-curvature ply covering. Aluminium cockpit side panels.
TAIL UNIT: All-wood structure, with fixed-incidence tailplane. Fixed surfaces plywood-covered, control surfaces fabric-covered.
LANDING GEAR: Non-retractable tailwheel type. Steerable tailwheel. Chrome-vanadium compression coil-spring shock-absorbers. Wheels of constructor's manufacture with 4-ply tyres size 5·00-4 and drum brakes.
POWER PLANT: One 63·5 kW (85 hp) Continental C85 flat-four engine, driving a Hegy wooden two-blade scimitar propeller. Glassfibre fuel tank between firewall and instrument panel, capacity 45·5 litres (10 Imp gallons).
ACCOMMODATION: Single seat, with aerobatic harness, under bubble canopy hinged along starboard side.
DIMENSIONS, EXTERNAL:

Wing span	5·72 m (18 ft 9 in)
Wing chord at root	1·37 m (4 ft 6 in)
Wing chord at tip	0·91 m (3 ft 0 in)
Wing area, gross	6·32 m² (68 sq ft)
Wing aspect ratio	5·14
Length overall	4·91 m (16 ft 1½ in)
Height overall	1·42 m (4 ft 8 in)
Tailplane span	1·98 m (6 ft 6 in)
Wheel track	1·52 m (5 ft 0 in)
Propeller diameter	1·52 m (5 ft 0 in)

WEIGHTS (A: 63·5 kW; 85 hp Continental engine, B: Volkswagen engine):

Weight empty: A	227 kg (500 lb)
B	185 kg (410 lb)
Max T-O weight: A	338 kg (745 lb)
B	290 kg (640 lb)

PERFORMANCE (prototype, at max T-O weight except where indicated):

Never-exceed speed	195 knots (362 km/h; 225 mph)
Max level speed	174 knots (322 km/h; 200 mph)
Normal cruising speed	135 knots (250 km/h; 155 mph)
Econ cruising speed	95·5 knots (177 km/h; 110 mph)
Best approach speed	65 knots (121 km/h; 75 mph)
Stalling speed, flaps up:	
A	50·5 knots (93·5 km/h; 58 mph)
B	46 knots (86 km/h; 53 mph)
Stalling speed, flaps down:	
A	43·5 knots (80·5 km/h; 50 mph)
B	40 knots (74 km/h; 46 mph)
T-O speed	54 knots (100 km/h; 62 mph)
Touchdown speed	48 knots (89 km/h; 55 mph)
Max rate of climb at S/L	335 m (1,100 ft)/min

TURNER
CHRISTOPHER TURNER
57 Field Lane, York YO1 5JD
Telephone: (0904) 413168

TURNER TSW
Mr Christopher Turner has built the prototype of an original-design biplane on which design work began in

June 1974. Construction started in April 1975, and the aircraft made its first flight on 14 October 1979.
TYPE: Two-seat lightweight biplane.
WINGS: Braced single-bay biplane. Wing section NACA M6. Thickness/chord ratio 12%. Dihedral on upper wings 0°; lower wings 3° 30'. Incidence on upper wings 3° 30'; lower wings 4°. Conventionally staggered wings, with N-type interplane and centre-section struts.

Streamline section flying and landing wires. Conventional wooden structure of spruce, with plywood leading-edge and fabric covering. Plain ailerons, of similar construction, on all four wings. No flaps. No trim tabs. Cut-out in trailing-edge of upper wing centre-section.
FUSELAGE: Conventional structure of wood with plywood skins.

TAIL UNIT: Cantilever wooden structure of spruce, with all surfaces fabric covered. Fixed-incidence tailplane. No trim tabs.

LANDING GEAR: Non-retractable tailskid type. Two side Vs and half-axles hinged to lower fuselage. Shock-absorption by rubber bungee. Goodyear main wheel tyres size 6·00-6, pressure 1·38 bars (20 lb/sq in). It is intended to fit Goodyear hydraulic disc brakes.

POWER PLANT: One 93 kW (125 hp) Avco Lycoming O-290-3 flat-four engine, driving a two-blade fixed-pitch wooden propeller with spinner. Fuel tank in fuselage, aft of firewall, capacity 63·6 litres (14 Imp gallons). Refuelling point on upper surface of fuselage. Oil capacity 7·6 litres (1·7 Imp gallons).

ACCOMMODATION: Pilot and passenger in tandem open cockpits. Removable cover for forward cockpit when aircraft flown solo. Baggage locker aft of pilot's cockpit.

DIMENSIONS, EXTERNAL:

Wing span (both)	6·10 m (20 ft 0 in)
Wing chord, constant (both)	1·07 m (3 ft 6 in)
Wing area, gross	13·01 m² (140 sq ft)
Wing aspect ratio	5·7
Length overall	5·79 m (19 ft 0 in)
Height overall	2·06 m (6 ft 9 in)
Tailplane span	2·13 m (7 ft 0 in)
Wheel track	1·52 m (5 ft 0 in)
Wheelbase	3·94 m (12 ft 11 in)
Propeller diameter	1·83 m (6 ft 0 in)

WEIGHTS:

Weight empty	349 kg (770 lb)
Max fuel weight	45 kg (100 lb)
Max T-O and landing weight	567 kg (1,250 lb)

PERFORMANCE (at max T-O weight):

Max level speed at S/L	130 knots (241 km/h; 150 mph)
Max cruising speed at S/L	87 knots (161 km/h; 100 mph)
Econ cruising speed at S/L	74 knots (137 km/h; 85 mph)
Stalling speed, engine idling	47 knots (87 km/h; 54 mph)
Max rate of climb at S/L	335 m (1,100 ft)/min
Range with max fuel, 9 litres (2 Imp gallons) reserves	174 nm (322 km; 200 miles)

UNITED STATES OF AMERICA

ABELS

L. GALE ABELS
Boulder, Colorado

ABELS GREENAPPLES AT-19

Mr L. Gale Abels, an architect of Boulder, Colorado, has designed and built a two-seat light monoplane known as the Greenapples AT-19. Construction took seven years, the aircraft beginning as a modified Thorp T-18. Constant redesign during construction led to only the landing gear and cockpit canopy of the finished aircraft being of Thorp type. First flight was made on 24 May 1979. It has been reported that the modified wing, of increased span and higher aspect ratio, using thicker skins and fitted with plain flaps, provides a slower landing speed and increased rate of climb compared with the Thorp T-18. The AT-19 received the Stan Dzik Memorial Award for 'Outstanding Design Contribution' at the 1979 EAA Fly-in.

TYPE: Side-by-side two-seat light aircraft.

POWER PLANT: One 134 kW (180 hp) Avco Lycoming O-360-A1A flat-four engine. Fuel capacity 125 litres (33 US gallons).

DIMENSIONS, EXTERNAL:

Wing span	7·42 m (24 ft 4 in)
Wing chord: at root	1·27 m (4 ft 2 in)
at tip	0·76 m (2 ft 6 in)
Length overall	6·40 m (21 ft 0 in)

WEIGHTS:

Weight empty	472 kg (1,040 lb)
Max T-O weight	771 kg (1,700 lb)

PERFORMANCE:

Cruising speed	186 knots (344 km/h; 214 mph)
Landing speed	61 knots (113 km/h; 70 mph)
Max rate of climb at S/L	762 m (2,500 ft)/min
Range with max fuel, 30 min reserves	521 nm (966 km; 600 miles)

ACE

ACE AIRCRAFT MANUFACTURING CO
106 Arthur Road, Asheville, North Carolina 28806
Telephone: (704) 252 4325
OWNER: Thurman G. Baird
SALES AND PUBLIC RELATIONS MANAGER: V. P. Baird

This company is a successor to the original Corben Aircraft Company, which was established in 1923 and began manufacturing the Baby Ace single-seat ultra-light monoplane in kit form in 1931. All rights in the current updated design were purchased by the present owner in 1965. Plans, kits and parts of the Baby Ace and Junior Ace are available to amateur builders from Ace Aircraft, together with plans of the Flaglor Scooter, described in this section of *Jane's.*

BABY ACE MODEL D

The prototype of the redesigned Baby Ace Model D flew for the first time on 15 November 1956. Large numbers have since been built by amateurs, some of whom have introduced authorised refinements to the basic design. At least one Baby Ace is flying with a float landing gear, and was illustrated in the 1975-76 *Jane's.* The floats were constructed of glassfibre, using a wood pattern and glassfibre mould, and have spruce struts wrapped in glassfibre, with cast aluminium end fittings. Twin water rudders are fitted for surface handling, and performance is claimed to be comparable with that of a Piper Cub seaplane with 48·5 kW (65 hp) engine.

TYPE: Single-seat ultra-light monoplane.

WINGS: Braced parasol monoplane. Wing section Clark Y (modified). Dihedral 1°. Incidence 1°. Fabric-covered two-spar wood structure. Fabric-covered wood ailerons. No flaps.

FUSELAGE: Welded steel tube structure, fabric-covered.

TAIL UNIT: Wire-braced steel tube structure, fabric-covered.

LANDING GEAR: Non-retractable tailwheel type. Combination special tubing and spring shock-absorption. Goodrich 8·00-4 main wheels. Scott hydraulic brakes. Wheel spats optional. Steerable tailwheel. Edo 1140 floats on seaplane version.

POWER PLANT: One Continental A65, A85, C65 or C85 flat-four engine of 48·5-63·5 kW (65-85 hp), driving a two-blade wooden fixed-pitch propeller. Fuel in tank aft of firewall with capacity of 63·6 litres (16·8 US gallons). Oil capacity 3·8 litres (1 US gallon).

ACCOMMODATION: Single seat in open cockpit. Wide door on starboard side. Space for 4·5 kg (10 lb) baggage.

DIMENSIONS, EXTERNAL:

Wing span	8·05 m (26 ft 5 in)
Wing chord, constant	1·37 m (4 ft 6 in)
Wing area, gross	10·43 m² (112·3 sq ft)
Wing aspect ratio	5·95
Length overall	5·40 m (17 ft 8¾ in)
Height overall	2·02 m (6 ft 7¾ in)
Tailplane span	2·13 m (7 ft 0 in)
Wheel track	1·83 m (6 ft 0 in)
Wheelbase	3·96 m (13 ft 0 in)

WEIGHTS:

Weight empty, equipped	261 kg (575 lb)
Max T-O weight:	
48·5 kW (65 hp)	431 kg (950 lb)
63·5 kW (85 hp) landplane or seaplane	522 kg (1,150 lb)

PERFORMANCE (48·5 kW; 65 hp engine, at max T-O weight):

Max level speed at S/L	96 knots (177 km/h; 110 mph)
Max cruising speed	87-91 knots (161-169 km/h; 100-105 mph)
Stalling speed	30 knots (54·7 km/h; 34 mph)
Max rate of climb at S/L	365 m (1,200 ft)/min
Service ceiling	4,875 m (16,000 ft)
T-O run	60 m (200 ft)
Landing run	76 m (250 ft)
Range with max fuel	304 nm (560 km; 350 miles)

JUNIOR ACE MODEL E

The Junior Ace Model E differs from the Baby Ace Model D in being a side-by-side two-seater. It is powered usually by a 63·5 kW (85 hp) Continental C85 flat-four engine, and the details refer to an aircraft with this power plant that was built by Mr Louis C. Seno of Melrose Park, Illinois.

First flown on 2 August 1966, it has a cockpit 7·5 cm (3 in) wider and 10 cm (4 in) deeper than that of the standard Model E, a full electrical system and increased fuel capacity of 85 litres (22·5 US gallons).

DIMENSIONS, EXTERNAL:

Wing span	7·92 m (26 ft 0 in)
Wing chord, constant	1·37 m (4 ft 6 in)
Wing aspect ratio	5·95
Length overall	5·50 m (18 ft 0 in)
Height overall	2·00 m (6 ft 7 in)

WEIGHTS:

Weight empty	367 kg (809 lb)
Max T-O weight	606 kg (1,335 lb)

PERFORMANCE:

Max level speed at S/L	113 knots (209 km/h; 130 mph)
Cruising speed	91 knots (169 km/h; 105 mph)
Landing speed	57 knots (105 km/h; 65 mph)
Service ceiling	3,050 m (10,000 ft)
T-O run	122 m (400 ft)
Landing run	183 m (600 ft)
Range with max fuel	304 nm (560 km; 350 miles)

AEROCAR

AEROCAR INC
PO Box 1171, Longview, Washington 98632
Telephone: (206) 423 8260
PRESIDENT AND GENERAL MANAGER: Moulton B. Taylor

In February 1948 Aerocar Inc began developing a flying automobile designed by Mr M. B. Taylor. The prototype Aerocar, with an Avco Lycoming O-290 engine, was completed in October 1949. It was followed by a pre-production Aerocar Model I, with an Avco Lycoming O-320 engine, and this was used for tests which led to FAA airworthiness certification of the Aerocar on 13 December 1956. Four additional Model I Aerocars were completed subsequently for demonstration tours of the United States and for sale to customers, and were followed by the prototype of a refined Model III Aerocar. Details of the development and history of these roadable aircraft can be found in the 1979-80 and earlier editions of *Jane's.*

Aerocar Inc, which is basically a three-person operation, decided that legislation and economics inhibited further development of the Aerocar, and has since devoted most of its activity to other projects, notably the single-seat Mini-Imp, which embodies features of the Aerocar and is suitable for amateur construction.

In 1966 Aerocar built the prototype of a light flying-boat for a private customer. It was followed by two further aircraft, named Coot, on similar lines but provided with tricycle landing gear for amphibious operation. Many sets of plans for this aircraft, now known as the Sooper-Coot, have been sold to amateur constructors.

Aerocar is also devoting much effort to the development of a low-cost and low-power aircraft engine, based on a Kawasaki motorcycle engine, which would be suitable for powering many types of light aircraft of the future. It originally flight tested for over 100 hours a 900 cc Kawasaki engine in a 1937 Taylorcraft. This was then replaced by a 1,000 cc Kawasaki engine, which had completed more than 200 flight hours by early 1980. During 1979 a turbocharger, Maloof three-blade constant-speed metal propeller, separate oil pump, and a Flexidyne dry fluid coupling in the Hy-Vo chain drive system have been incorporated in this power plant. Aerocar was investigating in 1980 the suitability of a solid state ignition system, with electronic spark advance, to facilitate engine starting and provide smoother running.

AEROCAR SOOPER-COOT MODEL A

The prototype of this aircraft flew for the first time in February 1971. It logged approximately 100 hours powered by an 89·5 kW (120 hp) Franklin 225 engine, driving a Sensenich fixed-pitch metal propeller. This was subsequently replaced by a 134 kW (180 hp) Franklin 335 engine, driving a Hartzell constant-speed metal propeller, and the aircraft has been flown extensively since 1972 with this more powerful engine.

The 'float-wing' configuration of the Sooper-Coot permits rough-water operation and, since the close proximity of the wings to the water forms a 'pressure wedge', unusually low take-off and landing speeds are possible without recourse to flaps or other lift-enhancing devices.

The structure is basically of wood, but the tailboom and tail unit can be of steel tube and fabric, wood monocoque or all-metal construction. The rearward-folding wings, of NACA 4415 section, can be folded by one person. The fabric-covered ailerons are of metal construction and statically balanced. There are no tip floats. Construction of the hull, which has only seven bulkheads, is straightforward, without the complication of wheel-well doors. Tailplane and elevators also fold and the elevators have trim tabs. All control surfaces are statically balanced. The tricycle-type landing gear is manually retractable into the wings, but an alternative powered retraction system is shown on the plans.

Recommended power plant for the Sooper-Coot is a Franklin flat-six engine of either 134 or 164 kW (180 or 220 hp). However, many builders of the Sooper-Coot are fitting a 157 kW (210 hp) Continental IO-360. To minimise expenditure, others are fitting Avco Lycoming O-320 and O-320-B engines of 119 kW (160 hp). These are reported to be satisfactory if only a limited weight of optional equipment is installed in the aircraft. However, a constant-speed propeller has proved essential to maintain reasonable performance with the O-320/320-B. Maximum fuel capacity is 189 litres (50 US gallons).

Certain component parts (including the glassfibre engine cowls, glassfibre hull shell, foredeck, instrument

Turner TSW two-seat lightweight biplane

Abels Greenapples AT-19 *(Howard Levy)*

Baby Ace Model D (Continental A65 engine) built by Capt Lloyd Windh of Air Canada *(Neil A. Macdougall)*

Side-by-side two-seat Junior Ace Model E *(J. M. G. Gradidge)*

Aerocar Sooper-Coot Model A lightweight homebuilt amphibian

Aerocar Mini-Imp single-seat homebuilt aircraft (1,900 cc Limbach engine)

panel, tail fairings, engine cooling-fan blades and spring steel main landing gear legs), and plans, are available to amateur constructors. The company also maintains a list of recommended suppliers of welded assemblies and machined components. More than 400 Sooper-Coots were under construction in early 1980, when 62 Coot-As and one Coot-B were known to be flying in the USA and other countries.

DIMENSIONS, EXTERNAL:
Wing span	10·97 m (36 ft 0 in)
Wing chord, constant	1·52 m (5 ft 0 in)
Wing area, gross	16·72 m² (180 sq ft)
Length overall	
	6·10 to 6·71 m (20 ft 0 in to 22 ft 0 in)
Height overall	2·44 m (8 ft 0 in)
Width folded	2·44 m (8 ft 0 in)
Tailplane span	3·04 m (10 ft 0 in)

WEIGHTS:
Weight empty	499 kg (1,100 lb)
Max T-O weight	884 kg (1,950 lb)

PERFORMANCE (134 kW; 180 hp engine, at max T-O weight):
Never-exceed speed	120 knots (223 km/h; 139 mph)
Max cruising speed	113 knots (209 km/h; 130 mph)
Econ cruising speed at 50% power	
	95·5 knots (177 km/h; 110 mph)
Max rate of climb at S/L	381 m (1,250 ft)/min
T-O run (land)	61 m (200 ft)
T-O (water)	6-8 s

AEROCAR IMP

Design of the Imp (an acronym derived from Independently Made Plane) began in January 1972. Many design features of the Aerocar were embodied, including folding wings and a pusher propeller aft of the tail unit. All-metal construction, using pop-rivets, bolt-together assemblies and limited welding, was specified to reduce building time.

Construction of a two-seat prototype Imp began in August 1972, but completion of the test programme was delayed by the need for further investigation into many aspects of the design. Subsequent non-availability of the Franklin engine which was intended to power the aircraft led to the decision to give priority instead to the single-seat Mini-Imp (which see).

More recently, it was decided to resume the Imp programme by converting the original prototype to two-plus-two configuration, with the pilot and one passenger seated side by side at the front of the cabin and two folding seats at the rear for children. The necessary new skins for the modification had been built by early 1977. However, the aircraft was transferred to another builder in St Louis, Missouri, in 1978, and he is continuing the conversion. The modified prototype will not incorporate all changes shown on the current Imp information sheet supplied by Aerocar, such as use of the GA (PC)-1 aerofoil section, Kawasaki engine and a lengthened fuselage. Therefore, the details below refer to subsequent Imps and not the prototype, which Aerocar hoped to display at the 1980 EAA Fly-in, at Oshkosh.

The future of the Imp programme will be determined largely by the outcome of Aerocar's work to evolve a low-cost and low-power aero-engine from the Kawasaki motorcycle engine. Two 1,000 cc 74·5 kW (100 hp) four-cylinder engines of this type might be geared to drive a single propeller, with centreline thrust and 'either/or' engine drive capability, via a chain drive.

TYPE: Four-seat light aircraft.

WINGS: Cantilever high-wing monoplane. Wing section GA(PC)-1. No dihedral. Incidence 4°. No sweepback. All-metal structure of constant chord. Wings fold aft, alongside fuselage, for towing or storage. All-metal ailerons, each with trim tab. No flaps.

FUSELAGE: All-metal structure with glassfibre shell.

TAIL UNIT: Inverted V type, of all-metal construction, with variable-incidence tailplane surfaces.

LANDING GEAR: Electrically-retractable tricycle type, main units retracting outward. Special highway-type wheels and 6-ply tyres suitable for road towing. Tyre pressure 2·76 bars (40 lb/sq in). Rosenhan wheel brakes. Nosewheel retracts separately from main wheels for road towing.

POWER PLANT: Prototype may be powered by the existing 93 kW (125 hp) Franklin engine or a new 149 kW (200 hp) Franklin engine. Plans show installation of the Kawasaki twin-engine arrangement. One fuel tank of 53 litres (14 US gallons) capacity in each wing root. Total fuel capacity 106 litres (28 US gallons). Refuelling points in upper surface of wings, inboard of wing fold. Oil capacity 7·5 litres (2 US gallons).

ACCOMMODATION: Two seats, side by side, at front of enclosed cabin, with two folding seats at rear. Large baggage space if rear seats folded against bulkhead. Airstair doors.

SYSTEM: Electrical system powered by 12V 60A engine-driven alternator.

ELECTRONICS: Narco Escort 110 radio and Type 50A transponder.

DIMENSIONS, EXTERNAL:
Wing span	8·84 m (29 ft 0 in)
Wing chord, constant	1·22 m (4 ft 0 in)
Wing area, gross	10·41 m² (112 sq ft)
Wing aspect ratio	7
Length overall	6·71 m (22 ft 0 in)
Width, wings folded	2·13 m (7 ft 0 in)
Height overall (propeller blades horizontal)	
	1·68 m (5 ft 6 in)
Tailplane span	2·44 m (8 ft 0 in)
Wheel track	1·78 m (5 ft 10 in)
Wheelbase	2·67 m (8 ft 9 in)
Propeller diameter	1·83 m (6 ft 0 in)

DIMENSION, INTERNAL:
Cockpit:	
Max width	1·12 m (3 ft 8 in)

WEIGHTS (estimated):
Weight empty	499 kg (1,100 lb)
Max T-O and landing weight	703 kg (1,550 lb)

PERFORMANCE (estimated):
Max cruising speed
more than 130 knots (241 km/h; 150 mph)
Stalling speed   44 knots (81 km/h; 50 mph)
Max rate of climb at S/L   244 m (800 ft)/min

AEROCAR MINI-IMP

The Mini-Imp is a single-seat version of the Aerocar Imp, to which it is generally similar. The basic structure, which is stressed to ±9g, is all metal and is assembled with bolts and pop-rivets, thereby eliminating the need for welding skill. It is claimed that only a bench drill, sander and bandsaw are needed for home construction of the Mini-Imp, in addition to the usual hand tools and a pop-riveter. Average time taken for construction is 700 working hours, at a cost of $8,000, excluding engine, instruments and electronics.

By early 1980 the Mini-Imp prototype had completed about 250 flying hours, powered by a 51 kW (68 hp) Limbach 1,900 cc flat-four engine driving a wooden propeller. During the Winter of 1975/76 Aerocar built a folding wing for this aircraft, which folds in a similar way to that of the Imp. This permits the builder to construct the aircraft in small areas, and is a standard feature on the plans for the aircraft.

All drawings for the Mini-Imp have been available since 1978, together with parts kits. More than 200 amateur-built examples were being constructed by early 1980 and several Mini-Imps are already flying. Recommended power plant is the turbocharged Revmaster 2100D, driving a Maloof metal constant-speed propeller; Aerocar has built a prototype fitted with this propeller, and this is 30 cm (12 in) longer overall than the original prototype. Individual builders are fitting a variety of engines, including the 74·5 kW (100 hp) Continental O-200, 86 kW (115 hp) Avco Lycoming O-235, and two-cylinder 44·5 kW (60 hp) Franklin. Another Aerocar-built Mini-Imp will be fitted with the turbocharged Kawasaki engine and Maloof propeller, after testing in the Taylorcraft has been completed.

The description of the Imp applies also to the Mini-Imp, except as follows:

TYPE: Single-seat light sporting aircraft.
WINGS: As for Imp. Wing pivots 90° to a fore and aft position for towing by motor car.
FUSELAGE, TAIL UNIT AND LANDING GEAR: As for Imp.
POWER PLANT: Recommended engine is the turbocharged Revmaster 2100D, driving a Maloof constant-speed metal propeller via the standard extended drive shaft incorporating a Flexidyne dry fluid coupling. Alterna-

tive engines in the 44·5-74·5 kW (60-100 hp) range may be installed. Fuel tank in wing centre-section, capacity 45·4 litres (12 US gallons), plus tip-tanks, each of 34 litres (9 US gallons) capacity. Refuelling point on wing upper surface.
ACCOMMODATION: Single semi-reclining moulded glassfibre bucket seat beneath sideways-opening (to port) transparent canopy. Seat folds forward to provide access to space for 46 kg (100 lb) of baggage.
DIMENSIONS, EXTERNAL:

Wing span	7·77 m (25 ft 6 in)
Wing chord, constant	0·91 m (3 ft 0 in)
Length overall	4·88 m (16 ft 0 in)
Height over fuselage	1·24 m (4 ft 1 in)
Height over propeller	1·89 m (6 ft 2½ in)
Tailplane span	1·98 m (6 ft 6 in)
Propeller diameter	1·45 m (4 ft 9 in)

WEIGHTS:

Weight empty	236 kg (520 lb)
Max T-O weight	362 kg (800 lb)

PERFORMANCE (Limbach engine, except where indicated):
Never-exceed speed 260 knots (482 km/h; 300 mph)
Max cruising speed at S/L
130 knots (241 km/h; 150 mph)
Max cruising speed (Revmaster engine and Maloof propeller, estimated)
over 173 knots (322 km/h; 200 mph)
Stalling speed   43·5 knots (80·5 km/h; 50 mph)
Max rate of climb at S/L   366 m (1,200 ft)/min
T-O run   183 m (600 ft)
Range   over 434 nm (804 km; 500 miles)

AEROCAR MICRO-IMP

The Micro-Imp is of similar configuration to the Mini-Imp, but is constructed primarily of glassfibre-reinforced paper known as TPG (Taylor Paper Glass). Static testing has shown this to be far stronger than originally estimated, resulting in the redesign of many components to reduce weight. Design had begun in August 1978, and construction of the prototype was started in December 1978. It was anticipated that the Micro-Imp with Citroen 2CV type engine would make its first flight in the Spring of 1980.
TYPE: Single-seat light sporting aircraft.
WINGS: Cantilever high-wing monoplane. Wing section NASA GA(PC)-1. Thickness/chord ratio 15%. No anhedral or dihedral. Incidence 3°. Glassfibre-reinforced paper structure, covered with rip-stop Dacron. Full-span constant-chord ailerons of similar construction to wings. Ailerons droop for flap function, and can be set in slight 'up' position for efficient cruise.

FUSELAGE: Glassfibre-reinforced paper structure. Non-structural and removable nosecone of moulded glassfibre.
TAIL UNIT: Inverted V type. Glassfibre-reinforced paper structure, covered with rip-stop Dacron. Variable-incidence tailplane surfaces.
LANDING GEAR: Manually-retractable tricycle type. Main units retract vertically. Cantilever spring steel tube main legs. Three plastics wheels, diameter 25·4 cm (10 in). Tyres size 3·00-4, pressure 3·45 bars (50 lb/sq in). Aerocar mechanical brakes.
POWER PLANT: One 18·6 kW (25 hp) modified and derated Citroen 2CV motor car engine, driving a tail-mounted Hendrickson two-blade wooden pusher propeller or a Maloof two-blade two-position propeller. One fuel tank aft of seat, capacity 26·5 litres (7 US gallons). Refuelling point on top of fuselage. NASA flush air intake ducts, plus cooling fan.
ACCOMMODATION: Single semi-reclining seat under sideways-hinged (to port) transparent canopy. Baggage space above engine.
AVIONICS: Radair 10A 10-channel radio, operated by nickel-cadmium battery.
DIMENSIONS, EXTERNAL:

Wing span	8·23 m (27 ft 0 in)
Wing chord, constant	0·91 m (3 ft 0 in)
Wing aspect ratio	9
Length overall	4·57 m (15 ft 0 in)
Max width of fuselage	0·69 m (2 ft 3 in)
Height overall	1·22 m (4 ft 0 in)
Tailplane span	2·13 m (7 ft 0 in)
Wheel track	1·22 m (4 ft 0 in)
Wheelbase	1·37 m (4 ft 6 in)
Propeller diameter	1·07 m (3 ft 6 in)
Propeller ground clearance	0·61 m (2 ft 0 in)

WEIGHTS:

Weight empty	118 kg (260 lb)
Max T-O weight	238 kg (525 lb)

PERFORMANCE (estimated):
Never-exceed speed 120 knots (223 km/h; 139 mph)
Max level speed   104 knots (193 km/h; 120 mph)
Max cruising speed 91 knots (169 km/h; 105 mph)
Econ cruising speed 87 knots (161 km/h; 100 mph)
Stalling speed   42 knots (78 km/h; 48 mph)
Max rate of climb at S/L   152 m (500 ft)/min
Service ceiling   3,050 m (10,000 ft)
T-O   152 m (500 ft)
T-O to 15 m (50 ft)   290 m (950 ft)
Landing from 15 m (50 ft)   274 m (900 ft)
Landing run   122 m (400 ft)

AERO DESIGN
AERO DESIGN ASSOCIATES

Hangar One, Building 147, Opa-Locka Airport, Opa-Locka, Florida 33054
Telephone: (305) 685 8128
PRESIDENT: David Garber

AERO DESIGN DG-1

This unorthodox monoplane is the first custom-built Unlimited Class racing aircraft constructed in the USA since the 1930s. Designated DG-1, it is intended to compete directly with the highly modified P-51 Mustangs, F8F Bearcats and Hawker Sea Furies, and also to be capable of breaking the existing world speed record for propeller-driven aircraft.

The DG-1 has a cigar-shaped fuselage embodying a flush cockpit canopy. It is powered by two engines—one at each end of the fuselage—with respective tractor and pusher propellers. The tailplane has marked anhedral and both dorsal and ventral tail fins are fitted. Stress limits are ±12g.

The President of Aero Design Associates, Mr David Garber, a pilot with Pan American World Airways, has several years' experience of racing in the Sport Biplane Class in modified Pitts Specials.

Design of the DG-1 was started in 1973 and construction began in late 1974. The aircraft made its first brief flight on 25 July 1977, when the port landing gear broke. Repairs were put in hand and at the same time the airscoop was moved to an underfuselage position, between the main landing gear legs. Flying resumed on 4 June 1978. After a number of flights indicated cooling problems with the rear engine, the DG-1 was fitted with new oil coolers. Flight testing was about to restart in January 1980.

TYPE: Single-seat racing monoplane.
WINGS: Cantilever monoplane. NACA 065 wing section. Thickness/chord ratio 12%. No dihedral or anhedral. Incidence 0° 30'. Glassfibre-reinforced spar; foam-filled wing interior and glassfibre covering. Ailerons of similar construction to wings.
FUSELAGE: Steel tube (4130) structure, covered with 2·4 mm (³/₃₂ in) plywood and glassfibre.
TAIL UNIT: All-moving tailplane with 10° anhedral, dorsal fin, and ventral fin and rudder, all constructed of foam and glassfibre.
LANDING GEAR: Fully retractable tricycle type, with single 0·25 m (10 in) diameter wheel on each unit. Tyre pressure 4·14 bars (60 lb/sq in). All three wheels retract rearward hydraulically into fuselage. Nosewheel lock coupled to control stick. Gerides brakes.
POWER PLANT: Two Mazda RX-3 rotary-combustion motor car engines, modified to produce an estimated 243 kW (330 hp) each at more than 8,000 rpm. Engines have fuel injection, and custom-built AiResearch turbochargers. Each drives a Hartzell three-blade constant-speed propeller. Usable fuel capacity 208 litres (55 US gallons) plus externally-carried 113·5 litre (30 US gallon) optional tank. Oil capacity of each engine 7·5 litres (2 US gallons).
ACCOMMODATION: Single semi-reclining seat under two-section Plexiglas canopy.
SYSTEMS: 14V DC electrical system, with AC for electric gyros. Full blind-flying, high-altitude capability, including oxygen system.
DIMENSIONS, EXTERNAL:

Wing span	6·10 m (20 ft 0 in)
Wing chord at root	1·07 m (3 ft 6 in)
Wing chord at tip	0·53 m (1 ft 9 in)
Wing area, gross	4·88 m² (52·5 sq ft)
Wing aspect ratio	7·6
Length overall	6·25 m (20 ft 6 in)
Height overall	1·68 m (5 ft 6 in)
Tailplane span	2·13 m (7 ft 0 in)
Wheel track	1·22 m (4 ft 0 in)
Wheelbase	2·24 m (7 ft 4 in)
Propeller diameter	1·73 m (5 ft 8 in)
Propeller ground clearance	0·25 m (10 in)

WEIGHTS:

Weight empty	816 kg (1,800 lb)
Max T-O weight, racing	1,043 kg (2,300 lb)
Max T-O weight	1,088 kg (2,400 lb)
Max landing weight	998 kg (2,200 lb)

PERFORMANCE (estimated):
Never-exceed speed   Mach 0·75
Max level speed at S/L with racing wing
391 knots (724 km/h; 450 mph)
Max level speed with special speed record wing
over 434 knots (804 km/h; 500 mph)
Normal cruising speed at 5,180 m (17,000 ft)
304 knots (563 km/h; 350 mph)
Stalling speed, flaps down
85 knots (158 km/h; 98 mph)
Max rate of climb at S/L   914 m (3,000 ft)/min
Service ceiling   7,315 m (24,000 ft)
Service ceiling, one engine out 5,180 m (17,000 ft)
Range with max fuel, 15 min reserves, at 60% power
600 nm (1,112 km; 691 miles)
Range with internal fuel, 15 min reserves, at 60% power   400 nm (740 km; 460 miles)
Range, 100% power, no reserves
290 nm (537 km; 334 miles)

AEROSPORT
AEROSPORT INC

Box 278, Holly Springs, NC 27540
Telephone: (919) 552 6375
PRESIDENT: E. B. Trent

Aerosport Inc was formed in 1970 by the late Mr H. L. Woods, former chief engineer of Bensen Aircraft Corporation, who designed and built a number of aircraft and air cushion vehicles, including flex-wing and rotating-wing aircraft, and a variety of gliders.

Since that time, the company has marketed plans and kits of a succession of light aircraft designed for construc-

tion by amateurs. Details of those which are still available follow. Construction plans for the Woody Pusher (see 1978-79 *Jane's*) are no longer available from Aerosport.

Aerosport also produces kits for a special agricultural cropspraying version of its single-seat Scamp, known as Scamp B. These kits are delivered to a company based in Colombia, South America, for commercial assembly and sale as completed aircraft. Details can be found in the main Aircraft section of this edition.

AEROSPORT RAIL Mk II

Plans and kits for this single-seat ultra-light aircraft are no longer being marketed. Full details can be found in the 1977-78 *Jane's*.

A new version was expected to be announced in 1980, but no details are currently available.

AEROSPORT QUAIL

Design of the Quail began in January 1970, and construction of the prototype was started in July 1971. It flew for the first time in December 1971, with an all-moving tailplane; but the designers incorporated a fixed-incidence tailplane with elevators before plans and construction kits were made available to amateur constructors. More than 375 sets of plans had been sold by 1980. Approximately 26 Quails are under construction and about ten are flying.
TYPE: Single-seat lightweight cabin monoplane.
WINGS: Cantilever high-wing monoplane. Wing section

Aerocar Micro-Imp, with additional side elevation (bottom) of four-seat Imp
(Michael A. Badrocke)

Aero Design DG-1 with fuselage covering and engine cowls removed

Aero Design DG-1 in revised form with underfuselage airscoop

Aerosport Quail single-seat lightweight cabin monoplane

Aerosport Scamp A single-seat biplane *(Peter M. Bowers)*

NACA 23015. No sweepback. All-metal two-spar structure of 2024-T3 and 6061-T6 light alloy. Plain ailerons of light alloy construction with piano hinge at upper surface. Trailing-edge flaps. Endplates optional.

FUSELAGE: Semi-monocoque all-metal structure of 2024-T3 light alloy.

TAIL UNIT: Cantilever all-metal structure of light alloy, with swept vertical surfaces. Fixed-incidence tailplane. Trim tab on rudder and elevator of prototype; optional for later aircraft.

LANDING GEAR: Non-retractable tricycle type. Cantilever spring main gear struts of light alloy. Nosewheel shock-absorption by rubber in compression. Main wheels and tyres size 5·30 × 4·50-6; nosewheel and tyre size 2·80 × 2·50-4. Tyre pressure 1·38 bars (20 lb/sq in). Barrel-type wheel brakes. Nosewheel steerable. Optional wheel fairings.

POWER PLANT: One 1,600 cc modified Volkswagen motor car engine, driving a 54-36 two-blade fixed-pitch wooden propeller. Provision for installation of Volkswagen engines from 1,500 cc to 1,800 cc capacity. Two fuel tanks in wings, and 7·5 litre (2 US gallon) meter tank, with total capacity of 38 litres (10 US gallons). Refuelling point in top of each wing.

ACCOMMODATION: Single seat in enclosed cabin, which is heated. Door on starboard side is hinged at top and opens upwards. Stowage for 9 kg (20 lb) baggage.

DIMENSIONS, EXTERNAL:
Wing span	7·32 m (24 ft 0 in)
Wing chord, constant	1·07 m (3 ft 6 in)
Wing area, gross	7·8 m² (84 sq ft)
Wing aspect ratio	6·87
Length overall	4·85 m (15 ft 11 in)
Height overall	1·69 m (5 ft 6½ in)
Tailplane span	1·83 m (6 ft 0 in)
Wheel track	1·52 m (5 ft 0 in)
Wheelbase	1·22 m (4 ft 0 in)
Propeller diameter	1·37 m (4 ft 6 in)

WEIGHTS:
Weight empty	242 kg (534 lb)
Normal T-O weight	345 kg (762 lb)
Max T-O weight	359 kg (792 lb)

PERFORMANCE (at max T-O weight):
Max level speed at S/L
113 knots (209 km/h; 130 mph)
Max cruising speed 100 knots (185 km/h; 115 mph)
Econ cruising speed 95·5 knots (177 km/h; 110 mph)
Max manoeuvring speed
78 knots (145 km/h; 90 mph)
Stalling speed, flaps down
42 knots (78 km/h; 48 mph)
Max rate of climb at S/L 259 m (850 ft)/min
Service ceiling (estimated) 3,660 m (12,000 ft)
T-O run 91 m (300 ft)
Landing run 122 m (400 ft)
Range with max fuel, no reserves
200 nm (370 km; 230 miles)

AEROSPORT SCAMP A

The prototype of the single-seat all-metal Scamp A flew for the first time on 21 August 1973. It was intended primarily for operation from grass strips, and tricycle landing gear was chosen as being more rational for a generation of amateur pilots who had received their initial flight training on aircraft equipped with landing gear of this configuration. Stressed to +6g and −3g, the Scamp A can be used for limited aerobatics; and emphasis has been placed on simple construction techniques to make it an easy project for the homebuilder.

Plans and kits of parts, except for the engine, are available to amateur constructors. More than 640 sets of plans had been sold by 1980. At least 12 Scamps are flying and approximately 30 more are under construction from Aerosport kits.

An agricultural cropspraying version, known as Scamp B, is assembled in South America from Aerosport kits and marketed commercially (see under Colombia in main Aircraft section).

TYPE: Single-seat light aircraft.

WINGS: Braced biplane structure, with V-type interplane strut each side. Flying and landing wires of streamline section. Single 5 cm by 12·5 cm (2 in by 5 in) extruded section of 6061-T6 light alloy forms a pylon to support the centre-section of the upper wing. Dihedral 3° on lower wings only. All-metal two-spar structures of light alloy. Plain ailerons of light alloy construction, with piano hinge at upper surface, on upper wing only. No flaps. No trim tabs.

FUSELAGE: Semi-monocoque all-metal structure of light alloy.

TAIL UNIT: Braced T-tail of light alloy construction. Single bracing strut on each side. Fixed-incidence tailplane. Ground-adjustable trim tab on rudder.

LANDING GEAR: Non-retractable tricycle type. Cantilever spring main-gear struts of light alloy. Wheel fairing on each unit optional.

POWER PLANT: Prototype has one 44·5 kW (60 hp) 1,834 cc Volkswagen modified motor car engine. Design suitable for Volkswagen engines of 1,700 cc to 2,100 cc, driving a 56-38 two-blade fixed-pitch wooden propeller. Fuel tank in fuselage nose, aft of firewall, capacity 30·5 litres (8 US gallons). Refuelling point on fuselage upper surface, forward of windscreen.

ACCOMMODATION: Single seat in open cockpit.

DIMENSIONS, EXTERNAL:
Wing span	5·33 m (17 ft 6 in)
Wing chord, constant	0·91 m (3 ft 0 in)
Wing area, gross	9·52 m² (102·5 sq ft)
Length overall	4·27 m (14 ft 0 in)
Height overall	1·69 m (5 ft 6½ in)
Wheel track	1·52 m (5 ft 0 in)
Wheelbase	1·17 m (3 ft 10 in)

WEIGHTS (prototype):
Weight empty	236 kg (520 lb)
Max T-O weight	348 kg (768 lb)

PERFORMANCE (prototype):
Never-exceed speed 108 knots (201 km/h; 125 mph)
Max level speed 82 knots (153 km/h; 95 mph)
Cruising speed 74 knots (137 km/h; 85 mph)
Max manoeuvring speed
72 knots (134 km/h; 83 mph)
Stalling speed 39 knots (73 km/h; 45 mph)
Service ceiling (estimated) 3,660 m (12,000 ft)
T-O run 91 m (300 ft)
Landing run 122 m (400 ft)
Range at cruising speed 130 nm (241 km; 150 miles)

ANDERSON
ANDERSON AIRCRAFT CORPORATION
c/o E. K. Morice Jr, PO Box 2048, Delray Beach, Florida 33444

Telephone: (305) 276 5207

Mr Earl Anderson, a Boeing 747 captain flying for Pan American World Airways, designed and built an original light amphibian which he named EA-1 Kingfisher. The

project occupied a period of nine years from start of design to completion, at a cost of around $5,500, and the first flight was made on 24 April 1969.

After a time, Mr Anderson replaced the original 74·5

kW (100 hp) Continental O-200 engine by an 86 kW (115 hp) Avco Lycoming O-235-C1, driving a Sensenich M76AM-4-44 propeller. With this power plant the Kingfisher has an empty weight of 495 kg (1,092 lb), a max T-O weight of 725 kg (1,600 lb) and improved performance. By January 1975 the prototype had accumulated a total of more than 600 flying hours.

Plans available to amateur constructors cover the increase in weight. The Kingfisher was designed originally to accept alternative power plants up to a maximum of 104·4 kW (140 hp), but on the basis of experience with the 86 kW (115 hp) Avco Lycoming engine, Mr Anderson is discouraging homebuilders from installing more powerful engines than this.

Mr Anderson formed Anderson Aircraft Corporation to market plans of the Kingfisher. By early 1980 well over 200 sets of plans had been sold, and more than 100 Kingfishers were under construction in the USA, Canada, Mexico, Sweden, West Germany and Panama. At least ten homebuilt Kingfishers are known to be flying.

The following details apply to Mr Anderson's Kingfisher in its original configuration:

ANDERSON EA-1 KINGFISHER

TYPE: Two-seat light amphibian.

WINGS: Braced high-wing monoplane with streamline-section Vee bracing struts each side (standard J3, PA-11 or PA-12 Piper Cub wing). Stabilising floats mounted beneath wings, adjacent to wingtips, are constructed of ³/₈ in square mahogany stringers, covered with ¹/₁₆ in mahogany plywood coated with glassfibre. Each float weighs 4·1 kg (9 lb).

FUSELAGE: Conventional flying-boat hull of wooden construction with spruce frames and longerons, covered with ¹/₁₆ in and ¼ in mahogany plywood coated with glassfibre.

TAIL UNIT: Conventional strut-braced tail unit of steel tubing, fabric covered.

LANDING GEAR: Retractable tailwheel type. Each main unit is retracted forward, manually and individually, with spring-loaded assist mechanism. Bungee shock-absorption.

POWER PLANT: One 74·5 kW (100 hp) Continental O-200 flat-four engine, driving a fixed-pitch two-blade tractor propeller. Alternatively an Avco Lycoming O-235-C1 of 86 kW (115 hp) or other engine of up to 112 kW (150 hp), can be fitted. Single fuel tank in hull, immediately forward of windscreen, capacity 76 litres (20 US gallons). Refuelling point on nose. Oil capacity 5·7 litres (1·5 US gallons).

ACCOMMODATION: Two seats, side by side, in enclosed cabin. Piper Tri-Pacer windscreen. Door on port side.

SYSTEM: 30A alternator for radios, lights and starter.

DIMENSIONS, EXTERNAL:
Wing span	11·00 m (36 ft 1 in)
Length overall	7·16 m (23 ft 6 in)
Height overall	2·44 m (8 ft 0 in)
Wheel track	1·52 m (5 ft 0 in)
Propeller diameter	1·83 m (6 ft 0 in)

WEIGHTS:
Weight empty	468 kg (1,032 lb)
Max T-O weight	680 kg (1,500 lb)

PERFORMANCE (at max T-O weight):
Never-exceed speed	104 knots (193 km/h; 120 mph)
Max level speed	104 knots (193 km/h; 120 mph)
Cruising speed at 305 m (1,000 ft)	74 knots (136 km/h; 85 mph)
Stalling speed	39 knots (72·5 km/h; 45 mph)
Max rate of climb at S/L	152-183 m (500-600 ft)/min
Service ceiling	3,050 m (10,000 ft)
T-O run	122-152 m (400-500 ft)
T-O to 15 m (50 ft)	305 m (1,000 ft)
Range with max fuel	173 nm (322 km; 200 miles)

BARNEY OLDFIELD
BARNEY OLDFIELD AIRCRAFT COMPANY

PO Box 5974, Cleveland, Ohio 44101
Telephone: (216) 449 6300
PRESIDENT: Harvey R. Swack
TECHNICAL DIRECTOR: Richard M. Lane

Barney Oldfield Aircraft Co markets plans and material kits for the 'Baby' Lakes, a scaled down version of the Great Lakes Sport Trainer, the prototype of which was designed and built by Mr Andrew Oldfield, who died during 1970. Over 650 sets of drawings had been sold by early 1980, and many 'Baby' Lakes are under construction. About 40 were flying by 1980.

A variant of the 'Baby' Lakes is the 'Super Baby', with a more powerful engine and other modifications. Plans are available and 25 sets had been sold by January 1979. Another new variant of the design is the 'Buddy Baby', of which all known details can be found below.

Under development are inverted oil and fuel systems for the 'Baby' Lakes, so that it can be used as a low-cost aerobatic aircraft. It is stressed for ±9g at the recommended 385 kg (850 lb) gross weight.

OLDFIELD 'BABY' LAKES

TYPE: Single-seat sporting biplane.

WINGS: Braced biplane, with N-type interplane struts, double landing and flying wires and N-type centre-section support struts. Wing section modified M6, tapering to USA 27 46 cm (18 in) from tips. Incidence 2° 30' on top wing, 1° 30' on bottom wing. Wood structure of spruce spars and Warren truss ribs, with overall fabric covering. Ailerons on lower wings only. No flaps.

FUSELAGE: Welded steel tube structure, fabric-covered.

TAIL UNIT: Wire-braced welded steel tube structure, fabric-covered.

LANDING GEAR: Non-retractable tailwheel type. Oleo main legs with size 5·00-4 wheels. Steerable tailwheel.

POWER PLANT: One 59·5 kW (80 hp) Continental A80 flat-four engine, driving a two-blade fixed-pitch propeller. Provision for alternative engines of between 37·25 and 74·5 kW (50 and 100 hp), and several aircraft now under construction will have 1,500 and 1,600 cc Volkswagen engines. Fuel tank in front fuselage, capacity 45 litres (12 US gallons).

ACCOMMODATION: Single seat, normally in open cockpit. Cockpit canopy optional.

DIMENSIONS, EXTERNAL:
Wing span: top	5·08 m (16 ft 8 in)
Wing chord (both wings, constant)	0·91 m (3 ft 0 in)
Wing area, gross	7·99 m² (86 sq ft)
Length overall	4·19 m (13 ft 9 in)
Height overall	1·37 m (4 ft 6 in)

WEIGHTS (A80 engine):
Weight empty	215 kg (475 lb)
Max T-O weight	385 kg (850 lb)

PERFORMANCE (A80 engine, at max T-O weight):
Max level speed at S/L	117 knots (217 km/h; 135 mph)
Cruising speed at S/L	102 knots (190 km/h; 118 mph)
Stalling speed	43·5 knots (81 km/h; 50 mph)
Max rate of climb at S/L	610 m (2,000 ft)/min
Service ceiling	5,200 m (17,000 ft)
T-O run	91 m (300 ft)
Landing run (no brakes)	122 m (400 ft)
Max range	217 nm (400 km; 250 miles)

OLDFIELD 'SUPER BABY' LAKES

Since 1976, a prototype 'Super Baby' Lakes (N362RB), based on the 'Baby' Lakes but with an 85·75 kW (115 hp) Avco Lycoming O-235 flat-four engine, has been under test by its constructors, Mr Ray Ball, Mr Alan Lane and Mr Richard Lane. Following completion of more than 100 flying hours by early 1977, plans were made available to other constructors, with provision for fitting Avco Lycoming engines of 80·5 to 93 kW (108-125 hp). At least two other plans-built 'Super Babies' were flying by early 1980.

The O-235 engine of the prototype drives a 69-54 Met-L-Prop two-blade metal propeller. Other modifications compared with the 'Baby' Lakes include use of a Burtch die spring landing gear, and routed wing spars which allow installation of wing fuel tanks without any appreciable increase in the empty weight by comparison with the wings of a standard 'Baby'. To prevent the possibility of fuel starvation, due to the high acceleration at take-off interupting forward fuel flow from the main tank, a 0·95 litre (1 US quart) header tank is installed forward of the carburettor. Covering is Dacron, finished with Stits Poly-Fiber and Imeron polyurethane colour.

Take-off distances are reduced by 20-25% compared with the 'Baby'. Other data measured with the prototype 'Super Baby' are as follows:

DIMENSIONS, EXTERNAL:
As for 'Baby' Lakes, except:
Length overall	4·34 m (14 ft 3 in)

WEIGHT:
Weight empty	218 kg (480 lb)
Max T-O weight	385 kg (850 lb)

PERFORMANCE:
Max level speed	135 knots (249 km/h; 155 mph) IAS
Cruising speed (75% power)	117 knots (217 km/h; 135 mph) IAS
Stalling speed	48 knots (88·5 km/h; 55 mph) IAS
Max rate of climb at S/L	915 m (3,000 ft)/min
T-O run	69 m (225 ft)
Landing run	130 m (425 ft)
Max range, with wing tanks	260 nm (483 km; 300 miles)

OLDFIELD 'BUDDY BABY' LAKES

Prototype construction and testing of the two-seat 'Buddy Baby' was under way in the first half of 1979, after a one-year delay due to relocation of the technical personnel and construction facilities from New York to Ohio. Flight testing was expected to be completed by the late Summer of 1979.

The 'Buddy Baby' utilises standard 'Baby' wings and tail unit. To prevent a significant increase in wing loading, a 41 cm (16 in) upper wing centre-section has been introduced, together with short stub-wings built integrally with the fuselage to increase the lower span by a similar amount.

The fuselage is a completely new design, which has been widened and stretched only enough to permit seating positions for two average-sized (77 kg; 170 lb) people in a configuration much like that of a 'buddy seat' on a motorcycle. Dual throttle and rudder pedals are provided, with a single dual-position joystick. The aircraft is flown solo from the rear seat and dual from the front position.

BARTON
WAYNE F. BARTON

11145 Cherokee Street, Northglenn, Colorado 80234
Telephone: (303) 452 8784

BARTON SYLKIE ONE MODEL B-1

Mr Wayne Barton, a pattern maker, has built a light aircraft known as the Sylkie One. Design and construction began in September 1966, and total cost of building was $6,600. First flight was made in April 1975. Plans were expected to be available to amateur builders by late 1979.

TYPE: Two-seat light aircraft.

WINGS: Cantilever tapered low-wing monoplane. Wing section NACA 23015 at root, NACA 23010 at tip. Dihedral from roots. Incidence 3° at root, 1° at tip. Spruce and mahogany structure, birch plywood and Dacron covered, with Butarae dope finish. Frise-type slotted ailerons and slotted flaps, of similar construction to wings. Trim tab on aileron.

FUSELAGE: Conventional spruce and mahogany truss structure, Dacron covered and dope finished.

TAIL UNIT: Cantilever structure, of similar construction to wings. Fin integral with fuselage. All-moving tailplane, with full-span trim/anti-servo tabs.

LANDING GEAR: Tricycle type, with spring-assisted mechanical retraction. Main wheels retract inward, nosewheel rearward. Steerable nosewheel. Shock-absorption by steel spring, with oil damping. Single Cleveland wheel on each unit, size 5·00-5, with 36 cm (14·2 in) diameter tyre. Tyre pressure: Main wheels 2·41 bars (35 lb/sq in), nosewheel 1·72 bars (25 lb/sq in). Cleveland hydraulic brakes.

POWER PLANT: One 112 kW (150 hp) Avco Lycoming O-320 flat-four engine, driving a two-blade wooden fixed-pitch propeller. Two fuel tanks forward of instrument panel, each with capacity of 26·5 litres (7 US gallons), and one glassfibre fuel tank aft of seat, capacity 106 litres (28 US gallons). Refuelling point on starboard side of fuselage. Oil capacity 7·5 litres (2 US gallons).

ACCOMMODATION: Two seats side by side under rearward-sliding transparent canopy. Baggage space aft of seat.

SYSTEM: 12V battery and 40A alternator.

AVIONICS: Genave 200B radio.

DIMENSIONS, EXTERNAL:
Wing span	7·57 m (24 ft 10 in)
Wing area, gross	10·22 m² (110 sq ft)
Wing chord at root	1·60 m (5 ft 3 in)
Wing chord at tip	0·76 m (2 ft 6 in)
Length overall	6·27 m (20 ft 7 in)
Height overall	2·14 m (7 ft 0½ in)
Tailplane span	2·67 m (8 ft 9 in)
Wheel track	2·43 m (7 ft 11¾ in)
Wheelbase	1·16 m (3 ft 9¾ in)
Propeller diameter	1·83 m (6 ft 0 in)

WEIGHTS:
Weight empty	463 kg (1,020 lb)
Max T-O weight	735 kg (1,620 lb)

PERFORMANCE:
Max level speed at 5,180 m (17,000 ft)	203 knots (376 km/h; 234 mph)
Max cruising speed at 2,440 m (8,000 ft)	167 knots (309 km/h; 192 mph)
Econ cruising speed at 2,440 m (8,000 ft)	148 knots (273 km/h; 170 mph)
Stalling speed, flaps down	43·5 knots (81 km/h; 50 mph) IAS
Max rate of climb at S/L	580 m (1,900 ft)/min
Service ceiling	over 5,790 m (19,000 ft)
T-O run at 1,735 m (5,700 ft)	564 m (1,850 ft)
T-O to 15 m (50 ft) at 1,735 m (5,700 ft)	823 m (2,700 ft)
Landing from 15 m (50 ft)	700 m (2,300 ft)
Landing run	366 m (1,200 ft)
Range with max fuel, 30 min reserves	833 nm (1,545 km; 960 miles)

Anderson EA-1 Kingfisher amphibian *(Howard Levy)*

Barton Sylkie One Model B-1 light aircraft

Oldfield 'Baby' Lakes built by Mr Jerry Rodgers of Los Angeles
(Continental A75 engine) *(Henry Artof)*

First Oldfield 'Super Baby' Lakes, built by Mr Ray Ball, Mr Alan Lane and Mr Richard Lane

Bensen B-8MJ jump take-off Gyro-Copter

Bensen Model B-8W Hydro-Glider being towed by a motorboat

BENSEN
BENSEN AIRCRAFT CORPORATION
Box 31047, Raleigh-Durham Airport, Raleigh, North Carolina 27612
Telephone: (919) 787-4224/0945
PRESIDENT: Dr Igor B. Bensen, PE

The Bensen Aircraft Corporation was formed by Dr Igor B. Bensen, formerly Chief of Research of the Kaman company, to develop a series of lightweight autogyros and rotary-wing gliders suitable for production in kit form for amateur construction as well as in ready-to-fly condition. According to Bensen, approximately 3,000 to 5,000 of these aircraft have been built and flown.

Production is centred on the B-8M/V and Super Bug Gyro-Copter powered autogyros, the twin-engined B-16S Gyro-Copter, and various land and waterborne versions of the B-8 rotor-kite. Research into new models and concepts continues, and Bensen has announced important new second-generation versions of the Gyro-Copter that are capable of 'jump' take-off and of hovering flight.

BENSEN MODEL B-8 GYRO-GLIDER
The Gyro-Glider is a simple unpowered rotor-kite which can be towed behind even a small motorcar and has achieved free gliding with the towline released. It is available as either a completed aircraft or kit of parts for amateur construction. Alternatively, would-be constructors can purchase a set of plans, with building and flying instructions. No pilot's licence is required to fly it in the United States and many hundreds of kits and plans have been sold.

The original Model B-7 Gyro-Glider was described in the 1958-59 *Jane's*. It was followed by the Model B-8, which is offered as either a single-seater or two-seater, the latter version being suitable for use as a pilot trainer.

The Model B-8 consists basically of an inverted square-section tubular aluminium T-frame structure, of which the forward arm supports the lightweight seat, towing arm, rudder bar and landing gear nosewheel. The rear arm supports a large stabilising fin and rudder, made normally of plywood, but optionally of metal. The main landing gear wheels are carried on a tubular axle near the junction of the T-frame. The free-turning two-blade rotor is universally-mounted at the top of the T-frame and is normally operated directly by a hanging-stick control. A floor-type control column is available as optional equipment. Pedal controls for the rudder are standard.

The Gyro-Glider rotor is made normally of laminated plywood, with a steel spar. Factory-built all-metal rotor blades are available as optional items.

The two-seat trainer version of the Gyro-Glider is fitted with castoring crosswind landing gear and has an extra-wide wheel track. It will maintain level flight down to 16·5 knots (30·5 km/h; 19 mph).

DIMENSIONS, EXTERNAL:
Diameter of rotor	6·10 m (20 ft 0 in)
Length of fuselage	3·45 m (11 ft 4 in)
Height overall	1·90 m (6 ft 3 in)

BENSEN MODEL B-8W HYDRO-GLIDER
The basic structure of this floatplane rotor-kite is similar to that of the B-8 Gyro-Glider and conversion from one to the other is simple. Main change is that the nosewheel landing gear is replaced by two floats. The original round-type floats have been superseded by flat-bottomed pontoons of polyurethane foam covered by glassfibre, which give better planing, with less spray.

The Hydro-Glider is towed by a motorboat.

BENSEN MODEL B-8M, B-8V and SUPER BUG GYRO-COPTERS and B-8MW HYDRO-COPTER
First flown on 6 December 1955, the Gyro-Copter is a powered autogyro conversion of the Gyro-Glider, designed for home construction from kits or plans. When fitted with floats it is known as a Hydro-Copter.

The current **B-8M** version of the Gyro-Copter has a more powerful engine than the original B-7M and can be equipped with an optional mechanical rotor drive. By engaging this drive, the rotor can be accelerated to flying speed while the aircraft is stationary. Then, by transferring the power to the pusher propeller, it is possible to take off in only 15 m (50 ft), with the rotor autorotating normally. Alternatively, a 1 hp Ohlsson & Rice Compact III two-stroke engine can be attached to the rotor for pre-rotation, automatically disengaging itself at take-off rpm.

Other non-standard items available optionally include a 67 kW (90 hp) engine instead of the normal 53·5 kW (72 hp) engine, a stronger aluminium bolted-together engine mounting, a larger-diameter rotor, an offset gimbal rotor head, a redundant mast consisting of a pair of closely matched alloy tubes instead of the normal square-tube mast, a floor-type control column instead of the normal overhead type of column, dual ignition, nosewheel arrester, Bensen-manufactured pontoons of polyurethane foam covered with glassfibre, and a detachable glassfibre open cabin nacelle for single-seat Gyro-Copters of 1976 or later type (only with redundant mast and aluminium engine mount of new design). All-metal rotor blades and tail surfaces are available as alternatives to the standard wooden components.

The prototype Model B-8M Gyro-Copter flew for the first time on 8 July 1957 and the first production model on 9 October 1957.

The B-8M is roadable, requiring no removal of, or changes in, its equipment for transition from air to ground travel. The rotor is merely stopped in a fore-and-aft position by a lock. Gyro-Copters have been driven on highways and have negotiated heavy city traffic with ease in a number of public demonstrations in the USA.

The **B-8V**, which flew for the first time in the Autumn of 1967, is basically a standard B-8M, but is powered by a 1,600 cc Volkswagen engine. In unmodified form the

VW1600 yields just adequate flight performance at 272 kg (600 lb) gross weight. Since Bensen engineers considered that most Gyro-Copters would not have a gross weight as high as 600 lb, the VW engine justified inclusion as an alternative power plant to the standard McCulloch engine.

Kits and parts for the B-8V, excluding engine and mounting, are available, as are plans and an instruction manual for converting the B-8M to a B-8V, or for mounting a VW engine on a standard B-8 airframe.

In May 1971, Bensen announced introduction of the **Super Bug**, an advanced version of the standard Model B-8M. This features a twin-engine installation to spin up the rotor prior to take-off. Bensen claims this as an intermediate step towards full VTOL capability, as this more powerful pre-rotation enables the Super Bug to take off and clear a 15 m (50 ft) obstacle within 137 m (450 ft) of starting its T-O run in zero wind conditions at max T-O weight. Other standard equipment of the Super Bug includes rotor brake, parking brake on main wheels, single control of rudder and nosewheel steering, soft suspension of the auxiliary tailwheel and an increase of 45·5 kg (100 lb) in max T-O weight.

In July 1979 it was announced that Bensen was to begin marketing a 'Gold Seal' kit containing all the component parts, including engine, necessary to construct a standard Gyro-Copter. Retail price was stated to be $6,995, and a fixed-price interest-free instalment plan spanning 28 months was to be offered. The price included a pre-flight checkout of the completed aircraft by an authorised Bensen dealer, and flying instruction for the builder.

The following description applies to the Models B-8M and B-8V:

TYPE: Single-seat light autogyro.

ROTOR SYSTEM: B-8M has single two-blade rotor of laminated plywood construction, with steel spar (optional all-metal rotor). Blade section Bensen G2. Teetering hub, with no lag hinges or collective pitch control. A similar rotor, of all-metal construction, is provided for the B-8V. A larger-diameter rotor is not available as an alternative for this latter model. No anti-torque rotor. Rotor speed 400 rpm.

ROTOR DRIVE (optional): An auxiliary 0·75 kW (1 hp) Ohlsson & Rice engine is available to spin up the rotor.

FUSELAGE: Square-section tubular 6061-T6 aluminium structure. Optional redundant twin rotor mast of alloy tubes.

TAIL SURFACES: Vertical fin and rudder of ¼ in plywood. Optional all-metal tail surfaces.

LANDING GEAR: Non-retractable tricycle type, with auxiliary tailwheel. No shock-absorbers. Steerable nosewheel. General Tire wheels, size 30·5-10·15 cm (12-4 in). Tyre pressure 0·69 bars (10 lb/sq in). Brake on nosewheel. Optional skis.

POWER PLANT: One 53·5 kW (72 hp) McCulloch Model 4318AX flat-four two-stroke engine (or, optionally, a 67 kW; 90 hp McCulloch 4318GX engine of similar weight and dimensions), driving a two-blade wooden fixed-pitch Aero Prop Model BA 48-A2 propeller with leading-edges covered with stainless steel. Alternatively, one 47·5 kW (64 hp) Volkswagen 1,600 cc flat-four four-stroke engine, driving a Troyer Model 50-24-65 two-blade wooden fixed-pitch pusher propeller. Fuel tank under pilot's seat, capacity 22·75 litres (6·0 US gallons). Can be fitted with auxiliary tank for ferrying. Optional plastics tank shaped as pilot's seat, replacing standard tank and seat and increasing fuel capacity to 36·5 litres (9·7 US gallons).

ACCOMMODATION: Open seat. Overhead azimuth stick and rudder pedal controls. Optional floor-type control column. Safety belt. Optional glassfibre open cabin nacelle.

DIMENSIONS, EXTERNAL:

Diameter of rotor:		
standard	6·10 m	(20 ft 0 in)
optional (on B-8M and B-8MW)	6·70 m	(22 ft 0 in)
Rotor blade chord	0·18 m	(7 in)
Length of fuselage	3·45 m	(11 ft 4 in)
Height overall	1·90 m	(6 ft 3 in)
Wheel track	1·52 m	(5 ft 0 in)
Propeller diameter:		
53·5 kW (72 hp) McCulloch	1·22 m	(4 ft 0 in)
47·5 kW (64 hp) Volkswagen	1·27 m	(4 ft 2 in)

AREAS (standard rotor):

Rotor blades (each)	0·54 m²	(5·83 sq ft)
Rotor disc	29·17 m²	(314 sq ft)

WEIGHTS (standard rotor):

Weight empty:		
B-8M	112 kg	(247 lb)
B-8V	158 kg	(348 lb)
Max T-O weight:		
B-8M	227 kg	(500 lb)
B-8V	272 kg	(600 lb)

PERFORMANCE (at max T-O weight, with standard rotor):

Max level speed at S/L:		
B-8M	74 knots	(137 km/h; 85 mph)
B-8V	52 knots	(96·5 km/h; 60 mph)
Max cruising speed at S/L:		
B-8M	52 knots	(96·5 km/h; 60 mph)
B-8V	43 knots	(80·5 km/h; 50 mph)
Econ cruising speed:		
B-8M, B-8V	39 knots	(72·5 km/h; 45 mph)
Min speed in level flight:		
B-8M	13 knots	(24 km/h; 15 mph)
B-8V	17·5 knots	(32 km/h; 20 mph)
T-O speed at S/L:		
B-8M	17·5 knots	(32 km/h; 20 mph)
B-8V	22 knots	(40 km/h; 25 mph)
Landing speed:		
B-8M	6 knots	(11·5 km/h; 7 mph)
B-8V	9 knots	(16 km/h; 10 mph)
Max rate of climb at S/L:		
B-8M	305 m	(1,000 ft)/min
B-8V	198 m	(650 ft)/min
Service ceiling:		
B-8M	3,800 m	(12,500 ft)
B-8V	2,440 m	(8,000 ft)
T-O run, unpowered rotor, zero wind:		
B-8M	92 m	(300 ft)
B-8V	122 m	(400 ft)
T-O run, powered rotor, zero wind:		
B-8M	15 m	(50 ft)
Landing run in 9 knot (16 km/h; 10 mph) wind:		
B-8M, B-8V		0 ft
Landing run in zero wind:		
B-8M	6 m	(20 ft)
B-8V	7·5 m	(25 ft)
Normal range:		
B-8M	86 nm	(160 km; 100 miles)
B-8V	130 nm	(241 km; 150 miles)
Ferry range:		
B-8M	260 nm	(482 km; 300 miles)
B-8V	345 nm	(643 km; 400 miles)
Endurance:		
B-8M		1·5 h
B-8V		2·25 h

BENSEN MODEL B-8HD

This 1979 Bensen Gyro-Copter is based on the Super Bug design, but uses hydraulic drive (hence the HD designation) to feed about 3 kW (4 hp) from the main engine to the rotor, instead of having a separate engine for pre-rotation. The rotor is thus engaged continuously during all aspects of flight. This is reported to give the aircraft a take-off run of less than 61 m (200 ft), and to improve climb and range, while allowing an increase in payload. A near-vertical landing is also possible.

The hydraulic drive is expected to be marketed as a retrofit kit for the current B-8M.

BENSEN B-8MJ

Bensen Aircraft Corporation announced in early 1977 that it was to market a Power Head to fit any standard B-8M Gyro-Copter, enabling the aircraft to take off without any ground roll. The Power Head is claimed to provide a 30° angle of climb. Hovering cannot be achieved.

Power Heads are offered only to builders or owners of Gyro-Copters with 50 or more hours of solo flight. The resulting aircraft are designated B-8MJ (for 'Jump' take-off).

BENSEN MODEL B-8MH HOVER-GYRO

Demonstrated in public for the first time in 1976, the B-8MH is described as a 'Hovering Gyro-Copter', a capability reflected by the 'H' in its designation.

Development dates from 1973. On 29 June that year, Dr Igor Bensen piloted a Gyro-Glider with two two-blade co-axial rotors during its first flight at Raleigh-Durham Airport. Nineteen further flights followed, during which the aircraft executed a full range of flight manoeuvres.

In the B-8MH the lower two-blade rotor is driven by a vertically-mounted engine; the upper rotor autorotates. A small engine mounted immediately forward of the tail-fin drives a pusher propeller.

Able to be built as a conversion of the standard B-8M Gyro-Copter, the B-8MH can fly forwards, sideways and backwards, as well as being able to hover. It is claimed to be safer than either an aeroplane or a helicopter, as it will not stall or spin and does not need any special skill to land with the engine stopped. A detachable glassfibre cabin enclosure is optional on the standard single-seater. Conversion to a side-by-side two-seat configuration for pilot training is quick and easy.

POWER PLANT: One 52·2-82 kW (70-110 hp) modified watercooled outboard engine, driving the lower two-blade main rotor. Upper rotor autorotates. One 10·4 kW (14 hp) modified aircooled go-kart engine driving a two-blade pusher propeller mounted at rear. Fuel consumption at cruising speed, 19 litres (5 US gallons) per hour.

DIMENSIONS, EXTERNAL:

Rotor diameter (each)	8·53 m	(28 ft 0 in)
Height overall	2·74 m	(9 ft 0 in)
Width overall	2·13 m	(7 ft 0 in)

WEIGHTS:

Max T-O weight		408 kg (900 lb)
Useful load		136 kg (300 lb)

PERFORMANCE:

Max cruising speed	56·5 knots	(105 km/h; 65 mph)
Range at optimum cruising speed		
	104 nm	(193 km; 120 miles)
Hovering endurance		45 min

BIRDMAN
BIRDMAN INC

701-B Glades Court, Port Orange, Florida 32019
Telephone: (904) 761 7672
PRESIDENT: Leonard I. Roberts
ENGINEERING: J. G. Ladesic
PRODUCTION: A. Kennan
SALES: J. Roberts

Birdman Aircraft Inc has developed an ultra lightweight sporting aircraft which, despite a wing span of 10·36 m (34 ft 0 in), has an empty weight of only 55·5 kg (122 lb) in its current form. The company's aim was to design a strong, lightweight and inexpensive aircraft that could be assembled easily by a novice builder. In achieving this aim, it introduced some unusual ideas and construction materials. The covering, for example, consists of a bi-axially orientated synthetic film known as aircraft Monokote, and this offers the key to the combination of light weight and strength. The airframe separates into four sections (wings, centre-sections, and tail cone/tail unit), for transporting and storage. Reassembly takes about 30 minutes.

Design of what proved to be the world's lightest powered aircraft, known as the Birdman TL-1, with an empty weight of 45 kg (100 lb) in prototype form, began in April 1969. The first flight was recorded almost six years later, on 25 January 1975, after considerable structural research and testing. The company is marketing the aircraft in kit form, with all materials, components, engine and accessories provided, together with plans for its construction and a builder's manual. Time of construction for the average person is 300 working hours or less, using home tools

only. First orders were taken in June 1975 and by early 1980 a total of 458 kits had been sold. One hundred and eighty-six TL-1As were then flying.

BIRDMAN TL-1A

The prototype TL-1 (N111ET) had full-span trailing-edge flaps. These were deleted on the TL-1A production version, which also has a V-tail instead of the T-tail fitted to the prototype. Current power plant is a Chrysler Power Bee, which replaces the earlier 8·5 kW (11·5 hp) McCulloch MC-101. The noise level is much reduced by this installation.

TYPE: Ultra lightweight sporting aircraft.

WINGS: Cantilever monoplane, built in three sections, with detachable outer panels. Wing section USA 35B modified. Thickness/chord ratio 14%. Dihedral on outer wing panels 5°. Incidence 3°. No sweepback. Composite structure, with single built-up spruce spar, wooden ribs, leading-edge D cell of reinforced expanded synthetic foam and aircraft Monokote covering. No ailerons. Sequentially-operated spoilers, immediately aft of main spar, for both yaw and roll control; the more the stick is moved, the more panels come into operation.

FUSELAGE: Three-part structure: forward portion of riveted semi-monocoque 2024-T3 light alloy, centre section of spruce and plywood, and an aft section comprising a tapered plywood monocoque.

TAIL UNIT: Braced V-tail. Two-spar structure with laminated plywood ribs and aircraft Monokote covering. No rudders.

LANDING GEAR: Non-retractable main units only, sited at point of balance. Pilot's legs and feet substitute as retractable nose gear. Castor at aft end of fuselage to support aircraft on ground. Shock-absorption by rubber bungee. Main-wheel tyres size 12 × 1·25, pressure 3·10 bars (45 lb/sq in). No brakes.

POWER PLANT: One 7·4 kW (10 hp) Chrysler Power Bee two-stroke engine, pylon-mounted from centre-section structure aft of pilot, and driving a two-blade fixed-pitch laminated wood pusher propeller through a 2·65:1 reduction gear. Fuel contained in one (normal) or two (auxiliary) aluminium tanks with combined capacity of 15 litres (4 US gallons). Lubricating oil mixed in fuel at ratio of 1 : 16. Standard recoil starter.

ACCOMMODATION: Exposed seat of aluminium tube and cloth, with harness, adjustable to allow pilot to fly the aircraft in an upright or semi-reclining position.

DIMENSIONS, EXTERNAL:

Wing span	10·36 m	(34 ft 0 in)
Wing chord, constant	1·30 m	(4 ft 3 in)
Wing area, gross	13·42 m²	(144·5 sq ft)
Wing aspect ratio		8
Length overall	5·92 m	(19 ft 5 in)
Height overall, tail up	2·18 m	(7 ft 2 in)
Tailplane span	2·59 m	(8 ft 6 in)
Wheel track	1·83 m	(6 ft 0 in)
Propeller diameter	1·07 m	(3 ft 6 in)

WEIGHTS:

Weight empty		55·5 kg (122 lb)
Normal T-O and landing weight		131 kg (288 lb)
Max T-O and landing weight		159 kg (350 lb)

Bensen Hover-Gyro, with co-axial rotors, being flight tested

Bensen Model B-8MW Hydro-Copter

Bensen B-8M Gyro-Copter constructed from a 'Gold Seal' kit

Bensen Model B-8HD hydraulic drive Gyro-Copter

Birdman TL-1A ultra-light homebuilt aircraft

Bond Sky Dancer single-seat gyroplane

PERFORMANCE (at max T-O weight):
Never-exceed speed 60·5 knots (112 km/h; 70 mph)
Max level speed at S/L
  56·5 knots (104 km/h; 65 mph)
Max cruising speed at 1,980 m (6,500 ft)
  48 knots (88 km/h; 55 mph)

Econ cruising speed at 1,220 m (4,000 ft)
  35 knots (64 km/h; 40 mph)
Stalling speed 12 knots (22·5 km/h; 14 mph)
Max rate of climb at S/L 152 m (500 ft)/min
Service ceiling 2,800 m (9,200 ft)
T-O run 26 m (85 ft)

T-O to 15 m (50 ft) 61 m (200 ft)
Landing from 15 m (50 ft) 30 m (100 ft)
Landing run 14 m (45 ft)
Min field length 61 m (200 ft)
Normal range 173·5 nm (322 km; 200 miles)
g limits ±6

BOND
JOHN BOND
c/o Hollmann Aircraft, 11082 Bel Aire Court, Cupertino, California 95014

BOND SKY DANCER

Mr John Bond has designed and built the prototype of a gyroplane known now as the Sky Dancer. Design was originated in 1971, construction beginning during 1972. Flown for the first time in 1973, its extremely low disc

loading and high thrust-to-weight ratio has enabled this homebuilt aircraft to demonstrate outstanding performance. Plans of the Sky Dancer are available to amateur builders from Hollmann Aircraft at the above address.
TYPE: Single-seat ultralight gyroplane.
ROTOR SYSTEM: Two-blade teetering rotor of modified NACA 4412 blade section. Rotordyne blades of 6061-T6 light alloy retained to hub by steel straps. Blades can be folded. No rotor brake.
FUSELAGE: Welded structure of 4130 steel tube, integrat-

ing landing gear, rotor pylon, pilot's seat structure, engine mounting and tail support booms.
TAIL UNIT: Fixed horizontal surface and fin, with conventional rudder, all constructed of glassfibre with foam core.
LANDING GEAR: Non-retractable tricycle type, with additional small tail bumper wheel. Shock-absorption of main wheels by coil spring in compression; tailwheel carried on spring steel arm. Steerable nosewheel. Main-wheel tyres 33 cm (13 in) diameter, pressure 1·52

bars (22 lb/sq in). Nosewheel tyre 28 cm (11 in) diameter, pressure 1·38 bars (20 lb/sq in). Fairings over main wheels.

POWER PLANT: One 67 kW (90 hp) RevMaster modified Volkswagen 2,100 cc motor car engine, driving a two-blade fixed-pitch pusher propeller manufactured by Troyer Boats. Fuel tank above engine, capacity 22·7 litres (6 US gallons). Refuelling point on tank. Oil capacity 2·8 litres (0·75 US gallons).

ACCOMMODATION: Pilot only, on exposed seat, immediately forward of rotor pylon.

DIMENSIONS, EXTERNAL:

Rotor diameter	7·01 m (23 ft 0 in)
Blade chord, constant	0·17 m (6¾ in)
Rotor disc	38·60 m² (415·5 sq ft)
Length of fuselage	3·30 m (10 ft 10 in)
Width, rotors folded	1·65 m (5 ft 5 in)
Height to top of rotor hub	2·02 m (6 ft 7½ in)
Wheel track	1·52 m (5 ft 0 in)
Propeller diameter	1·27 m (4 ft 2 in)

WEIGHTS:

Weight empty	127 kg (280 lb)
Max fuel weight	18 kg (40 lb)

Max T-O weight	245 kg (540 lb)

PERFORMANCE (at max T-O weight):
Never-exceed and max level speed
82 knots (153 km/h; 95 mph)
Max cruising speed at S/L
65 knots (121 km/h; 75 mph)
Econ cruising speed at S/L
48 knots (89 km/h; 55 mph)

Max rate of climb at S/L	366 m (1,200 ft)/min
Service ceiling	4,875 m (16,000 ft)
T-O run	46 m (150 ft)
Range with max fuel	104 nm (193 km; 120 miles)

BOWERS
PETER M. BOWERS
10458 16th Avenue South, Seattle, Washington 98168

Mr Peter Bowers, an aeronautical engineer with Boeing in Seattle, is a principal source of detailed information on vintage aircraft in the United States, and has provided much of the data for a number of replicas of first World War aircraft now under construction or flying.

Mr Bowers has built a number of aircraft himself. In particular, he designed and constructed prototypes of a single-seat light aircraft known as the Fly Baby, which is flying in both monoplane and biplane forms, and a side-by-side two-seat light monoplane named Namu II.

BOWERS FLY BABY 1-A
The prototype Fly Baby monoplane was produced to compete in an Experimental Aircraft Association design contest, organised to encourage the development of a simple, low-cost, easy-to-fly aeroplane that could be built by inexperienced amateurs for recreational flying. It was built in 720 working hours, at a cost of $1,050, and flew for the first time on 27 July 1960. As only one other aircraft was completed by the specified closing date, the contest was postponed for two years.

When the EAA contest was finally held in the Summer of 1962, Fly Baby was placed first and won a prize of $2,500. Home construction plans of the aircraft are available and 3,925 sets had been sold by May 1980. Construction of well over 700 Fly Babies is known to have been undertaken, of which 366 had been completed and flown by 1980, including some based on detailed drawings and instructions published in *Sport Aviation*, journal of the EAA.

The Fly Baby monoplane has been tested as a twin-float seaplane, in which configuration it has a max AUW of 454 kg (1,000 lb) and cruising speed of 84 knots (156 km/h; 97 mph).

During 1968, Mr Bowers designed and built biplane wings for the Fly Baby, which are interchangeable with the monoplane wings. The monoplane version is known as the Fly Baby 1-A, and the biplane as the Fly Baby 1-B (described separately).

Mr Bowers amended his plans during 1973 to allow for construction of a two-seat version of the Fly Baby. The changes include a 0·97 m (3 ft 2 in) wide fuselage, a 1·52 m (5 ft 0 in) span wing centre-section to support a shock-absorbing landing gear similar to that of the Ryan ST/PT-22 of 1934-42, the use of heavier flying wires with swaged fork ends, a raised aft turtledeck to offset the drag of the larger cockpit and a recommendation to use an engine of 63·5 to 80 kW (85 to 107 hp). The outer wing panels are unchanged, giving the two-seat Fly Baby a span of 9·45 m (31 ft 0 in) and wing area of 12·4 m² (133·5 sq ft).

Mr Bowers feels that the use of side-by-side seating is a great performance handicap to the basic design, and approves the tandem arrangement worked out by Mr Vic-

tor F. Meznarsic (see accompanying illustration). At present, he is developing a stretched tandem two-seater, to be fitted with longer two-bay biplane wings, in a deliberate attempt to resemble a First World War type such as the B.E.2C. This will be a low-performance 'fun flier' on engines up to 74·5 kW (100 hp), and will not be aerobatic.

Because of the shortage of aircraft engines in the 48·5-63·5 kW (65-85 hp) range, Mr Bowers has been asked repeatedly by would-be builders about the suitability of Volkswagen conversions for the Fly Baby. He has consistently recommended against this, but now that a Finnish constructor has had some success, first with a 1,600 cc and later with an 1,800 cc conversion, Mr Bowers approves the use of VW engines of over 1,800 cc.

The following description applies to the original single-seat Fly Baby 1-A:

TYPE: Single-seat light monoplane.
WINGS: Wire-braced low-wing monoplane. Double ½ in 1 × 19 stainless steel bracing wires. Wing section NACA 4412. Wooden two-spar structure, covered with Dacron fabric and finished with two coats of nitrate dope and one coat of automotive enamel. Wings rotate about a special fitting to fold back alongside the fuselage for towing.
FUSELAGE: Conventional plywood-covered wood structure of rectangular section. Decking behind cockpit, including pilot's headrest, is removable and can be replaced with higher transparent section matched with a sliding transparent cockpit canopy for enclosed cockpit operation.
TAIL UNIT: Wire-braced wood structure, fabric-covered.
LANDING GEAR: Non-retractable tailwheel type. Main landing gear struts of laminated wood, braced by crossed steel wires. Steel tube straight-across axle faired with streamline-section steel tube. Ends of axles project beyond wheel hubs to serve as anchor points for wing bracing wires. Shock-absorption by low-pressure 8·00-4 tyres, carried on Piper Cub wheels, with hydraulic brakes.
POWER PLANT: One 63·5 kW (85 hp) Continental C75 flat-four engine, driving a two-blade fixed-pitch propeller. Fuel tank from Piper J-3 Cub, capacity 60·5 litres (16 US gallons).
ACCOMMODATION: Single seat in open or enclosed cockpit. Baggage in underfuselage 'tank' which can be removed and carried like a suitcase.
DIMENSIONS, EXTERNAL:

Wing span	8·53 m (28 ft 0 in)
Wing chord, constant	1·37 m (4 ft 6 in)
Length overall	5·64 m (18 ft 6 in)
Height, wings folded	1·98 m (6 ft 6 in)

WEIGHTS:

Weight empty	274 kg (605 lb)
Max T-O weight	419 kg (924 lb)

PERFORMANCE (at max T-O weight):
Max level speed at S/L
over 104 knots (193 km/h; 120 mph)

Cruising speed
91-96 knots (169-177 km/h; 105-110 mph)

Landing speed	39 knots (72·5 km/h; 45 mph)
Max rate of climb at S/L	335 m (1,100 ft)/min
T-O and landing run	76 m (250 ft)
Range with max fuel	277 nm (515 km; 320 miles)

BOWERS FLY BABY 1-B
During 1968 Mr Bowers designed and built a set of interchangeable biplane wings for the original prototype Fly Baby and with these fitted it flew for the first time on 27 March 1969. About four more biplanes, designated Fly Baby 1-B, have been completed and flown.

The biplane wings have the same aerofoil section and incidence as those of the monoplane version, but the rib webs are made of 1/16 in instead of 1/8 in plywood and the wingtip bows are formed from ½ in aluminium tube instead of laminated wood strips. This lightweight construction limits weight increase to only 21 kg (46 lb) for an increase of 2·79 m² (30 sq ft) in wing area. Span is reduced by 1·83 m (6 ft) and chord by 0·30 m (1 ft). Ailerons are fitted to the lower wings only.

To facilitate entry to the cockpit the upper wing has been located well forward, and in order to bring the centre of lift in line with the original CG, both planes have been given 11° of sweepback. Changeover from monoplane to biplane configuration can be accomplished by two people in approximately one hour.

The biplane is intended to use the same engines as the monoplane, for which Mr Bowers does not recommend anything heavier than the Continental O-200. Since some biplane builders have desired to use the 93 kW (125 hp) Avco Lycoming O-290, a modification has been authorised for the biplane, whereby the wing sweep is decreased by 5° for CG reasons.

TYPE: Single-seat light biplane.
WINGS: Forward-stagger single-bay biplane with N-type interplane and centre-section struts. Landing and flying bracing wires. Sweepback 11°. Wooden structure with Dacron covering. Rib webs constructed of 1/16 in plywood, wingtip bows formed of ½ in aluminium tube. Ailerons on lower wings only.
POWER PLANT: One 63·5 kW (85 hp) Continental C85 flat-four engine.
DIMENSIONS, EXTERNAL:

Wing span	6·71 m (22 ft 0 in)
Wing chord, both wings, constant	1·07 m (3 ft 6 in)
Wing area, gross	13·94 m² (150 sq ft)
Height overall	2·08 m (6 ft 10 in)

WEIGHTS:

Weight empty	295 kg (651 lb)
Max T-O weight	440 kg (972 lb)

PERFORMANCE (at max T-O weight):

Cruising speed	75·5 knots (140 km/h; 87 mph)
Max rate of climb at S/L	267 m (875 ft)/min

BROKAW
BROKAW AVIATION INC
2625 Johnson Point, Leesburg, Florida 32748
Telephone: (904) 787 2329
PRESIDENT: Bergon F. Brokaw, MD, FACFP

BROKAW BULLET
Dr B. F. Brokaw, a former US Navy pilot, and Dr E. Jones, who has a PhD in aeronautical engineering, combined their talents to design and build a low-wing monoplane which was claimed to be the world's fastest two-seat homebuilt. Dr Brokaw was concerned primarily with overall design and construction, Dr Jones with stress analysis and structural design.

Basic intention was to develop a high-speed all-weather two-seat homebuilt suitable for cross-country flying. Aerobatic potential was of secondary consideration, but the Bullet, which was known originally as the BJ-520, is stressed to ±6g for aerobatics and 9g ultimate.

Design began in August 1966 and construction of the prototype started six months later. First flight was made on 18 November 1972, and during the Summer of 1973 work was carried out to clean up the airframe to take better advantage of the design potential. This included the provision of wheel-well doors, and reduction of the drag of the engine cooling system, achieved by the use of baffles, ducts and direct ram-air cooling.

Further major redesign and modification were undertaken in 1976, and the prototype resumed flying in 1977 as the Bullet. The latest refinements include changes to the wing span and section, and power plant, as described below. (For performance and other data relating to the original version, powered by a 212·5 kW (285 hp) Continental TSIO-520-B turbocharged engine, see 1975-76 *Jane's*.) By early 1980 the aircraft had logged more than 750 flying hours and had been flown in all weather conditions, including light ice.

Dr Brokaw formed Brokaw Aviation Inc to market plans, a construction manual and pilot handbook to amateur constructors. Although full kits are not available, it is intended also to supply certain components such as the canopy, cowling and, possibly, bulkheads and ribs, to simplify the task of the homebuilder. By early 1980 ten sets of plans had been sold and 9 or 10 Bullets were under construction, one with a tailwheel landing gear and a 410 kW (550 hp) Ranger twelve-cylinder V engine.

TYPE: Two-seat sporting aircraft.
WINGS: Cantilever low-wing monoplane. Laminar-flow wing section: NACA 64A412 at root, NACA 64A410 at tip. Dihedral 4° 30'. Incidence 1° at root, 0° at tip. Conventional structure of 2024-T3 light alloy. Ailerons and trailing-edge flaps of light alloy.
FUSELAGE: Semi-monocoque structure of light alloy.

TAIL UNIT: Cantilever light alloy structure. Fixed-incidence tailplane. Electrically-operated trim tabs in elevators and rudder.
LANDING GEAR: Hydraulically-retractable tricycle type. Main and nose units and associated hydraulic system are from a Navion aircraft. Main units retract inward and nosewheel rearward. Single wheel on each main unit, with 15 × 6·00-6 low-profile tyre, pressure 4·48 bars (65 lb/sq in). Nosewheel tyre size 14 × 5·00-4, pressure 3·10 bars (45 lb/sq in). Goodyear hydraulic brakes on main wheels.
POWER PLANT: One 283 kW (380 hp) Avco Lycoming TIO-541-E flat-six engine, driving a Sensenich three-blade metal constant-speed propeller with spinner. Alternative power plant is 213 kW (285 hp) Teledyne Continental TSIO-520-B flat-six engine, driving a McCauley three-blade metal constant-speed propeller with spinner, or other engine of 223-373 kW (300-500 hp). Four integral wing fuel tanks, with capacity of 363 litres (96 US gallons). Refuelling points at wingtips. Oil capacity 11·3 litres (3 US gallons).
ACCOMMODATION: Two seats in tandem beneath transparent individual canopies. Port half of each canopy hinged at centreline to open upwards. Baggage space, which accommodates 31·8 kg (70 lb), aft of rear seat. Cabin heated and ventilated.

Bowers Fly Baby 1-A (1,600 cc Volkswagen engine) operated on skis in Finland by its builder, Mr Olavi Sakselin

Bowers Fly Baby 1-B with O-290-G engine and reduced sweep, built by David Cronk *(Peter M. Bowers)*

Bowers Fly Baby 1-A (Continental A65) converted into a tandem two-seater by Mr Victor F. Meznarsic *(Howard Levy)*

Brokaw Bullet in its latest form

Bushby M-II Mustang II (Avco Lycoming O-320 engine), built by Mr Glenn Breitsprecher of Seattle *(Peter M. Bowers)*

Bushby/Long Midget Mustang built by Mr Bert Beverly of Blue Grass, Iowa *(J. M. G. Gradidge)*

SYSTEMS: Hydraulic system at 103·5 bars (1,500 lb/sq in) for landing gear retraction and brakes. 28V 70A alternator for electrical system. Oxygen system for pilot and passenger, with capacity of 5 hours.

AVIONICS AND EQUIPMENT: Full IFR instrumentation, including DGO 10, DME 70, dual Narco 360-channel transceivers and dual VORs, ADF, transponder, marker beacon and ILS. Landing gear warning lights, navigation lights and external power socket.

DIMENSIONS, EXTERNAL:

Wing span	7·32 m (24 ft 0 in)
Wing chord at root	1·52 m (5 ft 0 in)
Wing chord at tip	0·76 m (2 ft 6 in)
Wing area, gross	8·79 m² (94·59 sq ft)
Wing aspect ratio	6
Length overall	6·25 m (20 ft 6 in)
Height overall	2·69 m (8 ft 10 in)
Tailplane span	2·69 m (8 ft 10 in)
Wheel track	2·54 m (8 ft 4 in)
Wheelbase	1·80 m (5 ft 11 in)
Propeller diameter	1·98 m (6 ft 6 in)

DIMENSIONS, INTERNAL:

Length	2·54 m (8 ft 4 in)
Max width	0·91 m (3 ft 0 in)
Max height	1·37 m (4 ft 6 in)

WEIGHTS (TIO-541-E engine):

Weight empty	922 kg (2,033 lb)
Max T-O weight	1,425 kg (3,142 lb)

PERFORMANCE (TIO-541-E engine):
Max level and normal cruising speed (75% power) at 7,315 m (24,000 ft)
303 knots (562 km/h; 349 mph)
Econ cruising speed (55% power) at 7,315 m (24,000 ft) 255 knots (473 km/h; 294 mph)
Stalling speed, clean 79 knots (147 km/h; 91 mph)
Stalling speed, wheels and flaps down 76 knots (142 km/h; 88 mph)
Max rate of climb at S/L 762 m (2,500 ft)/min
Service ceiling over 8,535 m (28,000 ft)
T-O run 396 m (1,300 ft)
T-O to 15 m (50 ft) 610 m (2,000 ft)
Landing from 15 m (50 ft) 853 m (2,800 ft)
Landing run 488 m (1,600 ft)
Range at econ cruising speed, 45 min reserves 1,600 nm (2,964 km; 1,842 miles)

BUSHBY
BUSHBY AIRCRAFT INC

Route 1, PO Box 13B, Minooka, Illinois 60447
Telephone: (815) 462 2346

Mr Robert W. Bushby, a research engineer with Sinclair Oil Co, began by building a Midget Mustang single-seat sporting monoplane, using drawings, jigs and certain components produced by the aircraft's designer, the late David Long. He has since produced the aircraft in kit form and also offers sets of plans of the Midget Mustang and a two-seat derivative known as the Mustang II to amateur constructors.

BUSHBY/LONG MM-1 MIDGET MUSTANG

The prototype of the Midget Mustang was completed in 1948 by David Long, then chief engineer of the Piper company. He flew it in the National Air Races that year, and in 1949 was placed fourth in the Continental Trophy Race at Miami.

Two basic versions have been developed by Robert Bushby, as follows:

MM-1-85. Powered by 63·5 kW (85 hp) Continental C85-8FJ or -12 engine. Flew for the first time on 9 September 1959.

MM-1-125. Powered by 101 kW (135 hp) Avco Lycoming O-290-D2 engine. Otherwise similar to MM-1-85. Flew for first time in July 1963. New propeller introduced during 1973 has improved max speed and cruising speed.

One hundred Midget Mustangs had been completed by the Spring of 1980, with 900 more under construction throughout the world. Several of those now flying have a 112 kW (150 hp) Avco Lycoming O-320 engine, providing a cruising speed of 234 knots (435 km/h; 270 mph) at 2,440 m (8,000 ft). Some have been fitted with retractable main landing gear.

The following details apply to the two basic versions:

TYPE: Single-seat fully-aerobatic sporting monoplane.

WINGS: Cantilever low-wing monoplane. Wing section NACA 64A212 at root, NACA 64A210 at tip. Dihedral 5°. Incidence 1° 30′. Two-spar flush-riveted stressed-skin aluminium structure. Aluminium statically-balanced ailerons and plain trailing-edge flaps.

FUSELAGE: Aluminium flush-riveted stressed-skin monocoque structure.

TAIL UNIT: Cantilever all-metal structure. Controllable trim tab in port elevator.

LANDING GEAR: Non-retractable tailwheel type. Cantilever spring steel main legs. Steerable tailwheel. Goodyear wheels and tyres, size 5·00-5, pressure 1·24 bars (18 lb/sq in). Goodyear hydraulic disc brakes.

POWER PLANT (MM-1-85): One 63·5 kW (85 hp) Continental C85-8FJ or -12 flat-four engine, driving a McCauley two-blade metal fixed-pitch propeller. Fuel tank aft of firewall, capacity 57 litres (15 US gallons). Optional integral wing fuel tanks, each with capacity of 57 litres (15 US gallons). Optional wingtip tanks, each with capacity of 13 litres (3·5 US gallons). Oil capacity 3·75 litres (1 US gallon).

POWER PLANT (MM-1-125): One 101 kW (135 hp) Avco Lycoming O-290-D2 flat-four engine, driving a Sensenich two-blade metal fixed-pitch propeller. Fuel tank aft of firewall, capacity 57 litres (15 US gallons). No provision for wingtip tanks. Oil capacity 5·75 litres (1·5 US gallons).

ACCOMMODATION: Single seat in enclosed cabin. Canopy hinged on starboard side. Space for 5·5 kg (12 lb) of baggage aft of seat. Room for back parachute.

AVIONICS AND EQUIPMENT: Radio optional. No provision for blind-flying instrumentation. Electrical system available on MM-1-85 only.

DIMENSIONS, EXTERNAL:

Wing span	5·64 m (18 ft 6 in)
Wing span over tip-tanks (MM-1-85)	5·99 m (19 ft 8 in)
Wing chord at root	1·53 m (5 ft 0 in)
Wing chord at tip	0·76 m (2 ft 6 in)
Wing area, gross	6·32 m² (68 sq ft)
Wing aspect ratio	4
Length overall	5·00 m (16 ft 5 in)
Height overall	1·37 m (4 ft 6 in)
Tailplane span	1·98 m (6 ft 6 in)
Wheel track	1·55 m (5 ft 1 in)

DIMENSIONS, INTERNAL:
Cabin:

Max width	0·56 m (1 ft 10 in)
Baggage space	0·057 m³ (2 cu ft)

WEIGHTS:
Weight empty:

MM-1-85	261 kg (575 lb)
MM-1-125	268 kg (590 lb)

Max T-O and landing weight:

MM-1-85	397 kg (875 lb)
MM-1-125	408 kg (900 lb)

PERFORMANCE (at max T-O weight):
Never-exceed speed:

	243 knots (450 km/h; 280 mph)

Max level speed at S/L:

MM-1-85	165 knots (306 km/h; 190 mph)
MM-1-125	195 knots (362 km/h; 225 mph)

Max cruising speed at 2,440 m (8,000 ft):

MM-1-85	171 knots (317 km/h; 197 mph)
MM-1-125	187 knots (346 km/h; 215 mph)

Econ cruising speed:

MM-1-85	129 knots (238 km/h; 148 mph)
MM-1-125	143 knots (265 km/h; 165 mph)

Stalling speed, flaps down:

MM-1-85	50 knots (92 km/h; 57 mph)
MM-1-125	53 knots (97 km/h; 60 mph)

Max rate of climb at S/L:

MM-1-85	533 m (1,750 ft)/min
MM-1-125	670 m (2,200 ft)/min

Service ceiling:

MM-1-85	over 4,875 m (16,000 ft)
MM-1-125	5,790 m (19,000 ft)

T-O run:

MM-1-85	137 m (450 ft)
MM-1-125	122 m (400 ft)

T-O to 15 m (50 ft):

MM-1-85	274 m (900 ft)
MM-1-125	213 m (700 ft)

Landing from 15 m (50 ft)	365 m (1,200 ft)
Landing run	152 m (500 ft)

Range with max fuel:

MM-1-85	347 nm (640 km; 400 miles)
MM-1-125	325 nm (603 km; 375 miles)

Range with max fuel and tip-tanks:

MM-1-85	651 nm (1,200 km; 750 miles)

BUSHBY M-II MUSTANG II

Design of this side-by-side two-seat derivative of the Midget Mustang was started in 1963. Construction of a prototype began in 1965 and it flew for the first time on 9 July 1966. During 1968 Mr Bushby designed an alternative non-retractable tricycle landing gear for the Mustang II, and amateur constructors have the option of either configuration. Another option is wing folding, to permit storage in a home garage. About 1,000 Mustang IIs were being built by amateurs in the Spring of 1980, at which time 80 were flying.

The description applies to the de luxe model, and the empty weight quoted includes IFR instrumentation and nav/com equipment. The M-II can also be operated as an aerobatic aircraft in what Bushby Aircraft calls the 'Sport' configuration. This is identical to the de luxe model except that the electrical system, radio and additional IFR instrumentation are deleted. The 'Sport' model has an empty weight of 340 kg (750 lb) and T-O weight of 567 kg (1,250 lb).

A Hartzell controllable-pitch propeller has replaced the original fixed-pitch propeller as standard, and the performance figures quoted for the 119 kW (160 hp) engine are obtained with this propeller. The figures quoted for the 93 kW (125 hp) engine are those obtained with the fixed-pitch propeller.

TYPE: Two-seat light sporting aircraft.

WINGS: Cantilever low-wing monoplane. Outer wings similar to those of Midget Mustang, attached to new constant-chord centre-section of short span. Wing section NACA 64A212 at root, NACA 64A210 at tip. Dihedral 5° on outer wings only. Incidence 1° 30'. Two-spar flush-riveted stressed-skin aluminium structure. Wing folding optional. Aluminium statically-balanced ailerons and plain trailing-edge flaps. No trim tabs.

FUSELAGE: Aluminium flush-riveted stressed-skin monocoque structure.

TAIL UNIT: Cantilever all-metal structure. Fixed-incidence tailplane. Controllable trim tab in starboard elevator.

LANDING GEAR: Standard version has non-retractable tailwheel type. Cantilever spring steel main legs. Goodyear 5·00-5 main wheels and tyres, pressure 1·38 bars (20 lb/sq in). Goodyear hydraulic disc brakes. Steerable tailwheel. Alternatively, non-retractable tricycle type. Cantilever spring steel main legs. Cleveland or Goodyear main wheels and tyres size 5·00-5. Non-steerable nosewheel, mounted on oleo-pneumatic shock-strut and free to swivel up to 16° either side. Goodyear nosewheel and tyre size 5·00-5. Goodyear or Cleveland hydraulic disc brakes. Wheel fairings optional on either type of landing gear.

POWER PLANT: Normally one 119 kW (160 hp) Avco Lycoming O-320 flat-four engine, driving a Hartzell two-blade controllable-pitch metal propeller. Provision for other engines including a 93 kW (125 hp) Avco Lycoming O-290 engine, driving a two-blade fixed-pitch metal propeller. Fuel tank aft of firewall, capacity 94·6 litres (25 US gallons). Optional integral wing fuel tanks, each with a capacity of 45 litres (12 US gallons). Refuelling point on starboard side of fuselage aft of firewall. Provision for wingtip tanks. Oil capacity 7·5 litres (2 US gallons).

ACCOMMODATION: Two seats side by side, under large rearward-sliding transparent canopy. Dual controls. Baggage space aft of seats, capacity 34 kg (75 lb).

SYSTEMS: 12V electrical system, supplied by Delco-Remy 15A generator and Exide 33A battery.

AVIONICS AND EQUIPMENT: Provision for full IFR instrumentation and dual nav/com system.

DIMENSIONS, EXTERNAL:

Wing span	7·37 m (24 ft 2 in)
Width folded	2·44 m (8 ft 0 in)
Wing chord at root	1·47 m (4 ft 10 in)
Wing chord at tip	0·79 m (2 ft 7 in)
Wing area, gross	9·02 m² (97·12 sq ft)
Wing aspect ratio	5·5

Length overall	5·94 m (19 ft 6 in)
Height overall	1·60 m (5 ft 3 in)
Height folded	1·73 m (5 ft 8 in)
Tailplane span	2·29 m (7 ft 6 in)
Wheel track	2·08 m (6 ft 10 in)

Propeller diameter:

93 kW (125 hp)	1·73 m (5 ft 8 in)
119 kW (160 hp)	1·82 m (6 ft 0 in)

DIMENSIONS, INTERNAL:
Cabin:

Max width	1·02 m (3 ft 4 in)
Baggage space	0·16 m³ (5·5 cu ft)

WEIGHTS:
Weight empty, equipped (N: nosewheel, T: tailwheel landing gear):

N 93 kW (125 hp) engine	413 kg (911 lb)
T 93 kW (125 hp) engine	408 kg (900 lb)
N 119 kW (160 hp) engine	425 kg (938 lb)
T 119 kW (160 hp) engine	420 kg (927 lb)
*Max T-O and landing weight	680 kg (1,500 lb)

*Except for countries that restrict max wing loading to 73·2 kg/m² (15 lb/sq ft), where T-O weight of 658 kg (1,450 lb) applies

PERFORMANCE (with tailwheel, at max T-O weight):
Never-exceed speed:

93 kW (125 hp)	173 knots (322 km/h; 200 mph)
119 kW (160 hp)	211 knots (391 km/h; 243 mph)

Max level speed at S/L:

93 kW (125 hp)	156 knots (290 km/h; 180 mph)
119 kW (160 hp)	200 knots (370 km/h; 230 mph)

Max cruising speed at 2,285 m (7,500 ft):

93 kW (125 hp)	152 knots (282 km/h; 175 mph)
119 kW (160 hp)	181 knots (335 km/h; 208 mph)

Stalling speed, flaps down:

93 kW (125 hp)	47 knots (87 km/h; 54 mph)
119 kW (160 hp)	51 knots (94 km/h; 58 mph)

Stalling speed, flaps up:

93 kW (125 hp)	51 knots (94 km/h; 58 mph)
119 kW (160 hp)	53 knots (96 km/h; 60 mph)

Max rate of climb at S/L:

93 kW (125 hp)	305 m (1,000 ft)/min
119 kW (160 hp)	670 m (2,200 ft)/min

Service ceiling:

93 kW (125 hp)	4,875 m (16,000 ft)
119 kW (160 hp)	6,400 m (21,000 ft)

T-O run:

93 kW (125 hp)	198 m (650 ft)
119 kW (160 hp)	137 m (450 ft)

T-O to 15 m (50 ft):

93 kW (125 hp)	320 m (1,050 ft)
119 kW (160 hp)	198 m (650 ft)

Landing from 15 m (50 ft):

93 kW (125 hp)	290 m (950 ft)
119 kW (160 hp)	259 m (850 ft)

Landing run:

93 kW (125 hp)	215 m (700 ft)
119 kW (160 hp)	168 m (550 ft)

Range with standard fuel (75% power):

93 kW (125 hp)	416 nm (770 km; 480 miles)
119 kW (160 hp)	373 nm (692 km; 430 miles)

Range with optional wingtip tanks:

119 kW (160 hp)	542 nm (1,005 km; 625 miles)

BUTTERWORTH
G. N. BUTTERWORTH

Richmond Airport, Heaton Orchard Road, West Kingston, Rhode Island 02892
Telephone: (401) 789 0384

BUTTERWORTH WESTLAND WHIRLWIND MARK II

Mr G. N. Butterworth has designed and built a ⅔-scale representation of a second World War Westland Whirlwind single-seat fighter. Design began on 20 October 1976, and construction of the prototype started simultaneously. Based on the wings and horizontal tail surfaces of a Grumman American AA-1A Trainer, construction took 900-950 working hours over a nine-month period. Estimated cost of construction was $3,000-4,000. First flight was made in July 1977.

Plans are available to amateur constructors.

TYPE: Single-seat ⅔-scale replica fighter.

WINGS: Cantilever low-wing monoplane, based on those of a Grumman American AA-1A Trainer. Dihedral 2°. Incidence 2°. Aluminium structure, except for outer

wing panels which are made of 29 mm (1·125 in) sitka spruce spars and solid polyurethane foam filling, covered with Dynel and polyester resins. Outer wings removable in 15 minutes to permit road trailering. No flaps or tabs.

FUSELAGE: Conventional all-aluminium semi-monocoque structure, with ·02 in skins and ·03 in bulkheads.

TAIL UNIT: Cantilever aluminium structure. High-mounted horizontal surfaces based on those of a Grumman American AA-1A Trainer. Trim tab on starboard elevator.

LANDING GEAR: Hydraulically-retractable tailwheel type. Main wheels retract forward into engine nacelles. Cleveland wheels. Main-wheel tyres size 6·00-6. Tailwheel diameter 10 cm (4in). Oleo shock-absorbers. Cleveland disc brakes.

POWER PLANT: Two 48·5 kW (65 hp) 1,600 cc Volkswagen modified motor car engines, each driving a Hegy fixed-pitch two-blade propeller. Two fuel tanks, total capacity 76 litres (20 US gallons). Refuelling points in top of glassfibre engine cowlings. Oil capacity (total) 5·5 litres (1·5 US gallons).

ACCOMMODATION: Single seat under rearward-sliding transparent canopy. No heating or ventilation.

DIMENSIONS, EXTERNAL:

Wing span	8·53 m (28 ft 0 in)
Wing chord, constant	1·22 m (4 ft 0 in)
Length overall	5·94 m (19 ft 6 in)
Height overall	2·16 m (7 ft 1 in)
Tailplane span	2·49 m (8 ft 2 in)
Wheel track	2·44 m (8 ft 0 in)
Propeller diameter	1·35 m (4 ft 5 in)
Distance between propeller centres	2·13 m (7 ft 0 in)

WEIGHTS:

Weight empty	472 kg (1,042 lb)
Max T-O weight	635 kg (1,400 lb)

PERFORMANCE:

Max level and cruising speed	126 knots (233 km/h; 145 mph)
Econ cruising speed	87 knots (161 km/h; 100 mph)
Stalling speed	55·5 knots (103 km/h; 64 mph)
Max rate of climb at S/L	229 m (750 ft)/min
Service ceiling	2,440 m (8,000 ft)
T-O run	366 m (1,200 ft)
T-O distance to 15 m (50 ft)	549 m (1,800 ft)
Landing distance from 15 m (50 ft)	549 m (1,800 ft)
Landing run	427 m (1,400 ft)
Range with max fuel	608 nm (1,126 km; 700 miles)

CHRISTEN
CHRISTEN INDUSTRIES INC

1048 Santa Ana Valley Road, Hollister, California 95023
Telephone: (408) 637 7405
PRESIDENT: Frank L. Christensen

Two aircraft make up the current Christen Eagle series of aerobatic biplanes. The **Eagle I** is a special-purpose single-seater intended solely for unlimited class aerobatic

competition and is structured to +9g, -6g operational. It is powered by a 194 kW (260 hp) Avco Lycoming AEIO-540-D4B5 flat-six engine, driving a Sensenich fixed-pitch propeller. The **Eagle II** is a less-austere two-seat sporting biplane that can be used for unlimited class aerobatics as well as for advanced aerobatic training and comfortable cross-country flying. It has the same structural limits as the Eagle I. All Eagles have a roll rate of 187° a second.

First version to become available was the Eagle II, which can be built by amateur constructors, using a series of 26 parts-kits supplied by Christen Industries. Each kit makes up a separate portion of the aircraft and is supported by a very detailed constructional manual. This allows the cost of building the aircraft to be spread over a period of time. Only common hand tools and power tools are required in construction, and no previous aircraft

G. N. Butterworth's ⅔-scale replica of a Westland Whirlwind

Christen Eagle I flown by Gene Soucy of the three-aircraft Eagles Aerobatic Flight

Christen Industries Eagle II two-seat aerobatic biplane

experience is thought necessary. Christen believes that a typical homebuilder could complete the aircraft in 1,400 to 1,600 man-hours.

CHRISTEN EAGLE I

Following completion of its flight test programme, the Eagle I became available in kit form in the Summer of 1980. It is generally similar to the Eagle II, but is a single-seater powered by a 194 kW (260 hp) Avco Lycoming engine. The firewall is moved aft for the larger engine, and a fuel tank replaces the forward seat. Aileron slave struts have been eliminated. Wing span is 6·07 m (19 ft 11 in); length overall 5·46 m (17 ft 11 in); and height 1·98 m (6 ft 6 in).

CHRISTEN EAGLE II

Design began in June 1974 and construction of a prototype started in August 1975. First flight was achieved in February 1977, when construction of other pre-production Eagles began. Manufacture of kits was initiated by Christen Industries in October 1977 and by January 1980 a total of 315 had been ordered.

TYPE: Two-seat unlimited class aerobatic biplane.

WINGS: Braced biplane with steel tube I-type main interplane struts. Symmetrical sections. Thickness/chord ratio 15%. Dihedral 0° 30′ on lower wings, 0° on upper wing. Incidence 0°. Sweepback at quarter-chord 7° 30′ on upper wing, 0° on lower wings. Wooden spars and ribs; metal leading- and trailing-edges, polyester fabric covered. Conventional ailerons on upper and lower

wings, of similar construction to wings. No flaps or tabs.

FUSELAGE: Conventional structure of welded 4130N steel tubing. Covered with removable light alloy panels from firewall to back of rear seat. Rear fuselage fabric covered.

TAIL UNIT: Conventional wire-braced structure, comprising a tailplane and elevators fitted with boost tabs, and fin and rudder, all of welded steel tube, polyester fabric covered.

LANDING GEAR: Non-retractable tailwheel type. Aluminium spring main legs. Main tyres size 5·00-5, pressure 1·52 bars (22 lb/sq in). Cleveland hydraulic disc brakes. Streamline wheel fairings.

POWER PLANT: One 149 kW (200 hp) Avco Lycoming AEIO-360-A1D flat-four engine, driving a Hartzell HC-C2YK-4/C7666A-2 constant-speed propeller. One fuel tank in fuselage, capacity 98·4 litres (26 US gallons). Refuelling point in upper fuselage. Oil capacity 7·5 litres (2 US gallons). Fuel system allows unlimited inverted flight.

ACCOMMODATION: Two seats in tandem beneath one-piece side-hinged bubble canopy. Heated. Baggage hold in turtledeck, capacity 13·6 kg (30 lb).

SYSTEMS: 12V DC battery for starting and radio.

AVIONICS: Edo-Aire RT-563 or RT-553 radio.

DIMENSIONS, EXTERNAL:

Wing span	6·07 m (19 ft 11 in)
Wing chord, constant	1·02 m (3 ft 4 in)
Wing area, gross	11·61 m² (125 sq ft)

Length overall	5·64 m (18 ft 6 in)
Height overall	1·98 m (6 ft 6 in)
Tailplane span	2·13 m (7 ft 0 in)
Wheel track	1·83 m (6 ft 0 in)
Wheelbase	3·96 m (13 ft 0 in)
Propeller diameter	1·93 m (6 ft 4 in)

DIMENSIONS, INTERNAL:

Cabin: Length	2·13 m (7 ft 0 in)
Max width	0·71 m (2 ft 4 in)
Max height	0·99 m (3 ft 3 in)

WEIGHTS:

Weight empty	465 kg (1,025 lb)
Max T-O and landing weight	716 kg (1,578 lb)

PERFORMANCE:

Never-exceed speed	184 knots (341 km/h; 212 mph)
Max level speed at S/L	160 knots (296 km/h; 184 mph)
Max cruising speed at 1,825 m (6,000 ft)	143 knots (265 km/h; 165 mph)
Econ cruising speed at 1,825 m (6,000 ft)	137 knots (254 km/h; 158 mph)
Stalling speed	50·5 knots (94 km/h; 58 mph)
Max rate of climb at S/L	640 m (2,100 ft)/min
Service ceiling	5,180 m (17,000 ft)
T-O run	244 m (800 ft)
T-O to 15 m (50 ft)	381 m (1,250 ft)
Landing from 15 m (50 ft)	480 m (1,575 ft)
Range with max fuel and max payload	330 nm (611 km; 380 miles)

CASSUTT

THOMAS K. CASSUTT

11718 Persuasion Drive, San Antonio, Texas 78216

While employed as an airline pilot, Capt Tom Cassutt designed and built in 1954 a small single-seat racing monoplane known as the Cassutt Special I (No. 111), in which he won the 1958 National Air Racing Championships. In 1959, he completed a smaller aircraft on the same lines, known as the Cassutt Special II (No. 11).

Plans of both aircraft, and of a sporting version of No. 111 with a larger cockpit, are available to amateur constructors, and a total of about 2,000 sets of plans had been sold by early 1979. Many Cassutt Specials are flying or are under construction, in Australia, France, West Germany, New Zealand, South Africa, Sweden, the UK and elsewhere. Brief details of a number of these were given in a table in the 1977-78 *Jane's*.

Following his retirement from airline flying, Tom Cassutt plans to develop a number of different aircraft to meet Formula I specifications. It is also his intention to modify the plans of the Special to show ways of improving performance, and possibly to evolve a tandem two-seat cockpit layout.

CASSUTT SPECIAL I

The following description applies to the original Cassutt Special I (No. 111), named *Jersey Skeeter*:

TYPE: Single-seat racing monoplane.

WINGS: Cantilever mid-wing monoplane. Wing section Cassutt 1107. No incidence or dihedral. All-wood two-spar structure with spruce ribs, solid spars and plywood skin, fabric-covered. Ailerons are of welded steel tube construction, fabric-covered. No flaps.

FUSELAGE: Steel tube structure, fabric-covered.

TAIL UNIT: Cantilever steel tube structure, with fabric covering.

LANDING GEAR: Non-retractable tailwheel type. Wittman cantilever spring steel main legs. Main-wheel tyres size 5·00-5. Wheel fairings standard.

POWER PLANT: Originally one Continental C85-8F flat-four engine, rated normally at 63·5 kW (85 hp) but capable of developing 83·5-85·75 kW (112-115 hp) in racing trim. Aircraft now fitted usually with an Avco Lycoming engine. Sensenich two-blade fixed-pitch propeller. Fuel capacity 57 litres (15 US gallons). Oil capacity 3·8 litres (1 US gallon).

ACCOMMODATION: Single seat in enclosed cockpit.

DIMENSIONS, EXTERNAL:

Wing span	4·54 m (14 ft 11 in)
Wing chord (mean)	1·37 m (4 ft 6 in)
Wing area, gross	6·13 m² (66·0 sq ft)
Wing aspect ratio	3·37
Length overall	4·88 m (16 ft 0 in)
Height overall	1·30 m (4 ft 3 in)

Tailplane span	1·19 m (3 ft 11 in)
Wheel track	1·37 m (4 ft 6 in)

WEIGHTS (with Continental engine):

Weight empty	234 kg (516 lb)
Max T-O weight	331 kg (730 lb)

PERFORMANCE (Continental engine at max T-O weight):

Max level speed	200 knots (370 km/h; 230 mph)
Max cruising speed	165 knots (306 km/h; 190 mph)
Stalling speed	61 knots (113 km/h; 70 mph)
Max rate of climb at S/L	610 m (2,000 ft)/min
Endurance with max fuel	3 h

CASSUTT SPECIAL II

TYPE: Single-seat racing monoplane.

WINGS: Cantilever mid-wing monoplane. Wing section Cassutt 13106. No incidence or dihedral. All-wood structure. No flaps.

FUSELAGE: Steel tube structure, fabric-covered.

TAIL UNIT: Cantilever steel tube structure, fabric-covered. The prototype (No. 11) has small centre fin and auxiliary fins on the tailplane tips.

LANDING GEAR: Non-retractable tailwheel type. Wittman cantilever spring steel main legs. Main-wheel tyre size 5·00-5. Wheel fairings standard.

POWER PLANT AND ACCOMMODATION: As for Cassutt Special I.

Cassutt Special built by Mr Robert MacGillivray of Essendon, Australia *(The Age)*

Condor Shoestring built by Mr Ralph Moore of Titusville, Florida

DIMENSIONS, EXTERNAL:				
Wing span	4·16 m (13 ft 8 in)	Height overall	1·16 m (3 ft 10 in)	PERFORMANCE (at max T-O weight):
Wing chord, constant	1·47 m (4 ft 10 in)	Tailplane span	1·14 m (3 ft 9 in)	Max level speed at S/L 204 knots (378 km/h; 235 mph)
Wing area, gross	6·13 m² (66 sq ft)	Wheel track	0·97 m (3 ft 2 in)	Max cruising speed 174 knots (322 km/h; 200 mph)
Wing aspect ratio	2·83	WEIGHTS:		Stalling speed 54 knots (100 km/h; 62 mph)
Length overall	4·88 m (16 ft 0 in)	Weight empty	196 kg (433 lb)	Max rate of climb at S/L 915 m (3,000 ft)/min
		Max T-O weight	363 kg (800 lb)	Endurance with max fuel 3 h

CONDOR
CONDOR AERO INC
PO Box 762, Vero Beach, Florida 32960
PRESIDENT: Landis G. Ketner

CONDOR SHOESTRING

The original Shoestring was designed and built by the Mercury Air Group, consisting of Mr Vincent Ast, Mr Carl Ast and Mr Rodney Kreimendahl, in 1949. As a racing monoplane (No. 16) it first competed at Miami in 1950 where, piloted by Bob Downey, it achieved third place at a speed of 157·474 knots (291·844 km/h; 181·334 mph). At San Jose, California, in the same year it finished first in the hands of Vincent Ast, at 152 knots (282 km/h; 175 mph). By 1974, when a new wing was fitted to Shoestring, the aircraft had achieved fourteen first places in air races, three seconds and four thirds.

A full description of the original Shoestring appeared in the 1959-60 *Jane's*.

In 1965 Shoestring was purchased by John Anderson and taken to Miami, where a set of drawings of the aircraft was made. The first new racer to be built from these drawings was *Yellow Jacket*, constructed by Jim Strode, which flew for the first time on 15 July 1970. Although this aircraft was very similar to the original Shoestring, the fuselage structure was made 5 cm (2 in) wider and 10 cm (4 in) longer to provide a more comfortable cockpit. The power plant installation, canopy and fairings were also of Jim Strode's design.

Since then other Shoestrings have been built in modified form, and plans are available to amateur constructors.

The Shoestring illustrated was built by Ralph Moore of Titusville, Florida. It was the sixth plans-built aircraft to fly, on 16 December 1978. The weight and performance data which follow apply to this aircraft.

TYPE: Single-seat sporting monoplane.

WINGS: Cantilever shoulder-mounted monoplane of wood construction, built as one unit and fabric covered. Front spar built of three pieces of spruce bonded together. Rear spar can be cut from one piece of spruce or built up from several pieces. Plywood ribs with capstrips bonded to top and bottom. Skins bonded to spars and ribs. Ailerons built as part of wing and cut out after the top skin has been bonded in place.

FUSELAGE: Steel tube structure, with plywood formers and fabric covering from instrument panel aft. Thin-gauge aluminium skin forward of panel and on each side of cockpit above wing. Roll-over structure of heavy gauge steel.

TAIL UNIT: Conventional cantilever spruce structure, with fabric-covered plywood skin.

LANDING GEAR: Non-retractable tailwheel type. Main wheels carried on one-piece formed aluminium member bolted directly to bottom of fuselage. Sheet aluminium fairings over legs; aluminium wheel fairings. Solid rubber tailwheel. Brakes fitted.

POWER PLANT: Originally one 63·5 kW (85 hp) Continental flat-four engine. Alternative 74·5 kW (100 hp)

engine to meet current PRPA regulations. Recommended engines are Continental C85, C90 and O-200 flat-fours. Fuel tank aft of firewall, capacity 38 litres (10 US gallons). Provision for auxiliary tank behind seat.

ACCOMMODATION: Single seat under blown Plexiglas canopy.

DIMENSIONS, EXTERNAL:
Wing span	5·79 m (19 ft 0 in)
Wing area, gross	6·13 m² (66 sq ft)
Length overall	5·38 m (17 ft 7¾ in)
Height overall	1·42 m (4 ft 8 in)

WEIGHTS (aircraft illustrated):
Weight empty, equipped (with oil)	358 kg (788 lb)
Max T-O weight	476 kg (1,050 lb)

PERFORMANCE (aircraft illustrated):
Max level speed at S/L	200 knots (370 km/h; 230 mph)
Max cruising speed at 305 m (1,000 ft)	174 knots (322 km/h; 200 mph)
Econ cruising speed at 610 m (2,000 ft)	148 knots (274 km/h; 170 mph)
Stalling speed, power off	69·5 knots (129 km/h; 80 mph)
Service ceiling	5,485 m (18,000 ft)
T-O run	245 m (800 ft)
T-O to 15 m (50 ft)	305 m (1,000 ft)
Landing from 15 m (50 ft)	610 m (2,000 ft)
Landing run, without braking	488 m (1,600 ft)
Range with max fuel	295 nm (547 km; 340 miles)

CVJETKOVIC
ANTON CVJETKOVIC
5324 West 121 Street, Hawthorne, California 90250
Telephone: (805) 498 3092

When living in Yugoslavia, Mr Anton Cvjetkovic designed a single-seat light aeroplane designated CA-51 and powered by a modified Volkswagen engine. A prototype was built by members of Zagreb Aeroclub in 1951, and was followed by five more aircraft of the same type.

After moving to the USA, Mr Cvjetkovic began work, in May 1960, on the design of an improved light aircraft which he designated CA-61. Construction of a prototype was started in February 1961 and it flew for the first time in August 1962. Plans of both single-seat and two-seat all-wood versions are available to amateur constructors, together with plans of a two-seat aircraft designated CA-65, of which the prototype was completed in 1965. Plans of an all-metal version of the CA-65, designated CA-65A, are also available.

By early 1980 more than 400 sets of plans of these aircraft had been sold, and completed aircraft were flying in Australia, Canada, South Africa and the USA.

CVJETKOVIC CA-61/-61R MINI ACE

The CA-61 can be built as a single-seat or side-by-side two-seat light aircraft, with any Continental engine of between 48·5 and 63·5 kW (65 and 85 hp). Alternatively, the single-seater can be fitted with a modified Volkswagen engine. Construction takes less than 1,000 h.

The design was modified during 1973 to allow for installation of retractable landing gear; when constructed in this form, the aircraft is designated CA-61R.

The following details refer specifically to the single-seat CA-61 prototype:

TYPE: Single-seat light aircraft.

WINGS: Cantilever low-wing monoplane. Wing section NACA 4415. Dihedral 3°. No incidence. Structure consists of two spruce spars, each built in one piece, built-up

spruce girder-type ribs and plywood-covered leading-edge torsion box, with fabric covering overall. Fabric-covered spruce ailerons. No flaps.

FUSELAGE: Conventional wooden structure of basic square section, plywood-covered.

TAIL UNIT: Cantilever wooden structure, covered with plywood. Fixed-incidence tailplane. Trim tab in elevator.

LANDING GEAR: Non-retractable tailwheel type. Cantilever main legs, with helical spring shock-absorption. Goodyear main wheels and tyres, size 5·00-5 Type III, and Model L5 brakes. Steerable tailwheel.

POWER PLANT: One 48·5 kW (65 hp) Continental A65 flat-four engine, driving a Flottorp 63-55 two-blade fixed-pitch propeller. Fuel in two steel tanks in fuselage, with capacities of 45 litres (12 US gallons) and 19 litres (5 US gallons) respectively. Total fuel capacity 64 litres (17 US gallons). Oil capacity 4·5 litres (1·25 US gallons).

ACCOMMODATION: Single seat in enclosed cockpit.

AVIONICS AND EQUIPMENT: Prototype fitted with Nova Star radio and Omni.

DIMENSIONS, EXTERNAL:
Wing span	8·38 m (27 ft 6 in)
Wing chord, constant	1·40 m (4 ft 7 in)
Wing area, gross	11·75 m² (126·5 sq ft)
Wing aspect ratio	6·0
Length overall	5·77 m (18 ft 11 in)
Height overall (in flying position)	2·08 m (6 ft 10 in)
Wheel track:	
Single-seat	2·49 m (8 ft 2 in)
Two-seat	2·62 m (8 ft 7 in)

WEIGHTS:
Weight empty:	
Single-seat	275 kg (606 lb)
Two-seat	363 kg (800 lb)
Max T-O weight:	
Single-seat	430 kg (950 lb)
Two-seat	590 kg (1,300 lb)

PERFORMANCE:
Max level speed at S/L	104 knots (193 km/h; 120 mph)
Normal cruising speed	87 knots (161 km/h; 100 mph)
Min flying speed:	
Single-seat	37 knots (67·5 km/h; 42 mph)
Two-seat	44 knots (80·5 km/h; 50 mph)
Range with max fuel:	
Single-seat	369 nm (685 km; 425 miles)
Two-seat	321 nm (595 km; 370 miles)

CVJETKOVIC CA-65

Design of this side-by-side two-seat light aircraft was started in September 1963. Construction of the prototype began in March 1964 and it flew for the first time in July 1965. Plans are available.

The CA-65 closely resembles the CA-61 in general appearance, but has a more powerful engine and retractable landing gear. A folding-wing version was introduced during 1967.

TYPE: Two-seat light aircraft.

WINGS: Cantilever low-wing monoplane. Modified NACA 4415 wing section. Dihedral 0° on centre-section, 3° on outer wings. Structure consists of two spruce spars, each built in one piece, and built-up spruce girder-type ribs, completely plywood-covered. Fabric-covered spruce ailerons. On the folding-wing version, the outer wings fold upward from their junction with the centre-section.

FUSELAGE: Conventional wooden structure of basically square section, plywood-covered. Manually-operated landing flap under fuselage.

TAIL UNIT: Cantilever wooden structure. Fixed surfaces covered with plywood. Elevator and rudder fabric-covered. Fixed-incidence tailplane.

LANDING GEAR: Mechanically-retractable tailwheel type. Main wheels retract inward. Goodyear main wheels and tyres, size 5·00-5 Type III. Goodyear type L5 brakes. Steerable tailwheel.

The single-seat Cvjetkovic CA-61R (Continental A65 engine)

First folding-wing version of the Cvjetkovic CA-65, built by Graham Scarr of Duffy, Australia

First Cvjetkovic CA-65A, built by students of the Kelowna Secondary School, Kelowna, British Columbia, Canada

D'Apuzzo D-260(1) Senior Aero Sport built by Mr Merrill Vallender of Downer's Grove, Illinois

POWER PLANT: One 93 kW (125 hp) Avco Lycoming O-290-G flat-four engine, driving a Sensenich 66-68 two-blade fixed-pitch propeller. Two aluminium fuel tanks in fuselage, each with capacity of 53 litres (14 US gallons). Total fuel capacity 106 litres (28 US gallons).

ACCOMMODATION: Two seats side by side in enclosed cockpit, with dual controls; although hydraulic brakes can be operated only by the pilot. Forward-opening canopy.

RADIO: Bayside BEI-990 radio fitted in prototype.

DIMENSIONS, EXTERNAL:
Wing span	7·62 m (25 ft 0 in)
Wing area, gross	10·03 m² (108 sq ft)
Width, wings folded	2·74 m (9 ft 0 in)
Length overall	5·79 m (19 ft 0 in)
Height overall (in flying position)	2·24 m (7 ft 4 in)
Height, wings folded	3·05 m (10 ft 0 in)
Wheel track	2·11 m (6 ft 11 in)
Propeller diameter	1·73 m (5 ft 8 in)

WEIGHTS:
Weight empty	408 kg (900 lb)
Max T-O weight	680 kg (1,500 lb)

PERFORMANCE (at max T-O weight):
Max level speed	139 knots (257 km/h; 160 mph)

Normal cruising speed
117 knots (217 km/h; 135 mph)
Stalling speed	48 knots (89 km/h; 55 mph)
Max rate of climb at S/L	305 m (1,000 ft)/min
Service ceiling	4,575 m (15,000 ft)
T-O run	137 m (450 ft)
Landing run	183 m (600 ft)
Range with max fuel	434 nm (804 km; 500 miles)

CVJETKOVIC CA-65A

This aircraft is an all-metal version of the wooden CA-65, with swept vertical tail surfaces. It is designed for +9g and −6g ultimate loading.

The general description of the CA-65 applies also to the CA-65A, except in the following details:

WINGS: The wing structure consists of a single main spar and an auxiliary wing spar, with aluminium sheet ribs and skin, riveted throughout. The main wing spar cap is made of extruded and bent-up sheet aluminium angles, tapered towards the tip to produce a wing of uniform bending strength. Ribs are formed from 0·025 in aluminium sheet. Wing skin is of 2024T-3 aluminium alloy sheet.

FUSELAGE: All-metal structure with four aluminium angle longerons and built-up frames. Fuselage skin is of 0·025-0·032 in 2024T-3 aluminium alloy sheet. To simplify formation of the curvature on the upper fuselage, the skins are broken up into small sections of flat panels.

TAIL UNIT: Cantilever all-metal structure, with swept vertical surfaces and dorsal fin. Construction similar to that of the wings.

POWER PLANT: The structure is designed to accommodate an Avco Lycoming engine of 80·5-112 kW (108-150 hp).

DIMENSIONS, EXTERNAL: As for Model CA-65 except:
Wing span	7·75 m (25 ft 5 in)
Wing area, gross	10·16 m² (109·4 sq ft)
Length overall	5·99 m (19 ft 8 in)
Height overall	2·29 m (7 ft 6 in)

PERFORMANCE (112 kW; 150 hp engine):
Max level speed	151 knots (280 km/h; 174 mph)

Normal cruising speed
130 knots (241 km/h; 150 mph)
Stalling speed	48 knots (89 km/h; 55 mph)
Max rate of climb at S/L	466 m (1,530 ft)/min
Service ceiling	4,570 m (15,000 ft)
T-O run	99 m (325 ft)
Landing run	183 m (600 ft)
Range with max fuel	460 nm (853 km; 530 miles)

D'APUZZO
NICHOLAS E. D'APUZZO
1029 Blue Rock Lane, Blue Bell, Pennsylvania 19422
Telephone: (215) 646 4792

Mr D'Apuzzo, who was formerly employed by the Naval Air Development Center, Warminster, Pennsylvania, as a project manager on specialised projects, retired from the Navy Department during 1973. He retains an association with the Navy on a consultant basis.

He has designed several sporting aircraft for amateur construction, among the best known of which are the Denight Special midget racer, described in the 1962-63 *Jane's*, and the PJ-260 single-seat aerobatic biplane described under the Parsons-Jocelyn heading in the 1974-75 *Jane's*. His other designs include the Senior Aero Sport, which is a two-seat version of the PJ-260, the smaller single-seat D-200 Freshman, and the D-201 Sportwing.

By early 1980 a total of 31 PJ-260s and Senior Aero Sports were known to have been completed by amateur constructors in the USA, with at least 33 more under construction.

D'APUZZO D-260/D-295 SENIOR AERO SPORT

There are six versions of the Senior Aero Sport, as follows:

D-260(1). With Avco Lycoming O-435 series engine.

D-260(2). With Continental O-470/E-185 series engine. Prototype first flown on 17 July 1965, with a 168 kW (225 hp) E-185 (modified) engine, driving an Aeromatic F-200H-O-85 propeller. Fuel in one 60·5 litre (16 US gallon) tank in fuselage and one 79·5 litre (21 US gallon) streamlined external tank under fuselage.

D-260(3). With Avco Lycoming GO-435 series engine. Construction of prototype started by Mr G. A. Shallbetter of Minneapolis in April 1961 and first flight made on 17 July 1965, with a 194 kW (260 hp) GO-435-C2 engine, driving a Hartzell controllable-pitch propeller of 2·29 m (7 ft 6 in) diameter. Four fuel tanks in fuselage, with total capacity of 136 litres (36 US gallons). Second D-260(3), completed by Mr Alfred Fessenden of Lafayette, New York, is fitted with a Hartzell constant-speed propeller.

D-260(4). With Ranger 6-440-C six-cylinder inverted aircooled engine.

D-260(5). With 224 kW (300 hp) Avco Lycoming R-680-E3 engine. Prototype built by Mr Henry Neys of Lake Stevens, Washington.

D-295. With 209 kW (280 hp) Avco Lycoming GO-480-G1D6 engine. First example built by Mr Ed Mahler; D-295-2 (illustrated in 1979-80 *Jane's*) completed in 1976 by Mr Geoffrey Geisz of Flint, Michigan.

TYPE: Two-seat sporting biplane.

WINGS: Conventional braced biplane type. Wing section NACA M-12 (modified). Dihedral 30′ on lower wings only. Incidence 2°. Sweepback 9° 15′ on upper wings. Two wood spars, metal ribs, fabric covering. Metal Frise ailerons on all four wings, with fabric covering. No flaps.

FUSELAGE: Steel tube structure, with aluminium alloy access panels forward of cockpit and fabric covering aft.

TAIL UNIT: Wire-braced fabric-covered steel tube structure. Trim tab in starboard elevator.

LANDING GEAR: Non-retractable tailwheel type. Cantilever spring steel main units. Goodyear 6·00-6 main wheels and tyres, pressure 1·38 bars (20 lb/sq in). Goodyear disc brakes.

POWER PLANT: One flat-six engine; details given under individual model listings. Fuel in 125 litre (33 US gallon) main tank and 41·5 litre (11 US gallon) aerobatic tank, both in fuselage. Total fuel capacity 166·5 litres (44 US gallons). Oil capacity 11 litres (3 US gallons).

ACCOMMODATION: Two seats in tandem in open cockpits. Baggage space behind headrest.

SYSTEM: 12V electrical system, with optional starter and navigation lights.

AVIONICS: Prototypes fitted with two-way radio and Omni.

DIMENSIONS, EXTERNAL:
Wing span	8·23 m (27 ft 0 in)
Wing chord, constant (both)	1·17 m (3 ft 10 in)
Wing area, gross	17·2 m² (185 sq ft)
Wing aspect ratio	4·22
Length overall	6·40 m (21 ft 0 in)
Height overall	2·32 m (7 ft 7½ in)
Tailplane span	3·10 m (10 ft 2 in)
Wheel track	2·57 m (8 ft 5 in)

Wheelbase	4·80 m (15 ft 9 in)

WEIGHTS:
Normal T-O weight:

D-260 (2)	930 kg (2,050 lb)
D-260 (3)	975 kg (2,150 lb)

Max T-O and landing weight:

All versions	975 kg (2,150 lb)

PERFORMANCE (D-260 (3) at max T-O weight. D-260 (2) comparable):

Never-exceed speed 165 knots (305 km/h; 190 mph)	
Max level speed at 2,135 m (7,000 ft)	
	135 knots (250 km/h; 155 mph)
Max cruising speed at 2,135 m (7,000 ft)	
	122 knots (225 km/h; 140 mph)
Econ cruising speed at 2,135 m (7,000 ft)	
	113 knots (209 km/h; 130 mph)
Stalling speed	48 knots (89 km/h; 55 mph)
Max rate of climb at S/L	610 m (2,000 ft)/min
Service ceiling	6,100 m (20,000 ft)
T-O run	122 m (400 ft)
T-O to 15 m (50 ft)	213 m (700 ft)
Landing from 15 m (50 ft)	275 m (900 ft)
Landing run	183 m (600 ft)
Range with max fuel and max payload	
	434 nm (805 km; 500 miles)

D'APUZZO D-200 FRESHMAN

The D-200 Freshman (formerly Junior Aero Sport) is a smaller single-seat version of the PJ-260. Its design was started in September 1963 and construction of two prototypes began in September 1964. The first of these was almost completed in early 1973 when the building in which it was being constructed was destroyed by fire. The Freshman was not damaged severely, but due to the delay in obtaining new workshop premises completion of this prototype was not resumed until early 1975. The aircraft has been inspected by the FAA and approved for final assembly.

TYPE: Single-seat sporting biplane.
WINGS: Conventional braced biplane type. Wing section NACA M-12 (mod). Dihedral 0° on top wing, 0° 30' on bottom wing. Incidence 2° on both wings. No sweepback. Spruce spars, wooden ribs and light alloy nose skin, with fabric covering. Fabric-covered aluminium alloy ailerons. No flaps.
FUSELAGE: Welded steel tube structure, with aluminium alloy panels forward of cockpit and fabric covering aft.

TAIL UNIT: Wire-braced welded steel tube structure with fabric covering. Fixed-incidence tailplane. Trim tab in each elevator.
LANDING GEAR: Non-retractable tailwheel type. Cantilever spring steel main legs. Goodrich-Hayes main wheels and tyres, size 5·00-4, pressure 1·38 bars (20 lb/sq in). Goodrich-Hayes brakes.
POWER PLANT: One 134 kW (180 hp) Avco Lycoming O-360 flat-four engine, driving a Hartzell two-blade constant-speed metal propeller. Fuel tank in fuselage, capacity 75 litres (20 US gallons). Oil capacity 7·5 litres (2 US gallons).
ACCOMMODATION: Single seat in open cockpit.

DIMENSIONS, EXTERNAL:

Wing span (both)	6·60 m (21 ft 8 in)
Wing chord, constant	1·02 m (3 ft 4 in)
Wing area, gross	13·0 m² (140 sq ft)
Wing aspect ratio	4·2
Length overall	5·56 m (18 ft 3 in)
Height overall	1·93 m (6 ft 4 in)
Tailplane span	2·18 m (7 ft 2 in)
Wheel track	1·52 m (5 ft 0 in)
Wheelbase	4·11 m (13 ft 6 in)

WEIGHTS:

Weight empty	381 kg (840 lb)
Max T-O and landing weight	578 kg (1,275 lb)

PERFORMANCE (estimated, at max T-O weight):

Never-exceed speed 191 knots (354 km/h; 220 mph)	
Max level speed at 2,135 m (7,000 ft)	
	139 knots (257 km/h; 160 mph)
Max cruising speed at 2,135 m (7,000 ft)	
	122 knots (225 km/h; 140 mph)
Stalling speed	48 knots (89 km/h; 55 mph)
Max rate of climb at S/L	762 m (2,500 ft)/min
Service ceiling	6,100 m (20,000 ft)
T-O run	122 m (400 ft)
T-O to 15 m (50 ft)	198 m (650 ft)
Landing from 15 m (50 ft)	260 m (850 ft)
Landing run	168 m (550 ft)
Range with max fuel	260 nm (480 km; 300 miles)

D'APUZZO D-201 SPORTWING

The D-201 is a completely redesigned development of the PJ-260/D-260 Senior Aero Sport series. Special attention has been given to reducing the cost and complexity of building the aircraft, while retaining the safety aspects of the previous models. The aircraft features long-span ailerons on the lower wings only, to reduce weight and to simplify construction; the front cockpit has been enlarged by 7·6 cm (3 in), without affecting the rear cockpit; and the wing panel structures and tailplane assembly have been redesigned. Many preformed parts are available to the homebuilder.

Construction of the prototype D-201 began in January 1977; by early 1980 it was at the final assembly stage, having been inspected by the FAA and approved for covering. Rollout was expected to be in late Spring 1980.
TYPE: Two-seat sporting biplane.
WINGS: Conventional braced biplane type. Wing section NACA M-12 (modified). Dihedral 0° on upper wings; 0° 30' on lower wings. Incidence 2° on all wings. Sweepback 9° 15' on upper wings only, outboard of centre-section. Long-span ailerons, on lower wings only. N-type interplane struts and cabane struts.
FUSELAGE: Conventional steel tube structure, with aluminium alloy panels forward of cockpit and fabric covering aft.
TAIL UNIT: Conventional wire-braced structure. Trim tab in starboard elevator. All control surfaces horn-balanced.
LANDING GEAR: Non-retractable tailwheel type. Cantilever spring steel main units. Wheel fairings.
POWER PLANT: One 119 kW (160 hp) Avco Lycoming IO-320-B1A flat-four engine driving a Hartzell constant-speed propeller in prototype. Design suitable for any Avco Lycoming engine from the 112 kW (150 hp) O-320 to the 149 kW (200 hp) O-360.
ACCOMMODATION: Two seats in tandem. Optional canopy over rear cockpit.
SYSTEM: Starter and generator standard.

DIMENSIONS, EXTERNAL:

Wing span, upper	8·23 m (27 ft 0 in)
Wing span, lower	7·86 m (25 ft 9½ in)
Wing chord, constant	1·17 m (3 ft 10 in)
Wing area, gross	17·14 m² (184·5 sq ft)
Length overall, tail up	6·59 m (21 ft 7½ in)
Height overall, tail down	2·34 m (7 ft 8 in)
Elevator span	3·15 m (10 ft 4 in)
Wheel track	2·57 m (8 ft 5 in)

WEIGHTS (estimated, with O-320 engine):

Weight empty	537·5 kg (1,185 lb)
Design max T-O weight	839 kg (1,850 lb)

PERFORMANCE:
No details yet available

DAVIS
LEEON D. DAVIS

PO Box 207, 405 North St Paul, Stanton, Texas 79782
Telephone: (915) 756 2100

Details of the first light aircraft designed by Mr Davis, the DA-1A five-seat high-wing monoplane, can be found in the 1960-61 *Jane's*. He completed subsequently the prototype of a two-seat low-wing monoplane designated DA-2A, of which plans are available to other builders.

For several years the prototype DA-3, a four-seat development of the DA-2A of which details appeared in the 1973-74 *Jane's*, remained uncompleted. It was completed in 1978 and brief details of the aircraft can be found below, together with a description of a single-seat sporting aircraft which has the designation DA-5A.

DAVIS DA-2A

This side-by-side two-seat light aircraft was flown for the first time on 21 May 1966, after 18 months of spare-time work and an expenditure of $1,600. At the Experimental Aircraft Association's annual Fly-in a few weeks later, it gained the awards for both the most outstanding design and the most popular aircraft. Plans are available to other amateur constructors.

By early 1976 the prototype had flown a total of 860 hours, and the twenty DA-2As that were then flying had accumulated approximately 4,000 flying hours. It is believed that about 100 other DA-2As are under construction.

The DA-2A is of simple all-metal construction and has an all-moving V-tail (included angle 100°) like Mr Davis's earlier DA-1A. The wings are of constant chord, without flaps. Dihedral is 5°. The non-retractable tricycle landing gear has cantilever spring steel main legs and a steerable nosewheel. Power plant is a 48·5 kW (65 hp) Continental A65-8 flat-four engine, but the DA-2A is stressed for engines of up to 74·5 kW (100 hp). Total fuel capacity is 75 litres (20 US gallons) and oil capacity 3·75 litres (1 US gallon).

There is baggage space aft of the side-by-side seats or, alternatively, a child's seat may be located in this position.

DIMENSIONS, EXTERNAL:

Wing span	5·86 m (19 ft 2¾ in)
Wing chord, constant	1·31 m (4 ft 3½ in)
Wing area, gross	7·66 m² (82·5 sq ft)
Wing aspect ratio	4·48
Length overall	5·44 m (17 ft 10¼ in)
Height overall	1·65 m (5 ft 5 in)

DIMENSIONS, INTERNAL:

Cabin: Length	1·49 m (4 ft 6¾ in)
Max width	1·04 m (3 ft 5 in)
Max height	1·14 m (3 ft 8¾ in)

WEIGHTS:

Weight empty	277 kg (610 lb)
Max T-O weight	510 kg (1,125 lb)

PERFORMANCE (at max T-O weight):

Max level speed at S/L	
	104 knots (193 km/h; 120 mph)
Cruising speed	100 knots (185 km/h; 115 mph)
Landing speed	54 knots (100 km/h; 62 mph)
Range with max fuel	390 nm (725 km; 450 miles)

DAVIS DA-3

The DA-3 is a four-seat scaled-up development of the DA-2A. Work on the prototype began in the latter 1960s but was abandoned before the fuselage had been completed. Although stressed for engines of up to 74·5 kW (100 hp), the prototype was to be powered by a 48·5 kW (65 hp) Continental A65 flat-four engine. This aircraft was later completed, and has been joined by a three-seat DA-3 built by Mr Marcel DeWulf of Lake Bluff, Indiana, which first flew on 8 July 1978. The latter aircraft is powered by a 74·5 kW (100 hp) Continental O-200 flat-four engine, and has a wing span and length of 6·78 m (22 ft 2¾ in) and 5·97 m (19 ft 7¼ in) respectively. Max T-O weight is 726 kg (1,600 lb).

Plans are not being made available to homebuilders.

DAVIS DA-5A

Design of this aircraft began in October 1972, and Mr Davis and his son began construction of the prototype on 4 May 1974. It had been intended to power the aircraft with a two-cylinder Franklin Sport 2 engine, but non-availability of this power plant enforced a design change to utilise a 48·5 kW (65 hp) Continental A65. Despite the extra work involved, the first flight of the DA-5A was made on 22 July 1974.

The distance record set by a modified DA-5A on 6-7 August 1976 (see 1979-80 *Jane's*) has since been beaten.

Plans of the DA-5A are available to amateur constructors.
TYPE: Single-seat sporting aircraft.
WINGS: Cantilever low-wing monoplane. Wing section Clark Y. Thickness/chord ratio 12%. Dihedral 5°. Incidence 0°. Light alloy structure with single spar, ribs of 2024T-3 alloy, and stressed skins. Plain ailerons of light alloy construction. No flaps. No trim tabs.
FUSELAGE: Light alloy stressed-skin structure with four frames and stainless steel firewall. Steel tube overturn structure aft of pilot's seat.
TAIL UNIT: All-moving V tail (included angle 100°) with steel tube spar and light alloy ribs and skins. Anti-servo tabs in trailing-edges.

LANDING GEAR: Non-retractable tricycle type. Main-wheel legs of light alloy streamline section mounted rigidly to wing spar. Shock-absorption by tyres and rubber grommets. Main wheels have tyres size 14 × 5-4, pressure 1·03 bars (15 lb/sq in). Steerable nosewheel with tyre size 10 × 3-4, pressure 1·03 bars (15 lb/sq in). Rosenhan drum brakes.
POWER PLANT: One 48·5 kW (65 hp) Continental A65 flat-four engine, driving a Hegy type 60-70 two-blade fixed-pitch wooden propeller with spinner. Fuel tank in fuselage, immediately aft of firewall, capacity 64·3 litres (17 US gallons). Refuelling point on fuselage upper surface forward of windscreen. Oil capacity 3·75 litres (1 US gallon).
ACCOMMODATION: Single seat beneath canopy hinged on port side.

DIMENSIONS, EXTERNAL:

Wing span	4·76 m (15 ft 7¼ in)
Wing chord, constant	1·12 m (3 ft 8 in)
Wing area, gross	5·31 m² (57·20 sq ft)
Wing aspect ratio	4·26
Length overall	4·80 m (15 ft 9 in)
Height overall	1·35 m (4 ft 5¼ in)
Span over V tail	1·60 m (5 ft 3 in)
Wheel track	1·55 m (5 ft 1 in)
Wheelbase	1·12 m (3 ft 8 in)
Propeller diameter	1·52 m (5 ft 0 in)
Propeller ground clearance	0·203 m (8 in)

DIMENSION, INTERNAL:

Cockpit: Max width	0·53 m (1 ft 9 in)

WEIGHTS:

Weight empty	208 kg (460 lb)
Max T-O weight	351 kg (775 lb)

PERFORMANCE (at max T-O weight):

Never-exceed speed 147 knots (273 km/h; 170 mph)	
Max level speed at S/L	
	139 knots (257 km/h; 160 mph)
Max cruising speed at S/L	
	122 knots (225 km/h; 140 mph)
Econ cruising speed at S/L	
	104 knots (193 km/h; 120 mph)
Stalling speed	52·5 knots (97 km/h; 60 mph)
Max rate of climb at S/L	244 m (800 ft)/min
Service ceiling	4,420 m (14,500 ft)
T-O run	183 m (600 ft)
T-O to 15 m (50 ft)	259 m (850 ft)
Landing from 15 m (50 ft)	335 m (1,100 ft)
Landing run	183 m (600 ft)
Range with max fuel	390 nm (724 km; 450 miles)

Partially completed airframe of D'Apuzzo D-200 Freshman

D'Apuzzo D-201 Sportwing, developed from the PJ-260/D-260 series
(Michael A. Badrocke)

DSK Airmotive DSK-1 Hawk single-seat sporting aircraft (Avco Lycoming O-145-B2 engine)

Davis DA-5A single-seat lightweight sporting aircraft *(left)* and Davis DA-2A two-seat aircraft

DSK
DSK AIRMOTIVE INC
PRESIDENT: Sarah R. Killingsworth

Mr Richard Killingsworth, then a US Air Force Chief Master Sergeant, designed and built a single-seat sporting aircraft which he designated DSK-1 Hawk. It flew for the first time on 26 May 1973, and interest in the design was such that he formed DSK Airmotive Inc to market plans and partial kits to amateur constructors. The business is being carried on by Mrs Killingsworth following her husband's death on 12 April 1975, when the prototype Hawk crashed as the result of an engine failure at take-off.

The fuselage structure of the prototype was basically a surplus Air Force/Navy 200 US gallon drop-tank; but Mr Killingsworth's plans provide for alternative bulkhead/stressed-skin construction for builders unable to obtain a suitable drop-tank. In this form the aircraft is designated DSK-2 Golden Hawk and is described separately.

By early 1980, about 49 Hawks were thought to be under construction.

DSK AIRMOTIVE DSK-1 HAWK
TYPE: Single-seat sporting aircraft. Structure stressed to 9g ultimate.

WINGS: Cantilever low-wing monoplane. Clark Y section. Thickness/chord ratio 15%. Slight dihedral on outer panels. No incidence. Conventional two-spar structure of 2024T-3 light alloy. Wingtips are drooped, raked and conical. Trailing-edge flaps of light alloy construction extend from inner edge of ailerons and continue beneath fuselage. Plain ailerons of light alloy construction. Optional aileron droop. No tabs. Wings detach for trailering or stowage.

FUSELAGE: All-metal structure utilising a surplus military drop-tank as its basis, with 2024T-3 alloy sheet and 6061T-6 structural angle reinforcement.

TAIL UNIT: Cantilever all-metal structure with swept vertical surfaces. Incidence of tailplane ground-adjustable. Trim tab on elevator.

LANDING GEAR: Non-retractable tricycle type. All units have a tubular steel strut with compression springs for shock-absorption. Nosewheel and main-wheel tyres size 14 × 5·00-5, pressure 2·07 bars (30 lb/sq in). Steerable and self-centering nosewheel. Mechanical disc brakes. Parking brake. Wheel fairings optional.

POWER PLANT: Prototype has one 48·5 kW (65 hp) Avco Lycoming O-145-B2 flat-four engine, driving a McCauley two-blade metal fixed-pitch propeller refurbished by Aero Prop. Provision for alternative engines of up to 93 kW (125 hp). Fuel contained in forward fuselage tank, capacity 34 litres (9 US gallons). Auxiliary tank, raising total fuel capacity to 68 litres (18 US gallons), optional. Refuelling point for front tank forward of windscreen, for rear tank in turtledeck aft of cockpit. Oil capacity 4·7 litres (1·25 US gallons).

ACCOMMODATION: Single seat in enclosed cockpit. Canopy slides aft for access. Baggage space aft of pilot's seat. Cockpit heated and ventilated. All control surfaces actuated by push-pull rods.

SYSTEM: Simple air-driven alternator under design by DSK Airmotive.

AVIONICS: Battery-powered Narco VHT-3 nav/com and Omni.

DIMENSIONS, EXTERNAL:
Wing span	6·21 m (20 ft 4½ in)
Wing chord, constant	0·97 m (3 ft 2 in)
Wing area, gross	5·95 m² (64 sq ft)
Wing aspect ratio	6·42
Length overall	4·57 m (15 ft 0 in)
Height overall	1·83 m (6 ft 0 in)
Tailplane span	1·88 m (6 ft 2 in)
Wheel track	1·63 m (5 ft 4 in)
Wheelbase	1·14 m (3 ft 9 in)
Propeller diameter	1·60 m (5 ft 3 in)

WEIGHTS:
Weight empty	238 kg (525 lb)
Max T-O and landing weight	405 kg (893 lb)

PERFORMANCE (at max T-O weight):
Max level speed at 1,525 m (5,000 ft)	127 knots (235 km/h; 146 mph)
Max cruising speed at 1,525 m (5,000 ft)	114 knots (211 km/h; 131 mph)
Econ cruising speed at 1,525 m (5,000 ft)	96 knots (177 km/h; 110 mph)
Stalling speed, flaps up	52·5 knots (97 km/h; 60 mph)
Stalling speed, flaps down	39-44 knots (73-81 km/h; 45-50 mph)
Max rate of climb at S/L	457 m (1,500 ft)/min
Service ceiling	3,660 m (12,000 ft)
T-O run	122-183 m (400-600 ft)
T-O to 15 m (50 ft)	244 m (800 ft)
Landing from 15 m (50 ft)	229 m (750 ft)
Landing run	107-168 m (350-550 ft)
Range with max fuel, 45 min reserves	477 nm (885 km; 550 miles)

DSK AIRMOTIVE DSK-2 GOLDEN HAWK
Generally similar to the DSK-1 Hawk, the DSK-2 was designed to eliminate the use of a military drop-tank as the basic fuselage structure and is 0·46 m (1 ft 6 in) longer overall. Design began in January 1974 and construction of the prototype was started four months later. It was hoped originally to complete the flight testing in 1976; instead the prototype was placed into storage. Flying subsequently resumed, and by early 1978 this DSK-2 had logged 29 flight hours. Two other Golden Hawks have been completed; that illustrated was constructed by Mr Don Kames of West Chicago and first flew in 1976.

TYPE: Single-seat sporting aircraft.

WINGS: As for DSK-1, with 6061T-6 light alloy structural angle reinforcement of spars. Ailerons droop collectively with flaps.

FUSELAGE: Light alloy semi-monocoque structure with five bulkheads, 6061T-6 structural angle longerons, and 2024T-3 alloy bulkheads and stressed skin.

TAIL UNIT: Cantilever structure of light alloy, with swept tail surfaces. Box-beam/rib/stressed-skin structure of 2024T-3 alloy. Incidence of tailplane ground-adjustable. Manually-adjustable trim tab on elevator.

LANDING GEAR: Non-retractable tricycle type, as on DSK-1 Hawk. Main legs of steel tube, with springs in compression. Corded neoprene for absorption of side loads. Self-centering steerable nosewheel. Main wheels and tyres size 14 × 5·50-5, pressure 2·07 bars (30 lb/sq in). Nosewheel and tyre size 13 × 5·00-5, 14 × 5·00-5 optional, pressure 2·07 bars (30 lb/sq in). Cleveland hydraulic brakes. Fairings on main legs.

POWER PLANT: As for DSK-1.

ACCOMMODATION: As for DSK-1, except new sliding canopy and seatback, and control column removable to provide room for pilot to sleep, between flights, during sporting trips. Aircraft can be flown with canopy open or closed. Tandem passenger seat can be installed. Baggage space.

SYSTEMS: Hydraulic system for brakes only. Power for electronics provided by rechargeable battery. DSK air-driven alternator optional.

AVIONICS: Prototype has, currently, Narco VHT-2 nav/com. It is intended to install a 90-channel nav/com.

DIMENSIONS, EXTERNAL:
As for DSK-1, except:
Wing area, gross	5·99 m² (64·5 sq ft)
Wing aspect ratio	6·43
Length overall	5·03 m (16 ft 6 in)
Height overall	1·91 m (6 ft 3 in)
Wheel track	1·64 m (5 ft 4½ in)

WEIGHTS (estimated):
Weight empty	251 kg (554 lb)
Max T-O weight	414 kg (914 lb)

DSK-2 Golden Hawk built by Mr Donald A. Kames of Chicago *(J. M. G. Gradidge)*

PERFORMANCE (estimated, at max T-O weight):
Max level speed at 1,525 m (5,000 ft)
135 knots (251 km/h; 156 mph)
Max cruising speed at 1,525 m (5,000 ft)
122 knots (227 km/h; 141 mph)
Econ cruising speed 104 knots (193 km/h; 120 mph)

Stalling speed, flaps up
52·5 knots (97 km/h; 60 mph)
Stalling speed, flaps down
43·5 knots (81 km/h; 50 mph)
Max rate of climb at S/L 457 m (1,500 ft)/min
Service ceiling 3,660 m (12,000 ft)

T-O run	122-183 m (400-600 ft)
T-O to 15 m (50 ft)	320 m (1,050 ft)
Landing from 15 m (50 ft)	274-320 m (900-1,050 ft)
Landing run	168 m (550 ft)

Range with 53 litres (14 US gallons) fuel at econ cruising speed 416 nm (772 km; 480 miles)

DURAND
DURAND ASSOCIATES INC
84th and McKinley Road, Omaha, Nebraska 68122
Telephone: (402) 571 7060

DURAND Mk V
Mr William H. Durand, a professional engineer, has designed and built a two-seat all-metal biplane known as the Durand Mk V. Design began in 1967 and construction in 1970, and the first flight was achieved on 28 June 1978. Flight testing has shown that the Durand Mk V cannot be stalled.

Plans of the Durand Mk V are available to amateur builders, and 20 were known to be under construction in early 1980.

TYPE: Two-seat sporting biplane.

WINGS: Negative stagger biplane with wings of constant chord. Wing section NACA 23012. Dihedral 0° upper wing, 2° 30′ lower wings. Incidence 3° both wings. No sweepback. Strut-braced light alloy stressed-skin structure with spars of box form. Full-span flaps on upper and lower wings. Spoilers in place of ailerons, forward of flaps on lower wings only.

FUSELAGE: Semi-monocoque structure of 2024-T3 light alloy. Cabin area of fuselage skinned externally and internally, and insulated for temperature and sound.

TAIL UNIT: Cantilever structure of light alloy. All-moving tailplane has built-up box spar; fin and rudder have U-section spars. Full-span combined trim tab and anti-servo tab in tailplane.

LANDING GEAR: Non-retractable tricycle type. Cantilever main legs of reinforced glassfibre. All three wheels of Cleveland manufacture, with tyres size 5·00-5, pressure 2·07 bars (30 lb/sq in). It is intended to design fairings for the main wheels. Cleveland hydraulic brakes.

POWER PLANT: One 112 kW (150 hp) Avco Lycoming O-320-E2A flat-four engine, driving a Sensenich two-blade fixed-pitch metal propeller with spinner. Fuel tank in forward fuselage, aft of firewall, capacity 93 litres (24·5 US gallons). Two auxiliary wing tanks optional, each 22·5 litres (6 US gallons), to provide max fuel capacity of 138 litres (36·5 US gallons). Refuelling point for main tank on upper surface of forward fuselage. Oil capacity 7·5 litres (2 US gallons).

ACCOMMODATION: Two seats side by side beneath forward-sliding canopy. Full dual controls. Baggage space aft of seats, max capacity 58 kg (128 lb). Windscreen defroster. Cabin heated and ventilated.

SYSTEMS: Hydraulic system for brakes only. Electrical system includes 60A engine-driven alternator and 12V storage battery.

AVIONICS: Edo-Aire Mitchell nav-com can be installed optionally. Prototype has full IFR instrumentation, but is intended basically for VFR flying.

DIMENSIONS, EXTERNAL:

Wing span, both	7·47 m (24 ft 6 in)
Wing chord, constant (both)	0·914 m (3 ft 0 in)
Wing area, gross	13·38 m² (144 sq ft)
Wing aspect ratio, effective biplane	5·1
Length overall	6·17 m (20 ft 3 in)

Height overall	2·03 m (6 ft 8 in)
Tailplane span	2·71 m (8 ft 10½ in)
Wheel track	2·13 m (7 ft 0 in)
Wheelbase	1·83 m (6 ft 0 in)
Propeller diameter	1·83 m (6 ft 0 in)

DIMENSIONS, INTERNAL:
Cabin:

Length	2·03 m (6 ft 8 in)
Max width	1·09 m (3 ft 7 in)
Max height	1·22 m (4 ft 0 in)

WEIGHTS:

Weight empty	549 kg (1,210 lb)
Max T-O weight	834 kg (1,840 lb)

PERFORMANCE (at max T-O weight):

Never-exceed speed	147 knots (272 km/h; 169 mph)
Max cruising speed at 2,285 m (7,500 ft)	117 knots (217 km/h; 135 mph)
Econ cruising speed at 2,285 m (7,500 ft)	109 knots (201 km/h; 125 mph)
Landing speed	48 knots (89 km/h; 55 mph)
Max rate of climb at S/L	366 m (1,200 ft)/min
Absolute ceiling, estimated	4,570 m (15,000 ft)
T-O run	168 m (550 ft)
T-O to 15 m (50 ft)	503 m (1,650 ft)
Landing from 15 m (50 ft)	274 m (900 ft)
Landing run	137 m (450 ft)

Range with standard fuel, no reserves
347 nm (644 km; 400 miles)
Range with max optional fuel, no reserves
451 nm (837 km; 520 miles)

DYKE
DYKE AIRCRAFT
2840 Old Yellow Springs Road, Fairborn, Ohio 45324
Telephone: (513) 878 9832

Mr John W. Dyke was the designer of a small delta-wing aircraft, designated JD-1 Delta, which he built with Mrs Jennie Dyke. This was described in the 1964-65 *Jane's*. Subsequently, Mr Dyke developed the design, and the first flight of the JD-2 Delta was made in July 1966.

DYKE AIRCRAFT JD-2 DELTA
Plans of the JD-2 are available to amateur constructors, and Mr Dyke has formed Dyke Aircraft to market them. A total of about 300 JD-2s was thought to be under construction in early 1980, in Australia, Brazil, Canada, France, West Germany, Japan, New Zealand, South Africa, the United Kingdom and the United States. About eleven had been completed and flown by then.

As a help to the homebuilder, hardware and tubing kits are available.

A feature of the Dyke Delta is that the outer wing panels can be folded flat above the cockpit for easy towing.

TYPE: Delta-winged sporting aircraft.

WINGS: Delta wing of modified NACA 63012 and 66015 wing section. No dihedral. No incidence. Sweepback of wing centre-section 61°. Sweepback of outer wing panels 31°. Welded steel tube structure, with stainless steel capstrips to which the laminated glassfibre skins are secured by Dupont explosive rivets. Aluminium skin optional; attached by aluminium pop rivets. Trailing-edge elevons extending from centreline to approximately two-thirds span. Elevons have a basic structure of metal but are fabric covered. Trim tab at inboard edge of each elevon. Wing outer panels fold upward and lay above the fuselage so that the JD-2 can be towed on the landing gear. Folding and unfolding can be carried out by one person.

FUSELAGE: Welded steel tube structure with stainless steel capstrips and glassfibre skins, except for fuselage undersurface which has 4130 steel tube capstrips and fabric covering.

TAIL UNIT: Welded steel tube structure with swept fin and rudder, both fabric covered. Optional all-moving T-tailplane, with steel tube main spar and aluminium

skin, for improved low-speed trim when a heavier engine, such as the 149 kW (200 hp) Avco Lycoming, is installed.

LANDING GEAR: Manually retractable tricycle type, all units retracting aft. Shock-absorption by torsion bars of 6150 heat-treated steel. Main wheels have tyres size 14 × 5-6, pressure 3·10 bars (45 lb/sq in). Nosewheel tyre size 12 × 5-4, pressure 2·07 bars (30 lb/sq in). Firestone hydraulic brakes.

POWER PLANT: Prototype has one 134 kW (180 hp) Avco Lycoming O-360 flat-four engine, driving a McCauley two-blade fixed-pitch propeller with spinner. Constant-speed propeller and 149 kW (200 hp) engine installation optional. Glassfibre fuel tank in fuselage, immediately aft of cabin, capacity 178 litres (47 US gallons), with pilot and two passengers. Fuel capacity reduced to 87 litres (23 US gallons) as a four-seat aircraft. Refuelling point on port side of aft fuselage upper surface. Oil capacity 7·5 litres (2 US gallons).

ACCOMMODATION: Standard accommodation for pilot, on single forward seat, and three passengers on aft bench seat. Access by upward-opening canopy, hinged on starboard side. Accommodation is ventilated. Space for limited baggage in starboard wing centre-section.

SYSTEMS: Hydraulic system for brakes only. Vacuum system for instruments. Electrical supply from 12V DC generator; solid-state inverter provides 110V AC at 400Hz.

ELECTRONICS AND EQUIPMENT: Genave Series 200A 200-channel nav and com transceiver. Blind-flying instrumentation standard.

DIMENSIONS, EXTERNAL:

Wing span	6·87 m (22 ft 2½ in)
Wing chord at root (centre-section)	4·27 m (14 ft 0 in)
Wing chord at root (outer panels)	2·90 m (9 ft 6 in)
Wing chord at tip	0·51 m (1 ft 8 in)
Wing area, gross	17·00 m² (183 sq ft)
Wing aspect ratio	2·7
Length overall	5·79 m (19 ft 0 in)
Width, wings folded	2·24 m (7 ft 4 in)
Height overall, wings folded	1·83 m (6 ft 0 in)
Tailplane span (T-tail)	0·91 m (3 ft 0 in)
Wheel track	1·97 m (6 ft 5½ in)

Wheelbase	2·13 m (7 ft 0 in)
Propeller diameter	1·88 m (6 ft 2 in)

DIMENSIONS, INTERNAL:

Cabin: Length	1·88 m (6 ft 2 in)
Max width	1·22 m (4 ft 0 in)
Max height	1·02 m (3 ft 4 in)
Floor area	1·67 m² (18 sq ft)
Baggage space	0·17 m³ (6 cu ft)

WEIGHTS (A: 134 kW; 180 hp, B: 149 kW; 200 hp engine):
Weight empty, basic equipped:

A, B	435 kg (960 lb)

Weight empty, IFR equipped:

A, B	483 kg (1,065 lb)

Max T-O weight:

A, B	862 kg (1,900 lb)

Max landing weight:

A, B	816 kg (1,800 lb)

PERFORMANCE (at max T-O weight with 134 kW; 180 hp engine, except where indicated):

Never-exceed speed	191 knots (354 km/h; 220 mph)
Max level speed at 2,285 m (7,500 ft)	165 knots (306 km/h; 190 mph)
Max cruising speed at 2,285 m (7,500 ft), fixed-pitch propeller	156 knots (290 km/h; 180 mph)
Max cruising speed, constant-speed propeller	165 knots (306 km/h; 190 mph)
Max cruising speed, with 149 kW (200 hp) engine and constant-speed propeller	174 knots (322 km/h; 200 mph)
Econ cruising speed at 2,285 m (7,500 ft)	135 knots (249 km/h; 155 mph)
Max rate of climb at S/L	610 m (2,000 ft)/min
Service ceiling	4,420 m (14,500 ft)
Service ceiling, with 149 kW (200 hp) engine	5,485 m (18,000 ft)
T-O run	213 m (700 ft)
T-O to 15 m (50 ft)	488 m (1,600 ft)
Landing from 15 m (50 ft)	549 m (1,800 ft)
Landing run	244-305 m (800-1,000 ft)

Range with max fuel and pilot only
625 nm (1,158 km; 720 miles)
Range with max payload
390 nm (724 km; 450 miles)

EAA
EXPERIMENTAL AIRCRAFT ASSOCIATION INC
PO Box 229, Hales Corners, Wisconsin 53130
Telephone: (414) 425 4860
PRESIDENT: Paul H. Poberezny
VICE-PRESIDENT: Ray Scholler
SECRETARY: S. H. Schmid
TREASURER: Arthur Kilps
EXECUTIVE DIRECTOR, INFORMATION SERVICES: Ben Owen

As a service to its members, the EAA decided in 1955 to develop a modern single-seat sporting biplane suitable for home construction by amateurs. The design drawings were prepared by Mr J. D. Stewart and Mr T. Seely of the

Allison Division, General Motors Corporation, with the assistance of Mr Paul H. Poberezny, President of the EAA, and this aircraft became known as the EAA Biplane. It was followed in 1972 by the Acro-Sport, an aerobatic aircraft designed by Mr Poberezny. These two designs were supplemented in 1973 by a more advanced aerobatic aircraft, the Super Acro-Sport.

Latest designs to emanate from the EAA President are the lightweight Pober P-9 Pixie, which flew for the first time in July 1974, and the Acro-Sport II.

EAA BIPLANE
The prototype of the EAA Biplane was built between 1957 and May 1960 as a classroom project by students of St Rita's High School, Chicago, under the supervision of

Mr Robert Blacker. It flew for the first time on 10 June 1960, powered by a 48·5 kW (65 hp) Continental A65 engine.

After this prototype had been taken over by the EAA, a number of modifications were made, including installation of a 63·5 kW (85 hp) engine. Mr Poberezny subsequently introduced further changes, including lighter wing spars and fittings, which reduced the empty weight of the aircraft, together with increases in the area of the tail surfaces and many other improvements. This modified version was known as the EAA Biplane Model P. Subsequent changes led successively to Models P1 and P2, with successively thinner spars and, in the P2, movement of the cockpit to a slightly more forward position.

More than 7,200 sets of plans of the EAA Biplane have

Durand Mk V all-metal two-seat biplane (Vern Goff)

Dyke Delta built by Avions Pierre Robin in France (Brian M. Service)

EAA Super Acro-Sports built by Mr Robert O. Johannes and his son, Robert D. Johannes. N42J (foreground) has a 112 kW (150 hp) Avco Lycoming O-320 engine; N47JG has a 134 kW (180 hp) Avco Lycoming O-360-A1A (Howard Levy)

EAA Acro-Sport II two-seat aerobatic biplane (Lee Fray)

EAA Acro-Sport I aerobatic biplane

EAA Biplane single-seat sporting aircraft

been sold by the EAA Museum Foundation, and many examples are flying and under construction.

The following details apply to the standard EAA Biplane Model P2:

TYPE: Single-seat sporting biplane.

WINGS: Braced biplane, with N-shape streamline-section cabane struts and interplane struts. Dihedral 0° on upper wing, 2° on lower wings. Incidence 2° on upper wing, 2° on lower wings. All-wood two-spar structure, with aluminium leading-edge and overall fabric covering. Spars 25·5 mm (1·0 in) thick. Ailerons of similar construction to wings, on lower wings only. No flaps.

FUSELAGE: Welded steel tube structure, fabric-covered.

TAIL UNIT: Wire-braced welded steel tube structure, fabric-covered.

LANDING GEAR: Non-retractable tailwheel type, modified from standard Piper J-3 components. Rubber cord shock-absorption. Brakes on main wheels. Wheel fairings optional.

POWER PLANT: Prototype Model P has a 63·5 kW (85 hp) Continental C85-8 flat-four engine, driving a two-blade metal fixed-pitch propeller. Provision for engines of up to 112 kW (150 hp); but most Model Ps have a 93 kW (125 hp) Avco Lycoming. Piper J-3 fuel tank aft of firewall in fuselage, capacity 68 litres (18 US gallons).

ACCOMMODATION: Single seat in open cockpit.

DIMENSIONS, EXTERNAL:
Wing span	6·10 m (20 ft 0 in)
Wing chord (both), constant	0·91 m (3 ft 0 in)
Wing area, gross	10·03 m² (108 sq ft)
Length overall	5·18 m (17 ft 0 in)
Height overall	1·83 m (6 ft 0 in)
Wheel track	1·71 m (5 ft 7½ in)
Propeller diameter:	
85 hp	1·78 m (5 ft 10 in)
150 hp	1·88 m (6 ft 2 in)

WEIGHTS (63·5 kW; 85 hp engine):
Weight empty	322 kg (710 lb)
Max T-O weight	522 kg (1,150 lb)

PERFORMANCE (A, with 63·5 kW; 85 hp Continental engine; B, with 112 kW; 150 hp Avco Lycoming engine, at max T-O weight):
Max level speed at S/L:		
A		109 knots (201 km/h; 125 mph)

Econ cruising speed:
A		96 knots (177 km/h; 110 mph)
Stalling speed: A		48 knots (89 km/h; 55 mph)
B		52 knots (97 km/h; 60 mph) CAS
Max rate of climb at S/L: A		305 m (1,000 ft)/min
B		370 m (1,210 ft)/min
Service ceiling: A		3,500 m (11,500 ft)
T-O run: A		91 m (300 ft)
Landing run: A		245 m (800 ft)
Range with max fuel:		
A		304 nm (560 km; 350 miles)
g limits		normal ±6, ultimate ±9

EAA ACRO-SPORT I

The Acro-Sport I was designed by Mr Paul Poberezny, President of the EAA, specifically for construction by school students, as a pupils' project. The EAA considers that such a project enables those who participate to discover their capabilities and potential in the manual crafts necessary to build an aircraft, possibly helping the individual to choose a career more wisely.

First flight of the prototype Acro-Sport (N1AC) was made on 11 January 1972, only 352 days after its design was started, although it represented a completely new design, unrelated to the EAA Biplane.

Plans and construction manuals are available to homebuilders from Acro-Sport Inc (see Super Acro-Sport for address), and about 850 sets had been sold by January 1980.

The following details apply to the prototype:

TYPE: Single-seat aerobatic biplane.

WINGS: Braced single-bay biplane, with single streamline-section interplane strut each side. N-type centre-section struts. Double streamline-section flying and landing wires. Wing section M-6. Dihedral: upper 0°, lower 2°. Incidence (both) 1° 30'. Conventional two-spar structure, with spruce spars and ribs, single wire drag and anti-drag truss, fabric-covered. Glassfibre wingtips. Ailerons, on all four wings, of wood construction with fabric covering. No flaps. Cutout in trailing-edge of upper wing.

FUSELAGE: Composite structure of welded steel tube, with wooden stringers, fabric-covered. Glassfibre nose cowl and light alloy engine cowlings.

TAIL UNIT: Wire-braced welded steel tube structure with fabric covering. Controllable trim tab on port side of elevator, servo tab on starboard side.

LANDING GEAR: Non-retractable tailwheel type, modified from Piper J-3 components. Two side Vees and half axles. Rubber bungee shock-absorption. Main-wheel tyres size 5·00-5, pressure 1·86-1·93 bars (27-28 lb/sq in). Cleveland or Goodyear hydraulic brakes. Glassfibre wheel fairings. Steerable tailwheel. Parking brake.

POWER PLANT: Prototype has a 134 kW (180 hp) Avco Lycoming engine, driving a Sensenich two-blade metal fixed-pitch propeller with spinner. Basic power plant is a 74·5 kW (100 hp) Continental O-200 flat-four engine. Single fuel tank immediately aft of firewall, capacity 104 litres (20 US gallons). Refuelling point on upper surface of fuselage. Small smoke oil tank, capacity 19 litres (5 US gallons), forward of instrument panel, could also be used for fuel.

ACCOMMODATION: Single seat in open cockpit, which is large enough to accommodate a pilot 1·95 m (6 ft 5 in) tall and weighing 115 kg (250 lb). Baggage space behind headrest, capacity 16 kg (35 lb).

DIMENSIONS, EXTERNAL:
Wing span, upper	5·97 m (19 ft 7 in)
Wing span, lower	5·82 m (19 ft 1 in)
Wing chord (both), constant	0·91 m (3 ft 0 in)
Wing area, gross	10·73 m² (115·5 sq ft)
Wing aspect ratio, upper	6·6
Length overall	5·33 m (17 ft 6 in)
Height overall	1·83 m (6 ft 0 in)
Tailplane span	2·16 m (7 ft 1 in)
Wheel track	1·78 m (5 ft 10 in)
Propeller diameter	1·93 m (6 ft 4 in)

WEIGHTS:
Weight empty, equipped	335 kg (739 lb)
Max T-O and landing weight	534 kg (1,178 lb)

PERFORMANCE (at max T-O weight):
Never-exceed speed	156 knots (289 km/h; 180 mph)
Max level speed	132 knots (245 km/h; 152 mph)
Max cruising speed	113 knots (209 km/h; 130 mph)
Econ cruising speed	91 knots (169 km/h; 105 mph)
Stalling speed	43·5 knots (80·5 km/h; 50 mph)
Max rate of climb at S/L	1,067 m (3,500 ft)/min
T-O run	46 m (150 ft)

T-O .o 15 m (50 ft)	107 m (350 ft)
Landing from 15 m (50 ft)	267 m (875 ft)
Landing run	244 m (800 ft)
Range with max fuel	304 nm (563 km; 350 miles)

EAA SUPER ACRO-SPORT

Design of a developed version of the Acro-Sport was started in January 1971. Construction began in the following year and the first flight of this prototype was made on 28 March 1973. Known as the Super Acro-Sport, it is intended for unlimited International Class aerobatic competition at a world championship level. Generally similar in external appearance to the Acro-Sport, it has a more powerful engine, nearly symmetrical aerofoil sections, a better rate of climb, and improved outside (negative g) aerobatic capability.

The differences by comparison with the standard Acro-Sport are covered in a supplement to the basic plans which are available from Acro-Sport Inc, PO Box 462, Hales Corners, Wisconsin 53130. The description of the Acro-Sport applies also to the Super Acro-Sport, except as follows:

TYPE: Single-seat advanced aerobatic biplane.
WINGS: As Acro-Sport, except wing section NACA 23012.
TAIL UNIT: As Acro-Sport, except controllable trim tab on starboard side of elevator, servo tab on port side.
LANDING GEAR: As Acro-Sport, except Cleveland hydraulic brakes. Steerable tailwheel has a solid tyre.
POWER PLANT: Prototype has one 149 kW (200 hp) Avco Lycoming IO-360-A2A flat-four engine, driving a Sensenich two-blade metal fixed-pitch propeller type 76EM8-0-60 with spinner. Fuel system and capacity as for Acro-Sport. Oil capacity 7·5 litres (2 US gallons).
DIMENSIONS, EXTERNAL: As for Acro-Sport, except:

Length overall	5·30 m (17 ft 4½ in)

WEIGHTS:

Weight empty	401 kg (884 lb)
Max T-O weight	612 kg (1,350 lb)

PERFORMANCE (at max T-O weight):

Never-exceed speed	156 knots (289 km/h; 180 mph)
Max level speed at S/L	135 knots (251 km/h; 156 mph)
Max cruising speed	117 knots (217 km/h; 135 mph)
Stalling speed	43·5 knots (80·5 km/h; 50 mph)
Max rate of climb at S/L	1,128 m (3,700 ft)/min
Service ceiling	4,570 m (15,000 ft)
T-O run	38 m (125 ft)
T-O to 15 m (50 ft)	91 m (300 ft)
Landing from 15 m (50 ft)	274 m (900 ft)
Landing run	244 m (800 ft)
Range with max fuel	260 nm (482 km; 300 miles)

EAA ACRO-SPORT II

The Acro-Sport II is a two-seat aerobatic biplane derived from the Acro-Sport I, by Mr Paul Poberezny, for the pilot with only a small number of flying hours to his credit. Design began in 1976 and construction started in 1977. The first flight was achieved on 9 July 1978. Plans are available to the homebuilder from Acro-Sport Inc (see Super Acro-Sport for address), and about 400 sets have been sold.

TYPE: Two-seat aerobatic biplane. Stress limits are +6·5g/−4·5g.
WINGS, FUSELAGE AND TAIL UNIT: As for Acro-Sport I.
LANDING GEAR: As for Acro-Sport I, except for main-wheel tyres size 6·00-6, pressure 1·86-1·93 bars (27-28 lb/sq in).
POWER PLANT: Prototype has one 134 kW (180 hp) Avco Lycoming O-360-A4B engine, driving a Sensenich two-blade metal fixed-pitch propeller with spinner. Can be powered by engines of 93-149 kW (125-200 hp). Fuel capacity 98·4 litres (26 US gallons).
ACCOMMODATION: Two seats in tandem in separate cockpits. Baggage space, capacity 13·6 kg (30 lb).
DIMENSIONS, EXTERNAL:

Wing span, upper	6·60 m (21 ft 8 in)
Wing span, lower	6·32 m (20 ft 9 in)
Wing chord, constant	1·09 m (3 ft 7 in)
Wing area, gross	14·12 m² (152 sq ft)
Length overall	5·75 m (18 ft 10¼ in)
Height overall	2·03 m (6 ft 7¾ in)
Wheel track	1·85 m (6 ft 0¾ in)

WEIGHTS:

Weight empty	397 kg (875 lb)
Max T-O weight	689 kg (1,520 lb)

PERFORMANCE (prototype):

Max cruising speed	107 knots (198 km/h; 123 mph)
Stalling speed	46 knots (86 km/h; 53 mph)
T-O run	91 m (300 ft)

EAA POBER P-9 PIXIE

Design and construction of this lightweight sporting aircraft began simultaneously in January 1974, and the first flight was made in July 1974.

It was conceived under 'Project Econoplane' to be economical in operation; and the prototype was originally powered by a converted Volkswagen motor car engine. The Pixie made its public debut at the 1974 EAA Fly-in at Oshkosh, Wisconsin. Soon afterwards, the prototype was re-engined with a Limbach-VW engine, and a special pressure cowl was fitted to improve cooling and increase the cruising speed.

Plans are available to amateur constructors from Acro-Sport Inc (see Super Acro-Sport for address), and more than 350 sets had been sold by January 1980.

TYPE: Single-seat lightweight sporting aircraft.
WINGS: Braced parasol monoplane. Two streamline-section struts and wire bracing each side. Wing section Clark Y. Dihedral 2°. Incidence 2°. Conventional wooden structure utilising spruce spars, mahogany plywood and fabric covering. Full-span Frise-type ailerons. No flaps. No trim tabs.
FUSELAGE: Welded structure of 4130 chrome molybdenum steel tubing with wood formers and fabric covering.
TAIL UNIT: Wire-braced structure of welded 4130 chrome molybdenum steel tubing, fabric covered. Fixed-incidence tailplane. No trim tabs.
LANDING GEAR: Non-retractable tailwheel type. Side Vees with half-axles carry main wheels. Shock-absorption by rubber bungee. Main wheels with tyres size 5·00-5, pressure 2·07 bars (30 lb/sq in). Tailwheel tyre of solid type. Cleveland brakes. Glassfibre fairings over main wheels.
POWER PLANT: One 44·5 kW (60 hp) Limbach SL 1700 EA flat-four engine, driving a Sensenich two-blade fixed-pitch propeller. Equally suited to Monnett Volkswagen engine conversions. Fuel tank in wing centre-section, capacity 46·6 litres (12·3 US gallons). Refuelling point on wing upper surface. Oil capacity 2·84 litres (0·75 US gallons).
ACCOMMODATION: Single seat in open cockpit. Door on starboard side. Baggage capacity 9 kg (20 lb).
DIMENSIONS, EXTERNAL:

Wing span	9·09 m (29 ft 10 in)
Wing chord, constant	1·37 m (4 ft 6 in)
Wing area, gross	12·47 m² (134·25 sq ft)
Length overall	5·26 m (17 ft 3 in)
Height overall	1·88 m (6 ft 2 in)
Wheel track	1·60 m (5 ft 3 in)
Propeller diameter	1·35 m (4 ft 5 in)

WEIGHTS:

Weight empty	246 kg (543 lb)
Max T-O weight	408 kg (900 lb)

PERFORMANCE (at max T-O weight):

Never-exceed speed	113 knots (209 km/h; 130 mph)
Max level speed at S/L	89 knots (166 km/h; 103 mph)
Max cruising speed	72 knots (134 km/h; 83 mph)
Stalling speed	26 knots (49 km/h; 30 mph)
Max rate of climb at S/L	213 m (700 ft)/min
Service ceiling	3,810 m (12,500 ft)
T-O and landing run	91 m (300 ft)
T-O to 15 m (50 ft)	305 m (1,000 ft)
Landing from 15 m (50 ft)	152 m (500 ft)
Range with max fuel	251 nm (466 km; 290 miles)

EAGLE
EAGLE HELICOPTER CORPORATION
Scottsdale, Arizona 85252

The Eagle Helicopter Corporation has developed and built prototypes of two lightweight helicopters. The Eagle II is a 'cold-jet' tip-driven helicopter (as illustrated) and the Eagle III is powered by two 0·178 kN (40 lb st) Gluhareff G8 pressure jet engines, mounted at the rotor tips and burning liquid propane. A 151 litre (40 US gallon) fuel tank is expected to give the Eagle III an endurance of about two hours.

EAGLE HELICOPTER EAGLE II

TYPE: Two-seat lightweight helicopter.
ROTOR SYSTEM: Two-blade rotor, driven by tip-mounted 'cold-jets' supplied with air from a bleed-air compressor. Rotor blades, which are hollow light alloy extrusions on prototype, are attached to the rotor hub by stainless steel torsion straps (production blades to be of stainless steel). Simple pylon structure immediately aft of cabin bulkhead. Max rotor speed 312 rpm. Normal rotor speed 212 rpm. No tail rotor. Cooling fan air is blown over rudder for control in hovering flight.
FUSELAGE: Rectangular-section forward fuselage, probably comprising basic steel tube structure and glassfibre shell.
TAIL UNIT: Small fin. Movable rudder, beneath fin, mounted centrally in efflux from compressor. Narrow-chord horizontal stabiliser mounted at base of fin trailing-edge.
POWER PLANT: One 175 kW (235 hp) Evinrude 200749 six-cylinder V engine. Compressor supplies air to cold-jets through hollow rotor mast and blades.
ACCOMMODATION: Two seats side by side in enclosed cabin. Probably conventional helicopter controls.
DIMENSIONS, EXTERNAL:

Rotor diameter	10·97 m (36 ft 0 in)
Rotor blade chord: prototype	0·23 m (9¼ in)
production	0·36 m (1 ft 2 in)
Length of fuselage	3·69 m (12 ft 1 in)
Width overall, less rotor	1·66 m (5 ft 5¼ in)
Height overall	2·13 m (7 ft 0 in)

WEIGHTS:

Weight empty	340 kg (750 lb)
Normal T-O weight	703 kg (1,550 lb)

PERFORMANCE (estimated):

Max cruising speed	78 knots (145 km/h; 90 mph)
Normal cruising speed	69·5 knots (129 km/h; 80 mph)
Max rate of climb at S/L	314 m (1,030 ft)/min
Vertical rate of climb at S/L	244 m (800 ft)/min
Hovering ceiling IGE	3,353 m (11,000 ft)
Hovering ceiling OGE	1,525 m (5,000 ft)
Service ceiling	4,575 m (15,000 ft)
Range at 60 knots (113 km/h; 70 mph)	174 nm (322 km; 200 miles)

EICH
JAMES P. EICH
1820 W Grand Avenue, Alhambra, California 91801
Telephone: (213) 289 1983

After gaining considerable experience from flying a Barnett J-3M rotorcraft, Mr Eich designed and built a two-seat gyroplane of which details follow. Design started in 1975 and construction of the prototype began the following year. First flight was achieved in 1977.

EICH JE-2 GYROPLANE

TYPE: Two-seat light autogyro.
ROTOR SYSTEM: Two-blade aluminium teetering rotor. Six struts forming the rotor pylon pick up the top of the fuselage structure at the corners of the front (passenger's) cockpit.
FUSELAGE: Square-section welded girder structure of chrome-molybdenum steel tubing, covered with Dacron and finished with Stits Poly-dope.
TAIL UNIT: Fixed horizontal stabiliser, triangular ventral fin and rudder. Fin is of Dacron, integral with fuselage covering. Stabiliser and rudder are of sheet aluminium, with simple ribs and spars of aluminium tubing.
LANDING GEAR: Non-retractable tricycle type. Spring-in-compression shock-absorption. Main-wheel tyres size 5·00-5. Steerable nosewheel with tyre size 4·00-5. Go-kart brakes.
POWER PLANT: One 48·5 kW (65 hp) Continental A65 engine, driving a two-blade Eich fixed-pitch tractor propeller. One fuel tank aft of firewall, capacity 60·5 litres (16 US gallons).
ACCOMMODATION: Two seats in tandem in open cockpits. Dual controls.
DIMENSIONS, EXTERNAL:

Diameter of main rotor	7·92 m (26 ft 0 in)
Rotor blade chord	0·187 m (7⅜ in)
Length overall	4·27 m (14 ft 0 in)
Height overall	2·44 m (8 ft 0 in)
Wheel track	1·83 m (6 ft 0 in)
Wheelbase	1·65 m (5 ft 5 in)
Propeller diameter	1·78 m (5 ft 10 in)

WEIGHTS:

Weight empty	200 kg (440 lb)
Max T-O weight	385·5 kg (850 lb)

PERFORMANCE:

Max cruising speed at 915 m (3,000 ft)	69·5 knots (129 km/h; 80 mph)
Econ cruising speed at 915 m (3,000 ft)	52 knots (96·5 km/h; 60 mph)
Max rate of climb at 915 m (3,000 ft)	91·5 m (300 ft)/min
T-O run	305 m (1,000 ft)
Landing run	15 m (50 ft)
Range	156 nm (290 km; 180 miles)

EVANS
EVANS AIRCRAFT
PO Box 744, La Jolla, California 92037

Mr W. S. Evans, while employed as a design engineer with the Convair Division of General Dynamics Corporation, set out to design for the novice homebuilder an all-wood aircraft that would be easy to build and safe to fly. He was prepared to sacrifice both appearance and performance to achieve this aim. Two years of spare-time design

EAA Pober P-9 Pixie *(Howard Levy)*

Evans VP-1 single-seat light aircraft *(Peter M. Bowers)*

Evans VP-2 two-seat monoplane

Prototype Eagle II 'cold-jet' helicopter *(Howard Levy)*

Eich JE-2 Gyroplane (Continental A65 engine)

and a year of construction produced a strut-braced low-wing monoplane with an all-moving tail unit, powered by a 30 kW (40 hp) Volkswagen engine, which Mr Evans named the Volksplane but which has since been designated VP-1.

The prototype was subsequently re-engined with a 39·5 kW (53 hp) Volkswagen, increasing the rate of climb to 183 m (600 ft)/min at sea level.

Mr Evans next developed a two-seat version of the VP-1, known as the VP-2. This is powered by a 44·5/48·5 kW (60/65 hp) Volkswagen engine, but in other respects has only minor constructional variations from the VP-1.

Plans of both models are available to amateur constructors, and approximately 6,000 sets had been sold by early 1980. The VP-1 is approved by the PFA for construction in the UK. VP-1 and VP-2 aircraft are currently flying in Australia, Belgium, Canada, France, West Germany, Italy, Ireland, Japan, New Zealand, the UK and the USA.

EVANS VP-1

TYPE: Single-seat light aircraft.
WINGS: Strut-braced low-wing monoplane. Two streamline-section bracing struts on each side. Wing section NACA 4412. Square tips. Dihedral 5°. Conventional wood structure with two rectangular spar beams, internal wooden compression struts and diagonal wire bracing, dispensing with the need for a complicated box spar. Fabric covering. Ailerons of wooden construction, fabric covered. No trim tabs. No flaps.
FUSELAGE: Rectangular-section all-wood stressed-skin structure, consisting essentially of three bulkheads, four longerons and plywood skin. Stressed-skin design eliminates the need for any diagonal bracing. Glassfibre fairing aft of pilot's seat.
TAIL UNIT: No fixed fin. The rudder is constructed of plywood ribs clamped to a 5·08 cm (2 in) aluminium tube which is mounted vertically through the rear fuselage and pivots in two nylon bushes. Leading- and trailing-edges are of wood and the whole unit is fabric-

covered. The fabric-covered all-moving tailplane is a wooden cantilever structure, comprising ply ribs blocked and glued to a simple constant-section box spar. Both rudder and tailplane have anti-servo tabs.
LANDING GEAR: Non-retractable main wheels and tailskid. Main wheels carried on a bent section of heavy-gauge 24ST-3 aluminium bar, wire-braced by diagonal cables. Shock-absorption by low-pressure tyres. Main wheels and tyres size 6·00-6. Tyre pressure 0·83 bars (12 lb/sq in). Hydraulic brakes operated by single hand lever.
POWER PLANT: One 30 kW, 39·5 kW or 44·5 kW (40 hp, 53 hp or 60 hp) modified Volkswagen motor car engine, driving a Hegy two-blade propeller, with pitch of 0·61 m (24 in) for 30 kW (40 hp) engine, 0·76 m (30 in) for 39·5 kW (53 hp) and 0·91 m (36 in) for 44·5 kW (60 hp). Glassfibre fuel tank aft of firewall and integral with the forward fuselage cowling, capacity 30 litres (8 US gallons). Filling point on top of fuselage, forward of windscreen.
ACCOMMODATION: Single seat in open cockpit. No baggage stowage.
DIMENSIONS, EXTERNAL:
Wing span	7·32 m (24 ft 0 in)
Wing chord, constant	1·27 m (4 ft 2 in)
Wing area, gross	9·29 m² (100 sq ft)
Length overall	5·49 m (18 ft 0 in)
Height overall	1·56 m (5 ft 1½ in)
Tailplane span	2·13 m (7 ft 0 in)
Wheel track	1·50 m (4 ft 11 in)
Propeller diameter	1·37 m (4 ft 6 in)
WEIGHTS:
Weight empty	200 kg (440 lb)
Max T-O weight	340 kg (750 lb)
PERFORMANCE (with 30 kW; 40 hp engine, at T-O weight of 295 kg; 650 lb):
Never-exceed speed	104 knots (193 km/h; 120 mph)
Cruising speed	65 knots (121 km/h; 75 mph)
Stalling speed	35 knots (65 km/h; 40 mph)
Max rate of climb at S/L	122 m (400 ft)/min

T-O run (average breeze)	137 m (450 ft)
Landing run (average breeze)	61 m (200 ft)

EVANS VP-2

TYPE: Two-seat light aircraft.
WINGS: Generally similar to VP-1, except for NACA 4415 wing section and increased wing span and chord.
FUSELAGE: Similar to VP-1, but width increased by 0·305 m (1 ft 0 in).
TAIL UNIT: Similar to VP-1. No fin. Increased rudder area; all-moving tailplane of increased span and chord.
LANDING GEAR: Similar to VP-1. Wheel track increased by 0·23 m (9 in).
POWER PLANT: One 44·5 kW (60 hp) 1,834 cc or 48·5 kW (65 hp) 2,100 cc modified Volkswagen motor car engine, driving a two-blade propeller. Glassfibre fuel tank aft of firewall, capacity 53 litres (14 US gallons).
ACCOMMODATION: Two seats side by side in open cockpit.
DIMENSIONS, EXTERNAL:
Wing span	8·23 m (27 ft 0 in)
Wing chord, constant	1·47 m (4 ft 10 in)
Wing area, gross	12·08 m² (130 sq ft)
Length overall	5·87 m (19 ft 3 in)
Tailplane span	2·44 m (8 ft 0 in)
Wheel track	1·73 m (5 ft 8 in)
Propeller diameter	1·52 m (5 ft 0 in)
WEIGHTS:
Weight empty	290 kg (640 lb)
Max T-O weight	471 kg (1,040 lb)
PERFORMANCE (44·5 kW; 60 hp engine, at max T-O weight):
Never-exceed speed	104 knots (193 km/h; 120 mph)
Max level speed	87 knots (161 km/h; 100 mph)
Max cruising speed	65 knots (121 km/h; 75 mph)
Stalling speed	35 knots (64·5 km/h; 40 mph)
Max rate of climb at S/L (pilot only)	213 m (700 ft)/min
Max rate of climb at S/L (pilot and passenger)	122 m (400 ft)/min

FIKE
WILLIAM J. FIKE

Mr W. J. (Bill) Fike, bush pilot and designer of a series

of light aircraft since 1929, died on 31 December 1979. Descriptions of his Model 'D' and Model 'E' can be found in the 1979-80 *Jane's*.

FISHER-VAN NORMAN
DICK FISHER and CHARLES VAN NORMAN
FISHER-VAN NORMAN REPLICA P-51D MUSTANG

Mr Dick Fisher, an operations project engineer with NASA, and Mr Charles Van Norman, an engineer with the USAF Flight Test Center at Edwards Air Force Base, have designed and built a ⅔-scale replica of a North American P-51D Mustang fighter of the Second World War. The complete project occupied their spare time for 14 years and each man devoted about 5,000 hours to construction of the aircraft over the final 11-year period. The first flight was made in July 1978.

TYPE: Single-seat scale replica fighter.

WINGS: Cantilever all-wood structure, covered with plywood and an outer skin of Dacron fabric, finished with automotive acrylic enamel. Electrically-actuated flaps.

FUSELAGE: All-wood semi-monocoque structure, covered with plywood and an outer skin of Dacron fabric, finished with automotive acrylic enamel.

TAIL UNIT: Conventional cantilever structure of similar construction to wings. Electric pitch trim.

LANDING GEAR: Retractable tailwheel type. Main legs from a Globe Swift. Hydraulically-actuated main units; electrically-actuated tailwheel.

POWER PLANT: One 149 kW (200 hp) Ranger 6-440-C5 engine, driving a two-blade propeller with spinner. Fuel capacity 113·5 litres (30 US gallons).

ACCOMMODATION: Single seat under blown canopy.

WEIGHTS:
Weight empty	658 kg (1,450 lb)
Max T-O weight	839 kg (1,850 lb)

PERFORMANCE:
Max level speed over 174 knots (322 km/h; 200 mph)
Max rate of climb at S/L
305-457 m (1,000-1,500 ft)/min
Range with max fuel at 148 knots (274 km/h; 170 mph)
434 nm (805 km; 500 miles)
Endurance with max fuel   3 h

FLAGLOR
FLAGLOR AIRCRAFT
1550A Sanders Road, Northbrook, Illinois 60062

The latest of a series of light aircraft designed and built in prototype form by Mr K. Flaglor is an ultra-light sporting monoplane named the Scooter. Design work began in July 1965, and construction was started in November of the same year.

The prototype Scooter was powered originally by a 13·5 kW (18 hp) Cushman golf-kart engine, and it was with this power plant that the first flight was made in June 1967. Performance was marginal and, as a result, Mr Flaglor replaced the Cushman with an 18·5-21 kW (25-28 hp) Volkswagen engine. Current power plant is a 1,500 cc Volkswagen engine developing 30 kW (40 hp). When flown to the 1967 EAA meet at Rockford, Illinois, the prototype Scooter won the 'Outstanding Ultra-light' and 'Outstanding Volkswagen-Powered Airplane' awards. Plans are available to amateur constructors from Ace Aircraft Manufacturing Company (which see), and many Scooters are flying.

FLAGLOR SCOOTER

The following description applies to the prototype Scooter in its current form:

TYPE: Ultra-light sporting monoplane.

WINGS: High-wing monoplane, braced by wires attached to fuselage and to kingpost mounted above centre-section. Wing section NACA 23012. Dihedral 2°. Incidence 3°. Two-spar all-wood structure with wood drag and anti-drag bracing. Aluminium leading-edge and plywood covering. Conventional wooden ailerons. No flaps. No trim tabs.

FUSELAGE: Wooden structure, plywood-covered in the forward cockpit area, fabric-covered aft. Fuselage of triangular section aft of the wing. Wing centre-section and engine mounting constructed of 4130 steel tube.

TAIL UNIT: All-wood construction with strut bracing. No fixed fin. No trim tabs.

LANDING GEAR: Non-retractable tailwheel type. Fixed spring steel main units. Steerable tailwheel. Main wheels of go-kart type, size 4·10 × 3·50-5. Tyre pressure 1·38 bars (20 lb/sq in). Vespa or Sears motor scooter brakes.

POWER PLANT: One 30 kW (40 hp) Volkswagen 1,500 cc flat-four engine, driving a two-blade Troyer 54-28 propeller. Single fuel tank in fuselage nose, capacity 19 litres (5 US gallons). Refuelling point on top of fuselage forward of windscreen. Oil capacity 2·37 litres (2·5 US quarts).

ACCOMMODATION: Single seat in cockpit protected by deep windscreen.

DIMENSIONS, EXTERNAL:
Wing span	8·64 m (28 ft 0 in)
Wing chord, constant	1·27 m (4 ft 2 in)
Wing area, gross	10·68 m² (115 sq ft)
Wing aspect ratio	6·7
Length overall	4·78 m (15 ft 8 in)
Height overall	2·13 m (7 ft 0 in)
Tailplane span	2·18 m (7 ft 2 in)
Wheel track	1·37 m (4 ft 6 in)

WEIGHTS:
Weight empty	177 kg (390 lb)
Max T-O and landing weight	295 kg (650 lb)

PERFORMANCE:
Never-exceed speed	82 knots (153 km/h; 95 mph)
Max level speed	78 knots (145 km/h; 90 mph)
Max cruising speed	69 knots (129 km/h; 80 mph)
Econ cruising speed	56 knots (105 km/h; 65 mph)
Stalling speed	30 knots (55 km/h; 34 mph)
Max rate of climb at S/L	183 m (600 ft)/min
T-O and landing run	76 m (250 ft)
Range with max fuel	152 nm (282 km; 175 miles)

FLIGHT DYNAMICS
FLIGHT DYNAMICS INC
PO Box 5070, State University Station, Raleigh, North Carolina 27607
Telephone: (919) 781 6198 or 834 6806
PRESIDENT: Thomas H. Purcell Jr

FLIGHT DYNAMICS SEASPRITE

The Seasprite is the unpowered Stage I version of the aircraft which in a fully-developed powered form will be designated Seasprite II. The Seasprite is of simplified construction, and is available in plans form to amateur sailplane constructors.

Flight Dynamics has modified the original design, replacing the single tail unit by one which has twin fins and rudders; the Seasprite has also been provided with non-reversing differential ailerons. It is planned to power this airframe with two West Bend engines, each of approximately 7·5 kW (10 hp).

The following description applies to the unpowered model:

TYPE: Single/two-seat homebuilt glider.

AIRFRAME: Fuselage, of aerofoil/hydrofoil cross-section, is built on a framework of aluminium tubing. Sides and top are covered with polyethylene foil, except for upper part of nose section, which has a transparent covering of polyester film and Plexiglas. Pilot sits in centre-section, between twin booms, each of which carries at the aft end a fin and rudder. The fins are linked by a tailplane, attached to the tops of the fins and carrying a full-span elevator. Underside of fuselage/hull has catamaran-type twin floats, built of plastics with a plywood covering. For only a minimal weight increase, structure can be covered instead with aluminium foil, which has a much longer life. Wings are of triangular planform, and are of sailwing type, with aluminium tube leading-edge, wire trailing-edge, and polyethylene covering. They are braced to fuselage sides, and can be folded rearward when not in use. Wingtips pivot about their leading-edges, to provide roll control.

DIMENSIONS, EXTERNAL:
Wing span	10·36 m (34 ft 0 in)
Wing area	15·42 m² (166 sq ft)
Wing aspect ratio	6·96
Length overall	6·10 m (20 ft 0 in)
Height overall	2·44 m (8 ft 0 in)

WEIGHTS:
Weight empty	75 kg (165 lb)
Max T-O weight	227 kg (500 lb)

PERFORMANCE:
Powered performance not known

FLYRAY
FLYRAY

FLYRAY

Few details are available of this foot-launched flying-wing aircraft, which was at an advanced stage of construction in the Summer of 1979. Power is provided by an 0·58 kN (130 lb st) Gluhareff jet unit, mounted on top of the central fin and rudder. Flyray is said to be stressed to +3·8g and −3g. Plans will be made available eventually to amateur constructors.

DIMENSIONS, EXTERNAL:
Wing span	12·19 m (40 ft 0 in)
Wing area, gross	13·94 m² (150 sq ft)

WEIGHT:
Max T-O weight	204 kg (450 lb)

PERFORMANCE:
T-O and landing speed
8·7-13 knots (16-24 km/h; 10-15 mph)

FREDERICK-AMES
FREDERICK-AMES RESEARCH CORPORATION
Novi, Michigan
PRESIDENT: Frederick Smith

FREDERICK-AMES EOS

Mr Fred Smith, president of Frederick-Ames Research Corporation, designed a small single-seat sporting aircraft called the EOS, which first appeared in an incomplete form at the 1973 EAA Fly-in at Oshkosh. After the meeting the EOS was completed; but on its maiden flight the Hirth engine seized and the aircraft crash landed, causing extensive damage. Although some restoration work was carried out, the aircraft was subsequently abandoned through lack of finance. In early 1978 the project was revived, with a Volkswagen modified motor car engine in place of the original engine. First flight of the reworked aircraft was in mid-1978, piloted by Mr Robert Bishop. By August 1978 the EOS had completed about ten flying hours, and further modifications to the aircraft had been made. Changes still to be made at that time included fitting new ailerons, and re-contouring the fin and rudder.

Kits to build the EOS will be made available to amateur constructors in due course. All aluminium sheet is bent and flat wrapped, with no complicated forming. Structures are pop riveted and bonded, requiring no welding.

TYPE: Single-seat light sporting aircraft.

WINGS: Cantilever tapered low-wing monoplane. Wing section NACA 651212. Light alloy all-metal structure, except for glassfibre wing fillets, pop riveted and epoxy resin bonded.

FUSELAGE: Conventional light alloy semi-monocoque structure, pop riveted and epoxy resin bonded. Glassfibre engine cowling.

TAIL UNIT: Cantilever light alloy structure, comprising triangular fin, integral with rear fuselage, rudder, and all-moving tailplane with projecting balance arms at roots. Tailplane actuated via servo tabs.

LANDING GEAR: Manually-retractable tricycle type. Main units retract inwards. Fully-castoring and steerable nosewheel. Rubber-in-compression shock-absorption. Disc brakes.

POWER PLANT: One 52 kW (70 hp) 1,834 cc Volkswagen modified motor car engine, driving through a 178 mm (7 in) extension shaft a Rand Robinson three-blade ground-adjustable propeller, with Mooney 201 spinner. Fuel capacity 56·75 litres (15 US gallons).

ACCOMMODATION: Single glassfibre seat under large transparent canopy.

SYSTEM: Electrical system includes 45A alternator and starter.

DIMENSIONS, EXTERNAL:
Wing span	7·92 m (26 ft 0 in)
Wing area, gross	6·97 m² (75 sq ft)
Wing aspect ratio	9
Length overall	5·05 m (16 ft 7 in)
Height overall	1·98 m (6 ft 6 in)
Propeller diameter	1·27 m (4 ft 2 in)

WEIGHTS:
Weight empty	304 kg (670 lb)
Max T-O weight	442 kg (975 lb)

PERFORMANCE (as tested by early 1979):
Max level speed (estimated)
174 knots (322 km/h; 200 mph)
Cruising speed (70% power) at 1,525 m (5,000 ft)
152 knots (281 km/h; 175 mph)
Stalling speed at 1,370 m (4,500 ft)
50 knots (92 km/h; 57 mph) IAS
Max rate of climb at S/L   305 m (1,000 ft)/min
T-O run   305 m (1,000 ft)

²⁄₃-scale replica of a P-51D Mustang, built by Mr Dick Fisher and Mr Charles Van Norman *(Howard Levy)*

Flaglor Scooter built by Japanese students of Tokyo Aeronautical College

Two views of the Flyray jet-powered homebuilt aircraft, minus outer wings *(Henry Artof)*

Flight Dynamics Seasprite single/two-seat homebuilt glider

Frederick-Ames EOS single-seat sporting aircraft *(Howard Levy)*

Beets G/B Special lightweight sporting aircraft (Volkswagen engine)

G/B AIRCRAFT
GLENN BEETS
460 Colorado Road, GVSR, Kingman, Arizona 86401
Telephone: (602) 565 3350

Mr Glenn Beets designed a lightweight sporting aircraft which he named the G/B Special. Construction of the prototype occupied two years and the first flight was made on 25 July 1973. Plans of the G/B Special, kits of components and materials are available to amateur constructors. Cost of building is about $7,500.

BEETS G/B SPECIAL
TYPE: Single-seat sporting aircraft.
WINGS: Braced parasol monoplane. Wing section Curtis 72. Sweepback 10°. V bracing struts each side with auxiliary struts. N-type cabane struts. Conventional wood structure with spruce spars and truss ribs, Dacron covered. Plain ailerons of similar construction. No trim tabs. Cutout in wing trailing-edge.
FUSELAGE: Welded structure of 4130 steel tube with Dacron covering.
TAIL UNIT: Cantilever structure of wood, with foam filling and covering of ¹⁄₁₆ in mahogany plywood.
LANDING GEAR: Non-retractable tailwheel type, with main wheels carried on braced tubular steel struts. Rubber-block shock-absorption; optional spring type or rigid gear. Glassfibre wheel fairings on main wheels.
POWER PLANT: One 52 kW (70 hp) Volkswagen 1,700 cc modified motorcar engine, driving a Hendrickson laminated birch two-blade fixed-pitch propeller through a 2½ : 1 reduction drive. Design will accept engines of 37·25-74·5 kW (50-100 hp). Fuel capacity 56·75 litres (15 US gallons).
ACCOMMODATION: Single seat in open cockpit.
DIMENSIONS, EXTERNAL:

Wing span	7·62 m (25 ft 0 in)
Wing area, gross	9·29 m² (100 sq ft)
Wing chord	1·27 m (4 ft 2 in)
Length overall	4·98 m (16 ft 4 in)
Height overall	1·83 m (6 ft 0 in)
Propeller diameter	1·98 m (6 ft 6 in)

WEIGHTS:

Weight empty	274 kg (603 lb)
Max T-O weight	420 kg (925 lb)

PERFORMANCE (at max T-O weight with cruise performance propeller):

Max level speed at S/L	135 knots (251 km/h; 156 mph)
Cruising speed	104 knots (193 km/h; 120 mph)
Landing speed	30·5 knots (56 km/h; 35 mph)
Max rate of climb at S/L	610 m (2,000 ft)/min
T-O run	61 m (200 ft)
Landing run	92 m (300 ft)
Range	520 nm (965 km; 600 miles)

GREGA
JOHN W. GREGA
355 Grand Boulevard, Bedford, Ohio 44146

In addition to the standard Aircamper design, of which plans are available from Mr Bernard H. Pietenpol (see under 'Pietenpol'), a modernised version has been evolved by Mr John Grega. Plans of this are available to homebuilders, and by 1980 about 600 sets had been sold.

GN-1 AIRCAMPER
The prototype of this modernised version of the Aircamper two-seat light monoplane flew for the first time in November 1965. It uses cut-down Piper J-3 Cub wings

and bracing struts and J-3 Cub landing gear. Other differences compared with the standard Aircamper (which see) are as follows:

POWER PLANT: One 48·5 kW (65 hp) Continental A65-8 flat-four engine in prototype, driving a two-blade 72/41 metal fixed-pitch propeller. Other engines of up to 63·5 kW (85 hp) can be installed. Fuel tanks aft of firewall, capacity 45 litres (12 US gallons), and in wing centre-section, capacity 22·5 litres (6 US gallons). Oil capacity 3·75 litres (1 US gallon).

DIMENSIONS, EXTERNAL:	
Wing span	8·84 m (29 ft 0 in)
Wing chord, constant	1·52 m (5 ft 0 in)
Wing area, gross	13·94 m² (150 sq ft)
Wing aspect ratio	6
Length overall	5·51 m (18 ft 1 in)
Height overall	2·06 m (6 ft 9 in)
Tailplane span	2·29 m (7 ft 6 in)
Wheel track	1·60 m (5 ft 3 in)
WEIGHT:	
Max T-O weight	499 kg (1,100 lb)

PERFORMANCE (at max T-O weight):	
Max level speed at S/L	100 knots (185 km/h; 115 mph)
Max cruising speed at S/L	78 knots (145 km/h; 90 mph)
Stalling speed	31 knots (56 km/h; 35 mph)
Max rate of climb at S/L	152 m (500 ft)/min
T-O run	122 m (400 ft)
Landing run	76 m (250 ft)
Range with max fuel	347 nm (640 km; 400 miles)

HARMON
HARMON ENGINEERING COMPANY

PO Box 227, Rt 4, Sherman, Texas 75090
Telephone: (214) 893 2682
PRESIDENT: James B. Harmon

Harmon Engineering Company designed and built the prototype of a single-seat sporting aircraft named Der Donnerschlag (The Thunderclap). Design began in December 1972, and construction of the prototype started six months later. The first flight of this aircraft took place in June 1974.

Four months later, the aircraft suffered an engine failure while being flown by Mr James Harmon. He hit the ground at 52 knots (96 km/h; 60 mph) at a 45° impact angle, but was able to walk away from the accident. The aircraft was so little damaged that the decision was made to rebuild it as the prototype of a variant of Der Donnerschlag named Mister America. Design of the variant was started in November 1974, simultaneously with the rebuilding, and first flight of Mister America took place on 31 October 1975.

Plans of Der Donnerschlag are no longer available, but full details of the aircraft can be found in the 1978-79 *Jane's*. Those for Mister America remain available and more than 30 sets had been sold by early 1980. Mr Harmon is currently working on a number of new projects; no details of these were available at the time of going to press.

HARMON 1-2 MISTER AMERICA
TYPE: Single-seat lightweight sporting aircraft.

WINGS: Wire-braced shoulder-wing monoplane. Original wing section, with thickness/chord ratio of 14·5%. Dihedral 1°-2°. Incidence 0°. Wooden structure with fabric covering. Two simple beam spars; built-up ribs. Plain ailerons of similar construction. No flaps. Provision for ground-adjustable tabs in ailerons, if required. Dual flying and landing wires each side, landing wires attached to cabane structure at forward end of fuselage, which also forms windscreen support.

FUSELAGE: Welded structure of 4130 chrome-molybdenum steel tube with fabric covering. Wooden stringer turtledeck, with fabric covering. Aluminium and glassfibre engine cowling.

TAIL UNIT: Wire-braced welded structure of 4130 chrome-molybdenum steel tube with fabric covering. Tailplane incidence ground-adjustable. Elevators fitted. Provision for ground-adjustable trim tabs, if required.

LANDING GEAR: Non-retractable tailwheel type. Main units consist of two Vees, attached to fuselage structure, wire-braced and with a through axle. Shock-absorption by rubber bungee. Cleveland 5·00-5 main wheels and tyres, pressure 1·03 bars (15 lb/sq in). Aviation Products 10 cm (4 in) steerable tailwheel. Cleveland disc brakes with air cooling. Faired main legs and wheels.

POWER PLANT: One 44·7-48·5 kW (60-65 hp) 1,650 cc Volkswagen modified motor car engine, driving a two-blade fixed-pitch 54-36 propeller. Fuel tank aft of engine firewall, capacity 34 litres (9 US gallons). Refuelling point forward of windscreen.

ACCOMMODATION: Single seat in open cockpit.

DIMENSIONS, EXTERNAL:	
Wing span	5·99 m (19 ft 8 in)
Wing chord, constant	1·22 m (4 ft 0 in)
Wing area, gross	7·06 m² (76·0 sq ft)
Wing aspect ratio	4·916
Length overall	4·62 m (15 ft 2 in)
Height overall	1·52 m (5 ft 0 in)
Tailplane span	1·78 m (5 ft 10 in)
Wheel track	1·52 m (5 ft 0 in)
Wheelbase	3·51 m (11 ft 6 in)
Propeller diameter	1·37 m (4 ft 6 in)
DIMENSIONS, INTERNAL:	
Cockpit: Max width	0·52 m (1 ft 8½ in)
WEIGHTS:	
Weight empty	195 kg (430 lb)
Max T-O weight	295 kg (650 lb)
PERFORMANCE:	
Never-exceed speed	143 knots (265 km/h; 165 mph)
Max level speed at S/L	109 knots (201 km/h; 125 mph)
Max cruising speed at S/L	95·5 knots (177 km/h; 110 mph)
Econ cruising speed at S/L	87 knots (161 km/h; 100 mph)
Stalling speed	42 knots (77·5 km/h; 48 mph)
Max rate of climb at S/L	244 m (800 ft)/min
Service ceiling	3,660 m (12,000 ft)
T-O run	61 m (200 ft)
T-O to 15 m (50 ft)	122 m (400 ft)
Landing from 15 m (50 ft)	152 m (500 ft)
Landing run	92 m (300 ft)
Range with max fuel	347 nm (643 km; 400 miles)

HATZ
HATZ AIRPLANE SHOP

Rt 2, Gleason, Wisconsin 54435
INFORMATION: Dudley Kelly, Rt 4, Versailles, Kentucky 40383

Mr John D. Hatz designed and built the prototype of a two-seat lightweight biplane, designated CB-1, of which plans are available to amateur constructors. Design and construction started in September 1959, and the first flight of the CB-1 was made on 19 April 1968. It was then powered by a 63·5 kW (85 hp) Continental C85-12 engine, but this was replaced subsequently by a 112 kW (150 hp) Avco Lycoming O-320.

The first plans-built CB-1 flew for the first time on 15 June 1975, powered by a Continental O-200 engine. Many more CB-1s are under construction, and at least six are flying.

HATZ CB-1 BIPLANE
The following amended details conform with the plans currently marketed by Hatz:
TYPE: Two-seat lightweight biplane.
WINGS: Braced single-bay biplane, with N-type interplane struts each side. N-type centre-section struts and streamline-section flying and landing wires. Wing section Clark Y. Dihedral 2°, on lower wings only. Incidence (both wings) 0°. Wooden two-spar structure with fabric covering. Cutout in trailing-edge of upper wing. Plain unbalanced ailerons of wood construction, with fabric covering, on both wings. No flaps. No trim tabs.

FUSELAGE: Welded steel tube structure, with fabric covering.

TAIL UNIT: Wire-braced welded steel tube structure, with fabric covering. Trim tab in elevator.

LANDING GEAR: Non-retractable tailwheel type. Two side Vs and half-axles hinged to fuselage structure. Steel spring shock-absorption. Main wheels size 6·50-6, with Goodyear tyres, pressure 1·03 bars (15 lb/sq in). Cleveland hydraulic wheel brakes. Glassfibre fairings on main wheels.

POWER PLANT: One 86 kW (115 hp) Avco Lycoming O-235 flat-four engine, driving a Sensenich two-blade metal fixed-pitch propeller. Single fuel tank in centre-section of upper wing, capacity 68 litres (18 US gallons). Refuelling point on upper surface of upper wing centre-section. Oil capacity 7·5 litres (2 US gallons).

ACCOMMODATION: Two seats in tandem in open cockpits.

SYSTEM: Electrical system, with 12V 12A DC engine-driven generator and 12V battery, for engine starting, navigation and instrument lights.

DIMENSIONS, EXTERNAL:	
Wing span (both)	7·72 m (25 ft 4 in)
Wing chord, constant (both)	1·27 m (4 ft 2 in)
Wing area, gross	16·54 m² (178 sq ft)
Wing aspect ratio	6·06
Length overall	5·79 m (19 ft 0 in)
Height overall	2·39 m (7 ft 10 in)
Tailplane span	2·74 m (9 ft 0 in)
Wheel track	1·83 m (6 ft 0 in)
Propeller diameter	1·78 m (5 ft 10 in)
WEIGHTS:	
Weight empty	397 kg (875 lb)
Max T-O weight	726 kg (1,600 lb)
PERFORMANCE (at max T-O weight):	
Never-exceed speed	130 knots (241 km/h; 150 mph)
Max cruising speed	78 knots (145 km/h; 90 mph)
Stalling speed	35 knots (64·5 km/h; 40 mph)
Max rate of climb at S/L	244 m (800 ft)/min
T-O run	approx 122 m (400 ft)
Range with max fuel, 30 min reserves	174 nm (322 km; 200 miles)

HOLLMANN
HOLLMANN AIRCRAFT

11082 Bel Aire Court, Cupertino, California 95014
Telephone: (408) 255 2194

The HA-2M Sportster two-seat gyroplane has been developed by Mr Martin Hollmann, a senior design engineer in the aerospace industry. It is claimed to be the first aircraft of its type designed for the homebuilder who has access to a minimum of power tools. About 90 per cent of the structure is bolted and riveted together, and a minimum of machined parts are used.

Two average-size people can fly in the Sportster, which is suitable for pilot training and for flying on short cross-country journeys of up to 78 nm (145 km; 90 miles). It has been designed for towing behind a car, with the rotor stowed in a box attached to the car's roof. From the towed condition, the Sportster can be ready for its pre-flight walk-round inspection in ten minutes.

Plans, materials and many components are available to amateur constructors, and a network of distributors has been organised.

HOLLMANN HA-2M SPORTSTER

Design of this gyroplane began in June 1969, and construction of the first prototype was started in December 1972. The first flight of the prototype was made in October 1974, with FAA certification in the Experimental category. The first passenger was Dr Tom Butler, Vice-President Engineering and Research of AMF Incorporated, who flew in October 1975; test flying was completed by January 1976. The same year the prototype won a 'Best Original Design' award at the EAA Oshkosh meeting and an 'Outstanding New Design' award at the PRA Fly-in at Rockford. In 1977 it received the 'Best Autogyro' award at the EAA's Annual Antique Fly-in and air show at Watsonville, California. The prototype Sportster had logged over 160 flying hours by early 1979.

The Sportster utilises a collective pitch mechanism and a mechanical pre-rotator which engages the engine, via a clutch, prior to take-off to pre-spin the rotor to 300 rpm. This allows the aircraft to take off after a very short run, and is expected to permit jump starts after brief further development. A rotor brake is utilised to slow down the rotor after landing and to stop the blades for taxying. A tension spring is adjusted from within the cockpit to trim the control stick in pitch.

By early 1980 more than 50 Sportsters were under construction in the USA, Canada, New Zealand and Sweden. Most of these will be powered by an Avco Lycoming O-320 engine, rated at 112 kW (150 hp). Several Sportsters are flying.

TYPE: Two-seat gyroplane.

ROTOR SYSTEM: Two-blade rotor of NACA 8-H-12 section. Solidity ratio 0·035. Pre-cone angle 2°. Blade pitch +2½°. Metal blades, each made up of a 2024-T8511 leading-edge extrusion, aluminium formed ribs and Alclad skin, riveted and bonded together. Rotor rpm 380.

FUSELAGE: Square-tube 6061-T6 aluminium structure, bolted together. Aluminium skin. Glassfibre fairings. Two mast tubes. Large rear window for 360° view.

TAIL UNIT: Twin fins and balanced rudders carried on short tailbooms. Aluminium structure, with 2024-T3 Alclad skins pop-riveted in place. Glassfibre tips. Fixed horizontal surface between fins.

LANDING GEAR: Non-retractable tricycle type, with single wheel on each unit. Two small tailwheels. Main-wheel tyres size 18 × 6, pressure 1·8 bars (26 lb/sq in). Nose-wheel tyre of 0·25 m (10 in) diameter, pressure 1·8 bars (26 lb/sq in). Mechanical drum brake on nosewheel only.

POWER PLANT: One 97 kW (130 hp) Franklin Sport 4B flat-four engine, driving a Troyer 6635 pusher propeller, on prototype. One fuel tank of 45·4 litres (12 US gallons) capacity, with refuelling point inside cockpit. Oil capacity 5·7 litres (1·5 US gallons). Most other aircraft fitted with an Avco Lycoming O-320 engine, rated at 112 kW (150 hp), driving a Troyer 6648 propeller.

Grega GN-1 Aircamper two-seat light monoplane

Harmon Mister America sporting aircraft

First plans-built Hatz CB-1 biplane, built by Mr Dudley Kelly

Hollmann HA-2M Sportster two-seat gyroplane

Hovey Beta Bird, a monoplane derivative of the Whing Ding II

Hovey Whing Ding II built by Mr Lin Bruty of Mt Emu Farm, Australia
(The Herald & Weekly Times, Melbourne)

ACCOMMODATION: Two seats side by side in cabin with open sides.
SYSTEMS: Standard aircraft instruments and Narco Mk IV radio in prototype. 12V battery. Rotor pre-rotation and collective pitch system to spin rotor to 300 rpm.
DIMENSIONS, EXTERNAL:

Rotor diameter	8·53 m (28 ft 0 in)
Blade chord, constant	0·23 m (9 in)
Length overall	3·66 m (12 ft 0 in)
Height to top of rotor hub	2·34 m (7 ft 8 in)
Tailplane span	1·17 m (3 ft 10 in)
Wheel track	2·06 m (6 ft 9 in)

Wheelbase	1·42 m (4 ft 8 in)
Propeller diameter	1·68 m (5 ft 6 in)

DIMENSIONS, INTERNAL:

Max width	0·914 m (3 ft 0 in)
Max height	1·45 m (4 ft 9 in)

WEIGHTS (A: prototype, B: 112 kW; 150 hp engine):

Weight empty, equipped: A	281 kg (620 lb)
Max T-O and landing weight: A	476 kg (1,050 lb)
B	500 kg (1,100 lb)

PERFORMANCE (A: prototype, B: 112 kW; 150 hp engine):
Never-exceed speed at S/L

A	78 knots (145 km/h; 90 mph)

Max cruising speed at S/L	
A	65 knots (121 km/h; 75 mph)
Econ cruising speed at S/L	
A	52 knots (97 km/h; 60 mph)
Stalling speed: A	24·5 knots (45 km/h; 28 mph)
Max rate of climb at S/L: A	152 m (500 ft)/min
B	213 m (700 ft)/min
Service ceiling	2,440 m (8,000 ft)
T-O run	107 m (350 ft)
Landing run	0·6 m (0-20 ft)
Range with max fuel	78 nm (145 km; 90 miles)
Range with max payload	61 nm (112 km; 70 miles)

HOVEY
ROBERT W. HOVEY
Aircraft Specialties Co, PO Box 1074, Canyon Country, California 91351
Telephone: (805) 252 4054

Mr Hovey designed and built an ultra-lightweight biplane of which plans are available to amateur constructors. His objective was to produce an aircraft which would require minimal construction time and have STOL performance, and which could be quickly disassembled for transportation. To achieve these ends the design has some unusual features, such as wing warping for roll control and use of an aluminium tube tailboom which has high-strength light alloy sheet and urethane foam stiffening. The original tail surfaces of craft paper over a styrofoam core have, however, been superseded by new horizontal and vertical tail surfaces of fabric-covered spruce construction.

Design began in October 1970, construction starting in the following month. First flight was made in February

1971, at which time the aircraft, known as Whing Ding II, received FAA certification in the Experimental category.

The original prototype was sold in Japan, where considerable interest was aroused among homebuilders. A second prototype was completed subsequently. Over 7,000 sets of plans had been sold and many Whing Dings were under construction or flying by early 1980. In January 1980 the original plans were revised to increase the wing span by 0·51 m (1 ft 8 in). This improves climb and load carrying performance, as a result of lower induced drag and reduced wing loading.

Mr Hovey's latest design is a monoplane derivative of the WD-II, known as the Beta Bird (originally Bushwacker), which was flown for the first time in April 1979.

HOVEY WHING DING II (WD-II)
TYPE: Single-seat ultra-lightweight biplane.
WINGS: Braced single-bay biplane with parallel streamline-section interplane struts. Aircraft's fuselage, into which wing spars are socketed, gives location of

inboard ends of wings. Landing and flying wires, the rear flying wires being used to control warping of upper wing. Wing section Hovey-10. Thickness/chord ratio 10%. Dihedral, both 1°. Incidence, both 4°. No sweepback. Wooden two-spar structure with ribs formed of 9·5 mm (⅜ in) light alloy tube. Wingtip bows of 9·5 mm (⅜ in) light alloy tube. Leading-edge faired in with rigid urethane foam. Wing structure fabric covered, tension of which retains the ribs in position. A plasticised fabric dope is used to ensure adequate flexibility for wing warping. No ailerons. No flaps. No trim tabs.
FUSELAGE: A closed box structure of 3·2 mm (⅛ in) mahogany plywood glued to 12·7 mm (½ in) square pine stringers, which is filled with urethane foam to stiffen and stabilise the plywood skin. This narrow fuselage provides attachment points for the seat, rudder bar and controls, and sockets for the wing spars. A reinforced extension at the top of the fuselage carries the engine. Aluminium tube tailboom is reinforced by high-strength alloy sheet at the forward end, this being

wrapped around the tube and bonded with epoxy resin. The entire tube is filled with free-foam urethane.

TAIL UNIT: Strut-braced structure. Horizontal and vertical surfaces constructed of 12·7 mm (½ in) square-section spruce, with fabric covering. All-moving tailplane, attached to tailboom by piano hinge. Rudder attached to fin by cloth hinges. No trim tabs.

LANDING GEAR: Non-retractable tailwheel type. Main wheels carried on spring-type strut of laminated fir covered with a layer of polyester glassfibre. Go-kart type main wheels with 28 cm (11 in) diameter tyres. Tyre pressure 1·38 bars (20 lb/sq in). Tailwheel has solid rubber tyre. Alternative steel tube landing gear available.

POWER PLANT: One 10·44 kW (14 hp) McCulloch MC-101A single-cylinder two-stroke aircooled go-kart engine, driving a two-blade hand-carved laminated birch or beechwood fixed-pitch pusher propeller. Original chain-drive reduction system now replaced by a double V belt drive. Fuel tank integral with engine, capacity 1·9 litres (0·5 US gallons).

ACCOMMODATION: Pilot only on open seat.

EQUIPMENT: Basic instrumentation only, comprising airspeed and engine speed indicators and cylinder head temperature gauge.

DIMENSIONS, EXTERNAL:
Wing span (both)	5·69 m (18 ft 8 in)
Wing chord (both), constant	0·91 m (3 ft 0 in)
Wing area, gross	9·85 m² (106 sq ft)
Wing aspect ratio	5·9
Length overall	4·27 m (14 ft 0 in)
Height overall	1·68 m (5 ft 6 in)
Tailplane span	1·93 m (6 ft 4 in)
Wheel track	1·22 m (4 ft 0 in)
Wheelbase	2·97 m (9 ft 9 in)
Propeller diameter	1·22 m (4 ft 0 in)

WEIGHTS:
Weight empty, incl fuel	55·5 kg (123 lb)
Max T-O weight	140 kg (310 lb)

PERFORMANCE (at max T-O weight):
Never-exceed speed	52 knots (96·5 km/h; 60 mph)
Max level speed at S/L	43·5 knots (80·5 km/h; 50 mph)
Econ cruising speed at S/L	35 knots (64·5 km/h; 40 mph)
Stalling speed	23 knots (42 km/h; 26 mph)
Service ceiling	1,220 m (4,000 ft)
T-O run	76 m (250 ft)
T-O to 15 m (50 ft)	107 m (350 ft)
Landing from 15 m (50 ft)	76 m (250 ft)
Landing run	46 m (150 ft)
Range	17 nm (32 km; 20 miles)

HOVEY BETA BIRD

The Beta Bird is basically a monoplane version of the Whing Ding II. Design began in June 1977, and construction of the prototype started three months later. It was first flown in April 1979; the 40 h flight test programme to lift FAA test area restrictions was completed on 14 December 1979, and in early 1980 approximately 200 sets of plans and kits had been sold. All available details follow:

TYPE: Single-seat ultra-lightweight monoplane.

WINGS: Braced monoplane structure, with V strut on each side. Wing section Hovey BB-14. Thickness/chord ratio 14%. No dihedral. Incidence 3°. No sweepback. Constant-chord structure, with two spruce spars and ribs of single-piece aluminium tubes. Fabric covering. Full-span ailerons which can be drooped to a maximum of 16° to reduce take-off and landing runs. No trim tabs. Wings fold aft about a pin joint in the rear spar.

FUSELAGE: Generally the same as for WD-II.

TAIL UNIT: Wire-braced structure of aluminium tube, connected with pop-riveted gussets and fabric covered. Conventional tailplane with elevators. No trim tabs.

LANDING GEAR: Generally as for WD-II, except for Gerdes toe-operated brakes, and steerable tailwheel.

POWER PLANT: One 33·5 kW (45 hp) Volkswagen 1,385 cc

modified motor car engine, driving a Hovey two-blade fixed-pitch pusher propeller. Fuel tank within the vertical fuselage extension to which the engine is mounted, capacity 28·4 litres (7·5 US gallons). Oil capacity 3·8 litres (1 US gallon).

ACCOMMODATION: Pilot only, on exposed seat.

SYSTEM: Battery only, as source of electric power for basic instruments and radio.

AVIONICS: Six-channel VHF com radio.

DIMENSIONS, EXTERNAL:
Wing span	7·77 m (25 ft 6 in)
Width, wings folded	2·44 m (8 ft 0 in)
Wing chord, constant	1·07 m (3 ft 6 in)
Wing area, gross	8·08 m² (87 sq ft)
Wing aspect ratio	7·3
Length overall	5·33 m (17 ft 6 in)
Height overall	1·83 m (6 ft 0 in)
Tailplane span	2·44 m (8 ft 0 in)
Wheelbase	1·52 m (5 ft 0 in)
Propeller diameter	1·37 m (4 ft 6 in)

WEIGHTS:
Weight empty	184 kg (405 lb)
Max fuel weight	20·4 kg (45 lb)
Max T-O weight	295 kg (650 lb)

PERFORMANCE (at max T-O weight):
Never-exceed speed	82·5 knots (153 km/h; 95 mph) IAS
Max level speed at 915 m (3,000 ft)	74 knots (137 km/h; 85 mph)
Max cruising speed at 915 m (3,000 ft)	61 knots (113 km/h; 70 mph)
Econ cruising speed	52 knots (96·5 km/h; 60 mph)
Stalling speed, flaps down, power on	35 knots (64·5 km/h; 40 mph)
Max rate of climb at S/L	over 122 m (400 ft)/min
T-O and landing run	76 m (250 ft)
T-O to and landing from 15 m (50 ft)	152 m (500 ft)
Range with max fuel, no reserves	113 nm (209 km; 130 miles)

HUMMER
THE HUMMER

Box 1655, Salt Lake City, Utah 84110
Telephone: (801) 867 5622

THE HUMMER

The Hummer is a single-seat ultralight aircraft designed by the late Mr Klaus Hill, using hang glider technology. Design began in August 1977 and construction of the first prototype started in October of the same year. Construction took just 50 working hours and cost $2,000. First flight was achieved in November 1977.

Earlier, non-powered, aircraft designed and built by Mr Hill included two sailplanes, a Rogallo-type and Voyager hang gliders, and the Fledge hang glider currently in production by Manta Products Inc (see Hang Glider section). On 10 October 1979 he was killed while test flying a motorised version of the Voyager.

Hummer kits and plans are being handled by several distributors, with Mountain Green East of Glen Rock, Pa, as the main supplier and manufacturer of component parts. By early 1980 at least 12 Hummers had been completed.

TYPE: Single-seat ultralight monoplane.

WINGS: Wire-braced high-wing monoplane. Dihedral 45·7 cm (18 in) from horizontal at tips. Leading-edge spar of 4·4 cm (1¾ in) diameter aluminium tube; trailing-edge spar of 3·8 cm (1½ in) diameter aluminium tube. Eleven ribs of 1·3 cm (½ in) diameter aluminium tubing. Structure bolted together. Dacron fabric covering sewn into shape and slipped over wing structure, avoiding use of dope, glue or rib stitching. No ailerons or spoilers. Wings fold back and attach to tail for transportation. Assembly and disassembly takes one man 15-20 mins.

FUSELAGE: Main boom comprises a 12·7 cm (5 in) diameter irrigation pipe, to which wing and engine supporting truss structures are attached.

TAIL UNIT: Strut-braced V tail, with tailplane and elevators/rudders set at dihedral angle of about 33°. Construction similar to wings. Control by cables.

LANDING GEAR: Non-retractable tailwheel type, with steerable tailwheel. Formed sheet metal main legs with two steel cross-tubes. Go-kart wheels. No brakes.

POWER PLANT: One 16·4 kW (22 hp) 250 cc Zenoah snowmobile two-stroke engine, driving a two-blade laminated wood pusher propeller. Plastics fuel tank aft of seat, capacity 19 litres (5 US gallons). Fuel consumption at full throttle 5·7 litres (1½ US gallons)/h.

ACCOMMODATION: Single seat in open position.

DIMENSIONS, EXTERNAL:
Wing span	10·06 m (33 ft 0 in)
Wing area, gross	11·89 m² (128 sq ft)
Wing chord, constant	1·32 m (4 ft 4 in)
Length overall	5·49 m (18 ft 0 in)
Height overall	2·51 m (8 ft 3 in)
Tailplane span	2·49 m (8 ft 2 in)
Wheel track	1·07 m (3 ft 6 in)
Propeller diameter	0·84 m (2 ft 9 in)

WEIGHTS:
Weight empty	82 kg (180 lb)
Max T-O weight	172 kg (380 lb)

PERFORMANCE:
Max level speed	39-48 knots (72·5-88·5 km/h; 45-55 mph)
Cruising speed	26 knots (48 km/h; 30 mph)
T-O and landing speed	22-24·5 knots (40·5-45 km/h; 25-28 mph)
Stalling speed	19·5-21 knots (35·5-39 km/h; 22-24 mph)
Rate of climb at S/L	at least 122 m (400 ft)/min
T-O run	91-122 m (300-400 ft)
Landing distance	18-46 m (60-150 ft)

INTERNATIONAL HELICOPTERS
INTERNATIONAL HELICOPTERS INC

PO Box 107, Mayville, New York 14757
PRESIDENT: Robert G. Dart
VICE-PRESIDENT: Winfield Babcock II

On 2 January 1979, this company announced that it had completed the purchase of Helicom Inc, which had produced and marketed kits for single-seat and two-seat homebuilt helicopters since the early 1960s. It transferred the entire operation from Long Beach, California, to the facilities of Aero Industries at Dart Airport (Detroit Sectional) in Mayville, NY, and began production of Commuter IIA kits immediately.

INTERNATIONAL HELICOPTERS COMMUTER IIA

A detailed description of the original Helicom Commuter Jr Model H-1A single-seat helicopter last appeared in the 1972-73 *Jane's*. The Commuter IIA is a more powerful two-seater, of generally similar configuration but embodying a number of refinements.

TYPE: Two-seat light helicopter.

ROTOR SYSTEM: Two-blade main rotor and two-blade tail rotor. Main rotor blades each comprise a solid extruded 7075-T6 aluminium leading-edge spar, extending to 30% chord, solid aluminium alloy V section trailing-edge, cast ribs and Alclad skins, bonded together, with some rivets for added strength. Tail rotor has blades of stainless steel riveted to an aluminium alloy spar. All-metal drive system. Conventional main rotor gearbox has specially designed centrifugal clutch, and steel shaft drive to tail rotor gearbox. Main rotor/engine rpm ratio 1:5·5. Tail rotor/engine rpm ratio 1:1.

FUSELAGE: Basic truss structure of 4130 chrome-molybdenum steel tube. Glassfibre and Plexiglas cabin enclosure. Rear structure not covered.

TAIL UNIT: Small horizontal stabiliser and triangular ventral fin.

LANDING GEAR: Steel tube skids, with optional ground handling wheels.

POWER PLANT: One 112 kW (150 hp) Avco Lycoming O-320 flat-four engine, with dual ignition, mounted vertically aft of cabin. Two cylindrical fuel tanks, one each side of main rotor driveshaft, above engine, with

combined capacity of 83 litres (22 US gallons). Cooling fan standard.

ACCOMMODATION: Pilot and passenger, side by side on bench seat. Cabin width 1·02 m (3 ft 4 in). Conventional helicopter controls.

DIMENSIONS, EXTERNAL:
Main rotor diameter	7·62 m (25 ft 0 in)
Main rotor blade chord	0·20 m (8 in)
Main rotor disc	45·6 m² (490·9 sq ft)
Tail rotor diameter	1·22 m (4 ft 0 in)
Length overall	8·84 m (29 ft 0 in)
Height overall	2·49 m (8 ft 2 in)

WEIGHTS:
Weight empty	318 kg (700 lb)
Max T-O weight	590 kg (1,300 lb)

PERFORMANCE (at max T-O weight):
Max level speed	87 knots (161 km/h; 100 mph)
Max cruising speed	78 knots (145 km/h; 90 mph)
Service ceiling	3,960 m (13,000 ft)
Hovering ceiling IGE	2,135 m (7,000 ft)
Range with max fuel	195 nm (362 km; 225 miles)

JAMES-DENNIS
JAMES-DENNIS ENTERPRISES INC

7215 South-West 61 Street, Miami, Florida 33143
Telephone: (305) 633 9961
DESIGNER: Mike Melfa

JAMES-DENNIS VCA-1

Mr Mike Melfa has designed and built a small single-seat aircraft designated VCA-1. Design started in February 1970 and construction of the aircraft began in July of the following year. First flight was achieved in October

1976. It is not the intention of James-Dennis Enterprises to sell plans or kits.

TYPE: Single-seat light monoplane.

WINGS: Cantilever low-wing monoplane. Wing section NASA (Whitcomb) GAW-1. Thickness/chord ratio

Hummer ultralight monoplane *(Howard Levy)*

International Helicopters Commuter IIA two-seat light helicopter

Amateur-built Javelin Wichawk (Continental O-470-R engine)

James-Dennis VCA-1, designed and built by Mr Mike Melfa

17%. Dihedral 3°. Incidence 0° 30'. No sweepback. Constant-chord all-metal structure of 2024-T3 aluminium alloy. Plain ailerons and electrically-actuated flaps, of 2024-T3 aluminium alloy. No tabs.

FUSELAGE: Conventional all-metal semi-monocoque structure of 2024-T3 aluminium alloy.

TAIL UNIT: All-metal (2024-T3) structure, comprising a fin of basically triangular shape, constant-chord large-area rudder and constant-chord T-tailplane with elevators. Adjustable tab in port elevator.

LANDING GEAR: Non-retractable tricycle type. Rigid 2024-T3 aluminium alloy cantilever legs. Nosewheel diameter 20·3 cm (8 in). Main wheel diameter 33 cm (13 in). Streamline wheel fairings. Cleveland brakes.

POWER PLANT: One 74·5 kW (100 hp) Continental O-200-A flat-four engine, driving a two-blade Sensenich fixed-pitch propeller. Two fuel tanks in wings, one in fuselage; total capacity 93 litres (24·5 US gallons). Oil capacity 5·7 litres (1·5 US gallons).

ACCOMMODATION: Single seat under sideways-opening (to starboard) canopy.

SYSTEM: Electrical system includes 60A alternator for Genave 200B com/nav radio.

DIMENSIONS, EXTERNAL:

Wing span	6·10 m (20 ft 0 in)
Wing chord, constant	1·02 m (3 ft 4 in)
Wing area, gross	6·19 m² (66·66 sq ft)
Wing aspect ratio	6
Length overall	5·49 m (18 ft 0 in)
Height overall	1·73 m (5 ft 8 in)
Wheel track	1·45 m (4 ft 9 in)
Wheelbase	1·45 m (4 ft 9 in)
Propeller diameter	1·75 m (5 ft 9 in)

WEIGHTS:

Weight empty	322 kg (710 lb)
Max T-O weight	499 kg (1,100 lb)

PERFORMANCE:

Never-exceed speed at S/L	156 knots (290 km/h; 180 mph)
Max level speed at S/L	130 knots (241 km/h; 150 mph)
Max cruising speed at S/L	113 knots (209 km/h; 130 mph)
Econ cruising speed at S/L	95·5 knots (177 km/h; 110 mph)
Stalling speed, flaps up	55 knots (102 km/h; 63 mph)
Stalling speed, flaps down	49·5 knots (92 km/h; 57 mph)
Max rate of climb at S/L	335 m (1,100 ft)/min
Range with max fuel	174 nm (322 km; 200 miles)

JAVELIN
JAVELIN AIRCRAFT COMPANY INC

1979 Easy Street, Wichita, Kansas 67230
Telephone: (316) 733 1011
PRESIDENT AND CHIEF ENGINEER: David D. Blanton

Javelin Aircraft Company was founded on 1 March 1953 to manufacture a low-cost automatic pilot for small aircraft; this was followed by equipment manufacture, and aircraft development work. Following restoration of a Curtiss Robin between 1957 and 1961, which won the National Championship award for the best restored antique aircraft in 1961, Javelin sought an Arrow Sport biplane for similar treatment. Unable to find a suitable aircraft, the company began design and development of a new biplane on 1 January 1964.

The resulting aircraft, named Wichawk, has structural geometry similar to a Stearman biplane, as well as some of its aerodynamic features, and is stressed for +12 and −6g. It flew for the first time on 24 May 1971 and had accumulated 420 flying hours by early 1979.

Javelin Aircraft does not produce any assembled Wichawks, but plans, wing ribs and fuel tanks are available to amateur constructors. Eventually, Javelin Aircraft intends to sell complete kits for amateur construction of the aircraft, and it has been reported that the type may go into production in a foreign country as a primary trainer. A total of 225 sets of plans had been sold by early 1979, and more than 100 Wichawks were under construction, including several in Canada and Australia, and one in Argentina. Seven aircraft built to Javelin plans were known to be flying. The first of these (N29JC), built by Mr Jim Crawford, a retired airline captain, made its first flight on 2 August 1975. A 168 kW (225 hp) Continental O-470-11 flat-six engine gives this aircraft maximum and cruising speeds very similar to those of the Avco Lycoming-engined prototype; max rate of climb is increased to 762 m (2,500 ft)/min.

Two other Wichawks are powered by 134 kW (180 hp) Avco Lycoming O-360 engines, one with a Continental E-225-8 (ex-Beechcraft Bonanza) engine, and one with a 172 kW (230 hp) Continental O-470-R engine taken from a Cessna 182. This last aircraft (illustrated) has a three-blade propeller. It is said to be very smooth to fly, and can take off in 2½ seconds, climb at 762 m (2,500 ft)/min, cruise on 65% power at 113 knots (209 km/h; 130 mph) IAS, and perform well aerobatically.

The main current production work of Javelin Aircraft involves manufacture of 190 litre (50·2 US gallon) glassfibre slipper fuel tanks for the Rockwell Commander and Turbo-Commander 680/690 series. The company is also flight testing a turbocharged Ford Pinto motor car engine in a 1956 Cessna 172; this develops 134 kW (180 hp), and Javelin will eventually sell plans for the conversion to amateur constructors.

JAVELIN WICHAWK

TYPE: Two/three-seat sporting biplane.

WINGS: Braced single-bay biplane, with N-shape streamline-section cabane and interplane struts. Streamline-section landing and flying wires. Wing section NACA 23015. 2° dihedral on lower wings only. Incidence 0°. No sweepback. Composite structure, with two wooden spars and 2024T3 light alloy ribs, fabric-covered. Simple sealed ailerons on lower wings only. No flaps. Geared trim tab.

FUSELAGE: Welded structure of 4130 chrome-molybdenum steel tube with light alloy tubular stringers, fabric-covered.

TAIL UNIT: Wire-braced welded structure of 4130 chrome-molybdenum steel tube with fabric covering. Fixed-incidence tailplane. Trim tab in starboard elevator.

LANDING GEAR: Non-retractable tailwheel type. Main wheels carried on side Vs hinged to lower fuselage longerons. Shock-absorption by automotive-type shock-struts, similar to those of Piper PA-20, and rubber shock cord. Main wheels and tyres size 6·00-6. Cleveland toe brakes. Steerable tailwheel.

POWER PLANT: Prototype has one 134 kW (180 hp) Avco Lycoming O-360 flat-four engine, driving a Sensenich two-blade fixed-pitch propeller type 76EM8-0-56. McCauley propellers optional. Provision for alternative horizontally-opposed or radial engines from 112 kW (150 hp) to 224 kW (300 hp), for which Javelin can provide installation drawings. Other engines currently being installed, other than those previously mentioned, include the 175 kW (235 hp) Avco Lycoming O-435, 224 kW (300 hp) Avco Lycoming O-540 and 224 kW (300 hp) Continental O-520. Fuel tank of 94·5 litre (25 US gallon) capacity in upper wing centre-section, and one of 56·8 litre (15 US gallon) capacity in fuselage aft of firewall. Refuelling points above tanks. Oil capacity of prototype 7·5 litres (2 US gallons).

ACCOMMODATION: Two seats, side by side, in open cockpit. Provision for tandem two-seat or three-seat configurations. Drawings available for rearward-sliding transparent cockpit canopy. Dual controls standard. Baggage compartment aft of seats, capacity 45·4 kg (100 lb). Baggage locker, in turtleback, capacity 9 kg (20 lb).

SYSTEMS: Electrical system powered by 12V 50A engine-driven generator. Hydraulic system for brakes only.

DIMENSIONS, EXTERNAL:	
Wing span (upper)	7·32 m (24 ft 0 in)
Wing chord (both), constant	1·27 m (4 ft 2 in)
Wing area, gross	17·2 m² (185 sq ft)
Wing aspect ratio	5·76
Length overall	5·87 m (19 ft 3 in)
Height overall	2·18 m (7 ft 2 in)
Tailplane span	2·44 m (8 ft 0 in)
Wheel track	1·87 m (6 ft 1½ in)

Propeller diameter	1·93 m (6 ft 4 in)
DIMENSIONS, INTERNAL:	
Cockpit: Max width	0·93 m (3 ft 0½ in)
Baggage compartment	0·34 m³ (12 cu ft)
WEIGHTS (prototype with 134 kW; 180 hp engine):	
Weight empty	580 kg (1,280 lb)
*Max T-O weight	907 kg (2,000 lb)

*Max T-O weight is increased to 998 kg (2,200 lb) with high-powered engines.

PERFORMANCE (prototype with 134 kW; 180 hp engine):
Never-exceed speed 156 knots (289 km/h; 180 mph)
Max level speed at S/L
121·5 knots (225 km/h; 140 mph)
Max cruising speed 110 knots (204 km/h; 127 mph)
Landing speed 39 knots (72·5 km/h; 45 mph)
Max rate of climb at S/L 518 m (1,700 ft)/min
T-O run 46 m (150 ft)
Load factors at max AUW +12g, −6g

JEFFAIR
JEFFAIR CORPORATION
PO Box 975, Renton, Washington 98055
Telephone: (206) 863 7992
PRESIDENT: Geoffrey L. Siers

This company was formed by Mr Geoffrey Siers, a former RAF fighter pilot and design engineer with BAC, who emigrated to the USA in 1964. In 1966 he began designing a high-performance all-wooden two-seat light aircraft, of which construction was started in June 1969. Now known as the Barracuda, this aircraft (N19GS) flew for the first time on 29 June 1975, and is certificated in the FAA's Experimental category. At the EAA Fly-in at Oshkosh in 1976, the Barracuda won the 'Most Outstanding New Design' award. Plans are available to amateur constructors, and about 350 Barracudas were being built by January 1980. An amateur-built example was illustrated in the 1979-80 *Jane's*.

JEFFAIR BARRACUDA

The prototype Barracuda flew originally with a 164 kW (220 hp) Avco Lycoming GO-435-2 engine. This was replaced with a more powerful O-540 engine in 1979, and the following details apply to the prototype in its current form.

TYPE: Two-seat all-wooden sporting monoplane.

WINGS: Cantilever low-wing monoplane, made in three pieces: two constant-chord outer panels and a centre-section which is integral with the fuselage. Wing section

NACA 64₂415. Upper surface of centre-section each side has slight anhedral, but bottom surface has neither anhedral nor dihedral. Dihedral of 5° on outer panels. No incidence. Basic structure of spruce, with mahogany and birch plywood covering. Box-section main spar with spruce booms and ply webs; truss-type ribs of spruce. Frise-type ailerons of wood and glassfibre. Electrically-actuated wooden plain flap on entire centre-section trailing-edge, extending under fuselage.

FUSELAGE: Conventional spruce structure, covered with birch plywood stressed skin.

TAIL UNIT: Cantilever spruce structure, plywood-covered. Glassfibre tips. Electrically-actuated trim tab in port elevator. Rudder has bungee trim.

LANDING GEAR: Retractable tricycle type. Electrohydraulic retraction, main wheels inward, nosewheel rearward; all wheels fully enclosed by doors when retracted. Emergency extension by gravity. Legs made from 4130 steel tubing, with steel coil spring shock-absorption. Cleveland wheels, size 5·00-5, with 0·36 m (14 in) diameter tyres. Cleveland aircooled brakes.

POWER PLANT: One 194 kW (260 hp) Avco Lycoming O-540-E4B5 flat-six engine, driving a Hartzell three-blade constant-speed propeller. Two glassfibre fuel tanks in centre-section forward of spar, total capacity 166·5 litres (44 US gallons). Oil capacity 11·5 litres (3 US gallons).

ACCOMMODATION: Two armchair seats, with thigh support, side by side under upward-hinged individual 'gull-wing' canopy doors. Dual controls. Baggage space behind seats. Cabin heated and ventilated.

SYSTEMS: Electric pump supplies hydraulic system. Electrical supply via 12V DC system.
AVIONICS: Edo-Aire 360-channel nav/com.
DIMENSIONS, EXTERNAL:
Wing span 7·54 m (24 ft 9 in)
Wing chord at root 2·11 m (6 ft 11 in)
Wing chord, outer panels, constant
1·45 m (4 ft 9 in)
Wing area, gross 11·15 m² (120 sq ft)
Length overall 6·55 m (21 ft 6 in)
Wheel track 2·54 m (8 ft 4 in)
Propeller diameter 2·18 m (7 ft 2 in)
DIMENSION, INTERNAL:
Cabin: Max width 1·07 m (3 ft 6 in)
WEIGHTS:
Weight empty 678 kg (1,495 lb)
Baggage capacity 18 kg (40 lb)
Max T-O weight 1,043 kg (2,300 lb)
PERFORMANCE:
Never-exceed speed 260 knots (482 km/h; 300 mph)
Max level speed at 2,135 m (7,000 ft)
198 knots (367 km/h; 228 mph)
Max cruising speed at 2,135 m (7,000 ft)
182 knots (338 km/h; 210 mph)
Cruising speed (62% power) at 2,750 m (9,000 ft)
156 knots (290 km/h; 180 mph)
Stalling speed, flaps down
54 knots (100 km/h; 62 mph)
Max rate of climb at S/L 762 m (2,500 ft)/min
Range at max T-O weight, 65% power, with 30 min reserves 390 nm (724 km; 450 miles)

JONAS
GERALD JONAS
San Francisco, California

JONAS HUMMINGBIRD

Mr Gerald Jonas, an architect, has designed a light two-seat aircraft known as the Hummingbird. By July 1977, about 75% of the airframe and mechanical parts had been built, with the help of two other constructors, on a part-time basis.

The design features a moulded glassfibre lifting fuselage and boundary layer control, with a symmetrical aerofoil.

The rear-mounted narrow-chord tapering wings are also constructed of moulded glassfibre, with spars of graphite, and have full-span electrically-actuated flaps, with spoilers for roll control. The constant-chord canard foreplane is of similar construction. Power is provided by a rear-mounted 58 kW (78 hp) Revmaster Volkswagen 2,000 cc modified motor car engine, driving a Maloof two-speed aluminium propeller. The tricycle landing gear is fully retractable and the graphite main legs fold scissor-like into the underfuselage.

Plans and kits are expected to be made available to amateur constructors.

DIMENSIONS, EXTERNAL:
Wing span 6·10 m (20 ft 0 in)
Wing area, gross (incl canard foreplane)
3·81 m² (41 sq ft)
Length overall 3·05 m (10 ft 0 in)
WEIGHTS:
Weight empty 197 kg (435 lb)
Max T-O weight 385 kg (850 lb)
PERFORMANCE (estimated):
Max cruising speed 191 knots (354 km/h; 220 mph)
Stalling speed 56 knots (103 km/h; 64 mph)
Range with max fuel 955 nm (1,770 km; 1,100 miles)

KELEHER
JAMES J. KELEHER
4321 Ogden Drive, Fremont, California 94538

In the early 1960s Mr J. Keleher designed and built a mid-wing sporting monoplane which he called the Lark. The design was revised in 1963, and the current model, for which plans are available to amateur constructors, is designated Lark-1B.

KELEHER LARK-1B

The following description applies to the Lark-1B with a 48·5 kW (65 hp) Continental engine. Examples are flying with 56 kW (75 hp) A75-8 and 74·5 kW (100 hp) O-200 Continental engines.

TYPE: Single-seat sporting monoplane.

WINGS: Braced mid-wing monoplane with streamline-section V bracing struts each side. Wing section NACA 2R₂12. No dihedral. Incidence 4° at root, 2° 30' at tip. All-wood structure of Sitka spruce, with built-up I beam front spar and ribs, fabric-covered. Stressed to 6g plus. Fabric-covered wooden ailerons; no trim tabs or flaps.

FUSELAGE: Welded steel tube structure, fabric-covered, stressed to 6g plus.

TAIL UNIT: Wire-braced welded steel tube structure with sheet steel ribs and fabric covering. Adjustable-incidence tailplane. Swept fin. No trim tabs.

LANDING GEAR: Non-retractable tailwheel type. Divided main landing gear with shock-absorption by rubber cord in fuselage. Cleveland main wheels and tyres size 5·00-5, pressure 1·38-1·72 bars (20-25 lb/sq in). Cleveland disc brakes. Wheel fairings optional.

POWER PLANT: Provision for alternative flat-four engines of 48·5-74·5 kW (65-100 hp), driving a two-blade metal fixed-pitch propeller. One galvanised steel fuel tank in the fuselage, aft of the firewall, capacity 56 litres (15 US gallons). Refuelling point on top of cowl, forward of windscreen. Oil capacity 5·7 litres (1·5 US gallons).

ACCOMMODATION: Single seat in enclosed cockpit under sliding canopy. Lowered turtledeck and bubble canopy optional. Stowage for 9 kg (20 lb) baggage aft of seat.

DIMENSIONS, EXTERNAL:
Wing span 7·01 m (23 ft 0 in)
Wing chord, constant 1·22 m (4 ft 0 in)
Wing area, gross 7·48 m² (80·5 sq ft)
Wing aspect ratio 5·75

Length overall 5·18 m (17 ft 0 in)
Height overall 1·65 m (5 ft 5 in)
Tailplane span 2·03 m (6 ft 8 in)
Wheel track 1·57 m (5 ft 2 in)
Propeller diameter:
A65-8 1·70 m (5 ft 7 in)
A75-8 1·66 m (5 ft 5½ in)
WEIGHTS (48·5 kW: 65 hp engine):
Weight empty 249 kg (550 lb)
Max T-O and landing weight 387 kg (855 lb)
PERFORMANCE (with 48·5 kW; 65 hp engine, at max T-O weight):
Never-exceed speed
160 knots (297·5 km/h; 185 mph)
Max level speed 115 knots (212 km/h; 132 mph)
Max cruising speed 103 knots (192 km/h; 119 mph)
Stalling speed 48 knots (89 km/h; 55 mph)
Max rate of climb at S/L 274 m (900 ft)/min
Service ceiling 5,950 m (19,500 ft)
T-O run 183 m (600 ft)
Range with max payload, with reserves
303 nm (563 km; 350 miles)

KELLY
DUDLEY R. KELLY
Route 4, Versailles, Kentucky 40383

Mr Dudley R. Kelly, builder of the Hatz CB-1 biplane illustrated on page 523, has since designed and built, with Mr Thomas Bradford, the prototype of a biplane known as the Kelly-D, with the emphasis on improved efficiency and easier and cheaper construction. Design was initiated on 22 May 1977, and construction began almost two years later, on 2 March 1979. Wing structure was completed at the end of that year, and the first flight is anticipated in the Spring of 1981.

KELLY-D
TYPE: Two-seat lightweight biplane.

WINGS: Braced single-bay biplane, with N-type interplane struts each side. Inverted V-type centre-section struts and streamline-section landing and flying wires. Wing section NACA 23012 (modified by Dr Robert Addoms). Dihedral 3°, on lower wings only. Incidence 3° on both wings. Constant chord, with no sweepback but considerable stagger. Wooden two-spar structure, with fabric covering. Aerodynamically-balanced ailerons of wooden construction, fabric-covered, on lower wing only.

FUSELAGE: Conventional welded steel tube structure, with fabric covering.

TAIL UNIT: Wire-braced structure of welded steel tube, fabric-covered. Fixed-incidence tailplane. Trim tab in port elevator.

LANDING GEAR: Non-retractable tailwheel type. Two side Vs and half-axles hinged to fuselage structure. Shock-absorption of main units by steel coil spring on each compression strut. Main-wheel tyres size 6·00-6, pressure 1·24 bars (18 lb/sq in). Tailwheel diameter 15·2 cm (6 in). Cleveland hydraulic disc brakes. Fairings over main wheels.

POWER PLANT: One 86 kW (115 hp) Avco Lycoming O-235 flat-four engine, driving a Sensenich two-blade fixed-pitch propeller. Fuel tank in fuselage, aft of firewall, with capacity of 79·5 litres (21 US gallons). Refuelling point on upper surface of fuselage, forward of front cockpit. Oil capacity 5·7 litres (1·5 US gallons).

ACCOMMODATION: Two seats in tandem in open cockpits. Baggage space aft of pilot's seat in rear cockpit.

Prototype Jeffair Barracuda two-seat sporting monoplane in its latest form

Uncompleted Hummingbird two-seat light aircraft, designed by Mr Gerald Jonas of San Francisco (*Howard Levy*)

Keleher Lark-1B single-seat sporting monoplane (*J. M. G. Gradidge*)

Kinman Super Simple I single-seat monoplane (*Howard Levy*)

Kelly-D two-seat lightweight biplane (*Michael A. Badrocke*)

SYSTEMS: Hydraulic system for brakes only. Electrical system includes starter-generator and 12V storage battery.
AVIONICS AND EQUIPMENT: Genave Alpha 200B radio. Navigation lights.
DIMENSIONS, EXTERNAL:

Wing span (both)	7·42 m (24 ft 4 in)
Wing chord, constant (both)	1·27 m (4 ft 2 in)
Wing area, gross	19·54 m² (210·38 sq ft)
Wing aspect ratio	5·84
Length overall	5·87 m (19 ft 3 in)
Height overall	2·51 m (8 ft 3 in)
Tailplane span	2·82 m (9 ft 3 in)
Wheel track	1·83 m (6 ft 0 in)
Wheelbase	4·04 m (13 ft 3 in)
Propeller diameter	1·88 m (6 ft 2 in)

WEIGHTS (estimated):

Weight empty, basic operating	352 kg (775 lb)
Max baggage	13·5 kg (30 lb)
Max fuel weight	54 kg (120 lb)
Max T-O and landing weight	635 kg (1,400 lb)

PERFORMANCE (estimated at max T-O weight):

Never-exceed speed	104 knots (193 km/h; 120 mph)
Max level speed at 1,525 m (5,000 ft)	91 knots (169 km/h; 105 mph)
Max cruising speed at 1,525 m (5,000 ft)	78 knots (145 km/h; 90 mph)
Econ cruising speed at 1,525 m (5,000 ft)	74 knots (137 km/h; 85 mph)
Stalling speed, power off	35 knots (64 km/h; 40 mph)
Max rate of climb at S/L	229 m (750 ft)/min
Service ceiling	3,050 m (10,000 ft)
T-O run	91 m (300 ft)
T-O to 15 m (50 ft)	274 m (900 ft)
Landing from 15 m (50 ft)	183 m (600 ft)
Landing run	76 m (250 ft)
Range with max fuel, 20 min reserves	234 nm (435 km; 270 miles)
Range with max payload, 20 min reserves	217 nm (402 km; 250 miles)

KINMAN
DUANE KINMAN
Rubidoux, California

KINMAN SUPER SIMPLE I

As its name suggests, the Super Simple I was designed by Mr Duane Kinman to be easy to construct. It is a small single-seater, the prototype of which was built in three weeks, at a cost of $2,680, from six sheets of 1·22 × 3·66 m (4 × 12 ft) aluminium. There are no compound curves, except in the glassfibre nose cowl, and no welding because of the extensive use of glue and pop rivets. Plans will be made available to amateur builders.
TYPE: Single-seat light monoplane.
WINGS: Cantilever low-wing monoplane. Wing section NACA 64212. Slight dihedral. No sweepback. Constant chord. Structure of 2024-T3 aluminium, bonded by Hysol 9410 glue. Full-span drooping ailerons. No tabs.
FUSELAGE: Conventional 2024-T3 aluminium structure, pop riveted. Tailcone is a 30 cm (12 in) propeller spinner.
TAIL UNIT: Conventional cantilever 2024 T3 aluminium structure, pop riveted. Constant-chord tailplane with full-span elevators. No tabs.
LANDING GEAR: Non-retractable tailwheel type. Cantilever main legs made from 1·9 cm (¾ in) thick 2024 T3 aluminium strip. Main wheels size 2·80-4. Hydraulic disc brakes.
POWER PLANT: One 42·5 kW (57 hp) 1,800 cc modified Volkswagen motor car engine, driving a Bob Mende four-blade wooden propeller, with spinner. Fuel tank in nose, capacity 38 litres (10 US gallons).
ACCOMMODATION: Single semi-reclining seat under a bubble canopy.

DIMENSIONS, EXTERNAL:

Wing span	5·54 m (18 ft 2 in)
Wing chord, constant	1·27 m (4 ft 2 in)
Length overall	4·88 m (16 ft 0 in)
Propeller diameter	1·27 m (4 ft 2 in)

DIMENSIONS, INTERNAL:

Cockpit: max width	0·51 m (1 ft 8 in)
max height	0·76 m (2 ft 6 in)

WEIGHTS:

Weight empty	201 kg (443 lb)
Max T-O weight	306 kg (675 lb)

PERFORMANCE (estimated):

Max level speed over	139 knots (257 km/h; 160 mph)
Max cruising speed	130 knots (241 km/h; 150 mph)
Landing speed	39-42 knots (72·5-77 km/h; 45-48 mph)
T-O run	152 m (500 ft)
Range with max fuel	174 nm (322 km; 200 miles)

KRAFT
KRAFT SYSTEMS INC
450 West California Avenue, PO Box 1268, Vista, California 92083
Telephone: (714) 724 7146

KRAFT K-1 SUPER FLI

Designed and built by Phil Kraft, with help from Paul White, the Super Fli was produced to model aircraft standards in terms of wing design, areas and moments, as Phil Kraft is a world champion model aircraft builder. After 1½ years of work, the Super Fli was first flown in December 1974 and was taken to the EAA Fly-in at Oshkosh in 1975. Aerobatic pilots at Oshkosh who flew the aircraft found it most satisfactory, and the prototype had logged more than 350 hours of almost continuous unlimited aerobatics by the Spring of 1977. Plans of the Super Fli are available to amateur constructors.
TYPE: Single-seat aerobatic monoplane.
WINGS: Cantilever low-wing monoplane. Spruce spars, plywood ribs and plywood covering. Horn-balanced ailerons.
FUSELAGE: Oval section fuselage of steel tube construction, aluminium covered.
TAIL UNIT: Wire-braced steel tube structure, fabric covered.
LANDING GEAR: Non-retractable tailwheel type. Faired main legs and faired wheels. Steerable tailwheel.
POWER PLANT: One 149 kW (200 hp) Avco Lycoming IO-360-A1D flat-four engine. Provision for fitting 134 kW (180 hp) Avco Lycoming.
ACCOMMODATION: Single seat under transparent canopy, hinged on starboard side.

Kraft Super Fli aerobatic monoplane (*Howard Levy*)

LACO-125, designed and built by Mr Joe Laven

DIMENSION, EXTERNAL:		Max T-O weight	635 kg (1,400 lb)	Landing speed	35 knots (65 km/h; 40 mph)
Wing span	7·32 m (24 ft 0 in)	PERFORMANCE:		Max rate of climb at S/L	914 m (3,000 ft)/min
WEIGHTS:		Max level speed	174 knots (322 km/h; 200 mph)	Service ceiling	3,660 m (12,000 ft)
Weight empty	445 kg (980 lb)	Cruising speed	143 knots (265 km/h; 165 mph)	Range with max fuel	260 nm (483 km; 300 miles)

LACO
LACO

Banning Municipal Airport, PO Box 415, Desert Hot Springs, California 92240
Telephone: (714) 329 0955

LACO-125

Mr Joe Laven designed, built and has flown a two-seat light biplane known as the LACO-125. Design started in May 1971 and, following construction of two scale models to check the basic configuration, construction of a prototype began in April 1972. First flight was achieved on 29 May 1977 at the hands of Stolp Starduster test pilot Mr Eric Shilling. Recent modifications have included the fitting of a new nose cowl and louvred lower cowl discharge, and an oil filter system. A second airframe has been completed, to the plans which are available to amateur constructors.

TYPE: Two-seat light biplane.
WINGS: Braced single-bay biplane. Wing section NACA 2412. Dihedral 2° on lower wings only. Incidence 2° on lower wings only. Conventional structure, with two spruce spars, spruce capstrips, mahogany ribs, aluminium leading- and trailing-edges and chrome-molybdenum steel fittings, all fabric covered. N-type interplane struts each side; two N-type struts support centre of upper wing above fuselage. Modified Frise-type ailerons on lower wings only, of similar construction to wings. No flaps or trim tabs.
FUSELAGE: Welded Warren truss structure of chrome-molybdenum steel tubing, with mahogany formers and spruce stringers, fabric covered.
TAIL UNIT: Conventional braced structure of welded chrome-molybdenum steel tube, fabric covered. Trim tab optional, but not fitted to prototype.
LANDING GEAR: Non-retractable tailwheel type, with steerable tailwheel. Polyurethane spring shock-absorption of LACO design. Cleveland main wheels, size 6·00-6. McKay Aero Research MF-7 main-wheel fairings. Cleveland hydraulic brakes.
POWER PLANT: One 93 kW (125 hp) Continental C-125-2 flat-four engine, driving a McCauley two-blade fixed-pitch propeller. Fuel tank in fuselage, capacity 91 litres (24 US gallons). Oil capacity 7·5 litres (2 US gallons).
ACCOMMODATION: Two seats in tandem in open cockpits.
SYSTEMS: Engine-driven generator, lights and 30A starting system.
AVIONICS: Genave-100 channel transceiver.

DIMENSIONS, EXTERNAL:	
Wing span, upper	6·93 m (22 ft 8¾ in)
Wing span, lower	6·29 m (20 ft 7½ in)
Wing chord, upper (constant)	1·14 m (3 ft 9 in)
Wing chord, lower (constant)	1·07 m (3 ft 6 in)
Wing area, gross	13·94 m² (150 sq ft)
Length overall	5·94 m (19 ft 6 in)
Height overall	2·18 m (7 ft 2 in)
Tailplane span	2·64 m (8 ft 8 in)
Wheel track	1·88 m (6 ft 2 in)
Wheelbase	4·47 m (14 ft 8 in)
Propeller diameter	1·83 m (6 ft 0 in)
WEIGHTS:	
Weight empty	390 kg (860 lb)
Max T-O weight	635 kg (1,400 lb)
PERFORMANCE:	
Never-exceed speed	139 knots (257 km/h; 160 mph)
Max level speed	108 knots (200 km/h; 124 mph)
Max cruising speed	98 knots (182 km/h; 113 mph)
Stalling speed, power off	49 knots (90 km/h; 56 mph)
Stalling speed, power on	43·5 knots (80·5 km/h; 50 mph)
Max rate of climb at S/L	274 m (900 ft)/min
Range with max fuel	282 nm (523 km; 325 miles)

LANGHURST
LOUIS LANGHURST

Route 1, Box 315, Carriere, Mississippi 39426

LANGHURST REPLICA JUNKERS Ju 87B-2 'STUKA'

Mr Louis Langhurst, a retired design engineer, has designed and built a ⁷/₁₀th-scale replica of the German Junkers Ju 87B-2 'Stuka' dive-bomber of World War Two. Research and design took two years and construction occupied 8,000 working hours over a six-year period. First flight was made on 19 July 1978. Construction is of steel tubing, with aluminium skinning. Power is provided by a 164 kW (220 hp) Avco Lycoming GO-435-B engine. Mr Langhurst was awarded the Replica Fighters of America Annual Award of Excellence for the aircraft at the 1979 EAA Fly-in.

DIMENSION, EXTERNAL:
Wing span   9·91 m (32 ft 6 in)

WEIGHTS:	
Weight empty	794 kg (1,750 lb)
Max T-O weight	1,025 kg (2,260 lb)
PERFORMANCE:	
Max level speed	119 knots (220 km/h; 137 mph)
Cruising speed	102·5 knots (190 km/h; 118 mph)
Landing speed	54 knots (100 km/h; 62 mph)
Max rate of climb at S/L	over 305 m (1,000 ft)/min

LARKIN
LARKIN AIRCRAFT COMPANY

PO Box 66899, 4865 Scotts Valley Drive, Scotts Valley, California 95066
Telephone: (408) 438 3883
PRESIDENT: Keith Larkin

Larkin Aircraft Corporation, a subsidiary of ACS Communications Inc, designed and built the prototype of a two-seat light aircraft known as the Model KC-3 Skylark. Design began in 1961 and prototype construction started in 1970, with the first flight on 8 June 1972. The first public showing was at the Watsonville Fly-in in May 1973. Emphasis was placed on producing a robust structure suitable for homebuilders, the primary skill necessary to build a Skylark being that of sheet metal riveting.

Plans and material kits are available to amateur constructors, who may also order from the company any part or parts which they consider beyond their ability to fabricate. At least one further Skylark has been constructed, in addition to the prototype.

In early 1977, the right to licence-build the Skylark in kit form was negotiated with another company, as well as possible licence manufacture in Australia. The outcome of these negotiations is not known.

LARKIN KC-3 SKYLARK

TYPE: Two-seat light aircraft.
WINGS: Cantilever shoulder-wing monoplane. Wing section NACA 4415. Light alloy two-spar structure, with metal ribs and skins. Cambered wingtips of glassfibre. Ailerons of aluminium construction. No flaps or tabs.
FUSELAGE: Light alloy square-section tubular keel, mast and triangular support structure. Mast carries engine, drive and propeller. Support structure carries wings and tailbooms. Keel supports landing gear and seats. Glassfibre lower and upper fairings. Optional V-shaped stepped lower hull of glassfibre for amphibious operations.
TAIL UNIT: Twin-boom structure of rectangular-section light alloy, attached to wings, with twin fins and rudders. Large trim tab in centre of elevator trailing-edge.
LANDING GEAR: Non-retractable tricycle type. Shock-absorption by low-pressure tyres. Nosewheel steerable. Goodyear main wheels with tyres size 6·00-6, pressure 1·38 bars (20 lb/sq in). Nosewheel tyre size 14 × 6·00-5, pressure 1·38 bars (20 lb/sq in). Goodyear disc brakes. Large glassfibre main-wheel fairings.
POWER PLANT: One 50 kW (67 hp) 1,679 cc Volkswagen LA-1700 modified motor car engine as standard, driving a Fahlin two-blade fixed-pitch wooden pusher propeller via Larkin seven-belt V-drive reduction gearing. Glassfibre spinner. Fuel tank aft of pilot's seat, capacity 57 litres (15 US gallons). Refuelling point on tank's upper surface. Oil capacity 1·9 litres (0·5 US gallons).
ACCOMMODATION: Two seats, side by side, in enclosed cockpit. Dual controls standard. Port side of transparent canopy is hinged on centreline to provide access. Cockpit heating optional.
SYSTEM: Electrical system standard, comprising engine-driven generator and storage battery for engine starting.
ELECTRONICS AND EQUIPMENT: Navigation lights, radio and additional electronics optional.

DIMENSIONS, EXTERNAL:	
Wing span	8·08 m (26 ft 6 in)
Wing chord, constant	1·27 m (4 ft 2 in)
Wing area, gross	10·59 m² (114 sq ft)
Wing aspect ratio	7·0
Length overall	5·55 m (18 ft 2½ in)
Height overall	1·89 m (6 ft 2½ in)
Tailplane span	2·54 m (8 ft 4 in)
Wheel track	1·57 m (5 ft 2 in)
Wheelbase	1·55 m (5 ft 1 in)
Propeller diameter	1·75 m (5 ft 9 in)
DIMENSION, INTERNAL:	
Cabin: Max width	1·04 m (3 ft 5 in)
WEIGHTS:	
Weight empty	358 kg (790 lb)
Baggage	45 kg (100 lb)
Max T-O weight	565 kg (1,246 lb)
PERFORMANCE:	
Never-exceed speed	156 knots (289 km/h; 180 mph)
Max level speed	100 knots (185 km/h; 115 mph)
Max cruising speed	91 knots (169 km/h; 105 mph)
Econ cruising speed	87 knots (161 km/h; 100 mph)
Stalling speed	37 knots (68 km/h; 42 mph)
Max rate of climb at S/L	168 m (550 ft)/min
Service ceiling (estimated)	3,660 m (12,000 ft)
T-O run	183 m (600 ft)
T-O to 15 m (50 ft)	225 m (740 ft)
Landing from 15 m (50 ft)	168 m (550 ft)
Landing run	122 m (400 ft)
Range	347 nm (644 km; 400 miles)

Langhurst ⁷/₁₀th-scale replica of a Junkers Ju 87B-2 'Stuka' *(Howard Levy)*

Prototype Larkin KC-3 Skylark (1,679 cc Volkswagen engine)

Mahugh Flying Bathtub two-seat monoplane *(Ted Koston)*

Lasher Renegade I Formula V single-seat racer

LASHER
LASHER

LASHER RENEGADE I

The Lasher-designed Renegade I Formula V racer (N73RL) was built by Mr M. Ricketts. Construction took 18 months and cost $4,000. First flight was made in 1974. It is owned currently by Mr Vernon Willingham of Sparta, Illinois and has logged more than 500 flying hours. It took second and third places in Formula V at the 1978 and 1979 Cleveland National Air Races respectively, and is used for aerobatic displays. Structure is conventional, with all-wood wings, and fabric-covered tubular steel fuselage and tail unit. Power is provided by a 41 kW (55 hp) modified Volkswagen motor car engine. Plans are available from Southern Aeronautical Corporation, 141 00 Lake Candlewood Court, Miami Lakes, Florida 33014.

DIMENSIONS, EXTERNAL:
Wing span	5·18 m (17 ft 0 in)
Wing chord, constant	1·52 m (5 ft 0 in)
Length overall	4·57 m (15 ft 0 in)
Height overall	1·30 m (4 ft 3 in)

WEIGHTS:
Weight empty	204·5 kg (451 lb)

Bryan Allen in Gossamer Albatross leaving the cliffs of Dover on 12 June 1979

Max T-O weight	304 kg (670 lb)	Landing speed	43·5 knots (80·5 km/h; 50 mph)
PERFORMANCE:		Max rate of climb at S/L	259 m (850 ft)/min
Max level speed	over 148 knots (273 km/h; 170 mph)	Service ceiling	3,660 m (12,000 ft)
Max cruising speed	126 knots (233 km/h; 145 mph)	Range with max fuel	195 nm (362 km; 225 miles)

MacCREADY
DR PAUL B. MacCREADY

AeroVironment Inc, 145 Vista Avenue, Pasadena, California 91107
Telephone: (213) 449 4392

GOSSAMER ALBATROSS

The Gossamer Albatross man-powered aircraft was developed from the Gossamer Condor, with which a team headed by Dr Paul MacCready won a £50,000 Kramer Prize for the first figure-of-eight flight around two pylons half a mile apart by an aircraft propelled entirely by a man, on 23 August 1977. The Albatross is similar in configuration to the Condor, but has fewer external bracing wires and has structural members made of carbon fibre reinforced plastics (CFRP) tubing for optimum strength/weight ratio. The piloting position is upright rather than semi-reclined. Weight of the Albatross slightly exceeds that of the Condor, due mainly to the 2 litres (3·5 Imp pints) of drinking water provided for the pilot and the installation of a small Motorola Handi Talki communications radio with Bell Telephone earphone.

On 12 June 1979 the Gossamer Albatross completed successfully the first crossing of the English Channel by an aircraft propelled entirely by a man. Piloted by Mr Bryan Allen, who had gained the £50,000 prize in the Condor in 1977, it took off from Folkestone, England, at 05.51 h BST and landed on the beach at Cap Gris Nez, France, at

08.40 h BST. Straight-line distance covered was about 20 nm (37 km; 23 miles). Indicated airspeed varied from an initial 12-13 knots (22-24 km/h; 14-15 mph) to a later 9·5-10·5 knots (17·5-19·5 km/h; 11-12 mph). Average height above the sea was 0·5-2 m (2-6 ft), with a minimum of about 0·15 m (6 in) and maximum of 7·5 m (25 ft). This achievement gained a Kremer Prize of £100,000.

A second Gossamer Albatross, built as a backup for the cross-Channel flight, differed only in detail from the aircraft used on the successful attempt and described hereafter:

TYPE: Single-seat man-powered aircraft.
WINGS: Wire-braced high-wing monoplane, made in four panels, joined by light alloy tubes inside spar. Wing section Lissaman 7776. Thickness/chord ratio 11·5%. Moderate dihedral, constant from roots. Average sweepback at spar (28% chord) 7° 30'. Single spar of 50 mm (2 in) diameter CFRP tube; Styrofoam (expanded polystyrene) ribs with CFRP capstrips and stiffeners; Styrofoam leading-edge skin and Du Pont Mylar transparent heat-shrunk plastic film covering. Wingtips warped by starboard 'handlebar' control. No other control surfaces on wings. Kingpost of 25 mm (1 in) CFRP tubing provides overwing attachment for bracing wires.
FUSELAGE: Basic structure of CFRP tubing; formers of CFRP strip with Styrofoam core; leading-edge and bottom covering of Styrofoam sheet, with inset window in line with pilot's head; Mylar film covering. Holes in leading-edge and vents in trailing-edge maintain flow of

air through interior. Rhomboidal shape and aerofoil section of fuselage gondola enable it to act as vertical stabilising surface, requiring no additional fin area.
FOREPLANE: Wire-braced universally-pivoted structure of similar construction to wings, carried on a bowsprit of 38 mm (1·5 in) CFRP tubing. Fore and aft movement of pilot's port 'handlebar' grip controls foreplane pitch. Sideways movement operates servo-tabs on trailing-edge near tips, to provide roll and directional control.
LANDING GEAR: Two small fixed wheels at base of fore and aft gondola structural members, diameter 125 mm (5 in) and 100 mm (4 in) respectively.
MOTIVE POWER: Man-power on bicycle pedals, transmitted by chain drive to two-blade pusher propeller mounted on light alloy/CFRP shaft. Computer-designed propeller has Eppler 193 basic section; each blade is made in six pieces from expanded polystyrene, bonded on to a CFRP tube and covered with Kevlar cloth.

DIMENSIONS, EXTERNAL:
Wing span	28·60 m (93 ft 10 in)
Wing area	44·03 m² (474 sq ft)
Wing aspect ratio	18·6
Canard span	5·59 m (18 ft 4 in)
Canard area	5·95 m² (64 sq ft)
Propeller diameter	4·11 m (13 ft 6 in)

WEIGHTS AND LOADING:
Weight empty	31·75 kg (70 lb)
T-O weight with 63·5 kg (140 lb) pilot	97·5 kg (215 lb)
Wing loading	2·21 kg/m² (0·45 lb/sq ft)

MAHUGH
G. IRVIN MAHUGH

3155 North 3rd Street, Baker, Oregon 97814

MAHUGH FLYING BATHTUB

Mr G. Irvin Mahugh has built a two-seat monoplane similar to Mr William H. Ramsey's 1931 Flying Bathtub,

using plans that he modified from those which appeared in a 1932 edition of *Flying and Glider Manual,* and were republished recently by the EAA. Compared with the original, the Flying Bathtub has been structurally strengthened and is powered by a 56 kW (75 hp) Continental engine, against only 22·5 kW (30 hp) in the original aircraft. Construction took 2½ years, aided by Mr Ellis

Moncrief, and cost $4,000. First flight was made on 15 May 1978; soon afterwards, the aircraft was flown cross-country a total distance of 2,432 nm (4,506 km; 2,800 miles), to and from the 1978 EAA Fly-in at Oshkosh, where it won the EAA's Vintage Aircraft Award for the Outstanding Replica.
TYPE: Two-seat homebuilt monoplane.

WINGS: Braced high-wing monoplane. Wing section Clark Y. Slight dihedral. Incidence 2° 30'. No sweepback. Constant-chord structure with spruce spars, spruce/mahogany ribs, Dacron covering, and bracing struts of 4130 steel tube. Plain ailerons of similar construction. No trim tabs.

FUSELAGE: Triangular-section open structure of welded 4130 steel tube, with 'bath tub' gondola for pilot built integrally at the forward end. Forward of a line determined by the door's leading edge, this gondola is covered with aluminium sheet; aft of this line by Dacron.

TAIL UNIT: Conventional wire-braced structure of welded 4130 steel tube with Dacron covering. Tailplane incidence ground-adjustable. Trim tab in port elevator.

LANDING GEAR: Non-retractable tailwheel type. Main wheels have shock-absorption by rubber bungee; steerable tailwheel by steel leaf springs. Main wheels are Yamaha 650 motorcycle wheels, with tyres size 23 × 2·75-17, pressure 2·42 bars (35 lb/sq in). Scott 15·2 cm (6 in) diameter solid-tyre tailwheel. Bonanza go-kart caliper brakes.

POWER PLANT: One 56 kW (75 hp) Continental A75-8F flat-four engine, driving a Sensenich Type 74CK-2-36 two-blade fixed-pitch metal propeller. Fuel tank in wing centre-section, capacity 76·8 litres (20·3 US gallons). Oil capacity 3·8 litres (1 US gallon).

ACCOMMODATION: Pilot and 'skinny' passenger side by side in open cockpit with windscreen. Door on starboard side, hinged at forward end. Baggage space behind seat. Dual rudder pedals and central control column.

SYSTEM: Electrical system includes two Solarex Model 1270 solar panels, each with a maximum output of 1·3 A at 13·7 V, adequate to maintain the charge of a 12 V 14 Ah motorcycle battery used to power the nav-com radio.

AVIONICS: Battery-powered Narco Escort 110 nav-com.

DIMENSIONS, EXTERNAL:

Wing span	10·64 m (34 ft 11 in)
Wing chord, constant	1·60 m (5 ft 3 in)
Wing area	16·81 m² (181 sq ft)
Length overall	7·24 m (23 ft 9 in)
Height overall	1·68 m (5 ft 6 in)
Tailplane span	2·54 m (8 ft 4 in)
Wheelbase	1·70 m (5 ft 7 in)
Propeller diameter	1·83 m (6 ft 0 in)

WEIGHTS:

Weight empty, equipped	364 kg (802 lb)
Max fuel weight	55 kg (122 lb)
Max T-O and landing weight	590 kg (1,300 lb)

PERFORMANCE (at max T-O weight):

Max cruising speed at 1,220 m (4,000 ft)	65 knots (121 km/h; 75 mph)
Econ cruising speed at 2,135 m (7,000 ft)	56 knots (105 km/h; 65 mph)
Stalling speed, power off 35 knots (64·5 km/h; 40 mph)	
Max rate of climb at S/L	approx 152 m (500 ft)/min
Service ceiling	approx 2,590 m (8,500 ft)
T-O run	approx 152 m (500 ft)
Landing run	approx 122 m (400 ft)
Range with max fuel, 30 min reserves	226 nm (418 km; 260 miles)
Endurance	4½ h

McCARLEY
Mrs CHARLES E. McCARLEY
1119 27 Avenue, Hueytown, Alabama 35020

McCARLEY MINI-MAC
Designed by the late Mr Charles E. McCarley, the prototype Mini-Mac took 1,600 working hours to build, at a cost of $1,800, and first flew in July 1970. It was totally destroyed, and Mr McCarley was fatally injured, in an accident on 28 October 1978. The aircraft was reportedly operating normally up to the time of the crash; Mr McCarley apparently was blinded by the sun and failed to see a powerline.

A modified version of the Mini-Mac (N75GH), built by George M. Harrison, was completed on 4 July 1974 and accumulated 122 flying hours in its first year. As well as having a shortened wing span, N75GH has 10° drooping ailerons.

The Mini-Mac is capable of limited aerobatics, and has a number of optional features, including a cockpit canopy, radio and an electrical system. Plans for sale to amateur constructors were being completed in early 1980. Three more Mini-Macs were then known to be under construction.

The following description generally applies to both aircraft mentioned above, except where indicated:

TYPE: Single-seat limited aerobatic monoplane.

WINGS: Cantilever low-wing monoplane. Clark Y wing section. All-metal construction. 10° drooping ailerons fitted to N75GH. Folding wings.

FUSELAGE: Conventional all-metal structure.

TAIL UNIT: Conventional cantilever all-metal structure. Tab in elevators.

LANDING GEAR: Non-retractable tricycle type. Wheels enclosed in streamline fairings. Small tail bumper skid.

POWER PLANT: One 1,834 cc (N152CM prototype) or 1,600 cc (N75GH) modified Volkswagen motor car engine, driving a two-blade propeller. Conventional fuel and oil systems, not modified for inverted flight.

ACCOMMODATION: Single seat in open or enclosed cockpit, latter with rearward-sliding canopy.

DIMENSIONS, EXTERNAL (A: prototype; B: N75GH):

Wing span:		
	A	6·25 m (20 ft 6 in)
	B	5·79 m (19 ft 0 in)
Wing chord:		
	A	1·02 m (3 ft 4 in)
	B	1·04 m (3 ft 5 in)
Length overall:		
	A	4·47 m (14 ft 8 in)
	B	4·39 m (14 ft 5 in)
Height overall:		
	A and B	1·73 m (5 ft 8 in)

WEIGHTS:

Weight empty:		
	A	233 kg (514 lb)
	B	208 kg (458 lb)
Max T-O weight:		
	A	363 kg (800 lb)
	B	318 kg (700 lb)

PERFORMANCE:

Max level speed:		
	A and B	139 knots (257 km/h; 160 mph)
Cruising speed:		
	A	109 knots (201 km/h; 125 mph)
	B	95 knots (177 km/h; 110 mph)
Landing speed:		
	A	44 knots (81 km/h; 50 mph)
	B	48 knots (89 km/h; 55 mph)
Max rate of climb at S/L:		
	A	305 m (1,000 ft)/min
	B	213 m (700 ft)/min
Service ceiling:		
	A and B	2,440 m (8,000 ft)
T-O run:		
	A	152 m (500 ft)
	B	183 m (600 ft)
Landing run:		
	A and B	152 m (500 ft)
Range with max fuel:		
	A	434 nm (804 km; 500 miles)
	B	260 nm (483 km; 300 miles)

MEAD
GEORGE MEAD
Box 354, Colwich, Kansas 67030

MEAD ADVENTURE MODEL 100
Mr George Mead, a flight test engineer with Cessna Aircraft Company, has designed and built a small single-seat sporting aircraft known as the Adventure Model 100. Construction took 1½ years and cost $5,000. First flight was made in October 1978.

Construction is of glassfibre/foam/epoxy composite sandwich, and the Adventure 100 is powered by a 59·7 kW (80 hp) Continental engine, although other engines of 48·5-63·4 kW (65-85 hp) could be installed. The wings are fitted with ailerons of only 0·61 m (2 ft 0 in) span, and wide-span flaps. Plans of the Adventure Model 100 are available to amateur constructors.

TYPE: Single-seat sporting aircraft.

DIMENSIONS, EXTERNAL:

Wing span	6·10 m (20 ft 0 in)
Wing chord: at root	0·76 m (2 ft 6 in)
at tip	0·46 m (1 ft 6 in)
Length overall	3·96 m (13 ft 0 in)
Height overall	1·68 m (5 ft 6 in)

WEIGHTS:

Weight empty	208·5 kg (460 lb)
Max T-O weight	351·5 kg (775 lb)

PERFORMANCE:

Max level speed	165 knots (306 km/h; 190 mph)
Cruising speed	156 knots (290 km/h; 180 mph)
Landing speed	52 knots (96 km/h; 60 mph)
Max rate of climb at S/L	488 m (1,600 ft)/min
T-O run	213 m (700 ft)
Landing run	244 m (800 ft)
Range with max fuel	695 nm (1,287 km; 800 miles)

MILLER
WILLIAM Y. MILLER
1439 West Second Street, Mesa, Arizona 85201

Mr William Y. Miller built the prototype of the WM-2 sporting aircraft, which had been designed by Mr W. Terry Miller for amateur construction.

MILLER WM-2
The WM-2 is a low-powered, high-performance aircraft, conceived originally for the exploration of wave soaring conditions, thermal soaring with the engine stopped, and high-altitude, economical powered sport flying. The prototype (N24832) was built by Mr William Miller between 1969 and 1972, and made its first flight in August 1972. Flight testing was undertaken during 1973-74, and by January 1978 the aircraft had completed 430 flying hours. Plans are available to amateur constructors, and approximately 12 WM-2s were under construction by January 1980.

TYPE: Single-seat sport aircraft.

WINGS: Cantilever low-wing monoplane. Modified NACA laminar-flow series wing sections. Thickness/chord ratio 15%. Dihedral 4°. Incidence 1°. Sweepback 0° 53' at quarter-chord. Conventional structure of spruce spars, with birch plywood, glassfibre and fabric covering. Wooden ailerons. No flaps or tabs. Metal spoiler in each upper surface.

FUSELAGE: Conventional spruce structure, with birch plywood and glassfibre covering.

TAIL UNIT: Plywood- and fabric-covered spruce cantilever structure.

LANDING GEAR: Manually-retractable monowheel (wheel and tyre size 6·00-6) and steerable tailwheel. Hydraulic brake.

POWER PLANT: One 48·5 kW (65 hp) Continental flat-four engine, driving a two-blade fixed-pitch metal propeller. Fuel tank, capacity 37·8 litres (10 US gallons), aft of firewall. Fuel consumption at an econ cruising speed of 69·5 knots (129 km/h; 80 mph) is less than 7·5 litres (2 US gallons)/hour.

ACCOMMODATION: Single seat under one-piece sideways-opening bubble canopy.

DIMENSIONS, EXTERNAL:

Wing span	12·19 m (40 ft 0 in)
Wing chord at root	1·37 m (4 ft 6 in)
Wing chord at tip	0·76 m (2 ft 6 in)
Wing area, gross	13·38 m² (144·0 sq ft)
Wing aspect ratio	11·11
Length overall	6·10 m (20 ft 0 in)
Height over tail	1·60 m (5 ft 3 in)
Tailplane span	2·44 m (8 ft 0 in)
Propeller diameter	1·88 m (6 ft 2 in)

WEIGHTS:

Weight empty, equipped	351 kg (775 lb)
Max T-O weight	476 kg (1,050 lb)

PERFORMANCE (at max T-O weight):

Never-exceed speed	130 knots (241 km/h; 150 mph)
Max level speed at S/L	118 knots (219 km/h; 136 mph)
Normal cruising speed at 3,050 m (10,000 ft), 50% power	109 knots (203 km/h; 126 mph)
Stalling speed	39·5 knots (72·5 km/h; 45 mph)
Max rate of climb at S/L	271 m (890 ft)/min
Rate of climb at 4,575 m (15,000 ft)	152 m (500 ft)/min
Service ceiling (computed)	7,315 m (24,000 ft)
Range at normal cruising speed at 3,050 m (10,000 ft) with 30 min reserves	291 nm (540 km; 336 miles)
Best glide ratio at 54 knots (100 km/h; 62 mph), power off	15

MINI-HAWK
MINI-HAWK INTERNATIONAL INC
1930 Stewart Street, Santa Monica, California 90404
Telephone: (213) 828 4078
DIRECTOR OF MARKETING: E. Y. Treffinger

Mini-Hawk International was formed to market plans and kits for construction of an all-metal single-seat monoplane known as the Mini-Hawk TH.E.01 Tiger-Hawk. Three officers of the corporation, designer William B. Taylor, engineer Thomas E. Maloney and pilot E. Y. Treffinger, combined their efforts to design and construct the prototype. This aircraft flew for the first time during 1974 and the test programme was completed in 1976.

Mini-Hawk offers amateur constructors a complete set of plans and a construction manual or a complete kit

The prototype Mini-Mac (1,834 cc Volkswagen engine)

Mead Adventure Model 100 (*Howard Levy*)

Prototype WM-2 sport aircraft built by Mr William Miller

Mini-Hawk TH.E.01 Tiger-Hawk with current, revised canopy

---

package with or without an engine; by early 1980 at least five sets had been sold.

MINI-HAWK TH.E.01 TIGER-HAWK

TYPE: Single-seat lightweight aircraft.

WINGS: Cantilever low-wing monoplane of all-metal construction. Constant-chord wing. Dihedral 4° on outer panels. Full-span ailerons of all-metal construction, operated by push/pull rods. All-metal trailing-edge flaps. Wings removable in 10 min for towing or storage.

FUSELAGE: Built-up structure of light alloy.

TAIL UNIT: Cantilever all-metal structure. Fixed-incidence tailplane. Elevator of light alloy construction. No trim tabs.

LANDING GEAR: Non-retractable tricycle type with steerable nosewheel. Hurst/Airheart hydraulic disc brakes. Single wheel with speed fairing on each unit.

POWER PLANT: One 53·5 kW (72 hp) Revmaster Model 1831D modified Volkswagen motor car engine, with dual ignition, driving an Eng. Duplicating 54/42 two-blade fixed-pitch propeller with spinner. Fuel tank in fuselage with capacity of 45·4 litres (12 US gallons). Suitable for Volkswagen engines of up to 67 kW (90 hp). Oil capacity 2·35 litres (5 US pints).

ACCOMMODATION: Single seat under transparent canopy.

EQUIPMENT: Genave radio optional.

DIMENSIONS, EXTERNAL:
Wing span	5·49 m (18 ft 0 in)
Wing chord, constant	0·99 m (3 ft 3 in)
Wing area, gross	5·30 m² (57 sq ft)
Length overall	4·04 m (13 ft 3 in)
Width overall, wings removed	1·83 m (6 ft 0 in)
Height overall	2·08 m (6 ft 10 in)
Tailplane span	1·83 m (6 ft 0 in)
Wheel track	1·78 m (5 ft 10 in)
Wheelbase	1·93 m (6 ft 4 in)
Propeller diameter	1·37 m (4 ft 6 in)

WEIGHTS:
Weight empty	238 kg (525 lb)
Max T-O weight	362 kg (800 lb)

PERFORMANCE (at max T-O weight):
Never-exceed speed	173 knots (321 km/h; 200 mph)
Max level speed	152 knots (282 km/h; 175 mph)
Max cruising speed	139 knots (257 km/h; 160 mph)
Stalling speed, flaps up	54 knots (100 km/h; 62 mph)
Stalling speed, flaps down	44 knots (81 km/h; 50 mph)
Max rate of climb at S/L	275-305 m (900-1,000 ft)/min
Service ceiling	3,050 m (10,000 ft)
Absolute ceiling	3,660 m (12,000 ft)
T-O and landing run	122 m (400 ft)
Range with max fuel	608 nm (1,126 km; 700 miles)

MITCHELL
MITCHELL AIRCRAFT CORPORATION

1900 South Newcomb, Porterville, California 93257
Telephone: (209) 781 0778
GENERAL MANAGER: Richard T. Avalon

Mitchell Aircraft Corporation, which produces the Mitchell Wing hang glider, is also marketing plans and kits for two versions of the Mitchell Wing Model B-10, and a new Mitchell Wing U-2, all three of these aircraft being in the ultra-lightweight category. Both B-10 versions utilise the basic hang glider wing, whereas the wing of the U-2 is of different design.

MITCHELL WING MODEL B-10

Design of this aircraft originated in 1975, construction of the prototype following very soon after, and it flew for the first time in 1976. Two powered versions are available as follows:

Model B-10F. Foot-launch powered version, which has a tubular frame structure that serves as fuselage, engine mounting, and open cockpit for the pilot. Only two main wheels are provided, at the aft end of the fuselage frame.

Model B-10. Powered version with similar tubular frame structure, but with a tricycle-type landing gear that allows conventional powered take-offs and landings.

Both of the above versions, as well as the unpowered hang glider, have standard attachments to unite wing and fuselage, the wing being common to all three.

By early 1980 approximately 500 kits and plan sets for B-10/10F versions had been sold.

TYPE: Single-seat ultralight monoplane.

WINGS: Tapered parasol monoplane. Wing section NACA 23015. Dihedral 6° on outer wing panels. Sweepback at quarter-chord 12°. Structure is composite, with D section leading-edge, its form retained by foam ribs, and attached to a wooden web spar. Trailing-edge ribs are of built-up truss type, those in the centre-section being of heavier material and carrying the rear spar for accessory attachment points. Dacron covering, with a small section of the wing undersurface, immediately above the cockpit, left uncovered to simplify access to seat. Mitchell patented 'stabilators' occupy the entire trailing-edge of each outer wing panel and function differentially as ailerons and collectively as elevators. Rudders, mounted above each wingtip, are operated conventionally for yaw control; they can also be actuated differentially as airbrakes for increased descent rates. Outer wing panels fold over centre-section for transportation.

FUSELAGE: Braced framework of aluminium tube, serving also as support structure for wing, landing gear, and power plant when installed.

LANDING GEAR: B-10F has two main wheels only; B-10 has non-retractable tricycle configuration with steerable nosewheel. All wheels of nylon, with tubed tyres size 4·10 × 3·50-4. No brakes.

POWER PLANT: Not included in kit, but recommended for installation in powered versions are Chrysler West Bend or McCulloch two-stroke engines. Powering the prototype was a 9 kW (12 hp) McCulloch MC101 engine, driving a two-blade pusher propeller. Fuel tank, which can be mounted within the wing or on the fuselage framework, has a capacity of 5·7 litres (1·5 US gallons).

ACCOMMODATION: Pilot only, seated within fuselage framework on reinforced canvas sling seat, with seat belt or full shoulder-harness.

DIMENSIONS, EXTERNAL:
Wing span	10·36 m (34 ft 0 in)
Wing chord at root	1·83 m (6 ft 0 in)
Wing chord at tip	0·61 m (2 ft 0 in)
Wing area, gross	12·63 m² (136 sq ft)
Wing aspect ratio	·8
Width, wings folded	5·49 m (18 ft 0 in)
Height overall	1·22 m (4 ft 0 in)
Wheel track	1·22 m (4 ft 0 in)
Wheelbase	1·52 m (5 ft 0 in)
Propeller diameter	1·22 m (4 ft 0 in)

WEIGHTS:
Weight empty	66 kg (145 lb)
Max T-O weight	170 kg (375 lb)

PERFORMANCE (B-10 prototype at max T-O weight):
Max level speed at S/L	48 knots (89 km/h; 55 mph)
Max cruising speed at S/L	43 knots (80·5 km/h; 50 mph)
Econ cruising speed at S/L	31 knots (58 km/h; 36 mph)
Stalling speed	14 knots (26 km/h; 16 mph)
Max rate of climb at S/L	122 m (400 ft)/min
Service ceiling	3,660 m (12,000 ft)
T-O run	61 m (200 ft)
T-O to 15 m (50 ft)	91 m (300 ft)
Landing from 15 m (50 ft)	61 m (200 ft)
Landing run	30 m (100 ft)
Range, with max fuel and payload	35 nm (64 km; 40 miles)
Best glide ratio, power off	17

MITCHELL WING U-2

With the aim of developing an ultralight powered aircraft that would be superior in controllability, performance and structure to powered hang gliders, Mr Don Mitchell has designed a new machine based on the Mitchell wing. Designated U-2, initiation of the design, and construction and first flight of the prototype, were all accomplished during 1979. In early 1980, orders for plans and/or kits totalled 75.

TYPE: Single-seat ultralight monoplane.

WINGS: Those of production kits are generally similar to the wings of the B-10, except that the wing section is modified Wortmann of 19% thickness/chord ratio, and the over-wingtip rudders have been replaced by com-

Mitchell Wing Model
B-10 powered
ultralight aircraft

Mitchell Wing U-2, Don Mitchell's latest ultralight prototype

bined fin and rudder assemblies, the aft 65% of each being movable. (The prototype had wholly-fixed fins above the wingtips, and spoilers mounted in the upper surface of each wing to replace conventional rudders and speedbrakes.)
FUSELAGE: Chrome-molybdenum steel tube structure within the wing centre-section. Two hardwood runners extend the full length of this fuselage structure, beneath the pilot's seat, for protection in a wheels-up landing.
LANDING GEAR: Manually-retractable tricycle type, all units retracting aft. Optional non-retractable landing gear. Steerable nosewheel. Nylon wheels with tubed tyres size 4·10 × 3·50-4. Friction brake operating on surface of nosewheel tyre.
POWER PLANT: Not supplied as part of kit, but recommended engine is a 9 kW (12 hp) McCulloch MC101,

driving via a V-belt reduction gear a two-blade fixed-pitch pusher propeller. Power plant mounted at aft end of fuselage structure. Plastics fuel tank mounted within wing has capacity of 5·7 litres (1·5 US gallons).
ACCOMMODATION: Pilot only on reinforced canvas sling seat, beneath one-piece bubble canopy which is secured by fore and aft locking pins, and easily removed for entry and exit. Mylar panels in cockpit floor to provide downward view. Cockpit is ventilated.
DIMENSIONS, EXTERNAL: As for B-10 except:

Length overall	2·84 m (9 ft 4 in)
Height overall	0·91 m (3 ft 0 in)
Wheel track	1·47 m (4 ft 10 in)
Wheelbase	0·97 m (3 ft 2 in)

WEIGHTS:

Basic operating weight	82 kg (180 lb)

Max T-O weight	195 kg (430 lb)

PERFORMANCE (prototype, with 9 kW; 12 hp McCulloch engine, at max T-O weight):

Max level speed at S/L	82 knots (153 km/h; 95 mph)
Max cruising speed at S/L	69 knots (129 km/h; 80 mph)
Econ cruising speed at S/L	56 knots (105 km/h; 65 mph)
Stalling speed	22 knots (40 km/h; 25 mph)
Max rate of climb at S/L	152 m (500 ft)/min
Service ceiling	3,660 m (12,000 ft)
T-O run	61 m (200 ft)
T-O to 15 m (50 ft)	84 m (275 ft)
Landing from 15 m (50 ft)	76 m (250 ft)
Landing run	38 m (125 ft)
Range, with max fuel and max payload	39 nm (72 km; 45 miles)
Best glide ratio, power off	27

MONNETT
MONNETT EXPERIMENTAL AIRCRAFT INC
955 Grace Street, Elgin, Illinois 60120
Telephone: (312) 741 2223
GENERAL MANAGER: Gregg Erikson
Mr John T. Monnett formed this company to market plans and certain components of an original-design Formula V racer. Known originally as the Monnett II Sonerai, this received the Best in Class Formula V Racer award at the EAA Fly-in at Oshkosh in 1971, as well as an award for its outstanding contribution to low-cost flying. Since that time Mr Monnett has designed a two-seat version of the Sonerai, with the result that the original single-seat model is now known simply as Sonerai, the two-seat model as Sonerai II. Under development is a new high-performance single-seat monoplane named the Monex.
Other products available from Monnett Experimental Aircraft include the company's Aero Vee light aero-engines. The two current models are the E-V and Super-Vee, supplied as either 1,600 cc or 1,700 cc units, with or without alternator. Both are stock Volkswagen direct-drive engines, producing 44·7-48·5 kW (60-65 hp) at 4,000 rpm. Customers can purchase either a conversion kit for any Volkswagen Type 3 case of 1969 or newer, or a ready-to-run engine.

MONNETT MONEX
In January 1980 Monnett was building the prototype of a new all-metal single-seat high-performance monoplane which is to be named Monex. Planned for demonstration at the 1980 EAA convention at Oshkosh, it will be powered by a 48·5 kW (65 hp) Zenoah 440 cc two-cylinder two-stroke liquid-cooled engine that will have a fuel consumption of about 15 litres (4 US gallons)/h. Features of this new design, which it is estimated will have maximum and cruising speeds of 173 knots (322 km/h; 200 mph) and 143 knots (266 km/h; 165 mph) respectively, include semi-reclined seating for the pilot and a V tail. Construction is intended to be very simple, with virtually all parts pre-formed.

MONNETT SONERAI
Mr Monnett began design of the Sonerai in September 1970, construction starting two months later. First flight was made in July 1971, with FAA certification in the Experimental category. Plans and certain components are available to amateur constructors, including glassfibre engine cowlings, clear or tinted Plexiglas cockpit canopy, main landing gear struts, formed aluminium ribs, tapered rod tail spring, fuel tanks, spar kits, instruments, injector

carburettor and wheels and brakes. Estimated building time is 850 working hours. The aircraft is stressed to ±6g.
Approximately 550 sets of plans have been sold, and more than 400 Sonerais are under construction or flying.
TYPE: Single-seat Formula V racing aircraft.
WINGS: Cantilever mid-wing monoplane. Wing section NACA 64212. No dihedral, incidence or sweepback. Conventional light alloy structure. Full-span light alloy ailerons. No flaps or tabs. Wings fold on each side of the fuselage to allow the aircraft to be towed tail-first.
FUSELAGE: Welded chrome-molybdenum steel tube structure with fabric covering. Glassfibre engine cowling.
TAIL UNIT: Cantilever structure of welded chrome-molybdenum steel tube with fabric covering. Tailplane incidence ground-adjustable. No trim tabs.
LANDING GEAR: Non-retractable tailwheel type. Cantilever spring main gear of light alloy. Main wheels and tyres size 5·00-5. Caliper type wheel-brakes. Glassfibre fairings on main wheels.
POWER PLANT: One 44·7 kW (60 hp) Volkswagen 1,600 cc modified motor car engine, driving a Hegy two-blade propeller with spinner. Fuel tank in fuselage, immediately aft of firewall, capacity 37·8 litres (10 US gallons). Refuelling point on fuselage upper surface forward of canopy. Oil capacity 2·82 litres (0·75 US gallons).
ACCOMMODATION: Single seat under jettisonable Plexiglas bubble canopy, hinged at the starboard side.
ELECTRONICS: Battery-powered 100-channel com transceiver.
DIMENSIONS, EXTERNAL:

Wing span	5·08 m (16 ft 8 in)
Wing chord, constant	1·37 m (4 ft 6 in)
Wing area, gross	6·97 m² (75 sq ft)
Length overall	5·08 m (16 ft 8 in)
Height overall	1·52 m (5 ft 0 in)
Tailplane span	1·98 m (6 ft 6 in)
Wheel track	1·22 m (4 ft 0 in)
Propeller diameter	1·27 m (4 ft 2 in)

WEIGHTS:

Weight empty	199 kg (440 lb)
Max T-O weight	340 kg (750 lb)

PERFORMANCE (at max T-O weight):

Max level speed at S/L	152 knots (281 km/h; 175 mph)
Max cruising speed	130 knots (241 km/h; 150 mph)
Econ cruising speed	109 knots (201 km/h; 125 mph)
Stalling speed	35 knots (64·5 km/h; 40 mph)
Max rate of climb at S/L	305 m (1,000 ft)/min
T-O run	183 m (600 ft)
Landing run	183 m (600 ft)
Range, with reserves	260 nm (482 km; 300 miles)

MONNETT SONERAI II
The success of the Sonerai encouraged Mr Monnett to begin the design and construction of a two-seat version in December 1972. Generally similar to the Sonerai, it differs by being slightly larger and by having a more powerful Volkswagen engine. It is stressed to ±4·4g in the Utility category and to ±6g in a single-seat Aerobatic category. The prototype made its first flight in July 1973. Orders had been received for 843 sets of plans and at least 140 Sonerai IIs were flying by early 1980. Many components, complete kits for fuselage and wings, and materials, are available to amateur constructors. Estimated building time is 850 working hours.
The description of the Sonerai applies also to Sonerai II, except as follows:
TYPE: Two-seat high-performance sporting aircraft.
WINGS: As for Sonerai, except span increased.
FUSELAGE: As for Sonerai, except length increased.
TAIL UNIT: As for Sonerai, except tailplane has fixed incidence and reduced span.
POWER PLANT: One 1,700 cc Volkswagen modified motor car engine, developing 48·5-52·2 kW (65-70 hp), driving a two-blade ground-adjustable wooden propeller. Fuel capacity 37·8 litres (10 US gallons); oil as for Sonerai.
ACCOMMODATION: Two seats in tandem beneath transparent bubble canopy, hinged on starboard side.
ELECTRONICS: Prototype has alternator-powered 100-channel radio.
DIMENSIONS, EXTERNAL: As Sonerai, except:

Wing span	5·69 m (18 ft 8 in)
Wing area, gross	7·80 m² (84 sq ft)
Length overall	5·74 m (18 ft 10 in)
Tailplane span	1·83 m (6 ft 0 in)
Propeller diameter	1·32-1·37 m (4 ft 4 in to 4 ft 6 in)

DIMENSION, INTERNAL:

Cockpit: Max width	0·61 m (2 ft 0 in)

WEIGHTS:

Weight empty	230 kg (506 lb)
Max T-O weight	419 kg (925 lb)

PERFORMANCE (at max T-O weight):

Max level speed at S/L	approx 143 knots (266 km/h; 165 mph)
Max cruising speed at S/L	122 knots (225 km/h; 140 mph)
Econ cruising speed at S/L	113 knots (209 km/h; 130 mph)
Stalling speed	39 knots (73 km/h; 45 mph)
Max rate of climb at S/L	229 m (750 ft)/min
T-O run, ISA	274 m (900 ft)
Landing run	152 m (500 ft)
Range, with reserves	217 nm (402 km; 250 miles)

MOONEY MITE
MOONEY MITE AIRCRAFT CORPORATION
PO Box 3999, Charlottesville, Virginia 22903

Mooney Mite Aircraft Corporation was formed to market to amateur constructors plans of the Mooney Mite,

a version of the Mooney M-18 first designed and built as a production aircraft by Mooney Aircraft Inc.

Monnett Sonerai (1,850 cc Volkswagen engine) built by Mr Zig Bergins of Montreal, Canada (*Neil A. Macdougall*)

Monnett Sonerai II two-seat sporting aircraft

Model of the Monnett Monex, designed for outstanding fuel economy

Murphy VM-7 Competitor Unlimited class aerobatic monoplane

Mooney Mite single-seat light aircraft

MOONEY MITE

TYPE: Single-seat sporting aircraft.

WINGS: Cantilever low-wing monoplane. Wing section NACA 63215 at root, NACA 64415 at tip. Dihedral 5° 30′ from roots. Incidence 4°. Conventional single-spar structure of wood, with plywood D-type leading-edge torsion box, and fabric covering aft of the spar. Ailerons and trailing-edge flaps of welded steel tube construction with fabric covering.

FUSELAGE: Forward section to aft of cockpit of welded steel tube with light alloy skins. Aft fuselage of wood monocoque construction with fabric covering.

TAIL UNIT: Cantilever welded steel tube structure, fabric-covered. Tailplane incidence variable by 'Safe-Trim' system that interconnects tail trim with trailing-edge flaps to establish automatically the correct settings for take-off, climb, approach and landing.

LANDING GEAR: Manually retractable tricycle type. Shock-absorption of main units by rubber-in-compression. Nosewheel steerable. Main wheels of Cleveland, Firestone or Goodyear manufacture, with tyres size 5·00-5. Hydraulic brakes.

POWER PLANT: One 48·5 kW (65 hp) Avco Lycoming O-145-B2 flat-four aircooled engine, driving a Sensenich Type 66CB-54 two-blade fixed-pitch propeller with spinner. Fuel tank in fuselage, capacity 41·5 litres (11 US gallons). Provision for auxiliary tank, capacity 23 litres (6 US gallons). Oil capacity 3·75 litres (1 US gallon).

ACCOMMODATION: Single seat beneath aft-sliding transparent canopy. Space for 18 kg (40 lb) baggage aft of seat.

SYSTEM: Electric power supplied by wind-driven generator mounted on pylon on upper surface of aft fuselage.

DIMENSIONS, EXTERNAL:
Wing span	8·19 m (26 ft 10½ in)
Wing area	8·83 m² (95 sq ft)
Length overall	5·37 m (17 ft 7¼ in)
Height overall	1·89 m (6 ft 2½ in)
Tailplane span	2·54 m (8 ft 4 in)
Wheel track	1·55 m (5 ft 1 in)
Wheelbase	1·22 m (4 ft 0 in)
Propeller diameter	1·60 m (5 ft 3 in)

WEIGHTS:
Weight empty	229 kg (505 lb)
Max T-O weight	353 kg (780 lb)

PERFORMANCE (at max T-O weight):
Max level speed at S/L	124 knots (230 km/h; 143 mph)
Econ cruising speed, 50% power at S/L	99 knots (183 km/h; 114 mph)
Min controllable speed, power on	33 knots (61·5 km/h; 38 mph)
Landing speed, power off	39 knots (72 km/h; 45 mph)
Stalling speed, power off	37·5 knots (69·5 km/h; 43 mph)
Max rate of climb at S/L	332 m (1,090 ft)/min
Service ceiling	5,915 m (19,400 ft)
T-O run	213 m (698 ft)
T-O to 15 m (50 ft)	305 m (1,000 ft)
Landing from 15 m (50 ft)	366 m (1,200 ft)
Landing run	73 m (240 ft)
Range at econ cruising speed, standard fuel	382 nm (708 km; 440 miles)
Range with auxiliary fuel	521 nm (965 km; 600 miles)

MURPHY
R. L. MURPHY

90 Pebble Woods Drive, Doylestown, Pennsylvania 18901

Mr Dick Murphy, a Captain with American Airlines, with 23 years of military and civil flying and engineering experience, designed and built a single-seat Unlimited class aerobatic aircraft known as the VM-7 Competitor (N5P). He had previously constructed a Van's RV-3, which was flown competitively during 1976; the VM-7 Competitor owes much to this aircraft and to ideas and suggestions from other designers and pilots. Design objectives for the VM-7 were that it should be easy to construct, should cost under $10,000, and should have good performance. Without the engine and propeller, it cost $6,000

and took 2,000 working hours to build. The prototype flew for the first time in March 1978, but was destroyed by fire during December 1979. Mr Murphy began construction of a second example immediately, with the intention of having it completed in time to compete in the 1980 World aerobatic contest. Plans may be made available to amateur builders when the aircraft has proved its capability in competitive aerobatics.

MURPHY VM-7 COMPETITOR

TYPE: Single-seat Unlimited class aerobatic monoplane.

WINGS: Cantilever mid-wing monoplane. Wing section NACA 23015. Constant chord. Light alloy structure, comprising a laminated main spar, passing through fuselage under pilot's knees, and twenty hydroformed

ribs, covered with light alloy skin panels, bonded and pop-riveted in place. Symmetrical, balanced and sealed ailerons.

FUSELAGE: Light-alloy semi-monocoque structure, mostly bonded but with some pop rivets.

TAIL UNIT: Cantilever light alloy structure. Fin integral with rear fuselage. Trim tab in port elevator.

LANDING GEAR: Non-retractable tailwheel type. Wittman type cantilever spring steel main legs. Main-wheel tyres size 5·00-5. Cleveland brakes. Streamline fairings over main wheels. Steerable tailwheel.

POWER PLANT: One 149 kW (200 hp) Avco Lycoming O-360 flat-four engine, driving a Hartzell two-blade constant-speed propeller, with spinner. Engine fitted with IO-360 sump, manifold and fuel injector. Main and

auxiliary fuel tanks in forward fuselage; total capacity 64·4 litres (17 US gallons). Second auxiliary tank optional. Oil capacity 7·6 litres (2 US gallons).
ACCOMMODATION: Single seat, inclined at about 15°, under forward-sliding canopy.
DIMENSIONS, EXTERNAL:

Wing span	5·94 m (19 ft 6 in)
Wing chord (constant)	1·37 m (4 ft 6 in)
Length overall	6·02 m (19 ft 9 in)
Propeller diameter	1·93 m (6 ft 4 in)
Propeller ground clearance	0·15 m (6 in)

WEIGHTS:

Weight empty, with starter and battery	361·5 kg (797 lb)
Max T-O and landing weight	567 kg (1,250 lb)

PERFORMANCE:

Never-exceed speed	186 knots (346 km/h; 215 mph)
Max level speed at S/L	174 knots (322 km/h; 200 mph)
Max cruising speed (75% power)	152 knots (282 km/h; 175 mph)
Econ cruising speed (50% power)	130 knots (241 km/h; 150 mph)
Stalling speed, power off	43·5 knots (80·5 km/h; 50 mph)
Rate of climb at S/L	over 915 m (3,000 ft)/min
Service ceiling, estimated	5,485 m (18,000 ft)
T-O run	46 m (150 ft)
T-O to 15 m (50 ft)	76 m (250 ft)
Landing from 15 m (50 ft)	366 m (1,200 ft)
Range with max fuel	217 nm (402 km; 250 miles)
g limits: normal	±9
ultimate	±14

NEUMANN
EVERETTE NEUMANN
Anoka, Minnesota

NEUMANN N2

Mr Everette Neumann, a machinist, has designed and built a single-seat light monoplane known as the N2. Construction required 2 years and cost $7,000. First flight was made in July 1979. Of all-aluminium construction, the N2 is said to be fully aerobatic and is stressed to ±6g. Power is provided by a 74·5 kW (100 hp) Continental O-200 engine.
DIMENSIONS, EXTERNAL:

Wing span	7·92 m (26 ft 0 in)
Wing chord, constant	2·13 m (7 ft 0 in)
Length overall	6·71 m (22 ft 0 in)

Height overall	2·39 m (7 ft 10 in)

WEIGHTS:

Weight empty	510 kg (1,125 lb)
Max T-O weight	635 kg (1,400 lb)

PERFORMANCE:

Cruising speed	61 knots (113 km/h; 70 mph)
Landing speed	52 knots (96 km/h; 60 mph)
T-O and landing run	91 m (300 ft)

NIEMI
LEONARD NIEMI
Greenville, South Carolina

NIEMI SPRINTER

Mr Leonard Niemi, an aeronautical engineer, has designed and built a small single-seat light aircraft known as the Sprinter. Construction took five years and cost $6,400. First flight was made in March 1978. Construction is all-metal, and the aircraft is powered by a 74·5 kW (100 hp) Continental O-200 flat-four engine. The Sprinter received an 'Honorable Mention' from the EAA at its 1979 Fly-in.
DIMENSIONS, EXTERNAL:

Wing span	6·40 m (21 ft 0 in)
Length overall	5·49 m (18 ft 0 in)

WEIGHTS:

Weight empty	326·5 kg (720 lb)
Max T-O weight	499 kg (1,100 lb)

PERFORMANCE:

Max level speed	156 knots (290 km/h; 180 mph)
Cruising speed	148 knots (273 km/h; 170 mph)
Landing speed	45 knots (84 km/h; 52 mph)
Max rate of climb at S/L	457 m (1,500 ft)/min
T-O run	213 m (700 ft)
Endurance with max fuel	3 h

OHMERT
VERNON R. OHMERT
Ypsilanti, Michigan

OHMERT BRISTOL F.2B FIGHTER REPLICA

Mr Vernon R. Ohmert and his two brothers have built six flying replicas of the Bristol F.2B Fighter of World War I vintage, and two other F.2Bs for destruction during filming of 'High Road to China'. The first F.2B replica made its initial flight on 4 July 1979 and had required 190 working days to build. Power is provided by a 149 kW (200 hp) Ranger 6-440-C in-line engine. Wings are of wood; fuselage construction is of steel tubing, with Stits Poly Fiber covering.
TYPE: Replica of the Bristol F.2B Fighter.
DIMENSIONS, EXTERNAL:

Wing span	12·19 m (40 ft 0 in)
Wing chord, constant	1·68 m (5 ft 6 in)
Length overall	7·32 m (24 ft 0 in)
Height overall	2·90 m (9 ft 6 in)

WEIGHTS:

Weight empty	839 kg (1,850 lb)
Max T-O weight	1,225 kg (2,700 lb)

PERFORMANCE:

Max level speed	126 knots (233 km/h; 145 mph)
Cruising speed	78 knots (145 km/h; 90 mph)
Landing speed	35 knots (64·5 km/h; 40 mph)
Max rate of climb at S/L	122 m (400 ft)/min
Service ceiling	4,575 m (15,000 ft)
T-O and landing run	183 m (600 ft)
Range with max fuel	260 nm (483 km; 300 miles)

OSPREY
OSPREY AIRCRAFT
3741 El Ricon Way, Sacramento, California 95825
Telephone: (917) 483 3004

Osprey Aircraft was formed originally to market to amateur constructors plans of the Osprey I aircraft designed and built by Mr George Pereira. This was an unusual project for the homebuilder, being a flying-boat, intended for operation on and from enclosed waters rather than the open sea. The plans drawn up by Mr Pereira included drawings of a special trailer for carriage of the aircraft, which allowed the pilot to launch and recover the Osprey unassisted. Details of this aircraft can be found in the 1974-75 *Jane's*.

Mr Pereira subsequently completed the prototype of a two-seat amphibian version designated Osprey II.

PEREIRA GP3 OSPREY II

Design and construction of the Osprey II, a two-seat amphibian development of the Osprey I, began in January 1972.

Mr Pereira evolved an unusual form of hull construction for this aircraft. When the all-wood fuselage structure had been completed and controls installed, the undersurface was given a deep coating of polyurethane foam. This was then sculptured to the requisite hull form before being covered with several protective layers of glassfibre cloth bonded with resin. The resulting structure is light, but extremely strong, with good shock resisting characteristics.

First flight of the Osprey II from water was made in April 1973, the amphibian becoming airborne in less than 244 m (800 ft), with no tendency to porpoise at any speed. In later tests from land it was found that with the landing gear retracted, and at a speed of about 104 knots (193 km/h; 120 mph), there was slight buffet aft of the cabin and the noise level was unacceptably high. Modifications carried out in early 1974 included lengthening of the cabin by 0·18 m (7 in), and installation of an Avco Lycoming O-320 engine in place of the original Franklin Sport, in a new cowling. Testing was resumed and completed satisfactorily during 1974, since when the shape of the tail fin has been changed. Sets of plans are available to amateur constructors, and the accompanying illustration shows an Osprey II built by Mr Carl McCain of Peru, Indiana. This departs from plans only in having additional cockpit upholstery. By early 1980 fifteen Ospreys were flying.
TYPE: Two-seat lightweight amphibian.
WINGS: Cantilever mid-wing monoplane, of constant chord. Wing section NACA 23012. Dihedral 4° 30'. Incidence 5°. All-wood structure, with single box spar and auxiliary rear spar for aileron attachment. Forward of the main spar the wing is plywood-covered to form a rigid 'D' section. Aft of the spar the wing is fabric-covered. Conventional ailerons, 100% mass-balanced, will be fitted with a ground-adjustable tab if this proves desirable. No trailing-edge flaps. Wingtip stabilising floats of polyurethane foam covered with glassfibre.
HULL: All-wood structure of longerons and frames, covered with 2·5 mm (3/32 in) marine plywood. Hull undersurface contours formed from polyurethane foam, protected by several layers of glassfibre cloth bonded with resin.
TAIL UNIT: Cantilever all-wood structure, with swept vertical surfaces; tailplane mounted high on fin, which is integral with hull. Incidence of tailplane ground-adjustable. Controllable trim tab in starboard elevator. Water rudder, contained within the base of the aerodynamic rudder, is spring-loaded in the down position and retracted by cable.
LANDING GEAR: Retractable tricycle type, with single wheel on each unit. Main units retract inward into the wing roots, the wheel wells being covered by doors in the retracted position. Nosewheel retracts forward into the nosecone and is also enclosed by a door. Manual retraction system. Shock-absorption by coil springs. Cleveland main wheels and tyres size 5·00-5. Nosewheel, of industrial type with roller bearings, has a tyre of 10 in diameter. Cleveland hydraulic disc brakes.
POWER PLANT: One 112 kW (150 hp) Avco Lycoming O-320 flat-four engine, mounted on a steel tube pylon structure which is bolted to the wing truss. Hendrickson 66 × 52 three-blade fixed-pitch wooden pusher propeller. One glassfibre fuel tank mounted beneath the main spar at the wing centre-section, usable capacity 98·4 litres (26 US gallons). Refuelling point on starboard side of hull, just aft of cabin.
ACCOMMODATION: Two seats side by side beneath transparent canopy, which is hinged at rear and swings upward. Dual controls standard; but toe-operated wheel brakes on starboard side only. Baggage compartment aft of seats, capacity 41 kg (90 lb).
SYSTEMS: Hydraulic system for brakes only. Electrical system powered by engine-driven generator.
DIMENSIONS, EXTERNAL:

Wing span	7·92 m (26 ft 0 in)
Wing chord, constant	1·52 m (5 ft 0 in)
Wing area, gross	12·08 m² (130 sq ft)
Wing aspect ratio	5·2
Length overall	6·25 m (20 ft 6 in)
Height overall (wheels down)	1·83 m (6 ft 0 in)
Tailplane span	2·44 m (8 ft 0 in)
Wheel track	2·59 m (8 ft 6 in)
Wheelbase	2·13 m (7 ft 0 in)
Propeller diameter	1·68 m (5 ft 6 in)

WEIGHTS:

Weight empty	440 kg (970 lb)
Max T-O weight	707 kg (1,560 lb)

PERFORMANCE (at max T-O weight unless specified otherwise):

Never-exceed speed	130 knots (241 km/h; 150 mph)
Max cruising speed at 75% power	113 knots (209 km/h; 130 mph)
Econ cruising speed at 55% power	94 knots (175 km/h; 109 mph)
Stalling speed	53 knots (97 km/h; 60 mph)
Max rate of climb at S/L, with pilot only	365 m (1,200 ft)/min
Rate of climb at S/L	305 m (1,000 ft)/min
T-O run, land	122 m (400 ft)
T-O run, water	159 m (520 ft)

OWL
GEORGE A. OWL Jr
17700 S. Western Avenue, Apartment 195, Gardena, California 90248
Telephone: (213) 323 3385

Mr George Owl, a member of the preliminary design staff of Rockwell International, is also the designer of two Formula One racing aircraft known as the Owl Racers OR-70 and OR-71. The former was designed to order for Bernadine and Jim Stevenson, both racing pilots, and was built by them (see 1977-78 *Jane's*). The OR-71 was produced in co-operation with Mr Vince DeLuca, proprietor of Vin-Del Aircraft, who has built a prototype and is making plans available to amateur constructors.

Prototypes of a version of the OR-71 with a new wing have been under construction since 1975. This wing, of all-wood construction and utilising a special laminar flow aerofoil section, is calculated to raise the maximum speed of the OR-71 by 5 knots (10 km/h; 6 mph). The designation of these aircraft will be OR-71B.

Vin-Del Aircraft
29718 Knollview Drive, Miraleste, California 90732
Mr Vince DeLuca, proprietor of Vin-Del Aircraft, built

Folding the wings of the Neumann N2 *(Howard Levy)*

Niemi Sprinter single-seat light aircraft *(Howard Levy)*

First Bristol F.2B Fighter replica built by Vernon R. Ohmert *(Howard Levy)*

Osprey II built from plans, by Mr Carl McCain, with Mr Pereira's prototype in background *(Howard Levy)*

Vin-Del/Owl OR-71 *Lil Quickie* Formula One racing aircraft

Parker Teenie Two powered by a modified Volkswagen engine

the prototype of a Formula One racer of Mr Owl's design which he designated OR-71 *Lil Quickie*. Construction began on 2 December 1971 and the first flight was made on 6 June 1972. Plans are available to amateur constructors.

VIN-DEL/OWL OR-71 LIL QUICKIE

Limit load factor of the OR-71 is ±7·33g, ultimate load factor ±11·0g.

TYPE: Single-seat Formula One racing aircraft.

WINGS: Cantilever mid-wing monoplane. Owl laminar flow aerofoil section, tapered in chord. Dihedral 0° 51′. Incidence 0°. Non-linear thickness distribution. Thickness/chord ratio is 13·7% at root, 10% on outer 60% of wing. All-wood structure. Laminated spruce one-piece main spar, plywood ribs with spruce caps, and plywood skins. Ailerons of spruce and plywood construction, mass-balanced at tip. No flaps. No trim tabs. Plans show optional high-lift leading-edge of larger radius and increased camber.

FUSELAGE: Welded steel tube structure, with light alloy fairings and Dacron covering. Glassfibre nose cowl

incorporates an annular cooling inlet. Engine cowl has controllable air exit flap.

TAIL UNIT: Cantilever wooden structure, with spruce spars and mahogany plywood ribs and skins. Fixed-incidence tailplane. No trim tabs.

LANDING GEAR: Non-retractable tailwheel type. Prototype has cantilever light alloy main legs. Spring steel legs optional. Main wheels and tyres size 5·00-5, pressure 2·41 bars (35 lb/sq in). Cleveland hydraulic disc brakes. Glassfibre fairings on main wheels. Tailwheel is a ball-bearing castor.

POWER PLANT: One 74·5 kW (100 hp) Continental O-200 flat-four engine, driving an Anderson, McCauley or Sensenich two-blade fixed-pitch propeller. Fuel tank in fuselage, immediately aft of firewall, capacity 34 litres (9 US gallons). Auxiliary integral fuel tank in each wing leading-edge, with combined capacity of 22·7 litres (6 US gallons). Total fuel capacity 56·7 litres (15 US gallons). Refuelling point on upper surface of fuselage, forward of windscreen. Oil capacity 5·7 litres (1·5 US gallons).

ACCOMMODATION: Single seat beneath small transparent

canopy, hinged on starboard side, opening upwards and to starboard.

DIMENSIONS, EXTERNAL:
Wing span	6·10 m (20 ft 0 in)
Wing chord at root	1·27 m (4 ft 2 in)
Wing chord at tip	0·76 m (2 ft 6 in)
Wing area, gross	6·13 m² (66 sq ft)
Wing aspect ratio	6
Length overall	4·98 m (16 ft 4 in)
Height overall	1·40 m (4 ft 7 in)
Wheel track	1·30 m (4 ft 3 in)
Wheelbase	3·63 m (11 ft 11 in)
Propeller diameter (max)	1·52 m (5 ft 0 in)

WEIGHTS:
Weight empty	251 kg (553 lb)
Max T-O weight	386 kg (850 lb)

PERFORMANCE (at max T-O weight):
Never-exceed speed	260 knots (482 km/h; 300 mph) IAS
Max level speed	more than 221 knots (410 km/h; 255 mph)
Stalling speed	60 knots (111 km/h; 69 mph)

PARKER
C. Y. PARKER
PO Box 625, Coolidge, Arizona 85228
Telephone: (602) 723 5660

PARKER TEENIE TWO

Mr Cal Parker completed and flew in 1969 the prototype of an improved version of the small lightweight all-metal homebuilt aircraft which he had designated Jeanie's Teenie. With completion of the new prototype, the original model became known as Teenie One. Plans for the Jeanie's Teenie were available for three years prior to Teenie Two plans being marketed.

Mr Parker's original aim was to build an aircraft specifically to utilise the Volkswagen motor car engine

and, at the same time, to evolve an all-metal design that would present few constructional problems even to homebuilders with virtually no metal-working experience. This has been achieved, and no special tools or jigs are needed beyond a tool to close and form the cadmium-plated steel pop rivets that are used for practically all assembly. One gauge of aluminium sheet and one size of light alloy angle section is used for almost all of the structure, except for chromoly steel tube and sheet which are used for construction of the landing gear and control actuation tubes respectively. For simplicity and economy, push/pull tubes are used for all flying controls.

Teenie One conformed to these ideas, but the Teenie Two was considerably refined to produce a much cleaner aeroplane. The prototype cost approximately $650 to

build, over a period of six months. Its structure is stressed for full aerobatics, but the fuel and oil systems are not suitable for inverted flight.

Teenie Two has been tested with various propellers, but a computer-designed propeller is available in the parts kit which gives optimum performance for take-off, climb and cruise.

Plans, complete kits of parts, and details of modifications for the Volkswagen engine are available to amateur constructors, and some Teenie Twos built from plans have completed well over 750 flying hours. The 1980 cost of constructing a Teenie Two was said to be about $2,600, including engine.

TYPE: Single-seat light aircraft.

WINGS: Cantilever low-wing monoplane. Wing section

NACA 4415. All-metal two-spar structure, with detachable outer wing panels. Light alloy ribs and skin. Plain ailerons of metal construction. No flaps.

FUSELAGE: All-metal semi-monocoque structure with longerons of light alloy angle, three built-up bulkheads and light alloy skin.

TAIL UNIT: Cantilever all-metal structure with swept vertical surfaces. Small dorsal fin eliminates the need for a fourth bulkhead by carrying loads from fin leading-edge to centre bulkhead. Conventional rudder and elevators of metal construction.

LANDING GEAR: Non-retractable tricycle type. Shock-absorption provided by springs in compression and rubber hose. All three wheels same size, with tyres size 10·5 × 4·00-4, pressure 1·72 bars (25 lb/sq in). Mechanically-actuated wheel brakes.

POWER PLANT: One 31·5 kW (42 hp) 1,600 cc or 30 kW (40 hp) 1,500 cc Volkswagen modified motor car engine (conversion parts sold by Parker), driving a two-blade fixed-pitch wooden propeller. Single fuselage fuel tank, immediately aft of firewall, capacity 34 litres (9 US gallons). Refuelling point on top of fuselage, forward of windscreen. Oil capacity 2·5 litres (0·66 US gallons).

ACCOMMODATION: Single seat in open cockpit. Drawings of optional canopy available; this increases max level speed to 122 knots (225 km/h; 140 mph).

SYSTEM: Prototype now fitted with alternator, starter and battery to power lights and radio, giving an increase in empty weight of 18 kg (40 lb).

DIMENSIONS, EXTERNAL:

Wing span	5·49 m (18 ft 0 in)
Wing chord, constant	1·02 m (3 ft 4 in)
Width, wings detached	1·83 m (6 ft 0 in)
Length overall	3·91 m (12 ft 10 in)

WEIGHTS:

Weight empty	140 kg (310 lb)
Max T-O weight	267 kg (590 lb)

PERFORMANCE (at max T-O weight, 1,600 cc engine):

Max level speed	104 knots (193 km/h; 120 mph)
Max cruising speed (75% power)	95·5 knots (177 km/h; 110 mph)
Landing speed	43·5 knots (80·5 km/h; 50 mph)
Max rate of climb at S/L (standard propeller)	244 m (800 ft)/min
Max rate of climb at S/L (52 × 37 propeller)	305 m (1,000 ft)/min
Service ceiling	4,575 m (15,000 ft)
Range	347 nm (643 km; 400 miles)

PAYNE
VERNON W. PAYNE

Route No. 4, PO Box 319M, Escondido, California 92025
Telephone: (714) 746 4465

Mr Vernon Payne is the designer of the Knight Twister, a light sporting biplane of which plans and kits are available for amateur construction. It exists in several versions.

KNIGHT TWISTER KT-85

The original prototype of the Knight Twister KT-85 single-seat sporting biplane flew in 1933. Considerable refinement of the design since that time has improved both the appearance and the performance of later models, which have been built in substantial numbers by amateur constructors in the United States and elsewhere.

Standard power plant is a Continental flat-four engine of 63·5-67 kW (85-90 hp), but alternative engines have been fitted by some constructors. Most powerful Knight Twister flown to date is one owned by Mr Charles Williams of Mount Prospect, Illinois, which has a 134 kW (180 hp) Avco Lycoming O-360 engine installed.

The following details refer to the standard Knight Twister built from Mr Payne's plans:

TYPE: Single-seat light biplane.

WINGS: Braced biplane type. Wing section NACA M-6. No dihedral. Incidence 1° 30'. All-wood two-spar structure, plywood-covered and with fabric covering overall. Ailerons on lower wings only, of fabric-covered wood construction. No flaps.

FUSELAGE: Steel tube truss structure with wood stringers and fabric covering.

TAIL UNIT: Cantilever type. Vertical surfaces have fabric-covered steel tube structure. Horizontal surfaces have plywood-covered wood structure, with fabric covering overall.

LANDING GEAR: Non-retractable tailwheel type. Cantilever main units. Rubber cord or hydraulic shock-absorption. Wheels size 6·00-6 with Goodyear tyres, pressure 0·345-0·69 bars (5-10 lb/sq in). Goodyear disc brakes.

POWER PLANT: One 67 kW (90 hp) Continental C90 flat-four engine, driving a two-blade wood or metal fixed-pitch propeller. Alternatively any other Continental or Avco Lycoming flat-four engine of 63·5-108 kW (85-145 hp). Fuel tank aft of engine firewall, capacity 68 litres (18 US gallons). Oil capacity 3·7-5·7 litres (1-1·5 US gallons).

ACCOMMODATION: Single seat, normally in open cockpit. Baggage compartment capacity 9 kg (20 lb). Radio optional.

DIMENSIONS, EXTERNAL:

Wing span: upper	4·57 m (15 ft 0 in)
lower	3·96 m (13 ft 0 in)
Wing chord (mean, both)	0·65 m (2 ft 1·6 in)
Wing area, gross	5·57 m² (60 sq ft)
Wing aspect ratio: upper	6·87
lower	6·13
Length overall	4·27 m (14 ft 0 in)
Height overall	1·60 m (5 ft 3 in)
Tailplane span	2·13 m (7 ft 0 in)
Wheel track	1·52 m (5 ft 0 in)
Wheelbase	5·23 m (17 ft 2 in)

DIMENSION, INTERNAL:

Cockpit: Width	0·53 m (1 ft 9 in)

WEIGHTS (67 kW; 90 hp engine):

Weight empty	243 kg (535 lb)
Max T-O weight	435 kg (960 lb)

PERFORMANCE (67 kW; 90 hp engine, at max T-O weight):

Max level speed at S/L	139 knots (257 km/h; 160 mph)
Max cruising speed	122 knots (225 km/h; 140 mph)
Econ cruising speed	109 knots (201 km/h; 125 mph)
Stalling speed	53 knots (97 km/h; 60 mph)
Max rate of climb at S/L	275 m (900 ft)/min
T-O run	125 m (410 ft)
T-O to 15 m (50 ft)	305 m (1,000 ft)
Landing from 15 m (50 ft)	366 m (1,200 ft)
Landing run	205 m (670 ft)
Range with max fuel	338 nm (625 km; 390 miles)

SUNDAY KNIGHT TWISTER SKT-125

This developed version of the Knight Twister has a 93 kW (125 hp) Avco Lycoming engine. Increased wing area makes it easier to fly and its name is meant to imply that it is for the 'Sunday flyer'.

A fully aerobatic Sunday Knight Twister, with a 134 kW (180 hp) engine, has been built by Mr J. F. Carter of Drewry, Alabama.

DIMENSIONS, EXTERNAL:

Wing span	5·94 m (19 ft 6 in)
Wing area, gross	7·71 m² (83 sq ft)

Length overall	4·72 m (15 ft 6 in)
Height overall	1·68 m (5 ft 6 in)

WEIGHTS:

Weight empty	318 kg (700 lb)
Max T-O weight	461 kg (1,016 lb)

PERFORMANCE (at max T-O weight):

Max level speed at S/L	146 knots (270 km/h; 168 mph)
Max cruising speed	144 knots (267 km/h; 166 mph)
Econ cruising speed	126 knots (233 km/h; 145 mph)
Stalling speed	43·5 knots (80·5 km/h; 50 mph)
Max rate of climb at S/L	366 m (1,200 ft)/min
T-O run	113 m (370 ft)
T-O to 15 m (50 ft)	232 m (760 ft)
Landing run	265 m (870 ft)
Range at max cruising speed with max fuel	307 nm (570 km; 354 miles)

KNIGHT TWISTER JUNIOR KT-75

The Knight Twister Junior has the same fuselage, tail unit and landing gear as the KT-85, but its tapered wings have a larger area. The prototype flew in 1947. Details are as for the KT-85, except for the following:

WINGS: Incidence 2°.

POWER PLANT: One Continental or Avco Lycoming flat-four engine of 56-93 kW (75-125 hp). Fuel capacity with 56 kW (75 hp) engine 45 litres (12 US gallons).

DIMENSIONS, EXTERNAL:

Wing span: upper	5·33 m (17 ft 6 in)
lower	4·11 m (13 ft 6 in)
Wing area, gross	6·76 m² (72·8 sq ft)
Wing aspect ratio: upper	7·78
lower	7·10

WEIGHTS (56 kW; 75 hp engine):

Weight empty	227 kg (500 lb)
Max T-O weight	404 kg (890 lb)

PERFORMANCE (56 kW; 75 hp engine, at max T-O weight):

Max level speed at S/L	117 knots (217 km/h; 135 mph)
Max cruising speed	109 knots (201 km/h; 125 mph)
Econ cruising speed	97 knots (180 km/h; 112 mph)
Stalling speed	42 knots (77·5 km/h; 48 mph)
Max rate of climb at S/L	275 m (900 ft)/min
T-O run	114 m (375 ft)
T-O to 15 m (50 ft)	277 m (910 ft)
Landing from 15 m (50 ft)	311 m (1,020 ft)
Landing run	190 m (625 ft)
Range with max fuel	247 nm (460 km; 285 miles)

PAZMANY
PAZMANY AIRCRAFT CORPORATION

Box 80051, San Diego, California 92138
Telephone: (714) 276 0424

This company was formed by Mr Ladislao Pazmany, to develop and market a two-seat light aircraft known as the PL-1 Laminar, which he had designed. Some 5,000 design hours and 4,000 hours of construction went into the prototype PL-1, which was flown for the first time on 23 March 1962. Editions of *Jane's* published since that time have recorded the subsequent history of the PL-1, of which about 375 sets of plans were sold, leading to construction of many amateur-built examples and quantity production in Taiwan for the Chinese Nationalist Air Force.

Pazmany Aircraft Corporation is no longer marketing plans of the PL-1, of which a full description can be found in the 1979-80 *Jane's*; instead, plans and instructions for building the improved PL-2 and a lightweight, low-cost single-seat monoplane designated PL-4A are available to amateur constructors and many aircraft of these types are being built. Mr Pazmany also contributed to the design of the Ryson Aviation Cloudster two-seat motor-glider, of which details can be found in the 'Sailplanes' section of this edition.

PAZMANY PL-2

Shortly after flight trials of the PL-1 began, Mr Pazmany initiated a complete redesign of the aircraft. The developed design, known as the PL-2, is almost identical with the PL-1 in external configuration. Cockpit width is increased by 5 cm (2 in); wing dihedral is increased, and the internal structure is extensively changed, to simplify construction and reduce weight.

Static tests of every major assembly up to ultimate loads had been made by early 1967. The first PL-2 to be completed, by Mr H. Pio of Ramona, California, made its first flight on 4 April 1969, powered by an Avco Lycoming O-290-G engine. A total of 360 sets of plans had been sold by early 1980. Aircraft built and flown include several examples for evaluation and use by foreign military training centres (see 1977-78 *Jane's*), and a PL-2 was under construction by the Sri Lanka Air Force in 1979.

TYPE: Two-seat light aircraft.

WINGS: Cantilever low-wing monoplane. Wing section NACA 63₂615. Dihedral 5°. Incidence −1° 20'. All-metal single-spar structure in one piece, with leading-edge torsion box. Plain piano-hinged ailerons and flaps of all-metal construction. No trim tabs.

FUSELAGE: Conventional all-metal semi-monocoque structure, with flat or single-curvature skins.

TAIL UNIT: Cantilever all-metal structure. One-piece horizontal surface, with anti-servo tab which serves also as a trim tab.

LANDING GEAR: Non-retractable tricycle type, with all three oleo-pneumatic shock-absorbers interchangeable. Goodyear wheels and tyres, size 5·00-5. Tyre pressure 2·14 bars (31 lb/sq in). Goodyear brakes. Steerable nosewheel.

POWER PLANT: One Avco Lycoming flat-four engine, driving a two-blade metal fixed-pitch propeller. Suitable power plants are the 80·5 kW (108 hp) O-235-C1, 93 kW (125 hp) O-290-G (ground power unit), 101 kW (135 hp) O-290-D2B and 112 kW (150 hp) O-320-A. Fuel in two glassfibre wingtip tanks, each of 47 litres (12·5 US gallons) capacity. Total fuel capacity 94 litres (25 US gallons). Oil capacity 4·5 litres (5 US quarts).

ACCOMMODATION: Two seats side by side under rearward-sliding transparent canopy. Dual controls. Space for 18 kg (40 lb) baggage aft of seats. Heater and airscoops for ventilation. VHF radio.

DIMENSIONS, EXTERNAL:

Wing span	8·53 m (28 ft 0 in)
Wing chord, constant	1·27 m (4 ft 2 in)
Wing area, gross	10·78 m² (116 sq ft)
Wing aspect ratio	6·7
Length overall	5·90 m (19 ft 3½ in)
Height overall	2·44 m (8 ft 0 in)
Tailplane span	2·44 m (8 ft 0 in)
Wheel track	2·60 m (8 ft 5½ in)
Wheelbase	1·30 m (4 ft 3 in)

DIMENSIONS, INTERNAL:

Cabin: Length	1·27 m (4 ft 2 in)
Width	1·07 m (3 ft 6 in)
Height	1·02 m (3 ft 4 in)

WEIGHTS (A with 80·5 kW; 108 hp engine, B with 93 kW; 125 hp, C with 101 kW; 135 hp, D with 112 kW; 150 hp):

Weight empty:

A	396 kg (875 lb)
B, C	408 kg (900 lb)
D	409 kg (902 lb)

Max T-O weight:

A	642 kg (1,416 lb)
B, C	655 kg (1,445 lb)
D	656 kg (1,447 lb)

PERFORMANCE (at max T-O weight):

Max level speed at S/L:

A	120 knots (222 km/h; 138 mph)
B	125 knots (232 km/h; 144 mph)
C	128 knots (238 km/h; 148 mph)
D	133 knots (246 km/h; 153 mph)

Knight Twister (Avco Lycoming O-235-C1 engine) built by Robert Ubel *(Howard Levy)*

PDQ-2 Model E all-metal lightweight sporting aircraft

Pazmany PL-2 built by Mr Kenneth Arnold *(Howard Levy)*

Pazmany PL-4A built by Mr John Pollock of Red Deer, Alberta, Canada

---

Econ cruising speed:

A	103 knots (192 km/h; 119 mph)
B	111 knots (206 km/h; 128 mph)
C	113 knots (209 km/h; 130 mph)
D	118 knots (219 km/h; 136 mph)

Stalling speed (flaps down):

A	45·5 knots (84 km/h; 52 mph)
B, C, D	47 knots (87 km/h; 54 mph)

Max rate of climb at S/L:

A	390 m (1,280 ft)/min
B	457 m (1,500 ft)/min
C	488 m (1,600 ft)/min
D	518 m (1,700 ft)/min

Range at econ cruising speed:

A	427 nm (790 km; 492 miles)
B	422 nm (780 km; 486 miles)
C	428 nm (792 km; 493 miles)
D	330 nm (610 km; 381 miles)

PAZMANY PL-4A

The prototype of a lightweight single-seat low-wing monoplane designated PL-4A flew for the first time on 12 July 1972. It was designed specifically for easy low-cost construction by amateur builders, to provide a safe aircraft that would be economical in operation. The prototype had completed 335 hours of flight by January 1978. Sets of plans, kits of prefabricated components, glassfibre wing-tips and fuel tank and transparent cockpit canopy are available to amateur constructors.

By the beginning of 1980 more than 650 sets of plans had been sold, and the PL-4A had received approval in Australia for construction by amateurs.

Two aircraft were built to evaluate three different power plant installations, comprising a Volkswagen engine with 2¼ : 1 V-belt reduction; a Limbach SL 1700 E Volkswagen with direct drive to the propeller; and a Continental A65 aircooled engine.

TYPE: Single-seat lightweight sporting aircraft.

WINGS: Cantilever low-wing monoplane. Wing section NACA 63₃418. Dihedral 5°. Incidence 3°. No sweepback. All-metal structure, with main spar, Z section rear beam, sheet metal ribs and skins. Wings fold alongside fuselage for towing or storage. Plain piano-hinged ailerons of all-metal construction. Cambered glassfibre wingtips. No flaps. No trim tabs.

FUSELAGE: All-metal structure, with bulkheads built up from bent sheet metal channels and standard extruded angles for longerons, and with sheet metal skins.

TAIL UNIT: All-metal cantilever T tail. All-moving tailplane with large anti-servo tab which serves also as a trim tab.

LANDING GEAR: Non-retractable tailwheel type. Spring steel cantilever main legs. Single go-kart type wheel on each main unit, with 4·10 × 3·50-6 four-ply tyre, pressure 4·48 bars (65 lb/sq in). Steerable and castoring tailwheel with solid tyre size 5 × 1·5-1·5. Go-kart type hydraulic disc brakes by Hurst-Airheart.

POWER PLANT: One 1,600 cc modified Volkswagen motor car engine with Becar V-belt reduction of 2¼ : 1, developing approximately 37·5 kW (50 hp) and driving a two-blade fixed-pitch wooden propeller of Pazmany design, manufactured by Ted Hendricksen. Glassfibre fuel tank immediately aft of firewall, usable capacity 45 litres (12 US gallons). Refuelling point on upper fuselage forward of windscreen. Oil capacity 2·8 litres (0·75 US gallons).

ACCOMMODATION: Single seat under transparent Plexiglas canopy, hinged on starboard side. Compartment aft of seat for 9 kg (20 lb) baggage. Cabin heated and ventilated.

SYSTEMS: Hydraulic system for brakes only. Electrical system powered by 12V 25Ah battery situated in baggage compartment.

DIMENSIONS, EXTERNAL:

Wing span	8·13 m (26 ft 8 in)
Wing chord, constant	1·02 m (3 ft 4 in)
Wing area, gross	8·27 m² (89·0 sq ft)
Wing aspect ratio	8·0
Length overall	5·04 m (16 ft 6½ in)
Width, wings folded	2·44 m (8 ft 0 in)
Height overall	1·73 m (5 ft 8 in)
Tailplane span	2·29 m (7 ft 6 in)
Wheel track	2·06 m (6 ft 9 in)
Wheelbase	3·56 m (11 ft 8 in)
Propeller diameter	1·73 m (5 ft 8 in)
Propeller ground clearance	0·25 m (10 in)

WEIGHTS:

Weight empty	262 kg (578 lb)
Max T-O and landing weight	385 kg (850 lb)

PERFORMANCE (at max T-O weight):

Never-exceed speed	161 knots (299 km/h; 186 mph)
Max level speed at S/L	109 knots (201 km/h; 125 mph)
Max cruising speed at S/L	85 knots (158 km/h; 98 mph)
Econ cruising speed at S/L	78 knots (145 km/h; 90 mph)
Stalling speed, power on	40 knots (74 km/h; 46 mph)
Stalling speed, power off	42 knots (77·5 km/h; 48 mph)
Max rate of climb at S/L	198 m (650 ft)/min
Service ceiling	3,960 m (13,000 ft)
Min ground turning radius	3·05 m (10 ft 0 in)
T-O run	148 m (486 ft)
Landing run	133 m (436 ft)
Range with max fuel, no allowances	295 nm (545 km; 340 miles)

PDQ
PDQ AIRCRAFT PRODUCTS

28975 Alpine Lane, Elkhart, Indiana 46514
Telephone: (219) 264 2906

Mr Wayne Ison formed this company to market plans of the PDQ-2 lightweight sporting aircraft which he had designed and built. The PDQ-2 is intended to provide a cheap, robust, easily and quickly built aircraft which is easy for an average pilot to fly.

Design of the prototype had begun in September 1972, and construction was started on 5 January 1973. Excluding the 27 kW (36 hp) Rockwell (Venture) JLO-LB-600-2 engine which was originally fitted, the cost of construction was only $350 at 1973 prices, and the first flight was made on 30 May that year.

During 1975 it became clear that an alternative power plant was needed, owing to the increasing scarcity of the JLO engine. One amateur constructor fitted a BMW motorcycle engine; but Mr Ison decided to test the prototype PDQ-2 with a converted Volkswagen motor car engine, a type of power plant which is readily available and inexpensive. The increased engine weight required a number of structural modifications, notably to the engine mounting, wing spars and landing gear; but flight testing

proved satisfactory, and details of the new engine installation have been sent to over 2,000 purchasers of sets of plans, in 35 countries. At least 50 to 60 PDQ-2s were flying by early 1980.

PDQ AIRCRAFT PRODUCTS PDQ-2

The version of this aircraft described below is the **PDQ-2 Model C** (unless otherwise stated), which has wings and tail constructed of wood and polyurethane foam. The **Model D** differs from the C only in having wings and tail of wood, with fabric covering; while the **Model E** (illustrated) has all-metal wings and tail, constructed from aluminium sheet. At least two aircraft have been fitted with wings of NASA GAW-1 section.

TYPE: Lightweight sporting aircraft.

WINGS: Wire-braced monoplane. Wing section NACA 63₂A615. Dihedral 5°. Incidence 3°. Composite structure with spruce spars, polyurethane foam ribs, sheet foam skins, covered with Sharkskin fabric. Full-span plain ailerons. No flaps or trim tabs. Wings quickly removable for towing and storage.

FUSELAGE: Basic structure consists of 0·05 m (2 in) square tubes of 6061-T6 light alloy. A lower forward tube carries the landing gear; attached to it is a vertical king-

post, to which the wing is attached and wire-braced. An aft horizontal tube attached to the kingpost carries the T-tail.

TAIL UNIT: Strut-braced T-tail, with swept vertical surfaces. Fixed-incidence tailplane. No trim tabs. Composite structure of polyurethane foam, spruce strips, plywood and Sharkskin fabric covering.

LANDING GEAR: Non-retractable tricycle type. Shock-absorption by spring steel leaf mounting struts. Go-kart type main wheels, diameter 0·28 m (11 in); steerable nosewheel, diameter 0·15 m (6 in). Go-kart type brakes.

POWER PLANT: Prototype flew originally with Rockwell (Venture) JLO-LB-600-2 engine, mounted on top of the kingpost and driving a two-blade fixed-pitch wooden pusher propeller. This engine remains suitable, but prototype now has a 1,385 cc converted Volkswagen motor car engine, developing 30 kW (40 hp), and this is recommended for amateur-built PDQ-2s. Plastics fuel tank mounted alongside pilot's seat on port side, capacity 22·7 litres (6 US gallons). Refuelling point on tank upper surface.

ACCOMMODATION: Single open seat mounted immediately forward of kingpost.

DIMENSIONS, EXTERNAL:				Normal T-O weight:				Max cruising speed at S/L	
Wing span	7·44 m (24 ft 5 in)			Model C	257 kg (566 lb)				61 knots (113 km/h; 70 mph)
Wing chord, constant	1·07 m (3 ft 6 in)			Model D	239 kg (526 lb)			Stalling speed:	
Wing area, gross	7·90 m² (85 sq ft)			Max T-O weight:				Model C	37·5 knots (69·5 km/h; 43 mph)
Length overall	4·42 m (14 ft 6 in)			Model C	281 kg (620 lb)			Model D	35 knots (65 km/h; 40 mph)
Height overall	1·27 m (4 ft 2 in)			Model D	263 kg (580 lb)			Max rate of climb at S/L	152 m (500 ft)/min
Tailplane span	1·83 m (6 ft 0 in)							Service ceiling	3,050 m (10,000 ft)
Wheel track	1·27 m (4 ft 2 in)			PERFORMANCE (Model C and D, at max T-O weight, Volkswagen engine):				T-O run	107 m (350 ft)
WEIGHTS (Volkswagen engine):				Never-exceed speed	78 knots (145 km/h; 90 mph)			Landing run	122 m (400 ft)
Weight empty: Model C	164 kg (360 lb)			Max level speed at S/L 69 knots (129 km/h; 80 mph)				Range with max fuel	173 nm (321 km; 200 miles)
Model D	145 kg (320 lb)								

PIETENPOL
DON PIETENPOL
215, 21st Street SE, Rochester, Minnesota 55901

The prototype of Mr Bernard H. Pietenpol's Aircamper two-seat parasol monoplane flew for the first time in 1929, powered by a 30 kW (40 hp) Ford Model A engine. Plans were published in the magazine *Modern Mechanics and Inventions* in the following year and large numbers of Aircampers, with a wide variety of power plants, were built by amateurs, either from the magazine plans or from kits of parts marketed by Mr Pietenpol.

The original Aircamper was of all-wood construction, with fabric covering, but some examples completed recently or currently being built have a steel tube fuselage and tail unit.

An illustration in the 1979-80 *Jane's* showed Mr Pietenpol's Aircamper, which he modified by extending the fuselage by 9 in (23 cm), fitting modified Piper J-3 Cub landing gear, strengthening the wings, and installing two 15 litre (4 US gallon) fuselage fuel tanks and a 38 litre (10 US gallon) fuel tank in the wing centre-section. This aircraft, which now has a converted Chevrolet Corvair motor car engine, rated at 45 kW (60 p), has completed over 600 flying hours.

The accompanying illustration shows another modified Aircamper, in the optional two-seat configuration. A further version, embodying many Piper Cub components, is described under the Grega entry in this section.

PIETENPOL B4 AIRCAMPER
TYPE: Single-seat light aircraft. (Basic design makes provision for second seat.)
WINGS: Parasol monoplane, with two parallel bracing struts each side and centre-section cabane structure. Pietenpol special wing section. Thickness/chord ratio 16·6%. No dihedral. Incidence 2°. Fabric-covered two-spar wood structure. Tips may be rounded or square. Plain wooden ailerons with fabric covering. No flaps.
FUSELAGE: Wooden de Havilland truss structure of Sitka spruce, covered with birch plywood to back of rear cockpit and fabric on rear fuselage.
TAIL UNIT: Wire-braced wood and steel tube structure, covered with fabric.
LANDING GEAR: Divided main gear, with spring shock-absorption, modified from Piper J-3 Cub gear. Main-wheel tyres size 8·00-4, pressure 1·03 bars (15 lb/sq in). Piper hydraulic brakes. Steerable tailwheel.
POWER PLANT (Mr Pietenpol's aircraft): One 45 kW (60 hp) Chevrolet Corvair converted motor car engine, driving a two-blade wooden propeller. A variety of other engines have been fitted in amateur-built Aircampers. One fuel tank in wing, capacity 38 litres (10 US gallons); two tanks in fuselage, total capacity 30 litres (8 US gallons). Oil capacity 4·75 litres (1·25 US gallons).
ACCOMMODATION: Single seat in open cockpit in Mr Pietenpol's Aircamper N7533U. Second seat is optional in basic design.

DIMENSIONS, EXTERNAL:
Wing span	8·84 m (29 ft 0 in)
Wing chord, constant	1·52 m (5 ft 0 in)
Wing area, gross	13·47 m² (145 sq ft)
Wing aspect ratio	6
Propeller diameter	1·52 m (5 ft 0 in)

WEIGHT:
Weight empty	282 kg (622 lb)

PERFORMANCE:
Max level and never-exceed speed	95·5 knots (177 km/h; 110 mph)
Max cruising speed	74 knots (137 km/h; 85 mph)
Econ cruising speed	69 knots (129 km/h; 80 mph)
Stalling speed	33 knots (61·5 km/h; 38 mph)
Max rate of climb at S/L	152 m (500 ft)/min
T-O and landing run	76 m (250 ft)
Range, with 30 min reserves	330 nm (611 km; 380 miles)

PITTS
PITTS AEROBATICS
PO Box 547, Afton, Wyoming 83110
Telephone: (307) 886 3151
GENERAL MANAGER: E. H. Andersen Jr

In addition to marketing factory-built examples of the single-seat and two-seat Pitts Special biplanes, Pitts Aerobatics, which bought all rights to this range of aircraft from Mr Curtis Pitts, supplies plans of the S-1D and S-1E single-seaters to amateur constructors. It also began, in 1977, to supply kits for both the S-1E and the two-seat S-2E. No plans are available separately for the S-2 series.

PITTS S-1D/E SPECIAL
The versions of the single-seat S-1 for which plans are currently available are designated S-1D and S-1E. Details are generally similar to those given for the factory-built S-1S in the main US Aircraft section of this edition, but there are important differences in the two versions. The plans for the S-1E now include drawings for the four-aileron symmetrical wings which have not been available previously. The S-1D has four-aileron wings of M-6 aerofoil section, which are not symmetrical.

There is also an S-1C version, but Pitts Aerobatics does not supply plans for its construction. By comparison with earlier models, this has flat-bottomed wings, and ailerons on the lower wings only, and can be fitted with engines of between 74·5 and 134 kW (100 to 180 hp).

POLLIWAGEN
POLLIWAGEN INC
8782 Hewitt Place, Garden Grove, California 92644
Telephone: (714) 897 9852
PRESIDENT: Joseph P. Alvarez

POLLIWAGEN
The Polliwagen is a side-by-side two-seat sporting aircraft, stressed for aerobatics and designed for amateur construction. The first of two prototypes flew for the first time in July 1977. Plans are available, together with a wide range of component parts, including pre-moulded glassfibre cowlings, landing gear fairings, canopy and ribs, landing gear assemblies, brakes and instrument panel. By 1 January 1980, a total of 217 sets of plans had been sold; three Polliwagens had been built, and about 30 were known to be under construction.
TYPE: Two-seat light sporting aircraft.
WINGS: Cantilever low-wing monoplane. Wortmann FX-67-K-150 wing section. Thickness/chord ratio 15%. Dihedral 4°. Incidence 1° 30'. No sweepback. Structure entirely of glassfibre epoxy composite, embodying sailplane technology. Ailerons and trailing-edge flaps of similar construction; both have an upward setting of 10° for higher cruising speed. Flaps have a maximum downward setting of 80°, so that they can be used for aerodynamic braking. Electrically-actuated trim tab in port aileron. Wingtip tanks increase effective span by reducing induced drag.
FUSELAGE: Glassfibre epoxy structure, consisting basically of one bottom and two side D spars, designed in such a way that the cockpit would break outward if subjected to impact loads.
TAIL UNIT: Cantilever T tail of similar construction to wings, with sweepback on all surfaces. Fin integral with fuselage. All-moving horizontal surfaces operated by electrically-actuated servo.
LANDING GEAR: Retractable tricycle type. Main units retract forward, nosewheel rearward. Polyurethane bumper shock-absorption. Rosenhan main wheels and nosewheel, all with tyres size 5·00-5. Main-wheel tyre pressure 2·62 bars (38 lb/sq in); nosewheel 1·38 bars (20 lb/sq in). Rosenhan hydraulic disc brakes. Main wheels remain semi-exposed to reduce damage in a wheels-up landing.
POWER PLANT: One 56 kW (75 hp) Revmaster 2100 D Turbo, which is a Revmaster-developed turbocharged Volkswagen engine, driving a Maloof two-blade constant-speed metal propeller. Total of 76 litres (20 US gallons) of fuel in two wingtip tanks (each 34 litres; 9 US gallons) and an 8 litre (2 US gallon) gravity-feed tank in the fuselage nose. Refuelling point on upper surface of each tip-tank.
ACCOMMODATION: Two seats side by side under rearward-articulating transparent canopy. Accommodation is heated and ventilated.
SYSTEMS: All flying controls actuated through pushrods and bearings. Electrical system powered by 20A engine-driven alternator and storage battery. Pneumatic system for landing gear retraction is optional. Oxygen system of 0·62 m³ (22 cu ft) capacity.
AVIONICS AND EQUIPMENT: Dual nav/coms. Provisions for three-axis electric trim adaptable to autopilot. Blind-flying instrumentation is standard.

DIMENSIONS, EXTERNAL:
Wing span, over tip-tanks	7·92 m (26 ft 0 in)
Wing chord, constant	1·07 m (3 ft 6 in)
Wing area, gross	8·45 m² (91 sq ft)
Wing aspect ratio	7·43
Length overall	4·88 m (16 ft 0 in)
Height overall	1·70 m (5 ft 7 in)
Tailplane span	2·18 m (7 ft 2 in)
Wheel track	1·52 m (5 ft 0 in)
Wheelbase	1·09 m (3 ft 7 in)
Propeller diameter	1·45 m (4 ft 9 in)

WEIGHTS:
Weight empty	273 kg (600 lb)
Max fuel weight	54 kg (120 lb)
Max T-O weight	499 kg (1,100 lb)

PERFORMANCE (at max T-O weight, except when stated otherwise):
Never-exceed speed	217 knots (402 km/h; 250 mph)
Max level speed	200 knots (370 km/h; 230 mph)
Max turbo cruising speed at 5,790 m (19,000 ft)	200 knots (370 km/h; 230 mph)
Econ cruising speed at 5,790 m (19,000 ft)	174 knots (322 km/h; 200 mph)
Stalling speed, flaps and gear down	39 knots (72·5 km/h; 45 mph)
Max rate of climb at S/L	198 m (650 ft)/min
T-O and landing run	122 m (400 ft)
Range with max payload and max fuel, 45 min reserves	868 nm (1,609 km; 1,000 miles)

POWELL
JOHN C. POWELL
4 Donald Drive, Middletown, Rhode Island 02840

John Powell, formerly a Commander in the US Navy, designed and built a two-seat parasol-wing monoplane, of which plans are available to amateur constructors. Known as the P-70 Acey Deucy, its design was started in 1966 and construction began during 1967. FAA certification in the Experimental homebuilt category was awarded on 19 June 1970 and the first flight was recorded on the following day. By the beginning of 1980 this prototype had accumulated 581 hours' flying time.

More than 170 sets of plans have been sold, and the first aircraft built from plans was flying by the Autumn of 1973. At least seven Acey Deucys had flown by early 1980, with many more under construction.

One Acey Deucy, powered by a 74·5 kW (100 hp) Continental O-200 engine, has been fitted with twin floats and is said to perform well at a take-off weight of about 725 kg (1,600 lb).

POWELL P-70 ACEY DEUCY
TYPE: Two-seat light monoplane.
WINGS: Braced parasol-wing monoplane with steel tube V bracing struts on each side, auxiliary bracing struts and N-type centre-section struts. Wing section NACA 4412. Dihedral 1° on outer panels. Incidence 2°. No sweepback. Composite structure of steel tube and wood, fabric covered. Frise-type ailerons of wooden construction, fabric covered. No flaps. No trim tabs.
FUSELAGE: Welded 4130 steel tube structure with wooden stringers, fabric covered.
TAIL UNIT: Wire-braced welded steel tube structure with U channel ribs. Tailplane incidence adjustable by screwjack at leading-edge. No trim tabs.
LANDING GEAR: Non-retractable tailwheel type. Two side

Modified Pietenpol B4 two-seat Aircamper *(Peter M. Bowers)*

Polliwagen two-seat light sporting aircraft *(Don Dwiggins)*

Powell P-70 Acey Deucy with new sliding canopy

Quickie Aircraft Corporation Quickie prototype *(Ian MacFarlane)*

Vs and half axles hinged to fuselage structure. Shock-absorption by springs in compression. Goodyear main wheels and tyres size 8·00-4, pressure 0·83 bars (12 lb/sq in). Motor scooter type caliper brakes. At least one Acey Deucy is flying as a seaplane, with floats of 750 kg (1,650 lb) displacement.

POWER PLANT: Designer recommends use of engines from 48·5-67 kW (65 to 90 hp), although at least one Acey Deucy has a 74·5 kW (100 hp) Continental (see introductory copy). Prototype has one 48·5 kW (65 hp) Continental A65 flat-four engine, driving a McCauley two-blade metal fixed-pitch propeller. One fuel tank in fuselage, immediately aft of firewall, capacity 53 litres (14 US gallons). Refuelling point on top of fuselage, forward of front cockpit. Oil capacity 3·75 litres (1 US gallon).

ACCOMMODATION: Two persons in tandem, normally in open cockpits. Sliding canopy available. Small door by front cockpit on starboard side.

DIMENSIONS, EXTERNAL:
Wing span	9·91 m (32 ft 6 in)
Wing chord, constant	1·52 m (5 ft 0 in)
Wing area, gross	14·4 m² (155 sq ft)
Wing aspect ratio	6·5
Length overall	6·32 m (20 ft 9 in)
Height overall	2·06 m (6 ft 9 in)
Tailplane span	2·59 m (8 ft 6 in)
Wheel track	1·83 m (6 ft 0 in)

WEIGHTS (prototype):
Weight empty	340 kg (750 lb)
Max T-O weight	578 kg (1,275 lb)

PERFORMANCE (prototype):
Never-exceed speed 126 knots (233 km/h; 145 mph)
Max level speed at S/L
90 knots (167 km/h; 104 mph)
Max cruising speed at 610 m (2,000 ft)
80 knots (148 km/h; 92 mph)
Stalling speed
23·5-26 knots (44-48·5 km/h; 27-30 mph)
Max rate of climb at S/L 190·5 m (625 ft)/min
Service ceiling (approx)
3,050-3,355 m (10,000-11,000 ft)
T-O run 76 m (250 ft)
T-O to 15 m (50 ft) approx 213 m (700 ft)
Landing run approx 76 m (250 ft)
Range, with 30 min reserves
217 nm (402 km; 250 miles)

QUICKIE
QUICKIE AIRCRAFT CORPORATION
PO Box 786, Mojave, California 93501 and Building 68, Mojave Airport, Mojave, California 93501
Telephone: (805) 824 4313

Quickie Aircraft Corporation is a company formed by Gene Sheehan and Tom Jewett to develop the Quickie aircraft and to sell complete kits, including engine, to amateur constructors who wish to build this type. Gene Sheehan has worked in the aerospace industry since 1964 and was involved in several previous homebuilt projects; Tom Jewett's career has been devoted to flight testing, and he was a Flight Test Engineer on board the Rockwell International B-1 supersonic bomber.

In early 1980, Quickie Aircraft was well advanced with the construction of a research aircraft which has been given the provisional name Big Bird. It has been designed to demonstrate efficient long-range single-engined flight, and subject to satisfactory results of flight testing, will be used to attempt to establish new world distance records.

QUICKIE AIRCRAFT CORPORATION QUICKIE
The Quickie is a single-seat light aircraft of unusual configuration. The project began in 1975 when Mr Sheehan and Mr Jewett started looking for a low-power engine that could be installed in a highly-efficient single-seat sporting aircraft, the design of which had not then been initiated. Not until 1977 was the Onan engine found and tested. Having proved its reliability, Burt Rutan of VariViggen fame was contacted to assist in designing an aircraft that would make optimum use of the engine. Having established the basic configuration, Tom Jewett and Burt Rutan began detailed design work, while Gene Sheehan continued engine development.

On 13 August 1977 construction of the prototype Quickie (N77Q) was started, and it was completed in 400 working-hours over a three-month period. First flight was achieved on 15 November 1977. Fifteen flights were made by the three designer/pilots during the first five days of the test programme.

The Quickie design was frozen on 14 April 1978, after 125 hours of flight testing. The full programme of air and ground testing included investigation of performance, stability and control, flutter testing to 156 knots (290 km/h; 180 mph) TAS, static load testing and landing gear drop

testing to FAA Pt 23 certificated aircraft standards, fuel economy measurements, and taxying, take-off and landing in surface winds of over 50 knots. Extensive stall/departure/spin testing revealed that the Quickie could not be made to spin.

In August 1978, the Quickie was flown to the Experimental Aircraft Association's Fly-in at Oshkosh, Wisconsin, where it received the 'Outstanding New Design' award for 1978. In 1979, a company-owned Quickie was again flown to Oshkosh, covering the 3,650 nm (6,760 km; 4,200 mile) return journey at an average speed of 100 knots (185 km/h; 115 mph) and at a fuel consumption of 29·75 km/litre (70 miles/US gallon). Two homebuilt Quickies were also flown to the Oshkosh meeting.

Complete kits, including engines, have been available since June 1978. Each includes prefabricated cowling, canopy, all machined parts, all welded parts, and some of the tools, in order to reduce the building time to 400 man-hours for the inexperienced builder. More recently, Quickie has broken down the complete kit into three separate packages, making it possible to spread the capital cost over a longer period.

By January 1980, more than 340 kits had been sold and more than 15 homebuilt Quickies were flying, with a further 15-20 within two months of completion. By then the Quickie prototype had logged more than 550 flying hours, at an average cost of only $3·25 per hour to operate, including fuel, oil, maintenance and insurance.

TYPE: Single-seat light sporting aircraft of canard configuration.

WINGS: Tapered cantilever shoulder-wing monoplane. Dihedral from roots. Two unidirectional glassfibre spars and shaped low-density rigid foam core, covered with glassfibre. Constant-chord inboard ailerons. No flaps.

FOREPLANE: Tapered and slightly sweptback cantilever foreplane, mounted low on forward fuselage. Marked anhedral. Construction similar to that of wings. Main-wheel housings attached to tips. Full-span tapered elevator/flaps.

FUSELAGE: Semi-monocoque structure of banana shape, formed from 25 mm (1 in) thick foam, with glassfibre covering inside and out, and tapering towards rear. Foam/glassfibre sandwich bulkheads.

TAIL UNIT: Cantilever sweptback vertical fin and narrow-chord rudder of similar construction to wings.

LANDING GEAR: Non-retractable tailwheel type. Main

wheels positioned at tips of canard foreplane in swept fairings. A kit to provide 50 per cent larger tyres for grass field operation is optional. Steerable tailwheel aft of fuselage.

POWER PLANT: One modified Onan horizontally-opposed two-cylinder four-stroke engine, developing originally 13·5 kW (18 hp) at 3,600 rpm and driving a two-blade fixed-pitch wooden propeller. Modifications to cylinder heads and exhaust system allow newly-supplied engines to develop 16·4 kW (22 hp) at 3,800 rpm: a retrofit kit is available to convert 13·5 kW (18 hp) engines to develop this increased output. Fuel capacity 30·3 litres (8 US gallons). Fuel consumption approx 44·2 km/litre (104 miles/US gallon).

ACCOMMODATION: Single seat under one-piece side-hinged canopy. Cockpit suitable for pilot up to 1·98 m (6 ft 6 in) tall and weighing up to 95 kg (210 lb). Max baggage capacity with lighter pilot 13·6 kg (30 lb). With engine developing 16·4 kW (22 hp), a 100 kg (220 lb) pilot, maximum fuel, and 5·4 kg (12 lb) of baggage can be carried.

DIMENSIONS, EXTERNAL:
Wing span	5·08 m (16 ft 8 in)
Wing area, gross	2·52 m² (27·08 sq ft)
Canard wing span	4·67 m (15 ft 4 in)
Canard wing area	2·47 m² (26·57 sq ft)
Length overall	5·28 m (17 ft 4 in)

DIMENSIONS, INTERNAL:
Cockpit: Length	1·63 m (5 ft 4 in)
Width	0·56 m (1 ft 10 in)
Height	0·86 m (2 ft 10 in)

WEIGHTS (A: 13·5 kW; 18 hp engine, B: 16·4 kW; 22 hp engine):
Weight empty: A, B	109 kg (240 lb)
Max T-O weight: A	218 kg (480 lb)
B	236 kg (520 lb)

PERFORMANCE:
Max level speed: A 109 knots (202 km/h; 126 mph)
B 122 knots (225 km/h; 140 mph)
Max cruising speed: A
105 knots (195 km/h; 121 mph)
Stalling speed, power off: A
46 knots (86 km/h; 53 mph)
Stalling speed, power on: A
43 knots (79 km/h; 49 mph)

Normal rate of climb at S/L: A	130 m (425 ft)/min
B	183 m (600 ft)/min
Max rate of climb at 1,525 m (5,000 ft):	
A	110 m (360 ft)/min
B	152 m (500 ft)/min
Service ceiling: A	3,750 m (12,300 ft)
B	4,665 m (15,300 ft)
T-O run: A	201 m (660 ft)
B	137 m (450 ft)
Landing run: A	255 m (835 ft)
B	183 m (600 ft)
Range at normal cruising speed	
A, B	477 nm (885 km; 550 miles)
Range at econ cruising speed	
A, B	712 nm (1,320 km; 820 miles)

QUICKIE AIRCRAFT CORPORATION
SUPER QUICKIE

Quickie Aircraft Corporation has designed an improved version of its Quickie aircraft; the prototype was nearing completion in January 1980 and was scheduled to make a first flight during March 1980. It was anticipated that if flight testing proceeded as planned the Super Quickie, as this version has been named, would be available in kit form for homebuilders by late 1980.

Generally similar in configuration to the Quickie, this new aircraft has been redesigned to simplify construction, to embody aerodynamic improvements, and to increase cockpit volume by 25%. Few details were available in early 1980, but it is known that fuel capacity will be 56·8 litres (15 US gallons), and that the Super Quickie is designed to achieve a fuel economy at maximum cruising speed of 32 km/litre (75 miles/US gallon) with an engine developing 26 kW (35 hp).

The following provisional specification details are estimates:

WEIGHTS:	
Max useful load	141 kg (310 lb)
Baggage	18 kg (40 lb)
PERFORMANCE:	
Max level speed	174 knots (322 km/h; 200 mph)
Stalling speed	49 knots (90 km/h; 56 mph)
Rate of climb at 3,050 m (10,000 ft)	
	335 m (1,100 ft)/min
Service ceiling	7,620 m (25,000 ft)
T-O and landing run	152 m (500 ft)
Range (normal)	1,042 nm (1,931 km; 1,200 miles)

QUICKIE AIRCRAFT CORPORATION
'BIG BIRD'

Scheduled to fly in the Autumn of 1980, 'Big Bird' (a temporary in-house name) is a single-seat single-engined aircraft designed to fly long distances with outstanding efficiency. It is intended solely for special-purpose research, and will attempt to set new world records for absolute distance between December 1980 and March 1981.

At the beginning of 1980, preliminary design of the aircraft systems was complete; the wings had been built and the remainder of the airframe was under construction. The only specification details available are as follows:

DIMENSION, EXTERNAL:	
Wing span	15·00 m (49 ft 2½ in)
WEIGHT:	
Max T-O weight	approx 1,815 kg (4,000 lb)
PERFORMANCE (estimated):	
Normal cruising speed	
	174 knots (322 km/h; 200 mph)
Service ceiling	above 10,650 m (35,000 ft)
Range with max fuel	
	more than 10,425 nm (19,310 km; 12,000 miles)
Endurance with max fuel at normal cruising speed	
	more than 85 h
Fuel consumption:	
normal	
	21·25-29·75 km/litre (50-70 miles/US gallon)
record attempts	
	32-42·5 km/litre (75-100 miles/US gallon)

RAND ROBINSON
RAND ROBINSON ENGINEERING INC

5842 K McFadden Avenue, Huntington Beach, California 92649
Telephone: (714) 898 3811

In 1974, the late Mr Kenneth Rand formed Rand Robinson Engineering Inc to market plans for the KR-1 single-seat lightweight sporting aircraft, and of a slightly larger two-seat version, designated KR-2. His last design was the KR-3 light amphibian, described in the 1978-79 *Jane's*.

RAND ROBINSON KR-1

Mr Kenneth Rand designed and built the prototype of a single-seat lightweight sporting aircraft known as the Rand KR-1. The design originated in 1969; construction of the prototype was started in 1970 and the first flight was made in February 1972. Plans are available to amateur constructors; 6,000 sets had been sold by the beginning of 1980 and about 200 KR-1s were known to be flying.

The performance figures that are quoted relate generally to the re-engined prototype fitted with a 67 kW (90 hp) 2,074 cc Volkswagen engine. Performance figures with the original 27 kW (36 hp) 1,200 cc VW engine can be found in the 1975-76 *Jane's*.

TYPE: Single-seat lightweight sporting aircraft.

WINGS: Cantilever low-wing monoplane. Wing section RAF 48. Thickness/chord ratio 15%. Dihedral 5°. Incidence 5° at root, 2° at tip. No sweepback. Composite two-spar structure. Front spar of spruce; rear spar built of spruce and plywood. Most ribs formed from polyurethane foam, spaces between ribs being filled with polyurethane foam slab. Structure covered with Dynel reinforced epoxy. Outer wing panels removable for storage. Ailerons of polyurethane foam, with Dynel reinforced epoxy covering, over full span of outer panels. Trailing-edge flaps standard.

FUSELAGE: Composite structure, lower half of spruce longerons with plywood skin, upper surface of carved Styrofoam covered with Dynel epoxy. Firewall is a plywood, asbestos and stainless steel lamination.

TAIL UNIT: Cantilever structure with spruce spars, the remainder of the structure being carved polyurethane foam, Dynel epoxy covered. Fixed-incidence tailplane. Trim tabs in rudder and elevator.

LANDING GEAR: Tailwheel type. Main units retract aft manually into wing centre-section. Shock-absorption by flat spring crossbar to which main units are attached. Main-wheel tyres size 10½ × 4·00-5, pressure 2·07 bars (30 lb/sq in). Steerable tailwheel with solid tyre of 7·6 cm (3 in) diameter. Manual drum brakes.

POWER PLANT: One Volkswagen modified motor car engine, driving a Maloof metal two-blade two-position propeller with spinner. Prototype has been re-engined with a Rajay-turbocharged 67 kW (90 hp) 2,074 cc VW. Fuel tankage with larger engine comprises one tank immediately aft of firewall, capacity 38 litres (10 US gallons), and one 76 litre (20 US gallon) tank in each wing, giving total capacity of 190 litres (50 US gallons). Refuelling point on fuselage upper surface, forward of windscreen. Oil capacity 2·8 litres (0·75 US gallons).

ACCOMMODATION: Pilot only, beneath rearward-sliding transparent cockpit canopy. Baggage space aft of seat.

SYSTEM: Electrical power supplied by 20A alternator and 12V 14Ah storage battery. Bosch electric starter.

AVIONICS AND EQUIPMENT: Edo-Aire 720-channel transceiver with 200-channel Auto Omni. Full blind-flying panel.

DIMENSIONS, EXTERNAL:	
Wing span	5·18 m (17 ft 0 in)
Wing chord at root	1·22 m (4 ft 0 in)
Wing chord at tip	0·91 m (3 ft 0 in)
Wing area, gross	5·76 m² (62 sq ft)
Wing aspect ratio	4·5
Length overall	3·89 m (12 ft 9 in)
Width, wings removed	1·52 m (5 ft 0 in)
Height overall	1·07 m (3 ft 6 in)
Tailplane span	1·52 m (5 ft 0 in)
Wheel track	1·27 m (4 ft 2 in)
Propeller diameter	1·35 m (4 ft 5 in)
DIMENSIONS, INTERNAL:	
Cockpit: Length	1·22 m (4 ft 0 in)
Max width	0·51 m (1 ft 8 in)
Max height	0·76 m (2 ft 6 in)
Baggage space	0·11 m³ (4 cu ft)
WEIGHTS (A: 27 kW; 36 hp. B: 67 kW; 90 hp):	
Weight empty, equipped: A	154 kg (340 lb)
B	218 kg (480 lb)
Max T-O and landing weight: A	272 kg (600 lb)
B	408 kg (900 lb)
PERFORMANCE (A: 27 kW; 36 hp. B: 67 kW; 90 hp, at max T-O weight):	
Never-exceed speed:	
A	140 knots (259 km/h; 161 mph)
B	217 knots (402 km/h; 250 mph)
Max level speed at S/L:	
A	130 knots (241 km/h; 150 mph)
B	191 knots (354 km/h; 220 mph)
Max cruising speed at 1,525 m (5,000 ft):	
A	130 knots (241 km/h; 150 mph)
B	191 knots (354 km/h; 220 mph)
Econ cruising speed at 5,485 m (18,000 ft):	
B	217 knots (402 km/h; 250 mph)
Stalling speed: A, B	39 knots (73 km/h; 45 mph)
Max rate of climb at S/L: A	182 m (600 ft)/min
B	457 m (1,500 ft)/min
Service ceiling: A	3,660 m (12,000 ft)
B	9,145 m (30,000 ft)
T-O run: A, B	122 m (400 ft)
T-O to 15 m (50 ft): A, B	244 m (800 ft)
Landing from 15 m (50 ft): A, B	305 m (1,000 ft)
Landing run: A, B	152 m (500 ft)
Range with max fuel:	
B	2,600 nm (4,825 km; 3,000 miles)

RAND ROBINSON KR-2

The KR-2 is a slightly larger two-seat version of the KR-1, to which it is generally similar in construction. Design began in 1973 and the prototype flew for the first time in July 1974. Construction occupied approximately 800 man hours, at a cost of about $2,000. Plans and kits of parts are available to amateur constructors.

By early 1980, about 4,500 sets of plans and 2,800 kits had been sold; about 350 KR-2s were flying at that time.

TYPE: Two-seat lightweight sporting aircraft.

WINGS: As for KR-1, except span increased by 1·07 m (3 ft 6 in).

FUSELAGE: As for KR-1, except dimensions increased.

TAIL UNIT AND LANDING GEAR: As for KR-1, except wheel track increased.

POWER PLANT: Airframe designed to accept Volkswagen modified motor car engines of 1,600 to 2,200 cc. Prototype has a Rajay turbocharged 2,074 cc Volkswagen engine, driving a Maloof two-position propeller with spinner. Fuel tank immediately aft of firewall, capacity 38 litres (10 US gallons). One fuel tank in each wing, capacity 53 litres (14 US gallons). Total fuel capacity 144 litres (38 US gallons). Refuelling point on fuselage upper surface, forward of windscreen.

ACCOMMODATION: Two persons, side by side, beneath transparent cockpit canopy.

AVIONICS AND EQUIPMENT: Provision for wide range of electronics and blind flying instruments. Prototype has full IFR panel, dual nav/com transceivers, glideslope receiver, three-light marker beacon receiver, and radar transponder with altitude reporting.

DIMENSIONS, EXTERNAL:	
Wing span	6·30 m (20 ft 8 in)
Wing chord at root	1·22 m (4 ft 0 in)
Wing chord at tip	0·91 m (3 ft 0 in)
Wing area, gross	7·43 m² (80 sq ft)
Wing aspect ratio	5·5
Length overall	4·42 m (14 ft 6 in)
Height overall	1·07 m (3 ft 6 in)
Tailplane span	1·52 m (5 ft 0 in)
Wheel track	1·52 m (5 ft 0 in)
Propeller diameter	1·32 m (4 ft 4 in)
DIMENSIONS, INTERNAL:	
Cockpit: Length	1·22 m (4 ft 0 in)
Max width	0·91 m (3 ft 0 in)
Max height	0·76 m (2 ft 6 in)
Baggage space	0·11 m³ (4 cu ft)
WEIGHTS (prototype, A: without turbocharger; B: with turbocharger):	
Weight empty, equipped: A	200 kg (440 lb)
B, with IFR and electrics	263 kg (580 lb)
Max T-O and landing weight: A	363 kg (800 lb)
B	499 kg (1,100 lb)
PERFORMANCE (prototype, at max T-O weight. A: without turbocharger; B: with turbocharger):	
Never-exceed speed:	
A, B	186 knots (346 km/h; 215 mph)
Max level speed at S/L:	
A	156 knots (290 km/h; 180 mph)
B	161 knots (298 km/h; 185 mph)
Max cruising speed:	
A at 1,525 m (5,000 ft)	156 knots (290 km/h; 180 mph)
B at 5,485 m (18,000 ft)	191 knots (354 km/h; 220 mph)
Econ cruising speed at 3,660 m (12,000 ft):	
A	148 knots (274 km/h; 170 mph)
Stalling speed: A	39 knots (73 km/h; 45 mph)
Max rate of climb: A at S/L	244 m (800 ft)/min
B at 5,485 m (18,000 ft)	244 m (800 ft)/min
Service ceiling: A	4,875 m (16,000 ft)
B	7,925 m (26,000 ft)
T-O run: A, B	122 m (400 ft)
T-O to 15 m (50 ft): A, B	244 m (800 ft)
Landing from 15 m (50 ft): A, B	305 m (1,000 ft)
Landing run: A, B	152 m (500 ft)
Range with max fuel:	
B	1,735 nm (3,215 km; 2,000 miles)

RLU
CHARLES ROLOFF, ROBERT LIPOSKY and CARL UNGER

c/o Charles B. Roloff, PO Box 358, Palos Park, Illinois 60464

Telephone: (312) 598 6210

Three professional pilots designed and built a unique light aircraft known as the Breezy Model RLU-1, the designation being made up of the initial letters of the surnames of the designers. Well over 700 sets of plans for the Breezy have since been sold, and many examples are flying, including some built in Australia, Canada, South Africa and Switzerland.

BREEZY MODEL RLU-1

Described as being of vintage configuration with all modern facilities, such as full radio, instruments and hyd-

Rand Robinson KR-1 built by Mr Melvin Boggs of Cols, Oklahoma (56 kW; 75 hp Avco Lycoming GO-145 engine) *(Howard Levy)*

The two-seat Rand Robinson KR-2

Breezy Model RLU-1 built by Mr R. J. Weller *(J. M. G. Gradidge)*

RotorWay Scorpion 133 with turbocharged engine

raulic brakes, the prototype Breezy is an open three-seat light aircraft powered by a 67 kW (90 hp) Continental engine. Construction took six months, at a cost of $3,400, including radio. First flight was made on 7 August 1964.

First Breezy to be built from the published plans was that constructed by Airpark Aero of Santa Rosa, California, for Mr Jack Gardiner of Pandora, Ohio. It differed from the prototype only by having two bucket seats, one of these replacing the usual two-place bench seat behind the pilot.

The following description applies to the prototype Breezy:

TYPE: Three-seat parasol-wing monoplane.

WINGS: Strut-braced parasol-wing monoplane. Standard Piper PA-12 wing, with V streamline-section bracing struts each side.

FUSELAGE: Triangular-section welded chrome-

molybdenum steel tube structure, without any covering.

TAIL UNIT: Welded chrome-molybdenum steel tube braced structure; all surfaces fabric-covered.

LANDING GEAR: Non-retractable tricycle type. Main wheels and tyres size 6·00-6, 4-ply; nosewheel and tyre size 5·00-5. Cleveland hydraulic brakes.

POWER PLANT: One 67 kW (90 hp) Continental C90-8F-P flat-four engine, driving a Flottorp 72A50 two-blade pusher propeller. Single fuel tank, capacity 68 litres (18 US gallons), in wing centre-section. Oil capacity 4·5 litres (1·25 US gallons).

ACCOMMODATION: Seats for three in tandem. Pilot on single seat forward, two passengers on bench seat aft.

DIMENSIONS, EXTERNAL:
Wing span	10·06 m (33 ft 0 in)
Wing area, gross	15·3 m² (165 sq ft)
Length overall	6·86 m (22 ft 6 in)

Height overall	2·59 m (8 ft 6 in)
Wheel track	1·83 m (6 ft 0 in)
Wheelbase	3·05 m (10 ft 0 in)

WEIGHTS:
Weight empty	317 kg (700 lb)
Max T-O weight	544 kg (1,200 lb)

PERFORMANCE:
Never-exceed speed	91 knots (168·5 km/h; 105 mph)
Cruising speed, 70% power	65 knots (121 km/h; 75 mph)
Stalling speed	26 knots (49 km/h; 30 mph)
Service ceiling	4,572 m (15,000 ft)
T-O run (grass)	137 m (450 ft)
T-O to 15 m (50 ft)	335 m (1,100 ft)
Landing from 15 m (50 ft)	335 m (1,100 ft)
Landing run (grass)	91 m (300 ft)
Range with max fuel	217 nm (402 km; 250 miles)

ROTORWAY
ROTORWAY AIRCRAFT INC

14805 S. Interstate 10, Tempe, Arizona 85284
Telephone: (602) 963 6652

Mr B. J. Schramm formed the Schramm Aircraft Company to market, in both ready-to-fly and prefabricated component form, a single-seat helicopter of his own design, named the Javelin. Details of this aircraft, which flew for the first time in August 1965, can be found in the 1967-68 *Jane's*.

Subsequently, a new company named RotorWay Aircraft Inc was formed to market to amateur constructors plans and kits of components to build Mr Schramm's Scorpion helicopter, described as a production version of the Javelin (see 1972-73 *Jane's*). After a period this aircraft was superseded by the two-seat Scorpion Too, now known as the Scorpion 133.

RotorWay currently offers a package deal which includes Scorpion 133 construction kits, a RotorWay RW 133 engine, and a complete training programme for the constructor/pilot which covers flight training, operation and theory, and maintenance. Plans by themselves are no longer available.

During 1978, a turbocharged version of the RW 133 engine became available as an alternative to the basic, normally aspirated model, for owners who require improved performance at altitude.

ROTORWAY SCORPION 133

TYPE: Two-seat light helicopter.

ROTOR SYSTEM: Two-blade semi-rigid main rotor, incorporating Schramm Tractable Control rotor system. Blade section NACA 0015. All-metal D-spar thermal-bonded blades, which do not fold, are attached to aluminium teetering rotor hub by retention straps. Two-blade aluminium teetering tail rotor. Swashplate for cyclic pitch control. Cable through rotor shaft to blades for collective pitch control.

ROTOR DRIVE: Drive from engine to vertical shaft via four power bands. Drive from vertical shaft to main rotor shaft via sprocketed triple-row chain. Tail rotor driven by V belt from first stage of reduction pulleys.

FUSELAGE: Basic 4130 steel tube structure of simplified form. Removable glassfibre body fairing.

TAIL UNIT: Braced steel tube tailboom only, to carry tail rotor.

LANDING GEAR: Tubular skid type.

POWER PLANT: One 99 kW (133 hp) RotorWay RW 133 watercooled flat-four engine, designed and produced for the Scorpion 133 by RotorWay and mounted aft of cabin area. Turbocharged version available, giving 119 kW (160 hp) at 70% boost. Standard fuel capacity 37·5 litres (10 US gallons) in tank mounted above drive chain, aft of main rotor shaft.

ACCOMMODATION: Two individual bucket seats, side by side, in enclosed cabin.

DIMENSIONS, EXTERNAL:
Diameter of main rotor	7·62 m (25 ft 0 in)
Diameter of tail rotor	1·10 m (3 ft 7¼ in)

Length, nose to tail rotor axis	6·26 m (20 ft 6½ in)
Height to top of main rotor	2·22 m (7 ft 3½ in)
Width of cabin	1·22 m (4 ft 0 in)
Landing skid track	1·64 m (5 ft 4¾ in)

WEIGHTS (A without turbocharger, B with turbocharger):
Weight empty: A	365 kg (805 lb)
B	372 kg (820 lb)
Max T-O weight: A, B	560 kg (1,235 lb)

PERFORMANCE (at max T-O weight. A without turbocharger, B with turbocharger):
Cruising speed: A, B	69·5 knots (129 km/h; 80 mph)
Max rate of climb at S/L: A	244 m (800 ft)/min
B	366 m (1,200 ft)/min
Service ceiling: A	3,050 m (10,000 ft)
B	4,875 m (16,000 ft)
Hovering ceiling IGE: A	1,675 m (5,500 ft)
B	2,745 m (9,000 ft)
Range with max fuel: A	104 nm (193 km; 120 miles)
B	100 nm (185 km; 115 miles)

ROTORWAY EXEC

Announced in 1980, this addition to the RotorWay range embodies a similar power plant and rotor system to those of the Scorpion 133, but has a completely new and streamlined fuselage of pod-and-boom type. The tail rotor is carried on the starboard side of the tapered cylindrical boom, with a small horizontal stabiliser and one-piece sweptback dorsal/ventral fin on the port side. No further details have been received.

RUTAN
RUTAN AIRCRAFT FACTORY

Building 13, Mojave Airport, Mojave, California 93501
Telephone: (805) 824 2645
PRESIDENT: Elbert L. Rutan

RUTAN VARIVIGGEN

The prototype of a light aircraft known as the VariViggen (N27VV) was rolled out on 27 February 1972. Mr Rutan had begun its design in 1963 and its configuration was developed via a low-cost automobile-mounted test system. This involved construction of a one-fifth scale

model which was mounted on a specially-built test rig attached to the roof of a motor car. Ailerons, rudders and canard elevators were operated by remote control from within the car, and transducers in the test rig allowed measurement of airspeed, angle of attack, lift, drag, sideslip, side force, roll moment and elevator/aileron/rudder positions. An extra data channel provided for measurement of stick forces and structural load.

A one-fifth scale radio-controlled model was used to confirm the design's spin-proof characteristics. Construction of the prototype began during 1968, and the first flight was made in May 1972. By early 1976 the VariViggen had

accumulated a total flying time of nearly 600 hours, and flight testing had confirmed the spin-free characteristics demonstrated by the free-flying scale model. The prototype had no conventional stall in its original form, and could climb, cruise, glide, turn and land with continuous full aft stick, giving a stable speed of 45 knots (83·5 km/h; 52 mph) throughout. Rate of climb at this speed is 152 m (500 ft)/min. The full-span ailerons provide a high rate of roll, and a 360° roll can be accomplished at a speed of only 80 knots (148 km/h; 92 mph) without loss of height. Manoeuvrability is such that the aircraft's turn radius is less than 61 m (200 ft) at speeds of 60-110 knots (111-204 km/h; 69-127 mph). Nosewheel rotation on take-off occurs at 50 knots (93 km/h; 58 mph), at which speed the aircraft will enter an immediate stable climb.

The full-span ailerons are described as 'reflexerons', since they serve both as ailerons and as an adjustable 'reflex' control for the main wing. Differential aileron motion is related mechanically to the stick, but the collective 'reflex' is electrically controlled. This is achieved by electrically controlled aileron droop, which causes the resulting nose-down trim to be countered by a nose-up deflection of the elevators on the forward canard surface. Thus both ailerons and elevators serve also as flaps. The ailerons are also adjusted at cruising speed to minimise trim drag and optimise the lift/drag ratio. Trim is achieved by an electrically-controlled bungee device on the mechanical elevator system.

In 1975 Mr Rutan began experimenting with a new SP (special performance) wing outer panel, constructed from urethane foam and unidirectional glassfibre, and with a Wortmann FX-60-126 section. With an increase of wing span to 7·23 m (23 ft 8½ in), and of area to 11·61 m² (125 sq ft), it was anticipated that this would provide a 25% increase in the max rate of climb and give a cruising speed 4·5-6 knots (8-11 km/h; 5-7 mph) greater than with the standard wing. Tests showed that the new wing increased rate of climb, but that the former 'no stall' characteristic had been sacrificed. With the SP wing, the VariViggen will 'roll off' if uncoordinated at full aft stick. It is, however, easier to build and stronger than the aluminium outer panel, and is covered on sets of plans currently available to amateur constructors.

A further refinement on the SP wing is the addition of NASA-developed 'winglets', designed by Dr Whitcomb, to enhance directional stability at no cost in performance.

The SP wing panels attach to the standard inboard wing panels, without modification. Each SP outer wing houses a 28·4 litre (7·5 US gallon) fuel tank, giving an additional 56·8 litres (15 US gallons) of auxiliary fuel.

About 900 sets of VariViggen plans have been sold; it is believed that approximately 300 aircraft are being built and four homebuilt examples were flying by early 1980. One aircraft assembled in France by M Chagnes is powered by two Microturbo TRS 18 turbojet engines, in which form it is known as the Microstar (see French section).

The following details apply to the VariViggen with the original type of outer wing panels:

TYPE: Two-seat (or 2+2) light aircraft.

WINGS: Cantilever low-wing monoplane of cropped delta configuration. Rutan wing section. Thickness/chord ratio 7% at root, 9% at tip. Dihedral 3° on outer wing panels. Incidence 0°. Sweepback at quarter-chord 27°. Composite structure with spruce spars, plywood ribs and skin, Ceconite-covered, except for outboard aft wing panels which are of flush-riveted metal construction. Inward-canted fin and rudder each side at approximately one-third span. Full-span ailerons, extending between fins and wingtips, constructed as a shell of 0·016 in aluminium with foam filling. Cutout in inboard trailing-edges to accommodate pusher propeller.

CANARD SURFACES: Cantilever structure mounted high on the nose, forward of the windscreen. Aerofoil section NACA 4414 (modified). Slotted flap-type elevator in trailing-edge.

FUSELAGE: Basically square-section fuselage of wooden construction, Ceconite-covered. Landing light in nosecone, which is hinged at top and opens upwards for access to equipment. Engine mounted in aft end of fuselage.

LANDING GEAR: Electrically-retractable tricycle type. Nosewheel retracts forward, main wheels inward in wings. Nosewheel mounted on oleo-pneumatic shock-strut. Shock-absorption of main units by rubber discs in compression. Goodyear main wheels, with tyres size 14 × 5·00-5, pressure 2·07 bars (30 lb/sq in). Scott nose-wheel with 228 mm (9 in) diameter tyre, pressure 2·07 bars (30 lb/sq in). Goodyear caliper brakes.

POWER PLANT: One 112 kW (150 hp) Avco Lycoming O-320-A2A flat-four engine, mounted in rear fuselage and driving a Hegy two-blade fixed-pitch wooden propeller. One fuel tank in fuselage, capacity 87 litres (23 US gallons) and one external fuel tank, mounted on aircraft centreline under fuselage, capacity 45 litres (12 US gallons). Total capacity 132 litres (35 US gallons). Refuelling point on fuselage upper surface. Oil capacity 7·5 litres (2 US gallons).

ACCOMMODATION: Two seats in tandem in individual cockpits, beneath transparent canopies which are hinged on the starboard side. Space for two children, each weighing not more than 22·5 kg (50 lb), or 45 kg (100 lb) of baggage aft of rear seat.

SYSTEMS: Dual 12V electrical systems. Storage battery. Hydraulic system for brakes only.

ELECTRONICS AND EQUIPMENT: ARC 360-channel VHF com transceiver, ARC 200-channel VHF nav receiver. Edo-Aire transponder. Angle of attack indicator.

DIMENSIONS, EXTERNAL:

Wing span	5·79 m (19 ft 0 in)
Wing chord at root	2·26 m (7 ft 5 in)
Wing chord at tip	0·89 m (2 ft 11 in)
Wing area, gross	11·06 m² (119 sq ft)
Wing aspect ratio	3
Length overall	5·79 m (19 ft 0 in)
Canard surface span	2·44 m (8 ft 0 in)
Wheel track	2·20 m (7 ft 2½ in)
Wheelbase	2·44 m (8 ft 0 in)
Propeller diameter	1·78 m (5 ft 10 in)
Propeller ground clearance	0·41 m (1 ft 4 in)

DIMENSIONS, INTERNAL:

Cabin: Length	2·54 m (8 ft 4 in)
Max width	0·64 m (2 ft 1 in)

WEIGHTS:

Weight empty, equipped	431 kg (950 lb)
Max T-O and landing weight	771 kg (1,700 lb)

PERFORMANCE (A: standard wing; B: SP wing, at max T-O weight, except as indicated):

Never-exceed speed:		
A		156 knots (289 km/h; 180 mph)
Max level speed at S/L:		
A		142 knots (262 km/h; 163 mph)
Max cruising speed at 2,135 m (7,000 ft):		
A		130 knots (241 km/h; 150 mph)
B		137 knots (254 km/h; 158 mph)
Econ cruising speed at 2,135 m (7,000 ft):		
A		109 knots (201 km/h; 125 mph)
Max rate of climb at S/L: A		244 m (800 ft)/min
B		305 m (1,000 ft)/min
Service ceiling: A		4,265 m (14,000 ft)
T-O run: A		259 m (850 ft)
T-O to 15 m (50 ft): A		290 m (950 ft)
Landing from 15 m (50 ft) at max landing weight		
A		183 m (600 ft)
Landing run at max landing weight: A		152 m (500 ft)
Range with max fuel, 30 min reserves		
A		347 nm (643 km; 400 miles)

RUTAN VARIEZE

Mr Rutan designed and built two prototypes of a high-performance two-seat aircraft of canard configuration, named the VariEze, of which plans are available. The name stems from its simplicity of construction, the entire structure being a composite of high-strength, primarily unidirectional glassfibre with rigid foam as core material.

The configuration of the VariEze is based on that of the VariViggen, with canard foreplanes; but the cropped-delta wings of that aircraft are replaced by more conventional swept wings of high aspect ratio. At the tip of each wing is a vertical fin, known as a 'winglet'. Developed by Dr Richard Whitcomb at NASA's Langley Research Center, each 'winglet' consists of large above-wing and small below-wing surfaces. That beneath the wing extends aft from the leading-edge to 33% of the tip chord, is cambered inward and inclined outward at 30° from vertical. The above-wing surface, extending aft from 33% of the tip chord, is cambered outward and also inclined outward at 15° from vertical. This 'winglet' system has been shown to 'unwind' the wingtip vortex to a maximum, limiting induced drag and resulting in a fuel saving of 6%; the inclination of the upper and lower surfaces also offsets 40% of the parasite drag of the vertical fins. These vertical surfaces include rudders, which are moved outward individually by single cables and centralised by return springs. The rudder control cables include in their run slotted bellcranks, so that extended movement of either rudder pedal causes the bellcrank to actuate its respective wheel-brake master cylinder. A conventional control column operates elevators mounted on the trailing-edges of the canard foreplanes and ailerons on the trailing-edges of the rear wings.

The tricycle landing gear has another unusual feature: the main units are fixed but the nosegear retracts both on the ground and in the air. Retracting the nose unit on the ground, termed kneeled parking, not only facilitates access to the cockpits but raises the propeller at a convenient height for hand-swinging and, at the same time, dispenses with a need for wheel chocks.

Designed in late 1974, the first VariEze (N7EZ) was built over a ten-week period in the Spring of 1975 and made its first flight on 21 May, powered by a 47 kW (63 hp; 1,834 cc) Volkswagen engine. By early 1977 it had logged approximately 260 flying hours. Optimum economy cruise performance was a primary design aim, so that the prototype could be used to attack existing world distance records in the under 500 kg gross weight class C1a. On 4 August 1975 the aircraft set a new closed-circuit distance record in this class, by covering 1,415·119 nm (2,620·80 km; 1,628·49 miles). In 1979 the aircraft was being prepared for an attempt to raise the record to around 2,780 nm (5,150 km; 3,200 miles).

A second prototype (N4EZ), embodying some modifications and powered by a Continental O-200 engine, was built during the Winter of 1975-76. It represents the prototype of the version for which plans are available, and is described in detail below.

All raw materials and certain component parts of the VariEze are also available to homebuilders, including the Plexiglas canopy, moulded glassfibre nosewheel and main landing gear struts, and glassfibre cowling.

A large underfuselage drag device has been added to the VariEze to enable it to land in shorter distances. About 2,000 VariEzes are being constructed by homebuilders in many countries, and 220 were flying by early 1980.

TYPE: Two-seat sporting aircraft.

WINGS: Cantilever mid-wing monoplane with sweptback surfaces. Single-spar structure of unidirectional glassfibre with rigid foam core. Inboard ailerons. Vertical above-wing 'winglet' surface at each wingtip includes rudder.

CANARD FOREPLANE: Cantilever structure of unidirectional glassfibre with rigid foam core. Trailing-edge elevators of similar construction.

FUSELAGE: Composite structure comprising large sheets of rigid urethane foam, with wood strips as corner fillers, and internal and external covering of unidirectional glassfibre. A standard-size light alloy extrusion is used for engine, landing gear, and control stick mounts, as well as for canopy latches and other parts.

LANDING GEAR: Tricycle landing gear, with fixed main units and mechanically-retractable nosewheel which is carried on a glassfibre strut moulded to conform to the outside contour of the fuselage, so eliminating need for a fairing door. Nose gear retracted by hand-lever. Main wheels carried on one-piece moulded glassfibre strut. Fairings on main wheels. Hydraulically-operated brakes.

POWER PLANT: One 74·5 kW (100 hp) Continental O-200-B flat-four engine, mounted in the aft fuselage and driving a two-blade fixed-pitch pusher propeller with spinner. Provision for Continental A75, C85 or C90 engines. Fuel tanks, of glassfibre/foam/glassfibre sandwich construction, form strakes on each side of the fuselage that fair the wing roots; total capacity 91 litres (24 US gallons). A small fuselage tank is also available. Refuelling points on each side of fuselage, on the upper surface of tanks.

ACCOMMODATION: Pilot and passenger on semi-reclining seats in individual cockpits. Side-stick controls. Dual controls limited to control stick at rear position. One-piece bubble canopy of moulded Plexiglas covers both cockpits and is hinged on starboard side. Roll-over structure. Space for 14 kg (30 lb) baggage in two specially designed suitcases which fit in rear seat area.

SYSTEMS: Hydraulic system for wheel brakes only. Can have simple electrical system with a single nav/com and gyro instrument.

DIMENSIONS, EXTERNAL:

Wing span	6·77 m (22 ft 2½ in)
Wing chord at root	0·91 m (3 ft 0 in)
Wing chord at tip	0·41 m (1 ft 4 in)
Wing area, gross	4·98 m² (53·6 sq ft)
Foreplane span	3·81 m (12 ft 6 in)
Foreplane chord, constant	0·32 m (1 ft 0½ in)
Foreplane area	1·21 m² (13 sq ft)
Length overall	4·32 m (14 ft 2 in)

WEIGHTS (Continental O-200 engine):

Weight empty	254 kg (560 lb)
Max T-O weight	476 kg (1,050 lb)

PERFORMANCE (at max T-O weight, Continental O-200 engine):

Max cruising speed	170 knots (313 km/h; 195 mph)
Econ cruising speed	143 knots (265 km/h; 165 mph)
Landing speed	60 knots (112 km/h; 70 mph)
Stalling speed	48 knots (90 km/h; 55·5 mph)
Max rate of climb at S/L	487 m (1,600 ft)/min
T-O and landing run	275 m (900 ft)
Range at 75% power	607 nm (1,126 km; 700 miles)
Range at econ cruising speed	738 nm (1,368 km; 850 miles)

RUTAN LONG-EZ

In late 1978, Mr Rutan began the design of an improved VariEze, to be powered by an Avco Lycoming O-235 engine that would have an electric starter and engine-driven alternator. The new model was intended specifically to have long range (hence the name Long-EZ), good forward visibility during landing, and lower approach and landing speeds than the VariEze, to make it more suitable for pilots of low proficiency. In its initial prototype form (N79RA), as first flown on 12 June 1979, it was generally similar to the VariEze; but in addition to the changed power plant, it had wings of increased span and sweep, a 'Rhino' rudder, mounted on the nose, and no control surfaces on the winglets. Flight testing revealed several deficiencies in flight characteristics. As a result a new wing was designed, with an Eppler section similar to that used in the Rutan Defiant, reduced wing sweep, increased area, ailerons of increased span, and the eventual introduction of rudders in larger winglets, leading to deletion of the 'Rhino' rudder.

When the Long-EZ was flown with the wing in this finalised form, the desired flight characteristics had been achieved. On 15 December 1979, piloted by Dick Rutan, it took off in an attempt to set a new closed-circuit distance record in FAI Class C1b. Landing 33 h 33 min and 41 s later, the Long-EZ had covered a distance of 4,171·3 nm (7,725·3 km; 4,800·3 miles) which ranks as a new world record, beating the former 20-year-old record by almost 1,602 nm (2,969 km; 1,845 miles).

Generally similar in construction to the VariEze, this new two-seat aircraft has an 80·5 kW (108 hp) Avco Lycoming O-235 flat-four engine, and a maximum fuel capacity of 197 litres (52 US gallons). Optional alternative power plant for the Long-EZ is the 74·5 kW (100 hp) Continental O-200 flat-four engine.

Rutan Defiant four-seat twin-engined lightplane (foreground)

Rutan Long-EZ, an improved version of the VariEze

Rutan VariEze high-performance tail-first monoplane (foreground) flying with the Rutan VariViggen two-seat canard delta; both aircraft are now fitted with NASA 'winglets' *(Don Dwiggins)*

Plans for construction of this aircraft are available to homebuilders, and available specification details follow:

DIMENSIONS, EXTERNAL:
Wing span	8·01 m (26 ft 3½ in)
Wing area, gross	8·74 m² (94·1 sq ft)

WEIGHTS:
Weight empty, basic	322 kg (710 lb)
Weight empty, equipped	340 kg (750 lb)
Max T-O weight	601 kg (1,325 lb)

PERFORMANCE (at max T-O weight A: solo; B: two-seat):
Max cruising speed, 75% power at 2,440 m (8,000 ft)	
A	161 knots (298 km/h; 185 mph)
B	159 knots (295 km/h; 183 mph)
Cruising speed, 40% power at 3,660 m (12,000 ft)	
	125 knots (232 km/h; 144 mph)
Max rate of climb at S/L:	
A	533 m (1,750 ft)/min
B	411 m (1,350 ft)/min
Service ceiling:	
A	8,230 m (27,000 ft)
B	6,705 m (22,000 ft)
T-O run: A	168 m (550 ft)
B	253 m (830 ft)
Landing run: A	137 m (450 ft)
B	207 m (680 ft)
Range with max fuel at max cruising speed, 40 min reserves:	
A	1,190 nm (2,205 km; 1,370 miles)
B	838 nm (1,553 km; 965 miles)
Range with max fuel at 40% power, 40 min reserves:	
A	1,746 nm (3,235 km; 2,010 miles)
B	1,242 nm (2,301 km; 1,430 miles)

SEQUOIA
SEQUOIA AIRCRAFT CORPORATION
900 West Franklin Street, Richmond, Virginia 23220
PRESIDENT: Alfred P. Scott

Sequoia Aircraft Corporation was formed by Mr Alfred P. Scott to develop the Sequoia cabin monoplane. Work on this aircraft was begun in July 1975, with all design and engineering by Mr David B. Thurston, a consultant whose other designs have included the Colonial Skimmer (now the Lake amphibian), the Teal and Marlin amphibians, and the TA-16 Trojan amphibian.

Two variations of the basic Sequoia design are available. The Model 300 Sequoia is a side-by-side two-seat aircraft, with two aft-facing rear seats optional and a sliding bubble canopy. The Model 302 Kodiak is a four-seat aircraft with an enclosed cabin.

These aircraft have a high degree of commonality of parts. Kits consisting of formed and machined parts have been produced and delivered to amateur constructors who are building the first examples of the aircraft. In May 1980, twenty aircraft were under construction; 40 sets of plans had been sold.

In addition to marketing plans and kits to amateur aircraft builders, Sequoia Aircraft Corporation has offered both aircraft as military trainers to countries that wish to

RUTAN DEFIANT
The Rutan Defiant (N78RA), which made its first flight in proof-of-concept prototype form on 30 June 1978, is a four-seat twin-engined light aircraft of unconventional design. Benefiting from experience gained with the smaller two-seat VariEze, it retains the latter's rear-mounted swept cantilever wings with winglet surfaces, canard foreplane and retractable nosewheel/fixed main-wheel type of landing gear, but is powered by two 119 kW (160 hp) Avco Lycoming O-320 engines which are installed at the front and rear of the fuselage in tractor and pusher configurations. One 170 litre (45 US gallon) fuel tank is provided for each engine. The aircraft also has two simple separate electrical systems, each with a battery and alternator. An IFR system is installed, with the avionics split between both electrical systems to provide additional safety in the event of one failing.

The Defiant is claimed to be a very basic aircraft with no flaps, fixed-pitch propellers and few complex systems, but to provide greater leg room and comfort than other twin-engined lightplanes of larger overall size. It is also claimed that the Defiant will have no minimum control speed, will require no pilot action or configuration changes in order to continue a climb if an engine fails, and will be able to climb at its minimum full-aft-stick speed, at maximum weight, with one propeller windmilling and the nosewheel down.

By early 1980, the Defiant prototype had accumulated about 520 flying hours. It has been found, however, that the aircraft has certain minor deficiencies in design. In particular, boarding is difficult because the canopy opens only to one side and the sill is 1·27 m (4 ft 2 in) from the ground, with no wing on which to stand. Also, the baggage area has no loading door. If the decision is taken to cer-

tificate a production version, it will be a five-seat aircraft, powered by two 134 kW (180 hp) engines, each driving a constant-speed metal propeller. It will have a large door on the starboard side of the cabin, opening upwards to allow step-in boarding and easy baggage loading, and will also have a more square upper fuselage section, to increase lateral headroom and baggage area.

In early 1980 the Defiant programme was in a state of suspension, awaiting suitable financing.

DIMENSIONS, EXTERNAL:
Wing span	8·89 m (29 ft 2 in)
Wing area, gross	11·83 m² (127·3 sq ft)
Propeller diameter	1·75 m (5 ft 9 in)

DIMENSIONS, INTERNAL:
Cabin width, forward	1·17 m (3 ft 10 in)
Cabin width, aft	1·09 m (3 ft 7 in)

WEIGHTS:
Weight empty (IFR)	730 kg (1,610 lb)
Max T-O weight	1,315 kg (2,900 lb)

PERFORMANCE:
Max cruising speed (70% power)	
	186 knots (344 km/h; 214 mph)
Normal cruising speed (65% power)	
	182 knots (337 km/h; 210 mph)
Stalling speed, nosewheel down	
	65 knots (121 km/h; 75 mph)
Econ cruising speed	170 knots (315 km/h; 196 mph)
Max rate of climb at S/L	488 m (1,600 ft)/min
Max rate of climb, one engine out	94 m (310 ft)/min
Range with max fuel, four adults and 36 kg (80 lb) baggage, 45 min reserves	
	980 nm (1,815 km; 1,128 miles)

assemble their own aircraft, using local labour. Aeronics (Pty) Ltd of the Republic of South Africa has signed an exclusive production agreement for manufacture of the aircraft for civilian use in South Africa, but start of manufacture is dependent on suitable financing being arranged.

Meanwhile, Sequoia has begun offering also plans to build the Italian Falco F.8L light aircraft.

MODEL 300 SEQUOIA
TYPE: Two-seat utility and aerobatic monoplane.

WINGS: Cantilever low-wing monoplane. Wing section NACA 64₂A215 at root, NACA 64A210 at tip. Dihedral 3° from roots. Incidence 3° 30′ at root. Washout 2°. All-metal flush-riveted structure with single I-beam spar, 2024-T4 Alclad ribs and 2024-T3 Alclad skin. Glassfibre tips. Frise balanced ailerons of aluminium construction with rubber seals. Slotted aluminium flaps.

FUSELAGE: Welded 4130 steel tube structure. Entire fuselage, including wing fillets, covered with lightweight shell of glassfibre/PVC foam/glassfibre sandwich, attached to tubing with glassfibre and epoxy resin. Kevlar is optional alternative to glassfibre.

TAIL UNIT: Conventional cantilever unit of flush-riveted

aluminium alloy construction. Elevators fitted, each with trim tab. Rudder trim is bungee system.

LANDING GEAR: Retractable tricycle type. Electrohydraulic retraction. Oleo-pneumatic shock-absorbers.

POWER PLANT: One 224 kW (300 hp) Avco Lycoming TIO-540-S1AD flat-six engine, driving a Hartzell two-blade constant-speed propeller. Other Avco Lycoming engines of 175-224 kW (235-300 hp) may be used. Two integral fuel tanks in wings, with total capacity of 291·5 litres (77 US gallons). Provision for tip-tanks of approximately 75 litres (20 US gallons) capacity each; and two underwing attachment points for additional fuel tanks, radar or stores of up to 272 kg (600 lb) combined weight. Refuelling points in wingtips.

ACCOMMODATION: Two seats side by side, beneath sliding Plexiglas canopy. An aft-facing rear seat can be installed to provide a two-plus-two layout. Baggage compartment, capacity 45·4 kg (100 lb).

SYSTEMS: A completely flush antenna system is being designed. The nav antennae will be in the glassfibre wingtips and the remainder will be under the fuselage shell.

DIMENSIONS, EXTERNAL:
Wing span	9·14 m (30 ft 0 in)
Wing chord at root	1·68 m (5 ft 6 in)
Wing chord at tip	0·91 m (3 ft 0 in)

Wing area, gross	12·08 m² (130 sq ft)
Wing aspect ratio	6·92
Length overall	7·62 m (25 ft 0 in)
Height overall	2·90 m (9 ft 6 in)
Propeller diameter	2·03 m (6 ft 8 in)

WEIGHTS:

Weight empty	816 kg (1,800 lb)
Max T-O weight, utility	1,270 kg (2,800 lb)
Max T-O weight, aerobatic	1,088 kg (2,400 lb)

PERFORMANCE (estimated):

Never-exceed speed	243 knots (450 km/h; 280 mph)
Max level speed at S/L	195 knots (362 km/h; 225 mph)
Max cruising speed at 2,440 m (8,000 ft)	185 knots (343 km/h; 213 mph)
Stalling speed 'clean'	75 knots (139 km/h; 86 mph)
Stalling speed, flaps and wheels down	60 knots (111 km/h; 69 mph)
Max rate of climb at S/L	664 m (2,180 ft)/min
Service ceiling	7,620 m (25,000 ft)
T-O run	457 m (1,500 ft)
T-O to 15 m (50 ft)	610 m (2,000 ft)
Landing run	548 m (1,800 ft)
Range at max cruising speed, with 45 min reserves	868 nm (1,609 km; 1,000 miles)

MODEL 301

Plans to develop this tandem two-seat version of the Model 300 Sequoia have been abandoned.

SEQUOIA MODEL 302 KODIAK

The Kodiak is a four-seat development of the Model 300 Sequoia, using the same wing assembly, tail unit, landing gear, power plant and mount, engine cowling, firewall, control system, instrument panel and windscreen. Wingtip fuel tanks can be fitted to increase range; gull-wing doors provide access to the enclosed cabin; and the aircraft is designed to be fully aerobatic.

Power plant will be in the 186-224 kW (250-300 hp) Avco Lycoming IO-540/TIO-540-S1AD range, driving a Hartzell two-blade constant-speed propeller with a diameter of 2·03 m (6 ft 8 in). Empty weight will be 839 kg (1,850 lb); max T-O weight 1,451 kg (3,200 lb); fuel capacity 341 litres (90 US gallons).

SEQUOIA FALCO F.8L

Sequoia Aircraft Corporation is offering plans to build the Falco F.8L high-performance low-wing monoplane, designed in Italy by Ing Stelio Frati and first flown on 15 June 1955. The aircraft was last marketed in Italy by Aeromere. In its current form, for amateur construction, it incorporates minor changes, and the performance data given below apply to the Sequoia Falco F.8L fitted with a 119 kW (160 hp) Avco Lycoming O-320-B3B flat-four engine, although Avco Lycoming engines of 100·5 kW (135 hp) and 112 kW (150 hp) can be installed. Component parts and kits for the Sequoia Falco F.8L are available from Sequoia Aircraft. A total of 134 Falcos were being built in June 1980.

TYPE: Two-seat light monoplane.

WINGS: Cantilever low-wing monoplane. Laminar-flow NACA 64₂212½ wing section at root, NACA 64₂210 at tip. Thickness/chord ratio 12½% at root and 10% at tip. Dihedral 5°. Incidence at root 3°. Washout 3°. All-wood one-piece single-spar structure built integrally with forward portion of fuselage. Plywood-covered, with overall fabric covering. Frise-type ailerons and electrically-operated split flaps can be of wood and fabric or all-metal construction. Optional leading-edge modification gives milder stall and slightly reduced cruising speed.

FUSELAGE: Plywood-covered semi-monocoque structure, with wooden frames and longerons, fabric covered overall. Normally built in two sections, comprising a centre-section integral with the wings, and a tailcone; but can be built in one piece.

TAIL UNIT: Cantilever type. All-wood tailplane and fin integral with rear portion of fuselage. Rudder and elevators can be of wood and fabric or all-metal construction. Controllable trim tab in starboard elevator.

LANDING GEAR: Retractable tricycle type. Manual or optional electrical retraction, with mechanical emergency actuation. Oleo-pneumatic shock-absorbers. Single-disc hydraulic brakes. Steerable nosewheel.

POWER PLANT: One Avco Lycoming O-290-D2B, O-320-A2A or O-320-B3B flat-four engine of 100·5 kW (135 hp), 112 kW (150 hp) or 119 kW (160 hp) respectively, driving a fixed-pitch or constant-speed (except for O-290 engine) two-blade propeller with spinner. Fuel in two metal tanks, capacity 118 litres (31·2 US gallons).

ACCOMMODATION: Enclosed cabin for two persons side by side. Rearward-sliding transparent canopy. Dual controls standard. Cabin heated and ventilated. Baggage locker behind seats. Provision for fitting seat for a child of not more than 40 kg (88 lb) weight in baggage space.

SYSTEMS: Electrical system of 12V or 24V for cabin lighting, landing lights, navigation lights, strobes, etc.

DIMENSIONS, EXTERNAL:

Wing span	8·00 m (26 ft 3 in)
Wing area, gross	10 m² (107·5 sq ft)
Wing aspect ratio	6·4
Length overall	6·50 m (21 ft 4 in)
Height overall	2·29 m (7 ft 6 in)

WEIGHTS (O-320-B3B engine):

Weight empty	550 kg (1,212 lb)
Max T-O weight	820 kg (1,808 lb)
Max aerobatic weight	748 kg (1,650 lb)

PERFORMANCE (O-320-B3B engine):

Never-exceed speed	208 knots (386 km/h; 240 mph)
Max level speed at S/L	184 knots (341 km/h; 212 mph)
Cruising speed at 1,830 m (6,000 ft), 75% power	165 knots (306 km/h; 190 mph)
Stalling speed, flaps and wheels down	54 knots (100 km/h; 62 mph)
Max rate of climb at S/L	347 m (1,140 ft)/min
Service ceiling	5,790 m (19,000 ft)
Range at econ cruising speed	755 nm (1,400 km; 870 miles)

SHEPPARD
H. GORDON SHEPPARD
Purcellville, Virginia

SHEPPARD S-2

Mr H. Gordon Sheppard, a pilot with Eastern Air Lines, has designed and built, without reference to other plans, a two-seat sporting biplane resembling the Pitts Special. Construction took place over a four-year period, at a cost of $7,100. First flight was made on 9 July 1979. The wings are of wooden construction, the fuselage and tail unit of steel tube, all Dacron fabric covered. Power plant is a 134 kW (180 hp) Avco Lycoming O-360-A flat-four engine.

DIMENSIONS, EXTERNAL:

Wing span	6·10 m (20 ft 0 in)
Wing chord	1·02 m (3 ft 4 in)

WEIGHTS:

Weight empty	416 kg (916 lb)
Max T-O weight	715 kg (1,575 lb)

PERFORMANCE:

Max level speed	176 knots (327 km/h; 203 mph)
Cruising speed	113 knots (209 km/h; 130 mph)
Max rate of climb at S/L	610 m (2,000 ft)/min
T-O run	107 m (350 ft)
Landing run	305 m (1,000 ft)
Range with max fuel	260 nm (483 km; 300 miles)

SINDLINGER
SINDLINGER AIRCRAFT
37030 204th Avenue SE, Auburn, Washington 98002

Mr Fred G. Sindlinger began the design of a ⅝-scale replica of the second World War Hawker Hurricane IIC fighter in April 1969. Construction of the prototype was started three months later and the first flight was made in January 1972. By February 1977, this aircraft had accumulated a total of approximately 400 flying hours; it was subsequently sold.

Plans and certain component parts are available to amateur constructors; 53 sets of drawings had been sold by early 1980, and about 17 Sindlinger Hurricanes were under construction, including examples being built in Australia, France, West Germany and the United Kingdom. The first plans-built aircraft to fly was constructed in South Africa and was flown in 1978; three more were nearing completion in early 1980.

SINDLINGER HH-1 HAWKER HURRICANE

TYPE: Single-seat sporting aircraft.

WINGS: Cantilever low-wing monoplane. Wing section NACA 2418 in centre-section, with progressive change to NACA 2412 at tip. Dihedral 3° 30' on outer panels only. Incidence 0° 36'. Sweepback at quarter-chord 3°. Two-spar structure of wood. Front spar is of I-beam construction in the centre-section and of built-up box section in the outer panels. Rear spar is an I-beam in the centre-section, and of U-channel form in the outer panels. Built-up truss ribs and 2·4 mm (³/₃₂ in) plywood skin, fabric-covered overall. Frise-type ailerons of wood construction, fabric-covered and statically balanced. Split trailing-edge flaps of wood.

FUSELAGE: All-wood monocoque structure of 3·2 mm (⅛ in) plywood from firewall to aft of cockpit. Rear fuselage is a built-up box truss frame, with formers and stringers. Entire structure fabric-covered.

TAIL UNIT: All-wood cantilever structure. Two-spar tailplane and fin have plywood skin, covered with fabric overall. Rudder and elevators are of wood construction with fabric covering. Elevator trimmed by internal spring tension. Ground-adjustable trim tab on rudder.

LANDING GEAR: Manually-retractable tailwheel type. Main wheels retract inward. Shock-absorption of main and tail units by coil spring inside steel tubes. Tailwheel steerable. Goodyear main wheels and tyres size 5·00-5. Goodyear hydraulic brakes.

POWER PLANT: One 112 kW (150 hp) Avco Lycoming O-320 flat-four engine, driving a Hartzell two-blade constant-speed metal propeller with spinner. Up to three fuel tanks: one in fuselage aft of firewall with capacity of 54 litres (14 US gallons) and, optionally, one in each wing root, with capacity of 38 litres (10 US gallons) each. Max total fuel capacity 130 litres (34 US gallons). Refuelling point in fuselage upper surface, forward of windscreen. Oil capacity 7·5 litres (2 US gallons). Glassfibre engine cowlings.

ACCOMMODATION: Pilot only, beneath rearward-sliding transparent canopy. Cockpit heated and ventilated. Space for 18 kg (40 lb) baggage aft of pilot's seat.

SYSTEMS: Hydraulic system for brakes only. Electrical system powered by 12V DC engine-driven generator. 12V 35Ah battery.

ELECTRONICS AND EQUIPMENT: 90-channel VHF com transceiver, VOR Omni nav receiver. Partial IFR instrumentation. Wooden imitation cannon or machine-guns in wing leading-edges.

DIMENSIONS, EXTERNAL:

Wing span	7·65 m (25 ft 1 in)
Wing chord on centre-section, constant	1·52 m (5 ft 0 in)
Wing chord at tip	0·91 m (3 ft 0 in)
Wing area, gross	9·38 m² (101 sq ft)
Wing aspect ratio	6·2
Length overall	5·99 m (19 ft 8 in)
Height overall, tail up	1·78 m (5 ft 10 in)
Tailplane span	2·24 m (7 ft 4 in)
Wheel track	1·83 m (6 ft 0 in)
Propeller diameter	1·93 m (6 ft 4 in)

DIMENSION, INTERNAL:

Cockpit: Max width	0·66 m (2 ft 2 in)

WEIGHTS:

Weight empty	446 kg (984 lb)
Max T-O weight	624 kg (1,375 lb)

PERFORMANCE (at max T-O weight):

Never-exceed speed	208 knots (386 km/h; 240 mph)
Max level speed at S/L	174 knots (322 km/h; 200 mph)
Max cruising speed, 65% power at 1,830 m (6,000 ft)	148 knots (273 km/h; 170 mph)
Econ cruising speed, 60% power at 2,745 m (9,000 ft)	135 knots (249 km/h; 155 mph)
Stalling speed, flaps up	58 knots (108 km/h; 67 mph)
Stalling speed, flaps down	54 knots (100 km/h; 62 mph)
Max rate of climb at S/L	564 m (1,850 ft)/min
Service ceiling	6,400 m (21,000 ft)
T-O run	150 m (490 ft)
Landing run	168 m (550 ft)
Range, 65% power, 30 min reserves	500 nm (925 km; 575 miles)
Max range, no reserves	542 nm (1,005 km; 625 miles)
g limits	+4·4 utility, +6·6 ultimate

SISLER
SISLER AIRCRAFT COMPANY
Box 20219, Bloomington, Minnesota 55420

Captain Bert Sisler is an airline pilot who had logged more than 15,000 flying hours on 67 types of aircraft by the beginning of 1979. During his flying career, he has piloted seaplanes and sailplanes, instructed on single-engined and multi-engined aircraft, and served five years as a test pilot.

The first aircraft he designed and built was the Pipit two-seater, now owned by another pilot. It was followed by the SF-2 Whistler, which gained the 'Outstanding Design Contribution' award at the 1973 EAA Fly-in at Oshkosh. Capt Sisler has subsequently improved this design, making it easier to build, aerodynamically cleaner and 23 kg (50 lb) lighter. Plans of the improved version, now known as the SF-2A Cygnet, are available to other constructors.

SISLER SF-2A CYGNET

TYPE: Two-seat light aircraft.

WINGS: Strut-braced shoulder-wing monoplane of all-wood construction, swept forward 5° from roots. Wing section NACA 3413. Dihedral 3° 30'. Each wing consists of a main spar, light front and rear auxiliary spars, six plywood ribs, some stringers, geodetic upper and lower coverings of spruce strips, and an overall Dacron

Model 300 Sequoia two-seat utility and aerobatic aircraft, with additional (lower) side view of Model 302 Kodiak *(Pilot Press)*

SF-2A Cygnet, designed and built by Capt Bert Sisler of Bloomington, Minnesota *(Eric Sisler)*

Skyote Aeromarine Skyote aerobatic biplane built by Mr Duane Burnett *(Howard Levy)*

Italian-built Falco F.8L two-seat light monoplane *(James Gilbert)*

Sheppard S-2 two-seat sporting biplane *(Howard Levy)*

Sindlinger ⅝-scale replica of a Hawker Hurricane IIC

covering. Fabric-covered wooden ailerons, without tabs. No flaps.

FUSELAGE: Conventional welded chrome molybdenum steel tube structure, Dacron-covered.

TAIL UNIT: Conventional strut-braced unit, comprising tailplane and elevators, vertical fin and rudder. Structure similar to that of fuselage. Trim tab in port elevator. Ground-adjustable tab on rudder.

LANDING GEAR: Non-retractable tailwheel type. Two side Vs and half axles of welded steel tube. Bungee shock-absorption. Main-wheel tyres size 5·00-5 on prototype; size 6·00-6 tyres or skis optional. Steerable tailwheel.

POWER PLANT: One 46 kW (62 hp) 1,834 cc Volkswagen modified motor car engine, driving a two-blade propeller. Fuel capacity 57 litres (15 US gallons).

ACCOMMODATION: Two seats side by side in enclosed cockpit. Windscreen made up of two door panels, hinged on centreline. Baggage capacity 23 kg (50 lb).

SYSTEM: Prototype has no electrical system, but lightweight alternator and battery are optional.

DIMENSIONS, EXTERNAL:
Wing span	9·14 m (30 ft 0 in)
Wing chord, constant	1·27 m (4 ft 2 in)
Wing area, gross	11·60 m² (124·8 sq ft)
Wing aspect ratio	7·1
Length overall	5·79 m (19 ft 0 in)
Height overall	1·78 m (5 ft 10 in)
Tailplane span	2·39 m (7 ft 10 in)
Propeller diameter	1·47 m (4 ft 10 in)

DIMENSION, INTERNAL:
Cockpit width	0·99 m (3 ft 3 in)

WEIGHTS:
Weight empty	265 kg (585 lb)
Max T-O weight	499 kg (1,100 lb)

PERFORMANCE (at max T-O weight):
Max level speed	94 knots (174 km/h; 108 mph)
Cruising speed at 2,440 m (8,000 ft)	87 knots (161 km/h; 100 mph)
Stalling speed	42 knots (78 km/h; 48 mph)
Max rate of climb at S/L	177 m (580 ft)/min
T-O and landing run	213 m (700 ft)
g limit	+ 4

SKYOTE
SKYOTE AEROMARINE LTD
PO Box 142, Boulder, Colorado 80306
PRESIDENT: O. E. Bartoe Jr

This company was formed to produce components for an aerobatic biplane named Skyote, which is intended for amateur construction. Its President is also President of Ball-Bartoe Aircraft Corporation (see main Aircraft section of 1979-80 *Jane's*).

SKYOTE AEROMARINE SKYOTE
Construction of the prototype Skyote (N8XX), with a 67 kW (90 hp) Continental C90F engine, began in March 1975 and the first flight of this aircraft took place on 23 April 1976. FAA certification in the Aerobatic category

was applied for on 17 February 1977. At that time, components for five other aircraft were being produced, the first of which was completed by Mr Duane Burnett of Boulder, and first flew in Summer 1978. This Skyote took 2,500 working hours to build. It is powered by a 67 kW (90 hp) Continental C-90-8 engine, which gives the aircraft a max cruising speed of 97 knots (180 km/h; 112 mph); a max rate of climb of 564 m (1,850 ft)/min; T-O run of 107 m (350 ft); and landing run of 168 m (550 ft). Plans are available to amateur constructors, and Univair is reportedly selling wing kits. By early 1980 a total of 21 sets of plans had been sold.

TYPE: Single-seat aerobatic biplane.

WINGS: Braced biplane, with two parallel interplane struts each side and two pairs of centre-section support struts.

Wing section NACA (1.8)412. No anhedral or dihedral. Incidence 2°. Sweepback on all wings at quarter-chord 7° 12'. Forward-staggered upper wing. All structure of 2024 aluminium, with hydroformed ribs, fabric covered. Plain ailerons on upper and lower wings, torque tube actuated.

FUSELAGE: Truss structure of welded 4130N chrome-molybdenum steel tubing, fabric covered.

TAIL UNIT: Wire-braced unit of 4130N steel tube, fabric covered. Ground-adjustable tailplane incidence. No tabs.

LANDING GEAR: Non-retractable tailwheel type. Main wheels carried on side Vees and half-axles. Type 1280HD bungee cord shock-absorption. Cleveland main wheels and tyres size 18 × 7-6. Tyre pressure 1·24 bars (18 lb/sq in). Cleveland hydraulically-actuated disc brakes.

POWER PLANT: Aircraft used for FAA certification programme has one 88 kW (118 hp) Avco Lycoming O-235-K2A flat-four engine, driving a Sensenich two-blade fixed-pitch propeller. Other engines can be installed, including 67 kW (90 hp) Continental C85 or C90 flat-four. Fuel tanks in wing centre-section and fuselage, each with capacity of 24·6 litres (6·5 US gallons). Total fuel capacity 49·2 litres (13 US gallons). Refuelling points in top of wing centre-section and top of fuselage. Oil capacity 7·5 litres (2 US gallons).

ACCOMMODATION: Single seat in open cockpit. Baggage compartment behind seat.

DIMENSIONS, EXTERNAL:

Wing span	6·10 m (20 ft 0 in)
Wing chord, constant	0·97 m (3 ft 2 in)
Wing area, gross	11·43 m² (123 sq ft)
Wing aspect ratio	4·22
Length overall	4·95 m (16 ft 3 in)
Height overall	2·03 m (6 ft 8 in)
Tailplane span	2·03 m (6 ft 8 in)
Wheel track	1·22 m (4 ft 0 in)
Wheelbase	3·66 m (12 ft 0 in)

Propeller diameter	1·88 m (6 ft 2 in)
WEIGHTS:	
Weight empty	270 kg (595 lb)
Max T-O weight	406 kg (895 lb)
PERFORMANCE (prototype):	
Never-exceed speed	137 knots (253 km/h; 157 mph)
Max cruising speed, at 2,135 m (7,000 ft)	
	100 knots (185 km/h; 115 mph)
Stalling speed	38 knots (71 km/h; 44 mph)
Max rate of climb at S/L	579 m (1,900 ft)/min
Service ceiling	5,180 m (17,000 ft)
Range with max fuel	180 nm (333 km; 207 miles)

SMITH
MRS FRANK W. (DOROTHY) SMITH
3502 Sunny Hills Drive, Norco, California 91760

The late Frank W. Smith built and flew in October 1956 the prototype of a single-seat fully-aerobatic sporting biplane which he designated the DSA-1 (Darn Small Aeroplane) Miniplane. This aircraft (N90P) is now in the EAA Museum. Plans continue to be marketed by Mrs Smith, and about 450 sets have been sold to constructors in several countries. Many Miniplanes have been completed and flown.

Mrs Smith's son designed a two-seat version of the DSA-1, which was provisionally designated Miniplane + 1; all available details of this aircraft appeared in the 1974-75 *Jane's*. It was expected to make its first flight in the Spring or Summer of 1980, with a 93 kW (125 hp) Avco Lycoming engine.

SMITH DSA-1 MINIPLANE
The following details refer to the standard Miniplane, built according to Frank Smith's original plans:

TYPE: Single-seat sporting biplane.

WINGS: Braced biplane with N-type interplane struts each side and two N-type strut assemblies supporting centre of top wing above fuselage. NACA 4412 wing section.
Dihedral 2° on lower wings only. Incidence 0° on top wing, 2° on lower wings. All-wood structure, fabric-covered. Fabric-covered wooden ailerons on lower wings only. No flaps.

FUSELAGE: Welded steel tube structure, fabric-covered.

TAIL UNIT: Wire-braced welded steel tube structure, fabric-covered. Adjustable-incidence tailplane.

LANDING GEAR: Non-retractable tailwheel type. Tripod streamlined-tube main legs. Compression-spring shock-absorbers optional (now fitted on prototype). Goodyear main wheels and tyres, size 7·00-4, pressure 1·38 bars (20 lb/sq. in). Goodyear shoe-type brakes. Scott tailwheel.

POWER PLANT: Designed to take any engine in 48·5-93 kW (65-125 hp) category. Prototype has 80·5 kW (108 hp) Avco Lycoming O-235-C flat-four engine, driving a Sensenich two-blade fixed-pitch metal propeller. Most aircraft have a 48·5 kW (65 hp) Continental A65, 56 kW (75 hp) Continental A75 or 93 kW (125 hp) Avco Lycoming flat-four engine. Fuel in tank in fuselage, capacity 64·5 litres (17 US gallons). Oil capacity 5·7 litres (1·5 US gallons).

ACCOMMODATION: Single seat in open cockpit. Space for 27 kg (60 lb) baggage.

DIMENSIONS, EXTERNAL:

Wing span (upper)	5·18 m (17 ft 0 in)
Wing span (lower)	4·80 m (15 ft 9 in)
Wing chord, constant (both)	0·91 m (3 ft 0 in)
Wing area, gross	9·29 m² (100 sq ft)
Length overall	4·65 m (15 ft 3 in)
Height overall	1·52 m (5 ft 0 in)
Wheel track	1·52 m (5 ft 0 in)
Propeller diameter	1·80 m (5 ft 11 in)

WEIGHTS (prototype):	
Weight empty, equipped	279 kg (616 lb)
Max T-O weight	454 kg (1,000 lb)
PERFORMANCE (prototype, at max T-O weight):	
Max level speed at S/L	
	117 knots (217 km/h; 135 mph)
Max cruising speed	102 knots (190 km/h; 118 mph)
Econ cruising speed	96 knots (177 km/h; 110 mph)
Stalling speed	48 knots (88·5 km/h; 55 mph)
Max rate of climb at S/L	380 m (1,250 ft)/min
Service ceiling	3,960 m (13,000 ft)
T-O run	107 m (350 ft)
Landing run	152 m (500 ft)
Endurance with max fuel	2 h 30 min

SMYTH
JERRY SMYTH
ADDRESS FOR PLANS AND KITS: George Blair, PO Box 815, Newbury Park, California 91320

In February 1958 Mr Smyth began the design of a sporting monoplane, setting out to develop an aircraft that would be reasonably easy to construct, easy to fly, stressed to 9g for limited aerobatics, of good appearance and offering economic operation. Construction of the prototype began in January 1967, and occupied two years before completion, at a cost of around $2,500. First flight of what Mr Smyth named the Model 'S' Sidewinder was made on 21 February 1969, and this aircraft received the 'Outstanding Design' award at the EAA Fly-in at Rockford, Illinois, in 1969. Plans and kits of parts are available to amateur constructors.

An illustration in the 1975-76 *Jane's* showed a Sidewinder with retractable landing gear, built by Mr Donald Adams of Columbia City, Indiana. Powered, like the prototype, by a 93 kW (125 hp) Avco Lycoming O-290-G engine, the retractable gear allows a max cruising speed of 156 knots (290 km/h; 180 mph), an increase of 17 knots (32 km/h; 20 mph) by comparison with Mr Smyth's prototype.

The current illustration shows a Sidewinder built by Mr Walter Brumm of Kingston, Ontario. Powered by 100·5 kW (135 hp) Franklin O-235 engine, it is modified to have a tailwheel type landing gear.

SMYTH MODEL 'S' SIDEWINDER
The following description applies to Mr Smyth's prototype:

TYPE: Two-seat sporting monoplane.

WINGS: Cantilever low-wing monoplane. Wing section NACA 64-612 at root, NACA 64-210 at tip. Dihedral 4°. Incidence 1° 30′. No sweepback. All-metal structure comprising a centre-section and two outer wing panels. Built-up main spar of ·040 in 2024-T3 aluminium 'U'-sections, to which flat aluminium capstrips are riveted;
secondary spar is of formed sections. Eleven equally-spaced ribs in each wing panel are made of ·025 in 6061-T4 aluminium. The wing skin, of ·025 in 2024-T3 aluminium, is in three sections: leading-edge, lower and upper skin, and is flush-riveted. Wings filled with epoxy. Simple sealed-gap ailerons of aluminium construction, attached to secondary spar by piano-type hinge. No trim tabs. No flaps.

FUSELAGE: Welded steel tube structure with aluminium formers and skin. Electrically-operated speed brake may be fitted on lower fuselage.

TAIL UNIT: Cantilever all-metal structure with swept vertical surfaces. All-moving horizontal surface with electrically-operated anti-servo tab.

LANDING GEAR: Non-retractable nosewheel type. Wittman cantilever spring steel main gear. Main wheels and tyres size 5·00-5, pressure 1·72 bars (25 lb/sq in). Nose unit carries a 25·4 cm (10 in) diameter tailwheel and smooth tyre, free-castoring and non-steerable, pressure 1·72 bars (25 lb/sq in). Cleveland hydraulic brakes. Glassfibre fairings on all wheels.

POWER PLANT: Provision for installation of engines from 67-134 kW (90-180 hp). Prototype has a 93 kW (125 hp) Avco Lycoming O-290-G flat-four engine, driving a two-blade fixed-pitch aluminium propeller with spinner. Fuel tank in fuselage, forward of instrument panel, capacity 66·2 litres (17·5 US gallons). Refuelling point on top of fuselage, forward of windscreen. Provision for wingtip tanks. Oil capacity 7·5 litres (2 US gallons).

ACCOMMODATION: Pilot and passenger, seated side by side under rearward-sliding bubble canopy. Compartment for 40·8 kg (90 lb) of baggage aft of seats. Cabin heated and ventilated.

SYSTEMS: Hydraulic system for brakes and, optionally, for operation of aerodynamic speed brake. Engine-driven generator provides 35A 12V DC for instruments, lights, electrically-operated stabilator tab and optional electrically-driven hydraulic pump to operate aerodynamic speed brake.

ELECTRONICS: Simple 10-channel VHF communications transceiver.

DIMENSIONS, EXTERNAL:

Wing span	7·57 m (24 ft 10 in)
Wing chord at root	1·52 m (5 ft 0 in)
Wing chord at tip	0·91 m (3 ft 0 in)
Wing area, gross	8·92 m² (96 sq ft)
Wing aspect ratio	6·85
Length overall	5·89 m (19 ft 4 in)
Height overall	1·66 m (5 ft 5½ in)
Tailplane span	2·33 m (7 ft 7¾ in)
Wheel track	1·70 m (5 ft 7 in)
Wheelbase	1·30 m (4 ft 3 in)
Propeller diameter	1·70 m (5 ft 7 in)

DIMENSIONS, INTERNAL:	
Cabin: Max width	0·97 m (3 ft 2 in)
Baggage compartment	0·25 m³ (9 cu ft)

WEIGHTS:	
Weight empty	393 kg (867 lb)
Max T-O and landing weight	657 kg (1,450 lb)
PERFORMANCE (at max T-O weight):	
Never-exceed speed	173 knots (321 km/h; 200 mph)
Max level speed at 610 m (2,000 ft)	
	161 knots (298 km/h; 185 mph)
Max cruising speed, 75% power at 610 m (2,000 ft)	
	139 knots (257 km/h; 160 mph)
Stalling speed	48 knots (89 km/h; 55 mph)
Max rate of climb at S/L:	
at 0°C	366 m (1,200 ft)/min
at 24°C	274 m (900 ft)/min
Service ceiling	4,570 m (15,000 ft)
T-O run	244 m (800 ft)
T-O to and landing from 15 m (50 ft)	
	610 m (2,000 ft)
Landing run	457 m (1,500 ft)
Range with max fuel, no reserves	
	369 nm (684 km; 425 miles)

SORRELL
SORRELL AVIATION
Route 1, Box 660, Tenino, Washington 98589
Telephone: (206) 264 2866

Sorrell Aviation designed and built a two-seat aerobatic biplane named the SNS-6 Hiperbipe, with the intention of providing a true HIgh PERformance BIPlane that would be suitable for construction by amateurs. Flight testing confirmed that the aircraft had an outstanding aerobatic performance and, when demonstrated and displayed at the EAA 1973 Fly-in at Oshkosh, it received the Outstanding New Design of 1973 award. Plans for the fully-developed SNS-7 'production' version are not sold separately; but a basic kit package, containing construction drawings for the aircraft and certain completed components, is available.

SORRELL SNS-7 HIPERBIPE
Design of the Hiperbipe began in 1964; construction of the SNS-6 first prototype started in June 1971. This aircraft made its initial flight in March 1973; a second prototype, modified to the SNS-7 standard offered to homebuilders, followed in March 1975.

The following details refer to the second prototype:

TYPE: Two-seat aerobatic biplane.

WINGS: Braced single-bay biplane, of modified NACA 0012 wing sections. Dihedral 1° 30′ on lower wings only. Incidence 1° 30′ on upper wing, 2° 30′ on lower wings. Sweepback 4° 30′ on lower wings only. Wide-chord welded 4130 steel I-type interplane struts and dual streamline-section landing and flying wires. Conventional structure of spruce spars, web ribs and stressed plywood skin, fabric covered overall. Centre-
section of upper wing is skinned with transparent plastics to allow improved view for aerobatics. Cambered wingtips. Four full-span 'flaperons' of aluminium alloy sheet pop-riveted to aluminium torque tubes. No tabs.

FUSELAGE: Conventional structure of welded 4130 chrome-molybdenum steel tube, fabric-covered. Glassfibre engine cowling.

TAIL UNIT: Wire-braced structure of welded 4130 chrome-molybdenum steel tube, fabric-covered. Large dorsal fin. Tailplane and inset elevator extend aft of rudder trailing-edge. No tabs.

LANDING GEAR: Non-retractable tailwheel type. Wittman-type tapered spring steel rod main gear, with single wheel, glassfibre wheel fairing, and leg fairing on each unit. Cleveland 6·00-6 main wheels, with low-profile tyres. Maule 0·15 m (6 in) steerable tailwheel. Cleveland hydraulic spot disc brakes.

Smith DSA-1 Miniplane built by Mr Lee Wainscott and Mr Howard Terrill
(Continental A75 engine)

Modified Smyth Sidewinder built by Mr Walter Brumm (Franklin O-235 engine)
(Neil A. Macdougall)

Sorrell Hiperbipe two-seat aerobatic biplane (Peter M. Bowers)

The prototype of the Spencer Amphibian Air Car (Don Dwiggins)

POWER PLANT: One 134 kW (180 hp) Avco Lycoming IO-360-B1E flat-four engine, driving a Hartzell HC-C2YK-4AF two-blade constant-speed metal propeller with spinner. Fuel tank in fuselage, capacity 147·5 litres (39 US gallons). Christen 801 inverted oil system, capacity 7·5 litres (2 US gallons).

ACCOMMODATION: Two seats side by side in enclosed cabin. Dual controls standard. Forward-hinged door on each side. Baggage capacity 36 kg (80 lb). Cabin heated and ventilated.

SYSTEM: Full electrical system, with lights.

ELECTRONICS AND EQUIPMENT: Narco Com 11A 360-channel radio.

DIMENSIONS, EXTERNAL:
Wing span ... 6·96 m (22 ft 10 in)

Wing chord, constant	1·016 m (3 ft 3·9 in)
Wing area (projected)	13·9 m² (150 sq ft)
Length overall	6·35 m (20 ft 10 in)
Height overall	1·80 m (5 ft 10¾ in)
Tailplane span	2·87 m (9 ft 5 in)
Wheel track	2·16 m (7 ft 1 in)
Propeller diameter	1·93 m (6 ft 4 in)

DIMENSIONS, INTERNAL:
Cabin: Length	1·40 m (4 ft 7 in)
Max width	1·07 m (3 ft 6 in)

WEIGHTS:
Weight empty	561 kg (1,236 lb)
Max T-O weight:	
Aerobatic	766 kg (1,690 lb)
Normal	867 kg (1,911 lb)

PERFORMANCE (at max T-O weight):
Never-exceed speed	195 knots (362 km/h; 225 mph)
Max level speed at S/L	149 knots (277 km/h; 172 mph)
Max cruising speed at S/L	139 knots (257 km/h; 160 mph)
Econ cruising speed	130 knots (241 km/h; 150 mph)
Stalling speed, flaperons down	43 knots (79 km/h; 49 mph)
Stalling speed, flaperons up	51 knots (94 km/h; 58 mph)
Max rate of climb at S/L	457 m (1,500 ft)/min
Service ceiling, estimated	6,100 m (20,000 ft)
T-O run	122 m (400 ft)
Landing run	181 m (595 ft)
Range	436 nm (807 km; 502 miles)

SPENCER
P. H. SPENCER
12780 Pierce Street, Pacoima, California 91331
Telephone: (213) 899 1010

Mr P. H. Spencer, who made his first solo flight in a powered aircraft on 15 May 1914, has been associated with the design of several single-engined amphibians, dating back to 1930, when Amphibians Inc of Garden City, Long Island, NY, put the Privateer amphibian into production. This was followed by the Spencer-Larsen, Spencer Air Car S-12, Republic Seabee RC 1, RC 2 and RC 3.

All of these designs, as well as the Trident TR-1 amphibian prototype (see entry in main Canadian section), are variations of Mr Spencer's basic Air Car configuration, on which he was granted a patent on 3 January 1950. This was originally a two-seat amphibian powered by an 82 kW (110 hp) engine, and was developed into a four-seat version, known as the S-12-C. Mr Spencer then completed the design of the more advanced S-12-D, of which plans are available to homebuilders as well as certain glassfibre mouldings and metal assemblies. Since that time development has continued, the installation of a Teledyne Continental Tiara 6-285-B engine resulting in a change of designation to S-12-E for the prototype (N111DA). This had accumulated a total of 800 hours' flying time by early 1978, 450 of them with the Tiara engine. The wing sweepback has also been increased, from 3° to 5°.

By early 1980 at least 36 Air Cars were known to be under construction, with a variety of power plants ranging from 149 to 212·5 kW (200 to 285 hp), and 140 sets of plans had been sold. Air Car parts are currently being produced at a new facility at the address quoted.

The first S-12-E Air Car to be completed from Mr Spencer's plans made its first flight on 1 August 1974. Built by Mr Peter Breinig of Sausalito, California, it had logged 200 flying hours by early 1976. Four more Air Cars flew for the first time in 1975, three in 1976, at least two in 1977, and a further two or three in 1978. Five are S-12-Es,

with 212·5 kW (285 hp) Tiara engine, and five aircraft soon to fly are also powered by Tiara engines.

The Tiara 6-285-B engine has been removed from the prototype Air Car, and replaced by the 'C' model engine, of 224 kW (300 hp). Performance figures with this more powerful engine are not yet available. A second aircraft was scheduled to be fitted with a similar engine by February 1980, together with a new constant-speed reversible-pitch propeller. Developed by Hartzell, this has no slip ring beta valve assembly, so offering a much refined installation.

Mr Spencer has also designed a new biplane hydroglider named Drag-N-Fly. This aircraft made its first flight at the hands of Mr Spencer in 1977, on his 80th birthday, towed behind a motorboat. The Drag-N-Fly is not available for homebuilding; deliveries of completed aircraft began in 1979 (see Sailplanes section).

SPENCER AMPHIBIAN AIR CAR MODEL S-12-E
TYPE: Four-seat amphibian.

WINGS: Braced high-wing monoplane with single streamline-section bracing strut on each side. Specially-designed STOL wing section. Thickness/chord ratio 15%. Dihedral 1°. Incidence 2°. Sweepback at quarter-chord 5°. Conventional two-spar structure of wood, steel and glassfibre. Frise-type ailerons of wooden construction. Electrically-operated trailing-edge flaps. Glassfibre stabilising float mounted on strut beneath each wing at approximately two-thirds span.

HULL: Conventional single-stepped hull with wood frames, longerons and skin. Welded steel tube structure to provide wing and engine mounting and attachment points for landing gear.

TAIL UNIT: Cantilever structure, comprising conventional fin and rudder, and all-moving tailplane set approximately midway up fin. Combined anti-servo and trim tab in tailplane. Retractable water rudder in base of aerodynamic rudder.

LANDING GEAR: Manually-retractable tricycle type. Main wheels retract aft to take up a near-vertical position on each side of the cabin. Nosewheel retracts forward through almost 180° and is partially housed in the nose of the hull, above the waterline, to form a nose fender. Cantilever spring steel main gear. Main wheels and tyres size 7·00-6. Nosewheel and tyre size 6·00-6. Cleveland hydraulic disc brakes.

POWER PLANT: One 212·5 kW (285 hp) Teledyne Continental Tiara 6-285-B flat-six engine, driving a Hartzell three-blade constant-speed reversible-pitch metal pusher propeller. Fuel tanks in fuselage and wing stabilising floats. Total fuel capacity 355 litres (94 US gallons). Oil capacity 8·5 litres (2·25 US gallons).

ACCOMMODATION: Four seats in pairs in enclosed cabin. Backs of front seats fold forward to improve access. Rear seats fold back against bulkhead to provide cargo or baggage space. Baggage space in rear fuselage, aft of rear cabin bulkhead. Door on each side of fuselage, hinged at forward edge. Bow access door on starboard side, hinged on centreline and opening upward. Dual controls standard. Accommodation heated and ventilated.

SYSTEMS: Hydraulic system for brakes only. Electrical system supplied by 24V 50A engine-driven alternator.

ELECTRONICS AND EQUIPMENT: Complete IFR instrumentation. Bendix 360 nav/com transceiver.

DIMENSIONS, EXTERNAL:
Wing span	11·38 m (37 ft 4 in)
Wing chord, constant	1·52 m (5 ft 0 in)
Wing area, gross	17·1 m² (184 sq ft)
Wing aspect ratio	7·4
Length overall	8·05 m (26 ft 5 in)
Height overall	2·90 m (9 ft 6 in)
Tailplane span	3·66 m (12 ft 0 in)
Wheel track	2·54 m (8 ft 4 in)
Wheelbase	3·10 m (10 ft 2 in)
Propeller diameter	2·13 m (7 ft 0 in)
Cabin doors (port and starboard, each):	
Height	0·97 m (3 ft 2 in)

Width	1·02 m (3 ft 4 in)	Max width	1·14 m (3 ft 9 in)	Econ cruising speed, 65% power at 2,315 m (7,600 ft)		
Height to sill	0·86 m (2 ft 10 in)	WEIGHTS:			117 knots (217 km/h; 135 mph)	

Cabin door (bow, starboard):
Weight empty 993 kg (2,190 lb)
Length 0·89 m (2 ft 11 in)
Max T-O weight 1,451 kg (3,200 lb)
Width 0·51 m (1 ft 8 in)
PERFORMANCE (at max T-O weight):
Max level speed at S/L 128 knots (237 km/h; 147 mph)
DIMENSIONS, INTERNAL:
Max cruising speed at 1,675 m (5,500 ft)
Cabin: Length 2·59 m (8 ft 6 in)
122 knots (225 km/h; 140 mph)

Econ cruising speed, 65% power at 2,315 m (7,600 ft)
117 knots (217 km/h; 135 mph)
Stalling speed, flaps up 46 knots (86 km/h; 53 mph)
Stalling speed, 35° flap 37·5 knots (70 km/h; 43 mph)
Max rate of climb at S/L 305 m (1,000 ft)/min
T-O time from calm water at S/L 16 s
Range, 65% power at 2,375 m (7,800 ft), 20 min
reserves 695 nm (1,285 km; 800 miles)

SPEZIO
WILLIAM EDWARDS
25 Madison Avenue, Northampton, Massachusetts 01060

Tony and Dorothy Spezio designed and built a two-seat light aircraft named the Tuholer, all rights of which were acquired by Mr Edwards in August 1973. He is continuing to market plans of the Tuholer to amateur constructors.

SPEZIO DAL-1 TUHOLER
Named Tuholer because of its two open cockpits, the prototype flew for the first time on 2 May 1961.

Folding wings enable the Tuholer to be kept in a normal home garage and it is towed behind a car on its own landing gear. It can be made ready for flight by two people in about 10 minutes or by one person in 20 minutes.

The following description applies to the Tuholer built by Mr Edwards to the current plans:
TYPE: Two-seat sporting aircraft.
WINGS: Strut-braced low-wing monoplane, with streamline-section V bracing struts each side. Jury struts brace centre of these struts. Clark Y wing section.

Dihedral 3°. Incidence 1°. Washout at wingtips 1°. Two-spar spruce structure, with plywood leading-edge and overall fabric covering. Conventional wooden ailerons. Drawings for Frise type ailerons are available. No flaps. Wings fold back along sides of fuselage for stowage.
FUSELAGE: Steel tube structure with wood or light alloy stringers and fabric covering.
TAIL UNIT: Braced steel tube structure, fabric covered. Tailplane incidence adjustable by screwjack.
LANDING GEAR: Non-retractable tailwheel type. Coil spring shock-absorption. Main units fitted with Cleveland wheels and tyres, size 6·00-6. Cleveland brakes. Tyre pressure 2·76 bars (40 lb/sq in). Steerable tailwheel. Wheel fairings optional.
POWER PLANT: One 112 kW (150 hp) Avco Lycoming O-320 flat-four engine. Sensenich two-blade fixed-pitch metal propeller. Glassfibre fuel tank aft of firewall, capacity 90·5 litres (24 US gallons). Oil capacity 7·5 litres (2 US gallons).
ACCOMMODATION: Two persons in tandem in open cockpits. Small baggage compartment aft of rear seat.

EQUIPMENT: Nova-Tech TR-102 radio.
DIMENSIONS, EXTERNAL:
Wing span 7·55 m (24 ft 9 in)
Wing chord, constant 1·52 m (5 ft 0 in)
Wing area, gross 11·21 m² (120·7 sq ft)
Wing aspect ratio 5
Length overall 5·56 m (18 ft 3 in)
Height overall 1·57 m (5 ft 2 in)
Tailplane span 2·26 m (7 ft 5 in)
Wheel track 1·57 m (5 ft 2 in)
WEIGHTS:
Weight empty 408 kg (900 lb)
Max T-O weight 680 kg (1,500 lb)
PERFORMANCE (at max T-O weight):
Max level speed at S/L
130 knots (241 km/h; 150 mph)
Cruising speed
109-117 knots (201-217 km/h; 125-135 mph)
Stalling speed 48 knots (89 km/h; 55 mph)
Max rate of climb at S/L 732 m (2,400 ft)/min
T-O and landing run 61 m (200 ft)
Endurance with max fuel 3 h

SPORT AIR CRAFT
SPORT AIR CRAFT INTERNATIONAL
PO Box 1, Hillsboro, Oregon 97123
Telephone: (503) 985 7612
PROPRIETOR: Bill W. Johnson

Known originally as Chris Tena Aircraft Association, this concern is responsible for a lightweight all-metal single-seat sporting aircraft known as the Mini Coupe. Design originated in June 1968, and construction of the first prototype began in July 1970. This aircraft made its first flight in September 1971 and FAA certification in the Experimental category was awarded on 2 June 1972. Kits of components and materials for two alternative versions, less engine, are available to amateur constructors. Building of the Mini Coupe has now been approved also in Australia and Switzerland, where aircraft are being constructed.

SPORT AIR CRAFT MINI COUPE
Glassfibre wingtips have been added to the Mini Coupe since its early testing, to increase the wing area by 0·47 m² (5·1 sq ft). This improves the glide ratio, makes the aircraft more stable during banks, and has reduced stalling speed. A total of 270 sets of plans of the Mini Coupe had been sold by early 1980, when about 60 aircraft were known to be flying.

There are two versions, as follows:
Mini Coupe. Basic model, similar to prototype, with tricycle landing gear and twin-fin tail unit. Most amateur-built Mini Coupes are of this type.
Mini Coupe TD. Generally similar to basic model, but with tailwheel landing gear and single fin and rudder. First TD was completed by Mr E. Argence of New Orleans, Louisiana, on 1 June 1977.
TYPE: Single-seat lightweight sporting aircraft.

WINGS: Cantilever low-wing monoplane. Wing section modified Clark Y. Thickness/chord ratio 7%. Incidence 0°. Conventional metal stressed-skin structure of constant chord, with glassfibre wingtips. Plain all-metal ailerons. No flaps. No trim tabs.
FUSELAGE: All-metal semi-monocoque structure.
TAIL UNIT: Cantilever all-metal structure with twin end-plate fins and rudders of constant chord. Fixed-incidence tailplane. Manually controlled trim tab in centre of elevator. Alternative single fin and rudder configuration available on Mini Coupe TD.
LANDING GEAR: Non-retractable tricycle type. Shock-absorption on all units depends on use of oversize tyres. Main wheels with tyres size 14 × 6·00-6, pressure 0·55 bars (8 lb/sq in). Nosewheel tyre size 12 × 6·00-5, pressure 0·34 bars (5 lb/sq in). Asuze drum and band brakes. Alternative non-retractable tailwheel type, with faired main wheels, on Mini Coupe TD.
POWER PLANT: One 48·5 kW (65 hp) modified Volkswagen 1,600 cc motor car engine, driving a Reese-Shores two-blade fixed-pitch wooden propeller. (Two aircraft fitted with 48·5 kW; 65 hp Continental.) One metal fuel tank in fuselage, immediately aft of firewall, capacity 49 litres (13 US gallons). Refuelling point on fuselage upper surface, forward of windscreen.
ACCOMMODATION: Single seat for pilot in open cockpit. Transparent cockpit canopy optional. Baggage compartment aft of headrest, volume 0·085 m³ (3 cu ft).
SYSTEM: Provision for electrical system, for engine starter and radio.
DIMENSIONS, EXTERNAL:
Wing span 7·32 m (24 ft 0 in)
Wing chord, constant 1·07 m (3 ft 6 in)
Wing area, gross 7·76 m² (83·5 sq ft)
Length overall 4·98 m (16 ft 4 in)

Height overall 1·80 m (5 ft 11 in)
Tailplane span 1·83 m (6 ft 0 in)
Wheel track 1·83 m (6 ft 0 in)
Wheelbase (tricycle landing gear) 0·97 m (3 ft 2 in)
Propeller diameter 1·37 m (4 ft 6 in)
WEIGHTS (A: tricycle landing gear; B: tailwheel landing gear):
Weight empty: A 225 kg (497 lb)
B 241 kg (532 lb)
Max T-O weight: A 385 kg (850 lb)
B 408 kg (900 lb)
PERFORMANCE (at max T-O weight with 1,600 cc engine; A and B as above):
Never-exceed speed:
A, B 125 knots (231 km/h; 145 mph)
Max level speed at 610 m (2,000 ft):
A 91 knots (169 km/h; 105 mph)
B 118 knots (219 km/h; 136 mph)
Max cruising speed at 610 m (2,000 ft):
A 78 knots (145 km/h; 90 mph)
B 100 knots (185 km/h; 115 mph)
Stalling speed, power off:
A 42 knots (78 km/h; 48 mph)
B 50·5 knots (94 km/h; 58 mph)
Stalling speed, power on:
A, B 38 knots (70 km/h; 43 mph)
Max rate of climb at S/L: A 229 m (750 ft)/min
B 305 m (1,000 ft)/min
Service ceiling: A, B 3,810 m (12,500 ft)
T-O run: A, B 122 m (400 ft)
T-O to 15 m (50 ft): A, B 274 m (900 ft)
Landing from 15 m (50 ft): A, B 274 m (900 ft)
Landing run: A, B 152 m (500 ft)
Range with max fuel, 20 min reserves:
A, B 260 nm (482 km; 300 miles)

SPRATT
SPRATT AND COMPANY INC
PO Box 351, Media, Pennsylvania 19063

Mr George G. Spratt, formerly a design engineer with The Boeing Company and Consolidated Vultee (now Convair Division of General Dynamics), has completed more than 30 years' work on developing a two-piece movable-wing control system, which he claims provides improved safety factors compared with the conventional aileron, elevator and rudder control system.

While he was with Consolidated Vultee, Mr Spratt designed a roadable aircraft which featured an earlier version of his wing control system, but this did not enter production. Since that time Mr Spratt has concentrated on perfecting his idea as a private venture.

To flight test his movable-wing control system, Mr Spratt built a lightweight experimental flying-boat (N910Z) constructed almost entirely of moulded plastics; details of this can be found in the 1974-75 *Jane's*. Two further designs have followed, and plans of the Model 107 movable-wing flying-boat are available to amateur constructors. Details of the Model 105 landplane can be found in the 1979-80 *Jane's*.

SPRATT MODEL 107
Following construction and flight testing of his first experimental flying-boat, Mr Spratt designed and constructed a more advanced prototype known as the Model

107 (N2236) for public demonstration. Dimensions and weights are essentially the same as those of the test vehicle, but construction has been simplified to facilitate fabrication. The Mercury 800 modified outboard marine engine of the Model 107 is of slightly increased capacity, and produces greater horsepower with better fuel economy as a result of improved combustion chamber and inlet port design.

Mr Spratt claims that the Model 107 will neither stall nor spin, and displays 75% less reaction to turbulence than a conventional design.

Plans of this aircraft are available to amateur constructors. By early 1980 more than 80 sets had been sold, and the first amateur-built Model 107 flew in the Autumn of 1975.

Details have been received of a new hull that has been constructed for the Model 107. It is made from PVC foam, with Kevlar skin, coated with epoxy resin. Flight testing began in Spring 1979. Power for the new Model 107 is being provided by a Mercury 850 modified outboard marine engine.

The following data apply to the original version:
TYPE: Two-seat lightweight flying-boat.
WINGS: Pivoted controllable parasol wings, with inverted V bracing struts each side. Wing section NACA 23112. No dihedral. No sweepback. Reinforced plastics structure. No ailerons, flaps or trim tabs. Flying controls so arranged that the wings are allowed to move freely and

collectively in incidence, while their incidence is controlled differentially by a steering wheel. The wings' angle of attack can be adjusted by a separate control.
HULL: Structure of polyurethane foam with reinforced plastics skin. Small water rudder interconnected with the control wheel.
TAIL UNIT: Butterfly-type tail unit, with no movable surfaces, constructed of reinforced plastics.
POWER PLANT: One 59·7 kW (80 hp) Mercury 800 modified outboard two-stroke marine engine, driving a two-blade plastics pusher propeller through an extended drive shaft, which locates the propeller between the butterfly tail surfaces. The pitch of the propeller, which is of Mr Spratt's design, is adjustable on the ground. Outboard engine type of fuel tank.
ACCOMMODATION: Two persons side by side, in open cockpit.
DIMENSIONS, EXTERNAL:
Wing span 7·32 m (24 ft 0 in)
Wing chord, constant 1·22 m (4 ft 0 in)
Wing area, gross 8·92 m² (96 sq ft)
Wing aspect ratio 6
Length overall 5·18 m (17 ft 0 in)
Height overall 1·52 m (5 ft 0 in)
Propeller diameter 1·52 m (5 ft 0 in)
WEIGHTS:
Weight empty 226 kg (500 lb)
Max T-O weight 453 kg (1,000 lb)

Spezio Tuholer two-seat sporting aircraft

Sport Air Craft Mini Coupe single-seat sporting aircraft

Spratt Model 107 two-seat movable-wing flying-boat

Statler Firefly homebuilt two-seat light monoplane *(Don Dwiggins)*

The first Steen Skybolt built and flown outside the USA and Canada, constructed by Mr W. R Penaluna of Cornwall, England. Power plant is a 123 kW (165 hp) Rolls-Royce Continental IO-346A

STATLER
WILLIAM H. STATLER
9300 Encino Avenue, Northridge, California 91325
Telephone: (213) 886 1854

While employed as an aeronautical engineer with Lockheed, from 1940 to 1972, Mr Statler built his first two homebuilt aircraft, Formula One racers known as *Ginny* and *Skeeter*. Following his retirement from Lockheed, he began work, in January 1973, on a two-seat homebuilt aircraft capable of limited aerobatic flying. Construction of what became the Firefly started in June 1973, with the help of Byrl Robinson and Claude Fiske. The Firefly was rolled out in May 1976, when taxying trials began. The first flight, piloted by Al Foss, took place on 8 October 1976.

Plans and a construction manual are available to amateur builders and 65 sets had been sold by early 1980. Meantime, work has begun on an Unlimited Class racing aircraft, of which no details are currently available.

STATLER FIREFLY
TYPE: Two-seat light monoplane.
WINGS: Cantilever low-wing monoplane. Wing section NACA 2412. Dihedral 5°. Incidence 2°. No sweepback. All-metal construction, with aluminium ribs and skins, flush-riveted. Glassfibre wingtips. All-metal ailerons and electrically-actuated plain trailing-edge flaps.

Ground-adjustable tab on starboard aileron. Wings detachable for transportation.
FUSELAGE: All-metal semi-monocoque structure, with flush-riveted aluminium skin. Glassfibre engine cowl.
TAIL UNIT: Cantilever all-metal structure, with swept vertical surfaces. Fixed tailplane set at −3° incidence. Trim tab on elevator, controllable from either cockpit.
LANDING GEAR: Non-retractable tricycle type. Cantilever spring main units made from a single piece of aluminium. Ercoupe nosewheel, on oleo strut. Mainwheel tyres size 12 × 6·00-6, pressure 1·93 bars (28 lb/sq in). Nosewheel tyre size 10 × 5·00-5, pressure 1·93 bars (28 lb/sq in). Gerdes hydraulic brakes. Glassfibre wheel fairings.
POWER PLANT: One 63·5 kW (85 hp) Continental C85-12F flat-four engine, driving two-blade Wayne's Woodcraft fixed-pitch 62 × 54 propeller. Two interconnected fuel tanks in fuselage, total capacity 68 litres (18 US gallons). Refuelling point on forward tank. Oil capacity 5·7 litres (6 US quarts).
ACCOMMODATION: Two seats in tandem, under GB bubble canopy which is hinged on starboard side. Baggage compartment, capacity 22·6 kg (60 lb), in turtleback aft of rear cockpit.
SYSTEMS: Hydraulic system for brakes. Electrical system includes engine-driven generator and 12V 35Ah battery for engine starting, wing flap actuation and instruments.
ELECTRONICS: Bayside portable transceiver.

DIMENSIONS, EXTERNAL:
Wing span	5·84 m (19 ft 2 in)
Wing chord, constant	1·27 m (4 ft 2 in)
Wing area, gross	7·43 m² (80 sq ft)
Wing aspect ratio	4·6
Length overall	5·77 m (18 ft 11 in)
Height overall	2·15 m (7 ft 0½ in)
Tailplane span	2·82 m (9 ft 3 in)
Wheel track	1·37 m (4 ft 6 in)
Wheelbase	1·50 m (4 ft 11 in)
Propeller diameter	1·57 m (5 ft 2 in)

WEIGHTS:
Weight empty	379 kg (835 lb)
Max T-O weight	590 kg (1,300 lb)

PERFORMANCE:
Never-exceed speed	208 knots (386 km/h; 240 mph)
Max cruising speed at S/L	139 knots (257 km/h; 160 mph)
Econ cruising speed at 1,980 m (6,500 ft)	124 knots (230 km/h; 143 mph)
Stalling speed, flaps up	55 knots (102 km/h; 63 mph)
Max rate of climb at S/L	244 m (800 ft)/min
Service ceiling	4,875 m (16,000 ft)
T-O run	283 m (930 ft)
T-O to 15 m (50 ft)	354 m (1,160 ft)
Landing from 15 m (50 ft)	488 m (1,600 ft)
Landing run	152 m (500 ft)
Range with max fuel, no reserves	347 nm (643 km; 400 miles)

STEEN
STEEN AERO LAB INC
15623 De Gaulle Circle, Brighton, Colorado 80601
Telephone: (303) 659 7182

Mr Lamar Steen, an aerospace teacher in a Denver, Colorado, high school, designed a two-seat fully-aerobatic biplane named Skybolt which was built as a class project in the school. Simplicity of construction was a primary aim of the design, begun in June 1968, and it is stressed to +12 and −10g. Construction began on 19 August 1969, costing approximately $5,000, and the first flight was made in October 1970. The Skybolt received an EAA award for Best School Project. Plans are available to amateur constructors, together with fuselage and wing kits; over 2,000 sets of plans have been sold and many Skybolts are flying.

STEEN SKYBOLT
The following description applies to the prototype with 134 kW (180 hp) Avco Lycoming engine, built under Mr Steen's supervision:
TYPE: Two-seat aerobatic biplane.
WINGS: Braced biplane with single interplane strut each side. N-type centre-section struts. Streamline-section

landing and flying wires. Wing sections: upper wing NACA 63₂A015, lower wing NACA 0012. Dihedral 0° on upper wing, 2° 30′ on lower wings. Incidence (both) 1° 30′. Sweepback 6° on upper wing only. Wooden two-spar structures with spruce spars, built-up ribs and fabric covering. Fabric-covered Frise-type ailerons on upper and lower wings. Cutout in centre-section trailing-edge of upper wing.
FUSELAGE: Welded structure of 4130 chrome-molybdenum steel tube, with fabric covering.
TAIL UNIT: Wire-braced welded structure of 4130 chrome-molybdenum steel tube, with fabric covering. Adjustable trim tab in port elevator.
LANDING GEAR: Non-retractable main wheels and tailwheel. Two side Vs and half axles hinged to fuselage structure. Shock-absorption by rubber bungee. Cleveland wheels with tyres size 6·00-6, pressure 1·72 bars (25 lb/sq in). Cleveland hydraulic disc brakes. Glassfibre fairings for main wheels.
POWER PLANT: One 134 kW (180 hp) Avco Lycoming HO-360-B1B flat-four engine, driving a McCauley two-blade fixed-pitch propeller with spinner. Provision for alternative engines of 93-194 kW (125-260 hp).

Fuselage fuel tank, immediately aft of firewall, capacity 110 litres (29 US gallons). Optional tank of 37·8 litres (10 US gallons) capacity can be installed in centre-section of upper wing. Total optional fuel capacity 151·2 litres (40 US gallons). Refuelling points on fuselage upper surface, forward of windscreen, and on top surface of upper wing. Oil capacity 7·5 litres (2 US gallons).
ACCOMMODATION: Two seats in open cockpits. Provision for canopy over rear cockpit. Space for 13·6 kg (30 lb) baggage aft of rear seat.
SYSTEM: Hydraulic system for brakes only.
ELECTRONICS: Battery-powered Alpha 200 nav/com transceiver.

DIMENSIONS, EXTERNAL:
Wing span, upper	7·32 m (24 ft 0 in)
Wing span, lower	7·01 m (23 ft 0 in)
Wing chord, constant (both)	1·07 m (3 ft 6 in)
Wing area, gross	14·2 m² (152·7 sq ft)
Length overall	5·79 m (19 ft 0 in)
Height overall	2·13 m (7 ft 0 in)
Propeller diameter	1·88 m (6 ft 2 in)

WEIGHTS:
Weight empty	490 kg (1,080 lb)

Max T-O weight	748 kg (1,650 lb)	Cruising speed	113 knots (209 km/h; 130 mph)	Service ceiling	5,500 m (18,000 ft)
PERFORMANCE (at max T-O weight):		Landing speed	43 knots (80·5 km/h; 50 mph)	T-O run	122 m (400 ft)
Max level speed	126 knots (233 km/h; 145 mph)	Max rate of climb at S/L	762 m (2,500 ft)/min	Range with max fuel	390 nm (720 km; 450 miles)

STEPHENS

STEPHENS AIRCRAFT

ADDRESS FOR PLANS: Gerry Zimmerman, 8563 West
Sixty-Eighth Place, Arvada, Colorado 80004

Mr C. L. Stephens designed a single-seat aerobatic
monoplane specifically for homebuilders who wish to own
an aircraft for competitive aerobatics. The prototype,
designated Model A, was designed for Margaret Ritchie,
US National Women's Aerobatic Champion in 1966, and
the second aircraft, the Model B, for Dean S. Engelhardt
of Garden Grove, California.

Stressed to +12g and −11g, it was the first US aircraft
known to be designed around the Aresti Aerocriptografic
System for competitive aerobatics. All control surfaces are
fully static-balanced and the entire aircraft comes very
close to being aerodynamically symmetrical. Design of the
Model A started in July 1966 and construction of the
prototype began a month later. First flight of this version
was made on 27 July 1967, and of the **Model B**, with wings
and ailerons of increased area and reduced fuel tankage,
on 9 July 1969. Plans of the Stephens Akro are available to
amateur constructors.

STEPHENS AKRO

The following description applies to the prototype with
134 kW (180 hp) Avco Lycoming engine:

TYPE: Single-seat sporting monoplane.

WINGS: Cantilever mid-wing monoplane. Wing section
NACA 23012. No dihedral, incidence or sweepback.
All-wood two-spar structure. One-piece wing, with
solid spar passing through fuselage and positioned by
means of removable top longeron sections. Rear spar in
two pieces. No internal wires or compression struts.
Wing covered with mahogany skin. Plain ailerons have a
4130 steel spar, and spruce ribs and trailing-edge, and
are fabric-covered. Ground-adjustable trim tabs on
ailerons, which are statically balanced. No flaps.

FUSELAGE: Welded 4130 steel tube structure, mostly of
0·75 in outside diameter tubing, with Ceconite covering.

TAIL UNIT: Wire-braced welded 4130 steel tube structure
with swept surfaces, fabric-covered. Tailplane has variable incidence. Ground-adjustable trim tab on rudder;
controllable trim tab in elevator. All control surfaces
statically balanced.

LANDING GEAR: Non-retractable tailwheel type. Cantilever spring steel main gear. Goodyear main wheels
and tyres size 5·00-5, pressure 1·93 bars (28 lb/sq in).
Cleveland disc brakes. Maule steerable tailwheel.
Glassfibre fairings on main wheels.

POWER PLANT: One 134 kW (180 hp) Avco Lycoming
AIO-360-A1A flat-four engine, driving a Sensenich
Type 7660 two-blade fixed-pitch metal propeller.
Model A has a fuel system for prolonged inverted flight,
Model B has both fuel and oil system so modified.
Model B can also have optional constant-speed propel-
ler. Fuel tank in fuselage, forward of instrument panel.
Model A has fuel capacity of 121 litres (32 US gallons),
Model B has capacity of 102 litres (27 US gallons).
Refuelling point on top of fuselage, forward of
windscreen. Oil capacity 7·5 litres (2 US gallons).

ACCOMMODATION: Single seat for pilot under rearward-
sliding bubble canopy. Large window in underfuselage,
forward of control column. Model B has, in addition, a
quarter window on each side of the fuselage, beneath the
wings. Forced-air ventilation.

SYSTEM: Hydraulic system for brakes only.

ELECTRONICS: Battery-operated Bayside transceiver.

DIMENSIONS, EXTERNAL:	
Wing span	7·47 m (24 ft 6 in)
Wing chord at root	1·60 m (5 ft 3 in)
Wing chord at tip: Model A	0·76 m (2 ft 6 in)
Model B	0·91 m (3 ft 0 in)
Wing area, gross: Model A	8·73 m² (94 sq ft)
Model B	9·29 m² (100 sq ft)
Length overall	5·82 m (19 ft 1 in)
Height overall	1·73 m (5 ft 8 in)
Tailplane span	2·44 m (8 ft 0 in)
Wheel track	1·37 m (4 ft 6 in)
Propeller diameter	1·93 m (6 ft 4 in)

WEIGHTS:	
Weight empty: Model A	385 kg (850 lb)
Model B	431 kg (950 lb)
Max T-O weight: Model A	544 kg (1,200 lb)
Model B	589 kg (1,300 lb)

PERFORMANCE (at 544 kg; 1,200 lb T-O weight):

Never-exceed speed	191 knots (354 km/h; 220 mph)
Max level speed at 610 m (2,000 ft)	148 knots (274 km/h; 170 mph)
Max cruising speed at 610 m (2,000 ft)	139 knots (257 km/h; 160 mph)
Econ cruising speed at 610 m (2,000 ft)	109 knots (201 km/h; 125 mph)
Stalling speed	48 knots (89 km/h; 55 mph)
Max rate of climb at S/L	1,220 m (4,000 ft)/min
Service ceiling	6,705 m (22,000 ft)
T-O run	61 m (200 ft)
T-O to 15 m (50 ft)	122 m (400 ft)
Landing from 15 m (50 ft)	457 m (1,500 ft)
Landing run	183 m (600 ft)
Range with max fuel	303 nm (563 km; 350 miles)

STEWART

STEWART AIRCRAFT CORPORATION

11420 State Route 165, Salem, Ohio 44460
Telephone: (216) 332 0865

Mr Donald Stewart formed this company to market
plans of a simple single-seat light aircraft named the
Headwind, of which he designed and built a prototype.
During 1969 he designed a new wing for the Headwind
and this is an integral part of the plans available to
homebuilders. A two-seat version is under construction,
and by early 1979 the wings, ailerons, fuselage and vertical
tail surfaces had been completed. Mr Stewart expected to
power this aircraft with either a 44·5 kW (60 hp) Franklin
or 1,600 cc Volkswagen modified motor car engine with
Maximizer. No more recent news has been received concerning progress with the project.

Work on the original single-seat Headwind was followed by design and construction of the JD₂FF Foo Fighter, which is described separately.

Latest of Mr Stewart's projects is a foot-launched ultra-
light aircraft, with wings that can be dismounted in 5
minutes, without tools. Power will be provided by a 7·45
kW (10 hp) Chrysler engine with Maximizer. Empty
weight will be 43·5 kg (96 lb), max T-O weight 159 kg
(350 lb), cruising speed 43·5-48 knots (80·5-88·5 km/h;
50-55 mph) and landing speed 10·5-13 knots (19·5-24
km/h; 12-15 mph).

STEWART JD₁ HW 1·7 HEADWIND

Built in only five months, the prototype Headwind flew
for the first time on 28 March 1962, and has since undergone considerable refinement. Plans are available to
amateur constructors, who can build the aircraft with
either an open or enclosed cockpit. The wings can be
removed or fitted in about 20 minutes by two people.

The power plant of the prototype Headwind has a belt-
driven propeller reduction drive designed by Mr Stewart.
Given the name Maximizer, this unit was put into production in the Spring of 1972 and is available to amateur
constructors for use with Volkswagen power plants.

Several thousand sets of plans for the Headwind have
been sold. About 250 aircraft are believed to be under
construction, with approximately 30 already flying, including examples in Mexico and South Africa.

TYPE: Single-seat light aircraft.

WINGS: Strut-braced high-wing monoplane, with
streamline-section V bracing strut each side. Wing section NACA 4412. Dihedral 2°. Incidence 2°. Two
spruce spars, steel tube compression members, drag and
anti-drag wires, plywood ribs, fabric covering. Frise-
type ailerons of similar construction to wings. No flaps.

FUSELAGE: Welded steel tube structure, fabric-covered.

TAIL UNIT: Braced steel tube structure, fabric-covered.
Ground-adjustable tailplane incidence. Fixed tabs on
rudder and starboard elevator.

LANDING GEAR: Non-retractable tailwheel type. Shock-
absorption by low-pressure tyres. Hayes main wheels
with Goodyear tyres size 8·00-4. Tyre pressure 0·83
bars (12 lb/sq in). Alternatively, rubber-in-compression
shock-struts, with Cleveland or Goodyear wheels and
tyres size 6·00-6, tyre pressure 1·24 bars (18 lb/sq in).
No brakes. Steerable tailwheel.

POWER PLANT: One 27 kW (36 hp) modified Volkswagen
1,192 cc motor car engine, driving a special
Stewart/Kirk two-blade fixed-pitch propeller via a
Stewart belt-driven reduction unit, ratio 1·6 : 1. Engines
weighing up to 84 kg (185 lb) can be utilised. Fuel tank
aft of firewall, capacity 19 litres (5 US gallons). Oil
capacity 2·4 litres (5 US pints).

ACCOMMODATION: Single seat in open or enclosed cockpit,
with door on starboard side. Provision for up to 4·5 kg
(10 lb) baggage in net, directly aft of cockpit.

DIMENSIONS, EXTERNAL:	
Wing span	8·61 m (28 ft 3 in)
Wing chord, constant	1·22 m (4 ft 0 in)
Wing area, gross	10·3 m² (110·95 sq ft)
Wing aspect ratio	7
Length overall	5·41 m (17 ft 9 in)
Height overall	1·68 m (5 ft 6 in)
Tailplane span	2·13 m (7 ft 0 in)
Wheel track	1·52 m (5 ft 0 in)
Wheelbase	4·11 m (13 ft 6 in)
Propeller diameter	1·57 m (5 ft 2 in)

WEIGHTS:	
Weight empty	198 kg (437 lb)
Max T-O and landing weight	317 kg (700 lb)

PERFORMANCE (at max T-O weight):

Never-exceed speed	95·5 knots (177 km/h; 110 mph)
Max level speed at S/L	69·5 knots (129 km/h; 80 mph)
Cruising speed	65 knots (121 km/h; 75 mph)
Stalling speed	32-33 knots (58-61 km/h; 36-38 mph)
Max rate of climb at S/L	122 m (400 ft)/min
Absolute ceiling	3,355 m (11,000 ft)
T-O run	91 m (300 ft)
T-O to 15 m (50 ft)	365 m (1,200 ft)
Landing from 15 m (50 ft)	490 m (1,600 ft)
Landing run	137 m (450 ft)
Endurance with max fuel, no reserves	2½ h

STEWART JD₂FF FOO FIGHTER

Design of Mr Stewart's Foo Fighter began in October
1967 and the first prototype (N2123) made its first flight in
June 1971 powered by a six-cylinder Ford Falcon motorcar engine developing 89·5 kW (120 hp) at 3,800 rpm.
This engine was replaced subsequently by a 93 kW (125
hp) Franklin Sport 4.

A second prototype of the Foo Fighter (N2124), with a
93 kW (125 hp) Avco Lycoming engine, was sold for
exhibition flights at Lafayette Escadrille 76 in Pennsylvania. During 1972, Mr Stewart designed new wings for
the Foo Fighter, of increased span and chord. Since that
time he has modified the design to allow for installation of
Avco Lycoming flat-four engines of up to 112 kW (150
hp), and has made refinements to the fuselage, tail unit and
landing gear. Sets of plans of the Foo Fighter are available
to amateur constructors. About 85 examples are thought
to be under construction, and one Foo Fighter has been
completed in Connecticut, reportedly with a Continental
C90 flat-four engine.

The following description is applicable to the aircraft in
fully-updated form:

TYPE: Single-seat lightweight sporting biplane.

WINGS: Braced single-bay biplane. Wing section NACA
4412. Dihedral 0° upper wing, 1° lower wing. Incidence
2° upper wing, 0° lower wing. Conventional structure
with two wooden spars and wooden truss ribs, fabric-
covered. N-type interplane struts each side; two N-type
struts, joined at their upper ends, support the centre of
the upper wing above fuselage. The lower wing extends
below the fuselage, being attached to a cabane, and is
faired over with light gauge light alloy sheet.
Streamline-section landing and flying wires. Cutout in
trailing-edges of both wings. Frise-type ailerons of similar construction to wings. No flaps. No trim tabs.

FUSELAGE: Welded steel tube structure with wood formers
and stringers, fabric-covered.

TAIL UNIT: Wire-braced welded steel tube structure with
fabric covering. Tailplane incidence adjustable on
ground or, optionally, controllable in flight. Fixed tab in
starboard elevator.

LANDING GEAR: Non-retractable tailwheel type, with
steerable tailwheel or tailskid. Two side Vs with half-
axles attached to fuselage structure. Shock-absorption
by rubber cords in tension. Stewart wheels with tyres
size 3·00-16, pressure 2·76 bars (40 lb/sq in). Stewart
mechanical band brakes.

POWER PLANT: One 93 kW (125 hp) Franklin Sport 4
flat-four engine, driving a two-blade fixed-pitch wooden
propeller. Provision for Avco Lycoming flat-four engine
of up to 112 kW (150 hp). Fuel contained in aluminium
tank mounted in fuselage immediately aft of firewall,
capacity 72 litres (19 US gallons). Refuelling point on
fuselage upper surface. Oil capacity 3·75 litres (1 US
gallon).

ACCOMMODATION: Single seat in open cockpit. Space for
4·5 kg (10 lb) baggage aft of seat.

DIMENSIONS, EXTERNAL:	
Wing span (both)	6·30 m (20 ft 8 in)
Wing chord, constant (both)	1·02 m (3 ft 4 in)
Wing area, gross	12·08 m² (130 sq ft)
Wing aspect ratio	6·075
Length overall	5·72 m (18 ft 9 in)
Height overall	2·13 m (7 ft 0 in)
Tailplane span	1·93 m (6 ft 4 in)
Wheel track	1·75 m (5 ft 9 in)
Wheelbase	3·76 m (12 ft 4 in)
Propeller diameter	1·83 m (6 ft 0 in)

WEIGHTS:	
Weight empty	328 kg (725 lb)
Max T-O weight	499 kg (1,100 lb)

PERFORMANCE (at max T-O weight):

Never-exceed speed	126 knots (233 km/h; 145 mph)
Max cruising speed	100 knots (185 km/h; 115 mph)
Stalling speed	42 knots (77·5 km/h; 48 mph)
Max rate of climb at S/L	366 m (1,200 ft)/min
T-O run	137 m (450 ft)
Landing run	168 m (550 ft)

Stephens Akro registered in the UK (*J. M. G. Gradidge*)

Stewart Headwind built by Mr Richard F. Geide Jr of Wichita, Kansas
(Volkswagen modified motor car engine)

Stolp Starduster Too with Continental W-670 radial engine (*J. M. G. Gradidge*)

Stewart JD₂FF Foo Fighter (Franklin Sport 4 engine) (*Howard Levy*)

Stolp SA-500 Starlet built in England by Mr S. S. Miles (*Air Portraits*)

Stolp SA-900 V-Star (Avco Lycoming O-290-D2 engine) (*Howard Levy*)

Stolp SA-700 Acroduster 1 (Avco Lycoming IO-360-A1A engine) (*Howard Levy*)

SA-750 Acroduster Too built by Mr Jim Osborne, President of Stolp Starduster
Corporation (Avco Lycoming IO-540-N1A5 engine) (*Howard Levy*)

STOLP
STOLP STARDUSTER CORPORATION
4301 Twining, Riverside, California 92509
Telephone: (714) 686 7943
PRESIDENT: Jim Osborne
GENERAL MANAGER: Eric Shilling
SECRETARY-TREASURER: Hanako Osborne

Mr Louis A. Stolp and Mr George M. Adams designed and built a light single-seat sporting biplane known as the Starduster, which flew for the first time in November 1957; and founded Stolp Starduster Corporation to market to amateur constructors plans, components and basic materials for the Starduster and subsequent designs. On 1 May 1972 this company was acquired by Jim and Hanako Osborne, who continue to trade under the original name.

Plans of the SA-100 Starduster are no longer available; but the company continues to market plans, kits and materials for the two-seat Starduster Too, single-seat Starlet, aerobatic V-Star, Acroduster 1 and Acroduster Too. In addition, it is marketing plans for a replica of the Fokker D.VII, the G/B Special designed by Glenn Beets and the Knight Twister designed by Vernon Payne.

STOLP SA-300 STARDUSTER TOO
The SA-300 Starduster Too is an enlarged two-seat version of the original SA-100 Starduster, and is suitable for engines of 93-194 kW (125-260 hp). The weight and performance figures quoted apply to the example registered N2MR, which won the Grand Champion award at the 1977 EAA Fly-in at Oshkosh and was illustrated in the 1979-80 *Jane's*. It has a 149 kW (200 hp) Avco Lycoming HIO-360-A1A engine, driving a McCauley constant-speed propeller.

Some Starduster Toos, including that illustrated, have radial engines. N9JR, built by Mr J. Ruddy, has a Continental W-670 engine. Another, illustrated in the 1973-74 *Jane's*, has a 123 kW (165 hp) Warner Super Scarab engine.

TYPE: Two-seat sporting biplane.
WINGS: Biplane wings of unequal span with a single interplane strut each side. Multiple centre-section bracing struts. Streamline section landing and flying wires. Wing section M-6 modified. Dihedral 1° 30′ on lower wings only. Incidence 1° on lower wings only. Sweepback on leading-edge of upper wing 6°. All-wood structure with spruce spars and ribs of 6·5 mm (¼ in) plywood, fabric-covered. Ailerons of wooden construction, fabric-covered, on both upper and lower wings. No trailing-edge flaps.
FUSELAGE: Welded 4130 steel tube structure with fabric covering. Glassfibre turtleback.

TAIL UNIT: Welded 4130 steel tube structure with fabric covering. Wire-braced fixed-incidence tailplane.
LANDING GEAR: Non-retractable tailwheel type. Rubber cord shock-absorption. Wheel fairings on main units. Hydraulic brakes.
POWER PLANT (prototype): One 134 kW (180 hp) Avco Lycoming O-360-A1A flat-four engine, driving a two-blade fixed-pitch propeller with spinner. Fuel tank in fuselage, immediately aft of firewall.
ACCOMMODATION: Two seats in tandem open cockpits.
DIMENSIONS, EXTERNAL:
Wing span, upper	7·32 m (24 ft 0 in)
Wing chord, constant (both)	1·22 m (4 ft 0 in)
Length overall	6·63 m (21 ft 9 in)
Height overall	2·21 m (7 ft 3 in)

WEIGHTS:
Weight empty	517 kg (1,139 lb)
Max T-O weight	907 kg (2,000 lb)

PERFORMANCE (at max T-O weight, except where stated):
Max level speed	174 knots (322 km/h; 200 mph)
Max cruising speed	133 knots (246 km/h; 153 mph)
Econ cruising speed	100 knots (185 km/h; 115 mph)
Stalling speed	51 knots (94 km/h; 58 mph)
Sustained rate of climb, pilot only	548 m (1,800 ft)/min

STOLP SA-500 STARLET

The SA-500 Starlet is a single-seat swept parasol-wing monoplane. The wing is of wooden construction with spruce spars, plywood web and capstrip ribs, with Dacron covering. It has a Clark YH section; sweepback is 9° and incidence 3° 30'. The fuselage is of welded 4130 steel tube with Dacron covering, and the tail unit is a braced structure of the same materials. The non-retractable tailwheel-type landing gear has cantilever main legs with wheel fairings. Power plant in the prototype consists of a 1,500 cc Volkswagen flat-four engine, driving a fixed-pitch two-blade propeller with spinner. Other engines of 63·5-93 kW (85-125 hp) may be fitted, the 80·5 kW (108 hp) Avco Lycoming being recommended.

Construction of the prototype occupied three months and cost $1,500. First flight was made on 1 June 1969. The following details refer to the prototype:

DIMENSIONS, EXTERNAL:
Wing span	7·62 m (25 ft 0 in)
Wing chord	0·91 m (3 ft 0 in)
Wing area, gross	7·71 m² (83 sq ft)
Length overall	5·18 m (17 ft 0 in)
Height overall	2·03 m (6 ft 8 in)

WEIGHT:
Max T-O weight	340 kg (750 lb)

PERFORMANCE (at max T-O weight):
Cruising speed	78 knots (145 km/h; 90 mph)
Landing speed	
	48-52 knots (89-97 km/h; 55-60 mph)

STOLP SA-700 ACRODUSTER 1

Introduced in 1973, the SA-700 is a single-seat fully-aerobatic biplane. Ailerons on both wings produce a roll rate in excess of 240° a second, and an interesting design feature is that the four ailerons are raised slightly when the control column is pulled back. This helps maintain aileron control when the aircraft is stalled in a normal attitude. Conversely, the ailerons are drooped slightly when the control column is pushed forward, which helps to maintain aileron control in an inverted stall. Plans and kits of components are available to amateur constructors.

TYPE: Single-seat aerobatic biplane.

WINGS: Braced single-bay biplane. Single I-type interplane strut each side. N-type centre-section struts. Streamline-section flying and landing wires. Aerofoil section Osborne A-1. Upper wing swept back 6°. Conventional two-spar structure. Spruce spars, plywood ribs and fabric covering. Ailerons on both wings. Upper wing built as two separate panels, joined by bolts at the centre. Stressed to ±9g ultimate.

FUSELAGE: All-metal semi-monocoque structure of light alloy.

TAIL UNIT: Cantilever structure of light alloy.

LANDING GEAR: Non-retractable tailwheel type. Main wheels carried on sprung cantilever legs of 2024-0 T-4 light alloy. Fairings for main wheels.

POWER PLANT: Prototype had originally a 149 kW (200 hp) Avco Lycoming flat-four engine, driving a two-blade fixed-pitch propeller with spinner, but was re-engined subsequently with a 134 kW (180 hp) engine. Design is suitable for engines of 93-149 kW (125-200 hp). Fuel tank in fuselage, aft of firewall, capacity 94·5 litres (25 US gallons). Refuelling point on upper fuselage forward of windscreen.

ACCOMMODATION: Single seat in open cockpit. Space for 23 kg (50 lb) of baggage in turtledeck compartment.

DIMENSIONS, EXTERNAL:
Wing span, upper	5·79 m (19 ft 0 in)
Wing area, gross	9·75 m² (105 sq ft)
Length overall	4·80 m (15 ft 9 in)
Height overall	1·91 m (6 ft 3 in)

WEIGHTS (prototype with 149 kW; 200 hp engine):
Weight empty	335 kg (740 lb)
Aerobatic T-O weight	476 kg (1,050 lb)
Max T-O weight	539 kg (1,190 lb)

PERFORMANCE (prototype with 149 kW; 200 hp engine, at AUW of 476 kg; 1,050 lb):
Max level speed	156 knots (290 km/h; 180 mph)
Cruising speed	143 knots (266 km/h; 165 mph)
Stalling speed	61 knots (113 km/h; 70 mph)
Max rate of climb at S/L	
	more than 914 m (3,000 ft)/min
Endurance at cruising speed, with reserves	2 h

STOLP SA-750 ACRODUSTER TOO

The SA-750 is basically a two-seat aerobatic biplane generally similar to the Starduster Too. Stressed to ±9g, it has symmetrical wings, the upper wing being swept back 6°. The prototype has a 149 kW (200 hp) Avco Lycoming IO-360 engine driving a two-blade constant-speed propeller. The front cockpit is open and has a small windscreen. A bubble canopy for the rear cockpit is faired neatly to the turtleback.

DIMENSIONS, EXTERNAL:
Wing span, upper	6·53 m (21 ft 5 in)
Wing area, gross	12·1 m² (130 sq ft)
Length overall	5·64 m (18 ft 6 in)
Height overall	2·08 m (6 ft 10 in)

PERFORMANCE (at max T-O weight):
Cruising speed	139 knots (257 km/h; 160 mph)
Stalling speed	48 knots (88·5 km/h; 55 mph)
Max rate of climb at S/L	701 m (2,300 ft)/min

STOLP SA-900 V-STAR

To meet the demand for low-cost, low-horsepower aircraft with aerobatic capability, Stolp has introduced the SA-900 V-Star, which is essentially a biplane version of the single-seat SA-500 Starlet.

It is stressed to ±9g. The wings, of Clark YH section, have N centre-section and I interplane struts. Incidence of the upper wing is 2° 30' and that of the lower wings 2°. The upper wing is swept back 6°.

The prototype has a 48·5 kW (65 hp) Continental flat-four engine, driving a two-blade fixed-pitch propeller, but engines of 44·5-93 kW (60-125 hp) may be installed.

DIMENSIONS, EXTERNAL:
Wing span, upper	7·01 m (23 ft 0 in)
Wing area, gross	13·1 m² (141 sq ft)
Length overall	5·23 m (17 ft 2 in)
Height overall	2·26 m (7 ft 5 in)

PERFORMANCE (prototype, at max T-O weight):
Cruising speed	65 knots (121 km/h; 75 mph)
Stalling speed	30·5 knots (56·5 km/h; 35 mph)
Max rate of climb at S/L	183 m (600 ft)/min

STRIPLIN
STRIPLIN AIRCRAFT CORPORATION

PO Box 2001, Lancaster, California 93534
Telephone: (805) 942 0768
PRESIDENT: Kenneth Striplin

This company is marketing kits to build a foot-launched powered hang glider known as the FLAC (Foot Launched Air Cycle). Its design was started in June 1977, and construction of the prototype began a year later. It was flown for the first time on 24 October 1978.

Striplin Aircraft Corporation is now marketing the FLAC in the form of a Quick Flight kit, which requires only assembly, and an Economy Kit containing all materials to build the complete glider. It does not sell engines, but is able to recommend suitable power plants.

STRIPLIN FLAC

In addition to two prototypes, five other FLACs had flown by January 1980. A total of 79 kits had been ordered at that time.

TYPE: Foot-launched rigid-wing powered hang glider.

WINGS: Cantilever high-wing monoplane of constant chord. Wortmann FX-126 wing section. Thickness/chord ratio 12%. No dihedral. Incidence 3°. Sweepback at quarter-chord 8°. Structure of glassfibre and epoxy with foam core, fabric-covered aft of spar. Elevon control surfaces attached to trailing-edge near tips operate collectively as elevators, differentially as ailerons. Large endplates on wingtips each carry a control surface at the rear, operated independently as rudders, collectively as airbrakes. Wings fold for transportation.

FUSELAGE: Pod, consisting of a moulded shell formed from glassfibre over foam reinforcement, is suspended from wings, and has a large windscreen and open sides. Bomb-bay type doors in bottom open for foot launching.

LANDING GEAR (auxiliary): Tricycle type, with non-retractable main units and rearward-retracting manually-actuated steerable nosewheel. Laminated glassfibre legs. Nylon main wheels and nosewheel each have tyre size 11 × 3·50-3, pressure 1·04 bars (15 lb/sq in). Friction brake operates on tyre surface. Optional main-wheel fairings, skis, and floats.

POWER PLANT (optional): Two 6 kW (8 hp) West Bend two-stroke engines geared to a common propeller shaft, and driving a Ritz two-blade wooden pusher propeller. Two glassfibre tanks in wing, with a combined fuel capacity of 19 litres (5 US gallons).

ACCOMMODATION: Pilot only, on hammock-type seat. Side-stick control actuates elevons; foot pedals operate rudders.

DIMENSIONS, EXTERNAL:
Wing span	9·75 m (32 ft 0 in)
Wing span, folded	5·64 m (18 ft 6 in)
Wing chord (constant)	1·37 m (4 ft 6 in)
Wing area, gross	14·4 m² (155 sq ft)
Wing aspect ratio	7·1
Length of fuselage pod	2·13 m (7 ft 0 in)
Height overall	1·22 m (4 ft 0 in)
Wheel track	1·07 m (3 ft 6 in)
Propeller diameter	1·22 m (4 ft 0 in)

WEIGHTS:
Weight empty	71 kg (156 lb)
Max fuel weight	13·6 kg (30 lb)
Max T-O weight	175 kg (386 lb)

PERFORMANCE (at max T-O weight):
Never-exceed speed	69 knots (129 km/h; 80 mph)
Max cruising speed	56 knots (105 km/h; 65 mph)
Econ cruising speed	39 knots (72 km/h; 45 mph)
Stalling speed	17·5 knots (32 km/h; 20 mph)
Max rate of climb at S/L	152 m (500 ft)/min
Rate of climb at S/L, one engine out	
	91 m (300 ft)/min
T-O run	46 m (150 ft)
Landing run	31 m (100 ft)
Range with max fuel	174 nm (322 km; 200 miles)

TAYLOR
C. GILBERT TAYLOR

Aero Industries, Camareo, California

TAYLOR BIRD

In 1976 Mr C. Gilbert Taylor, founder of the original Taylor Aircraft (Taylorcraft) Company and creator of the Cub design, unveiled his latest aircraft. Named the Bird, this is a two-seat lightplane of unusual configuration, designed for operation from small fields.

At the 1976 Oshkosh meeting, the Taylor Bird received the EAA award for the 'Best New Design or Innovation'. Built with the help of Bruce Taylor, the designer's son, the prototype (N303TB) flew for the first time on 17 July 1979. Flight tests have indicated that it 'stalls flat' due to the use of leading-edge slots. A T tail is to be fitted later.

Plans are available to amateur constructors. Materials and component parts, such as the main load bearing member and pre-formed graphite-epoxy fairings, are also available from Aero Industries.

TYPE: Two-seat ultra-light aircraft.

WINGS: Cantilever shoulder-wing monoplane. Wing section NACA 23015. No dihedral. Conventional aluminium alloy structure, with rectangular box-type main spar, drawn ribs and pop-riveted Alclad T3 skin. Plastics composite root section, which remains attached to fuselage when main wing panels are removed for towing or storage. Endplates at tips, toed-in 2° and canted 10° for directional stability. Full-span metal ailerons. Leading-edge slot, 0·61 m (2 ft) long, near each wingtip. No flaps or tabs.

FUSELAGE: Main load-bearing member comprises a 5·4 m (17 ft 8½ in) long, 150 mm (6 in) diameter 6061-T6 aluminium alloy tube, to which are bolted two pylons for the cabin/landing gear/engine/wing group and the tail unit assembly. All fairings, including cabin enclosures, of graphite-epoxy.

TAIL UNIT: Cantilever structure of aluminium alloy honeycomb, with plastics leading-edges. Constant-chord horizontal surfaces, with one-piece elevator.

LANDING GEAR: Non-retractable tailwheel type. Cantilever aluminium alloy main units, with solid industrial wheels and toe-operated disc brakes. Steerable tailwheel.

POWER PLANT: One 48·5 kW (65 hp) watercooled Subaru 1,400 cc converted motor car engine, driving a two-blade pusher propeller via a timing belt speed reduction.

ACCOMMODATION: Two seats in tandem in fully-enclosed cabin. Access by sliding forward entire nose fairing and windscreen assembly.

DIMENSIONS, EXTERNAL:
Wing span	7·92 m (26 ft 0 in)
Width, wings removed	2·29 m (7 ft 6 in)
Wing chord, constant	1·27 m (4 ft 2 in)
Length overall	5·49 m (18 ft 0 in)
Height overall	1·68 m (5 ft 6 in)

WEIGHTS:
Weight empty	254 kg (560 lb)
Max T-O weight	454 kg (1,000 lb)

PERFORMANCE:
Max level speed	109 knots (201 km/h; 125 mph)
Max cruising speed	100 knots (185 km/h; 115 mph)
Landing speed	35 knots (64·5 km/h; 40 mph)
T-O run	76 m (250 ft)
Endurance	4 h

THOMPSON
THOMPSON AIRCRAFT

336 Fitzwater Street, Philadelphia, Pennsylvania 19147

Telephone: (215) 925 8942
PRESIDENT: Richard R. Thompson

THOMPSON BOXMOTH

Mr Richard R. Thompson has designed and built the

Striplin FLAC foot-launched powered hang glider

Thompson Boxmoth (one two-cylinder snowmobile engine)

Taylor Bird two-seat lightplane *(Howard Levy)*

Thorp T-18 built by Mr W. C. Griffin *(J. M. G. Gradidge)*

Thompson Boxmoth with wing fabric furled

prototype of a unique light aircraft known as the Thompson Boxmoth. Intended as an easy-to-build low-speed lightweight type for the homebuilder, its construction requires no welding, machining, sheet metal, woodwork, or conventional fabric or dope. All materials and components can be purchased from local hardware and farm supply stores and from distributors of recreational vehicles. Any high-performance, lightweight snowmobile, motorcycle or outboard engine can be fitted. The wings fold against the main frame for towing behind a car or for storage in a one-car garage.

Licences to build the Boxmoth are available, together with three-view drawings, detail photos, notes and progress reports of the development and flight testing of the prototype; but it is not intended to sell completed aircraft or certificated plans at present. Estimated time to build a Boxmoth, by bolting together and wire-bracing the strong but flexible rhomboidal and triangular structure that supports the eight wing panels, seat, power plant and landing gear, is 134 man-hours; estimated cost of the aircraft is $1,555. By early 1980 25 licences had been issued.

Development of the Boxmoth began in October 1968; construction of the prototype was started in January 1970. It flew for the first time in November 1975 and had made approximately a dozen flights by early 1978. An FAA Experimental Airworthiness Certificate was granted on 18 May 1978.

Patent rights in the Boxmoth are reserved by Mr Richard R. Thompson, and no unauthorised production, use or sale of the Boxmoth concept is permitted without authorisation.

During the Summer of 1979, Mr Thompson increased the span of the rear cell so that it equalled that of the front cell (7·32 m: 24 ft 0 in), bringing the total wing area to 44·59 m² (480 sq ft). Other major modifications include the addition of secondary wing spars for both fore and aft wing cells, and removal of the main cross spar (which can be seen in the illustrations that appeared in the 1979-80 *Jane's*). These improvements hold the wing-panels flatter for greater efficiency, reduce drag, and give increased

strength. The landing gear is now braced fore and aft with aluminium tube.

TYPE: Single-seat tandem biplane type.

WINGS: Rhomboidal wings at front and rear of aircraft. The four panels making up each wing assembly consist of aluminium leading-edge and secondary wing spars of irrigation pipe and single-surface sail-type panels of Mothsilk nylon-reinforced vinyl, with curved ribs of lightweight aluminium tubing sewn into the fabric. Each pair of top and bottom spars is pivoted to the centre-frame and bolted together at the tip, to form a triangular structure. Spars of forward wing fold backward, spars of rear wing fold forward for stowage, with fabric panels furled and lashed to centre frame. Lateral control by differential flexing of the main cell trailing-edges.

FUSELAGE FRAME: Wire-braced open frame, mainly of 50 mm (2 in) aluminium tubing, bolted together. Vertical centre-frame comprises a pair of bottom longerons supporting the pilot's seat, controls and engine; an upper longeron carried on a forward N structure and two forward-sloping parallel members at rear. A further longeron extends the full length of the aircraft on each side, from the leading-edge of the forward wing to the trailing-edge of the rear wing, providing wingtip attachments for both sets of spars and for the flexible trailing-edges of the Mothsilk panels.

TAIL UNIT: All-moving elevator pivoted at mid-point of rearmost vertical frame member. Rudder between this member and the parallel member forward of it. Both surfaces made of Mothsilk on aluminium frame. Elevator is supplemented by collective flexing of trailing-edges of rear wing panels in low-speed flight.

LANDING GEAR: Non-retractable tailwheel type. Main legs of Tuf-Rod plastic, braced rigidly fore and aft only, by light alloy tube. Utility type tyres. No brakes required.

POWER PLANT: Prototype has one 41 kW (55 hp) 650 cc two-cylinder two-stroke snowmobile engine, driving a Thompson Aircraft two-blade variable-pitch propeller via two-strand chain drive 3:1 reduction gearing. Provi-

sion for variety of alternative engines. One 9·5 litre (2·5 US gallon) translucent plastics utility container serves as fuel tank. Provision for larger tankage.

ACCOMMODATION: Underslung PVC seat for pilot, mounted between two bottom longerons.

DIMENSIONS, EXTERNAL:

Wing span (original panels) approx 6·10 m (20 ft 0 in)	
Wing span (current long span panels) approx 7·32 m (24 ft 0 in)	
Wing chord, front	1·83 m (6 ft 0 in)
Wing chord, rear	1·22 m (4 ft 0 in)
Wing area, gross (original panels) 37·16 m² (400 sq ft)	
Wing area gross (current long span panels) 44·59 m² (480 sq ft)	
Wing aspect ratio (original panels)	3·3
Length overall	7·92 m (26 ft 0 in)
Width, wings folded	1·37 m (4 ft 6 in)
Height overall	3·35 m (11 ft 0 in)
Tailplane span	3·05 m (10 ft 0 in)
Wheel track	1·37 m (4 ft 6 in)
Wheelbase	3·66 m (12 ft 0 in)
Propeller diameter	1·83 m (6 ft 0 in)

WEIGHTS:

Weight empty	159 kg (350 lb)
Max T-O weight	249 kg (550 lb)

PERFORMANCE:

Never-exceed speed	48 knots (88 km/h; 55 mph)
Max level and cruising speed	39 knots (72 km/h; 45 mph)
Econ cruising speed	35 knots (64·5 km/h; 40 mph)
Stalling speed	26 knots (48·5 km/h; 30 mph)
Max rate of climb (estimated)	152 m (500 ft)/min
Service ceiling (estimated)	3,050 m (10,000 ft)
T-O run	61 m (200 ft)
T-O run to 15 m (50 ft)	91 m (300 ft)
Landing from 15 m (50 ft)	91 m (300 ft)
Landing run	30·5 m (100 ft)
Range, with 38 litres (10 US gallons) of fuel	173 nm (321 km; 200 miles)

THORP
THORP ENGINEERING COMPANY
PO Box 516, Sun Valley, California 91352

This company was founded by Mr John W. Thorp, who is well known as a designer of light aircraft. It markets plans of the T-18 Tiger two-seat all-metal sporting aircraft. More than 1,300 sets of drawings had been sold and over 200 T-18s were flying by early 1980.

THORP T-18 TIGER

First T-18 to be completed was N9675Z with a 134 kW (180 hp) Avco Lycoming O-360 engine. Built by Mr W. Warwick, it flew for the first time on 12 May 1964 and was illustrated in the 1964-65 *Jane's*.

More than 160 of the T-18s under construction and flying in 1980 were T-18Cs, with folding wings designed by Mr Luther Sunderland of Apalachin, NY. These wings

can be folded back on each side of the fuselage, for road transport, in less than five minutes.

Between 1 August and 30 September 1976, a T-18 piloted by Mr Don Taylor became the first homebuilt aircraft to circumnavigate the world, covering more than 21,400 nm (39,633 km; 24,627 miles) in 171·5 flying hours.

The following details apply to the standard Thorp T-18, built to plans:

TYPE: Two-seat high-performance sporting aircraft.

WINGS: Cantilever low-wing monoplane, with 8° dihedral on outer panels only. All-metal two-spar structure. Normally no flaps, but a flap installation is under design. Folding wings optional. With these, the centre-section span is reduced but the outer panels are lengthened to give an overall wing span of 7·67 m (25 ft 2 in).

FUSELAGE: All-metal structure, without double curvature.

TAIL UNIT: Cantilever all-metal structure.

LANDING GEAR: Non-retractable tailwheel type. Cantilever main legs. Steerable tailwheel. Main-wheel tyres size 5·00-5.

POWER PLANT: One Avco Lycoming or Continental flat-four engine in 80·5-149 kW (108-200 hp) category, driving a two-blade fixed-pitch propeller. Fuel tank aft of firewall, capacity 110 litres (29 US gallons).

ACCOMMODATION: Two seats side by side in open cockpit, with dual controls. Space for 36 kg (80 lb) baggage. Canopy optional.

DIMENSIONS, EXTERNAL:

Wing span (non-folding)	6·35 m (20 ft 10 in)
Wing chord, constant	1·27 m (4 ft 2 in)
Wing area, gross	8·0 m² (86 sq ft)
Length overall	5·54 m (18 ft 2 in)
Height overall	1·47 m (4 ft 10 in)
Tailplane span	2·10 m (6 ft 11 in)

Propeller diameter	1·60 m (5 ft 3 in)

WEIGHTS (134 kW; 180 hp Avco Lycoming):

Weight empty	408 kg (900 lb)
Max T-O weight	683 kg (1,506 lb)

PERFORMANCE (134 kW; 180 hp Avco Lycoming):

Max level speed at S/L	174 knots (321 km/h; 200 mph)
Max cruising speed	152 knots (282 km/h; 175 mph)
Stalling speed	57 knots (105 km/h; 65 mph)
Max rate of climb at S/L	610 m (2,000 ft)/min
Service ceiling	6,100 m (20,000 ft)
T-O run	91 m (300 ft)
Landing run	275 m (900 ft)
Range with max fuel	434 nm (805 km; 500 miles)

TURNER
TURNER AIRCRAFT

5803 Waterview Drive, Arlington, Texas 76016
Telephone: (817) 457 5081

The 1966-67 *Jane's* contained details of a single-seat sporting aircraft designated T-40, which was designed and built by Mr E. L. Turner and flew for the first time on 3 April 1961. This aircraft was modified by Mr Turner and his son into a prototype of the two-seat T-40A and has since formed the basis of a succession of developed versions of the same general design.

Plans are available to homebuilders, and more than 410 sets had been sold by January 1980.

The latest version of the basic T-40 design is the T-77 (T-40C), utilising the NASA GAW general aviation wing section; spoilers without ailerons for roll control; and aerodynamically-operated leading-edge slats. The T-77 will undergo flight testing and development as a testbed for a new series of single-engined sporting aircraft, beginning with a four-seater.

All existing Turner aircraft have folding wings, for reduced hangar space requirements and for transport by trailer. Approval for construction by amateur builders is being sought in Australia, England and South Africa.

In early 1980, Turner Aircraft had two new lightweight aircraft in the design stage. To be constructed of composite materials, each will be powered by a watercooled Rotorway RW-100 engine, developing approximately 75 kW (100 hp). One is an amphibian, the other a conventional low-wing monoplane; both are expected to have a cruising speed of between 130-139 knots (241-257 km/h; 150-160 mph) at a T-O weight of approximately 500 kg (1,100 lb).

TURNER T-40A

The prototype T-40A was produced by conversion of the original T-40. Modification took about four months and the aircraft flew for the first time in this form on 29 July 1966.

The T-40A is small enough to fit in a single-car garage and is transported on a small trailer. It has built-in skids in the fuselage, to protect the pilot in a minor crash landing, and an overturn structure.

TYPE: Two-seat sporting aircraft.

WINGS: Cantilever low-wing monoplane. Wing section NACA 65-215. Dihedral 4°. Incidence 1° 30′. All-wood (fir) two-spar structure with mahogany plywood covering. Hoerner low-drag tips. Plain ailerons. Large plain flaps. Wings fold rearward for stowage.

FUSELAGE: All-wood (fir) structure, covered with mahogany plywood. Glassfibre engine cowling.

TAIL UNIT: Cantilever all-wood (fir) structure with mahogany plywood covering. Horizontal surface of all-flying type with anti-servo tabs. Glassfibre dorsal fin.

LANDING GEAR: Non-retractable tailwheel type. Cantilever spring steel main units attached to front spar. Cleveland main wheels and tyres, size 5·00-5, pressure 3·10 bars (45 lb/sq in). Cleveland brakes.

POWER PLANT: One Continental flat-four engine of 63·5-74·5 kW (85 to 100 hp), driving a McCauley two-blade fixed-pitch propeller, type 65/57. Fuel tank in front fuselage, capacity 75 litres (20 US gallons). Oil capacity 3·75 litres (1 US gallon).

ACCOMMODATION: Pilot and passenger side by side. Each half of transparent canopy is hinged on centreline of aircraft to form a door, folding in two as it opens upward. Space for 11·5 kg (25 lb) baggage aft of seats.

EQUIPMENT: Prototype had Narco Mark III radio.

DIMENSIONS, EXTERNAL:

Wing span	7·67 m (25 ft 2 in)
Wing chord, constant	1·08 m (3 ft 6½ in)
Wing area, gross	8·35 m² (89·9 sq ft)
Wing aspect ratio	7·2
Length overall	6·02 m (19 ft 9 in)
Width, wings folded	2·39 m (7 ft 10 in)
Height overall	1·83 m (6 ft 0 in)
Tailplane span	1·96 m (6 ft 5 in)
Wheel track	2·24 m (7 ft 4 in)

DIMENSION, INTERNAL:

Cabin: Max width	1·02 m (3 ft 4 in)

WEIGHTS:

Weight empty	376 kg (828 lb)
Max T-O and landing weight	640 kg (1,410 lb)

PERFORMANCE (63·5 kW; 85 hp engine, at max T-O weight):

Never-exceed speed	191 knots (354 km/h; 220 mph)
Max level speed at S/L	130 knots (241 km/h; 150 mph)
Max cruising speed at S/L	113 knots (209 km/h; 130 mph)
Econ cruising speed at S/L	104 knots (193 km/h; 120 mph)
Stalling speed, flaps up	51·5 knots (95 km/h; 59 mph)
Stalling speed, flaps down	47 knots (87 km/h; 54 mph)
Max rate of climb at S/L	229 m (750 ft)/min
Service ceiling	3,660 m (12,000 ft)
T-O run	380 m (1,250 ft)
T-O to 15 m (50 ft)	730 m (2,400 ft)
Landing from 15 m (50 ft)	520 m (1,700 ft)
Landing run	305 m (1,000 ft)
Range with max payload, 20 min reserves	412 nm (756 km; 475 miles)

TURNER SUPER T-40A

The Super T-40A differs from the standard T-40A by having a larger wing, more powerful engine, swept tail, bubble canopy and other improvements. The prototype made its first flight in early 1972.

WINGS: As for T-40A, except span and chord increased.

TAIL UNIT: As for T-40A, except swept vertical surfaces, and vertical and horizontal surfaces of increased area.

LANDING GEAR: Non-retractable tailwheel type standard, with optional non-retractable or retractable tricycle type.

POWER PLANT: One 93 kW (125 hp) flat-four engine standard; provision for engines of up to 112 kW (150 hp).

ACCOMMODATION: As for T-40A, except for having a bubble canopy.

DIMENSIONS, EXTERNAL:

Wing span	8·13 m (26 ft 8 in)
Wing chord, constant	1·17 m (3 ft 10 in)
Wing area, gross	9·5 m² (102·5 sq ft)
Wing aspect ratio	6·98
Length overall	6·12 m (20 ft 1 in)

WEIGHTS:

Weight empty	445 kg (980 lb)
Max T-O weight	703 kg (1,550 lb)

PERFORMANCE (at max T-O weight):

Max level speed at S/L	152 knots (282 km/h; 175 mph)
Max cruising speed	135 knots (249 km/h; 155 mph)
Stalling speed, flaps down	43·5 knots (81 km/h; 50 mph)
Max rate of climb at S/L	425 m (1,400 ft)/min

TURNER T-77 (T-40C)

The T-77 utilises the T-40A fuselage and incorporates simplified model aeroplane type construction. The wing has a highly modified and computer-developed version of the NASA GAW general aviation section and incorporates a quick-folding mechanism. A retractable tandem-type landing gear was intended to be fitted; but in order to get the aircraft completed without further delay, a non-retractable gear has been substituted initially.

In January 1980 the prototype T-77 was expected to fly within five months.

TYPE: Two-seat sporting aircraft.

WINGS: Cantilever low-wing monoplane. NASA GAW-2 general aviation wing section. All-wood (fir) two-spar structure, with mahogany plywood covering. Hoerner low-drag tips. Aerodynamically-operated leading-edge slats. Hydraulically-actuated, single-slotted, full-span Fowler flaps. Spoilers without supplemental ailerons, in six sections, for roll control, and ground spoilers. Wings fold rearward, incorporating a quick-folding mechanism.

FUSELAGE: All-wood (fir) structure, covered with mahogany plywood. Glassfibre engine cowling. Central section embodies the wing centre-section structure, landing gear, engine mounting and cockpits. Rear fuselage carries the tail unit.

TAIL UNIT: Cantilever all-wood (fir) T-tail structure with mahogany plywood covering. Horizontal surface of all-flying type with anti-servo tab, which serves also as a trim tab. Glassfibre dorsal fin.

LANDING GEAR: Non-retractable tricycle type fitted initially. Electrically-retractable tandem type, with retractable balancer wheels at mid-span, is being considered. Cantilever main units attached to front spar. Cleveland main wheels and tyres, size 5·00-5, pressure 3·10 bars (45 lb/sq in). Cleveland brakes.

POWER PLANT: One 112 kW (150 hp) Avco Lycoming flat-four engine, driving a McCauley two-blade fixed-pitch propeller, type 65/57. Fuel tanks in front fuselage, capacity 95 litres (25 US gallons), and in centre-section, capacity 60 litres (16 US gallons). Oil capacity 3·75 litres (1 US gallon).

ACCOMMODATION: Pilot and passenger side by side under rearward-sliding transparent canopy. Space for 22·5 kg (50 lb) baggage aft of seats.

EQUIPMENT: Prototype has Narco Mark III, Com III, Nav II, transponder, AM/FM radio receiver and CB transceiver.

DIMENSIONS, EXTERNAL:

Wing span	8·53 m (28 ft 0 in)
Wing chord	1·08 m (3 ft 6½ in)
Wing area, gross	9·48 m² (102 sq ft)
Wing aspect ratio	9·2
Length overall	6·12 m (20 ft 1 in)
Width, wings folded	2·39 m (7 ft 10 in)
Height overall	1·83 m (6 ft 0 in)
Tailplane span	1·96 m (6 ft 5 in)

DIMENSIONS, INTERNAL:

Cabin: Length	1·78 m (5 ft 10 in)
Max width	1·02 m (3 ft 4 in)

WEIGHTS:

Weight empty	376 kg (828 lb)
Max T-O and landing weight	748 kg (1,650 lb)

PERFORMANCE (112 kW; 150 hp engine, at max T-O weight):

Never-exceed speed	225 knots (418 km/h; 260 mph)
Max level speed at S/L	165 knots (306 km/h; 190 mph)
Max cruising speed at S/L	152 knots (282 km/h; 175 mph)
Econ cruising speed at S/L	122 knots (225 km/h; 140 mph)
Stalling speed, flaps up	51 knots (94 km/h; 58 mph)
Stalling speed, flaps down	41 knots (76 km/h; 47 mph)
Max rate of climb at S/L	457 m (1,500 ft)/min
Estimated service ceiling	6,400 m (21,000 ft)
T-O run	152 m (500 ft)
T-O to 15 m (50 ft)	305 m (1,000 ft)
Landing run	91 m (300 ft)
Range, max payload, 20 min reserves	521 nm (965 km; 600 miles)

TURNER
BILL TURNER

Riverside, California

TURNER GEE BEE MODEL Z SUPER SPORTSTER

Mr Bill Turner and Mr Ed Marquart have built a replica of the 1931 Gee Bee Model Z Super Sportster racer *City of Springfield.* Construction took five years. Powered, like the original, by a 335 kW (450 hp) Pratt & Whitney Wasp radial engine, construction is conventional, with wooden wings of M-6 section and steel tube fuselage and tail unit, all fabric covered. Differences compared with the original include use of a Hamilton Standard propeller, tailwheel instead of tailskid, and installation of radio. In June 1979 the aircraft was involved in an accident, following brake problems when landing at a speed of 70 knots (129 km/h; 80 mph). Repairs to the wings and upper fuselage have been completed. The pilot, Bill Turner, suffered only minor injuries. Econ cruising speed is stated to be 182 knots (338 km/h; 210 mph), and range 608 nm (1,126 km; 700 miles) with 30 minute fuel reserves.

Turner Super T-40A built by Dr Jim Mandley

Turner Gee Bee Model Z Super Sportster replica *(Howard Levy)*

Turner T-77 (T-40C) two-seat sporting and aerobatic aircraft with non-retractable landing gear *(Roy J. Grainge)*

UFM Solar Riser, solar-powered aeroplane *(Henry Artof)*

Van's RV-3 single-seat sporting monoplane

UFM
ULTRALIGHT FLYING MACHINES
Santa Clara, California

UFM SOLAR RISER

Mr Larry Mauro, designer of the Easy Riser biplane hang glider, has built a solar-powered aircraft, called the Solar Riser. Based on the hang glider, the Solar Riser has a power system incorporating solar panels with 300 cells, giving a total of 40V 10A power output. Associated equipment includes a battery and a 2·24 kW (3 hp) General Design electric motor of the type developed originally for the Apollo spacecraft programme. To convert the hang glider into a simple research aeroplane, a pilot nacelle and a tricycle landing gear are also fitted.

The Solar Riser is claimed to have been the first solar-powered aircraft to fly, and by mid-1979 had completed six flights, totalling 10 minutes flying time. The first flight, in late April 1979, covered a distance of about 805 m (2,640 ft), at an altitude of 12·2 m (40 ft). Normal flying time is from 1 to 3 minutes. The current research and development programme is aiming at a flight of one hour, but improvements to the aircraft and its power system could eventually lead to flights of about two hours.

TYPE: Single-seat solar-powered biplane.
WINGS: Based on Easy Riser hang glider, with aluminium alloy spars, ribs, leading- and trailing-edges, stainless steel interplane struts, and Dacron skin. Upper wing top surface is covered with solar panels made up of 300 cells.
FUSELAGE: Small and basic nacelle for pilot, with electric motor mounted at rear.

LANDING GEAR: Non-retractable tricycle type.
POWER PLANT: One 2·24 kW (3 hp) General Design electric motor, driving a 1·04 m (3 ft 5 in) diameter Soarmaster pusher propeller.

DIMENSIONS, EXTERNAL:

Wing span	9·14 m (30 ft 0 in)
Wing chord (constant)	1·04 m (3 ft 5 in)
Length overall	2·44 m (8 ft 0 in)

WEIGHTS:

Weight empty	57 kg (125 lb)
Max T-O weight	131·5 kg (290 lb)

PERFORMANCE:

Max level speed, approx 17·3 knots (32 km/h; 20 mph)	
T-O run	23-61 m (75-200 ft)
Endurance (to date)	1 to 3 min

VAN'S
VAN'S AIRCRAFT
22730 SW Francis, Beaverton, Oregon 97005
Telephone: (503) 649 5378

Mr Richard VanGrunsven designed and built a single-seat all-metal sporting aircraft known as Van's RV-3. It was built over a 2½-year period, from 1968, at a cost of approximately $2,000, and won its designer the Best Aerodynamic Detailing award at the 1972 EAA Fly-in.

After the RV-3's first flight, and subsequent EAA award, Mr VanGrunsven formed Van's Aircraft to market plans to amateur constructors. By early 1980 at least 750 sets of plans had been sold, with about 220 aircraft under construction and 45 RV-3s flying, including the prototype.

VAN'S RV-3

Illustrated in the 1979-80 *Jane's* was an RV-3, powered by a 119 kW (160 hp) Avco Lycoming O-320 engine, which was built by Mr William M. Pomeroy of Norval, Ontario, Canada. With this aircraft, Mr Pomeroy set the current FAI Class C1a speed record of 172·40 knots (319·28 km/h; 198·39 mph) over a 3 km course on 11 July 1976.

The following data apply to the basic plans-built RV-3:
TYPE: Single-seat sporting monoplane.
WINGS: Cantilever low-wing monoplane. Wing section NACA 23012. Dihedral 3° 30'. Incidence 1°. Conventional 2024-T3 light alloy structure of constant chord, with I-beam main spar, light rear spar, pressed ribs and moulded glassfibre tips. All-metal bottom-hinged plain

trailing-edge flaps. All-metal Frise-type ailerons. No tabs.
FUSELAGE: All-metal semi-monocoque structure of 2024-T3 light alloy. Glassfibre engine cowling.
TAIL UNIT: Cantilever structure of light alloy, with glassfibre tips. Trim tab in port elevator.
LANDING GEAR: Non-retractable tailwheel type. Cantilever tapered steel-spring main gear struts, with streamline fairings. Cleveland main wheels with tyres size 14 × 5·00-5, pressure 1·38 bars (20 lb/sq in). Steerable tailwheel with 0·15 m (6 in) diameter tyre. Cleveland brakes. Glassfibre streamlined fairings on main wheels.
POWER PLANT: One 93 kW (125 hp) Avco Lycoming O-290-G (GPU) flat-four engine, driving a Sensenich two-blade fixed-pitch propeller with spinner. Fuel capacity 91 litres (24 US gallons).
ACCOMMODATION: Pilot only, beneath rearward-sliding Plexiglas bubble canopy. Baggage space aft of seat, capacity 0·23 m³ (8 cu ft).

DIMENSIONS, EXTERNAL:

Wing span	6·07 m (19 ft 11 in)
Wing chord, constant	1·37 m (4 ft 6 in)
Wing area, gross	8·36 m² (90 sq ft)
Wing aspect ratio	4·43
Length overall	5·79 m (19 ft 0 in)
Height overall	1·55 m (5 ft 1 in)
Tailplane span	2·13 m (7 ft 0 in)
Wheel track	1·73 m (5 ft 8 in)
Wheelbase	4·29 m (14 ft 1 in)
Propeller diameter	1·73 m (5 ft 8 in)

DIMENSION, INTERNAL:

Cabin: Width	0·64 m (2 ft 1 in)

WEIGHTS:

Weight empty	315 kg (695 lb)
Max T-O weight	476 kg (1,050 lb)

PERFORMANCE (at max T-O weight):

Never-exceed speed 191 knots (354 km/h; 220 mph)	
Max level speed at S/L 169 knots (314 km/h; 195 mph)	
Max cruising speed at 2,440 m (8,000 ft)	
	161 knots (298 km/h; 185 mph)
Econ cruising speed at 3,050 m (10,000 ft)	
	139 knots (257 km/h; 160 mph)
Stalling speed, flaps up 45·5 knots (84 km/h; 52 mph)	
Stalling speed, flaps down	
	42 knots (78 km/h; 48 mph)
Max rate of climb at S/L	579 m (1,900 ft)/min
Service ceiling	6,400 m (21,000 ft)
T-O run	61 m (200 ft)
Landing run	91·5 m (300 ft)
Range, no reserves	520 nm (965 km; 600 miles)

VAN'S RV-4

This tandem two-seat sportsplane for homebuilders is similar in external appearance to the RV-3; it is, however, some 20% larger and there is no commonality of airframe components. The design goal was to retain in a two-seat aircraft the overall performance and flight characteristics of the single-seat RV-3. The first flight of the prototype RV-4 (N14RV) was made on 21 August 1979. Some 50 hours of intensive flight testing had been completed by mid-January 1980, confirming that all design goals had been achieved or exceeded. Work began immediately to prepare plans and kits for sale to homebuilders, and these became available during the Summer of 1980.

TYPE: Two-seat sporting monoplane.

WINGS: As for RV-3, except wing section Van's Aircraft 135.

FUSELAGE, TAIL UNIT: As for RV-3.

LANDING GEAR: As for RV-3, except main-wheel tyre pressure 1·52 bars (22 lb/sq in).

POWER PLANT: One 112 kW (150 hp) Avco Lycoming O-320-E1F flat-four engine, driving a Cassidy two-blade fixed-pitch wooden propeller with spinner. Fuel capacity 121 litres (32 US gallons).

ACCOMMODATION: Two seats in tandem; pilot seated forward under side-opening canopy, passenger aft beneath rear-sliding Plexiglas canopy. Limited baggage capacity in compartments forward of instrument panel and aft of rear seat.

DIMENSIONS, EXTERNAL:
Wing span	7·01 m (23 ft 0 in)
Wing chord, constant	1·47 m (4 ft 10 in)
Wing area, gross	10·22 m² (110 sq ft)
Wing aspect ratio	4·76
Length overall	6·21 m (20 ft 4½ in)
Height overall	1·60 m (5 ft 3 in)
Tailplane span	2·54 m (8 ft 4 in)
Wheel track	1·88 m (6 ft 2 in)
Propeller diameter	1·73 m (5 ft 8 in)

DIMENSIONS, INTERNAL:
Cabin: Max width	0·71 m (2 ft 4 in)
Max height	1·12 m (3 ft 8 in)

WEIGHTS:
Weight empty	404 kg (890 lb)
Max T-O weight	680 kg (1,500 lb)

PERFORMANCE (at max T-O weight):
Never-exceed speed	182 knots (338 km/h; 210 mph)
Max level speed at S/L	175 knots (325 km/h; 202 mph)
Max cruising speed at 2,440 m (8,000 ft)	162 knots (301 km/h; 187 mph)
Econ cruising speed at 3,050 m (10,000 ft)	139 knots (257 km/h; 160 mph)
Stalling speed, flaps up	48 knots (88·5 km/h; 55 mph)
Stalling speed, flaps down	43·5 knots (80·5 km/h; 50 mph)
Max rate of climb at S/L	503 m (1,650 ft)/min
Service ceiling	6,100 m (20,000 ft)
T-O run	137 m (450 ft)
Landing run	122 m (400 ft)
Range with max fuel, no reserves	651 nm (1,207 km; 750 miles)

VAN'S RV-6

This side-by-side two-seat light aircraft, a variation of the RV-4, was designed by Mr VanGrunsven at the request of Mr Art Chard of Bronson, Missouri, who completed detail design of the fuselage and built it in 15 months. First flight was made on 26 April 1977. Like the RV-3 and RV-4, it is of all-metal construction, with glassfibre cowlings, wingtips and fairings. The basic wing and tail unit components are the same as those of the RV-4. Power plant is a 112 kW (150 hp) Avco Lycoming O-320 flat-four engine.

It is intended to offer the RV-6 in both plan and kit form as soon as the marketing programme of the RV-4 has become established.

DIMENSIONS, EXTERNAL:
Wing span	7·32 m (24 ft 0 in)
Wing chord, constant	1·47 m (4 ft 10 in)
Length overall	6·10 m (20 ft 0 in)

WEIGHTS:
Weight empty	454 kg (1,000 lb)
Max T-O weight	680 kg (1,500 lb)

PERFORMANCE:
Max level speed	156 knots (290 km/h; 180 mph)
Max cruising speed	139 knots (257 km/h; 160 mph)
Landing speed	44 knots (81 km/h; 50 mph)
Range with max fuel	417 nm (772 km; 480 miles)

VOLMER
VOLMER AIRCRAFT

Box 5222, Glendale, California 91201

Telephone: (213) 247 8718

Mr Volmer Jensen, well known as a designer of sailplanes and gliders, also designed and built a two-seat light amphibian named the Sportsman. Construction of the prototype began in September 1957 and this aircraft flew for the first time on 22 December 1958. It has since logged more than 1,600 flying hours.

Plans of the Sportsman are available to amateur constructors. Over 800 sets had been sold by early 1980 and more than 100 Sportsman amphibians are flying. Some have tractor propellers, but this modification is not recommended by Mr Jensen.

VOLMER VJ-22 SPORTSMAN

The following details refer to Mr Jensen's prototype:

TYPE: Two-seat light amphibian.

WINGS: Braced high-wing monoplane. Dihedral 1°. Incidence 3°. Wings are standard Aeronca Chief or Champion assemblies with wooden spars, light alloy ribs and fabric covering, and carry stabilising floats under the tips. Plans of newly-designed wing, with wooden ribs and spars, available. Streamline V bracing struts each side.

FUSELAGE: Conventional flying-boat hull of wooden construction, covered with mahogany plywood and coated with glassfibre.

TAIL UNIT: Strut-braced steel tube structure, fabric-covered.

LANDING GEAR: Retractable tailwheel type. Rubber-cord shock-absorption. Manual retraction. Cleveland wheels and mechanical brakes. Tyre pressure 1·38 bars (20 lb/sq in). Castoring retractable tailwheel with integral water rudder.

POWER PLANT: 63·5 kW (85 hp) Continental C85, 67 kW (90 hp) or 74·5 kW (100 hp) Continental O-200-B flat-four engine, driving a Sensenich two-blade fixed-pitch pusher propeller. Fuel in a single tank, capacity 76 litres (20 US gallons). Oil capacity 4·25 litres (4·5 US quarts).

ACCOMMODATION: Two seats side by side in enclosed cabin with dual controls.

DIMENSIONS, EXTERNAL:
Wing span	11·12 m (36 ft 6 in)
Wing chord	1·52 m (5 ft 0 in)
Wing area, gross	16·3 m² (175 sq ft)
Wing aspect ratio	7·2
Length overall	7·32 m (24 ft 0 in)
Height overall	2·44 m (8 ft 0 in)

WEIGHTS (63·5 kW; 85 hp):
Weight empty	454 kg (1,000 lb)
Max T-O weight	680 kg (1,500 lb)

PERFORMANCE (63·5 kW; 85 hp, at max T-O weight):
Max level speed at S/L	83 knots (153 km/h; 95 mph)
Max cruising speed	74 knots (137 km/h; 85 mph)
Stalling speed	39 knots (72 km/h; 45 mph)
Max rate of climb at S/L	183 m (600 ft)/min
Service ceiling	3,960 m (13,000 ft)
Range with max fuel, no reserves	260 nm (480 km; 300 miles)

WAG-AERO
WAG-AERO INC

PO Box 181, 1216 North Road, Lyons, Wisconsin 53148

Telephone: (414) 763 9588

PRESIDENT: Richard H. Wagner

Wag-Aero supplies plans and kits of parts which enable amateur constructors to build modern versions of the Piper Cub and Vagabond light aircraft.

WAG-AERO CUBy

Wag-Aero plans and kits offer homebuilders the choice of four different modern versions of the famous Piper Cub.

Known as the CUBy Sport Trainer, the basic two-seat sporting aircraft follows the original design, but benefits by utilising up-to-date constructional techniques. The wing has a wooden main spar and ribs, light alloy leading-edge and fabric covering. The fuselage and tail unit are of welded 4130 chrome molybdenum steel tube with fabric covering. The CUBy can be powered by any flat-four Continental, Franklin or Avco Lycoming engine of between 48·5 and 93 kW (65 and 125 hp).

Also available are the CUBy Acro Trainer which differs from the standard version by having a strengthened fuselage, shortened wings, modified lift struts, improved wing fittings and rib spacing, and a new leading-edge; the CUBy Observer which is a replica L-4 military liaison aircraft; and the Super-CUBy with structural modifications to accept engines of up to 112 kW (150 hp), making it suitable for glider towing, bush operations, or for operation as a floatplane.

Design of the CUBy began in 1974 and construction of a prototype started in December of that year. First flight took place on 12 March 1975. By February 1979 plans for approximately 610 CUBys had been ordered.

The following details apply to the standard CUBy Sport Trainer:

DIMENSIONS, EXTERNAL:
Wing span	10·73 m (35 ft 2½ in)
Wing chord, constant	1·60 m (5 ft 3 in)
Wing area, gross	16·58 m² (178·5 sq ft)
Wing aspect ratio	6·96
Length overall	6·82 m (22 ft 4½ in)
Height overall	2·03 m (6 ft 8 in)

WEIGHTS:
Weight empty	327 kg (720 lb)
Max T-O weight	635 kg (1,400 lb)

PERFORMANCE (at max T-O weight):
Max level speed at S/L	89 knots (164 km/h; 102 mph)
Cruising speed	82 knots (151 km/h; 94 mph)
Stalling speed	34 knots (63 km/h; 39 mph)
Max rate of climb at S/L	149 m (490 ft)/min
Service ceiling	over 3,660 m (12,000 ft)
T-O run	114 m (375 ft)
Range at cruising speed with standard fuel (45 litres; 12 US gallons)	191 nm (354 km; 220 miles)
Range with auxiliary fuel (98 litres; 26 US gallons)	395 nm (732 km; 455 miles)

WAG-AERO WAG-A-BOND

The name Wag-A-Bond covers two aircraft which can be built by amateur constructors: a replica of the Piper PA-15 Vagabond, known as the Classic, and the Traveler. The latter is a modified and updated version of the Vagabond with port and starboard doors, overhead skylight window, extended sleeping deck (conversion from aircraft to camper interior taking about two minutes and accommodating two persons), extended baggage area, engine of up to 85·7 kW (115 hp), and provision for a full electrical system.

A prototype Wag-A-Bond was completed by Wag-Aero in May 1978 and has been test flown successfully. The following details apply to both versions, unless stated otherwise:

TYPE: Two-seat light monoplane.

WINGS: Strut-braced high-wing monoplane. Fabric-covered all-wood structure of spruce spar and ribs, with mahogany plywood gussets. Fabric-covered aluminium ailerons. V bracing struts. Steel drag and anti-drag wires.

FUSELAGE: Welded 4130 steel tube and flat plate structure, fabric-covered.

TAIL UNIT: Wire-braced structure, comprising tailplane with elevators, vertical fin and rudder, all of welded 4130 steel tube, fabric-covered.

LANDING GEAR: Non-retractable tailwheel type. Welded steel tube side Vs and half-axles. Bungee shock-absorption. Cleveland wheels, size 6·00-6, and 7·00-6 tyres, covered by fairings. Cleveland brakes. Skis optional.

POWER PLANT: Traveler can be powered by an Avco Lycoming engine of 80·5-85·7 kW (108-115 hp), driving a two-blade wooden or metal propeller. Classic can be powered by a Continental engine of 48·5-74·5 kW (65-100 hp) driving a similar propeller. Fuel capacity of Traveler 98·5 litres (26 US gallons). Fuel capacity of Classic 45·5 litres (12 US gallons).

ACCOMMODATION: Two persons side by side in enclosed cabin. Baggage area, capacity 27·2 kg (60 lb) for Traveler, 18 kg (40 lb) for Classic.

SYSTEMS: Traveler has provision for full electrical system.

DIMENSIONS, EXTERNAL:
Wing span	8·32 m (29 ft 3½ in)
Wing area, gross	13·70 m² (147·5 sq ft)
Length overall	5·70 m (18 ft 8½ in)
Height overall	1·83 m (6 ft 0 in)

WEIGHTS (A: Traveler, B: Classic):
Weight empty: A	329 kg (725 lb)
B	290 kg (640 lb)
Max T-O weight: A	658 kg (1,450 lb)
B	567 kg (1,250 lb)

PERFORMANCE (A: Traveler with 80·5 kW; 108 hp engine, B: Classic):
Max level speed: A	106 knots (196 km/h; 122 mph)
B	91 knots (169 km/h; 105 mph)
Cruising speed: A	100 knots (185 km/h; 115 mph)
B	83 knots (153 km/h; 95 mph)
Stalling speed: A, B	39 knots (72·5 km/h; 45 mph)
Max rate of climb at S/L: A	259 m (850 ft)/min
B	190 m (625 ft)/min

WAR
WAR AIRCRAFT REPLICAS

348 South Eighth Street, Santa Paula, California 93060

PRESIDENT: Kenneth L. Thoms

War Aircraft Replicas is a company formed to market plans and kits from which amateur constructors can build ½-scale replicas of a series of second World War aircraft. The term '½-scale' is not strictly accurate, but refers to the general overall dimensions of the aircraft. For example, to provide adequate accommodation for the pilot, the cockpit is considerably larger than ½-scale, and the area of the horizontal and vertical tail surfaces has been increased beyond scale to ensure adequate stability.

The basic concept involves the use of a common-design wooden fuselage box and spar structure. The desired contours to duplicate a particular aircraft are obtained by using carved polyurethane foam, covered with high-strength laminating fabric and epoxy resin to form a lightweight and rigid structure that is stressed to ±6g, allowing for aerobatic manoeuvres. By changing fuselage contours,

Van's RV-6, a side-by-side two-seat development of the RV-4

The original Volmer VJ-22 Sportsman, named *Chubasco*

Wag-Aero Super-CUBy floatplane with 112 kW (150 hp) engine *(J. M. G. Gradidge)*

Van's RV-4, a larger tandem two-seat version of the RV-3

Wag-Aero Wag-A-Bond, a version of the Piper Vagabond suitable for home-builders

WAR half-scale replica of the F4U Corsair built by Fred Bauer Jr of Winona (Avco Lycoming O-235 engine) *(Howard Levy)*

WAR half-scale replica of the Focke-Wulf Fw 190 (nearest) built by Ivan Munninghoff of San Antonio (Continental O-200-A engine) *(Howard Levy)*

using different engine cowlings and wingtips, and by shape changes to tail unit surfaces, it was considered that a number of different aircraft could be copied with reasonable similarity to the full-scale combat types.

The Focke-Wulf 190 was chosen as the first prototype to be completed, its design starting in July 1973 and construction in February 1974. The first flight of this aircraft was made on 21 August 1974. At least 197 sets of plans of the WAR Focke-Wulf 190 had been sold by early 1980, as well as more than 200 sets of plans for the Vought F4U Corsair. Approximately 100 sets of plans have been sold for the construction of replica Republic P-47 Thunderbolts. Prototype replicas of the Hawker Sea Fury and North American P-51 Mustang have been completed. Prototype replicas of the Mitsubishi Zero and P-40 Warhawk are known to be under construction. Development continues on a P-38 Lightning replica.

The description which follows applies specifically to the Focke-Wulf 190 replica, but is applicable generally to the range of aircraft for which the company is producing plans, components and kits.

WAR AIRCRAFT REPLICAS FOCKE-WULF 190

TYPE: Half-scale combat aircraft replica.
WINGS: Cantilever low-wing monoplane, built in three sections: nominal 2·44 m (8 ft) centre-section, integral with fuselage box, and two nominally 1·83 m (6 ft) outer panels. Wing section NACA 23015 at root, 23012 at tip. Dihedral 5°. Incidence 2°. Washout 2°. Primary

structure of wood, with a laminated hollow plywood-covered front spar and solid laminated rear spar. Plywood ribs are used at the root, both faces of the centre-section joints and at the tip sections, with intermediate ribs of polyurethane foam. Aerofoil contours built up with carved polyurethane foam, bonded in place. High-strength laminating fabric and epoxy resin used for covering and for internal strengthening. Frise-type ailerons with wooden front spar bonded to a shaped form of urethane foam with fabric/epoxy covering. No flaps. Ground-adjustable tab on each aileron.
FUSELAGE: Of similar general construction to wings, with a standard four-longeron box built from ¾ in fir stringers, ¾ in by ½ in diagonals and cross pieces, 1/16 in birch plywood covering and a metal-faced ⅛ in plywood firewall. Fuselage contoured by carved polyurethane foam with fabric/epoxy covering.
TAIL UNIT: Cantilever wooden structure, utilising the same construction technique as for the wings. Fixed tailplane with elevators. Ground-adjustable trim tab on rudder and each elevator.
LANDING GEAR: Electrically-retractable tailwheel type, with manual emergency retraction system. Main wheels retract inward into wings. Fixed tailwheel. Oleo-pneumatic shock-struts on main units. Main wheels and tyres size 3·50 × 4·10-6. Cleveland hydraulic disc brakes.
POWER PLANT: One 74·5 kW (100 hp) Continental O-200 flat-four engine, driving a three-blade fixed-pitch

wooden propeller with spinner. Fuel tank in fuselage, immediately aft of firewall, with capacity of 45·5 litres (12 US gallons). Refuelling point on upper surface of fuselage, forward of windscreen.
ACCOMMODATION: Single seat beneath rearward-sliding cockpit canopy. Accommodation heated and ventilated.
SYSTEMS: Hydraulic system for brakes only. Electrical system powered by 12V engine-driven alternator.
DIMENSIONS, EXTERNAL:

Wing span	6·10 m (20 ft 0 in)
Wing chord at root	1·37 m (4 ft 6 in)
Wing chord at tip	0·94 m (3 ft 1 in)
Wing area, gross	6·50 m² (70 sq ft)
Wing aspect ratio	5·7
Length overall	5·05 m (16 ft 7 in)
Height overall	2·13 m (7 ft 0 in)
Tailplane span	2·29 m (7 ft 6 in)
Wheel track	2·03 m (6 ft 8 in)
Wheelbase	3·25 m (10 ft 8 in)
Propeller diameter	1·52 m (5 ft 0 in)

WEIGHTS:

Weight empty	286 kg (630 lb)
Max T-O weight	408 kg (900 lb)

PERFORMANCE (at max T-O weight):
Max level speed at 1,065 m (3,500 ft)
169 knots (314 km/h; 195 mph)
Max cruising speed at 1,065 m (3,500 ft)
126 knots (233 km/h; 145 mph)

Econ cruising speed at 1,065 m (3,500 ft)
               108 knots (201 km/h; 125 mph)
Stalling speed   48 knots (89 km/h; 55 mph)
Max rate of climb at S/L   305 m (1,000 ft)/min
Service ceiling   3,810 m (12,500 ft)
T-O run   305 m (1,000 ft)
Landing from 15 m (50 ft)   550 m (1,800 ft)
Landing run   365 m (1,200 ft)
Range with max fuel   347 nm (643 km; 400 miles)

WAR AIRCRAFT REPLICAS F4U CORSAIR

The F4U Corsair illustrated was built by Mr Fred Bauer

Jr of Winona, Minnesota, to War Aircraft Replicas plans. Construction is as described for the WAR Focke-Wulf 190, and the aircraft is powered by an 80·5 kW (108 hp) Avco Lycoming O-235 flat-four engine, driving a three-blade propeller. The external fuel tank under the fuselage has a capacity of 25 litres (6·5 US gallons). First flight was made in May 1979.

DIMENSIONS, EXTERNAL:
Wing span   6·10 m (20 ft 0 in)
Wing chord, constant   1·37 m (4 ft 6 in)
Length overall   4·88 m (16 ft 0 in)
Height overall   1·53 m (5 ft 0 in)

WEIGHTS:
Weight empty   418 kg (921 lb)
Max T-O weight   544 kg (1,200 lb)

PERFORMANCE (at max T-O weight):
Max level speed   147 knots (273 km/h; 170 mph)
Max cruising speed 121 knots (225 km/h; 140 mph)
Landing speed   78 knots (145 km/h; 90 mph)
Rate of climb at S/L   426 m (1,400 ft)/min
T-O run   305 m (1,000 ft)
Landing run   457 m (1,500 ft)
Range with max fuel 347 nm (643 km; 400 miles)

WATSON
WATSON WINDWAGON COMPANY
Rt 1, Newcastle, Texas 76372

WATSON GW-1 WINDWAGON

Mr Gary Watson has designed and built a diminutive single-seat all-metal monoplane known as the GW-1 Windwagon (N64614). Although this is Mr Watson's first design, he was previously a member of a team that constructed a Parker Teenie Two.

Construction of the prototype Windwagon took six months and cost $1,222·74, including the engine taken from a derelict Volkswagen 'Beetle' cut in half and reworked. First flight was made on 19 April 1977.

Plans to build the Windwagon are available to amateur builders, and by early 1980 at least 67 sets had been sold (including details for modifying the VW engine). Complete kits and individual parts are also available.

TYPE: Single-seat light monoplane.

WINGS: Cantilever low-wing monoplane. Wing section Clark Y. Constant chord. All-metal pop-riveted structure of aluminium alloy, built in three 1·83 m (6 ft 0 in) sections, the outer wing sections being removable for trailering. Conventional ailerons. No flaps.

FUSELAGE: Conventional pop-riveted aluminium alloy semi-monocoque structure.

TAIL UNIT: Cantilever all-metal structure of aluminium alloy, comprising constant-chord tailplane with elevators, slightly swept fin and rudder. No tabs.

LANDING GEAR: Non-retractable tricycle type, employing tubular legs. No shock-absorbers. Hydraulic brakes.

POWER PLANT: One 22·4 kW (30 hp) 900 cc half-Volkswagen modified motor car engine, driving normally a four-blade propeller made by Dick Bohls, with spinner. A 1·27 m (4 ft 2 in) two-blade propeller was fitted initially. Fuel capacity 15·14 litres (4 US gallons). Oil capacity 1·4 litres (1·5 US quarts).

ACCOMMODATION: Single semi-reclining seat in open cockpit. Large windscreen.

DIMENSIONS, EXTERNAL:
Wing span   5·49 m (18 ft 0 in)
Wing chord, constant   0·91 m (3 ft 0 in)
Length overall   3·96 m (13 ft 0 in)
Height overall   1·07 m (3 ft 6 in)
Propeller diameter (four blade) 1·02 m (3 ft 4 in)

WEIGHTS:
Weight empty   124 kg (273 lb)
Max T-O weight   220 kg (485 lb)

PERFORMANCE:
Max level speed   117 knots (217 km/h; 135 mph)
Normal cruising speed
              82·5 knots (153 km/h; 95 mph)
Landing speed   39 knots (72·5 km/h; 45 mph)
Max rate of climb at S/L   137 m (450 ft)/min
T-O run   76 m (250 ft)
Landing run   91 m (300 ft)
Range with max fuel   260 nm (483 km; 300 miles)

WEEDHOPPER
WEEDHOPPER OF UTAH INC
PO Box 2253, 1148 Century Drive, Ogden, Utah 84404
Telephone: (801) 621 3941

WEEDHOPPER JC-24 WEEDHOPPER

This single-seat ultralight aircraft represents the 23rd design by Mr John F. Chotia; the others comprised 18 hang-gliders and four powered lightplanes. Design of the original wooden version of the Weedhopper (which is reminiscent in configuration of the 1909 Demoiselle of Alberto Santos-Dumont) began in 1975. Two prototypes were tested, after which the decision was taken to switch to metal structures. The first of two pre-production metal prototypes flew in February 1978. In November 1979 a prototype with an increased-area wing flew for the first time, and two versions of the JC-24 are available currently:

JC-24B. Basic version, as described in detail below. Compared with original JC-24, the 'B' has simplified structure and improved manoeuvrability. Full 360° turns have been completed in less than 8 s, with a turn radius of less than 21 m (70 ft). Stalls are now preceded by greater warning buffet. Foot-launch has been demonstrated, but is discouraged by Weedhopper.

JC-24BL. Soaring version, with wing of increased span and area that gives greater lift, and reduces both drag and stalling speed. Because the increased-span wing is more affected by gusts and turbulence, spoilers have been introduced, mounted adjacent to the wingtips on the upper surface of the wings, to function as ailerons. In their neutral position they serve as wingtip leading-edge slots, inhibiting wingtip stalls. These supplementary aerofoils are available optionally for installation also on the standard wing of the JC-24B, and offer considerable aerodynamic improvement to the basic version.

Kits of parts to build the Weedhopper first became available to homebuilders in July 1978. By 1 January 1980 orders for kits totalled 410, of which 330 had been supplied: about 100 Weedhoppers were known to be flying.

Production of kits was at a rate of approximately 15 per week in early 1980.

It is claimed that the JC-24B Weedhopper will recover from a stall, with power on, within an altitude loss of 3 m (10 ft). If the optional spoilers are not fitted to this version, bank and roll control are effected by using the rudder, or by optional wing warping.

TYPE: Single-seat light monoplane.

WINGS: Strut-braced high-wing monoplane. Thickness/chord ratio 11%. Dihedral 12°. Incidence 3°. Washout 4° 30'. Sweepback 4° on JC-24B, 5° on JC-24BL. Aluminium tube structure, covered with Dacron fabric. Upper surface of JC-24B wing is fabric-covered, undersurface optional; but JC-24BL has both surfaces covered as standard. Aluminium tube V bracing struts each side, from landing gear axle to wing leading- and trailing-edges. Wingtip spoilers for roll control standard on JC-24BL, optional for JC-24B. Alternative wing warping system also available.

FUSELAGE: Open triangulated structure of aluminium tubing, bolted together. Upper fuselage tube supports wing roots, tailplane and engine.

TAIL UNIT: Cantilever structure, comprising tailplane with elevators, ventral fin and rudder. Tailplane incidence and rudder trim ground-adjustable. Aluminium tube structure, Dacron fabric covered.

LANDING GEAR: Non-retractable tricycle type. Steerable nosewheel. All three tyres size 3·50-4. Brake on nosewheel optional. Ski landing gear optional.

POWER PLANT: One Chotia 460 two-stroke engine, developing 18·6 kW (25 hp) at 4,500 rpm, and driving a Weedhopper-built two-blade fixed-pitch wooden propeller. Single fuel tank of standard 3·8 litre (1 US gallon) capacity, or optional 13·25 litre (3·5 US gallon) capacity.

ACCOMMODATION: Single semi-reclined and adjustable open seat.

SYSTEMS: 6V battery for ignition system.

DIMENSIONS, EXTERNAL (A: JC-24B; B: JC-24BL):
Wing span: A   8·53 m (28 ft 0 in)

B	10·46 m (34 ft 4 in)
Wing chord at root	2·44 m (8 ft 0 in)
Wing chord at tip	1·22 m (4 ft 0 in)
Wing area, gross: A	15·61 m² (168 sq ft)
B	19·32 m² (208 sq ft)
Wing aspect ratio: A	4·7
B	5·7
Length overall	5·64 m (18 ft 6 in)
Height overall	1·98 m (6 ft 6 in)
Tailplane span	2·44 m (8 ft 0 in)
Wheel track	1·30 m (4 ft 3 in)
Wheelbase	0·99 m (3 ft 3 in)
Propeller diameter	1·12 m (3 ft 8 in)

WEIGHTS:
Weight empty: A	75 kg (165 lb)
B	82 kg (180 lb)
Max fuel weight	9 kg (20 lb)
Max T-O weight: A	175 kg (385 lb)
B	204 kg (450 lb)

PERFORMANCE (at max T-O weight):
Never-exceed speed and max level speed:
  A   43 knots (80 km/h; 50 mph)
  B   35 knots (64 km/h; 40 mph)
Max cruising speed at S/L:
  A   30 knots (56 km/h; 35 mph)
  B   26 knots (48 km/h; 30 mph)
Econ cruising speed at S/L:
  A   26 knots (48 km/h; 30 mph)
  B   22 knots (40 km/h; 25 mph)
Stalling speed, power on:
  A   16 knots (29 km/h; 18 mph)
  B   13·5 knots (25 km/h; 15·5 mph)
Max rate of climb at S/L: A   183 m (600 ft)/min
  B   198 m (650 ft)/min
Service ceiling: A   over 3,050 m (10,000 ft)
T-O run: A   30·5 m (100 ft)
T-O to 15 m (50 ft): A   91 m (300 ft)
Landing run: A   18 m (60 ft)
Range with optional fuel 78 nm (145 km; 90 miles)

WENDT
WENDT AIRCRAFT ENGINEERING
9900 Alto Drive, La Mesa, California 92041
Telephone: (714) 463 8473

Wendt Aircraft Engineering designed and built the prototype of a two-seat sporting monoplane which is known as the WH-1 Traveler. The design originated on 4 September 1969, and construction of the prototype began on 26 November of the same year. The first flight was made on 15 March 1972, and FAA certification in the Experimental category was awarded on 30 May 1972. Plans of the Traveler are available to amateur constructors, and at least 60 sets had been sold by early 1980, at which time eight aircraft were under construction and two completed.

WENDT WH-1 TRAVELER

TYPE: Two-seat sporting aircraft.

WINGS: Cantilever low-wing monoplane. Wing section NACA 64₁A-418. Dihedral 5° 30'. Incidence 2°. No sweepback. Constant-chord two-spar structure. Spruce

spars, marine plywood ribs, pine leading- and trailing-edges and ³/₃₂ in mahogany plywood skin from leading-edge to 37% chord. Aft of main spar, wing is Dacron-covered. Plain ailerons, hinged at upper surface, made of spruce with plywood ribs, and Dacron-covered. No flaps. Bungee trim on control column. Glassfibre wingtips.

FUSELAGE: Conventional structure of spruce frames and longerons, plywood formers and tension ties, with steel tube overturn structure in the cockpit section. Fuselage undersurface and sides covered with ¼ in mahogany plywood. Upper surface Dacron-covered. Glassfibre nose cowl.

TAIL UNIT: Cantilever wooden structure with swept vertical surfaces and all-moving tailplane. Each surface has a spruce spar, spruce and plywood ribs, and a ¹/₁₆ in mahogany plywood torsion box. All surfaces Dacron-covered. Static balance weights near tips of tailplane leading-edge. Tailplane has a half-span trim and anti-balance tab. Tailplane tips of glassfibre.

LANDING GEAR: Non-retractable tricycle type. Cantilever spring steel main gear. Steerable nosewheel has coil spring shock-absorption. Cleveland 5·00-5 wheels with Armstrong tyres, pressure 2·07 bars (30 lb/sq in). Cleveland caliper-type brakes. Glassfibre wheel fairings.

POWER PLANT: Prototype has one 56 kW (75 hp) Continental A75 flat-four engine, driving a McCauley Type 1C90 two-blade fixed-pitch metal propeller with glassfibre spinner. Design is suitable for installation of engines from 48·5-74·5 kW (65 to 100 hp). One aerofoil-shaped glassfibre fuel tank at each wingtip, capacity 41·5 litres (11 US gallons). Total fuel capacity 83 litres (22 US gallons). Refuelling points on upper surface of each wingtip. Oil capacity 3·8 litres (1·0 US gallon).

ACCOMMODATION: Pilot and passenger in tandem, beneath canopy which has large transparent panels at each side. Canopy hinged on port side. Dual controls standard. Stowage for 23 kg (50 lb) baggage aft of rear seat.

Watson GW-1 Windwagon (half an 1,800 cc Volkswagen modified motor car engine) *(Howard Levy)*

Wendt WH-1 Traveler two-seat homebuilt aircraft

Weedhopper JC-24BL Weedhopper with increased-span wings

White Der Jäger D.IX built by Mr B. W. Salyer *(J. M. G. Gradidge)*

SYSTEM: Electrical system powered by 30A engine-driven alternator. 12V 25Ah storage battery in glassfibre battery box in aft fuselage.
ELECTRONICS: Prototype has a Narco Escort 110 com transceiver.
DIMENSIONS, EXTERNAL:

Wing span	9·14 m (30 ft 0 in)
Wing chord, constant	1·20 m (3 ft 11¼ in)
Wing area, gross	10·96 m² (118 sq ft)
Wing aspect ratio	7·63
Length overall	5·94 m (19 ft 6 in)
Height overall	2·08 m (6 ft 10 in)
Tailplane span	2·44 m (8 ft 0 in)
Wheel track	1·93 m (6 ft 4 in)

Wheelbase	1·45 m (4 ft 9 in)
Propeller diameter	1·80 m (5 ft 11 in)

DIMENSION, INTERNAL:

Max width	0·71 m (2 ft 4 in)

WEIGHTS:

Weight empty, equipped	408 kg (900 lb)
Max T-O and landing weight	635 kg (1,400 lb)

PERFORMANCE (at max T-O weight):
Never-exceed speed 142 knots (264 km/h; 164 mph)
Max level speed at 1,220 m (4,000 ft)
114 knots (211 km/h; 131 mph)
Max cruising speed at 1,220 m (4,000 ft)
107 knots (198 km/h; 123 mph)

Econ cruising speed at 1,220 m (4,000 ft)
100 knots (185 km/h; 115 mph)
Stalling speed   50 knots (92 km/h; 57 mph)
Max rate of climb at S/L (no passenger)
229 m (750 ft)/min
Max rate of climb at S/L (with passenger)
152 m (500 ft)/min

Service ceiling	3,960 m (13,000 ft)
T-O run	244 m (800 ft)
Landing run	213 m (700 ft)

Range with max fuel, no reserves
503 nm (933 km; 580 miles)
Range with max payload, no reserves
416 nm (772 km; 480 miles)

WHITE
E. MARSHALL WHITE
Meadowlark Airport, 5141 Warner Avenue, Huntington Beach, California 92649
Telephone: (714) 846 2409

WHITE WW-1 DER JÄGER D.IX
Mr Marshall White, a staff engineer of TRW Systems at Redondo Beach, California, designed an unusual homebuilt aircraft named Der Jäger D.IX, which is reminiscent of several German designs, mainly of first World War vintage. The wings are patterned on those of an Albatros D.Va, with the landing gear fairings of the Focke-Wulf Stösser and tail unit of the Fokker D.VII.

Design and construction of the prototype started simultaneously at the beginning of 1969, as Mr White's fifth homebuilt, and first flight of the prototype was made on 7 September 1969.

Plans and kits of materials, as well as some of the more difficult-to-construct parts in finished form, are available to amateur constructors, and at least 75 Der Jäger D.IXs are under construction. The first completed aircraft to be seen at an EAA Fly-in at Oshkosh, in 1974, was N1007, built by Mr Ray D. Fulwiler of Algoma, Wisconsin, with a 112 kW (150 hp) Avco Lycoming engine.

The following details apply to the prototype in its original form. It has since been re-engined with a 112 kW (150 hp) Avco Lycoming, but no details have been received of performance with this more powerful engine.

TYPE: Single-seat sporting biplane.
WINGS: Forward-stagger single-bay biplane with N-type interplane and centre-section struts. Single streamlined lift strut from each side of lower fuselage to attachment point of forward interplane strut on upper wing. No flying or landing wires. Aerofoil section M-6. Incidence 3° upper wing, 2° lower wings. Spruce spars and plywood ribs, fabric covered. Internal steel tube bracing. Ailerons in both top and bottom wings. Scalloped trailing-edge to both wings.
FUSELAGE: Welded 4130 steel tube structure, fabric covered. Aluminium engine cowling.
TAIL UNIT: Wire-braced welded 4130 steel tube structure, with sheet metal ribs, fabric covered. Balanced rudder and elevator. Ground-adjustable trim tabs in elevator.
LANDING GEAR: Non-retractable tailwheel type. Main legs each consist of an A frame, welded into the fuselage, with tension springs in the centre-fuselage to cushion landing shock. Main wheels and tyres size 5·00-5. Glassfibre wheel fairings.
POWER PLANT: One 86 kW (115 hp) Avco Lycoming O-235-C1 flat-four engine, driving a McCauley two-blade propeller. Structure suitable for alternative power plants from 1,600 cc Volkswagen up to 112 kW (150 hp). Fuel contained in two tanks, one in upper wing centre-section, capacity 53 litres (14 US gallons), one in fuselage, capacity 38 litres (10 US gallons); total 91 litres (24 US gallons).

ACCOMMODATION: Single seat in open cockpit, with headrest faired into wood or glassfibre fuselage turtleback.
EQUIPMENT: Two dummy machine-guns mounted on top of fuselage, forward of cockpit. Dummy bomb, carried between legs of main landing gear, can be adapted as oil tank for smoke discharge system.
DIMENSIONS, EXTERNAL:

Wing span, upper	6·10 m (20 ft 0 in)
Wing span, lower	4·88 m (16 ft 0 in)
Wing chord, upper at root	1·07 m (3 ft 6 in)
Wing chord, upper at tip	1·22 m (4 ft 0 in)
Wing chord, lower, constant	0·91 m (3 ft 0 in)
Wing area, gross	10·68 m² (115 sq ft)
Length overall	5·18 m (17 ft 0 in)
Tailplane span	2·44 m (8 ft 0 in)
Wheel track	1·52 m (5 ft 0 in)
Propeller diameter	1·68 m (5 ft 6 in)

WEIGHTS:

Weight empty	242 kg (534 lb)
Max T-O weight	403 kg (888 lb)

PERFORMANCE (at max T-O weight):
Never-exceed speed 152 knots (282 km/h; 175 mph)
Max level speed at 610 m (2,000 ft)
126 knots (233 km/h; 145 mph)
Max cruising speed at 610 m (2,000 ft)
116 knots (214 km/h; 133 mph)
Stalling speed   47 knots (87 km/h; 54 mph)
Max rate of climb at S/L   732 m (2,400 ft)/min
T-O run   46 m (150 ft)

WITTMAN
S. J. WITTMAN
Box 2672, Oshkosh, Wisconsin 54901

Famous as a racing pilot since 1926, Steve Wittman has designed and built a large number of different racing and touring aeroplanes at Winnebago County Airport, of which he became manager in 1931.

Most popular current Wittman design is the W-8 Tailwind side-by-side two-seat light aeroplane. The prototype was built in 1952-53 and proved so successful that sets of plans and prefabricated components were made available to amateur builders. By early 1980 there were more than 325 Model W-8 Tailwinds flying, including a number built in foreign countries, and more than 100 were known to be under construction. In January 1968 Mr Wittman's plans

were approved by the Australian Department of Civil Aviation.

In 1966, a more powerful six-cylinder Continental engine was installed in a Tailwind redesigned to take the added weight and power. This version is designated W-9 and was described in the 1978-79 *Jane's*. Also flying is a Tailwind Model W-10 with a converted Oldsmobile motor car engine (see 1979-80 *Jane's*).

Wittman W-8 Tailwind built in South Africa *(R. Kunert)*

Replica of the Travel Air Mystery S racer built by Mr Jim Younkin *(Howard Levy)*

WITTMAN TAILWIND MODEL W-8

Some Tailwinds have been built with tricycle landing gear, retractable main wheels and other design changes. The following data refer to the standard W-8 Tailwind built to Mr Wittman's plans:

TYPE: Two-seat cabin monoplane.

WINGS: Braced high-wing monoplane. Wing section is a combination of NACA 4309 (upper surface) and NACA 0006 (lower surface). Thickness/chord ratio 11·5%. No dihedral. Incidence 1°. Wooden structure with plywood and fabric covering. Single bracing strut each side. Ailerons and flaps of steel and stainless steel construction.

FUSELAGE: Steel tube structure, fabric-covered.

TAIL UNIT: Cantilever structure of steel and stainless steel. Ground-adjustable trim tabs in control surfaces.

LANDING GEAR: Non-retractable tailwheel type. Spring steel cantilever main legs. Goodyear 15 × 5 main wheels and tyres, pressure 2·21 bars (32 lb/sq in). Goodyear brakes.

POWER PLANT: Normally one 67 kW (90 hp) Continental C90-12F flat-four engine, driving a Sensenich or Flottorp two-blade fixed-pitch wood propeller. Alternative engines are the 63·5 kW (85 hp) Continental C85, 74·5 kW (100 hp) Continental O-200, 86 kW (115 hp) Avco Lycoming O-235 or 104·5 kW (140 hp) Avco Lycoming O-290. One fuel tank of 94·5 litres (25 US gallons) capacity in fuselage. Oil capacity 1·85-2·8 litres (4-6 US quarts).

ACCOMMODATION: Two seats side by side in enclosed cabin, with door on each side. Space for 27 kg (60 lb) baggage.

DIMENSIONS, EXTERNAL:
Wing span	6·86 m (22 ft 6 in)
Wing chord, constant	1·22 m (4 ft 0 in)
Wing area, gross	8·36 m² (90 sq ft)
Wing aspect ratio	5·5
Length overall	5·87 m (19 ft 3 in)
Height overall	1·73 m (5 ft 8 in)
Tailplane span	2·03 m (6 ft 8 in)
Wheel track	1·65 m (5 ft 5 in)
Propeller diameter	1·63 m (5 ft 4 in)

WEIGHTS (74·5 kW; 100 hp Continental engine):
Weight empty	318 kg (700 lb)
Max T-O weight	590 kg (1,300 lb)

PERFORMANCE (74·5 kW; 100 hp Continental engine at max T-O weight):
Never-exceed speed	160 knots (297 km/h; 185 mph)
Max level speed at S/L	143 knots (265 km/h; 165 mph)
Max cruising speed	139 knots (257 km/h; 160 mph)
Econ cruising speed	113 knots (209 km/h; 130 mph)
Stalling speed, flaps down	48 knots (89 km/h; 55 mph)
Max rate of climb at S/L	275 m (900 ft)/min
Service ceiling	4,876 m (16,000 ft)
T-O run	245 m (800 ft)
T-O to 15 m (50 ft)	405 m (1,325 ft)
Landing from 15 m (50 ft)	350 m (1,150 ft)
Landing run	183 m (600 ft)

Range with max payload at 3,050 m (10,000 ft), no reserves:
at 139 knots (257 km/h; 160 mph)	521 nm (965 km; 600 miles)
at 122 knots (225 km/h; 140 mph)	607 nm (1,125 km; 700 miles)

YOUNKIN
JIM YOUNKIN
Springdale, Arkansas

YOUNKIN TRAVEL AIR MYSTERY S REPLICA

Mr Jim Younkin has built a replica of the Travel Air Mystery S racer which won the 1929 Thompson Trophy contest. Construction took 2¾ years at a cost of $15,000. First flight was made in March 1979. Unlike the original, the replica has a fuselage and tail unit constructed of steel tubing, with wood and fabric covering; the wings are of wood. Power is provided by a 224 kW (300 hp) Avco Lycoming R-680 engine, inside a modified cowling from a Beech AT-10. Fuel capacity is 227 litres (60 US gallons).

TYPE: Replica of the Travel Air Mystery S.

DIMENSIONS, EXTERNAL:
Wing span	9·14 m (30 ft 0 in)
Wing chord, constant	1·60 m (5 ft 3 in)
Length overall	6·25 m (20 ft 6 in)
Wheel track	1·73 m (5 ft 8 in)

WEIGHTS:
Weight empty	816·5 kg (1,800 lb)
Max T-O weight	1,111 kg (2,450 lb)

PERFORMANCE:
Cruising speed	161 knots (298 km/h; 185 mph)
Landing speed	61 knots (113 km/h; 70 mph)
Max rate of climb at S/L	488 m (1,600 ft)/min
Service ceiling	3,660 m (12,000 ft)
Range with max fuel	565 nm (1,046 km; 650 miles)

SAILPLANES

(For specification data, see Tables at end of Section)

AUSTRALIA

BETTERIDGE
DAVID BETTERIDGE

c/o Box 390, Morphett Vale, South Australia 5162

Mr Betteridge has designed an unusual motor glider, the general appearance of which is shown in an accompanying photograph. It was test-flown by Mr Colin Scott at Aldinga, South Australia, in early 1979, and was due to be

put into production by Free Flight Gliders towards the end of that year.

Of sweptwing tail-less configuration, with a swept fin and rudder at each wingtip, the aircraft has a single-seat open cockpit and is powered by a 175 cc Yamaha motorcycle engine, driving a pusher propeller. A tailwheel-type non-retractable landing gear is fitted.

The prototype is built of aluminium and plywood, but

glassfibre will be used for production aircraft, which will be capable of being dismantled and carried on a car trailer.

SPECIFICATION:
Wing span	10·00 m (32 ft 9¾ in)
Length overall	3·00 m (9 ft 10 in)
Weight empty	180 kg (397 lb)
T-O and landing run	50 m (165 ft)

BUCHANAN
JOHN BUCHANAN

Mr Buchanan is building the prototype of a new sailplane which he describes as "just a pod big enough to fit the pilot, with a wing attached". The wing, constructed of carbonfibre and glassfibre, is of swept configuration, with a

15 metre span (49 ft 2½ in), narrow chord and very high aspect ratio. It is mid-mounted on the small, streamlined fuselage pod, at the rear of which is a small sweptback fin; there are no horizontal tail surfaces. A flush-fitting one-piece cockpit transparency encloses the pilot. Fuselage

length is 3·70 m (12 ft 1¾ in).

Mr Buchanan, who is a graduate aeronautical engineer from the Cranfield Institute of Technology in England and a former RAAF pilot, is building the sailplane under a $A10,000 grant from the Australian government.

SUNDERLAND
GARY SUNDERLAND

1 Nicholas Grove, Heatherton, Victoria 3202
Telephone: 551 2564

Mr Sunderland has built a 15 metre sailplane known as the MOBA-2C.

SUNDERLAND MOBA-2C

The original 2A version of the MOBA was one of two 13 metre sailplanes which competed with one another in 1972 in a design competition held by the Australian Gliding Federation. The MOBA-2B was a 15 metre version of

the 2A, and the MOBA-2C represents an improved version of both earlier models.

Construction of the MOBA-2C began in 1975, and it flew for the first time on 12 December 1979. Series production is not intended.

TYPE: Single-seat 15 metre Standard Class sailplane; *g* limits +4; −1·5.

AIRFRAME: Cantilever high-wing monoplane, with T tail. Box-spar wings, of Wortmann FX-67-K-150 section, built in three pieces. Dihedral 1° at tips. Plywood ribs, with urethane foam infill; spar of pop-riveted

aluminium alloy sheet. Epoxy-resin glasscloth skin. Aluminium alloy plain flaps on trailing-edges, serving also as airbrakes; GRP-covered wooden ailerons. Nose and central fuselage are riveted aluminium alloy box structures, with sliding nose of balsa/GRP sandwich; centre fairing of foam with GRP skin; tailboom is of riveted aluminium alloy sheet. Tail unit of wood, with foam infill and GRP skin. Elevator has spring trim. Manually retractable monowheel and non-retractable tailwheel, both from a Standard Libelle. Cockpit canopy slides forward with fuselage nose section. No water ballast provision.

TODHUNTER
R. W. TODHUNTER

5 Leemon Street, Condell Park, New South Wales 2200

Mr Reg Todhunter, designer and builder of the Skycycle man-powered aircraft (see Homebuilts section of the 1979-80 *Jane's*), is developing an ultralight powered sailplane known as the Blue Wren.

TODHUNTER T-5 BLUE WREN

Basic design and stressing of the Blue Wren had been completed by early 1980, and it was expected that the aircraft itself would be completed by November 1980. It has been designed to comply initially with the Australian Dept of Air Transport ANO Section 95-10. In parallel

development is a horizontally-opposed two-stroke engine, which will feature a reduction drive to the propeller shaft. Extremely economical fuel consumption is anticipated.

No illustration was available in early 1980, but the following are the Blue Wren's salient characteristics:
TYPE: Single-seat ultralight powered sailplane.
AIRFRAME: Cantilever tapered high-wing monoplane, with Wortmann wing section. Pod-type fuselage of glassfibre over a steel tube frame. Tapered 2024-T3 aluminium alloy tailboom faired to bottom of pod. Engine, mounted above boom, is faired in behind streamlined cockpit canopy and drives a pusher propeller centred behind wing trailing-edge. Propeller can be stopped in horizontal position to reduce drag in soaring mode. T

tailplane, with elevators. Non-retractable monowheel, with brake.
POWER PLANT: One 11-12 kW (15-16 hp) RTS 162 two-stroke flat-twin engine, driving (on prototype) a 0·91 m (3 ft) diameter fixed-pitch pusher propeller.

DIMENSIONS, EXTERNAL:
Wing span	10·97 m (36 ft 0 in)
Wing area, gross	8·08 m² (87·0 sq ft)
Wing aspect ratio	14·89
Length overall	5·49 m (18 ft 0 in)

WEIGHTS:
Weight empty	100 kg (220 lb)
Max T-O weight	181 kg (400 lb)

AUSTRIA

BRDITSCHKA
H. W. BRDITSCHKA OHG

A-4053 Haid, Dr Schärfstrasse 42, Postfach 12
Telephone: 07229/8355
Telex: 21909
DIRECTOR: Heinz W. Brditschka

BRDITSCHKA HB-21

The HB-21, which first flew on 22 March 1974, is essen-

tially an enlarged version of the HB-3 (1977-78 *Jane's*), with increased-span wings, tandem seating for two persons, and a Volkswagen engine. Four prototypes were built. Certification was granted in February 1978, and 15 HB-21s had been built by early 1980.
TYPE: Two-seat motor glider; *g* limits +5·3; −2·7.
AIRFRAME: Fabric-covered wooden wings, with Wortmann sections (FX-61-184 at root, FX-60-126 at tip). Dihedral 2°. Incidence 3°. All-wood ailerons and

upper-surface spoilers. Steel tube fuselage with glassfibre covering. Fixed-incidence all-wood tailplane. Non-retractable tricycle landing gear, with Tost mechanical main-wheel brakes.
POWER PLANT: One 35·75 kW (48 hp) VW-Westermayer 1600G flat-four piston engine, driving a Hoffmann HO 14-175 117 LD two-blade fixed-pitch pusher propeller. Aluminium fuel tank in wing, capacity 54 litres (11·9 Imp gallons). Fuel is 100LL avgas.

BRAZIL

CTA
CENTRO TÉCNICO AEROESPACIAL

São José dos Campos, São Paulo State
IPD (Instituto de Pesquisas e Desenvolvimento)/PAR (Divisão de Aeronaves)

The IPD is the aeronautical research and development institute of the CTA (see Aircraft section). The PAR is its Aircraft Division, having responsibility for flight testing, evaluating, certificating and developing new aircraft projects. One of these is the Urubu two-seat all-metal training sailplane.

IPD/PAR PE-80367 URUBU

The PE-80367 programme is intended to develop a modern training sailplane which, after testing and certification, is to be handed over to the Brazilian aircraft industry for series production, as a replacement for the Czechoslovak Blanik sailplanes used at present. One static test prototype, and one (PP-ZUR) for flight test and certification, have been built; first flight was scheduled to take place in 1979.
TYPE: Tandem two-seat training sailplane; *g* limits: semi-aerobatic, +6·2/−3·4; fully aerobatic, +6·5/−3·5.

AIRFRAME: Cantilever shoulder-wing monoplane. Wing section NACA 63₂A-615 at root, NACA 63₁A-412 at tip. Dihedral 3° on lower surface. Sweepforward 1° 51' at quarter-chord. Incidence 3° at root. All-metal two-spar wings, with light alloy airbrakes in upper and lower surfaces, and all-metal ailerons. All-metal semi-monocoque oval-section fuselage. All-metal tail unit, with fixed-incidence tailplane; controllable trim tab in each elevator. Non-retractable rubber-sprung monowheel, with mechanical brake; non-retractable tailwheel.

Prototype motor glider designed by Mr David Betteridge of South Australia
(Advertiser Newspapers Ltd)

Sunderland MOBA-2C single-seat Standard Class sailplane

Brditschka HB-21 two-seat motor glider

EEUFMG (CEA)
ESCOLA DE ENGENHARIA DA UNIVERSIDADE FEDERAL DE MINAS GERAIS (Centro de Estudos Aeronáuticos)

Rua Espirito Santo 35, 30.000 Belo Horizonte, Minas
Gerais State
Telephone: 222 4011
HEAD OF CEA: Prof Cláudio Pinto de Barros

CB-2/B MINUANO

The Air Research Centre of the Engineering School at
Minas Gerais Federal University began the design of this
single-seat sailplane in 1969. Its designation indicates that
it is the second design by Professor Cláudio Barros. The
CB-2 prototype (PP-ZPZ) flew for the first time on 20
December 1975 and was described in the 1977-78 *Jane's*.

A further four Minuanos were ordered, and the second
aircraft was scheduled for completion by the end of 1979.
This incorporates several modifications, and is designated
CB-2/B; the description applies to this version. The
Minuano is named after a strong, cold wind in southern
Brazil.

TYPE: Single-seat high-performance sailplane; *g* limits (at
safety factor of 1·72): normal, +5·3/−3·0; ultimate,
+9·14/−5·19.

AIRFRAME: High-wing monoplane, with Wortmann
FX-67-K-170/17 (root) and FX-60-126 (tip) wing sections. Single aluminium alloy main spar; wing skin of
plywood/glassfibre honeycomb sandwich. Flaps and
ailerons, similar except for wooden spars, are interconnected; flaps can be used also as airbrakes. Provision for
80 kg (176 lb) of water ballast. All-wood semi-
monocoque fuselage. Plywood-covered tail surfaces,
stiffened with foam plastics. All-moving tailplane, with
trim tab in each half. Retractable unsprung monowheel
(tyre pressure 2·45 bars; 35·5 lb/sq in), with internal
shoe brake, and sprung tailskid.

IPE
INDÚSTRIA PARANAENSE DE ESTRUTURAS

J. Durski 357, 80.000 Curitiba, Paraná State
MANAGER: Eng J. C. Boscardin

IPE has recently completed building the KW 1 b 2
Quero Quero II single-seat training sailplane, and in 1980
was continuing to develop a two-seat training sailplane
known as the IPE 02 Nhapecam. A licence has also been
acquired for the construction of three examples of the
Swiss Neukom Elfe 4, with wings and part of the fuselage
of sandwich construction.

IPE KW 1 b 2 QUERO QUERO II

The KW 1 b 2 made its first flight on 1 October 1972,
and CTA certification was awarded in December 1976.

By 7 February 1980, IPE had completed one static and
three flying prototypes, four first-series production aircraft (one of which was lost in a non-fatal accident), a
second-series batch of 20, and a final batch of eight aircraft. This last batch each have an Akaflieg Braunschweig
variometer compensation device.

The Quero Quero II was described and illustrated in the
1979-80 *Jane's*.

IPE 02 NHAPECAM

The general appearance of this aircraft can be seen from
the accompanying illustration. The prototype (PP-ZQL)
flew for the first time on 24 May 1979, and had accumulated more than 50 hours' flying by mid-February 1980.

Two more prototypes were then under construction,
and an order for at least 30, for Brazilian flying clubs, was
awaiting confirmation.

TYPE: Tandem two-seat training sailplane.
AIRFRAME: Shoulder-wing monoplane with Scheibe Spatz
(modified) wing section. Ailerons and upper/lower surface spoilers. Fabric-covered elevators and rudder.
Non-retractable monowheel, in streamlined fairing, and
tailwheel.

IPE 03

The IPE 03, of which brief details were given in the
1979-80 *Jane's*, has been shelved for the time being.

RIO CLARO
AÉRO CLUBE DE RIO CLARO

Rua Cinco 1152, 13500 Rio Claro (Caixa Postal 147), São
Paulo State

The Rio Claro aero club is building, under the direction
of Eng Sylvio de Oliveira, an all-wood sporting glider
known as the **Araponga**. General appearance can be seen
from the accompanying three-view drawing; first flight
was expected in March 1980.

SIDOU
ENG ANTONIO MENEZES SIDOU

Rua Luciana de Abreu 184, Moinhos de Vento, 90.000
Porto Alegre, Rio Grande do Sul

SIDOU JOÃO GRANDE (STORK)

Eng Sidou is developing the João Grande at Passo Fun-
do, Rio Grande do Sul, currently with GRP construction
instead of the original wooden-construction version. For
general appearance, see accompanying three-view drawing.

TYPE: Tandem two-seat Open Class and advanced training
sailplane (OSTIV aerobatic category A); *g* limits
+9·75; −6·00 (ultimate).
AIRFRAME: Cantilever mid-wing monoplane, with cambered wingtips and T tail. Wortmann wing sections:
FX-61-184 (modified) at root, FX-60-126 (modified)
at tip. Dihedral 3° 36'. GRP structure, with wide-span
ailerons and upper/lower surface Schempp-Hirth airbrakes. All wing and tail control surfaces statically and
dynamically balanced. GRP semi-monocoque fuselage.
Jettisonable cockpit canopy. Retractable rubber-sprung
monowheel, with mechanical brake, and tail bumper.

CANADA

MARSDEN
PROF DAVID J. MARSDEN

c/o Dept of Mechanical Engineering, University of
Alberta, Edmonton, Alberta T6G 2G8
Telephone: (403) 432 3705

Prof Marsden of the University of Alberta acquired
from Operation Sigma Ltd the **Sigma** variable-geometry
sailplane last described in the 1974-75 *Jane's*; it now carries the Canadian registration C-GVJW-X. He replaced
the former area-increasing flap system by full-span slotted
flaps similar to those used on the Gemini, a two-seat
sailplane of his own design. Modification work was carried
out at the Cranfield Institute of Technology in the UK,
where Prof Marsden spent a sabbatical year during 1977-
78. Two half-hour test flights were made at Cranfield
before his return to Canada. After 16 hours of flight testing in 1979, handling and performance are considered to
be very satisfactory. Plans for 1980 included entry into
competition at the Nationals level, record attempts, and
continuing flight test evaluation.

MARSDEN GEMINI

This successful variable-geometry sailplane flew for the
first time in October 1973.

The full-span slotted-flap configuration has a number of
advantages over the chord-extending type as used originally on Sigma. Apart from the obvious advantage of
simpler flap extension mechanisms, it is possible to achieve
higher overall lift coefficient; even more significant is the
excellent aileron effectiveness when the flaps are
extended. Climb capability is similar to that of unballasted

CTA (IPD/PAR) PE-80367 Urubu *(Roberto Pereira de Andrade)*

First prototype of the IPE 02 two-seat training sailplane

Marsden Gemini two-seat variable-geometry sailplane

Prototype EEUFMG CB-2 Minuano single-seat sailplane

Rio Claro Araponga all-wood sporting glider *(Michael A. Badrocke)*

Sidou João Grande *(Michael A. Badrocke)*

Sigma variable-geometry sailplane (see Marsden entry) flying over Alberta

15 metre sailplanes, and high-speed glide performance is comparable to that of Open Class sailplanes when the Gemini is flown at its normal wing loading of just over 43·9 kg/m² (9 lb/sq ft) with two occupants.

The performance figures given in the table are those measured in October 1978, but Gemini was expected to improve upon these after air leaks between the fuselage and wing, and around the canopy joints and wheel-well doors, had been sealed.

Type: Side-by-side two-seat variable-geometry sailplane; g limits +6·0; −6·0.
Airframe: Cantilever mid-wing monoplane, with T tail. Wing section Wortmann FX-61-163, modified for slotted flap. Dihedral 3°. Incidence 0°. All-metal single box-spar structure, built in four portions, with metal skins providing torsional stiffness. Full-span all-metal (2024-T3 aluminium alloy) slotted flap system, outer segments of which function also as ailerons. No spoilers

or airbrakes. Inboard flap segments can be deflected up to 75° for approach control. Forward fuselage has a structural glassfibre shell, with a steel tube frame to carry wing loads, and sheet metal internal bulkheads. Tailcone is a monocoque of aluminium alloy sheet. All-metal tail unit, with full-span anti-balance tab on all-moving tailplane. Mechanically retractable oleo-sprung monowheel, with hydraulic disc brake. Non-retractable tailwheel.

CZECHOSLOVAKIA

OMNIPOL
OMNIPOL FOREIGN TRADE CORPORATION
Nekázanka 11, 11221 Prague 1
Telephone: 268261-8

Telex: 121299
Sales Manager: Ing Miloslav Branný
Omnipol handles all exports of products of the Czechoslovak aircraft industry.

LET
LET NÁRODNI PODNIK (Let National Corporation)
Uherské Hradiste-Kunovice

In addition to its work on powered aircraft, Let National Corporation manufactured the L-13 Blaník sailplane.

LET L-13 BLANÍK
The Blaník was designed for training in all categories

from elementary to 'blind' flying and for high-performance flight. It is fully aerobatic when flown solo and capable of basic aerobatic manoeuvres when carrying a crew of two. First flight was made in March 1956.
Production terminated at the end of 1978, and a total of

2,623 had been delivered by January 1980. Of these, over 2,000 had been exported to customers in more than 40 countries, including more than 1,000 to the USSR, approx 200 to the USA, approx 150 to the UK and more than 100 each to Australia and Canada.

A description of the standard Blanik can be found in the 1978-79 *Jane's*. During the course of its career, a number of Blaniks were converted into motor gliders, and all known details of these were given in the 1979-80 *Jane's*. Since then, further details have been received of the L-13SW (listed incorrectly in the 1979-80 edition as the L-13SV). These details are as follows:

L-13SW. With Walter Mikron IIIA engine mounted in nose. First flown (OK-068) on 10 May 1978.

POWER PLANT: One Walter Mikron IIIA piston engine, rated at 48 kW (65 hp) for T-O and 35 kW (47 hp) maximum cruising power, driving an Avia V 218 two-blade propeller.

DIMENSIONS, EXTERNAL:
Wing span	17·00 m (55 ft 9¼ in)
Length overall	8·20 m (26 ft 10¾ in)
Height over tail	2·30 m (7 ft 6½ in)

WEIGHTS:
Weight empty	440 kg (970 lb)
Max T-O weight	670 kg (1,477 lb)

PERFORMANCE (at max T-O weight, powered, except where indicated):
Never-exceed speed	132 knots (245 km/h; 152 mph)
Max cruising speed	108 knots (200 km/h; 124 mph)
Stalling speed, power off	32·5 knots (60 km/h; 37 mph)
Max rate of climb at S/L	162 m (531 ft)/min
T-O run	240 m (788 ft)
T-O to 15 m (50 ft)	520 m (1,706 ft)
Landing from 15 m (50 ft)	370 m (1,214 ft)
Landing run	110 m (361 ft)
Best glide ratio at 49 knots (90 km/h; 56 mph)	24

VSO
VYVOJOVÁ SKUPINA ORLICAN
c/o Orlican Národní Podnik, 565 37 Chocen
Telephone: Chocen 70 and 80
Telex: 0 196 210
CHIEF DESIGNER: Dipl Ing Jan Janovec

This group was formed by members of the former VSB (1973-74 *Jane's*) and some of the design staff of the Orlican National Works. Its first product is the VSO 10.

VSO 10
Design of the VSO 10 began in March 1972. Construc-

tion of three prototypes (one for structural test and two for flight test) began in 1975, and the first flight took place on 26 October 1976. Series production began in December 1978, with first deliveries being made to the Aeroclub of the Czechoslovakian SSR.

In 1979, VSO also produced a number of the VSO 10C Club Class version, with non-retractable monowheel. Two of these were placed 1st and 2nd in the International Club Class Competition at Örebro, Sweden, in that year.

TYPE: Single-seat high-performance sailplane; *g* limits +5·3/−3·5.

AIRFRAME: Cantilever shoulder-wing monoplane, with

Wortmann wing sections: FX-61-163 at root, FX-60-126 at tip. Dihedral 3°. All-wood single-spar forward-swept wings with sandwich skin. All-metal DFS airbrakes on upper surfaces. All-wood slotted ailerons. Glassfibre monocoque front and centre fuselage sections, latter reinforced by steel tube frame. Monocoque rear fuselage of aluminium alloy sheet. Metal T tail with fabric-covered elevators and rudder. Fixed-incidence tailplane. Retractable rubber-sprung monowheel (tyre pressure approx 2·45 bars; 35·5 lb/sq in), with drum brake. Semi-recessed unsprung tailwheel. Detachable cockpit canopy.

DENMARK

PROJEKT 8
PROJEKT 8 I/S
Fynsvej 56, DK-4000 Roskilde

DOLPHIN
The Projekt 8 I/S company, formed by Mr Helge Petersen and 10 other glider pilots, is building a two-seat motor glider known as the Dolphin. Construction is taking place at three separate sites near Copenhagen. The fuselage, power plant installation and tail unit have been completed, and successful initial taxying trials have been carried out using a spar-and-outrigger-wheels assembly in place of the wings. Construction of the wings was proceeding in early 1980.

Dolphin is a testbed for the power system to be used in developing an improved motor glider known as Dolphin M2. The latter is described separately; the following description applies to the Dolphin prototype:

TYPE: Tandem two-seat motor glider; *g* limits +6; −4.
AIRFRAME: Cantilever mid-wing monoplane with T tail. Wortmann and NACA wing sections: FX-67-K-170 on centre-section; outer panels vary through FX-67-K-150 to NACA 64-212 at tip. Dihedral 4°. Aluminium

wing centre-section; outer panels, including flaps and ailerons, of wood and glassfibre. Aluminium upper-surface airbrakes. Welded steel tube forward fuselage, covered by light glassfibre shell; wooden rear fuselage, reinforced by glassfibre. Wooden tail unit, with fixed-incidence tailplane. Central trim tab in elevator, inset tab at base of rudder. Semi-retractable rubber-sprung Tost main wheel; Tost nosewheel; steerable solid-tyre tailwheel; retractable wingtip balancer wheels. Cockpit canopy opens sideways.

POWER PLANT: One 40·25 kW (54 hp) VW 1600 engine, driving a two-blade tractor propeller, mounted on pylon which retracts rearward into top of fuselage when not in use.

DOLPHIN M2
Dolphin M2 is a developed version of the original Dolphin, from which it differs mainly in having a redesigned fuselage of improved aerodynamic shape, and sweptback fin and rudder. Design of the fuselage, of which the plug for the moulds was being made in early 1980, was by Mr Petersen's son Lars. Manufacture of the M2 will be under-

taken by KFI (Kalundborg FlyIndustri) of Holbaekvej 109, DK-4400 Kalundborg.

TYPE: Side-by-side two-seat motor glider.
AIRFRAME: Cantilever mid-wing monoplane with swept-back fin and rudder. Construction generally similar to that of Dolphin prototype. Outer wing panels detachable, reducing span to 7·60 m (24 ft 11¼ in) for hangarage. Retractable twin monowheels; steerable tailwheel. Seats for two persons under two-piece upward-opening clamshell canopy; right-hand seat is staggered 25 cm (10 in) aft of left-hand seat. Towing hooks in nose and at CG for launching training.

POWER PLANT: One 45 kW (60 hp) VW engine, driving a two-blade tractor propeller, mounted on pylon which retracts rearward into top of fuselage when not in use. Propeller pylon movement is actuated by push-button electrical control from cockpit; engine clutch is operated automatically by pylon movement. When retracted, propeller is automatically aligned longitudinally in fuselage. Engine can be started before pylon is raised, to facilitate transition from gliding to powered flight with minimum loss of height.

FINLAND

ALANNE
PENTTI ALANNE
Orapihlajantie 9, 02620 Espoo 62

Mr Pentti Alanne has been concerned with a number of motor glider conversions since the second World War. In 1949, with Mr Vilho Swahn, he modified a Grunau Baby glider by installing a Poinsard engine in the nose and fitting a landing gear similar to that of a Piper Cub. The Motorlerche, described hereafter, is a Rhönlerche II glider fitted with similar landing gear and a modified Volkswagen engine. Currently, Mr Alanne is converting a Czechoslovak Blanik sailplane to receive a dorsally-mounted VW

engine; this was expected to make its first flight in the Summer of 1980.

ALANNE MOTORLERCHE
The Motorlerche, which flew for the first time on 10 August 1973, is a conversion of the Rhönlerche II, a former training glider now readily obtainable at a low cost. The forward section of the fuselage is removed, and attachments welded on for a modified Volkswagen 1,500 cc engine. Landing gear consists of main-wheel and tail-wheel units similar to those of a Piper Cub, and the complete conversion can be accomplished in approx 200 h.

By the Spring of 1980, six Motorlerche were flying and five more were under construction.

TYPE: Single-seat motor glider. Aerobatics prohibited.
AIRFRAME: As for Rhönlerche II, except for modifications necessary to install power plant and non-retractable landing gear.
POWER PLANT: One 37·2 kW (50 hp) modified Volkswagen 1,500 cc engine (Ted Barker conversion), driving a two-blade propeller. Usable fuel capacity 26 litres (5·7 Imp gallons). Oil capacity 2·5 litres (0·5 Imp gallons).

EIRI
EINO RIIHELÄ KY (Eiriavion Dept)
Box 107, SF-15101, Lahti 10
Telephone: (918) 339 211
Telex: 16165 eiri sf
SALES MANAGER: Eero Horma
Technical Dept and Works: 38800 Jämijärvi
Telephone: (930) 71 200
Telex: 26254 eiri sf
TECHNICAL DIRECTOR: Stefan Nyström

EIRI PIK-20E
Production of the PIK-20D 15 metre Contest Class sailplane has ended during the past year; a total of 162 were built. Details of this and earlier versions of the PIK-20 can be found in the 1979-80 and previous editions of *Jane's*. The PIK-20E powered version is now the only

model in current (1980) production; a total of 50 had been built by 31 January 1980.

An experimental powered prototype of the PIK-20E was flown for the first time on 2 October 1976; this was described in the 1977-78 *Jane's*. The production prototype, based on the PIK-20D and powered by a manually retractable Rotax 503 engine, made its first (aero-tow) flight on 16 March 1978, and its first powered flight two days later. The production version has a Rotax 501 engine, longer nose and 25% more tailplane area than the PIK-20D. Series production began in late 1978, and was at the rate of two per week in early 1980.

TYPE: Single-seat self-launching 15 metre Class sailplane.
AIRFRAME: Cantilever shoulder-wing monoplane with T tail. Wortmann wing sections: FX-67-K-170 at root, FX-67-K-150 at tip. Dihedral 3°. Sweepback 1° 21·6'. Glassfibre/epoxy/PVC foam sandwich wings. Spars of

carbonfibre-reinforced epoxy. Schempp-Hirth airbrakes standard. Plain flaps ('flaperons') function as both flaps and ailerons. Provision for 120 litres (26·4 Imp gallons) of water ballast. Glassfibre/epoxy monocoque fuselage, reinforced with ribs and carbonfibre. Optional Tost towing hook. T tail of similar construction to wings. Fixed-incidence tailplane, with one-piece elevator. Retractable sprung Tost monowheel with drum brake. Steerable rubber-sprung tailwheel. Fixed wingtip wheels. Cockpit canopy opens sideways.

POWER PLANT: One 32 kW (43 hp) Rotax 501 two-cylinder two-stroke engine, driving a Hoffmann two-blade fixed-pitch wooden propeller, retracting manually into fuselage aft of cockpit when not in use. Electric starter. Kevlar fuel tank, capacity 30 litres (6·6 Imp gallons).

Let L-13SW powered version of the Blanik sailplane

VSO 10 single-seat high-performance sailplane

Alanne Motorlerche motor glider (modified VW engine)

Projekt 8 Dolphin tandem two-seat motor glider, partially complete and undergoing taxying trials

Projekt 8 Dolphin M2 side-by-side two-seat motor glider (Michael A. Badrocke)

Eiri PIK-20E self-launching sailplane, with retractable power plant

Calvel Frelon ultralight powered glider (J. M. G. Gradidge)

FRANCE

CALVEL
JACQUES CALVEL
Hotel des Causses, 12230 La Cavalerie, Aveyron

CALVEL FRELON (HORNET)
Illustrated in an accompanying photograph, the Frelon was built by M Jacques Calvel, a specialist in the use of laminated plastics materials. It was exhibited at the Paris Air Show in the Summer of 1979.
TYPE: Single-seat ultralight powered glider.

AIRFRAME: Braced high-wing monoplane. Wing section Wortmann FX-61-184. Slight dihedral from roots; single wing bracing strut each side. Airbrake in upper surface of each wing, well inboard of aileron and close to trailing-edge. Main load-bearing structure of cabin is of metal tubing, around which is built a streamlined pod-shaped nacelle tapering off to a 12 cm (4¾ in) diameter tubular tailboom. Cantilever tail unit comprises a sweptback fin with horn-balanced rudder, a small ventral fin, and a low-set, non-swept, one-piece all-moving tailplane. Non-retractable tricycle landing gear, with streamlined wheel fairings. Steerable nosewheel has metal leg, main units have legs of glassfibre laminates. Except for cabin framework and nosewheel leg, entire airframe is of glassfibre/epoxy laminates, with metal fittings. One-piece flush-fitting cockpit transparency.

POWER PLANT: One 20 kW (27 hp) piston engine, installed in nacelle on top of fuselage, aft of cabin, and driving a two-blade fixed-pitch wooden propeller with spinner.

CARMAM
CARMAM SOCIÉTÉ ANONYME
Aérodrome de Moulins, BP 201, 03001 Moulins Cédex
Telephone: (70) 44 36 18
PRESIDENT: Xavier Laguette
DIRECTOR GENERAL: Jean Pottier
TECHNICAL DIRECTOR: Christian Rocheteau

Since July 1979, CARMAM has been a member of the Siren group, together with Issoire-Aviation (which see), Siren SA and Pelletier Exploitation. Its current products are the J.P.15-36A and AR, the Pottier Kit Club 15-34, the C.38 (formerly CARMAM 15-38), and a new sailplane known as the C.40.

CARMAM J.P.15-36A and AR AIGLON (EAGLET)
The Aiglon was designed as a private venture by M Robert Jacquet and M Jean Pottier. Design began in September 1971, and prototype construction started at the end of 1972. The prototype (F-WCAP) made its first flight on 14 June 1974.

Series production by CARMAM began in 1976, and the first production **J.P.15-36A** flew for the first time on 16 October 1976. With retractable monowheel, the aircraft is designated **J.P.15-36AR**.

More than 40 J.P.15-36A and J.P.15-36AR Aiglons had been built by January 1980.
TYPE: Single-seat Standard Class sailplane; g limit +5·3.
AIRFRAME: Cantilever mid-wing monoplane, with Wortmann wing sections: FX-67-K-170 at root, FX-60-126 at tip. Dihedral 3°. Single glassfibre wing spar, with glassfibre/Rohacell/epoxy sandwich skin and steel-tipped wingtip 'salmons'. Plastics plain ailerons, which can be operated differentially or in unison. Schempp-Hirth upper/lower surface airbrakes. Provision for 55 kg (121 lb) water ballast. Semi-monocoque glassfibre fuselage, moulded in two halves and joined at centre-line. Single bulkhead forms cockpit backrest and shock-absorbing structure for monowheel. Sweptback fin, integral with fuselage, with fabric-covered wooden rudder. All-moving plastics tailplane. Non-retractable monowheel, with brake, and tail bumper on J.P.15-36A. Retractable monowheel on J.P.15-36AR. Detachable cockpit canopy.

CARMAM (POTTIER) KIT CLUB 15-34
CARMAM produces factory-built examples of the Kit Club 15-34 homebuilt sailplane described under the Pottier heading in this section; 14 were under construction by CARMAM in January 1980.

CARMAM C.38
Construction of this single-seat Standard Class sailplane, known originally as the 15-38, began in February 1977, and the prototype flew for the first time on 17 January 1979. It utilises the same wings as the J.P.15-36A, but with provision for 100 kg (220 lb) water ballast; the fuselage is of new design, but of similar construction to the

CARMAM J.P.15-36A Aiglon Standard Class sailplane (*Peter F. Selinger*)

CARMAM C.40 single-seat carbonfibre sailplane (*Michael A. Badrocke*)

J.P.15-36A; it has a T tail, with elevator spring trim, and a mechanically retractable unsprung monowheel.

Certification was expected in Spring 1980, with production then beginning during the following Summer.

CARMAM C.40

Construction of the prototype C.40 was due to begin in April 1980, with first flight expected to take place in October 1980. General appearance of the C.40 can be seen from the accompanying three-view drawing.

TYPE: Single-seat 15/17 metre sailplane; g limit +6.

AIRFRAME: Cantilever mid-wing monoplane. Wings as for J.P.15-36, but of carbonfibre and epoxy construction, with detachable tips to extend span to 17 m. Fuselage is a thin-skin carbonfibre and epoxy structure, over a plywood frame in the centre-section. Sweptback fin and rudder, and cantilever fixed-incidence T tail, of similar construction to wings. Elevator spring trim. Retractable unsprung monowheel, tyre size 4·00-4, with Tost brake; tailskid. Provision for 180 kg (397 lb) water ballast.

ENSMA
ÉCOLE NATIONALE SUPÉRIEURE DE MÉCANIQUE ET D'AÉROTECHNIQUE

20 rue Guillaume-VII-le-Troubadour, 86034 Poitiers
Telephone: 41 37 11

ENSMA FS-25 S CUERVO

Led by MM Gauthier and Piquereau, students of the ENSMA are building at Poitiers a modified version of the Akaflieg Stuttgart FS-25 Cuervo, described and illustrated in the 1973-74 *Jane's*. Known as the FS-25 S, it has a retractable monowheel and modifications to the internal structure and wing/fuselage attachments. The aircraft was expected to fly in March 1980.

TYPE: Single-seat sailplane; g limits +5·3/−2·65.

AIRFRAME: Wings as for FS-25, but with 0° incidence. Ailerons of glassfibre/balsa sandwich and carbonfibre. Fuselage and tail unit as FS-25. Manually retractable monowheel (tyre size 300 × 100 mm), without brake; tailskid.

FAUVEL
CHARLES FAUVEL

M Fauvel has been killed in an accident in a powered light aircraft since the 1979-80 edition of *Jane's* was published. Details of some of the powered and unpowered homebuilt sailplanes that he designed can be found in that edition.

FOURNIER
FOURNIER AVIATION

Aérodrome de Nitray, 37270-Montlouis
Telephone: (47) 50 68 30
MANAGING DIRECTOR: René Caillet
CONSULTANT: René Fournier

This company was formed in the Spring of 1978 as a successor to Avions Fournier (see 1977-78 *Jane's*).

FOURNIER RF-9

The prototype RF-9 (F-WARF) flew for the first time on 20 January 1977. A second prototype made its first flight in April 1979, and French certification was granted on 20 December 1979. The RF-9 then entered production.

TYPE: Side-by-side two-seat training and sporting motor glider.

AIRFRAME: Cantilever low-wing monoplane, of all-wood construction. NACA 64₃-618 section wings, with dihedral from roots. Ailerons and upper-surface air-brakes. Outer portion of each wing can be folded inward for stowage (span folded 10·00 m; 32 ft 9½ in), with connect/disconnect aileron controls. Semi-monocoque fuselage, slightly-swept fin and rudder, and small dorsal fin. Retractable main wheels, with oleo-pneumatic suspension and hydraulic disc brakes; steerable tailwheel. One-piece cockpit canopy opens upward and rearward.

POWER PLANT: One 50 kW (68 hp) Limbach SL 1700 E flat-four engine, driving a Hoffmann two-blade three-position propeller. Fuel capacity 30 litres (6·6 Imp gallons).

GEPAS
GROUPE D'ÉTUDES POUR L'AVIATION SPORTIVE

Allée Gabriel Voisin, BP No. 3, 78370 Plaisir
PRESIDENT: M Collard

GEPAS 01 COMPACT

This single-seat sailplane prototype (F-CRRL) was flown for the first time on 9 June 1978. Series production is not planned at present.

TYPE: Single-seat homebuilt sailplane; g limit +5·33.

AIRFRAME: Cantilever mid-wing monoplane, built of glassfibre and epoxy resin, with carbon roving. Wortmann wing section, of 16·5% thickness/chord ratio. Dihedral 3°. No sweepback at quarter-chord. Ailerons of GRP. Upper-surface metal and GRP airbrakes. Fuselage of GRP, with carbon roving stiffeners. GRP tail unit. Non-retractable monowheel. Flush-fitting one-piece cockpit canopy.

ISSOIRE
ISSOIRE-AVIATION SA

Aérodrome d'Issoire-le-Broc (Puy-de-Dôme), BP No. 7, 63501 Issoire Cédex
Telephone: (73) 89 01 54
Telex: ISSAVIA 990 185 F
PRESIDENT-DIRECTOR GENERAL: Xavier Laguette
TECHNICAL DIRECTOR: Philippe Moniot
DESIGNER: Bruno Boulnois

This company was formed in late 1977 by the President of Siren SA, following the bankruptcy of Wassmer Aviation. It is responsible for the Siren (formerly CERVA CE 75) Silène and the Siren D 77 Iris sailplanes. It is now one of four companies forming the Siren group, the others being Siren SA and CARMAM (which see), and Pelletier Exploitation.

ISSOIRE (SIREN) D 77 IRIS

Design of the Iris began in 1973, and the prototype (F-WAQA) flew for the first time on 26 February 1977. French certification was granted in early February 1979 and BGA certification in May 1979 (semi-aerobatic category).

By 1 January 1980 a total of 20 Iris had been ordered, of which five had been completed. Fuselages and tail units are manufactured by Siren; Issoire builds the wings, and undertakes final assembly and flight testing.

The D 77 is also available in kit form for amateur construction.

TYPE: Single-seat training sailplane; g limits +5·3/−2·65 (normal), +8·0/−4·0 (ultimate).

AIRFRAME: Cantilever mid-wing monoplane. Bertin E55-166 wing section. Dihedral 3°. Glassfibre/polyester/PMC sandwich construction, with glassfibre ailerons and Schempp-Hirth metal airbrakes on upper surfaces. Glassfibre/polyester monocoque fuselage, built in two halves. Cantilever tail unit, of similar construction to wings. Fixed-incidence tailplane. Spring tab in each elevator. Non-retractable unsprung monowheel, tyre size 330 × 130, pressure 1·8 bars (26 lb/sq in); tailskid. Siren hydraulic brake. Cockpit canopy opens sideways to starboard. Winch-launching and bungee-launching equipment available.

ISSOIRE (SIREN) E 78 SILÈNE

Design of the original E 75 Silène (by Siren SA) began on 1 January 1972. Construction by CERVA of a CE 75 prototype started on 1 February 1973, and this aircraft (F-CCFF) made its first flight at Argenton on 2 July 1974. French certification was granted on 3 February 1978, and BGA certification in March 1979 (semi-aerobatic category).

Ten E 78s had been built by 1 January 1980, of 20 then on order, including examples for customers in Australia, the Federal Republic of Germany, the UK and the USA. Production is on the same basis as for the Iris, with fuselages and tail units built by Siren; the wings are built by Issoire, which also carries out final assembly and flight testing.

Current versions of the Silène are designated as follows:

E 78. Cockpit improvements by comparison with E 75 include a larger canopy, lowered seats, increased width at shoulder level, and repositioned starboard rudder pedals. Retractable monowheel. Certificated 1 August 1978. In production.

E 78B. Basic version, with non-retractable monowheel. Certificated 1 August 1978.

I 79. Advanced version, with wing flaps and water ballast. Under development in 1979-80. Fuselage as for E 78, but modified wings incorporating carbonfibre components; Bertin E55-166 V.M2 wing section; aspect ratio 20. Monowheel, wing flaps and airbrakes actuated hydraulically.

The following description applies to the E 78 and E 78B:

TYPE: Side-by-side two-seat training sailplane; g limits +5·3/−2·65 (normal), +8·0/−4·0 (ultimate).

AIRFRAME: Cantilever mid-wing monoplane, built entirely of glassfibre/polyester/PMC sandwich. Bertin E55-166 wing section. Dihedral 2°. Sweepforward 2° at quarter-chord. Two-section ailerons, with spring tabs. Schempp-Hirth airbrakes above and below each wing. Semi-monocoque fuselage. Cantilever tail unit, with fixed-incidence tailplane. Spring tab in each elevator. Retractable or non-retractable rubber-sprung monowheel, tyre size 330 × 130, pressure 2·4 bars (35 lb/sq in). Siren hydraulic brake optional. Tailskid. Winch-launching and bungee-launching equipment available.

Prototype Fournier RF-9 two-seat training motor glider

GEPAS Compact homebuilt sailplane

Issoire (Siren) D 77 Iris single-seat training sailplane

Issoire (Siren) E 78 Silène two-seat training sailplane *(Peter F. Selinger)*

Pottier Kit Club 15-34 prototype homebuilt sailplane *(Geoffrey P. Jones)*

Akaflieg Braunschweig SB-12 *(Peter F. Selinger)*

POTTIER
JEAN POTTIER
4 rue de Poissy, 78130 Les Mureaux
Telephone: 099 13 85

POTTIER KIT CLUB 15-34
This is essentially the same sailplane as the CARMAM J.P.15-36A Aiglon (which see), with some constructional simplification to make it suitable for amateur builders.

Prototype construction began in November 1975; first flight was made on 6 November 1976.

French certification was received on 15 February 1979. First kits for homebuilders became available in mid-March 1979, and by mid-April of that year two Kit Clubs had been completed, both by M Jean Magne of Livry Gargan.

The Kit Club is also produced in factory-built form by CARMAM (which see).

The description of the Aiglon applies also to the Kit Club, except in the following respects:
TYPE: Single-seat homebuilt sailplane; *g* limits +8·3/−4·0.
AIRFRAME: As Aiglon, but of plywood-covered spruce construction except for glassfibre nosecone. Provision for 80 kg (176 lb) of water ballast. Rudder and rear part of tailplane fabric-covered. Non-retractable unsprung monowheel, with cable-operated drum brake for production aircraft.

SCAP
SOCIÉTÉ DE COMMERCIALISATION AÉRONAUTIQUE DU PLESSIS, SàRL
Aérodrome de Bailleau-Armenonville, 28320 Gallardon
Telephone: (37) 23 43 74 and 23 54 32

SCAP is marketing, as the Cirrus 78L, the former Schempp-Hirth Standard Cirrus, and has developed the SL-2 two-seat all-plastics sailplane.

SCAP CIRRUS 78L
The Cirrus 78L is a current version of the Standard Cirrus sailplane produced originally by Schempp-Hirth in Germany. It is manufactured in France by the holding

company Dubigeon-Normandie, and distributed by SCAP. Thirty had been completed by 1 January 1979.
TYPE: Single-seat high-performance Standard Class sailplane; *g* limit +10.
AIRFRAME: Cantilever mid-wing monoplane with T tail. Wortmann wing section. Dihedral 3°. Sweepback 1°18′ at leading-edge. Glassfibre/foam sandwich wings, ailerons and tail surfaces. Schempp-Hirth glassfibre airbrakes on wing upper surface. Provision for 130 litres (28·6 Imp gallons) of water ballast. Glassfibre fuselage shell, stiffened with bonded-in foam rings. Fixed tailplane, with elevator. Retractable monowheel standard.

Non-retractable faired monowheel optional. Tost wheel with drum brake and Continental tyre, pressure 3·45 bars (50 lb/sq in). New-design canopy, opening sideways to starboard.

SCAP-LANAVERRE SL-2
First flown on 15 October 1977, the SL-2 is a development of the Schempp-Hirth Janus (which see), from which it differs chiefly in having a fixed tailplane with elevators instead of a one-piece all-moving tailplane. There is provision for 200 litres (44 Imp gallons) of water ballast in the wings, and a more comfortable cockpit for both occupants, with provision for back-type parachutes.

SIREN
SIREN SA
Route des Chambons, BP 42, 36200 Argenton-sur-Creuse
Telephone: (54) 04 14 47

Telex: 750534 Chamco-Châteauroux Siren 200-1
DIRECTOR: Xavier Laguette

In addition to Siren SA, the Siren group has since July 1979 comprised CARMAM and Issoire-Aviation (which

see), and Pelletier Exploitation.

The current activities of Siren SA in 1980 included the manufacture of fuselages and tail units for the Issoire D77 Iris and E78 Silène sailplanes.

GERMANY
(FEDERAL REPUBLIC)

AKAFLIEG BRAUNSCHWEIG
AKADEMISCHE FLIEGERGRUPPE BRAUNSCHWEIG eV
3300 Braunschweig, Flughafen Akafliegheim
Telephone: 0531 3952149
DIRECTOR: Martin Hansen

The students of Brunswick University have built a series of high-performance sailplanes (see 1977-78 and earlier editions of *Jane's*). The SB-10 (1974-75 *Jane's*) remains

the largest sailplane in the world; in December 1979/January 1980, flown by H.-W. Grosse and H.-H. Kohlmeier, it established in central Australia (subject to FAI confirmation) a series of new world records for two-seat sailplanes. The most outstanding of these were a distance of 600 nm (1,112 km; 691 miles) around a triangular course, and a speed of 70·15 knots (130 km/h; 80·78 mph) around a 1,000 km triangular circuit.

The SB-11 Antares high-performance research sail-

plane, described in the 1979-80 *Jane's,* in 1978 won the unlimited 15 metre Class contest at the World Gliding Championships, piloted by Dr Helmut Reichmann, who thus became the only person to win the title of World Champion three times. In 1978 the SB-11 received the Wolf Hirth prize for the best development in light aircraft and gliding.

The latest design by Akaflieg Braunschweig is the SB-12.

AKAFLIEG BRAUNSCHWEIG SB-12

The SB-12 is a Standard Class sailplane using a new wing aerofoil section developed for high cruising performance; its general appearance is shown in an accompanying illustration. Design began in the Summer of 1979, and the prototype construction started in the following November. First flight was made on 9 April 1980. Production is not intended.

TYPE: Single-seat experimental Standard Class sailplane; g limits +5·3/−2·65.

AIRFRAME: Cantilever mid-wing monoplane. Specially-designed HQ 014 wing section, with thickness/chord ratio of 18·4%. Dihedral 3°. Incidence 0° 30'. No sweep. Single I spar, with carbonfibre flanges and GRP shear web; outer skin of carbonfibre and plastics foam. GRP ailerons and wide-span trailing-edge airbrakes. No flaps or spoilers. GRP monocoque fuselage. Cantilever T tail, with fixed surfaces of GRP/plastics foam sandwich, rudder and elevators of GRP only. Retractable unsprung monowheel, size 5·00-5, with Tost internal drum brake; semi-recessed tailwheel. Canopy hinged at front to open upward.

AKAFLIEG DARMSTADT
AKADEMISCHE FLIEGERGRUPPE DARMSTADT eV

6100 Darmstadt, Technische Hochschule, Hochschulstrasse 1
Telephone: 06151 162790
The Fliegergruppe of Darmstadt University has been designing, building and flying sailplanes since 1921. Its postwar products have been described in previous editions of *Jane's*.

AKAFLIEG DARMSTADT D-39

The D-39 motor glider utilises the basic D-38 airframe, except for a low-mounted wing and a nose-mounted power plant.
The prototype flew for the first time on 28 June 1979.
TYPE: Single-seat motor glider; g limits +5·3/−3·6.
AIRFRAME: Cantilever low-wing monoplane with T tail. Wortmann wing sections: FX-61-184 at centreline, FX-60-126 at tip. Dihedral 4° from roots. Glassfibre/balsa sandwich wings, tail and monocoque fuselage, with glassfibre/Klégécel foam sandwich ailerons. All-moving one-piece swept tailplane, with Flettner tab. Retractable sprung monowheel, with Tost drum brake, and small tailwheel.

POWER PLANT: One 51 kW (68 hp) Limbach SL 1700 E engine, driving a two-blade propeller. Fuel capacity 35 litres (7·7 Imp gallons).

AKAFLIEG KARLSRUHE
AKADEMISCHE FLIEGERGRUPPE KARLSRUHE eV

Technische Hochschule, 7500 Karlsruhe 1, Postfach 6380, Kaiserstrasse 12
Telephone: 0721 6081
PUBLIC RELATIONS: Adolf Herlitzka

AKAFLIEG KARLSRUHE AK 2

A prototype of the AK 2 was under construction in 1979. All known details are given hereafter; appearance of the AK 2 can be seen in the accompanying three-view drawing.
TYPE: Single-seat motor glider.

AIRFRAME: Cantilever mid-wing monoplane with upper-surface airbrakes, trailing-edge flaps and ailerons. GFK wings. Cantilever T tail. Monowheel and tailwheel.
POWER PLANT: One 41 kW (55 hp) Hirth O-28 two-cylinder two-stroke engine, driving a tractor propeller and retractable into fuselage when not in use.

AKAFLIEG MÜNCHEN
AKADEMISCHE FLIEGERGRUPPE MÜNCHEN eV

8000 München 2, Arcisstrasse 21, Postfach 202420
Telephone: (089) 28 61 11
DIRECTOR: Klaus Raeder
DESIGN MANAGER: Werner Pattermann
Recent designs by students at Munich University have included the Mü 27 and Mü 28.

AKAFLIEG MÜNCHEN Mü 27

The prototype Mü 27 (D-2827) flew for the first time on 24 February 1979 at Oberpfaffenhofen.
TYPE: Tandem two-seat high-performance sailplane.

AIRFRAME: Cantilever shoulder-wing monoplane with T tail. Wortmann FX-67-VC-170/136 section, with electrically-actuated Fowler-type flaps which increase wing area by 36% when fully extended. Aluminium alloy wing spar and metal webs, with glassfibre/foam sandwich wing and tail skins; all-glassfibre semi-monocoque fuselage. Double ailerons, linked to flaps when latter are extended. Carbonfibre airbrakes on wing upper surfaces. Retractable monowheel and fixed tailwheel. Front portion of canopy opens sideways to starboard; rear portion opens upward.

AKAFLIEG MÜNCHEN Mü 28

A prototype of the Mü 28 is under construction, and was expected to fly for the first time in the Spring of 1980. Its general appearance is shown in the accompanying three-view drawing.

TYPE: Single-seat sailplane for full aerobatics and training.

AIRFRAME: Cantilever mid-wing monoplane, with detachable tips to extend span from 12 m to 14 m. Wings are of Wortmann FX-71-L-150/20 symmetrical section, fitted with automatic trailing-edge flaps/ailerons ('flaperons'), and are of glassfibre/foam sandwich construction. Airbrakes in upper surfaces. All-glassfibre monocoque fuselage. Retractable monowheel; non-retractable tailwheel. Canopy opens forward and upward.

BLESSING
GERHARD BLESSING

205 Hamburg 80, Ochsenwerder Landstrasse 33

BLESSING REBELL

The Rebell is a single-seat homebuilt motor glider, with provision for a second occupant. The prototype (D-KEBO) first flew on 3 June 1973 and was powered originally by a 40·5 kW (54 hp) Hirth engine driving a pusher propeller; it was subsequently flown with a modified VW power plant.

The Rebell is no longer available in its 'pusher-engined' form. The fuselage has been redesigned to accept a front-mounted 46 kW (62 hp) Limbach SL 1700 engine, driving a tractor propeller. In this form it was expected to fly again in early 1980.

GLASER-DIRKS
GLASER-DIRKS FLUGZEUGBAU GmbH

7520 Bruchsal 4, Postfach 47, Im Schollengarten 19-20
Telephone: 07257 (1071)
DIRECTORS: Gerhard Glaser and Dipl-Ing Wilhelm Dirks

GLASER-DIRKS DG-100

Manufacture of the DG-100 series is now carried out under licence by Elan in Yugoslavia, under whose entry a description and illustration can be found. By the end of 1978, production by Glaser-Dirks totalled 89 DG-100 Standard Class sailplanes and 16 examples of the generally similar DG-100G. Elan built 10 DG-100s and 10 DG-100Gs in 1979.

GLASER-DIRKS DG-200

The DG-200 (D-8200), which flew for the first time in prototype form on 22 April 1977, is an improved DG-100 fitted with wing flaps, and was developed for unlimited international competition.

Five versions have been announced, as follows:
DG-200. High-performance 15 metre Class standard version. Total of 89 built by beginning of 1980.
DG-200A Acroracer. As DG-200, but with detachable wingtips to reduce span for aerobatics. No water ballast. First flown on 28 October 1978. One only built.
DG-200/17. As DG-200, but with insertable wingtips to extend span for Open Class competition. First flown 14 March 1979. Total of 15 built by beginning of 1980.
DG-200C. Similar to DG-200, but with spar boom, wing skin, ailerons and wing flaps made of carbonfibre. Weights empty 220 kg (485 lb), max T-O weight 450 kg (992 lb), max wing loading 45·0 kg/m² (9·22 lb/sq ft); other data as given in table for DG-200. First flights scheduled for February 1980 (prototype) and March 1980 (production aircraft).
DG-200/17C. Similar to DG-200/17, but with carbonfibre wing construction as in DG-200C. Weight empty 228 kg (503 lb), max T-O weight 450 kg (992 lb), max wing loading 42·6 kg/m² (8·72 lb/sq ft); other data as given in table for DG-200/17. Type certification granted in January 1980. In production.
The following description applies to the standard DG-200, unless indicated otherwise:

TYPE: Single-seat high-performance sailplane.

AIRFRAME: Cantilever shoulder-wing monoplane. Wing section Wortmann FX-67K-170-17 at root, FX-60K-126 at tip. Dihedral 3° from roots. Incidence 0°. Glassfibre roving main spar. Glassfibre/Conticell/foam sandwich wings, with glassfibre flaps and carbonfibre ailerons. All-glassfibre semi-monocoque fuselage, fin and rudder. Glassfibre/foam sandwich T tailplane, with all-glassfibre elevator. Schempp-Hirth aluminium airbrakes on upper wing surfaces. Water ballast tank in each wing (except Acroracer), combined capacity 130 kg (286 lb). Manually-retractable monowheel, size 5·00-5, with Tost drum brake; size 200 × 50 tailwheel.

GLASFLÜGEL
GLASFLÜGEL GmbH (Deutsch-Brasilianische Flugzeug- und Fahrzeugbau GmbH)

7318 Lenningen 1 Schlattstall, Württ 1
Telephone: 07026 855
Telex: 7267785 gafud
DIRECTOR: Erich Weinzierl

The present company was formed on 4 April 1979. The products of the former Glasflügel company were described in the 1979-80 and earlier editions of *Jane's*. Those no longer in production include the Libelle H-301 (108 built), BS-1 (18 built), Standard Libelle (601 built), Kestrel (129 built), Glasflügel 604 (10 built), Club Libelle (171 built) and Mosquito (100 built). Sailplanes in production in 1980 were the Mosquito B, Hornet and Hornet C.

GLASFLÜGEL HORNET

The Hornet is a derivative of the Club Libelle (1977-78 *Jane's*), from which it differs principally in having a retractable monowheel, provision for water ballast, and an enlarged flush-fitting canopy. The prototype (D-9432) flew for the first time on 21 December 1974. Approx 90 Hornets had been delivered by the beginning of 1980.
TYPE: Single-seat Standard Class sailplane; g limits +5·3/−3·25 (safety factor 1·5).
AIRFRAME: Cantilever mid-wing monoplane with T tail. Wortmann FX-66-17AII-182 wing section. Entire structure of glassfibre monocoque and glassfibre/foam sandwich. Rotating airbrakes on wing trailing-edges; partially mass-balanced ailerons. Elevator spring trim. Retractable unsprung monowheel, with internally-expanding brake; tyre size either 5·00-5, pressure 3·5 bars (51 lb/sq in), or 4·00-4, pressure 5·0 bars (73 lb/sq in). Non-retractable tailwheel. Provision for 170 kg (375 lb) water ballast.

GLASFLÜGEL HORNET C

First flown on 6 April 1979, the Hornet C has a wing of carbonfibre construction, reducing the aircraft empty weight to 210 kg (463 lb). Five examples of this version had been built by the beginning of 1980.

GLASFLÜGEL MOSQUITO B

Glasflügel began building a prototype of this Mosquito version in September 1977. It differs from the original Mosquito (1979-80 *Jane's*) in having GRP ailerons, no fuselage/wing fairings, reduced wing weight and slimmer horizontal tail surfaces.
The Mosquito B flew for the first time on 24 March 1978; approx 90 had been delivered by January 1980.
TYPE: Single-seat 15 metre Class sailplane.
AIRFRAME: Cantilever mid-wing monoplane with T tail. Wortmann FX-67-K-150 wing section. Dihedral 3° on wing upper surface; sweepback 0° 9' at quarter-chord. Construction generally similar to Hornet, but with GRP mass-balanced ailerons. Camber-changing trailing-edge flaps; spoiler forward of each flap combines with flap to act as trailing-edge airbrake. Flap, aileron and airbrake controls linked automatically. Fixed-incidence tailplane; elevator has spring trim. Retractable unsprung monowheel, with internally-expanding brake; non-retractable semi-recessed tailwheel. Provision for 120 kg (265 lb) water ballast.

Akaflieg Braunschweig SB-11 Antares variable geometry sailplane *(Peter F. Selinger)*

Akaflieg Darmstadt D-39 single-seat motor glider *(Peter F. Selinger)*

Akaflieg Karlsruhe AK 2 motor glider *(Michael A. Badrocke)*

Akaflieg München Mü 28 single-seat sailplane *(Michael A. Badrocke)*

Akaflieg München Mü 27 prototype tandem two-seat sailplane

Glaser-Dirks DG-200A Acroracer aerobatic sailplane

Glaser-Dirks DG-200 standard 15 metre Class sailplane

17 metre span version of the Glaser-Dirks DG-200, the DG-200/17

Glasflügel Hornet C 15 metre competition sailplane *(Peter F. Selinger)*

Glasflügel Mosquito B single-seat 15 m Contest Class sailplane *(Peter F. Selinger)*

GROB
BURKHART GROB FLUGZEUGBAU GmbH & Co KG

Flugplatz Mindelheim-Mattsies, 8939 Mattsies
Telephone: 08268 411
Telex: 53 96 23
DIRECTOR: Ernst Grob

This company built the Schempp-Hirth Standard Cirrus under licence between 1972 and 1975. It is now manufacturing the Astir series and other sailplanes of its own design.

GROB ASTIR II

Prototype construction of the Astir CS (Club Standard) single-seat Standard Class sailplane began in March 1974, and this aircraft (D-6102) made its first flight on 19 December 1974. German certification by the LBA was awarded in September 1975. The Astir CS77, first flown on 26 March 1977, introduced modified tailplane actuation.

The Astir is produced currently in two forms: the **Standard Astir II**, and the **Club Astir II**, the latter having a non-retractable monowheel and no water ballast provision. By Spring 1978, a total of more than 550 of the successive versions had been delivered, and 160 more were on order; these figures included 110 and 140 respectively of the Club version. No later production figures than these have been received.

TYPE: Single-seat Standard and Club Class sailplanes.
AIRFRAME: Cantilever mid-wing monoplane with T tail.

Eppler E 603 wing section. Wing sweepback 1°. Carbonfibre main spar; wings and tail surfaces have glassfibre/epoxy resin sandwich skin. Ailerons are of glassfibre sandwich, with elastic gap seals. Schempp-Hirth upper-surface aluminium airbrakes. Glassfibre semi-monocoque fuselage, with towing/launching hook. Carbonfibre used to reinforce fuselage and fin, and for canopy frame. Retractable Tost monowheel standard (non-retractable on Club version), tyre pressure 2·5 bars (36·3 lb/sq in), with internally-expanding drum brake; rubber-sprung tailwheel. Canopy opens sideways to starboard. Provision for 90 kg (198 lb) water ballast.

GROB SPEED ASTIR IIB

The prototype Speed Astir II made its first flight in mid-April 1978. More than 50 were then on order; deliveries began in 1979.

TYPE: Single-seat 15 metre Class sailplane.
AIRFRAME: Cantilever mid-wing monoplane with T tail. Generally similar to Standard Astir except for wings, which have reduced area, Eppler E 662 section, a carbonfibre spar, and 'elastic flaps' (ie, the gaps are elastically sealed) which can be deflected upward or downward. Ailerons actuated by a similar system. Provision for 180 litres (39·5 Imp gallons) water ballast.

GROB TWIN ASTIR

The Twin Astir tandem two-seat development of the Standard Astir, described in the 1979-80 *Jane's*, is no longer in production.

GROB G 103 TWIN II

This new tandem two-seat sailplane (known originally as the G 118) for training and club flying is the successor to the Twin Astir (1979-80 *Jane's*), from which it differs mainly in having lower-mounted wings, a more streamlined fuselage, modified landing gear, improved cockpit layout and reduced weight. General appearance is shown in an accompanying three-view drawing. First flight was made in late 1979.

TYPE: Tandem two-seat training and club sailplane.
AIRFRAME: Cantilever low/mid-wing monoplane, of similar construction to Astir. Wings have ailerons and trailing-edge 'elastic flaps', similar to those of Speed Astir. Cantilever T tail. Non-retractable nosewheel and monowheel, both semi-recessed; plus tailwheel. No water ballast provision.

GROB G 109

The prototype of the G 109 (D-KBGF) flew for the first time on 14 March 1980.

TYPE: Side-by-side two-seat motor glider.
AIRFRAME: Cantilever low-wing monoplane with T tail. Wings of E 572 (modified Eppler E 603) section. Construction mainly of glassfibre (GfK). Non-retractable tailwheel-type landing gear, with Scheibe hydraulic brakes. One-piece fully-transparent canopy.
POWER PLANT: One 59 kW (80 hp) Limbach L 2000 EI engine, driving a Hoffmann two-blade variable-pitch wooden propeller. Fuel capacity 80 litres (17·5 Imp gallons).

ISF
INGENIEUR-BÜRO DIPL-ING STRAUBER — FROMMHOLD GmbH & Co KG

6140 Bensheim 3-Auerbach, Wilhelm-Leuschner-Strasse 13
Telephone: 06251/74561

ISF MODEL 2 MISTRAL-C

The original Mistral was described and illustrated under

the Strauber heading in the 1976-77 *Jane's*. Design of a second model, known as the ISF Mistral-C, was started in October 1974, and this made its first flight on 21 October 1976. A total of 20 had been completed by the beginning of 1979.

TYPE: Single-seat Standard Class sailplane; *g* limits +5·8/−3·8.
AIRFRAME: Cantilever shoulder-wing monoplane with T tail. Wortmann wing sections: FX-61-163 at root,

FX-60-126 at tip. Dihedral 4° 18′. Sweepforward 1° at quarter-chord. Structure: main wings and tail of GRP/foam/Conticell CC60 sandwich, ailerons of GRP. Schempp-Hirth aluminium airbrakes on upper wing surfaces. GRP monocoque fuselage. Fixed-incidence tailplane, with spring trim. Non-retractable monowheel, tyre pressure 2·5 bars (36·25 lb/sq in), with Tost brake; tailskid.

KORTENBACH & RAUH
KORTENBACH & RAUH KG

5650 Solingen 15, Postfach 150121, Weyerstrasse 277
Telephone: (02122) 312031
Telex: 8514848 kora d

KORTENBACH & RAUH KORA 1

The Kora 1 first prototype flew for the first time on 13 September 1973. It was designed by Herren Schultes, Seidel and Putz, and was described in the 1977-78 *Jane's*.

The second prototype, which made its first flight on 9 April 1976, differs in having a non-retractable main landing gear. It was described and illustrated in the 1979-80 *Jane's*.

KUFFNER
LEICHTFLUGZEUGBAU KUFFNER GmbH & Co KG

5485 Sinzig/Koisdorf, Postfach 1233

KUFFNER WK-1

The design of this all-metal motor glider was started by Werner Kuffner in 1973, and a prototype was under construction in 1978. No later information has been received. All known details, and an illustration, were published in the 1979-80 *Jane's*.

PFLUMM & RICHTER
MANFRED PFLUMM and K. J. RICHTER

Öschwende 17, 7900 Ulm-Lehr

Herr Pflumm of Stuttgart and Herr Richter of Ulm have produced a small, ultralight collapsible motor glider known as the **Faltente**, designed to be carried on the roof rack of a motor-car. General appearance can be seen in the accompanying three-view drawing; all known details are given in the table at the end of this section. Power plant is a 7·5 kW (10 hp) Sachs-Wankel KM 48 piston engine.

ROLLADEN-SCHNEIDER
ROLLADEN-SCHNEIDER FLUGZEUGBAU GmbH

6073 Egelsbach, Mühlstrasse 10 (Postfach 1130)
Telephone: Langen (06103) 4126
OFFICERS: Walter Schneider and Dipl-Ing Wolf Lemke

All models of Rolladen-Schneider's LS1 sailplane are now out of production. A total of 224 examples of the models LS1-o/a/b/c/d/e/ef were built, as well as 240 examples of the LS1-f. Current (1980) production is concerned with two versions of the LS3, and the company is also developing a new sailplane known as the LS4.

ROLLADEN-SCHNEIDER LS3

The LS3 was developed from the LS1-f. Design and construction began in 1975, and the prototype flew for the first time on 4 February 1976. A total of 358 of all versions had been built by the beginning of 1980.

Three versions have been built, as follows:
LS3. Standard FAI 15 metre Class sailplane. Total of 155 built; no longer in production.
LS3-a. Similar to LS3, but with horizontal and vertical tail surfaces of greater area and different aerofoil sections, and reduced empty weight. First flown on 18 February 1978; deliveries began in Spring 1978. Total of 177 built by beginning of 1980.
LS3-17. Extended-span (17 metre) version of LS3; first flown on 10 February 1979. Total of 26 built by beginning of 1980.
The following description applies to the LS3-a:
TYPE: Single-seat FAI 15 metre Class sailplane.

AIRFRAME: Cantilever mid-wing monoplane, with modified Wortmann wing section. Dihedral 4°. Ailerons and flaps over entire trailing-edge. Schempp-Hirth airbrakes on upper wing surfaces. Semi-monocoque fuselage. Cantilever T tailplane, with elevator. Entire structure of Gfk sandwich. Retractable Tost rubber-sprung monowheel, tyre pressure 2·94 bars (43 lb/sq in), with drum brake; tailskid. Provision for 150 kg (330 lb) water ballast.

ROLLADEN-SCHNEIDER LS4

Design of this new Standard Class sailplane began in the Winter of 1978, and the prototype (D-6680) flew for the first time on 28 March 1980. It is claimed to have a best glide ratio of 40.

SCHEIBE
SCHEIBE FLUGZEUGBAU GmbH

HEAD OFFICE AND WORKS: D-8060 Dachau, August-Pfaltz-Strasse 23, Postfach 1829, near Munich
Telephone: Dachau 4047, 6813 and 81886
MANAGERS: Dipl-Ing Egon Scheibe and Ing Christian Gad

Scheibe Flugzeugbau GmbH was founded at the end of 1951 by Dipl-Ing Scheibe; its first type produced in quantity was the Mü-13E Bergfalke I.

Subsequently, Scheibe has built many new types of sailplane, and since 1957 has become the major producer of motor gliders in the Federal Republic of Germany. Currently in production or under development are the SF-25C, C-S and K Falke, SF-25E Super-Falke and SF-28 Tandem-Falke motor gliders, in addition to the Bergfalke-IV and SF-H34 sailplanes.

Scheibe has built more than 2,000 aircraft of various types, in addition to many kits for home construction by amateurs. Gliders of Scheibe design are being built under licence by gliding clubs as well as by foreign companies.

SCHEIBE SF-25C and C-S FALKE '80 (FALCON)

The SF-25C is an improved version of the SF-25B Falke, to which it is structurally similar. The primary difference is in the use of a more powerful engine, giving an enhanced performance.

By January 1980 a total of 295 SF-25C Falkes had been built by Scheibe; a further 50 were built under licence by Sportavia in Germany. Type certification was granted in September 1972.

With a Hoffmann feathering propeller, adjustable engine cowl flap and slightly modified fuselage, the aircraft is known as the **SF-25C-S** and has a best glide ratio of 25 at 43·5 knots (80 km/h; 50 mph). Twenty of this version had been built by January 1980.

Optional features include an additional exhaust outlet and a slower-turning propeller. With this installation the nominal noise level is reduced to less than 60 dB. In addition, Scheibe has developed an optional folding wing, which reduces the span to 9·50 m (31 ft 2 in) for easier hangar storage.

Current models, known as **C-Falke '80**, introduced a number of design improvements, as listed in the 1977-78 *Jane's*. With fully-folding wings, they are known as **K-Falke '80**.

TYPE: Side-by-side two-seat motor glider, particularly suitable for basic and advanced training.

Grob Club Astir II single-seat sailplane *(Peter F. Selinger)*

Grob G 103 two-seat training and club sailplane *(Michael A. Badrocke)*

ISF Mistral-C single-seat Club Class sailplane

Grob G 109 two-seat motor glider *(Michael A. Badrocke)*

Pflumm & Richter Faltente ultralight motor glider *(Michael A. Badrocke)*

Rolladen-Schneider LS3-17 single-seat 17 metre sailplane

Scheibe Bergfalke-IV two-seat training and competition sailplane
(Peter F. Selinger)

Rolladen-Schneider LS3-a 15 metre Class sailplane

Scheibe SF-H34 two-seat training and sporting sailplane

British-registered Scheibe SF-28A Tandem-Falke motor glider

AIRFRAME: Cantilever low-wing monoplane. Forward-swept wooden wings, with airbrakes and aerodynamically balanced ailerons. Wing folding optional. Fabric-covered welded steel tube fuselage; forward section coated with laminated glassfibre. Tow hitch optional. Wooden tail unit. Non-retractable unsprung mono-wheel with brake and aerodynamic fairing; steerable tailwheel; spring outrigger stabilising wheel under each wing. Rubber-sprung monowheel optional. Alternative twin-wheel main gear available optionally, with streamlined wheel fairings.

POWER PLANT: One 48·5 kW (65 hp) Limbach SL 1700 EA I modified Volkswagen engine, driving a two-blade propeller. Electric starter. Fuel in single fuselage tank, capacity 45 litres (9·9 Imp gallons) standard, 55 litres (12·1 Imp gallons) optional.

SCHEIBE SF-25E SUPER-FALKE

Developed from the SF-25C-S, the Super-Falke has an increased wing span and a rubber-sprung monowheel; a cabin heater is fitted as standard. Production aircraft have a tailwheel, and upper-surface Schempp-Hirth airbrakes.

A 48·5 kW (65 hp) Limbach SL 1700 EA I engine is fitted, with a 12V battery and alternator for electrical engine starting. Fuel capacity is 45 litres (9·9 Imp gallons). Optionally, the outer wing panels can be made foldable to facilitate transportation and storage.

The Super-Falke was flown for the first time in the Summer of 1974; 52 had been delivered by January 1980.

SCHEIBE SF-28A TANDEM-FALKE

The Tandem-Falke, as its name implies, is a further development of the Falke series of motor gliders in which the two seats are arranged in tandem. Design began in 1970, and the prototype (D-KAFJ) flew for the first time in May 1971, powered by a 33·5 kW (45 hp) Stamo MS 1500 engine. Details apply to the production version, of which 112 had been built by January 1980.

TYPE: Tandem two-seat motor glider.

Scheibe SF-25C Falke '80, version with twin-wheel main gear

Scheibe SF-25K Falke '80, with fully-folding wings

AIRFRAME: Cantilever low-wing monoplane. Wing section Gö 533. Single-spar wooden wings, with wooden ailerons. No flaps. Spoiler on upper surface of each wing. Fabric-covered steel tube fuselage. Wooden tail unit, with trim tab in elevator. Non-retractable monowheel, with internal brake, and steerable tailwheel. Nylon leg with outrigger stabilising wheel under each wing. Can be flown solo from front seat, with space for 90 kg (198 lb) of baggage on rear seat.

POWER PLANT: One 48·5 kW (65 hp) Limbach SL 1700 EAI engine, driving a Hoffmann two-blade feathering (optionally, fixed-pitch) propeller. 12V alternator standard, for engine starting. Fuel capacity 40 litres (8·8 Imp gallons).

SCHEIBE BERGFALKE-IV

The Bergfalke-IV is a developed version of the Bergfalke-III, with a new wing which provides improved performance. Construction of the prototype began in early 1969 and first flight was accomplished a few months later. A total of 70 had been built by the beginning of 1980.

TYPE: Tandem two-seat training and competition sailplane; g limit +8 (ultimate).

AIRFRAME: Cantilever mid-wing monoplane, primarily of plywood-covered wooden construction except for welded steel tube fuselage, which is covered with moulded glassfibre shell (nose section) and fabric. Wortmann wing sections: SO 2 at root, SO 2/1 at tip. Dihedral 3°. Wooden ailerons and Schempp-Hirth airbrakes. Flettner trim tab on starboard elevator. Non-retractable monowheel and tailwheel.

SCHEIBE SF-H34

Design of the SF-H34 sailplane began in 1978, and it flew for the first time on 28 October that year. One production-standard aircraft was completed in early 1979; series production began at the end of that year, and was expected to reach an output of five or six per month.

TYPE: Tandem two-seat training and sporting sailplane.

AIRFRAME: Cantilever mid-wing monoplane. Wortmann wing sections: FX-61-184 at root, FX-60-126 at tip. Glassfibre roving main spar. Wings and tail unit of Gfk honeycomb sandwich construction; fuselage is a Gfk shell. Schempp-Hirth airbrake in upper surface of each wing. Non-retractable semi-exposed monowheel and nosewheel, tyre sizes 5·00-4 and 265 × 85 respectively; tailskid. Tandem seats under frameless one-piece flush canopy. Towing hooks under nose and at CG.

SCHEMPP-HIRTH

SCHEMPP-HIRTH GmbH & Co KG

7312 Kirchheim-Teck, Krebenstrasse 25, Postfach 143
Telephone: (07021) 2441 and 6097
Telex: 7267817 hate
DIRECTOR: Dipl-Ing Klaus Holighaus

Schempp-Hirth specialises in the production of high-performance Open Class and Standard Class sailplanes. In 1970 Dipl-Ing Klaus Holighaus became a 50% shareholder of Schempp-Hirth KG, later becoming its director following the retirement of Herr Martin Schempp.

Production by Schempp-Hirth of the original Cirrus ended in late 1971, after 120 had been built; but manufacture has continued since early 1972 by VTC in Yugoslavia, under which heading the description of the Cirrus can now be found.

SCHEMPP-HIRTH NIMBUS 2C

Generally similar to the HS-3 Nimbus (1972-73 *Jane's*), from which it was developed, the Nimbus 2 differs principally by having reduced span and a wing built in four pieces to limit weight and dimensions for rigging, storage and trailer transport. The first flight was made in April 1971; in the 1976 World Championships at Räyskälä, Finland, Nimbus 2s took no fewer than 14 of the first 25 places.

On 7 January 1978, a Nimbus 2 flown by G. Eckle of West Germany set a speed record of 76·20 knots (141·1 km/h; 87·69 mph) over a 750 km triangular course. A similar record over 500 km was set in a Nimbus 2 on 27 November 1976 by Edward Pearson of Rhodesia at 77·235 knots (143·04 km/h; 88·881 mph). The world distance record to a goal, for single-seat gliders, was set by a group of three Nimbus 2s flown by S. H. Georgeson, B. L. Drake and D. N. Speight, who covered 677·25 nm (1,254·26 km; 779·36 miles) in New Zealand on 14 January 1978.

A total of 132 of the original Nimbus 2, with all-moving tailplane, were built. Aircraft from No. 133 onward (Nimbus 2B) introduced a fixed-incidence tailplane. The current model, the Nimbus 2C, is similar, but has a new brake/flap system, higher gross weight and (optionally) wings and horizontal tail surfaces of carbonfibre construction. A total of 78 Nimbus 2B/2C had been built by 1 January 1980.

The following description applies primarily to the Nimbus 2C:

TYPE: Single-seat Open Class sailplane; g limit +10·5.

AIRFRAME: Cantilever mid-wing monoplane. Wortmann wing section. Dihedral 2°. Sweepback at leading-edge 1° on inner panels, 2° on outer panels. Glassfibre/foam sandwich (optionally carbonfibre) wings and tail. Combined flap/airbrake on each wing trailing-edge. Central tubular steel fuselage framework. Glassfibre shell, stiffened with bonded-in foam bulkheads. Cantilever T tail, with fixed-incidence tailplane. Retractable rubber-sprung monowheel, tyre pressure 3·45 bars (50 lb/sq in). Tost drum brake. Tailskid. Canopy opens sideways to starboard. Provision for up to 250 kg (550 lb) of water ballast.

SCHEMPP-HIRTH HS-7 MINI-NIMBUS C

As its name implies, the Mini-Nimbus is a scaled-down version of the Nimbus 2, the chief differences being a shorter wing, fitted with trailing-edge flaps/airbrakes, designed to qualify under the new FAI regulations for 15 metre Standard Class sailplanes. With optional fixed-incidence tailplane it is known as the Mini-Nimbus B; with the same new features as listed for the Nimbus 2C, it is known as the Mini-Nimbus C.

The prototype Mini-Nimbus (D-3119) flew for the first time on 18 September 1976. A total of 155 Mini-Nimbus had been delivered by 1 January 1980. The following details apply primarily to the Mini-Nimbus B/C:

TYPE: Single-seat 15 metre Class sailplane.

AIRFRAME: Cantilever mid-wing monoplane. Wortmann wing section. Dihedral 3°. Glassfibre/foam sandwich (optionally carbonfibre) wings and tail; flaps/airbrakes and ailerons are glassfibre shells. Glassfibre fuselage shell, stiffened with bonded foam rings and a central tubular steel frame. Fixed-incidence T tailplane; fin integral with fuselage. Manually-retractable rubber-sprung monowheel, tyre pressure 3·45 bars (50 lb/sq in), with Tost drum brake. Provision for up to 190 kg (418 lb) of water ballast.

SCHEMPP-HIRTH JANUS B

The Janus is of all-glassfibre construction. Original design work, begun by Dipl-Ing Holighaus in 1969, was continued from early 1972 onward, and the prototype made its first flight in the Spring of 1974.

A Janus flown by E. Mouat Biggs and S. Murray set three speed records over triangular courses in South Africa in November 1977. On 16 November, it averaged 73·171 knots (135·513 km/h; 84·204 mph) over 300 km; next day it achieved 75·631 knots (140·068 km/h; 87·034 mph) over 500 km; on 21 November it averaged 79·476 knots (147·19 km/h; 91·46 mph) over 100 km. The record of 66·015 knots (122·26 km/h; 75·97 mph) over a 750 km course was set by Erwin Müller and Otto Schäffner of West Germany in a Janus on 26 November 1978, in South Africa. The record for distance around a triangular course was set by C. M. Greaves and C. R. Simpson of the UK in a Janus, at 411·84 nm (762·72 km; 473·93 miles), on 28 December 1977.

Production began in January 1975 with the second, improved aircraft; a **Janus B** version became available in March 1978, with fixed-incidence tailplane; the **Janus C** has 20 m span carbonfibre wings and carbonfibre tailplane. A total of 100 Janus, Janus Bs and Janus Cs had been delivered by early 1980. The **Janus CM** is a powered version of the C, first flown in 1978; it has a 37 kW (50 hp) engine, pylon-mounted aft of the cockpit and retracting into the top of the fuselage when not in use. Empty and max T-O weights are 465 kg (1,025 lb) and 680 kg (1,500 lb) respectively. Three Janus CMs had been completed by early 1980.

The following description applies to the Janus B:

TYPE: Tandem two-seat high-performance training sailplane; g limits +5·3/−2·65.

AIRFRAME: Cantilever mid-wing monoplane. Wortmann wing sections: FX-67-K-170 at root, FX-67-K-15 at tip. Dihedral 4°. Sweepforward 2° on leading-edge. Glassfibre/foam sandwich wings, with glassfibre monocoque ailerons, trailing-edge flaps and Schempp-Hirth upper-surface airbrakes. Glassfibre monocoque fuselage with bonded-in foam bulkheads. Cantilever glassfibre/foam sandwich fixed-incidence T tailplane. Non-retractable monowheel and nosewheel. Continental tyres: pressure 2·69 bars (39 lb/sq in) on main wheel; pressure 0·79 bars (11·5 lb/sq in) on nosewheel. Tost drum brake on main wheel. Bumper under rear fuselage. Tail drag 'chute. Provision for 200 kg (440 lb) of water ballast.

SCHLEICHER

ALEXANDER SCHLEICHER SEGEL-FLUGZEUGBAU

HEAD OFFICE AND WORKS: D-6416 Poppenhausen/Wasserkuppe
Telephone: (06658) 225

This company is one of the oldest manufacturers of sailplanes in the world. Its founder, Alexander Schleicher, won a contest for training sailplanes in 1927 at the Wasserkuppe. In the same year he built at Poppenhausen a small factory for manufacturing gliders, two of his best-known pre-war products being the Rhönbussard and Rhönadler, designed by Hans Jacobs.

During the second World War, the factory was engaged in the repair of Baby IIb sailplanes. For a time afterwards it became a furniture factory, but it began producing sailplanes once more in 1951.

Descriptions of sailplanes in current production follow. Those designed by Ing Rudolf Kaiser are prefixed ASK; those with ASW designations are designed by Ing Gerhard Waibel. Schleicher also manufactures and markets spare parts, constructional materials and dust- and weather-proof covers for sailplanes.

SCHLEICHER ASK 13

This tandem-seat sailplane was developed from the K 7, which is in worldwide use by gliding clubs. The prototype first flew in July 1966.

Production by Schleicher, which totalled 617 of these aircraft, has ended, but the ASK 13 is expected to continue being manufactured, under licence, by another Federal German company.

TYPE: Tandem two-seat training and high-performance sailplane; g limit +4·0 (safety factor of 2).

AIRFRAME: Cantilever mid-wing monoplane. Wing section developed from Göttingen 535 and 549. Sweepforward at quarter-chord 6°. Dihedral 5°. Single-spar wooden wings, with fabric covering. Wooden ailerons, with plywood covering; Schempp-Hirth metal airbrakes above and below each wing. Welded steel tube fuselage with spruce formers and fabric main covering. Nose made of glassfibre. Turtledeck aft of canopy is plywood shell. Cantilever wooden tail unit, plywood-covered except for fabric-covered rear portion of rudder and elevators. Flettner tab in starboard elevator. Non-retractable sprung monowheel, with Tost drum brake; skid in front of wheel; steel tailskid. Canopy opens sideways to starboard.

Schempp-Hirth Nimbus 2C high-performance Open Class sailplane

Schempp-Hirth Janus two-seat all-glassfibre training sailplane

Schempp-Hirth HS-7 Mini-Nimbus C single-seat 15 metre sailplane
(Peter F. Selinger)

Schleicher ASW 19 Club single-seat sailplane

Schempp-Hirth Janus C, with 20 metre carbonfibre wings

Schleicher ASW 20 15 metre Class sailplane

Schleicher ASK 21 tandem two-seat sailplane

SCHLEICHER ASW 19

This sailplane, which flew for the first time on 23 November 1975, is essentially an improved version of the ASW 15 B (1977-78 *Jane's*), from which it differs in having a T tail unit. Production began in the Spring of 1976, and approx 300 had been built by the beginning of 1980. The ASW 19 took 1st place in the Standard Class at the 1978 World Championships at Châteauroux, France.

There are two current production versions:

ASW 19B. Standard Class version, with retractable monowheel, water ballast provision.

ASW 19 Club. Club Class version, with non-retractable unsprung monowheel, no water ballast provision and larger-area airbrakes. Best glide ratio of 36; other data as for ASW 19B.

TYPE: Single-seat Standard Class and Club Class sailplane.

AIRFRAME: Cantilever mid-wing monoplane. Wortmann wing sections: FX-61-163 at root, FX-60-126 at tip. Dihedral 2°. Glassfibre roving wing main spar. Wings and tail surfaces of glassfibre/foam sandwich, with Schempp-Hirth metal upper-surface airbrakes. Glassfibre/honeycomb sandwich fuselage, with reinforced keel. T tailplane with elevator. Retractable monowheel (non-retractable on Club version), size 5·00-5, with internal drum brake; rubber tailskid. Canopy hinged at front and opens upward. Provision for 100 kg (220 lb) water ballast (19B only). Towing hook at CG; optional second hook in nose.

SCHLEICHER ASW 20

The ASW 20 is intended to take advantage of the March 1975 CIVV regulations for unlimited 15 metre sailplanes, and is fitted with trailing-edge flaps as well as large upper-surface spoilers. It has an additional high-drag flap range incorporating a special mechanism to eliminate pitch and airspeed changes when changing flap position between 30° and 55°.

The prototype ASW 20 made its first flight on 29 January 1977, and aircraft of this type won 2nd, 3rd, 4th, 6th and 7th places in their class at the 1978 World Championships. Approx 300 had been built by the beginning of 1980. A version designated **ASW 20F** is being built under licence in France by Centrair; this received French certification on 31 March 1978.

TYPE: Single-seat 15 metre Class sailplane.

AIRFRAME: As described for ASW 19B, but with Wortmann FX-62K-131 (modified) wing section at root, FX-60-126 at tip, no dihedral, addition of wing flaps, no option for nose towing hook, and max water ballast increased to 120 kg (265 lb).

SCHLEICHER ASW 20 L

The ASW 20 L (for Lang: long), first flown in May 1977, is a version of the ASW 20 with detachable outer wing panels increasing the span to 16·59 m (54 ft 5¼ in) for Open Class competition. Production began in late 1978, and a total of 48 (about one-third of those then on order) had been built by the beginning of 1980.

TYPE: Single-seat Open Class sailplane; g limits +5·3/−2·65.

AIRFRAME: Generally as for ASW 20 except for wings, which have detachable span-increasing outer panels and no provision for water ballast.

SCHLEICHER ASK 21

Latest design by Ing Kaiser, the ASK 21 prototype flew for the first time on 6 February 1979, it received LBA certification on 18 April 1980.

TYPE: Tandem two-seat competition and training sailplane.

AIRFRAME: Cantilever mid-wing monoplane. Two-piece wings, primarily of GRP/foam sandwich construction with GRP roving spar. Wortmann wing sections: FX S 02-196 from root to inboard of ailerons, FX-60-126 at tip. Dihedral 4°. Schempp-Hirth upper-surface metal airbrakes. Fixed T tailplane and separate elevator. Non-retractable semi-recessed nosewheel (size 4·00-4) and rubber-sprung monowheel (size 5·00-5), the latter with hydraulic disc brake; steel-shod rubber tailskid. Front and rear canopies hinged at front and rear respectively, both opening upward.

SPORTAVIA
SPORTAVIA-PÜTZER GmbH u Co KG

HEAD OFFICE AND WORKS: D-5377 Dahlem-Schmidtheim, Flugplatz Dahlemer Binz

Telephone: (02447) 277/8

Telex: 08 33 602 spkg

This company was formed in 1966 by Comte Antoine d'Assche, director of the French company Alpavia SA, and Herr Alfons Pützer, to take over from Alpavia manufacture of the Avion-Planeur series of motor gliders designed by M René Fournier.

In 1969, RFB (see Aircraft section), a subsidiary of VFW, acquired a percentage holding in Sportavia.

Current Sportavia products include the RS 180, described in the Aircraft section of this edition.

SPORTAVIA RF5B SPERBER

The RF5B Sperber, first flown in May 1971, is an improved, high-performance development of the RF5 (1978-79 *Jane's*), differing chiefly in having increased wing span/area and reduced fuselage side area. The Sperber was certificated by the LBA in March 1972, and by the end of 1978 a total of about 35 had been delivered. Production rate was later reduced, and since 1979 the Sperber has been available only to firm order. A description and illustration can be found in the 1979-80 *Jane's*.

VALENTIN
**VALENTIN GmbH GERÄTE-
und MASCHINENBAU**

8901 Königsbrunn, Germanenstrasse 2 (Postfach 1165)

Telephone: (08231) 4033/4
DESIGNER: Dipl-Ing Jörg B. Stieber

VALENTIN TAIFUN

The Taifun (typhoon) motor glider is proposed in four versions, as follows:

Taifun 15S. Basic model, with 15 m span wings and non-retractable tailwheel-type landing gear.

Taifun 15E. With 15 m span wings and retractable tricycle landing gear.

Taifun 17S. With 17 m span wings and non-retractable tailwheel-type landing gear.

Taifun 17E. With 17 m span wings and retractable tricycle landing gear.

Construction of the first prototype, to Taifun 17E configuration, began in July 1979, and this aircraft was expected to make its first flight in July 1980.

TYPE: Two-seat motor glider; g limits +5·3/−3·0.

AIRFRAME: Cantilever low-wing monoplane with T tail. Wortmann FX-67K-170/17 wing section. Dihedral 3°. Incidence 0° 48'. Sweepforward 0° 38' 4" at quarter-chord. Wings and ailerons of glassfibre/foam sandwich construction. All-glassfibre trailing-edge flaps. Schempp-Hirth upper-surface airbrakes. Fuselage is a stressed-skin structure of glassfibre and foam sandwich. Fixed-incidence T tailplane, with horn-balanced elevator, of similar construction to wings. Flettner tab in port half of elevator. Non-retractable or mechanically retractable tricycle or tailwheel-type landing gear (see model listings), with Goodyear 5 in main-wheel tyres, pressure 2·5 bars (36 lb/sq in), and Cleveland disc brakes. Single nosewheel or tailwheel. Cockpit seats two persons side by side under rearward-sliding canopy.

POWER PLANT: One 59 kW (80 hp) Limbach L 2000 EB four-cylinder four-stroke engine, driving a Hoffmann HO-V62 two-blade propeller.

INDIA

CIVIL AVIATION DEPARTMENT
TECHNICAL CENTRE, CIVIL AVIATION DEPARTMENT

Civil Aviation Department, R. K. Puram, New Delhi 22
WORKS: Technical Centre, opposite Safdarjung Airport, New Delhi 110003
Telephone: 611504
DIRECTOR GENERAL: Air Marshal J. Zaheer, PVSM, AVSM (Retd)
DEPUTY DIRECTOR GENERAL: K. B. Ganesan
DIRECTOR (R & D): P. R. Chandrasekhar

The Technical Centre is the research and development establishment of the Indian Civil Aviation Department. It is equipped with all facilities necessary for the development of design, airworthiness and operational standards, operational research, development testing and standardisation of indigenous aircraft materials, type certification of prototype aircraft and equipment, and the scientific investigation of accidents.

Since 1950 the Technical Centre has undertaken the design and development of gliders utilising predominantly indigenous materials. The first of these gliders, of the open-cockpit primary type, was flown in November 1950. Since then the Technical Centre has built gliders of eight types for service at civil gliding centres in India, as listed in the 1972-73 *Jane's*. Of these, five have been original designs.

The Technical Centre does not undertake quantity production of gliders. Drawings of designs developed at the Centre are supplied to interested organisations with permission to manufacture them in series.

HS-II MRIGASHEER

This single-seat Standard Class sailplane is the first to be designed and developed at the Technical Centre by the team of designers and engineers led by Mr K. B. Ganesan, then the Director of Research and Development. The original HS-I made its first flight in November 1970 and was last described and illustrated in the 1973-74 *Jane's*.

The further-developed HS-II flew for the first time in April 1973. The second prototype, fitted with trailing-edge slotted flaps instead of airbrakes, made its first flight in May 1977, and the following description applies to this aircraft. Production of the Mrigasheer was under consideration in early 1980.

TYPE: Single-seat Standard Class sailplane.
AIRFRAME: Cantilever high-wing monoplane. Wortmann wing sections: FX-61-184 at root, varying through FX-61-163 to FX-60-126 at tip. Dihedral 1° 30'. Entire airframe is of plywood-covered wooden construction, with plain wooden ailerons and trailing-edge slotted flaps, except for rudder, which is fabric-covered. Retractable unsprung monowheel, tyre pressure 2·07 bars (30 lb/sq in), with drum-type brake. Rubber-sprung nose-skid with replaceable steel shoe. Rubber-sprung tailskid. Forward-opening jettisonable canopy.

ATS-1 ARDHRA

Recorded previously in *Jane's* as the TG-1 Arudhra, this two-seat training sailplane was designed by the same team that was responsible for the Mrigasheer. The prototype (VT-GEJ) made its first flight on 5 March 1979 and, after extensive flight testing, was certificated by the Indian DGCA in November of that year.

The Ardhra has been evaluated and found suitable for use by the National Cadet Corps, and in early 1980 plans were under way for large-scale production, both for the NCC and for civil flying clubs. A second prototype was then under construction, with 2° geometric twist (washout) from 50% span to tip, and 3° (instead of 1° 30') dihedral. The following description applies to this second prototype:

TYPE: Tandem two-seat advanced training sailplane; g limits +5·3/−2·65.
AIRFRAME: Cantilever shoulder-wing monoplane. Wortmann FX-61-184 wing section from root to tip. Dihedral 3°. Incidence 3°. Sweepforward 3° at leading-edge; 2° geometric twist on outer panels. Plywood-covered two-spar wooden wings, plywood covered on leading- and trailing-edges; plain wooden ailerons; wooden airbrakes in upper and lower wing surfaces. Tail unit of similar construction, but with rear portions of rudder and elevator fabric covered. Horn-balanced rudder; mass- and horn-balanced elevator. Plywood-covered tab in starboard elevator. Semi-monocoque wooden fuselage, with plywood covering. Nosecone of glassfibre. Non-retractable unsprung monowheel, tyre size 6·00-4. Rubber-sprung nose-skid, with replaceable steel shoe, and rubber-sprung tailskid.

ITALY

CAPRONI VIZZOLA
CAPRONI VIZZOLA COSTRUZIONI AERONAUTICHE SpA

20122 Milano, Via Durini 24
Telephone: (02) 700826 and 781975
WORKS: 21010 Vizzola Ticino (Varese)
Telephone: (0331) 230826 and 230727
Telex: Caproni 332554 CAVIZ I

PRESIDENT: Dott Giovanni Caproni di Taliedo

The Caproni company, formed in 1910, is the oldest Italian aircraft manufacturer. Its works at Vizzola Ticino have approx 30,000 m² (322,917 sq ft) of covered space, and are adjacent to Malpensa Airport. They are equipped to manufacture complete structural subassemblies for helicopters and medium-sized fixed-wing aircraft. Caproni Vizzola also produces ground support equipment for General Electric T64/CT64, J79, J85 and CF6 and Turbo Union RB.199 turbojet and turbofan engines.

In 1969 Caproni Vizzola began producing a series of Calif sailplanes designed by Carlo Ferrarin and Livio Sonzio. Details of the earlier A-10 (one built), A-12 (two built), A-14 (one built), A-15 (one built), A-20 and A-21 have been given in the 1972-73 and subsequent *Jane's*.

Development of an improved two-seat version of the A-20, designated A-20S, is at present in abeyance.

CAPRONI VIZZOLA CALIF A-21S

The original A-21 was a two-seat version of the A-14, from which it differed in having a wider (to accommodate two side-by-side seats) and slightly longer fuselage. This version (1975-76 *Jane's*) was superseded by the A-21S which has been certificated by the RAI, FAA, LBA and DGAC.

It was in an A-21S that, on 18 August 1974, Adele Orsi and Franca Bellingeri set the current Class D2 speed record for women over a 300 km closed circuit at 52·742 knots (97·741 km/h; 60·733 mph).

By January 1980 a total of 54 A-21S had been ordered, of which 29 had been delivered.

TYPE: Side-by-side two-seat high-performance sailplane; g limit +5·0 (ultimate).
AIRFRAME: Cantilever mid-wing monoplane. Wing section Wortmann FX-67-K-170 at root, FX-60-126 at tip. Dihedral 0° at root, 1° 30' on outer panels. Incidence 4°. No sweep. Single-spar wings, of aluminium alloy stressed-skin construction, with glassfibre tips. Extruded aluminium alloy ailerons are aerodynamically balanced. Extruded aluminium alloy plain trailing-edge flaps. Extruded aluminium alloy airbrakes on upper wing surface move in conjunction with flaps. Glassfibre/foam plastics semi-monocoque forward fuselage, with load-carrying light alloy frame; all-metal stressed-skin rear fuselage. T tail of aluminium alloy, with glassfibre tailplane tips; spring-adjusted elevator trim. Manually retractable twin main wheels, with rubber-in-compression shock-absorbers, tyre size 3·50-5, pressure 3·54 bars (51·3 lb/sq in) and Tost drum brake; non-retractable steerable tailwheel, size 200 × 50. Canopy hinged at rear to open upward.

CAPRONI VIZZOLA CALIF A-21SJ

An A-21J jet-powered version of the A-21 two-seat sailplane, fitted with a 0·90 kN (202 lb st) Microturbo TRS 18 turbojet, flew for the first time at the end of January 1972. In 1976 this prototype was acquired by Lockheed-Georgia, USA, for use in a joint research programme with Mississippi State University. Details of this programme were given in the 1977-78 *Jane's*.

Now known as the A-21SJ, this version is based on the A-21S sailplane (which see).

TYPE: Side-by-side two-seat jet-powered sailplane.
AIRFRAME: As A-21S, except for modifications necessary to incorporate power plant aft of cockpit. Main-wheel tyre size 5·00-5. Steerable tailwheel, tyre size 210 × 65.
POWER PLANT: One 1·08 kN (242·5 lb st) Microturbo TRS 18 turbojet engine (or 1·1 kN; 247 lb st KHD T317 turbojet), installed to rear of cockpit. Fuel load, in one tank in fuselage and two flexible wing tanks, 110 kg (242·5 lb). 24V/600W starter/generator and 24V 12Ah batteries for in-flight and ground starting.

GLASFASER
GLASFASER ITALIANA SrL

24030 Valbrembo (Bergamo), Via Locatelli 1
Telephone: (035) 612617
PRESIDENT: Dott Ing Sergio Aldo Capoferri
TECHNICAL DIRECTOR: Giampaolo Ghidotti

This company's factory occupies an area of 1,600 m² (17,225 sq ft) and is insulated and heated to maintain a controlled temperature of 20°C, essential for work on glassfibre structures.

Glasfaser holds RAI licences to build glassfibre sailplanes and to repair, maintain and modify sailplanes and training aircraft.

Glasfaser built 25 single-seat 17 metre Kestrel sailplanes, described under the Glasflügel entry in the German section of this edition. The company has built 130 complete fuselage assemblies for the Kestrel and assembled 10 Hornets. It has also completed 15 Glaser-Dirks DG-200s, and is an agency for Grob sailplanes (see Federal German section).

Other activities include construction of glassfibre trailers for road transportation of sailplanes, the repair and maintenance of sailplanes of glassfibre, wood and metal construction, and installation and modification work on sailplanes of all types.

MAGGI
ANGELO MAGGI

c/o Club Aviazione Popolare, Via Dante 80, 21015 Lonate Pozzolo (Varese)

MAGGI MG3-15L CONDOR

This homebuilt sailplane, of which construction began in May 1975, was expected to make its first flight in February 1979. No more recent news had been received at the time of closing for press.

TYPE: Single-seat homebuilt sailplane.
AIRFRAME: Cantilever shoulder-wing monoplane. Wing section NACA 65₃-618. Dihedral 4°. Incidence 4°.

Model of the Valentin Taifun two-seat motor glider

Caproni Vizzola Calif A-21S two-seat high-performance sailplane

Caproni Vizzola Calif A-21SJ jet-powered sailplane

First prototype Nippi NP-100A, with original Kawasaki H2 engine

Second prototype HS-II Mrigasheer single-seat Standard Class sailplane

First prototype of the Civil Aviation Dept ATS-1 Ardhra advanced training sailplane

Maggi MG3-15L Condor homebuilt sailplane (*Michael A. Badrocke*)

First Japanese-built Nippi Pilatus B4-PC11AF Standard Class sailplane

Single light alloy main spar; wing leading-edges of PVC resin, coated with glassfibre. NASA (Whitcomb) winglets at each wingtip. Fiat light alloy ailerons; airbrakes and plain trailing-edge flaps, also of light alloy. Fuselage has light alloy structure with glassfibre/polyurethane foam covering. Cantilever tailplane of light alloy, leading-edges of which are of balsa with glassfibre coating; separate elevators, with spring trim. Retractable unsprung monowheel, tyre size 5·00-5, pressure 3·2 bars (46·4 lb/sq in), with drum brake; non-retractable tailskid.

JAPAN

NIPPI
NIHON HIKOKI KABUSHIKI KAISHA (Japan Aircraft Manufacturing Co Ltd)

HEAD OFFICE AND SUGITA PLANT: 3175 Showa-machi, Kanazawa-ku, Yokohama 236
Telephone: Yokohama (045) 771 1251
Telex: (3822) 267 Nippi J
CHIEF, SAILPLANE SALES SECTION: Norio Kagata
OTHER OFFICERS: see Aircraft section

NIPPI NP-100A ALBATROSS

Nippi began the design of this motor glider in late 1973, and the prototype (NP-100) made its first flight on 25 December 1975. Flight testing was carried out during 1976, as a result of which several modifications were made. Principal point of interest in the NP-100A is the power plant, which is of the ducted-fan type and is fully buried within the fuselage aft of the main landing gear.

A secondary flight test programme took place between March and July 1978, to determine the final specification for a production version. The planned production programme is awaiting final selection of a type-certificated power plant.

The following description applies to the first prototype in its current form:

TYPE: Side-by-side two-seat motor glider.
AIRFRAME: Cantilever shoulder-wing monoplane. Wing section Wortmann FX-67-K-170 (modified) from root

to tip. No dihedral or sweepback. All-metal single-spar structure, with two-section metal-skinned flaps on each trailing-edge (designed for upward or downward deflection) and plain ailerons. No spoilers. All-metal semi-monocoque fuselage. All-metal tail unit, with conventional elevators and rudder. Forward-retracting twin-wheel main landing gear, operated mechanically with spring assistance. Steerable, non-retractable tailwheel, linked to rudder movement.

POWER PLANT (prototype): One modified 50·7 kW (68 hp at 6,000 rpm) M2 1,000 cc two-stroke aircooled flat-four engine, installed in centre of fuselage and driving a four-blade wooden ducted fan. Triple 'Venetian blind' air intake doors, on each side of fuselage, interconnected with engine starting circuit to prevent engine operating when doors are closed. Fuel in single fuselage tank, capacity 40 litres (8·8 Imp gallons).

NIPPI PILATUS B4-PC11AF

Pilatus Flugzeugwerke of Switzerland designed and built this single-seat Standard Class sailplane for multi-purpose training and aerobatics. Swiss certification was granted on 12 June 1972, and by March 1978 more than 330 had been delivered by Pilatus to customers in 30 countries in all parts of the world. For these aircraft, Pilatus continues to be responsible for after-sales service.

Production and marketing rights in the aircraft were transferred to Nippi in June 1978, and it is now known as the Nippi Pilatus B4-PC11AF. The first Nippi-built example flew for the first time on 25 November 1979. Initial production after JCAB certification, is to be at the rate of three per month.

TYPE: Single-seat Standard Class and Club Class sailplane; g limits +6·32/−4·32 (Normal); +7·0/−4·79 (Aerobatic).

AIRFRAME: Cantilever shoulder-wing monoplane with T tail. Wing section NACA 64₃-618. Dihedral 1°. Conventional light alloy wings with single U spar and hard PVC foam ribs between metal ribs; conventional ailerons of similar construction. Light alloy spoilers at 60% chord on wing upper surfaces. Semi-monocoque light alloy fuselage, with flush-riveted skin. Rear fuselage consists of two half-shells, riveted together. Cantilever light alloy tail unit, with PVC ribs. Fixed-incidence tailplane. Elevator spring trim. Retractable (optionally non-retractable) unsprung Tost monowheel, and fixed tailwheel, in tandem. Main wheel faired by doors when retracted. Mechanical independent drum brakes. Canopy jettisonable in flight.

TAINAN

TAINAN INDUSTRY CO LTD (Tainan Kogyo KK)

5139-3 1-chome, Komatsubara, Zama-shi, Kanagawa-ken 228
Telephone: 0462 54 2332/3/4

This company took over the manufacture of sailplanes from LADCO (see 1971-72 *Jane's*). Details of the former company's Mita III, which Tainan continued to build under licence, can be found in the 1979-80 *Jane's*. Tainan's latest known design is the TN-1.

TAINAN TN-1

The TN-1 (manufacturer's designation F5) was designed by Yukio Tanaka. Construction of a prototype began in August 1974, and this made its first flight in December 1976. Certification trials by the JCAB were under way in the Spring of 1978, but no later information had been received at the time of closing for press.

TYPE: Single-seat sailplane; g limits +5·3/−2·65.

AIRFRAME: Cantilever high-wing monoplane. Modified Göttingen wing sections. Dihedral 3°. Sweepforward 2°

4' at quarter-chord. Single-spar wings of spruce and plywood, with fabric covering. Plywood-covered wooden ailerons. Schempp-Hirth airbrakes. Steel tube fuselage with wooden stringers and fabric covering. Glassfibre nose. Cantilever wooden tail unit, with fabric-covered elevators and rudder. Trim tab in starboard elevator. Non-retractable unsprung monowheel at CG, tyre pressure 2·94 bars (42·7 lb/sq in); Tainan band brake; tailskid.

POLAND

SZD
PRZEDSIEBIORSTWO DOSWIADCZALNO-PRODUKCYJNE SZYBOWNICTWA (Experimental and Production Concern for Gliders) PZL-BIELSKO

HEAD OFFICE AND WORKS: 43-300 Bielsko-Biala 1, ul. Cieszynska 325
Telephone: 250 21 to 250 26
Telex: 031-259 SZD PL
DIRECTOR: Ing Kazimierz Jasinski
SALES REPRESENTATIVE: Pezetel, 02-344 Warszawa, ul. Czestochowska 4a

The Instytut Szybownictwa (Gliding Institute), formed officially in January 1946 at Bielsko-Biala, has since undergone several changes of name, as detailed in the 1977-78 *Jane's*. The change to the present title took place in July 1975, but the well-known designation initials SZD are retained. This organisation is responsible for the design and development of all Polish gliders and sailplanes. Production plants are situated at Bielsko-Biala, Wroclaw and Jezów.

Between 1947 and 1979 the Polish aircraft industry produced 3,914 gliders of more than 100 different types, and SZD sailplanes have been exported all over the world in substantial numbers. The SZD-9 Bocian, last described in the 1978-79 *Jane's*, was in production for 25 years.

SZD-30C PIRAT

Designed by Ing Jerzy Smielkiewicz, the prototype of this single-seat Standard Class sailplane flew for the first time on 19 May 1966. It is suitable for the full range of duties from training to competition flying and is cleared for cloud flying, spinning and basic aerobatics.

Production of the Pirat started in 1967 and ·776 had been built by the beginning of 1980, including 430 completed by the WSK-Swidnik works, where production was also undertaken until October 1977. Pirats have been exported to 24 countries, including Argentina, Australia, Austria, Canada, Denmark, Egypt, Finland, France, Germany (Democratic Republic), Germany (Federal Republic), Hungary, Italy, North Korea, Netherlands, New Zealand, Norway, Spain, Sweden, Switzerland, UK, USA, USSR, Venezuela and Yugoslavia.

The improved version from 1978 was the SZD-30C, to which the description applies; the first SZD-30C was flown on 10 January 1978. Production has now ended.

TYPE: Single-seat Standard Class sailplane; g limits +5·3/−2·65.

AIRFRAME: Cantilever high-wing monoplane with T tail. Wortmann wing sections: FX-61-168 at root, FX-60-1261 at tip. Dihedral 2° 30' on outer panels only. Plywood-covered wooden wings, comprising multi-spar rectangular centre-section and single-spar tapered outer panels. Epoxy/glassfibre, partially mass-balanced ailerons (smaller than on earlier Pirat models). Double-plate airbrakes. Plywood monocoque fuselage, with glassfibre nose and cockpit floor. Forward fuselage reinforced with thick layer of glassfibre, instead of original front skid. Towing hooks in nose and near CG. Wooden tail unit, with trim tab on elevator trailing-edge. Non-retractable monowheel, size 350 × 135 mm, with disc brake and roller bearings; tailwheel replaceable with rubber-sprung tailskid. Canopy opens sideways. Two cockpit baggage compartments.

SZD-41A JANTAR STANDARD (AMBER)

This single-seat Standard Class sailplane was designed by Ing W. Okarmus on the basis of the prototype Open Class SZD-38 Jantar-1. The fuselage and tail unit are the same for both types; the wings of the SZD-41A are designed to OSTIV Standard Class requirements.

The Jantar Standard was flown for the first time at Bielsko-Biala on 3 October 1973, piloted by A. Zientek. Polish pilots flying the SZD-41 in the 1974 World Championships at Waikerie, Australia, gained third and seventh places in the Standard Class competition. Jantar Standards gained fourth, sixth and eighteenth places in the World Championships at Räyskälä, Finland in June 1976. The current production version is designated SZD-41A.

A total of 160 Jantar Standards had been built by the beginning of 1980, for customers in Argentina, Australia, Austria, Belgium, Bulgaria, Canada, Denmark, Finland, Germany (Democratic Republic), Germany (Federal Republic), Hungary, Poland, Sweden, Switzerland, UK, the USA, the USSR and Yugoslavia.

TYPE: Single-seat Standard Class sailplane; g limits +5·3/−2·65.

AIRFRAME: Cantilever mid-wing monoplane. Wing section NN-8. Dihedral 1° 30'. Sweepback 0° 30' at quarter-chord. Single-spar ribless wings with foam-filled glassfibre/epoxy resin sandwich skin. Multi-hinged ailerons; no flaps. DFS glassfibre airbrakes above and below each wing. All-glassfibre/epoxy resin shell fuselage; centre portion has a steel tube frame coupling together the wings, fuselage and landing gear. Cantilever T tail, of glassfibre/epoxy resin. Elevator spring trim. Fin integral with fuselage. Retractable monowheel, tyre pressure 3·43 bars (49·8 lb/sq in), with disc brake; non-retractable tailwheel. Provision for 80 kg (176 lb) water ballast.

SZD-42-1 JANTAR 2 (AMBER)

This high-performance single-seat Open Class sailplane, originally designated SZD-42, was developed by Dipl-Ing Adam Kurbiel from the series-built all-plastics SZD-38A Jantar-1, and flew for the first time on 2 February 1976.

A total of 23 Jantar-2s had been built by the beginning of 1979. Production then ceased in favour of the later Jantar 2B. A description and illustration of the Jantar 2 can be found in the 1979-80 *Jane's*.

SZD-42-2 JANTAR 2B

Designed by Dipl-Ing Adam Kurbiel, the SZD-42-2 Open Class sailplane is based on the SZD-42-1. The prototype flew for the first time on 13 March 1978, and 32 Jantar 2Bs had been built by the beginning of 1980.

TYPE: Single-seat Open Class sailplane; g limits +5·3/−2·65.

AIRFRAME: Generally similar to SZD-41A, but with wings raised from mid-mounted to shoulder position, 2° dihedral and incidence reduced by 1° 30'. Light alloy DFS-type airbrakes. Cantilever cruciform tail unit of glassfibre/epoxy resin. Monowheel tyre pressure 2·96 bars (43 lb/sq in). Tailskid instead of tailwheel. Water ballast provision is increased to 170 kg (375 lb). Improvements made to elevator spring trim, monowheel retraction system and cockpit comfort. Hinged canopy and provision for CG tow hook.

SZD-45A OGAR (GREYHOUND)

This two-seat school and training motor glider was designed by Dipl Ing Tadeusz Labuc, originally with a 33·5 kW (45 hp) Stamo engine and later with a 50·7 kW (68 hp) Sportavia Limbach engine. The first prototype (SP-0001) made its first flight on 29 May 1973, and was described in the 1973-74 *Jane's*. This prototype made a new 'first' flight on 10 September 1979, after being fitted with wing-tip winglets, a modification devised by Mr W. Blazewicz of Warsaw Technical University.

A total of 65 Ogars had been built by the beginning of 1980, for customers in Germany (Democratic Republic), Germany (Federal Republic), Sweden, the UK and the USA. Production has now ended.

The first flight was made on 13 March 1979 of the **SZD-45-2 Ogar-F**, with a 44·7 kW (60 hp) PZL-Franklin 2A-120C two-cylinder engine.

TYPE: Side-by-side two-seat school and training motor glider; g limits +5·3/−2·65.

AIRFRAME: Cantilever shoulder-wing monoplane. Wortmann wing sections: FX-61-168 at root, FX-60-1261 at tip. Dihedral 1° 30'. Sweepback 1° at quarter-chord. Single-spar wooden wings, with moulded plywood stressed skin covered with glassfibre. Glassfibre sandwich slotless ailerons; airbrake above and below each wing. Pod and boom fuselage; main nacelle is glassfibre/epoxy resin shell built on two wooden frames which carry wings, engine mounting, fuel tank, and tubular duralumin boom which supports tail unit. Cantilever T tail, fin being integral with tailboom. Semi-retractable monowheel with shock-absorber and disc-type brake. Fully-castoring tailwheel. For school use, outrigger legs and wheels are mounted adjacent to wing-tips. Canopy opens upward. Dual controls standard.

POWER PLANT: One 50·7 kW (68 hp) Limbach SL 1700 EC four-cylinder four-stroke aircooled engine, mounted behind cabin and driving a two-blade Hoffmann pusher propeller. Fuel load 22 kg (48·5 lb).

SZD-48 JANTAR STANDARD 2

This Standard Class sailplane is a development of the SZD-41A Jantar Standard (which see), and was designed by Ing Wladyslaw Okarmus. The prototype flew for the first time on 10 December 1977, and 96 had been built by the beginning of 1980.

With simple modifications to the trim and speed measuring systems, the SZD-48 can be converted quickly to the **SZD-48-2** version, which has a never-exceed speed of 151 knots (280 km/h; 174 mph).

TYPE: Single-seat Standard Class sailplane.

AIRFRAME: Cantilever shoulder-wing monoplane, with NN-8 wing section. Dihedral 1° 30'. Single glassfibre roving main spar, with glassfibre/foam/glassfibre moulded skins (no ribs) and plain ailerons. Duralumin upper/lower surface airbrakes. Glassfibre fuselage, with steel tube central support structure, rear portion stiffened by half-frames and ribs. Cantilever T tail of similar construction to wings. Elevator spring trim. Retractable monowheel, with disc brake; semi-recessed tailwheel. Provision for 150 litres (33 Imp gallons) water ballast.

Tainan TN-1 (F5) single-seat sailplane

SZD-50-2 Puchacz two-seat training sailplane

SZD-45A Ogar side-by-side two-seat motorised training glider

SZD-30C Pirat single-seat Standard Class sailplane

SZD-42-2 Jantar 2B single-seat Open Class sailplane

SZD-41A Jantar Standard single-seat Standard Class sailplane

SZD-48-2 Jantar Standard 2 single-seat sailplane

SZD-49 JANTAR K

The Jantar K is an FAI 15 metre Class version of the Jantar Standard, fitted with wing flaps. A prototype (SP-2583) flew for the first time on 10 October 1978.

SZD-50-2 PUCHACZ (EAGLE OWL)

The Puchacz, designed by Dipl-Ing Adam Meus, is a high-performance sailplane intended particularly for training and performance flying. It has been modified and developed from a prototype, designated SZD-50-1 Dromader, which first flew on 21 December 1976.

A second prototype made its initial flight on 20 December 1977, and the first production Puchacz (SP-3151) followed on 13 April 1979. A total of nine had been built by the beginning of 1980.

TYPE: Tandem two-seat high-performance training sailplane; g limits +5·2/−2·65.

AIRFRAME: Cantilever mid-wing monoplane, mainly of glassfibre sandwich construction. Wortmann wing sections. Plain ailerons. Upper/lower surface airbrakes. Glassfibre fuselage, supported in central portion by two wooden frames. Glassfibre sandwich cruciform tail unit, with fabric-covered rudder. Non-retractable semi-recessed nosewheel and sprung monowheel (latter with disc brake), and tailskid. Canopy opens sideways.

ROMANIA

ICA
INTREPRINDERE DE CONSTRUCTII AERONAUTICE (Aeronautical Construction Enterprise)

Brasov

As detailed in the Aircraft section, the current activities of the Romanian aircraft industry are divided between two main industrial centres, IAvB in Bucharest and ICA at Brasov. In addition to its work on powered aircraft, the ICA is responsible for all sailplane development and production previously undertaken by URMV-3 (up to 1959) and IIL (Ghimbav) up to 1968. The principal Romanian designer of sailplanes is Dipl Ing Iosif Silimon, whose designs are prefixed with the letters IS. Details of his earlier designs appeared in the 1961-62, 1965-66 and 1972-73 Jane's.

IS-28B2

Despite its similar designation, this high-performance training sailplane represents a considerable advance over the IS-28 (1975-76 Jane's), from which it differs principally in having 17 m span all-metal wings, a longer and more slender fuselage, and reduced wing and tailplane dihedral. Design began in the Autumn of 1971, and the first IS-28B made its first flight on 26 April 1973.

There have been two production versions, as follows:

IS-28B1. Version without wing flaps. No longer in production. Described in 1976-77 Jane's.

IS-28B2. Current (since 1976) production version, with Schempp-Hirth type (instead of DFS type) airbrakes and trailing-edge split flaps. Description applies to this version, of which more than 100 have been sold, chiefly in Australia and the USA. Production in 1979 was continuing at a rate of 70-100 per year, but was expected to be replaced from mid-1980 by the IS-30. The IS-28B2 has also been certificated in the UK and the Federal Republic of Germany.

TYPE: Tandem two-seat high-performance training sailplane; g limits (single-seat) +6·4/−4·2; (two-seat) +5·3/−2·65.

AIRFRAME: Cantilever shoulder-wing monoplane. Wortmann wing sections: FX-61-163 at root, FX-60-126 at tip. Forward-swept all-metal wings, with L-section main spar booms and dural web, dural auxiliary spar, and dural ribs. Schempp-Hirth metal airbrake above and below each wing. Ailerons and split trailing-edge flaps fabric-covered. No tabs. All-metal semi-monocoque forward and centre fuselage. Rear fuselage is duralumin monocoque. Cantilever T tail, with moderate tailplane

dihedral. Elevator trailing-edges and rudder fabric-covered. Trim tab in each elevator. Semi-retractable monowheel with oleo-pneumatic shock-absorber and disc brake; sprung tailskid. Canopy opens sideways (to starboard) and can be jettisoned in flight. Nose towing hook, with Tost cable release, is standard; CG towing hook optional.

IS-28M

Two motor glider versions of the IS-28B2 have been developed. The rear fuselage, tail unit and main wings are virtually unchanged from the IS-28B2, but the powered versions are of low-wing configuration and have redesigned forward fuselages, cockpit canopies and main landing gear. The wings of both versions can be folded from a point immediately inboard of the ailerons.

The two versions are designated as follows:

IS-28M1. Tandem two-seater, with main landing gear comprising a retractable central monowheel, with balloon tyre, and underwing outrigger wheels. Otherwise generally similar to IS-28M2, except that wing span is increased. Reported that deliveries were due to begin in late 1979.

IS-28M2. Side-by-side two-seater, with main landing gear comprising two retractable wheels side by side under-fuselage centre-section, with shock-absorbers. Steerable

Close-up of cabin and main landing gear of IS-28M1 *(Brian M. Service)*

IS-28B2 tandem two-seat high-performance training sailplane
(The Age, Melbourne)

IS-28M2 side-by-side two-seat motor glider *(Brian M. Service)*

tailwheel, also with shock-absorber. Prototype (YR-1013) flew for the first time on 26 June 1976. The first 10 aircraft of this type were allocated to the UK, where they are marketed by Morisonics Ltd of The Parade, Frimley, Surrey. Supplied also to customers in Canada and the USA. In production.

TYPE: Two-seat motor glider; g limits +4·0/−1·5 (M1), +5·3/−2·65 (M2).

AIRFRAME: Cantilever low-wing monoplane, of mainly metal construction. Wortmann wing sections: FX-61-163 at root, FX-60-126 at tip. Dihedral 2°. Sweepforward 2° 30′ at quarter-chord. Single-spar wings, with aluminium ribs and skin, fabric-covered metal ailerons and (optionally) all-metal split flaps on trailing-edges. Flaps can be set to a negative position. All-metal two-section Hütter airbrakes on upper surfaces. Optional folding of outer wing panels, inward over inboard panels. Conventional fuselage, in three parts: metal front portion, built up on two longerons and cross-frames and having glassfibre fairings and engine cowling panels; aluminium alloy monocoque centre portion; and rear portion of aluminium alloy frames and skin. Cantilever aluminium alloy T tail, with dihedral tailplane. Rudder and elevator trailing-edges fabric-covered. Trim tab in each elevator. Landing gear as described under model listings. Rearward-sliding canopy. Dual controls standard.

POWER PLANT: One 50·7 kW (68 hp) Limbach SL 1700 EI flat-four engine, driving a Hoffmann HO-V-62/R160T two-blade variable-pitch fully-feathering propeller. Single fuel tank aft of cockpit, capacity 40 litres (8·8 Imp gallons).

IS-29, IS-31 and IS-33

The IS-29, designed under the leadership of Dipl Ing Iosif Silimon, can be adapted to suit a variety of requirements or weather conditions. All versions have an identical fuselage and tail unit, and a choice of wings is available. The versions so far announced are as follows:

IS-29B. Standard Class version, with 15 m all-wooden wings. First flown April 1970; certificated September 1970. Not now in production. See 1975-76 *Jane's*.

IS-29D. Standard Class version, with all-metal 15 m span wings. First flown in November 1970; certificated in

1971. Approx 30 built by 1974. Described in 1975-76 *Jane's*.

IS-29D2. Current Standard Class version, with improved cockpit and controls, Hütter airbrakes, separate tailplane and elevator, and improved rigging system. More than 60 sold in Australia and the USA. Production continuing in 1979 at rate of 10-15 a year.

The following are all variants of the IS-29D2 design:

IS-29D3. Club Class version, with 16·5 m span wings, non-retractable landing gear and unpainted (allochrome) finish.

IS-29D4. 15 m Class version, with 80° max flap setting, airbrakes, and (to come) provision for 120 litres (26·4 Imp gallons) water ballast.

IS-29DM. Powered version of D2; see separate description which follows.

IS-29E. Open Class version, having increased-span wings fitted with ailerons, flaps, Schempp-Hirth airbrakes and integral water ballast tanks. First flown in August 1971 with 17·60 m (57 ft 9 in) span wings, as described in 1975-76 *Jane's*.

IS-29E2. With 19 m span wings and interconnected flaps and ailerons. To be offered with 100 litres (22 Imp gallons) water ballast.

IS-29E4. High-performance version, with 24 m span wings, built in four sections, water ballast, and interconnected flaps and ailerons.

IS-29EM. Powered version of E3; see separate description which follows.

IS-29G. Club version, with all-metal 16·5 m span wings. Prototype completed in 1972. Described in 1975-76 *Jane's*.

IS-31 (E3). With 20 m span wings and interconnected flaps and ailerons. To be offered with 100 litres (22 Imp gallons) water ballast. Prototype flying; not certificated up to mid-1979.

IS-33. Racing version, with 15 m span wings fitted with 'flaperons'. To be offered with 150 litres (33 Imp gallons) water ballast.

The following description applies to the IS-29D2 and E2, except where a specific model is indicated:

TYPE: Single-seat Standard Class (D2) and Open Class (E2) sailplanes; g limits (29D3, 29D4, 31(E3) and 33) +5·3/−2·65; (D4) +4·0/−1·5.

AIRFRAME: Cantilever shoulder-wing monoplane, with T tail. Wortmann wing sections: FX-61-165 at root, FX-61-124 at tip on D2; FX-K-170 (root) and FX-K-150 (tip) on E2 and E3. All-metal wings, with main spar, false rear spar and riveted dural skin. Full-span trailing-edge flaps and ailerons, coupled to operate in unison but can be disconnected for separate operation during landing. Airbrakes (see under model listings for type) in upper and lower surface of each wing (upper surface only on D2). All-metal semi-monocoque fuselage identical on all versions except for local variations at wing attachment points. Detachable glassfibre nosecap. Cantilever all-metal T tail, with full-span elevator. Retractable sprung monowheel (non-retractable on D3), with brake; non-retractable tailwheel. Canopy hinges sideways to starboard and can be jettisoned in flight. Provision for water ballast in E2 and E3.

IS-29DM and IS-29EM

These two motor gliders, of which prototypes have been flown, are respectively powered versions of the IS-29D2 and IS-29E3, fitted with a 29 kW (39 hp) Rectimo 4AR-1200 engine driving a Hoffmann HO-V42 propeller; fuel capacity is 27 litres (6 Imp gallons). A retractable rubber-sprung Tost monowheel, diameter 345 mm, is fitted; the Tost tailwheel has a diameter of 210 mm. Production aircraft were expected to be available by mid-1980.

IS-30

The IS-30, which underwent flight testing in the Spring of 1978, is a development of the IS-28B2 with 18·00 m (59 ft 0¾ in) span wings, the redesigned tail of the IS-32, and no water ballast provision; g limits are the same as for the IS-28B2. The IS-30 prototype appeared at the Hanover Air Show in May 1980 fitted with a power plant and retractable propeller pylon aft of the cockpit.

IS-32

First shown publicly at the Paris Air Show in June 1977, the IS-32 tandem two-seat Open Class sailplane is developed from the IS-28B2. Of all-metal construction, it has 20 m wings of an improved Wortmann FX-K-170 (root) and FX-K-150 (tip) section, with interconnected flaps and ailerons and water ballast tanks, and redesigned tail surfaces; g limits are +4·0/−1·5. Certification has been awarded, and deliveries were intended to begin in 1980.

SPAIN

CASES
FRANCISCO CASES MASIÁ

Miguel Hernandez 44, Benetússer, Valencia
Telephone: (93) 3754380

Sr Cases designed the Libel-Lula lightweight glider in early 1977, and began building it later that year. He is currently working, as time permits, on the design of a Standard Class sailplane.

CASES LIBEL-LULA

This lightweight homebuilt glider, built by an experienced aeromodeller and glider pilot, was flown for the first time on 14 September 1979.

TYPE: Single-seat homebuilt sailplane; g limits +4/−1·5.

AIRFRAME: Braced high-wing monoplane. Dihedral 3°. Incidence 3°. Wings of glassfibre/polyester construction, with constant Wortmann FX-S-02-196 section except in area of ailerons; built in two halves and joined to fuselage upper beam. D-section torsion box formed

from leading-edge and main spar; glassfibre/polyester moulded ribs; overall nylon covering (wings and ailerons). Single duralumin tube bracing strut each side. Fuselage comprises wooden triangular-section beam to carry wings and tail unit, with pear-shaped polyester fibre nacelle, moulded in two halves, below and forward of wings. Tail surfaces of balsa and glassfibre, with nylon covering. Rubber-sprung glassfibre landing skid beneath nacelle. Tip of underfin acts as tailskid. Single seat in open cockpit. Windscreen optional.

SWITZERLAND

AVIAFIBER
AVIAFIBER AG

Sagenrainstrasse 4, CH-8636 Wald
Telephone: (055) 952055
PRESIDENT: Dipl-Ing Hans U. Farner

AVIAFIBER CANARD-2 FL

First flown on 7 September 1977, the Canard-2 FL was designed by Dipl-Ing Hans U. Farner, who also designed the Colibri 1 SL canard motor glider described in this

section. It can be bungee-launched in a conventional manner, foot-launched, or rolled downhill on wheels for take-off. Production of the Canard-2 FL began in 1978. A

ICA IS-32 two-seat Open Class sailplane

IS-29EM motor glider (Rectimo 4AR-1200 engine)

Cases Libel-Lula single-seat homebuilt glider

Aviafiber Canard-2 FL ultralight sailplane with jettisonable four-wheel take-off gear

IS-29D2 single-seat Standard Class sailplane produced by ICA

ICA IS-31(E3) single-seat Open Class sailplane

EFF Prometheus twin-jet motor glider

powered version was scheduled for completion in the Summer of 1979.

The following description applies to the production version:

TYPE: One-man ultralight sailplane; *g* limits +5·3 (limit)/+7·9 (ultimate).

AIRFRAME: 'Parasol monoplane' configuration, with main wing at rear, supported by Vee-form pylons which act as both lifting surfaces and 'vertical' fins; fixed-incidence canard foreplane. Wings, pylons and canard surface have Wortmann FX-63-137 section. Wings have external aerofoil ailerons; trailing-edges of Vee-tail pylons movable to act as Venom-type airbrakes. Wing is a single-spar structure, with vacuum-formed shell of laminated resin (Du Pont Kevlar, CIBA-Geigy 2878) and glassfibre, and core of styrofoam plate; other struc-tures have a similar shell, with cores of hard foam cells (ailerons) or solid hard foam (airbrakes). Leg and head doors for foot-launch, after which pilot swivels into prone position, on sliding board, and closes both doors. One-piece canopy/windscreen, open at rear. Retractable front skid for landing; monowheel, or jettisonable twin main- and tailwheels, optional for downhill rolling take-off.

EFF
ENTWICKLUNGSGEMEINSCHAFT FÜR FLUGZEUGBAU

c/o Dr H. K. Stiffler, Dufourstrasse 101, CH-8000 Zürich
Telephone: (01) 813 3244
PRESIDENT: Thomas Bircher

EFF PROMETHEUS

After four years of design work, construction of the Prometheus began in 1975, and it flew for the first time on 22 June 1978.

This original version, with 19·40 m (63 ft 7¾ in) wing span, is known as the Prometheus 19. A Prometheus 12 version, with 12·63 m (41 ft 5¼ in) span, flew for the first time on 17 September 1979. Another version, with tip-tanks and winglets, was scheduled to fly in early 1980. No production of the Prometheus is intended at present.

TYPE: Two-seat twin-jet motor glider; *g* limits +4·0/−4·0.

AIRFRAME: Cantilever monoplane. Wing section Wort-mann FX-67-170-17. Wings have aluminium main spar, with plywood skin and glassfibre/foam sandwich infill. Trailing-edge 'flaperons'. DFS upper-surface air-brakes. Forward fuselage built of wood, with glassfibre skin; rear fuselage is of glassfibre sandwich, as are the fixed-incidence T tailplane and elevator. Retractable tricycle landing gear, comprising twin main wheels with Goodyear tyres (diameter 127 mm; 5 in, pressure 4·3 bars; 62·4 lb/sq in) and Tost brake; and single nose-wheel with General Tire and Rubber Co tyre (pressure 5 bars; 72·5 lb/sq in). Nosewheel is oleo-sprung, main wheels by rubber blocks. Seats for two persons side by side; VFR instrumentation standard, IFR optional.

POWER PLANT: Two 0·88 kN (198 lb st) Microturbo TRS 18 turbojet engines. Fuel in two 82 litre (18 Imp gallon) wing tanks and two 14 litre (3 Imp gallon) fuselage tanks in Prometheus 19, giving total capacity of 192 litres (42 Imp gallons). Prometheus 12 has two 35 litre (7·75 Imp gallon) tip-tanks, increasing total capacity to 262 litres (57·5 Imp gallons). Oil capacity 2 litres (0·4 Imp gallons).

FARNER
DIPL-ING ETH HANS ULRICH FARNER

c/o Aviafiber AG, Sagenrainstrasse 4, CH-8636 Wald
Telephone: (055) 952055

FARNER HF COLIBRI 1 SL

Herr Farner has designed, built and flown an unusual experimental motor glider, known as the HF Colibri 1 SL and registered HB-2036. Its general appearance can be seen in the accompanying illustration.

TYPE: Single-seat motor glider; two-seat version under development.

AIRFRAME: Cantilever gull-wing monoplane, with canard

foreplane. Main wing of very high aspect ratio, mounted on top of fuselage at rear. It has dihedral on constant-chord, constant-section (Wortmann FX-61-184) inner portions, and anhedral on the all-moving outer panels, which have leading-edge taper and a Wortmann FX-60-1261 section. No flaps or ailerons. Constant-chord, constant-section foreplane (Wortmann FX-60-1261), mounted on telescopic extension of long, tapering nose to vary moment arm, can be pivoted about fuselage longitudinal axis. Adjustment of telescopic nose also permits foreplane incidence to be varied. Very short, narrow fuselage, with telescopic nose tube permitting overall length to be varied in flight. Rear fuselage ends in split-wedge section which acts as vertical fin when closed and airbrake when opened. Retractable tricycle landing gear, of narrow track. Yaw control by pivoting canard surface about fuselage longitudinal axis; pitch control by varying canard moment arm; roll (bank) control by operating all-moving wingtips ('tiperons') with dynamically irreversible drive.

POWER PLANT: Two 10·14 kW (13·6 hp) McCulloch MC-101A 123 cc single-cylinder two-stroke engines. mounted aft of cabin and driving, via a reduction gear, a two-blade pusher propeller aft of the wing trailing-edge. Propeller blades are of Wortmann section, and can be folded to the rear when not in use. Fuel capacity 21 litres (4·6 Imp gallons).

NEUKOM
ALBERT NEUKOM SEGELFLUGZEUGBAU
Flugplatz Schmerlat, CH-8213 Neuenkirch

NEUKOM S-4A ELFE 15
The S-4A Elfe 15 is a developed version of the Standard Class S-3 (see 1974-75 Jane's). The prototype flew for the first time in 1970, and 10 had been built by early 1973. Production continues, though at a relatively slow rate. The Elfe 15 is also available in kit form for amateur construction.
TYPE: Single-seat Standard Class sailplane.
AIRFRAME: Cantilever high-wing monoplane. Wortmann wing sections: FX-61-163 at root, FX-60-126 at tip.

Single wing spar of aluminium alloy, with plywood/foam sandwich skin. Plain ailerons. Schempp-Hirth airbrakes on upper surfaces. Forward fuselage of reinforced glassfibre; rear portion and tail unit of plywood/foam sandwich. Elevator spring trim. Retractable rubber-sprung monowheel, with brake. Detachable canopy. Universal aero-tow/winch coupling forward of monowheel.

NEUKOM ELFE 17
The Elfe 17 is an Open Class version of the S-4A, employing the same fuselage, but having a two-piece wing of 17 metres span with provision for a tank in each leading-edge to contain a total of 60 kg (132 lb) water ballast. A braking parachute is carried on this version.

A total of 10 Elfe 17s had been built by the Spring of 1973. Production continues, though at a relatively slow rate. The Elfe 17 is available also in kit form for amateur construction.

NEUKOM AN-21
The latest known design by Mr Neukom is the AN-21 ultra-lightweight glider, of sweptwing configuration with a canard foreplane and elevator (see accompanying three-view drawing). The main wings have a Wortmann FX-63-137 section and area of 11·5 m² (123·8 sq ft); canard surface area is 1·0 m² (10·76 sq ft). Weights are 56 kg (123 lb) without, and 150 kg (330 lb) including, the pilot.

UNION OF SOVIET SOCIALIST REPUBLICS

LAK
LITOVSKAYA AVIATSIONNAYA KON-STRUKTSIYA (Lithuanian Aircraft Construction)
Litovsk SSR (Lithuanian SSR)
DIRECTOR: Vitautas Pakarskas
CHIEF DESIGNER: Balis Karvyalis

This factory originated in the late 1960s with a 12-man 'initiative group', led by designers B. Oshkinis, B. Karvyalis and A. Paknis, and assisted by the Lithuanian branch of DOSAAF. Its primary objective was the evaluation of a plastics-construction sailplane. A workshop, opened in the Summer of 1969, began by building the Oshkinis BRO-11 elementary training glider. At that time it was known as the Experimentalnii Zavod Sportivnoi Aviatsii (Experimental Sports Aviation Factory). Its first plastics sailplane, designed by Balis Karvyalis, was the BK-7 Lietuva, which was first flown by Alexander Ionushas in December 1972 and was described and illustrated in the 1975-76 Jane's. This was followed by a small experimental production batch designated BK-7A, two of which took part in an international competition between Socialist countries at Kishinev in April 1976. As a result, a number of modifications were introduced in a developed version, the LAK-9, then under construction to participate in the 1976 World Championships in Finland.

In the early 1970s further experience was gained by repairing Czechoslovak Blanik sailplanes. More than 300 Blaniks had been overhauled by mid-1977, and LAK is now the sole overhaul centre in the USSR for this type of sailplane. Repairs were also undertaken of German MBB Phoebus and Schleicher ASW 15 plastics sailplanes. The factory has its own static test laboratory; design calculations and wind tunnel testing of LAK designs are carried out by the Central Aero-Hydrodynamic Institute (TsAGI) in Moscow. Branch factories now handle Blanik overhauls and BRO-11 production, and a new, larger, sports aviation factory is under construction.

Other recent activities have included the fitting of an engine to a standard L-13 Blanik, and this aircraft (the LAK-6, illustrated in the 1977-78 Jane's) serves as a flying testbed for a new plastics-construction motor glider, of which a prototype was under construction in 1977. A report in the August 1979 issue of the Soviet monthly magazine Krilya Rodiny included reference to a national out-and-return record of 335·6 nm (622 km; 386·5 miles), at an average speed of 60·4 knots (112 km/h; 69·6 mph), by Oleg Pasetsnik in a sailplane designated LAK-10. The latest known LAK design is a new Standard Class sailplane, designed by Ionas Bankauskas and known as the LAK-11.

OSHKINIS BRO-11 ZILE (ACORN)
The BRO-11 was first built in 1954, and has since been built in considerable numbers as an elementary training glider for use by the DOSAAF. A modified version, designated BRO-11-M, was illustrated in the 1975-76 Jane's; the 1977-78 edition contained brief details of a biplane seaplane version, the BRO-16, first flown in August 1973, and a shorter-span (experimental?) version of this, known as the BRO-17U Utochka.

The BRO-11 is believed to be still in production by a branch factory of the LAK.
TYPE: Single-seat basic training glider.
AIRFRAME: Strut-braced high-wing monoplane, of fabric- and plywood-covered wooden construction. Towing hook under nose. Semi-recessed monowheel landing gear.

LAK-9 LIETUVA
As indicated in the introductory copy, the LAK-9 is a developed version of the Karvyalis BK-7/7A; its chief designer was Kestutis Gechas. The first LAK-9, registered CCCP-6301, was flown by O. Pasetsnik in the Open Class of the June 1976 World Championships at Räyskälä, Finland. It was not placed among the first 25 aircraft on that occasion, and it was reported that the three LAK-9s then built had not, at that time, fully completed flight testing.

The LAK-9 has since entered full production; the fourth series, begun in the Winter of 1976-77, is reported to have the designation LAK-9M, indicating 'Modernised'.
TYPE: Single-seat Open Class sailplane; g limits +6·0/−3·0.
AIRFRAME: Cantilever shoulder-wing monoplane. Single-spar wings, of Wortmann FX-67-K-170 section, with flaps and ailerons on trailing-edges. Glassfibre/epoxy construction. Retractable monowheel and tailwheel. Provision for 180 kg (397 lb) water ballast.

UNITED KINGDOM

SLINGSBY
SLINGSBY ENGINEERING LTD (Aircraft Division)
HEAD OFFICE AND WORKS: Kirkbymoorside, N Yorks YO6 6EZ
Telephone: 0751 31751
Telex: 57911
MANAGING DIRECTOR: J. S. Tucker, BSc
SALES MANAGER, AIRCRAFT DIVISION: Roger Bull

Slingsby's present aircraft production includes the Vega 15 metre Class sailplane, the Sport Vega sport class sailplane, the T.61F Venture, which is a 'military' version of the T.61A built between 1971 and 1974, and the T.61G Falke, the latest civilian development of the type.

Slingsby also manufactured parts of the Aerospace Developments AD-500 airship.

SLINGSBY VEGA
The first sailplane entirely of Slingsby design to appear since the failure of the previous Slingsby company in 1969, the Vega was designed to take advantage of the change in the rules for Standard Class sailplanes permitting, after 1976, the installation of flaps in this class. Designed for optimum performance in its class, its wings have a unique flap and airbrake speed limiting system fitted to their trailing-edges, operated by a single control lever in the cockpit. The fuselage is gently 'waisted' to reduce the possibility of flow separation over the fuselage/wing junction.

The prototype Vega flew for the first time on 3 June 1977. A total of 34 had been delivered by the beginning of 1980.
TYPE: Single-seat 15 metre Class sailplane.
AIRFRAME: Cantilever mid-wing monoplane with T tail. Wing section Wortmann FX-67-K-150 from root to tip. Wings of foam plastics sandwich, with single carbonfibre main spar. Combined flaps/airbrakes inboard, ailerons outboard, on trailing-edges; glassfibre ailerons can be operated independently or in conjunction with flaps. Turned-down wingtips. Conventional semi-monocoque plastics fuselage, with retractable tow hook. Cantilever T tail, with GRP/carbonfibre tailplane spar; elevator spring trim. Tost monowheel (size 5·00-5), with Tost drum brake, and tailwheel, both fully retractable. Canopy opens forward and upward, and is jettisonable. Provision for 159 kg (350 lb) water ballast.

SLINGSBY T.65C SPORT VEGA
A prototype of the Sport Vega flew for the first time on 18 December 1979. Ten had been ordered by early 1980, and deliveries were due to begin in March of that year.
TYPE: Single-seat sporting sailplane; g limit +5·3.
AIRFRAME: Generally similar to Vega, but with glassfibre main spar, rotating trailing-edge airbrakes instead of flaps, and non-retractable monowheel and tailwheel. No provision for water ballast.

SLINGSBY T.61F VENTURE
RAF name: Venture T.Mk 2
Slingsby began producing the Scheibe SF-25B Falke motor glider under licence in 1970, and completed a total of 35.

The Venture is a special version, of which 40 have been ordered by the Ministry of Defence (Air) for the Air Training Corps. It features a special glassfibre spar, encased in plywood, which simultaneously reduces the empty weight and increases the max permissible T-O weight of the aircraft. Many other glassfibre components are used in the aircraft, including a new seat designed to improve comfort and to reduce the hazard of loose articles slipping under the seat into the control area. The power plant is a Rollason-modified Volkswagen 33·5 kW (45 hp) 1,600 cc motor car engine, driving a two-blade fixed-pitch propeller.

First flight of a production Venture T.Mk 2 (XZ550) was made on 2 July 1977. Deliveries began in Autumn 1977, and 19 had been completed by the beginning of 1980.

SLINGSBY T.61G FALKE
The T.61G is a civil development of the T.61F Venture, differing mainly in having a 45 kW (60 hp) Limbach SL 1700 EA flat-four engine driving a Hoffmann two-blade fixed-pitch (optionally variable-pitch) propeller. Fuel capacity is 32 litres (7 Imp gallons).

SWALES
SWALES SAILPLANES
Long Street, Thirsk, North Yorkshire
Telephone: 0845 23096

OFFICERS:
Bryan Swales, MBIM, Eng Dip, MIMI
G. L. Kemp, BEM (Chief Inspector)

SWALES SD3-15T
Construction of the prototype SD3 started in September 1974, and it flew for the first time in March 1975.

Farner HF Colibri 1 SL experimental motor glider (*J. Urech*)

Neukom S-4A Elfe 15 single-seat Standard Class sailplane (*Martin Fricke*)

Oshkinis (LAK) BRO-11 primary training glider (*reproduced from* **Krilya Rodini**)

Neukom AN-21 ultralight glider (*Michael A. Badrocke*)

LAK-9 Lietuva single-seat Open Class sailplane (*reproduced from* **Krilya Rodini**)

Slingsby Vega high-performance 15 metre sailplane

Slingsby T.61F Venture T.Mk 2 in service with UK Air Cadets

Swales SD3-15T single-seat sailplane

This aircraft was designated SD3-13V. Production aircraft were designated SD3-15V (first flight July 1975) and SD3-15T (first flight December 1976), the suffix letter denoting the tail configuration. By mid-1979, six SD3-15s had been built. Construction is now to order, and is restricted to the T tail version, of which one was nearing completion at that time.

TYPE: Single-seat sailplane; *g* limits +3·5/−1·0.
AIRFRAME: Cantilever mid-wing monoplane. Wortmann FX-61-168 wing section. Dihedral 3°. Wings built mainly of metal, with metal and polystyrene ribs and GRP wingtips. All-metal trailing-edge flaps/airbrakes. Metal plain ailerons, with foam ribs. Semi-monocoque fuselage with metal skin and GRP nosecone. Cantilever

T tail, of metal construction with 50% foam ribs. Full-span elevator with spring trim. Non-retractable mono-wheel, tyre pressure 2·41 bars (35 lb/sq in), with internally-expanding brake. Canopy opens sideways to starboard.

UNITED STATES OF AMERICA

AmEAGLE
AmEAGLE CORPORATION
841 Winslow Court, Muskegon, Michigan 49441
Telephone: (616) 780 4680
PRESIDENT: Larry Haig

This company was formed by Mr Larry Haig, a 1958 graduate engineer from Wayne State University, following seven years experience in gas turbine engine development with the research laboratories of General Motors; a further seven years in automotive and diesel engine design and application work for the Allison Division of General

Motors and Teledyne Continental Motors; and two years experience with composite laminate structures with Brunswick Corporation.

Its first product is a homebuilt self-launching sailplane known as the American Eaglet.

AmEAGLE AMERICAN EAGLET
Design of the American Eaglet began in September 1974. Construction of the prototype started in June 1975, and this aircraft (N101EA) made its first flight on 19 November of that year.

A total of 400 kits had been ordered by early 1980, of which 20 had been completed.
TYPE: Single-seat homebuilt self-launching sailplane; *g* limits +4·4/−2·2 (safety factor 1·5).
AIRFRAME: Shoulder-wing monoplane, with single aluminium tube bracing strut on each side. Wing section Wortmann FX-61-184. Dihedral 1° 30' from roots. Sparless stressed-skin structure with urethane foam core, moulded glassfibre leading-edges and wingtips, and epoxy-bonded pre-cured glassfibre skin. 'Spoile-rons' (for both roll and glidepath control) at 30% chord

AmEagle American Eaglet single-seat self-launching sailplane (*J. M. G. Gradidge*)

Applebay Zuni 15 metre sailplane (*Michael A. Badrocke*)

on each upper surface. Pod-and-boom fuselage, the forward portion comprising two pre-formed glassfibre half-shells pop-riveted to tubular aluminium longerons. Tailboom is a thin-wall aluminium tube with a moulded glassfibre tailcone. Combined pitot tube/lifting handle in nose. Cantilever inverted-Vee tailplane and elevators, suspended from rear of tailboom. Tail surfaces have urethane foam core and epoxy/glassfibre skin. Manually-retractable monowheel, tyre pressure

2·41 bars (35 lb/sq in), with external friction-pad brake, forward of CG. Tailwheel under tip of each half-tailplane.

POWER PLANT: One 9 kW (12·2 hp at 8,000 rpm) McCulloch MC-101B single-cylinder two-stroke engine, installed aft of cockpit and driving a two-blade fixed-pitch pusher propeller with folding plastics blades. Recoil starting. Engine is for T-O and self-recovery only, and not for cross-country continuous operation.

Fuel tank capacity 2 litres (0·5 US gallons). Normal fuel load of approx 1·81 kg (4 lb) (consumption at max power is 5·5 kg/h; 12 lb/h) is sufficient for one T-O and climb to 610 m (2,000 ft) and three airborne restarts and climbs from 150 m (500 ft) to 610 m (2,000 ft).

PERFORMANCE (powered):

Max rate of climb at S/L	137 m (450 ft)/min
T-O run	305 m (1,000 ft)
Landing run	90 m (300 ft)

APPLEBAY
APPLEBAY SAILPLANES

206 Industrial Park Road, Rio Rancho, New Mexico 87124
DIRECTOR: George Applebay

APPLEBAY ZUNI

This sailplane, known originally as the Aero Tek Model V, made its first flight on 18 November 1976. Its appearance is shown in the accompanying three-view drawing.

TYPE: Single-seat 15 metre sailplane.

AIRFRAME: Cantilever shoulder-wing monoplane, with T tail, of glassfibre construction. Wortmann wing section. Full-span camber-changing flaps/ailerons. One-piece all-moving tailplane. Retractable monowheel; non-retractable semi-recessed tailwheel. Provision for 109 kg (240 lb) water ballast.

BRYAN
BRYAN AIRCRAFT INC

HEAD OFFICE AND WORKS: Williams County Airport, PO Box 488, Bryan, Ohio 43506
Telephone: (419) 636 1340
DIRECTOR: R. E. Schreder

This company markets plans and kits for the RS-15 and HP-18 high-performance 15 metre Class sailplanes, and is developing the more recent HP-19.

BRYAN (SCHREDER) RS-15

The RS-15 was designed by Mr Schreder to meet OSTIV Standard Class specifications. It is designed for simple, rapid assembly by the homebuilder and is licensed in the amateur-built Experimental category. No jigs are required, and most major components are prefabricated, to reduce assembly time to approx 500 man-hours for a builder with average mechanical aptitude.

TYPE: Single-seat 15 metre Class sailplane.

AIRFRAME: Cantilever shoulder-wing monoplane. Wing section Wortmann FX-67-K-150. Dihedral 2° 18'. All-metal wings except for polyurethane foam plastics ribs. Main wing spar caps of aluminium plate. Water

ballast carried inside wing box spars. Plain ailerons. Optional trailing-edge flaps/airbrakes, of aluminium sheet bonded to PVC foam ribs, which can be linked with ailerons. Monocoque fuselage: prefabricated glassfibre forward pod, complete with bulkheads, floorboards and finish; aluminium tube tailboom. All-metal V tail, which can be folded upward for towing or storage. Retractable monowheel, with hydraulic shock-absorber and brake, and non-retractable steerable tailwheel. Provision for 91 kg (200 lb) water ballast.

BRYAN (SCHREDER) HP-18

The HP-18 was flown for the first time in 1975. Approx 170 had been built or were under construction by early 1979. Assembly time is approx 700 man-hours.

TYPE: Single-seat 15 metre Class sailplane.

AIRFRAME: Generally similar to the RS-15, the HP-18 has a slightly longer fuselage, with low profile circular instead of oval section, and other features designed to reduce drag and produce a superior competition aircraft; g limits are +12/−12. Incidence 2°. Improvements include better gap seals, new wingtips, faired tailwheel and better streamlining; ailerons and 90° flaps

are coupled, to improve cross-country speed; use of full flap permits steeper approaches and slower landing speeds. NASA-type winglets can be added to increase glide ratio and improve aileron control. Fuselage comprises a prefabricated glassfibre pod and aluminium monocoque tailboom. The Tost monowheel has a tyre pressure of 2·07 bars (30 lb/sq in) and is fitted with a mechanically-expanding brake.

BRYAN (SCHREDER) HP-19

Expected to fly in mid-March 1979, the HP-19 is an improved version of the HP-18. A carbonfibre main spar and other weight savings reduce wing weight by 32 kg (70 lb), while increasing water ballast capacity to 136 kg (300 lb). A new Schreder wing section with higher maximum lift coefficient, together with NASA-type winglets, decrease thermalling and landing speeds, decrease minimum sink rate, improve aileron control and increase glide ratios. Coupled flaps and ailerons improve performance at all speeds, while 90° flaps permit steeper approaches and slower landing speeds than were possible with conventional airbrakes. Simplified constructional materials and methods reduce assembly time to about 500 man-hours.

DSK
DSK AIRCRAFT CORPORATION

13161 Sherman Way, North Hollywood, California 91605
VICE-PRESIDENT, MARKETING: Rodney E. Gage

In addition to the well-established Duster homebuilt sailplane, DSK is developing an improved version known as the DS-1. It has also acquired all production and marketing rights in the Woodstock homebuilt sailplane designed and originally built by Mr Jim Maupin.

DSK BJ-1b DUSTER

The Duster is available in the form of plans and/or

component kits for amateur construction. Average construction time is approx 600-700 hours.

TYPE: Single-seat homebuilt sailplane; g limits +5·3/−3·1.

AIRFRAME: Cantilever shoulder-wing monoplane. NACA 4415 (modified) wing section, with 2° washout at tips. Single wooden main spar, with plywood ribs and plywood covering. Wing built in three portions: two outer panels, and a 2·13 m (7 ft) span centre-section integral with fuselage. Trailing-edge flaps/airbrakes; top-hinged ailerons. Straight-sided plywood fuselage shell, having an elongated hexagonal cross-section in the cockpit area, changing to triangular section aft of wings. Ventral plywood keel, reinforced by two bulk-

heads shaped to seat contour and supporting floor-mounted seat. Glassfibre nosecone and fairings. Cantilever tail unit, with tailplane mounted on top of fuselage. Construction similar to that of wings. All tail surfaces plywood skinned. Non-retractable semi-recessed monowheel beneath keel, and tailwheel. Aircraft can be flown with one-piece flush-fitting canopy, or with open cockpit and windscreen only.

POWER PLANT: Auxiliary power package, using a 19·4 kW (26 hp) engine, under development in 1977. Plans detail all hardware necessary to support an engine mount, which can be added at builder's option without further alteration of airframe.

EXPLORER
EXPLORER AIRCRAFT COMPANY INC
(Sierra-Nevada Soaring Division)

PO Box 60036, 4895 Texas Avenue, Reno-Stead Airport, Reno, Nevada 89506
Telephone: (702) 972 7757

Explorer Aircraft markets plans of the biplane Aqua Glider. Designed by Colonel William L. Skliar, USAF (Ret'd), it is intended for tethered gliding by unlicensed pilots, towed behind any motor boat able to attain a speed of 30 knots (56 km/h; 35 mph). If the pilot has the necessary licence, he can cast off from the motor boat when airborne and make a free flight before landing back on the water.

EXPLORER PG-1 AQUA GLIDER

Design of the Aqua Glider began in September 1958, and the prototype made its first flight in July 1959. Plans are available to amateur constructors and approx 1,000 sets have been sold in more than 20 countries all over the world. About 12 Aqua Gliders are known to have flown, in the USA, the Bahamas, Brazil and Japan, and about 200 more are under construction.

The prototype, after making about 1,000 flights and being flown by about 60 pilots, was donated to the Experimental Aircraft Association Museum in 1970.

TYPE: Single-seat homebuilt waterborne glider; g limit +4·0.

AIRFRAME: Forward-stagger single-bay biplane with N

interplane and parallel centre-section struts. Wing section (both) NACA 4412. Dihedral 2° 30' on lower wing only. Conventional single-spar wooden structure with fabric covering. Spoiler-type light alloy ailerons on lower wing only, immediately aft of main spar. Balancer floats at lower wingtips. Unstepped watertight wooden hull of spruce with mahogany plywood bow, bottom skins and sides. Plywood is glassfibre-covered below waterline. Tow hook on nose. Wire-braced spruce tail unit, with plywood and fabric covering, carried on welded steel tube or wire-braced wooden boom. All-moving one-piece tailplane with bungee trim. Conventional rudder. Standard jumper skis, 1·83 m (6 ft) in length, attached to small wire-braced struts below hull. Open cockpit.

Known as the Airmate, this Bryan (Schreder) HP-18 has been modified by its Canadian builders Don Band and Peter Masak to have Wortmann FX-60-126 section winglets of glassfibre and balsa at the wingtips (Neil A. Macdougall)

Bryan (Schreder) RS-15 Standard Class sailplane built by Mr Gordon Anderson of Michigan (Howard Levy)

DSK BJ-1b Duster single-seat homebuilt sailplane

Explorer PG-1 Aqua Glider built by Sr Fernando de A. Botelho of São Paulo, Brazil

Bryan (Schreder) HP-19 high-performance sailplane (Michael A. Badrocke)

Marske Monarch B single-seat ultralight glider

MARSKE
MARSKE AIRCRAFT CORPORATION

130 Crestwood Drive, Michigan City, Indiana 46360
Telephone: (219) 879 7039
PRESIDENT: James J. Marske

MARSKE MONARCH C

The first Monarch single-seat ultralight glider was designed and built by Mr Jim Marske in 1973-74, and made its first flight on 4 July 1974. Plans and kits are available to amateur constructors. A total of 71 Monarchs were under construction by the beginning of 1979, of which four were then known to have been completed.

Mr Marske has successfully test-flown the Monarch prototype with a 9 kW (12 hp) McCulloch engine installed behind the pilot's seat, driving a 0·635 m (2 ft 1 in) diameter pusher propeller. It is considered, however, that an engine of approx 15 kW (20 hp) should be fitted to homebuilt aircraft.

The earlier Monarch B was described in the 1977-78 *Jane's*; the following description applies to the current Monarch C version, which replaced it:

TYPE: Single-seat ultralight homebuilt glider; *g* limits +8·0/−4·0 (ultimate).

AIRFRAME: Braced high-wing monoplane, with single steel strut each side. Wing section NACA 43012R or 43112. Dihedral 2°. Sweepforward 3° at quarter-chord. Moulded glassfibre D leading-edge, with glassfibre front spar web and booms, wood and foam plastics ribs, wooden rear spar and trailing-edge, and fabric covering. Ailerons (outboard) and elevators (inboard) have single Sitka spruce spars with foam plastics ribs. Fixed tab on each elevator. All control surfaces Dacron-covered. Aluminium spoiler above each wing. Simple minimal beam-type fuselage of laminated glassfibre, moulded in two halves and joined at centreline. Forward section supports pilot's seat, with nose fairing over instrument panel; rear section forms integral fin leading-edge. CG tow hook on each side of nose fairing. Fin and rudder, above and below level of wings. Glassfibre leading-edge (fin), wooden trailing-edge (rudder), foam ribs and fabric covering. No horizontal tail surfaces. Reinforced underfuselage landing skid. Single landing wheel, below pilot's open seat. Conventional floor-mounted control column.

MONNETT
MONNETT EXPERIMENTAL AIRCRAFT INC

955 Grace Street, Elgin, Illinois 60120
Telephone: (312) 741 2223
GENERAL MANAGER: Gregg Erikson

In addition to its Sonerai powered aircraft (see Homebuilts section), Monnett produces kits of parts for the Monerai single-seat homebuilt sailplane.

By mid-January 1980 more than 210 Monerai kits had been sold, of which 173 had been delivered since 1 November 1978. Eight aircraft had flown by the beginning of 1980.

MONNETT MONERAI S

The Monerai, development of which began in 1976, was designed to fill a need for a low-cost homebuilt sailplane with better-than-average performance. It flew for the first time in March 1978. The kit includes many extruded or preformed components, to permit quick construction with a minimum of equipment or experience. Average construction time is 300 hours.

TYPE: Single-seat homebuilt sailplane; *g* limits +6/−6.

AIRFRAME: Cantilever mid-wing monoplane. Wing section Wortmann FX-61-192 (modified). Dihedral 4°. Aluminium main spar of extruded, modified I section; rear spar is an aluminium C channel. Constant chord allows all the preformed ribs to be identical, and single-piece aluminium skin to wrap around from trailing-edge to trailing-edge. Skin bonded to spars and ribs with Hysol epoxy. Glassfibre wingtips. Aileron and flap skins are preformed and ready for assembly. Fuselage is built up from chrome-molybdenum steel tube and is covered by a non-structural premoulded glassfibre shell. A 12·7 cm (5 in) diameter extruded aluminium tube is attached to the frame and extends 3·66 m (12 ft) to the rear where an upright, all-flying, all-aluminium V tail is attached. Non-retractable monowheel, with mechanical brake; tailskid. One-piece flush-fitting canopy. No provision for water ballast.

MONNET MONERAI P

Exhibited at Oshkosh in 1978, the Monerai P is identical to the S version, but has a small auxiliary engine (15 kW; 20 hp 250 cc Zenoah single-cylinder two-stroke) to permit self-launch. Fuel capacity is 4·25 litres (1·13 US gallons). A combination turnover structure and power pod mount, aft of the cockpit, allows the sailplane to be converted to the P version in only five minutes. The engine and propeller do not fold away when not in use, but a streamlined glassfibre fairing encloses the engine and pylon. The Monerai P has a rate of climb of 91-122 m (300-400 ft)/min.

Monnett Monerai S single-seat homebuilt sailplane

Monnett Monerai P, powered version of the S for self-launch

RAND ROBINSON
RAND ROBINSON ENGINEERING INC

5842 K McFadden Avenue, Huntington Beach, California
92649
Telephone: (714) 898 3811

RAND ROBINSON KR-1B

Under this designation, Rand Robinson was in late
1979 proposing to market plans for a motor glider version
of the KR-1 (see Homebuilts section), with enlarged wing
outer panels to increase the span to 8·23 m (27 ft 0 in).

RYSON
RYSON AVIATION CORPORATION

548 San Fernando Street, San Diego, California 92106
Telephone: (714) 278 4791
PRESIDENT: T. Claude Ryan
EXECUTIVE VICE-PRESIDENT AND OPERATIONS MANAGER:
Jerome D. Ryan
CHIEF ENGINEER: L. Pazmany

Ryson Aviation Corporation was founded by Mr T.
Claude Ryan, until 1969 Chairman and Chief Executive
Officer of the Ryan Aeronautical Company (now Teledyne Ryan Aeronautical). Other executives include his
son, Mr Jerry Ryan, and Mr Ladislao Pazmany. The aim of
the Corporation is to develop aeronautical products and
make them available for manufacture by other companies.

First design from Ryson was the STP-1 Swallow two-
seat motor glider, described in the 1973-74 *Jane's.*

Since early 1975 the company has been working on the
ST-100 (Soaring/Touring—100 hp) motor glider.

RYSON ST-100 CLOUDSTER

The ST-100, design of which was started on 18 March
1974, incorporates all-metal construction, fully-folding
wings, power-operated flaps for air braking, and ailerons
which operate with the flaps. It is designed to be aerobatic

and to meet current FAR Pt 23 gust load requirements
(15·25 m; 50 ft/s); is capable of performing as an aero-tow
aircraft for unpowered sailplanes; and can be used as a
conventional powered aircraft for cross-country flying.

The ST-100 prototype (N2RY) flew for the first time on
21 December 1976. By January 1980 it had accumulated
about 700 hours of flight testing and demonstration,
including an economy record flight from California to
Oshkosh, Wisconsin (1,456 nm; 2,697 km; 1,676 miles),
on 28 of the available 32 US gallons of fuel (106 of 121
litres); and a 5,214 nm (9,656 km; 6,000 mile) flight
around the perimeter of the United States. FAA certification was expected by March 1980. A production programme by a licensee is planned.

TYPE: Tandem two-seat motor glider; *g* limits
+6·75/−3·5.
AIRFRAME: Cantilever low-wing monoplane. Wing section
Wortmann FX-67-K-170/17 throughout, with max
thickness at 40% chord. Dihedral 4° from roots. All-
metal safe-life structure, with some fail-safe features,
built of extruded 2024-T4 and other alloys of
aluminium, with sheet aluminium skin. Aluminium
plain ailerons and plain trailing-edge flaps, with foam
core. Flaps, powered by electrically-operated screwjack, can be deflected downward for use as airbrakes.
Ailerons operate with flaps. No spoilers or tabs. Wings

fold back alongside fuselage for stowage or transportation. Conventional all-metal semi-monocoque fuselage,
with extruded aluminium longerons, and sheet metal
frames, bulkheads and skins. Cantilever T tail, with
sweptback fin and rudder and non-swept horizontal surfaces, latter comprising fixed-incidence tailplane and
one-piece balanced elevator. Rudder and elevator have
riveted sheet aluminium primary ribs, bonded intermediate foam ribs, and bonded sheet aluminium skin.
Elevator tips removable for transportation or storage.
Anti-servo and trim tab, of similar construction, in
centre of elevator. Two-wheel main gear and steerable
tailwheel, all non-retractable. Ryson oleo-pneumatic
shock-absorbers. Cleveland main wheels, with Cleveland hydraulic disc brakes, and Goodyear tailwheel.
Streamlined glassfibre fairings on main gear legs, main
wheels and tailwheel. Canopy opens sideways to starboard. Dual controls standard. Baggage space aft of rear
seat.
POWER PLANT: One 74·5 kW (100 hp) Continental O-200
flat-four engine, driving a Hoffmann HO-V-62
variable-pitch fully-feathering propeller with two composite blades. Fuel in two integral tanks in leading-
edges of wing centre-section, with combined capacity of
121 litres (26·6 Imp gallons; 32 US gallons). Oil capacity 5·7 litres (1·25 Imp gallons; 1·5 US gallons).

SCHWEIZER
SCHWEIZER AIRCRAFT CORPORATION

HEAD OFFICE AND WORKS: Box 147, Elmira, New York
14902
Telephone: (607) 739 3821
Telex: 932459
PRESIDENT AND CHIEF ENGINEER: Ernest Schweizer
SALES MANAGER: W. E. Doherty Jr

Schweizer Aircraft Corporation is the leading American
designer and manufacturer of sailplanes. Its current products include the SGS 1-26E, SGS 2-33A, SGS 1-35
series and SGS 1-36.

By agreement with Gulfstream American, Schweizer
also manufactures the Super Ag-Cat agricultural biplane,
a description of which can be found under the Gulfstream
heading in the Aircraft section. Other subcontract work
includes production of fuselage assemblies for Piper Aircraft Corporation and major structures for Bell Helicopter
Textron.

About 320 people were employed by Schweizer in
1980.

SCHWEIZER SGS 1-26

This relatively small sailplane was developed for one-
design class activities. It was designed to be produced both
complete and in kit form for the homebuilder. The prototype was first flown in January 1954, and with award of
the FAA Type Certificate production of complete sailplanes and kits began in November of that year.

The current production version, the **SGS 1-26E**, introduced an all-metal semi-monocoque fuselage. More than
700 SGS 1-26 sailplanes had been produced by January
1980, of which approximately 200 were in kit form.

TYPE: Single-seat medium-performance sailplane.
AIRFRAME: Cantilever mid-wing monoplane. Dihedral 3°
30′. All-metal structure of aluminium alloy, with metal
skin. Fabric-covered ailerons. Balanced airbrakes
immediately aft of spar on each wing. Production SGS
1-26E has an all-metal semi-monocoque fuselage.
Fabric-covered aluminium alloy tail unit. Non-
retractable unsprung monowheel, with Schweizer
brake, aft of rubber-sprung nose-skid. Small tailwheel.

SCHWEIZER SGS 2-33A

The SGS 2-33 was developed to meet the demand for a
medium-priced two-seat sailplane for training and general
family soaring. The prototype was first flown in the
Autumn of 1966 and received FAA Type Approval in
February 1967. Production began in January 1967, and
570 SGS 2-33 sailplanes had been built by January 1980.
The current 2-33A is also available in kit form.

TYPE: Tandem two-seat training sailplane.
AIRFRAME: Strut-braced high-wing monoplane.
Aluminium alloy structure with metal skin and all-metal
ailerons. Airbrakes fitted. Welded chrome-
molybdenum steel tube fuselage. Nose covered with
glassfibre, remainder with Ceconite fabric. Steel tube
tail unit, covered with Ceconite fabric. Braced tailplane.
Non-retractable Cleveland monowheel immediately aft
of nose-skid. Rubber-block shock-absorption for skid.
Wingtip wheels.

SCHWEIZER SGS 1-35 SERIES

The SGS 1-35 is an all-metal single-seat high-
performance 15 metre Class sailplane, the prototype of
which was flown for the first time in April 1973. The FAA
certification programme was completed in Spring 1974.

The 1-35 is claimed to have the widest wing loading
range in the FAI 15 metre Class (28·22 to 43·75 kg/m²;
5·78 to 8·96 lb/sq ft), and carries 146·5 kg (323 lb) of water
ballast. It can thus compete effectively in both light and
strong soaring conditions. The 80° landing flaps are used
instead of the more conventional airbrakes.

Two newer models are also available, as follows:

SGS 1-35A. Unrestricted 15 metre Class version.
Monowheel forward of CG, large tailwheel and no nose-
skid. Interconnected flaps and ailerons standard. Data as
for standard 1-35 except for empty equipped weight of
222 kg (490 lb) and best glide ratio of 41.

SGS 1-35C (Club-35). Simplified, lower-cost version
for club or syndicate ownership. Non-retractable Cleveland unsprung monowheel aft of CG, Cleveland hydraulic
brake, nose-skid, and no water ballast provision. Flush
rivets used on aft fuselage. Data as for standard 1-35
except for empty equipped weight of 192 kg (425 lb), max

T-O weight of 310 kg (685 lb), max wing loading of 32·16
kg/m² (6·59 lb/sq ft), and best glide ratio of 36.

A total of 96 SGS 1-35s of all versions had been produced by January 1980. The following description applies
to the standard SGS 1-35:

TYPE: Single-seat 15 metre Class sailplane; *g* limits
+8·33/−5·33.
AIRFRAME: Cantilever shoulder-wing monoplane. Wortmann wing sections: FX-67-K-170 at root, FX-67-K-
150 at tip. Dihedral 3° 30′. Aluminium stressed-skin
and stringer wing structure. Bottom-hinged trailing-
edge flaps and top-hinged ailerons of aluminium torque
cell construction. No airbrakes or spoilers. All-
aluminium monocoque fuselage. Cantilever aluminium
T tail, with fixed-incidence tailplane and fabric-covered
elevator. No tabs. Mechanically-retractable unsprung
monowheel, tyre pressure 2·41 bars (35 lb/sq in). Hydraulic brake. Nose-skid and tailwheel or tailskid.
Detachable canopy. Provision for 146·5 kg (323 lb)
water ballast.

SCHWEIZER SGS 1-36

The SGS 1-36 was designed to offer modern performance, handling and appearance to up to 99% of the solo
glider pilots in the USA and overseas as a personal, school
or club sailplane. At the same time, it is intended that it
should be capable of being flown and soared by an inexperienced pilot shortly after becoming competent in his
first solo training flight.

Alternatively, the 1-36 is easily capable of diamond
distance flights for club and partnership owners, and a
one-design competition class is planned.

The general appearance of the SGS 1-36 is shown in an
accompanying three-view drawing. The prototype flew for
the first time on 2 August 1979; production plans were
being finalised in the late Winter of 1979-80.

TYPE: Single-seat multi-purpose sailplane.
AIRFRAME: Cantilever mid-wing monoplane, of all-metal
construction. Wortmann wing sections: FX-61-163 at
root, FX-60-126 at tip. Incidence 1° at root, 0° 4′ at tip.
Airbrakes in upper and lower wing surfaces. Cantilever
T tail, with elevator. Non-retractable monowheel and
tailwheel.

Rand Robinson KR-1B motor glider (*Don Dwiggins*)

Ryson ST-100 Cloudster (Continental O-200 engine)

Schweizer SGS 2-33A two-seat general-purpose sailplane

Schweizer SGS 1-26E single-seat medium-performance sailplane

Schweizer SGS 1-35C Club version of the 1-35A

Schweizer SGS 1-35A single-seat 15 metre sailplane

Volpar-Spencer single-seat Drag-N-Fly

Schweizer SGS 1-36 training and club sailplane (*Michael A. Badrocke*)

VOLPAR
VOLPAR INC

7929 Hayvenhurst Avenue, Van Nuys, California 91406
Telephone: (213) 787-4393 and 873-5599
Officers: See Aircraft section

Volpar Inc is engaged primarily in the conversion and manufacture of light/medium-sized turboprop-powered aircraft, as described in the Aircraft section.

In February 1977 the company retained Mr Percival H. Spencer to design a small but fully manoeuvrable water-based glider, utilising modern plastics and foam materials for high strength and low cost, and having simple controls that could be operated safely by an amateur or non-pilot. Mr Spencer is a pioneer pilot, amphibious aircraft designer and manufacturer of the Spencer Amphibian Air Car (see Homebuilts section).

VOLPAR-SPENCER DRAG-N-FLY

The Drag-N-Fly is intended to be towed in tethered flight by a conventional motor-boat. The tether may be disconnected by the pilot in an emergency, and will disconnect automatically if the glider tends to overrun the tow boat. An unusual feature is the hinged fuselage, which permits the glider to be transported on a light road trailer without exceeding a width of 2·44 m (8 ft 0 in).

The prototype was first flown, by Mr Spencer, on 20 April 1977. Development testing, continued throughout 1978, resulted in the addition of a 0·305 m (1 ft) tip extension on each wing in order to reduce tow-boat power requirements. Flight and water characteristics, including control response, were then regarded as entirely satisfactory, and in early 1979 the Drag-N-Fly was ready for production.

TYPE: Single-seat waterborne glider; *g* limit +6.

AIRFRAME: Strut-braced biplane. Aerofoil-shaped styrofoam blocks, with plywood spar caps bonded to styrofoam shear web with epoxy resin. Wooden blocks between capstrips at each end provide bolt attachments to join panels. Wings covered in glasscloth laminate, bonded with epoxy resin. Spoilers on outer panels of lower wing. Fuselage and floats built of plywood internal frames and bulkheads, covered in polyester resin-bonded moulded glassfibre cloth laminate. Cantilever tail unit with styrofoam core, wooden frame edges (vertical surfaces) and plywood spar caps (horizontal surfaces); glassfibre laminate covering. Horizontal tail is one-piece unit, hinged at fuselage aft bulkhead and statically balanced with bob-weight; bungee spring for trim adjustment. Water rudder, operated from cockpit, for towing control. Single open cockpit forward of wings.

YUGOSLAVIA

ELAN
Begunje

This factory has, since the beginning of 1979, assumed responsibility for licence production of the DG-100 sailplane formerly built by Glaser-Dirks of the Federal Republic of Germany (which see).

ELAN (GLASER-DIRKS) DG-100 ELAN

The DG-100 is a modified and lighter-weight development of the Akaflieg Darmstadt D-38 described in the 1973-74 *Jane's*. Its design, by Dipl-Ing Wilhelm Dirks, began in August 1973, and the prototype (D-7100) flew for the first time on 10 May 1974. By the end of 1978,

Glaser-Dirks had completed 105 DG-100s, including 16 examples of the DG-100G (first flight 11 June 1976), which differs in having a tailplane similar to that of the Glaser-Dirks DG-200. A Club version of the DG-100, without water ballast, is also available.

From early 1979, the DG-100 entered licence production in Yugoslavia, and the two versions are now known as the **DG-100 Elan** and **DG-100G Elan**. Ten of each version were built by Elan during 1979. The following description applies to the former (standard) version:
TYPE: Single-seat Standard Class sailplane; g limit +6·1.

AIRFRAME: Cantilever shoulder-wing monoplane. Wortmann wing sections: FX-61-184 at centreline, FX-60-126 at tip. Dihedral 3° from roots. Glassfibre roving main spar. Glassfibre/Conticell/foam sandwich wings, ailerons and all-moving T tailplane; all-glassfibre semi-monocoque fuselage, fin and rudder. Schempp-

Hirth duralumin airbrakes on wing upper surfaces. Water ballast tank in each wing (except on Club version), combined capacity 100 kg (220 lb). Full-span Flettner tab in tailplane. Manually-retractable monowheel, tyre pressure 2·0 bars (29 lb/sq in), with Tost drum brake, and tailwheel.

JASTREB
JASTREB AEROPLANE AND GLIDER FACTORY
Vrsac
Telephone: (013) 813157, 813051, 813639 and 815491
JASTREB SOLE-77
The Jastreb SOLE-77, illustrated in an accompanying three-view drawing, is a tandem two-seat motor glider for elementary and advanced training, and can be used for basic aerobatics. Other applications include atmospheric sampling, photogrammetry, and study of air currents. The monowheel is said to be retractable; the tailwheel, linked to the rudder pedals, is fully castoring. The cockpit canopy, which opens forward, is jettisonable. Power off,

the SOLE-77 has a best glide ratio of 29. The engine, of unknown type, develops 54 kW (72 hp) and drives a two-blade propeller; there is provision for an auxiliary fuel tank. Without this tank, standard fuel load is 50 kg (110 lb) and powered flight endurance 5 h.
All other known details are given in the Table.

MF
MASINSKI FAKULTET (Faculty of Mechanical Engineering, Aeronautical Institute ATI)
27 Marta 80, 11000 Belgrade
Telephone: (011) 329 362
SAILPLANE DESIGNER: Prof Dr Tomislav Dragovic, Dipl Eng

The Faculty of Mechanical Engineering at the University of Belgrade is the leading research and educational institution for aircraft engineering in Yugoslavia. It has tackled many important light aviation projects in recent years, and collaborates closely with the national aerospace industry. Among its recent designs was the UTVA-75, described in the Aircraft section.

MF VUK-T
The prototype of this single-seat all-plastics sailplane was designed and built at the MF in 1976, and made its first flight in 1977. It entered production in the Jastreb Aeroplane and Glider Factory at Vrsac (which see) in January 1979. At that time 110 had been ordered by the Yugoslav Aeronautical Union.
Chief features of the VUK-T are an entirely new technique of plastics stressed-skin construction and the use of a supercritical wing section. The sailplane is designed to OSTIV airworthiness requirements, and is cleared for cloud flying, aerobatics and spinning.
TYPE: Single-seat high-performance basic and advanced training sailplane; g limits +5·3/−2·65 (safety factor 1·5).

AIRFRAME: Cantilever mid-wing monoplane. NASA GAW-1 supercritical wing section from root to tip, with no twist. Thickness/chord ratio 17%. Dihedral 3°. Glassfibre roving main spar, integral with the upper and lower wing skins, which are of glassfibre/Conticell foam sandwich. Auxiliary rear spar carries the top-hinged plain ailerons. Schempp-Hirth airbrakes in upper surfaces at 50% chord. Fuselage is of glassfibre sandwich construction forward, glassfibre monocoque aft. Cantilever T tailplane, with separate elevator, of similar construction to wings. Retractable monowheel, with brake, and non-retractable tailwheel. Semi-reclining seat under one-piece flush-fitting jettisonable canopy. No water ballast provision.

VTC
VAZDUHOPLOVNO TEHNICKI CENTAR—VRSAC
Vrsac, 29 Novembra b.b. Guduricki put
Telephone: 80-111
DIRECTOR: Veselinovic Zivota
CHIEF DESIGNER: Dipl Ing Ivan Sostaric

The VTC at Vrsac is producing the Schempp-Hirth Cirrus and Standard Cirrus under licence. The first production Cirrus built at Vrsac was delivered in late 1971.

VTC (SCHEMPP-HIRTH) CIRRUS
This single-seat high-performance sailplane was designed in the Federal Republic of Germany by Dipl-Ing

Klaus Holighaus, who utilised a thick Wortmann series wing section, without flaps, to achieve good low-speed and climb characteristics.
The first prototype Cirrus flew for the first time in January 1967 with a V tail unit. The second prototype had a conventional tail unit, as fitted to production models.
Schempp-Hirth built a total of 120 Cirrus sailplanes

DATA: SAILPLANES AND MOTOR GLIDERS (POWER OFF)

Manufacturer and Model	Wing span: m; ft in	Wing aspect ratio	Wing area (gross): m²; sq ft	Length overall: m; ft in	Height over tail: m; ft in	Empty: kg; lb	Max T-O: kg; lb	Max wing loading: kg/m²; lb/sq ft
AUSTRALIA								
Sunderland MOBA-2C	14·99; 49 2	24·7	9·08; 97·7	6·78; 22 3	1·36; 4 5½	263; 580	361; 796	39·8; 8·15
AUSTRIA								
Brditschka HB-21	16·24; 53 3½	13·9	18·98; 204·3	8·10; 26 7	2·60; 8 6¼	505; 1,113	710; 1,565	37·4; 7·66
BRAZIL								
CTA PE-80367 Urubu	17·80; 58 4¾	15·1	20·915; 225·1	8·96; 29 4¾	2·00; 6 6¾	370; 816	550; 1,212	26·3; 5·39
EEUFMG (CEA) CB-2/B Minuano	15·00; 49 2½	22·1	10·20; 109·8	7·00; 22 11¾	1·43; 4 8¼	230; 507	400; 882	39·22; 8·03
IPE 02 Nhapecam	17·20; 56 5¼	15·4	19·26; 207·3	8·40; 27 6¾	1·57; 5 1¾	370; 816	570; 1,256	29·6; 6·06
Sidou João Grande	18·00; 59 0¾	25·0	12·96; 139·5	9·00; 29 6¼	2·52; 8 3¼	270; 595	450; 992	34·72; 7·11
CANADA								
Marsden Gemini	18·45; 60 6½	29·7	11·45; 123·2	7·60; 24 11¼	1·50; 4 11	357; 787	545; 1,201	47·6; 9·75
CZECHOSLOVAKIA								
VSO 10	15·00; 49 2½	18·75	12·00; 129·2	7·00; 22 11¾	1·38; 4 6¼	250; 551	380; 837	31·67; 6·49
VSO 10C	15·00; 49 2½	18·75	12·00; 129·2	7·00; 22 11¾	1·38; 4 6¼	250; 551	380; 837	31·67; 6·49
DENMARK								
Projekt 8 Dolphin	18·72; 61 5	16·8	20·80; 223·9	8·50; 27 10¾	1·30; 4 3¼	480; 1,058	750; 1,653	36·0; 7·37
Projekt 8 Dolphin M2	18·60; 61 0¼	16·6	20·80; 223·9	8·40; 27 6¾	1·52; 4 11¾	520; 1,146	750; 1,653	36·0; 7·37
FINLAND								
Alanne Motorlerche	13·00; 42 7¾	10·3	16·34; 175·9	6·86; 22 6	1·58; 5 2¼	288; 635	400; 882	23·8; 4·88
Eiri PIK-20E	15·00; 49 2½	22·5	10·00; 107·6	6·53; 21 5	1·47; 4 10	300; 661	470; 1,036	47·0; 9·63

n.k. = not known; n.a. = not applicable

Jastreb SOLE-77 two-seat motor glider *(Michael A. Badrocke)*

VUK-T all-plastics training sailplane, designed by the Yugoslav Faculty of Mechanical Engineering

Federal German-built Glaser-Dirks DG-100s. This sailplane is now produced under licence by Elan in Yugoslavia

before ending production in late 1971. Since then the Cirrus has been produced under licence by VTC in Yugoslavia, which had completed about 60 by early 1979. According to Schempp-Hirth, production was continuing in 1980.

TYPE: Single-seat high-performance sailplane.

AIRFRAME: Cantilever mid-wing monoplane. Wortmann FX-66 series section. Dihedral 3° at spar centreline. Wing shell is a glassfibre/foam sandwich structure, with an all-glassfibre box spar. Hinged ailerons of glassfibre/balsa sandwich. No flaps. Schempp-Hirth aluminium alloy airbrakes. Glassfibre fuselage shell, stiffened with foam rings, secured with resin. Cantilever tail unit of glassfibre/foam sandwich. Retractable rubber-sprung Tost monowheel, tyre pressure 3·38 bars (49 lb/sq in). Tost drum brake.

VTC (SCHEMPP-HIRTH) STANDARD CIRRUS 75-VTC

Designed by Dipl-Ing Klaus Holighaus, this Standard Class version of the Schempp-Hirth Cirrus entered production in the Federal Republic of Germany in the Summer of 1969, following the first flight of the prototype in March 1969.

By April 1977 a total of 700 Standard Cirrus had been built, including 200 under licence by Grob Flugzeugbau in West Germany. Production by Grob ended in July 1975, and by Schempp-Hirth in April 1977. Since then licence manufacture has been undertaken by Lanaverre in France, and from January 1979 by VTC in Yugoslavia. VTC had built 14 Standard Cirrus by the Spring of 1979. According to Schempp-Hirth, production was continuing in 1980.

TYPE: Single-seat Standard and Club Class sailplane; g limit +10.

AIRFRAME: Cantilever mid-wing monoplane. Wortmann wing section. Dihedral 3°. Sweepback 1°18' at leading-edge. Glassfibre/foam sandwich wings, ailerons and tail surfaces. Schempp-Hirth glassfibre airbrakes on upper surfaces. Glassfibre fuselage shell, stiffened with bonded-in foam rings. All-moving T tailplane. Retractable monowheel standard; non-retractable faired monowheel optional. Tost wheel with drum brake and Continental tyre, pressure 3·45 bars (50 lb/sq in). Canopy opens sideways to starboard. Provision for 60 kg (132 lb) of water ballast.

Performance (at max T-O weight except where indicated)

Best glide ratio	at (speed): knots; km/h; mph	Min sinking speed: m (ft)/s	at (speed): knots; km/h; mph	Stalling speed: knots; km/h; mph	Max speed (smooth air): knots; km/h; mph	Max speed (rough air): knots; km/h; mph	Max aero-tow speed: knots; km/h; mph	Max winch-launching speed: knots; km/h; mph	Remarks
38	55; 102; 48	0·64; 2·10	48; 89; 42	*40; 74; 46	117; 217; 102	80; 148; 92	80; 148; 92	75; 139; 86·5	*Flaps up (35 knots; 65 km/h; 40·5 mph flaps down)
24-26	56·5; 105; 65	1·20; 3·94	45; 84; 52	38; 70; 43·5	108; 200; 124	94; 174; 108	n.a.	n.a.	
30·6	46; 85; 53	0·70; 2·30	39; 72; 45	35; 64; 40	139; 257; 160	87; 161; 100	81; 150; 93	n.k.	
39	51; 95; 59	0·60; 1·97	45; 83; 51·5	35; 65; 40·5	140; 260; 161	86; 160; 99	86; 160; 99	n.a.	
28	43; 80; 50	0·75; 2·46	37; 68; 42·5	30; 55; 35	108; 200; 124	81; 150; 93	65; 120; 75	n.a.	
43·9	51; 95; 59	0·57; 1·87	44; 81; 50·5	37·5; 69; 43	162; 300; 186	97; 180; 112	97; 180; 112	59·5; 110; 68·5	
37	60; 111; 69	*0·72; 2·36	45; 83; 52	35; 65; 40·5	140; 260; 161	120; 222; 138	75; 139; 86	n.a.	*Flaps extended
36	49; 90; 56	0·64; 2·10	39; 73; 45·5	37; 68; 42·5	135; 250; 155	86; 160; 99	86; 160; 99	65; 120; 75	
34	51; 95; 59	0·72; 2·36	43; 79; 49	38; 70; 43·5	135; 250; 155	86; 160; 99	86; 160; 99	65; 120; 75	
32	54; 100; 62	0·70; 2·30	43·5; 80; 50	38; 70; 43·5	141·5; 263; 163	141·5; 263; 163	67·5; 125; 77·5	59; 110; 68	
33	54; 100; 62	0·70; 2·30	43·5; 80; 50	n.k.	n.k.	n.k.	n.k.	n.k.	
17	42; 78; 48·5	1·00; 3·28	35; 65; 40·5	24·5; 45; 28	81; 150; 93	65; 120; 75	n.a.	n.a.	
41	63; 117; 73	0·70; 2·30	47·5; 88; 55	40·5; 75; 47	154; 285; 177	119; 220; 136	105; 195; 121	67; 125; 78	

Manufacturer and Model	Dimensions					Weights and Loading		
	Wing span: m; ft in	Wing aspect ratio	Wing area (gross): m²; sq ft	Length overall: m; ft in	Height over tail: m; ft in	Empty: kg; lb	Max T-O: kg; lb	Max wing loading: kg/m²; lb/sq ft
FRANCE								
Calvel Frelon	10·40; 34 1½	13·5	7·80; 83·96	5·40; 17 8½	1·50; 4 11	135; 297	220; 485	28·0; 5·70
CARMAM J.P. 15-36A Aiglon	15·00; 49 2½	20·4	11·00; 118·4	6·18; 20 3¼	1·40; 4 7	229; 505	390; 860	35·0; 7·16
CARMAM C.38	15·00; 49 2½	20·6	11·00; 118·4	6·70; 21 11¾	1·45; 4 9	230; 507	440; 970	40·0; 8·19
CARMAM C.40	15·00; 49 2½	20·6	11·00; 118·4	6·65; 21 9¾	1·40; 4 7	240; 529	370; 816	34·0; 6·97
or	17·00; 55 9½	24·7	11·70; 125·9	6·65; 21 9¾	1·40; 4 7	250; 551	470; 1,036	40·0; 8·20
ENSMA FS-25 S Cuervo	15·00; 49 2½	26·4	8·55; 92·0	6·48; 21 3	1·42; 4 8	160; 353	250; 551	29·2; 5·98
Fournier RF-9	17·00; 55 9½	16·1	18·00; 193·75	7·86; 25 9½	1·93; 6 4	520; 1,146	750; 1,653	41·67; 8·53
GEPAS Compact	12·80; 42 0	17·2	9·50; 102·3	6·00; 19 8¼	1·30; 4 3¼	160; 352	266; 586	28·0; 5·73
Issoire (Siren) D 77 Iris	13·50; 44 3½	16·0	11·40; 122·7	6·37; 20 10¾	1·20; 3 11¼	220; 485	345; 760	30·3; 6·21
Issoire (Siren) E 78 Silène	18·00; 59 0½	18·0	18·00; 193·8	7·95; 26 1	1·50; 4 11	365; 805	565; 1,245	31·3; 6·43
Pottier Kit Club 15-34	15·00; 49 2½	20·6	11·00; 118·4	6·25; 20 6	1·40; 4 7	225; 496	420; 926	39·0; 7·99
SCAP Cirrus 78L	15·00; 49 2½	22·5	10·00; 107·6	6·41; 21 0½	1·32; 4 4¾	218; 480	450; 992	45·0; 9·22
SCAP-Lanaverre SL-2	18·20; 59 8½	19·95	16·60; 178·7	8·57; 28 1½	1·00; 3 3¼	370; 815	620; 1,366	37·3; 7·64
GERMANY (FEDERAL REPUBLIC)								
Akaflieg Braunschweig SB-12	15·00; 49 2½	22·6	9·95; 107·1	6·40; 21 0	1·40; 4 7	225; 496	450; 992	45·2; 9·26
Akaflieg Darmstadt D-39	15·00; 49 2½	20·5	11·00; 118·4	7·15; 23 5½	*1·02; 3 4¼	370; 816	470; 1,036	42·0; 8·61
Akaflieg Karlsruhe AK 2	20·00; 65 7½	27·6	14·50; 156·1	7·60; 24 11¼	1·67; 5 5¾	n.k.	580; 1,278	40·0; 8·19
Akaflieg München Mü 27 (flaps in)	22·00; 72 2¼	27·5	17·60; 189·4	10·30; 33 9½	2·10; 6 10¾	710; 1,565	900; 1,984	51·0; 10·45
Akaflieg München Mü 27 (flaps out)	22·00; 72 2¼	20·2	23·90; 257·3	10·30; 33 9½	2·10; 6 10¾	710; 1,565	900; 1,984	37·6; 7·70
Akaflieg München Mü 28	12·00; 39 4½	10·9	13·20; 142·1	6·78; 22 3	1·53; 5 0¼	250; 551	360; 794	27·27; 5·59
or	14·00; 45 11¼	13·2	14·56; 156·7	6·78; 22 3	1·53; 5 0¼	260; 573	370; 816	25·41; 5·21
Glaser-Dirks DG-200	15·00; 49 2½	22·5	10·00; 107·6	7·00; 22 11¾	1·40; 4 7	238; 525	450; 992	45·0; 9·22
Glaser-Dirks DG-200A Acroracer	13·10; 42 11¾	18·6	9·25; 99·6	7·00; 22 11¾	1·40; 4 7	237; 522	360; 793	38·9; 7·97
Glaser-Dirks DG-200/17	17·00; 55 9¼	27·3	10·57; 113·8	7·00; 22 11¾	1·40; 4 7	248; 547	450; 992	42·5; 8·71
Glasflügel Hornet	15·00; 49 2½	22·96	9·80; 105·5	6·40; 21 0	1·40; 4 7	227; 500	420; 926	42·9; 8·79
Glasflügel Hornet C	15·00; 49 2½	22·96	9·80; 105·5	6·40; 21 0	1·40; 4 7	210; 463	450; 992	45·9; 9·40
Glasflügel Mosquito B	15·00; 49 2½	22·8	9·86; 106·1	6·40; 21 0	1·40; 4 7	235; 518	450; 992	46·0; 9·42
Grob Standard Astir II	15·00; 49 2½	18·2	12·40; 133·5	6·80; 22 3¾	1·40; 4 7	260; 573	450; 992	36·3; 7·43
Grob Club Astir II	15·00; 49 2½	18·2	12·40; 133·5	6·80; 22 3¾	1·40; 4 7	255; 562	380; 837	30·6; 6·27
Grob Speed Astir IIB	15·00; 49 2½	19·6	11·50; 123·8	6·60; 21 7¾	1·27; 4 2	260; 573	515; 1,135	44·8; 9·18
Grob G 103 Twin II	17·50; 57 5	17·2	17·80; 191·6	8·18; 26 10	1·55; 5 1	360; 794	580; 1,278	32·6; 6·68
Grob G 109	15·00; 49 2½	11·8	19·10; 205·6	7·80; 25 7	1·80; 5 10¾	500; 1,102	750; 1,653	39·3; 8·05
ISF Mistral-C	15·00; 49 2½	20·7	10·85; 116·8	6·73; 22 1	1·45; 4 9	230; 507	350; 771	32·3; 6·62
Rolladen-Schneider LS3-a	15·00; 49 2½	21·4	10·50; 113·0	6·84; 22 5¼	1·20; 3 11¼	240; 529	472; 1,040	45·0; 9·22
Scheibe Bergfalke-IV	17·20; 56 5¼	17·4	17·00; 183·0	8·00; 26 3	1·50; 4 11	300; 661	500; 1,102	29·4; 6·02
Scheibe SF-25C and C-S Falke '80	15·25; 50 0¼	12·8	18·20; 195·9	7·55; 24 9¼	1·85; 6 0¾	375; 826	610; 1,345	33·5; 6·86
Scheibe SF-25K Falke '80	14·60; 47 10¾	12·5	17·10; 184·1	7·55; 24 9¼	1·85; 6 0¾	*410; 904	610; 1,345	35·7; 7·32
Scheibe SF-25E Super-Falke	18·00; 59 0¾	17·8	18·20; 195·9	7·50; 24 7¼	1·85; 6 0¾	440; 970	650; 1,433	35·0; 7·17
Scheibe SF-28A Tandem-Falke	16·30; 53 5¾	14·4	18·50; 199·1	8·10; 26 7	1·55; 5 1	410; 904	610; 1,345	33·0; 6·76
Scheibe SF-H34	15·80; 51 10	16·9	14·80; 159·3	7·50; 24 7¼	1·50; 4 11	306; 675	500; 1,102	33·8; 6·92
Schempp-Hirth Nimbus 2C	20·30; 66 7¼	28·6	14·40; 155·0	7·33; 24 0½	1·45; 4 9	*355; 782	650; 1,433	45·0; 9·22
Schempp-Hirth Mini-Nimbus C	15·00; 49 2½	22·8	9·86; 106·1	6·41; 21 0½	1·32; 4 4	*235; 518	500; 1,102	51·0; 10·45
Schempp-Hirth Janus B	18·20; 59 8½	19·95	16·60; 178·7	8·62; 28 3¼	1·45; 4 9	370; 815	620; 1,366	37·0; 7·58

n.k. = not known; n.a. = not applicable

					Performance (at max T-O weight except where indicated)				
Best glide ratio	at (speed): knots; km/h; mph	Min sinking speed: m (ft)/s	at (speed): knots; km/h; mph	Stalling speed: knots; km/h; mph	Max speed (smooth air): knots; km/h; mph	Max speed (rough air): knots; km/h; mph	Max aero-tow speed: knots; km/h; mph	Max winch-launching speed: knots; km/h; mph	Remarks
n.k.	n.k.	n.k.	n.k.	n.k.	n.k.	n.k.	n.k.	n.k.	
36·9	43·5; 80; 50	0·62; 2·03	39; 72; 45	33·5; 62; 39	119; 220; 136	89; 166; 103	89; 166; 103	n.k.	
38	54; 100; 62	0·60; 1·97	40; 75; 46·5	35; 64; 40	119; 220; 136	89; 166; 103	119; 220; 136	89; 166; 103	
39	49; 90; 56	n.k.	n.k.	31·5; 58; 36	146; 270; 168	97; 180; 112	97; 180; 112	97; 180; 112	} Data for 15 m version without water ballast, 17 m version with water ballast
41	37; 68; 42	n.k.	n.k.	31·5; 58; 36	146; 270; 168	97; 180; 112	97; 180; 112	97; 180; 112	
38	49; 90; 56	0·60; 1·97	43; 80; 50	31; 57; 35·5	119; 220; 137	86; 160; 99	65; 120; 75	86; 160; 99	Performance data estimated
28	49; 90; 56	0·80; 2·62	43·5; 80; 50	39·5; 73; 45·5	119; 220; 136	99; 183; 114	n.a.	n.a.	
31	49; 90; 56	0·70; 2·30	38; 70; 43·5	32·5; 60; 37·5	113; 210; 130	81; 150; 93	76; 140; 87	65; 120; 75	
33	51; 95; 59	0·65; 2·13	43·5; 80; 50	32·5; 60; 37·5	121; 225; 140	91; 170; 105	91; 170; 105	67; 125; 78	
38	51; 95; 59	0·67; 2·20	43·5; 80; 50	40·5; 75; 47	119; 220; 136	91; 170; 105	91; 170; 105	70; 130; 81	
36	41·5; 77; 48	0·63; 2·07	39; 72; 45	34; 62; 39	135; 250; 155	135; 250; 155	135; 250; 155	n.k.	
38·5	49; 90; 56	0·60; 1·97	40·5; 75; 47	34; 62; 39	135; 250; 155	135; 250; 155	81; 150; 93	65; 120; 75	
40	55; 102; 63	0·65; 2·13	47; 87; 54	n.k.	119; 220; 136	91; 169; 105	81; 150; 93	n.k.	
—	—	—	—	—	*135; 250; 155	*81; 150; 93	*81; 150; 93	*81; 150; 93	*Estimated
**36	56·5; 105; 65	**0·70; 2·30	45; 84; 52	43·5; 80; 50	151; 280; 174	151; 280; 174	97; 180; 112	59; 110; 68	*Height over fuselage **Without propeller
47	54; 100; 62	0·65; 2·13	38; 70; 43·5	35; 64; 40	n.k.	n.k.	n.k.	n.k.	
47	62; 115; 71·5	0·65; 2·13	58; 108; 67	53; 98; 61	162; 300; 186	162; 300; 186	108; 200; 124	108; 200; 124	
36	50; 93; 58	0·66; 2·16	41·5; 77; 48	37; 68; 42	75·5; 140; 87	75·5; 140; 87	75·5; 140; 87	75·5; 140; 87	
28	51; 95; 59	0·84; 2·76	43·5; 80; 50	32·5; 60; 37·5	205; 380; 236	167; 310; 193	108; 200; 124	108; 200; 124	Performance estimated
32	51; 95; 59	0·72; 2·36	40·5; 75; 47	32; 59; 37	156; 290; 180	108; 200; 124	86; 160; 99	86; 160; 99	Performance estimated
42·5	59·5; 110; 68·5	0·59; 1·94	43; 80; 50	*34; 62; 39	146; 270; 168	102; 190; 118	102; 190; 118	70; 130; 80·5	*At 300 kg (661 lb) AUW; other performance at 420 kg (926 lb)
37	57; 106; 66	0·70; 2·30	46; 85; 53	35; 64; 40	156; 290; 180	121; 225; 140	102; 190; 118	70; 130; 80·5	
44·6	59·5; 110; 68·5	0·53; 1·74	43; 80; 50	32·5; 60; 37·5	146; 270; 168	102; 190; 118	102; 190; 118	70; 130; 80·5	
38	41; 75; 47	*0·60; 1·97	41; 75; 47	39; 72; 45	135; 250; 155	135; 250; 155	81; 150; 93	65; 120; 74·5	*At 345 kg (760 lb) AUW
38·5	58; 107; 66·5	0·59; 1·94	40; 74; 46	35; 65; 40·5	135; 250; 155	135; 250; 155	81; 150; 93	81; 150; 93	
42	59·5; 110; 68·5	0·67; 2·20	51; 95; 59	42·5; 78; 48·5	135; 250; 155	108; 200; 124	81; 150; 93	81; 150; 93	
37·5	51; 95; 59	0·58; 1·90	41; 75; 47	32·5; 60; 37·5	135; 250; 155	135; 250; 155	91; 170; 105	65; 120; 74·5	
36	51; 95; 56	0·60; 1·97	41; 75; 47	32·5; 60; 37·5	135; 250; 155	135; 250; 155	91; 170; 105	65; 120; 74·5	
41·5	64·5; 120; 74·5	0·57; 1·87	41; 75; 47	34·5; 64; 40	146; 270; 168	108; 200; 124	91; 170; 105	65; 120; 74·5	
37	56; 105; 65	0·64; 2·10	43; 80; 50	33·5; 62;* 39	135; 250; 155	108; 200; 124	91; 170; 105	65; 120; 74·5	*With pilot only
30	65; 120; 75	0·90; 2·95	n.k.	40·5; 75; 47	118; 220; 136	n.k.	n.k.	n.k.	
37	50; 92; 57	0·66; 2·17	44·5; 82; 51	36·5; 67; 42	135; 250; 155	135; 250; 155	86; 160; 99·5	70; 130; 80·5	
41·8	54; 100; 62	0·60; 1·97	38; 70; 43·5	34; 62; 39	146; 270; 168	102·5; 190; 118	102·5; 190; 118	70; 130; 80·5	
34	51·5; 95; 59	0·75; 2·46	46; 85; 53	35·5; 65; 40·5	108; 200; 124	92; 170; 106	76; 140; 87	59·5; 110; 68·5	
23	41; 75; 47	1·00; 3·28	38; 70; 43·5	32·5; 60; 37·5	102·5; 190; 118	102·5; 190; 118	n.a.	n.a.	
*22	n.k.	*1·10; 3·61	97; 180; 112	35; 65; 40	n.k.	n.k.	n.k.	n.k.	*Approx
28/29	46; 85; 53	0·85; 2·79	41; 75; 47	37; 68; 42·5	102·5; 190; 118	102·5; 190; 118	n.a.	n.a.	
26/27	51·5; 95; 59	0·90; 2·95	38; 70; 43·5	32·5; 60; 37·5	102·5; 190; 118	102·5; 190; 118	n.a.	n.a.	
35	51·5; 95; 59	0·70; 2·30	41; 75; 47	35·5; 65; 40·5	135; 250; 155	135; 250; 155	88; 163; 101	67·5; 125; 78	
49	62; 115; 71	0·47; 1·54	43; 80; 50	46; 77; 48	146; 270; 168	146; 270; 168	97; 180; 112	81; 150; 93	*315 kg (694 lb) with carbonfibre wings and tail
42	65; 120; 75	0·70; 2·30	46; 85; 53	43·5; 80; 50	135; 250; 155	135; 250; 155	97; 180; 112	81; 150; 93	*215 kg (474 lb) with carbonfibre wings and tail
*39·5	*59·5; 110; 68·5	*0·70; 2·30	*48·5; 90; 56	*38; 70; 43·5	118; 220; 136	118; 220; 136	91; 170; 105	65; 120; 74·5	*At wing loading of 36·5 kg/m² (7·48 lb/sq ft)

Manufacturer and Model	Dimensions					Weights and Loading		
	Wing span: m; ft in	Wing aspect ratio	Wing area (gross): m²; sq ft	Length overall: m; ft in	Height over tail: m; ft in	Empty: kg; lb	Max T-O: kg; lb	Max wing loading: kg/m²; lb/sq ft
Schempp-Hirth Janus C	20·00; 65 7½	23·0	17·40; 187·3	8·62; 28 3¼	1·45; 4 9	355; 783	700; 1,543	40·0; 8·20
Schleicher ASK 13	16·00; 52 6	14·6	17·50; 188·4	8·18; 26 9½	1·60; 5 3	290; 640	480; 1,060	26·8; 5·49
Schleicher ASW 19 B	15·00; 49 2½	20·4	11·00; 118·4	6·82; 22 4½	1·45; 4 9	245; 540	454; 1,000	41·3; 8·46
Schleicher ASW 20	15·00; 49 2½	21·4	10·50; 113·0	6·82; 22 4½	1·45; 4 9	250; 551	454; 1,000	43·0; 8·81
Schleicher ASW 20 L	16·59; 54 5¼	24·9	11·05; 118·9	6·82; 22 4½	1·45; 4 9	*255; 562	380; 838	34·385; 7·05
Schleicher ASK 21	17·00; 55 9¼	16·1	17·95; 193·2	8·35; 27 4¾	1·55; 5 1	360; 794	600; 1,323	37·0; 7·58
Valentin Taifun 15	15·00; 49 2½	13·8	16·35; 176·0	7·785; 25 6½	2·16; 7 1	480; 1,058	725; 1,598	44·0; 9·02
Valentin Taifun 17	17·00; 55 9¼	16·4	17·60; 189·4	7·785; 25 6½	2·16; 7 1	480; 1,058	725; 1,598	41·0; 8·40
INDIA								
Civil Aviation Dept HS-II Mrigasheer (2nd prototype)	15·00; 49 2½	19·85	11·24; 121·0	7·59; 24 10¾	2·50; 8 2½	237; 522	335; 738	29·55; 6·05
Civil Aviation Dept ATS-1 Ardhra (2nd prototype)	16·50; 54 1½	12·5	21·83; 235·0	8·61; 28 3	2·464; 8 1	328; 723	508; 1,120	23·28; 4·77
ITALY								
Caproni Vizzola Calif A-21S	20·38; 66 10¼	25·65	16·19; 174·3	7·737; 25 4½	1·615; 5 3½	436; 961	644; 1,419	39·8; 8·15
Maggi MG3-15L Condor	15·00; 49 2½	20·0	11·25; 121·1	6·80; 22 3¾	1·56; 5 1½	340; 750	510; 1,124	45·3; 9·28
JAPAN								
Nippi NP-100A Albatross (1st prototype)	18·00; 59 0¾	18·0	18·00; 193·75	8·00; 26 3	2·02; 6 7½	500; 1,102	680; 1,499	37·8; 7·74
Nippi Pilatus B4-PC11AF	15·00; 49 2½	16·0	14·04; 151·1	6·57; 21 6¾	1·57; 5 1¾	230; 506	350; 770	25·0; 5·13
Tainan TN-1	15·50; 50 10½	15·0	15·98; 172·0	7·64; 25 0¾	2·203; 7 2¾	270; 595	380; 837	23·78; 4·87
POLAND								
SZD-30C Pirat	15·00; 49 2½	16·3	13·80; 148·5	6·92; 22 8½	1·67; 5 5¾	255; 562	370; 816	26·8; 5·49
SZD-41A Jantar Standard	15·00; 49 2½	21·1	10·66; 114·7	7·11; 23 4	1·60; 5 3	250; 551	440; 970	41·3; 8·46
SZD-42-2 Jantar 2B	20·50; 67 3	29·2	14·25; 153·4	7·18; 23 6¾	1·76; 5 9¼	356; 785	649; 1,430	45·6; 9·34
SZD-45A Ogar	17·53; 57 6¼	16·2	19·10; 205·6	7·95; 26 1	1·72; 5 7¾	473; 1,042	700; 1,543	36·6; 7·50
SZD-48 Jantar Standard 2	15·00; 49 2½	21·1	10·66; 114·7	6·71; 22 0¼	1·50; 4 11	247; 544	520; 1,146	48·8; 9·99
SZD-50-2 Puchacz	16·67; 54 8¼	15·3	18·16; 195·5	8·38; 27 6	1·92; 6 3½	331; 729	550; 1,212	30·3; 6·20
ROMANIA								
IS-28B2	17·00; 55 9¼	15·8	18·24; 196·3	8·17; 26 9¾	1·80; 5 11	360; 793	590; 1,300	32·34; 6·62
IS-28M1	18·00; 59 0¾	17·1	18·95; 204·0	7·96; 26 1½	1·90; 6 2¾	485; 1,069	730; 1,609	38·52; 7·89
IS-28M2	17·00; 55 9¼	15·8	18·24; 196·3	7·50; 24 7¼	2·15; 7 0¾	495; 1,091	745; 1,642	40·8; 8·36
IS-29D2	15·00; 49 2½	21·6	10·40; 111·9	7·30; 23 11½	1·68; 5 6¼	230; 507	360; 793	34·62; 7·09
IS-29D3	16·50; 54 1½	23·4	11·61; 125·0	7·30; 23 11½	1·68; 5 6¼	230; 507	360; 793	31·0; 6·35
IS-29D4	15·00; 49 2½	21·6	10·40; 111·9	7·30; 23 11½	1·68; 5 6¼	230; 507	480; 1,058	46·1; 9·45
IS-29DM	15·00; 49 2½	22·1	10·20; 109·8	7·00; 22 11½	1·75; 5 9	310; 683	440; 970	43·1; 8·83
IS-29E2	19·00; 62 4	26·5	13·60; 146·4	7·30; 23 11½	1·68; 5 6¼	320; 705	500; 1,102	36·76; 7·53
IS-29E4	24·00; 78 9	30·8	18·70; 201·3	7·30; 23 11½	1·68; 5 6¼	420; 926	530; 1,168	28·3; 5·80
IS-29EM	20·00; 65 7½	27·2	14·68; 158·0	7·00; 22 11½	1·75; 5 9	400; 882	530; 1,168	36·1; 7·40
IS-30	18·00; 59 0¾	17·1	18·92; 203·6	8·36; 27 5¼	1·90; 6 2¾	365; 804	590; 1,300	31·71; 6·49
IS-31 (E3)	20·00; 65 7½	27·2	14·68; 158·0	7·30; 23 11½	1·68; 5 6¼	350; 771	530; 1,168	36·1; 7·40
IS-32	20·00; 65 7½	27·2	14·68; 158·0	8·36; 27 5¼	1·90; 6 2¾	390; 860	590; 1,300	40·6; 8·31
IS-33	15·00; 49 2½	21·2	10·61; 114·2	6·35; 20 10	1·68; 5 6¼	240; 529	500; 1,102	47·1; 9·65
SPAIN								
Cases Libel-Lula	10·50; 34 5½	11·7	9·45; 101·7	5·00; 16 4¾	2·26; 7 5	75; 165	180; 397	19·05; 3·90

n.k. = not known; n.a. = not applicable

Best glide ratio	at (speed): knots; km/h; mph	Min sinking speed: m (ft)/s	at (speed): knots; km/h; mph	Stalling speed: knots; km/h; mph	Max speed (smooth air): knots; km/h; mph	Max speed (rough air): knots; km/h; mph	Max aero-tow speed: knots; km/h; mph	Max winch-launching speed: knots; km/h; mph	Remarks
*43.5	*62; 115; 71.5	*0.60; 1.97	*48.5; 90; 56	*38; 70; 43.5	135; 250; 155	135; 250; 155	97; 180; 112	81; 150; 93	*At wing loading of 36.5 kg/m² (7.48 lb/sq ft)
28	49; 90; 56	0.80; 2.62	38; 70; 43.5	33; 61; 38	108; 200; 124	75.5; 140; 87	75.5; 140; 87	54; 100; 62	Performance at 470 kg (1,036 lb) AUW
38.5	60.5; 112; 70	0.73; 2.40	48.5; 90; 56	36.5; 67; 42	137; 255; 158	137; 255; 158	92; 170; 106	67.5; 125; 78	
*42	52; 96; 60	0.59; 1.94	45.5; 84; 52.5	37.5; 69; 43	143; 265; 165	97; 180; 112	97; 180; 112	67.5; 125; 78	*At 350 kg (772 lb) AUW
46	52; 96; 60	0.55; 1.80	46.5; 86; 53.5	37; 68; 42.5	135; 250; 155	89; 165; 102.5	86; 160; 99.5	65; 120; 74.5	*Approx
34	46; 85; 53	0.65; 2.13	36; 67; 42	33.5; 62; 39	151; 280; 174	135; 250; 155	94; 175; 109	70; 130; 80.5	
28	65; 120; 75	0.99; 3.25	47; 87; 54	n.k.	143; 265; 165	100; 185; 115	n.a.	n.a.	Performance data (estimated) are for 15E
30	59.5; 110; 68.5	0.85; 2.79	43; 80; 50	38.5; 71; 44.5	143; 265; 165	100; 185; 115	n.a.	n.a.	Performance data (estimated) are for 17E
32	47; 87; 54	0.58; 1.90	37; 68.5; 42.5	36.5; 68; 42	115; 213; 132	80; 148; 92	62; 115; 71.5	53.5; 99; 61.5	
26	47; 87; 54	0.78; 2.56	39; 72; 45	33; 61; 38	108; 200; 124	68.5; 127; 79	59.5; 110; 68	59.5; 110; 68	
43	56.5; 105; 65	0.60; 1.97	46; 85; 53	34; 63; 39.5	136; 252; 156	91; 169; 105	75.5; 140; 87	70; 130; 81	
42	62; 115; 71.5	0.66; 2.16	47; 87; 54	40.5; 74.5; 46.5	137; 254; 158	137; 254; 158	n.k.	n.k.	
30	54; 100; 62	0.90; 2.95	49; 90; 56	35.5; 65; 40.5	n.k.	n.k.	n.k.	n.k.	
35	46; 85; 53	0.64; 2.10	39; 72; 45	33; 61; 38	129; 240; 149	129; 240; 149	88; 163; 101	70.5; 130; 81	
26	42.5; 79; 49	0.79; 2.59	n.k.	31.5; 58; 36.5	102; 190; 118	70; 130; 81	70; 130; 81	59.5; 110; 68	
34	45.5; 84; 52	0.70; 2.30	41; 75; 47	32.5; 60; 37.5	135; 250; 155	78.5; 145; 90	75.5; 140; 87	65; 120; 74.5	
40	56.5; 105; 65	0.62; 2.03	42; 78; 48.5	37; 68; 42.5	135; 250; 155	86; 160; 99	81; 150; 93	59.5; 110; 68.5	Performance = without water ballast at 360 kg (793 lb) AUW
50.3	56; 103; 64	0.93; 3.05	52; 95; 59	43; 79; 49	151; 280; 174	108; 200; 124	75.5; 140; 87	62; 115; 71.5	Performance at 645 kg (1,422 lb) AUW
22.6	51; 95; 59	1.10; 3.61	43.5; 80; 50	42.5; 78; 48.5	121; 225; 140	121; 225; 140	n.a.	n.a.	
39.5	70; 130; 81	0.77; 2.53	50; 92; 57	46; 85; 53	135; 250; 155	135; 250; 155	81; 150; 93	67.5; 125; 78	
30	52; 96; 60	0.70; 2.30	42; 78; 48.5	32.5; 60; 37.5	118; 220; 136	81; 150; 93	81; 150; 93	64.5; 120; 74.5	
34	54; 100; 62	0.67; 2.20	43.5; 80; 50	39; 72; 45	124; 230; 143	89; 136; 84.5	n.k.	n.k.	Performance at 540 kg (1,190 lb) AUW
32	54; 100; 62	0.81; 2.66	42; 78; 48.5	*35; 64; 40	113; 210; 130	n.k.	n.k.	n.k.	*Flaps down
29	54; 100; 62	0.87; 2.85	43.5; 80; 50	*36; 66; 41	113; 210; 130	n.k.	n.k.	n.k.	*Flaps down
37	50; 93; 58	0.58; 1.90	42; 78; 48.5	38; 70; 43.5	121; 225; 140	108; 200; 124	102; 190; 118	70; 130; 81	
37.5	50; 93; 58	0.58; 1.90	42; 78; 48.5	37; 68; 42.5	121; 225; 140	n.k.	n.k.	n.k.	
37	59; 110; 68.5	0.65; 2.13	46.5; 86; 53.5	41.5; 76; 47.5	121; 225; 140	n.k.	n.k.	n.k.	
32	n.k.	0.70; 2.30	n.k.	43.4; 80.3; 50	n.k.	n.k.	n.k.	n.k.	
46	60.5; 112; 70	0.58; 1.90	47; 87; 54.5	40.5; 75; 47	121; 225; 140	n.k.	n.k.	n.k.	
51	57; 105; 65.5	0.40; 1.31	45.5; 84; 52.5	37; 68; 42.5	119; 220; 137	n.k.	n.k.	n.k.	
42	n.k.	0.55; 1.80	n.k.	42; 77; 48	n.k.	n.k.	n.k.	n.k.	
36.5	54; 100; 62	0.62; 2.03	44; 82; 51	38; 70; 43.5	124; 230; 143	n.k.	n.k.	n.k.	
48	59; 110; 68.5	0.50; 1.64	49; 90; 56	41.5; 76; 47.5	119; 220; 137	n.k.	n.k.	n.k.	
46	58; 107; 66.5	0.53; 1.74	47; 87; 54	40; 74; 46	124; 230; 143	n.k.	n.k.	n.k.	
41	61.5; 114; 71	0.64; 2.10	46.5; 86; 53.5	40.5; 75; 47	130; 240; 149	n.k.	n.k.	n.k.	
19	32; 60; 37	1.00; 3.28	n.k.	27; 50; 31.5	81; 150; 93	65; 120; 75	59; 110; 68.5	49; 90; 56	

Manufacturer and Model	Dimensions					Weights and Loading		
	Wing span: m; ft in	Wing aspect ratio	Wing area (gross): m²; sq ft	Length overall: m; ft in	Height over tail: m; ft in	Empty: kg; lb	Max T-O: kg; lb	Max wing loading: kg/m²; lb/sq ft
SWITZERLAND								
Aviafiber Canard-2 FL	13·50; 44 3½	14·0	13·00; 139·9	4·94; 16 2½	1·80; 5 11	58; 128	170; 375	12·5; 2·56
Farner HF Colibri 1 SL	17·50; 57 5	31·7	9·65; 103·9	7·20; 23 7½	1·45; 4 9	255; 562	362; 798	32·8; 6·71
Neukom S-4A Elfe 15	15·00; 49 2½	19·1	11·80; 127·0	7·10; 23 3½	1·50; 4 11	230; 507	350; 771	29·6; 6·06
Neukom Elfe 17	17·00; 55 9¼	21·8	13·20; 142·1	7·10; 23 3½	1·50; 4 11	255; 562	380; 837	28·8; 5·90
USSR								
Oshkinis BRO-11 Zile	7·28; 23 10½	5·05	10·50; 113·0	5·17; 16 11½	n.k.	58; 128	118; 260	11·24; 2·30
LAK-9 Lietuva	20·02; 65 8¼	26·8	14·99; 161·35	7·27; 23 10¼	1·53; 5 0¼	382; 842	670; 1,477	44·7; 9·15
UK								
Slingsby Vega	15·00; 49 2½	22·4	10·05; 108·2	6·72; 22 0½	1·50; 4 11	233; 515	508; 1,120	50·51; 10·35
Slingsby Sport Vega	15·00; 49 2½	22·4	10·05; 108·2	6·72; 22 0½	1·50; 4 11	233; 515	354; 780	35·2; 7·21
Slingsby Venture T.Mk 2	15·25; 50 0¼	13·8	18·20; 195·9	7·55; 24 9¼	1·85; 6 0¾	376·5; 830	612; 1,350	33·6; 6·88
Slingsby T.61G Falke	15·25; 50 0¼	13·8	18·20; 195·9	7·55; 24 9¼	1·85; 6 0¾	376·5; 830	612; 1,350	33·6; 6·88
Swales SD3-15T	15·00; 49 2½	23·7	9·48; 102·0	6·10; 20 0	1·30; 4 3	218; 480	331; 730	34·96; 7·16
USA								
Aero Tek Model V Zuni	15·00; 49 2½	22·2	10·13; 109·0	6·71; 22 0	1·30; 4 3	222; 490	431; 950	42·5; 8·71
AmEagle American Eaglet	10·97; 36 0	18·0	6·69; 72·0	4·88; 16 0	0·91; 3 0	72·5; 160	163; 360	24·41; 5·00
Bryan (Schreder) RS-15	15·00; 49 2½	21·4	10·50; 113·0	6·71; 22 0	1·17; 3 10	204; 450	431; 950	41·04; 8·41
Bryan (Schreder) HP-18	15·00; 49 2½	21·4	10·50; 113·0	7·06; 23 2	1·22; 4 0	213; 470	440; 970	41·87; 8·58
Bryan (Schreder) HP-19	15·00; 49 2½	21·4	10·50; 113·0	7·06; 23 2	1·22; 4 0	181; 400	453; 1,000	43·18; 8·85
DSK BJ-1b Duster	13·00; 42 7¾	17·4	9·72; 104·65	n.k.	n.k.	177; 390	281; 620	28·9; 5·92
Explorer PG-1 Aqua Glider	4·88; 16 0	5·0	8·73; 94·0	4·17; 13 8	1·52; 5 0	81; 180	181; 400	20·5; 4·20
Marske Monarch C	12·80; 42 0	9·5	17·19; 185·0	3·51; 11 6	2·39; 7 10	100; 220	204; 450	11·72; 2·40
Monnett Monerai S	10·97; 36 0	16·6	7·25; 78·0	5·97; 19 7	1·32; 4 4	100; 220	204; 450	28·11; 5·76
Ryson ST-100 Cloudster	17·58; 57 8	15·6	19·79; 213·0	7·78; 25 6·4	1·78; 5 10	550; 1,212	794; 1,750	37·82; 7·75
Schweizer SGS 1-26	12·19; 40 0	10·0	14·87; 160·0	6·57; 21 6½	2·21; 7 2½	195; 430	317; 700	21·34; 4·37
Schweizer SGS 2-33A	15·54; 51 0	11·85	20·39; 219·48	7·85; 25 9	2·83; 9 3½	272; 600	472; 1,040	23·14; 4·74
Schweizer SGS 1-35	15·00; 49 2½	23·29	9·64; 103·8	5·84; 19 2	1·35; 4 5	199; 440	422; 930	43·75; 8·96
Schweizer SGS 1-36	14·07; 46 2	15·15	13·07; 140·7	6·25; 20 6	1·42; 4 7¾	204; 450	322; 710	24·64; 5·05
Volpar-Spencer Drag-N-Fly	5·79; 19 0	5·57	11·24; 121·0	4·85; 15 11	1·75; 5 9	113; 250	204; 450	18·15; 3·72
YUGOSLAVIA								
Elan (Glaser-Dirks) DG-100/DG-100G Elan	15·00; 49 2½	20·5	11·00; 118·4	7·00; 22 11¾	1·40; 4 7	*230; 507	418; 921	38·0; 7·78
Elan (Glaser-Dirks) DG-100 Club Elan	15·00; 49 2½	20·5	11·00; 118·4	7·00; 22 11¾	1·40; 4 7	*225; 496	385; 848	35·0; 7·17
MF VUK-T	15·00; 49 2½	18·75	12·00; 129·2	6·50; 21 4	1·30; 4 3¼	245; 540	355; 783	29·7; 6·08
VTC (Schempp-Hirth) Cirrus	17·74; 58 2½	24·98	12·60; 135·6	7·20; 23 7¼	1·56; 5 1½	260; 573	400; 882	31·7; 6·49
VTC (Schempp-Hirth) Standard Cirrus 75	15·00; 49 2½	22·5	10·00; 107·6	6·41; 21 8½	1·32; 4 4¾	215; 474	330; 727	33·0; 6·76

n.k. = not known; n.a. = not applicable

					Performance (at max T-O weight except where indicated)				
Best glide ratio	at (speed): knots; km/h; mph	Min sinking speed: m (ft)/s	at (speed): knots; km/h; mph	Stalling speed: knots; km/h; mph	Max speed (smooth air): knots; km/h; mph	Max speed (rough air): knots; km/h; mph	Max aero-tow speed: knots; km/h; mph	Max winch-launching speed: knots; km/h; mph	Remarks
31	32; 60; 37	0·50; 1·64	27; 50; 31	21; 38; 24	54; 100; 62	54; 100; 62	n.a.	n.a.	
41-43	54·5; 101; 63	0·55; 1·80	42; 77; 48	37·6; 69·6; 43·3	119; 220; 137	97; 180; 112	n.a.	n.a.	
37·5	49; 90; 56	0·60; 1·97	38; 70; 43·5	35·5; 65; 40·5	113; 210; 130	113; 210; 130	75·5; 140; 87	54; 100; 62	
40·5	49; 90; 56	0·56; 1·84	40·5; 75; 46·5	35·5; 65; 40·5	113; 210; 130	113; 210; 130	75·5; 140; 87	54; 100; 62	
n.k.	n.k.	1·00; 3·28	n.k.	21·5; 30; 19	n.k.	n.k.	n.k.	n.k.	
48	55·5; 103; 64	0·51; 1·67	40; 74; 46	.35; 64; 40	n.k.	113; 210; 130	75·5; 140; 87	n.k.	
42	62; 115; 71	0·67; 2·21	44; 82; 51 (EAS)	41; 76·5; 47·5	135; 250; 155	105; 195; 121	80; 148; 92	70; 129; 80	
39	50; 93; 58	0·70; 2·30	44; 82; 51 (EAS)	37; 69; 43	135; 250; 155	105; 195; 121	100; 185; 115	70; 129; 80	
20·5	50·5; 93·5; 58	1·00; 3·30	43·5; 80·5; 50	37; 69; 43	100; 185; 115	80; 148; 92	n.a.	n.a.	
21	47; 87; 54	n.k.	n.k.	37; 69; 43	100; 185; 115	79; 146; 91	n.a.	n.a.	
36	48; 88·5; 55	0·73; 2·40	42; 78; 48·5	34; 63·5; 39·5	109; 201; 125	86; 159; 99	78; 145; 90	65; 121; 75	
n.k.	n.k.	0·51; 1·67	45; 84; 52	36·5; 68; 42	156; 290; 180	n.k.	n.k.	n.k.	
27	45; 84; 52	0·76; 2·50	35; 64·5; 40	33; 61·5; 38	100; 185; 115	69·5; 129; 80	69·5; 129; 80	n.a.	
38	59; 109; 68	*0·64; 2·10	43·5; 80; 50	**40; 74; 46	130; 241; 150	104; 193; 120	104; 193; 120	78; 145; 90	*At 284 kg (626 lb) AUW; **at 335 kg (740 lb) AUW
40	59; 109; 68	*0·52; 1·70	39; 73; 45	**35; 64·5; 40	130; 241; 150	104; 193; 120	104; 193; 120	78; 145; 90	*At 275 kg (606 lb) AUW; **at 326 kg (720 lb) AUW
42	n.k.	*0·46; 1·50	35; 64·5; 40	*30·5; 56·5; 35	130; 241; 150	104; 193; 120	104; 193; 120	78; 145; 90	*At 266 kg (586 lb) AUW
n.k.	n.k.	n.k.	n.k.	n.k.	n.k.	n.k.	n.k.	n.k.	
6·5	39; 72·5; 45	n.a.	n.a.	*30·5; 56·5; 35	56·5; 105; 65	56·5; 105; 65	56·5; 105; 65	56·5; 105; 65	*At 149 kg (330 lb) AUW
19	35; 64; 40	0·82; 2·70	26; 48·5; 30	21; 39; 24	61; 113; 70	43·5; 80; 50	43·5; 80; 50	43·5; 80; 50	
30	52; 97; 60	0·79; 2·60	48; 88·5; 55	33; 61·5; 38	104; 193; 120	78; 145; 90	78; 145; 90	n.k.	
28	52; 97; 60	0·90; 2·95	47; 87; 54	36·5; 68; 42	139; 258; 160	139; 258; 160	n.a.	n.a.	
23	46; 85; 53	0·79; 2·60	35; 64·5; 40	29; 54; 33	99; 183; 114	99; 183; 114	99; 183; 114	55; 101; 63	
22·25	45; 84; 52	0·91; 3·00	33; 61; 38	30·5; 57; 35	85; 158; 98	85; 158; 98	85; 158; 98	60; 111; 69	
39	46; 85; 53	0·61; 2·00	43; 79; 49	28; 51·5; 32	121; 223; 139	121; 223; 139	121; 223; 139	n.a.	
31	49; 92; 57	0·68; 2·25	40; 74; 46	31; 58; 36	107; 198; 123	107; 198; 123	107; 198; 123	69; 127; 79	
n.k.	n.k.	n.k.	n.k.	n.k.	65; 120; 75	n.k.	n.k.	*35; 65; 40	*Required speed for T-O
39	56·5; 105; 65	0·59; 1·94	40; 74; 46	32·5; 60; 37·5	140; 260; 161	140; 260; 161	89; 165; 102·5	70; 130; 80·5	*With normal tailplane; 235 kg (518 lb) with all-moving tailplane
36	49; 90; 56	0·60; 1·97	40; 74; 46	32·5; 60; 37·5	n.k.	n.k.	n.k.	n.k.	*With normal tailplane; 230 kg (507 lb) with all-moving tailplane
37·5	51; 95; 59	0·65; 2·13	42; 78; 48·5	32; 59; 37	129; 240; 149	81; 150; 93	67·5; 125; 78	59; 110; 68	
44	46; 85; 53	0·50; 1·64	39; 73; 45	33·5; 62; 39	119; 220; 137	119; 220; 137	76; 140; 87	59; 110; 68	
38·5	49; 90; 56	0·60; 1·97	39·5; 75; 47	33·5; 62; 39	119; 220; 137	119; 220; 137	81; 150; 93	65; 120; 75	

DATA: MOTOR GLIDERS (POWER ON)

Manufacturer and Model	Wing span: m; ft in	Wing aspect ratio	Wing area (gross): m²; sq ft	Length overall: m; ft in	Height over tail: m; ft in	Empty: kg; lb	Max T-O: kg; lb	Max power loading: kg/kW; lb/hp
AUSTRIA								
Brditschka HB-21	16·24; 53 3½	13·9	18·98; 204·3	8·10; 26 7	2·60; 8 6¼	505; 1,113	710; 1,565	15·80; 26·00
FINLAND								
Alanne Motorlerche	13·00; 42 7¾	10·3	16·34; 175·9	6·86; 22 6	1·58; 5 2¼	288; 635	400; 882	12·07; 19·84
Eiri PIK-20E	15·00; 49 2½	22·5	10·00; 107·6	6·53; 21 5	1·44; 4 8¾	300; 661	470; 1,036	14·62; 24·03
FRANCE								
Calvel Frelon	10·40; 34 1½	13·5	7·80; 83·96	5·40; 17 8½	1·50; 4 11	135; 297	220; 485	10·93; 17·96
Fournier RF-9	17·00; 55 9½	16·1	18·00; 193·75	7·86; 25 9½	1·93; 6 4	520; 1,146	750; 1,653	14·79; 24·31
GERMANY (FEDERAL REPUBLIC)								
Akaflieg Darmstadt D-39	15·00; 49 2½	20·5	11·00; 118·4	7·15; 23 5½	†1·02; 3 4¼	370; 816	470; 1,036	9·20; 15·12
Akaflieg Karlsruhe AK 2	20·00; 65 7½	27·6	14·50; 156·1	7·60; 24 11¼	1·67; 5 5¾	n.k.	580; 1,278	14·14; 23·23
Grob G 109	15·00; 49 2½	11·8	19·10; 205·6	7·80; 25 7	1·80; 5 10¾	500; 1,102	750; 1,653	12·71; 20·66
Pflumm and Richter Faltente	8·80; 28 10½	5·4	14·26; 153·5	4·05; 13 3½	n.k.	49·5; 109	134·5; 296·5	18·03; 29·65
Scheibe SF-25C and C-S Falke '80	15·25; 50 0¼	12·8	18·20; 195·9	7·55; 24 9¼	1·85; 6 0¾	375; 826	610; 1,345	12·58; 20·68
Scheibe SF-25K Falke '80	14·60; 47 10¾	12·5	17·10; 184·1	7·55; 24 9¼	1·85; 6 0¾	*410; 904	610; 1,345	12·58; 20·68
Scheibe SF-25E Super-Falke	18·00; 59 0¾	17·8	18·20; 195·9	7·50; 24 7¼	1·85; 6 0¾	440; 970	650; 1,433	13·41; 22·04
Scheibe SF-28A Tandem-Falke	16·30; 53 5¾	14·4	18·50; 199·1	8·10; 26 7	1·55; 5 1	410; 904	610; 1,345	12·58; 20·68
Valentin Taifun 15	15·00; 49 2½	13·8	16·35; 176·0	7·785; 25 6½	2·16; 7 1	480; 1,058	725; 1,598	12·1; 19·9
Valentin Taifun 17	17·00; 55 9¼	16·4	17·60; 189·4	7·785; 25 6½	2·16; 7 1	480; 1,058	725; 1,598	12·1; 19·9
ITALY								
Caproni Vizzola Calif A-21SJ	20·38; 66 10¼	25·65	16·19; 174·3	7·737; 25 4½	1·615; 5 3½	528; 1,164	808; 1,781	915 kg/kN; 8·97 lb/lb st
JAPAN								
Nippi NP-100A Albatross (first prototype)	18·00; 59 0¾	18·0	18·00; 193·75	8·00; 26 3	2·02; 6 7½	500; 1,102	680; 1,499	13·4; 22·0
POLAND								
SZD-45A Ogar	17·53; 57 6¼	16·2	19·10; 205·6	7·95; 26 1	1·72; 5 7¾	473; 1,042	700; 1,543	13·8; 22·7
ROMANIA								
IS-28M1	18·00; 59 0¾	17·1	18·95; 204·0	7·96; 26 1½	1·90; 6 2¾	485; 1,069	730; 1,609	14·4; 23·6
IS-28M2	17·00; 55 9¼	15·8	18·24; 196·3	7·50; 24 7¼	2·15; 7 0¾	495; 1,091	745; 1,642	14·7; 24·1
IS-29DM	15·00; 49 2½	22·1	10·20; 109·8	7·00; 22 11½	1·75; 5 9	310; 683	440; 970	15·1; 24·9
IS-29EM	20·00; 65 7½	27·2	14·68; 158·0	7·00; 22 11½	1·75; 5 9	400; 882	530; 1,168	18·2; 29·9
SWITZERLAND								
EFF Prometheus 12	12·63; 41 5¼	12·1	13·21; 142·2	8·30; 27 2¾	1·70; 5 7	*668/688; 1,472/1,516	n.k.	n.k.
EFF Prometheus 19	19·40; 63 7¾	21·3	17·64; 189·9	8·30; 27 2¾	1·70; 5 7	735; 1,620	999; 2,202	567·6 kg/kN; 5·56 lb/lb st
Farner HF Colibri 1 SL	17·50; 57 5	31·7	9·65; 103·9	7·20; 23 7½	1·45; 4 9	255; 562	362; 798	17·8; 29·3
UK								
Slingsby Venture T.Mk 2	15·25; 50 0¼	13·8	18·20; 195·9	7·55; 24 9¼	1·85; 6 0¾	376·5; 830	612; 1,350	18·3; 30·0
Slingsby T.61G Falke	15·25; 50 0¼	13·8	18·20; 195·9	7·55; 24 9¼	1·85; 6 0¾	376·5; 830	612; 1,350	13·69; 22·5
USA								
Ryson ST-100 Cloudster	17·58; 57 8	15·6	19·79; 213·0	7·78; 25 6·4	1·78; 5 10	550; 1,212	794; 1,750	10·0; 16·5
YUGOSLAVIA								
Jastreb SOLE-77	16·40; 53 9¾	n.k.	n.k.	7·67; 25 2	n.k.	500; 1,102	n.k.	n.k.

n.k. = not known

Performance at max T-O weight (powered)

Max cruising speed: knots; km/h; mph	Econ cruising speed: knots; km/h; mph	Stalling speed: knots; km/h; mph	Max rate of climb at S/L: m; ft/min	Service ceiling: m; ft	T-O run: m; ft	Landing run: m; ft	Range with max fuel: nm; km; miles	Remarks
86; 160; 99	70·5; 130; 81	39·5; 75; 47	198; 650	6,300; 20,675	100; 330	80; 262	431; 800; 497	
65; 120; 75	54; 100; 62	24·5; 45; 28	150; 492	n.k.	n.k.	n.k.	162; 300; 186	
73; 135; 84	73; 135; 84	40·5; 75; 47	162; 531	5,200; 17,050	*500; 1,640	300; 985	156; 290; 180	*To 15 m (50 ft)
*43; 80; 50	n.k.	*24·5; 45; 28	n.k.	n.k.	n.k.	n.k.	n.k.	*Estimated
86; 160; 112	n.k.	35·5; 65; 40·5	180; 590	6,000; 19,685	n.k.	n.k.	n.k.	
*97; 180; 112	n.k.	43·5; 80; 50	240; 787	n.k.	150; 492	200; 656	324; 600; 373	†Height over fuselage *Max level speed
n.k.	n.k.	n.k.	n.k.	n.k.	n.k.	n.k.	n.k.	
108; 200; 124	n.k.	40·5; 75; 47	156; 512	n.k.	200; 656	n.k.	*540; 1,000; 621	*Approx
*30; 55; 34	24; 45; 28	n.k.	30; 98	n.k.	n.k.	n.k.	n.k.	Wing loading 9·5 kg/m² (1·95 lb/sq ft) *Max level speed
86; 160; 99	70·5; 130; 81	35·5; 65; 40·5	138; 453	5,000; 16,400	180; 590	100; 328	404; 750; 466	
86; 160; 99	70·5; 130; 81	35·5; 65; 40·5	138; 453	5,000; 16,400	*180; 590	100; 328	*378; 700; 435	*Approx
*97; 180; 112	81; 150; 93	37; 68; 42·5	150; 492	5,000; 16,400	150-200; 490-655	100; 328	323-600; 372	*Max level speed
*97; 180; 112	81; 150; 93	33·5; 62; 39	132; 435	5,000; 16,400	150-200; 490-655	150; 492	280; 520; 323	*Max level speed
114; 212; 132	102; 190; 118	n.k.	162; 531	n.k.	n.k.	n.k.	566; 1,050; 652	Performance data (estimated) are for Taifun 15E
112; 208; 129	102; 190; 118	38·5; 71; 44	174; 571	n.k.	n.k.	n.k.	486; 900; 559	Performance data (estimated) are for Taifun 17E
124; 230; 143	102·5; 190; 118	34; 63; 39·5	240; 787	9,000; 29,525	300; 985	200; 656	189; 350; 217	Max wing loading 49·9 kg/m² (10·22 lb/sq ft)
65; 120; 74	48·5; 90; 56	35·5; 65; 40·5	120; 394	n.k.	365; 1,200	*400; 1,312	108; 200; 124	*From 15 m (50 ft)
*97·5; 180; 112	75·5; 140; 87	37; 68; 42·5	159; 522	3,100; 10,175	200; 656	155; 508	296; 550; 341	*Max level speed
95; 176; 109	86; 159; 99	38; 70; 44	192; 630	5,500; 18,050	180; 590	90; 295	242; 450; 280	
92; 170; 106	81; 150; 93	35·5; 65; 40·5	186; 610	5,000; 16,400	240; 788	90; 295	242; 450; 280	
92; 170; 106	n.k.	43·4; 80·3; 50	180; 590	4,500; 14,765	*370; 1,215	n.k.	270; 500; 310	*To 15 m (50 ft)
86; 160; 99	n.k.	42; 77; 48	150; 492	4,500; 14,765	*400; 1,315	n.k.	270; 500; 310	*To 15 m (50 ft)
n.k.	n.k.	n.k.	366+; 1,200+	n.k.	450; 1,476	n.k.	n.k.	*Without/with tip-tanks
*140; 260; 161	n.k.	n.k.	244+; 800+	n.k.	450; 1,476	n.k.	n.k.	*Max attained speed (88% power)
65; 120; 75	51; 95; 59	37; 68; 42·5	240; 787	n.k.	120; 394	n.k.	n.k.	
76; 140; 87	65; 121; 75	37·5; 69·5; 43	125; 410	4,267; 14,000	198; 650	100; 330	217; 402; 250	
90; 167; 104	75; 139; 86	36; 67; 41·5	140; 460	5,000; 16,400	*180; 590	100; 330	217; 402; 250	*To 15 m (50 ft)
130; 241; 150	*69; 129; 80	37·5; 69·5; 43	256; 840	7,315; 24,000	290; 950	244; 800	595; 1,104; 686	*At 26% power
92; 170; 106	n.k.	39; 72; 45	186; 610	4,500; 14,760	*350; 1,148	n.k.	378; 700; 435	*To 15 m (50 ft)

HANG GLIDERS

CIVL
COMMISSION INTERNATIONALE DE VOL LIBRE

c/o Fédération Aéronautique Internationale, 6 rue Galilée, 75782 Paris, Cédex 16, France

PRESIDENT: Erwin Kjellerup (Sweden)
HONORARY PRESIDENTS:
Daniel F. Poynter (USA)
Mrs Ann Welch (UK)
VICE-PRESIDENTS:
Tom Hudson (Ireland)
Stein Arne Fossum (Norway)
SECRETARY: Tom Hudson

INTERNATIONAL REPRESENTATIVES:
Austria: Sepp Himberger, A-6345 Kössen
Belgium: Dimitri Caloussis, Aéro-Club Royal de Belgique, 1 rue Montoyer, 1040 Brussels
Denmark: Palle J. Christensen (address not known)
France: René Coulon, 3 rue Ampère, 94200 Ivry-sur-Seine; alternate: Maurice Bourgueil (address not known)
Germany (Federal Republic): Klaus Tänzler, Agnesstrasse 48, 8000 München 40
Hungary: M. Ordody, 11 Szilagyi E.f. 13-15, 1024 Budapest
Ireland: Tom Hudson, 60 Hillcourt Road, Glenageary, Co Dublin

Italy: Heinz Kostner, 39033 Coruara
Japan: Asahi Miyahara, 2-27, Uehara Shibuya-ku, Tokyo 151
Korea (Republic): Kim Suk Whan (address not known)
Luxembourg: Jean Willems, 15 rue de la Sûre, Echternach, 62 Rabatt
Mexico: Miguel G. Aldrete (address not known); alternate: Alfonso Espinoza (address not known)
Netherlands: Floor C. G. Gremmen, G. Doustraat 7, Assen
Norway: Stein Arne Fossum, Brendöyveien 21, 6900 Florö; alternate: John P. Coldwell, 3640 Skollenborst
Poland: Dr Jerzy Wolf, Instytut Lotnictwa, Al. Krakowska 110/114, 02-256 Warsaw
South Africa: Martin van der Merwe (address not known)
Spain: Roman Camps, Beethoven 12, Barcelona 6; alternate: Eugenio M. Rubio (address not known)
Sweden: Hans Saevenberg (address not known)
USSR: E. Elizarov, FAS of the USSR, PO Box 395, Moscow D-362
UK: R. J. Spooner, Clifton House, Bath Road, Cowes, Isle of Wight; alternate: Roy D. Hill, 68 Besselsleigh Road, Abingdon, Oxford
USA: Harry W. Robb, 2909 Gulf to Bay 0203, Clearwater, Florida 33515; alternate: Richard Heckman, 3401 Lookout Drive, Huntsville, Alabama 35801

The CIVL held its first meeting in June 1975. One of its first actions was to define a hang glider as "a heavier-than-air, fixed-wing (not rotating) glider, capable of being carried, foot-launched and landed solely by the energy and use of the pilot's legs". It has since defined three Competition classes of hang glider. Other tasks of the commission include safety and pilot ratings.

The listing which follows, while not complete, includes data for all hang gliders of which details had been received at the time this edition closed for press; however, many manufacturers have failed to supply information for the present edition.

Also included, for the first time this year, are some of the new and growing family of 'featherweight' and 'micro-light' aircraft which, it is felt, do not strictly belong in the Homebuilt Aircraft section. Most of these aircraft are more or less standard hang gliders, fitted with a power plant and wheeled landing gear, and at present the FAA regards them as powered hang gliders provided the capability for foot launch and landing is retained.

Types retained in the Homebuilt Aircraft section this year include the following:
Australia: **Kimberley Sky-Rider**
USA: **Birdman TL-1A**
(Hill) Hummer
Mitchell Wing B-10 and U-2
Striplin FLAC
UFM Solar Riser
Weedhopper JC-24

ARGENTINA
LADAS (LIGA ARGENTINA DE AERODESLIZA-DORES SUPERLIVIANOS)

San Martin 359, 5539 Las Heras, Mendoza
PRESIDENT: Johan F. Byttebier

Sr Byttebier was responsible for a series of hang gliders based on the US Seagull III; reference to these can be found in the 1979-80 and earlier editions of *Jane's*.

Current activities concern the higher-performance Johan SH1, based on the Seagull Seahawk, of which LADAS had produced nine and sold seven by the end of 1979. This aircraft set an Argentinian soaring record of 1 h 30 min 2 s in 1979. Sr Byttebier has also test-flown a larger Johan SH2 version, but this was not yet in production in early 1980.

Johan SH1. Similar to Seagull Seahawk (which see), with same sail and leading-edge characteristics, but utilising an entirely new keel and A-frame. Suitable for private and competition flying (prone pilot position). Airframe of 6061-T6 aluminium alloy and duralumin, with single-thickness Dacron sail and stainless steel cables. Kingpost standard. Features include ribs, pre-formed battens and single deflexers. Airframe stressed to $+3/-2g$. For other details see table.

In addition, LADAS markets a powered sailwing-type hang glider known as the **Chimango**. This weighs 140 kg (308 lb) including power plant, fuel and tricycle landing gear; no other details were received for publication.

LADAS Johan SH1

AUSTRALIA
FREE FLIGHT SYSTEMS

8/3 First Avenue, Ascot Park, South Australia 5043
For 1978 details see 1979-80 *Jane's*; no 1979 or 1980 details received.

MOYES DELTA GLIDERS PTY LTD

173 Bronte Road, Waverley, Sydney, NSW 2024

Manufacturer of the Stinger range, of which the following models were available in 1980. By January 1980, some 2,000 Stinger types had been sold. Maxi Stingers won 22 of the 30 international competitions held in 1979.

Maxi Stinger Mark III. Class 2 competition model, for expert pilots only. Aluminium alloy airframe, with Dacron sail and vinyl-coated stainless steel cables. Kingpost standard. Features include floating keel pocket, keel pocket battens, folding crossbar, cambered sail, deflexers, and provisions for tow launch and passenger-carrying. Airframe stressed to $+7/-4g$.
Maxi Stinger Mark IV. Similar to Mk III, but with reduced sail area, shorter keel and higher aspect ratio.
Maxi Stinger SP. Similar to Maxi Mark III, but scaled down 5% for lighter-weight pilots; folding crossbar.
Mega Stinger II. Competition model for advanced pilots only. Features include feathered radial tip, pre-formed keel pocket battens, deep fin floating keel pocket, folding crossbar, and double-thickness covering on 40% of sail area.
Redtail Stinger. In production since 1978. Basic Class 1 model, with single-batten roached tip and moderate speed range; easy to fly and suitable for learner pilots and experts.
Stingray. Low-speed model, suitable for small ridge and sand-dune soaring, and for learner pilots. No deflexers. Produced in two sizes.

For other details see table.

Moyes Maxi Stinger

WINTON AIRCRAFT

D4/1 Campbell Parade, Manly Vale, Sydney, NSW 2093
This company markets two single-seat 'micro-light' aircraft, the Grasshopper and the Cricket, both designed by Mr Col Winton.

WINTON GRASSHOPPER

AIRFRAME: Cantilever shoulder-wing monoplane, built mainly of aluminium alloy tube and glassfibre. Wing leading-edges, wingtips and ailerons are of glassfibre; remainder of wings, and all tail surfaces, are Dacron-covered. Wings detachable for transportation and stowage. Pod-shaped fuselage nacelle, to accommodate pilot and to support power plant, with slender boom to carry tail unit. Three-axis control by ailerons, elevators and rudder. Non-retractable tricycle-type sprung landing-gear. Cockpit equipped with upholstered seat and windscreen.
POWER PLANT: One 17 kW (23 hp) 432 cc two-cylinder two-stroke engine, mounted on top of fuselage pod aft of cockpit and driving a two-blade pusher propeller.
DIMENSIONS:
Wing span   approx 8·23 m (27 ft 0 in)
WEIGHT:
Weight empty   115 kg (253 lb)
PERFORMANCE:
Max level speed   65 knots (120 km/h; 74 mph)

WINTON CRICKET

AIRFRAME: Extremely simple minimum airframe comprising constant-chord 'plank' wings and a keel-type boom to support the power plant and a constant-chord cruciform fin/rudder/tailplane/elevator assembly. Lower (dependent) part of fin is strut-braced to 'fuselage' boom, as are the pilot's seat and tricycle sprung landing gear forward, below the wings. Construction is of aluminium alloy, with Dacron-covered glassfibre wings and tail surfaces built in same way as those of Grasshopper. Three-axis control by ailerons, elevators and rudder.
POWER PLANT: Same engine as in Grasshopper, but mounted at front of aircraft and driving a tractor propeller.
DIMENSIONS:
No details received
WEIGHT:
Weight empty   100 kg (220 lb)
PERFORMANCE:
Max level speed   54 knots (100 km/h; 62 mph)

CANADA
ADVENTURE FLIGHT CENTRES INC

Box 172, Station A, Winnipeg, Manitoba R3K 2A1

AFC SKYSEEKER

The Skyseeker is a powered version of the US Eipper-Formance/Lovejoy Quicksilver (which see). AFC imports Quicksilvers from the USA, and adds a power plant package (7·5 kW; 10 hp Chrysler engine, reduction gear, and 6·5 litre; 1·4 Imp gallon fuel tank) and landing gear.
WEIGHTS:
Weight empty, incl power package and landing gear
                                      54 kg (120 lb)
Max T-O weight   158 kg (350 lb)
PERFORMANCE:
Best glide ratio   6
Min sinking speed, power off   67 m (220 ft)/min
Max level speed approx 39 knots (72 km/h; 45 mph)
Cruising speed 22-26 knots (40-48 km/h; 25-30 mph)
T-O speed   15 knots (27·5 km/h; 17 mph)
Stalling speed   14 knots (26 km/h; 16 mph)
Endurance   1 h 15 min

BIRDMAN ENTERPRISES LTD
8027 Argyll Road, Edmonton, Alberta T6C 4A9

Producer in 1980 of the **Falcon I and II, MJ-5, MJ-6 and XC** hang gliders (see table for details). All airframes are of aluminium alloy, with vinyl-coated stainless steel cables, single-thickness Dacron sail, and a kingpost as standard. All are stressed to a *g* limit of +6·5. Both Falcon models are suitable for training; MJ-5, MJ-6 and XC are suitable for competition flying. Falcons have floating keel pocket, single deflexers and ribs, but no fin; and can be tow-launched. The two MJ models have a stabilising fin, floating keel pocket and ribs, but no deflexers; MJ-5 can be tow-launched. The XC has a fin, floating keel pocket, triple deflexers and ribs.

Birdman also markets power plant packs suitable for most high-performance hang gliders.

Birdman MJ-5 with engine

Birdman MJ-6

HIGH PERSPECTIVE INC
RR No. 2, Claremont, Ontario L0H 1E0

By early 1979, High Perspective had sold 50 examples of its **HP IV** Class 2 glider. Suitable for training or private flying, this has an aluminium alloy airframe with vinyl-coated stainless steel cables and a single-thickness Dacron sail. A kingpost is standard; other features include a floating keel pocket, pre-formed battens and double deflexers; and the glider can be tow-launched. Details in the table are for the medium-sized model: smaller and larger models are available, for pilot weights of 32-54·5 kg (70-120 lb) and 72·5-100 kg (160-220 lb) respectively.

High Perspective's main activities in 1979 were training, and the manufacture of safety landing wheels, floats, tow frames and winches. No information for 1980 was received.

High Perspective HP IV

RECREATIONAL FLIGHT CENTRES INC
RR 2, Lucknow, Ontario N0G 2H0

RFC SKYRIDER
The Skyrider is a modified, powered version of the US Eipper-Formance/Lovejoy Quicksilver (which see). A choice of power plants includes a 7·5 kW (10 hp) Chrysler, 8·2 kW (11 hp) McCulloch go-kart engine, and 11·2 kW (15 hp) Komet go-kart engine. Fuel tank capacity is 6·5 litres (1·4 Imp gallons).

WEIGHTS:
Weight empty, incl power package and landing gear
54 kg (120 lb)
Max T-O weight   170 kg (375 lb)
PERFORMANCE:
Best glide ratio   6
Min sinking speed, power off   67 m (220 ft)/min
Max level speed   43 knots (80 km/h; 50 mph)
Cruising speed 26-30 knots (48-56 km/h; 30-35 mph)
T-O speed   15 knots (27·5 km/h; 17 mph)
Stalling speed   14 knots (26 km/h; 16 mph)

ULTRAFLIGHT INC
6 George Street, Port Colborne, Ontario L3K 3S1

ULTRAFLIGHT LAZAIR
The Lazair twin-engined rigid-wing hang glider was designed by Mr Dale Kramer in 1977-78, making its first flight in November 1978. It is available in kit form for amateur construction.
AIRFRAME: Braced high-wing monoplane, with inverted-V tail unit. Wings have an aluminium tube and foam plastics D-section leading-edge, with foam plastics ribs. Wings and tail surfaces are Mylar- or Dacron-covered. Non-retractable tricycle landing gear. Airframe stressed to +4/−2g at gross weight of 140 kg (310 lb).
POWER PLANT: Two 4 kW (5·5 hp) 100 cc Pioneer chain-saw engines, each driving a two-blade carbonfibre tractor propeller.
DIMENSIONS:
Wing span   11·07 m (36 ft 4 in)
Wing chord at root   1·52 m (5 ft 0 in)
Wing chord at tip   0·91 m (3 ft 0 in)
Wing area, gross   13·19 m² (142·0 sq ft)
Wing aspect ratio   9·3
Length overall   4·27 m (14 ft 0 in)
Height overall   1·93 m (6 ft 4 in)
WEIGHTS AND LOADING:
Weight empty   61 kg (135 lb)
Max T-O weight   158 kg (350 lb)
Max wing loading   12·2 kg/m² (2·5 lb/sq ft)
PERFORMANCE:
Best glide ratio   13
Min sinking speed   76 m (250 ft)/min
Never-exceed speed   47 knots (88 km/h; 55 mph)
Cruising speed   30 knots (56 km/h; 35 mph)
Manoeuvring speed   26 knots (48 km/h; 30 mph)
Stalling speed (AUW of 140 kg; 310 lb)
15 knots (27·5 km/h; 17 mph)
Max rate of climb at S/L:
at 140 kg (310 lb) AUW   76 m (250 ft)/min
at max T-O weight   61 m (200 ft)/min
T-O run   46 m (150 ft)
Landing run   30 m (100 ft)
Range   35 nm (64 km; 40 miles)

Ultraflight Lazair (*Howard Levy*)

FRANCE
DAHU PLANE (ÉTABLISSEMENTS NOIN AÉRONAUTIQUE)
Le Logis-Neuf, RN85 Châteauvieux, 05130-Tallard

Models in production in 1979 were as follows:
Baby 18. For learner pilots. Airframe of duralumin, with anodised stainless steel cables and Dacron sail.
Nimbus. High-performance competition glider, for expert pilots; stressed to +5/−2g. Airframe materials as for Baby. Kingpost standard; other features include rudder, floating keel pocket, pre-formed battens, triple deflexers, and double-thickness sail over 85% of area.

Dahu Plane Nimbus

Stratus IV. Class 1 glider, flown in several 1978 competitions in France. Airframe materials similar to Nimbus. Double-thickness sail forward of kingposts; shallow stabilising fin.

For other details see table. No 1980 information received.

LA MOUETTE
1 rue de la Petite Fin, 21121 Fontaine les Dijon

Manufacturer of the **Atlas 14 and 16** (25 and 90 sold respectively by early 1979); **Lotus 15 and 17** (sales 5 and 5); and **Mouette 15, 17, 19 and 23B** (sales 25, 240, 780 and 90). All continued to be available in 1980.

The two Atlas models are suitable for competition flying; the Lotus 15 and all four Mouettes are suitable for training. All have duralumin frames (with kingpost as standard), vinyl-coated stainless steel cables, and Dacron sails (double thickness on both Atlas, single on Lotus and Mouette models); all are stressed to +6/−4g. All eight models have a floating keel pocket; Lotus and Mouette have ribs, Atlas models have pre-formed battens. For other details see table.

La Mouette Atlas

SOFREC 'VÉLIPLANE' (Société Française de Représentation et d'Échanges Commerciaux)
16 rue Georges-Appay, 92150 Surèsnes

The well-known **Strato** continued in production (two models) in 1979, together with the more recent **Starga** (three models). Both types are suitable for training and competition flying; the Stargas are stressed to +6/−4g, Strato models to +5/−4g. Airframes are of duralumin, with vinyl-coated anodised stainless steel cables and single Dacron sail; kingpost standard on all models. All are fitted with fin, pre-formed battens and tips; Starga models have a floating keel pocket. For other details see table; no information for 1980 was received.

Véliplane Starga

GERMANY
(Federal Republic)
WOLF HIRTH GmbH
7312 Kirchheim/Teck-Nabern

Producer of the **W-17 Dracula** series, of which 22 had been built and 17 sold by early 1979. Current model (from mid-1978) was the **W-17B** (see table for details); the 1980 **W-17C** is similar except for an automatically operated rudder. Special features claimed are very quick assembly (one cable connection only), and curve steering with external slip (opposite control movements compared with conventional Rogallos). Marketed jointly with Peraves AG für Flugentwicklungen, Oberfeldstrasse 44A, CH-8408 Winterthur, Switzerland.

Suitable for training and competition flying, Dracula does not fit precisely into any FAI-defined class. It is fitted with a fin, rudder and damping elevator, and has an aluminium alloy frame, stainless steel cables and Dacron sail. The airframe is stressed to +6/−3g.

A motorised version, designated W-17CM, has been tested.

Hirth W-17B Dracula B

ENTWICKLUNG UND ERPROBUNG VON LEICHTFLUGZEUGEN
Fichtenstrasse 7, 8077 Reichertshofen

ULF-1

The ULF-1 (Ultra Leicht Flugzeug) is a one-man rigid-wing high-wing monoplane, designed by Dieter Reich and built by Heiner Neumann. First flight was made in November 1977, and certification flying was completed in the late Summer of 1979. Plans (but not kits or materials) are available to amateur constructors, and 15 were being built by mid-1979.

AIRFRAME: Cantilever high-wing monoplane. Wings have Wortmann FX-63-137 section, and comprise a single wooden (spruce) spar, plywood nose section, plywood/balsa ribs and fabric covering. Thickness/chord ratio 18% at root, 15% at tip. Fuselage is a fabric-covered wooden frame, of triangular cross-section aft of cockpit. Cantilever tail unit, of similar construction to wings. Single sliding seat for pilot, who retracts his legs after foot-launch to operate rudder pedals. Landing is made on a nose-skid and glassfibre tube (fishing rod) tailskid. Three-axis aerodynamic control by ailerons, one-piece elevator and rudder.

DIMENSIONS:
Wing span	10·40 m (34 ft 1½ in)
Wing chord at root	1·53 m (5 ft 0¼ in)
Wing chord at tip	1·07 m (3 ft 6¼ in)
Wing aspect ratio	8
Length overall	5·55 m (18 ft 2½ in)
Height overall	2·55 m (8 ft 4½ in)
Tailplane span	2·90 m (9 ft 6¼ in)

AREAS:
Wings, gross	13·40 m² (144·24 sq ft)
Vertical tail surfaces (total)	1·50 m² (16·15 sq ft)
Horizontal tail surfaces (total)	2·40 m² (25·83 sq ft)

WEIGHTS AND LOADING:
Weight of glider	45 kg (99 lb)
Pilot weight	60-90 kg (132-198 lb)
Max T-O weight	135 kg (297 lb)
Max wing loading	10·1 kg/m² (2·07 lb/sq ft)

PERFORMANCE:
Best glide ratio at 30 knots (55 km/h; 34 mph)	15
Min sinking speed at 19-21·5 knots (35-40 km/h; 22-25 mph)	48 m (157 ft)/min
Stalling speed	16·5 knots (30 km/h; 19 mph)
Max speed	38 knots (70 km/h; 43·5 mph)

Reich & Neumann ULF-1

PROF DIPL-ING BERNHARD E. R. J. DE TEMPLE
Am Pfingstborn 23, 6501 Heidesheim/Rhein

TEMPLE-WING TE-F1

The Temple-Wing (Temple-Flügel) TE-F1 rigid-wing hang glider is unusual in that pre-stressed sheets of foam plastics are used in the wings and tail unit to provide firm lifting surfaces which are virtually insensitive to dynamic loads. Because these surfaces are pre-stressed, they do not become deformed in flight. Other advantages accruing from the use of foam plastics include low constructional and repair costs.

Prof de Temple first tested this concept in the form of a model, which was flown in 1963. A full-size prototype was

Temple-Wing TE-F1 rigid-wing hang glider

built in 1978, and the first manned flight in this aircraft was made in Austria on 13 August of that year.

AIRFRAME: Constant-chord non-swept wings, with bowed profile and 4° dihedral from roots. Basic airframe structure is of aluminium alloy tubes and U-sections, with ferritic and stainless steel bolts and screws. Tail unit is an inverted V, supported by twin tailbooms and having an included angle of 104°. Wing and tail lifting surfaces are of pre-stressed Styropor foam plastics, a biologically inert material; their profiles are especially suitable for flight at low Reynolds numbers, though this type of wing could possibly be flown at higher speeds. Steel cables above and below wings permit control of the aircraft by wing-warping and raising tail unit.

DIMENSIONS:
Wing span	10·30 m (33 ft 9½ in)
Wing chord, constant	1·46 m (4 ft 9½ in)
Length overall	5·00 m (16 ft 4¾ in)
Height overall	3·00 m (9 ft 10 in)
Tail unit span	2·80 m (9 ft 2¼ in)

AREAS:
Wings, gross	15·00 m² (161·5 sq ft)
Tail unit (projected):	
horizontal	2·52 m² (27·13 sq ft)
vertical	1·00 m² (10·76 sq ft)

WEIGHTS:
Weight empty	48 kg (106 lb)
Max T-O weight	138 kg (304 lb)

PERFORMANCE:
Best glide ratio	8·8
Min sinking speed	1·38 m (4·53 ft)/s
Max level speed	approx 24 knots (44 km/h; 27 mph)

TEMPLE-WING TE-F2

Built in the Spring of 1979, the TE-F2 has a rigid wing, made of the same materials as that of the TE-F1, and a similar inverted-V tail unit. All pre-stressed sheets are secured firmly by thin strips of polypropylene. The glider can be dismantled and folded to half-span dimensions for transportation and stowage. The TE-F2 was tested by the DAeC-Testauto at Malmsheim in August 1979, and aerodynamic results were sufficiently encouraging to lead to a new design, the TE-F3, which is a powered hang glider with a multi-propeller propulsion system. It was hoped to fly the TE-F3 during 1980.

The following details apply to the TE-F2:

DIMENSIONS:
Wing span	11·00 m (36 ft 1 in)
Wing chord, constant	1·36 m (4 ft 5½ in)
Length overall	3·52 m (11 ft 6½ in)
Height overall	2·80 m (9 ft 2¼ in)
Tail unit span	2·60 m (8 ft 6½ in)

AREAS:
Wings, gross	15·00 m² (161·5 sq ft)
Tail unit (projected):	
horizontal	1·82 m² (19·59 sq ft)
vertical	0·80 m² (8·61 sq ft)

WEIGHTS:
Weight empty	35 kg (77 lb)
Weight of pilot	75 kg (165 lb)

PERFORMANCE:
Best glide ratio	12
Min sinking speed	0·80 m (2·62 ft)/s
Max level speed	27 knots (50 km/h; 31 mph)

Temple-Wing TEF2, folded for road transportation

POLAND
VLADIMIR TALANCZUK
ul. Dubois 16a m 18, 50-207 Wroclaw

Mr Talanczuk, of the Aeroklub Wroclaw, was responsible for the **Mars-Agat WT-8** competition glider, of which eight had been built by early 1979. His previous designs included the WT-6 Mars-S and WT-7 Mars-2S.

Details of the WT-8 were published in the 1979-80 *Jane's*. No 1980 information was received.

PAWEL WIERZBOWSKI
ul. Wroblewskiego 25/506, 51-627 Wroclaw

Mr Wierzbowski's **Vega 106** was available in two models, the Uni and the Sport. Ten had been built and sold by early 1979; in addition, 50 sets of plans had been sold by that time, and 30 Vega 106s were under construction by amateur builders.

Details of the Vega 106 were published in the 1979-80 *Jane's*. No 1980 information was received.

DR JERZY WOLF
Stepinska 6 m 63, 00-739 Warsaw

Dr Wolf, of the Instytut Lotnictwa (Aviation Institute) in Warsaw, has worked since 1970 on developing a stretched-membrane sailwing for various low-speed applications (including sailing applications: see *Jane's Surface Skimmers*).

Details of this work, and of hang gliders embodying this concept, appeared in the 1978-79 and 1979-80 *Jane's*. No new information was received for 1980.

UNITED KINGDOM
BIRDMAN SPORTS LTD
Overtown House, Mildenhall, Marlborough, Wiltshire

Producer of the **Cherokee**, of which 250 had been sold by the beginning of 1980. The Cherokee is suitable for private and competition flying, and is stressed to +6·5/−2·5g. Airframe is of aluminium alloy, with single-thickness Dacron sail and vinyl-coated galvanised cables. Kingpost standard. Features include floating keel pocket, single deflexers, adjustable camber, and provision for tow launch.

The Cherokee was the first hang glider to make a cross-country flight in the UK of more than 43 nm (80 km; 50 miles). It is available in several sizes; details of only one size were received, and are given in the table.

BREEN MICROLIGHT AIRCRAFT CENTRE
New Road, Crickhowell, near Abergavenny, South Wales

Markets the US Electra Flyer Eagle (which see).

CHARGUS HANG GLIDERS
Wagland Engineering, Gawcott, Buckingham

This company, one of the leading UK hang glider concerns, has not yet responded to any *Jane's* request for information about its products.

In Spring 1980 it flew a prototype of the **Vortex** powered hang glider (see accompanying photograph), which has an 8·2/10·6 kW (11/19 hp) 244 cc Fuji Robin engine and three-blade pusher propeller. Stalling speed is approx 16 knots (29 km/h; 18 mph). No other details known at the time of closing for press.

Chargus Vortex *(Peter R. March)*

DAVID COOK
Hillcrest, Aldeburgh Road, Aldringham, near Leiston, Suffolk

Mr David Cook acquired a Volmer VJ-23 Swingwing hang glider (which see) in the Spring of 1974, subsequently fitting it with a McCulloch MC-101B piston engine and two 5 litre (1·1 Imp gallon) fuel tanks. In this form, Mr Cook piloted the aircraft across the Channel from Walmer Castle, Deal, to Blériot Plage, France, on 9 May 1978 in a flying time of 1 h 15 min. This VJ-23E thus became the lowest-powered aeroplane to make a cross-Channel flight up to that time.

David Cook and the VJ-23E Swingwing powered glider on which he crossed the Channel in May 1978
(Dr Alan Beaumont)

ECLIPSE
7 Exbridge Road, Dulverton, Somerset

Markets the **Super Eagle** 'micro-light' powered hang glider shown in an accompanying photograph. No other details known.

Eclipse Super Eagle *(Peter R. March)*

EURO WING
Unit 20, Dixon Place, College Milton North, East Kilbride G74 5JF

This company, formerly known as Scot-Kites, was in 1980 the distributor for the US Catto CA 15 and Electra Flyer Eagle powered hang gliders (which see). Fifty Eagles had been sold by early 1980.

FLEXI-FORM SKYSAILS
Unit 24, Nassau Mill, Cawdor Street, Patricroft, Manchester

Current models (1979) were **Skyline, Spirit** and **Vector,** sales of which had totalled 70, 230 and 60 respectively by early 1979. No 1980 details were received.

All models have an aluminium alloy airframe, with kingpost as standard, PVC-coated galvanised steel cables, flexible PVC battens and single-thickness Terylene sail. Skyline and Vector are stressed to +6·5/−5g, Spirit to +5/−5g. Other features include floating keel pocket and a roached tip design with minimum fixed washout (Skyline); adjustable keel camber and adjustable double deflexers (Spirit); floating keel pocket, triple deflexers, and a truncated tip design with fully tensioned sail (Vector).

Skyline is suitable for competition flying.

HIGH SCHOOL OF HANG GLIDING
Wellesbourne Airfield, Wellesbourne, near Warwick

Run by Mr Paul Baker and Mr David Garrison, this organisation was preparing in the Spring of 1980 to assemble in the UK the Pterodactyl Fledgling powered hang glider (which see) developed in the USA by Mr Jack McCornack. The HSHG also planned to provide a course of instruction for those wishing to fly this aircraft.

HIWAY HANG GLIDERS LTD
Sirhowy Hill, Tredegar, Gwent NP2 4XP

Current gliders (1979) were the **Gemini, Harrier** (two models), **Spectrum** (two models) and **Super Scorpion** (three models). All have an aluminium alloy frame, with kingpost as standard, vinyl-coated galvanised steel cables, and a single-thickness Dacron sail; and are stressed to +6·6/−3g. Other features include adjustable sail camber, ribs, and a floating keel pocket. Gemini can carry two persons; Super Scorpion has small tip-struts, to facilitate quick recovery from a dive.

Hiway does not release performance figures, but all other known details are given in the table.

No details for 1980 were received, but press reports have referred to a powered version of the Super Scorpion known as **Skytrike** (see accompanying photograph), which has a landing gear/seat/power plant unit in which the engine drives a pusher propeller.

Hiway Skytrike *(Peter R. March)*

FRANK MARSHALL
19 Station Road, Filton, Bristol BS12 7BZ

Mr Marshall, whose Fantail hang glider was described under the South African section in the 1978-79 *Jane's*, has since designed and built the Heatwave and Madcap powered hang gliders. No recent news of these has been received.

MARSHALL HEATWAVE
The Heatwave is of conventional semi-rigid design, but quick-folding for carriage on a car roof rack. The double-surface wing has a pre-sewn sail bag, with removable pre-formed battens in top and bottom surfaces. Tailplane and rudder are rigid, but easily detachable. Control in pitch is by weight shift, control for turning by a long vertical twist bar moving the rudder. Power plant is a Rowena 6424 210 cc engine driving a 0·91 m (3 ft) diameter propeller. First flight was made in January 1978.

Marshall Heatwave

DIMENSIONS:
Wing span	9·91 m (32 ft 6 in)
Wing area, gross	15·33 m² (165 sq ft)
Wing aspect ratio	6·4
Length overall	5·33 m (17 ft 6 in)

WEIGHTS:
Weight of glider	47·6 kg (105 lb)
Pilot weight range	54-77 kg (120-170 lb)

PERFORMANCE (with 63·5 kg; 140 lb pilot):
Best rate of climb at S/L, at 22 knots (40 km/h; 25 mph)
70 m (230 ft)/min

MARSHALL MADCAP
The Madcap has a canard layout, chosen to provide static balance when using the Rowena 6424 engine in a 'pusher' installation. The fin forms the engine mount, and incorporates a 4·5 litre (1 Imp gallon) GRP fuel tank in its leading-edge. The wing uses the proven pre-stressed curved spar technique developed for the Fantail, resulting in only 2-3° washout while retaining the single-spar, flexible wing structure. Control is by weight shift in both axes. First flight took place in South Africa in May 1978.

DIMENSIONS:
Wing span	12·19 m (40 ft 0 in)
Wing area, gross	18·58 m² (200 sq ft)
Wing aspect ratio	8
Length overall	5·18 m (17 ft 0 in)

WEIGHTS:
Weight of glider	44 kg (97 lb)
Pilot weight range	79-104 kg (175-230 lb)

PERFORMANCE (with 86 kg; 190 lb pilot):
Best rate of climb at S/L, at 20 knots (37 km/h; 23 mph)
91 m (300 ft)/min

Marshall Madcap

SKYHOOK SAILWINGS LTD
Vale Mill, Chamber Road, Hollinwood, Oldham, Lancashire OL8 4PG

Current models for 1980 are as follows:
Cutlass. Illustrated in an accompanying photograph. No details received.

Silhouette. Single-seater, for training, private and competition flying. Airframe of anodised aluminium alloy, with single-thickness Dacron sail and vinyl-coated stainless steel cables. Kingpost standard. Features include pre-formed battens, floating keel pocket and (optionally) provision for tow launch. Airframe is stressed to +6/−3g (minimum), and can be broken down to 4·1 m (13 ft 6 in) for transportation and stowage.

In addition, Skyhook Sailwings has evaluated a number of 'micro-light' powered hang gliders, and expected to enter this market later in 1980 with one or more types of canard configuration.

Skyhook Sailwings Cutlass

Skyhook Sailwings Silhouette

UNITED STATES OF AMERICA
CATTO AIRCRAFT
PO Box 1619, Cupertino, California 95015

CATTO GOLDWING
The Goldwing, designed and built by 21-year-old Mr Craig Catto, is a rigid-wing powered hang glider of canard configuration; it flew for the first time in January 1979. Mr Catto planned to market plans of the Goldwing in the Autumn of that year.

AIRFRAME: Canard monoplane configuration, with swept-back main wings and non-swept foreplane. Construction is of foam plastics, glassfibre, epoxy resin, carbon/graphite fibre and balsa wood composites, with Mylar covering. Wings fitted with trailing-edge flaps and ailerons, foreplane with elevators. Drag rudder above each wingtip. Pilot is enclosed in an aerodynamic nacelle, to reduce drag.

POWER PLANT: One 7·5 kW (10 hp) Chrysler go-kart engine, driving a two-blade pusher propeller.

DIMENSIONS:
Wing span	10·97 m (36 ft 0 in)
Wing aspect ratio	14·2
Wing chord at root	1·07 m (3 ft 6 in)
Wing chord at tip	0·53 m (1 ft 9 in)
Foreplane span	5·18 m (17 ft 0 in)
Foreplane chord (constant)	0·61 m (2 ft 0 in)
Foreplane aspect ratio	8·0
Wing and foreplane area (total)	11·06 m² (119·0 sq ft)

WEIGHTS:
Weight of glider	41 kg (90 lb)
Power plant	11·5 kg (25 lb)

PERFORMANCE (estimated):
Best glide ratio	24
Min sinking speed	46 m (150 ft)/min
Cruising speed 35-39 knots (64-72 km/h; 40-45 mph)	
Stalling speed: flaps up	21 knots (39 km/h; 24 mph)
flaps down	17 knots (31 km/h; 19 mph)
Max rate of climb at S/L	122-152 m (400-500 ft)/min

Catto Goldwing *(J. M. Gradidge)*

CATTO CA 15

The CA 15 is a powered rigid-wing monoplane hang glider. It is stressed to +5g, and is available in fully-built or kit form.

AIRFRAME: Constant-chord cantilever sweptback flying-wing monoplane. Sweepback 17°. 'Elliptical' dihedral (i.e., curving upsweep). Pre-moulded glassfibre D-section leading-edge, reinforced with plywood. Aft of this are pre-stamped aluminium ribs. Mylar covering. Overwing 'rudderon' at each wingtip, combining functions of ailerons and rudders. Non-retractable tricycle landing gear, with front-wheel steering and braking.

POWER PLANT: One 130 cc Chrysler Power Bee engine, mounted at rear of 'fuselage', with reduction gear to a large-diameter two-blade pusher propeller. Standard fuel tank capacity 15 litres (4 US gallons). Long-range fuel tanks available optionally.

DIMENSIONS:
Wing span	9·14 m (30 ft 0 in)
Wing area, gross	13·94 m² (150·0 sq ft)
Wing aspect ratio	6·7

WEIGHTS AND LOADING:
Glider	26·5 kg (58 lb)
Power plant	12·25 kg (27 lb)
Max wing loading	9·03 kg/m² (1·85 lb/sq ft)

PERFORMANCE:
Best glide ratio: with engine	12
without engine	15
Min sinking speed, with engine, at 22 knots (40 km/h; 25 mph)	49 m (160 ft)/min
Max recommended speed, powered	43·5 knots (80 km/h; 50 mph)
Stalling speed	15 knots (27·5 km/h; 17 mph)
Rate of climb (depending on pilot weight and air density)	116-137 m (380-450 ft)/min

CGS AVIATION INC

4252 Pearl Road, Cleveland, Ohio 44109

Known previously as Chuck's Glider Supplies (see earlier editions of *Jane's*), this company had two basic sailwing-type hang gliders in production in 1980: the Falcon V and Falcon 5+. It also markets the rigid-wing Manta Fledge 2 (which see), and the Power Hawk, a reduction-drive power package suitable for various types of hang glider. The Power Hawk is used in Mitchell and Birdman homebuilts, and as a power plant for such types as the UFM Easy Riser and the Volmer VJ-23 and VJ-24. The Power Hawk unit for the Easy Riser comprises a 7·5 kW (10 hp) Chrysler West Bend engine, full reduction gear, fuel tank and a 1·07 m (3 ft 6 in) diameter two-blade propeller. A conversion pack for the McCulloch MC-101 engine is also available, as is a tricycle landing gear package for the Easy Riser.

Falcon V. Anodised aluminium tube airframe, with Dacron sail and anodised cables. Negative deflexers standard on 18 ft leading-edge model. Options include applied leading-edge pockets, and dual rigging for both seated and prone flying. Capable of max speed of 39 knots (72 km/h; 45 mph). Certificated by HGMA. Available in three sizes (see table).

Falcon 5+. Improved version of Falcon V, with keel pocket as standard, triple deflexers and floating tip limiters. Options as for Falcon V.

DELTA WING KITES AND GLIDERS INC

PO Box 483, Van Nuys, California 91408

Current (1980) models were as follows:

Phoenix 6D. Single-place glider for training and private flying; 853 sold by 1 January 1980. Aluminium alloy (6061-T6) airframe, with single-thickness Dacron sail and vinyl-coated stainless steel cables. Kingpost standard. No deflexers. Features include floating keel pocket and provision for tow launch. Available in four sizes: details of one of these are given in the table; data for the other three were not received. Larger sizes can carry a passenger. All can be flown seated or prone.

Delta Wing Phoenix 6D

Phoenix Lazor. Single-place glider for private and competition flying; 1,200 sold by 1 January 1980. Airframe construction similar to Phoenix 6D. Kingpost standard. Features include floating keel pocket, 'window' panels and provision for tow launch. Available in three sizes: details of two of these are given in the table; data for the other were not received. Largest size can carry a passenger. All can be flown seated or prone.

Delta Wing Phoenix Lazor

DELTA SAILPLANE CORPORATION

13161 Sherman Way, North Hollywood, California 91605

DELTA DS-26a NOMAD

Intended as a fully prefabricated kit for homebuilders, the Nomad ultralight rigid hang glider is designed specifically for powered operation, and is a successor to the DSK Flatlander described in the 1979-80 *Jane's*. The airframe is stressed to g limits of +4·67/−1·67 (normal) and +7/−2·5 (ultimate), and meets FAA sailplane Utility category requirements. Deliveries began in mid-March 1980.

AIRFRAME: Strut-braced high-wing monoplane. All-aluminium frame, assembled with bolts and pop-rivets. Tubular wing spars and fuselage boom. Auxiliary wing box-spar, of formed sheet metal, to support ailerons. All flying surfaces covered with polyester fabric and doped. Full aerodynamic control in all three axes by ailerons, elevators and rudder. Foldaway seat for pilot. Single main wheel and steerable tailwheel. Wings and tail detachable for transportation.

POWER PLANT: One 7·5 kW (10 hp) Star/Tek 134 cc piston engine, with overhead starter; 9 kW (12 hp) engine available optionally.

DIMENSIONS:
Wing span	11·00 m (36 ft 1 in)
Wing area, gross	13·69 m² (147·34 sq ft)
Wing aspect ratio	8·84
Propeller diameter	1·07 m (3 ft 6 in)

WEIGHTS AND LOADING:
Weight empty	69 kg (152 lb)
Max T-O weight	175 kg (387 lb)
Max wing loading	12·83 kg/m² (2·63 lb/sq ft)

PERFORMANCE:
Best glide ratio	14·5
Min sinking speed, power off	51 m (168 ft)/min
Never-exceed speed	47·5 knots (88 km/h; 55 mph) IAS
Cruising speed	31 knots (58 km/h; 36 mph) IAS
Stalling speed	18·5 knots (34 km/h; 21 mph) IAS
Landing speed	16 knots (29 km/h; 18 mph) IAS
Max rate of climb (77 kg; 170 lb pilot, 7·5 kW; 10 hp engine)	73 m (240 ft)/min
Service ceiling (85% power)	1,980 m (6,500 ft)
Absolute ceiling (powered)	3,660 m (12,000 ft)
Min T-O run (firm ground)	46 m (150 ft)
T-O to 15 m (50 ft)	256 m (840 ft)
Range at 85% power	92 nm (170 km; 106 miles)
Endurance at 75% power	3 h 20 min

DELTA DS-22a DRIFTER

In production since February 1979, the Drifter homebuilt powered glider is a wooden-construction version of the DSK Flatlander described in the 1979-80 *Jane's*.

EIPPER-FORMANCE INC

1070 Linda Vista Drive, San Marcos, California 92069

Current models in 1980 were Flexi 2, Flexi 3 and Antares sailwing-type hang gliders, and the rigid-construction Quicksilver.

Antares. Single-place glider for training, private and competition flying; 400 sold by 1 January 1980. Aluminium alloy airframe, with Dacron sail (double over 40% of area) and vinyl-coated stainless steel cables. Kingpost standard. Features include raised cambered keel pocket, total camber-shaping throughout sail, bowsprit

Eipper-Formance Antares

replacing usual crossbar, pre-formed battens, ribs, and triple deflexers. Stressed to +5/−2g; can be flown either seated or prone.

Flexi 2. Single-place glider for training and private flying; 500 sold by 1 January 1980. Single-thickness Dacron sail, otherwise construction as for Antares. Kingpost standard. Features include glassfibre flat battens and single deflexers. Stressed to +4·5/−2g; can be flown either seated or prone.

Flexi 3. As for Flexi 2, but with glassfibre tubular battens and triple deflexers; 800 sold by 1 January 1980.

Eipper-Formance Flexi 2

Eipper-Formance Flexi 3

EIPPER-FORMANCE (LOVEJOY) QUICKSILVER

Designed by Mr Bob Lovejoy, the Quicksilver has been in production by Eipper-Formance for several years, and some 1,500 had been sold by the beginning of 1980. The Quicksilver C version was first flown in September 1974, and is currently produced in slightly modified form as the **Quicksilver CM.** It is also available in powered form from Eipper-Formance as the **Quicksilver M**; other companies (e.g. Rotec, which see) also market power plant packages for this aircraft.

Eipper-Formance Quicksilver CM

TYPE: One-man hang glider; design g limit +4·0.

AIRFRAME: High-wing monoplane, with rudder and one-piece fixed horizontal tail supported on U-shaped rear twin booms. Wing dihedral 8°, incidence 2° 30'. Kingpost above centre-section. Framework of anodised aluminium alloy tubing. Stainless steel fittings; vinyl-coated stainless steel cables. Dacron-covered wings, tailplane and rudder.

POWER PLANT (Quicksilver M): One 9·7 kW (13 hp) Chrysler 82026 two-stroke engine, driving a two-blade pusher propeller. Fuel capacity 6·5 litres (1·7 US gallons).

DIMENSIONS:
Wing span	9·75 m (32 ft 0 in)
Wing area, gross	14·86 m² (160·0 sq ft)
Wing aspect ratio	6·4
Length overall (excl landing gear)	
	3·96 m (13 ft 0 in)
Height overall (excl landing gear)	
	2·90 m (9 ft 6 in)

WEIGHTS:
Weight of glider: CM	31 kg (68 lb)
M	59 kg (130 lb)
Pilot weight range	54-100 kg (120-220 lb)

PERFORMANCE (Quicksilver CM, with 77 kg; 170 lb pilot):
Best glide ratio	7
Min sinking speed	76 m (250 ft)/min
Max level speed	35 knots (64 km/h; 40 mph)
Cruising speed	19 knots (35 km/h; 22 mph)
Stalling speed	16 knots (29 km/h; 18 mph)

PERFORMANCE (Quicksilver M, with 72·5 kg; 160 lb pilot, at S/L, zero wind):
Max level speed	30 knots (56 km/h; 35 mph)
Cruising speed 17-22 knots (32-40 km/h; 20-25 mph)	
Stalling speed	15 knots (27·5 km/h; 17 mph)
Max rate of climb	106 m (350 ft)/min
T-O run	30 m (100 ft)
Landing run	15 m (50 ft)

Eipper-Formance Quicksilver (Peter R. March)

ELECTRA FLYER INTERNATIONAL
700 Comanche NE, Albuquerque, New Mexico 87107

The latest known (1979) models produced by Electra are listed below and in the table. No details were received for 1980.

Cirrus 5. Airframe of anodised aluminium, with vinyl-coated stainless steel cables. Standard features include quick tensioner kingpost, triple deflexers, keel pocket. Available in four sizes.

Dove. Airframe of similar materials to Cirrus. Standard features include quick tensioner kingpost, keel pocket. No deflexers. Available in four sizes.

Electra Floater. High-performance glider for intermediate and advanced pilots. Airframe of similar materials to Cirrus. Standard features include applied leading-edge, coated cables, quick-folding crossbar. Available in four sizes.

Olympus. High-performance glider, with which many national and international distance and altitude gain records have been set. Airframe of similar materials to Cirrus. Standard features include triple deflexers, glassfibre battens, locking tips for 18° washout . Can be fitted with 7·5 kW (10 hp) Chrysler two-stroke engine in Soarmaster PP-106 power pack with 2 litres (0·5 US gallons) fuel and Kevlar propeller. The standard unpowered Olympus is available in three sizes.

ELECTRA FLYER EAGLE
TYPE: One-man powered hang glider, stressed to +6/−5g.
AIRFRAME: Sweptback flexible-wing monoplane configuration, with non-swept canard surface; dependent rudders at wingtips. Main frame is of aluminium alloy, with Dacron sail and vinyl-coated stainless steel cables. Kingpost standard. Elevator fitted to foreplane.

Electra Flyer Eagle

Features include floating keel pocket and pre-formed battens.
POWER PLANT: One or two 130 cc Chrysler Power Bee engines (each approx 6 kW; 8 hp), driving a single pusher propeller via a reduction gear. Fuel tank capacity 7·5 litres (2 US gallons).

DIMENSIONS:
Wing span	9·75 m (32 ft 0 in)
Wing area, gross	16·72 m² (180·0 sq ft)

WEIGHTS:
Glider weight	62 kg (136 lb)
Pilot weight range	54-91 kg (120-200 lb)

PERFORMANCE:
Cruising speed approx 30 knots (56 km/h; 35 mph)	
T-O and landing run	23 m (75 ft)
Typical endurance	2 h

FLIGHT DESIGNS
PO Box 1503, Salinas, California 93902

Markets the New Zealand-designed **Lancer** (two models). All known details given in table.

HIGHSTER AIRCRAFT INC
Produces the **Highster** intermediate-performance hang glider in 13·94, 15·79 and 17·65 m² (150, 170 and 190 sq ft) sizes. No other details known.

TARAS KICENIUK JR
976 La Vuelta, Santa Paula, California 93060

KICENIUK ICARUS II
The Icarus tail-less sweptwing biplane hang glider made its first flight in August 1971. The improved Icarus II is approved by the FAA for amateur construction, and is available in kit form only.
TYPE: One-man amateur-built hang glider; g limit +3·0.
AIRFRAME: Sweptback, staggered flying-wing biplane. Modified Eiffel 32 wing section. Dihedral approx 8°. Incidence 2° 15′ upper wing, 0° lower wing. Sweepback approx 15°. Aluminium tube leading-edge and trailing-edge spars, wood and styrofoam ribs, and Dacron covering. Balsa and plywood vertical rudders, one attached to each outermost rear interplane strut, actuated independently to provide strong lateral control because of effects of sweep and dihedral angle. When actuated simultaneously, rudders act as airbrakes. No other control surfaces needed, pitch control being effected by pilot's body movement. Aircraft is inherently stable, and returns to straight and level flight when flown hands-off. No fuselage or tail surfaces.

DIMENSIONS:
Wing span	8·84 m (29 ft 0 in)
Wing area, gross	18·12 m² (195·0 sq ft)
Wing aspect ratio (geometric)	8·7
Length overall	2·74 m (9 ft 0 in)

WEIGHTS AND LOADING:
Weight empty	25 kg (55 lb)
Max T-O weight	115 kg (255 lb)
Max wing loading	6·34 kg/m² (1·3 lb/sq ft)

PERFORMANCE:
Best glide ratio at 17 knots (32 km/h; 20 mph)	8
Min sinking speed at 17 knots (32 km/h; 20 mph)	
	64 m (210 ft)/min
Stalling speed	15 knots (27 km/h; 17 mph)
Max speed (smooth air) 35 knots (64 km/h; 40 mph)	

KICENIUK ICARUS V
The Icarus V monoplane hang glider flew for the first time on 1 September 1973; it is suitable for both thermal soaring and cross-country flying.
TYPE: One-man amateur-built hang glider; g limit +6·0.
AIRFRAME: Constant-chord sweptback flying-wing monoplane. TK 7315 high-lift, low-moment wing section. Dihedral from roots. Sweepback 20°. No incidence. Aluminium tube frame, foam sheet leading-edge, doped fabric covering. Dependent fin and rudder at each wingtip. Yaw and roll control through independently-controlled rudders, pitch control by pilot weight shift. Aircraft can spiral continuously at bank angles of 60°, is extremely stable, and has a very gentle stall.

DIMENSIONS:
Wing span	9·75 m (32 ft 0 in)
Wing area, gross	14·86 m² (160·0 sq ft)
Wing aspect ratio	6·4
Length overall	3·81 m (12 ft 6 in)
Height overall	1·83 m (6 ft 0 in)

WEIGHTS AND LOADING:
Weight empty	29·5 kg (65 lb)
Max T-O weight	129 kg (285 lb)
Max wing loading	8·7 kg/m² (1·78 lb/sq ft)

PERFORMANCE:
Best glide ratio at 17 knots (32 km/h; 20 mph)	10
Min sinking speed at 16 knots (29 km/h; 18 mph)	
	64 m (210 ft)/min
Stalling speed	14 knots (26 km/h; 16 mph)
Max speed (smooth air)	
	43·5 knots (80·5 km/h; 50 mph)

MANTA PRODUCTS
1647 East 14th Street, Oakland, California 94606

MANTA FLEDGE
This rigid sweptwing tail-less monoplane can be flown from either a seated or prone position, and is suitable for training, private or competition flying. Total sales had reached 500 by early 1979.

It is produced as the Fledge 1 and 2, respectively with single-surface and double-surface wing covering; each model is available in two sizes, designated A and B.

The Fledge 2 is also marketed by CGS Aviation (which see).
TYPE: One-man rigid-wing hang glider; g limits +7·5/−7·5.
AIRFRAME: Sweptback flying-wing monoplane, with 18° sweep on leading-edges, 2° washout, and dihedral which raises wingtips 56 cm (22 in) above keel. Each half-wing has two aluminium alloy spars, and compression struts; wings are linked by vinyl-coated stainless steel sweep/flying wires. Structure includes ten pre-formed aluminium ribs and tip ribs. Kingpost standard. Fledge 1 has drag rudder extending above and below each wingtip. Fledge 2 has swept and canted drag rudders above 'booster' wingtips which facilitate turning, take-off and landing. All surfaces Dacron-covered (single thickness on Fledge 1, double on wings of Fledge 2). Provision for power plant and landing gear.

DIMENSIONS:
Wing span (included): A	8·84 m (29 ft 0 in)
B	10·06 m (33 ft 0 in)
Wing leading-edge length: A	4·42 m (14 ft 6 in)
B	5·03 m (16 ft 6 in)
Wing chord at root (keel length):	
A, B	1·68 m (5 ft 6 in)
Wing chord at tip: A, B	1·37 m (4 ft 6 in)
Wing area, gross: A	13·19 m² (142·0 sq ft)
B	15·05 m² (162·0 sq ft)
Wing aspect ratio: A	6·0
B	6·8
Nose angle	144°
Billow angle	not applicable

WEIGHT:
Weight empty: A	26 kg (57 lb)
B	28·5 kg (63 lb)
Pilot weight: A	54-70 kg (120-155 lb)
B	72·5-100 kg (160-220 lb)

PERFORMANCE:
Best glide ratio	11
Min sinking speed	61 m (200 ft)/min
Max speed	39 knots (72 km/h; 45 mph)
Cruising speed 16-22 knots (29-40 km/h; 18-25 mph)	
Stalling speed	12·5 knots (23 km/h; 14 mph)

Manta Fledge 2 in powered form (Peter R. March)

MOTORIZED GLIDERS
Clear Lake, Iowa

This company markets the Eipper-Formance (Lovejoy) Quicksilver C rigid-wing hang glider (which see) in both unpowered kit form, without landing gear; or with a 0·4 kN (100 lb st) power plant kit, plus tailwheel or tricycle landing gear.

PERFORMANCE:
Max level speed	35 knots (64 km/h; 40 mph)
Cruising speed 22-26 knots (40-48 km/h; 25-30 mph)	
Max rate of climb with 91 kg (200 lb) pilot	
	76 m (250 ft)/min

PACIFIC GULL
150 H, Los Obreros Lane, San Clemente, California 92672

For details of 1979 **Alpine** series, see table. Airframes are of aluminium alloy tube, with kingpost as standard, and are stressed to g limits of +6·0 (+4·8 rolling) and −3·0. Cables are of vinyl-coated stainless steel, sails of Dacron. All have pre-formed battens, triple deflexers

Pacific Gull Alpine 1·0

and a floating keel pocket. Alpine 2·5 can carry two persons in tandem; all models are suitable for training, private or competition flying.

Total sales had reached 159 by early 1979. No 1980 details were received.

PTERODACTYL LTD
Monterey, California

Mr Jack McCornack, President of Pterodactyl Ltd, designed and built the prototype of the Fledgling powered hang glider, which is based on the Manta Fledge (which see). Plans are being marketed by Tim and Wesley Friesen, reportedly trading as the Wrong Brothers. Mr McCornack and Mr Keith Nicely each flew one of these aircraft from Monterey to the EAA Fly-in at Oshkosh, Wisconsin, in 1979, averaging about 174 nm (322 km; 200 miles) per day. The High School of Hang Gliding (which see) was planning in the Spring of 1980 to import kits into the UK for assembly and sale.

Mr McCornack has also developed a version with conventional tailplane and elevators.

PTERODACTYL FLEDGLING
TYPE: Single-seat powered hang glider.
AIRFRAME: Braced monoplane wing, with tubular leading-edge spar, tubular secondary spar and lightweight light alloy ribs. Nylon or Dacron covering on upper surface only. Wing wires braced to light alloy tube 'fuselage' and to kingpost extending above wing. Controllable drag rudder above each wingtip. Non-retractable tricycle landing gear.
POWER PLANT: One 18 kW (24 hp) Sachs 340 cc two-stroke snowmobile engine, driving a two-blade fixed-pitch pusher propeller. Fuel in two plastics tanks.

DIMENSIONS:

Wing span	10·06 m (33 ft 0 in)
Wing chord at root	1·68 m (5 ft 6 in)
Wing chord at tip	1·37 m (4 ft 6 in)
Length	2·44 m (8 ft 0 in)
Height	3·05 m (10 ft 0 in)

WEIGHTS:

Weight empty	68 kg (150 lb)
Max T-O weight	192 kg (425 lb)

PERFORMANCE:

Max level speed	56 knots (105 km/h; 65 mph)
Cruising speed range	30-47 knots (56-88 km/h; 35-55 mph)
Landing speed	17 knots (32 km/h; 20 mph)
Max rate of climb at S/L	107 m (350 ft)/min
Service ceiling	5,180 m (17,000 ft)
T-O run	61 m (200 ft)
Landing run	6 m (20 ft)
Range with max fuel	174 nm (322 km; 200 miles)

Pterodactyl Fledgling

ROTEC ENGINEERING INC
PO Box 124, Duncanville, Texas 75166

This company markets, in ready-to-fly or kit form, a powered version of the Eipper-Formance (Lovejoy) **Quicksilver** (which see), available either in foot-launch form or with wheel landing gear. Power plant is a 7·5 kW (10 hp) Chrysler engine, driving a 1·07 m (3 ft 6 in) diameter laminated propeller. Weight empty is 41 kg (90 lb).

PERFORMANCE (powered):

Max level speed	39 knots (72 km/h; 45 mph)
Cruising speed	26 knots (48 km/h; 30 mph)
Stalling speed	14 knots (26 km/h; 16 mph)

Also marketed by Rotec are a powered version of the UFM **Easy Riser** (which see), with a 7·8 kW (10·5 hp)

Chrysler engine driving a pusher propeller, and an empty weight of 38·5 kg (85 lb); and the 'micro-light' Rally. The latter is available with 7·5 kW (10 hp) Chrysler 82026 or 13 kW (17·5 hp) Chrysler 206 engine, in each case driving a pusher propeller. There are two versions: **Rally 1** with a swing seat and weight shift control, and **Rally 2**, with stick and pedal for full three-axis control.

Rotec Powered Quicksilver

SEAGULL AIRCRAFT
1160 Mark Avenue, Carpinteria, California 93013

In production in early 1980 were the **9, 10 and 11 Meter** gliders and the **Seahawk 155, 180 and 200**. The former are suitable for private and competition flying, and are normally flown prone; the Seahawk series can be used for training and private flying, and can be flown either seated or prone. More than 2,000 Seahawks and over 1,500 Meters had been sold by early 1980.

Seagull 10 Meter

Both series have airframes of aluminium alloy, with a kingpost as standard, a Dacron sail (double thickness over 20% of area), and vinyl-coated stainless steel cables; all are stressed to +4·5/−2·0g. Features include floating keel pocket, deflexers (single or triple on 9/10/11 Meter, single only on Seahawk), ribs (9/10/11 Meter only), provision for tow launch, and (on larger sizes) the capability to carry a passenger. A Seagull 10 Meter holds the world record for height gain by a hang glider of 3,566 m (11,700 ft). Other details given in table.

Seagull Sierra

Seagull Seahawk

At the beginning of 1980, prototypes had been completed of two new models, the **Sierra** and **Sailwing**, and these were due to be released for production in February and April 1980 respectively. Sierra, available in two sizes (see table), is designed for cross-country flying, with a fairly broad speed range and very high performance; Sailwing is of 'flying-wing' configuration, with a V tail, and is claimed to be the first of its type in which the wing is controlled entirely by weight shift. Airframe construction of both types is generally similar to existing models, though a greater proportion of the sail is double-covered, and production aircraft may incorporate some composite materials.

SKY SPORTS INC
PO Box 507, 394 Somers Road (Route 83), Ellington, Connecticut 06029

Current 1979 types (see table for details) were the **Eaglet, Bobcat IV, Osprey II** and **Sirocco III**, all of which have aluminium tube airframes, stainless steel cables and double-surface Dacron sails. Bobcat has a two-position double billow wing; Sirocco has a buried cross-member.

For other details see table. In 1979 all models were available in other sizes; some have provision for power plant. No details received for 1980, but a photograph in the Addenda shows the **Humbug**, a multi-purpose design which, with wings and tail removed, can be used as a snowmobile, ice boat, air boat or dune buggy.

SUNBIRD ULTRALIGHT GLIDERS
12501 Gladstone Avenue, No. A4, Sylmar, California 91324

Sunbird's 1980 hang glider was the **Nova**, first flown in 1978 and now produced in five models. Suitable for private and competition flying, the Nova can be flown in a prone, seated or supine position. The airframe is of aluminium alloy, with kingpost as standard; cables are of vinyl-coated stainless steel, and sail of Dacron. Other features include a floating keel pocket, leading-edge without deflexers, and floating tips.

Two hundred Novas had been built and sold by the beginning of 1980.

Sunbird Nova

ULTIMATE HI
14328 Lolin Lane, Poway, California 92064

Producer of the **Starship** series (three sizes). All known details given in table.

ULTRALIGHT FLYING MACHINES OF WISCONSIN (UFM)
PO Box 248, Kansasville, Wisconsin 53139

This company produces John Moody's power package and crosswind landing gear for the **Easy Riser**, a rigid-wing powered hang glider stressed to +11/−5g. More than 700 had been delivered by early 1980, many of them for construction by homebuilders.

A solar-powered version, known as the **Solar Riser**, is described in the Homebuilt Aircraft section of this edition.

UFM EASY RISER
AIRFRAME: Constant-chord sweptback (15°) flying-wing biplane, of LM 7610 aerofoil section and unequal span, built of aluminium alloy with double-thickness Dacron covering. No fuselage. Drag rudder aft of each wing, attached to outermost rear interplane strut. Crosswind tricycle landing gear optional.

POWER PLANT (optional): One McCulloch MC-101 or Chrysler West Bend 820 single-cylinder two-stroke piston engine, driving a two-blade wooden pusher propeller. Either engine can be fitted with a 'Maximizer' reduction gear assembly and larger-diameter propeller. Fuel capacity 4·25 litres (9 US pints) standard; additional tank of similar capacity is available optionally.

DIMENSIONS:
Wing span (trailing-edge)	9·14 m (30 ft 0 in)
Wing chord (streamwise, constant)	1·04 m (3 ft 5 in)
Wing area, gross	15·98 m² (172 sq ft)
Aspect ratio (upper wing)	8·8
Propeller diameter:	
with direct drive engine	0·71 m (2 ft 4 in)
with Maximizer unit	1·07 m (3 ft 6 in)

WEIGHTS AND LOADING:
Weight of glider without engine or landing gear	22·7 kg (50 lb)
Weight of glider with engine:	
foot-launched	38·5 kg (85 lb)
with landing gear	47 kg (104 lb)
Pilot weight range	54·5-95 kg (120-210 lb)
Max wing loading	7·17 kg/m² (1·47 lb/sq ft)

PERFORMANCE (A: unpowered; B: with direct drive engine; C: with Maximizer unit):
Best glide ratio:		
A		over 10
B at 22-24 knots (40-45 km/h; 25-28 mph)		9·6
C at 22-24 knots (40-45 km/h; 25-28 mph)		9·3
Min sinking speed:		
A		55 m (180 ft)/min
B, C, foot-launched, at 16·5-18 knots (31-34 km/h; 19-21 mph)		70 m (230 ft)/min
B, C, with landing gear, at 16·5-18 knots (31-34 km/h; 19-21 mph)		76 m (250 ft)/min
Max speed: B, C		39-43 knots (72-80 km/h; 45-50 mph)
Cruising speed: B, C		22-30 knots (40-56 km/h; 25-35 mph)
Stalling speed: A		14 knots (26 km/h; 16 mph)
B, C		15-17 knots (27·5-31 km/h; 17-19 mph)
Typical rate of climb:		
B (McCulloch engine)		53-84 m (175-275 ft)/min
C (West Bend engine)		76-106 m (250-350 ft)/min
C (McCulloch engine)		91-122 m (300-400 ft)/min
Typical endurance: B, C		1 h

UFM (John Moody) powered Easy Riser

UP INC (ULTRALITE PRODUCTS)
PO Box 582, 28011 Front Street, Rancho California, Temecula, California 92390

UP's major model for 1980 was the **Mosquito**, which is available in three sizes; details are given in the Table. The Mosquito has an airframe of 6061-T6 aluminium alloy tube, with kingpost as standard, single-thickness Dacron sail, vinyl-coated stainless steel cables, and a floating keel pocket. It is stressed to +7/−4·5g, and can be flown from a prone or seated position. A total of nearly 180 had been sold by January 1980.

Details of the UP Condor, Firefly and Spyder series can be found in the 1979-80 *Jane's*.

UP Mosquito 196

VOLMER AIRCRAFT
PO Box 5222, Glendale, California 91201

VOLMER VJ-23 SWINGWING
This monoplane hang glider was designed in 1971 by Volmer Jensen and Irving Culver, making its first flight towards the end of that year. Subsequent modifications made the aircraft safer and more controllable. Volmer Aircraft markets plans (but not kits or materials) for the VJ-23; several hundreds have been sold.

Following the success of David Cook in the UK (which see) in installing an engine in his Swingwing, drawings for a **VJ-23E** powered version are now also available from Volmer Aircraft.

AIRFRAME: Cantilever high-wing monoplane, constructed of steel tube, spruce, mahogany and plywood, with Dacron or fabric covering. Control by means of ailerons, elevators and rudder. Airframe stressed to +3/−3g.

DIMENSIONS:
Wing span	9·93 m (32 ft 7 in)
Wing area, gross	16·63 m² (179·0 sq ft)
Length overall	5·31 m (17 ft 5 in)
Height overall	1·83 m (6 ft 0 in)

WEIGHTS:
Weight empty: VJ-23	45·5 kg (100 lb)
VJ-23E	63·5 kg (140 lb)
Pilot weight range	45-91 kg (100-200 lb)
Max T-O weight: VJ-23	136 kg (300 lb)

PERFORMANCE (VJ-23):
Best glide ratio	9
Cruising speed	17 knots (32 km/h; 20 mph)
Stalling speed	13 knots (24 km/h; 15 mph)

Volmer Jensen flying a VJ-23 Swingwing

Volmer VJ-23E powered Swingwing

VOLMER VJ-24 SUNFUN
The VJ-24 rigid-wing monoplane hang glider is essentially a simplified-construction version of the earlier VJ-23 Swingwing, from which it differs primarily in having wings and tail of fabric-covered aluminium tube instead of wooden spars and ribs; rectangular instead of tapered planform wings, of increased span, with V bracing struts; and a pair of ground handling wheels.

A **VJ-24E** is also available, with a 7·5 kW (10 hp) engine and fuel tank installed beneath the wing, aft of the pilot, to permit take-offs from level ground or uphill.

NASA has undertaken a study involving covering the wings of a VJ-24 with solar cells, to produce electricity to power an electric motor power plant for the aircraft.

The following details apply to the unpowered VJ-24:

DIMENSIONS:
Wing span	11·13 m (36 ft 6 in)
Wing area, gross	15·14 m² (163·0 sq ft)
Length overall	5·54 m (18 ft 2 in)
Height over tail	1·73 m (5 ft 8 in)

WEIGHTS:
Weight empty	50 kg (110 lb)
Max T-O weight	140·5 kg (310 lb)

PERFORMANCE: As for VJ-23.

Volmer VJ-24E powered Sunfun

WILLS WING INC
1208-h, East Walnut, Santa Ana, California 92701

Formerly known as Sport Kites Inc, this company marketed the Wills Wing and Swallowtail gliders, as listed in the 1978-79 *Jane's*. Its current (1980) products are the **Alpha, Omega, Omni** and **Raven,** of which details are given in the table; more than 1,000 of these had been sold by early 1980. All are stressed to g limits of +8/−4, and are suitable for private and competition flying. Airframes are of aluminium alloy and composite materials, with a kingpost as standard; cables are of vinyl-coated stainless steel; double-surface sail is of Dacron. Other features include applied leading-edge pockets, adjustable camber, triple deflexers (except on Raven), foam/glassfibre battens (Alpha), pre-formed battens (Omega), and washout control tips. All are capable of tow launch, and the larger sizes are capable of carrying two persons.

In January 1980 Wills Wing had completed a prototype of the **Boomer**, a Class 2 competition model stressed to g limits of +9/−7. This has an aluminium alloy airframe, with kingpost, a double-thickness Dacron sail, and stainless steel cables. Other features include floating keel pocket, prone pilot position, ribs, and provision for tow launch. All other details are given in the table.

WILLIAM H. WOLF
18703 S.E. 44th Place, Issaquah, Wichita 98027

WOLF VALKYRIE
The Valkyrie is a rigid, non-swept tail-less monoplane hang glider with a drag rudder near each wingtip. Construction is of aluminium alloy tube, with stainless steel cables and Dacron covering. Wings have 7° dihedral.

No further news was received in 1980. It is not known whether the Valkyrie is in production.

DIMENSIONS:
Wing span	9·37 m (30 ft 9 in)
Wing chord (constant)	1·37 m (4 ft 6 in)
Wing area	12·82 m² (138·0 sq ft)
Wing aspect ratio	6·83
Length overall	1·91 m (6 ft 3 in)
Height overall	2·29 m (7 ft 6 in)

WEIGHT:
Weight empty	21·8 kg (48 lb)

PERFORMANCE (at 95·25 kg; 210 lb gross weight):
Best glide ratio at 15·5 knots (29 km/h; 18 mph)	8
Min sinking speed	60 m (197 ft)/min
Stalling speed	10·5 knots (19·5 km/h; 12 mph)

Wolf Valkyrie

FLEXIBLE WING HANG GLIDER DATA

Manufacturer and Model	FAI class	Span: m/ft-in	Leading-edge: m/ft-in	Keel: m/ft-in	Nose/Billow angle: degrees	Wing area: m²/sq ft	Wing aspect ratio	Weight: kg/lb	Glide ratio	Sink rate: m/ft per min	Pilot weight kg (lb)	Stalling speed knots (km/h; mph)	Remarks
ARGENTINA													
LADAS													
Johan SH1	n.k.	9·20/30-2¼	5·60/18-4½	3·20/10-6	108/n.k.	16·00/172	n.k.	21·0/46·3	n.k.	72/236	40-75 (88-165)	7 (13; 8·5)	
AUSTRALIA													
Moyes													
Maxi-Stinger Mark III	2	10·40/34-1½	6·10/20-0	4·00/13-1½	117/1·0	20·00/215	5·40	28·0/61·7	8·2	61/200	50-100 (110-220)	11 (20·5; 13)	Mk IV sail area 18 m² (194 sq ft); otherwise similar
Maxi Stinger SP	2	10·00/32-9¾	5·80/19-0½	4·00/13-1½	117/1·0	18·00/194	5·55	26·0/57·3	8·5	61/200	n.k.	10 (18; 11·5)	
Mega Stinger II	2	10·00/32-9¾	5·80/19-0½	4·00/13-1½	120/0·0	16·00/172	6·00	26·0/57·3	8·6	67/220	n.k.	13·5 (25; 16)	
Redtail Stinger	1	9·00/29-6½	5·50/18-0½	4·00/13-1½	109/1·5	16·00/172	4·40	25·0/55·1	5·5	87/285	55-75 (121-165)	10 (18; 11·5)	
Stingray	1	9·00/29-6½	5·00/16-4¾	4·00/13-1½	120/1·0	18·60/200	4·50	25·0/55·1	5·5	70/230	n.k.	10 (18; 11·5)	
Stingray	1	9·40/30-10	5·20/17-0¾	4·00/13-1½	115/1·0	20·00/215	4·50	26·0/57·3	5·5	67/220	n.k.	10 (18; 11·5)	
CANADA													
Birdman Enterprises													
Falcon I	1	8·23/27-0	5·49/18-0	3·96/13-0	96/1·5	15·33/165	4·40	20·4/45	6	87/285	45-72·5 (100-160)	10·5 (19·5; 12)	
Falcon II	1	8·84/29-0	5·79/19-0	4·27/14-0	96/1·5	16·72/180	4·60	20·4/45	6	87/285	61-91 (135-200)	10·5 (19·5; 12)	
MJ-5	2	9·60/31-6	5·49/18-0	3·05/10-0	120/0·5	16·72/180	5·50	22·2/49	8+	68·5/225	63·5-88·5 (140-195)	9 (16·5; 10)	
MJ-6	3	10·06/33-0	5·61/18-5	3·35/11-0	115/0·0	17·00/183	5·70	22·7/50	8·5	61/200	63·5-95 (140-210)	9 (16·5; 10)	
XC	2	10·21/33-6	5·94/19-6	3·51/11-6	116/0·75	19·51/210	5·40	24·9/55	9+	61/200	82-104 (180-230)	9 (16·5; 10)	
High Perspective *(1979: no 1980 details received)*													
HP IV	2	8·53/28-0	5·49/18-0	3·66/12-0	100/2·0	14·86/160	5·00	15·9/35	6+	68·5/225	50-72·5 (110-160)	13 (24·5; 15)	Smaller and larger models available
FRANCE													
Dahu Plane (Noin) *(1979: no 1980 details received)*													
Baby 18	n.k.	8·00/26-3	n.k.	4·50/14-9¾	92/n.k.	18·00/193·7	3·50	18·0/39·7	5-6	96/315	n.k.	n.k.	
Nimbus	2	10·40/34-1½	5·60/18-4½	3·00/9-10	122/0·0	13·40/144·2	8·10	26·0/57·3	10-11	59/194	60-75 (132-165)	14·5 (26; 16·5)	
Stratus IVB	1	8·35/27-4¾	n.k.	4·00/13-1½	100/n.k.	17·00/183·0	4·40	19·0/41·9	n.k.	84/276	n.k.	11 (20; 12·5)	
La Mouette													
Atlas 14	2	9·30/30-6¾	5·36/17-7	3·50/11-5¾	120/0·5	13·80/148·5	6·25	24·5/54·0	9	54/177	65-75 (143-165)	10 (18; 11·5)	
Atlas 16	2	9·80/32-1¾	5·70/18-8½	3·50/11-5¾	120/0·5	15·50/166·8	6·20	25·0/55·1	9	54/177	65-100 (143-220)	10 (18; 11·5)	
Lotus 15	2	9·45/31-0	5·40/17-8½	3·50/11-5¾	120/2·0	15·50/166·8	5·70	23·0/50·7	7·5	66/217	40-75 (88-165)	11 (20; 12·5)	
Lotus 17	2	9·80/32-1¾	5·70/18-8½	3·50/11-5¾	120/2·0	17·00/183·0	5·60	24·0/52·9	7·5	66/217	65-95 (143-209)	11 (20; 12·5)	
Mouette 15	1	8·00/26-3	5·00/16-4¾	3·80/12-5½	102/2·0	15·00/161·5	4·30	15·0/33·1	6·5	78/256	40-55 (88-121)	10 (18; 11·5)	
Mouette 17	1	8·50/27-10½	5·21/17-1	4·00/13-1½	102/2·0	17·00/183·0	4·30	17·0/37·5	6·5	78/256	50-68 (110-150)	10 (18; 11·5)	
Mouette 19	1	9·00/29-6¾	5·40/17-8½	4·20/13-9¾	102/2·0	19·00/204·5	4·30	19·0/41·9	6·5	78/256	65-100 (143-220)	10 (18; 11·5)	
Mouette 23B	1	10·60/34-9¾	5·40/17-8½	4·50/14-9¾	102/2·0	23·00/247·6	4·30	30·0/66·1	6·5	78/256	100-180 (220-397)	11 (20; 12·5)	
SOFREC Véliplane *(1979: no 1980 details received)*													
Starga 15	2	9·14/30-0	4·85/15-11	3·60/11-9¾	140/1·0	15·00/161·5	5·60	25·0/55·1	10	66/217	40-60 (88-132)	12 (22; 14)	
Starga 16	2	10·00/32-9¾	4·85/15-11	3·60/11-9¾	140/1·0	16·00/172·2	6·25	25·0/55·1	10	66/217	55-75 (121-165)	12 (22; 14)	
Starga 17	2	10·00/32-9¾	4·85/15-11	3·60/11-9¾	140/1·0	17·00/183·0	5·88	25·0/55·1	10	66/217	70-95 (154-209)	12 (22; 14)	
Strato 16	2	9·20/30-2¼	4·80/15-9	4·80/15-9	123/0·0	16·30/175·5	5·19	25·0/55·1	9	75/246	55-75 (121-165)	13·5 (25; 16)	
Strato 18	2	9·20/30-2¼	4·80/15-9	4·80/15-9	123/0·0	17·30/186·2	4·89	25·0/55·1	9	75/246	70-90 (154-198)	13·5 (25; 16)	
GERMANY (Federal Republic)													
Hirth *(1979: no 1980 details received)*													
W-17B Dracula B	—	10·00/32-9¾	5·00/16-4¾	5·00/16-4¾	180/0·0	16·00/172·2	6·25	28·0/61·7	7-8	78/256	65-95 (143-209)	13·5 (25; 16)	
UNITED KINGDOM													
Birdman													
Cherokee	1	10·06/33-0	5·49/18-0	3·35/11-0	120/0·0	18·58/200	n.k.	24·9/55	9	61/200	55-95 (121-209)	13(24·5; 15)	Other sizes available
Flexi-form Skysails *(1979: no 1980 details received)*													
Skyline	n.k.	10·06/33-0	n.k.	2·44/8-0	114/1·0	15·79/170	6·40	20·9/46	7	61/200	51-63·5 (112-140)	14 (26; 16)	
Skyline	n.k.	10·26/33-8	n.k.	2·44/8-0	114/1·0	16·26/175	6·40	22·2/49	7	61/200	63·5-76 (140-168)	14 (26; 16)	
Skyline	n.k.	10·36/34-0	n.k.	2·59/8-6	114/1·0	18·12/195	6·00	24·0/53	7	61/200	76-89 (168-196)	14 (26; 16)	
Skyline	n.k.	10·82/35-6	n.k.	2·90/9-6	114/1·0	19·97/215	5·90	24·5/54	7	61/200	89-102 (196-225)	14 (26; 16)	
Spirit	n.k.	n.k.	6·25/20-6	n.k.	102/2·5	17·65/190	5·00	23·6/52	7	61/200	59-77 (130-170)	13·5 (24·5; 15)	
Spirit	n.k.	n.k.	6·71/22-0	n.k.	102/2·5	19·97/215	5·00	24·9/55	7	61/200	77-102 (170-225)	13·5 (24·5; 15)	
Vector	n.k.	10·67/35-0	6·25/20-6	2·26/7-5	114/0·0	15·79/170	7·30	24·0/53	8+	55/180	59-77 (130-170)	14 (26; 16)	
Vector	n.k.	11·10/36-5	6·48/21-3	2·26/7-5	114/0·0	16·72/180	7·40	24·0/53	8+	55/180	77-102 (170-225)	14 (26; 16)	

Manufacturer and Model	FAI class	Span: m/ft-in	Leading-edge: m/ft-in	Keel: m/ft-in	Nose/Billow angle: degrees	Wing area: m²/sq ft	Wing aspect ratio	Weight: kg/lb	Glide ratio	Sink rate: m/min per min	Pilot weight kg (lb)	Stalling speed knots (km/h; mph)	Remarks
Hiway Hang Gliders *(1979: no 1980 details received)*													
Gemini	1	10·29/33-9	6·50/21-4	5·00/16-5	105/n.k.	24·15/260	4·30	29·0/64	—	—	n.k.	—	Two-man glider: can carry weight of up to 165 kg (364 lb); enlarged, strengthened version of Spectrum
Harrier Standard	1	n.k.	5·49/18-0	3·96/13-0	100/n.k.	18·12/195	4·25	20·4/45	—	—	n.k.	—	
Harrier Large	1	n.k.	6·10/20-0	4·27/14-0	100/n.k.	20·44/220	4·25	23·1/51	—	—	n.k.	—	
Spectrum Small	1	8·18/26-10	5·18/17-0	4·04/13-3	105/n.k.	15·33/165	4·45	20·4/45	—	—	50-76 (110-167)	—	
Spectrum Large	1	8·97/29-5	5·64/18-6	4·57/15-0	105/n.k.	17·93/193	4·45	23·1/51	—	—	57-90 (125-198)	—	
Super Scorpion B	2	9·32/30-7	5·49/18-0	3·68/12-1	120/n.k.	16·07/173	5·60	20·9/46	—	—	57-82 (125-181)	—	
Super Scorpion C	2	10·21/33-6	5·99/19-8	4·04/13-3	120/n.k.	18·39/198	5·70	23·6/52	—	—	70-90 (154-198)	—	
Super Scorpion C+	2	10·21/33-6	5·99/19-8	4·04/13-3	120/n.k.	18·39/198	5·70	n.k.	—	—	89-98 (196-217)	—	
Skyhook Sailwings													
Silhouette	2	10·06/33-0	5·79/19-0	3·76/12-4	120/0·5	18·58/200	5·45	24·5/54	10	61/200	63·5-91 (140-200)	12·5 (23; 14)	Smaller and larger versions under development
UNITED STATES OF AMERICA													
CGS Aviation													
Falcon V	2	8·66/28-5	5·49/18-0	n.k.	105/1·65	14·31/154	5·25	17·7/39	8	61/200	45-63·5 (100-140)	16-19·5 (29-35·5; 18-22)	
Falcon V	2	9·63/31-7	6·10/20-0	n.k.	105/1·65	17·65/190	5·28	18·6/41	8	61/200	61-84 (135-185)	16-19·5 (29-35·5; 18-22)	
Falcon V	2	10·59/34-9	6·71/22-0	n.k.	105/1·65	21·18/228	5·30	19·5/43	8	61/200	77-113 (170-250)	16-19·5 (29-35·5; 18-22)	
Falcon 5+	2	8·66/28-5	5·49/18-0	n.k.	105/1·5	14·31/154	5·25	19·1/42	n.k.	n.k.	45-63·5 (100-140)	n.k.	
Falcon 5+	2	9·63/31-7	6·10/20-0	n.k.	105/1·5	17·65/190	5·28	20·0/44	n.k.	n.k.	61-84 (135-185)	n.k.	
Falcon 5+	2	10·59/34-9	6·71/22-0	n.k.	105/1·5	21·18/228	5·30	20·9/46	n.k.	n.k.	77-113 (170-250)	n.k.	
Delta Wing Kites and Gliders													
Phoenix 6D	n.k.	9·14/30-0	5·49/18-0	3·05/10-0	110/0·25	17·19/185	n.k.	25·4/56	n.k.	61/200	45-125 (100-275)	14 (26; 16)	Three other sizes available
Phoenix Lazor 170	n.k.	9·45/31-0	5·26/17-3	2·44/8-0	130/0·0	15·79/170	5·70	n.k.	n.k.	n.k.	61-79 (135-175)	n.k.	
Phoenix Lazor 190	n.k.	10·06/33-0	5·56/18-3	2·59/8-6	130/0·0	17·65/190	5·70	24·9/55	9·5	55/180	75-100 (165-220)	15 (27·5; 17)	
Eipper-Formance													
Antares 18	n.k.	10·16/33-4	5·49/18-0	2·13/7-0	130/0·25	14·40/155	7·25	24·0/53	8·5*	61/200*	59-75 (130-165)	16 (29; 18)*	*At wing loading of 5·86 kg/m² (1·2 lb/sq ft)
Antares 19	n.k.	10·78/35-4¼	5·79/19-0	2·29/7-6	130/0·25	15·98/172	7·25	24·9/55	8·5*	61/200*	68-84 (150-185)	16 (29; 18)*	*At wing loading of 5·86 kg/m² (1·2 lb/sq ft)
Antares 20	n.k.	11·34/37-2½	6·10/20-0	2·44/8-0	130/0·25	17·65/190	7·25	25·9/57	8·5*	61/200*	77-95 (170-210)	16 (29; 18)*	*At wing loading of 5·86 kg/m² (1·2 lb/sq ft)
Flexi 2-18	n.k.	8·08/26-6	5·49/18-0	3·96/13-0	95/2·5	15·33/165	n.k.	16·8/37	6*	79/260*	50-68 (110-150)	11·5 (21; 13)*	*At wing loading of 5·17 kg/m² (1·06 lb/sq ft)
Flexi 2-20	n.k.	8·99/29-6	6·10/20-0	4·42/14-6	95/2·5	19·05/205	n.k.	18·6/41	6*	79/260*	63·5-82 (140-180)	11·5 (21; 13)*	*At wing loading of 5·17 kg/m² (1·06 lb/sq ft)
Flexi 2-22	n.k.	9·88/32-5	6·71/22-0	5·03/16-6	95/2·5	22·76/245	n.k.	20·9/46	6*	79/260*	77-100 (170-220)	11·5 (21; 13)*	*At wing loading of 5·17 kg/m² (1·06 lb/sq ft)
Flexi 3-18	n.k.	8·71/28-7	5·49/18-0	3·05/10-0	105/1·0	13·94/150	5·40	17·2/38	6·5*	70/230*	45-66 (100-145)	11·5 (21; 13)*	*At wing loading of 5·17 kg/m² (1·06 lb/sq ft)
Flexi 3-20	n.k.	9·68/31-9	6·10/20-0	3·35/11-0	105/1·0	17·19/185	5·40	18·1/40	6·5*	70/230*	61-84 (135-185)	11·5 (21; 13)*	*At wing loading of 5·17 kg/m² (1·06 lb/sq ft)
Flexi 3-22	n.k.	10·64/34-11	6·71/22-0	3·66/12-0	105/1·0	20·44/220	5·40	20·4/45	6·5*	70/230*	79-100 (175-220)	11·5 (21; 13)*	*At wing loading of 5·17 kg/m² (1·06 lb/sq ft)
Electra Flyer *(1979: no 1980 details received)*													
Cirrus 5A	n.k.	10·12/33-2½	6·10/20-0	2·93/9-7¼	112/1·0	18·58/200	5·50	23·1/51	8	76/250	73-100 (160-220)	16 (29;18)	
Cirrus 5B	n.k.	9·45/31-0	5·67/18-7¾	2·74/9-0	112/1·0	16·26/175	5·50	20·9/46	8	76/250	59-77 (130-170)	16 (29;18)	
Cirrus 5C	n.k.	8·75/28-8½	5·27/17-3½	2·53/8-3½	112/1·0	13·94/150	5·50	18·6/41	8	76/250	50-63·5 (110-140)	16 (29;18)	
Cirrus 5D	n.k.	7·99/26-2½	4·81/15-9½	2·32/7-7¼	112/1·0	11·61/125	5·50	17·7/39	8	76/250	36-50 (80-110)	16 (29;18)	
Dove A	n.k.	10·12/33-2½	6·10/20-0	3·23/10-7¼	112/1·75	20·44/220	1·80	23·1/51	7	55/180	73-100 (160-220)	14 (26;16)	
Dove B	n.k.	9·45/31-0	5·67/18-7¾	3·05/10-0	112/1·75	18·02/194	1·80	20·9/46	7	55/180	59-77 (130-170)	14 (26;16)	
Dove C	n.k.	8·75/28-8½	5·27/17-3½	2·83/9-3½	112/1·75	15·61/168	1·80	18·6/41	7	55/180	50-63·5 (110-140)	14 (26;16)	
Dove D	n.k.	7·99/26-2½	4·81/15-9½	2·62/8-7¾	112/1·75	13·47/145	1·70	17·7/39	7	55/180	36-50 (80-110)	14 (26;16)	
Electra Floater 165	n.k.	9·21/30-2½	5·18/17-0	2·81/9-2½	120/0·5	15·33/165	5·53	24·0/53	n.k.	n.k.	45-68 (100-150)	15-16 (27·5-29;17-18)	
Electra Floater 185	n.k.	9·75/32-0	5·49/18-0	2·97/9-9	120/0·5	17·19/185	5·53	24·9/55	n.k.	n.k.	59-77 (130-170)	15-16 (27·5-29;17-18)	
Electra Floater 205	n.k.	10·27/33-8¾	5·79/19-0	3·12/10-3	120/0·5	19·05/205	5·53	25·9/57	n.k.	n.k.	68-86 (150-190)	15-16 (27·5-29;17-18)	
Electra Floater 230	n.k.	10·88/35-8¾	6·10/20-0	3·32/10-10¾	120/0·5	21·37/230	5·53	29·5/65	n.k.	n.k.	77-100 (170-220)	15-16 (27·5-29;17-18)	
Olympus 140	n.k.	10·06/33-0	5·79/19-0	1·86/6-1¾	122/0·15	12·91/139	7·83	21·8/48	9	61/200	52-63·5 (115-140)	11·5 (21;13)	
Olympus 160	n.k.	10·67/35-0	5·94/19-6	2·29/7-6	123/0·15	14·68/158	7·70	22·7/50	9	61/200	66-77 (145-170)	11·5 (21;13)	
Olympus 180	n.k.	10·92/35-10	6·20/20-4	2·62/8-7¾	123/0·15	16·63/179	7·20	23·6/52	9	61/200	79-100 (175-220)	11·5 (21;13)	
Flight Designs													
Lancer IVS	n.k.	9·91/32-6	n.k.	2·74/9-0	120/n.k.	n.k.	6·90	20·9/46	n.k.	n.k.	n.k.	n.k.	
Lancer IVL	n.k.	10·36/34-0	n.k.	3·00/9-10	120/n.k.	n.k.	6·90	22·7/50	n.k.	n.k.	n.k.	n.k.	
Pacific Gull *(1979: no 1980 details received)*													
Alpine 1-0	n.k.	9·91/32-6	5·79/19-0	2·74/9-0	115/1·0	15·79/170	6·21	23·1/51	9·5	63-66/205-215	54-75 (120-165)	8 (14·5;9)	
Alpine 1-5	n.k.	9·91/32-6	5·79/19-0	2·74/9-0	115/1·0	16·54/178	6·21	23·4/51·5	9·5	63-66/205-215	63·5-79 (140-175)	8 (14·5;9)	
Alpine 2-0	n.k.	10·36/34-0	6·10/20-0	3·05/10-0	115/1·0	17·28/186	6·22	23·6/52	9·5	63-66/205-215	75-100 (166-220)	8 (14·5;9)	
Alpine 2-5	n.k.	10·36/34-0	6·10/20-0	3·05/10-0	115/1·0	19·14/206	6·22	24·0/53	9·5	63-66/205-215	84-106 (185-235)	8 (14·5;9)	

Manufacturer and Model	FAI class	Span: m/ ft-in	Leading-edge: m/ ft-in	Keel: m/ ft-in	Nose/ Billow angle: degrees	Wing area: m²/ sq ft	Wing aspect ratio	Weight: kg/lb	Glide ratio	Sink rate: m/ft per min	Pilot weight kg (lb)	Stalling speed knots (km/h; mph)	Remarks
Seagull Aircraft													
9 Meter	1	9·14/30-0	5·49/18-0	2·49/8-2*	110/0-0	14·68/158	5·70	20·4/45	8·5	61/200	45-63·5 (100-140)	12·5 (23;14)	*Root chord
10 Meter	1	9·91/32-6	6·10/20-0	2·92/9-7*	110/0-0	17·09/184	5·71	24·9/55	8·5	61/200	59-82 (130-180)	12·5 (23;14)	*Root chord
11 Meter	1	10·46/34-4	6·40/21-0	2·92/9-7*	110/0-0	19·60/211	5·58	27·2/60	8·5	61/200	77-100 (170-220)	12·5 (23;14)	*Root chord
Sailwing	1	n.k.	n.k.	n.k.	180/n.k.	n.k.	n.k.	n.k.	11-12*	55/180*	59-86 (130-190)	13·5 (24·5;15)	*Estimated
Seahawk 155	1	8·31/27-3	5·18/17-0	3·26/10-8½*	102/n.k.	14·40/155	4·80	19·1/42	7	61/200	41-59 (90-130)	10·5 (19·5;12)	*Root chord
Seahawk 180	1	9·30/30-6	5·79/19-0	3·58/11-9*	102/n.k.	16·72/180	5·20	20·9/46	7	61/200	59-77 (130-170)	10·5 (19·5;12)	*Root chord
Seahawk 200	1	9·75/32-0	6·10/20-0	3·89/12-9*	102/n.k.	18·58/200	5·10	22·7/50	7	61/200	77-100 (170-220)	10·5 (19·5;12)	*Root chord
Sierra 185	1	10·36/34-0	n.k.	n.k.	132/0-0	17·19/185	n.k.	29·5/65	10	55/180	54-82 (120-180)	12·5 (23;14)	
Sierra 205	1	10·06/33-0	n.k.	n.k.	132/0-0	19·05/205	n.k.	29·5/65	10	55/180	75-104 (165-230)	12·5 (23;14)	
Sky Sports (1979: no 1980 details received)													
Bobcat IV	1	9·07/29-9	5·79/19-0	3·96/13-0	100/1·5	19·51/210	4·21	21·8/48	7	n.k.	n.k.	n.k.	All available in other sizes
Eaglet	1	8·46/27-9	5·79/19-0	3·96/13-0	105/1·5	13·10/141	4·00	15·9/35	6	n.k.	n.k.	n.k.	
Osprey II	2	9·88/32-5	6·02/19-9	3·66/12-0	110/1·0	19·23/207	5·08	21·8/48	8	n.k.	n.k.	n.k.	
Sirocco III	2	10·67/35-0	6·40/21-0	2·74/9-0	120/0-0	17·19/185	6·62	24·5/54	10	n.k.	n.k.	n.k.	
Sunbird Ultralight Gliders													
Nova 150	2	8·92/29-3	4·88/16-0	3·66/12-0	130/1-0	13·94/150	5·70	20·4/45	8·5	58/190	45-63·5 (100-140)	15 (27·5;17)	
Nova 170	2	9·45/31-0	5·18/17-0	3·81/12-6	130/1-0	15·79/170	5·70	22·2/49	8·5	58/190	54-72 (120-160)	15 (27·5;17)	
Nova 190	2	10·00/32-9¾	5·49/18-0	3·96/13-0	130/1-0	17·65/190	5·70	23·6/52	8·5	58/190	63·5-86 (140-190)	15 (27·5;17)	
Nova 210	2	10·52/34-6	5·79/19-0	4·27/14-0	130/1-0	19·51/210	5·70	27·2/60	8·5	58/190	72-91 (160-200)	15 (27·5;17)	
Nova 230	2	10·97/36-0	6·10/20-0	4·42/14-6	130/1-0	21·37/230	5·70	28·1/62	8·5	58/190	79-100 (175-220)	15 (27·5;17)	
Ultimate Hi													
Starship 170	n.k.	10·46/34-4	5·79/19-0	2·44/8-0	124/1-0	15·79/170	6·10	23·6/52	n.k.	n.k.	54-82 (120-180)	n.k.	
Starship 190	n.k.	10·67/35-0	5·94/19-6	2·59/8-6	124/1-0	17·65/190	6·00	24·9/55	n.k.	n.k.	68-100 (150-220)	n.k.	
Starship 220	n.k.	11·38/37-4	6·35/20-10	2·84/9-4	124/1-0	20·44/220	6·20	26·3/58	n.k.	n.k.	82-113 (180-250)	n.k.	
UP Inc													
Mosquito 146	2	10·00/32-9¾	5·32/17-5⅝	1·78/5-10	136·4/0·2	13·47/145	7·40	22·7/50	10+	55/180	56-83 (123-183)	13·5 (24·5;15) IAS	
Mosquito 166	2	10·61/34-9½	5·70/18-8½	1·91/6-3	136·4/0·2	15·14/163	7·40	24·5/54	10+	55/180	64-94 (141-207)	13·5 (24·5;15) IAS	
Mosquito 196	2	11·55/37-10¾	6·22/20-4⅞	2·08/6-10	136·4/0·2	18·02/194	7·40	29·0/64	10+	55/180	78-113 (172-249)	13·5 (24·5;15) IAS	
Wills Wing													
Alpha 155	2	8·94/29-4	5·18/17-0	3·35/11-0	111/0·5	14·40/155	5·55	20·0/44	10+	<61/200	50-66 (110-145)	16 (29;18)	
Alpha 185	2	9·70/31-10	5·64/18-6	3·66/12-0	111/0·5	17·19/185	5·50	21·3/47	10+	<61/200	63·5-79 (140-175)	16 (29;18)	
Alpha 215	2	10·52/34-6	6·10/20-0	3·96/13-0	111/0·5	19·97/215	5·50	23·6/52	10+	<61/200	75-93 (165-205)	16 (29;18)	
Alpha 245	2	11·28/37-0	6·55/21-6	4·27/14-0	111/0·5	22·76/245	5·60	26·3/58	10+	<61/200	86-113 (190-250)	16 (29;18)	
Boomer (prototype)	2	11·58/38-0	5·49/18-0	2·13/7-0	140/0-0	18·58/200	7·20	24·9/55	10+	<61/200	56-91 (125-200)	16 (29;18)	
Omega 180	2	10·82/35-6	6·17/20-3	3·58/11-9	120/0·5	16·72/180	7·00	24·9/55	10+	<61/200	59-79 (130-175)	16 (29;18)	
Omega 220	2	11·58/38-0	6·68/21-11	3·78/12-5	120/0·5	20·44/220	6·60	29·0/64	10+	<61/200	75-100 (165-220)	16 (29;18)	
Omega 260	2	12·34/40-6	7·14/23-5	3·99/13-1	120/0·5	22·76/245	6·70	32·7/72	10+	<61/200	91-120 (200-265)	16 (29;18)	
Omni 187 ('200')	2	10·85/35-7	6·25/20-6	3·66/12-0	120/0·2	17·37/187	6·80	26·3/58	10+	<61/200	70-88 (155-195)	16 (29;18)	
Omni 213	2	11·73/38-6	6·78/22-3	3·91/12-10	120/0·2	19·79/213	7·00	29·0/66	10+	<61/200	79-102 (175-225)	16 (29;18)	
Raven 179	2	9·60/31-6	5·55/18-2½	3·75/12-3½	115/1-0	16·63/179	5·50	22·2/49	10+	<61/200	52-77 (115-170)	16 (29;18)	
Raven 209	2	10·52/34-6	6·10/20-0	3·84/12-7¼	115/1-0	19·42/209	5·70	26·3/58	10+	<61/200	68-95 (150-210)	16 (29;18)	
Raven 229	2	11·04/36-2½	6·40/21-0	4·11/13-6	115/1-0	21·27/229	5·70	28·1/62	10+	<61/200	77-104 (170-230)	16 (29;18)	

n.k. = not known

— = not available

LIGHTER-THAN-AIR: AIRSHIPS

JAPAN

Latest radio-controlled research airship in the Fuji Model 500 Aero-Ship series

FUJI
FUJI MANUFACTURING CO LTD

16 Hotoku-cho, Kita-ku, Nagoya
Telephone: (052) 991 8171
PRESIDENT: Yasushi Koizumi

In the Autumn of 1974 Fuji Manufacturing Co began construction of a small remotely controlled pilotless research airship (construction number 2) which flew for the first time on 23 December 1974. (It is believed that No. 1 was the airship built by members of the Japan Experimental Aircraft Association and described under the JEAA heading in the 1975-76 *Jane's*.)

Airship No. 3 flew on 28 July 1975, this being a modified version of No. 2. No details are known of Nos 4, 5 and 6; but No. 7, which first flew on 21 November 1975, has an overall length of 6·0 m (19 ft 7½ in) and was supplied to Tohoku University Geographical Laboratory. Airship No. 12 was under test at the end of 1978, but no recent information on the progress of this programme has been received from the company.

FUJI MODEL 500 AERO-SHIP

The word Aero-Ship, which forms a part of the designation of the Fuji Model 500, is an allusion to the unique aeroplane-type horizontal lifting surface which is attached to the lower structure of the gondola. The Aero-Ship's envelope is helium filled, and it is claimed that the wing not only provides additional lift but, in conjunction with the fairly large tail surfaces, ought to make the vessel highly manoeuvrable. Flown under radio control, it is suggested that the Aero-Ship could be utilised for such applications as aerial photography, various forms of meteorological and pollution measurement, seed and fertiliser distribution, and advertising.

The envelope of the Model 500 is of plastics, the gondola and cruciform tail surfaces of wood, with silk cover-

ing. Tailplane incidence is normally 3°, but is ground adjustable. Trim tabs in elevators. The wing is also of wood, with silk covering. Wing section is Göttingen Gö 535 and the wing is normally mounted without incidence. Two handling wheels, with tyres of 365 mm (14·4 in) diameter, are mounted beneath the wing, one at the aft end of the gondola and one beneath the lower fin. Two ENYA 60 IIIB aircooled engines, each developing 0·97 kW (1·3 hp), are mounted at the rear of the gondola, at each end of an outrigger. The forward part of the gondola is able to house a camera or other equipment. Radio control equipment and batteries are accommodated in the central area, and a fuel tank in the aft section.

Limited range of the radio control equipment used to date has prevented full evaluation of the Aero-Ship's performance, but a speed range of 5·4-43 knots (10-80 km/h; 6·2-50 mph) and ceiling of 1,000 m (3,280 ft) have been demonstrated.

DIMENSIONS:
Length overall	8·0 m (26 ft 3 in)
Wing span	3·26 m (10 ft 8½ in)
Wing chord, constant	0·68 m (2 ft 2¾ in)
Tailplane span	2·25 m (7 ft 4½ in)

DIMENSIONS, ENVELOPE:
Max diameter	1·90 m (6 ft 2¾ in)
Volume, gross	18·28 m³ (645 cu ft)

AREAS:
Wings, gross	1·01 m² (10·87 sq ft)
Rudders (total)	0·43 m² (4·63 sq ft)
Tailplane	0·86 m² (9·26 sq ft)
Elevators (incl tabs)	0·49 m² (5·27 sq ft)

WEIGHTS AND LOADING:
Weight empty, equipped	22·7 kg (50 lb)
Weight, helium filled	4·0 kg (8·8 lb)
Max T-O weight	6·0 kg (13·2 lb)
Max wing loading	5·96 kg/m² (1·22 lb/sq ft)

UNITED KINGDOM

AIRSHIP INDUSTRIES
AIRSHIP INDUSTRIES LTD

HEAD OFFICE: Meadows Court, Ramsey, Isle of Man
LONDON OFFICE: 2 York Street, London W1H 1FA
Telephone: (01) 486 3356
Telex: 299964 Bitco G

On 12 June 1980 Thermo-Skyships Ltd, an airship design company based on the Isle of Man, acquired the assets of Airship Developments Ltd (formerly Aerospace Developments, a CAA approved manufacturer) for the sum of £1·1 million: the resulting company is known as Airship Industries Ltd. It is the intention of this company to build initially two new Skyship 500s (formerly AD-500), and it is planned that the first of these will be flown during 1981 from new facilities, including an airship hangar, that are to be built on the Isle of Man. The original AD-500 airframe is now to be used for static and structural testing.

It was understood in mid-1980 that there is considerable interest in the Skyship 500 in Australia, and that the Royal Navy and the United States Navy both wish to carry out flight test and evaluation of this vessel. This emphasises the current interest in airships for such duties as maritime patrol, fishery protection, and anti-submarine warfare, as a result of which Airship Industries is to complete by 1981 the tooling to build to order a special-purpose AEW version which has been allocated the designation Skyship 5000. This would carry comprehensive avionics, possibly including the MSA (Mission System Avionics) which Marconi Avionics Ltd has developed for the British Aerospace Nimrod AEW Mk 3.

Details of the Skyship 600 (formerly AD-600) appear in this entry, but the company will build examples of this vessel only to specific order.

On 11 July 1980, Redcoat Cargo Airlines, a Surrey-based freight operator, announced that it had concluded an agreement with Airship Industries covering the supply of four rigid cargo airships, with options for ten more. Allocated the provisional designation Model 4060 by Airship Industries, detail design was in progress in the Summer of 1980. It is planned that the second Skyship 500 will be used for test and evaluation by Redcoat Cargo Airlines.

AIRSHIP INDUSTRIES SKYSHIP 500

The envelope of the Skyship 500 (originally AD-500) is manufactured from a strong-in-weft single-ply polyester fabric, developed by Airship Industries, and coated with titanium dioxide polyurethane sealant to minimise loss of

Airship Industries' original prototype AD-500 non-rigid airship moored at its transportable mast

the helium lifting gas. The nose structure consists of a domed disc, moulded from Kevlar and carrying the fitting by which the airship is moored to its transportable mast. Two ballonets, which together comprise 25 per cent of the envelope volume, are installed fore and aft, so that differential inflation will provide some degree of fore and aft trim. Catenary curtains carry 12 main cables of Kevlar within the envelope for suspension of the gondola. The tail unit is of conventional cruciform layout, each surface being attached to the envelope at its root and braced by four wires on each side. All four surfaces are constructed from interlocking ribs and spars of Fibrelam and have GRP skins: their hinged rudder and elevator control surfaces are cable-operated and each has a trim tab.

The gondola is a one-piece moulding of Kevlar-reinforced plastics, with flooring and bulkheads of Fibre-

lam panels; those which form the engine compartment at the rear of the gondola are faced with stainless steel for fire protection. There is accommodation for a pilot and co-pilot, with dual controls, although the vessel is designed to be flown by a single pilot; there are seven individual seats for passengers. Door on port side, just aft of flight deck. Transparent plastics dome in ceiling of flight deck for visual internal inspection of envelope. Ballast in the form of lead shot is contained in a box situated below the crew seats, and water ballast totalling 513 kg (1,130 lb) is contained in tanks at the rear of the gondola. A single fully-castoring wheel with pneumatic tyre is mounted on an oleo-pneumatic strut beneath the gondola to ensure that the latter is not damaged by contact with the ground.

Power plant comprises two 149 kW (200 hp) Porsche six-cylinder aircooled motorcar engines. Each drives, via a modified Lynx helicopter tail rotor gearbox, a ducted propulsor designed by Airship Industries, consisting of a Hoffmann five-blade reversible-pitch metal propeller rotating within an annular duct constructed of GRP, reinforced with carbon fibre. Each propulsor can be rotated about its pylon attachment to the gondola through an arc of 210°: 90° upward and 120° downward. The 30° of movement past centre with the ducted propulsors facing downward is to maintain cable tension while the airship is being moored to its mast. The vectored thrust available throughout this range of 210° simplifies the tasks of take-off and landing. A fuel tank, capacity 536 litres (118 Imp gallons), is mounted at rear of engine compartment. Max fuel capacity is 1,577 litres (347 Imp gallons). Engine modifications include provision of automatic mixture control, fuel injection and electronic ignition. The 28V electrical system is supplied by engine-driven alternators. Avionics installed in the prototype Skyship 500 include Bendix 2000 series dual nav/com, ADF, VOR/ILS and Omega, Bendix 1400 weather radar, and Decca Doppler 80 nav system with PBDI and automatic chart display.

DIMENSIONS, ENVELOPE:
Length overall	50·00 m (164 ft 0½ in)
Max diameter	14·00 m (45 ft 11¼ in)
Volume, gross	5,130 m³ (181,160 cu ft)
Volume, ballonets	1,282·5 m³ (45,290 cu ft)

DIMENSIONS, GONDOLA:
Length overall	9·25 m (30 ft 4 in)
Height	2·26 m (7 ft 4⅞ in)
Max width	2·41 m (7 ft 10¾ in)

WEIGHT:
Nominal payload to 610 m (2,000 ft)	
	2,540 kg (5,600 lb)

PERFORMANCE (estimated):
Max level speed	62 knots (114 km/h; 71 mph)
Cruising speed	49 knots (90 km/h; 56 mph)
Pressure altitude	3,050 m (10,000 ft)
Range with 1,577 litres (347 Imp gallons) of fuel, 15% reserves:	
at 15 knots (28 km/h; 17 mph)	
	6,375 nm (11,800 km; 7,335 miles)
at max speed	600 nm (1,110 km; 690 miles)

AIRSHIP INDUSTRIES SKYSHIP 600

Airship Industries has completed the design of what is basically a 'stretched' version of the Skyship 500. The increased volume of the envelope will provide approximately 1,016 kg (2,240 lb) more lift, and the lengthened gondola would have a usable floor area of 11·15 m² (120 sq ft). Developed to meet the needs of operators who require greater payload and/or endurance than are provided by the Skyship 500, it is considered to be suited to roles which require long-endurance patrols or extended time on station. With the maximum fuel that can be carried, patrols of up to three days' duration would be possible, and the large cabin would permit a high degree of crew comfort and efficiency.

Airship Industries believes that the size and capability of the Skyship 600 would make it particularly suitable for deployment in a surveillance role, but other obvious military applications include minesweeping, ASW and electronic warfare. It is understood that the Royal Navy and US Navy are interested in evaluating such a vessel for maritime applications.

ENVELOPE: Of ellipsoidal form with parallel mid-body. Four load curtains and two ballonets. Envelope fabric comprises a Terylene strength layer, with a weather protection coating of titanium oxide-loaded polyurethane, and an internal helium-retention layer of Saran film.

TAIL FINS: Of conventional cruciform layout, each aerofoil section has ribs and spars constructed from Ciba Geigy Fibrelam-bonded honeycomb structure panels. Control surfaces have setback hinges, balance tabs, and adjustable gearing to minimise control forces.

GONDOLA: A one-piece shell, moulded from Kevlar. Fireproof bulkheads in engine bay are honeycomb panels, faced with stainless steel skins. For patrol, or associated military duties, accommodation can be provided for a crew of up to seven, with bunks, galley, mess, and toilet facilities. In a passenger-carrying role, up to 20 passenger seats can be installed at a pitch of 0·91 m (36 in). For use as a cargo carrier in an emergency, the gondola can be configured to provide a maximum disposable freight capacity of 28·32 m³ (1,000 cu ft).

POWER PLANT: Two 186·4 kW (250 hp) Porsche Turbo 930 turbocharged engines. Each drives, via a Westland bevel gearbox, a ducted propulsor designed by Airship Industries which houses a Hoffmann five-blade variable-pitch fan. Each propulsor can be rotated about its pylon attachment to the gondola through an arc of 180°, thus simplifying the tasks of take-off and landing. A fuel tank, mounted at the rear of the engine compartment, has a maximum capacity of 2,273 litres (500 Imp gallons).

AVIONICS AND EQUIPMENT: Full equipment and instrumentation for IFR operation by day or night is standard. Optional avionics considered suitable for surveillance and patrol include Bendix RDR 1400 digital radar, Ferranti Sea Spray, or MEL Marec. Bendix radar and Omega VLF navigation is optional for civil versions of the AD-600, and is considered suitable also for a surveillance role.

DIMENSIONS, ENVELOPE:
Length overall	56·00 m (183 ft 8¾ in)
Max diameter	14·00 m (45 ft 11¼ in)
Height overall	18·65 m (61 ft 2¼ in)
Tail fin span	17·00 m (55 ft 9¼ in)
Volume, gross	6,055 m³ (213,830 cu ft)
Volume, ballonets	1,332·1 m³ (47,040 cu ft)
Helium volume, at 85% inflation	
	5,146 m³ (181,730 cu ft)
L/D ratio	4·0

DIMENSIONS, GONDOLA:
Length overall	12·10 m (39 ft 8¼ in)
Length between cabin bulkheads	
	7·00 m (22 ft 11½ in)
Height	1·96 m (6 ft 5¼ in;
Max width	2·41 m (7 ft 10¾ in)

WEIGHTS (estimated, A: patrol configuration; B: passenger configuration):
Weight empty, basic: A, B	3,331 kg (7,344 lb)
Fuel weight: A	1,633 kg (3,600 lb)
B	816 kg (1,799 lb)
Max T-O weight: A	6,220 kg (13,713 lb)
B	6,087 kg (13,420 lb)
Gross lift at 85% inflation, ISA, plus vectored thrust	
	6,270 kg (13,823 lb)

PERFORMANCE (estimated):
Max level speed	65 knots (120 km/h; 75 mph)
Max cruising speed	50 knots (93 km/h; 58 mph)
Cruising speed (43·3 kW; 58 hp rating per engine)	
	40 knots (74 km/h; 46 mph)
Cruising speed (26·1 kW; 39 hp rating per engine)	
	35 knots (64 km/h; 40 mph)
Max rate of climb at S/L	610 m (2,000 ft)/min
Rate of climb at S/L, at max cruising power	
	549 m (1,800 ft)/min
Cruising altitude	610 m (2,000 ft)
Pressure height (85% inflation at S/L)	
	1,675 m (5,500 ft)
Max altitude pressure height, with ballonets full at S/L	
	2,440 m (8,000 ft)

AIRSHIP INDUSTRIES MODEL 4060

This airship, under detail design for Redcoat Cargo Airlines, is of rigid configuration and will have a cargo capacity of 1,069 m³ (37,755 cu ft), compared with the total cargo volume of 670·83 m³ (23,690 cu ft) for a Boeing 747-200F Freighter. Apart from offering considerably more economical operation than a fixed-wing aircraft, which it is believed will open up new export markets because of lower airfreight rates, it is anticipated that such a vessel will allow cargoes to be flown directly from factory to factory, since landing sites can be established at low cost. It is planned that construction of the prototype will begin in early 1982.

As envisaged prior to final design, the Model 4060 will have conventional lines for a rigid airship, except that the flight deck will be located in the nose of the vessel. It will have four cruciform tail fins, with control surfaces; the power plant will comprise four 835 kW (1,120 shp) Pratt & Whitney Aircraft of Canada PT6A-50 turboprop engines.

DIMENSIONS:
Length overall	182·88 m (600 ft)
Diameter	36·58 m (120 ft)
Span over tail fins	54·86 m (180 ft)
Volume, gross	128,559 m³ (4,540,000 cu ft)
Volume, gas	119,498 m³ (4,220,000 cu ft)

AREAS:
Hull surface area	16,201 m² (174,395 sq ft)
Total nett fin area	826·8 m² (8,900 sq ft)

WEIGHTS:
Weight empty	51,030 kg (112,500 lb)
Aerostatic lift at pressure altitude	
	103,455 kg (228,080 lb)
Max vertical T-O weight	113,800 kg (250,890 lb)

PERFORMANCE (estimated at 915 m; 3,000 ft altitude):
Design diving speed 103·5 knots (192 km/h; 119 mph)	
Max level speed at max continuous power	
	95·3 knots (177 km/h; 110 mph)
Cruising speed, at cruising power	
	67·6 knots (126 km/h; 78 mph)
Ferry range, still air, at cruising speed of 50 knots (92·5 km/h; 57·5 mph) 10,420 nm (19,310 km; 12,000 miles)	
Range with 58 ton payload	
	435 nm (805 km; 500 miles)
Range with 45 ton payload	
	1,735 nm (3,215 km; 2,000 miles)
Range with 40 ton payload	
	2,170 nm (4,020 km; 2,500 miles)

CAMERON
CAMERON BALLOONS LTD
1 Cotham Park, Bristol BS6 6BZ
Telephone: (0272) 41455

DIRECTORS:
D. A. Cameron, BSc (Aero Eng), MIE, MRAeS
Kim Cameron
R. I. M. Kerr, BSc, MRAeS
Tom Sage, ARPS, AIIP

Cameron Balloons Ltd, which designs and manufactures a wide range of hot-air balloons (which see), also designed and built the world's first hot-air airship, of which production versions are available. A new airship has been designed and built, and in early 1980 was undergoing a development programme. It is intended to be available as a kite balloon, or as a one-pilot airship, under the respective designations C-38 and D-38. Gross volume of the envelope is 1,075 m³ (38,000 cu ft).

CAMERON D96 HOT-AIR AIRSHIP

First flight of the prototype (G-BAMK) was made at Wantage, Berkshire, on 7 January 1973. Since that time a considerable amount of work has been carried out to improve and develop the airship, and the current production model has two vertical and two horizontal stabilisers. An improved method of suspending the gondola has also been developed, eliminating distortion of the envelope which occurred in the early stages. During 1978, further development led to an increase in the length and volume of the envelope. Like the envelopes of Cameron hot-air balloons, this is made from a light but high-strength nylon

The C-38 kite balloon version of Cameron's new hot-air airship during early tests

fabric. A lightweight gondola carries the propane burner, gas supply, pilot and power plant. A maximum of two passengers can be accommodated.

Power plant is a 33·5 kW (45 hp) 1,600 cc Volkswagen modified motor car engine, using propane as fuel and driving a large-diameter semi-shrouded pusher propeller.

The first production airship was completed for a customer in the USA; several more have been constructed for customers in Australia, Belgium, Canada, France, the Netherlands, Sweden and the UK.

The following data apply to the current version, with the envelope lengthened by 3·66 m (12 ft):

DIMENSIONS, ENVELOPE:
Length overall	34·14 m (112 ft 0 in)

Max diameter	13·72 m (45 ft 0 in)
Volume, gross	2,917 m³ (103,000 cu ft)

PERFORMANCE:
Max speed	13 knots (24 km/h; 15 mph)
Turning radius at 8·7 knots (16 km/h; 10 mph)	30·5 m (100 ft)
Endurance	2 h

THUNDER
THUNDER BALLOONS LTD

75 Leonard Street, London EC2A 4QS
Telephone: (01) 739 0775/0776
Telex: 261234 reference H5758D
CHAIRMAN: K. F. Simonds

DIRECTORS:
T. M. Donnelly (Managing)
A. R. Wirth

Thunder Balloons has been involved in the design and development of a hot-air airship during the past two years. A one-fifth-scale radio controlled model has been flown successfully, confirming flight characteristics. The full-size airship was still under construction in the Spring of 1980,

and was scheduled for delivery to an English customer later in the year. No new details had been released in early 1980, and it is known only that the envelope length is approximately 38·10 m (125 ft), diameter 12·19 m (40 ft), and gross volume 3,965 m³ (140,000 cu ft). The gondola, with burner mounted above, will accommodate three persons. Design maximum speed is quoted as 25 knots (46 km/h; 29 mph).

UNITED STATES OF AMERICA

BOLAND
BOLAND BALLOON

Pine Drive, RD 2, Burlington, Connecticut 06013
Telephone: (203) 673 1307

BOLAND A-1 ALBATROSS

Mr Brian Boland, an art and photographic teacher at Farmington High School, Connecticut, has, with his wife Kathy, designed and built several hot-air balloons, described in the Balloons section, as well as a hot-air airship named *Albatross*. Construction began in January 1975 and it was flown for the first time on 11 October 1975.

The envelope is made from 32 separate strips of polyurethane-coated rip-stop nylon. The gondola, which can accommodate four persons, has a basic structure of light alloy, around which wicker sidewalls have been woven. It has oak landing skids on its undersurface, and is mounted on a wheeled trailer for easy ground handling, this being left on the ground on lift-off. The gondola is suspended from the envelope by 28 flexible steel cables which run through its light alloy tubular framework and are attached to two catenary suspension curtains. The tubular framework of the gondola serves also as mounting for three 8 million BTU propane burners. The fuel supply comprises six low-pressure cylinders, with a combined capacity of 227 litres (60 US gallons) of liquid propane, and a 22·7 litre (6 US gallon) tank of fuel/oil mixture for the propulsion engine. This is a 29·8 kW (40 hp) Rockwell JLO two-stroke engine, driving a Banks Maxwell two-blade ducted pusher propeller.

On the basis of flight experience with *Albatross* Mr Boland designed a number of improvements, including shortening each of the original catenary cables by 2·29 m (7 ft 6 in); adding 7·32 m (24 ft) of catenary curtain aft of the original curtains; and improving the structural integrity of the gondola by heliarc welding of all metal fittings. The rigid-frame fabric-covered fin and rudder, with which *Albatross* was flown originally, was replaced by a multi-chambered inflatable fin and rudder with three times the surface area. Initial flight testing showed that this could deflate during prolonged turns, and an enlarged-scoop fin pressurisation sleeve has been designed and installed. The *Albatross* was flown in this form for the first time at the end

Boland A-1 *Albatross* in flight, giving clear view of fin and rudder pressurisation scoop

of August 1979. Testing has shown that it is possible to operate this vessel as a free balloon, with the power plant closed down.

A second hot-air airship, named *Roover*, was designed in 1978. This will have a volume of about 1,982-2,265 m³ (70,000-80,000 cu ft) and is described as being ultra-lightweight, responsive and compact. Construction was expected to start in 1980.

The following details apply to *Albatross*:

DIMENSIONS, OVERALL:
Length	34·14 m (112 ft 0 in)
Height	19·81 m (65 ft 0 in)
Width	15·24 m (50 ft 0 in)
Volume	3,965 m³ (140,000 cu ft)

DIMENSIONS, GONDOLA:
Length overall	3·35 m (11 ft 0 in)
Height	3·05 m (10 ft 0 in)
Width	1·22 m (4 ft 0 in)

WEIGHTS:
Flight weight, fuelled	658 kg (1,450 lb)
Max design gross weight	1,089 kg (2,400 lb)

PERFORMANCE:
Max speed	approx 8·7 knots (16 km/h; 10 mph)
Turning radius	approx 91 m (300 ft)

GOODYEAR
THE GOODYEAR TIRE & RUBBER COMPANY—AIRSHIP OPERATIONS

1144 East Market Street, Akron, Ohio 44316
Telephone: (216) 794 4045
CHAIRMAN OF THE BOARD AND CHIEF EXECUTIVE OFFICER:
Charles J. Pilliod Jr
CORPORATE DIRECTOR PUBLIC RELATIONS:
William L. Newkirk

Goodyear has built over 300 airships, more than any other company in the world. Of these, over 250 were constructed under contract for the US Army and Navy, and included the USS *Akron* and USS *Macon,* the largest rigid airships constructed in the USA. The remainder have been commercial airships, of which the first was the *Pilgrim,* launched in 1925.

Goodyear operates currently four non-rigid airships for public relations and sales promotion activities: *America, Columbia, Europa* and *Enterprise. Europa* is based near Rome, Italy, the other three airships in the USA. Details of the newly constructed *Enterprise* follow. In size, equipment and performance it is generally the same as the three other airships in the fleet.

Goodyear has been studying the development of heavy-lift airships, and believes that existing technology can provide such a vehicle in the 1980s if adequate funding is available. The company suggests that a helium-filled airship, using helicopter-type rotors for lift and conventional propellers for forward flight, would prove more economical than helicopters in a flying-crane role, and

The new non-rigid airship *Enterprise*, constructed by Goodyear during 1979

would also have a very much greater lift capability. Studies indicate that by using such techniques a 73,625 m³ (2·6 million cu ft) airship would have a useful lifting capacity of 76·2 tonnes (75 tons).

ENTERPRISE

The *Enterprise* (N1A) was constructed during 1979 and erected at Houston, Texas, where it was flown for the first time in late October 1979. Some two weeks later it was flown to its base at Pompano Beach, Florida. Like its sister ships, it has a gross volume of 5,740 m³ (202,700 cu ft) and envelope surface area of 2,006 m² (21,600 sq ft). The envelope is made of two-ply Neoprene-coated Dacron and is helium-filled. On each side is a four-colour sign 32·00 m (105 ft 0 in) long and 7·47 m (24 ft 6 in) high, containing 3,780 lamps to flash static or animated messages. These can be read at a distance of 1·6 km (1 mile) when the airship is cruising at a height of 305 m (1,000 ft). A turbojet APU, mounted in a removable pod on the undersurface of the 'ship's gondola, drives a 500A 28V generator to supply electrical power for the signs and their control equipment. The turbojet is designed to operate without developing any appreciable amount of forward thrust for the airship.

The gondola, attached to the undersurface of the envelope, has accommodation for a pilot and six passengers, and has a single non-retractable landing wheel mounted beneath it.

Power plant consists of two 157 kW (210 hp) Continental IO-360-D flat-six engines, each driving a Hartzell two-blade metal reversible-pitch pusher propeller. Tankage is provided for 527 litres (138 US gallons) of fuel.

DIMENSIONS, OVERALL:
Length	58·67 m (192 ft 6 in)
Width	15·24 m (50 ft 0 in)
Height	18·14 m (59 ft 6 in)

DIMENSIONS, ENVELOPE:
Length	58·00 m (190 ft 3½ in)
Max diameter	14·00 m (45 ft 11½ in)

Model of heavy-lift airship studied by the Goodyear company

Fineness ratio		14·4	Max design gross weight	5,824 kg (12,840 lb)
Volume, gross	5,740 m³ (202,700 cu ft)		PERFORMANCE:	
Volume, ballonets	1,662·2 m³ (58,700 cu ft)		Max speed	43·5 knots (80 km/h; 50 mph)
DIMENSIONS, GONDOLA:			Normal cruising speed	
Length overall		6·93 m (22 ft 9 in)		30-35 knots (56-64 km/h; 35-40 mph)
Height		2·47 m (8 ft 1¼ in)	Max rate of climb at S/L	732 m (2,400 ft)/min
Height, incl landing gear		3·59 m (11 ft 9½ in)	Max rate of descent	427 m (1,400 ft)/min
Width at ceiling		2·13 m (7 ft 0 in)	Normal operational altitude	
Width at floor		1·31 m (4 ft 3½ in)		305-915 m (1,000-3,000 ft)
WEIGHTS:			Service ceiling	2,285 m (7,500 ft)
Weight empty		4,252 kg (9,375 lb)	Endurance at cruising speed	approx 10 h

HOV-AIR-SHIP
HOV-AIR-SHIP INC
1427 West 22nd Street, Miami Beach, Florida 33140
Telephone: (305) 531 8968/8969

HOV-AIR-SHIP HX-1
Designed by Mr Saul I. Slater, who formed Hov-Air-Ship Inc to hold the patents of this and other designs he has produced, the HX-1 is a small-scale remotely controlled airship 5·79 m (19 ft) long and 2·13 m (7 ft) in diameter, with cruciform tail surfaces. It has been test-flown tethered to a 110V electrical power source and piloted by a controller on the ground; a magnetic device was provided to moor the airship, without any need for groundcrew assistance.

A feature which at the present time is unique to this airship is an ability to hover over a fixed point, and ascend or descend above that point.

The HX-1 was acquired by the US Navy, and was delivered on 16 October 1978 for extensive tests at the Naval Air Development Center, Warminster, Pennsylvania. In late 1979, the Navy was removing the electric motors which then powered the HX-1, replacing them by nitro-alcohol fuelled engines of the type used to power model aircraft. Simultaneously, the magnetic mooring device was being removed to save weight so that, with the small engines operating, it would be possible to fly this research airship without the restrictions imposed by the electric tether.

Hov-Air-Ship's HX-1 small experimental airship, which was being tested by the US Navy in 1979

Mr Slater has proposed an enlarged HX-2 version to the US Navy and Coast Guard. This would be approximately 33·5 m (110 ft) long and 7·6 m (25 ft) in diameter, with an envelope volume of 1,218 m³ (43,000 cu ft), and would carry a crew of two. Power would be provided by two small turboshaft engines. The dimensions of the HX-2 have been revised since the project was proposed originally, to make it suitable for wind tunnel testing. In addition to manual control, the HX-2 could be operated in remotely piloted form, untethered, as a cargo carrier.

TUCKER
TUCKER AIRSHIP COMPANY
13218 Lake Street, Los Angeles, California 90066
Telephone: (213) 792 5429; (213) 354 5176
PRESIDENT: Curtis E. Tucker

The Tucker Airship Company was founded in 1973 by Mr Curtis Tucker, with the object of building airships that would benefit from the latest technology and materials.

Production of three prototype airships was planned originally, but only the initial TX-1 was nearing completion in early 1980.

TUCKER TX-1 SILVER HAWK
Design of the TX-1 originated in October 1972 and construction began in May 1973. During 1976 the company encountered a problem with its envelope sealing process, but this was subsequently resolved. Funding was reduced in 1977, but additional finance was made available during 1978 and 1979 so that the vessel could become operational and available for company use. In early 1980 the envelope had been coated with a 0·018 mm (0·0007 in) thickness of light alloy by means of a new metalising process, and testing of the envelope was being carried out. It was planned to complete installation of wiring and instrumentation during the Summer of 1980, with a first flight to be made before the end of the year.

The TX-1 is very much an experimental vessel, intended to provide experience in design, construction and operation, and will be used to test new design ideas, materials and ground handling concepts. Should the future airship proposals develop, it is envisaged that the TX-1 type would serve as a low-cost primary trainer. It is intended to be available for research use by scientific, military and industrial organisations upon request.

A semi-rigid design was chosen to provide for multi-mission roles, permitting the carriage of external loads; all

Tucker TX-1 airship Silver Hawk during inflation checks in August 1978

of the superstructure, including the tail control surfaces, is located beneath the envelope. Oversize ballast and trim tanks are provided to keep the airship level irrespective of load disposition, and to provide additional safety during pilot training. A unique feature of the design is its modular construction. The TX-1 breaks down into twelve units for transportation or storage, and can be assembled and inflated in an open field. A portable mooring mast, which can be erected in 30 minutes, has been designed and built, and this accepts the company's Mk 1 pneumatic mooring spindle which requires only one man on the ground to carry out mooring and castoff operations. When broken down for transit, the entire vessel can be accommodated in a standard-width trailer, 4·57 m (15 ft) in length, and there is sufficient space in the trailer for a power generating unit,

air-to-ground communication system, and other essential supplies and equipment. During 1978 a portable double-wall air-inflated hangar was developed to accommodate the TX-1. Measuring 33·5 × 12·2 × 10·7 m (110 × 40 × 35 ft), it has an air-operated upward-opening clamshell door.

The forward-mounted gondola of the TX-1 airship provides accommodation for the pilot and one passenger, seated in tandem. Excellent view is provided by a wide and deep windscreen, plus large sliding side windows. Standard airship controls are provided and equipment includes VFR instrumentation and communication radio. A monowheel is mounted beneath the gondola. Tail control surfaces comprise a large fin and rudder, with a wide-span horizontal tail surface and elevator. Power plant consists of an 89 kW (120 hp) McCulloch O-150-O two-stroke six-cylinder engine, mounted beneath the keel structure at approximately its mid-point, and driving an AAF tractor propeller 1·12 m (3 ft 8 in) in diameter. Total fuel capacity is 227 litres (60 US gallons).

Three holds are provided within the keel structure, each with a capacity of 90·7 kg (200 lb), and are available for equipment or baggage. Hardpoints are provided for the carriage of external loads.

The envelope, which contains a single ballonet, is intended to be hydrogen filled for short test flights. For operational use the envelope would be inflated with helium. Special equipment includes pneumatic ballast controls, and there are provisions for full IFR instrumentation.

Details of proposals for the developed prototypes can be found in the 1979-80 *Jane's*.

DIMENSIONS, OVERALL:
Length	32·00 m	(105 ft 0 in)
Height	7·92 m	(26 ft 0 in)

DIMENSIONS, ENVELOPE:
Length	27·74 m	(91 ft 0 in)
Max diameter	6·10 m	(20 ft 0 in)
Length of constant-diameter section	13·11 m	(43 ft 0 in)
Volume	651 m³	(23,000 cu ft)

DIMENSIONS, GONDOLA:
Length overall	2·74 m	(9 ft 0 in)
Height	1·37 m	(4 ft 6 in)
Max width	0·91 m	(3 ft 0 in)

AREAS:
Fin	6·97 m²	(75·0 sq ft)
Rudder	2·93 m²	(31·5 sq ft)
Tailplane	7·43 m²	(80·0 sq ft)
Elevator	5·39 m²	(58·0 sq ft)

WEIGHTS (estimated):
Weight empty	368 kg	(810 lb)
Max design gross weight	635 kg	(1,400 lb)

PERFORMANCE (estimated, with 89 kW; 120 hp engine):
Max speed	56 knots	(105 km/h; 65 mph)
Service ceiling	1,370 m	(4,500 ft)
Range with max fuel	434 nm	(804 km; 500 miles)
Range with max payload	43 nm	(80 km; 50 miles)

LIGHTER-THAN-AIR: BALLOONS

FRANCE

CHAIZE
BALLONS CHAIZE
48 rue Balay, 42000 Saint-Étienne
Telephone: (77) 33 43 76

M Maurice Chaize was offering five hot-air balloons at the beginning of 1980, one in the FAI AX-6 class, three in the AX-7 class and, the most recently introduced, a 4,000

m³ (141,260 cu ft) balloon in the AX-9 class. The envelopes are made from high-strength nylon, with the lower panels in the throat made from Nomex flame-resistant fabric. They are supplied in a ready-to-fly state, complete with basket, burners, and gas cylinders, but without instruments. Several options are available to customer requirements.

The company holds the French Certificat de Navigabi-

lité de Type for all five models, details of which can be found in the accompanying tables.

The prototype balloon was flown for the first time in December 1972. Deliveries began in the Summer of 1977, and totalled 20 by late 1979. On 20 October 1979 two Chaize balloons, one of 2,000 m³ (70,630 cu ft) and one of 4,000 m³ (141,260 cu ft) capacity, crossed the Alps from France to Italy, flying directly over Mont Blanc.

GERMANY
(FEDERAL REPUBLIC)

BALLONFABRIK
BALLONFABRIK SEE- UND LUFT-AUSRÜSTUNG GmbH und Co KG
Austrasse 35, 89 Augsburg 1, Postfach 101327
Telephone: (0821) 41 50 41

Ballonfabrik is currently manufacturing and marketing a range of seven gas balloons, all of which are within the FAI categories AX-3/-4/-5/-6. All available details of these balloons are given in the accompanying table.

UNITED KINGDOM

CAMERON
CAMERON BALLOONS LTD
1 Cotham Park, Bristol BS6 6BZ
Telephone: (0272) 41455
DIRECTORS: See Airships subsection

Cameron Balloons has been manufacturing hot-air balloons in Bristol since 1968. The company is the second largest manufacturer of hot-air balloons in the world, and has built the world's largest hot-air balloon, the *Gerard A. Heineken* of 14,158 m³ (500,000 cu ft). Cameron balloons hold the absolute distance record for hot-air balloons and the absolute duration record of 18 h 56 min. The company holds CAA, FAA, Certificat de Navigabilité de Type and the West German Musterzulassungsschein type certificates for its balloons. It constructed also the world's first hot-air airship (see Airships subsection).

Envelopes are made from rip-stop nylon which has been treated with a polyurethane sealant to reduce porosity. The lower section of the envelope is made from Nomex flame-resistant fabric. The envelopes are available with either a Velcro seal or parachute deflation system, and those with the Velcro seal have also a vertical flap-type vent. Cameron offers a wide range of balloons, details of which can be found in the accompanying table. Each is supplied complete with willow and cane basket, burner and gas cylinders and is ready to fly when delivered. Optional items include instrument pack, envelope thermometer, pressure scoop, Nomex skirt, rigid-suspension basket, trail rope and additional gas cylinders.

During 1976 the company initiated the design of specially shaped balloons for advertising purposes. Three new sporting balloons were introduced during 1979, compris-

ing the N-65 and V-65 in the AX-7 class, and the O-105 in the AX-8 class.

During 1978 an attempt was made by Don Cameron and Maj Christopher Davey to be the first balloonists to cross the North Atlantic, in the combination helium/hot-air balloon *Zanussi*. This flight had to be abandoned on 30 July, when a rip which had developed in the inner (helium) envelope on 27 July extended. At that time they were little more than 87 nm (161 km; 100 miles) from the French coast. Their Cameron AT-165 balloon, which was categorised in the FAI AM-10 class, had a gross volume of 4,672 m³ (165,000 cu ft), of which 4,248 m³ (150,000 cu ft) represented helium volume. Total lift developed was 4,422 kg (9,750 lb). The crew was carried in a light alloy gondola, manufactured by Aalco Ltd, which was designed to serve as a boat in the event of a descent at sea.

THUNDER
THUNDER BALLOONS LTD
75 Leonard Street, London EC2A 4QS
Telephone: (01) 739 0775/0776
Telex: 261234 reference H5758D
CHAIRMAN: K. F. Simonds
DIRECTORS:
   T. M. Donnelly (Managing)
   A. R. Wirth
Thunder Balloons manufactures a range of ready-to-fly

hot-air balloons, details of which can be found in the accompanying table. In early 1980 there were five basic types, all of them incorporating a fail-safe plug-parachute deflation system. A new model has been introduced in the AX-3 Class. Known as the Sky Chariot, it is available in three versions designated Mini, Midi, and Maxi.

Envelopes are made from coated polyamide or polyester fabrics, with lower panels of Nomex flame-resistant fabric. All balloons are supplied complete with basket, burner and fuel cylinders, and are certificated for use

throughout the world. Series 1, 2 and Z balloons are available with an instrument dashboard which covers the fuel cylinders and provides more room within the basket. 'Bolt' type balloons, in a lower price range, were introduced during 1978. The British team competing in the World Championship events in 1979 flew Z-type Thunder balloons.

The company is developing also a hot-air airship, all available details of which are given in the Airships subsection.

UNITED STATES OF AMERICA

ADAMS
MIKE ADAMS' BALLOON LOFT INC
PO Box 12168, Atlanta, Georgia 30355
Telephone: (404) 261 5818

Mike Adams' Balloon Loft is manufacturing a range of hot-air balloons, of which details can be found in the accompanying table.

Envelopes are made from rip-stop nylon, which may be coated optionally with a polyurethane or aluminised sea-

lant to reduce porosity. Nomex flame-resistant fabric is used to protect the envelope throat. Two manoeuvring vents are located in the crown of the balloon and there is a duffle bag type of deflation system.

In 1978 Adams introduced the first two of a series of balloons named 'Little Devil' models. These feature a deflation system which the company calls MultiVent. A single control line creates 16 diamond-shape openings which snap shut immediately the control line is released,

so providing an improved measure of control.

Adams balloons are supplied complete with a woven rattan basket, burner, aluminium fuel cylinders, and instruments which include a sensitive altimeter, rate of climb indicator, envelope temperature gauge, bubble type compass and fuel gauges. Optional items include tank-mounted pressure gauge, Nomex skirt, MultiVent deflation system, inflator fan and additional fuel cylinders.

Some new designs were under development in 1979.

Maurice Chaize CS.4000 balloon in the FAI AX-9 class

Cameron V-77 balloon which is in the AX-7 class

British team's Thunder balloons at Uppsala, Sweden

One of the Mike Adams' Balloon Loft range of hot-air balloons

Avian Balloon 20-gore envelope in the AX-7 class

Boland *Dimples* AX-5 class balloon

AVIAN
AVIAN BALLOON COMPANY

South 3722 Ridgeview Drive, Spokane, Washington 99206
Telephone: (509) 928 6847

Avian Balloon completed FAA certification of two hot-air balloons: these are in FAI classes AX-7 and AX-8 and are named Falcon II and Skyhawk respectively. Only the Falcon II is currently available, but the company was working in early 1980 to complete the certification of a new competition balloon in the FAI AX-5 class, identified as the Avian Sparrow.

Avian balloon envelopes are made from rip-stop nylon, which can be treated with a sealant to reduce porosity, or can optionally be made from aluminised balloon fabric. Four design patterns and twelve fabric colours are available to customer's choice. A feature of the design is the incorporation of a mechanical rapid deflation system. The basket is of wicker and, in addition to the burner and gas cylinders, an instrument panel that includes an altimeter, rate of climb indicator and envelope temperature gauge is standard. Details of Avian's balloons are given in the accompanying table.

BALLOON WORKS
THE BALLOON WORKS

Rhyne Aerodrome—RFD2, Statesville, North Carolina 28677
Telephone: (704) 873 0503
DIRECTORS:
Tracy Barnes
Dodds Meddock

The Balloon Works is currently marketing four category sizes of hot-air balloons, details of which are given in the accompanying table.

The envelopes of this company's balloons are made of a polyester fabric, which tests have shown to be less affected by heat and sunlight exposure than other materials, and

are coated with a urethane sealant to reduce porosity. Rapid deflation is made possible by use of a wide-diameter envelope valve, which is self-sealing immediately the valve line is released. Triangular wicker baskets are leather trimmed and are available in three sizes. One high-output burner is fitted.

Standard equipment includes the Barnes triple burner, one main tank and related fuel lines, apex handling line, thermometer, rate of climb indicator, sensitive altimeter, and a fuel pressure gauge.

Optional equipment includes Fire 2 supplementary quiet burner system, Nomex envelope skirt, electronic temperature and rate of climb indicators, extra fuel tanks and tethering kit. A wide variety of envelope artwork can be provided.

BOLAND
BOLAND BALLOON

Pine Drive, RD 2, Burlington, Connecticut 06013
Telephone: (203) 673 1307

Mr Brian Boland, designer and builder, with his wife Kathy, of the *Albatross* hot-air airship (described in the Airships section) has also designed and built a number of

hot-air balloons. Early examples included the very small *Piccolo,* and the somewhat larger *Fred II* of which Mr Boland built six examples. A plan/construction manual and materials source book is available for *Fred II,* and details of both of these early balloons can be found in the 1978-79 *Jane's.*

During 1978 the Bolands built three new balloons, two of them in the lower-size FAI categories. These included

Boland *Peaches* AX-6 balloon, showing translucent semi-sphere

the XXUS in the AX-1 class, *High Fred* in the A-3 class, and *Spirit of Lake Garda* in the AX-8 class. Details of these are given in the accompanying table; additional information can be found in the 1979-80 *Jane's.*

During 1979 the Bolands originated two more designs, the first being a very lightweight balloon with the model name *Peaches,* which is categorised in the AX-6 class. Believed to be the lightest-weight balloon yet built in relation to volume, it has a duration of 2-3 h with a crew of two. A feature of its design is the use of translucent material above, and black opaque material below, the equator line to gain some benefit from solar heating at high altitude. The second new design, the AX-5 class *Dimples,* is intended for one-person operation, and has a duration of about 1 h 30 min with two gas cylinders.

Available details of these balloons are given in the accompanying table.

PICCARD
PICCARD BALLOONS
PO Box 1902, Newport Beach, California 92663
Telephone: (714) 642 3545

Piccard Balloons manufactures a range of hot-air balloons, of which seven different models are available, all classified within the FAI's AX-3 to AX-8 ranges. Details of these can be found in the accompanying table.

RAVEN
RAVEN INDUSTRIES INC
Box 1007, Sioux Falls, South Dakota 57101
Telephone: (605) 336 2750

Raven Industries has been manufacturing hot-air balloons since the early 1960s, and also built the STAR hot-air airship of which details were given in the 1977-78 *Jane's*.

In 1979 Raven introduced a new balloon designated RX-7, which falls within the FAI class AX-7 and joins the RX-6 in Raven's Rally II economy balloon class. In addition, the company markets five sizes of custom design balloons. Details of these may be found in the accompanying table.

Raven envelopes are made from rip-stop nylon treated with ultra-violet inhibitors to prolong fabric life. They embody to the customer's choice either a parachute-style deflation system or a Velcro rapid deflation port. All models have woven rattan wicker baskets. Standard equipment includes the burner, gas cylinders, and an instrument case which includes a sensitive altimeter, rate of climb indicator and envelope temperature gauge. A range of options includes fire retardant Kynol skirt liner, Kynol throat liner, stainless steel or additional aluminium gas cylinders, electric variometer, special colours, designs and decorations for the envelope, banners, bunting and repair fabrics.

Group of balloons made by Raven Industries; largest is the new RX-7

HOT-AIR AND GAS BALLOON DATA

Country	Company	Model	Volume m³/cu ft	Diameter m/ft	Height m/ft	Crew	Basket	Fuel Cylinders	Burners	Lift, S/L ISA kg/lb
FAI CLASS AX-1										
United States	Boland Balloon	XXUS	239/8,450	7·62/25	8·53/28	1	Harness seat	1	1	—
FAI CLASS AX-2										
United States	Boland Balloon	Piccolo	345/12,200	8·53/28	9·75/32	1	Harness seat	1	1	136/300
FAI CLASS AX-3										
West Germany	Ballonfabrik	K 630/1-Ri	630/22,250	10·59/34·75	18·0/59	3-4	—	NA	NA	730/1,609
United Kingdom	Cameron Balloons	O-20	566/20,000	—	—	1	Harness	2	1	—
United Kingdom	Thunder Balloons	Sky Chariot (Mini)	—	—	—	1	Harness seat	1	1	159/350
United States	Boland Balloon	Fred II	566/20,000	10·4/34·25	12·2/40	1	Wicker	1	1	181/400
United States	Boland Balloon	High Fred	595/21,000	10·06/33	—	1	Harness seat	1	1	—
United States	Piccard Balloons	Piccup-3	595/21,000	10·67/35	12·2/40	1	Harness seat	1	1	200/440
FAI CLASS AX-4										
West Germany	Ballonfabrik	B 800/2-Ri	800/28,250	11·4/37·4	20·12/66	4	—	NA	NA	928/2,046
West Germany	Ballonfabrik	K 780/2-Ri	780/27,500	11·4/37·4	19·81/65	4	—	NA	NA	905/1,995
West Germany	Ballonfabrik	K 945/2-Ri	945/33,400	12·28/40·3	20·42/67	5-6	—	NA	NA	1,095/2,416
United Kingdom	Cameron Balloons	N-31	890/31,430	12·5/41	14·63/48	1	Willow/Cane	2	1	—
United Kingdom	Cameron Balloons	O-31	890/31,430	—	—	1	Willow/Cane	2	1	—
United Kingdom	Cameron Balloons	V-31	890/31,430	—	—	1	Willow/Cane	2	1	—
United Kingdom	Thunder Balloons	31Z	890/31,430	—	—	1	Rattan	2	1	—
United States	Piccard Balloons	Lightning 33	934/33,000	12·19/40	14·33/47	1-2	—	2	1	272/600
United States	Raven Industries	S-40	900/31,779	12·19/40	16·76/55	1	Aluminium Chair	1	1	299/660
FAI CLASS AX-5										
West Germany	Ballonfabrik	K 1050/3-Ri	1,050/37,100	12·6/41·3	20·7/68	5-6	—	NA	NA	1,218/2,685
West Germany	Ballonfabrik	K 1260/3-Ri	1,260/44,500	13·4/44	22·25/73	6	—	NA	NA	1,460/3,219
United Kingdom	Cameron Balloons	O-42	1,190/42,024	—	—	2	Willow/Cane	2	1	—
United Kingdom	Thunder Balloons	42	1,190/42,024	13·4/44	14·1/46·4	2	Rattan	2	1	—
United Kingdom	Thunder Balloons	42 Bolt	1,190/42,024	—	—	2	Willow	2	1	—
United States	Adams' Balloon Loft	LD	964/34,029	12·95/42·5	15·54/51	1	Rattan	1/2	1	318/700
United States	Adams' Balloon Loft	LD-S	1,104/38,978	12·95/42·5	16·46/54	1-2	Rattan	1/2	1	318/700
United States	Boland Balloon	Dimples	906/32,000	—	—	1	Wicker	2	1	272/600
United States	The Balloon Works	FireFly 5	1,182/41,742	13·9/45·6	14·8/48·4	2	Wicker	2	2	393/867
United States	Piccard Balloons	Ballymurray	1,189/42,000	14·02/46	14·63/48	1-2	—	2	1-2	363/800
United States	Piccard Balloons	Lightning 45	1,274/45,000	13·72/45	15·24/50	1-2	—	2	1	363/800

HOT-AIR AND GAS BALLOON DATA

Country	Company	Model	Volume m³/cu ft	Diameter m/ft	Height m/ft	Crew	Basket	Fuel Cylinders	Burners	Lift, S/L ISA kg/lb
FAI CLASS AX-6										
France	M. Chaize	CS. 1600	1,600/56,503	—	—	2	Rattan	2	—	—
West Germany	Ballonfabrik	K 1680/4-Ri	1,680/59,300	14·78/48·5	24·4/80	6	—	NA	NA	1,960/4,321
United Kingdom	Cameron Balloons	O-56	1,590/56,150	—	—	3	Willow/Cane	2	1	—
United Kingdom	Cameron Balloons	Viva 56	1,590/56,150	—	—	3	Willow/Cane	2	1	—
United Kingdom	Cameron Balloons	N-56	1,590/56,150	15·25/50	17·07/56	3	Willow/Cane	2	1	—
United Kingdom	Thunder Balloons	56	1,590/56,150	14·8/48·4	15·5/50·9	3	Rattan	2	1	—
United Kingdom	Thunder Balloons	56Z	1,590/56,150	14·51/47·6	15·7/51·5	3	Rattan	2	1	—
United Kingdom	Thunder Balloons	56 Bolt	1,590/56,150	—	—	3	Willow	2	1	—
United States	Adams' Balloon Loft	A50	1,557/54,985	15·24/50	17·68/58	2	Rattan	1-4	1	544/1,200
United States	Boland Balloon	Peaches	1,416/50,000	—	—	2	Wicker	2	1	454/1,000
United States	The Balloon Works	FireFly 6	1,576/55,656	15·3/50·1	16·1/52·8	3	Wicker	3	2	476/1,050
United States	Piccard Balloons	Le Mans	1,586/56,000	14·94/49	16·45/54	2-3	—	2	2	454/1,000
United States	Raven Industries	S-50A	1,597/56,400	15·24/50	17·68/58	2-4	Wicker	3	1	635/1,400
United States	Raven Industries	RX-6	1,597/56,400	15·24/50	17·68/58	2-3	Wicker	2	1	—
FAI CLASS AX-7										
France	M. Chaize	CS. 1800	1,800/63,565	—	—	—	Rattan	2	—	—
France	M. Chaize	CS. 2000	2,000/70,629	—	—	3-4	Rattan	3	—	—
France	M. Chaize	CS. 2200	2,200/77,682	—	—	3-4	Rattan	3	—	—
United Kingdom	Cameron Balloons	O-65	1,840/64,980	—	—	3	Willow/Cane	3	1	—
United Kingdom	Cameron Balloons	O-77	2,190/77,339	—	—	4	Willow/Cane	4	1	—
United Kingdom	Cameron Balloons	N-65	1,840/65,000	16·15/53	18·0/59	3	Willow/Cane	3	1	—
United Kingdom	Cameron Balloons	V-65	1,840/65,000	—	—	3	Willow/Cane	2	1	—
United Kingdom	Cameron Balloons	V-77	2,190/77,339	—	—	4	Willow/Cane	2	1	—
United Kingdom	Cameron Balloons	N-77	2,190/77,339	17·07/56	18·9/62	4	Willow/Cane	4	1	—
United Kingdom	Thunder Balloons	65	1,840/64,980	15·5/50·8	16·3/53·5	3	Rattan	2	1	—
United Kingdom	Thunder Balloons	65Z	1,840/64,980	—	—	3	Rattan	2	1	—
United Kingdom	Thunder Balloons	65 Bolt	1,840/64,980	—	—	3	Willow	2	1	—
United Kingdom	Thunder Balloons	77	2,190/77,339	16·4/53·8	17·3/56·6	4	Rattan	2	1	—
United Kingdom	Thunder Balloons	77Z	2,190/77,339	15·97/52·38	16·66/54·66	4	Rattan	2	1	—
United Kingdom	Thunder Balloons	77 Bolt	2,190/77,339	—	—	4	Willow	2	1	—
United States	Adams' Balloon Loft	A50S	1,755/61,977	15·24/50	18·59/61	3	Rattan	1-4	1	544/1,200
United States	Adams' Balloon Loft	A55	2,123/74,973	16·76/55	19·51/64	3	Rattan	1-4	1	680/1,500
United States	Avian Balloon	Falcon II	1,700/60,000	15·39/50·5	20·42/67	1-2	Wicker	2	1	376/830
United States	The Balloon Works	FireFly 7	2,167/76,526	17·0/55·8	17·7/58·2	3	Wicker	3	2	753/1,660
United States	Piccard Balloons	Stretch	1,982/70,000	16·15/53	17·68/58	3	—	4	2	549/1,210
United States	Raven Industries	S-55A	2,195/77,500	16·76/55	19·2/63	3-4	Wicker	3	1	657/1,450
United States	Raven Industries	RX-7	2,195/77,500	16·76/55	19·2/63	3	Wicker	3	1	657/1,450
FAI CLASS AX-8										
United Kingdom	Cameron Balloons	O-84	2,380/84,047	—	—	4	Willow/Cane	4	1	—
United Kingdom	Cameron Balloons	A-105	2,970/104,884	—	—	6	Willow/Cane	6	2	—
United Kingdom	Cameron Balloons	N-105	2,970/104,884	18·9/62	20·72/68	6	Willow/Cane	6	2	—
United Kingdom	Cameron Balloons	O-105	2,970/104,884	—	—	6	Willow/Cane	6	2	—
United Kingdom	Thunder Balloons	84	2,380/84,047	—	—	4	Rattan	2	1	—
United Kingdom	Thunder Balloons	90	2,550/90,050	17·5/57·5	17·5/57·5	5	Rattan	2	2	—
United Kingdom	Thunder Balloons	105	2,970/104,884	18·44/60·5	18·44/60·5	6	Rattan	2	2	—
United States	Adams' Balloon Loft	A55S	2,350/82,990	16·76/55	20·42/67	4	Rattan	1-4	1	680/1,500
United States	Avian Balloon	Skyhawk	2,265/80,000	16·46/54	22·56/74	3-4	Wicker	3	1	544/1,200
United States	The Balloon Works	FireFly 8	2,956/104,400	18·8/61·8	19·5/64	4-5	Wicker	6	2	916/2,020
United States	Boland Balloons	*Spirit of Lake Garda*	2,322/82,000	—	—	4	Wicker	3/6	2	—
United States	Piccard Balloons	Newport	2,265/80,000	16·75/55	18·6/61	4	—	4	2	549/1,210
United States	Raven Industries	S-60A	2,973/105,000	18·29/60	21·03/69	3-4	Wicker	3	1	680/1,500
FAI CLASS AX-9										
France	M. Chaize	CS.4000	4,000/141,260	—	—	8	Rattan	—	2	—
United Kingdom	Cameron Balloons	A-140	3,960/139,846	—	—	8	Willow/Cane	6	2	—
United Kingdom	Thunder Balloons	140	3,965/140,022	20·36/66·8	20·36/66·8	8	Rattan	2	2	—
United States	Raven Industries	S-66A	4,000/141,260	—	—	4-6	Wicker	2	2	998/2,200

RPVs AND TARGETS

ARGENTINA

AMC
AREA DE MATERIAL CÓRDOBA, FUERZA AÉREA ARGENTINA
(Fábrica Militar de Aviones)

Avenida Fuerza Aérea Argentina Km 5½, 5103 Guarnicion Aérea Córdoba
Telephone: 45011/15
Telex: 51965 AMCOR AR
HEAD OF AMC: Brigadier Jorge A. Martinez Castro
DIRECTOR OF IIAE: Comodoro Roberto M. Cajal

FMA IA 59

Designed to Argentinian Air Force requirements by the IIAE (Instituto de Investigaciónes Aeronáuticas y Espaciales: Aerospace Research Institute), the IA 59 target drone was built by the Grupo Fabricación of the FMA. Original research towards an experimental vehicle embodying radio guidance and control techniques was started in the late 1960s. Construction of a prototype vehicle, designated IA-X-59-1, began in 1975, and this made its first flight in December 1976. A second prototype flew in July 1977, and a third was completed for static tests.

The primary purpose of the IA 59 is as an aerial target for anti-aircraft guns and surface-to-air missiles.
TYPE: Remotely controlled aerial target.

AIRFRAME: Cantilever high-wing monoplane, with torpedo-shaped fuselage and twin-fin tail unit. Single-spar duralumin wings are of constant section (NACA 65_1-212) and chord, fitted with ailerons. Fuselage is of circular cross-section, with four main longerons; steel central section forms the fuel tank; tapered forward and rear sections are of duralumin. All-dural tail unit comprises tailplane, with electrically-actuated elevator, mounted on top of rear fuselage; and rectangular twin fins (no rudders). Target floats to permit recovery from water.
POWER PLANT: One 54/67 kW (72/90 hp) McCulloch O-100-2 four-cylinder two-stroke aircooled piston engine, driving a two-blade fixed-pitch wooden propeller. Fuel (petrol/oil mixture) in steel centre-fuselage tank, capacity 40 litres (8·75 Imp gallons).
LAUNCH AND RECOVERY: Zero-length launch, from ground or ship's deck, using portable launcher and jettisonable booster rockets. Parachute system for recovery from land or water.
GUIDANCE AND CONTROL: Radio command guidance system, developed by IIAE, using 30W FM/FM ground transmitter operating in 138·67MHz bandwidth. Receiver/decodifier separates command signals into two control channels, plus another which stops the engine and deploys the recovery parachute. Backup system to initiate recovery sequence automatically if radio control link is broken. IIAE onboard autopilot acts under command from ground radio controller to govern pitch and roll. Vertical gyro provides attitude signals which, when amplified, govern the electrical actuators. Aerodynamic control by ailerons and elevator.
SYSTEM: 24V 15Ah lead-acid battery for general electrical supply; 18V 0·5Ah nickel-cadmium battery for signal circuits.

DIMENSIONS, EXTERNAL:
Wing span	3·60 m (11 ft 9¾ in)
Wing chord (constant)	0·625 m (2 ft 0½ in)
Wing area, gross	2·25 m² (24·2 sq ft)
Wing aspect ratio	5·76
Length overall	4·06 m (13 ft 3¾ in)
Tailplane span	1·00 m (3 ft 3¼ in)
Propeller diameter	1·10 m (3 ft 7¼ in)

WEIGHTS:
Max launching weight	170 kg (375 lb)
Max landing weight	150 kg (330 lb)

PERFORMANCE (at max launching weight):
Max level speed at S/L	172 knots (320 km/h; 199 mph)
Stalling speed	65 knots (120 km/h; 75 mph)
Max rate of climb at S/L	1,200 m (3,935 ft)/min
Service ceiling	7,000 m (22,950 ft)
Range with max fuel	172 nm (320 km; 199 miles)
Endurance with max fuel	1 h

AUSTRALIA

GAF
GOVERNMENT AIRCRAFT FACTORIES

Fishermen's Bend, Private Bag No. 4, Post Office, Port Melbourne, Victoria 3207
Telephone: 64 0661
Telex: AA 34397
OFFICERS: see Aircraft section

GAF's current products include the Jindivik weapons target drone.

GAF JINDIVIK Mk 3B

The Jindivik continues to be a standard weapons target in Australia and Great Britain.

Design began in March 1948. Construction of the prototype Jindivik Mk 1 started in December 1950, and it flew for the first time on 28 August 1952.

A total of 486 Jindiviks had been ordered by 1 January 1980, of which 466 had been delivered, as detailed in the 1979-80 *Jane's*.

Only the 700 Series Mks 103BL and 203B versions are still in production; deliveries of these versions began in 1976. Customers include the UK (40 Mk 103BL) and Royal Australian Navy (12 Mk 203B). These models were designed to cater for low-level trials at speeds in excess of 500 knots (925 km/h; 575 mph). The autopilot is the improved Marconi L4 or L5, and system 'black boxes' incorporate printed-circuit techniques.

An improved Mk 4 Jindivik was at an advanced design stage in January 1980, and production of 40 of this version is due to begin in 1981. The Mk 4 has a rationalised electrical/electronic system, increased manoeuvring capability (to +6g), and improved endurance. No other details were available at the time of going to press.

For low-altitude work, the standard-span Jindivik can be fitted either with Mk 5 wingtip camera pods, or with larger Mk 8 pods each containing two cameras, a Luneberg lens and a small amount of fuel. For high-altitude work (also with a choice of Mk 5 or Mk 8 wing pods), constant-chord wing extension panels can be added outboard of the pods. For extra high altitude flying (with Mk 5 pods only), these panels can be replaced by increased-span panels, tapered on the leading-edge. A ventral tail fin is also fitted in this configuration.

Up to 1 January 1980, Jindiviks had flown more than 3,710 sorties at the RAE, Llanbedr, North Wales; one particular Mk 3A drone (WRE 418) was eventually destroyed after successfully completing 285 sorties at Woomera. Total sorties by all Jindiviks at that date amounted to more than 6,400.
TYPE: Pilotless target drone.

WINGS: Cantilever low/mid-wing monoplane. Wing section NACA 64A-106 with modified trailing-edge. Dihedral 2° 30′. Incidence 1°. Araldite-bonded multi-spar box structure of aluminium alloy. Interspar torsion box utilised as integral fuel tankage. Aluminium alloy monocoque flaps and ailerons. Ailerons fitted with inset geared tab and driven by GAF-designed twin-motor servo motor. Flaps operated pneumatically.
FUSELAGE: Aluminium alloy semi-monocoque structure, built in front, centre and rear sections. Front fuselage carries all control equipment, autopilot amd telemetry equipment. Pitot head and wave-guide boom mounted on permanent nose probe. Moulded glassfibre canopy, which lifts off for access to equipment, forms ram-type air intake. Rear end of front fuselage and front end of centre-fuselage form bay for all special trials equipment. Centre-fuselage also houses landing skid. Rear fuselage carries engine and jetpipe.
TAIL UNIT: Cantilever multi-spar light alloy tailplane. Elevators driven by GAF-designed twin-motor servo motor. Inset geared tabs. Fin of light alloy skin bonded to two spars, stabilised by metal honeycomb filling. No rudder. Ventral fin on extra high altitude version.
LANDING GEAR: Pneumatically-extended, manually retracted (on ground) central skid. Pneumatic jack acts as shock-absorber. Steel auxiliary skids at wingtips. See also paragraph on 'Take-off and Landing'.
POWER PLANT: One Rolls-Royce Viper Mk 201 turbojet engine, rated at 11·1 kN (2,500 lb st). Engine relight capability available in the event of flameout. Flexible rubber main fuselage fuel tank, capacity 291 litres (64 Imp gallons), and two integral wing tanks, total capacity 173 litres (38 Imp gallons). Oil capacity 4·5 litres (1 Imp gallon).
TAKE-OFF AND LANDING: Take-off from aircraft trolley, steered by gyro and servo-controlled nosewheel which responds to signals from ground controller. Aircraft/trolley combination accelerates under normal jet power with flaps retracted and with aircraft set at negative incidence. When unstick speed (125 knots; 231 km/h; 144 mph) is reached, aircraft is rotated to take-off incidence and flaps are lowered rapidly. Rotation of aircraft initiates trolley release system and the aircraft climbs away. When Jindivik is in approach run, flaps and skid are selected down for landing. On touchdown, at approx 120 knots (222 km/h; 138 mph), a 'sting' extended below main skid rotates on impact and initiates rapid retraction of flaps. Fuel supply terminated by radio command.
REMOTE-CONTROL EQUIPMENT: Radio control equipment comprises two receivers and GAF relay receiving set. Telemetry equipment consists of NIC transducers and Australian-designed transmitter and junction box.
SYSTEMS: No hydraulic system. Non-regenerative pneumatic system: air stored at 138 bars (2,000 lb/sq in) in power pack which supplies air to flaps and landing skid reduced to 39·6 bars (575 lb/sq in). Engine-driven 11·5kVA alternator delivers 208V AC 3-phase electrical supply at 300-550Hz. In event of alternator failure, a 24V DC battery provides limited power for essential control functions. Automatic orbit and/or destruct systems provided, consistent with range safety requirements.
TRIALS EQUIPMENT: Transponders and microwave reflectors for trials of active, semi-active or beam-riding missiles. Heat sources, including infra-red flare packs mounted on rear of fuselage, can be fitted to provide low-frequency IR output. Transponders in X, S and C bands can be fitted for target acquisition and to enable Jindivik to be tracked at greater range. Provision for Tonic Beam under each wing, on which can be carried recoverable Tonic Tow Bodies. These Tow Bodies can carry either active radar, in-flight-commanded IR flares, or forward-looking Luneberg lens. They can be towed at 15-150 m (50-500 ft) behind aircraft; recovery by electric winch mounted in centre of fuselage. Other types of special tow may also be carried.
RECORDING EQUIPMENT: Cameras fitted with wide-angle lenses are carried in wingtip pods, with all-round viewing capability. Variants are Mk 5 pod with cameras only and Mk 8 with cameras, fuel and provision for fitment of microwave reflectors in leading-edge and trailing-edge radomes. By fitting rearward-looking prisms to the lower cameras they can be used to film and record missile performance when Tonic towed targets are used.

DIMENSIONS, EXTERNAL:
Wing span:	
short span, low altitude	6·32 m (20 ft 8·99 in)
extended, high altitude	7·92 m (26 ft 6 in)
extended, extra high altitude	9·78 m (32 ft 1·4 in)
Wing area, gross: short span	7·06 m² (76·0 sq ft)
extended span, high altitude	9·48 m² (102·0 sq ft)
extended span, extra high altitude	10·68 m² (115·0 sq ft)
Length overall: incl nose probe	8·15 m (26 ft 8¾ in)
excl nose probe	7·11 m (23 ft 3¾ in)
Height overall, skid extended	2·08 m (6 ft 9·85 in)

WEIGHTS:
Weight empty, equipped (min)	1,315 kg (2,900 lb)
Max payload: short-span version	249 kg (550 lb)
extended-span versions	181 kg (400 lb)

IA 59 target drone, under development by FMA, on its launcher

GAF Jindivik Mk 203B target drone, with Mk 1 in background

Canadair CL-89 airborne surveillance/target acquisition drone system

Canadair CL-227 surveillance/target acquisition RPV

Max T-O weight:
  short span, Mk 5 wing pods   1,451 kg (3,200 lb)
  short span, Mk 8 wing pods   1,655 kg (3,650 lb)
  high altitude, Mk 5 wing pods   1,474 kg (3,250 lb)
  high altitude, Mk 8 wing pods   1,655 kg (3,650 lb)
  extra high altitude, Mk 5 wing pods
                                    1,496 kg (3,300 lb)
PERFORMANCE (A: short span, Mk 5 pods; B: short span,
Mk 8 pods; C: high altitude, Mk 5 pods; D: high
altitude, Mk 8 pods; E: extra high altitude, Mk 5 pods):
Max level speed at max operational ceiling:
  A, B, C, D
          Mach 0·86 (490 knots; 908 km/h; 564 mph)
  E   Mach 0·82 (470 knots; 871 km/h; 541 mph)

Min operating height: A, B   15 m (50 ft)
Max operational ceiling: A   17,375 m (57,000 ft)
  B   16,460 m (54,000 ft)
  C   19,200 m (63,000 ft)
  D   18,595 m (61,000 ft)
  E   20,420 m (67,000 ft)
Time to max operational ceiling: A   26 min
  B, C   30 min
  D, E   34 min
Typical max on-station endurance: A, C   1 h 6 min
  B   1 h 38 min
  D   1 h 52 min
  E   1 h 3 min

Max range: A   430 nm (796 km; 495 miles)
  B   670 nm (1,240 km; 771 miles)
  C   540 nm (1,000 km; 621 miles)
  D   900 nm (1,667 km; 1,036 miles)
  E   700 nm (1,297 km; 806 miles)

GAF TURANA

The Turana target drone programme has been discontinued. Full details can be found in the 1979-80 *Jane's*.

HAWKER DE HAVILLAND
HAWKER DE HAVILLAND AUSTRALIA PTY LTD (Member Company of Hawker Siddeley Group)
PO Box 30, Bankstown, NSW 2200
Telephone: 772 8111

Telex: 20719
TECHNICAL DIRECTOR: S. S. Schaetzel

HAWKER DE HAVILLAND HDH-11 BEEMOTH
The HDH-11 Beemoth has a similar planform to the Promoth, but has double the linear dimensions, greatly increased payload capacity, and a pusher propeller.

HAWKER DE HAVILLAND HDH-12 PROMOTH
The Promoth mini-RPV is designed specifically as a rugged, low-cost expendable target for small-arms gunnery practice. Three prototypes have been flown, and development has been completed.
Details can be found in the 1979-80 *Jane's*.

CANADA

CANADAIR
CANADAIR LTD
PO Box 6087, Montreal, Quebec H3C 3G9
Telephone: (514) 744 1511

OFFICERS: see Aircraft section

In addition to its work on manned aircraft, Canadair is developing or producing various drone systems, including the CL-289 described in the International section.

CANADAIR CL-89
NATO designation: AN/USD-501
British Army name: Midge

The Canadair CL-89 (AN/USD-501) airborne surveillance drone system evolved from a need of the western Allied armed forces for an intelligence-gathering device

for battlefield commanders; details of its early history can be found in the 1977-78 and earlier editions of *Jane's*.

With a very high probability of survival against all known air defence systems, the CL-89 can acquire timely and accurate battlefield intelligence using its photographic and infra-red line-scanning equipment. The system, consisting of the air vehicles plus the related ground support and operational maintenance equipment, is totally integrated, mobile, and independent of such external services as electrical power supplies.

The CL-89 system has been produced for Canada, the Federal Republic of Germany (five battalions, each with 12 drones and two launchers), Italy (jointly with Meteor, which see) and the UK. Well over 500 drones have been manufactured and by early 1980 had made more than 2,000 flights. An order from the French government was announced in August 1978.

TYPE: Recoverable airborne surveillance drone system.

AIRFRAME: Cylindrical metal body, with curved nosecone and tapering tailcone. Three detachable dorsal packs for forward and rear landing bags and flare container; two detachable ventral packs for sensor equipment and parachute recovery system. Four rectangular stub-wings at rear of body, in cruciform arrangement at 45° to horizontal and vertical centrelines. Upper pair fold out of way when landing airbags are inflated. Ailerons on port upper and starboard lower stub-wings. Two pairs of canard foreplanes aft of nosecone on horizontal and vertical centrelines, for pitch and yaw trim respectively.

POWER PLANT: One 0·56 kN (125 lb st) Williams Research WR2-6 turbojet engine, with variable exhaust nozzle, installed in tailcone aft of wings. Air intake duct on each side of fuselage, forward of wings. Fuel and oil tanks in central body compartment, forward of air intakes. One 22·24 kN (5,000 lb st) average thrust BAJ Vickers

Wagtail booster rocket motor, attached to body of drone by three V-shaped thrust arms and cable.

LAUNCH AND RECOVERY: Launched from truck-mounted zero-length ramp; booster separates automatically after 2·5 s of flight. For recovery, after final positioning by ground homing beacon, drone is slowed by drogue parachute until main parachute deploys. Drone is then inverted, and forward and rear airbags are inflated and deployed automatically to absorb landing impact.

GUIDANCE AND CONTROL: Flight path, altitude and sensor on/off commands are controlled by preset programmer which receives information from onboard Air Distance Measuring Unit (ADMU) and combines this with preset programme to control flight path. Ground homing beacon positions drone in final stages of flight to ensure accuracy of landing.

EQUIPMENT: Engine-driven alternator for electrical power during flight. Two main sensor systems currently in use: Carl Zeiss KRb 8/24C camera system and British Aerospace Dynamics Type 201 infra-red linescan system. Aft of sensor pack is compartment for fuel and oil tanks. Compartment aft of tanks has ventral forward-hinged door providing access to engine start air connector, and dorsal pack containing 12 photoflares just forward of rear landing bag container. Final cylindrical compartment houses rear landing bag container and parachute recovery pack, between dorsal and ventral pairs of wings respectively. Other onboard equipment includes forward and rear landing airbags; Air Distance Measuring Unit (ADMU); programmer; static power converter; homing receiver; amplifier; flash detector; directional and vertical gyros; transponder antenna; and air bottle to inflate airbags.

DIMENSIONS, EXTERNAL:
Length overall, excl nose probe:	
with booster	3·73 m (12 ft 3 in)
without booster	2·60 m (8 ft 6½ in)
Body diameter	0·33 m (1 ft 1 in)
Span of wings	0·94 m (3 ft 1 in)
Span of foreplanes	0·48 m (1 ft 7 in)

WEIGHTS:
Weight dry (excl fuel, oil and payload)	78·2 kg (172·4 lb)
Payload	17-20 kg (37·5-44 lb)
Max launching weight: with booster	156 kg (343 lb)
without booster	108 kg (238 lb)

PERFORMANCE:
Max speed	400 knots (741 km/h; 460 mph)
Max operating altitude	3,050 m (10,000 ft)
Max range	65 nm (120 km; 74 miles)

CANADAIR CL-227

The CL-227 is designed as a highly survivable real-time surveillance and target acquisition system for use at medium range. It has VTOL capability, can translate to horizontal flight and hover, and is launched and recovered using a platform mounted on a truck or small ship.

It has a peanut-shaped body housing the power plant in the upper sphere, with the sensors and autopilot in the lower sphere. Two three-blade contra-rotating rigid propellers, mounted amidships, provide the lift and attitude control. Current power plant in the development vehicle is a 15·7 kW (21 hp) Fichtel & Sachs Wankel-type rotating-piston engine, but a small US turboshaft engine, driving 2·59 m (8 ft 6 in) propellers, will power the production version of the CL-227. Payload capacity (TV camera or infra-red sensor and laser designator) will be increased to 36 kg (80 lb).

First flight took place on 25 August 1978; the initial phase of the flight test programme, consisting of more than 200 tethered flights, was completed in November 1978. A new test facility has been put into operation which allows for increased horizontal motion of the air vehicle, simulating free flight. This facility will also be used for production system testing and training.

A unique characteristic of the CL-227 is the landing concept, in which the air vehicle is winched on to the landing device to provide an automatic landing capability. This platform also acts as the transportation platform and minimises ground handling of the air vehicle between flights.

DIMENSIONS, EXTERNAL:
Height overall	1·32 m (4 ft 4 in)
Body diameter (max)	0·51 m (1 ft 8 in)
*Propeller diameter (approx)	2·29 m (7 ft 6 in)

*WEIGHTS:
Payload	20 kg (44 lb)
Max T-O weight	93 kg (205 lb)

*PERFORMANCE (estimated):
Max level speed	70 knots (130 km/h; 81 mph)
Max operating altitude	2,500 m (8,200 ft)
Typical operating radius	27 nm (50 km; 31 miles)
Typical mission endurance	2-3 h

* *Larger-diameter propellers (see introductory notes) will be used on the production CL-227, for heavier payloads and longer endurance*

FRANCE

AÉROSPATIALE
SOCIÉTÉ NATIONALE INDUSTRIELLE AÉROSPATIALE
Division des Engins Tactiques
2-18 rue Béranger, BP 84, 92320 Châtillon-sous-Bagneux
Telephone: 657 14 21
Telex: AIRSPA 250881 F
OFFICERS: see Aircraft section

Aérospatiale (Division des Engins Tactiques) is currently producing the CT.20 target drone for the French armed forces. Approx 50 examples of the C.20, referred to in the 1978-79 *Jane's*, were produced. Under development as a high-performance subsonic target is the C.22.

AÉROSPATIALE CT.20

The CT.20 is a turbojet-powered radio-controlled target of medium performance, which is also used as a tug for a towed target. Series production began in 1958; by 1 January 1980 a total of 1,431 had been ordered, including more than 300 for export to NATO and non-NATO countries. Rate of production in 1979 was approx five to six per month.

It is standard equipment for training military units in the use of air-to-air and surface-to-air missiles, in particular the Hawk. A version known as the **CT.20 TBA**, with very low altitude capability, is also operational.

The CT.20, fitted with a Thomson-CSF active homing radar, and with a warhead in place of the recovery system, also formed the basis of the M.20 anti-ship missile designed by Aérospatiale for the Swedish Navy and built by Saab-Scania as the RB08.

TYPE: Turbojet-powered radio-controlled target.

AIRFRAME: Body in three main sections. Forward section, of aluminium alloy, contains command guidance, autopilot, batteries and principal recovery parachute. Central section consists of structural steel tank divided into two parts, one for fuel and one containing chemicals for tracking smoke. Rear fuselage, of aluminium alloy, contains engine and carries aluminium alloy V-tail. Braking parachute in cone above jet nozzle. Mid-mounted swept wings, of aluminium alloy, have wingtip spoilers for lateral control; elevators controlled simultaneously by single jack. Ventral fin.

POWER PLANT: One Turboméca Marboré II (3·92 kN; 880 lb st) turbojet engine in CT.20 Version IV; Marboré VI (4·7 kN; 1,056 lb st) turbojet in CT.20 Version VII.

LAUNCH AND RECOVERY: Launched by booster rockets from nearly-zero-length vehicle-mounted ramp. Recovery by parachute and impact-absorbing airbag, deployed after engine is stopped by transmission of landing signal. Can be recovered from land or water.

GUIDANCE AND CONTROL: Radio command guidance system, operated by controller on ground or in airborne director aircraft. Nine basic signals can be transmitted: turn right; turn left; nose up; nose down; increase power; decrease power; trace smoke; operate cameras; and land.

EQUIPMENT: Can be used to tow Dornier target which is pylon-mounted under starboard wing at launch; or can be used with trailed target system developed for the Centre d'Essais des Landes, primarily for training in use of air-to-air missiles with electro-magnetic (BEY target) or infra-red homing (EMIR target) systems. CT.20 TBA version has TRT AVH-6 radio altimeter for very low (about 30 m; 100 ft) altitude capability, and an improved remote guidance system.

DIMENSIONS, EXTERNAL (A: standard version; B: extended version with trailed target):
Wing span	3·16 m (10 ft 4½ in)
Wing area, gross	3·20 m² (33·34 sq ft)
Length overall:	
A	5·45 m (17 ft 10½ in)
B	5·60 m (18 ft 4½ in)
Body diameter (max)	0·66 m (2 ft 2 in)

WEIGHTS (A: standard version; B: extended version with trailed target):
Weight empty: A	490 kg (1,080 lb)
B	610 kg (1,344 lb)
Fuel load: A	164 kg (361 lb)
B	192 kg (423 lb)
Max launching weight: A	660 kg (1,455 lb)
B	800 kg (1,763 lb)

PERFORMANCE (A: standard version; B: extended version with trailed target):
Max speed at 10,000 m (32,800 ft):	
Marboré II	485 knots (900 km/h; 560 mph)
Marboré VI	512 knots (950 km/h; 590 mph)
Max Mach number (A, B)	Mach 0·85
Service ceiling: Marboré II	12,000 m (39,375 ft)
Marboré VI	15,000 m (49,200 ft)
Max operating height: A	14,000 m (45,925 ft)
B	13,000 m (42,650 ft)
Time to max operating height: A, B	15 min
Time to 10,000 m (32,800 ft)	6 min
Endurance at max operating height: A	50 min
B	1 h 10 min
Min operating height: A, B	30 m (100 ft)
Practical range of command guidance and tracking system	135 nm (250 km; 155 miles)
Endurance at min operating height: A	15 min
B	21 min
Average endurance at 10,000 m (32,800 ft)	45 min

AÉROSPATIALE C.22

The C.22, which first flew on 6 June 1980, has been designed for use as a variable-speed target for anti-aircraft weapons and, especially, for training land or air force units equipped with conventional guns or surface-to-air or air-to-air missiles. Its dimensions, low radar signature and high performance enable it to perform equally realistically whether representing a bomber at 12,200 m (40,000 ft) or a sea-skimming anti-ship missile.

TYPE: High-performance variable-speed subsonic target.

AIRFRAME: Moulded plastics wings, with symmetrical profile and no control surfaces. Fuselage of wound glassfibre, impregnated with epoxy resin, reinforced by metal inserts at attachment points. Nosecone and tailcone of moulded plastics. Cruciform light alloy tail-fins, with four control surfaces operated by electrical actuators.

POWER PLANT: One 3·4 kN (772 lb st) Microturbo TRI 60 turbojet engine, mounted in pod on top of fuselage; and two jettisonable solid-fuel booster rockets (each 28·3 kN; 6,360 lb st) attached beneath wings on sides of fuselage. Fuel tanks for TRI 60 in centre of fuselage, capacity 245 litres (54 Imp gallons).

LAUNCH AND RECOVERY: Launched by jettisonable rockets from ground or ship base. Parachute system for recovery from land or sea. Inflatable airbag beneath fuselage to absorb landing impact.

GUIDANCE AND CONTROL: Radio command guidance system. Flight control, based upon a mini-computer, permits complex manoeuvres at more than 6g. Aerodynamic control by cruciform tail-fins indexed at 45° from vertical axis.

SPECIAL EQUIPMENT: Nose compartment available for equipment, including tow winch. Tail compartment includes smoke generator and recovery parachutes. Equipment/payload includes up to 75 kg (165 lb) of Luneberg lenses or infra-red augmentation devices; active or passive countermeasures; recording equipment for assessing the effectiveness of weapon systems during training; or equipment for towing successively two 30 kg (66 lb) secondary targets at speeds of more than 485 knots (900 km/h; 559 mph), with 1,000 m (3,280 ft) cable for each target.

DIMENSIONS, EXTERNAL:
Wing span	2·50 m (8 ft 2½ in)
Span over tail-fins	1·20 m (3 ft 11¼ in)
Length overall	5·10 m (16 ft 8¾ in)
Height overall	1·15 m (3 ft 9¼ in)
Body diameter	0·40 m (1 ft 3¾ in)

WEIGHTS:
Weight empty	255 kg (562 lb)
Total payload, incl towed targets	up to 135 kg (297·5 lb)
Max launching weight	570 kg (1,257 lb)

PERFORMANCE:
Max speed	Mach 0·95
Time to 12,000 m (39,375 ft)	less than 6 min
Service ceiling	14,000 m (45,950 ft)
Minimum operating altitude	15 m (50 ft)
Endurance at Mach 0·9 at 13,000 m (42,650 ft)	2 h
g limit	more than +6

Aérospatiale CT.20 target drones on launching ramps

Aérospatiale C.22 variable-speed subsonic target drone

EERM SAM-B meteorological drone

EERM SAM-D adverse-weather meteorological drone

EERM SAM-C MAR atmospheric sounding vehicle

EERM
ÉTABLISSEMENT D'ÉTUDES ET DE RECHERCHES MÉTÉOROLOGIQUES (Direction de la Météorologie Nationale)

77 rue de Sèvres, 92106 Boulogne-Billancourt Cédex
Telephone: (1) 604 91 51
DIRECTOR: A. Villevieille

Several types of SAM (Sonde Aérologique Motorisée) have been used in considerable numbers by the EERM since 1976 as pilotless atmospheric sounding vehicles.

EERM SAM-B

As the accompanying photograph shows, SAM-B is an extremely simple vehicle, of disc-shaped planform with the trailing-edges hinged to act as control surfaces. It is powered by a 1·2 kW (1·6 hp) Webra 61 10 cc two-stroke piston engine, driving a two-blade fixed-pitch glassfibre propeller, and is used under line-of-sight radio control for low-altitude sounding flights up to 500 m (1,640 ft). No other details are known.

EERM SAM-C

SAM-C is an atmospheric sounding vehicle for work at higher altitudes than SAM-B, up to cloud level. Design began in January 1977, and the first of two prototypes made its initial flight on 5 May that year. This version, with the engine pod-mounted on a pylon above the centre-fuselage, is designated **SAM-C MP** (moteur en pylône). A later version, which began flight testing in July 1978, is known as the **SAM-C MAR** (moteur arrière) and has the engine mounted at the rear, driving a pusher propeller.

First high-altitude (3,200-4,000 m; 10,500-13,125 ft) tests with a SAM-C MP were made in May 1978 at Deux-Alpes, and in the following month one was flown over the 3,300 m (10,825 ft) Mount Etna in Sicily, to measure thermal conditions in the vicinity of the volcano and to take gas samples to determine their chemical composition.

Five production SAM-C MAR vehicles, to which version the following description applies, had been built by 1 February 1980; production was continuing at that time.
TYPE: Pilotless atmospheric sounding vehicle.
AIRFRAME: Cantilever shoulder-wing monoplane, with inverted-V tail surfaces. Wings, of Aérospatiale RA 16 RC3 section, have 10° dihedral and 3° incidence, and are of glassfibre/polystyrene foam construction without spars or ribs. Schempp-Hirth metal airbrakes, or plastics trailing-edge flaps, with upward travel only and actuated by electrical servo. Glassfibre frameless

monocoque fuselage, in four sections: nose, front, centre and tail. Tail surfaces of similar construction to wings; elevators actuated by electrical servo. No landing gear.
POWER PLANT: One 1·2 kW (1·6 hp) Webra 61 10 cc two-stroke piston engine, mounted in rear fuselage and driving a two-blade fixed-pitch glassfibre pusher propeller. Fuel tank in centre fuselage section, capacity 0·5 to 2·0 litres (0·9 to 3·5 Imp pints). Refuelling point in fuselage tail section. NACA-type flush air intake above rear fuselage.
LAUNCH AND RECOVERY: Launched by catapult from 3·10 m (10 ft 2 in) ramp.
GUIDANCE AND CONTROL: Line-of-sight radio control. Aerodynamic control by airbrakes/flaps and elevators.
SYSTEM: 12V 0·5Ah nickel-cadmium battery for sounding systems; 4·8V 1·2Ah nickel-cadmium battery for radio controls.
EQUIPMENT: Temperature, humidity and atmospheric pressure sensors.
DIMENSIONS:

Wing span	3·15 m (10 ft 4 in)
Wing chord (constant)	0·35 m (1 ft 1¾ in)
Wing area, gross	1·10 m² (11·85 sq ft)
Wing aspect ratio	9
Length overall	2·10 m (6 ft 10¾ in)
Body diameter	0·16 m (6·3 in)
Height overall (on ground)	0·20 m (7·9 in)
Propeller diameter	0·30 m (11·8 in)

WEIGHTS AND LOADINGS:
Weight empty:

MP with minimum 0·5 kg (1·1 lb) ballast in forward fuselage	6·5 kg (14·33 lb)
MAR with 2 kg (4·5 lb) ballast	8 kg (17·63 lb)
Max payload	2·5 kg (5·5 lb)
Max fuel	1·3 kg (2·9 lb)
Max launching and landing weight	9·5 kg (20·9 lb)
Max wing loading	8·63 kg/m² (1·76 lb/sq ft)
Max power loading	7·9 kg/kW (13·1 lb/hp)

PERFORMANCE (at max launching weight except where indicated):

Never-exceed speed	68 knots (126 km/h; 78 mph)
Max level speed at S/L	50 knots (92 km/h; 57 mph)
Max cruising speed	30 knots (55 km/h; 34 mph)
Econ cruising speed at S/L 25 knots (46 km/h; 29 mph)
Stalling speed, power off 15 knots (28 km/h; 17·5 mph)
Max rate of climb at S/L at 8·5 kg (19 lb) normal operating weight	210 m (690 ft)/min
Service ceiling	5,000 m (16,400 ft)

EERM SAM-D

Design of SAM-D began at the same time as that of SAM-C, and the first of two prototypes made its initial flight in March 1978. To be used to obtain aerological measurements under difficult conditions (wind speeds of up to 29 knots; 54 km/h; 33 mph), it has a wide speed range of 17-64 knots (32-119 km/h; 20-74 mph) and entered production in 1979. Three production SAM-Ds had been completed by 1 February 1980.
TYPE: Pilotless atmospheric sounding vehicle.
AIRFRAME: Cantilever monoplane, with cropped-delta mid-mounted main wings at rear and shoulder-mounted canard foreplanes with elevons. Main wings have 15% thickness/chord ratio, 4° dihedral, 2° incidence and 20° sweepback at quarter-chord; they are of glassfibre/polystyrene foam construction, without spars or ribs, and have no movable control surfaces. Foreplanes are of similar construction, the elevons being actuated by electrical servos. Single sweptback fin; no rudder. Glassfibre frameless monocoque fuselage, of rectangular cross-section. No landing gear.
POWER PLANT: As for SAM-C. Single plastics fuel tank, capacity 0·5 to 1·0 litre (0·9 to 1·75 Imp pints), in fuselage centre-section beneath wing roots. Refuelling point in rear fuselage.
LAUNCH AND RECOVERY: No details received.
GUIDANCE AND CONTROL: No details received.
SYSTEM: Electrical power sources as for SAM-C.
EQUIPMENT: No details received.
DIMENSIONS, EXTERNAL:

Wing span	1·40 m (4 ft 7¼ in)
Wing chord at root	0·60 m (1 ft 11½ in)
Wing area, gross	0·63 m² (6·78 sq ft)
Wing aspect ratio	3·1
Length overall	1·55 m (5 ft 1 in)
Fuselage: Max width	0·14 m (5½ in)
Height overall	0·47 m (1 ft 6½ in)
Propeller diameter	0·30 m (11¾ in)

WEIGHTS:

Weight empty	4·4 kg (9·7 lb)
Max payload	1 kg (2·2 lb)
Max fuel load	0·6 kg (1·3 lb)
Max launching and landing weight	6 kg (13·2 lb)

PERFORMANCE (at max launching weight):

Max level speed	60 knots (111 km/h; 69 mph)
Max cruising speed	50 knots (92 km/h; 57 mph)
Stalling speed, power off 15 knots (28 km/h; 17·5 mph)
Max rate of climb at S/L	360 m (1,180 ft)/min
Service ceiling	4,000 m (13,125 ft)

FRANCE-ENGINS
SOCIÉTÉ ANONYME FRANCE-ENGINS

c/o Microturbo SA, BP 2089, Chemin du Pont-de-Rupé,
31019 Toulouse Cédex
Telephone: (61) 70 07 77
Telex: 531442 miturbo
PRESIDENT-DIRECTOR GENERAL: André de Boysson

This company was formed, in early 1975, by Microturbo SA (see Aero-Engines section) and Société Soulé.

FRANCE-ENGINS MITSOUBAC

The Mitsoubac is a low-cost target drone for naval operation, designed for high-*g* manoeuvrability at medium altitude and very low-level flight over water. Maximum use of watertight equipment minimises refurbishing. Mitsoubac is intended to provide a target for ships' armament without the need for support by land-based installations.

Flight trials began in 1975 as a private venture, using a Bell 47 light helicopter as the launch aircraft, and continued subsequently using an Alouette III helicopter. A low-cost launching system, using a Dornier Do 28 as the launch aircraft, has been developed, capable of operating 135 nm (250 km; 155 miles) offshore from its base.

A long-range version of the Mitsoubac is under development. This will have an engine thrust of 1·13 kN (253·5 lb st); payload of 30 kg (66 lb); launch weight of 200 kg (441 lb); max range of 324 nm (600 km; 373 miles) at 330 m (1,000 ft) or 450 nm (835 km; 519 miles) at 3,280 m (10,000 ft); and endurance of 35 min at 330 m (1,000 ft) at a max speed of 450 knots (835 km/h; 519 mph).

The following details apply to the present standard version, of which a fuller description can be found in the 1979-80 *Jane's*.

POWER PLANT: One 0·98 kN (220 lb st) Microturbo TRS 18-056 turbojet. Fuel capacity 31 litres (6·8 Imp gallons).

DIMENSIONS, EXTERNAL:
Wing span	1·35 m (4 ft 5¼ in)
Length overall	2·86 m (9 ft 4½ in)
Height overall	0·72 m (2 ft 4½ in)

WEIGHTS:
Payload	15 kg (33 lb)
Launching weight	150 kg (330 lb)

PERFORMANCE:
Max level speed at 100 m (330 ft)
437 knots (810 km/h; 503 mph)
Cruising speed at 1,500 m (5,000 ft)
324 knots (600 km/h; 373 mph)

Range, no reserves:
at max level speed	71 nm (131 km; 81 miles)
at cruising speed	93 nm (173 km; 107 miles)
Typical endurance	15 min

GERMANY
(FEDERAL REPUBLIC)

DORNIER
DORNIER GmbH

Postfach 2160, 8000 München 66
Telephone: München 8715480
Telex: 05-23543
OFFICERS: see Aircraft section

Current activities of Dornier GmbH include the development of drones, RPVs, reconnaissance systems, missiles and air target systems.

Dornier Aerial Target Systems (DATS) can be adapted to a wide variety of aircraft and target drones, and the original DATS was described briefly in the 1975-76 *Jane's*. Later systems include DATS 2, now entering service with the German armed forces and employed for all-calibre surface-to-air and air-to-air gunnery training. It is used with piloted aircraft in the high subsonic speed range (up to 500 knots; 925 km/h; 575 mph), and consists of two underwing-mounted Dornier Do-TLU 2 target launcher and reel units; a Do-TCU 2 launcher control unit; an aircraft installation kit; rigid, re-usable Do-SK 4 or Do-SK 5 towed targets, with up to 3,000 m (9,840 ft) of cable; ground control stations; and test and support equipment. DATS 3, for air-to-air gunnery in the high subsonic and transonic speed ranges, comprises Do-SK 10 A 1 dart-shaped tow targets, a radar reflector, a DS-SETA 1 scoring sensor, Do-TLU 3 launcher/reel unit, a DS-SUIT 1 scoring indicator unit, and appropriate ground support equipment. DATS 3 was tested successfully by the Luftwaffe in late 1979, and in early 1980 was in the procurement phase for operation with that service's F-4 Phantom and F-104 Starfighter aircraft. DATS 5, which uses Do-SK 4 towed targets, is designed for operation with target drones but is otherwise identical to DATS 2; DATS 6, operable with either target drones or piloted aircraft, is also similar to DATS 2 but uses Do-SK 4s with 2,500 m (8,200 ft) of cable stowed on a reel mounted internally in the towed target.

Dornier developed the Do 34 Kiebitz mobile drone system, based on the Do 32 K Experimental Kiebitz; and the Aerodyne unmanned VTOL research vehicle, described in previous editions of *Jane's*. It is currently developing the LA-RPV, and is active in the fields of tactical RPVs, stand-off missiles, mini-RPVs and helicopter drones. Under subcontract to LMSC (see US section), it is supplying the net recovery system for the new tactical mini-RPV ordered by the US Army.

Jointly with Canadair and SAT, Dornier is developing the AN/USD-502, details of which can be found in the International section.

DORNIER Do 34 KIEBITZ (PEEWIT)

In August 1972 Dornier announced the receipt of a DM 7 million contract from the Federal Ministry of Defence for the first development phase of a prototype of an operational Kiebitz system, to be used for reconnaissance, fire control, communications and traffic monitoring duties. This followed the completion in mid-1972 of the design of a Do 34 operational model as a sensor platform with a payload of 140 kg (308 lb). Full-scale mockups of the Do 34 were followed by the construction of two prototype flight vehicles and two ground stations. Under a bilateral agreement between the West German and French governments, both flight vehicles are fitted with an advanced version of the French LCT Orphée II radar, to define, integrate and test a new battlefield reconnaissance system known as **Argus** (see International section). The first Argus prototype made its initial flight on 14 May 1979.

Flight testing of the first Do 34 Kiebitz (F 01) began on 1 February 1978, and on 3 March the maximum flight altitude of more than 300 m (985 ft) was reached, the Kiebitz staying aloft for 40 minutes. By February 1980 the prototypes had made more than 240 successful flights, totalling approx 90 flying hours.

The following details apply to the basic Do 34 flight vehicle:

AIRFRAME: Flight vehicle is roughly cone-shaped, to reduce radar signature. Approximately cylindrical payload compartment located beneath this, enabling sensors to be changed quickly and allowing space for large-volume radome. Two-blade rotor, with foldable blades attached by straps and driven by cold air expelled through blade-tip nozzles. Air to nozzles supplied by MTU radial compressor driven by engine.

POWER PLANT: One 313 kW (420 shp) Allison 250-C20B turboshaft engine, installed at an angle to give good air intake position.

LAUNCH AND RECOVERY: Not applicable. Kiebitz is cable-tethered, housed in vehicle which incorporates its landing platform, winch, control post, fuel tank and auxiliary equipment.

GUIDANCE AND CONTROL: After arrival on site, can be in position at operational height of 300 m (985 ft) in 8 min; limiting factors are wind speed of 14 m (46 ft)/s, added gusts of 8 m (26 ft)/s, available thrust reserves, and sensor requirements. Control system aligns drone according to airframe attitude and position in relation to ground. Electromagnetic sensor measures any drift from desired position.

EQUIPMENT: Bodenseewerk autopilot and Lear Siegler 3 kW starter/generator. Appropriate payload packages for reconnaissance, target acquisition, fire control, communications relay or traffic monitoring.

DIMENSIONS, EXTERNAL:
Diameter of rotor	8·00 m (26 ft 3 in)
Height overall	2·70 m (8 ft 10¼ in)
Body diameter (max) at bottom	2·00 m (6 ft 6¾ in)

WEIGHTS AND LOADING:
Weight without cable or payload	350 kg (772 lb)
300 m (985 ft) cable	85 kg (187 lb)
Max payload to 300 m (985 ft), ISA	140 kg (309 lb)
Max launching weight	550 kg (1,212 lb)
Disc loading	10·9 kg/m² (2·2 lb/sq ft)

DESIGN PERFORMANCE:
Reel-in/reel-out speed	3 m (9·8 ft)/s
Operating altitude	300 m (985 ft)
Mission endurance	more than 24 h

DORNIER LA-RPV

Formerly known as the UKF, the LA (Luft-Angriffs: air attack) RPV has been proposed by Dornier, under the Federal Defence Ministry's Component Air Testing Programme, as a means of examining the basic problems of target acquisition, armament and flight guidance for ground support RPVs.

The principal tasks of the LA-RPV are seen as air strike (especially battlefield interdiction) against highly defended fixed and transient ground targets; tactical reconnaissance; and electronic warfare including air defence suppression. Several different possible configurations have been studied, the one most favoured in 1979-80 (see accompanying photograph) being a ground-launched re-usable vehicle with retractable landing gear, an internal weapon load, an externally-mounted turbojet engine, and inertial navigation updated by satellite data or terrain comparison. This would take off and land conventionally, having provision for booster-assisted take-off and an arrester system for landing.

Particular attention is being paid to accuracy of navigation and weapons delivery, with or without terminal guidance or with remote-based ground control. Since most missions will be against preselected targets, there will be no onboard detection sensors for an enemy to jam. Most missions will be undertaken at high speed and low altitude, and will be pre-programmed out and back, with provision for the ground controller to override the mission programme during the take-off, formation, flight monitoring and recovery phases. Target attack would be by means of 'scatter' weapons ejected from an onboard munitions container.

An Aeritalia (Fiat) G91R aircraft is serving as a multipurpose RPV testbed, and will be used in co-operation with VFW in a remote target acquisition programme. This aircraft is manually piloted, and has been modified by Dornier to carry an AEG-Telefunken underwing television camera, an Eltro forward-looking infra-red (FLIR) sensor, a two-axis stabilisation system, and a TV transmitter, all housed in an underwing pod. The TV/infra-red experiments were completed by the beginning of 1979, and the G91 is being used by the two companies in other programmes.

DIMENSIONS:
Wing span	3·80 m (12 ft 5½ in)
Length overall	6·50 m (21 ft 4 in)
Height overall	1·90 m (6 ft 2¾ in)

DORNIER KDAR-LOCUST

Dornier has been studying for some years the development of mini-RPVs, and a vehicle of this type was displayed for the first time at the Paris Air Show in May/June 1977. A half-scale model has been flight-tested, as well as experimental full-scale prototypes of the Dornier/Texas Instruments KDAR (Kleindrohne Antiradar; anti-radiation mini-drone).

Typical missions for which the vehicle is intended include electro-optical reconnaissance, target acquisition and fire control, anti-radar operations, anti-tank or point target attack, and target presentation. For the reconnaissance and target acquisition and fire control missions, the integration of a sensor package comprising a stabilised TV camera, with auto-track facility coupled with a laser illuminator, is under investigation. Anti-radar missions and attacks on tanks or point targets are 'kamikaze' missions in which the vehicle homes on to and attacks the target after a search flight using, for example, passive or active radar and/or infra-red seeker heads. For target missions, it can be fitted with various augmentation devices, including smoke cartridges, flares or Luneberg lenses. It can also be used to test missile proximity fuses or homing heads. The flight guidance, data transmission and ground control systems are adapted to suit specific mission requirements.

The Dornier vehicle is one of three designs (others are by MBB and VFW, which see) competing in a joint US-West German competition for the development of the **Locust** harassment weapon system.

AIRFRAME: Consists essentially of two glassfibre half-shells. Wings built integrally with fuselage, and fitted with elevons on trailing-edges. Tail surfaces comprise a main fin and an underfin, the latter also serving as a keel surface to protect the propeller during landing.

POWER PLANT: One 16·4 kW (22 hp) Limbach two-cylinder two-stroke piston engine, mounted in rear of fuselage and driving a four-blade pusher propeller. Fuel in two fuselage tanks; provision to install a third tank in centre of fuselage instead of main recovery parachute. Provision for booster engine for launch.

LAUNCH AND RECOVERY: During initial flight tests, drone was launched by catapult from hydraulically operated launching sled. When required for re-use, the RPV is fitted with an electro-mechanically deployed parachute recovery system (drogue parachute in fin-tip fairing, main parachute in centre-fuselage), activated by radio command, with automatic activation in the event of onboard systems failure. Inflatable airbags to absorb landing impact. For expendable missions, parachute can be replaced by an additional fuel tank or other equipment.

GUIDANCE AND CONTROL: Automatic or remote radio command guidance system. Aerodynamic control by elevons.

France-Engins Mitsoubac in Do 28 launch configuration

Dornier delta-winged KDAR-Locust tactical mini-RPV

Dornier Spähplattform on truck-towed trailer

Dornier Spähplattform in flight

Model of possible Dornier LA-RPV strike RPV (Brian M. Service)

MBB KDAR-Locust anti-radar RPV, with flip-out wings, tail fins and propeller

DIMENSIONS, EXTERNAL:
Wing span	2·10 m (6 ft 10½ in)
Length overall	2·00 m (6 ft 6¾ in)

DIMENSIONS, INTERNAL:
Payload compartment: Length	0·60 m (1 ft 11½ in)
Diameter	0·20 m (8 in)

WEIGHTS:
Payload	15 kg (33 lb)
Max launching weight	70 kg (154 lb)

PERFORMANCE:
Max diving speed	194 knots (360 km/h; 223 mph)
Max level speed at S/L, ISA	135 knots (250 km/h; 155 mph)
Max operating height	3,000 m (9,850 ft)
Max endurance	3 h

DORNIER SPÄHPLATTFORM

The Spähplattform (spotting platform) is an unpowered camera-carrying device being developed for battlefield surveillance. To improve mobility, the experimental system has been installed, under government contract, in a Unimog 1·4 ton truck with a two-wheeled trailer. Field tests, simulating military missions, were planned to take place during 1980.

AIRFRAME: Small, domed payload compartment, mounted on top of an upper gyroscopic ring encircling a four-blade rotor, and a lower stationary ring, in which four control vanes are mounted.

POWER SOURCE: 25 kW (33·5 hp) is available for initial rotor spin-up; 90 N is required to maintain the hover mode.

LAUNCH AND RECOVERY: Not applicable. The Spähplattform is vehicle-mounted, and tethered to its control vehicle by an umbilical cable, via which drive from the parent vehicle is transmitted to spin up the four-blade flywheel rotor to 4,000 rpm for take-off. The blade-tips of the rotor are attached to the upper gyroscopic ring, in which the energy from spin-up is stored; the four control vanes, mounted on cruciform tubes within the stationary lower ring, can be actuated to control the platform in azimuth. A conventional cyclic pitch control of the rotor determines the platform's position, and gyroscopic effect stabilises its attitude. The Spähplattform is started and reeled out from a transportation box with automatic covers, and hovers on the energy stored in the flywheel rotor.

GUIDANCE AND CONTROL: Control and sensor signals are transmitted via the tethering cable from the ground control vehicle.

SPECIAL EQUIPMENT: Still camera of 12·5 mm to 75 mm focal length, or TV camera, in payload compartment.

DIMENSION:
Rotor diameter	1·20 m (3 ft 11¼ in)

WEIGHTS:
Weight of twin-ring assembly	20 kg (44 lb)
Weight of complete vehicle, without payload	30 kg (66 lb)
Payload	5 kg (11 lb)
Max T-O weight	35 kg (77 lb)

PERFORMANCE:
Reel-in/reel-out speed	5 m (16·4 ft)/s
Operating altitude	50 m (164 ft)
Mission endurance	1 min

MBB
MESSERSCHMITT-BÖLKOW-BLOHM GmbH

Ottobrunn bei München, 8 München 80, Postfach 801220
OFFICERS: see Aircraft section

MBB's drone/RPV activities include development of the KDAR-Locust, of which all known details follow. Other programmes include studies for a modular-concept weapon-carrying RPV, for use against heavily defended, previously reconnoitred targets, or for electro-optical reconnaissance. All-weather navigation, and the ability to deliver weapons even under adverse conditions of visibility, would be achieved with the aid of a combined flight guidance and fire control system also under development by MBB. The RPV would be truck-launched, using a booster, and recovered either by arrester cable or in a horizontal, parachute-assisted glide landing.

MBB KDAR-LOCUST

This miniature harassment drone is being developed under Federal German Ministry of Defence contract, to combat the radar equipment of enemy air defence installations. It is a competitor for US/German contracts that are intended to have Locust vehicles in service with field units by the end of FY 1983.

The drone is launched by means of a booster directly from its storage and transport container. When inside the container the wings, tail control surfaces and propeller are folded; they flip out for use immediately upon launch. Designed to search for, and attack, enemy air defence radars, this small RPV was evolved in collaboration with Teledyne Brown Engineering of Huntsville, Alabama, USA. Components for the terminal phase guidance system are manufactured by Motorola.

VFW
VEREINIGTE FLUGTECHNISCHE WERKE GmbH
Hünefeldstrasse 1-5, 28 Bremen 1, Postfach 1206

VFW MINI-RPV
To meet a German Defence Ministry requirement, VFW developed a catapult-launched mini-RPV of canard configuration. The first prototype, designed in association with Northrop of the USA, had a tapered wing and was powered by a 1·5 kW (2 hp) piston engine, mounted at the extreme tail and driving a two-blade pusher propeller. This prototype carried no telemetry equipment and had a weight of only 5 kg (11 lb).

The second prototype, displayed at the 1978 Hanover Air Show, was described as the Mini-RPV 2012. It has constant-chord wings, a 4·5 kW (6 hp) single-cylinder piston engine and onboard telemetry equipment, increasing the take-off weight to 20 kg (44 lb). Its general configuration is shown in the accompanying illustration.

The wing has a Wortmann section, and is fitted with spoilers. There are elevators on the canard foreplane, and a tail fin but no rudder.

The later and larger RT 910 Tucan (which see) has a similar configuration.

VFW VF-500
This larger RPV, of delta-winged aircraft configuration with twin fins and rudders, was displayed in model form at the 1978 Hanover Air Show.
DIMENSIONS, EXTERNAL:

Wing span	4·00 m (13 ft 1½ in)
Length overall	7·80 m (25 ft 7 in)
Height overall	1·95 m (6 ft 4¾ in)

WEIGHT:
Max launching weight 1,940 kg (4,277 lb)

VFW RT 910 TUCAN
This mini-RPV, developed under contract to the Federal Ministry of Defence, was displayed in model form at

the 1979 Paris Air Show. Intended for real-time target detection and acquisition, the Tucan has a broadly similar configuration to the prototype mini-RPV No. 2012 (which see), but without the latter's canard control surfaces. The Tucan is of modular design, with a radio command guidance system, and telemetry for relaying visual and signal data. Power plant is a horizontally-opposed piston engine, driving a two-blade pusher propeller. Launch is by catapult, recovery by parachute. Payloads, accommodated in the long fuselage nose, can include cameras and transmitters; the CG of the vehicle can be adjusted, according to the weight of payload, by positioning the wings accordingly. Targets are detected by means of a TV or infra-red camera, the images from which are relayed via TV/radio link to the ground control station.
WEIGHT:
Max launching weight 100 kg (220 lb)
PERFORMANCE:
Max level speed 135 knots (250 km/h; 155 mph)
Operational radius, incl 30 min hold
38 nm (70 km; 43 miles)

INDONESIA

LAPAN
LEMBAGA PENERBANGAN DAN ANTARIKSA NASIONAL (National Aeronautics and Space Institute)
HEADQUARTERS: Jalan Pemuda Persil No. 1, PO Box 3048, Jakarta Timur
Telephone: (021) 465125, 482808 and 482653
Telex: 45675 LAPAN IA

OFFICERS: see Aircraft section
This Institute, established in 1963, designed and built an experimental mini-RPV, known as the XTG-01.

LAPAN XTG-01
Test-flown for the first time at Rumpin airfield in FY

1977, the XTG-01 was being developed in 1979 for such applications as aerial photography, emergency transmitter aerial, and flight research.
TYPE: Experimental mini-RPV.
AIRFRAME: High-wing monoplane configuration, built basically of balsa wood; wings have 2° dihedral, 2° incidence, and a flat-bottomed section. Balsa fuselage, laminated with synthetic fibres.
POWER PLANT: One 1·28 kW (1·71 hp) Hirtenberger HP 61 FS single-cylinder aircooled piston engine, driving a two-blade fixed-pitch wooden propeller. Fuel capacity 2·5 litres (0·55 Imp gallons).
LAUNCH AND RECOVERY: Conventional T-O and landing.
GUIDANCE AND CONTROL: Futaba FP-6FN six-channel radio command flight control system; transmitter and

receiver operate in 27MHz band. Aerodynamic control by ailerons, elevators and rudder.
EQUIPMENT: 9·6V battery.
DIMENSIONS, EXTERNAL:

Wing span	2·43 m (7 ft 11¾ in)
Wing area, gross	0·814 m² (8·76 sq ft)
Length overall	1·60 m (5 ft 3 in)
Height overall	0·575 m (1 ft 10¾ in)

WEIGHTS:

Weight empty	5·3 kg (11·7 lb)
Max payload	2 kg (4·4 lb)
Max T-O weight	7·0 kg (15·4 lb)

PERFORMANCE:

Speed	60 knots (112 km/h; 70 mph)
Endurance	1 h

INTERNATIONAL PROGRAMMES

AN/USD-502
PRIME CONTRACTOR:
Canadair Ltd, PO Box 6087, Montreal, Quebec H3C 3G9, Canada
Telephone: (514) 744 1511

PRINCIPAL SUBCONTRACTOR:
Dornier GmbH, Postfach 2160, 8000 München 66, Federal Republic of Germany
Telephone: München 8715480
Telex: 05-23543

AN/USD-502/CL-289
The AN/USD-502 originated as a joint Canadair/Dornier programme, based on AN/USD-501 (Canadair CL-89, which see) technology, to meet a German military technical requirement for a longer-range drone for service from about 1983. It has the NATO designation AN/USD-502, and the Canadair designation **CL-289**.

The main contract was awarded in July 1976 to Canadair, as part of a shared-cost project between Canada and West Germany. Dornier is subcontracted for approximately half the work. France joined the programme on 29 March 1977, and assigned SAT as the industrial subcontractor. The SAT work represents approx 10 per cent of the total programme.

Resembling a scaled-up CL-89, the AN/USD-502 has greater payload capacity and is equipped with both a Zeiss reconnaissance camera and an SAT infra-red linescan (IRLS) sensor with real-time data transmission, plus a ground recording system. The navigation/control system comprises a Canadian Marconi Doppler sensor and a Dornier System airborne digital computer. The mission programme is stored in the computer, which generates the command signals required for navigation, attitude control and sensor activation. A 1·08 kN (242·5 lb st) KHD T117 turbojet engine gives the drone a high-subsonic cruising speed; a 32 kN (7,200 lb st) Bristol Aerospace solid-propellant booster rocket is used to accelerate the drone

off the mobile zero-length launcher. Heading correction before landing, descent on the recovery parachute, and damping of the landing impact by inflatable landing bags, correspond to the well-proven concepts of the CL-89, which are characterised by their high landing accuracy and the avoidance of damage to the flight vehicle. The launcher is also of similar design to that for the CL-89.

The first AN/USD-502/CL-289, together with its launching vehicle, were rolled out on 4 September 1979 at Löwental airfield, near Friedrichshafen. First flight was made on 3 March 1980. Operational trials of the CL-289 are due to take place in 1981; production is scheduled to begin in 1983.

DIMENSIONS, EXTERNAL:

Wing span	1·32 m (4 ft 4 in)
Length overall (excl ADMU):	
with booster	4·67 m (15 ft 4 in)
without booster	3·61 m (11 ft 10 in)
Body diameter (max)	0·38 m (1 ft 3 in)

ARGUS
Dornier GmbH, Postfach 2160, 8000 München 66, Federal Republic of Germany
Telephone: München 8715480
Telex: 05-23543

LCT (Laboratoire Central de Télécommunications), 18-20 rue Grange-Dame-Rose, 78140 Vélizy-Villacoublay, BP 40, France
Telephone: 946 96 15
Telex: 690892

ARGUS
Argus (Autonomes Radar Gefechtsfeld Uberwachungs

System) is a battlefield surveillance system being developed under a German-French government agreement signed on 6 March 1974. Dornier has the main contract for co-ordinating, integrating and testing the system, and the programme is administered by a board of directors representing the two governments.

The Argus prototypes consist of the two prototypes of the Dornier Do 34 Kiebitz, each fitted with an advanced version of the LCT Orphée II radar as the primary sensor. The first Argus prototype made its initial flight on 14 May 1979 and the second prototype at the end of 1979. The first part of the troop demonstration was also completed in

that year. The second part was due to be carried out in the latter half of 1980, using an improved Orphée II airborne radar and ground control station.

The complete Argus system incorporates a mobile ground station and a tether cable. The ground station is installed in a container mounted on a cross-country 10 ton truck and provided with all equipment necessary for transportation and up to 24 h operation of the system. Operating height of the flight vehicle is 300 m (985 ft).

A description of the Kiebitz appears under the Dornier heading in the German section.

VFW second prototype mini-RPV (No. 2012) *(Brian M. Service)*

VFW RT 910 Tucan target acquisition mini-RPV *(Brian M. Service)*

AN/USD-502/CL-289 surveillance drone and launcher in starting position

LAPAN XTG-01 prototype experimental mini-RPV

Exploded view of the Canadair/Dornier AN/USD-502 surveillance drone

Dornier Do 34 Kiebitz in Argus configuration

1 Air distance measuring unit (ADMU)
2 Nosecone
3 Heading reference unit
4 Airborne computer
5 Servo amplifier
6 Forward landing bag container
7 Power supply unit
8 Video data link
9 Barometric altitude reference unit
10 Lanyard valve
11 Fuel tank
12 Command receiver/decoder
13 Air reservoir
14 Aft landing bag container
15 Wing (one of four)
16 Transponder unit
17 Air charging door
18 Access panel
19 Pressure regulator
20 Engine air intake
21 T 117 engine
22 Tailcone
23 Recovery parachute door
24 Drogue parachute
25 Main parachute
26 Transponder antenna
27 Data link antenna
28 Fuel expulsion unit
29 28V regulator
30 Doppler antenna
31 IRLS sensor
32 Optical sensor
33 Doppler electronic sensor unit
34 Yaw canard surface
35 Yaw actuator
36 Vertical gyro
37 Terminal guidance unit
38 Non-tactical payload telemetry unit

ISRAEL

IAI
ISRAEL AIRCRAFT INDUSTRIES
Ben Gurion International Airport, Lydda (Lod)
Telephone: (03) 973 111
Telex: Isravia 031102 and 031114

IAI SCOUT
Israel Aircraft Industries has designed and built a mini-RPV system known as Scout, primarily for real-time battlefield reconnaissance and surveillance. The complete system comprises the Scout aircraft, ground control station, launcher and retrieval net.

Military and civil applications include missile site reconnaissance, battlefield control, target identification, strike force control, artillery targeting, border patrol, coastal and waterway control, and damage assessment.

Scouts are operational with a number of export customers.

AIRFRAME: Cantilever high-wing monoplane. Fuselage is a rectangular-section nacelle; twin inward-canted fins and rudders, supported by twin tailbooms extending from wings outboard of fuselage. No landing gear on catapult-launched version, but a non-retractable tricycle gear can be fitted, if required, for operation from paved strips. Modular construction, with large access panels. Low detection signatures.

POWER PLANT: One 13·4 kW (18 hp) two-cylinder air-cooled piston engine, installed in rear of fuselage nacelle, driving a specially designed two-blade pusher propeller. Fuel is a 20:1 petrol/oil mixture.

LAUNCH AND RECOVERY: Truck-mounted pneumatic rail launcher, and trailer- or truck-mounted recovery net, are standard. Conventional runway T-O and landing available optionally, if landing gear is fitted.

GUIDANCE AND CONTROL: Real-time guidance by auto-tracker and two-way data link. Pre-programmed dead reckoning capability. For recovery, aircraft is guided semi-automatically by an optical device into centre of retrieval net.

SPECIAL EQUIPMENT: TV camera, with telephoto lens, mounted in fuselage on stabilised platform servo-controlled for vibration damping. Large transparent hemispherical blister under centre of fuselage nacelle. Camera can rotate and scan through 360° in azimuth and 0-90° in pitch. Field of view adjustable, varying between 47·5° and 3·4°. The mini-RPV is also fitted with panoramic camera to scan an area within 60° on each side of flight path. Configuration permits development of other payload packages, to customer's requirements.

DIMENSIONS, EXTERNAL:
Wing span	3·60 m (11 ft 9¾ in)
Length overall	3·68 m (12 ft 1 in)

WEIGHTS:
Payload	22·7 kg (50 lb)
Fuel	14·5 kg (32 lb)
Launching weight	113·4 kg (250 lb)

PERFORMANCE (typical):
Max level speed	80 knots (148 km/h; 92 mph)
Speed for max range	55 knots (102 km/h; 63 mph)
Stalling speed	42 knots (78 km/h; 49 mph)
Rate of climb at S/L	152 m (500 ft)/min
Max operating altitude	3,050 m (10,000 ft)
Flight endurance	4 h 30 min

TADIRAN
TADIRAN ISRAEL ELECTRONICS INDUSTRIES LTD
3 Hashalom Road, PO Box 648, Tel-Aviv 61000
Telephone: 267272
Telex: 03-3537
MANAGING DIRECTOR: E. Caspi
ADVERTISING MANAGER: N. Leshem
PLANNING AND DEVELOPMENT: A. Mayer

TADIRAN MASTIFF
This mini-RPV completed over 100 test flights with great success, and is now in production for the Israeli armed forces and for export.

Designed for a wide range of intelligence and reconnaissance missions, its applications include real-time reconnaissance, remotely controlled photography, decoy manoeuvres, electronic interference and jamming, and other uses within the limitations of payload size and weight.

AIRFRAME: High-wing monoplane, with low-set tailplane, non-retractable tailwheel landing gear, and a ventral payload compartment within the centre-fuselage. Very low radar signature.

POWER PLANT: One 10·4 kW (14 hp) two-cylinder piston engine, driving a two-blade propeller. Fuel capacity 22·7 litres (5 Imp gallons); fuel is a 16:1 petrol/oil mixture.

LAUNCH AND RECOVERY: Conventional take-off and landing, using non-retractable tailwheel-type landing gear.

GUIDANCE AND CONTROL: Remotely controlled from ground radio control station or, independently, by a pre-programmed airborne autopilot controller. Aerodynamic control by ailerons, elevators and rudder.

EQUIPMENT: Electrical power system, supplied by alternator and standby battery. Onboard avionics, to control flight and stability, include autopilot, vertical gyro, barometric altitude transducer, and magnetic compass. Standard payload incorporates a TV camera, with 7° to 35° zoom lens, mounted on a bi-axial platform capable of motion in pitch and roll of up to 45° to each side of vertical axis. The ground controller can control camera pitch and roll angles by joystick or by potentiometer dialling to the required angle relative to the RPV. He can also control the viewing angle of the zoom lens. Camera angles are controlled directly by payload servo-actuators and a zoom servo system.

DIMENSIONS, EXTERNAL:
Wing span	4·20 m (13 ft 9½ in)
Wing area	2·00 m² (21·53 sq ft)
Length overall	2·60 m (8 ft 6¼ in)
Height overall	1·00 m (3 ft 3¼ in)

WEIGHTS:
Weight empty	52 kg (114·5 lb)
Max payload	15 kg (33 lb)
Max launching weight	80 kg (36·3 lb)

PERFORMANCE:
Max level speed	80 knots (148 km/h; 92 mph)
Typical cruising speed	40-60 knots (74-111 km/h; 46-69 mph)
Stalling speed	35 knots (65 km/h; 40·5 mph)
Max operating altitude	3,050 m (10,000 ft)
T-O and landing run	150 m (492 ft)
Range	38 nm (70 km; 43·5 miles)
Endurance	4 h

ITALY

METEOR
METEOR SpA AIRCRAFT AND ELECTRONICS INDUSTRY
146 Via Nomentana, 00162 Rome
Telephone: (06) 830991
Telex: 680136 Meteor
PRESIDENT: Comm Avv Furio Lauri
GENERAL MANAGER: Dott Antonio Castelli
PRODUCTION PLANT: 34074 Monfalcone, Stazioni F.S. Ronchi Nord
Telephone: (0481) 778001
Telex: 460288 METMON
PLANT MANAGER: Ing Carlo Spanò
PRODUCTION AND TECHNICAL DIVISION MANAGER: P. I. Paolo Raiteri
ADMINISTRATIVE DIVISION MANAGER: Mrs Mirella Tiburzio

Meteor was established in Trieste as a joint stock company in 1947. Its present head office is in Rome, supported by facilities at Monfalcone (Trieste) and Cagliari (Sardinia). The former is a production factory, the latter being equipped for flight operations and for technical assistance to the users of the tri-service range at Salto di Quirra.

Meteor is producing for the Italian and foreign armed forces various propeller-driven and turbojet-powered radio-controlled drones covering a speed range from 323 knots (600 km/h; 372 mph) up to Mach 2·8, and altitudes from 10 m (35 ft) to 25,000 m (82,000 ft) above sea level. It also co-produces the Northrop-Ventura Meteor 1 and 2 (NVM-1 and NVM-2), Northrop-Ventura Meteor/USD-1, Aérospatiale Meteor 20 (AM/CT.20) target drones and the BM-1 (Beech Meteor 1) missile target system. Under licence from Canadair, Meteor produces 50 per cent of the AN/USD-501 (CL-89) reconnaissance systems ordered by Italy.

METEOR ANDROMEDA/MIRACH SYSTEM
The Andromeda system is designed to meet a basic operational requirement which synthesises and integrates the requirements of most potential operators. Such a multi-role system, equipped with various types of RPV for combat or training use by air, land and naval forces in natural and operational environments, could reduce the attrition of conventional piloted aircraft used in conjunction with them and/or replaced by them in missions operationally suited to the use of RPVs.

The Andromeda system, which is characterised by completely independent operation, maximum utilisation and considerable mobility, is composed of the following subsystems:

1st Subsystem (Alamak). Ground station for accomplishing and/or controlling the mission by the ground crew (Standard and RID versions). Produced for foreign markets.

2nd Subsystem. Equipment for launch, recovery and maintenance of the aerial vehicles. Produced for foreign markets.

3rd Subsystem. Equipment for preparation, recovery, maintenance and operation and/or evaluation of the payload and/or its results. Produced for foreign markets.

4th Subsystem. The aerial vehicle system, configured in a range of five types of vehicle, known as **Mirach**, compatible with the Andromeda system to guarantee maximum effectiveness.

The Andromeda system can be adapted, with only slight modification, to use other types of air vehicle which operators may already have at their disposal. It is being developed in collaboration with Aerosystem Electronic AG of Switzerland.

The following versions of the Mirach flight vehicle are available:

Mirach-10. RPV for target acquisition, location and designation; surveillance; 'kamikaze' missions; and enemy defence saturation. Powered by single 16·4 kW (22 hp) piston engine. Meteor radio command guidance system. Equipped with real-time TV, photo-reconnaissance cameras and laser designator. Under development for foreign markets.

Mirach-70. Target, or RPV for surveillance, target acquisition, electronic warfare, or decoy saturation. Powered by single 52 kW (70 hp) McCulloch piston engine. Meteor radio command guidance system. Various combat or training payloads. In production for foreign markets.

Mirach-100. Target, or RPV for surveillance; reconnaissance; target acquisition, location and designation; electronic warfare strike; and defence saturation. Powered by single 1·13 kN (253·5 lb st) Microturbo TRS 18-076 turbojet engine. Meteor radio command guidance, or programmed guidance with real-time updating. Various combat or training payloads. In production for Italian Navy and foreign markets.

Mirach-300. Target, or RPV for surveillance, reconnaissance, target acquisition, location and designation, electronic warfare strike, and defence saturation. Powered by single 3·34 kN (750 lb st) Microturbo TRI 60 turbojet engine. Guidance as for Mirach-100. Various combat or training payloads. Under development for foreign markets.

Mirach-600. Target, or RPV for training and evaluation, area reconnaissance, electronic warfare strike, and defence suppression. Powered by two 3·34 kN (750 lb st) Microturbo TRI 60 turbojet engines. Guidance as for Mirach-100. Various combat or evaluation payloads.

DIMENSIONS, EXTERNAL:
Span overall (wings or fins):	
10	2·71 m (8 ft 10¾ in)
70	3·57 m (11 ft 8½ in)
100	2·80 m (9 ft 2¼ in)
300	2·83 m (9 ft 3½ in)
600	3·60 m (11 ft 9¾ in)
Length overall (excl booster):	
10	2·25 m (7 ft 4½ in)
70	3·66 m (12 ft 0 in)
100	3·91 m (12 ft 10 in)
300	4·88 m (16 ft 0 in)
600	6·10 m (20 ft 0 in)

WEIGHTS:
Weight empty: *10	50 kg (110 lb)
70	200 kg (441 lb)
100	210 kg (463 lb)
*300	320 kg (705 lb)
*600	680 kg (1,499 lb)
Combat payload (internal): 70	20 kg (44 lb)
100	40 kg (88 lb)
300	80 kg (176 lb)
600	160 kg (352 lb)

Israel Aircraft Industries Scout mini-RPV

Tadiran Mastiff mini-RPV

Mirach-70 RPV on its launch trailer

Mirach-10 multi-purpose RPV

Helicopter-launched Mirach-100

Meteor Mirach-300 target/RPV on launching ramp

Fuji-built BQM-34A Firebee target drone of the JMSDF

Max T-O weight (incl booster): *10	70 kg (154 lb)	PERFORMANCE:		Max endurance: 10	3 h 0 min
70	260 kg (573 lb)	Max level speed:		70	1 h 0 min
100	310 kg (683 lb)	10	97 knots (180 km/h; 112 mph)	100	1 h 10 min
*300	450 kg (992 lb)	70	167 knots (310 km/h; 193 mph)		
*600	1,000 kg (2,204 lb)	100	512 knots (950 km/h; 590 mph)		
*estimated		300, 600	Mach 0·9		

JAPAN

FUJI
FUJI JUKOGYO KABUSHIKI KAISHA (Fuji Heavy Industries Ltd)
Subaru Building, 7-2, 1-chome, Nishi-Shinjuku, Shinjuku-ku, Tokyo
Telephone: Tokyo (03) 347 2505
Telex: 0-232-2268
OFFICERS: see Aircraft section

Under contract from the Japan Defence Agency, Fuji is building the Teledyne Ryan BQM-34A Firebee I subsonic target drone (see US section) for use in the training of Tartar missile and gunnery crews and for the evaluation of air-to-air missile systems. The first shipboard launch of a Fuji-built drone was carried out successfully in 1970, and 180 flights had been made by the beginning of 1980.
Fuji-built BQM-34As include two fitted with RALACS (Radar Altimeter Low Altitude Control System: see

Teledyne Ryan entry in US section), for training the crews of defensive weapons against attack by anti-shipping missiles.
Twenty-four Fuji-built BQM-34As had been completed and delivered to the Japan Maritime Self-Defence Force, and two to the Technical Research and Development Institute of the Japan Defence Agency, by the beginning of 1980. A total of 29 were scheduled to be completed by the end of FY 1979 (March 1980).

NEC
NIPPON ELECTRIC CO LTD (Nippon Denki Kabushiki Kaisha)

33-1 Shiba Gochome, Minato-ku, Tokyo 108
Telephone: Tokyo (03) 454 1111
Telex: NECTOK A J22686

PRESIDENT: Tadao Tanaka
MANAGER, OVERSEAS RELATIONS: Kiyoshi Yamauchi

Under a technical aid agreement with Northrop Corporation, USA, NEC is responsible for production and repair of Northrop KD2R5 (Shelduck) target drones for the

Japan Maritime Self-Defence Force and Ground Self-Defence Force. Delivery of these drones to the JMSDF and JGSDF began in 1961, and a total of 283 had been delivered by the beginning of 1980. Production was expected to continue at the rate of approx 15 per year.

SAUDI ARABIA

MCS
MID-CONTINENT SCIENTIFIC CO (A subsidiary of Qutub International Ltd)

PO Box 3603, Riyadh
PRESIDENT: Dr Musa Qutub, PhD

MCS PL-60

The PL-60 is a twin-engined mini-RPV capable of use for surveillance and other military duties, border patrol, forest fire surveillance, aerial photography, traffic patrol, air pollution and weather monitoring, and similar applications. It is claimed that it cannot be detected by radar.

Design began, in the USA, in 1971; a prototype PL-60 was flown in 1972, and production began in the same year. By March 1979 a total of 1,580 had been ordered and built

in two versions, designated **PL-60A** and **PL-60B**, the latter having a strengthened structure to carry a heavier payload.
POWER PLANT: Two 1·4 kW (1·9 hp) piston engines, mounted in overwing nacelles and each driving a two-blade propeller. Fuel capacity 1·9 litres (0·5 US gallons) standard, 7·6 litres (2 US gallons) optional.
LAUNCH AND RECOVERY: Conventional T-O, using tailwheel-type fixed landing gear. Wire recovery.
EQUIPMENT: Automatic navigation system, TV or other camera installations, optional.
DIMENSIONS, EXTERNAL:
Wing span 3·30 m (10 ft 10 in)
Wing area, gross 1·57 m² (16·94 sq ft)
Length overall 1·96 m (6 ft 5 in)
Height overall 0·58 m (1 ft 11 in)

WEIGHTS:
Payload: PL-60A 11·3 kg (25 lb)
PL-60B 22 kg (48 lb)
Max T-O weight 27·2 kg (60 lb)

PERFORMANCE:
Max level speed
65-87 knots (121-161 km/h; 75-100 mph)
Cruising speed 56·5 knots (105 km/h; 65 mph)
Max operating height 3,050 m (10,000 ft)
T-O run (hard surface) 99 m (325 ft)
Range: standard fuel 30·5 nm (56·5 km; 35 miles)
max optional fuel 121·5 nm (225 km; 140 miles)

SOUTH AFRICA

NATIONAL DYNAMICS
NATIONAL DYNAMICS (PTY) LTD

PO Box 20163, Virginia Airport, Durban North 4016

Telephone: Durban 845350
MANAGING DIRECTOR: S. J. Reed

In addition to its piloted aircraft programmes, National

Dynamics developed the ND-100 Observer mini-RPV described and illustrated in the 1979-80 *Jane's*.
No recent news of this programme has been received.

SWEDEN

FOA
FÖRSVARETS FORSKNINGSANSTALT (National Defence Research Institute), Applied Electronics Dept (FOA 3)

Box 1165, S-581 11, Linköping
Telephone: (013) 11 80 00

HEAD OF DEPARTMENT: Torsten Linell

FOA SKATAN

The Skatan system was designed for a feasibility study concerning short-range daylight-only reconnaissance and surveillance over zones immediately behind the forward edge of the battle area (FEBA). The complete system comprises miniature aircraft, a radio transmitter and telescopic antenna, two pairs of binoculars, and a case for cameras and film processing equipment. The first phase of the Skatan programme had been completed by the end of 1979.
TYPE: Short-range battlefield reconnaissance mini-RPV.
AIRFRAME: Strut-braced shoulder-wing monoplane, with constant-chord wings and square-section fuselage. Non-retractable tailwheel-type landing gear. Construction of balsa wood proposed, which would give typical lifetime of 5-10 missions. Extremely small radar signature; not affected by ECM in programmed flight.
POWER PLANT: One 1·2 kW (1·6 hp) O.S. Max H80/RC 13·23 cc single-cylinder glow-plug engine, driving a

two-blade propeller. Fuel, contained in a tank of 0·5 litres (0·11 Imp gallons) capacity, is a mixture of methanol (70%), castor oil (25%) and nitromethane (5%).
LAUNCH AND RECOVERY: Conventional T-O and landing, under radio control, is standard; alternative parachute recovery system available optionally.
GUIDANCE AND CONTROL: Radio command guidance. Aircraft can be guided by manual control throughout flight, controlled in line-of-sight by use of two pairs of binoculars (one of low magnification for very close range control, and a higher-magnification pair for use at longer range), mounted coaxially; manual guidance can also be effected by use of radar data and triangulation instead of binoculars. Of these, the distance-calculation method has proved to be the most effective. Alternatively, drone can be fitted with an automatic flight control system for pre-programmed flight. An aneroid altimeter is linked to an onboard control to maintain operating altitude within an accuracy of 20 m (66 ft). Course is controlled by means of a special device based on a magnetic terrain compass. Using this system, the onboard radio receiver can be switched off over the surveillance area, avoiding ECM while the aircraft photographs the area below. Aerodynamic control of the drone is by movement of conventional ailerons and tail control surfaces.
SPECIAL EQUIPMENT: Several onboard camera systems have been tested. The best results were obtained with a

Hasselblad 500 EL (70 frames) and a Nikon F (36 frames), both cameras having an electric motor to advance the film. Various lenses, depending on mission configuration, have also been tested. Other potential payloads include radio relay equipment, jammers, smoke generators, laser target designator, TV camera, radar reflector, or (in 'kamikaze' role) small attack weapons.

DIMENSIONS, EXTERNAL:
Wing span 2·14 m (7 ft 0¼ in)
Length overall 1·61 m (5 ft 3½ in)

WEIGHTS:
Weight without camera 4·4 kg (9·7 lb)
T-O weight with 0·4 litres (0·09 Imp gallons) fuel:
with Canomatic M70 camera 6·0 kg (13·2 lb)
with Nikon F camera 7·4 kg (16·8 lb)

PERFORMANCE:
Max level speed 54 knots (100 km/h; 62 mph)
Optimum operating height 300-500 m (985-1,640 ft)
T-O run (on tarmac, zero wind) 7 m (23 ft)
Landing run 20 m (66 ft)
Line-of-sight control range 2·7 nm (5 km; 3·1 miles)
Typical mission times:
briefing and preparation 5-10 min
out and back flight 7-10 min
film removal and processing 5-10 min
total time 17-30 min

UNION OF SOVIET SOCIALIST REPUBLICS

UR-1

According to press reports appearing in early 1979, and unconfirmed at the time of closing for press, the designation UR-1 applies to a target drone observed during tests of late-model MiG-25 'Foxbat' interceptors equipped

with AA-X-9 radar-guided air-to-air missiles. These tests were said to have been successful against drones flying at low level, in ground clutter, and at altitudes up to approx 21,335 m (70,000 ft). The drones, used to simulate targets of some 25·00 m² (269 sq ft) gross area, are air-launched

from Tu-16 carrier aircraft. They are said to operate normally between 19,810 m (65,000 ft) and 30,500 m (100,000 ft), but to be capable of flying as high as 39,625 m (130,000 ft).

UNITED KINGDOM

AEL
AERO ELECTRONICS (AEL) LTD

Gatwick House, Horley, Surrey RH6 9SU
Telephone: 02 934 5353

Telex: 877362 and 87116
MANAGING DIRECTOR: M. H. Nicholas
MANAGER, AERIAL TARGET DIVISION: I. Matyear

This company manufactures small, low-cost radio- and optically-guided systems for target drone, reconnaissance or other RPV applications.

AEL4111 SNIPE Mk II

The AEL Snipe aerial target system was developed as a dynamic target for use with air defence gun systems, of up to 40 mm calibre, and close-range missile systems. It com-

bines simplicity of design with outstanding performance and ease of operation. Its high manoeuvrability enables it faithfully to reproduce any of the complex attack profiles which are normally executed by full-size, manned ground attack aircraft.

The Mk II Snipe is a development of the original aircraft (see 1978-79 *Jane's*) which is in service in six countries and is on order or under evaluation by several others.

MCS PL-60 twin-engined mini-RPV

NEC-built Northrop Shelduck target drone

AEL Snipe miniature target aircraft

FOA Skatan experimental battlefield reconnaissance mini-RPV

BAe Stabileye Mk 1 day/night surveillance mini-RPV

AIRFRAME: High-wing monoplane configuration. Built of wood and plywood veneer covering a polystyrene foam core. Finish is to customer's specification, but is normally a high gloss red paint.

POWER PLANT: One 76 cc single-cylinder two-stroke air-cooled engine, with electronic ignition. Petrol/oil mixture (25:1), contained in a 2·3 litre (0·5 Imp gallon) tank.

LAUNCH AND RECOVERY: Launch by simple rubber bungee catapult mounted on two-wheel transporting trailer. Recovery by orthodox belly landing or by parachute. Fail-safe system automatically closes throttle and deploys parachute in event of loss of command signal, heavy radio interference or loss of internal power supplies.

GUIDANCE AND CONTROL: Radio control by modified commercial equipment operating in VHF band (27-72MHz); available with either AM or FM mode. Two transmitters normally supplied with each trailer, on frequencies specified by customer. Aerodynamic control by ailerons and elevators.

SPECIAL EQUIPMENT: For visual enhancement, underwing pylons can be fitted to carry four smoke flares which can be ignited sequentially. The 40 s burning time is adequate to allow full target engagement. For weapons employing infra-red homing techniques, heat from engine is normally sufficient to allow lock-on and full target engagement. For special applications, one infra-red flare with 25 s burning time can be fitted to each wingtip and fired sequentially. For radar enhancement, a special radar-reflective mesh is incorporated between foam core and skin of aircraft which is sufficient to provide a return on most radars operating between 2-10 GHz. For customers requiring a greater radar response, a corner reflector can be mounted in rear of fuselage. For special applications a robot camera can be supplied for aerial photography. Under development are a Doppler miss-distance indicating equipment (by an

associate company) and an airborne lightweight closed-circuit TV system. For naval air defence training, target aircraft are specially waterproofed for recovery from sea. GSE (ground support equipment) comprises trailer, launcher, and all ground-based stores needed to fly aircraft. Trailer is matched to standard Land-Rover truck with Avonride suspension. Trailer can carry two target aircraft and has built-in workbench for ease of maintenance. For naval air defence training, GSE can be supplied without trailer, for shipboard mounting.

DIMENSIONS, EXTERNAL:
Wing span	2·44 m (8 ft 0 in)
Wing area	0·99 m² (10·64 sq ft)
Length overall	2·13 m (7 ft 0 in)

WEIGHT:
Max launching weight	18 kg (40 lb)

PERFORMANCE:
Max speed	113 knots (209 km/h; 130 mph)
Average sortie	45 min

BAe
BRITISH AEROSPACE, DYNAMICS GROUP
Manor Road, Hatfield, Hertfordshire
Telephone: Hatfield (30) 62300

BAe FLYBAC

This small RPV has been used many times by the Royal Aircraft Establishment, in a continuing programme of research and testing, concerned with the military applications of RPVs. Few details are available, except that a primary need in the programme has been to instrument all vehicles to permit autonomous or remote pilot control, telemetry of the onboard systems, and parachute recovery for reasons of range safety.

Flybac is powered by a 1·34 kW (1·8 hp) Webra piston engine.

DIMENSIONS, EXTERNAL:
Wing span	2·00 m (6 ft 6¾ in)
Length overall	1·47 m (4 ft 9¾ in)
Height overall	0·41 m (1 ft 4¼ in)

WEIGHTS:
Max payload	3 kg (6·6 lb)
Max launching weight	11 kg (24·25 lb)

PERFORMANCE:
Cruising speed	39 knots (72 km/h; 45 mph)
Max range	13 nm (24 km; 15 miles)
Max endurance	20 min

BAe STABILEYE

Exhibited at the 1979 Paris Air Show, Stabileye is a mini-RPV for day and night surveillance, equipped with a Linescan 204 infra-red camera system. The image obtained by the camera can be projected on a screen in the ground control station, signals being transmitted by radio data link, or recorded on film for analysis on completion of mission.

General configuration is that of a bulbous, pod-shaped nacelle, with shoulder-mounted constant-chord wings, twin tailbooms and twin fins and rudders. The power plant drives a 'pusher' propeller at the rear of the central nacelle.

Stabileye Mk 1 has been flown hundreds of times with different payloads during the RAE's RPV research programme. At least 18 had been built by the Autumn of 1979, one of which had flown 40 times. This version has a 60 cc Rowena piston engine, rated at 3 kW (4 hp).

Stabileye Mk 2, which had not flown by September 1979, has a 5·5 kW (7·5 hp) Weslake 116 engine.

DIMENSIONS, EXTERNAL:
Wing span	3·10 m (10 ft 2 in)
Wing area	1·65 m² (17·75 sq ft)
Length overall	2·60 m (8 ft 6½ in)
Height overall	0·89 m (2 ft 11 in)

WEIGHTS (A, Stabileye Mk 1; B, Mk 2):
Max payload: A		8 kg (17·6 lb)
B		15 kg (33 lb)
Max launching weight: A		42 kg (92·5 lb)
B		55 kg (121 lb)

PERFORMANCE:
Max level speed: A		78 knots (144 km/h; 90 mph)
B		93 knots (173 km/h; 107 mph)
Cruising speed: A		68 knots (126 km/h; 78 mph)
B		83 knots (155 km/h; 96 mph)
Stalling speed: A		39 knots (72 km/h; 45 mph)
B		43 knots (79 km/h; 49 mph)
Max range: B		86 nm (160 km; 99 miles)
Max endurance: A		30 min
B		1 h 0 min

FR
FLIGHT REFUELLING LTD
Wimborne, Dorset BH21 2BJ
Telephone: 0202 882121
Telex: 41247
CHAIRMAN: M. J. Cobham, MA, FRAeS, Barrister

For more than 20 years, Flight Refuelling Ltd has been engaged, inter alia, in the design and manufacture of control systems for pilotless aircraft. It was responsible for the conversion of more than 250 Gloster Meteor aircraft to pilotless or drone configuration. Some of these aircraft are still in service use for missile development trials and practice firings.

An initial batch of 25 Hawker Siddeley Sea Vixen D. Mk 3 aircraft are being fitted with Flight Refuelling's Universal Drone Pack (UDP), a packaged system which enables most types of aircraft to be readily converted to drone or pilotless configuration with only minor modifications to their conventional flying control system inputs, and without degrading the original manned performance. The pack is designed for installation on the existing seat rail in the aircraft's cockpit.

Flight Refuelling is continuing its work on RPVs and target drones, and currently has under development the ASAT target vehicle for the UK Ministry of Defence.

FR ASAT
Flight Refuelling Ltd has designed a jet-propelled target drone to meet a Ministry of Defence requirement known as ASAT (Advanced Subsonic Aerial Target). This requirement calls for a level speed in excess of 400 knots (741 km/h; 461 mph) and a steady state manoeuvring capability of up to 6g. Design began in May 1979, and a contract has been received to build eight flight vehicles, of which the first is scheduled to fly during the second quarter of 1981. If approved, the drone is expected to be produced at the rate of about 50 per year.

The max fuel load of 60 kg (132 lb) permits sortie times in excess of 1 h. Approach and intercept legs of a typical mission total nearly 5·5 nm (10 km; 6·2 miles), over the whole of which the target vehicle is flown at more than 400 knots (741 km/h; 461 mph) at S/L. Ten such circuits can be repeated at 4·5 min intervals. During less demanding operations, or where more time is required between presentations, the rate of fuel usage will be lower and the vehicle can be loitered at 3,000 m (9,845 ft) altitude for more than 90 min, with full allowances for T-O, climb, descent and recovery.

TYPE: Subsonic target drone.

AIRFRAME: Cantilever low/mid-wing monoplane. Wings, tailplane and elevators folded from flat aluminium alloy sheet, without compound forming. Wings are each attached to fuselage by four bolts, are fitted with plain ailerons, and are interchangeable port/starboard. Tailplane held in place by GRP fin, via two studs. Aluminium alloy stressed-skin fuselage, of circular cross-section, with crushable nosecone to absorb nose-down ground impact. Nosecone attachment and body joints made by band-clamps. Nosecone is expendable, and is replaced after each flight. Cylindrical GRP canister in rear fuselage houses recovery parachutes. Engine pod attached under fuselage by two bolts.

POWER PLANT: One 1·08 kN (242·5 lb st) Microturbo TRS 18-075 turbojet engine, built under licence by Ames Industrial Ltd and mounted in pod under centre of fuselage. Single integral fuel tank in centre of fuselage, between wings; this has a capacity of 75 litres (16·5 Imp gallons) and is pressurised at 1·5 bars (22 lb/sq in). Refuelling point on top of fuselage. Aft of fuel tank is a smaller tank for oil, which can be injected into jetpipe, on command from ground, to produce smoke.

LAUNCH AND RECOVERY: Takes off under own power from three-wheeled trolley, running on a circular track 100 m (330 ft) in diameter and tethered to a pylon in the centre. Aircraft will reach T-O speed in three laps of this track, equivalent to a straight-line T-O run of more than 1,000 m (3,280 ft), and with this system can always be launched into wind. Day and night parachute recovery system, consisting of a cluster of three Irvin cruciform 'chutes, stowed in GRP canister which is rear-loaded into aft fuselage and covered by an ejector spring and drogue tailcone.

GUIDANCE AND CONTROL: Radio command guidance system, with Skyleader receiver and Marconi Avionics autopilot complemented by a microprocessor-based ground control station which utilises radar data as the basis for more sophisticated control and guidance functions. Aerodynamic control by ailerons and elevators, actuators for which are in rear fuselage, between fuel/oil tanks and parachute compartment.

SYSTEMS: Fuel and smoke/oil tanks pressurised by engine compressor bleed air. 400W direct-drive alternator/PCU.

EQUIPMENT: Large bay in forward fuselage, aft of nosecone, for avionics and optional payload.

DIMENSIONS, EXTERNAL:
Wing span	2·90 m (9 ft 6¼ in)
Wing area, gross	1·40 m² (15·1 sq ft)
Wing aspect ratio	6
Length overall	4·00 m (13 ft 1½ in)
Body diameter (max)	0·387 m (1 ft 3¼ in)
Height overall	1·32 m (4 ft 4 in)
Tailplane span	1·32 m (4 ft 4 in)

WEIGHTS:
Max fuel load	60 kg (132 lb)
Max launching weight	200 kg (441 lb)

PERFORMANCE (estimated):
Max level speed at S/L	430 knots (796 km/h; 495 mph)
Min loitering speed	150 knots (278 km/h; 173 mph)
Max rate of climb at S/L	2,600 m (8,530 ft)/min

RCS
RCS GUIDED WEAPONS SYSTEMS
(Division of Radio Control Specialists Ltd)
6 Wolsey Road, Ashford, Middlesex TW15 2RB
Telephone: 078 42 53661/2
DIRECTORS:
E. A. Falkner, CEng, MRAeS, FIED
P. R. Conway, BSc (Eng), CEng, MICE
K. E. Mackley, CEng, MIERE

This company manufactures a range of small, low-cost radio- and optically-guided systems for target drone, reconnaissance or other RPV applications. All types listed were in full-scale production at the beginning of 1979; their present status is not known.

The standard systems offer payload capabilities of up to 13·6 kg (30 lb) and a visual control range of up to 2·7 nm (5 km; 3·1 miles). Non-standard systems can be produced with payload capabilities of up to 22·7 kg (50 lb). To simplify control, an autostabiliser is available, with options of height lock and heading lock. An autopilot is under development to permit automatic out-and-back sorties beyond, and returning to, visual control. All systems are controlled using a standard tripod-mounted transmitter, and each system operates in a slot with an approximate bandwidth of 25kHz and an ERP (effective radiated power) maximum of 10W.

Also available for the larger drones is an airborne RF television link, weighing 2·3 kg (5 lb) and having a line-of-sight range of up to 8 km (5 miles).

RCS MERLIN
The Merlin system consists of a delta-shaped flying-wing drone, built of polystyrene foam with a plywood skin, powered by a 10 cc piston engine and fitted with a tricycle landing gear. A six-function pulse width modulated VHF guidance system with RF output of 5W is used.

Three versions are available, as follows:

RCS4018 Target System. For training air defence weapon crews to acquire and track target aircraft. Can carry X- and S-band radar enhancement devices. A 2·13 m (7 ft) drogue target can be towed on a 152 m (500 ft) cable for live firing work.

RCS4019 Camera System. For short-range aerial reconnaissance with radio-triggered Robot f/2·8 35 mm camera at heights up to 915 m (3,000 ft). Optional kit for rapid film processing and printing.

RCS4020 Composite Target/Camera System. Combines facilities of RCS4018 and 4019.

LAUNCH AND RECOVERY: T-O from ground or launch from system launcher; orthodox landing.

DIMENSIONS, EXTERNAL:
Wing span	1·45 m (4 ft 9 in)
Length overall	1·22 m (4 ft 0 in)

WEIGHTS:
Payload	1·4 kg (3 lb)
Max launching weight	4·8 kg (10·5 lb)

PERFORMANCE:
Max speed	78 knots (145 km/h; 90 mph)
Max controllable range (optical)	
	1·6 nm (3 km; 1·9 miles)
Endurance	30 min

RCS FALCON
The Falcon is generally similar to the Merlin, but is larger, has a greater payload and longer endurance, and is powered by a 7·5 kW (10 hp) engine. Guidance, launch and recovery are as for the Merlin.

Three versions are available, as follows:

RCS4012 Target System. For training air defence weapon crews to acquire and track low-level high-speed aircraft. Can carry X- and S-band radar enhancement devices. Facility for trailing a 3·05 m (10 ft) towed target on a 152 m (500 ft) cable. Supplied to Libyan government in 1973-74.

RCS4015 Camera System. For short-range aerial reconnaissance; same equipment as Merlin, including optional processing/printing kit. Target location by photo/map comparison. Supplied to Libyan government 1973-74.

RCS4017 Composite Target/Camera System. Combines facilities of RCS 4012 and 4015.

DIMENSIONS, EXTERNAL:
Wing span	2·13 m (7 ft 0 in)
Length overall	1·98 m (6 ft 6 in)

WEIGHTS:
Payload	5·4 kg (12 lb)
Max launching weight	16·3 kg (36 lb)

PERFORMANCE:
Max speed	110 knots (204 km/h; 126·5 mph)
Max controllable range (optical)	
	2·7 nm (5 km; 3·1 miles)
Endurance	45 min

RCS4024 HERON
This high-wing monoplane RPV is powered by a 7·5 kW (10 hp) engine. Fuel capacity is 4·5 litres (1 Imp gallon). Although designed specifically for target work, payload capability and 0·03 m³ (1 cu ft) payload bay make it equally suitable for other applications, and up to 5 kg (11 lb) of total payload may consist of pylon-mounted underwing stores such as flares or small bombs. A good X-band radar signature is provided for tracking. Guidance, launch and recovery as for Merlin system. Controllable in winds gusting up to 30 knots (56 km/h; 34·5 mph). Ordered by British Army.

Both Heron and Heron HS can be supplied with a laser gun hit simulating system, in which hits are recorded on an airframe counter and marked with a small flare or flash when a hit is made.

DIMENSIONS, EXTERNAL:
Wing span	3·00 m (9 ft 10 in)
Length overall	2·13 m (7 ft 0 in)
Fuselage: Max width	0·254 m (10 in)

WEIGHTS:
Max payload:	
catapult launch	6·8 kg (15 lb)
ground T-O	13·6 kg (30 lb)
Max weight:	
catapult launch	15·4 kg (34 lb)
ground T-O	24 kg (53 lb)

PERFORMANCE:
Max speed	104 knots (193 km/h; 120 mph)
Max controllable range (optical)	
	2·7 nm (5 km; 3·1 miles)
Endurance	30 min

RCS HERON HS
High-speed version of standard Heron, improved aerodynamically by reducing wing thickness and area, introducing linear taper and eliminating wing struts and pylons. Wheeled landing gear replaced by sprung metal skid and catapult launching points; take-off dolly can be provided, permitting a 25 per cent increase in payload. Dimensions as for standard Heron, except for 2·44 m (8 ft 0 in) wing span. Max payload is 4·5 kg (10 lb); max speed 121·5 knots (225 km/h; 140 mph).

RCS4030 TRAINING DRONE
Designed to train operators of operational drone/RPVs, RCS4030 is broadly similar externally to Heron, but slightly smaller and powered by a 10 cc engine. Six-channel proportional radio control, designed for use with standard RCS ground control system.

DIMENSIONS, EXTERNAL:
Wing span	2·13 m (7 ft 0 in)
Length overall	1·83 m (6 ft 0 in)

WEIGHTS:
Payload	1·8 kg (4 lb)
Weight dry	5 kg (11 lb)

PERFORMANCE:
Max speed	52·1 knots (96·6 km/h; 60 mph)
Max controllable range	0·9 nm (1·6 km; 1 mile)
Endurance	35 min

RCS SATS
SATS (Small Arms Target System) is used as live target for infantry anti-aircraft firing practice with rifles and sub-machine-guns. Controlled with hand-held transmitter.

DIMENSIONS, EXTERNAL:
Wing span	2·21 m (7 ft 3 in)
Length overall	1·98 m (6 ft 6 in)

WEIGHTS:
Payload	0·68 kg (1·5 lb)
T-O weight	4·1 kg (9 lb)

PERFORMANCE:
Max speed	74 knots (137 km/h; 85 mph)
Endurance	40 min

RCS SWIFT
Photographic or target drone, of sweptwing aircraft configuration. Glassfibre fuselage; plywood-covered wings with styrofoam core.

LAUNCH AND RECOVERY: Launched from specially designed toggle action catapult; flown along fixed heading at fixed climb angle, using optical tracking system.

GUIDANCE AND CONTROL: Tripod-mounted high-power radio transmitter (range 5·4 nm; 10 km; 6·2 miles) and optical sight. Can be operated with 6-channel hand-held transmitter.

SPECIAL EQUIPMENT: 35 mm camera, barometric trip switch and marker flash.

Flight Refuelling ASAT (Advanced Subsonic Aerial target)

RCS4020 Merlin miniature drone

Mounted on its ground transporter, an FR Universal Drone Pack awaits installation in a Sea Vixen aircraft

RCS4024 Heron target drone, operated by the British Army

RCS Falcon mini-RPV and its ground control equipment

RCS Swift photo-reconnaissance or target drone, on its catapult launcher

RCS Small Arms Target System (SATS)

DIMENSIONS, EXTERNAL:
Wing span   1·83 m (6 ft 0 in)
Length overall   0·91 m (3 ft 0 in)
WEIGHTS:
Payload   0·9 kg (2 lb)
Max T-O weight   4·5 kg (10 lb)
PERFORMANCE:
Max speed
   100-120 knots (185-222 km/h; 115-138 mph)
Range   4·3 nm (8 km; 5 miles)
Endurance   30 min

RCS TELEDRONE II

Real-time TV reconnaissance drone. Airframe of glassfibre, plywood, expanded foam and duralumin. Pow-

ered by two 1·5 kW (2 hp) or one 4·5 kW (6 hp) piston engine. Launched from catapult or T-O dolly; skid landing or parachute recovery. Standard TV payload; options include chaff dispenser, ECM, radar augmentation or radar transponders. Radio guidance (8-channel VHF), with 20W power amplifier optional.

DIMENSIONS, EXTERNAL:
Wing span   2·90 m (9 ft 6 in)
Length overall   1·98 m (6 ft 6 in)
WEIGHTS:
Weight empty   10 kg (22 lb)
Fuel   3·85 kg (8·5 lb)
Normal payload (incl fuel)   9 kg (20 lb)
Max launching weight   approx 20·4 kg (45 lb)

PERFORMANCE:
Max speed   90 knots (167 km/h; 104 mph)
Cruising speed   65 knots (120 km/h; 75 mph)
Max operating height   3,050 m (10,000 ft)
Max range   5·4 nm (10 km; 6·2 miles)
Endurance   up to 2 h

RCS SMALL ROTARY-WING DRONE

Small rigid-rotor target drone, intended primarily to train operators of radar-controlled missiles; powered by 0·9 kW (1·2 hp) 10 cc piston engine. Fuel capacity 0·5 litres (0·1 Imp gallons).

LAUNCH AND RECOVERY: Conventional helicopter T-O and landing, using non-retractable tricycle landing gear.

GUIDANCE AND CONTROL: Six-channel proportional radio control system (four for pitch, roll, yaw and throttle control, and two for camera controls).

SPECIAL EQUIPMENT: Choice of half-frame (f/2·8) or full-frame (f/2·5) 35 mm camera, each with 18 exposures per wind and automatic film advance. Heavy-duty 12 V electric starter optional.

DIMENSIONS, EXTERNAL:

Main rotor diameter	1·63 m (5 ft 4 in)
Tail rotor diameter	0·36 m (1 ft 2 in)
Length overall	1·83 m (6 ft 0 in)

WEIGHTS:

Payload	0·9 kg (2 lb)
Weight dry	5 kg (11 lb)

PERFORMANCE:

Max speed	61 knots (113 km/h; 70 mph)
Range	0·9 nm (1·6 km; 1 mile)
Endurance	20 min

RCS LARGE ROTARY-WING RPV

Surveillance mini-RPV, powered by 7·5 kW (10 hp) two-stroke piston engine; details apply to this version. Twin-engined version, capable of carrying 18 kg (40 lb) payload, has been tested.

LAUNCH AND RECOVERY: Conventional helicopter T-O and landing, using wide-track tubular skid landing gear.

SPECIAL EQUIPMENT: Standard payload comprises ground surveillance TV system, cameras, sensors and other equipment. Gyroscopic stabilisation optional.

DIMENSIONS, EXTERNAL:

Main rotor diameter	2·29 m (7 ft 6 in)
Length overall	1·83 m (6 ft 0 in)

WEIGHTS:

Payload	8·5 kg (18·7 lb)
Max T-O weight	20 kg (44 lb)

PERFORMANCE:

Max speed	32 knots (60 km/h; 37 mph)
Guidance radius	2·7 nm (5 km; 3·1 miles)
Endurance	1 h

SHORTS
SHORT BROTHERS LIMITED

PO Box 241, Airport Road, Belfast BT3 9DZ, Northern Ireland
Telephone: 0232 58444
Telex: 74688

OFFICERS: see Aircraft section

SHORTS SKEET

The Skeet, a development of Short Brothers' highly successful MATS-B drone (see 1979-80 *Jane's*) now in service with the British Army, provides a realistic and cost-effective aerial target for use with close-range weapon systems. Like MATS-B, it combines simplicity with high manoeuvrability and ease of operation, but offers the additional advantages of higher speed, greater range and better payload, and has a maximum endurance twice that of the parent drone. The Skeet completed acceptance trials in September 1979, and is now in production under MoD contract. Developments of the design are being pursued.

AIRFRAME: Modular construction cantilever high-wing monoplane. Fuselage of metal and GRP. Polyurethane foam-filled glassfibre wings, fin and tailplane.

POWER PLANT: One 13·4 kW (18 hp) Weslake 274-6 274 cc two-cylinder two-stroke aircooled engine. Fuel capacity 9·1 kg (20 lb).

LAUNCH AND RECOVERY: Launched pneumatically from self-contained two-wheel launcher having a capacity of eight launches from one charging. Recovery by parachute or by conventional landing, using fuselage underfairing as a skid. Launches can be carried out in headwinds of up to 25 knots (46 km/h; 29 mph).

GUIDANCE AND CONTROL: Eight-channel (elevator, aileron, throttle, smoke generator firing, ignition/fail-safe, height hold, and two spare) radio command system (hand-held transmitter and 10W rf amplifier), in the 68MHz band. Automatic barometric height hold available. Visual control sight with binoculars to assist pilot in flying the aircraft visually to over 2·7 nm (5 km; 3·1 miles) range and to enable repeatable race tracks to be flown.

SPECIAL EQUIPMENT: Reflector in rear fuselage, and parachute in forward fuselage. Sixteen 40 s smoke

generators fitted in landing skid. Two wing-mounted pods can carry such items as miss-distance indicator and Simflak, as required. Skeet can accept payloads of a non-target nature (e.g. for surveillance and tactical aggression), according to customer's requirements. An automatic parachute release can be provided. An autopilot, complete with heading device, is under development for out-of-sight operation.

DIMENSIONS, EXTERNAL:

Wing span	3·35 m (11 ft 0 in)
Wing area	1·53 m² (16·5 sq ft)
Length overall, incl MDI aerial	2·72 m (8 ft 11 in)

WEIGHTS:

Payload	8 kg (17·6 lb)
Max launching weight	63 kg (139 lb)

PERFORMANCE:

Max level speed	125 knots (232 km/h; 144 mph)
Stalling speed	50 knots (93 km/h; 58 mph)
Max in-sight range	2·7 nm (5 km; 3·1 miles)
Max range under control	more than 5·4 nm (10 km; 6·2 miles)
Endurance at full throttle	1 h 15 min

SKYLEADER
SKYLEADER RADIO CONTROL LTD

Airport House, Purley Way, Croydon, Surrey CR0 0XZ
Telephone: 01-686 6688 or 0700

MANAGING DIRECTOR: S. E. Uwins

This company designed and produced the MATS-A target system, in use for several years by the British Army and described in the 1979-80 *Jane's*. A further version,

with sweptback wings and designed to simulate the Panavia Tornado, was under development in 1979; no details of this have been received for publication.

WESTLAND
WESTLAND HELICOPTERS LTD

Yeovil, Somerset BA20 2YB
Telephone: 0935 5222

Telex: 46277
OFFICERS: see Aircraft section

WESTLAND WIDEYE

The programme for the Wideye remotely piloted rotor-

craft, and the Supervisor surveillance system of which it formed a part, has been cancelled by the Ministry of Defence. An illustration and all known details of the Wideye can be found in the 1979-80 *Jane's*.

UNITED STATES OF AMERICA

APL
APPLIED PHYSICS LABORATORY, THE JOHNS HOPKINS UNIVERSITY

Johns Hopkins Road, Laurel, Maryland 20810
Telephone: (301) 953 7100 and 792 7800

In addition to the RPD2, which is described briefly and illustrated, APL had under development in the Spring of 1979 a new drone of which testing was to begin in August 1979. No details of this had been received at the time of closing for press.

APL RPD2

This drone, developed by APL from an earlier US Army programme vehicle, first flew on 13 June 1975 at the US Naval Surface Weapons Center. It is a miniature target for evaluating improved shipboard fire control systems.

Four RPD2s were built, of which two were still operable in Summer 1979, when testing was to be resumed.

POWER PLANT: One 7·5 kW (10 hp) McCulloch MC-101A single-cylinder piston engine, driving two-blade pusher propeller at tail.

LAUNCH AND RECOVERY: Launch by catapult system. Parachute recovery system, with airbag impact absorbers stowed in each wing. Fin tip comes off for parachute release.

GUIDANCE AND CONTROL: System includes autopilot which uses Earth's electrostatic field for pitch and roll stabilisation.

SPECIAL EQUIPMENT: Includes passive radar augmentation device in nose and Luneberg lens in fairing on fin trailing-edge. Pitch sensor above nose; roll sensors at wingtips.

DIMENSIONS:

Wing span	2·083 m (6 ft 10 in)
Wing area	1·74 m² (18·75 sq ft)
Length overall	2·057 m (6 ft 9 in)
Height overall	0·72 m (2 ft 4¼ in)
Propeller diameter	0·51 m (1 ft 8 in)

WEIGHTS:

Weight empty	23 kg (50·5 lb)
Payload	12 kg (26·4 lb)
Max launching weight	46 kg (101 lb)

PERFORMANCE:

Max level speed	150 knots (278 km/h; 173 mph)
Cruising speed	65 knots (120 km/h; 75 mph)
Service ceiling	5,500 m (18,000 ft)
Endurance	2 h 30 min

BEECHCRAFT
BEECH AIRCRAFT CORPORATION

Wichita, Kansas 67201
Telephone: (316) 689 7111
OFFICERS: see Aircraft section

In addition to manufacturing piloted aircraft, Beech has been designing and producing pilotless target drones since 1955. By 1 January 1980 it had built a total of 6,193 target drones. This figure includes 403 MQM-61As for the US Army, and 3,560 AQM-37As.

Beech has also carried out design studies to examine the suitability of its range of light aircraft for operation under remote control.

BEECHCRAFT MODEL 1019 SERIES
US military designation: AQM-37A

This normally non-recoverable, supersonic air-launched missile target system is designed to simulate invader aircraft and missile threats, and to provide defence weapon system evaluation and crew training. The target provides both active and passive radar augmentation for

radar acquisition and tracking, and a chemical flare is provided for infra-red homing. Two optical miss-distance systems are available.

The original Model 1019 won a 1959 US Navy/Air Force design competition, and has since entered service in a variety of versions with the US Navy (1962), US Air Force (1968) and US Army (1973), as well as the air forces of the UK (1966), Italy (1969), France (1974) and Israel (1975). Total deliveries of all versions had reached 3,560 by January 1980.

The Model 1019 is the basic AQM-37A target. Other versions are as follows:

Model 1019A. Twenty AQM-37As built to a 1975 US Navy contract. Capable of flying at heights of 10-300 m (33-985 ft) for weapon system evaluation. These 'Sea Skipper' vehicles were equipped with an autopilot which incorporated a homing device for longitudinal guidance and a radar altimeter for altitude control.

Model 1072 (Shorts SD.2 Stiletto). Version for UK, substantially re-engineered by Shorts to meet British requirements, including incorporation of telemetry and

radar systems and control system changes. Vehicle is fitted by Beech with single-chamber rocket motor to give Mach 2 performance at 18,300 m (60,000 ft). Principal modifications made by Shorts were detailed in the 1978-79 *Jane's*. Current Stiletto system consists of basic target vehicle plus a number of optional mission kits which can either be installed by Shorts or be delivered separately for customer installation. Total of 110 ordered by early 1980.

Model 1088. Manufacturer's designation of 11 targets for Italian Air Force, used primarily for weapon systems evaluation. Pre-programmed dive manoeuvre to give supersonic presentation at medium altitudes. Radio controlled lateral manoeuvring capability to position target accurately.

Model 1094. Manufacturer's designation of 45 targets for French Air Force, used primarily for air-to-air weapon systems evaluation. French name **Vanneau** (Lapwing). Modified by Matra to be compatible with appropriate weapon system. Modifications include addition of scoring, radar augmentation, telemetry, and tracking beacon systems. Primary missions are performed at Mach 1·6 at 16,750 m (55,000 ft) and Mach 2 at 21,335 m (70,000 ft).

RCS Teledrone II TV reconnaissance drone

Single-engined version of RCS's large rotary-wing surveillance RPV

RCS small rotary-wing drone, of mini-helicopter configuration

Shorts Skeet military aircraft target drone on its pneumatic launcher

RPD2 naval weapons target, developed by APL, on its launch trolley

Model 1095. Manufacturer's designation of 30 targets ordered by British Ministry of Defence. Modified to MoD specifications for use in crew training exercises on Hebrides range.

Model 1098. Manufacturer's designation of 20 targets for Israeli Air Force.

Models 1100 and 1101. The US Army contracted with Beech in 1975 to provide 48 AQM-37As for weapon system evaluation. These were the first production vehicles to incorporate a two-stage parachute recovery system. Under the Army contract, Beech produced two versions of the AQM-37A. One (the Model 1101) is a supersonic, high-altitude target capable of operation at speeds up to 1,182 knots (2,188 km/h; 1,360 mph) and altitudes up to 21,335 m (70,000 ft). The other (the Model 1100) is a low-altitude version which can be flown to within 15 m (50 ft) of the terrain. Both models are equipped with a radio controlled guidance system permitting both longitudinal and vertical positioning.

Model 1102. Version of AQM-37A for US Navy, incorporating a solid-state autopilot, improved wing design, and other changes yielding improved performance. Initial contract for 100 placed in November 1976; total of 415 ordered by early 1980.

The following description applies to the standard Model 1019/AQM-37A:

TYPE: Air-launched expendable or recoverable target.

AIRFRAME: Mid-wing monoplane, of canard configuration, with slim-delta main wings (of double-wedge section) at rear having 76° sweep on leading-edges, 0° dihedral, 0° incidence, and full-span ailerons. Movable canard foreplanes, of modified double-wedge section. Fixed endplate fin at tip of each main wing. Cylindrical centre-fuselage, with ogival nose section and tapering rear section over rocket chambers. Underbelly tunnel for

Beechcraft Model 1089, Swedish RB06 version

Beechcraft Model 1019 AQM-37A target drone

rocket-engine cartridge-operated start valves, plumbing, infra-red flare and miss-distance scoring system antenna.

POWER PLANT: One Rocketdyne/AMF LR64 P-4 two-chamber liquid-propellant rocket engine (2·81 kN; 631 lb st). Three propellant tanks, for nitrogen pressurant, mixed amine fuel (MAF-4) and IRFNA oxidiser, form integral part of centre-fuselage.

LAUNCH AND RECOVERY: Air-launched from launcher which is adaptable to various fighter aircraft. Normally non-recoverable, but US Army Models 1100/1101 have parachute recovery system.

GUIDANCE AND CONTROL: Programmed guidance system. Flight normally terminated by automatic destruct system, which also operates in event of a major failure. Command standby destruct system for added range safety.

SPECIAL EQUIPMENT: Approx 0·04 m³ (1·4 cu ft) of space in nose section for optional scoring and augmentation systems (see introductory paragraph). Target is compatible with many non-co-operative scoring systems.

DIMENSIONS, EXTERNAL:
Wing span	1·00 m (3 ft 3½ in)
Wing area (exposed)	0·87 m² (9·35 sq ft)
Length overall	3·82 m (12 ft 6½ in)
Height overall	0·51 m (1 ft 8 in)
Diameter of fuselage	0·33 m (1 ft 1 in)

WEIGHT:
Max launching weight	256 kg (565 lb)

PERFORMANCE (rated):
Operating speed	Mach 0·4 to Mach 3·0
Operating height	300-24,385 m (1,000-80,000 ft)
Endurance (powered)	8 min
Range	more than 100 nm (185 km; 115 miles)

BEECHCRAFT MODEL 1070 HAST

Beyond the initial development stages, detailed in the 1979-80 and earlier editions of *Jane's*, Beech is no longer associated with this programme.

It is now known as HAHST (High Altitude High Speed Target), and is being continued by Teledyne Ryan (which see) as a full-scale development programme for the US Air Force.

BEECHCRAFT MODEL 1089
US Army designation: MQM-107A Streaker
Swedish Air Force designation: RB06 Girun

After a performance and cost competition, Beech was awarded a multi-year production contract by the US Army in 1975 for the Model 1089 Variable-Speed Training Target, under the designation MQM-107A Streaker. Final assembly is performed at Beech's Boulder Division in Colorado. Beech designed, developed and now delivers ground support equipment, spares and ancillaries; and also provides operation of the system.

In addition to purchase for its own use, the US Army has supplied the MQM-107A system through Foreign Military Sales to Iran, the Republic of Korea, Sweden and Taiwan for operational use. Other foreign governments are making plans to use the system. The US Navy and Air Force have also completed evaluation programmes, involving firings of air-to-air and surface-to-air missiles. More than 375 Model 1089s had been ordered by early 1980.

The principal function of the Streaker is to tow a variety of targets for missile training and evaluation, including gunnery banners, or sophisticated infra-red and radar-augmented tow targets with cable lengths of up to 2,438 m (8,000 ft).

The MQM-107A itself also serves as an aerial target for air defence systems such as Chaparral, Redeye, Hawk and improved Hawk, and is the primary subsonic missile training target for the US Army.

Programmes are under way which will enhance the speed performance of the MQM-107A through the use of higher-thrust engines. The pod arrangement for the propulsion system makes this uprating feasible. Additional improvements being investigated are increased internal payload, improved control of high-*g* manoeuvres, and a digital flight control system.

TYPE: Re-usable variable-speed target.

AIRFRAME: Low-wing monoplane configuration, with sweptback wings and tail surfaces. Engine suspended on pylon beneath centre of fuselage. Modular design throughout, with flat-section wings and tail surfaces of bonded honeycomb and foam-filled aluminium ailerons and elevators. Cylindrical body, with ogival nose and tail cones.

POWER PLANT: One 2·85 kN (640 lb st) Teledyne CAE 372-2 (J402-CA-700) turbojet engine in underfuselage pod, with 242 litres (64 US gallons) of fuel. JATO bottle for surface launch boost. New solid-propellant rocket booster developed and qualified by Atlantic Research Corporation.

LAUNCH AND RECOVERY: Lightweight surface launcher and checkout system, easily transportable in two suitcase-size containers. Can also be air-launched. Drogue and main parachute command recovery system.

GUIDANCE AND CONTROL: Radio command guidance of manoeuvre and recovery, which can be either preprogrammed or maintained directly during flight. In flight, guidance and control system automatically stabilises about roll, yaw and pitch attitudes, and provides altitude and speed hold modes.

SPECIAL EQUIPMENT: Principal function is to tow a variety of tow targets for missile training and evaluation. Two TA-8 radar or IR augmentation targets can be carried on each mission and towed separately up to 2,440 m (8,000 ft) behind MQM-107A. Streaker serves as aerial target for such air defence systems as Chaparral, Redeye, Hawk, Roland and Stinger, and is expected to become primary subsonic missile training target for US Army. Internal payload capacity for avionics; wingtip payload capacity for decoy augmentation and additional avionics; capacity for up to 113 kg (250 lb) beneath each wing.

DIMENSIONS, EXTERNAL:
Wing span	3·00 m (9 ft 10 in)
Length	5·23 m (17 ft 2 in)
Height (total)	1·47 m (4 ft 10 in)
Body diameter	0·38 m (1 ft 3 in)

AREAS:
Wings (total projected)	2·52 m² (27·16 sq ft)
Vertical tail surfaces	0·43 m² (4·63 sq ft)
Horizontal tail surfaces	0·79 m² (8·50 sq ft)

WEIGHTS:
Weight empty	295 kg (650 lb)
Usable fuel	173 kg (382 lb)
Launching weight (incl booster)	460 kg (1,014 lb)

PERFORMANCE:
Operating speed range	247-500 knots (459-925 km/h; 285-575 mph)
Operating height range	S/L to 12,200 m (40,000 ft)
Endurance	more than 3 h

BRUNSWICK
BRUNSWICK DEFENSE DIVISION

3333 Harbor Boulevard, Costa Mesa, California 92626
Telephone: (714) 546 8030

MARKETING DIRECTOR: A. H. Bickel

On behalf of the US Air Force Avionics Laboratory, Brunswick developed the small Maxi-Decoy glider, and the larger rocket-powered Propelled Decoy, to be carried by US strike aircraft. Equivalent to an 'iron' bomb, the decoys are carried with wings folded on the aircraft external stores points. Shortly after release the wings are opened by internal command. Flight profiles and manoeuvres are pre-programmed.

BRUNSWICK MAXI-DECOY

Unpowered decoy glider, having a square-section body and flip-out sweptback wings. Capable of high subsonic speed. Under development by US Air Force primarily as active or passive ECM carrier, using F-4 Phantom carrier aircraft. Three Maxis can be accommodated in each of F-4's four underfuselage Sparrow missile recesses, and two on each 340 kg (750 lb) underwing hardpoint; several decoys can be deployed simultaneously. Electronic warfare payloads are designed and manufactured by Automated Systems Division of RCA. Series of payload test flights conducted at Eglin AFB during 1977. Typical payloads include a C-band jammer; or a G-band jammer combined with radar signature augmentation. Further details are classified.

DIMENSIONS:
Wing span	approx 0·76 m (2 ft 6 in)
Body width	0·13 m (5 in)
Length	1·14 m (3 ft 9 in)
Payload volume	0·008 m³ (500 cu in)

WEIGHT:
Max launching weight	59 kg (130 lb)

PERFORMANCE:
Max speed	Mach 0·8-0·9

BRUNSWICK PROPELLED DECOY

Larger than Maxi-Decoy, with circular-section body, flip-out sweptback wings and cruciform sweptback tail surfaces; powered by Atlantic Research solid-propellant rocket motor. Flight testing began in 1974. Two-axis (roll and heading/altitude) autopilot allows decoy to manoeuvre at high cruising speeds as well as performing in glide modes; unlike Maxi, Propelled Decoy can cruise at high subsonic speeds. Six successful launchings from F-4 carrier aircraft made at Eglin AFB in 1974. One Propelled Decoy can be carried on each of Phantom's 340 kg (750 lb) underwing hardpoints. Further details are classified.

DIMENSIONS:
Wing span	1·40 m (4 ft 7 in)
Body diameter	0·25 m (10 in)
Length	2·24 m (7 ft 4 in)
Payload volume	0·03 m³ (1,800 cu in)

WEIGHT:
Launch weight	136 kg (300 lb)

PERFORMANCE:
Burn time	5 min
Max speed	Mach 0·8-0·9

DSI
DEVELOPMENTAL SCIENCES INC

15757 East Valley Boulevard, PO Box 1264, City of Industry, California 91749

Telephone: (213) 330 6865

PRESIDENT: Dr Gerald R. Seemann

DSI designed and built, under contract to NASA, a prototype oblique-wing RPRA which made its first flight in mid-1976 and was described and illustrated in the 1976-77 *Jane's*. The company also designed and built the Sky Eye and Scout mini-RPVs, and, for LMSC, the Aquila, based on the Sky Eye. In 1977 it undertook, for the US Army, a study of the feasibility of equipping mini-RPVs with 2·75 in FFAR rockets for attack duties. A further contract, for test and analysis of projectiles launched from small RPVs, was awarded in 1978 by the US Army Research and Technology Laboratories. Also in 1978, DSI completed, for the US Army, a recovery programme using LMSC Aquila drones fitted with a parachute and an inflatable airbag. Since early 1978 the company has been investigating, with promising results, the feasibility of a solar-powered aeroplane.

DSI is currently engaged in several classified RPV programmes, and in 1979 began a programme for the US Air Force concerned with an electric propulsion system for micro- and mini-RPVs. This involves an 'exotic' primary battery as the energy source, a rare earth electric motor, and a composite-material propeller.

DSI RPA-12 SKY EYE

The prototype Sky Eye first flew on 26 April 1973; details of this and early models can be found in previous editions of *Jane's*. The last two Sky Eye I-Bs, which were being flown as testbeds, were taken out of service in mid-1978.

Current models are as follows:

Sky Eye II-E. Expendable version of II-R, developed from Sky Eye I-B (1977-78 *Jane's*).

Sky Eye II-R. Recoverable version, 6% larger than II-E but with endplate fins at wingtips and lower radar signature. Basically similar to I-B, but of glassfibre/foam construction. Endplate fins later deleted and propeller duct added. Non-retractable tricycle landing gear. Orders for several Sky Eye IIs received, from the US Army and various aerospace companies.

Sky Eye R-4D. Upgraded version of II-R with improved wing; larger, flat-bottomed fuselage; no landing gear; and upgraded flight control system. More powerful engine, increased payload and higher gross weight. Endurance more than 8 h with 36 kg (80 lb) payload. By 1979 the R-4D was the version mainly in use and the only version being sold. DSI was then engaged, with All American Engineering Inc, in an overseas programme involving the R-4D version.

The following description applies to the Sky Eye R-4D:

AIRFRAME: Predominantly of Kevlar 49 honeycomb sandwich materials, giving a lightweight but robust vehicle capable of sustaining ±6*g* (normal) and 8*g* axial loading at max gross weight, and of surviving rough handling in operation. Sweptback high-wing monoplane, with servo-actuated trailing-edge elevons and turned-down wingtips. Wing section NACA 23-015 (modified). Incidence 3° at root. Aerodynamic twist (washout) 3°. Removal of wing and nosecone provides access to entire payload installation in nose and central bays. Fuselage consists of four basic components: nose fairing, central body, cowling and propeller shroud. Flat-bottomed fuselage has three quickly removable structural bottom panels, intended specifically for easy pallet-style installation and interchanging of a wide variety of payloads.

POWER PLANT: One 11·9 kW (16 hp) or 16·4 kW (22 hp) DH 220 or 280 engine, driving a two-blade wooden pusher propeller turning within a 0·69 m (2 ft 3 in) diameter annular duct.

LAUNCH AND RECOVERY: Ramp launch; parachute or net recovery.

GUIDANCE AND CONTROL: VHF radio command guidance system. Aerodynamic control by elevons.

AVIONICS AND EQUIPMENT: Autopilot and uplink. Equipped initially with 600W electrical system; 1,200W system under development. Flight control system built by LSI-AD, based on a DSI-LSI-AD design.

DIMENSIONS, EXTERNAL (R-4D):
Wing span	3·78 m (12 ft 4¾ in)
Wing area, gross	2·99 m² (32·2 sq ft)
Wing aspect ratio	4·75
Length overall	2·01 m (6 ft 7¼ in)
Body: Max diameter	0·356 m (1 ft 2 in)

Brunswick Maxi-Decoy unpowered decoy, with flip-out wings

DSI armed Sky Eye R-4D, with underwing rocket launch tubes

DSI RPMB airship drone, 7·92 m (26 ft) version

DSI Gunsight low-cost target

The active expendable decoy developed by DSI for the US Navy, showing the flying surfaces folded (left) and deployed (right)

WEIGHTS (R-4D):

Weight empty, dry	45·4 kg (100 lb)
Fuel load (standard tanks)	13·6 kg (30 lb)
Payload	36·3 kg (80 lb)
Launching weight	99·3 kg (219 lb)

PERFORMANCE (R-4D 'clean' at 99·3 kg; 219 lb gross weight, 22 hp engine):

Max level speed:

at S/L	130 knots (241 km/h; 150 mph)
at 3,050 m (10,000 ft)	
	128 knots (237 km/h; 147 mph)
at 6,100 m (20,000 ft)	
	125 knots (232 km/h; 144 mph)
at 9,150 m (30,000 ft)	
	113 knots (209 km/h; 130 mph)
Stalling speed	39 knots (72·5 km/h; 45 mph)

Max rate of climb:

at S/L	600 m (1,970 ft)/min
at 3,050 m (10,000 ft)	375 m (1,230 ft)/min
at 6,100 m (20,000 ft)	194 m (638 ft)/min
at 7,625 m (25,000 ft)	118 m (386 ft)/min
Service ceiling (46 m; 150 ft/min climb)	
	6,100 m (20,000 ft)
Endurance with 13·6 kg (30 lb) standard fuel	6 h

DSI RPMB

Details of DSI's original 4·88 m (16 ft) long RPMB (Remotely Piloted Mini-Blimp) appeared in the 1977-78

Jane's; and of a later 7·92 m (26 ft) long version in the 1978-79 and 1979-80 editions.

For 1979, DSI designed a third, larger RPMB to what it describes as a final configuration, powered by a 15 kW (20 hp) D & H two-stroke engine driving a Sensenich two-blade wooden propeller. The envelope is of 6 oz Neoprene-coated Dacron. The following details apply to this version:

GUIDANCE AND CONTROL: Radio command guidance system. Pitch and yaw control provided by gimballing engine. If command link is lost, engine shuts down and helium is dumped (dumping 8·5 m³; 300 cu ft makes craft 9 kg; 20 lb 'heavy'). If engine fails, helium is dumped in same way; if altitude hold malfunctions, and vehicle escapes from 152 m (500 ft) to higher altitude, independent transducer triggers helium dump.

AVIONICS AND EQUIPMENT: Dufresne 28V 650W alternator for electrical power; guidance and control equipment; servo motors; data link; payload (camera, bullhorn and spotlight); transponder and running lights; ballast.

DIMENSIONS:

Length overall	11·94 m (39 ft 2 in)
Envelope max diameter	3·40 m (11 ft 2 in)
Envelope fineness ratio	3·5
Envelope volume	85 m³ (3,000 cu ft)

WEIGHTS:

Payload	20·5 kg (45 lb)
Fuel	11 kg (25 lb)
Max T-O weight	97·5 kg (215 lb)

PERFORMANCE (estimated):

Max level speed	43 knots (80 km/h; 50 mph)
Min flying speed (full fuel)	4·3 knots (8 km/h; 5 mph)
Endurance at 17·5 knots (32 km/h; 20 mph)	24 h

DSI/US NAVY ACTIVE EXPENDABLE DECOY

Since 1976, DSI has been working with the Naval Research Laboratory and other US Navy agencies on a programme for an active expendable decoy vehicle. Cruising flight, and boost launch from a folded position, were demonstrated successfully in 1978 in the Mojave Desert and at the Naval Weapons Center, China Lake, California.

No other details of this programme are known, but two accompanying photographs show that the decoy is basically of long and narrow cylindrical shape, with three foldaway/flip-out tail control surfaces and a one-piece pivoting wing.

DSI GUNSIGHT

Gunsight is a low-cost target for tracking and actual weapon-firing use; it was in the feasibility demonstration phase in early 1980.

POWER PLANT: One 11·2 kW (15 hp) McCulloch flat-twin piston engine. Alternative power plant available, depending upon the speed desired.

LAUNCH AND RECOVERY: Rocket launch; parachute recovery.

EQUIPMENT: Two-axis autopilot. Visual (smoke), infra-red (flares) and R/F (three Luneberg lenses) augmentation available.

DIMENSIONS, EXTERNAL:
Wing span	1·02 m (3 ft 4 in)
Length overall	2·03 m (6 ft 8 in)
Body diameter	0·22 m (8⅝ in)

WEIGHT:
Max launching weight	34 kg (75 lb)

PERFORMANCE (with 11·2 kW; 15 hp engine):
Never-exceed speed at S/L	
	300 knots (555 km/h; 345 mph)
Max level speed at S/L 240 knots (444 km/h; 276 mph)	
Service ceiling	6,100 m (20,000 ft)
Endurance at S/L	40 min

E-SYSTEMS
E-SYSTEMS INC
PO Box 6030, Dallas, Texas 75222

MELPAR DIVISION: 7700 Arlington Boulevard, Falls Church, Virginia 22046

Telephone: (703) 560 5000

E-Systems Inc's activities lie predominantly in aerospace systems development and manufacture, in addition to which it has carried out specialised conversion work on nearly 400 C-135 and KC-135 series aircraft for the US Air Force. Its Greenville Division designed and built the L450F, a single-engined aircraft capable of manned or unmanned operation and described in previous editions of *Jane's.* Melpar Division has designed a number of mini-RPVs, including those of which details follow.

E-SYSTEMS E-55
The E-55 is an improved version of the E-45 mini-RPV (1978-79 *Jane's*), with a more powerful engine and higher gross weight. All existing E-45 vehicles have been upgraded to the E-55 configuration.

The E-55 is designed to carry a variety of electronic payloads for real-time reconnaissance, jamming, targeting, and homing missions. Several E-55s were employed successfully during a harassment weapons systems concept demonstration at Meppen in the Federal Republic of Germany in early 1977. Three modified E-55S were undergoing US Army evaluation in early 1980 (see Addenda).

AIRFRAME: High-wing twin-tailboom monoplane, with pod-shaped central nacelle. Dihedral on outer wing panels. Twin endplate fins and rudders; enclosed tailplane with full-span elevator.

POWER PLANT: One 2·76 kW (3·7 hp) single-cylinder two-stroke Roper engine, mounted in rear of fuselage nacelle and driving a two-blade pusher propeller. Fuel capacity 3·4 litres (0·9 US gallons).

LAUNCH AND RECOVERY: Launch by vehicle-mounted launcher, using jettisonable take-off dolly, or by catapult. Recovery by conventional landing, on skid beneath central nacelle, or by net.

GUIDANCE AND CONTROL: Either by real-time tracking radar mounted on top of two-man mobile van, or by standard non-tracking radio control link. Radar system can control RPV effectively for approx 43·5 nm (80·5 km; 50 miles). This can be extended to 130 nm (241 km; 150 miles) by pre-programming flight and using airborne relay for video downlink. Aircraft can be controlled either manually or by combination of pre-programmed flight and manual landing.

EQUIPMENT: Melpar-designed five-axis autopilot weighing 0·9 kg (2 lb), which can be used for dead reckoning or Omega navigation. Melpar TV surveillance system provides means for remote manual control, target identification, and navigational assistance away from launch site.

DIMENSIONS, EXTERNAL:
Wing span	2·41 m (7 ft 11 in)
Wing area, gross	0·68 m² (7·36 sq ft)
Length overall	2·36 m (7 ft 9 in)
Height overall	0·51 m (1 ft 8 in)
Width over tailbooms	0·71 m (2 ft 4 in)
Fuselage diameter	0·20 m (8 in)

WEIGHTS:
Weight empty, equipped	11·3 kg (25 lb)
Payload	13·6 kg (30 lb)
Fuel	2·7 kg (6 lb)
T-O weight	25 kg (55 lb)

PERFORMANCE:
Cruising speed	52 knots (97 km/h; 60 mph)
Stalling speed	39 knots (72 km/h; 45 mph)
Rate of climb at S/L	198 m (650 ft)/min
Service ceiling	3,050 m (10,000 ft)
Endurance	4 h

DSI LOCOMP
Locomp, also in the feasibility demonstration phase in early 1980, is a multi-purpose system for operation at high subsonic speeds.

POWER PLANT: No details known.

LAUNCH AND RECOVERY: Air or ground launch; recoverable from land or water (floats with 50% fuel or less).

DIMENSIONS:
Wing span	1·37 m (4 ft 6 in)
Length overall	2·31 m (7 ft 7 in)
Body diameter	0·33 m (1 ft 1 in)
Payload volume	0·057 m³ (2 cu ft)

WEIGHTS:
Weight empty (incl 52 kg; 115 lb payload)	
	136 kg (300 lb)
Max launching weight	200 kg (440 lb)

E-SYSTEMS E-90
The E-90 is a 41 kg (90 lb) version of the E-75 'harassment' vehicle (1978-79 *Jane's*). The use of a more powerful engine improves performance and allows an increase in payload weight. It was first flown in October 1977, and development was continuing in early 1980.

In addition to its potential mission as a passive radar homing system, future applications for the E-90 include loiter over enemy defences while carrying RV reconnaissance jamming, FLIR, or photographic payloads.

AIRFRAME: High-wing single-boom monoplane, with side-force generator panel under each wing. Glassfibre wings, with high/low-density foam core; moulded polyethylene fuselage; internal phenolic resin coated cardboard tubes to stiffen tailboom and tail surfaces.

POWER PLANT: One 8·2 kW (11 hp) Herbrandson DH-160 flat-twin two-stroke piston engine, driving a two-blade pusher propeller. Standard fuel capacity of 5·7 litres (1·5 US gallons) can be increased by reducing payload.

EQUIPMENT: Pre-programmed autonomous autopilot/navigation system using onboard microprocessor.

DIMENSIONS, EXTERNAL:
Wing span	3·05 m (10 ft 0 in)
Wing area, gross	1·11 m² (12 sq ft)
Length overall	2·29 m (7 ft 6 in)
Height overall	0·51 m (1 ft 8 in)
Fuselage: Max width	0·25 m (10 in)

WEIGHTS:
Weight empty, equipped	22·7 kg (50 lb)
Normal payload	9 kg (20 lb)
Fuel	4·5 kg (10 lb)
T-O weight	41 kg (90 lb)

PERFORMANCE (typical):
Max level speed	95 knots (177 km/h; 110 mph)
Max cruising speed	69 knots (128 km/h; 80 mph)
Stalling speed	44 knots (81 km/h; 50 mph)
Rate of climb at S/L	488 m (1,600 ft)/min
Service ceiling	3,660 m (12,000 ft)
Range at 1,525 m (5,000 ft)	
	191 nm (354 km; 220 miles)
Endurance at 1,525 m (5,000 ft)	4 h 0 min

E-SYSTEMS E-100X
Essentially, the E-100X is an enlarged development of the E-45 (1978-79 *Jane's*), having extended-span wings, greater engine power, and increased payload volume. It consists of three major assemblies (fuselage pod, wing, and booms and tail unit), designed for quick and simple assembly or dismantling. The wing contains a sealed fuel tank. The pod is a sealed unit accommodating the onboard avionics and power plant.

Some 0·085 m³ (3 cu ft) of volume and more than 22·7 kg (50 lb) of weight can be devoted to possible payloads such as a low-cost miniature TV reconnaissance system, similar to that developed for the E-45, or packages for photographic reconnaissance, electronic jamming, tactical strike support, communications relay, and remote communications interception. Programme ended in December 1979.

AIRFRAME: Similar to E-45/55.

POWER PLANT: One 6·7 kW (9 hp) Rosspower flat-four two-stroke piston engine, driving a two-blade fixed-pitch pusher propeller. Fuel in integral wing tank, capacity approx 11·4 litres (3 US gallons).

LAUNCH, RECOVERY, GUIDANCE AND CONTROL: Similar to E-45/55.

EQUIPMENT: According to mission (see introductory copy).

DIMENSIONS, EXTERNAL (typical):
Wing span	3·28 m (10 ft 9 in)
Wing area, gross	1·33 m² (14·33 sq ft)
Length overall	2·74 m (9 ft 0 in)
Height overall	0·57 m (1 ft 10½ in)
Fuselage diameter	0·27 m (10¾ in)

WEIGHTS (typical):
Weight empty, equipped	18 kg (40 lb)
Payload	22·7-23·6 kg (50-55 lb)
Fuel	8·2 kg (18 lb)
T-O weight	49 kg (108 lb)

PERFORMANCE:
Max level-flight Mach No. at S/L	0·80
Max level-flight Mach No. at 6,100 m (20,000 ft) 0·82	
Endurance at max Mach No. at S/L	37 min
Endurance at max Mach No. at 6,100 m (20,000 ft)	
	1 h 0 min

DSI MARS ASTROPLANE
Among concepts being studied by NASA for future exploration of the planet Mars is one for a series of recoverable, remotely controlled small aircraft able to photograph terrain, take atmospheric soundings, and acquire other useful data. DSI submitted proposals to NASA for an aircraft, the Mars Astroplane, capable of meeting such a requirement, and a detailed description of this aircraft, with illustrations, appeared in the 1979-80 *Jane's.*

This study is now completed. Any subsequent phase is dependent upon future NASA funding for Mars exploration.

PERFORMANCE (typical):
Max level speed	95 knots (175 km/h; 109 mph)
Cruising speed	75 knots (139 km/h; 86 mph)
Stalling speed	42 knots (78 km/h; 48·5 mph)
Rate of climb at S/L	305 m (1,000 ft)/min
Service ceiling	above 3,050 m (10,000 ft)
Endurance	more than 5 h

E-SYSTEMS E-130
Like the E-200, the E-130 is a growth development of the E-90, and is powered by a 13·5 kW (18 hp) engine. For further details see Addenda.

E-SYSTEMS E-150
The E-150, which flew for the first time on 4 August 1978, was designed to carry a 27·2 kg (60 lb) stabilised TV camera. It was constructed with as many standard Melpar parts as possible, but with new nose structure and fairings; extended wings, tailboom and horizontal tail; additional fin area; rudder control; and a new shock-absorbing landing gear.

AIRFRAME: Derived from that of E-75 (197879 *Jane's*).

POWER PLANT: One 9·7 kW (13 hp) Herbrandson DH-174 horizontally-opposed two-stroke piston engine, driving a two-blade wooden pusher propeller. Fuel capacity 9·5 litres (2·5 US gallons).

LAUNCH AND RECOVERY: Launched from truck top, free in yaw and pitch. Lands on shock-absorbing, self-stabilising skid/castor gear.

GUIDANCE AND CONTROL: Autopilot-guided, similar to E-45/55.

DIMENSIONS, EXTERNAL:
Wing span	3·96 m (13 ft 0 in)
Wing area, gross	1·45 m² (15·6 sq ft)
Length overall	2·22 m (7 ft 3½ in)
Height overall	0·89 m (2 ft 11 in)
Fuselage width	0·25 m (10 in)

WEIGHTS:
Weight empty, equipped	37·6 kg (83 lb)
Payload	27·2 kg (60 lb)
Fuel	6·8 kg (15 lb)
Max T-O weight	71·6 kg (158 lb)

PERFORMANCE:
Max level speed	74 knots (137 km/h; 85 mph)
Cruising speed	56·5 knots (105 km/h; 65 mph)
Stalling speed	46 knots (86 km/h; 53 mph)
Endurance	2 h

E-SYSTEMS E-200
Due to begin flight testing in late 1979, the E-200 is a scaled-up derivative of the E-75 (described in the 1978-79 *Jane's*) and E-55. Its 91 kg (200 lb) take-off gross weight will allow a 31·75 kg (70 lb) payload to be flown at altitudes of up to 3,660 m (12,000 ft). The vehicle is configured for use as a flying testbed, permitting flight demonstration of airborne reconnaissance, jamming, or navigation systems without incurring the costs of manned flight test programmes. Electrical power for the payload and the Melpar-designed digital autopilot/flight control system is provided by a 0·5kW engine-driven alternator.

AIRFRAME: A formed and machined aluminium backbone joins the firewall, propulsion unit, tailboom and wing spars. Fuselage structure and payload covered with cast plastics fairing. Firewall provides for structural mounting of payload. Wings and horizontal tail surfaces are shaped foam cores covered with glassfibre-reinforced skin. Wing spars and tailboom are structural tubes. Fin of cast plastics. Nosecone removable for ease of access to payload; wings and horizontal tail surfaces removable for transportation. Lifting yoke at CG.

POWER PLANT: One 18 kW (24 hp) flat-twin two-stroke piston engine, driving a two-blade fixed-pitch pusher propeller. Fuel capacity 8·7 litres (2·3 US gallons).

LAUNCH AND RECOVERY: Vehicle-mounted launcher. Recovery by conventional landing on skid beneath central nacelle.

GUIDANCE AND CONTROL: Radio command control for launch and recovery. In-flight guidance by three-axis Melpar-designed autopilot. Aerodynamic control by ailerons, elevator and rudder.

EQUIPMENT: Volume of 0·06 m³ (2·08 cu ft) available for user-defined payload.

DSI Locomp high-subsonic multi-purpose target

E-Systems E-55 mini-RPV at a desert test site

E-Systems E-150 TV-carrying RPV

E-Systems E-100X multi-purpose mini-RPV

E-Systems E-90 mini-RPV with underwing side-force panels

Provisional drawing of E-Systems E-200 testbed RPV *(Michael A. Badrocke)*

Flight Systems Inc QF-86E drone conversion of the Canadair Sabre 5

DIMENSIONS, EXTERNAL (provisional):

Wing span	4·27 m (14 ft 0 in)
Wing area, gross	3·07 m² (33·0 sq ft)
Length overall	3·35 m (11 ft 0 in)
Height overall	0·71 m (2 ft 4 in)
Fuselage: Max width	0·305 m (1 ft 0 in)

WEIGHTS (typical):

Weight empty, incl flight controls	52·1 kg (115 lb)
Payload	31·75 kg (70 lb)
Fuel	6·8 kg (15 lb)
Max T-O weight	91 kg (200 lb)

PERFORMANCE (estimated):

Max level speed	96 knots (177 km/h; 110 mph)
Cruising speed	82 knots (153 km/h; 95 mph)
Stalling speed	39 knots (73 km/h; 45 mph)
Rate of climb at S/L	610 m (2,000 ft)/min
Service ceiling	3,660 m (12,000 ft)
Endurance	2 h

EHI
EGLEN HOVERCRAFT INC (RPV Division)
PO Box 1671, Terre Haute, Indiana 47808
Telephone: (812) 234 4307

CHAIRMAN: Jan Alan Eglen

EHI produced two target RPVs: the Falcon, and the more recent Matador for RC/MATS programmes. No news of these targets has been received for the past two years; both were described and illustrated in the 1979-80 *Jane's*.

FSI
FLIGHT SYSTEMS INC
4000 Westerly Place, PO Box 2400, Newport Beach, California 92663
Telephone: (714) 833 9661
DIRECTOR, AERIAL TARGETS: S. C. Warrick

FSI QF-86E SABRE

FSI demonstrated to the US Army in 1975 two remotely controlled North American F-86 Sabre jet fighters, the converted aircraft actually being Canadair-built Sabre 5s, structurally similar to the US-built F-86E.

Thirty-six QF-86Es had been ordered by 1 January 1980; deliveries began in mid-1977. They are being produced to test and evaluate US Army air defence systems. Manoeuvres of up to 8g can be performed, and the QF-86Es can also deploy stores, initiate jamming and provide other countermeasures, all under remote control.

A description of the basic F-86 airframe can be found in the 1959-60 *Jane's;* the following details apply to the FSI QF-86E/Sabre 5:

POWER PLANT: One Orenda 10 turbojet engine, rated at 28·15 kN (6,325 lb st). Fuel capacity 1,571 litres (415 US gallons) internal, plus provision for two 454 or 757 litre (120 or 200 US gallon) underwing drop-tanks.

LAUNCH AND RECOVERY: Conventional runway T-O and landing, on retractable tricycle landing gear. Aircraft programmed to come to a halt, or continue and make safe T-O and climb-out, if ground control link is lost during T-O run.

GUIDANCE AND CONTROL: Radio command guidance system. Primary mode of operation is NOLO (No Local Operator), over full range of pre-programmed flight manoeuvres including T-O and landing; but provision for onboard human pilot is retained (eg for manned practice presentations, or maintenance or ferry flights). Remote control exercised from one fixed and one mobile ground station, both manufactured by Vega Precision Laboratories; or by the drone formation control system manufactured by IBM Corporation.

SPECIAL EQUIPMENT: Onboard avionics and instrumentation comprise three basic installations: autopilot, with FSI avionics; Vega Precision Laboratories command/telemetry data system; and FSI interface coupler for processing uplink command and downlink telemetry data to and from drone aircraft. A fourth installation, the IBM drone formation control system, is optional. Radar altimeter optional, for simulated low-level attack

presentations. Ancillary equipment, according to mission, may include scoring gear, infra-red flare dispenser, chaff dispensers or ECM pods. Television has been added as an optional T-O and landing aid.

DIMENSIONS, EXTERNAL:
Wing span	11·31 m (37 ft 1·2 in)
Length overall	11·43 m (37 ft 6 in)
Height overall	4·48 m (14 ft 8·4 in)

WEIGHTS:
Basic weight empty	4,921 kg (10,850 lb)
T-O weight 'clean'	6,123 kg (13,500 lb)
T-O weight with two 454 litre (120 US gallon) drop-tanks	6,894 kg (15,200 lb)

PERFORMANCE:
Max level speed above 11,000 m (36,000 ft)	Mach 0·92 (527 knots; 977 km/h; 607 mph)
Service ceiling	13,715 m (45,000 ft)
Max range at 9,145 m (30,000 ft) with two 454 litre (120 US gallon) drop-tanks	600 nm (1,112 km; 691 miles)
Max endurance, conditions as above	2 h 0 min
g limit	+7·0

ILC DOVER
ILC INDUSTRIES INC
Dover Division
PO Box 266, Frederica, Delaware 19946
Telephone: (302) 335 3911

VICE-PRESIDENT AND GENERAL MANAGER: Homer D. Reihm

MANAGER, INFLATABLE PRODUCTS: George P. Durney

This company, which has for some years been a manufacturer of tethered balloons, has recently evaluated the application of inflatable surfaces to lightweight RPVs. Early experiments with winch- or tow-launched hang glid-

ers have been followed by development of the Apteron, an inflatable-wing mini-RPV.

ILC APTERON
This small, lightweight RPV was built to prove the feasibility of a 'flying wing' vehicle using an inflatable aerofoil. It is claimed that the principle could be applied to much larger vehicles of up to 22·86 m (75 ft) wing span, capable of operation at altitudes of up to 21,340 m (70,000 ft).

AIRFRAME: 'Flying wing' monoplane. Moderate sweepback. Reflex-section fabric wing, inflated by compressed air prior to flight. To maintain inflation pressure irrespective of barometric or ambient temperature changes during flight, aircraft carries a small tank of

Freon gas in fuselage. Wing is fitted with elevons, of Mylar-covered balsa construction. Aerofoil-shaped plywood fuselage. Non-retractable tricycle landing gear. Fabric wing has virtually no radar signature.

POWER PLANT: One 0·4 kW (0·5 hp) piston engine, driving a two-blade pusher propeller.

LAUNCH AND RECOVERY: Conventional T-O and landing.

GUIDANCE AND CONTROL: Radio command guidance system. Pitch and roll control by elevons.

DIMENSION, EXTERNAL:
Wing span	1·55 m (5 ft 1 in)

WEIGHTS:
Weight empty	1·8 kg (4 lb)
Payload	1·4 kg (3 lb)

KAMAN
KAMAN AEROSPACE CORPORATION
Old Windsor Road, Bloomfield, Connecticut 06002
Telephone: (203) 242 4461

OFFICERS: see Aircraft section

KAMAN STAPL
Kaman began design of the STAPL (Ship Tethered Aerial Platform) under contract to the US Office of Naval Research in September 1972, and construction of two concept feasibility demonstrators began in the following month. Testing of the two aircraft and their mobile launch and recovery platform and control system began in 1974; low-altitude testing was completed in 1979.

The demonstrators are of autogyro configuration, and are equipped with automatic flight control systems and data recording equipment. A photograph of the first demonstrator appeared in the 1977-78 *Jane's;* since that time, modifications have been made to the tail unit to

include a horizontal stabiliser with vertical fins at the tips. The self-contained AFCS, engineered by Kaman, provides three-axis stabilisation and automatic flight path control, and incorporates redundancy for mission reliability.

AIRFRAME: Welded steel tube fuselage and skid-type landing gear. Sheet metal vertical fin and aerodynamically balanced rudder. Electrically actuated variable-incidence plywood horizontal stabiliser, with plywood endplate fins. Two-blade Bensen G2 teetering and autorotating rotor, with metal blades bolted to hub. Blades do not fold. No rotor brake.

POWER PLANT: One 67 kW (90 hp) McCulloch 4318G piston engine, driving a Bensen BA-48-A8-70 two-blade fixed-pitch propeller. Single fuselage fuel tank, capacity 22·4 litres (6 US gallons).

LAUNCH AND RECOVERY: Tethered T-O and landing.

GUIDANCE AND CONTROL: Electrically-driven automatic flight control system (AFCS).

EQUIPMENT: Two 12V batteries to drive AFCS.

DIMENSIONS:
Rotor diameter	6·63 m (21 ft 9⅛ in)
Rotor blade chord	0·18 m (7 in)
Length overall (excl rotor)	3·27 m (10 ft 8¾ in)
Width overall	1·75 m (5 ft 9 in)
Height to top of rotor hub	1·92 m (6 ft 3½ in)
Propeller diameter	1·22 m (4 ft 0 in)

AREAS:
Rotor blades (each)	0·59 m² (6·3 sq ft)
Rotor disc	34·56 m² (372 sq ft)
Fins (total)	0·69 m² (7·4 sq ft)
Rudder	0·32 m² (3·4 sq ft)
Horizontal stabiliser	0·71 m² (7·6 sq ft)

WEIGHTS AND LOADING:
Weight empty	172 kg (380 lb)
Fuel load	17·7 kg (39 lb)
Max payload	34 kg (75 lb)
Max T-O weight	224 kg (494 lb)
Max disc loading	6·35 kg/m² (1·3 lb/sq ft)

PERFORMANCE: No details available

LMSC
LOCKHEED MISSILES AND SPACE COMPANY INC
1111 Lockheed Way, Sunnyvale, California 94088
Telephone: (408) 742 4321

PUBLIC RELATIONS: Paul J. Binder

LMSC AQUILA
US Army designation: XMQM-105
The Aquila (Latin for 'eagle') mini-RPV was developed under US Army contract to demonstrate available technology for RPV use in surveillance, target acquisition, artillery adjustment, and laser designation for precision-guided munitions. One complete system consists of an RPV, a truck-mounted ground control station (GCS), pneumatic rail launcher and vertical-ribbon barrier retrieval system.

The GCS houses the system computer, TV displays, position plotters, automatic tracking system, command and data link equipment, and control consoles for the RPV and sensor operators. Design and development of the Aquila by LMSC utilised prior efforts by DSI (which see) with its Sky Eye RPV, and DSI supplied LMSC with technology demonstration airframe parts.

A total of 23 RPVs, and two each of the GCS, launchers and recovery systems were delivered, following the first flight of an Aquila in December 1975. More than 150 flights had been made by January 1978 in the US Army's demonstration programme to develop utilisation measures, doctrine and operational specifications. Flights were continued subsequently at the White Sands Missile Range, New Mexico; Fort Bliss, Texas; and Fort Huachuca, Arizona.

During the 188th flight, on 3 June 1978, an Aquila demonstrated its laser designation capability by enabling a Martin Marietta Copperhead cannon-launched guided projectile to achieve a direct hit on a stationary tank. The RPV was at a height of 350 m (1,150 ft), 0·75 nm (1·40 km; 0·87 miles) from the target and 6·5 nm (12 km; 7·5 miles) from its control station when the hit occurred. The Copperhead was fired from 5·9 nm (11 km; 6·8 miles) and intentionally aimed 500 m (1,650 ft) short of the tank to test the performance of the seeker. In another US Army test, to determine RPV survivability, more than 3,000

rounds of 0·50 in and other ammunition were fired at an Aquila over ranges between 460 and 1,830 m (1,500-6,000 ft), without a single hit being registered.

In its production form, Aquila would have a more powerful engine, lower radar signature and ability to carry a variety of sensors. Development was continuing in early 1980, with funding of $49·4 million approved in FY 1980 and $54·2 million requested in FY 1981.

AIRFRAME: Shoulder-wing monoplane of near-delta planform, built of Kevlar 49 honeycomb material, for low radar signature. Elevons on trailing-edges; turned-down wingtips. Airframe dismantles into four major components (centrebody, two wings, and propeller duct), and has quick-disconnect bladder fuel system.

POWER PLANT: One 8·2 kW (11 hp) McCulloch MC-101M/C single-cylinder piston engine, driving a two-blade pusher propeller mounted in an annular duct.

LAUNCH AND RECOVERY: Catapult-launched from mobile pneumatic-tube launcher at airspeed of 44 knots (81·5 km/h; 51 mph); recovered in vertical ribbon arrester net and parallel-strap retrieval net system. Parachute/air-bag recovery system tested successfully by DSI in 1978.

GUIDANCE AND CONTROL: Radio pre-programmed guidance system, with operator override capability.

SPECIAL EQUIPMENT: Lockheed autopilot, Aacom data link and Honeywell laser designator. Four different payloads being evaluated: for real-time surveillance (TV camera), target acquisition, laser target designation (Honeywell designator), and target location and artillery adjustment. Crash-resistant payload protection system standard.

DIMENSIONS, EXTERNAL:
Wing span	3·76 m (12 ft 4·2 in)
Length	1·83 m (6 ft 0 in)

WEIGHTS:
Payload	17·2 kg (38 lb)
Max launching weight	64·9 kg (143 lb)

PERFORMANCE:
Max speed	118 knots (219 km/h; 136 mph)
Min speed to become airborne	44 knots (81·5 km/h; 51 mph)
Service ceiling	3,660 m (12,000 ft)
Max range	10·4 nm (19·3 km; 12 miles)
Max endurance	3 h

LMSC TACTICAL MINI-RPV
The US Army has awarded LMSC a $101 million contract for full-scale development of a new tactical mini-RPV, based on the Aquila, for target acquisition, laser designation and reconnaissance missions. The target acquisition system can be used for conventional artillery as well as for laser homing missiles such as Copperhead. It will also provide damage assessment data, and accuracy in locating a target is such that, at a range of 11 nm (20 km; 12·5 miles) it offers a circular area prediction of only 70 m (230 ft).

Under the US Army contract LMSC is to supply, over a 43-month period, a total of 22 of these tactical RPVs, together with four ground control stations, three launchers, three recovery units, three maintenance shelters, training simulators and training manuals. An operational section equipped with the system would consist of seven trucks, three trailers, 13 troops and an officer in charge, and would be air-transportable (incl five RPVs) in a Lockheed C-5A Galaxy transport aircraft. Set-up and launching can be done in 1 hour after arrival at a tactical site; stowage and make-ready for transport takes 30 min.

TYPE: Recoverable tactical mini-RPV.

AIRFRAME: Generally similar to Aquila (which see), except for pointed nose. Modular construction throughout.

POWER PLANT: One Herbrandson two-stroke piston engine (18 kW; 24 hp at 8,000 rpm), driving a fixed-pitch wooden pusher propeller within an annular duct. Fuel is a petrol/oil mixture.

LAUNCH AND RECOVERY: Launched from Fairchild Stratos launcher mounted on a 5 ton truck. Recovered by Dornier vertical ribbon net, raised on back of truck and capable of being lowered quickly after recovery in order to maintain low profile.

GUIDANCE AND CONTROL: Operates independently of ground control, inertial navigation being provided via an onboard computer.

EQUIPMENT: Variety of payloads, depending upon mission.

DIMENSIONS, EXTERNAL:
Wing span	3·96 m (13 ft 0 in)
Length overall	1·98 m (6 ft 6 in)
Propeller diameter	1·83 m (2 ft 0 in)

WEIGHT:
Max launching weight	100 kg (220 lb)

PERFORMANCE:
Range	more than 27 nm (50 km; 31 miles)

ILC Dover Apteron inflatable-wing mini-RPV

Kaman STAPL demonstrator, with all-moving horizontal tail and twin fins

LMSC tactical mini-RPV, under full-scale development for the US Army (*Howard Levy*)

Antenna testing of an LMSC Aquila in an anechoic chamber

NASA Mini-Sniffer II, with variable-dihedral wingtips

NASA ARW-1 supercritical wing on a quarter-scale wind tunnel model of a Project DAST Firebee II

NASA

NATIONAL AERONAUTICS AND SPACE ADMINISTRATION

1520 H Street NW, Washington, DC 20546

HUGH L. DRYDEN FLIGHT RESEARCH CENTER

PO Box 273, Edwards, California 93523

Telephone: (805) 258 3311

NASA MINI-SNIFFER II

The Mini-Sniffer is a simple, low-cost vehicle platform, designed for high-altitude atmospheric research in remote areas, to measure air turbulence and atmospheric trace gas and to determine the constituents of particles in the atmosphere.

The first two prototype vehicles, designated Mini-Sniffer I, were described and illustrated in the 1975-76 *Jane's*. A third prototype, designated Mini-Sniffer II, made its first flight in the Summer of 1975; the description applies to the mission vehicle, which is fitted with a hydrazine-burning engine to permit flights to altitudes of up to 27,430 m (90,000 ft). The first flight with this engine was made in November 1976.

Payload instrumentation is being developed by the Wallops Flight Center and the National Oceanic and Atmospheric Administration to measure nitric oxide, chlorine,

Freon 11 and 12, free oxygen, and the hydroxyl radical. Langley Research Center plans to use the Mini-Sniffer to make accurate measurements of fine turbulence which cannot be obtained with faster aircraft. Equipped with lightweight wire impact particle grab samplers developed by Ames Research Center, and a real-time telemetered particulate density sensor, the Mini-Sniffer can make low-speed manoeuvres through aerospace vehicle wakes or other suspected particle concentrations. Radiation sensor payloads being developed by the Atomic Energy Commission may allow the multiple and prompt monitoring of nuclear activity.

The Mini-Sniffer is also under consideration by the Jet Propulsion Laboratory as a potential RPV to collect rock samples and data on Mars.

TYPE: Remotely piloted research vehicle.

AIRFRAME: Mid-wing monoplane of twin-tailboom configuration, built entirely of foam plastics, glassfibre and wood. Wings have 20° sweepback at quarter-chord, 13% thickness/chord ratio, and variable dihedral on outer panels. Elevons on wing trailing-edges. Twin sweptback fins and rudders and enclosed tailplane. Non-retractable tricycle landing gear, without tyres.

POWER PLANT: One 3-22·4 kW (4-30 hp) Akkerman 235 piston engine, driving a two-blade constant-speed variable-pitch feathering pusher propeller. Typical rat-

ing 15 kW (20 hp). Single aluminium integral fuel tank in fuselage, for 26·5 litres (7 US gallons) of hydrazine monopropellant. Oil capacity 0·95 litres (1 US quart).

SYSTEMS AND EQUIPMENT: Alternator on Akkerman 235 engine provides electrical power during climb and cruise; 28V nickel-cadmium battery for use during unpowered flight. Resdel uplink control. SCI-680-PCM 16-channel data telemetry system. Vega radar transponder. NASA autopilot. Sun and magnetic sensors for wing levelling, airspeed hold and heading hold.

DIMENSIONS, EXTERNAL:

Wing span	6·71 m (22 ft 0 in)
Wheel track	1·14 m (3 ft 9 in)

DIMENSION, INTERNAL:

Payload compartment volume	0·033 m³ (1·16 cu ft)

WEIGHTS:

Max payload	22·7 kg (50 lb)
Max T-O weight	89 kg (196 lb)

PERFORMANCE (estimated):

Max level speed at 21,340 m (70,000 ft)	
	160 knots (296 km/h; 184 mph)
Stalling speed	26 knots (49 km/h; 30 mph) IAS
Max rate of climb at S/L	792 m (2,600 ft)/min
Service ceiling	27,430 m (90,000 ft)
Range with max payload	
	434 nm (805 km; 500 miles)

LANGLEY RESEARCH CENTER

Hampton, Virginia 23665
Telephone: (804) 827 1110

NASA PROJECT DAST

Project DAST (Drones for Aerodynamic and Structural Testing) is conducted jointly by NASA's Langley and Dryden Flight Research Centers, utilising modified Firebee IIs as testbeds for high-risk evaluation of various research wing configurations.

The first of these, designated ARW-1 (for aeroelastic research wing), was due to begin flight testing in August 1979. Fabrication of a second type of wing (ARW-2), also of supercritical type, was to begin later the same year.

NORTHROP
NORTHROP CORPORATION—VENTURA DIVISION

1515 Rancho Conejo Boulevard, Newbury Park, California 91320
Telephone: (805) 498 3131
Telex: 659 220
General Manager: Kent Kresa
Vice-President, Aeronautical Systems:
Vincent W. Howard
Manager, Corporate Communications: Park H. Irvine

Northrop's Ventura Division designs and manufactures pilotless target aircraft and related equipment. It also produces glassfibre wing fairings for the Boeing 747 transport aircraft, as well as various parts and subassemblies for Northrop F-5E/F and McDonnell Douglas F-18A combat aircraft.

Northrop Ventura (formerly Radioplane) undertook the design, development and construction of its first radio controlled target drone in the mid-thirties. Since then it has become a leader in the field of pilotless aircraft. More than 77,000 drones have been delivered to the US military services and 25 allied nations.

NORTHROP KD2R5 BASIC TRAINING TARGET

This target drone is currently in use by the armed forces of 18 countries as a training device for ground-to-air gunnery and is used as a training target for surface-to-air missiles such as Seacat, Tigercat, Redeye, Blowpipe, Sparrow, Chaparral and Hawk.

Design began in 1946 and the prototype flew for the first time in 1947. Since then more than 65,000 of this type, including early KD2R versions, have been built and production continues.

Northrop has received a $3 million US Army contract for 57 examples of a modified version of the BTT, designated **MQM-33C**. This version will incorporate a new Northrop-developed G-band command control system.

The following description applies to the standard version:

Type: Remotely controlled aerial target.
Airframe: High-wing monoplane, of aluminium alloy construction. No dihedral. Wing incidence 1° at root, −2° at tip. Ailerons and elevator servo-operated by D-9 actuators.
Power Plant: One 67 kW (90 hp) Northrop O-100-3 flat-four engine, driving a two-blade fixed-pitch wooden propeller. Steel integral fuel tank in mid-fuselage, capacity 44 litres (11·6 US gallons). Refuelling point in fuselage forward of wing.
Launch and Recovery: Surface launch from land or ship, by either rotary or zero-length launcher. Recovery by parachute released by radio command. Engine is stopped and parachute deploys automatically in event of serious damage by gunfire, or loss of radio control or electrical power.
Guidance and Control: AN/ARW-79 radio command guidance system, with automatic altitude hold. Visual or radar tracking (radar or FM type tracking systems or equivalent).
Equipment: 28V battery for all electrical power. L-band tracking system, smoke generating kit, tow banner and many other accessories available to customer's requirements. For radar augmentation, two wingtip reflector pods are optional.
Dimensions, external:
Wing span	3·50 m (11 ft 6 in)
Wing area, gross	1·74 m² (18·7 sq ft)
Length overall	3·85 m (12 ft 7½ in)
Height overall	0·76 m (2 ft 6 in)

Weights:
Weight empty	123 kg (271 lb)
Max launching weight	181 kg (400 lb)
Max zero-fuel weight	133 kg (292 lb)
Max landing weight	154 kg (340 lb)

Performance:
Max level speed at S/L and max cruising speed
194 knots (359 km/h; 223 mph)
Stalling speed	58 knots (108 km/h; 67 mph)
Max rate of climb at S/L	1,341 m (4,400 ft)/min
Service ceiling	8,230 m (27,000 ft)

Range at S/L with max fuel
183 nm (338 km; 210 miles)

NORTHROP CHUKAR II
US military designation: MQM-74C

The MQM-74C is an improved version of the MQM-74A (1974-75 *Jane's*), evolved via an MQM-74B developmental model to meet requirements for a 500 knot (926 km/h; 576 mph) target. Since early 1974 more than 1,300 MQM-74Cs have been delivered to the US Navy, making more than 3,700 MQM-74 Chukars manufactured in all. Production of the MQM-74C is continuing.

Modified versions of the MQM-74C have been tested and operated as reconnaissance, electronic warfare and strike RPVs under the US Navy's Persistent Anti-Radiation Missile (PARM) and US Air Force's TED programmes. More recently, Northrop has developed a tactical reconnaissance and target acquisition version, known as the **Chukar-R**, fitted with a modular nose section mounting a Perkin-Elmer 35 mm camera and a Teledyne Brown TV camera, and incorporating preprogrammed navigation. Under US Navy contract, Northrop is producing a new version of the MQM-74C known as the **BQM-74C** (described separately), for use by the US Navy as a cruise missile simulator and standard Navy aerial training target.

The basic Chukar II/MQM-74C target aircraft was designed to meet requirements for a small, lightweight target for anti-aircraft gunnery, surface-to-air missile training and weapon system evaluation. Chukar II is used at the NATO Missile Firing Installation (NAMFI) on the island of Crete in the Mediterranean. Meteor of Italy (which see) was selected by NATO's Hawk management office to provide Chukar II services at the Salto di Quirra range in Sardinia.

Type: Radio-controlled recoverable target.
Airframe: Shoulder-wing monoplane, of aluminium construction. No-dihedral detachable wings, each with electrically-actuated aileron. Tapered circular-section body, with underslung air intake duct. Inverted-Y tail unit, with 30° anhedral on tailplane, fixed vertical fin and electrically-actuated elevators.
Power Plant: One Williams Research Corporation Model WR24-7 (J400-WR-401) turbojet engine, rated at 0·8 kN (180 lb st). Fuel tank in centre of fuselage.
Launch and Recovery: Zero-length launching by means of two Mk 91 Mod 0 JATO rockets and a ZL-5 launcher. Normal recovery by automatic drone pull-up followed by main parachute deployment, initiated automatically in emergencies such as interruption of continuous radio signal or loss of parachute command channel. Alternative method consists of direct main parachute deployment and is initiated automatically on loss of electrical power. Main parachute housed in fuselage immediately aft of wing, with automatic disconnect on impact.
Guidance and Control: Radio command guidance system. Out-of-sight control by automatic stabilisation and command, with radar tracking; in-sight control with visual acquisition aids. Proportional feedback stabilisation and control system for pitch and bank. Engine throttle position, altitude hold initiation and recovery system initiation controlled by audio tone signals. Components include receiver, decoder, autopilot, aileron and elevator servos, altitude hold and airspeed pressure transducers. Command control antenna in upper forward fuselage.
Equipment (target): Electrical power from engine-driven alternator through a rectifier-regulator. 28V nickel-cadmium battery secondary power source used during glide. Onboard acquisition and tracking aids include fore and aft Luneberg lenses for passive radar augmentation, four wingtip-mounted MK-28 Mod 3 infra-red flares, pyrotechnic infra-red plume augmentors, active L-band augmentation, and a smoke system, designed to improve visual detection. Main payload compartment is in front fuselage between control equipment bay and fuel tank. Improved Manoeuvrability Package (IMP) successfully flight tested in 1976 has closed-loop control device installed in flight control system, enabling Chukar II to perform constant g manoeuvres at any of five selected levels up to and including 6g. A low-cost infra-red tow target, for use with the Chukar II system, was successfully flight-tested in early 1978. One can be attached to each wingtip and towed approx 30 m (100 ft) behind the Chukar.
Dimensions, external:
Wing span	1·76 m (5 ft 9¼ in)
Length overall	3·87 m (12 ft 8½ in)
Body diameter	0·38 m (1 ft 3 in)
Height overall	0·71 m (2 ft 4 in)

Weights:
Weight empty	128·4 kg (283 lb)
Max launching weight	223 kg (492 lb)

Performance:
Max level speed at 6,100 m (20,000 ft)
515 knots (954 km/h; 593 mph)
Max level speed at S/L
475 knots (880 km/h; 547 mph)

Econ cruising speed at S/L
250 knots (463 km/h; 288 mph)
Max rate of climb at S/L with full fuel
1,780 m (5,840 ft)/min
Service ceiling	12,200 m (40,000 ft)

Range at max speed at S/L
205 nm (380 km; 236 miles)
Range at max speed at 6,100 m (20,000 ft)
330 nm (611 km; 380 miles)
Range at econ cruising speed at S/L
245 nm (454 km; 282 miles)

NORTHROP BQM-74C
US Navy designation: BQM-74C

The BQM-74C is a US Navy target version of the MQM-74C Chukar II (which see) with added air-launch capability. It can be used as a cruise missile simulator, in training pilots for air-to-air combat, and as a target for anti-aircraft gunnery and surface-to-air missiles. Design began in November 1977, and construction of 10 pre-production examples started in September 1978. Initial flight trials have proved successful, and testing was continuing in 1980. Production deliveries to the US Navy were expected to begin later in that year.

Type: Radio controlled recoverable target.
Airframe: Shoulder-wing monoplane of aluminium construction. Northrop G-9224-080 wing section of 8% thickness/chord ratio. No-dihedral non-swept wings, each with electrically-actuated aileron. Semi-monocoque aluminium body, similar to that of MQM-74C, houses all equipment, power plant and fuel tank. Nose and tail skins removable for access to equipment and power plants. Underslung engine air intake. Inverted-Y aluminium tail unit, comprising fixed vertical fin, fixed tailplane halves (anhedral 30°) and two electrically actuated elevators.
Power Plant: One Williams Research Corporation Model WR24-7A (J400-WR-402) turbojet engine, rated at 0·8 kN (180 lb st). Pressurised fuel tank in centre of fuselage.
Launch and Recovery: Can be launched from ground or shipborne launcher in same manner as MQM-74C. Can also be air-launched from Grumman A-6E Intruder or McDonnell Douglas TA-4J Skyhawk (one under each wing); is also compatible with underwing launchers of Lockheed DP-2 Neptune or DC-130A Hercules. Parachute recovery, on land or from water, as for MQM-74C.
Guidance and Control: Out-of-sight control by automatic stabilisation and command; radar tracking in-sight control, with visual acquisition aids. Proportional feedback stabilisation and control system for pitch and bank. Engine throttle position, altitude hold initiation and recovery initiation are controlled by audio tone signals. Components include a Northrop digital avionics processor, vertical gyro, Motorola AN/DKW-3 integrated target control system, aileron and elevator servos, and altitude hold pressure transducer.
Equipment: Electrical power from engine-driven alternator through a rectifier-regulator. 28V nickel-cadmium battery secondary power source. Onboard acquisition and tracking aids include fore and aft Luneberg lenses, for passive radar augmentation, and a smoke system. Main payload compartment is in forward fuselage section. Equipment includes locator beacon, radar altimeter, seeker simulator (to duplicate cruise missile emissions), radar transponder for IFF, and scoring. Provisions include flight profile programmer with UHF command override; radar altimeter; active J-band, B-band, L-band and X-band radar augmentation; and Tacan receiver. System also includes payload kits for mobile sea range (MSR) operations.
Dimensions, external:
Wing span	1·76 m (5 ft 9·4 in)
Wing area, gross	0·74 m² (8·0 sq ft)
Length overall	3·94 m (12 ft 11·4 in)
Height overall	0·72 m (2 ft 4·3 in)

Weights and Loading:
Basic operating weight empty	133 kg (294 lb)
Max payload	78·5 kg (173 lb)
Max launching weight	204 kg (451 lb)
Max wing loading	273 kg/m² (56 lb/sq ft)

Performance (at max T-O weight):
Max level speed at 6,100 m (20,000 ft)
500 knots (927 km/h; 576 mph)
Econ cruising speed	300 knots (555 km/h; 345 mph)
Service ceiling	9,145 m (30,000 ft)
Max range	450 nm (833 km; 518 miles)

DAST Firebee II with ARW-1 wing on B-52 launch aircraft *(Erik Simonsen)*

Launch of a Northrop MQM-74C Chukar II at the Pacific Missile Test Range

MQM-33C version of the Northrop Basic Training Target (BTT)

Northrop Chukar-R, with interchangeable nosecones for tactical reconnaissance or target use

One of the two Rockwell HiMAT research RPV prototypes

Northrop BQM-74C air-launchable target under the wing of a US Navy Grumman A-6 Intruder

ROCKWELL INTERNATIONAL
ROCKWELL INTERNATIONAL CORPORATION, NORTH AMERICAN AIRCRAFT DIVISION

PO Box 92098, Los Angeles, California 90009

ROCKWELL INTERNATIONAL/NASA/US AIR FORCE HiMAT

HiMAT (Highly Manoeuvrable Aircraft Technology) is a programme evolved by NASA's Dryden Flight Research Center at Edwards AFB, California, and the US Air Force Flight Dynamics Laboratory (AFFDL) at Wright-Patterson AFB, Ohio. Its basic purposes are to speed up the progress of advanced design technology into the flight test phase; to assist designers in taking larger technological steps forward between generations of aircraft; and, more specifically, to provide a low-cost, low-risk means of testing the advanced manoeuvring capability of future aircraft. NASA began evolving control techniques for the HiMAT programme in 1975, first with ⅜-scale unpowered glassfibre models of the F-15 fighter and later with two modified BQM-34F Firebee IIs.

After receipt of programme proposals from Grumman Aerospace, McDonnell Aircraft Co and Rockwell International, NASA announced in October 1975 the award of an $11·8 million contract to Rockwell for the design and construction of two prototype HiMAT remotely piloted research vehicles (RPRVs). Major subcontractors are Teledyne Ryan Aeronautical (airborne flight control system) and Hydraulic Research Corpn (servo actuators).

To meet the requirements of the programme, HiMAT's design consists of a basic core vehicle which includes the engine and all essential subsystems. To the core vehicle are added, as modular units, the main wings, canard surfaces, tail surfaces, and engine intake and afterburner/exhaust structures. In this way the modular components can be replaced during the programme, at minimum cost, with others of alternative design. Among these is expected to be a so-called '2D' vectored-thrust exhaust nozzle; other features to be tested include advanced supercritical wings; variable-camber wings; deformable, self-trimming outer wings; CCV (control configured vehicle) techniques; a digital fly-by-wire system; and a variable-thrust engine control system.

The first HiMAT RPRV was delivered to NASA on 7 March 1978 and the second on 12 June 1978. The first free flight was made on 27 July 1979, initiating the 'envelope expansion' phase of the flight test programme. This phase, scheduled for completion in 1980, is to be followed by a 30-month research test programme.

The HiMAT is flown by a pilot in a ground-based control centre in which all of the aeroplane's flight parameters are displayed via telemetry from the RPRV. The ground-based cockpit is equipped with conventional aircraft controls. The pilot is aided in the landing manoeuvre by a televised view of the landing area taken with a TV camera mounted in the HiMAT.

The following description applies to the HiMAT prototypes:

TYPE: Remotely piloted research vehicle.

AIRFRAME: Mid-wing monoplane, of roughly tandem-delta configuration, with sharply-swept main wings and canard forebody surfaces having graphite composite skins. Glassfibre outer leading-edges; remainder of wings of aluminium, titanium and other materials. Main wings have neither dihedral nor anhedral, and have ailerons, elevons and elevators on the trailing-edges, and NASA 'winglets' at tips. Canard surfaces have marked dihedral and are fitted with elevators. Semi-monocoque area-ruled fuselage, with graphite composite skin. Twin, swept, outward-canted pivoted fins on short booms extending from trailing-edges of main wings at approx mid-span. Graphite composite fin skins. Retractable tricycle landing gear, of skid type for landing on dry lake bed at Edwards AFB. All units retract rearward, main units to form continuous fairing with wing/tail booms, nose unit into underside of engine air intake trunk.

POWER PLANT: One General Electric J85-GE-21 turbojet engine (15·6 kN; 3,500 lb st dry and 22·25 kN; 5,000 lb st with afterburning), mounted centrally in fuselage. Fuel capacity (JP-5) 295 kg (650 lb).

LAUNCH AND RECOVERY: Air-launched from B-52 carrier aircraft. Recovered by conventional runway landing.

GUIDANCE AND CONTROL: Primary control from ground console, by TV, telemetry, and radar link with onboard systems. If ground control is lost, backup inputs from the RPRV will be relayed to a TF-104G chase-plane. On occasions when the TF-104G is out of control range,

the HiMAT has an onboard self-righting system that will bring the RPRV into constant-altitude, orbiting, subsonic flight until the former can resume control.

EQUIPMENT: Onboard equipment includes flight and control parameter sensors, 164 research instrumentation sensors (pressures, strain gauges, accelerometers), signal processors, data link to ground and chase-plane, backup flight control system computer, and TV camera.

DIMENSIONS, EXTERNAL:
Wing span	4·755 m (15 ft 7¼ in)

Length overall, incl probe	6·86 m (22 ft 6 in)
Height overall	1·31 m (4 ft 3·6 in)

WEIGHTS:
Weight empty	1,200 kg (2,645 lb)
Max air-launching weight	1,528 kg (3,370 lb)
Thrust/weight ratio	approx 1

PERFORMANCE (estimated):
Max level speed	Mach 1·6
Touchdown speed	180 knots (333 km/h; 207 mph)
Average research flight duration	30 min
g limit	+12

RS
RS SYSTEMS
Beltsville, Maryland

RS RCMAT
US Army designation: FQM-117A

The US Army has ordered 14,000 examples of this miniature expendable aerial target, as a training vehicle for air defence gunners, tank and armoured vehicle gunners, air-to-air gunners and infra-red systems tracking; and for payload missions. At a distance of 200 m (650 ft) and a speed of 80 knots (148 km/h; 92 mph), the RCMAT simulates a full-size aircraft 1,200 m (3,935 ft) away,

travelling at 480 knots (890 km/h; 550 mph).

TYPE: Radio controlled miniature aerial target.

AIRFRAME: Simple styrofoam structure, of cropped-delta monoplane planform with V tail surfaces. No landing gear.

POWER PLANT: One 0·75 kW (1 hp) K & B 0·6 cu in two-stroke model aircraft engine.

LAUNCH AND RECOVERY: Hand-launched; non-recoverable (expendable).

GUIDANCE AND CONTROL: Radio command guidance system.

EQUIPMENT: Aluminium tube along top of fuselage provides infra-red target signature.

DIMENSIONS, EXTERNAL:
Wing span	1·60 m (5 ft 3 in)
Length overall	0·81 m (2 ft 8¹/₁₆ in)
Height overall	0·19 m (7⅝ in)

WEIGHT:
Payload	1·4 kg (3 lb)

PERFORMANCE:
Max level speed	87 knots (161 km/h; 100 mph)
Min flying speed	25 knots (47 km/h; 29 mph)
Service ceiling	3,050 m (10,000 ft)
Endurance at max speed	10 min

SPERRY
SPERRY FLIGHT SYSTEMS DIVISION, SPERRY CORPORATION
PO Box 21111, Phoenix, Arizona 85036
Telephone: (602) 869 2765

SPERRY (CONVAIR/GENERAL DYNAMICS) F-102A DELTA DAGGER
US Air Force designations: QF-102 and PQM-102

Conversion of US Air Force F-102A fighters for remotely piloted operation, under the Pave Deuce programme, has resulted in three versions, as follows:

QF-102. Prototypes, with provision for manned operation. Five converted by Fairchild Aircraft Service Division.

PQM-102A. Initial unmanned version, of which 63 produced under subcontract to Sperry by Fairchild Aircraft Service Division. Details in 1977-78 *Jane's.*

PQM-102B. Current unmanned version; more than 140 being converted by Sperry Flight Systems. Retains same operational characteristics as PQM-102A except for one low-altitude mode, which can be implemented for special missions by installing radar altimeter. Retains also dual autopilots (the manoeuvre programmer of the PQM-102A being used as a backup flight control and stability system) and dual Vega command guidance and telemetry systems. Scoring system; smoke, brake and explosive destruct systems; and lift compensation in altitude hold mode, are all improved. Modification of basic aircraft; avionics and operational complexity; and throttle quadrant, are all simplified. Additional batteries are reduced to one; second transformer installation is deleted, a slightly modified form of the basic F-102A AC system being used; aircraft wiring is simplified; and engine start is done in cockpit, eliminating need for external control unit. Flight control avionics are located in the nose bay. Manoeuvres can be initiated and programmed from fixed ground control site, using new PQM-102B auxiliary panel.

The PQM-102s are the first-ever fighter aircraft converted for drone duties with no provision whatever for manned operation, and cannot be flown except under remote control. The following description applies to the PQM-102B:

AIRFRAME: As F-102A (see 1961-62 *Jane's*).

POWER PLANT: One Pratt & Whitney J57-P-23A turbojet engine, rated at approx 45·4 kN (10,200 lb st) dry and 71·2 kN (16,000 lb st) with afterburning.

LAUNCH AND RECOVERY: Normal runway T-O and landing.

GUIDANCE AND CONTROL: Fully redundant digital tracking control system, in conjunction with AN/FPS-16 range radar. Simultaneous control of two targets has been demonstrated.

SPECIAL EQUIPMENT: Aft avionics bay, missile bay, cockpit and two pylon-mounted underwing pods available for payload. Digidops miss-distance scoring system standard (antennae aft of cockpit, under fuselage, and in fairing each side of tailpipe); installation and test of vector miss-distance indication (VMDI) is planned. Two types of scoring camera operational, covering forward and aft areas to provide missile approach angle, velocity and miss distance; these are mounted in front and at rear of cockpit. Flight control stabilisation system, comprising flight reference computer, interface coupler and air data computer, provides eight longitudinal/vertical and four lateral/directional modes, and interface between aircraft systems and command/telemetry system. Automatic control modes are provided for take-off, loss of command carrier, take-off abort, and other safety modes. Redundant AC and DC power systems, and redundant autopilot. Manoeuvre programmer can be pre-programmed for three or four manoeuvres, to run in any required sequence. Command/telemetry system provides for four proportional and 48 discrete commands, 22 proportional and 40 discrete telemetry channels; nine additional commands available in standard payload modification. Manoeuvre destruct and explosive destruct systems incorporated. Radar and infra-red augmentation not required, due to size of aircraft.

DIMENSIONS:
Wing span	11·62 m (38 ft 1½ in)
Wing area, gross	64·57 m² (695·0 sq ft)
Length overall	20·84 m (68 ft 4⅔ in)
Height overall	6·46 m (21 ft 2½ in)
Payload volume (max, excl wing pods)	5·66 m³ (200 cu ft)

WEIGHTS:
Basic mission weight	9,076 kg (20,010 lb)
Payload (max)	1,905 kg (4,200 lb)
Mission operational T-O weight	14,186 kg (31,276 lb)

PERFORMANCE:
Max speed at altitude
Mach 1·2 (688 knots; 1,274 km/h; 792 mph)
Operating height range
61 m (200 ft) to 17,070 m (56,000 ft)

Range (dictated by effective control range of guidance radar)   more than 174 nm (322 km; 200 miles)
Normal endurance of mission	40-55 min
g limit	+8

SPERRY (NORTH AMERICAN) F-100 SUPER SABRE
US Air Force designation: QF-100

Conversion of US Air Force /Air National Guard F-100 fighter-bombers for remotely piloted operation as QF-100 aerial targets is being undertaken by Sperry under a full-scale engineering development contract from the US Air Force Armament Development and Test Center, Eglin AFB, Florida. Nine pre-production examples were being converted in early 1980 at Sperry's facility at Phoenix-Litchfield Airport (formerly the Naval Air Facility, Litchfield Park). First delivery is scheduled to be made in February 1981, to Tyndall AFB, Panama City, Florida; initial operational capability is due to be achieved by June 1983. The development contract includes a production option for up to 72 aircraft conversions.

The QF-100 uses current Sperry PQM-102 drone ground control and test equipment, as well as many PQM-102 airborne subsystems. While sharing a common conversion and operational scheme with the PQM-102 series, the QF-100 utilises a digital flight control computer instead of four analogue computers for ease of testing and flexibility for future growth of operational modes.

AIRFRAME: As F-100 (see 1961-62 *Jane's*).

POWER PLANT: One Pratt & Whitney J57-P-21 turbojet engine with afterburning.

LAUNCH AND RECOVERY: Normal runway T-O and landing.

GUIDANCE AND CONTROL AND SPECIAL EQUIPMENT: As for PQM-102 (which see).

DIMENSIONS:
Wing span	11·82 m (38 ft 9⅓ in)
Wing area, gross	35·79 m² (385·2 sq ft)
Length overall, incl probe	16·54 m (54 ft 3 in)
Height overall	4·95 m (16 ft 2⅔ in)

WEIGHTS:
Mission operational T-O weight	14,060 kg (31,000 lb)

PERFORMANCE:
Max speed at altitude
Mach 1.2 (688 knots; 1,274 km/h; 792 mph)
Range, nominal (guidance radar range-limited)
120 mm (222 km; 138 miles)
Normal mission endurance	40-55 min
g limit	+8

TELEDYNE RYAN
TELEDYNE RYAN AERONAUTICAL
2701 Harbor Drive, San Diego, California 92138
Telephone: (714) 291 7311
PRESIDENT: R. S. McCarter
SENIOR VICE-PRESIDENT, ADMINISTRATION: C. E. McGill
VICE-PRESIDENTS:
J. R. Reichardt (Target Programmes)
H. B. Starkey (Special Programmes)
D. L. Arney (Administration, incl Public Relations)
R. R. Schwanhausser (International RPV Requirements)
F. E. Oldfield (Aerospace Engineering)

The former Ryan Aeronautical Company was an indirect successor to Ryan Airlines Inc, which produced the aeroplane in which Charles A. Lindbergh made the first nonstop flight from New York to Paris in 1927. In December 1969 the company was renamed Teledyne Ryan Aeronautical.

Current activities fall into two major categories, under the headings of Aerospace Systems and Electronic and Space Systems. The former group is concerned principally with the design, production and field operation of high-performance aerial jet targets and RPV systems.

Major production items at Teledyne Ryan's plant for many years have been the Firebee jet-powered targets and special-purpose vehicles (pre-programmed and remotely piloted) for various types of reconnaissance mission.

Teledyne Ryan BQM-34F Firebee II supersonic drones are being used in remotely piloted research vehicle (RPRV) test programmes at NASA's Dryden and Langley Research Centers. Teledyne Ryan itself conducted, under contract to NASA, a feasibility study involving the fitting of various different wing planforms and aerofoil sections to the Firebee II for test purposes. These included three types of supercritical wing, three types of supersonic wing, and a laminar-flow wing, and have led to NASA's DAST programme (which see).

Among other recent activities, Teledyne Ryan has studied a number of concepts for mini-RPVs.

TELEDYNE RYAN MODEL 124 FIREBEE I
US Air Force designation: BQM-34A
US Army designation: MQM-34D
US Navy designations: BQM-34A and BQM-34S

The Firebee I remotely piloted vehicle was developed as a joint US Air Force/Army/Navy project, in collaboration with the US Air Force Air Research and Development Command.

Glide flight tests of the original version began in March 1951, and the first powered flights were made that Summer at the US Air Force Holloman Air Development Center, Alamogordo, New Mexico. A total of 1,280 of these early Q-2A and KDA versions were built eventually for all three US services and for the Royal Canadian Air Force, and full details of these can be found in previous editions of *Jane's.*

Rockwell International HiMAT research RPV *(Michael A. Badrocke)*

RS Systems RCMAT (FQM-117A) low-cost expendable target for the US Army
(Howard Levy)

Pre-production QF-100 Sperry conversion of an F-100 Super Sabre fighter-bomber

Sperry PQM-102 target drone conversion of the Convair/GD F-102A

BQM-34S Firebee I target drone of the US Navy

Teledyne Ryan AQM-34V electronic warfare RPV with ALE-38 chaff pods

Development of the current **BQM-34A** (originally Q-2C) improved Firebee began on 25 February 1958. Construction of the prototype started on 1 May and it flew for the first time on 19 December 1958. The first production model flew on 25 January 1960.

By May 1980, a total of 6,103 Firebee Is (including more than 4,840 BQM-34A/S and MQM-34D targets) had been produced. These included Firebees supplied under contract to NATO for use in a missile test and evaluation programme, and a contract from the Japan Defence Agency for Firebees to support the training of missile and gunnery crews. The latter are being built by Fuji (which see). The latest US contract, for 189 more Firebee Is, includes 127 powered by 10·9 kN (2,450 lb st) General Electric J85-7 turbojets.

Current Firebee targets for the US Navy incorporate a Motorola integrated track and control system (ITCS) and have the designation **BQM-34S**; US Air Force BQM-34A targets have a Vega Drone Tracking and Control System (DTCS).

By 1 January 1980 Firebee I targets had provided more than 28,400 flights in support of weapon system and target research, development, test, evaluation, quality assurance, training and annual service practices conducted by the US Army, Navy and Air Force, and certain foreign governments. Since the current Firebee I and its predecessor models have been in operational use, target presentations have been made to virtually every surface-to-air and air-to-air weapon system in the US arsenal. To reduce the vulnerability of the target, and increase its cost-effectiveness, a 'non-kill' environment has been created and extensive use made of infra-red and/or radar augmented towed targets ('Towbees') or cloth banners, towed behind the Firebee on cables.

In November 1977 Teledyne Ryan successfully flew a BQM-34A using a company-developed all-digital Microprocessor Flight Control System (MFCS). This sys-

tem permits the precise high-g manoeuvres required in test and evaluation of modern weapon systems.

RPVs (remotely piloted vehicles) using airframes developed from that of the Firebee I are described separately.

The following details refer to the standard BQM-34A target vehicle:

TYPE: Remotely piloted jet target vehicle.

AIRFRAME: Cantilever mid-wing monoplane, of aluminium alloy semi-monocoque construction. Three-spar wings, incorporating leading-edge droop. No dihedral or incidence. Sweepback at quarter-chord 45°. Single-spar ailerons, with Lear servo-actuators. Wingtips detachable. Provision for wingtip extensions. Tapered, circular-section body, with chemical-etched components. Glassfibre tailcone and nose section. Keel under central portion, to absorb landing impact. All tail surfaces swept 45° at quarter-chord. Multi-spar fin, with glassfibre tip housing guidance and control antenna. Trim rudder operated electrically by Bendix actuator. Single-spar tailplane, with glassfibre tips housing radar echo enhancing antennae. Ventral fin under tailcone, aft of main tail unit. Magnesium elevators powered by Lear servo.

POWER PLANT: One 7·56 kN (1,700 lb st) Teledyne CAE J69-T-29 turbojet engine. Integral fuel tank in forward fuselage, capacity 378 litres (100 US gallons). Provision for one 94·5 litre (25 US gallon) auxiliary fuselage tank and one 378 litre (100 US gallon) drop-tank under each wing. Oil capacity 5·75 litres (1·5 US gallons).

LAUNCH AND RECOVERY: Either air-launching, from suitably-modified aircraft, or ground-launching, using 50·3 kN (11,300 lb st) (nominal) solid-propellant JATO bottle. US Navy has launched BQM-34As from ships under way at up to 15 knots (27·5 km/h; 17 mph). Two-stage parachute recovery system operates automatically in event of target hit, loss of radio wave

carrier from remote control station, engine failure, or upon command by remote control operator. To prevent damage by dragging, recovery system incorporates disconnect which releases parachute from Firebee on contact with ground or water.

GUIDANCE AND CONTROL: Remote control methods include choice of radar, radio, active seeker and automatic navigator, developed and designed by Teledyne Ryan. Normal method is through UHF radio link using AN/FRW-2 or SRW-4 ground transmitter and AN/DRW-29 airborne receiver. Target can be controlled either from manned aircraft or from surface station. Remote command includes activation of special scoring and augmentation equipment in target. Onboard beacon facilitates radar tracking; provision to install telemetry system to relay pertinent flight data to controller. Basic commands consist primarily of on/off functions, received by onboard radio receiver and relayed to appropriate subsystem. Motorola ITCS (integrated tracking and control system) in BQM-34S. BQM-34As currently being fitted with Vega DTCS (drone tracking and control system). Other types of remote command and tracking system can include microwave command and guidance system to control Firebee beyond line-of-sight from ground station through airborne relay station. Operational Firebees can be equipped with increased manoeuvrability flight control system for tactical air combat simulation which gives target capability to perform 4, 5 or 6g manoeuvres. Other systems include active and passive radar augmentation, and afterburning plume devices. Radar Altimeter Low Altitude Control System (RALACS), when added to Firebee I control system, permits precision low-altitude flights at 15 m (50 ft) over water and 30 m (100 ft) over land.

SYSTEMS: Electrical power only. Primary power furnished by 28V 200A DC engine-driven generator. Power for control systems furnished by 400Hz 115V 250W AC inverter; 28V 12·5Ah lead-acid battery provides power for electrical devices of recovery system and for control during pre-landing glide phase.

AVIONICS AND EQUIPMENT: AN/DRW-29 radio receiver with Dorsett TM-4-31A telemetry system, or DKW-2 guidance transponder, or DTCS Model 685-2 guidance system. A/A37G-3 or A/A37G-8 flight control system. Wide range of 'building block' operational equipment includes visual or radar-reflecting banner targets; radar or infra-red Towbee towed targets or tow target Doppler 'bird'; two underwing drop-tanks, 500 lb bombs or bomblet dispensers; AN/ALE-33 or other ECM containers; wingtip tow launchers, camera pods, scoring equipment, flares or other forms of infra-red augmentation, or reflector pods for radar augmentation. BQM-34A can be equipped with adjustable travelling wave tube amplifiers for use as radar echo enhancers in L, S, X and C frequency bands.

DIMENSIONS, EXTERNAL:

Wing span	3·93 m (12 ft 10·8 in)
Wing area, gross	3·34 m² (36·00 sq ft)
Length overall	6·98 m (22 ft 10·8 in)
Body diameter	0·94 m (3 ft 1·2 in)
Height overall	2·04 m (6 ft 8·4 in)

WEIGHTS:

Weight empty	680 kg (1,500 lb)
Basic gross weight	934 kg (2,060 lb)
Max launching weight	1,134 kg (2,500 lb)

PERFORMANCE:

Never-exceed speed	Mach 0·96
(635 knots; 1,176 km/h; 731 mph at 15,240 m; 50,000 ft)	
Max level speed at 1,980 m (6,500 ft)	600 knots (1,112 km/h; 690 mph)
Max cruising speed at 15,240 m (50,000 ft) at 816 kg (1,800 lb) AUW	547 knots (1,015 km/h; 630 mph)
Stalling speed, power on, at 816 kg (1,800 lb) AUW	101 knots (187 km/h; 116 mph)
Max rate of climb at S/L at 1,000 kg (2,200 lb) AUW	4,875 m (16,000 ft)/min

Operating height range
    15 m-18,300 m (50 ft to more than 60,000 ft)

Endurance at 15,240 m (50,000 ft), incl 2 min 40 s glide after fuel expended	75 min 30 s
Max range	692 nm (1,282 km; 796 miles)
Flotation time with 25% fuel	24 h

TELEDYNE RYAN MODELS 147 and 255
US Air Force designation: AQM-34

The Model number 147, and the basic US Air Force designation AQM-34, encompass a large family of surveillance, reconnaissance and ECM RPVs evolved from the subsonic Firebee I target. The original Model 147A, which was little more than a modified Firebee I with a new guidance system and increased fuel capacity, was developed in 1962. Since then many hundreds of Model 147s have been delivered for operational use.

Details of all Model 147s, and their uses from 1964-74, can be found in the 1975-76 and later editions of *Jane's*. The surviving US Air Force RPVs are now in store, though available for reactivation if required. The major recent versions are as follows:

Model 147SD (AQM-34M). Low-altitude photographic reconnaissance version. Total of 78 built under US Air Force Compass Bin and Buffalo Hunter programmes. Pre-programmed digital computer, with Doppler guidance system. Fairchild KS-120A or F-415Y camera. Radar altimeter standard; some fitted in 1972 with Teledyne Systems Co Loran receivers and redesignated **Model 147SD Loran/AQM-34M(L)**. Extended-range version, with underwing drop-tanks, also built. Served with 22nd Tactical Drone Squadron. One AQM-34M underwent flight testing at Edwards AFB, California, under US Air Force Compass Robin programme (see 1975-76 *Jane's* for details).

Model 147TF (AQM-34R). Built under US Air Force Compass Bin programme. Was also the second Combat Dawn version for Strategic Air Command: twenty ordered in 1971. Airframe externally similar to 147TE (see 1978-79 *Jane's*), but probe-type fairing on nose is omitted and there is a small blade antenna on top of the nosecone. Provision for underwing stores. Capable of cruising above 18,300 m (60,000 ft) at a speed of 420 knots (780 km/h; 485 mph).

Model 255 (AQM-34V). Tactical recoverable electronic warfare RPV. Update of 47 AQM-34H and J tactical electronic warfare RPVs, and 16 new-built AQM-

34Vs, delivered in 1976 and later served with 432nd Tactical Drone Group, 11th Tactical Drone Squadron, Davis-Monthan AFB, Arizona. First flight conducted May 1976 by 6514th Test Squadron at Hill AFB, Utah. Incorporates active jamming provided by E-Systems (Melpar Division) and carries two Lundy ALE-2 or MB Associates ALE-38 chaff dispenser pods on underwing pylons. Primary mission was to precede strike aircraft to target, confusing enemy tracking equipment with chaff or other countermeasures. Air or ground launch capability, with prime recovery by MARS (mid-air retrieval system) by CH-3 or HH-53 helicopters. Compatible with Sperry Univac MDC (Multi Drone Control) installed in DC-130H, controlling up to eight vehicles at a time.

POWER PLANTS: Single Teledyne CAE turbojet engine, as follows:
147 SD: 8·54 kN (1,920 lb st) J69-T-41A.
147 TF: 12 kN (2,700 lb st) J100-CA-100.
255: J69-T-29.

LAUNCH AND RECOVERY: All models normally air-launched from DC-130A, E or H Hercules carrier/director aircraft. Recovery by CH-3 helicopter mid-air retrieval system (MARS). AQM-34V tested in ground launch in 1975 using Thiokol booster rocket and TRW thrust vector control.

GUIDANCE AND CONTROL: Teledyne Ryan radio command; or programme and command; or radio/microwave command guidance system. See also under individual model listings.

EQUIPMENT: See under individual model listings.

DIMENSIONS, EXTERNAL:

Wing span:	
147 SD	4·42 m (14 ft 6 in)
147 TF	9·75 m (32 ft 0 in)
Length overall:	
147 SD and TF	9·14 m (30 ft 0 in)
Body diameter:	
147 SD	0·94 m (3 ft 1·2 in)
147 TF	1·01 m (3 ft 3·6 in)

WEIGHTS:

Max launching weight:	
147 SD	1,412 kg (3,113 lb)
147 TF:	
without underwing stores	1,859 kg (4,100 lb)
with underwing stores	2,812 kg (6,200 lb)
AQM-34V	2,041 kg (4,500 lb)

TELEDYNE RYAN MODEL 166 FIREBEE II
US Navy designations: BQM-34E and BQM-34T
US Air Force designation: BQM-34F

The Model 166 Firebee II supersonic target vehicle, an advanced development of the BQM-34A Firebee I, is now out of production. A full description and illustration can be found in the 1979-80 *Jane's*.

US Air Force BQM-34F Firebee IIs are currently being equipped with a Vega Drone Tracking and Control System (DTCS) for tracking, command control and telemetry functions.

TELEDYNE RYAN FIREBRAND
US Navy designation: ZBQM-111A

Initial US Navy funding of approx $3 million was announced in May 1977 for this new supersonic target, designed to simulate the threat posed by Soviet anti-shipping missiles. The total value of the development and construction programme will be $41·7 million.

The initial contract calls for the completion of nine targets: six for research and development and three for special tasks. Known as the ZBQM-111A Firebrand, the target will serve as a realistic 'enemy' in testing US Navy shipboard defence weapons under simulated combat conditions. Subject to the satisfactory completion of flight testing, which is due to begin in October 1981, production Firebrands are expected to be ordered in 1982.

TYPE: Recoverable supersonic target drone.

AIRFRAME: Shoulder-wing monoplane, with small delta wings (approx 63° sweep on leading-edges) set well back on tapered, circular-section body. Built mainly of aluminium alloy, with wings of aluminium honeycomb and bonded stainless steel skins. Differentially-operating elevons and rudder. Ram-air intake in base of fin.

POWER PLANT: Two Marquardt ramjets, mounted externally one on each side of fuselage at rear. Fuel tank in centre of fuselage. Thiokol booster rockets.

LAUNCH AND RECOVERY: Air or surface launch. Fail-safe parachute recovery system, housed in fuselage between payload compartment (forward) and fuel tank.

GUIDANCE AND CONTROL: Pre-programmed radio command guidance system, using AN/AYK-14 flight control computer. Provision for manual override.

EQUIPMENT: Ram-air turbogenerator; batteries; Honeywell 7193 altimeter; Tacan; drag 'chute, recovery parachute and flotation bag; locator beacon; and destruct receiver. Mission equipment, in 0·17 m³ (6 cu ft) payload compartment in nose, includes ECM; active and passive radar augmentation; IR augmentation; expendable H-, I- and J-band emitter; and scoring system.

DIMENSIONS, EXTERNAL:

Wing span	2·74 m (9 ft 0 in)
Wing area, gross	3·72 m² (40·0 sq ft)
Length overall	10·36 m (34 ft 0 in)
Body diameter	0·71 m (2 ft 4 in)

WEIGHTS (surface launch):

Fuel	998 kg (2,200 lb)
Payload	113 kg (250 lb)
Max gross weight (incl booster)	2,812 kg (6,200 lb)

TELEDYNE RYAN MODEL 305 FIREBOLT
US Air Force designation: AQM-81A

Teledyne Ryan is conducting, for the US Air Force Armament Division at Eglin AFB, Florida, full-scale development of the Firebolt High Altitude High Speed Target (HAHST). HAHST is a continuation and refinement of the High Altitude Supersonic Target (HAST) which was an advanced development programme conducted by Beech Aircraft Corporation. Teledyne Ryan was the winner in a competitive procurement bid for the full-scale engineering development of this target, and on 10 December 1979 was awarded a contract to produce and deliver nine test vehicles. The four-year programme includes a series of 30 test flights, which will begin in August 1982 and end in December 1983.

The flight performance envelope of the Firebolt covers a range from Mach 1·2 at 12,200 m (40,000 ft) to Mach 4·0 at 30,500 m (100,000 ft).

TYPE: Supersonic air-launched recoverable target drone.

AIRFRAME: Mid-wing monoplane, with slim-delta main wings swept 75° on leading-edges and of constant thickness except for leading-edges. Full-span aileron on each trailing-edge. Arrow-planform canard foreplanes for longitudinal control. Fixed endplate fin at tip of each main wing. Cylindrical body, with 3·5 calibre von Kármán nose section and conical boat-tail section. Ventral fin under rear fuselage.

POWER PLANT: CSD hybrid rocket engine. Propellant is polybutadiene and polymethyl-methacrylate, with IRFNA oxidiser. System is inherently safe, since propellants will not burn unless external ignition is applied. Engine is throttleable, with thrust variable from 0·53 to 5·34 kN (120-1,200 lb st). The 0·33 m (13 in) thrust chamber forms integral part of fuselage assembly. Oxidiser pressurisation and electrical power provided by ducted power unit. This unit, developed by Marquardt, is powered by ram-air turbine with air intake and exit on lower side of fuselage mid-section. Manoeuvring requirements dictate positive expulsion system for oxidiser.

LAUNCH AND RECOVERY: Air-launched from carrier aircraft at speeds between Mach 1·2 and 2·5. Recovery by 13·72 m (45 ft) diameter parachute from land, water or mid-air.

GUIDANCE AND CONTROL: Manoeuvres can be either pre-programmed or initiated via ground command radio link. Manoeuvres of between 5g at 10,670 m (35,000 ft) and 1·15g at 27,400 m (90,000 ft) are part of flight test programme; vehicle also capable of 'S' and 180° turns in horizontal plane and altitude changes in vertical plane.

SPECIAL EQUIPMENT: The flight test vehicles include provisions for a Scaler miss-distance scoring system and a point source radar augmentation system.

DIMENSIONS, EXTERNAL:

Wing span	1·02 m (3 ft 4 in)
Wing area (total exposed)	0·97 m² (10·44 sq ft)
Length	5·18 m (17 ft 0 in)
Height (stabiliser)	0·66 m (2 ft 2 in)
Body diameter	0·33 m (1 ft 1 in)

VOLUME:

Payload volume	0·033 m³ (1,970 cu in)

WEIGHTS:

Launching weight	558 kg (1,231 lb)
Propellant	29·7 kg (65·5 lb)

PERFORMANCE:

Endurance at Mach 3	5 min

US DEPARTMENT OF DEFENSE

Major areas in which the Department of Defense was concentrating RPV research during the late 1970s include the testing of a missile- or aircraft-launched mini-RPV; development and test of shipboard launch and recovery techniques; battery- and solar-powered RPVs; miniature infra-red and laser designator and rangefinder systems that will enable a mini-RPV to find targets and guide weapons at night; and data links resistant to hostile jamming. The use of mini-RPVs for hostile weapon and radar location is foreseen, using the air vehicle as a platform equipped with a lightweight high-performance radar, or a laser line-scanner, and a direct line-of-sight flash detector, or with an explosive charge to destroy a target. A small, low-cost system for locating a mortar projectile is being designed, and investigation of radar options for projectile tracking is in progress.

In addition to drone/RPV programmes for which hardware contracts have been awarded (described under the appropriate contractor's heading in this section), the following are among the more important programmes recently receiving attention by the three US services:

US AIR FORCE
Office of Information, Aeronautical Systems Division (AFSC), Wright-Patterson AFB, Ohio 45433
Telephone: (513) 253 7111

Teledyne Ryan ZBQM-111A Firebrand naval supersonic target

Mockup of the Teledyne Ryan Model 305 HAHST

The seventh US Air Force Flight Dynamics Laboratory XBQM-106, equipped with side-force control surfaces on the wings and a McCulloch MC-101A engine

Terminal attack of a target by a US Air Force Locust defence suppression mini-RPV

Locust. Mini-drone programme to develop a small, low-cost system to provide defence suppression of hostile air defences. Formerly known as LCEHV (Low Cost Expendable Harassment Vehicle) and later as HWS (Harassment Weapons System). Will be ground-launched, and pre-programmed to navigate to, and loiter in, the area of hostile air defences. Its presence will draw the defences' fire, provoke radar silence, or (if ignored) will home in to allow an explosive charge to damage a hostile radar.

The Locust vehicle will be able to re-loiter in the event of a hostile radar being turned off during a terminal attack. A concept validation flight test was conducted in early 1979, using a US Air Force Flight Dynamics Laboratory XBQM-106 vehicle (see next entry) with a DH 220 two-stroke engine and existing modified sensor and warhead. A Memorandum of Agreement is expected to be signed with West Germany, leading to joint development of the production Locust vehicle. If testing is successful, this should reach field units in late FY 1983 (see also MBB in German section).

In advance of the airframe, the US Air Force has awarded competitive sensor contracts to General Dynamics and Texas Instruments for full-scale engineering development of the Locust passive radio frequency homing sensor.

XBQM-106. This experimental mini-RPV was designed and is built by the US Air Force Flight Dynamics Laboratory, and was first flown in 1975. It is designed for easily-obtainable flexibility; up to early 1980, 18 vehicles had been built and 10 variants had flown, incorporating various alternative wing, nose, tail and engine configurations, and with payloads ranging from 11·3 to 59 kg (25-130 lb).

Launch has been demonstrated from a Fairchild catapult. Flight tests with a fluidic autopilot were completed successfully in 1979. The XBQM-106 has also been used to demonstrate several seeker/warhead combinations for a variety of expendable mini-RPV strike missions.

The following description applies to the current (1980) configuration:

AIRFRAME: Cantilever high-wing monoplane. Slightly-swept wings, of NACA 2512/2515 root/tip section, with glassfibre skins and foam core. Pod-and-boom fuselage of glassfibre cloth and resin, with moulded polyurethane foam bulkheads; Kevlar and graphite in highly-stressed areas. Sweptback single fin, integral with rear fuselage; rudder and all-moving tailplane have glassfibre or balsa skin with foam core. Modified Futaba FP-S14 electrical trim and servo actuators for ailerons, rudder and tailplane. Side-force panels above and below wings. Twin dependent endplate fins and rudders have also been flight tested.

POWER PLANT: One 13·5 kW (18 hp) D.H. Enterprises (Herbrandson) Dyad 220 two-cylinder two-stroke piston engine, mounted above wing centre-section and driving a two-blade fixed-pitch wooden pusher propeller. Single fuel tank in fuselage, capacity 11·5 litres (2·5 Imp gallons; 3 US gallons). Fuel is a petrol/oil mixture.
LAUNCH AND RECOVERY: Launched pneumatically by catapult. Normal recovery by landing on ventral skid. Recovery using powered ram-air canopy has also been demonstrated.
GUIDANCE AND CONTROL: Radio and radar command guidance system standard. Real-time ground-based control system; USAF-developed autopilot or manual control optional. Aerodynamic control by ailerons, rudder and all-moving tailplane. Special wings-level steering available via wing-mounted side-force control surfaces for accurate target strike experiments.
SYSTEMS AND EQUIPMENT: Bosch 28V 17A engine-driven alternator for electrical power. Air-to-ground uplink and downlink telemetry; tracking sensors; downlinked video from nose-mounted camera standard. Variable military payloads, up to 13·6 kg (30 lb) in weight, accommodated in nose sections of standard or modified shape.
DIMENSIONS, EXTERNAL:
Wing span	3·63 m (11 ft 11 in)
Wing area, gross	1·80 m² (19·4 sq ft)
Length overall	3·07 m (10 ft 1 in)
Height overall	0·84 m (2 ft 9 in)
Propeller diameter	0·71 m (2 ft 4 in)

WEIGHTS:
Weight empty	47·6 kg (105 lb)
Max payload	50·8 kg (112 lb)
Max fuel load	8·2 kg (18 lb)
Max launching weight	106·6 kg (235 lb)

PERFORMANCE (at max launching weight):
Max level speed at S/L	100 knots (185 km/h; 115 mph)
Max cruising speed at S/L	90 knots (167 km/h; 104 mph)
Econ cruising speed at S/L	75 knots (139 km/h; 86 mph)
Stalling speed, power on	55 knots (102 km/h; 64 mph)
Max rate of climb at S/L	305 m (1,000 ft)/min
Service ceiling	3,050 m (10,000 ft)
Landing from 15 m (50 ft)	244 m (800 ft)
Landing run	122 m (400 ft)
Range with max fuel	675 nm (1,250 km; 777 miles)
Range with max payload	112 nm (207 km; 129 miles)
Max endurance	5 h

US ARMY

Public Affairs Office, US Army Troop Support and Aviation Materiel Readiness Command, 4300 Goodfellow Boulevard, St Louis, Missouri 63120

Electronic Warfare RPV. Programme to demonstrate 22·7-54·5 kg (50-120 lb) expendable/non-expendable mini-RPVs as an airborne platform for communication and non-communication jammers. Feasibility programme was tentatively scheduled for completion in 1979. Future programme to be determined.

US NAVY

Office of Information, Naval Air Systems Command, Department of the Navy, the Pentagon, Washington, DC 20361

David W. Taylor Naval Ship Research and Development Center VATOL (XBQM-108A). This US Navy programme, described in detail in the 1979-80 *Jane's*, was aimed at demonstrating vertical attitude take-off and landing (VATOL) aboard non-aviation ships. Tethered hover flight tests were successfully demonstrated on 29 September 1976, after which the programme was terminated.

Naval Air Development Center HI-SPOT. HI-SPOT (High altitude Surveillance Platform for Over-the-horizon Targeting) is a programme to develop an unmanned platform for high altitude (18,500 to 24,000 m; 60,700 to 78,750 ft) ocean surveillance and communications relay. It will be designed to remain on station for periods of more than 30 days. Programme is sponsored by the Naval Air Systems Command, with technical management by the Naval Air Development Center. Model testing is scheduled to begin in 1982.

Naval Air Development Center QF-4B. QF-4B target version of McDonnell Douglas F-4B was developed by Naval Air Development Center for use at Pacific Missile Test Center. First aircraft was delivered in Spring 1972 to PMTC at Point Mugu.

Seven QF-4B conversions were produced by Naval Air Rework Facility, Cherry Point, North Carolina. Target is equipped for high-g manoeuvring and has provisions for photo and electronic scoring and ECM. Production continuing into 1980s. A follow-on version is under development to incorporate all-attitude manoeuvring.

Naval Weapons Center QF-86. Thirty-one North American F-86H Sabres were converted by Naval Weapons Center, China Lake, California, into QF-86H pilotless target aircraft, as described in 1977-78 *Jane's*. Three F-86F Sabres underwent prototype conversion at the NWC in 1979 into QF-86F pilotless target aircraft. Approx 117 F-86Fs are to be converted to QF-86F drones. The QF-86Fs and QF-86Hs are used as interim all-attitude manoeuvring targets.

AIR-LAUNCHED MISSILES

ARGENTINA

CITEFA
ARMED FORCES SCIENTIFIC AND TECHNICAL RESEARCH CENTRE

It was announced in the Spring of 1978 that two types of missile were under advanced development in Argentina. One is an anti-tank missile, in the class of the West Ger-

man Cobra, and was expected to become operational in 1979. The other is an air-to-surface missile in the class of the French AS.20, to arm naval fixed-wing aircraft and helicopters. Eight R & D rounds had been built by the Armed Forces Scientific and Technical Research Centre at the time of the announcement, with an evaluation batch of 50 missiles to follow. Guidance is by radio command. Only

other details released by mid-1980 are as follows:

WEIGHTS:
Warhead 40 kg (88 lb)
Launching weight 115 kg (254 lb)

PERFORMANCE:
Max range 3·75 nm (7 km; 4·35 miles)

FRANCE

AÉROSPATIALE
SOCIÉTÉ NATIONALE INDUSTRIELLE AÉROSPATIALE
Division des Engins Tactiques
EXECUTIVE OFFICE: 2 rue Béranger, BP 84, 92320 Châtillon sous Bagneux
Telephone: 657 14 21
Telex: AISPA 250881 F

When Nord-Aviation became part of Aérospatiale, responsibility for its guided missiles, target vehicles and test vehicles was allocated to Aérospatiale's Tactical Missiles Division. Subsequently, this Division developed and put into production a new generation of short-range battlefield weapons, in association with MBB of Federal Germany (see Euromissile entry in International section).

A total of 489,259 tactical missiles and 1,906 target and reconnaissance RPVs had been ordered from the Division and its overseas partners by January 1980. Employees totalled 6,065 at the beginning of 1980.

AÉROSPATIALE AS.11

The AS.11 is an air-to-surface version of the SS.11 line-of sight wire-guided battlefield missile. It is powered by a two-stage solid-propellant rocket motor. Directional control is achieved by varying the sustainer efflux through two side-nozzles.

In action, with a typical helicopter installation, the operator acquires the target by means of a stabilised and magnifying optical sight. As soon as the missile enters his field of vision after launch, he passes to it the signals needed to align it with the target, while keeping it above the terrain until impact. The signals are given by the operator by means of a control stick which makes it possible to send simultaneously up or down and port or starboard commands. The signals are transmitted to the missile over wires, wound on twin spools. Tracer flares are installed on the rear of the missile for visual reference.

The current AS.11 B.1 version is available with a variety of warheads, including an inert type for practice, the Type 140AC anti-tank warhead capable of perforating 60 cm (24 in) of armour plate, the Type 140AP02 explosive warhead (2·6 kg; 5·72 lb of explosive) which will penetrate an armoured steel plate 1 cm (0·4 in) thick at a range of 3,000 m (9,840 ft) and explode about 2·1 m (7 ft) behind the point of impact, and the Type 140AP59 high-fragmentation anti-personnel type with contact fuse.

The AS.11 B.1 and the basic surface-launched SS.11 B.1 have been supplied to all three French services and the armed forces of 27 other countries, including the USA and UK. Orders totalled 173,666 by January 1980, including surface-to-surface Harpons with automatic infra-red command guidance. Of these, 60 per cent were for export. Licence manufacture was undertaken in Federal Germany and India. Production by Aérospatiale is expected to continue on a reduced scale until about 1985.
DATA: See table

AÉROSPATIALE AS.12

This spin-stabilised missile was derived from the AS.11 and has a warhead weighing 28·4 kg (62·6 lb), which makes it suitable for use against fortifications as well as tanks, ships and other vehicles. The current OP.3C warhead can pierce 40 mm (1·5 in) of armour and explode on the other side.

The AS.12 has a two-stage solid-propellant rocket motor and a command to line-of-sight guidance system. It can be air-launched at speeds up to about 200 knots (370 km/h; 230 mph), in conjunction with an APX 260 or APX 334 gyro-stabilised sight, and can be used at night with target illuminating equipment.

The AS.12 arms seven types of fixed-wing aircraft and eight types of helicopter in service with 16 navies or air forces. They include Breguet Atlantic and P-2 Neptune aircraft of the Royal Netherlands Navy, the Breguet Alizé, and helicopters of the French Navy and Royal Navy.

A total of 8,651 AS.12s and surface-to-surface SS.12s had been ordered by January 1980, when manufacture was continuing. Of these, 79 per cent were for export.
DATA: See table

AÉROSPATIALE AS.15TT

The AS.15TT is projected by Aérospatiale as a light-weight all-weather missile for attacking surface targets of all tonnages at sea. It could be operated from comparatively slow-flying aircraft, such as ship-based or shore-based helicopters and maritime patrol aircraft, or from surface ships or coastal defence batteries. A helicopter such as the SA 365 Dauphin II could carry four, in pairs, on fuselage-side racks.

The general appearance of the AS.15TT is shown in the accompanying photograph of a model. It would use an extremely accurate automatic guidance system, and carry a warhead identical to that of the AS.12 missile.

Associated surface-surveillance radar is the Thomson-CSF Agrion 15, which has a 360° scan; is designed for automatic target tracking and determination of the differential target/missile range and bearing; and is able to operate in an ECM environment. As well as forming part of the AS.15TT system, the Agrion 15 can be used to designate over-the-horizon targets for long-range anti-ship missiles in the Exocet class.

In operation, the target would be detected and identified; the radar would be switched to automatic tracking and the missile launched. After a shallow descent, the AS.15TT would then follow a sea-skimming trajectory to the target, under entirely automatic guidance. The characteristics of the system are such that approach to the target and missile launch could be performed at very low altitude.
DATA: See table.

AÉROSPATIALE AS.30 LASER

Developed as a successor to the original command-guided AS.30 (see 1976-77 *Jane's*), this tactical air-to-surface supersonic missile is intended to be compatible with all types of modern single-seat or multi-seat combat aircraft, for use against heavy surface targets on land or at sea. It has a cylindrical body, cruciform sweptback wings which are canted to impart spin stabilisation, cruciform 'flip-out' tail-fins indexed in line with the wings, and a two-stage (boost and sustainer) solid-propellant rocket motor. A two-phase guidance system is utilised, comprising a pre-guidance phase on gyro reference, followed by automatic (TV) target tracking combined with semi-active laser terminal homing, by means of the missile's Thomson-CSF Ariel homing head.

Standard equipment required in the launch aircraft consists of an armament control panel, pilot's sight and TV screen, a firing button on the control column and an emergency jettison switch. Equipment associated specifically with the AS.30 Laser missile comprises launchers with the appropriate firing circuits, and a Thomson-CSF Atlis target illuminating pod.

Tests of an Atlis II pod under a French Air Force Jaguar A were made successfully at the CEV, Cazaux, in 1977. Test firings of the AS.30 Laser missile were made successfully in 1979.
DATA: See table

AÉROSPATIALE EXOCET AM39

Exocet is a missile that was devised originally to provide warships with all-weather attack capability against other surface vessels. The air-to-surface version is designated AM39. Propulsion is by a tandem two-stage solid-propellant motor, and the highly-destructive warhead is in the same order as that of a torpedo.

Compared with the surface-to-surface versions, the AM39 air-to-surface Exocet has a reduced launch weight and a new rocket motor that burns for 150 s, giving an increased range. Another modification to the propulsion system ensures a one-second delay in ignition after launch, allowing the missile to drop clear of the launch aircraft.

The AM39 has been selected for carriage by the French Navy's Atlantic NG (Nouvelle Génération) and Super Etendard aircraft. It is suitable for operation from medium-size helicopters, and has been ordered to equip Pakistani Sea Kings and Iraqi Super Frelons.

The missile's high subsonic flight profile consists of a pre-guidance phase, during which it travels towards the target, whose range and bearing have been determined by an airborne radar and fire control computer and set up in the missile pre-guidance circuits before launch; an inertially-guided midcourse phase; and a final guidance phase during which the missile flies directly towards the target under the control of its active homing head. Throughout its flight the missile is maintained at a very low altitude (reported to be 2 to 3 m; 6·5 to 10 ft) by an FM radio altimeter. Its homing head is reported to pick up the target over a range of up to 6·5 nm (12 km; 7·5 miles). Exocet is intended to operate efficiently in an ECM (electronic countermeasures) environment. Subcontractors to Aérospatiale include Electronique Marcel Dassault for the ADAC homing head, TRT for the AHV-7 radio altimeter, SNPE for the solid propellants, SERAT for the explosive charge, SFENA and SAGEM for accelerometers and gyroscopes, and Jaeger for control surface actuators.

Launch tests from a Super Frelon helicopter began in April 1973. The type of missile employed was an intermediate version of Exocet designated AM38, which consisted of a surface-to-surface MM38 fitted with the one-second ignition delay that is embodied in the AM39. In each of the powered launches, the missile dropped about 10 m (33 ft) in a stable, horizontal attitude from its pylon before ignition, despite rotor downwash.

Firings of AM39 missiles from a Super Frelon began in December 1976, and were followed by the first launches from a Super Etendard in the first half of 1977.

Carrying two Exocet AM39s and 5,000 litres (1,100 Imp gallons) of fuel, a Super Frelon can carry out a 6-h patrol near its shore or ship base, or attack a specific target up to 350 nm (650 km; 400 miles) from base. Equipment added to the helicopter consists of two launch pylons, an operator's console, an Omera ORB-31D X-band search and tracking radar capable of acquiring targets the size of a fast patrol boat over a range of 28·5 nm (53 km; 33 miles) in sea state 4 or 5, an EMD Alto-2 Doppler radar altimeter, a SFIM CV-153 vertical gyro for a compass system, a compensated airspeed indicator and a Crouzet 70 computer.

Of the 140 production AM39s ordered by January 1980, more than 60 per cent were for export.
RANGE (estimated):
launched from a helicopter at 60 knots (110 km/h; 69 mph) at a height of 100 m (330 ft)
28 nm (52 km; 32·25 miles)
launched from an Atlantic aircraft at heights between 300 and 5,000 m (1,000 ft and 16,400 ft)
29-32·25 nm (54-60 km; 33·5-37·25 miles)
launched from a Super Etendard aircraft at heights between 100 m (330 ft) and 10,000 m (33,000 ft)
32-37 nm (60-70 km; 37-43 miles)
For other data see table

ASMP

As mentioned in the 1977-78 *Jane's*, the original missile that was being developed under the ASMP (Air-Sol Moyenne Portée) designation reverted to definition study status when the ACF (Avion de Combat Futur) programme was cancelled. However, on 6 April 1978 it was announced that a new design and development contract for an air-to-surface medium-range missile (ASMP) had been awarded to Aérospatiale's Tactical Missiles Division, which will collaborate with ONERA and SNPE. Intended as the vehicle for the French Air Force's latest tactical nuclear warhead, ASMP was stated to benefit from ramjet engine research carried out by Aérospatiale and its pre-

Launch of an Aérospatiale AS.11 air-to-surface missile from an Alouette III helicopter

Aérospatiale AS.12 air-to-surface missile on an Alouette III helicopter

Model of Aérospatiale AS.15TT (Brian M. Service)

decessors, and from experience gained in developing the guidance systems for the Exocet and Pluton missiles. It will be carried by 15 Dassault Mirage IV bombers and by Dassault Mirage 2000 tactical fighters, from about 1985.

The ASMP will be powered in supersonic cruising flight by a kerosene-burning ramjet, supplied with air by a pair of two-dimensional side intakes which will serve also as wings. Stability and control will be provided by two pairs of tail-fins and rudders, with guidance by an inertial system. Range is expected to be in the order of 40-54 nm (75-100 km; 46-62 miles) depending on launch and cruising height. Yield of the nuclear warhead is said to be between 100 and 150 kT, and ASMP is intended for stand-off use against heavily defended targets such as airfields, and command and communications centres.

It seems likely that the power plant will be a rocket-ramjet, with the solid-propellant launch booster integrated in the ramjet combustion chamber.

MATRA
SA MATRA

HEAD OFFICE: 4 rue de Presbourg, 75116 Paris
MANAGEMENT AND WORKS, POSTAL ADDRESS: BP No. 1, 78140 Vélizy
Telephone: 946 96 00
Telex: ENMATRA 698077F
PRESIDENT DIRECTOR-GENERAL: Jean-Luc Lagardère
DIRECTOR OF PUBLIC RELATIONS: Philippe Chassagny
PRESS DEPARTMENT: 6 rond-point des Condamines, 78000 Versailles
Telephone: 953 00 05
Telex: DREMATRA 695 413 F
CHIEF OF PRESS DEPARTMENT: Roland Sanguinetti

Since 1948, Matra has been engaged in extensive research and experimental work in the guided missile, propulsion and guidance fields. The wide range of weapon systems in current production includes a total of eight air-to-air, surface-to-air, air-to-surface and anti-ship missiles.

Other Matra weapon systems include the Durandal rocket-propelled penetration bomb for attacking runways; and the Beluga cluster weapon, developed in association with Thomson/Brandt, which dispenses 151 grenades or other munitions, lowered to the ground on individual brake-chutes.

MATRA R.530

Since 1963, more than 3,000 R.530 air-to-air missiles have been delivered to arm aircraft of 14 countries, including Mirage III and Mirage F1 interceptors of the French Air Force, F-8E(FN) Crusaders of the French Navy, and Mirages of the air forces of Argentina, Australia, Brazil, Colombia, Pakistan, South Africa and Venezuela. Production was scheduled to continue into 1979.

Suitable for use at heights from sea level to 21,000 m (69,000 ft), the R.530 is an all-weather missile, with interchangeable EMD AD-26 semi-active radar and SAT AD-3501 infra-red homing heads. It can be fired at the target from any relative direction.

The R.530 has a cylindrical body, with cruciform delta wings, two of which are fitted with ailerons, and cruciform tail control surfaces. It is powered by a dual-thrust (boost and sustainer) Hotchkiss-Brandt/SNPE Marie Antoinette solid-propellant rocket motor, rated at 83·36 kN (18,740 lb st).

Interchangeable Hotchkiss-Brandt fragmentation or continuous-rod warheads are available, each weighing 27 kg (60 lb) and fitted with a proximity fuse. Anti-jamming ECM devices are fitted to the AD-26 head.
DATA: See table

MATRA SUPER 530

This air-to-air weapon is being deployed initially as armament for the Dassault Mirage F1 interceptors of the French Air Force and will eventually arm also the Mirage 2000. Compared with the R.530, it has much improved aerodynamics, structure, radome, electronics and power plant, doubling both the acquisition distance and the effective range. It is an all-weather and all-sector weapon, with the ability to attack targets flying at an altitude 9,000 m (29,500 ft) higher or lower than that of the launch aircraft. Range limits are described as being from 'several hundreds of metres' to 'several tens of km'.

The Super 530 has skin, wings and tail surfaces of sheet steel and steel honeycomb, with a ceramic radome over its EMD Super AD-26 semi-active pulse radar homing head. Its Angèle dual-thrust rocket motor, supplied by Thomson/Brandt, utilises Butalane propellant, with a much higher specific impulse than the motor of the R.530. The fragmenting warhead is supplied by Thomson/Brandt, with a proximity fuse by Thomson-CSF; and advanced ECM anti-jamming circuits are fitted. Control is by means of the cruciform tail-fins. Transverse acceleration limit is 20g on each axis up to 17,000-18,000 m (56,000-59,000 ft) and 6g from that height up to 25,000 m (82,000 ft).

Ramp-launch tests of the Super 530 began in January 1971, and the first controlled model was fired successfully on 27 February 1973. Five complete missiles had been fired successfully against airborne targets by early 1975; the first launch from a Mirage F1 was conducted successfully in January 1976. Manufacture for the Air Force was started at the end of 1977, reaching mass production levels by January 1979. The Super 530 has been operational on French home defence interceptors since December 1979.
DATA: See table

MATRA R.550 MAGIC

This air-to-air weapon system was intended initially to meet a French Air Force requirement for a highly-manoeuvrable short/medium-range 'dogfight' missile. Development was started in 1967 as a private venture and has continued under official contract since 1969.

The R.550 Magic has a 'double-canard' configuration, with a set of movable foreplane control surfaces immediately behind and indexed in line with cruciform fixed surfaces. The missile has an SNPE Romeo single-stage solid-propellant motor, an AD-3601 infra-red homing head with a cooled cell, manufactured by SAT, and a 12·5 kg (27·5 lb) warhead with 6 kg (13·2 lb) of explosive, impact and proximity fuses. It can utilise the same aircraft launcher as the Sidewinder which it replaces.

The Magic has wide range limits, is stressed for 30g manoeuvres and can be fired from an aircraft in a 6g turn, singly or at one second interval between rounds. There is no minimum launch speed; maximum is more than 700 knots (1,300 km/h; 805 mph), against targets in a forward sector of 140°.

The first air-launch of an R.550 complete with guidance equipment, against a target, took place at the Landes Test Centre on 11 January 1972, from a Gloster Meteor test aircraft. Delivery of the first production missiles for operational testing and evaluation by the French Air Force began in 1974. Full series manufacture began in 1975 and by the beginning of 1979 a total of 3,200 Magics had been delivered. Orders for training and operational rounds totalled 5,000, for 11 countries, at that time, and production was continuing at the rate of 100 a month at Salbris.

Adaptation to the Mirage III, Mirage 5, Mirage F1 and French Navy Crusader has been completed; adaptation to the Jaguar, Alpha Jet, Aermacchi M.B. 326K, and Super Étendard is under way, and Magic will also form the basic weapon of the Mirage 2000.
DATA: See table

GERMANY
(FEDERAL REPUBLIC)

BODENSEEWERK
BODENSEEWERK GERÄTETECHNIK GmbH

HEAD OFFICE: Postfach 1120, 7770 Überlingen
Telephone: (07 551) 811

Telex: 07 33924
LIAISON OFFICE: Bundeskanzlerplatz HI 1002, 5300 Bonn
Telephone: (02 221) 214432

UK OFFICE: 27-28 Crossway House, Bracknell, Berkshire RG12 1DA, England
Telephone: (0344) 26070 and 54782

Under the original NATO European production programme for the Sidewinder air-to-air missile, Bodenseewerk was prime contractor for the licence manufacture of 13,000 of the AIM-9B and FGW Mod 2 versions. The company is now prime contractor for European production of the advanced AIM-9L Sidewinder, described under the NWC heading in the US section.

In the late 1960s, Bodenseewerk began developing the Viper close-range air-to-air missile system, comprising the high-performance all-aspect Viper infra-red homing missile, a new launcher, and a launcher-mounted passive infra-red target acquisition unit. When Dornier entered the programme in 1972, a joint management team was set up. After cancellation of Viper in 1974, the joint US/FRG missile programme known as ALASCA (all aspect capability) was launched, combining the Viper IR seeker with the aft section of the AIM-9L/H Sidewinder. Under this programme, 12 ALASCA guidance and control sections were built for flight testing. The project was stopped later in favour of the AIM-9L, but flight tests of ALASCA seekers were being performed during 1980.

Bodenseewerk has been selected as West German lead contractor to carry out with British Aerospace studies for a new generation of air-to-air missiles.

Aérospatiale AS.30 Laser air-to-surface homing missile on a Jaguar

Versions of the Matra R.530 air-to-air missile with semi-active radar guidance (left) and infra-red homing head (right)

Matra R.550 Magic air-to-air missile on wingtip of Dassault Mirage F1

Matra Super 530 air-to-air missiles on the underwing mountings of Mirage F1

AM39 Exocet air-to-surface missile on an Aéronavale Super Étendard

MBB Kormoran missile under wing of F-104G Starfighter

MBB
MESSERSCHMITT-BÖLKOW-BLOHM GmbH

HEAD OFFICE AND WORKS: Ottobrunn bei München, 8000 München 80, Postfach 801220

Telephone: (089) 60 00 25 90

In addition to its manufacture of piloted aircraft, MBB has engaged in the development and manufacture of guided weapons for many years. It has achieved considerable success with its short-range surface-to-surface and surface-to-air battlefield missiles, some of which result from partnership with Aérospatiale of France.

Weapons in current production include an air-launched anti-shipping missile known as the Kormoran.

MBB KORMORAN

This roll-stabilised all-weather anti-shipping missile can be carried by any aircraft which is able to maintain a speed between Mach 0·6 and 0·95 during the attack, and which is equipped with target detection radar and an autonomous navigation system such as an inertial platform. The aircraft's electronics must be supplemented by a position and homing indicator (PHI) and Kormoran firing equipment. Launch information is obtained from the aircraft's target detection radar, navigation system, and a navigation support device which adapts the signals representing velocity for the Kormoran airborne computer. In addition, if the missile is operated in an optical mode, instead of through target detection radar, the PHI has to be used in conjunction with computer co-ordinated data (CCD) and a vector addition unit (VAD).

Two built-in SNPE Prade boosters accelerate Kormoran to high subsonic cruising speed, which is then maintained by the SNPE Eole IV solid-propellant sustainer motor. The guidance system employs pre-guidance and homing phases, using a Thomson-CSF RE-576 radar terminal seeker. The new-type high-energy warhead, developed at MBB's Schrobenhausen works, weighs 160 kg (352 lb) and can penetrate 70-90 mm (2·75-3·5 in) of steel plate, making it effective against ships up to the size of a destroyer.

The launch aircraft can approach the target area at very low level, to escape detection by the ship's radar, by means of the PHI, with radar switched off. With the radar then turned on, the target is acquired and its position is fed into the PHI; the radar is again switched off while the aircraft takes up the optimum attack position. The radar is switched on, locked on to the target, and initial data are transmitted automatically to the missile. As soon as the missile has been launched under power, directly from the pylon, as little as 30 m (100 ft) above the water, the aircraft breaks away, outside the range of enemy anti-aircraft defences. The missile descends to its programmed flight level and locks on to the target, guided by inertial naviga-

tion aided by its radar altimeter. At a prescribed distance, the inertial system releases the active radar seeker. After this has locked on target, the inertial guidance is slaved and corrected in azimuth and range by the seeker head. At a short distance from the target the missile descends to its terminal flight level in order to hit the target just above the waterline.

The secondary optical firing mode, in which the pilot aims the missile by means of his optical weapon sight, is used against surprise targets, in the presence of extreme enemy ECM, or when the target is a small vessel, such as a fast patrol boat or minesweeper. Kormoran itself is immune to all known kinds of ECM.

In-plant testing of Kormoran was completed by early 1974, at which time official tests from F-104G Starfighter aircraft were under way. A preliminary production contract to equip West German naval air arm F-104Gs was placed in 1974; it was followed by a full contract in November 1976, for 350 missiles and 56 aircraft installations, for which MBB is prime contractor. Seven qualification test firings in Autumn 1977 resulted in six direct hits on target and a seventh which met specification requirements. Kormoran has been in series production since December 1977, and will arm West German Navy Tornadoes when these aircraft replace the F-104G Starfighters now in service.

DATA: See table

INTERNATIONAL PROGRAMMES

EMDG
EUROMISSILE DYNAMICS GROUP

7 rue Béranger, BP 84, 92320 Châtillon, France
Telephone: 657 12 44
Telex: EUROM 204691 F
SUPERVISORY BOARD:
Michel Allier (Aérospatiale)
G. R. Jefferson (British Aerospace)
Gunther Kuhlo (MBB)

Formation of this guided weapons company was announced by Aérospatiale, British Aerospace and MBB on 2 January 1980, following the signing of a memorandum of understanding by the governments of France, the UK and the German Federal Republic. EMDG is subject to French law. Its supervisory board is made up of the Chief Executives of Aérospatiale's Division Engins Tactiques, MBB Unternehmensbereich Apparate and British Aerospace Dynamics Group.

Initially, EMDG will be involved in research, development, production and marketing of third-generation anti-tank guided weapon systems, both medium and long range. It is also the intention of the three participating companies that other weapon systems undertaken jointly by them, on behalf of their respective governments, shall be the responsibility of EMDG.

Aérospatiale, MBB and British Aerospace were already working together on an anti-ship missile system through a joint company known as Anti-Ship Euromissile (ASEM). It is intended to absorb ASEM into EMDG as soon as practicable.

EUROMISSILE
EUROMISSILE GROUPEMENT D'INTÉRÊT ÉCONOMIQUE

12 rue de la Redoute, 92260 Fontenay-aux-Roses, France
Telephone: 661 33 11
Telex: EUROM 204691 F

PRESIDENT: Marcel Morer
SALES DIRECTORS: Pierre Froget and Georg Erlenwein

Euromissile is a Groupement d'Intérêt Economique formed by Aérospatiale of France and MBB of Federal Germany. First products of the Euromissile team are three short-range battlefield weapons known as Milan, Hot and Roland, developed initially for the armed services of France and Federal Germany. Hot is in production for both air-launched and surface-launched operation.

HOT

The Hot (High-subsonic, optically-guided, tube-launched) is a tube-launched wire-guided anti-tank missile suitable for both surface-to-surface and air-to-surface use. It has fins which fold down against the body when it is in its launching tube, and open out in flight. The power plant is a two-stage solid-propellant rocket motor. A jet-vane is used to steer the missile. Guidance is by automatic command to line of sight, with infra-red tracking.

The HLVS (Hot, stabilised localiser-sight) system offers magnifications of 3·2 × 17° field and 10·8 × 5° field. Sight limits are ±118° in bearing and +28°/−20° in elevation. To engage a target, the aimer maintains a sighting cross on the target, switches on the firing installation and selects a missile on the control box.

Flight testing of an operational Hot installation on an Aérospatiale/Westland SA 341 Gazelle helicopter, in conjunction with the HLVS stabilised sight system, was performed in 1973. With the target hidden from the sight of the pilot and missile operator before take-off, the helicopter proved able to acquire the target and launch a missile within 4 s of lift-off. Hit probability proved to be 90 per cent over ranges varying from a minimum 400 m (1,310 ft) to a maximum of 4,000 m (13,125 ft) in hovering flight and 4,300 m (14,100 ft) in translational flight at speeds up to 100 knots (185 km/h; 115 mph). During missile flight, the helicopter was able to take evasive action at a turning speed of up to 6° per second.

Further helicopter trials, by the official services of France and Federal Germany, took place during 1974, from a Gazelle and a BO 105 respectively. Since then France has adopted Hot as armament for the Gazelle helicopter; Federal Germany has selected it for the BO 105 M (PAH 1), and several other nations have ordered this weapon system for helicopter use. Series production began in 1976, and the first production units to equip helicopters were delivered in 1977. Hot was fired from Lynx and Dauphin helicopters during 1978.

A system known as Venus (Viseur Ecartometric Nuit Stabilisé) is under development to permit firing at night, and will be fitted eventually on the Dauphin helicopter.
DATA: See table.

ISRAEL

RAFAEL
RAFAEL ARMAMENT DEVELOPMENT AUTHORITY

Ministry of Defence, POB 2082, Haifa
Telephone: 04 714168

SHAFRIR

Shafrir is a short-range infra-red homing dogfight missile developed for use against aircraft at heights up to 18,000 m (60,000 ft). Many rounds have been fired against enemy aircraft since the current Mk 2 version entered service in 1969, with considerable success. This was particularly evident during the Yom Kippur War of October 1973, when Shafrir is claimed to have destroyed more than 100 Arab aircraft in air combat, representing a success rate of 60% in terms of the number of missiles fired.

Relatively small in size and simple in conception, Shafrir has a solid-propellant rocket motor and is a solid-state weapon, fully transistorised and with guidance by proportional navigation, for optimum results against manoeuvring targets.

The missile and its launcher are mounted under the wing of the aircraft on a specially-designed adapter which is capable of carrying other types of weapon as an alternative to Shafrir. Attachment is mechanical and the missile requires no support from the aircraft except for the firing circuit. When a target is detected within firing range, an audio signal is heard and a light is switched on automatically on the pilot's control panel as an indication that the firing button should be pressed. After launch, the missile tracks the target entirely automatically, and the warhead is detonated either on impact or by the proximity fuse within optimum distance of the target.

Shafrir Mk 3, under development, is expected to offer greater manoeuvrability and all-aspect launch capability.

Sales of the Mk 2 version are reported to have been made to several overseas customers, including Chile and Taiwan.
DATA: See table

LUZ

First reported in the 1974-75 *Jane's*, Luz-1 is now confirmed as a TV-guided air-to-surface missile developed and produced by Rafael Armament Development Authority. No details have been released officially, but in mid-1977 the Israeli Air Force was reported to be modifying its F-4E Phantom and IAI Kfir-C2 fighters to carry Luz. The missile's main purpose is said to be the destruction of enemy surface-to-air weapons, with a conventional warhead. Impervious to jamming, Luz is believed to have a maximum range of 43 nm (80 km; 50 miles) and a launch weight of 200 kg (440 lb).

ITALY

SELENIA
SELENIA INDUSTRIE ELETTRONICHE ASSOCIATE SpA

HEAD OFFICE AND WORKS: Via Tiburtina km. 12.400, 00131 Rome
POSTAL ADDRESS: PO Box 7083, 00100 Rome
Telephone: 43601
Telex: 61106 Seleniat
PUBLIC RELATIONS: Gen Clemente Paolozzi

ASPIDE

This missile, which is in series production for use by nine navies in the Albatros naval surface-to-air defence system, is also under development as an all-weather all-aspect weapon for high-performance interceptors. It will improve their effectiveness in terms of maximum missile range, operation at very low altitudes, multiple target engagement and resistance to advanced ECM. In particular, it is expected to enhance the dogfight and shootdown capabilities of the F-104S interceptors of the Italian Air Force.

Aspide has a single-stage solid-propellant rocket motor, supplied by SNIA Viscosa, which gives it a speed described as being "well in the hypersonic field". Its guidance system is of the semi-active radar type, developed by Selenia. The warhead is a fragmentation type produced by SNIA Viscosa.

The missile's final configuration is almost identical to that of the US Sparrow and the five missiles used in first-phase firing tests, concluded on 17 December 1975, were each powered by a licence-built Rocketdyne Mk 38 motor, as fitted in Sparrow. Second-phase testing involved five surface-to-air and five air-to-air firings, using missiles powered by the SNIA Viscosa motor developed especially for Aspide and fitted with an improved autopilot. Final air-to-air verification trials, phased in with Italian Air Force priorities, took place in 1979 and 1980.
DATA: See table

SISTEL
SISTEL—SISTEMI ELETTRONICI SpA

HEAD OFFICE: via Tiburtina 1210, 00131 Rome
Telephone: 41 25 841
Telex: 68112 Sistelro
MANAGING DIRECTOR: Dott Manlio Lo Cascio

MARTE

In 1967, the Italian Navy initiated a development programme, known as Project Marte, to enhance the capabilities of shore-based or shipborne helicopters by arming them with anti-shipping missiles. Eventually, Sistel's Sea Killer family of missiles was chosen as most suitable for this application, because of the weapons' all-weather operability, automatic guidance system, inherent insensibility to ECM and sea-skimming flight profile. The system has been studied for installation on a wide range of Agusta helicopters, with take-off weights varying from 3,000 kg to more than 10,000 kg (6,600-22,050 lb), dependent on the number of missiles to be carried and the possible requirement for simultaneous anti-submarine and surface strike capability.

Equipment added to the Marte helicopter is lightweight and easily operated. The radar performs navigation, search and target tracking as well as guidance of the missile in azimuth. Thus an SH-3D helicopter, fully equipped for surface strike and anti-submarine duties, and with an autopilot for instrument flying, can be assigned a 4¼ h maritime patrol at a search speed of 100 knots (185 km/h; 115 mph), carrying a crew of four. Total weight of the system is 1,320 kg (2,910 lb), including 158 kg (348 lb) for the radar, 600 kg (1,323 lb) for two Sea Killer Mk 2 missiles, 300 kg (661 lb) for electronic warfare equipment, and 22 kg (48 lb) for an optical sight.

In action, it can be assumed that the helicopter will locate a target in a few seconds of radar operation at the limit of radar range. To reduce the possibility of enemy recognition of the helicopter's radar interrogation, the airborne radar is then switched off and the aircraft descends in order to fly toward the target at the lowest practical height above the water. At an estimated distance just beyond missile range, the helicopter climbs again to missile launching height, re-acquires the target and launches a Sea Killer, which takes slightly more than one minute to reach the enemy ship.

The Sistel radar altimeter in the missile can be pre-set before launch to control the cruising height at values down to 3 m (9 ft 10 in) or less, depending on factors such as sea state. The altitude can be changed by command signal during flight, if required. Control in azimuth can be achieved either by automatic radar mode in all-weather conditions or by a standby fair-weather system, using an optical sight and joystick controller.

Initial firing trials of the Marte system, in flight, had been made successfully from an AB 204 helicopter by the Spring of 1973. The system was put into production subsequently for installation on Agusta SH-3D helicopters of the Italian Navy, utilising two Sea Killer Mk 2/Marte missiles and chin-mounted APQ-706 X-band track-while-scan radar supplied by SMA.

Launching a Hot missile from a Gazelle helicopter

Ground-to-air firing of an Aspide missile in Sardinia

Artist's impression of Penguin Mk 3 on an F-16 of the Norwegian Air Force

Shafrir under wing of a Kfir fighter (Israir)

Sistel Sea Killer Mk 2 missile, as used in Marte air-to-surface weapon system

Mitsubishi ASM-1 anti-shipping missile

SISTEL SEA KILLER Mk 2

This two-stage missile is a development of the Sea Killer Mk 1 (see 1977-78 *Jane's*), with a heavier warhead and extended range. It is operational in surface-to-surface form on board four Vosper Mk 5 frigates of the Iranian Navy. With a small receiver modification, it is also the sea-skimming missile utilised in the Marte air-to-surface weapon system for helicopters.

POWER PLANT: SEP 299 solid-propellant booster, rated at 43·16 kN (9,702 lb st) for 1·6 s. SEP 300 solid-propellant sustainer, rated at 0·98 kN (220·5 lb st) for 73 s.

GUIDANCE: Alternative all-weather beam-rider/ command/radio altimeter guidance, or optical radio command/radio altimeter guidance.

WARHEAD: High-explosive semi-armour-piercing with impact/proximity fuse.

DATA: See table

JAPAN

MITSUBISHI
MITSUBISHI DENKI KABUSHIKI KAISHA (Mitsubishi Electric Corporation)

HEAD OFFICE: 2-3, Marunouchi 2-chome, Chiyoda-ku, Tokyo 100

Telephone: 218 2111

PRESIDENT: Sadakazu Shindo

Mitsubishi Electric is prime contractor for licence production of Sparrow air-to-air missiles to arm F-4EJ fighters of the JASDF. This work began in FY 1972, and more than 800 Sparrows were delivered, for air-to-air use, between 1974 and 1979. Production is continuing, the current version being the advanced AIM-7F Sparrow (see Raytheon entry in US section).

MITSUBISHI JUKOGYO KABUSHIKI KAISHA (Mitsubishi Heavy Industries, Ltd)

HEAD OFFICE: 5-1 Marunouchi 2-chome, Chiyoda-ku, Tokyo 100

Mitsubishi Heavy Industries has Japanese government contracts to develop an air-to-surface anti-shipping missile.

MITSUBISHI AAM-2

Further development of this air-to-air missile was suspended in 1978, but the Japan Defence Agency is developing a new air-to-air 'daylight' missile in co-operation with Mitsubishi, utilising technology evolved during the AAM-2 programme.

MITSUBISHI ASM-1

The Japanese government approved the expenditure of $44 million between FY 1973 and FY 1977 to cover the initial development phase of an anti-shipping missile to be carried by Mitsubishi F-1 attack aircraft of the JASDF. In November 1973 Mitsubishi Heavy Industries was selected as prime contractor for this missile, which is also suitable for ship or ground launching when fitted with a rocket booster. Subcontractors include Nissan Motor Co for the rocket motors.

Known as the ASM-1, the missile is intended to travel to the target at a low altitude, using a Japan Aviation Electronics inertial system and TRT/Japan Radio ANV-7 radio altimeter for mid-course guidance, and a Mitsubishi Electronics active radar seeker for terminal guidance.

Twenty-five prototype missiles were bought in FY 1977-78 and the first two launches were made from a Mitsubishi T-2, flying at a height of 760 m (2,500 ft), on 12 and 13 December 1977, off Fukui in the Sea of Japan. Testing by the JDA's Technical Research and Development Institute was completed in 1979, enabling the programme to be taken over by the JASDF. For this purpose, 10 more XASM-1s were ordered for 1980 testing, and were followed by 12 pre-production YASM-1s. Procurement of an initial quantity of 25 production ASM-1s for the JASDF was approved in the FY 1980 defence budget. Delivery of these is scheduled to begin in 1981.

DATA: See table

NORWAY

KONGSBERG
A/S KONGSBERG VAAPENFABRIKK

HEAD OFFICE AND WORKS: Postboks 25, N-3601 Kongsberg
Telephone: 034 38250
Telex: 11491 vaapn n
Defence Products Division
MARKETING MANAGER, DEFENCE EQUIPMENT: Jens Ch. Width
PUBLIC RELATIONS MANAGER: E. Frisvaag

This government-owned company was prime contractor for European production of the Bullpup air-to-surface missile and participated in other NATO-co-ordinated programmes such as those for the Sidewinder air-to-air missile and NATO Sea Sparrow. It is manufacturer of the Norwegian-developed Penguin anti-ship missile system.

PENGUIN

This anti-ship missile system was developed by the Norwegian Defence Research Establishment and A/S Kongsberg Vaapenfabrikk. It is in quantity production, and can be installed on ships, helicopters and other platforms.

In its ship-to-ship version, Penguin is delivered in a container with integral launch-rail and can utilise most existing types of shipboard fire-control systems. It embodies a two-stage solid-propellant rocket motor and an inertial guidance system with infra-red terminal homing. Its warhead weighs 120 kg (264 lb) and is similar to that of Bullpup, with a contact fuse.

The air-launched Penguin Mk 3 version is under development for carriage by F-16 fighters of the Norwegian Air Force. The Mk 3 will have an extended range and reduced wing span, and will dispense with the booster stage of the rocket motor fitted to the ship-launched versions. No dimensions, weights or performance data may yet be published; details of the ship-launched Penguin Mk 2 are included in the table at the end of this section.

SOUTH AFRICA

ARMSCOR
ARMAMENTS CORPORATION OF SOUTH AFRICA

The Kentron branch of ARMSCOR is reported to have brought a new air-to-air missile, designated V3, beyond the development stage to the start of production.

V3

The V3 air-to-air missile was stated, in 1979, to have been totally developed and produced by Kentron, with support from the Council for Scientific and Industrial Research (CSIR), Atlas Aircraft Corporation and the South African Air Force. No details have been released,

except that it is derived from the earlier Whiplash programme (see 1976-77 *Jane's*) and is claimed to be superior to the Matra 550 Magic. The V3 is said to be ready for operational use by the SAAF, to supplement and eventually replace the Sidewinders and Magics now in service.

SWEDEN

SBMC
SAAB-BOFORS MISSILE CORPORATION
Stureplan 15, S-111 45 Stockholm

Telephone: 08 21 49 17
Telex: 12798 SBMC S

PRESIDENT: Arne Hult

This company was created jointly by Saab-Scania and Bofors, on 14 April 1978, to co-ordinate future missile activities within the two companies and to be responsible for marketing. The intention is that the work will continue to be located in the facilities of both parent companies, which remain responsible individually for weapons developed before the creation of SBMC. Details of three of these, the air-to-surface Saab RB04E and RB05A and

Bofors RB53 Bantam wire-guided anti-tank missile, can be found in the 1977-78 *Jane's*.

In July 1979, SBMC was awarded a contract for the RBS 15 ship-to-ship weapon system for the Swedish Navy, with Saab-Scania as prime contractor.

RBS 15

The RBS 15 anti-ship missile, shown in an accompanying illustration, is the first project undertaken by the Saab Bofors Missile Corporation. Other Swedish companies such as Philips Electronics Industries will participate in the programme, which was launched after studies of the capability of existing foreign missiles such as Harpoon and Exocet to satisfy the requirements.

As currently envisaged, the RBS 15 will require very little pre-launch preparation. All calculations will be performed automatically by a fire control computer, which

will also control the status of the complete weapon system. The missile itself will be of the 'fire and forget' type, with a turbojet engine for long range at sea-skimming height, an ECM-resistant homing system, and a heavy and effective warhead.

The RBS 15 will be deployed initially as armament for Swedish torpedo boats of the 'Spica' class, with which it will become operational in 1985. Second stage of the programme will involve adapting the same weapon to meet Swedish Air Force requirements for its next type of attack aircraft.

DIMENSIONS:

Length overall	4·35 m (14 ft 3¼ in)
Body diameter	0·50 m (1 ft 7¾ in)
Wing span, folded	0·85 m (2 ft 9½ in)

WEIGHT:

Launching weight, without booster 560 kg (1,235 lb)

UNION OF SOVIET SOCIALIST REPUBLICS

AIR-TO-AIR MISSILES

AA-1
NATO reporting name: Alkali

This Soviet air-to-air missile was produced as standard armament for the older generation of PVO-Strany interceptors, such as the Sukhoi Su-9 and all-weather versions of the MiG-19, and can be expected to disappear from service soon. Radars fitted to the interceptors are known to NATO as 'Spin Scan' and 'Scan Odd' respectively.

'Alkali' is a solid-propellant missile, with large delta cruciform wings at the rear and small cruciform foreplanes indexed in line with the wings. There appear to be control surfaces in the trailing-edges of the wings and 'Alkali' employs I/J-band semi-active radar homing. The warhead is carried immediately aft of the foreplanes.

DATA: See table

K-13A (AA-2)
NATO reporting name: Atoll

This missile, which has the Soviet designation K-13A, has long been standard equipment on home and export versions of the MiG-21, and is carried by export models of the MiG-23 and Sukhoi Su-22. It is almost identical to the first-generation American Sidewinder (AIM-9B) in size and configuration and has a similar infra-red guidance system.

The body is cylindrical with cruciform control surfaces near the nose, indexed in line with the fixed cruciform tail-fins. There are no external cable or control conduits.

The triangular control surfaces have a compound sweep averaging about 60° on the leading-edge and 10° on the trailing-edge. They are linked in opposite pairs, with a maximum movement of 20-30°.

Leading-edge sweep on the tail-fins is about 40°, with straight trailing-edges. A small gyroscopically-controlled tab is inset in the trailing-edge of each fin, at the tip, presumably for anti-roll stabilisation but possibly with an added control function.

Nozzle diameter of the solid-propellant motor is 8 cm (3⅛ in). Weight and performance of 'Atoll' should be very similar to those of Sidewinder.

DATA: See table

AA-2-2
NATO reporting name: Advanced Atoll

The latest multi-role versions of the MiG-21 ('Fishbed-J, K, L and N') carry a mix of standard infra-red 'Atolls' and a version of this weapon with a radar homing head. The radar version is known as 'Advanced Atoll'.

AA-3
NATO reporting name: Anab

First seen as underwing armament on the Yakovlev Yak-28P fighter ('Firebar') in the 1961 Soviet Aviation Day display, 'Anab' is a standard air-to-air missile in the Soviet Air Force. It was carried by Yak-28, Sukhoi Su-11 and Sukhoi Su-15 interceptors taking part in the 1967 air display at Domodedovo. All three types are fitted with the radar known to NATO as 'Skip Spin'.

'Anab' has a cylindrical body, with small cruciform canard control surfaces indexed in line with very large

cruciform tail-fins. Both infra-red and I/J-band semi-active radar homing versions are operational, and have been built in thousands.

DATA: See table

AA-5
NATO reporting name: Ash

'Ash' is the large air-to-air missile carried under the wings of Tupolev Tu-28P ('Fiddler') fighters. It has cruciform wings and tail surfaces indexed in line, and is operational in two versions, which have infra-red and I/J-band semi-active radar homing heads respectively. active radar homing heads respectively.

The radar fitted to the Tu-28P is known to NATO as 'Big Nose'. It has been suggested that the MiG-25 ('Foxbat-A') also carries 'Ash' as one of its alternative weapons. Several thousand of these missiles have been built.

DATA: See table

AA-6
NATO reporting name: Acrid

This air-to-air missile was identified during 1975 as one of the weapons carried by the 'Foxbat-A' interceptor version of the MiG-25, which has fire control radar known to NATO as 'Fox Fire'. Its configuration is similar to that of 'Anab' but it is considerably larger. Photographs suggest that the version of 'Acrid' with an infra-red homing head is normally carried on each inboard underwing pylon, with a radar-homing version on each outer pylon. The latter is about 6·10 m (20 ft) long, with an estimated range of at least 20 nm (37 km; 23 miles). The wingtip fairings on the fighter, different in shape from those of 'Foxbat-B', are thought to house continuous-wave target illuminating equipment for the radar-homing missiles.

'Fox Fire' radar is believed to be evolved from the Tu-28P's 'Big Nose', with a detection range of 43-54 nm (80-100 km; 50-62 miles) and ability to track targets at 27 nm (50 km; 31 mile) range.

AA-7
NATO reporting name: Apex

This long-range air-to-air missile is one of two types of missile known to be carried as standard armament by interceptor versions of the MiG-23. No details are yet available, except that 'Apex' has a solid-propellant rocket motor and exists in two versions, with infra-red and semi-active radar homing heads, the latter operating in conjunction with the MiG-23's 'High Lark' fire control radar. 'Apex' is also reported to be an alternative weapon for the MiG-25.

DATA: See table

AA-8
NATO reporting name: Aphid

Second type of air-to-air missile carried by the MiG-23, 'Aphid' is a close-range solid-propellant weapon with infra-red homing guidance.

The accompanying illustration suggests that it has a canard configuration, with small cruciform control surfaces immediately behind the hemispherical nose, indexed in line with the cruciform rear-mounted wings, which are similar in shape to those of 'Acrid'.

DATA: See table

AA-X-9

The missile known in the West as AA-X-9 is reported to have achieved successes against simulated cruise missiles, after 'look-down/snap-down' launch from a modified MiG-25 interceptor. No details are available.

HELICOPTER MISSILES

AT-2
NATO reporting name: Swatter

This standard Soviet anti-tank weapon formed the original missile armament of the Mil Mi-24 ('Hind-A and D') helicopter gunship, and is carried by the 'Hip-E' version of the Mi-8. 'Swatter' is controlled by elevons on the trailing-edges of its rear-mounted cruciform wings, and embodies infra-red terminal homing, guiding the missile via two small, movable canard surfaces at the nose. The motor appears to exhaust through two vents diametrically opposed between the wings. Two more tubes, projecting rearward from opposite wings, probably house tracking flares.

DATA: See table

AT-3
NATO reporting name: Sagger

In conformity with the Soviet practice of not supplying advanced equipment on its export aircraft, the wire-guided 'Sagger' replaces 'Swatter' on the 'Hip-F' version of the Mi-8, and 'Hind-F' version of the Mi-24, as well as arming the Polish-built Mi-2. It has a short cylindrical body, with conical nose. Rear-mounted cruciform wings, which fold for storage, are swept near the body of the missile but unswept outboard. A hollow charge warhead is fitted.

DATA: See table

AT-6
NATO reporting name: Spiral

Unlike previous Soviet helicopter-launched anti-tank missiles, 'Spiral' does not appear to have a surface-launched application. Few details are yet available, except that it is tube-launched and homes on targets illuminated by a laser designator. It equips the 'Hind-E' version of the Mi-24, and is said to have a range of 3·75-5·3 nm (7-10 km; 4·3-6·2 miles).

AIR-TO-SURFACE MISSILES

AS-2
NATO reporting name: Kipper

First seen in the 1961 Soviet Aviation Day flypast, this aeroplane-configuration missile, with swept wings and underslung turbojet engine, was described by the commentator at Tushino Airport as an anti-shipping weapon. Radar is carried in the nose of the Tu-16 ('Badger-C') carrier aircraft, and guidance is believed to comprise initial beam-riding, subsequent pre-programmed flight under autopilot control, and infra-red terminal homing. A nuclear warhead can be fitted.

DATA: See table

AS-3
NATO reporting name: Kangaroo

Largest of the air-to-surface missiles first seen in the Soviet Aviation Day display at Tushino in 1961, and

Artist's impression of the Swedish RBS 15 anti-ship missile

'Anab' air-to-air missiles on a Yak-28P ('Firebar') fighter *(Flug Revue)*

Infra-red (left) and radar versions of 'Ash'

'Atoll' air-to-air missile under wing of 'Ash' MiG-21

Two views of the missile known to NATO as 'Alkali' *(Tass)*

'Swatter' anti-tank missiles on BRDM vehicle. Missiles of this type arm Soviet helicopters *(Tass)*

Soviet Tu-16 carrying a 'Kingfish' missile under each wing *(JASDF)*

known still to equip more than half of the Tu-95s ('Bears') of the Soviet Long-Range Aviation bomber force, 'Kangaroo' is a winged missile with an airframe similar in size and shape to a sweptwing turbojet-powered fighter aircraft. The tail unit is conventional, with sweepback on all surfaces. The vertical surfaces, concealed inside the launch aircraft until the missile is dropped, are of rhomboid form. A nuclear or high-explosive warhead can be fitted.

What was believed originally to be a radome on the missile's nose was identified subsequently as either a duct through which air can be fed to start the missile's turbojet engine prior to launching or a fairing over the air intake. Radar is carried in the nose of the Tu-95 launch aircraft and guidance is assumed to be by initial beam-riding and subsequent pre-programmed flight under autopilot control.

DATA: See table

AS-4
NATO reporting name: Kitchen

Developed as a stand-off weapon for the Tu-95 and Tu-22 strategic bombers, and now carried also by the variable-geometry 'Backfire', the AS-4 was first seen on a single Tu-22 ('Blinder-B') in 1961. Most of the 22 Tu-22s which participated in the 1967 Aviation Day display at Domodedovo carried an AS-4, semi-submerged in the fuselage, and production by 1976 was stated by the UK Defence Minister to be around 1,000. The missile, which has been seen in more than one form, has an aeroplane configuration, with stubby delta wings and cruciform tail surfaces. Propulsion is believed to be by liquid-propellant rocket motor. Guidance is reported to be inertial, with infra-red terminal homing. The speed of 'Kitchen' is probably high, and a choice of nuclear or high-explosive warhead can be assumed.

DATA: See table

AS-5
NATO reporting name: Kelt

This air-to-surface missile, carried by the Tu-16 bomber, is externally similar to the earlier turbojet-powered 'Kennel' missile, which looked rather like a scaled-down unpiloted version of the MiG-15 fighter with a hemispherical radome above its air intake. On 'Kelt', both the ram-air intake and radome are replaced by a hemispherical nose fairing, probably housing a larger radar. 'Kelt' is liquid-propellant rocket-powered and appears to be longer than 'Kennel'. Guidance is said to be by autopilot on a pre-programmed flight path, with radar terminal homing which can be switched from active to passive as required. Well over 1,000 'Kelts' are thought to

Launch of AS-2 ('Kipper') missile from a Tupolev Tu-16 ('Badger-C')

AA-7 Apex

AA-8 Aphid

'Apex' and 'Aphid' missiles (*Michael A. Badrocke, with reference to data from Hasegawa Seisokusho Company*)

have been delivered, with high-explosive warheads.

According to Israeli reports, about 25 'Kelts' were launched against Israeli targets by Tu-16s from Egypt during the Arab-Israeli War of October 1973. Twenty of the missiles were claimed as destroyed by the air and ground defences; the others hit two radar sites and a supply centre in Sinai.

DATA: See table

AS-6
NATO reporting name: Kingfish

First sighting of this air-to-surface missile was by the pilot of a Japan Air Self-Defence Force F-86F in December 1977. When investigating a Tu-16 ('Badger') flying 43 nm (80 km; 50 miles) to the north of the Noto Peninsula, he was able to photograph the bomber, carrying a 'Kingfish' under its port wing. The missile has a cylindrical body with ogival nose, two short-span longchord wings, and a cruciform tail unit with folding ventral fin. Propulsion is said to be by liquid-propellant rocket

motor, with inertial midcourse guidance and active radar terminal homing, giving exceptional accuracy. Primary carrier was expected to be the variable-geometry 'Backfire'; there has been little evidence of this, but a Tu-16 was photographed near Japan in early 1980 with a 'Kingfish' under each wing.

DATA: See table

AS-7
NATO reporting name: Kerry

This tactical air-to-surface missile is reported to be carried by the Sukhoi Su-24 ('Fencer') fighter-bomber and other current Soviet close-support aircraft. It is said to have a radio command guidance system, to weigh about 1,200 kg (2,650 lb) and to have a range of 5·4 nm (10 km; 6·2 miles).

AS-8 and AS-X-10

There is reason to believe that these designations were applied, mistakenly, to the missile now known as the AT-6 ('Spiral').

AS-X-9

A reported anti-radiation missile, with a range of 43-48 nm (80-90 km; 50-56 miles), to arm the Sukhoi Su-24 ('Fencer').

NEW MISSILE

US administration officials are reported to have said, on 1 February 1979, that the Soviet Union had begun to test a missile in the category of the USAF's ALCM. They claimed that at least eight missiles had been test-launched from 'Backfire' bombers during preceding months, over ranges of about 650 nm (1,200 km; 750 miles). This was said to be the first suggestion that the Soviet Union was testing long-range cruise missiles from its bombers.

The same US officials were quoted as saying that the maximum range of the new Soviet missile could be as much as 1,300 nm (2,400 km; 1,500 miles), but that it did not appear to have the high accuracy of the US ALCM designs or their ability to approach targets at tree-top heights.

UNITED KINGDOM

BAe
BRITISH AEROSPACE CORPORATION

CORPORATE HEADQUARTERS: Brooklands Road, Weybridge, Surrey KT13 0SJ
Telephone: Weybridge (97) 45522
Telex: 27111

BRITISH AEROSPACE DYNAMICS GROUP

HEADQUARTERS: Six Hills Way, Stevenage, Herts SG1 2DA
Telephone: Stevenage (0438) 2422
Telex: 825125
CHAIRMAN AND CHIEF EXECUTIVE: G. R. Jefferson, CBE, BSc, CEng, MIMechE, FRAeS
GROUP DEPUTY CHAIRMAN: Admiral Sir Raymond Lygo
GROUP DEPUTY CHIEF EXECUTIVE: T. G. Kent
GROUP SALES AND MARKETING DIRECTOR: L. A. Sanson, OBE
SECRETARY: M. W. Plimley, LLB
HEAD OF PUBLIC RELATIONS: M. K. Hird
Stevenage Division (Army Weapons)
MANAGING DIRECTOR: R. J. Parkhouse, MSc, BSc, CEng
Hatfield Division (Air Weapons)
MANAGING DIRECTOR: L. G. Evans, MA, CEng, FRAeS
Bristol Division (Naval Weapons)
MANAGING DIRECTOR: H. Metcalfe, OBE, BSc, ARCS, CEng, FRAeS
Space and Communications Division (Stevenage Site B)
MANAGING DIRECTOR: P. L. V. Hickman

British Aerospace Dynamics Group was established on 1 January 1978 as a separate operating unit within British Aerospace, to continue the guided weapon and associated business of the predecessor companies. On 1 January 1980 it was reorganised to comprise the Group Board and Headquarters, and four business units (Divisions). Lostock works continues as a separate self-accounting centre and a main production unit of Dynamics Group. Total number of employees on 1 January 1980 was approximately 17,500.

Among weapons for which the Dynamics Group of British Aerospace is currently prime contractor are the Rapier and Seawolf surface-to-air missiles, the Sea Dart ship-to-air and ship-to-surface missile, and the Swingfire series of wire-guided anti-tank missiles; details of all of these can be found in *Jane's Weapon Systems*.

Production of the Martel long-range air-to-surface weapon jointly with Engins Matra of France (see 1978-79 *Jane's*) has been completed, but the Dynamics Group of British Aerospace is developing a new airlaunched sea-skimming missile known as Sea Eagle. In production are a medium-range all-weather air-to-air missile known as Sky Flash and the Sea Skua lightweight all-weather sea-skimming anti-ship missile.

Dynamics Group is the British 'daughter firm' for the

Australian-developed Ikara long-range anti-submarine weapon for the Royal Navy. Other defence work includes development and manufacture of infra-red linescan systems which equip the Jaguar aircraft and the CL-89 surveillance RPV (see RPVs section).

SEA SKUA

This lightweight all-weather sea-skimming anti-ship missile is designed for operation from the Royal Navy's Lynx helicopter, to meet the threat from missile-firing fast patrol craft and to provide a good stand-off capability for the helicopter, with consequent protection from counterattack. The complete helicopter-borne weapon system includes surveillance and tracking radar, fire control equipment, launching arrangements and up to four of the semi-active homing missiles. Main contractors are Dynamics Group of British Aerospace for the missile and fire control, Ferranti for the Sea Spray radar, and Westland for the Lynx helicopter.

In addition to its ability to engage fast patrol boat targets, Sea Skua has a significant effectiveness against larger warships. It offers high lethality, with the capability of firing salvoes. The radar provides continuous surveillance, and includes facilities for weapon control and target identification.

Sea Skua is a quick-reaction system, at immediate readiness throughout the helicopter sortie, with a high degree of system reliability and full capability in a complex ECM environment. Wherever possible, it embodies existing, proven techniques and components. The solid-propellant boost and sustainer motor provides a high subsonic speed. Sea-skimming capability is conferred by a licence-built TRT radio altimeter, with Marconi Space and Defence Systems semi-active radar for terminal homing and a high-efficiency warhead actuated by a direct-action fuse. Simple go/no-go testing is all that is required on board ship before the missile is mounted on the helicopter.

The weapon system is in full production and will enter service on Lynx helicopters of the Royal Navy in the early 1980s as the Navy's principal all-weather light strike weapon for defence of the fleet. It can be fitted to other medium-size helicopters and long-range maritime patrol aircraft.

DATA: See table

SEA EAGLE (P3T)

On 17 August 1977, Dr John Gilbert, UK Minister of State for Defence, announced that a sea-skimming 'fire and forget' anti-ship missile designated P3T was to be developed to replace Martel on RAF aircraft in the early 1980s. Since given the name Sea Eagle, it will be an active radar development of the present Martel (see 1978-79 *Jane's*), powered by a Microturbo TRI-60 turbojet engine instead of a rocket motor, to give much longer range. An artist's impression of Sea Eagle was made available at the 1979 Paris Air Show. As anticipated, the configuration

follows closely that of Martel, except for the addition of an underbelly air intake for the Microturbo engine.

The Sea Eagle's height control system is already well proven in flight trials. It is an all-weather missile, with an onboard computer employing the latest microprocessing technology, and an active radar homing head developed by Marconi Space & Defence Systems. Prior to launch, the computer is supplied with target positional information from the carrier aircraft. The computer controls the flight path of the Sea Eagle until the target is acquired by the seeker during the final sea-skimming phase of the attack. The missile is designed to operate against targets operating sophisticated ECM.

British Aerospace Dynamics Group announced on 31 July 1979 that it had completed the definition phase of the programme, as a result of which it had been awarded a contract to complete development and evaluation of Sea Eagle, and to supply an initial production quantity. Wholly funded by the UK Ministry of Defence, the weapon will arm RAF Buccaneer and Tornado GR.Mk 1 aircraft and the Royal Navy's Sea Harriers.

SKY FLASH
Swedish Air Force designation: RB71

On 17 April 1973 Hawker Siddeley Dynamics (now British Aerospace Dynamics Group) announced that it had received a prime contract from the Ministry of Defence for project definition and pre-development studies of a new medium-range all-weather air-to-air missile based on the American AIM-7E Sparrow, which is itself in service with the RAF. The name Sky Flash was given subsequently to the new missile. Raytheon, the US Sparrow prime contractor, is participating in the programme through cross-licensing agreements with British Aerospace and Marconi Space and Defence Systems Ltd.

Project definition was completed in 1973, and it was announced on 26 February 1974 that Dynamics Group had received instructions from the Ministry of Defence to proceed with full development and initial production of the basic **Sky Flash Mk 1**. A contract for full production was awarded in 1975, initially to arm the RAF's Phantom and, later, the Tornado F.Mk 2.

The 'boost and coast' Sky Flash has the same general configuration and dimensions as the Raytheon AIM-7E, but is fitted with a semi-active radar homing head of inverse monopulse design, developed by Marconi Space and Defence Systems under a Ministry of Defence contract. This has been designed as a completely selfcontained unit with modular construction, which provides considerable flexibility in the overall design to cater for a wide range of different applications. Microstrip circuitry and the latest types of solid-state technology and microcircuits have offered reliability, reduced size and high performance. The complete homing head is only 283 mm (11 in) long and can be fitted in any appropriate missile body of 180 mm (7 in) internal diameter.

The 'Badger-G' version of the Tupolev Tu-16, with two 'Kelt' missiles on underwing launchers

Two views of Tupolev Tu-95 ('Bear-B') with AS-3 ('Kangaroo') air-to-surface missile

Lynx HAS. Mk 2 of the Royal Navy, armed with Sea Skua missiles

Sky Flash medium-range all-weather air-to-air missiles on RAF Phantom

The advanced radar proximity fuse is designed by EMI Electronics Ltd, and is claimed to offer a high single-shot kill capability against targets at high, medium and low altitudes. Dynamics Group has updated the autopilot and power systems, and is responsible for building the missile structure, as well as for assembly and test.

The successful completion of Sky Flash Mk 1 firing trials was announced in December 1977, by which time 22 missiles had been launched from US Navy F-4J Phantom aircraft over the Pacific Missile Test Center, California, in a variety of attack situations against targets representative of a range of hostile aircraft types. These included targets flying at subsonic and supersonic speeds, singly and in formation, and in severe ECM environments. Several missiles scored direct hits and others were classified as partial successes, simple remedial modifications being made to subsequent missiles. During the trials the snapdown capability of Sky Flash was demonstrated when a missile launched from medium altitude achieved a target 'kill' against an unaugmented QF-86 drone flying only 150 m (500 ft) above the ground. Aircraft from which Sky Flash Mk 1 has since been launched successfully include the General Dynamics F-16. The weapon has shown itself able to engage hostile aircraft at ranges in excess of 21 nm (40 km; 25 miles) at high altitudes or as low as 75 m (250 ft).

The first firing of a Sky Flash Mk 1 in the UK from an

Artist's impression of the Sea Eagle anti-ship missile

RAF aircraft was made on 15 August 1979 from a Phantom of No. 29 Squadron, which shot down a Meteor target aircraft flying at a lower level over the Aberporth test range.

The first export contract, valued at £60 million, was announced in December 1978 and is providing Sky Flash missiles to arm the Swedish Air Force's Saab JA 37 Viggen all-weather fighter. The Sky Flash integration programme for the Viggen, involving many air firings, with a 100 per cent success rate, had been completed by the end of 1979, and delivery of production missiles was to begin in mid-

1980.

On 23 April 1980, it was announced that the improved Sky Flash Mk 2 was to be developed and produced under a £75 million contract from the UK Ministry of Defence. Compared with the Mk 1 version, this will offer greater all-round coverage, increased range, enhanced performance against manoeuvring targets and greater resistance to ECM. In particular, the snap-up and lookdown/shoot-down capabilities have been further improved.

DATA: See table

UNITED STATES OF AMERICA

BOEING
BOEING AEROSPACE COMPANY

HEAD OFFICE AND WORKS: Seattle, Washington 98124

ALCM
USAF designation: AGM-86

The Air-Launched Cruise Missile (ALCM) is a small unmanned winged air vehicle capable of sustained subsonic flight following launch from an airborne carrier aircraft. It is propelled by a turbofan engine, incorporates a nuclear warhead for 'hard target' kill capability, and is programmed to strike a pre-determined surface target. Guidance is by a combination of inertial and terrain comparison (Tercom) techniques. In the terrain comparison mode the missile is kept on course by a computer which compares pre-programmed geographical features on its flight plan with the geography seen by its sensors during actual flight.

When launched in large numbers, each of the missiles would have to be countered, making defence against them difficult and costly. The missiles are intended both to serve as stand-off weapons and to dilute defences and improve the ability of manned aircraft to penetrate to major targets. Small radar signature and low-level flight capability would enhance their effectiveness.

In its initial form, designated **AGM-86A**, Boeing's ALCM design made maximum use of the air vehicle developed under the former AGM-86A Subsonic Cruise Armed Decoy (SCAD) programme, for which Boeing was prime contractor. It was similar in overall dimensions to SRAM (short-range attack missile; see 1977-78 *Jane's*) and was suitable for carriage on the rotary launcher developed for this latter weapon, with wings and tail folded and engine air intake retracted. A B-52G was expected to carry 12 AGM-86As externally and 8 internally, complementing the aircraft's SRAMs and free-fall weapons. When carried externally, the missile was to have an underbelly auxiliary fuel tank fitted to increase its range.

Six test flights (three performance and three navigation/guidance) were conducted with AGM-86As between March and November 1976. Development was then switched to the **AGM-86B**. This has a fuselage more than 30% longer than that of the AGM-86A, to house sufficient fuel for double the range of the basic 'A'. On 1 February 1978, Boeing Aerospace received the first increment of a contract calling for a competitive fly-off between the AGM-86B and an AGM-109 air-launched version of the General Dynamics Tomahawk SLCM. Department of Defense contracts funded a total of 24 Boeing/GD ALCMs in FY 1978, and a similar quantity in FY 1979. Ten examples of each missile were used in the competitive fly-off, which ended on 8 February 1980. Three of the AGM-86Bs crashed, and another flight suffered unscheduled termination; four of the AGM-109s crashed. Programme officials considered that, overall, the fly-off had achieved its targets, and Boeing was declared the winner on 25 March 1980. Reasons for the choice were given as better guidance system software, aerodynamic features that offered better terrain following in rough country, and promise of superior field maintenance characteristics. A follow-on series of up to 19 test and evaluation flights began in June 1980.

Current plans envisage procurement of 3,418 ALCMs between FY 1980 and FY 1987, with deliveries to be completed in FY 1989. Initial FY 1980 purchase is 225 missiles, at a cost of $364·4 million, plus $111 million for initial spares, RDT&E and military construction. Requests for a further increment of 480 missiles are included in the FY 1981 budget. Scheduled date for fitting an AGM-86B to the first operational B-52G, at Griffiss AFB, NY, is September 1981. Initial operational capability, comprising one squadron of 14 B-52Gs externally loaded with missiles (six under each wing) is expected to be achieved in December 1982. Subsequently, each bomber is intended to be modified to have a bomb-bay rotary launcher for eight more ALCMs, eight SRAMs, or a mix of both.

Boeing will manufacture initial quantities of AGM-86B airframes, although General Dynamics will be entitled to tender for a share of the total programme. The F107-WR-100 turbofan engine (2·67 kN; 600 ib st) will continue to be produced by Williams Research Corporation, as prime contractor; but Teledyne CAE will be permitted to tender as second source contractor from FY 1981. McDonnell Douglas will be responsible for supplying guidance systems, with Litton of California and Litton Systems Canada competing as subcontractor for inertial navigation platforms. DATA: See table.

FORD
FORD AEROSPACE & COMMUNICATIONS CORPORATION

HEAD OFFICE: 20th Floor, 300 Renaissance Center, PO Box 43342, Detroit, Michigan 48243

Aeronutronic Division
Ford Road, Newport Beach, California 92663
Telephone: (714) 759 5996

Ford Aerospace & Communications Corporation, and its Philco predecessor, have produced Sidewinder air-to-air missiles and Chaparral surface-to-air missiles for the US armed services for many years. Details of the Sidewinder can be found under the NWC entry in this section.

GENERAL DYNAMICS
GENERAL DYNAMICS CORPORATION

HEAD OFFICE: Pierre Laclede Center, St Louis, Missouri 63105

Convair Division
5001 Kearny Villa Road, San Diego, California 92123
VICE-PRESIDENT AND GENERAL MANAGER: Dr Leonard F. Buchanan

Pomona Division
PO Box 2507, Pomona, California 91766
VICE-PRESIDENT AND GENERAL MANAGER: Ralph E. Hawes

The Pomona Division of General Dynamics is responsible for development and production of a wide variety of tactical weapon systems for the US Navy, US Army, US Air Force and friendly foreign powers. Current and recent products include the Standard Missile-1 naval ship-launched weapon, the Standard ARM anti-radiation missile, the Stinger advanced man-portable air defence weapon and Phalanx, the Navy's all-weather automatic gun fire-control system. In pilot production is the longer-range Standard Missile-2.

In addition, the US Naval Air Systems Command has awarded a contract to Pomona for second-source production of the AIM-7F Sparrow air-to-air missile (see Raytheon entry).

Convair Division was selected in 1976 to develop the US Navy's Sea Launched Cruise Missile, under the designation BGM-109 Tomahawk. Variants include the USAF's Ground Launched Cruise Missile.

TOMAHAWK
USAF designation: AGM-109

Following a competitive fly-off, Boeing's AGM-86B air-launched cruise missile (ALCM) was selected in preference to the AGM-109 version of Tomahawk to equip B-52G bombers of USAF's Strategic Air Command. General Dynamics is expected to tender as second-source contractor for the AGM-86B (described under the Boeing entry in this section).

Details of Tomahawk can be found in the 1979-80 *Jane's*.

MRASM

Shortly after announcing selection of the AGM-86B rather than the AGM-109 Tomahawk as the USAF's air-launched cruise missile, Under-Secretary of Defense William J. Perry stated that a new medium-range air-to-surface missile (MRASM) was to be based on Tomahawk. Intended to provide both the US Air Force and the US Navy with a reasonable-cost stand-off weapon with which to attack high-value land and sea targets, MRASM will be produced in two forms. The first, utilising the same Tercom inertial navigation/terrain contour matching guidance system as the ALCM, is expected to be operational by 1983. The other, with imaging infra-red guidance, will follow one year later and will be suitable for use against targets at sea as well as overland.

MRASM is described as being shorter than Tomahawk, with a length of 5·0 m (16 ft 5 in) and launch weight of about 900 kg (2,000 lb). Its wings will be of the variable-geometry type, to compensate for CG changes in flight. Armed with a 1,000 lb non-nuclear warhead, similar to that fitted to the Tomahawk tactical sea-launched cruise missile (SLCM), it will have a range of about 260 nm (480 km; 300 miles), and is expected to offer a high degree of accuracy.

HUGHES
HUGHES AIRCRAFT COMPANY

CORPORATE OFFICE: Culver City, California 90230
CHAIRMAN OF THE BOARD AND CHIEF EXECUTIVE OFFICER: Dr Allen E. Puckett
PRESIDENT: John H. Richardson
Missile Systems Group
Canoga Park, California 91304
Telephone: (213) 883 2400

VICE-PRESIDENT AND GROUP EXECUTIVE: Dr Malcolm R. Currie
Electro-Optical & Data Systems Group
Culver City, California 90230
VICE-PRESIDENT AND GROUP EXECUTIVE: H. W. Boehmer

Hughes Aircraft began developing an air-to-air missile for the USAF in 1947, and this weapon has been in squadron use for many years as the Falcon. Currently, Hughes is producing an air-to-air missile named Phoenix for the US Navy, an air-to-surface missile named Maverick for the USAF, and a wire-guided anti-tank missile named TOW for the US Army and other customers. It is also engaged in prototype validation of an advanced medium-range air-to-air missile (AMRAAM).

PHOENIX
US Navy designation: AIM-54

Phoenix arms the Grumman F-14A Tomcat two-seat carrier-based fighter and is claimed to have capabilities exceeding those of any other air-to-air missile yet operational. It has a solid-propellant rocket motor, and is fitted with a large proximity-fused high-explosive warhead.

The launch aircraft's AWG-9 weapon control system is able to track an enemy target, at high or low altitude, in any kind of weather, and launch the Phoenix missile. The data from the radar is processed by a high-speed digital computer, the output of which is displayed to the missile control officer in the launch aircraft on two displays: a 254 mm (10 in) cathode-ray tube and a 127 mm (5 in) multi-mode storage tube. The long-range high-power pulse Doppler radar has a 'look-down' capability that enables it to pick out moving targets from the ground clutter that normally obscures them on a conventional radar. The AWG-9 has a track-while-scan radar mode that makes it possible to launch up to six missiles and keep them on course while searching for other possible targets, all in the presence of sophisticated enemy countermeasures.

All F-14s built for the US Navy are equipped to carry Phoenix. Production was initiated in late 1970, and continued missile purchases are envisaged until at least 1991. Details of early testing can be found in the 1979/80 *Jane's*. Phoenix entered first-line service in September 1974, when two squadrons of US Navy F-14s were deployed on board the nuclear-powered USS *Enterprise* for a six-month tour of duty in the Western Pacific. Eight US carriers were operating F-14 fighter squadrons in 1979.

There are two versions of Phoenix, as follows:
AIM-54A. Initial production version, to which all details above apply. More than 2,000 had been built by the beginning of 1980, with manufacture of 120 approved for FY 1979.

AIM-54C. Improved version, with much enhanced ECCM capability and reliability. New target detecting device, digital electronics unit, solid-state transmitter/receiver and strap-down inertial reference system for improved accuracy and greater range. First of 15 engineering development models delivered in Summer 1979, with firings scheduled to extend over 12 months from late 1979. Thirty pilot production missiles to follow in 1981-82, leading to series production of approximately 1,400 AIM-54Cs in 1982-90. The 2,000 AIM-54As in USN inventory may also be updated with AIM-54C electronics.
DATA: See table

AMRAAM

On 5 February 1979, the USAF announced that it had selected Hughes Aircraft Company's Missile Systems Group and Raytheon Company's Missile Systems Division to begin prototype validation on an advanced medium-range air-to-air missile (AMRAAM). This weapon is intended to replace the AIM-7 Sparrow in USAF and US Navy service, as primary armament of the F-14, F-15, F-16 and F/A-18 fighters.

The AMRAAM programme was initiated by a 13-month USAF/USN/USMC study of the likely air-to-air threat for the next 30 years, and the kind of beyond-visual-range weapon that would best meet such a threat.

Basic parameters laid down by the AMRAAM Joint System Program Office included an upper weight limit of about 160 kg (350 lb), with 90 kg (200 lb) as the desirable goal; all-weather capability; snapdown capability to per-

Boeing AGM-86B air-launched cruise missile in flight

Model of Hughes' AMRAAM on F-15 fuselage station

First engineering development model AIM-54C Phoenix air-to-air missile

BGM-71A TOW missile undergoing final inspection

---

mit interception of low-flying targets over land or sea; a resistance to ECM at least as good as that offered by current monopulse techniques; all-aspect launch and tracking ability; a minimum range at least equal to that of the AIM-7F Sparrow and a maximum range as great as the state of the art permits. These requirements seemed likely to demand inertial midcourse guidance and self-contained terminal homing such as active radar; however, it seemed likely that a missile with these features would appproach its target so closely that a conventional proximity-fused warhead weighing only 14-22 kg (30-50 lb) would be adequate.

No details of Hughes' AMRAAM missile have been released, but its general appearance is shown in the accompanying photograph of a full-scale model mounted on an F-15 fuselage station. Hughes claims that it will outperform the Sparrow, cost less to build and be one half as heavy as the earlier weapon. Its version of AMRAAM will offer maximum independence of the launching aircraft, and will enable the pilot to make launches against multiple targets with no changes in current cockpit procedures.

The AMRAAM validation phase is expected to last 33 months, after which the winning design will be taken through full-scale engineering development into production.

TOW
US Army designation: BGM-71A

Hughes Aircraft was prime contractor for development of this high-performance surface-to-surface and air-to-surface anti-tank missile, the basic characteristics of which are indicated by its name, as TOW is an acronym for Tube-launched, Optically-tracked, Wire-guided.

The basic ground-fired TOW system consists of a glassfibre launch tube, a tripod, a traversing and sighting unit, an electronic package, and missiles encased in shipping containers. Total weight of the entire weapon system, including missile, is approximately 91 kg (200 lb).

The missile has low aspect ratio wings and tail control surfaces that remain folded while in the launcher and flick open as the missile leaves the launch tube. The wings flick forward during extension, the tail surfaces rearward.

TOW is inserted into the rear end of the tube in its container, which forms an extension of the tube. Electrical and mechanical connections to the missile are made automatically during this operation. The Hercules K-41 solid-propellant motor gives two separate boost periods. It

fires first to propel the missile from the launcher. The missile then coasts for a period after leaving the mouth of the tube, before the second stage of the booster fires.

The operator guides the missile by keeping the target centred in a telescopic sight. Movement of the sight generates electronic signals to correct the missile's course, the signals being passed through two wires. The warhead is a high-explosive shaped charge, developed under the Army Munitions Command, Picatinny Arsenal, New Jersey.

In its current form, TOW is a heavy assault weapon for use against tanks, armoured vehicles and gun emplacements over ranges of more than 3,750 m (12,300 ft). To permit its use from helicopters, Hughes developed under US Army contract a gyro-stabilised sight that would eliminate the effects of aircraft vibration and manoeuvres. As part of the XM-26 missile/launcher/sight subsystem, this was installed on a UH-1B helicopter, from which air-to-surface firing tests of TOW missiles were then made successfully at Redstone Arsenal, Alabama, with hits on moving tank targets over ranges of more than one mile.

Two UH-1Bs with early-model Hughes XM26 sighting systems were shipped to Viet-Nam on 24 April 1972. After a short training period, during which each pilot-gunner fired one TOW missile for the first time, the aircraft were committed at Kontum to meet an expected armour threat. By 27 June, in 77 combat launches, they had scored 62 hits on point targets and had destroyed 39 armoured vehicles, trucks and howitzers, without themselves being hit by hostile fire.

As a result of these successes, the US Army embarked on a programme to convert AH-1G HueyCobras to AH-1Q/S Cobra/TOW standard, with improved M65 missile system. In addition, TOW arms helicopters of various types selected by foreign services, including the Hughes 500M-D Defenders of South Korea, Italy's Agusta A 109, and the British Army Lynx.

TOW has been in production for the US Army since 29 November 1968. By the beginning of 1979 a total of 220,000 missiles had been delivered from Hughes' factory at Tucson, Arizona, with production continuing at a rate of about 3,000 a month. Deployment to US troops in the USA and Europe began in November 1970, to replace the 106 mm recoilless rifle and the Entac and SS.11 missiles. Subsequently, TOW was ordered by 30 other countries. In more than 10,500 firings, including combat, TOW has demonstrated an operational reliability better than 96%, and 83% of the missiles have hit their target.

During the late Summer of 1979, at Fort Hood, Texas,

first tests were conducted of an AH-1S HueyCobra fitted with a modified TOW system that provides a FLIR (forward-looking infra-red) night vision capability. Known as the FLIR Augmented Cobra TOW Sight (FACTS), the system utilises a standard US Army thermal imaging night vision sensor. Following an initial firing using the sight's daylight viewing channel, two TOWs were fired in early evening and two in total darkness. All five missiles scored hits on stationary targets. US Army evaluation tests were to follow.
DATA: See table

MAVERICK
USAF designation: AGM-65

The Maverick is a precision-guided air-to-surface missile in the 500 lb class, which developed from a 1965 USAF concept. A three-year total package contract, covering development, testing, support equipment, launchers, and initial production, was put into effect in July 1968. The production option was exercised in July 1971 and first deliveries of the AGM-65A Maverick were made in August 1972. By the end of 1978, deliveries totalled more than 26,000, all TV-guided versions. Maverick is operational on the A-7D, A-10A, F-4D/E and F-5E/F and has been integrated with the F-16 and F-111. The A-4M Skyhawk II will be equipped with the new AGM-65E version of the missile, when development has been completed. Another carrier-based aircraft with which Maverick will be integrated is the F/A-18 Hornet, and plans call for integration on the A-6E and AV-8B. It has been possible to adapt existing controls and displays in launch aircraft to operation of the Maverick weapon system. The minimum aircraft requirement is a raster-scan TV-type display in the cockpit and conventional control functions. A single-rail launcher has been developed for wing stations which cannot accommodate the standard three-round launcher.

More than 600 Mavericks have been launched during testing, training, operational evaluation, demonstrations, and actual combat, with over 87 per cent achieving direct hits on their targets. First combat employment was by the USAF in South East Asia. In October 1973, Mavericks were used operationally by the Israeli Air Force during the Yom Kippur War, with spectacular success. Others have been delivered to Greece, Iran, Saudi Arabia, Sweden and Turkey. Sweden has integrated Maverick with the AJ37 version of the Viggen.

Two TV-guided versions were produced in quantity:

AGM-65A. Basic model with 5° field of view camera in the seeker, centroid tracker and single-stage solid-propellant boost/sustain rocket motor. Warhead in central portion of airframe. When triggered by contact fuse in the nose, a shaped-charge jet fires through the axis of the guidance unit into the target. First employed by USAF in Viet-Nam and the only version of Maverick yet made available to friendly foreign nations. Production terminated in favour of AGM-65B.

AGM-65B. 'Scene magnification' version of TV Maverick, with 2·5° field of view camera and associated minor changes to the guidance equations. Generally similar to AGM-65A, with same warhead. The USAF was training with this version in early 1978. Manufacture of 6,000 completed.

The basic 57 kg (125 lb) shaped-charge warhead is designed to defeat heavy armour and reinforced concrete, making it most suitable for use against tanks and pillbox-type targets. Missile reliability obviates the need for a missile check on aircraft, and operational use is in the 'fire and forget' mode. The pilot can slew the seeker for rapid lock-on to the target, using a TV visual display, launch the missile and immediately take evasive action while the missile guides itself to the target. Simplicity of operation was demonstrated by a successful firing from a Teledyne Ryan BGM-34 RPV.

Two further versions of Maverick are under development:

AGM-65D. Has imaging infra-red (IIR) seeker, which tracks passively the natural thermal image of a tactical target, providing a pictorial display of the target to the pilot in darkness, haze and smoke. Lock-on, launch and 'fire and forget' homing flight as for AGM-65A/B. Full-scale engineering development for USAF started October 1978.

AGM-65E. Fitted with a Rockwell laser seeker which homes on a target illuminated by a ground or airborne laser designator. Can be used by day or night, as the pilot of the launch aircraft does not need to acquire the target visually. Provision is made for rendering the warhead inert, to protect friendly troops in the event of a designator failure or other loss of lock-on during close-support missions. Contractor and USAF flight test launches were made against moving and stationary tanks, armoured personnel carriers and simulated bunkers, by day and night, from high and low altitudes, at various ranges, and at speeds from slow to supersonic. After 19 direct hits had been achieved in 22 firings, development was switched from the original AGM-65C model to the AGM-65E, combining the laser seeker with a new 135 kg (298 lb) blast/penetrator warhead. This is being developed to extend Maverick's capability against larger targets. Intended for US Navy and Marine Corps utilisation.

DATA: See table

GBU-15

Hughes Aircraft Company is responsible for developing the wing module and digital autopilot for the planar wing version of the US Air Force's GBU-15 air-to-surface glide bomb family, and for system integration.

The planar wing weapon (PWW), which is 4·04 m (13 ft 3 in) long, has 3·45 m (11 ft 4 in) span pivoted wings which extend after launch to increase its range. This enables the pilot of the launch aircraft to stand off at a safe distance while guiding the weapon accurately to the target. Its launching weight is 1,360 kg (3,000 lb).

The initial PWW is based on an Mk 84 2,000 lb general-purpose bomb, with added TV guidance seeker and data link. It is planned eventually to deploy with Tactical Air Command a DME-guided PWW, which will be used in conjunction with the Lockheed U-2R Precision Location Strike System (PLSS) for all-weather area target attack. In this application, both the DME PWW and its target will be located in an electronic grid, and a ground-based computer will supply guidance commands to the weapon through the DME data link.

The GBU-15 series of weapons is described in more detail under the Rockwell International entry in this section. Flight testing of the planar wing version continued in 1979.

WASP

The Statement outlining the FY 1981 Department of Defense Programme for Research, Development and Acquisition advised Congress that the DoD had "begun the development of a family of area munitions, dispensers, warheads and guidance systems in the Advanced Attack Weapons programme. The Wide Area Anti-Armour Munitions (WAAM) programme will provide a system capable of multiple kills of armour targets per aircraft pass, even at night and in adverse weather. The four munitions concepts originally in development have been reduced to three: the Anti-Armour Cluster Munitions (ACM), the Extended Range Anti-Tank Mine (ERAM), and the Wasp mini-missile. The Army and the Air Force will co-ordinate Wasp and Hellfire (see Rockwell entry in this section) developments to determine the opportunities to utilise common systems or subsystems to meet both Air Force and Army anti-armour requirements".

Announcing its involvement in Wasp development, in February 1980, Hughes Aircraft Company described it as "the first weapon with built-in ability to identify and aim itself at a target". Wasps will be fired from aircraft in clusters of ten or more, by day or night and in inclement weather, in a 'fire and forget' mode. On-board computers will direct each mini-missile in the 'swarm' to a different target as long as there are more targets than missiles. Thus, it will not be necessary for the aircrew to see and designate a target for the missile before it is fired. Wasp will be programmed to fly to the area where enemy armour has been located. A terminal guidance seeker will then take over, identifying the armour and steering the Wasp to its individual target. Meanwhile, the launch aircraft can withdraw from the area.

Despite its potential, Wasp will be approximately one-fifth the weight of the Maverick air-to-surface missile currently in production by Hughes. Under an initial $42·9 million competitive validation phase contract, the company will evaluate both infra-red and millimetre wave radar seekers for Wasp.

MARTIN MARIETTA
MARTIN MARIETTA CORPORATION

CORPORATE HEADQUARTERS: 6801 Rockledge Drive, Bethesda, Maryland 20034
Telephone: (301) 897-6000
EXECUTIVES: See Spaceflight section.

Martin Marietta Aerospace produces missiles, spacecraft, launch vehicles, communications systems and electronic systems. It also fabricates precision components for the US Department of Defense and NASA, and conducts research related to defence and space systems.

WALLEYE
US Navy designation: AGM-62A

When introduced into service, the original version of Walleye was described by the US Navy as "the most accurate and effective air-to-surface conventional weapon ever developed anywhere". It was designed and developed at the NOTS (now Naval Weapons Center), China Lake, California. A production contract awarded to Martin Marietta on 21 January 1966 covered manufacture of qualification weapons as well as an initial quantity for operational use, and carried options for continued production in succeeding years. These options were taken up, the work being performed at Orlando Division. Hughes Aircraft was for a period second source manufacturer.

Walleye is simple in configuration, comprising a torpedo-shaped body with cruciform wings of long-chord cropped-delta form. Control surfaces are hinged to the wing trailing-edges. A ram-air turbine provides the electrical and hydraulic power to operate the guidance/control system. The target seeker is housed behind a window in the nose, and a conventional high-explosive warhead is fitted.

Walleye has undergone considerable development, and the following versions may now be listed:

Walleye 1 (Guided Weapon Mk 1 Mod 0). Basic version with 385 kg (850 lb) warhead. Before launch, the pilot focussed the missile's gyro-stabilised TV camera on target, with the aid of a CRT monitor screen in the cockpit. Once the camera had been locked on target, the missile could be released. Mechanism inside Walleye then took over, using signals from the TV seeker to correct any deviation from the flight path to the target during the bomb's unpowered descent.

Walleye 2 (Guided Weapon Mk 5 Mod 4). Larger than Walleye 1, with warhead in 907 kg (2,000 lb) class for attacking semi-hard targets such as bridges, air base facilities, and ships. Development by Martin Marietta started in Spring 1971.

Extended-Range Data Link Walleye (Guided Weapon Mk 13 Mod 0). Larger wings, to extend glide range, and data link equipment. These improvements permit earlier release, and subsequent remote acquisition and lock-on of the Walleye's TV seeker by the pilot of the launch aircraft (or the pilot of a companion aircraft), after the initiation of evasive action and withdrawal from the target area. Initial batch of 170 Walleye 2s had been updated to ER/DL standard by October 1976, and work on a further batch of 430 then started. Conversion of Walleye 1s began in FY 1978. Current plans envisage conversion of a total of about 1,400 Walleye 1s and 2,400 Walleye 2s.

IR Walleye. Hughes Aircraft has developed an imaging infra-red seeker for Walleye, aimed at achieving guidance system commonality with the GBU-15 glide bomb and the AGM-65D version of the Maverick missile. This provides night and adverse weather capability, together with improved tracking precision. First IR Walleye was scheduled for delivery in Summer 1980.

DATA: See table.

MDAC
MCDONNELL DOUGLAS ASTRONAUTICS COMPANY (A Division of McDonnell Douglas Corporation)

5301 Bolsa Avenue, Huntington Beach, California 92647
Telephone: (714) 896 3311
PRESIDENT: Robert L. Johnson
VICE-PRESIDENT AND GENERAL MANAGER:
C. James Dorrenbacker
VICE-PRESIDENT, ENGINEERING: Adrian P. O'Neal
VICE-PRESIDENT, MARKETING: Paul L. Smith
McDonnell Douglas Astronautics Company-St Louis
Box 516, St Louis, Missouri 63166
Telephone: (314) 232 0232
VICE-PRESIDENT AND GENERAL MANAGER: Erwin F. Branahl
VICE-PRESIDENT AND PROGRAMME MANAGER, HARPOON:
Clifford D. Marks
VICE-PRESIDENT, ADVANCED MISSILE PROGRAMMES: R. Wayne Lowe

McDonnell Douglas Astronautics Company was formed on 26 June 1968, by merging the former Douglas Missile and Space Systems Division and the McDonnell Astronautics Company into a single management structure.

In the missile field, McDonnell Douglas Astronautics Company has developed and is producing the Harpoon anti-shipping missile for the US Navy and other customers, and is developing cruise missile guidance systems for the USAF's ALCM and GLCM, US Navy's SLCM, and the new Medium-Range Air-to-Surface Missile (MRASM).

HARPOON
US Navy designations: AGM-84A and RGM-84A

The US Navy selected McDonnell Douglas as prime contractor for development of the Harpoon all-weather anti-ship missile in June 1971. The work was allocated to McDonnell Douglas Astronautics Company-East, with Texas Instruments Inc and Sperry Systems Management as major subcontractors.

The initial contract covered the development and demonstration of a number of engineering-model missiles over a two-year period. This phase of the programme was completed successfully on schedule, and was followed by a 30-month final development phase in which more than 30 missiles were launched from Harpoon-designated aircraft, ships and submarines. Production of 100 pilot missiles was authorised in 1974. A proportion of them was used for operational evaluation, which began in November 1975 and was completed in February 1977. The go-ahead for initial production had been given in July 1975, and authorisation for deployment on aircraft, surface ships and submarines was granted in July 1977.

The US Navy plans to equip all of its guided missile cruisers, guided missile destroyers, FF-1052 frigates, FFG-7 patrol frigates, DD-963 ASW destroyers and PHM-1 hydrofoil patrol craft; P-3C, A-6E and S-3A aircraft; and 594, 637, 688 and 700 class nuclear attack submarines with the Harpoon Weapon System (HWS). By the beginning of 1980, the missiles equipped 65 destroyers, frigates and cruisers, 19 nuclear attack submarines, and 13 P-3C aircraft of the US Navy. Patrol Squadron 23 was the first P-3C unit to carry operational Harpoons, in August 1979. In addition the HWS has been procured by 12 allied nations for launch from surface ships, submarines and aircraft.

By early 1980, a total of 1,753 of the missiles had been ordered. The 1,000th Harpoon produced by MDAC was delivered in late 1979, with production continuing at the rate of 40 per month. Manufacture will continue until at least 1986, and could be increased to 55 per month if justified by further orders.

The general configuration of the **AGM-84A** air-launched version of Harpoon is shown in the accompanying illustration. The Teledyne CAE J402-CA-400 turbojet power plant is housed in the rear of the body, with a ventral flush air intake.

Prior to launch, targeting data for Harpoon are provided by the command and launch subsystem, which interfaces with onboard systems. The Harpoon data processor, a general-purpose digital computer, receives targeting and attitude data from existing systems, and computes the necessary missile and launcher orders. After launch, guidance is provided by a midcourse guidance system consisting of a strapdown attitude reference assembly and digital computer. No inputs from the launch platform are required by the missile after launch. Cruise altitude is monitored by a radar altimeter, enabling the flight to the target to be made at low altitude, so offering both

Planar wing version of GBU-15 glide bomb, with wings stowed, on B-52

Production line of AGM-65A Maverick TV-guided missiles

AGM-62A Walleye 1 TV-guided glide bomb

Extended-Range Walleye and data link pod on A-7 Corsair II

Grumman A-6 Intruder carrying two Harpoons on underwing pylons

AGM-84A Harpoon air-to-surface anti-shipping missile

optimum target acquisition capability through reduction of clutter effects, and the ability to penetrate enemy defences. Offset launch capability is provided for all launch modes.

When the target comes within the search area of the active radar seeker, the high-resolution system detects and locks on to the target, even in rain and high sea states. Seeker lock-on is maintained until impact. Capability to perform high-g manoeuvres throughout flight permits successful operation against fast manoeuvring targets. A terminal 'pop-up' manoeuvre counters close-in defences and

offers maximum warhead effectiveness. Counter-countermeasures devices are installed. The warhead is a penetration/high-explosive blast type.

Advanced versions of Harpoon are under development, including some with an alternative guidance system, using an imaging infra-red seeker.
DATA: See table

ASALM

The Advanced Strategic Air-Launched Missile

(ASALM) was conceived as a supersonic, highly-accurate, long-range missile, powered by an integral rocket/ramjet and capable of use in both air-to-surface and air-to-air bomber defence roles, including the destruction of enemy AWACS aircraft. By Spring 1980 it had completed five of a planned series of seven test flights. The USAF then decided to terminate development of ASALM and to limit the programme to demonstration of the feasibility of ramjet propulsion for such applications.

Further details of ASALM can be found in the 1979-80 Jane's.

NWC
NAVAL WEAPONS CENTER
China Lake, California 93555
Telephone: (714) 939 3511

The Naval Weapons Center is located 250 km (155

miles) northeast of Los Angeles, in the Mojave Desert. Its current mission is to be the principal US Navy RDT&E centre for air warfare systems (except anti-submarine warfare systems) and missile weapon systems, and to operate the National Range/Facility for parachute T&E.

Weapons developed at the Center have included the

Mighty Mouse 2·75 in folding-fin aircraft rocket, the 11·75 in Tiny Tim rocket, the Zuni 5 in folding-fin aircraft rocket, the Sidewinder air-to-air guided missile, the Snakeye 250/500 lb bomb with folding dive-brake retardation system to avoid fragmentation damage to the launch aircraft during low-level strikes, the Shrike and Standard ARM air-to-surface anti-radar missiles and the Walleye glide bomb. Production of many of these weapons was entrusted to commercial companies under whose entries they are, or were, described in *Jane's*.

SIDEWINDER

US military designation: AIM-9

The **AIM-9A** prototype version of the Sidewinder air-to-air missile was developed by the NWC and was first fired successfully on 11 September 1953. The **AIM-9B** first-generation production version was manufactured by Philco (now Ford Aerospace & Communications Corporation) and General Electric for the US Navy and the USAF, with a Naval Propellant Plant solid-propellant rocket motor and infra-red seeker, and was supplied to many foreign services. Production in the USA, from 1955, totalled more than 80,000 AIM-9Bs.

Although the US services no longer deploy the AIM-9B and its semi-active radar counterpart, the **AIM-9C**, other countries continue to utilise the 'B', of which licence manufacture was undertaken in Germany by Bodenseewerk, in association with subcontractors in the Netherlands, Denmark, Norway, Greece, Portugal and Turkey.

Also no longer deployed was the **AIM-9D**, which had higher speed and greater range than the 'B', from which it could be distinguished by its tapering nose, longer-chord nose fins and greater sweepback on the tail fins. This version had a Rocketdyne Mk 36 Mod 5 solid-propellant rocket motor, different guidance unit and continuous-rod warhead with proximity and impact fuses.

Of the developed versions of the infra-red homing Sidewinder produced for air-to-air use, to enhance and update the missile's capabilities, those in service with, or in production for the US services in 1979 were as follows:

AIM-9E. Approximately 5,000 of this version were produced by Philco for the USAF, by modification of AIM-9Bs to have a new seeker section, Thiokol Mk 17 solid-propellant motor, refurbished electronics and wiring. Major increase in capability claimed. Production completed.

AIM-9G. Similar to AIM-9D but with off-boresight target acquisition and lock-on. Production by Raytheon for US Navy completed in FY 1970.

AIM-9H. Version for US Navy with improved close-range 'dogfight' capability. Basically similar to AIM-9G, but with solid-state guidance instead of vacuum tube electronics for improved reliability and maintainability, decreased minimum ranges and faster angle tracking rates. Production completed.

AIM-9J. Conversion of AIM-9Bs and 9Es, with new 'front end' to enhance 'dogfight' capability by improved manoeuvring ability. About 14,000 modified for USAF by Ford Aerospace to equip the F-15 Eagle and other types. Deliveries began in 1977 and have been completed.

AIM-9L. Third-generation version of Sidewinder. Hercules/Bermite Mk 36 Mod 7 and 8 solid-propellant motors. Double-delta nose fins for improved inner boundary performance and better manoeuvrability. AM-FM conical scan for increased seeker sensitivity and improved tracking stability. Active optical fuse for increased lethality and low susceptibility to countermeasures. Annular blast fragmentation warhead. Series of 20 joint service technical evaluation firings completed on 1 March 1975, including successful firings against PQM-102 targets, and with particular emphasis on difficult shots on the beam or forward quarter of the target. Planned procurement between FY 1976 and FY 1980 totals 3,550 for US Navy and more than 5,000 for the USAF (to arm the F-15 and

F-16). Eventual total for the two services is expected to be 14,950. In FY 1976, Raytheon was contracted to deliver 1,300 AIM-9Ls and Ford Aerospace the remaining 210 missiles to qualify them for full production. Total of 2,900 provided under FY 1978 budget and 3,150 in FY 1979, with a further 2,370 requested in FY 1980 and 1,120 proposed for FY 1981. The AIM-9L was chosen in August 1977 to arm Phantom and Tornado F.Mk 2 aircraft of the Royal Air Force and Sea Harriers of the Royal Navy. It is also produced under licence by a consortium of manufacturers in NATO countries.

AIM-9N. Version of AIM-9P for Foreign Military Sales. Deliveries have been completed.

AIM-9P. Improved version of AIM-9J produced by Ford Aerospace for USAF. Increased lethality due to fuse improvements. Reduced-smoke rocket motor.

Versions of Sidewinder under development for proposed air-to-air use are as follows:

AIM-9J+ (J-3). Further improvement of AIM-9J, under development for USAF by Ford Aerospace. Increased target acquisition envelope, solid-state electronics and increased lethality due to seeker improvements. Proposed production by conversion of existing AIM-9Es and 9Js.

AIM-9M. Improved version of AIM-9L with new closed-cycle IR cooling unit claimed to be easier to service and more effective than the open-cycle gas unit used in earlier versions. Under development for US Navy and USAF. Increased ECCM capability, improved background discrimination, reduced-smoke rocket motor. A pilot production contract for 50 units was awarded to Raytheon, for delivery in 1979-80. Ninth consecutive successful flight test scored a direct hit on a QF-86 target flying well below the F-15 launch aircraft. DATA: See table.

RAYTHEON
RAYTHEON COMPANY

141 Spring Street, Lexington, Massachusetts 02173
Telephone: (617) 862 6600
Telex: 92-3455

CHAIRMAN OF THE BOARD AND CHIEF EXECUTIVE OFFICER:
  Thomas L. Phillips
PRESIDENT: D. Brainerd Holmes

Raytheon Company is prime contractor for the US Army's Patriot and Improved Hawk surface-to-air missile systems, and the US Navy/USAF Sparrow air-to-air missile. It produces the Dragon anti-tank missile for the US armed services, and versions of the US Navy/USAF Sidewinder air-to-air missile (described under NWC heading), and is the major subcontractor on the US Navy's Aegis advanced surface missile system.

Raytheon Company's Equipment Division is prime contractor for the NATO Sea Sparrow system, under development for the US Navy, the Royal Norwegian Navy, the Royal Danish Navy, the Royal Netherlands Navy, the Royal Belgian Navy and the Italian Navy.

SPARROW
US military designations: AIM-7 and RIM-7H

The AIM-7 Sparrow, developed by Raytheon Company

for the US Naval Air Systems Command, is a radar-homing air-to-air missile with all-weather all-altitude operational capability. It can also be used against shipping targets from aircraft or ships.

The Sparrow equips McDonnell Douglas F-4 Phantom II aircraft of the US Navy, USAF, Royal Air Force, Greek Air Force, Iranian Air Force, Israeli Air Force, Republic of Korea Air Force and Spanish Air Force. The Lockheed F-104S fighters licence-built in Italy are Sparrow-armed, and both the USAF's McDonnell Douglas F-15 Eagle and the US Navy's Grumman F-14 Tomcat employ this missile. Mitsubishi is manufacturing more than 800 in Japan for the Japan Air Self-Defence Force, under licence from Raytheon.

Without change, the Sparrow is used on US Navy ships as a surface-to-air and anti-shipping weapon in the Basic Point Defense Surface Missile System. It is also used in Canadian ships in the Close Range Missile System.

The advanced **AIM-7F** Sparrow, in production by both Raytheon and Mitsubishi in 1980, is powered by a Hercules Mk 58 Mod 0 solid-propellant motor and has a Raytheon semi-active Doppler radar homing system, with a smaller solid-state seeker than that of earlier versions. The heavier continuous-rod warhead is actuated by a proximity fuse or contact fuse, and is mounted forward of the wings, instead of aft as on earlier versions. Manoeuvrability has been improved, and Sparrow is now considered a good dogfight missile as well as a good medium-

range weapon with all-aspect capability, including shoot-down.

The AIM-7F is the fourth operational version of the Sparrow and is the only one that can be carried by the F-15. It has been fired successfully from a YF-16, but there is no current requirement for Sparrow armament on USAF F-16s. Production of the earlier AIM-7C, D and E models totalled 34,000 missiles, and the AIM-7F is being produced for both the US Navy and USAF, with General Dynamics as second-source contractor. Total procurement under the AIM-7F programme is expected to provide 9,804 missiles for the US Navy and 9,150 for the USAF. The missile was approved for deployment at the beginning of 1977. Production of 1,725 was funded under the FY 1978 budget and 1,910 in FY 1979, with a further 1,560 requested in FY 1980 and 1,700 proposed for FY 1981 to meet USAF and USN requirements.

An advanced monopulse seeker has now been developed for Sparrow, with the aims of reducing cost and overcoming present shortcomings in the ECM and look-down/clutter areas. It has been fitted to a new version of the missile, designated **AIM-7M**, of which production began in FY 1980. In FY 1981, all Sparrow production will switch to the AIM-7M.

A missile known as Sky Flash, evolved from Sparrow, is in production for the Royal Air Force by Dynamics Group of British Aerospace (which see).
DATA: See table

ROCKWELL INTERNATIONAL
ROCKWELL INTERNATIONAL CORPORATION

Missile Systems Division
4300 East Fifth Avenue, Columbus, Ohio 43216

Rockwell International's Columbus (Ohio) Missile Systems Division is playing a major role in several important US weapon programmes. Brief details are given of the GBU-15 air-to-surface weapons and the Hellfire anti-armour weapon system which the Division is developing and/or producing for the US Army and Air Force.

HELLFIRE

The US Army announced in October 1976 that Rockwell International had won the competition for engineering development of the Hellfire (HELicopter-Launched, FIRE and forget) modular missile system. The company was awarded a $66·7 million contract for full-scale engineering development, including design, manufacture, testing and evaluation of the missile, launcher, ground and logistics support equipment. Rockwell is performing most of the work at Columbus, but propellant loading and final assembly are done at Redstone Arsenal, Alabama, under subcontract with Thiokol Chemical Company.

The initial version of Hellfire uses a laser seeker as its guidance module, and will equip the US Army's AH-64 advanced attack helicopter. Use of laser homing in the initial application of Hellfire is based on successful testing by the Army Missile Research and Development Command in Huntsville, Alabama, using design, engineering and Rockwell International Hornet missile airframes and Rockwell laser seekers. Hellfire is designed to accept a variety of other terminal homing seeker modules, including TV, imaging infra-red (IR) radio frequency (RF), and dual-mode RF/IR.

In November 1974 two test missiles, fitted with laser seekers supplied by Rockwell International, scored direct hits on two tank targets in the first successful ripple fire demonstration of such weapons at Redstone Arsenal. A US Army crew, flying an AH-1G HueyCobra helicopter, 'popped up' from cover and fired the first test missile at a tank illuminated by a ground-based laser designator. Less than one second later, the second missile was launched against a tank situated about 20 m (65 ft) from the first target and illuminated by an airborne laser on board a second AH-1G.

The Hellfire system's demonstrated rapid, ripple and indirect fire performance and effectiveness, coupled with the capability of being launched from a variety of helicopters, ground vehicles and fixed-wing aircraft, provides a significant improvement over current systems. Its 178 mm (7 in) warhead has a high level of effectiveness against present and near-term future types of armour.

Hellfire is being developed in accordance with international standards of measurement (metric). Launch weight of the missile will be in the region of 41 kg (90 lb).

Engineering Development (ED) flight testing of Hellfire began in mid-1978. Testing up to the beginning of 1979 included unguided ballistic launches, a pre-programmed launch, and fully guided laser launches using the Tri-Service Laser Seeker also developed by Rockwell. One laser-guided Hellfire was launched from a JAH-1G testbed helicopter flying at low altitude.

The first guided flight of a Hellfire from a YAH-64 helicopter took place on 18 September 1979, and a total of 21 guided firings had been completed by February 1980. Initial production of laser Hellfire has been delayed for about one year to be consistent with the AH-64 production schedule. Full-scale development of an imaging infra-red seeker will start in FY 1981, to provide the

missile with true 'launch and leave' capability, and the US Army has been directed to pursue a parallel detector development approach, evaluating a focal plane array detector as the primary effort. R & D funding of $54·6 million for a laser Hellfire and $24·9 million for an imaging IR seeker are requested for FY 1981. Procurement funding of $20·8 million is requested for initial production facility set-up and long lead items for laser Hellfire.

GBU-8 (HOBOS) and GBU-15

The GBU-8 HOBOS (HOming BOmb System) is a modular weapon system developed under the USAF's electro-optical guided bomb (EOGB) programme. It consists of a guidance and control kit designed for easy installation on MK 84 (2,000 lb) and M118H1 (3,000 lb) general-purpose bombs. This installation does not alter the conventional bomb suspension, release or jettison functions, thus permitting the conversion of standard bombs into highly-accurate guided weapon systems.

Each kit consists of a forward guidance section, the warhead or interconnect section (including the bomb), and the aft control section.

The guidance or nose section consists of target seeker optics and sensor mounted on a gyro-stabilised platform, and the associated electronics which include a camera, platform and tracker electronics, and associated power supplies. The guidance section also furnishes reference signals to the autopilot located in the control section.

The warhead section consists of the MK 84 or M118H1 bomb with an interconnect assembly made up of four strakes, external electrical conduit, umbilical receptacle, and strake and umbilical receptacle attachment bands. The strakes are indexed in line with the wings to provide aerodynamic stability. The conduit transmits electrical

AIM-9H Sidewinder on McDonnell F-4 Phantom II

Sparrow (lower) and Sidewinder (upper, with protective nosecap) missiles on an F-14A Tomcat fighter of the US Navy *(Brian M. Service)*

Hellfire missiles on Hughes YAH-64 advanced attack helicopter

AIM-9L advanced version of Sidewinder on US Navy F-4

MK 84 GBU-8 with new midcourse guidance, including DME, for increased accuracy

Cruciform Wing Weapon developed under GBU-15 programme

Left to right: TV-guided HOBOS based on 2,000 lb MK 84 bomb; IR-guided HOBOS based on 2,000 lb MK 84 bomb; TV-guided HOBOS based on 3,000 lb M118 bomb

signals between the guidance and control sections. The umbilical receptacle provides the necessary aircraft signal interface. Fusing of the HOBOS can be accomplished either electrically or mechanically.

The control or aft section consists of a cylindrical body with cruciform wings fitted with trailing-edge flap control surfaces for flight manoeuvring. The weapon system batteries and flight control system components are located within this section, including the autopilot which collects pitch and yaw steering data from the guidance section and converts this information into signals which drive the pneumatic control surface actuators.

The effectiveness of the HOBOS modular weapon system has been demonstrated fully in a large number of successful air drops, notably against targets such as aircraft in revetments, jungle roads and bridges in Viet-Nam.

Missile Systems Division has produced this weapon for the US Air Force, and it has been sold to several other countries through Foreign Military Sales.

USAF designation for this weapon system in its latest form is GBU-15(V)/B, covering a family of modular guided weapons. Development of an alternative CBU-75·

cluster munition warhead has been undertaken; and several alternative types of guidance system may be utilised, including a laser seeker, imaging infra-red (IIR), and a midcourse system that includes distance measuring equipment (DME) for increased accuracy. Each system provides a glide bomb with self-contained guidance, high accuracy and moderate/long-range stand-off capability.

The modular elements consist of a group of interchangeable major assemblies which are combined to produce specific guided glide weapons. These configurations differ according to guidance, fusing, warhead and type of mission (direct attack or indirect attack).

In the indirect attack version, a data link module is used which allows control after launch. Further options available are cruciform and planar wings which provide the two basic weapons in the GBU-15(V)/B system.

Under Congressional direction, the USAF initiated testing of the TV-guided CWW integrated with a Naval Avionics Command weapon data link in December 1979. Integration of the Maverick imaging infra-red (IIR) seeker into the CWW is also underway, and the Air Force is funding its share of the hardened Joint Service Weapon

Data Link (JSWDL) under this programme. These efforts will provide the GBU-15 CWW with night and adverse weather attack capability, with much reduced susceptibility to ECM. RDT&E funding of $37·2 million is requested in FY 1981 for GBU-15 CWW-IIR-Data Link development. A further $31 million is requested for GBU-15 CWW-TV-Data Link production. (See also GBU-15 entry under the Hughes Aircraft heading in this section.)

DIMENSIONS:

Length overall:	
MK 84	3·78 m (12 ft 5 in)
M118E1	3·71 m (12 ft 2 in)
Body diameter:	
MK 84	0·46 m (1 ft 6 in)
M118E1	0·61 m (2 ft 0 in)
Wing span:	
MK 84	1·12 m (3 ft 8 in)
M118E1	1·32 m (4 ft 4 in)

WEIGHT:

Launching weight:	
MK 84	1,016 kg (2,240 lb)
M118E1	1,544 kg (3,404 lb)

Paveway II laser-guided bombs

Paveway laser-guided weapons on a USMC AV-8A Harrier

AGM-88A HARM air-to-surface missile

TEXAS INSTRUMENTS
TEXAS INSTRUMENTS INCORPORATED
PO Box 6015, Dallas, Texas 75222
Telephone: (214) 238 2011
Telex: 7-3324

Texas Instruments has played a major part in many US missile programmes. The latest missile for which it is prime contractor is the AGM-88A HARM, of which brief details follow:

HARM
US Navy designation: AGM-88A

On 24 May 1974, Texas Instruments was named as prime contractor for HARM (High-speed Anti-Radiation Missile) by the US Naval Air Systems Command. The initial phase of the contract covered four months of basic design co-ordination and was followed by the Advanced Development Phase; during 1979 development continued in the company's Dallas facilities, where production of the Shrike anti-radiation missile took place for more than a decade.

Few details of HARM may yet be published. Its basic configuration is conventional, with a slim cylindrical body, ogival head, cruciform double-delta wings at mid-length for simplified roll control, and cruciform tail fins indexed in line with the wings. The fixed antenna for proportional navigation is in the extreme nose, with the seeker. The smokeless solid-propellant dual-thrust rocket motor is provided by Thiokol.

The emphasis on high speed reflects experience gained in Viet-Nam, where Soviet surface-to-air missile radar systems sometimes detected the approach of US anti-radiation missiles such as the first-generation Shrike and ceased operation before the missile could lock on to them. In the case of the Navy's A-7E aircraft, HARM can cover a wide range of frequency spectra through the use of programmable digital processors in both the aircraft's AN/AWG-25 avionics equipment and the missile. The USAF will also utilise HARM on the F-4G 'Wild Weasel'. The missile has been launched successfully from F-4, A-6 and A-7 aircraft, and is readily adaptable to the F-18, AV-8B and F-16.

For technical and budgetary reasons, the planned procurement of 80 pilot production HARMs for early Navy IOC (initial operational capability) was delayed. The first procurement for the Air Force is now planned for FY 1982.

DATA: See table

PAVEWAY LASER GUIDED BOMBS

The Laser Guided Bomb (LGB) concept was introduced by Texas Instruments Incorporated in 1965. The US Air Force initiated an extensive development programme and the name Paveway was assigned to this. Texas Instruments builds the guidance units and rear wing assemblies, which are fitted to US MK 80 series bomb bodies. With minor modifications, the Paveway units have been installed on other aircraft ordnance, including the British MK 13/18 and 540 lb stores.

Paveway LGBs are semi-active laser-guided munitions which home on reflected laser energy from a target being illuminated by a laser designator. Day and night attacks can be accomplished against all types of tactical targets, since no intrinsic target signature is required. LGBs have been used effectively against anti-aircraft gun and missile installations, tanks, tracks, bridges, power stations, railroads, buildings, ships and caves.

Conventional bomb handling equipment is used for loading and fusing. No electrical interface to the delivery aircraft is required. Paveway munitions are delivered in a similar manner to conventional unguided munitions.

Continued development and engineering upgrading has added Paveway II to the family of weapons proven in Southeast Asia. Folding rear wings on the Paveway II have increased weapon performance and aircraft load density, increasing the number of aircraft, worldwide, that are compatible with the Paveway system.

The same laser detector and guidance unit is used with all weapons. The rear wing and control canards vary in size according to the size of the weapon.

Both Paveway I and II are currently in production for customers that include the US Air Force and Navy, Royal Air Force, Royal Netherlands Air Force, Iranian Air Force, Hellenic Air Force, Turkish Air Force, Canadian Forces, Royal Saudi Air Force and Republic of Korea Air Force.

AIR-LAUNCHED MISSILES

Note: entries in italics are estimated

Country	Prime Contractor	Model	Length m (ft in)	Body diam cm (in)	Wing span m (ft in)	Launch weight kg (lb)	Cruising speed knots (km/h; mph)	Range	
France	Aérospatiale	AS.11	1·21 (3 11½)	16·4 (6½)	0·50 (1 7½)	29·9 (66)	214-370 (396-685; 246-425)	350-3,000 m (1,150-9,850 ft)	Time of flight (propelled) 18-20 s. Min turning radius 1,000 m (3,300 ft)
	Aérospatiale	AS.12	1·87 (6 2)	21 (8¼)	0·65 (2 1½)	76 (168)	at impact 505 (936; 581)	8,000 m (26,250 ft) launch speed 180 (333; 207)	Range in relation to surface. Time of flight 32 s. Warhead 30 kg (66 lb)
	Aérospatiale	AS.15TT	2·16 (7 1)	18·5 (7¼)	0·53 (1 8¾)	96 (212)	540 (1,000; 620)	more than 8 nm (15 km; 9·3 miles)	Warhead 30 kg (66 lb) Time of flight (propelled) 45·2 s
	Aérospatiale	AS.30 Laser	3·65 (11 11¾)	34·2 (13½)	1·00 (3 3¼)	520 (1,146)	supersonic	1·6-5·4 nm (3-10 km; 1·8-6·2 miles)	Warhead 240 kg (529 lb) Time of flight 21 s
	Aérospatiale	Exocet AM39	4·68 (15 4¼)	35 (13¾)	1·10 (3 7¼)	652 (1,438)	Mach 0·93	see p. 645	Warhead *160 kg (352 lb)*
	Matra	R.530	3·28 (10 9¼)	26 (10¼)	1·10 (3 7¼)	195 (430)	Mach 2·7	9·5 nm (18 km; 11 miles)	
	Matra	Super 530	3·54 (11 7¼)	26 (10¼)	0·64 (2 1¼)	250 (550)	Mach 4-5	*16-19 nm (30-35 km; 18·5-21·75 miles)*	Fin span 0·90 m (2 ft 11½ in). Operational ceiling above 21,350 m (70,000 ft). Warhead greater than 30 kg (66 lb)

Note: entries in italics are estimated

Country	Prime Contractor	Model	Length m (ft in)	Body diam cm (in)	Wing span m (ft in)	Launch weight kg (lb)	Cruising speed knots (km/h; mph)	Range	
	Matra	R.550 Magic	2·80 (9 2¼)	15·7 (6)	0·47 (1 6½)	88 (194)	Mach 2+	3·25 nm (6 km; 3·75 miles) at medium altitude 5·4 nm (10 km; 6·2 miles) at high altitude	Fin span 0·65 m (2 ft 1½ in) Min range 500 m (1,640 ft)
Germany, Federal Rep	MBB	Kormoran	4·40 (14 5)	34 (13½)	1·00 (3 3¼)	600 (1,320)	*Mach 0·95*	20 nm *(37 km; 23 miles)*	
International	Euromissile	Hot	1·28 (4 2½)	14·4 (5¾)	*0·31 (1 0¼)	23·5 (51·8)	486 (900; 560)	400-4,000 m (1,310-13,125 ft)	Time of flight to 4,000 m 17 s. Warhead 6 kg (13·2 lb)
Israel	Rafael	Shafrir	2·47 (8 1¼)	16 (6¼)	0·52 (1 8½)	93 (205)	NA	2·7 nm (5 km; 3·1 miles)	Warhead 11 kg (24.25 lb)
Italy	Selenia	Aspide	3·70 (12 1½)	20·3 (8)	1·00 (3 3¼)	220 (485)	*Mach 4*	27-54 nm *(50-100 km; 31-62 miles)*	Warhead (estimated) 33 kg (73 lb)
	Sistel	Sea Killer Mk 2	4·70 (15 5)	20·6 (8⅛)	1·00 (3 3¼)	300 (660)	Mach 0·74	over 10·8 nm (20 km; 12·4 miles)	Warhead 70 kg (154 lb)
Japan	Mitsubishi	ASM-1	4·00 (13 1½)	35 (13¾)	1·20 (3 11¼)	610 (1,345)	Mach 0·9	43-48 nm (80-90 km; 50-56 miles)	Warhead 200 kg (440 lb)
Norway	Kongsberg	Penguin Mk 2	3·05 (10 0)	28 (11)	1·40 (4 7)	330 (727)	Mach 0·8	15 nm (27 km; 17 miles)	Air-launched Mk 3 has shorter span, extended range
USSR		AA-1 'Alkali'	1·88 (6 2)	17·8 (7)	0·58 (1 10¾)	*90 (200)*		3·2-4·3 nm (6-8 km; 3·7-5 miles)	
		AA-2 'Atoll' (K-13A)	2·80 (9 2)	12·0 (4¾)	0·45 (1 5¾)	70 (154)	Mach 2·5	2·5-3·5 nm (5-6·5 km; 3-4 miles)	Span of tail fins 0·53 m (1 ft 8¾ in)
		AA-3 'Anab'	*4·10 (13 5)*	*28·0 (11)*	*1·30 (4 3)*			over 8·75 nm (16 km; 10 miles)	Length for IR version; radar version is 4·0 m (13 ft 1 in) long
		AA-5 'Ash'	*5·50 (18 0)*					16 nm (30 km; 18·5 miles)	Length for IR version; radar version is 5·2 m (17 ft 0 in) long
		AA-7 'Apex'	*4·30 (14 1¼)*	*24·0 (9½)*	*1·05 (3 5½)*	*320 (705)*		15 nm (27 km; 17 miles)	
		AA-8 'Aphid'	*2·00 (6 6¾)*	*13·0 (5)*		*55 (121)*		*3-4 nm (5·5-8 km; 3·5-5 miles)*	*Warhead 6 kg (13·2 lb)*
		AT-2 'Swatter'	0·90 (2 11½)	15·0 (6)	0·65 (2 2)	25 (55)	290 (540; 335)	300-2,200 m (985-7,220 ft)	
		AT-3 'Sagger'	0·86 (2 10)	*12·0 (5)*	0·46 (1 6)	11·3 (24·9)		500-3,000 m (1,640-9,840 ft)	
		AS-2 'Kipper'	*9·50 (31 0)*	*90 (35·4)*	*4·88 (16 0)*	*4,200 (9,260)*	*Mach 1·2*	115 nm (213 km; 132 miles)	*Warhead 1,000 kg (2,200 lb)*
		AS-3 'Kangaroo'	*14·90 (48 11)*	*185 (72·8)*	*9·15 (30 0)*	*11,000 (24,250)*	Mach 1·8	350 nm (650 km; 400 miles)	*Nuclear or HE warhead 2,300 kg (5,070 lb)*
		AS-4 'Kitchen'	*11·30 (37 0)*	*90 (35·4)*	*3·00 (9 10)*	*6,000+ (13,225)*	*Mach 2+*	160 nm *(300 km; 185 miles)*	Range at low altitude *Warhead 1,000 kg (2,200 lb)*
		AS-5 'Kelt'	*9·45 (31 0)*	*100 (39·5)*	*4·57 (15 0)*	*3,500 (7,715)*	*Mach 0·9 at low altitude; Mach 1·2 at 9,150 m (30,000 ft)*	over 85 nm *(160 km; 100 miles)*	Range at low altitude; doubled at height HE warhead; 1,000 kg (2,200 lb)
		AS-6 'Kingfish'	*10·50 (34 6)*		*2·50 (8 2½)*		*Mach 3*	120 nm (220 km; 135 miles)	Range at low altitude
UK	British Aerospace	Sea Skua	*2·83 (9 3½)*	*27 (10½)*	*0·60 (1 11½)*	*147 (325)*	NA	NA	*Warhead 20 kg (44 lb)*
	British Aerospace	Sky Flash	3·66 (12 0)	20·3 (8)	1·02 (3 4¼)	193 (425)	Mach 4	27 nm (50 km; 31 miles)	
USA	Boeing Aerospace	AGM-86B ALCM	6·32 (20 9)	62 (24½)	3·66 (12 0)	1,282 (2,825)	approx 435 knots (805 km/h; 500 mph)	approx 1,350 nm (2,500 km; 1,550 miles)	Height overall 1·19 m (3 ft 11 in)
	Hughes	AIM-54A Phoenix	3·95 (13·0)	38 (15)	0·91 (3 0)	447 (985)	Mach 5+	108 nm + (200 km; 124 miles)	
	Hughes	BGM-71A TOW	1·17 (3 10)	15 (6)	0·34 (1 1½)	19 (42)	High subsonic	500-3,750 m (1,640-12,300 ft)	Warhead 3·9 kg (8·6 lb) Max range increased by 25% in 1978
	Hughes	AGM-65A Maverick	2·46 (8 1)	30 (12)	0·71 (2 4)	210 (462)	NA	*12 nm (22 km; 14 miles)*	Alternative 135 kg (298 lb) warhead under development
	Martin Marietta	AGM-62A Walleye 1	3·44 (11 3½)	38·1 (15)	1·14 (3 9)	499 (1,100)	Subsonic	—	Warhead 385 kg (850 lb)
	Martin Marietta	AGM-62 Walleye 2	4·04 (13 3)	45·7 (18)	1·30 (4 3)	1,061 (2,340)	Subsonic	—	Warhead 907 kg (2,000 lb)
	MDAC	AGM-84A Harpoon	3·84 (12 7)	34 (13½)	NA	526 (1,160)	High subsonic	NA	
	NWC/ Raytheon	AIM-9G/H Sidewinder	2·87 (9 5)	13 (5)	*0·63 (2 0¾)	86 (190)	Mach 2·5	over 1·75 nm (3·35 km; 2 miles)	Warhead 11·4 kg (25 lb)
	Ford Aerospace	AIM-9J/J + N/P Sidewinder	2·83 (9 3½)	13 (5)	*0·56 (1 10)	72 (159)	Mach 2·5	over 1·75 nm (3·35 km; 2 miles)	Warhead 11·4 kg (25 lb)
	NWC/ Raytheon/ Ford Aerospace	AIM-9L Sidewinder	2·87 (9 5)	13 (5)	*0·63 (2 0¾)	86 (190)	Mach 2·5	over 3·75 nm (7 km; 4·35 miles)	Warhead 11·4 kg (25 lb)
	Raytheon	AIM-7F Sparrow	3·66 (12 0)	20 (8)	1·02 (3 4)	227 (500)	*Mach 3·5+*	*24 nm (44 km; 28 miles)*	
	Texas Instruments	AGM-88A HARM	4·18 (13 8½)	25·4 (10)	1·13 (3 8½)	362 (798)		over 8·5 nm (16 km; 10 miles)	Altitude limits S/L to 12,200 m (40,000 ft)

*Fin span

SPACEFLIGHT

CANADA

SPAR
SPAR AEROSPACE LIMITED

Royal Bank Plaza, South Tower, PO Box 83, Toronto, Ontario M5J 2J2
Telephone: (416) 865-0480
Telex: 065-24240 Sparcal Tor

CHAIRMAN OF THE BOARD AND CHIEF EXECUTIVE OFFICER:
L. D. Clarke
PRESIDENT AND CHIEF OPERATING OFFICER:
R. D. Richmond
VICE-PRESIDENT, MARKETING: R. E. Marcille
DIRECTOR, PUBLIC RELATIONS: Hugh A. MacLean

Spar is an independent Canadian public company, active in varied fields of advanced technology and serving commercial, scientific and military markets.

ANIK

Anik B, Canada's latest domestic communications satellite (see RCA entry in US section of 1979-80 *Jane's*), which was launched on 15 December 1978, contained two communications systems developed and built by Spar Aerospace Electronic Group.

The **Anik C** series of three further satellites, to be launched during 1981 and 1982, will provide 14/12GHz services to the Trans-Canada Telephone System. Hughes Aircraft Company of California, USA, as prime contractor, has awarded to Spar major Anik C subcontracts, under which Spar's Mechanical and Electrical Group will supply the Anik C structures, thermal hardware, solar panel positioners and antenna positioners.

The first of two 6/4GHz **Anik D** satellites, to replace the second of the original Anik A series, will be launched in early 1982. The second Anik D will replace Anik B in 1985. Spar is prime contractor for the Anik D series of spacecraft.

SHUTTLE REMOTE MANIPULATOR SYSTEM (RMS)

Under Canadian/US co-operative arrangements, a Canadian team led by Spar is developing the remote manipulator system for the Space Shuttle programme. The team has, in addition, established a computer-controlled facility capable of simulating under laboratory conditions the performance of remote manipulator systems for space, Arctic, underwater and nuclear applications.

The RMS consists of a 15 m (50 ft) long mechanical arm with joints similar to a human shoulder, elbow and wrist. It will be operated by an astronaut, from the port-side aft crew station of the Orbiter flight deck, to deploy satellites into space from the vehicle's cargo bay, and to retrieve orbiting satellites for onboard servicing or return to Earth. It will be capable of handling satellites weighing up to 29,480 kg (65,000 lb), with a length of up to 18·28 m (60 ft) and maximum diameter of 4·57 m (15 ft). A second arm may be installed on the opposite side of the cargo bay when mission requirements dictate such a move.

NASA has placed a contract for three RMS systems, for delivery in 1982, 1983 and 1984. These, together with the first flight system developed by Spar for the National Research Council of Canada, will be installed on the NASA fleet of four Space Shuttle vehicles. The first RMS was to be delivered in 1980 and will be tested on the second shuttle flight.

Engineering model of RMS under test at Spar's Toronto facility

RMS deploying a satellite *(artwork by MBB)*

Artist's impression of Anik D in orbit

CHINA
(PEOPLE'S REPUBLIC)

China launched her first satellite (Norad designation *Chicom 1*) on 24 April 1970, and thus became the fifth country to orbit a payload using national resources, following the USSR, USA, France and Japan. The launch is believed to have taken place from the main Chinese rocket centre near Shuang Cheng Tsu, 800 km (500 miles) east of the nuclear test establishment of Lop Nor.

Brief details of the China 2, 3, 4 and 5 satellites were given in the 1976-77 *Jane's*. China 6 and 7 were briefly described in the 1978-79 *Jane's*. China 8, launched on 26 January 1978, and weighing an estimated 3,600 kg (8,000 lb), returned a re-entry module to Earth.

In 1979 a Japanese delegation was told that China is developing a new three-stage launch vehicle, named Long March III, capable of placing an 800 kg (1,764 lb) payload in geostationary orbit. It is reported that the first and second stages have been developed and tested, and that the third stage was being tested in 1979. China is also reported to be developing a communications satellite and a weather satellite.

A Chinese spokesman has announced that China has long-range plans for launching manned spacecraft and space laboratories, and a documentary film has shown men in space suits undergoing stress tests and weightlessness. It is reported that a dog has been sent into orbit and recovered, as a preliminary stage of the manned spaceflight programme.

In 1978 a Chinese delegation, led by Dr Ren Xinmin,

President of the Chinese Academy of Space Technology, held discussions with US officials regarding possible US-Chinese co-operation in the peaceful utilisation of space technology. The discussions resulted in an informal agreement for purchase by the Chinese Communications Satellite Corporation of a complete US civil satellite communications system.

The discussions also led to the signing of a Memorandum of Understanding between NASA and the Chinese Academy of Sciences in January 1980, covering China's participation in an experimental Landsat programme. Under the agreement, China will establish a ground station in the Beijing area to read out Earth resources data from Landsat D.

CZECHOSLOVAKIA

ACADEMY OF SCIENCES
Narodni Trida 3, 111 42 Praha 1

MAGION

Magion, the first satellite to be designed and built in Czechoslovakia, was launched into orbit with the Soviet satellite Intercosmos 18 on 24 October 1978. The satellite carried experiments to study the Earth's magnetosphere and ionosphere. Magion was ejected into independant orbit on 14 November 1978, the purpose of the mission being to obtain simultaneous data from a pair of slowly diverging satellites. Telemetry data from both satellites were received by ground stations in the USSR and by the Observatory of the Academy of Sciences at Panska Ves. Magion exceeded its design life of three weeks by many weeks.

Assembling the Magion satellite

FRANCE

AÉROSPATIALE
SOCIÉTÉ NATIONALE INDUSTRIELLE AÉROSPATIALE
Division Systèmes Balistiques et Spatiaux
MANAGEMENT: Route de Verneuil, BP 96, 78130 Les Mureaux
Telephone: 33 (1) 474 72 13
Telex: AIRSPA 696 759F
DIRECTOR: P. M. Usunier

The Space and Ballistic Systems Division of Aérospatiale handles research, development, testing and engineering for entire missile and space vehicle systems, including a range of solid-propellant sounding rockets (see 1977-78 *Jane's*). Satellite programmes to which it is contributing include Intelsat V, Exosat, MAROTS, Phebus and Meteosat, for which it is prime contractor.

Aérospatiale is a member of the CIFAS and COSMOS international consortia (see International section) and has founded a joint subsidiary, named Eurosatellite, with MBB and ETCA, for the development and marketing of applications satellites. Studies are currently underway for direct-to-home TV broadcast satellites and communications satellites in both the 500 kg (1,102 lb) and 1,000 kg (2,204 lb) classes.

ARIANE

This heavy three-stage launch vehicle is being developed and produced in Europe as a co-operative project involving ten countries. The programme is financed by the European Space Agency, with the French space agency CNES as prime contractor. Ariane's payload potential is 1,700 kg (3,748 lb) into a transfer orbit, or applications satellites of up to 925 kg (2,035 lb) weight in geostationary orbit. Geostationary satellite weight can be increased to 967 kg (2,134 lb) by use of an ESA-developed apogee motor.

Aérospatiale is responsible for the design of Ariane and for integration of the entire vehicle. It is producing major structural elements of the first stage and is responsible for the final delivery of all three stages and the fairings.

SEP is producing the engines and associated subsystems. Matra is building the vehicle equipment bay, and ETCA is responsible for the checkout and launch command facilities.

The first test flight was made successfully on 24 December 1979, with a payload consisting of a technological capsule (CAT) and a dummy payload weighing 1,600 kg (3,527 lb). The second test flight was scheduled for May 1980, with a payload consisting of Amsat, CAT and Firewheel; the third for September 1980 with a payload of APPLE, CAT and Meteosat 2, the fourth for December 1980, with a payload of CAT and MARECS A. The vehicle is expected to be fully operational by that time, and the fifth launch, in May 1981, will put into orbit MARECS B and Sirio 2, followed by an Intelsat V launch two months later. Payloads have been allocated provisionally up to the fifteenth launch in February 1984, with options on others. A dual launch system, known as SYLDA (described separately) will be used on missions requiring the simultaneous launch of two large satellites.

Projected developments include lengthening the third stage fuel tank (Ariane 2) and the addition of strap-on boosters (Ariane 3) to increase the transfer orbit payload respectively to 1,950 kg (4,299 lb) and 2,400 kg (5,291 lb).

Details of the individual stages of the basic Ariane are as follows:

L 140 FIRST STAGE

This first stage is made up of two identical steel tanks for the 145,000 kg (319,670 lb) of UDMH and nitrogen tetroxide propellants, linked together by means of a cylindrical skirt. It is powered by four Viking engines (each 611·25 kN; 137,412 lb st), carried on a cylindrical thrust frame and protected by fairings with fins. Burn time is 145 s.

An interstage skirt joins the first and second stages.

L 33 SECOND STAGE

The second stage comprises two light alloy tanks for 34,000 kg (74,955 lb) of UDMH and nitrogen tetroxide propellants, separated by a common bulkhead. The single Viking engine (713 kN; 160,280 lb thrust in vacuum) is linked to the stage by a conical thrust frame. Burn time is 132 s.

A cylindrical interstage skirt connects the second and third stages.

H 8 THIRD STAGE

The third stage is made of light alloy and houses 8,200 kg (18,075 lb) of liquid hydrogen and liquid oxygen propellants for its single HM7 cryogenic engine (60 kN; 13,485 lb thrust). Burn time is 570 s.

A cylindrical vehicle equipment bay is situated above the third stage. The equipment platform is an annular plate, the inside flange of which supports the payload attachment fittings.

DIMENSIONS:

Length: L 140 1st stage	18·40 m	(60 ft 4½ in)
L 33 2nd stage	10·40 m	(33 ft 1 in)
H 8 3rd stage	8·60 m	(26 ft 2½ in)
Overall length	47·0 m	(154 ft 2 in)
Body diameter: L 140	3·80 m	(12 ft 5½ in)
L 33, H 8, equipment bay	2·60 m	(8 ft 6½ in)

WEIGHTS:

L 140 1st stage	165,000 kg	(363,762 lb)
L 33 2nd stage	37,600 kg	(82,895 lb)
H 8 3rd stage	9,400 kg	(20,725 lb)
Total weight at lift-off	207,000 kg	(456,355 lb)

SONATE

Sonate is a drum-shape telecommunications satellite, weighing 300 to 400 kg (660-880 lb). It is optimised for

Model of the Sonate communications satellite

First launch of Ariane

domestic or regional missions, involving point-to-point telecommunications, relay, data collection and transmission.

Utilising proven technologies and existing hardware, Sonate will be reliable and relatively inexpensive. Its configuration is based on the Meteosat spacecraft platform, and on Symphonie (4-6GHz) or OTS (12-14GHz) payloads, with a mechanically de-spun antenna. It will be spin-stabilised and will have more than 300W power at the end of its lifetime.

Sonate is configured for dual launch with Ariane/SYLDA, but users can choose between this method and the Space Shuttle with an upper stage (SSUS-D).

SYLDA

The first use of SYLDA (SYstem for Launching Dual payloads with Ariane) is scheduled for May 1981, on the fifth flight, with MARECS B and Sirio 2. SYLDA is an egg-shaped device of carbonfibre/metal honeycomb material. Its height in the current version is 3·9 m (12 ft 9½ in) and its diameter 2·8 m (9 ft 2½ in), making SYLDA the largest carbonfibre structure yet made in Europe. It weighs only 180 kg (397 lb) fully equipped, but can place a total mass (two spacecraft) of 1,520 kg (3,351 lb) into transfer orbit with Ariane 1. A stretched version of SYLDA will be ready for Ariane 2 and 3 by mid-1983, and will accommodate two satellites of 1,400 kg (3,086 lb) total mass, destined for transfer orbit.

TDF-1

This is a joint Franco-German programme for the development of direct-to-home TV broadcast satellites. Under a decision made by the heads of state in October 1979, two satellites are planned, TDF-1 for France and TV-Sat for West Germany, using the same spacecraft platform. Aérospatiale and Thomson-CSF in France, and MBB and AEG-Telefunken in West Germany, will develop jointly the two three-channel pre-operational satellites, and subsequent operational versions.

SYLDA dual launch system

Artist's impression of TDF-1 TV satellite

MATRA
SA MATRA

SPACE BRANCH: 37 avenue Louis Breguet, 78140 Vélizy
Telephone: 946 96 00
Telex: MATRA 698 077F
OFFICERS: See Missiles section

On 18 September 1979, Matra was appointed prime contractor for Telecom 1, the first French telecommunications satellite. It is also prime contractor for the French Earth Observation Satellite SPOT, which is being developed in association with Sweden and Belgium. Other current commitments include the Command and Data Management System for Spacelab, as contractor for ESA, and the vehicle equipment bay for the Ariane European launch vehicle.

Following successful operation in orbit of the Orbital Test Satellite (OTS), for which Matra developed the attitude and orbit control system, the company is developing within the MESH international consortium the attitude and orbit control system of the European Communications Satellite (ECS) and its maritime version (MARECS), and will integrate ECS.

MATRA is also working, under ESA contract, on the Faint Object Camera (FOC) for NASA's Space Telescope.

TELECOM 1

This telecommunications satellite utilises the platform of MARECS (see MESH entry in International section).

Artist's impression of Telecom 1

When put into orbit by the twelfth Ariane launch, in December 1982, the first Telecom 1 will be employed for inter-computer data transfer, video conferences, video transmissions, telecopying, and telephone and TV hook-up with overseas French territories. Its general appearance is shown in the accompanying illustration.

SPOT

Matra is prime contractor for the SPOT Earth Observation Satellite which, utilising advanced instrumentation, is expected to provide images of greater resolution than

Mockup of SPOT Earth Observation Satellite

those obtained from the US Landsat series of spacecraft.

SPOT comprises two modules: a lower platform housing the stabilisation subsystem, power supplies, onboard management systems, telemetry and solar array; and an upper payload module housing the mission instrumentation. The solar panel array will provide 1,800W power. Overall length of the satellite is 7·35 m (24 ft 1½ in) and weight with maximum payload 1,750 kg (3,858 lb).

SPOT is scheduled to be launched by Ariane in March 1984.

GERMANY
(FEDERAL REPUBLIC)

DORNIER
DORNIER SYSTEM GmbH

Postfach 6136048, 7990 Friedrichshafen
Telephone: Immenstaad (07545) 81
Telex: 073 4359

GENERAL MANAGERS:
Dipl-Ing Silvius Dornier
Dipl-Ing Dr Jr Karl-Wilhelm Schäfer
Dr Ing Bernhard Schmidt
Dr Ing Helmut Ulke
Dipl-Kfm Klaus-Peter Thomé

PUBLIC RELATIONS: Gerhard Patt

Dornier System, a member company of the Dornier group, is engaged in activities involving spaceflight, new technologies, electronics and research. It is a major European contractor for the development of equipment for satellites, and for associated equipment such as the communications terminals mounted on West German ships for use with the Marisat satellite system.

Within the STAR international consortium, Dornier System is leading the development programme for the ISPM (International Solar Polar Mission) scientific satellite. Two spacecraft, the second developed by NASA

(which see), will be launched by Space Shuttle in 1983 into planetary trajectories towards Jupiter, the gravitational field of which will deflect them out of the ecliptic plane in opposite directions for unique observations of our solar system.

Dornier System is also developing the environmental control and life support subsystem (ECLSS) and the instrument pointing system (IPS) for the Spacelab which is to be carried into orbit by the US Space Shuttle.

For Ariane, the European launch vehicle, Dornier has developed the second-stage tank structure.

ERNO
ERNO RAUMFAHRTTECHNIK GmbH

Hünefeldstrasse 1-5, Postfach 10 59 09, 2800 Bremen 1
Telephone: (0421) 5391
Telex: 024 5548

DIRECTORS:
Dipl-Ing Hans E. W. Hoffmann
Bernd Kosegarten

ERNO is the prime contractor for Spacelab, which is to be carried into orbit by the Space Shuttle. It is also

involved in work on the Ariane European launch vehicle and subsystem work for communications satellites such as the European Communications Satellite (ECS), MARECS, the French Telecom 1, and the Franco-German direct-broadcast TV-Sat project.

SPACELAB

Under development by a ten-nation consortium led by ERNO, Spacelab is the only manned payload for the American Space Shuttle. A typical payload will comprise a two-segment module and two pallets with an overall length of 13·80 m (45 ft 3 in) and a diameter of 4·06 m (13 ft 4 in).

The first launch of the Space Shuttle with a Spacelab is scheduled for 1982. Up to four payload specialists can work in two shifts for a period of seven days; extensions up to 30 days are envisaged. Spacelab will remain in the cargo bay of the Orbiter during the mission and will be brought back to Earth when the Orbiter lands. The payload specialists will be able to work under normal atmospheric conditions in the pressurised module. For work on the pallet section pressure suits will be necessary.

Diagram of Spacelab, including two experiment pallets

MBB

MESSERSCHMITT-BÖLKOW-BLOHM GmbH

Space Division

8012 Ottobrunn bei München
Telephone: (089) 60 00 25 90

In addition to its manufacture of piloted aircraft, Messerschmitt-Bölkow-Blohm is engaged in the development of guided weapons (see Air-Launched Missiles section), research rockets and satellites. Contributions to ten space programmes have been made since 1968, including the two Helios solar probes, the Symphonie communications satellites and the cryogenic engine for the third stage of the Ariane European launch vehicle. Currently the company is building the Exosat

X-ray satellite, under contract to ESA, and is a major subcontractor for the Intelsat V communications satellite (which see).

MBB is also developing the trajectory and attitude control system for the Galileo Jupiter probe, sponsored by NASA and the Federal German Ministry of Research and Technology, and subsystems for the SPAS (Shuttle Pallet Satellite) family of satellites for use with the Space Shuttle. The company is also engaged in the Franco-German programme for a domestic TV-Sat satellite, designed to transmit three television programmes directly into every home from a geostationary orbit. The satellite is designed for a life of seven years in orbit, and includes triple-redundancy for critical electronic components and electric thrust units for orbit control.

Artist's impression of TV-Sat

OTRAG

ORBITAL TRANSPORT- UND RAKETEN AG

Herzogstrasse 39, 8000 München 40
Telephone: 089 320 1079
Telex: 528548 otragd

CHAIRMAN: Dr-Ing Kurt H. Debus
PRESIDENT: Dipl-Ing Lutz T. Kayser
PUBLIC RELATIONS: Dipl-Ing Frank K. Wukasch

OTRAG is developing as a private venture a low-cost satellite launch vehicle based on a building block concept, by which tank-plus-engine modules are clustered in increasing numbers to form larger vehicles.

The basic OTRAG building block is a two-tank/two-engine module, one tank containing white fuming nitric acid and the other kerosene. The two throttleable engines each develop 29·36 kN (6,600 lb st). Two such building blocks together form the smallest flight vehicle.

The tanks, which have a diameter of 27·0 cm (10·6 in), are made from cold-spun stainless steel and are built up from modular segments each 3·0 m (9 ft 10 in) long. Length of the tanks on the basic vehicle is 6·0 m (19 ft 8 in), but this is increased for the larger vehicles. Each tank is filled with propellant to about two-thirds capacity. An adiabatic blow-down feed system utilising compressed air occupies the remaining space and forces the propellant into the engine during flight. Radial injection and ablative thrust chambers are used, lined with a coating of asbestos and phenolic plastics resin.

Engine throttling capability is provided by ball valves, which allow propellants to pass from the tanks to the engines, and are opened or closed by actuators to provide full, 50 per cent or zero thrust.

To achieve low cost, existing aerospace components and commercially available components are used wherever possible, examples of the latter being the fuel valves and their actuators.

Guidance is by an inertial platform and computer in the payload section. These send signals to each engine actuator unit, which in turn throttles the engines on one side or the other to control the attitude of the vehicle.

A basic flight vehicle, consisting of two modules, was successfully test-launched from North-Shaba in Zaïre on 17 May 1977, when an altitude of about 12,000 m (39,370 ft) was reached. A second launch, on 20 May 1978, utilised a cluster of four modules and reached a height of 30,000 m (98,400 ft). No 3 flight test took place on 5 June 1978, with a cluster of four modules and tank length of 12·0 m (39 ft 4 in). OTRAG has been asked to stop using the Zaïre site, for political reasons, and was negotiating with other countries in early 1980, for the establishment of a new flight test range.

From these basic flight vehicles OTRAG plans to evolve a series of efficient but relatively inexpensive launchers capable of undertaking a wide variety of duties. The first orbital insertion is planned for late 1981, with a 64-module vehicle; by 1984 it is hoped to launch a vehicle of more than 600 modules. On the larger vehicles the propellant tanks will be lengthened to a maximum of 40 m (131 ft), and the basic modules will be clustered in stages one inside the other. As one stage or 'layer' burns out, it will be jettisoned when the next outermost layer or stage ignites. The process will continue until only a slender core stage is left to insert the payload into orbit.

A 600-module vehicle could place a 10,000 kg (22,500 lb) payload in low Earth orbit, or 2,000 kg (4,409 lb) in geosynchronous orbit.

OTRAG 4-module launch vehicle

INDIA

ISRO

INDIAN SPACE RESEARCH ORGANISATION

F Block, Cauvery Bhavan, District Office Road, Bangalore 560 009
Telephone: 27371/76
Telex: 0845-499 IN

CHAIRMAN: Prof S. Dhawan
PUBLIC RELATIONS OFFICER: V. K. Nair

The Government of India set up a Space Commission in June 1972, backed by the Department of Space (DOS),

and entrusted DOS with responsibility for conducting India's space programme. ISRO functions under DOS as its research and development organisation and for executing the space research activities.

ISRO operates and maintains the UN-sponsored Thumba Equatorial Rocket Launching Station (TERLS) near Trivandrum, and encourages international collaboration in space research experiments using rockets.

The activities of ISRO, which has its Headquarters at Bangalore, are carried out at the following centres:

Vikram Sarabhai Space Centre (VSSC)

ISRO PO, Trivandrum 695 022

Telephone: 4671 and 4791

Telex: 0884-201 IN and 0884-202 IN

DIRECTOR: Dr V. R. Gowarikar

VSSC serves as the main research and development centre for space technology. It is engaged in the development of sounding rockets and satellite launch vehicles.

Space Applications Centre (SAC)

Jodhpur Tekra, Ahmedabad 380 053
Telephone: 442700 and 443296
Telex: 012-239 IN
DIRECTOR: Prof Yash Pal

This Centre is concerned with space applications programmes of ISRO in the areas of satellite communications, TV broadcasting via satellite, survey of Earth resources and meteorological parameters from space/aerial platforms using remote sensing and satellite geodesy.

SHAR Centre

Sriharikota PO 524 124, Nellore District (AP)
Telephone: 2001 and 2345 (via Madras)
Telex: 041-394 and 041-7353 IN
DIRECTOR: N. Pant

This centre contains facilities for launching and flight testing large multi-stage sounding rockets. Facilities for launching satellites are under development. The centre also has facilities for the production of solid propellants and for the static testing of rocket motors. The main Indian ground station for tracking, commanding ISRO satellites and receiving telemetry data is located at this centre.

ISRO Satellite Centre (ISAC)

Peenya Industrial Estate, Bangalore 560 058
Telephone: 38261-69
Telex: 0845-325 IN
DIRECTOR: Prof U. R. Rao

This centre provides inputs for planning satellite programmes/missions of ISRO, and for the fabrication of satellites. It is the research centre for satellite technology.

The latest ISRO programmes are as follows:

SATELLITE LAUNCH VEHICLE (SLV-3)

This VSSC project has the objective of developing an indigenous satellite launch vehicle capable of putting a 40 kg (88 lb) Rohini satellite into a near-Earth orbit. The four-stage solid-propellant vehicle, designated SLV-3, has a length of 22·77 m (74 ft 8 in), with a maximum diameter of 1 m (39 in) and weighs 16,900 kg (37,258 lb) at lift-off. Thrust of the first stage is 422 kN (95,000 lb). Inertial guidance is employed.

The first experimental flight on 10 August 1979 was only partially successful; a second flight was planned for mid-1980.

APPLE

APPLE (Ariane Passenger Payload Experiment), weighing about 657 kg (1,448 lb) is India's first three-axis stabilised geostationary experimental communications satellite. Its communications payload is being built by the Space Applications Centre, Ahmedabad. Major subsystems, such as the Apogee Boost Motor, C-Band Antenna, Momentum Wheel and Solar Array Drive, are under development at VSSC. The satellite was due to be launched by an Ariane vehicle of the European Space Agency in 1980. APPLE is a forerunner of future Indian operational communications satellites and represents a significant advance in indigenous satellite technology.

BHASKARA

The second Indian satellite, known as Bhaskara (originally SEO) and designed primarily for Earth observation experiments, was launched from the Soviet Union on 7 June 1979. The 444 kg (979 lb) satellite carries microwave radiometers and TV cameras, fabricated by SAC, to obtain data in the areas of hydrology, forestry, oceanography and meteorology. The radiometers are providing useful ocean and land-surface temperature data. Efforts are continuing to circumvent a malfunction in the TV power system, so that the TV cameras can be switched on. Earth resources satellites are expected to be of great importance to India, in view of the country's vast size, immense unexplored resources and the need for constant monitoring of agricultural and forestry activities.

INSAT

To further the objective of the Indian Space Programme to use space technology for practical applications, the government has approved the establishment of the Indian National Satellite (INSAT) system by 1981. INSAT is a multi-purpose geostationary satellite system for telecommunications and meteorology, and also has the capability for nation-wide direct TV broadcast to community TV receivers in rural areas. INSAT involves the departments of Space, Communications and Meteorology, as well as the Ministry of Information and Broadcasting.

Each of the two first-generation INSAT (INSAT-1) satellites will combine capability for long-distance telephony, continuous meteorological Earth observations in the visible and infra-red bands, relay of meteorological

Artist's impression of the CAT/APPLE/Meteosat payload for the third Ariane launch

data from unattended data platforms, disaster warning, direct TV broadcasting and programme distribution.

The Ford Aerospace & Communcations Corporation, USA, has been awarded a contract for fabrication of the INSAT-1 spacecraft and associated equipment for the master control facility (MCF) that is being created near Hassan, Karnataka.

ROHINI

The Rohini Satellite (RS-1), which weighs about 40 kg (88 lb), is designed to evaluate the performance of the fourth stage of the SLV-3 vehicle which will inject the satellite into an Earth orbit.

INTERNATIONAL PROGRAMMES

CIFAS
CONSORTIUM INDUSTRIEL FRANCO-ALLEMAND POUR LE SATELLITE SYMPHONIE (DEUTSCH-FRANZÖSICHES INDUSTRIE-KONSORTIUM FÜR DEN SATELLITEN SYMPHONIE)

BP 62, 78130 Les Mureaux, France
Telephone: 474 72 13
Telex: AIRSPA 60159F
ADMINISTRATOR: P. M. Usunier

This consortium was formed on 25 April 1968 in response to a request from the French and West German governments for proposals to develop a telecommunications satellite named Symphonie. Members of the con-

sortium, under the technical, industrial and commercial direction of Société Nationale Industrielle Aérospatiale (Division Systèmes Balistiques et Spatiaux), are Messerschmitt-Bölkow-Blohm, Thomson-CSF, SAT, Siemens-AG and AEG-Telefunken.

SYMPHONIE

The first operational Symphonie telephone/television satellite was launched by a Delta vehicle on 19 December 1974, and reached its geostationary position over the South Atlantic, at longitude 11·5°W, on 8 January 1975, giving coverage of two zones through two elliptical beams, each of 13° × 8°. The first beam covers Europe, North and Central Africa; the second beam covers South America and the eastern parts of North and Central America. The

second Symphonie was launched on 26 August 1975, and is also positioned at longitude 11·5°W.

The two satellites are used constantly for experiments, demonstrations, and a wide variety of operational services, including educational broadcasts to Africa, commercial television programmes and communications for the UN and UNESCO. Two transponders have a transmission capacity of 600 two-way telephone channels.

Symphonie was intended for 24-h use over a five-year period. The basic programme called for three flight units, plus the necessary spares. The third satellite, a refurbished prototype, has not yet been launched.

An illustration of Symphonie can be found in the 1979-80 *Jane's*.

COSMOS
ÉTUDES TECHNIQUES ET CONSTRUCTIONS AÉROSPATIALES SA (ETCA)

BP 97, 6000 Charleroi 1, Belgium
SOCIÉTÉ NATIONALE INDUSTRIELLE AÉROSPATIALE

BP 96, 78130 Les Mureaux, France
SOCIÉTÉ ANONYME DE TÉLÉCOMMUNICATIONS (SAT)

41 rue Cantagrel, 75624 Paris Cédex 13, France
MESSERSCHMITT-BÖLKOW-BLOHM GmbH (MBB)

8 München 80, Postfach 801 169, West Germany
CONSTRUCCIONES AERONAUTICAS SA (CASA)

Division Espacial, Getafe, Madrid, Spain
MARCONI SPACE & DEFENCE SYSTEMS LTD (MSDS)

The Grove, Stanmore, Middlesex HA7 4LY, England
SELENIA SpA

CP 7083, 00100 Rome, Italy

The COSMOS consortium was formed in November 1970. It is involved in several major space programmes, notably Exosat and Meteosat, of which details follow:

EXOSAT

In 1978, MBB of West Germany, acting as prime contractor for the COSMOS consortium, was awarded a con-

tract by ESA for development of the European X-Ray Observatory Satellite (Exosat). This satellite will extend the understanding of both point source and distributed cosmic X-ray sources.

MSDS is responsible for the attitude control system, which is so precise (about 2 arc seconds peak-to-peak in fine pointing) that astronomers will be able to identify for the first time point sources with very faint visible stars. In addition, MSDS is responsible for the orbit control system which, by adjusting the satellite velocity, will cause selected X-ray objects to be acculted by the Moon, giving further definition of the location of point sources and the distribution of extended ones. Exosat will be launched in November 1981 by a European Ariane.

METEOSAT

Aérospatiale of France, acting as prime contractor for the COSMOS consortium, was awarded a $56·76 million contract by ESA for development of this geosynchronous meteorological satellite in December 1973. The work culminated in launch of Meteosat 1 by a Delta 2914 vehicle on 23 November 1977. Launch of the second Meteosat was scheduled for September 1980, by an Ariane vehicle.

Ford Aerospace assists Aérospatiale's Cannes establishment in co-ordinating and integrating the project. Of the other COSMOS members, MBB is responsible for the spacecraft structure; Marconi Space & Defence Systems supplies the attitude and orbit control system and checkout equipment. MSDS is also responsible for the satellite's main communications package for all future missions.

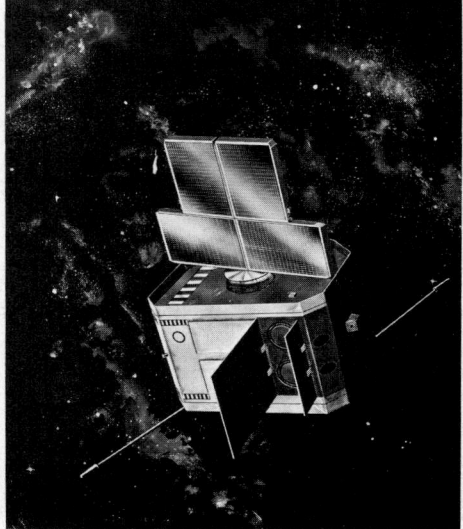

Artist's impression of Exosat

Meteosat represents Europe's contribution to a worldwide Global Atmospheric Research Programme (GARP), intended to utilise also US and Japanese satellites to provide data for the World Weather Watch Organisation. Meteosat's main mission is to transmit images of the Earth and its cloud cover every half-hour, using both visible light and the infra-red spectrum. It also relays processed images from the main station in Darmstadt to user stations. Data are collected from land-based, marine or airborne platforms at various points in the coverage zone.

Meteosat geostationary meteorological satellite

MESH
AERITALIA SpA
Piazzale V. Tecchio 51/A, 80125 Naples, Italy
BRITISH AEROSPACE DYNAMICS GROUP
Space and Communications Division, Gunnels Wood Road, Stevenage, Hertfordshire SG1 2AS, England
ERNO RAUMFAHRTTECHNIK GmbH
28 Bremen 1, Hünefeldstrasse 15, Postfach 1199, Germany
FOKKER-VFW
PO Box 7600, Schiphol Oost. The Netherlands
INTA
Departamento de Equipo y Armamento, Paseo del Pintor Rosales 34, Torrejon de Ardoz, Madrid 8, Spain
SA MATRA
BP No. 1, 78140 Vélizy, France
SAAB-SCANIA
S-581 88 Linköping, Sweden

This international consortium was formed in October 1966, the word MESH being an acronym of the initial letters of the four original founder members.

In addition to the OTS and ECS satellite programmes, MESH is involved in the maritime communications satellite MARECS, which employs basic ECS technology.

ECS
Five European Communications Satellites (ECS) are being developed and built, with British Aerospace Dynamics Group as prime contractor. ECS, based on the technology of OTS, will offer a fully operational indigenous regional satellite communications system, and will be capable of carrying a significant proportion of future European telephone, telex and TV traffic. The first ECS will be placed in geostationary orbit in 1981, by the European Ariane launcher, and it is planned that this should be followed by others between then and 1990, each satellite being designed for a minimum operational life of seven years. The launches will be made from the equatorial site at Kourou in French Guiana.

MARECS
This maritime communications programme, for which British Aerospace Dynamics Group is lead contractor, involves the initial procurement of three MARECS (the maritime version of ECS) satellites. Two will serve the

Eastern Atlantic and Indian Oceans, providing merchant shipping with instant communications to shore terminals by links vastly superior to the present highly congested HF circuits.

The basic structure, control and power systems are those of ECS, to which will be fitted complete communications packages being developed by MSDS. The first satellite was scheduled to be launched in 1980, into geostationary orbit over the western Indian Ocean. The system will be augmented by further launches into different orbital locations, until INMARSAT has established a worldwide maritime satellite communications system.

To permit the use of simple shipborne and shore-based terminals, MARECS will be equipped with a high-efficiency 'shaped beam' antenna, coupled with a transistorised L-band power amplifier. Ships will use L-band frequencies to communicate to and from the satellite. As shore terminals will be able to use more sophisticated equipment, the shore-to-satellite frequency will be in the 6GHz band and satellite-to-shore communications will use the 4GHz band.

OTS
This Orbital Test Satellite was produced under a three-year contract, with British Aerospace Dynamics Group as prime contractor, responsible for both development and launch support. It is intended to demonstrate the operational capabilities of high-technology communications systems, and to test experimental advanced communications concepts and propagation assumptions in space, as a preliminary to the ECS programme.

A failure in the Delta launch vehicle caused the first OTS to be lost in September 1977. The second OTS was

Artist's impression of OTS satellite in orbit

launched successfully on 11 May 1978 and arrived on station at 10°E on 21 May.

OTS has exceeded the performance standards specified, and has demonstrated its ability to transmit TV signals to, and receive them from, small mobile ground stations.

STAR
BRITISH AEROSPACE DYNAMICS GROUP
Bristol Division, PO Box 5, Filton, Bristol BS 12 7QW, England
CONTRAVES AG
Schaffhauserstrasse 580, CH-8052 Zurich 11, Switzerland
CGE-FIAR
Via G.B. Grassi 93, 20157 Milan, Italy
DORNIER SYSTEM GmbH
Postfach 648, 799 Friedrichshafen/Bodensee, West Germany
TELEFONAKTIEBOLAGET L. M. ERICSSON
126 25 Stockholm, Sweden

MONTEDEL (MONTECATINI EDISON ELETRONICA SpA)
Via E Bassini 15, 20133 Milan, Italy
SENER SA
Guzman el Bueno 133, Madrid 3, Spain
SOCIÉTÉ EUROPÉENNE DE PROPULSION
Tour Roussel-Nobel, 92080 Paris Défense Cédex 3, France
THOMSON-CSF
173 boulevard Hausmann, 75360 Paris Cédex 08, France

STAR (Satellites for Telecommunications, Applications and Research) companies are involved in several

major space programmes, including development of the ISPM satellite, described under the NASA entry.

Details of STAR's earlier ISEE-2 satellite can be found in the 1979-80 Jane's.

GEOS
The GEOS-2 spacecraft in geostationary orbit, launched on 14 July 1978 and described in the 1977-78 Jane's, continues to provide a wealth of data about the Earth's magnetic environment; data transmission is equivalent to ten pages of 2,000 characters every second. British Aerospace Dynamics was prime contractor for GEOS-1 and 2. The possibility of launching a third GEOS satellite is being studied.

ITALY

AERITALIA
AERITALIA-SOCIETÀ AEROSPAZIALE ITALIANA p.a.
DIVERSIFIED ACTIVITIES GROUP
HEADQUARTERS: See Aircraft section
EXECUTIVE DIRECTOR: Ing Stefano Abba
Space Sector
Corso Marche, 41-10146 Turin
Telephone: (011) 33321
Telex: 23076 AERITOR

Aeritalia is engaged in research and development of missile and space vehicle systems. It is a member of the

ERNO Spacelab consortium and of the MESH European satellite consortium.

The Space Sector's current activities include work on the structure and heat shields for the Italian Alfa vehicle (described in 1977-78 Jane's) and its engine; development of the Iris interorbital satellite launch system; work on the OTS, MARECS and ECS satellites and on the thermal control system for Spacelab.

IRIS
Aeritalia has an agreement with SNIA (Space and Defence Division) for the development and production of

a new vehicle to facilitate interorbital space transportation. IRIS (Italian Research Interim Stage) is a propulsive stage conceived to transfer from low orbit into transfer orbit any kind of geosynchronous satellite.

IRIS would be used as the last stage of a complete satellite launching system. Once in orbit, its motor would be fired by radio command, or by a preprogrammed signal, to give the satellite the necessary additional thrust to reach an altitude of 36,000 km (22,370 miles), corresponding to geosynchronous orbit. It is intended to be used primarily from the Space Shuttle Orbiter, but could be utilised for special missions involving launch rockets such as the European Ariane.

CNA
COMPAGNIA NAZIONALE AEROSPAZIALE

Via Salaria Km 9·3, 00199 Rome

Telephone: (06) 840 2021

Telex: 610295 CNASPA

DIRECTOR GENERAL: Dott Antonio Teofilatto

This company succeeds the former Compagnia Industriale Aerospaziale, which was formed in 1965 for the design and development of aerospace systems. Its current parent companies are Aeritalia, Montedison Sistemi, Selenia and SNIA Viscosa.

The company was involved primarily in development of the Sirio satellite, produced under the sponsorship of the Consiglio Nazionale Ricerche (CNR) of Rome and launched on 25 August 1977. Sirio reached station at 15°W longitude on 8 September 1977 where it is involved in SHF propagation experiments. Brief details of this satellite were given in the 1977-78 *Jane's*.

CN Aerospaziale is currently developing Sirio 2, designed to support the METEOSAT and LASSO missions, under contract to the European Space Agency.

JAPAN

MITSUBISHI
MITSUBISHI JUKOGYO KABUSHIKI KAISHA
(Mitsubishi Heavy Industries Ltd)

5-1, Marunouchi, 2-chome, Chiyoda-ku, Tokyo 100
OFFICERS: See Aircraft section
MANAGER, SPACE SYSTEMS DEPARTMENT: M. Hamada

Mitsubishi Heavy Industries has co-operated with the National Space Development Agency of Japan in the programme for the N-I and N-II launch vehicles; with the National Aerospace Laboratory, which supports rocket research; and with the Institute of Space and Aeronautical Science, University of Tokyo, which is a major contributor to scientific satellite programmes. It is also a designer and manufacturer of space subsystems, and ground support equipment.

Mitsubishi had delivered six N-Is by early 1980 and is scheduled to produce two more before 1983. It is also developing the second stage of the H-1 launch vehicle for NASDA, and GS-1, Japan's first geosurvey satellite, in co-operation with Kawasaki and Canon Corporation. The GS-1 is to be launched by NASDA into a geosynchronous orbit with the eighth and last N-I rocket in FY 1983.

MITSUBISHI ELECTRIC CORPORATION
(MELCO)

2-3, Marunouchi, 2-chome, Chiyoda-ku, Tokyo 100

Mitsubishi Electric Corporation has designed and manufactured a succession of satellites for NASDA (which see), often in partnership with Ford Aerospace & Communications Corporation. Among the latest of these was Japan's second Experimental Communications Satellite, ECS-B. This was launched successfully on 22 February 1980, but was lost in orbit three days later during a boost motor burn towards geostationary orbit.

NASDA
NATIONAL SPACE DEVELOPMENT AGENCY OF JAPAN

2-4-1, Hamamatsu-cho, Minato-ku, Tokyo 105
Telephone: (03) 435 6111
Telex: J28424
PRESIDENT: Akiyoshi Matsuura
DIRECTOR, INTERNATIONAL AFFAIRS DEPARTMENT: Hiroshi Uda

This Agency was established on 1 October 1969, with primary responsibility for Japanese development of satellites, launch vehicles, tracking systems, and associated facilities and equipment.

In addition to the programme of satellites to be launched by the N vehicle (which see), NASDA has another programme involving three geostationary satellites launched by US vehicles—Geostationary Meteorological Satellite (GMS-1) launched on 14 July 1977 and described in 1977-78 *Jane's*, the experimental Communications Satellite (CS) Sakura, launched on 15 December 1977, and the experimental Broadcasting Satellite (BSE) Yuri launched on 7 April 1978. CS and BSE are described in the 1978-79 *Jane's*.

The future NASDA programme calls for the launching of two more engineering satellites, a second met-sat, a geosurvey satellite, second and third com-sats, the second and third TV-sats and a maritime observation satellite.

H-1 LAUNCH VEHICLE

This three-stage vehicle is being designed to launch heavy satellites in the mid-eighties. The H-1 will employ Japan's first liquid hydrogen/liquid oxygen rocket motor, developed by Mitsubishi, as its second stage, and will be able to launch satellites weighing 500 kg (1,102 lb) into geostationary orbit.

N LAUNCH VEHICLE

The three-stage N-I launch vehicle is capable of putting a 1,200 kg (2,645 lb) satellite into a 300 km (186 mile) circular orbit, or a 130 kg (286 lb) satellite into a geostationary orbit. The first stage consists of a Douglas DSV-3N-1 liquid-propellant (liquid oxygen/kerosene) rocket, with three Nissan (Thiokol TX-354-5) solid-propellant strap-on boosters (approx 1,471 kN; 330,600 lb st); the LE-3 second stage is powered by a storable liquid rocket (NTO/A-50), and the third stage by a Thiokol TE-364-14 solid rocket. The guidance system is of the strap-down radio command type. The N-II vehicle has an extended long-tank DSV-3P-1, nine strap-on boos-

Artist's impression of GMS-2

ters and inertial guidance, and is designed to put a 350 kg (772 lb) satellite into geostationary orbit. It is scheduled to be tested in 1981, and will have an Aerojet AJ10-118FJ second stage instead of the LE-3 of the N-I.

With the N vehicle NASDA launched the Ionosphere Sounding Satellite-B (ISS-B) Ume on 16 February 1978, and the Experimental Communications Satellite (ECS-A) Ayame on 6 February 1979. ECS-B, the backup of Ayame, was launched successfully on 22 February 1980. ETS-III, which is being designed to establish the production and operational technology of three-axis stabilised satellites with a high-accuracy attitude control system, is to be launched in 1982. Other satellites planned for launch by N-II vehicles are ETS-IV, designed to prove the operational technology required for later large-scale satellites; GMS-2, CS-2 and BS-2 (second-generation developments of Himawari, Sakura and Yuri); and AMES, which is to establish operational technology for aeronautical and maritime satellite systems. CS-2 is scheduled for launch in 1983 and AMES in 1985.

First launching of N rocket

The main parameters of the N-I and N-II vehicles are:

DIMENSIONS (approx):	
Length overall: N-I	32·6 m (106 ft 11 in)
N-II	35·4 m (116 ft 2 in)
Diameter of first stage:	
N-I and N-II	2·4 m (8 ft 2½ in)
WEIGHT (approx): N-I	90,400 kg (199,298 lb)
N-II	134,700 kg (296,963 lb)

NISSAN
NISSAN JIDOSHA KABUSHIKI KAISHA
(Nissan Motor Co Ltd)

HEAD OFFICE: 17-1, 6-chome, Ginza, Chuo-ku, Tokyo
AERONAUTICAL AND SPACE DIVISION: 5-1, 3-chome, Momoi, Suginami-ku, Tokyo
Telephone: (390) 1111
Telex: 232 2271
CHAIRMAN: Katsuji Kawamata
PRESIDENT: Takashi Ishihara

MANAGING DIRECTOR AND GENERAL MANAGER, AERONAUTICAL AND SPACE DIVISION: Kazuo Shibata

The Aeronautical and Space Division of Nissan has a major share of the market for solid rocket motors in Japan. It has produced many sounding rockets and space launch vehicles for the Institute of Space and Aeronautical Science, University of Tokyo (ISAS); National Aerospace Laboratory; Meteorological Agency; and Antarctic Research Centre. Nissan has also fabricated a number of strap-on boosters for the N satellite launch vehicles of the National Space Development Agency of Japan (NASDA), under licence from Thiokol Corporation, USA. The third-stage solid-propellant motors of the N vehicle are procured from Thiokol and serviced by Nissan.

Mu ROCKET

Details of Mu-4S, Mu-3C, Mu-3C-1 and Mu-3C-2 satellite launching rockets were given in the 1977-78 *Jane's*. The Mu-3H launch vehicle is basically an Mu-3C with an improved M13 first stage. The latest development,

Mu-3S, is basically an Mu-3H with thrust vectoring control (TVC) on both the first and second stages. The M13-TVC first stage develops 925 kN (208,000 lb st). The new rocket was used to launch the 185 kg (408 lb) engineering test satellite MS-T4 on 17 February 1980. When developed, the Mu-3S will be able to place payloads of around 270 kg (595 lb) into a nominal 250 km (155 mile) orbit.

Nissan is also developing a new launch rocket, similar in size to Mu-3S, but with improved second and third stages, and two large strap-on boosters for the first stage. This rocket will be able to place a 700 kg (1,543 lb) payload into a 750 km (466 mile) circular orbit, and is to be used to send Japan's first interplanetary spacecraft, Planet-A, to Venus in FY 1985.

Brief details of the MS-T3 Tansei 3 and Exos-A satellites launched by Mu vehicles were given in the 1978-79 *Jane's*. Exos-B was launched on 16 September 1978 and placed in a 30,558 × 230 km (18,987 × 143 mile) orbit; when in orbit this scientific satellite was named Jikiken. Corsa-B (Hakucho), an X-ray observation satellite, was launched on 21 February 1979. The 120 kg (265 lb) ISAS scientific satellites Astro-A, Astro-B and Exos-C will be launched by the improved Mu-3S boosters in the 1980s.

The following details apply to the Mu-3H:
TYPE: Solid-propellant three-stage satellite launch vehicle.
POWER PLANT: M13 first stage gives 866 kN (194,670 lb st) at sea level, and is supplemented by eight SB-310 strap-on boosters, giving a total of 690 kN (155,200 lb st). The M22-TVC second stage gives 252 kN (56,800 lb st), and is fitted with liquid-injection thrust vector control. The M3A third stage gives 51·6 kN (11,600 lb st) and has a similar control system.
DIMENSIONS:
Length overall:
M13 1st stage   14·9 m (48 ft 11 in)
M22 2nd stage   4·6 m (15 ft 1 in)
M3A 3rd stage   2·0 m (6 ft 7 in)
Diameter:
M13 1st stage   1·41 m (4 ft 7½ in)
M22 2nd stage   1·41 m (4 ft 7½ in)
M3A 3rd stage   1·14 m (3 ft 9 in)

WEIGHTS:
At launch:
M13 1st stage   32,264 kg (71,130 lb)
SB boosters (8)   3,825 kg (8,432 lb)
M22 2nd stage   8,635 kg (19,037 lb)
M3A 3rd stage   1,240 kg (2,734 lb)

Upper-stage spherical motor and Jikiken satellite

Mu-3H-3 launch vehicle

UNION OF SOVIET SOCIALIST REPUBLICS

Available details of Soviet satellites, space probes and spacecraft have appeared in *Jane's* since the 1959-60 edition, together with descriptions of the A-2 and A-3 research rockets and meteorological rockets which are standard vehicles in constant use.

Recent sounding rocket activities included the launch, using an SS-5 'Skean', of the Vertical-8 payload on 26 September 1979. A joint Soviet-Polish-Czechoslovakian mission, this was designed to measure short-wave radiation, and the recoverable instrument container was separated from the main payload as it descended through 95 km (59 miles).

COSMOS SATELLITES

This series of satellites is continuing the Soviet programme of research into physical phenomena in space and the Earth's upper atmosphere; and into the technical problems involved in spaceflight and the development of spacecraft design and their systems; as well as conducting experiments of an applied nature of interest to science and the Soviet economy.

The wide terms of reference mean that a Cosmos satellite can vary from a small uninstrumented device to a large spacecraft capable of life support, and military applications. The majority of the scientific satellites are of a basic standard design in which various experiment payloads can be accommodated. They are cylindrical in shape, approximately 1·83 m (6 ft) long by 1·05 m (3 ft 6 in) in diameter and weigh about 360 kg (800 lb).

Cosmos 637, launched on 26 March 1974, was the first satellite in the series to be placed in a synchronous orbit. Positioned over the Indian Ocean, it is assumed to have been an early version of the Statsionar communications satellite announced by the Soviet authorities in 1970. Statsionar 1, the first operational satellite of this class, was launched on 22 December 1975. (See the Raduga entry in this section.)

In October 1976, the Soviet authorities announced the creation of the Morsvyazsputnik Organisation, which is responsible for the management of Soviet maritime communications satellites.

MILITARY COSMOS

As the satellite table at the end of this section indicates, Cosmos designations are given to Soviet reconnaissance satellites and other types of military spacecraft.

Cosmos reconnaissance satellites are launched from the bases at Plesetsk and Tyuratam, usually into orbits with inclinations of 52°, 65° or 72°. Most eject capsules after 8 or 13 days and these are recovered. Some have the capacity for in-flight frequency changing; others have a small manoeuvring capability for precise target coverage.

A number of test vehicles for the Soviet Union's Fractional Orbital Bombardment System were given Cosmos designations. Cosmos designations have also been given to

Cosmos scientific satellite (*Maurice Allward*)   **Mockup of Cosmos 782 biological satellite, embodying components of Vostok manned spacecraft** (*Tass*)

spacecraft which have the capability of intercepting other satellites. Early 'interceptors' were Cosmos 249, 252, 374 and 375. In the first of a later series of typical tests, Cosmos 803, launched on 12 February 1976, was the target and was intercepted by Cosmos 804 and 814. Cosmos 804 executed three major manoeuvres and achieved a close intercept, after which it was manoeuvred out of orbit. Other Cosmos satellites used for intercept tests were described in the 1977-78 *Jane's*. Three distinct attack procedures appear to be used: Eccentric Orbit mode, where the attack satellite is launched into an eccentric orbit in which it makes a flyby of the target; Circular Orbit mode, where the attack satellite is injected into a circular orbit similar to that of the target, the interception being made at a slower flyby speed; Pop-Up mode, where the attack satellite intercepts within one revolution, in contrast to the other two modes, which require several revolutions. The Pop-Up mode of attack is difficult to counter, as there is little advance indication of an intended target. It was reported in 1980 that at least one of the Soviet anti-satellite systems was then operational.

A number of Cosmos satellites have been launched into orbits suitable for ocean surveillance missions. The first of these was Cosmos 198, launched on 27 December 1967. Cosmos 651 and subsequent spacecraft in this series appear to be bigger, with a length of about 12 m (40 ft) compared with 6 m (20 ft) of the earlier satellites. All the satellites were launched into an initially low orbit of about 250 km (155 miles) but after a few weeks moved into an approximately circular orbit of 1,000 km (620 miles).

COSMOS LAUNCHERS

Two categories of launch vehicle appear to be used for Cosmos and Intercosmos satellites, and other Soviet spacecraft. One category is based on the structures and power plants of standard missiles, such as the SS-4 ('Sandal'), SS-5 ('Skean') and SS-9 ('Scarp'), with additional upper stages as required. The other combines the basic core vehicle developed originally for the Vostok manned spacecraft with a variety of upper stages. Examples are as follows:

SS-4 + Cosmos stage. First stage powered by 706·34 kN (158,800 lb st) RD-214 four-chamber liquid-propellant rocket engine, burning nitric acid and kerosene. Second stage powered by RD-119 single-chamber engine, burning liquid oxygen and dimethyl-hydrazine, and giving 107·87 kN (24,250 lb thrust) in vacuum. Typical launch, on 26 June 1974, orbited Cosmos 662, a 408 kg (900 lb) ellipsoid, 1·83 m (6 ft) long with a diameter of 1·22 m (4 ft), intended for scientific research. (Referred to as B-1 Cosmos in drawing on page 684).

SS-5 + Restart stage. A typical application for the SS-5 is to orbit satellites like Cosmos 655 and 661. Shaped as cylinders, 1·83 m (6 ft) long and 0·91 m (3 ft) in diameter, with paddle-type solar panels, these are thought to have navigation and/or electronic intelligence missions. (Referred to as C-1 Cosmos in drawing on page 684).

SS-9 + FOBS stage. Frequent launches of this vehicle are expected to contribute to continued development of Fractional Orbital Bombardment System techniques and/or to ocean surveillance missions. Satellites like Cosmos 651 and 654 normally remain in low parking orbit for two months, then split and move into a 104 min orbit.

Vostok core + Venus stage. This standard launch vehicle has many applications. It is used with an escape stage to orbit the 1,250 kg (2,750 lb) uprated Molniya 2 communications satellites. Typical military payloads were Cosmos 639, a manoeuvrable reconnaissance satellite intended probably to study the breakup of Arctic pack ice; and Cosmos 658, a reconnaissance satellite in the form of a four-ton sphere-cylinder, 5·0 m (16 ft 6 in) long, which remained in orbit for 12 days.

EKRAN

Ekran (Screen) is the name given by Vasily Shamshin, Soviet First Deputy Minister of Communications, to a new generation of geostationary television relay satellites, although the first spacecraft in the series was given the international registration of Statsionar T.

Purpose of the satellite is to make it possible to set up a system of television communications throughout the whole of the Soviet Union.

Ekran is a direct-broadcast satellite, relaying television signals directly to community aerials throughout the country. Earlier Statsionar satellites are conventional relay spacecraft, transmitting programmes from Moscow to special Earth satellite stations in the USSR and bordering countries.

The Ekran spacecraft is operating at 714MHz and, in addition to advanced relay equipment, embodies a three-axis Earth-directed orientation system, a power supply system using solar batteries which is independently orientated on the Sun, an orbital correction system, a radio telemetry system to transmit information on the functioning of the various systems, and a radio system for the accurate measurement of the orbital parameters and spacecraft control.

Ekran 1 (Statsionar T) was launched on 26 October 1976 into a geostationary orbit and then manoeuvred into its scheduled position at 90° E.

Ekran geostationary TV relay satellite, displayed at 1977 Paris Air Show *(Flight International)*

HORIZONT

Horizont (Horizon) is the name given to a series of communications satellites for telephone and television transmissions. The use of an inclined orbit gives better coverage for areas in the far north of the Soviet Union. The first Horizont satellite was launched on 19 December 1978 into an elliptical orbit with a significantly higher perigee than Molniya satellites.

INTERCOSMOS SATELLITES

Launched on 14 October 1969, Intercosmos 1 involved the co-operation of seven Socialist countries: Bulgaria, Czechoslovakia, Germany (Democratic Republic), Hungary, Poland, Romania and the USSR. The satellite carried scientific instruments developed and made in Czechoslovakia and Germany as well as in the USSR. Its programme was devoted mainly to research connected with the Sun, and involved simultaneous observations in the seven participating countries into radio-astronomical, ionospheric and optical phenomena.

Details of subsequent Intercosmos launches have been given in successive editions of *Jane's*. Spacecraft in this series launched during 1979 are listed in the satellite table at the end of this section.

METEOR

Meteor is the name given to the Soviet series of first-generation operational meteorological satellites, developed from Cosmos prototypes.

The Meteor system consists of three satellites in orbital planes at 90° and 180° to each other, so that they pass over a given area of the Earth on the northbound pass at intervals of about 6 h and 12 h, and again during the southbound pass.

The satellites, which provide information about the state of the atmosphere both on the 'daylight' and 'night' sides of the Earth, are stabilised so that the camera lenses and infra-red instruments always point towards the Earth.

Information received from Meteors is supplied to the Soviet hydro-meteorological service and to the World Meteorological Service. Cloud cover picture charts are transmitted to Washington, Geneva, Tokyo, Sydney and other foreign weather services.

Meteor 1 was launched on 26 March 1969; and launchings have continued at a current rate of three or four per year. An improved version, **Meteor 2**, is now in service. Launchings of both types are recorded in the annual satellite table.

MOLNIYA

Molniya 1 (Lightning), launched on 23 April 1965, was a communications satellite placed in a highly elliptical orbit designed to provide the longest possible communications sessions between Moscow and Vladivostok. It was the first Soviet communications satellite. On 24 November 1971, **Molniya 2A**, the first of a new uprated version, was launched from Plesetsk.

Launches of both versions have continued, and the current operational system consists of four pairs of each type of Molniya circling the Earth in orbital planes spaced at 90° intervals. The planes rotate at the rate of about 1° a day, in order to maintain stationary ground tracks over the Earth throughout the year, thus providing predictable communications coverage over the whole of the USSR.

Full-scale model of Molniya 2 communications satellite *(Brian M. Service)*

Molniya 3 is the latest version, embodying improved communications equipment able to accommodate colour television and new communications frequencies. The first of the new spacecraft was launched on 21 November 1974, and was placed in a normal Molniya-type 12 h 17 min orbit, with its 650 km (400 mile) perigee over the southern hemisphere and its apogee of 40,690 km (25,283 miles) over the northern hemisphere.

The Molniya satellites, together with the Ekran and Raduga satellites (which see), operate in conjunction with 60 ground stations to provide the Orbita national communications system. The ground network cost 100 million roubles and took seven years to construct. To achieve similar results using radio relay systems, or land lines, would have taken more than 20 years and cost thousands of millions of roubles.

PROGNOZ

Launched on 14 April 1972, Prognoz 1 (Forecast) was the first of a series of satellites designed specifically to study processes of solar activity, and their influence on the interplanetary medium and the Earth's magnetosphere.

Prognoz is basically spherical, with four cruciform solar panels extended to provide power via an internal rechargeable chemical battery. The sphere, filled with an inert gas, contains telemetry equipment, temperature control components and the electrical system. Experiments on board are intended to measure: electromagnetic solar radiation generated simultaneously with solar flares; solar cosmic radiation; solar wind plasma; and radio waves.

Subsequent Prognoz launches have been recorded in the annual tables of satellites.

PROGRESS

Progress is a non-reusable unmanned spacecraft, designed to ferry supplies and equipment up to space stations of the Salyut type. A development of the basic two-man Soyuz spacecraft, it is lightened as much as possible, with all the normal Soyuz life support systems removed, to permit carriage of the maximum practicable payload. The propulsion module is almost unchanged; but the size of the instrument module is increased. The major change entails replacement of the standard Soyuz descent module with a tanker module carrying propellants.

Positioning, rendezvous, approach and docking can be effected automatically or controlled from Salyut. The freight compartment of Progress is hermetically sealed, so that, after the vehicle has docked, cosmonauts can work in comfort while transferring supplies to their space station.

After transfer of the supplies, the spacecraft is used as a receptacle for waste material such as spent oxygen regenerators and filters, empty food and water cartons, sewage and redundant flight documentation. It is then jettisoned, to burn up in the atmosphere on re-entry; recovery is not attempted.

Weight of the first Progress was announced as 7,020 kg (15,476 lb), of which 2,300 kg (5,071 lb) was cargo, 1,000 kg (2,204 lb) fuel and 1,300 kg (2,866 lb) food etc. Weight varies according to mission. Progress is 10·8 m (35 ft 5 in) long with a maximum diameter of 3·7 m (12 ft 2 in)

Progress 1. Launched on 20 January 1978, ferried supplies to Salyut 6, with which it docked on 22 January.

Prognoz 2 solar research satellite *(Tass)*

While docked, the first-ever refuelling in space was conducted on 3 February, following checks by the crew of Soyuz 26. The spacecraft undocked on 6 February, and re-entered and burned up the next day.

Details of **Progress 2 to 7**, which supported the Soyuz 26-28 and Soyuz 29-34 missions to Salyut 6, were given in the 1979-80 *Jane's*.

RADUGA/STATSIONAR

Raduga (Rainbow) is the name of a Soviet system of geostationary-orbit communications satellites, the first operational version of which, **Statsionar 1**, was launched on 22 December 1975.

Statsionars are three-axis stabilised, and transmit at higher power levels than comparable US-launched Intelsat IV spacecraft. This enables them to communicate with smaller and therefore cheaper ground terminals. Currently, the spacecraft communicate with the Orbita network of ground stations set up for the Molniya programme.

Details of Statsionar launches can be found in the annual tables of satellites.

SALYUT

Salyut (Salute) spacecraft have served as orbital scientific stations for the crews of Soyuz manned spacecraft. Basically, the station is a stepped cylinder about 13 m (42 ft 8 in) long, from 2·13 m (7 ft) to 4·0 m (13 ft) in diameter, with a weight of 18½ tons.

Details of Salyut 1 and 2 can be found in the 1973-74 *Jane's*. Salyut 3 was described in the 1975-76 edition. Salyut 4 and 5 were described in the 1977-78 edition.

Salyut 6, launched on 29 September 1977, is a major development of Salyut 5, the main change being the embodiment of a second docking port so that two Soyuz-type spacecraft can be docked simultaneously. The additional port is located on the instrument section, opposite the original port on the transfer compartment. The two ports are identical, and the automatic rendezvous procedure is the same at both, but only the new port embodies refuelling facilities. Normal crew is two, increasing for

Launch vehicle for Vertical 4 payload *(Tass)*

Full-scale representation of the Salyut 3/4 type of space station *(Tass)*

Launch vehicle for Intercosmos 16 satellite *(Tass)*

short periods of time to four. Soviet sources indicate that the station can support six cosmonauts.

Internal modifications by comparison with early Salyuts include the installation of a folding shower cubicle, into which hot water is sprayed and recovered by an extractor pump. Sensors are fitted to register the impact of micrometeorites.

Major items of equipment installed in the Working Compartment include a BST-IM submillimetre telescope, an MKF-6M multi-spectral camera and a KT-140 high-resolution topographical camera system.

An initial programme of research involving Soyuz 26, 27 and 28, and Progress 1, was described in the 1978-79 *Jane's*. A second programme started on 16 June 1978 with the docking of Soyuz 29 (see 1979-80 *Jane's*), crewed by Vladimir Kovalyonok and Alexander Ivanchenkov, who set a new endurance record for manned space flight of 140 days, ending on 2 November 1978.

During this period the two cosmonauts carried out an extensive programme of research and experiments, were visited by the crews of Soyuz 30 and 31 (see 1979-80 *Jane's*), and were resupplied with fuel, food and equipment ferried up by the Progress 2, 3 and 4 unmanned transport spacecraft. Activities during the 140-day programme included a 2 h 5 min EVA on 29 July 1978 by Kovalyonok and Ivanchenkov, and a burn of the Progress 4 engines on 20 October to raise the Salyut's orbit. The second programme ended on 2 November 1978 with the return to Earth of the two cosmonauts in Soyuz 31.

A third programme started on 26 February 1979 with the docking of Soyuz 32 and the boarding of cosmonauts Lyakhov and Ryumin. During this mission, Soyuz 33 and 34 and Progress 5, 6 and 7 (see Addenda to 1979-80 *Jane's*) docked with the space station. The mission ended on 19 August 1979 with the return to Earth of Lyakhov and Ryumin in Soyuz 34 after a record endurance for manned spaceflight of 175 days and 36 min in space.

SOYUZ SPACECRAFT

Developed for the Soviet Earth-orbital space station programme, Soyuz spacecraft each comprise three basic sections or modules: a laboratory-cum-rest compartment (orbital module), a descent compartment (landing module) and a propulsion and instrument section (service module). The orbital module is mounted on the extreme nose of the craft, and communicates with the landing module via a hermetically-sealed hatch. The orbital and landing modules are pressurised to 1·01 bars (14·7 lb/sq in), have a combined internal volume of 9 m³ (318 cu ft) and can accommodate up to four cosmonauts.

The service module contains the main systems for orbital flight, together with a liquid-propellant propulsion system embodying two motors (one a standby) each with a thrust of 3·92 kN (880 lb). These allow midcourse manoeuvres, up to heights of 1,300 km (800 miles), and are used for the de-orbit manoeuvre. Another system provides attitude control. Attached to the service module is a solar-cell array having an area of about 14 m² (150 sq ft).

The landing module contains the parachutes and landing rockets. A backup parachute system is available in case of failure. The main parachute, preceded by a pilot 'chute, is deployed at 8,000 m (27,000 ft). Retro-rockets, operating at a height of 1 m (3 ft) above the ground, ensure a landing velocity not exceeding 3 m/s (10 ft/s). The aerodynamic design of the landing module permits landing loads to be kept within 3-4*g*, although ballistic re-entries, involving loads of 8-10*g*, can be made if required. The overall length of the craft is about 9 m (30 ft), the diameter of the crew compartments about 2·1 m (7 ft) and the all-up weight about 6,000 kg (13,000 lb).

The Soyuz craft are equipped with an automatic control system for approach and docking manoeuvres, the technique and external aerials being similar to those employed on the Cosmos spacecraft 186 and 188, and 212 and 213.

The missions of Soyuz 1 to 34 were described in previous editions of *Jane's*, including the Addenda to the 1979-80 edition.

Soyuz 35. Launched on 9 April 1980, with Lt Col Leonid Popov (commander) and Valery Ryumin (engineer), Soyuz 35 docked with Salyut 6 on 10 April to begin a fourth programme of research. The space station had been orbiting unmanned since the return to Earth of Lyakhov and Ryumin in Soyuz 34, on 19 August 1979, after a record 175 days in space.

SOYUZ T SPACECRAFT

Soyuz T is a new version of the spacecraft used normally to orbit two-man crews. Dr Konstantin Feoktistov, the cosmonaut and spacecraft designer, described the spacecraft as being similar to earlier Soyuz craft in external appearance, but with many changes to internal layout and equipment. The onboard digital computer, which controls manoeuvring operations and the systems, also transmits processed data to Earth. For example, when docking, the computer displays on a visual display unit (VDU) at mission control how all the main systems are working. A new propulsion system is embodied, in which all engines (main propulsion, manoeuvre and attitude control) use a common source of propellants. The landing system has also been changed.

Soyuz T was first launched on 16 December 1979, unmanned, and docked with Salyut 6 (also unmanned) on 19 December on a test mission. Earlier tests of Soyuz T systems were carried out on Cosmos 1001, launched on 4 April 1978, and Cosmos 1074, launched on 31 January 1979.

SOYUZ LAUNCHER

The vehicle used for launching Soyuz spacecraft appears to be a development of the booster used for launching the original Vostok spacecraft, with some 11·8 m (36 ft) of additional upper staging and structures. To cater for the increased weight and bending moment the inter-stage truss is strengthened. During launch, the Soyuz vehicle is surmounted by an escape tower.

It is not possible to identify the current engines in the launch vehicle, or give their individual ratings. However, official Soviet reports have stated that the vehicle has a total thrust of around 60 million horsepower, which is three times the power quoted for the original Vostok launcher. The basic configuration has not changed. Thus, the first stage consists of a central core, powered by an engine with four primary nozzles and four verniers. This is surrounded by four wrap-round boosters, each with four primary nozzles and two verniers, so that 32 rocket chambers are fired simultaneously during lift-off.

Data given in a brochure issued by Aérospatiale of France suggest that the Soyuz launcher can insert payloads of up to 7,500 kg (16,535 lb) into low circular orbit; 2,400 kg (5,290 lb) into geostationary transfer orbit; and satellites of up to 1,100 kg (2,425 lb) into geostationary orbit.

VENUS

Venus is the name given to a series of spacecraft developed specifically to explore the planet Venus. Details of Venus 1 to 12 were given in earlier editions of *Jane's*, and the basic spacecraft was described in the 1977-78 edition.

VENUS LAUNCHER

Although basically similar in configuration to the launchers used for the Soviet manned spacecraft, the launcher for Venus probes appears to have elongated first and second stages, giving an increase in propellant tankage.

ZONDA LAUNCHER

A drawing purporting to show this largest known Soviet launch vehicle appeared in a brochure issued by Aéro-

Launch of Soyuz 28 (Note: photograph could not be trimmed to show true vertical lift-off) *(Tass)*

spatiale of France in 1977. The drawing, of which a copy appears on page 684, suggests that Zonda has the same configuration as the Soyuz vehicle. The first stage is shown as a large-diameter core, surrounded by six large boosters. The upper stages are attached by a truss structure.

Overall height of Zonda is shown as about 61·33 m (201 ft). It is stated to be able to insert a payload of 22,000 kg (48,500 lb) into low circular orbit; 5,000 kg (11,020 lb) into geostationary transfer orbit; and satellites weighing up to 1,600 kg (3,525 lb) into geostationary orbit.

UNITED KINGDOM

BAe
BRITISH AEROSPACE DYNAMICS GROUP

HEAD OFFICE: Six Hills Way, Stevenage, Hertfordshire SG1 2DA
CHAIRMAN AND CHIEF EXECUTIVE: G. R. Jefferson, CBE, BSc, CEng, MIMechE, FRAeS
HEAD OF PUBLIC RELATIONS: M. K. Hird

Space and Communications Division
Gunnels Wood Road, Stevenage, Hertfordshire SG1 2AS
MANAGING DIRECTOR: P. L. V. Hickman
SALES DIRECTOR: R. G. T. Munday, BSc, ARCS, CEng, FRAeS

Following nationalisation of major units of the UK aerospace industry, British Aircraft Corporation's Guided Weapons Division and Hawker Siddeley Dynamics Ltd became the Dynamics Group of British Aerospace on 1 January 1978; on 1 January 1980 the Space and Communications Division was established as a separate business unit within the Dynamics Group. Both of the former concerns had played major roles in British and international space projects for many years, as described in previous editions of *Jane's*.

Among a wide variety of space technology programmes currently in hand, under contract to the European Space Agency and US companies, BAe Dynamics is leading the MESH international consortium as prime contractor for ESA's European Communications Satellite (ECS) and MARECS, a maritime version of ECS. The ECS project aims to provide a fully operational satellite communications system for Europe in the 1980s, providing bulk telephone transmissions in 'time division multiple-access' mode, and TV distribution to complement existing terrestrial systems. MARECS (described in the MESH entry) will provide direct telephone and telex links between ships in distant oceans and shore stations in the UK and elsewhere.

BAe Dynamics has been appointed prime contractor by ESA for the L-Sat large communications satellite which will be about twice the size of ECS. Also for ESA, BAe Dynamics in 1979 completed a study of the payload for an Earth Resources Survey Satellite System, and is currently developing and manufacturing the 33 m² (356 sq ft) 4kW solar array and the photon detector assembly for NASA's Space Telescope being built by Lockheed Missiles and Space Company. Other solar array work for spacecraft applications, under contract to ESA, includes development of a 6kW lightweight flexible fold-out array for direct-broadcast television satellites of the next decade, and proposals to augment Space Shuttle power, using solar power modules of up to 60kW.

BAe Dynamics is to develop the attitude and orbit control equipment for the interplanetary satellite being manufactured by the STAR consortium for the International Solar Polar Mission (ISPM). Under contract to Marconi Space & Defence Systems, it was design authority for Britain's Ariel 6 scientific satellite, launched on 3 June 1979 for investigations into high energy physics. It is also prime contractor for the SAMS (stratospheric and mesospheric) experiment carried on the Nimbus 7 advanced atmospheric research satellite.

BAe has initiated long-term studies of the feasibility of Solar Power Satellites (SPS). Stationed in geosynchronous orbit, these satellites would receive energy via large arrays of photo electric cells, convert it on board into microwave radio energy, and beam it towards receiving antennae on the Earth's surface. There, the microwave energy would be converted to usable electrical power and fed into a supply grid. Under contract to the Department of Industry, BAe Dynamics is studying the industrial implications to the UK of such satellites.

As a member of the nine-nation European Spacelab consortium led by ERNO of West Germany, British Aerospace is making the pallets (experiment-mounting platforms) for the Spacelab that is to be carried into orbit by the US Space Shuttle. By mid-1980, thirteen pallets had been completed. Study has been made to assess the feasibility of using the pallets as the basic structure of free-flying spacecraft and as elements of a space station.

Other space engineering work performed by BAe Dynamics includes the design, testing and supply of satellite power and electrical subsystems; attitude and orbit control systems; solar array drives; and satellite reaction and momentum control wheels; and studies of reusable spacecraft and Small Payload Kits for the Space Shuttle. BAe Dynamics also designed and built the hold-down launch release system for the Ariane European launcher.

British Aerospace has developed under contract to Intelsat a microprocessor-based computer intended primarily for satellite attitude and orbit control applica-

Artist's impression of the MARECS maritime communications satellite

Artist's impression of the European Communications Satellite (ECS)

tions. The system, designed to operate on less than 1W of power, is of modular construction so that its built-in memory can be expanded to meet a variety of needs.

Manufacture of the widely-used Skylark high-altitude sounding rocket continues. For details see 1977-78 *Jane's*.

L-SAT

BAe has been appointed by ESA as prime contractor for the L-Sat programme. L-Sat is a communications satellite, about twice the size of the European Communications

Satellite (described in the International pages of this section) and several times more powerful, developing up to 7 kW of electrical power. In addition to transmitting TV broadcasts at high power, for direct reception on Earth by individual houses equipped with small rooftop-mounted antennae, L-Sat will also carry a significant volume of telephone and data traffic.

Configured for launch by either Ariane or the Space Shuttle, L-Sat is scheduled to be placed in geosynchronous Earth orbit in 1984, to provide communications coverage in Europe.

MSDS
MARCONI SPACE AND DEFENCE SYSTEMS LTD

HEAD OFFICE: The Grove, Stanmore, Middlesex HA7 4LY

Telephone: 01 954 2311

Telex: 22616

CHAIRMAN: General Sir Harry Tuzo, GCB, OBE, MC, MA

Marconi Space and Defence Systems, a member of GEC-Marconi Electronics, assembled and tested the hydrazine propulsion subsystem used to keep the NATO III communications satellite on station in its synchronous orbit. This series of satellites also embodies local oscillators built by MSDS; these act as highly stable frequency sources with which incoming signals to the satellites are mixed to produce the intermediate frequency suitable for the onboard electronics.

As a member of COSMOS consortium, MSDS provided the attitude control system and other equipment for the first Meteosat which was launched on 23 November 1977.

MSDS is providing similar equipment for the second Meteosat, scheduled to be launched by an Ariane vehicle in September 1981, and for Exosat, a precision three-axis stabilised X-ray observatory. Under subcontract to Aérospatiale, it is responsible for onboard software for the Ariane European launch vehicle. In association with the MESH international consortium, it is totally responsible for the maritime payload modules which will be mounted on the ECS platform to form the MARECS spacecraft.

Details of the UK 6 (Ariel) scientific satellite, for which MSDS was prime contractor, can be found in the 1979-80 *Jane's*.

UOSAT
UNIVERSITY OF SURREY
UOSAT

Students at the University of Surrey, in conjunction with the UK branch of the Amateur Satellite Corporation

(Amsat), are designing and building a satellite to provide radio enthusiasts with a means of studying radio propagation in the ionosphere. For this purpose the satellite, named Uosat, will carry high-frequency beacons, transmitting on 7, 14, 21 and 28MHz. Other equipment will include a three-axis magnetometer, supplied by a US

enthusiast, and radiation counters. To assist the project, which has a budget of £85,000, BAe Dynamics has carried out a structural analysis of Uosat.

NASA has agreed to launch the satellite, as a piggyback payload, on the Delta vehicle scheduled to orbit the Solar Mesosphere Explorer in September 1981.

UNITED STATES OF AMERICA

BOEING
THE BOEING COMPANY

HEAD OFFICE AND WORKS: Seattle, Washington 98124

Boeing Aerospace Company
PO Box 3999, Seattle, Washington 98124
OFFICERS: See Aircraft section

INERTIAL UPPER STAGE (IUS)

In August 1976 Boeing was selected by the US Air Force Space and Missile Systems Organization (SAMSO) to develop the Inertial Upper Stage (IUS) that will carry Space Shuttle payloads either to orbits not attainable by the Shuttle Orbiter or on to interplanetary trajectories. It has also been chosen as the upper stage for the Air Force's Titan 34-D rocket.

The IUS vehicles are designed in three sizes, using common components.

The basic two-stage vehicle is 5·0 m (16 ft 4½ in) long and 2·9 m (9 ft 6 in) in diameter. It consists of an aft skirt, a 9,707 kg (21,400 lb) aft-stage solid rocket motor generating an average of 189·5 kN (42,600 lb) of thrust, an interstage, a 2,722 kg (6,000 lb) forward stage solid rocket motor generating an average of 77·5 kN (17,430 lb) of thrust, and an equipment support structure which contains electronics for guidance and navigation, reaction control subsystem and electrical power. Its weight is 14,515 kg (32,000 lb).

The NASA twin-stage IUS uses two 9,707 kg (21,400 lb) motors and, except for the larger forward-stage motor and minor modifications to the interstage and equipment

support structure, is quite similar to the basic two-stage vehicle. Tooling is identical for both vehicles. The NASA two-stage version is 6·64 m (21 ft 9½ in) long and weighs 20,956 kg (46,200 lb).

The three-stage vehicle combines the NASA twin-stage vehicle with a spinning version of the smaller 2,722 kg (6,000 lb) motor, acting as the third stage and providing increased performance for planetary missions. The three-stage vehicle is 8·3 m (27 ft 6 in) long and weighs 24,767 kg (54,600 lb).

Boeing's propulsion team member, Chemical Systems Division of United Technologies, will design and test all solid motors. Production deliveries are programmed to begin in 1981.

FAIRCHILD
FAIRCHILD SPACE & ELECTRONICS COMPANY

Germantown, Maryland 20767
Telephone: (301) 428 6000

Fairchild is responsible for producing the Stage Vehicle System for use on the Atlas E/F launch vehicle. Used as an interstage between Atlas and the NavStar Global Positioning Satellite System, it contains two tandem-mounted TE-M-364-4 solid rocket motors for providing transfer orbit insertion of the satellites. Of the planned total of eight satellites, five have been launched successfully into orbit; the sixth and seventh were scheduled for launch in 1980, and the eighth for the first quarter of 1981.

Fairchild was responsible for the integration and test, and the manufacture of subsystems for the ISEE-3 satellite. Current contracts include manufacture of the Multimission Modular Spacecraft (MMS).

ISEE-3

Launched on 12 August 1978 by a Delta rocket from Cape Canaveral, the International Sun-Earth Explorer-3 (ISEE-3) entered a giant 'halo orbit' above Earth at the end of November. Performance of the spacecraft is meeting all expectations. The ISEE-3 (ISEE-C before launch) is designed to measure the isotropic concentration of solar and galactic cosmic rays, and investigate various solar, interplanetary and recently discovered astrophysical and magnetic phenomena. It carries twelve scientific experiments, and will provide a reference measurement for data collected by ISEE-1 and 2, launched into elliptical Earth orbits.

ISEE-3, on the other hand, was designed to operate at a hypothetical point in space where the gravity of the Sun and Earth/Moon systems balance out. This point, known as the Libration point, is about 1,500,000 km (930,000 miles) from the Earth. If placed exactly at this point, the spacecraft would move round the Sun at the same rate as

Artist's impression of ISEE-3 in orbit

the Earth. At this point, however, communications would be difficult, and to minimise the Sun's interference ISEE-3 is revolving about the Libration point at a distance of 145,000 km (89,900 miles). Frequent course corrections are necessary to maintain this unusual heliocentric orbit.

The ISEE-3 spacecraft is drum-shaped; it weighs about 453 kg (1,000 lb), and is 1·73 m (68 in) in diameter and 3·30 m (10 ft 10 in) high.

MMS

In 1978 Fairchild was selected by NASA as the integration and test contractor for the Multimission Modular Spacecraft (MMS), a standard bus for many future NASA and DoD missions. The MMS standardises into modules basic spacecraft functions such as power supply, attitude control, communications and data handling, and propul-

sion. The first launch using MMS was the Solar Maximum Mission, on 14 February 1980. The second mission will be Landsat-D, scheduled for 1981. Shuttle-compatible, retrievable and refurbishable, the MMS is also being considered for such missions as GRO, ERBS, UARS and COASTSAT.

Under separate contract, Fairchild builds the Communications and Data (C&DH) module for the MMS. This module provides full telemetry and command link between the host spacecraft and the ground facility; onboard control of all spacecraft functions; and retrieval of spacecraft housekeeping and scientific payload data. Besides its application in the MMS, the C&DH can be interjected into other systems, and Fairchild is under contract to build one version of the C&DH for Lockheed's Space Telescope Programme.

Solar Maximum Mission, first spacecraft to use the MMS

FORD
FORD AEROSPACE & COMMUNICATIONS CORPORATION

20th Floor, 300 Renaissance Center, PO Box 43342, Detroit, Michigan 48243
Telephone: (313) 568 7640

In addition to satellites built for US agencies and NATO, Ford Aerospace manufactured the Sakura Experimental Communications Satellite, described under the NASDA entry in the Japanese section of the 1978-79 *Jane's*. It also built jointly with Mitsubishi Japan's second Experimental Communications Satellite, ECS-B, which was launched successfully on 22 February 1980, but was lost in orbit three days later during a boost motor burn towards geostationary orbit.

INTELSAT V

Ford Aerospace, under a contract administered by the Communications Satellite Corporation (COMSAT), is building seven Intelsat V communications satellites for the 102-nation International Telecommuncations Satellite Organisation (INTELSAT). The first Intelsat V was scheduled to be launched in 1980.

Intelsat V's capacity of 24,500 telephone half-circuits is twice that of Intelsat IVA. It is also the first satellite of the Intelsat series to be three-axis stabilised, using technology developed during the European Symphonie programme. Launch weight of the 6.4 m (21 ft) high satellite is 1,860 kg (4,100 lb). Planned life span is seven years.

Intelsat V structural thermal model

GENERAL DYNAMICS
GENERAL DYNAMICS CORPORATION

HEAD OFFICE: Pierre Laclede Center, St Louis, Missouri 63105
Convair Division
San Diego, California 92138
OFFICERS: See Aircraft section

Convair Division devotes a major part of its activity to production and launch of Atlas and Centaur space launch vehicles, as well as production of DC-10 fuselages. Convair is also developing the Tomahawk cruise missile for the US Navy, and producing the Space Shuttle Orbiter mid-fuselage for NASA.

ATLAS E and F

Atlas E and F series rockets were formerly ICBMs deployed at Strategic Air Command bases as part of the US strategic missile force. Phase-out of the Atlas ICBM force in 1965 made them available for conversion into launch vehicles, as described in previous editions.

ATLAS SLV

The Atlas Standardised Launch Vehicle (SLV) had its inception in Atlas, the USA's first intercontinental ballistic missile (ICBM). Two versions are currently in service:
SLV-3A, for use with Agena.
SLV-3D, for use with the Centaur D-1A.

These vehicles differ from their immediate predecessor, the SLV-3, mainly in increased tank length and rocket engine thrust.

Atlas is a 'stage-and-a-half' vehicle, consisting of side booster and central sustainer sections. The sustainer section includes the propellant tanks and a single rocket engine. The booster engines receive fuel from the sustainer tanks and are jettisoned midway into flight.

The engine system is the Rocketdyne MA-5, using liquid oxygen and RP-1 propellants. Total thrust developed is 1,917·4 kN (431,040 lb), including 1,646 kN (370,000 lb) total from the two boosters, 266·9 kN (60,000 lb) from the sustainer, and 4·6 kN (1,040 lb) total axial thrust from the two vernier rockets. All engines are ignited at lift-off.

Most of the electronic command and control functions for the SLV-3D are generated by its Centaur D-1A upper-stage electronics system. The SLV-3A has its own systems, independent of the upper stage, including radio guidance.

Atlas has many space 'firsts' to its credit, including launch of the world's first communications satellite, in 1958, and the first US manned orbital flights (Mercury). All US planetary spacecraft have been launched by Atlas or Centaur. In 1972 Pioneer 10 was started on its flight

path to Jupiter with the highest velocity ever imparted to a spacecraft.
DIMENSIONS:
Diameter	3·05 m (10 ft 0 in)
Length:	
SLV-3A	24·0 m (78 ft 11 in)
SLV-3A/Agena	36·0 m (118 ft 0 in)
SLV-3D	21·2 m (69 ft 6 in)
SLV-3D/Centaur	39·9 m (131 ft 0 in)

PERFORMANCE:
Atlas/Centaur: See Centaur entry
Atlas SLV-3A/Agena:
3,856 kg (8,500 lb) into 185 km (115 mile) orbit
1,238 kg (2,730 lb) into synchronous transfer orbit

CENTAUR

Centaur was the first US high-energy upper stage and the first to utilise liquid hydrogen as a propellant. The current version is combined with the Atlas SLV-3D.

In April 1973, the first Atlas/Centaur D-1A launched Pioneer 11 on a Jupiter fly-by mission. Three more Intelsat IVs, Mariner 10, seven Intelsat IVAs, three Comstars (domestic communication satellites leased to AT and T by Comsat), three High Energy Astronomy Observatories (HEAO) and two US Navy fleet satellite communications spacecraft have also been launched successfully by this vehicle. In early 1979, Atlas/Centaur D-1A had been assigned future missions extending into 1981. They include further launches of Comstars, Fleetsatcoms, High Energy Astronomy Observatories and Pioneer missions to orbit Venus and probe its atmosphere.

Centaur was also used as an upper stage for Titan IIIE, described in previous editions of *Jane's*.

Centaur D-1A retains the same propulsion and structural features as its predecessor, Centaur D, with stainless steel pressurised tanks and two 66·72 kN (15,000 lb st) Pratt & Whitney RL10A liquid oxygen/liquid hydrogen rocket engines. Specific impulse with this propellant combination is 445 s, the highest of any current space vehicle. Total propellants carried weigh 13,950 kg (30,750 lb). Attitude control is achieved by gimballing the two main engines or by clusters of small hydrogen peroxide rocket motors.

Several of the electronics components were redesigned for Centaur D-1A. The most significant addition is a 16,000 word capacity Teledyne digital computer. Navigation, guidance, vehicle stability, tank pressurisation, propellant management, telemetry formats and transmission, and event initiation are all controlled by the computer. Guidance, control and sequencing for the Atlas booster are provided by the Centaur D-1A electronics system.

Payloads are carried on adapters mounted on the for-

Atlas/Centaur AC-36 launch vehicle

ward end of the Centaur. A 3·05 m (10 ft) diameter fairing protects payloads for Centaur D-1A.
DIMENSIONS:
Centaur length	9·14 m (30 ft 0 in)
Centaur diameter	3·05 m (10 ft 0 in)
Atlas/Centaur length	39·9 m (131 ft 0 in)

PERFORMANCE:
Atlas/Centaur:
5,080 kg (11,200 lb) into 185 km (115 mile) circular orbit
1,860 kg (4,100 lb) into synchronous transfer orbit
590 kg (1,300 lb) to near planet

GENERAL ELECTRIC
GENERAL ELECTRIC COMPANY SPACE DIVISION

HEAD OFFICE: Valley Forge Space Center, PO Box 8555, Philadelphia, Pennsylvania 19101

General Electric's Space Division is vehicle contractor for NASA's Landsat programme (formerly Earth Resources Technology Satellite, ERTS). Other satellites designed and manufactured by this Division have included Nimbus meteorological satellites, BSE (Broadcast Satellite Experimental) and DSCS III (Defense Satellite Communications Systems).

LANDSAT (ERTS)

Designed to study the resources of Earth from space, ERTS-1 (Earth Resources Technology Satellite) was launched by NASA on 23 July 1972. It was subsequently renamed Landsat-1 and is described in the 1977-78 *Jane's*. This spacecraft was retired by NASA on 16 January 1978, after operating for 5½ years and after revolutionising the technology of observing the Earth from space.

Landsat-2 (known formerly as ERTS-B) was launched on 22 January 1975, into an orbit similar to that of Landsat-1 but 180° out of phase from it to allow repetitive coverage of all portions of the Earth every nine days with two spacecraft, instead of once every 18 days with one spacecraft. Brief details of Landsat-2, which was retired on 22 January 1980 because of wear-induced failure of its primary flight control system, were given in the 1977-78

Jane's. A third spacecraft in the series, Landsat-3, was launched on 5 March 1978. This embodies refined sensors which are supplying data significantly improved over those obtained from Landsats 1 and 2. The multispectral scanner subsystem (MSS) detects temperature differences in vegetation, bodies of water and urban areas by day and night. An improved return beam vidicon (RBV) sensor has increased the resolution of recorded images by 50 per cent, enabling areas as small as half an acre to be identified. The thermal data is providing information on plant stress, vigour and other changes characterised by temperature differences.

NIMBUS

Nimbus-7, the seventh satellite in an atmospheric research programme, was launched on 23 October 1978. Designed to gather data from the atmosphere and oceans, it is obtaining global information on air and water pollution for continuing research on climate and weather. In addition one of the sensors, called a Coastal Zone Colour Scanner (CZCS), is available to identify and track oil spills over eleven major ocean areas traversed by tankers.

Since Nimbus-1 was launched on 28 August 1964, the spacecraft in the series have returned more than 400,000 TV pictures of the Earth's cloud cover, 51,000 h of infra-red data, 42,000 h of ultra-violet data, 185,000 h of 'sounder' data on temperature and pressure and more than 16,000 h of data on the Earth's heat balance.

Details of earlier Nimbus spacecraft are given in the 1974-75 *Jane's*.

Landsat-3 Earth resources technology satellite

HUGHES
HUGHES AIRCRAFT COMPANY
Space and Communications Group

PO Box 92919, Los Angeles, California 90009
Telephone: (213) 648 0884

Current space programmes for which Hughes Aircraft is prime contractor include development and manufacture of the US Navy's LEASAT; Telesat Canada's Anik C; Satellite Business Systems' SBS satellite; Western Union's Westar IV and Indonesia's Palapa B communications satellites; Japan's Geostationary Meteorological Satellite (GMS-2); the Geostationary Operational Environmental Satellites (GOES-D, E, F) for the US National Oceanic and Atmospheric Administration (NOAA); and the Ku-band Integrated Radar and Communications Subsystem for NASA's Space Shuttle. The company is also engaged on development and manufacture of Earth stations for satellite telecommunications; classified military satellite systems; Visible/Infrared Spin-Scan Radiometers (VISSR), used as the primary sensor on GMS and, with atmospheric sounder (VAS), on GOES-D, E, and F; Multispectral Scanners (MSS) used on Landsat spacecraft and a Thermatic Mapper for Landsat D; and on investigation and flight testing of experimental ion engines for advanced spacecraft. Hughes is a major subcontractor on Anik D, being built by Spar Aerospace Ltd for Telesat Canada.

INTELSAT IVA

Pending the availability of Intelsat V (see Ford entry), Hughes built six improved Intelsat IVA spacecraft, brief details of which were given in the 1979-80 *Jane's*.

LEASAT

In September 1978, the US Navy announced a contract award to Hughes Communication Services Inc, a Hughes Aircraft Company subsidiary, to provide worldwide communications satellite service to the Department of Defense for at least five years at each of four orbital locations. The new satellite, known as LEASAT, will begin service in 1982. Users will include mobile air, surface, subsurface, and fixed Earth stations of the US Navy, Marine Corps, Air Force and Army. Hughes Space and Communications Group will build the satellites, which will occupy geostationary positions over the USA and over the Atlantic, Pacific and Indian Oceans.

The satellites will be spin-stabilised, with the spun portion containing the solar array and Sun and Earth sensors for attitude determination and Earth pointing reference, batteries for eclipse operation, and all propulsion and attitude control hardware. The despun platform will contain Earth-pointing communications antennae, communications repeaters, and the majority of the telemetry, tracking and command equipment.

Designed to be launched from the Space Shuttle, each satellite is approx 4·22 m (13 ft 10 in) in diameter and 6·16 m (20 ft 2½ in) long with the UHF and omnidirectional antennae deployed. Total payload weight in the Shuttle

Artist's impression of LEASAT

will be 7,938 kg (17,500 lb). Weight after separation from the Shuttle will be 6,849 kg (15,100 lb), and the satellite's weight on station at beginning of life will be nearly 1,315 kg (2,900 lb).

PALAPA B

Permumtel, Indonesia's state-owned telecommunications company, has chosen Hughes to build a new generation of Palapa B communications satellites, to succeed the Hughes-built system placed in orbit in 1976-77. The new satellites will be more than twice as big and four times as powerful as those currently in use.

The Palapa B satellites will provide voice, video, telephone and high-speed data services. Each will have 24 transponders, compared with 12 for the present model, and each of the transponders will have 10W power output, compared with 5W on the earlier spacecraft. This increased capability reduces the expense of extended coverage to small rural terminals in remote locations.

The new satellites have outer cylindrical sleeves which, together with folding antennae, deploy in space. The vehicles' cylindrical bodies and their extensions are covered with solar cells. This arrangement nearly doubles the area of power-producing solar cells usable with the same-size satellite. Palapa B will have a height of 6·83 m (22 ft 5 in) when deployed in space and a diameter of 2·16 m (7 ft 1 in). In-orbit weight at the start of the satellite's eight-year lifetime will be 628 kg (1,385 lb).

SBS

In December 1977, Satellite Business Systems (a consortium of IBM, Comsat General Corporation, and Aetna Life and Casualty) selected Hughes Aircraft Company to

Artist's impression of Palapa B

build three SBS commercial communications satellites for service over the continental USA.

First US domestic commercial communications satellite system to utilise 12/14GHz (K-band) frequencies, SBS will provide point-to-point voice, high-speed data, facsimile and teleconferencing service to its users. With K-band communications, small, relatively inexpensive Earth stations can be used. Another advantage of SBS is that its solar panel almost doubles the power output over that obtainable with other spin-stabilised satellites of the same size.

Since the SBS satellite will operate in the 12/14GHz bands, small antennae may be used in urban areas to communicate with the satellite, without causing interference to terrestrial systems or other spacecraft.

Designed to be launched by NASA on either the Space Shuttle or a Delta 3910 booster, the first launch was scheduled for mid-1980. Using a folding antenna reflector and a deployable solar panel, the compact satellite will be able to stow upright in the Shuttle bay. This configuration will reduce Shuttle charges, which are proportional to the length of payload bay used. After the satellite is separated from the Shuttle, the antenna will be erected and the outer section of the telescoping solar panel deployed.

The spacecraft is 2·16 m (7 ft 1 in) in diameter and 6·60 m (21 ft 8 in) high with the solar panel and antenna deployed. It weighs 1,057 kg (2,326 lb) following injection into elliptical transfer orbit by the perigee motor, part of the payload assist module (PAM). After the apogee engine fires, the on-station weight of the satellite will be 555 kg (1,222 lb), of which 96 kg (211 lb) will be on-orbit propellant.

LOCKHEED
LOCKHEED MISSILES & SPACE COMPANY INC (Subsidiary of Lockheed Corporation)

1111 Lockheed Way, Sunnyvale, California 94086
Telephone: (408) 742 6688
PRESIDENT: Robert A. Fuhrman
OTHER FACILITIES: Palo Alto and Santa Cruz, California
DIRECTOR, PUBLIC INFORMATION: George Mulhern

Lockheed Missiles & Space Company is heavily engaged in both missile work and the design, development and production of satellites and space vehicles.

AGENA D

The Agena satellite is used normally as the upper stage of a two-stage launcher, in combination with an Atlas, Thor, or Titan IIIB. The current Agena D version consists of a cylindrical body containing a Bell Aerosystems Model

8096 (YLR81-BA-11) restartable liquid-propellant rocket engine (71·2 kN; 16,000 lb st) and propellant tanks, telemetry, instrumentation, guidance and attitude control systems. It has carried most types of power supply, including a nuclear reactor electric power supply and an ion engine. The payload section (nosecone) can accommodate a wide variety of Earth-orbiting and space probes weighing up to several hundred pounds. The Agena system and its attached payload have functioned for more than six months in some missions for the US Air Force.

Agena D differs from earlier versions in being able to accept a variety of payloads, whereas its predecessors had integrated payloads. The restartable engine permits the satellite to change its orbit in space.

Since 1959, Agenas have served as satellite or booster on more missions than any other spacecraft in the world, having been used on well over 300 flights, representing approximately half of all US space missions.

Agena forms the basis of the new Seasat ocean survey satellite, described separately in this entry. A high proportion of the unidentified US satellites included in the table at the end of this section can be assumed to be Agena payloads of various kinds.

The following details refer to Agena D:

DIMENSIONS:
Length (typical)	7·09 m (23 ft 3 in)
Diameter	1·52 m (5 ft 0 in)

WEIGHTS (typical):
Propellant weight	6,148 kg (13,553 lb)
Vehicle weight empty	673 kg (1,484 lb)
Weight in orbit, less payload	579 kg (1,277 lb)

LOCKHEED/USAF 467 BIG BIRD

First launched on 15 June 1971, from Pt Arguello, this highly-advanced photographic reconnaissance satellite is reported to weigh about 11,340 kg (25,000 lb) and to be 15·25 m (50 ft) long. The first Big Bird was launched by a Titan IIID into an orbit of 299 × 183 km (186 × 144 miles), with an inclination of 96·41°. Its capabilities clearly included the same kind of close-look high-resolution photography as that of the recoverable type of Agena vehicle; and it is reported to have ejected a series of capsules for air-snatch recovery.

Big Bird is believed to process photographs taken by cameras and transmit information to Earth in the form of digital data by radio link. Some reports suggest that it also carries infra-red mapping and side-looking radar equipment. Its orbit takes its cameras within range of every point on the Earth twice in each period of 24 h.

Big Birds continue to be launched at four-to-six-monthly intervals and have demonstrated an endurance of up to four months in orbit.

Although no official data have been released on US reconnaissance satellites, acknowledgement of their use for military purposes was made by President Carter during a speech at the Kennedy Space Center. In his statement, the President said: "Photo reconnaissance satellites have become an important stabilizing factor in world affairs in the monitoring of arms agreements. They make an immense contribution to the security of all nations. We shall continue to develop them." An earlier indication of the value placed on information gained by satellite reconnaissance was given by the late President Lyndon Johnson, who said in March 1967: "We have spent $35-40,000 million on the space programme, and if nothing else had come out of it except the knowledge we have gained from space photography, it would be worth 10 times what the whole programme has cost, because tonight we know how many missiles the enemy has."

SEASAT

Seasat, an experimental oceanographic satellite built for NASA, was launched on 27 June 1978 from Vandenberg Air Force Base into a near-circular polar orbit of about 800 km (495 miles), so that it circled the Earth 14 times daily and covered 96 per cent of the world's oceans every 36 h. Radars and radiometers aboard the spacecraft were used to see through clouds and provide data on wave heights, currents, ocean temperatures, icebergs, storms, and coastal features. On 9 October, after three months of gathering extensive data, the satellite was silenced by an apparent power failure due, it is thought, to an electrical short in the slip ring assembly of the solar array. Nevertheless, the satellite proved its primary objective: that precise information on the state of the oceans could be obtained in this manner. Processing of extensive data from all sensors was completed in late 1980, and data will be made available to interested user groups. Full details of the 2,274 kg (5,000 lb) satellite and its special sensors were given in the 1978-79 *Jane's*. Future ocean survey satellites are planned for Space Shuttle launches in the mid-80s.

SPACE TELESCOPE

Lockheed Missiles & Space Company is building for

Artist's impression of NASA's Space Telescope

NASA a Space Telescope which will be launched in 1983 as the most ambitious space astronomy project yet undertaken. Operating well above the optically obscuring effects of Earth's atmosphere, the telescope will be able to detect objects 50 times more faint and seven times further away than those which can be seen by telescopes on Earth. The solar array and photon detector assembly are being developed and manufactured by British Aerospace under contracts from the European Space Agency.

MARTIN MARIETTA
MARTIN MARIETTA CORPORATION

CORPORATE HEADQUARTERS: 6801 Rockledge Drive, Bethesda, Maryland 20034
Telephone: (301) 897 6000
CHAIRMAN AND CHIEF EXECUTIVE OFFICER: J. Donald Rauth
PRESIDENT AND CHIEF OPERATING OFFICER: Thomas G. Pownall
VICE-PRESIDENT, PUBLIC RELATIONS: Roy Calvin
AEROSPACE HEADQUARTERS: 6801 Rockledge Drive, Bethesda, Maryland 20034
PRESIDENT, MARTIN MARIETTA AEROSPACE: Laurence J. Adams

Baltimore Division
103 Chesapeake Park Plaza, Baltimore, Maryland 21220
Denver Division
PO Box 179, Denver, Colorado 80201
Telephone: (303) 973 3000
Orlando Division
PO Box 5837, Orlando, Florida 32805
Telephone: (305) 352 2000

Martin Marietta Aerospace produces missiles, spacecraft, launch vehicles, communications systems and electronic systems. It also fabricates precision components for the US Department of Defense and NASA, and conducts research related to defense and space systems.

The Denver Division produces the Titan III family of space boosters, defence systems, command and information systems, mobile transporter systems and external tanks for the Space Shuttle. Orlando Division produces advanced strategic air-launched missiles, communications systems, the Pershing surface-to-surface ballistic missile, the Patriot surface-to-air missile, strategic terminal interceptors, and tactical weapons systems. Baltimore Division fabricates structural components of aircraft, space vehicles and defence systems.

TITAN III

Titan III is America's standard heavy-duty space 'workhorse' booster and is used for both military and non-military space launch missions. It provides a high frequency launch capability for a wide variety of payloads, ranging from 15,875 kg (35,000 lb) in Earth orbit to 3,175 kg (7,000 lb) for planetary missions to Mars, Jupiter and Saturn.

Martin Marietta, in addition to its role as systems integrating contractor, builds the airframe and liquid-propellant stages, supplies the flight control system, and is integrating contractor for facilities and launch operation at Cape Canaveral. Aerojet-General produces the liquid-propellant engines. UTC's Chemical Systems Division supplies the solid-propellant boosters used in the more powerful models. Guidance systems for the Titan IIIC and D are built by General Motors Corporation's Delco Division and Western Electric respectively.

The core section of Titan III consists of elements which provide a high degree of commonality throughout all configurations. It consists of two booster stages and an upper stage, known as Transtage, that can function both in the boost phase of flight and as a restartable space tug propulsion vehicle. All stages use storable liquid propellants and have gimbal-mounted thrust chambers for vehicle control.

Titan III exists in three current configurations:

Titan IIIB. Basically the first two stages of the core section. It can accommodate a variety of specialised upper stages. First launched on 29 July 1966. Series of launches continued through 1978, all with Agena upper stages and classified US Air Force payloads.

Titan IIIC. Consists of the core section, including the Transtage upper stage, with solid-propellant rocket motors attached to each side to function as a booster stage before ignition of main engines. Payloads include US Air Force and NASA military, scientific and communications satellites, including about 80 per cent of all those placed into synchronous equatorial orbit from US launch sites.

Titan IIID. Basically similar to IIIC but has only a two-stage liquid-propellant core (without Transtage) and radio guidance instead of the standard inertial guidance. Able to accept a variety of upper stages. Reported to have been used to orbit the first Lockheed Big Bird advanced photo-reconnaissance spacecraft, weighing about 11,340 kg (25,000 lb), from Pt Arguello on 15 June 1971.

The first stage of the core section is 22·25 m (73 ft) long and 3·05 m (10 ft) in diameter. Its engines, which use a blend of hydrazine and unsymmetrical dimethylhydrazine (UDMH) for fuel, and nitrogen tetroxide as an oxidiser, have a 15 : 1 expansion ratio and are ignited at an altitude where efficiency is increased, giving a thrust of 2,339·6 kN (526,000 lb) in vacuum. The second stage is 7·10 m (23 ft 3½ in) tall and 3·05 m (10 ft) in diameter. Its engine uses the same propellants as the first stage and develops 453·7 kN (102,000 lb st).

The Transtage space propulsion vehicle is 4·57 m (15 ft) tall and 3·05 m (10 ft) in diameter and also uses UDMH/hydrazine and nitrogen tetroxide as propellants. The twin-chamber engine produces 71·17 kN (16,000 lb) of thrust and is capable of multiple restarts in space, which permits a wide variety of manoeuvres, including change of plane, change of orbit, and transfer to deep-space trajectory. Transtage also houses the control module for the entire vehicle, including the guidance system and segments of the flight control and vehicle safety systems.

Titan IIIC/D's solid-propellant booster motors are each 25·91 m (85 ft) long and 3·05 m (10 ft) in diameter. Each motor is built in five segments and develops more than 5,115 kN (1,150,000 lb st). The booster stage is steered by a thrust vector control system, which injects nitrogen tetroxide into the engine nozzle.

Titan IIIC heavy duty launch vehicle

TITAN 34-D

Instead of Transtage, future Titan IIIs will use the Boeing Inertial Upper Stage (which see) that is being developed for the Space Shuttle. Designated Titan 34-D, these vehicles will be used for some primary launches, as well as for backup of the Space Shuttle during that vehicle's transition period. The Titan 34-D is expected to replace current Titans, with an estimated requirement for 23 in the 1980s.

MDAC
MCDONNELL DOUGLAS ASTRONAUTICS COMPANY
McDonnell Douglas Astronautics Company

5301 Bolsa Avenue, Huntington Beach, California 92647

In March 1977 MDAC was awarded a Spacelab integration contract by NASA involving the design, development and fabrication of most of the Spacelab hardware for which NASA is responsible. This includes the crew transfer tunnel, verification flight instrumentation, mockups and ground support equipment. The contract also covers systems engineering and integration to develop Spacelab operational capability.

DSV-3 DELTA

Details of early versions of the Delta can be found in the 1971-72, 1972-73 and 1977-78 *Jane's*. Production is now centred on the DSV-3P, of which details follow:

DSV-3P Extended Long Tank Delta (also known as 'Straight-Eight' or '2000 Series Delta'). This launch vehicle has a constant 2·44 m (8 ft) diameter from the base of the boat-tail to the conical nose section of the shroud. This provides an enlarged volume, to accommodate larger payloads. The second stage, with a TRW LMDE engine, is suspended within the 2·44 m (8 ft) diameter barrel section. The first-stage length is increased by 3·05 m (10 ft) by comparison with earlier long-tank versions, providing an increase of 13,600 kg (30,000 lb) in propellant capacity. In addition, the MB-3-III main engine is replaced by a Rocketdyne RS-27 of 911·84 kN (205,000 lb st). As an alternative to the TE-364-3 motor, a higher-performing motor, the TE-364-4, is available as a third stage. The two-stage capability is increased to 1,880 kg (4,150 lb) into a 370 km (230 mile) circular orbit. The three-stage capability is increased to 700 kg (1,550 lb) into a synchronous transfer orbit.

DSV-3P (Delta 3914). First launched on 12 December 1975, this uprated version of the standard 'Straight-Eight' Delta utilises nine Castor IV solid-propellant strap-on motors in place of the nine Castor IIs used on the Delta 2914. Development costs were borne by MDAC, and will be recovered through a user charge imposed on non-government users of the vehicle. Dimensions are the same as for the standard DSV-3P Delta 2914, but firing weight is increased to 191,400 kg (422,000 lb). Delta 3914 is capable of putting a 930 kg (2,050 lb) payload into a geosynchronous transfer orbit. The payload is increased to 1,091 kg (2,400 lb) with PAM (see separate entry).

DSV-3P (Delta 3920). This version, development of which was authorised by NASA in March 1980, has an upgraded second-stage propulsion assembly produced by Aerojet. This new stage has a larger propellant tank than the present second stage, extending the burn time by 30 per cent, and uses an AJ10-118K-ITIP (Improved Transtage Injector Programme) engine supplied by Aerojet Liquid Rocket Company.

Delta 3920 with PAM (described separately) is designed to place 1,250 kg (2,750 lb) into a geosynchronous transfer orbit. The first launch, expected in early 1982, is scheduled to orbit Landsat-D for NASA.

The number of Deltas ordered, in many versions, totalled 157 by Spring 1979. They had completed 139 successful flights in 151 attempts between 13 May 1960 and 11 March 1980.

DIMENSIONS:

Length overall	35·15 m (115 ft 4 in)
Body diameter	2·44 m (8 ft 0 in)

WEIGHTS:
Firing weight of DSV-3P (2000 Series):

3 solid motors	104,330 kg (230,000 lb)
6 solid motors	117,930 kg (260,000 lb)
9 solid motors	131,540 kg (290,000 lb)

PAYLOAD ASSIST MODULE (PAM)

Two Payload Assist Module (PAM) rocket systems are being developed to improve the load-carrying capability of the McDonnell Douglas launch vehicle and for use on Space Shuttle missions. As many as four satellites, with PAM stages attached, could be launched during a single flight of the Shuttle Orbiter.

Both PAMs are solid-propellant spinning rockets. One, known as PAM-D, will be carried into low Earth orbit by the Space Shuttle and from that position will carry payloads of up to 1,110 kg (2,450 lb) into transfer orbit. Kick motors will then insert payloads into 35,880 km (22,300 mile) high geosynchronous orbits.

Six PAM-Ds have been ordered by Hughes Aircraft Company, and two by Ford Aerospace and Communications Corporation to help launch satellites which Ford is developing for the Government of India.

The second type of rocket, PAM-A, is intended to be used for handling payloads weighing up to 2,000 kg (4,400 lb) during Space Shuttle missions.

After insertion into low Earth orbit by the Shuttle, the upper stage will carry payloads into a transfer orbit where a kick motor will insert it into a circular geosynchronous orbit 35,880 km (22,300 miles) above the Earth. This upper stage will accommodate payloads of a size now being launched by Atlas-Centaur rockets. Six PAM-As were ordered by NASA in 1978.

Delta 117 launch vehicle for Explorer 55 satellite

NASA
NATIONAL AERONAUTICS AND SPACE ADMINISTRATION

HEADQUARTERS: Washington, DC 20546
ADMINISTRATOR: Dr Robert A. Frosch

NASA is responsible for co-ordinating and conducting virtually all US non-military space projects. Its Office of Space Transportation Systems is responsible for the Space Shuttle programme.

DYNAMICS EXPLORER

Dynamics Explorer is a NASA-sponsored programme which will investigate the interactive coupling between the earth's magnetosphere, ionosphere and plasmasphere. It will utilise two coplanar polar orbiting spacecraft, constructed by RCA Astro-Electronics and described under the RCA entry in this section.

IUE SATELLITE

This International Ultraviolet Explorer satellite was launched into a synchronous Earth orbit by NASA on 26 January 1978, in co-operation with the European Space Agency and the British Research Council. It is obtaining high-resolution ultraviolet observations of bright stars, planets, and stellar and planetary atmospheres, and providing experience in the combined use of satellite and ground-based observations. By 1980 the spacecraft had returned more than 9,000 images that could not be obtained by ground-based instruments, helping to answer the most basic questions in astronomy, such as the nature of stars, nebulae and galaxies, and how they develop.

MAGSAT

Magsat (Magnetic Field Satellite) was launched by a Scout-G-1 from the Air Force Western Space and Missile Center, on 30 October 1979, as the third Applications Explorer mission. It is the first spacecraft designed specifically to measure the near-Earth magnetic field and crustal anomalies.

It is hoped that Magsat data will reflect important geological features, such as composition, temperature of rock formation, residual magnetism and geological structure on a regional scale.

Weighing 181 kg (399 lb), the spacecraft is made up of two parts: an instrument module with an optical bench,

Artist's impression of Space Shuttle launch. The two boosters and the Orbiter main engine fire in parallel

star cameras, altitude transfer system, magnetometer boom and gimbal systems, scalar and vector magnetometers, and precision Sun sensor; and a base module housing the electrical power supply, telemetry, altitude control and command data handling systems. Solar panels provide 160 W of power.

Goddard Space Flight Center is responsible for the design and data processing. Applied Physics Laboratory, Johns Hopkins University, is spacecraft contractor.

ISPM

In March 1979 NASA announced that it had signed an agreement with the European Space Agency for a joint International Solar Polar Mission (ISPM) to be launched in 1983. Under the agreement, NASA and ESA will each provide a spacecraft. Both spacecraft will be launched simultaneously by the Space Shuttle, and will then be directed on a trajectory in the ecliptic plane (the plane containing all the planets) to Jupiter. The gravity of Jupiter will be used to redirect their paths out of the ecliptic plane, back to the Sun in trajectories—one northbound and one southbound—that are mirror images of each other, passing over the solar poles. Purpose of the mission is to extend scientific knowledge of the Sun.

Orbiter vehicle in Earth orbit, with Spacelab in payload compartment

At low altitude the Orbiter goes into horizontal flight for an aircraft-type approach and landing

SAGE (AEM-B)

SAGE (Stratospheric Aerosol and Gas Experiment) was launched on 18 February 1979 by a Scout vehicle, from Wallops Flight Center, into a nominal 600 km (370 miles) orbit.

Its purpose is to obtain measurements of global, spatial and temporal distributions of stratospheric aerosols and ozone, and to use these to study their effects on the Earth's radiation budget and environment.

Known also as the Applications Explorer Mission-B satellite, SAGE is a small, versatile, low-cost spacecraft which provides three-axis stabilisation for its viewing instruments. Structure consists of a base module containing attitude control, data handling, communications, command and power subsystems for the instrument module; and an instrument module containing the spectrometer and its supporting equipment. Two solar paddles for converting sunlight to electricity extend from the structure. A yo-yo despin system is located on the base module, below the solar array.

The SAGE sensor is a four-spectral channel radiometer, which measures the extinction of solar radiation during solar occultation. The spacecraft locks on to the Sun as it experiences a sunrise or sunset, and measures the Sun's brightness at four wavelengths. This information is interpreted in terms of vertical profiles of the atmospheric constituent that attenuated or dimmed the sunlight. Thirty profiles per day are being obtained in this manner, spread over latitude and longitude. Over a year, 10,000 profiles will be measured from latitude 78° S to 78° N.

Comparable aerosol data for the polar regions obtained by Nimbus 7 (which see) will complement SAGE.

SMM

The SMM (Solar Maximum Mission) spacecraft was launched on 14 February 1980 by a Delta 3914 from Cape Canaveral Air Force Station. Carrying seven scientific instruments, SMM is the first spacecraft designed specifically for the study of solar flares, and is expected to provide observations over a wide band of wavelengths in the ultraviolet, X-ray and gamma-ray regions of the spectrum. The mission is designed to coincide with the solar maximum period, the peak of an 11-year sunspot cycle, when particularly explosive activity disrupts the Sun's surface.

The satellite is a three-axis inertially-stabilised platform providing precise stable pointing to any region on the solar disc to within 5 s of arc. It weighs 2,315 kg (5,105 lb) and is 4·0 m (13 ft) long by 2·3 m (7 ft) diameter. It is of modular construction, and an intrument module houses all the solar payload instruments and a fine-pointing Sun sensor for aiming control. Below the instrument module, separated by the transition adapter, are three modules housing the attitude control system, power supply and communications and data handling. Two fixed solar arrays, each having three panels, supply up to 3,000W of power. Three nickel-cadmium batteries supply power during eclipses, or when the spacecraft is operating in the Earth's shadow.

The Solar Maximum Mission is managed by the Goddard Spaceflight Center. At the end of the mission, the spacecraft may be retrieved by the Space Shuttle.

SPACE SHUTTLE TRANSPORTATION SYSTEM

The Space Shuttle is the first re-usable space vehicle, consisting basically of two stages: a booster and an Orbiter. The Orbiter has a delta wing and looks very like a conventional aeroplane, but is powered by rocket engines. The liquid propellants for these engines are carried in a large external jettisonable tank, which will be attached to the orbiter at lift-off. Two large solid-propellant jettisonable boosters will be mounted on opposite sides of the propellant tank for lift-off.

Prime contractors are Rockwell International (which see) for the Orbiter, Martin Marietta for the external tank, and Thiokol for the booster. In operation, the Shuttle will be launched vertically, with all engines firing in both the boosters and Orbiter. At an altitude of about 43 km (27 miles), the booster stages will separate and descend into the sea by parachute, for recovery. The Orbiter will continue under its own power, and will jettison its large external propellant tank just before attaining orbit.

In space, the Orbiter will manoeuvre by means of two smaller rocket engines, also mounted in the rear-fuselage propulsion cluster. For minor course corrections and adjustments of attitude, the Orbiter has a series of small thrusters.

The Orbiter's main tasks are to place satellites into orbit, retrieve satellites from orbit, and repair and service satellites in orbit. It could be used to put a propulsive stage and satellite into precise low Earth orbit, for subsequent transfer to synchronous orbit or to an 'escape' mission into space. It could also be used for short-duration scientific and applications missions, as an orbiting research laboratory or reconnaissance vehicle, for space rescue, as a tanker for space refuelling, and for support of orbiting space stations.

On some flights a pressurised Spacelab, being developed by ten European countries, under the leadership of the European Space Agency, will be carried in the payload bay.

Spacelab will be the means by which man-associated experiments can be performed in the Orbiter payload bay. It includes a pressurised enclosure housing support equipment (to make it habitable) as well as the experimen-

Orbiter OV-101 *Enterprise*, **mated with an external tank and solid rocket boosters, to check out launch facilities and procedures in mid-1979**

tal equipment. When sensors require direct exposure to the space environment, a pallet will be used in association with the pressurised enclosure. On other types of missions, a pallet may be used alone, with control of the instruments being exercised from the Orbiter cabin or even from the ground. The Spacelabs are being designed around a basic seven-day mission, which is extendable up to 30 days by trading payload weight and volume for the additional consumables necessary to accommodate the further time in orbit.

On conclusion of its mission, the Orbiter will fly back into the atmosphere towards its land base, protected by a new form of heat shielding which will survive 100 missions, unlike current ablative-type heatshields. Once through the re-entry phase, the Orbiter will be able to glide up to 950 nm (1,760 km; 1,100 miles) to its base, steered by aerodynamic controls.

Special equipment being developed for use on the Space Shuttle includes a new type of spacesuit and a rescue system known as a Personal Rescue Enclosure. This consists of a 0·86 m (34 in) diameter ball which contains its own short-term simplified life support and communication systems. The ball has three layers (Urethane, Kevlar and an outside thermal protective layer) and a small viewing port of tough Lexan.

Orbiter OV-101 *Enterprise* completed approach and landing tests at NASA's Dryden Flight Research Center, California, in 1977, and ground vibration tests in 1978. On 1 May 1979 the craft was moved to launch Complex 39, Pad A, at the Kennedy Space Center, where it remained until 23 July 1979. Mated with an external tank and solid rocket boosters, it was used to check out ground support equipment, procedures and launch complex facilities.

The first operational orbital mission is scheduled to be flown by the second Orbiter, OV-102, from the Kennedy

Jupiter-Saturn Voyager being vibration tested

Space Center, Florida, in 1981, following a series of test flights. Orbiter OV-102 is named *Columbia*; OV-099 will be named *Challenger*; OV-103, *Discovery*; and OV-104, *Atlantis*, after vessels used for exploration at sea.

Basic dimensions and weights of the complete Space Transportation System are as follows:

DIMENSIONS, EXTERNAL:

Wing span	23·79 m (78 ft 0·68 in)
Length overall	56·14 m (184 ft 2·4 in)
Length of external tank	47 m (154 ft 2·4 in)
Length of boosters	45·46 m (149 ft 2·0 in)
Height overall	23·35 m (76 ft 7·2 in)

WEIGHTS:

Shuttle complete	1,984,305 kg (4,374,573 lb)
Orbiter (empty)	68,040 kg (150,000 lb)
External tank (full)	743,253 kg (1,638,565 lb)
Boosters (2), each	586,506 kg (1,293,004 lb)

THRUST:

Total, at lift-off	30,622 kN (6,925,000 lb)
Orbiter, main engines (3), each	
	1,608 kN (375,000 lb)
Boosters (2), each	12,899 kN (2,900,000 lb)

PERFORMANCE:

Payload:
In 185 km (115 mile) orbit, due east
29,485 kg (65,000 lb)
In 500 km (310 mile) orbit, 55° inclin
11,340 kg (25,000 lb)
In 185 km (115 mile) polar orbit
14,515 kg (32,000 lb)

VOYAGER

Two Mariner-type spacecraft, designated Voyager 1 and 2, were launched on a Jupiter-Saturn mission in 1977—Voyager 1 on 5 September and Voyager 2 on 20 August. They were intended to fly by both planets, and conduct exploratory investigations of the Jupiter and Saturn planetary systems. Voyager 1, flying faster than its companion, encountered Jupiter in March 1979, passing within 357,000 km (222,000 miles) of the planet. It took the first close-up pictures of Jupiter's four largest moons. The craft arrived at Saturn in November 1980, flying past at a distance of 209,000 km (130,000 miles) and within 4,000 km (2,500 miles) of Titan, Saturn's largest moon. Voyager 2 reached Jupiter in July 1979.

The Voyagers discovered a 14th moon orbiting the planet, a previously unknown Jovian ring, and that the inner Galilean moon, Io, is by far the most volcanically active member of the solar system.

Voyager 2 will reach Saturn in August 1981, and if all goes well, it will then be targeted for the first encounter with Uranus, some 2,700 million km (1,700 million miles) from Earth, in January 1986, before leaving the solar system.

The Voyagers were designed and built at NASA's Jet Propulsion Laboratory, California. Each of the 825 kg (1,820 lb) spacecraft carries wide-angle and narrow-angle television cameras and 10 scientific instruments. Major investigations will include imaging, radio science, infra-red and ultraviolet spectroscopy, magnetometry, charged particles, cosmic rays, photopolarimetry, planetary radio astronomy, plasma and particulate matter.

RCA
RCA CORPORATION

PRESIDENT AND CHIEF EXECUTIVE OFFICER: Edgar H. Griffiths
GROUP VICE-PRESIDENT: Dr James Vollmer
DIRECTOR, PUBLIC AFFAIRS: Nicholas F. Pensiero
Government Systems Division
Cherry Hill Offices, Camden, New Jersey 08101
Telephone: (609) 234 1234

RCA is prime contractor for a number of major defence programmes, including the US Navy's Aegis advanced ship-to-air missile system, the US Air Force's Block 5D satellites, and Tiros meteorological satellites. It also produces many satellite subsystems and components, including the Closed Circuit Television (CCTV) camera system for the Space Shuttle.

BLOCK 5D SATELLITE

Block 5D is the name given to series of advanced meteorological satellites forming part of the Defense Meteorological Satellite Program (DMSP) managed by the Air Force Space and Missile Systems Organisation.

Twenty-one DMSP satellites had been launched successfully by early 1980, including four in the series of the advanced Block 5D Integrated Spacecraft. The first Block 5D-1 was placed into orbit on 11 September 1976, the second on 4 June 1977, the third on 30 April 1978, and the fourth on 6 June 1979. Largest and most complex in the US Air Force's weather satellite series, the Block 5D is designed to provide high-quality meteorological data to tri-service users worldwide. The spacecraft is designed to handle all manoeuvres automatically, from guiding the booster to the accurate positioning of the satellite and its sensors in orbit. This is accomplished by a high-accuracy attitude control system using a star sensor, inertial platform, and two onboard computers which can be reprogrammed from the ground if desired.

The latest Block 5D-2 spacecraft are improved versions of the 5D-1, and are each 155 kg (342 lb) heavier. The extra weight results from added redundant systems and an advanced computer that gives the Block 5D-2 an in-orbit operational life of three years (twice that of 5D-1 satellites).

DYNAMICS EXPLORER

Dynamics Explorer (DE) is a NASA-sponsored programme which will investigate the interactive coupling between the Earth's magnetosphere, ionosphere and plasmasphere. It will utilise two coplanar polar orbiting spacecraft, designed by RCA Astro-Electronics; these will be launched by a single Delta 3914 into low and high elliptical orbits. The planned perigee altitude of both satellites is 250 km (155 miles); the apogee altitude of the low spacecraft is 1,000 km (620 miles) and that of the high spacecraft 4 to 6 Earth radii geocentric. The Dynamics Explorer launch is scheduled for 1981.

The Dynamics Explorer spacecraft is a derivative of the Atmosphere Explorer satellite. DE-A is estimated to weigh 258 kg (569 lb), of which 30 kg (66 lb) is science payload. DE-B will weigh approximately 305 kg (672 lb), of which 70 kg (154 lb) is for the experiments.

Of particular interest is the variety of experiment antennae and booms carried on both spacecraft. The high mission configuration (DE-A) accommodates two wire antennae 213 m (700 ft) long tip-to-tip, two 4 m (13 ft) flexible stem antennae, and two rigid booms 6 m (20 ft) long. The low mission spacecraft (DE-B) contains six 32 mm (1·25 in) diameter flexible stem antennae 11 m (36 ft) long, and a single rigid boom 6 m (20 ft) in length.

ITOS (NOAA)

Designed and built by RCA Astro-Electronics for NASA's Goddard Space Flight Center, the Improved Tiros Operational Satellite is capable of mapping the Earth's cloud cover at night as well as by day. Two complete scans of the Earth are thus possible in each 24 h rather than one.

When in orbit ITOS spacecraft are handed over to the National Oceanic and Atmospheric Administration and

Artist's impression of Block 5D-2 Air Force meteorological satellite

Artist's impression of Nova navigational satellite

Artist's impression of ITOS (NOAA-A) satellite

given the designation NOAA. Details of early ITOS spacecraft and NOAA launchings are given in the 1977-78 *Jane's*. Recent launchings are listed in the table of satellites at the end of this section.

NOVA

The Nova satellite is an advanced version of the US Navy's Transit, and is part of the Navy's Navigation Satellite System.

Among various improvements, the satellite is equipped with its own onboard station-seeking and station-keeping propulsion systems. The satellite also requires fewer position-updating transmissions from ground control stations than Transit. The new design was developed by the Applied Physics Laboratory of Johns Hopkins University, with support from RCA.

Artist's impression of Dynamics Explorer spacecraft

Artist's impression of RCA Satcom

Artist's impression of TIROS-N weather satellite

In operation, Nova satellites will transmit signals that indicate their orbital positions. Using information derived from these signals, a ship or aircraft with the required onboard equipment will be able to determine its longitude and latitude to an accuracy 20 times greater than that offered by conventional radio or astro navigation.

Nova will weigh approximately 136 kg (300 lb) in orbit and will utilise a 7·6 m (25 ft) long gravity boom for stabilisation. The first of three satellites was scheduled for launch in mid-1980 from Vandenberg Air Force Base, California, by a Scout rocket.

SATCOM

Satcom domestic communications satellites are designed and built by RCA Astro-Electronics of Princeton, New Jersey. The satellites are operated by RCA

American Communications, which provides more hours of nationwide television distribution than any other carrier in the world.

RCA Satcom I was launched on 12 December, 1975; RCA Satcom II followed into orbit on 26 March, 1976. A third RCA Satcom is scheduled for launch in 1981. All have a design life of more than eight years, with continuous full power.

The RCA Satcoms have 24 channels, each of which can carry 1,000 voice circuits, one FM/colour TV transmission, or 64 million bits per second of computer data. They are the first of a new generation of communications satellites with three-axis stabilisation, which gives them extra weight and power margins. The RCA Satcoms cover Alaska, Hawaii and the contiguous 48 States.

TIROS N

The first of a new generation of polar-orbiting weather satellites, designated TIROS-N, was launched on 13 October 1978 and is providing more information, more accurately and at a higher rate than the ITOS satellites. This is accomplished by carrying more advanced sensing devices, including: the Advanced Very High Resolution Radiometer (AVHRR), the Tiros Operational Vertical Sounder (TOVS), a French Data Collection System (DCS), and a Solar Environment Monitor (SEM). The data provided by these instruments will enable forecasters to predict climatic trends accurately up to a week in advance, and eventually to two weeks.

TIROS-N has an overall diameter of 1·88 m (6 ft 2 in) and is 3·71 m (12 ft 2 in) long. Weight at lift-off is 1,421 kg (3,127 lb); in-orbit weight is 689 kg (1,520 lb). Eight of the satellites have been procured to meet NOAA's operational requirements until 1984. Each will be launched by an Atlas E/F vehicle into a near-polar Sun-synchronous orbit at a nominal height of 833 km (517 miles) or 870 km (540 miles).

ROCKWELL INTERNATIONAL
ROCKWELL INTERNATIONAL CORPORATION
Space Systems Group
12214 Lakewood Boulevard, Downey, California 90241
Telephone: (213) 922 2111
PRESIDENT: George W. Jeffs

Rockwell's Space Systems Group is comprised of two divisions: the Space Transportation System Development and Production Division which is responsible for design, development and test of Space Shuttle Orbiters and integration of NASA's Space Transportation System and payloads; and the Space Operations and Satellite Systems Division which has responsibility for design, development and test of the NavStar satellites of the Global Positioning System, as well as government and commercial space operations, payload/cargo integration, and manned space business areas.

NAVSTAR

The NavStar global positioning system is intended to satisfy future precise positioning and navigation needs of all the US military services, and to have potential civil applications. NavStar is designed to provide suitably equipped users with highly accurate (to within 10 m; 30 ft) three-dimensional position and velocity information and a precise timing reference in real time. The NavStar spacecraft will be placed in subsynchronous, 12-h circular orbits of about 17,525 km (10,890 miles) in three orbital planes at 63° inclination, with eight satellites per ring. The complete system of 24 satellites should be operational by 1985.

NavStar I was launched on 22 February 1978 by an Atlas F from Vandenberg AFB, and was followed by three more NavStars as detailed in the table of satellites at the end of this section. In concept validation phase testing, these four satellites have, in signals to ground, air and sea units, provided navigational data with three-dimensional accuracies better than design specifications.

The Global Positioning System (GPS) set (the user's or receiver's equipment) may be one of several models, installed or even hand-held in land, sea, air or space vehicles. The set comprises a combined radio receiver and computer, which locks on to NavStar signals from the four satellites that are most favourably located and computes the signal's time and range into navigational data. Key to the system is the use of highly accurate atomic clocks, of which three are installed on each of the 759 kg (1,673 lb) satellites; these will lose or gain only one second in 36,000 years.

In 1979, it was announced that funding had been made available for the development of electronic countermeasures technology for NavStar and other US military satellites. Work includes development of onboard sensors capable of detecting whether a spacecraft has been illuminated by laser energy or has been touched by another spacecraft.

SPACE SHUTTLE ORBITER

The National Aeronautics and Space Administration's Space Shuttle will be the world's first re-usable space transportation system, and will be the keystone of America's space programme through this century.

The Shuttle system includes the Orbiter stage, capable of carrying up to 29,484 kg (65,000 lb) of cargo into Earth orbit; an external propellant tank; and two solid-propellant rocket boosters. The Orbiter will lift off from Earth like a rocket, operate in orbit as a spacecraft, and return to land in a manner similar to that of a conventional aeroplane.

The first Shuttle spacecraft, *Enterprise* (OV-101), has been returned to Rockwell's Palmdale, California, facility following completion of the mated vertical ground vibration tests at NASA's Marshall Space Flight Center, and fit and function checkout of the launch facilities and equipment at Kennedy Space Center. *Columbia* (OV-102), the first Shuttle spacecraft scheduled for Earth orbital flight, was transported to the Kennedy Space Center in March 1979 and continues to undergo preparations for launch in 1981. The *Challenger* (STA-099) has returned to Rockwell's Palmdale facility, following successful load-limit structural testing. *Challenger* is being prepared for modification leading to structural renovation, systems installation, and final assembly as the second Earth orbital flight spacecraft. *Discovery* (OV-103) and *Atlantis* (OV-104) are in the initial stages of fabrication, and are scheduled for final assembly at Palmdale in 1982-83.

Details of the overall operation of the Space Shuttle Transportation System are given in the NASA entry in this section.

The following description applies to Orbiter vehicle OV-102:

TYPE: Re-usable space transportation vehicle.

WINGS: Cantilever low-wing monoplane, of double-delta planform. Wing section NACA 0010 (modified). Sweepback 81° on inner leading-edges, 45° on outer leading-edges. Dihedral 3° 30′ on trailing-edges. The main wing assembly, for which Grumman is responsible, is primarily a conventional aluminium alloy structure made up of a corrugated spar web, truss-type ribs, and riveted skin/stringer and honeycomb skins. Wing has a very blunt leading-edge and is more than 1·52 m (5 ft) thick at the thickest point. Two-segment hydraulically-actuated elevons on each trailing-edge, for pitch and roll control, are of aluminium honeycomb construction with a titanium rubbing strip on each of their leading-edges. Hinged panels on the wing upper surface, of titanium sandwich, are used to seal the wing/elevon gap; these are the only areas of the wing not covered by the thermal protection system.

FUSELAGE: Conventional semi-monocoque aluminium alloy structure, built in three main portions. Forward fuselage contains the crew module, three forward electronics bays, forward reaction control system and nose-wheel unit. The mid-fuselage portion is an 18·28 m (60 ft) long section of primary load-carrying structure, built by General Dynamics (Convair) and includes the wing carry-through structure. Upper half of the mid-fuselage consists of structural payload bay doors, hinged along the side and meeting at the top centreline. These doors are of graphite epoxy bonded honeycomb sandwich construction, with a Nomex core, and are opened and closed by Curtiss-Wright actuators. The forward 9·14 m (30 ft) of each door incorporates Vought radiator panels that are hinged and latched to the inside of the door and are deployed in orbit. Fixed aft radiator panels are attached to the remaining inner surface of each door if required by a specific mission. The aft fuselage interfaces with the removable orbital manoeuvring system (OMS) pods, the wing rear spar, the vertical tail assembly, the underbody flap, the external tank rear supports, the main propulsion system, the launch umbilical panel, the three aft electronics bays, and other discrete system equipment. A bulkhead heatshield at the rear of the vehicle protects the main engine systems. A large body flap under the rear fuselage protects the main engine nozzles during re-entry, and is hydraulically-actuated to serve also as a trimming surface, particularly to compensate for the nose-up pitching moment induced when the rudder is in use as a speed brake.

TAIL UNIT: Vertical surfaces only, built by Fairchild Republic, of wedge-shaped section with 45° sweepback on fin leading-edge. Fin is a conventional aluminium alloy structure. The rudder/speed brake assembly has an aluminium honeycomb skin and is divided into upper and lower sections. Each of these is also split longitudinally and actuated individually to serve as both rudder and speed brake, operated by a Sundstrand hydraulic rotary actuator. The Inconel honeycomb seal over these is the only part of the vertical tail not covered by the thermal protection system. Mission requirements call for a locked rudder/speed brake during boost, orbit and re-entry. The speed brake control is provided from approx Mach 10 to Mach 5; from Mach 5 to landing the rudder and speed brake controls are combined as required. Primary system control is automatic, with manual override.

THERMAL PROTECTION SYSTEM: Almost the whole of the exterior of the Orbiter, a total area of some 1,105 m² (11,895 sq ft), is covered in one of four main types of thermal insulation. Two of these, known as HRSI (high-temperature re-usable surface insulation) and LRSI (low-temperature re-usable surface insulation) are the responsibility of Lockheed Missiles and Space Co, and are in the form of silica fibre-based quartz tiles. Some 34,000 tiles will cover 70 per cent of the surface (479·8 m²; 5,164 sq ft of HRSI and 254·6 m²; 2,741 sq ft of LRSI, covering most of the wings, fuselage and tail

NASA/Rockwell International Space Shuttle Orbiter (*Michael A. Badrocke*)

Space Shuttle Orbiter vehicle OV-101, *Enterprise,* **approaching the runway at the end of an unpowered flight test**

areas). The tiles are coated with reaction cured glass (RCG), the HRSI tiles giving protection from temperatures of 649-1,260°C (1,200-2,300°F) and the LRSI tiles from temperatures of 371-649°C (700-1,200°F). For temperatures below 371°C, some 332·7 m² (3,581 sq ft) of the surface, mostly on the cargo bay doors, upper wing and mid-fuselage, is covered with coated Nomex felt. The nose-cap, and most of the wing leading-edges, a total of 38·00 m² (409 sq ft), are covered in a reinforced carbon-carbon (RCC) composite for which Vought is the subcontractor. Metal insulation is used along the elevon hinge lines. Total weight of the thermal insulation is 8,074 kg (17,800 lb).

LANDING GEAR: Retractable tricycle type, with twin wheels and Menasco oleo-pneumatic shock-absorbers on each unit. Hydraulic release, with a pyrotechnic backup for deployment in flight. Landing gear cannot be retracted in flight, after release. Nose unit is retracted forward into fuselage and main units forward into wings before launch. Nose unit is steerable; main units are fitted with B. F. Goodrich brakes and Hydro-Aire anti-skid units. All units have Goodrich wheels and tyres. Landing gear is designed to facilitate safe landing at speeds of up to 225 knots (415 km/h; 258 mph). The main gear tyres are rated at 20,410 kg (45,000 lb) and the brakes at 240 × 10⁶ ft-lb.

BOOSTERS: Two Thiokol solid-propellant rocket boosters (each 12,899 kN; 2,900,000 lb st for lift-off) will be attached one on each side of the external propellant tank.

MAIN PROPULSION: Three Rocketdyne SSME (Space Shuttle Main Engines) high-pressure liquid oxygen/liquid hydrogen engines, each rated at 1,668 kN (375,000 lb) st for lift-off and 2,090 kN (470,000 lb) thrust in space.

EXTERNAL PROPELLANT TANK: Contains the main propellants for the Orbiter. It is of aluminium alloy semi-monocoque construction, with a 25 mm (1 in) thick foam external insulation. In the forward end of the tank is a 552 m³ (19,495 cu ft) tank holding 604,185 kg (1,332,000 lb) of liquid oxygen; in the aft end is a 1,573·1 m³ (55,552 cu ft) tank holding 101,604 kg (224,000 lb) of liquid hydrogen. Total propellant weight 743,240 kg (1,638,565 lb).

ORBIT MANOEUVRING ENGINES: Two Aerojet Liquid Rocket Company (ALRC) bi-propellant liquid rocket engines, running on monomethylhydrazine (MMH) and nitrogen tetroxide (N₂O₄), are used for the Orbiter's orbit manoeuvring subsystem (OMS). These engines are housed in pods, one on each side of the Orbiter's aft fuselage. The OMS engines, for which a usable total of 10,830 kg (23,876 lb) of propellant is carried, are used to position the Orbiter in orbit; each develops 26·7 kN (6,000 lb) thrust in space.

REACTION CONTROL ENGINES: The Orbiter's reaction control subsystem (RCS) utilises thirty-eight Marquardt R-40A bipropellant liquid rocket engines (each 3·87 kN; 870 lb vacuum thrust) and six Marquardt R-1E bipropellant liquid rocket vernier thrusters (each 0·11 kN; 24 lb vacuum thrust). Fourteen of the R-40A engines are on the Orbiter's nose and 24 on the aft end, 12 in each OMS/RCS pod; there are two of the R-1E verniers on the nose and two in each aft pod. Propellants are the same as for the OMS engines; 1,096 kg (2,418 lb) is carried in the RCS tanks, and there is provision for crossfeed between the OMS and RCS tanks.

CREW COMPARTMENT: Self-contained crew module has a fuselage-side hatch for access, a hatch into the airlock

from the mid-section, and a hatch from the airlock into the payload bay. It is divided into three levels, the upper (flight deck) level having side-by-side seating for two flight crewmen with dual controls. Behind them are seats for one or two mission specialists. On the middle deck are seats for three more mission specialists, three bunks, galley, hygiene section, airlock, three electronics bays, and payload bay access; for rescue missions, seats for three more persons can be fitted in place of the bunks. The lower deck contains environmental control equipment and crew equipment storage.

PAYLOAD BAY: In centre of fuselage, 18·29 m (60 ft) long and 4·57 m (15 ft) in diameter. Retractable manipulator arm on left hand side (with provision for a second one on the right), for deploying and retrieving payloads. Complete closed-circuit TV system by RCA Astro-Electronics includes a colour camera in the crew compartment and several black and white cameras in the cargo bay and on the manipulator arm. These will facilitate payload handling and provide TV coverage for engineers and the general public on Earth.

SYSTEMS: Environmental control and life support system, made up of four subsystems: atmosphere revitalisation subsystem (ARS), to control atmospheric environment for occupants and thermal environment for electronics; food, water and waste subsystem (FWW), to provide cooking, hygiene, and other life support functions; active thermal control subsystem (ATCS), to maintain subsystems and components within specified temperature limits and to provide, via payload door radiator panels, active heat rejection to protect payloads; and an airlock support subsystem. Three redundant hydraulic systems, each of 207 bars (3,000 lb/sq in), supply actuators for the elevons, body flap, rudder/speed brake, and power to actuate main engine thrust vector controls, landing gear, brakes and steering. Electrical power subsystem (EPS) consists, functionally, of a fuel cell power plants (FCP) subsystem, and a power reactant storage and distribution (PRSD) subsystem. There are three FCPs, each providing power at 27·5V to 32·5V DC over a power range of 2-12kW and each connected to one of the three main DC buses; these supply the primary in-flight electrical power used by the Shuttle, generated through the chemical combination and conversion of cryogenic oxygen and hydrogen. In the PRSD subsystem, enough of these materials is stored to provide a total of 1,530kWh of electrical energy to the Orbiter, including 50kWh to a payload over a seven-day period. Westinghouse remote power control system and master timing unit. Honeywell four-channel fly-by-wire electrical flight control subsystem for operation of all control surfaces and main engine controls. APU subsystem consists of three Sundstrand independent APUs (each 100·7 kW; 135 shp), deriving their energy from the decomposition of hydrazine (N₂H₄).

ELECTRONICS AND EQUIPMENT: Fully fail-operational/fail-safe guidance, navigation and control system, including three Singer-Kearfott KT-70/SKN-2600 type inertial measuring units; triplex Ku-band microwave scan beam landing system, by the AIL Division of Cutler-Hammer; three Northrop rate gyro assemblies; three Hoffman L-band Tacan; three Bendix accelerometer assemblies; two Honeywell C-band radar altimeters; four AiResearch air data transducers; three Lear Siegler attitude director indicators; two Collins horizontal situation indicators; two Sperry alpha/Mach indicators; two Bendix altitude/vertical velocity indicators;

Artist's impression of NavStar satellite

two Bendix surface position indicators; two Sperry barometric altimeters; and two Sperry ATC transponders. Communications and tracking equipment includes one (optionally two) Ku-band rendezvous radar/satellite com; two Ball star trackers; two one-way Doppler extractors; two 100W Watkins-Johnson S-band TWT amplifiers; two P-band UHF for EVA/ATC com; Conrac S-band FM for Orbiter/ground and Orbiter/payload com; and Ku-band radio for Orbiter/ground com. Central data processing is by means of five IBM Advanced System/4 Pi Model AP-101 (modified) digital computers (each with a capacity for 65,000 32-bit words) and two mass memory units (each with capacity of 134 megabits). Four of the computers are interconnected to process guidance, navigation and control inputs and to relay commands to FBW flight control systems; the fifth is provided for independent backup and systems management.

Basic dimensions and weights of the Orbiter are:

DIMENSIONS, EXTERNAL:

Wing span	23·79 m (78 ft 0·68 in)
Wing aspect ratio	2·265
Wing mean aerodynamic chord	12·06 m (39 ft 6·81 in)
Length	37·19 m (122 ft 0·2 in)
Height	17·25 m (56 ft 7 in)

DIMENSIONS, INTERNAL :

Payload bay:

Length	18·29 m (60 ft 0 in)
Diameter	4·57 m (15 ft 0 in)
Crew module: Volume	74·33 m³ (2,625 cu ft)

AREAS :

Wings, gross	249·91 m² (2,690 sq ft)
Elevons (total)	38·38 m² (413·14 sq ft)
Rudder/speed brake	9·09 m² (97·84 sq ft)
Vertical tail surfaces (total)	38·39 m² (413·25 sq ft)
Body flap	12·61 m² (135·75 sq ft)

WEIGHTS:

Weight empty	68,040 kg (150,000 lb)
Design landing weight with	14,515 kg (32,000 lb)
payload	96,162 kg (212,000 lb)

PERFORMANCE:

Orbital speed

approx 15,285 knots (28,325 km/h; 17,600 mph)

Nominal touchdown speed (unpowered)

180 knots (334 km/h; 208 mph) EAS

TRW
TRW DEFENSE AND SPACE SYSTEMS GROUP

1 Space Park, Redondo Beach, California 90278
Telephone: (213) 535 4321
VICE-PRESIDENT AND GENERAL MANAGER: Dr George E. Solomon
PUBLIC AFFAIRS AND COMMUNICATIONS DIRECTOR: R. E. Trudel

TRW Defense and Space Systems Group has provided technical direction and systems engineering for the US Air Force Atlas/Titan/Minuteman missile programme since 1954. The company has also designed and built more than 150 spacecraft and scores of major subsystems. Its recent and current military and civilian contracts have included prime contracts for the NASA Pioneer, US Air Force DSCS II, international communications satellites and US Navy Fleet Communications Satellite.

DEFENSE SATELLITE COMMUNICATIONS SYSTEM, PHASE II (DSCS II)

The Phase II Defense Satellite Communications System (DSCS II) utilises synchronous-orbit, high-capacity, super high frequency communications satellites and surface terminals to provide reliable worldwide circuits for carrying essential military communications. The satellites are developed and produced by TRW Inc for the US Air Force.

Protected against interference, the satellites are each equipped with steerable narrow-beam antennae that focus a portion of the satellite's energy to areas 870 nm (1,600 km; 1,000 miles) in diameter. Within these specially

illuminated areas, the narrow beam antennae allow small terminals to be used in place of more costly large terminals. The narrow beams are designed to be steered in a matter of minutes to different locations on the Earth's surface, and the satellites are so designed that they can be moved in a few days to new synchronous orbital positions. In this way coverage can be tailored to fit defence contingency communications all over the world.

The Phase II satellites each weigh 590 kg (1,300 lb), are 2·75 m (9 ft) in diameter and 3·95 m (13 ft) tall with antennae extended. Electrical power is supplied by solar arrays with an output of 535W at launch, decreasing to a minimum of 358W after five years. The X-band single-frequency conversion repeater has a bandwidth of 410MHz and capacity of 1,300 voice channels or up to 100 megabits per second of data.

The Earth-coverage antennae have a transmit beamwidth of 18°, a gain of 16·8 dbi, and effective radiated power of 28 dbw. The narrow-coverage antennae have beamwidths of 2·6° and 6·5°, a gain of 33 dbi and 22 dbi, and an effective radiated power of 43 dbw and 32 dbw. They are steerable to ±10°.

First launch of two DSCS II satellites was on 3 November 1971, by Titan IIIC launch vehicle, from Cape Kennedy. Five more pairs had been launched by early 1979, at which time contracts were expected to fund a total of at least 16 satellites, to extend coverage into the 1980s.

FLEETSATCOM

The US Navy-sponsored Fleetsatcom satellite system will provide worldwide high-priority UHF communications between naval aircraft, ships, submarines, ground

DSCS II defence communications satellite

stations, Strategic Air Command and the Presidential command networks.

The first Fleetsatcom was launched by an Atlas-Centaur on 19 February 1978 and the second on 4 May 1979. In all, four of the three-axis stabilised satellites will be placed into geosynchronous equatorial orbit to provide complete Earth coverage, except for the polar regions. A fifth satellite will serve as a contingency spare. Fleetsatcoms have a design life of five years and provide more than 30 voice and 12 teletype channels.

The satellite consists of two major components, each with a basic 2·44 m (8 ft) hexagonal body. The payload module contains UHF and X-band communications equipment and antennae. Each of its six side panels carries related communications components. The 4·88 m (16 ft) parabolic UHF antenna is made up of ribs and mesh, and opens like an umbrella. The solar array, never shadowed, is exposed to sunlight in both folded and deployed configurations. Three nickel-cadmium batteries provide power during eclipse.

WEIGHTS:

At lift-off	1,860 kg (4,100 lb)
In orbit	885 kg (1,950 lb)

HEAO

HEAO, a High Energy Astronomy Observatory, is designed to study some of the most intriguing mysteries in the universe; including pulsars, quasars, exploding galaxies and 'black holes' in space.

Three spacecraft, HEAO-A, B and C, are involved in a three-mission programme.

HEAO-A surveyed and mapped X-ray sources throughout the celestial sphere and also measured low-energy gamma-ray flux. Rotating end-over-end, it was able to survey the entire sky in six months.

HEAO-B is manoeuvring to point for long periods at selected X-ray sources mapped by HEAO-A and smaller X-ray spacecraft. HEAO-C is conducting a survey of gamma ray emissions and cosmic ray particles from our galaxy.

HEAO is 5·8 m (19 ft) long and weighs about 3,150 kg (7,000 lb), including 1,350 kg (3,000 lb) of experiments. Basically, the spacecraft consists of a common equipment module plus a mission-peculiar experiment module. The HEAO-A experiment module structure is six-sided. Three of the four experiments are designed to study certain attributes of the low-to-medium energy X-rays from galactic and extra-galactic discrete X-ray sources, as well as the diffuse X-ray background. The fourth experiment extends the observations into the low-energy gamma ray region of the spectrum.

In HEAO-B, which must point to specific stars or points in the sky, reaction wheels are added to provide a precise and highly accurate pointing capability of one arc minute or better.

HEAO-A, designated HEAO-1 in orbit, was launched by Atlas-Centaur 45 on 12 August 1977, from Cape Canaveral Air Force Station at the Kennedy Space Center, Florida. It returned excellent quality data, studying more than 300 stellar sources, until its supply of attitude control gas became exhausted in January 1979 and its mission ended. HEAO-B, designated HEAO-2 in orbit, was launched on 13 November 1978. Nicknamed *Einstein Observatory,* the spacecraft carries the first telescope capable of producing focused images showing the structure of X-ray objects. By the end of 1979, among the 500 images transmitted were pictures of the brightest, most distant and most powerful objects yet observed to emit X-rays—quasars estimated to be more than 10,000 million light years from Earth.

HEAO-C, designated HEAO-3 in orbit, was launched on 20 September 1979.

IMEWS (USAF 647 SATELLITE)

The US Air Force's 647 series of satellites, for which TRW Systems is prime contractor, is intended to provide early warning of a hostile ballistic missile launch by detecting the infra-red emission from the missiles by means of an Aerojet-General infra-red 'telescope'. The programme is believed to be known now by the acronym IMEWS (Integrated Missile Early Warning Satellite) and to be the operational successor to the original Midas project.

A first launch, on 6 November 1970, was unsuccessful. The second launching, by a Titan IIIC from Cape Kennedy on 5 May 1971, is believed to have been successful. IMEWS-3 was launched on 1 March 1972, and IMEWS-4 on 12 June 1973. French reports suggest that the IMEWS satellite is cylindrical, weighs 820 kg (1,800 lb) at launch, has an inertial three-axis stabilisation system and measures approximately 3 m (9 ft 10 in) in diameter and 3 m (9 ft 10 in) in height; cruciform solar panels are said to span 7 m (23 ft). The same reports stated that the satellite carries high-resolution cameras, able to transmit photographs of any missiles that are located to a ground station 500 km (300 miles) north-west of Adelaide, Australia, for onward transmission via synchronous-orbit relay satellites to NORAD headquarters, Colorado Springs, USA.

Debriefing reports of an espionage trial held in 1977 contain references to two US satellite surveillance systems known as Argus and Rhyolite. Developed by TRW and stationed in geosynchronous orbit over Asia, the Rhyolite satellites are reported to intercept telemetry signals transmitted by Soviet missiles during test launchings and when they deliver dummy payloads in Eastern Siberia or in the Pacific Ocean. The system can also monitor Chinese missile tests. Argus satellites are reported to intercept

Artist's impression of Fleetsatcom satellite

Soviet and Chinese telephonic and radio microwave communications and to have other classified capabilities. A third satellite surveillance system is reported to be code named Keyhole.

VOUGHT

VOUGHT CORPORATION (Subsidiary of THE LTV CORPORATION)

HEADQUARTERS: PO Box 225907, Dallas, Texas 75265
OFFICERS: See Aircraft section

Vought Corporation is prime contractor for the NASA/DoD Scout launch vehicle. It is also engaged in the fields of aircraft, advanced defence systems, ramjet propulsion systems and laser technology.

SCOUT (XRM-91)

Scout was designed to make possible space, orbital and re-entry research at comparatively low cost. On 16 February 1961, it became the first solid-propellant vehicle ever to put a satellite into orbit when it was used to launch Explorer 9. In its current form, the first-stage motor is an Algol III, manufactured by Chemical Systems Division of UTC and providing a total impulse of 3,266,000 kg/s (7,200,000 lb/s); the second stage is the 266·9 kN (60,000 lb) Castor II by Thiokol; the third stage is the 83·1 kN (18,700 lb) Antares III by Thiokol; the current Altair III fourth stage, by Thiokol, develops 26·7 kN (6,000 lb st). Honeywell provides the simplified gyro guidance system. Spin stabilisation of the fourth stage is by Vought.

In this standard four-stage form, Scout is able to put a 193 kg (425 lb) payload into a 500 km (310 mile) easterly orbit. A five-stage version is also available, which increases the Scout's hypersonic re-entry performance and makes possible highly-elliptical deep-space orbits.

In addition to its use by NASA and the Department of Defense, Scout is used for international programmes, including those of the United Kingdom, Italy, France, West Germany, the Netherlands and the European Space Agency (ESA). A total of 101 had been launched by January 1980.

DIMENSIONS:

Overall height	22·92 m (75 ft 2½ in)
Max body diameter	1·14 m (3 ft 9 in)

WEIGHT:

Launching weight	21,400 kg (47,185 lb)

ASAT

In FY 1979 the LTV Corporation was awarded a $78·2 million contract to develop a new miniature anti-satellite (ASAT) vehicle. Few official details are available, but it is reported that ASAT is fitted with a simple seeker and does not carry an explosive warhead, targets being destroyed or incapacitated by direct collision. According to Lt. Gen. Tom Stafford, then US Air Force Deputy Chief of Staff for Research, Development and Acquisition, the weapon is to be tested against a co-operative target satellite instrumented to evaluate ASAT performance. These trials will "concentrate on kill verification, pointing and tracking".

The ASAT programme received a further $80·5 million in FY 1980, with $124·9 million requested for FY 1981.

Scout four-stage solid-propellant launch vehicle

LAUNCH VEHICLES

Launch vehicles: 1, Scout (USA); 2, Diamant BP-4 (France); 3, B-1 Cosmos (USSR); 4, N (Japan); 5, C-1 Cosmos (USSR); 6, Delta 3914 (USA); 7, Atlas-Centaur (USA); 8, Ariane (France); 9, A-2 Soyuz (USSR); 10, Titan IIIC (USA); 11, D-1e Zonda (USSR); 12, Space Shuttle (USA) *(Michael A. Badrocke)*

Salyut 6 Space Station *(M. A. Barnes)*

1 Forward and aft hatches
2 External TV camera mount
3 Rendezvous antenna
4 Exploration hatch?
5 External instrument package
6 EVA handrails
7 Airlock pneumatic controls
8 External thermal control panel
9 Airlock controls
10 Sunsensor
11 Protective screen
12 Rotating solar arrays
13 Telemetry antennae
14 Zero-gravity cosmonaut weighing scale
15 Sleeping berth
16 Airlock for debris ejection
17 Dust filter
18 Pneumatic and hydraulic systems for attitude control and main propulsion engines
19 Attitude control engines

20 Air Ventilator
21 TV camera for aft docking operations
22 Sanitary facilities
23 Toilet
24 Food lockers
25 Sighting device (12 × magnification, for aligning the BST-1M telescope)
26 Container for scientific instruments (BST-1M telescope)
27 Fresh water storage
28 Garbage containers
29 Electronic control panels for instrument module
30 Running track for cosmonaut exercises
31 Veloergometer exerciser
32 Photographic apparatus
33 Electronics bay
34 Solar panel rotating mechanism
35 Commander's control panel
36 TV camera
37 EVA spacesuits (stowage)

38 Transport spaceship Soyuz
39 Active docking system of Soyuz
40 Passive docking system of the Salyut station
41 Sun sensor
42 Porthole
43 Compressed air cylinders
44 Oxygen cylinders for station's atmosphere
45 Fresh water tank
46 Vacuum cylinder
47 Attachment point for launch shroud
48 MFK-6M photographic apparatus
49 High-pressure airlines
50 High-pressure air storage cylinder
51 Communications antenna
52 Propellant tank
53 Main propulsion system engine
54 Visual docking target
55 Soyuz orbital module
56 Soyuz descent module

SATELLITES AND SPACECRAFT LAUNCHED DURING 1979

Note: Both the USA and USSR have withheld information on some launchings and this listing may be incomplete.
Data in italics are approximate or estimated.

Date	Origin	Name	Total Weight kg	lb	Launch Vehicle	Perigee km	miles	Apogee km	miles	Inclin- ation	Lifetime	Remarks
11 Jan	USSR	Cosmos 1070	*6,000*	*13,230*	—	205	127	296	184	62·80	13 days	*Reconnaissance satellite. Recovered.*
13 Jan	USSR	Cosmos 1071	*6,000*	*13,230*	—	178	111	338	210	62·79	13 days	Manoeuvrable satellite. Purpose not disclosed.
16 Jan	USSR	Cosmos 1072	*700*	*1,543*	—	963	598	1,018	632	82·92	*1,200 years*	*Navigation satellite.*
18 Jan	USSR	Molniya 3 (11)	*1,500*	*3,307*	—	434	270	39,942	24,818	62·80	*12 years*	Communications satellite.
25 Jan	USSR	Meteor 1 (29)	*2,200*	*4,850*	—	621	386	643	399·5	98·00	*60 years*	Meteorological satellite. In retro- grade, Sun-synchronous orbit.
30 Jan	USSR	Cosmos 1073	*6,000*	*13,230*	—	181	112·5	327	203	62·81	13 days	*Reconnaissance satellite. Recovered.*
30 Jan	USA	SCATHA	360	794	Delta	180	112	43,260	26,880	27·32	Unlimited	Spacecraft Charging AT High Al- titude satellite; investigating build-up of electrical charges in spacecraft.
31 Jan	USSR	Cosmos 1074	*7,000*	*15,430*	—	197	122·5	240	149	51·60	60 days	*Test of manned spacecraft. Recovered.*
6 Feb	Japan	ECS (Ayame)	260	573	N-I	190	118	34,583	21,489	24·09	Unlimited	Experimental communications satellite. Damaged during launch.
8 Feb	USSR	Cosmos 1075	*1,000*	*2,205*	—	428	266	516	321	65·83	*2 years*	Purpose not disclosed.
12 Feb	USSR	Cosmos 1076	*1,000*	*2,205*	—	635	394·5	664	412·5	82·53	*60 years*	Oceanographic survey satellite.
13 Feb	USSR	Cosmos 1077	*2,500*	*5,510*	—	623	387	630	391	81·23	*60 years*	Purpose not disclosed.
18 Feb	USA	SAGE	147	324	Scout	549	341	661	411	54·93	*40 years*	Stratospheric Aerosol and Gas Experiment satellite.
21 Feb	Japan	CORSA (Hakucho)	100	220	Mu-3C	541	336	573	356	29·90	*30 years*	Scientific satellite; studying X-rays.
21 Feb	USSR	Ekran (3)	*2,000*	*4,410*	—	35,635	22,143	35,935	22,329	0·34	—	Communications satellite.
22 Feb	USSR	Cosmos 1078	*6,000*	*13,230*	—	168	104·5	280	174	72·85	8 days	*Reconnaissance satellite. Man- oeuvrable. Recovered.*
24 Feb	USA	Solwind			Scout	562	349	600	373	97·66	*40 years*	Research satellite. Studying ionosphere and magnetosphere.
25 Feb	USSR	Soyuz 32	*6,600*	*14,550*	—	193	120	256	159	51·59	105 days	Docked with and reactivated Salyut 6. Crew Vladimir Lyakhov and Valery Ryumin. Crew set endurance record of 175 days.
27 Feb	USSR	Cosmos 1079	*6,000*	*13,230*	—	171	106	337	209·5	67·14	12 days	*Reconnaissance satellite. Recovered.*
27 Feb	USSR	Intercosmos 19	*550*	*1,212*	—	500	311	990	615	73·98	*100 years*	Scientific satellite. Carries experiments from Bulgaria, Czechoslovakia, Poland, Hungary and USSR.
1 Mar	USSR	Meteor 2 (4)	*2,750*	*6,063*	—	837	520	896	557	81·22	*500 years*	Meteorological satellite.
12 Mar	USSR	Progress 5	*7,000*	*15,430*	—	183	114	256	159	51·65	22 days	Unmanned supply craft. Carried food, equipment and fuel to Salyut 6.
14 Mar	USSR	Cosmos 1080	*6,000*	*13,230*	—	167	104	292	181·5	72·85	14 days	*Reconnaissance satellite. Man- oeuvrable. Recovered.*
15 Mar	USSR	Cosmos 1081-88	*40*	*88*	—	1,406	874	1,455	904	74·03	*10,000 years*	*Military communications satellites.*
16 Mar	USA	USAF	13,300	29,320	Titan IIID	159	99	245	152	96·39		'Big Bird' reconnaissance satellite.
	USA	USAF	60	132	}	619	385	628	390	97·23	*60 years*	'Ferret' sub-satellite.
21 Mar	USSR	Cosmos 1089	*700*	*1,543*	—	971	603	1,003	623	82·97	*1,200 years*	*Navigation satellite.*
31 Mar	USSR	Cosmos 1090	*5,500*	*12,125*	—	201	125	329	204	72·85	13 days	*Reconnaissance satellite. Recovered.*
7 Apr	USSR	Cosmos 1091	*700*	*1,543*	—	967	601	1,011	628	82·93	*1,200 years*	*Navigation satellite.*
10 Apr	USSR	Soyuz 33	*6,600*	*14,550*	—	194	120·5	261	162	51·61	2 days	Crew: Nikolai Rukavishnikov and Georgi Ivanov. Failed to dock with Salyut 6.
11 Apr	USSR	Cosmos 1092	*700*	*1,543*	—	966	600	1,008	626	82·95	*1,200 years*	*Navigation satellite.*
12 Apr	USSR	Molniya 1 (43)	*1,000*	*2,205*	—	622	386·5	40,595	25,225	62·91	*12 years*	Communications satellite; replaces Molniya 1 (32).
14 Apr	USSR	Cosmos 1093	*2,500*	*5,510*	—	620	385	633	393	81·25	*60 years*	
18 Apr	USSR	Cosmos 1094			—	427	265	445	276·5	65·02		*Reconnaissance satellite. Ocean survey.*
20 Apr	USSR	Cosmos 1095	*6,000*	*13,230*	—	197	122·5	379	235·5	72·85	14 days	*Reconnaissance satellite. Recovered.*
25 Apr	USSR	Raduga 5			—	35,789	22,238	35,789	22,238	0·41	Unlimited	Communications satellite.
25 Apr	USSR	Cosmos 1096			—	430	267	444	276	65·05	29 days	*Reconnaissance satellite. Ocean survey.*
27 Apr	USSR	Cosmos 1097	*5,500*	*12,125*	—	174	108	336	209	62·79	13 days	*Reconnaissance satellite. Recovered.*
4 May	USA	Fleetsatcom 2	1,884	4,154	Atlas-Centaur						Unlimited	Military communications satellite.
13 May	USSR	Progress 6	*7,000*	*15,430*	—	190	118	247	153·5	51·62	27 days	Unmanned supply craft. Carried food, materials and fuel to Salyut 6.
15 May	USSR	Cosmos 1098	*6,000*	*13,230*	—	168	104	356	221	72·87	13 days	*Reconnaissance satellite. Recovered.*
17 May	USSR	Cosmos 1099	*6,000*	*13,230*	—	214	133	244	152	81·34	13 days	Manoeuvrable *reconnaissance sat- ellite.* Recovered.
22 May	USSR	Cosmos 1100	*7,000*	*15,430*	—	195	121	210	130·5	51·6	90 minutes	Dual launch. Satellites recovered immediately. Purpose not known.
	USSR	Cosmos 1101	*7,000*	*15,430*	}	195	121	210	130·5	51·6	90 minutes	

Date	Origin	Name	Total weight kg	lb	Launch Vehicle	Perigee km	miles	Apogee km	miles	Inclin- ation	Lifetime	Remarks
25 May	USSR	Cosmos 1102	6,000	13,230	—	211	131	259	161	81·34	13 days	*Reconnaissance satellite. Recovered.*
28 May	USA	USAF	13,300	29,320	Titan IIID	133	82·5	291	181	96·41		'Big Bird' reconnaissance satellite.
31 May	USSR	Cosmos 1103	6,000	13,230	—	255	158·5	374	232·5	62·82	14 days	*Reconnaissance satellite. Recovered.*
31 May	USSR	Cosmos 1104	700	1,543	—	961	597	1,009	627	82·95	*1,200 years*	*Navigation satellite.*
2 June	UK	Ariel 6	154	340	Scout D	599	372	656	408	54·95	*60 years*	Scientific satellite.
5 June	USSR	Molniya 3 (12)	1,500	3,307	—	438	272	40,772	25,335	62·84	*12 years*	Domestic communications satellite.
6 June	USSR	Soyuz 34	6,800	14,990	—	192	119	254	158	51·61	74 days	Unmanned replacement for the crew of Salyut 6, following docking failure of Soyuz 33.
6 June	USA	AMS 4	513	1,131	Thor-Burner 2	818	508	837	520	98·78	*100 years*	Advanced Meteorological Satellite.
7 June	India	Bhaskara	444	979	—	519	322·5	541	336	50·67	*10 years*	Earth observation satellite.
8 June	USSR	Cosmos 1105	6,000	13,230	—	210	130·5	246	153	81·33	13 days	Reconnaissance satellite.
10 June	USA	USAF	35,801	22,246	Titan IIIC	35,801	22,246	36,261	22,531	1·95	Unlimited	Purpose not disclosed.
12 June	USSR	Cosmos 1106	6,000	13,230	—	214	133	236	147	81·37	13 days	*Reconnaissance satellite. Recovered.*
15 June	USSR	Cosmos 1107	6,000	13,230	—	197	122·5	302	188	72·87	14 days	*Reconnaissance satellite. Recovered.*
22 June	USSR	Cosmos 1108	6,000	13,230	—	213	132·5	244	151·5	81·34	13 days	*Reconnaissance satellite. Recovered.*
27 June	USA	NOAA 6	723	1,594	Atlas F	810	503	826	513	98·74	*100 years*	Meteorological satellite. Working with Tiros 11.
27 June	USSR	Cosmos 1109	1,000	2,205	—	613	381	40,058	24,891	62·90	*12 years*	*Missile early warning satellite.*
28 June	USSR	Progress 7	7,000	15,430	—	271	168·5	346	215	51·63	22 days	Unmanned supply craft. Carried fuel, equipment and supplies to Salyut 6.
28 June	USSR	Cosmos 1110	750	1,653	—	790	491	812	504·5	74·01	*120 years*	—
29 June	USSR	Cosmos 1111	6,000	13,230	—	255	158·5	373	232	62·83	15 days	*Reconnaissance satellite. Recovered.*
5 July	USSR	Horizont	5,000	10,023	—	36,531	22,699	36,627	22,759	0·59	Unlimited	Communications satellite.
6 July	USSR	Cosmos 1112	550	1,212	—	345	214·5	544	338	50·68		—
10 July	USSR	Cosmos 1113	6,000	13,230	—	172	107	318	197·5	65·01	13 days	*Reconnaissance satellite. Recovered.*
11 July	USSR	Cosmos 1114	900	1,984	—	504	313	550	342	74·04	*10 years*	—
13 July	USSR	Cosmos 1115	6,000	13,230	—	210	130·5	235	146	81·35	13 days	*Reconnaissance satellite. Recovered.*
20 July	USSR	Cosmos 1116	2,500	5,510	—	592	368	642	399	81·20	*60 years*	*Electronics ferret satellite.*
25 July	USSR	Cosmos 1117	6,000	13,230	—	179	111	324	201·5	62·80	13 days	*Reconnaissance satellite. Recovered.*
27 July	USSR	Cosmos 1118	6,000	13,230	—	211	131	246	153	81·36	13 days	*Reconnaissance satellite. Recovered.*
31 July	USSR	Molniya 1 (44)	1,000	2,205	—	452	281	39,902	24,794	62·84	*12 years*	Communications satellite.
3 Aug	USSR	Cosmos 1119	5,500	12,125	—	214	133	240	149	81·35	12 days	*Reconnaissance satellite. Recovered.*
10 Aug	USA	Westar 3	572	1,261	Delta							Domestic communications satellite.
11 Aug	USSR	Cosmos 1120	6,000	13,230	—	169	105	361	224	70·56	13 days	*Reconnaissance satellite. Recovered.*
14 Aug	USSR	Cosmos 1121	6,000	13,230	—	170	105·5	346	215	67·16	30 days	*Reconnaissance satellite. Recovered.*
17 Aug	USSR	Cosmos 1122	5,500	12,125	—	212	132	238	148	81·34	13 days	*Reconnaissance satellite. Recovered.*
21 Aug	USSR	Cosmos 1123	6,000	13,230	—	210	130·5	232	144	81·36	13 days	*Reconnaissance satellite. Recovered.*
28 Aug	USSR	Cosmos 1124	1,000	2,205	—	566	352	40,259	25,016	62·99	*12 years*	*Early warning satellite.*
28 Aug	USSR	Cosmos 1125	750	1,653	—	782	486	811	504	74·05	*120 years*	—
31 Aug	USSR	Cosmos 1126	6,000	13,230	—	378	235	394	245	72·86	14 days	*Reconnaissance satellite. Recovered.*
5 Sept	USSR	Cosmos 1127	6,000	13,230	—	213	132·5	271	168·5	81·35	13 days	*Reconnaissance satellite. Recovered.*
14 Sept	USSR	Cosmos 1128	6,000	13,230	—	174	108	330	205	62·82	13 days	
20 Sept	USA	HEAO-3	3,150	6,945	Atlas-Centaur	484	301	500	311	43·60		High Energy Astronomical Observatory.
25 Sept	USSR	Cosmos 1129	6,000	13,230	—	218	135·5	377	234	62·82	20 days	International co-operative bio-satellite.
28 Sept	USSR	Cosmos 1130-1137	40	88	—	1,400	870	1,482	921	74·03	*10,000 years*	*Military communications satellite.*
28 Sept	USSR	Cosmos 1138	6,000	13,230	—	199	124	373	232	72·86	14 days	*Reconnaissance satellite.*
1 Oct	USA	USAF	—	—	Titan IIIC	In geostationary orbit					Unlimited	*Early warning satellite.*
3 Oct	USSR	Ekran (4)	2,000	4,410	—	In geostationary orbit					Unlimited	Domestic communications satellite.
5 Oct	USSR	Cosmos 1139	6,000	13,230	—	201	125	333	207	72·86	13 days	*Reconnaissance satellite. Recovered.*
11 Oct	USSR	Cosmos 1140	750	1,653	—	779	484	800	500	74·07	*120 years*	
16 Oct	USSR	Cosmos 1141	700	1,543	—	960	596·5	1,001	622	82·95	*1,200 years*	*Navigation satellite.*
20 Oct	USSR	Molniya 1 (45)	1,000	2,205	—	618	384	40,624	25,242	62·82	*12 years*	Domestic communications satellite.
22 Oct	USSR	Cosmos 1142	6,000	13,230	—	197	122	381	237	72·87	13 days	*Reconnaissance satellite. Recovered.*
26 Oct	USSR	Cosmos 1143	2,500	5,510	—	622	386	645	401	81·25	*60 years*	*Electronic surveillance satellite.*
30 Oct	USA	Magsat	181	399	Scout G	354	220	561	348	96·80	*6 months*	Scientific satellite.
31 Oct	USSR	Meteor 2 (5)	2,750	6,063	—	872	542	889	552	81·21	*500 years*	Meteorological satellite.
1 Nov	USSR	Intercosmos 20	550	1,212	—	465	289	510	317	74·03	*18 months*	Co-operative scientific satellite.
2 Nov	USSR	Cosmos 1144	6,000	13,230	—	167	104	357	222	67·15		*Reconnaissance satellite.*
21 Nov	USA	DSCS II (13)	550	1,212	Titan IIIC	35,594	22,117	35,594	22,117	2·42	Unlimited	Military communications satellite.
21 Nov	USA	DSCS II (14)	550	1,212	Titan IIIC	35,792	22,240	36,357	22,591	2·41	Unlimited	Military communications satellite.
27 Nov	USSR	Cosmos 1145	2,500	5,510	—	623	387	634	394	81·21	*60 years*	*Electronic surveillance satellite.*
5 Dec	USSR	Cosmos 1146	1,000	2,205	—	444	276	494	307	65·85	*2 years*	—
7 Dec	USA	RCA SATCOM	895	1,973	Delta	162	101	35,798	22,244	23·85	Unlimited	Domestic communications satellite. Failed in orbit.
12 Dec	USSR	Cosmos 1147	6,000	13,230	—	195	121	380	236	72·86	—	
16 Dec	USSR	Soyuz T	7,000	15,430	—	195	121	215	133	51·6	—	Test recoverable transport spacecraft.
24 Dec	France	CAT	1,602	3,532	Ariane	202	125	36,000	22,370	17·55	*10 years*	Test satellite for first launch of European Ariane launcher.
28 Dec	USSR	Horizont 3	5,000	11,023	—	36,290	22,550	36,333	22,576	0·80	Unlimited	Communications satellite.
28 Dec	USSR	Cosmos 1148	6,000	13,230	—	173	107	342	212	67·14	—	Reconnaissance satellite.

AERO-ENGINES

ARGENTINA

CICARÉ
CICARÉ AERONAUTICA SC

Ave Ibañez Frocham s/n, CC24, Saladillo, Provincia de Buenos Aires (Comodoro Mantel, in Buenos Aires)

Telephone: 41 5260

Several types of Cicaré automotive engine have been produced in quantity for surface applications. Cicaré Aeronautica was formed in 1972 to develop light helicop-

ters and light-aircraft engines. Details of the 4C2T (four-cylinder two-stroke) appeared in several editions of *Jane's* up to 1979-80.

AUSTRALIA

CAC
COMMONWEALTH AIRCRAFT CORPORATION LIMITED

HEAD OFFICE AND WORKS: GPO Box 779H, Melbourne 3001, Victoria
Telephone: (03) 640 771
OFFICERS: See Aircraft section

This company built the Rolls-Royce Avon and Viper and SNECMA Atar 9C turbojets, and supports these engines in service with the RAAF.

BELGIUM

FN
FABRIQUE NATIONALE HERSTAL SA

HEAD OFFICE AND WORKS: B-4400 Herstal
Telephone: (041) 64 08 00

FN has been making and overhauling jet engines since 1949. Its major current programme involves the production of components for the Pratt & Whitney F100-PW-100 fan module and core engine module for Belgium, Denmark, the Netherlands and Norway, and also for the US Air Force and for third-party countries; assembly and test of these modules; and final building and testing of the complete engines for the European consortium and for third-party countries. The first engine ran at FN in July 1978, and deliveries to F-16 production centres began two months later.

Participation in the Larzac jet engine programme involves final building and testing of the engines for Alpha Jet trainers supplied to the Belgian Air Force.

FN is also a member of the consortium which has put the Rolls-Royce Tyne turboprop back into production to power the Transall C-160 and Dassault-Breguet Atlantic ANG.

FN's share in the CFM56 project amounts to 5 per cent of the 50 per cent work-split due to SNECMA in this SNECMA-General Electric joint programme.

FN is still making parts for major engine manufacturers including Rolls-Royce (marine Tyne, Dart), SNECMA (Atar 9C, M53) and Pratt & Whitney (JT8D). FN also makes spare parts for the General Electric J79-11A and SNECMA Atar 9C, and for the FN-Boeing 553 gas turbine powering Swedish S tanks.

CANADA

ORENDA
HAWKER SIDDELEY CANADA LTD, Orenda Division

PO Box 6001, Toronto, AMF, Ontario L5P 1B3
Telephone: (416) 677 3250

VICE-PRESIDENT AND GENERAL MANAGER: R. F. Tanner
DIRECTOR OF ENGINEERING: B. A. Avery

DIRECTOR OF OPERATIONS: P. K. Peterson
DIRECTOR OF MARKETING: D. J. Caple
DIRECTOR OF FINANCE: K. R. Church

Main activities of Orenda Division are the manufacture of aircraft turbine engines and components, and the design and manufacture of industrial gas turbines.

An important activity is repair, overhaul and spares

manufacture of J85-CAN-15 turbojets. These engines, similar to the J85-GE-15 described under General Electric on a later page, were in production at Orenda from 1967 until 1974.

Orenda also overhauls J85-CAN-40, J79-OEL-7 and Orenda turbojet engines. It supplies parts to Belgium, Canada, West Germany, Italy, the Netherlands, Norway, Pakistan, the USA and Venezuela.

P&WC
PRATT & WHITNEY AIRCRAFT OF CANADA LTD

HEAD OFFICE AND WORKS: PO Box 10, Longueuil, Quebec J4K 4X9
Telephone: (514) 677 9411

PRESIDENT AND CHIEF EXECUTIVE OFFICER: E. L. Smith
VICE-PRESIDENTS:
  K. H. Sullivan (Marketing)
  L. D. Caplan (Finance and Administration)
  J. P. Beauregard (Materials and Procurement)
  A. L. Tontini (Personnel)
  R. H. Guthrie (Industrial and Marine Division)
  R. G. Raven (Helicopter and Systems Division)
  E. H. Schweitzer (Product Support)
  C. B. Wrong (Engineering)
  E. L. Hunter (Production)
  C. J. C. Pascoe (Counsel)

Pratt & Whitney Aircraft of Canada is a major subsidiary of United Technologies Corporation, Connecticut, USA, and is the UTC company responsible for engines for general aviation.

Original turbine work by the company was initiated in 1957 by the concept and preliminary design of the JT12 (J60) turbojet, development and manufacture of which were completed subsequently by Pratt & Whitney Aircraft. Design, development and manufacture of the PT6, ST6, PT6T and JT15D series of small turbine aero-engines represents more than 70 per cent of the company's activities.

P&WC is owned 97 per cent by the United Technologies Corporation. Approximately 15 per cent of its sales are linked to defence requirements. It occupies more than 139,400 m² (1·5 million sq ft) of space in three plants and employs more than 6,500 persons.

P&WC JT15D-1 two-spool turbofan engine

In 1979 a total of 2,240 new engines were delivered. By 1 January 1980 P&WC had delivered more than 15,670 PT6A and 6B engines, and over 1,610 JT15D turbofans.

P&WC JT15D

Following a comprehensive performance study of small turbofan engines carried out by P&WC during 1965, detail design of a definitive engine, the 8·9-11·12 kN (2,000 lb to 2,500 lb st) JT15D was initiated in June 1966. First run of the new turbofan was on 23 September 1967.

Intended to power business aircraft, small transports and training aircraft in the 8,000 lb to 12,500 lb AUW category, the JT15D is an advanced technology two-spool front-fan engine having a minimum number of aerodynamic components. Major design objectives were a significant improvement in sfc, and simplicity of construction to ensure low first cost and maintenance costs. Other objectives were low noise levels, ease of handling, and the attainment of airline standards of reliability.

Initial application for the JT15D was the twin-engined Cessna Citation. Flightworthy prototype engines were delivered in August 1969 for the Citation's first flight in mid-September. Certificated to FAR 36 noise specifications, the Citation is claimed to be the quietest executive jet flying. Up to 1976 Cessna produced the Citation powered by the JT15D-1. Late that year it announced the Citation I powered by the improved-performance JT15D-1A and the Citation II powered by the JT15D-4. More than 1,170 JT15D-1/D-1A and 340 JT15D-4 engines had been delivered for these aircraft by January 1980.

Other twin-engined business jets powered by the JT15D-4 are the Aérospatiale Corvette and Mitsubishi Diamond I. More than 80 engines had been delivered for these aircraft by January 1980. TBO is 3,000 h for the JT15D-1/D-1A, and 2,000 h for the JT15D-4. By January 1980 the total operating time was 2,446,780 h.

The following description relates to the JT15D-1 (JT15D-4 features in brackets):

TYPE: Two-shaft turbofan.

AIR INTAKE: Direct pitot intake without inlet guide vanes. Hot-air anti-icing for nose bullet.

FAN: Single-stage axial fan, aerodynamically related to that of the JT9D but on a much smaller scale. Forged disc fitted with 28 solid titanium blades secured by dovetail fixings riveted to disc. Blades have part-span shrouds. Casing, which forms the engine air intake, of forged stainless steel. Circular splitter ring behind fan, held between two rows of 33 inner wrapped-sheet stators and single row of 66 outer stator blades. Total air mass flow, 34 kg (75 lb)/s; bypass ratio about 3·3:1; bypass flow typically 26 kg (57·5 lb)/s; primary core air flow 8 kg (17·5 lb)/s; fan pressure ratio 1·5:1.

COMPRESSOR: Primary airflow enters eye of single-stage titanium centrifugal compressor. Single-sided impeller, with 16 full vanes and 16 splitter vanes, secured to shaft by special bolt and key-washer. Two-piece casing with diffuser in form of pipes containing straightening vanes. Overall pressure ratio almost 10:1. (JT15D-4 compressor airflow augmented by axial boost stage between fan and compressor.)

COMBUSTION CHAMBER: Annular reverse-flow type. Outer casing of heat-resistant steel; flame tube of nickel alloy, supported on low-pressure turbine stator assembly. Spark igniters at 5 and 7 o'clock positions (viewed from rear).

FUEL SYSTEM: Engine-driven sandwich-mounted pump delivering through FCU, flow divider and dual manifolds at 44·8 bars (650 lb/sq in); DP-LI pneumatic control unit mounted on pump on first 246 engines, subsequent engines having DP-L2 with dual metering valve.

FUEL GRADES: JP-1, JP-4, JP-5 conforming to PWA Spec. 522.

NOZZLE GUIDE VANES: High-pressure ring of 15, air-cooled, integrally cast in cobalt alloy.

TURBINE: Single-stage HP with 71 solid blades held in fir-tree roots. Two-stage LP with nickel alloy discs, first stage being cast integrally with 61 blades and second stage carrying 55 blades in fir-tree roots. LP fan shaft drives fan, with ball thrust bearing behind fan and roller gear and intershaft bearings; HP shaft drives centrifugal

Cutaway drawing of the P&WC JT15D-1 turbofan (9·8 kN; 2,200 lb st)

First simplified cutaway drawing of the P&WC PT7, revealing independent LP and HP centrifugal compressors and a free power turbine with front drive. By mid-1980 the PT7 had been selected for the DHC-8 as well as the EMB-120

compressor, with front ball thrust bearing and rear roller bearing. Gas temperature 960°C before turbine, 562°C after turbine.

JET PIPE: Nickel alloy cone and sheet-metal pipe. Provision made for adjusting the area to match engines and to trim performance.

ACCESSORY DRIVES: Package under front of engine driven by power offtake from front of HP shaft.

LUBRICATION SYSTEM: Integral oil system, with gear-type pump delivering at up to 5·52 bars (80 lb/sq in). Capacity, 9·0 litres (2·4 US gallons; 2·0 Imp gallons).

OIL SPECIFICATION: PWA521 Type II.

MOUNTING: Hard or soft, according to customers' choice. Four main pads on front casing, arranged two on each side at 30° above and below horizontal. One rear mount at top or on either side of centreline.

STARTING: Air-turbine starter or electric starter/generator.

DIMENSIONS:

Diameter:	
JT15D-1, -1A	691 mm (27·2 in)
JT15D-4	686 mm (27·0 in)
Length overall:	
JT15D-1, -1A	1,506 mm (59·3 in)
JT15D-4	1,600 mm (63·0 in)
Frontal area	0·37 m² (4 sq ft)

WEIGHT, EQUIPPED:

JT15D-1, -1A	232·5 kg (514 lb)
JT15D-4	253 kg (557 lb)

PERFORMANCE RATINGS:

T-O:	
JT15D-1, -1A	9·8 kN (2,200 lb st)
JT15D-4	11·12 kN (2,500 lb st)
Max continuous:	
JT15D-1, -1A	9·3 kN (2,090 lb st)
JT15D-4	10·56 kN (2,375 lb st)

SPECIFIC FUEL CONSUMPTION (T-O):

JT15D-1, -1A	15·30 mg/Ns (0·540 lb/h/lb st)
JT15D-4	15·92 mg/Ns (0·562 lb/h/lb st)

One of the first P&WC PT7 turboprops, to be rated at up to 1,865 kW (2,500 shp) but limited by gearbox to 1,119 kW (1,500 shp)

P&WC PT7A

The PT7A is an advanced-technology turboprop designed for the 30/40-passenger short-haul transports and executive aircraft being developed for introduction in the 1980s. An all-new free-turbine engine, the PT7A is claimed to offer 20 per cent improvement in specific fuel consumption over current engines. Features include electric starting, electronic management, compatibility with new lightweight propellers, and a unique ground APU capability.

The PT7A is scheduled for certification in 1983. In 1979 it was selected for the EMBRAER EMB-120. The following data are estimated:

DIMENSIONS:
Length	2,083 mm (82 in)
Width	584 mm (23 in)
Height	838 mm (33 in)

WEIGHT, DRY: 363 kg (800 lb)
PERFORMANCE RATING (T-O, S/L, thermodynamic):
1,525 ekW (2,047 ehp)
SPECIFIC FUEL CONSUMPTION (T-O as above):
85·0 μg/J (0·503 lb/h/ehp)

P&WC PT6A

The PT6A is a free-turbine turboprop, built in many versions. By January 1980 more than 11,500 had logged 33,600,000 h in some 4,500 aircraft registered in 120 countries.

An experimental PT6 ran for the first time in November 1959 and flight trials in the nose of a Beech 18 began in May 1961. Civil certification of the first production model, the 578 ehp PT6A-6, was granted in late 1963. Progressively higher rated versions have followed to power a wide variety of aircraft. In September 1977 P&WC introduced the PT6A-10 series, with ratings extending down to 354 kW (475 shp) for light and agricultural aviation.

Principal versions of the PT6A are as follows:

PT6A-6. Flat rated at 431 ekW; 410 kW (578 ehp; 550 shp) at 2,200 propeller rpm to 21°C, this version received civil certification in December 1963. A total of 350 PT6A-6s were built between then and November 1965. Among aircraft powered are de Havilland Canada Turbo-Beaver and early DHC-6 Twin Otter Series 100.

PT6A-10. Flat rated at 374 ekW; 354 kW (502 ehp; 475 shp) at 2,200 propeller rpm to 38°C. Certification expected early 1980.

PT6A-11. Flat rated at 394 ekW; 373 kW (528 ehp; 500 shp) at 2,200 propeller rpm to 42°C. Certificated December 1977. Fitted to Piper Cheyenne I.

PT6A-110. Flat rated at 374 ekW; 354 kW (502 ehp; 475 shp) at 1,900 propeller rpm to 38°C. Certification expected early 1980. Selected to power Dornier Turbo-Skyservant.

PT6A-11AG. Flat rated at 394 ekW; 373 kW (528 ehp; 500 shp) at 2,200 propeller rpm to 42°C. Certificated in May 1979, it embodies design features for agricultural aviation, including operation on diesel fuel. Fitted to Ayres Turbo-Thrush and selected for Weatherly 620 TP.

PT6A-112. Flat rated at 394 ekW; 373 kW (528 ehp; 500 shp) at 1,900 propeller rpm to 56°C. Certificated October 1978. Fitted to Cessna Corsair.

PT6A-15AG. Flat rated at 533 ekW; 507 kW (715 ehp; 680 shp) at 2,200 propeller rpm to 22°C. Certificated October 1977, including operation on diesel fuel. Embodies design features for agricultural aviation. Fitted to Ayres Turbo-Thrush, Frakes Turbo-Cat and Gulfstream American Turbo Ag-Cat D. Selected for Air Tractor AT-400.

PT6A-20. Flat rated at 432 ekW; 410 kW (579 ehp; 550 shp) at 2,200 propeller rpm to 21°C, the -20 offered improved reliability and increases in max continuous, max climb and max cruise power ratings over the PT6A-6. The PT6A-20 was certificated in October 1965. Between then and 1974 approximately 2,400 were built to power the Beech King Air B90, Beech Model 99, prototypes of the EMBRAER EMB-110 Bandeirante, de Havilland Canada DHC-6 Twin Otter Series 100 and 200, James Aviation (Fletcher FU-24) conversion, Marshall of Cambridge (Grumman) Goose conversion, McKinnon G-21C and G-21D Turbo-Goose (Grumman Goose) conversions, Pilatus PC-6/B1-H2 Turbo-Porter, prototype Pilatus PC-7 Turbo Trainer and the Swearingen Merlin IIA (which can be re-engined with the PT6A-27).

PT6A-20A. Similar to A-20; fitted to early Beech King Air C90.

PT6A-21. Flat rated at 432·5 ekW; 410 kW (580 ehp; 550 shp) at 2,200 propeller rpm to 21°C, the A-21 offers improved fuel consumption and reliability, mainly by mating the A-27 power unit with the A-20A gearbox. Certificated on 10 December 1974. Fitted to current Beech King Air C90. Total deliveries of -20, -20A and -21 exceed 2,800.

PT6A-25. Flat rated at 432·5 ekW; 410 kW (580 ehp; 550 shp) at 2,200 propeller rpm to 33°C. Special oil system for sustained inverted flight. Certificated May 1976. Fitted to Beech T-34C.

PT6A-25A. Identical to -25 except for certain castings being made of magnesium alloy instead of aluminium alloy. Fitted to Pilatus PC-7.

PT6A-25C. Flat rated at 584 ekW; 559 kW (783 ehp; 750 shp) at 2,200 propeller rpm to 31°C. Basically an

The 553 ekW (715 ehp) P&WC PT6A-27 free-turbine turboprop

A-25 with standard A-34 hot end and A-27 first-stage reduction gearing. The A-25C, whilst maintaining aerobatic capabilities, offers an increased power rating over that of the A-25 and A-25A. Certification expected late 1981. Selected to power EMBRAER EMB-312.

PT6A-27. Flat rated at 553 ekW; 507 kW (715 ehp; 680 shp) at 2,200 propeller rpm to 22°C, attained by 12½ per cent increase in mass flow provided by larger-diameter compressor, at lower turbine temperatures than in PT6A-20. Production began in November 1967 and 1,892 had been delivered by January 1980. Production continues. Applications include the Hamilton Westwind II/III (Beech 18) conversions, Beech Model 99, Beech Model 99A, Beech U-21A and U-21D, de Havilland Canada DHC-6 Twin Otter Series 300, Pilatus/Fairchild Industries PC-6/B2-H2 Porter, Frakes Aviation (Grumman) Mallard conversion, IAI Arava, Let L-410A Turbolet, Saunders Aircraft ST-27A (de Havilland Heron) conversion and EMBRAER EMB-110 Bandeirante and EMB-312 single-engined military trainer.

PT6A-28. Similar to the PT6A-27 and with the same T-O and max continuous ratings, this version has an additional normal cruise rating of 562 ehp available up to 21°C corresponding to the max cruise conditions of the -27. In addition the max cruise rating of the -28 gives 652 ehp up to the higher ambient of 33°C. This model continues in production, with 2,212 engines delivered by the beginning of 1980. Applications are Beech King Air E90 and A100 Piper Cheyenne II and EMBRAER Xingu.

PT6A-34. Flat rated at 584 ekW; 559 kW (783 ehp; 750 shp) at 2,200 propeller rpm to 31°C, this version has aircooled nozzle guide vanes to allow operation at higher turbine entry temperatures. For the IAI Arava, Saunders ST-28, Frakes Aviation (Grumman) Mallard conversion, Jetstream conversion and EMBRAER EMB-111.

PT6A-34B. Identical to -34 except for aluminium alloy replacing magnesium in major castings. Fitted to Beech T-44A.

PT6A-34AG. First model intended specifically for agricultural use, and certificated on diesel fuel. Retrofitted to Frakes conversion of Ag-Cat and Ayres Turbo-Thrush.

PT6A-135. Flat rated at 587 ekW; 559 kW (787 ehp; 750 shp) at 1,900 rpm. Changed drive ratio reduces propeller noise; hot-end modifications to permit higher cycle temperatures. Certificated July 1977. Fitted to Jetcrafters Taurus and Beech King Air C100.

PT6A-36. Flat rated at 586 ekW, 559 kW (786 ehp, 750 shp) at 2,200 rpm to 36°C. Similar to -34 but higher ratings. Certificated June 1977. Fitted to IAI Arava.

PT6A-38. Derated A-41, flat rated at 597 ekW; 559 kW (801 ehp; 750 shp) to 39°C. Certificated May 1975. Installed in Beech C-12A.

PT6A-41. Higher mass flow, aircooled stage-one turbine nozzle guide vanes and two-stage free turbine. T-O rating of 673 ekW; 634 kW (903 ehp; 850 shp) at 2,000 propeller rpm, available up to 41°C. Thermodynamic power is 812 ekW (1,089 ehp). By the beginning of 1980 more than 1,480 engines had been delivered for Beech Super King Air 200, Piper Cheyenne III and Gulfstream American Hustler.

PT6A-42. Identical to A-41, but with detailed improvements to give approx 10 per cent increase in cruise performance. Certificated August 1979.

PT6A-45A. Similar to PT6A-41 but with redesigned gearbox to transmit higher powers at reduced propeller speeds. Rated at 876 ekW; 875 kW (1,174 ehp; 1,173 shp) at 1,700 rpm to 8°C, or to 21°C with water injection. Certificated February 1976. Powers Shorts 330 and Mohawk 298.

PT6A-45B. Identical to PT6A-45A, but with increased water injection to give improved thermodynamic performance. Rated at 916 ekW; 875 kW (1,229 ehp; 1,173 shp) at 1,700 rpm to 11°C or to 30°C with water injection. Certificated March 1979. Powers Shorts 330.

PT6A-50. Similar to PT6A-41 with a longer, higher-ratio reduction gear to give lower propeller tip speed for quieter operation at T-O. Rating at T-O is 875·5 ekW; 835 kW (1,174 ehp; 1,120 shp) available with water injection up to 34°C at 1,210 propeller rpm. Certificated September 1976, and delivered same month for de Havilland Canada DHC-7.

Current TBO is 3,500 h on all models except -11AG, -15AG, -25, -25A, -38, -41, -42, -45A and -45B, for which TBO is 3,000 h, and -50, for which TBO is 2,000 h.

The following data apply generally to the PT6A series:
TYPE: Free-turbine axial-plus-centrifugal turboprop engine.
PROPELLER DRIVE (all models up to and including PT6A-41): Two-stage planetary gear train. Ratio 15 : 1. Rotation clockwise when viewed from rear. Drive from free turbine. Flanged propeller shaft. Plain bearings. Higher-ratio reduction gears developed for PT6A-45A and -50.
AIR INTAKE: Annular air intake at rear of engine, with intake screen. Aircraft-supplied alcohol anti-icing system or inertial separation anti-icing system.
COMPRESSOR: Three axial-flow stages, plus single centrifugal stage. Single-sided centrifugal compressor, with 26 vanes, made from titanium forging. Axial rotor of disc-drum type, with stainless steel stator and rotor blades. The stator vanes (44 first-stage, 44 second-stage, 40 third-stage) are brazed to casing. The rotor blades (16 first-stage, 32 second-stage and 32 third-stage) are dovetailed to discs. Discs through-bolted, with centrifugal compressor, to shaft. Fabricated one-piece stainless steel casing and radial diffuser. PT6A-27: compression ratio 6·7 : 1, air mass flow 3·1 kg/s (6·8 lb/s).
COMBUSTION CHAMBER: Annular reverse-flow type of stainless steel construction, with 14 simplex burners around periphery of chamber. All versions up to A-34 have two glow plug igniters with option of two spark igniters; A-38 onwards, two spark igniters. PT6A-27 has one plug at 64° on starboard side of vertical centreline and one at 90° on port side.
FUEL SYSTEM: Bendix DP-F2 pneumatic automatic fuel control system. Pneumatic computing section, fuel metering and regulating section, gas generator governor and free turbine governor. Primary and secondary flow manifolds with seven nozzles per manifold. PT6A-50 has DP-F3 with starting spill valve and motive flow systems.
FUEL GRADE: Commercial jet fuels JP-1, JP-4, JP-5, MIL-J-5624. Use of aviation gasolines (MIL-G-5572) grades 80/87, 91/98, 100/130 and 115/145 permitted for a period of up to 150 h during any overhaul period.

The 876 ekW (1,174 ehp) P&WC PT6A-45A free-turbine turboprop

NOZZLE GUIDE VANES: 29 nozzle guide vanes; A-34 onward, 14 aircooled HP vanes.

TURBINES: Models up to A-34 have two single-stage axial; HP turbine (with 58 blades) drives compressor, and LP turbine (with 41 shrouded blades) drives output shaft. PT6A-38 onward have two-stage LP turbine. All blades have fir-tree root fixings.

BEARINGS: Each main rotor (gas generator and free turbine) supported by one ball and one roller anti-friction bearing.

JET PIPE: Collector duct surrounding free-turbine shaft, exhaust through two ports on horizontal centreline.

ACCESSORIES: Mounting pads on accessory case (rear of engine) for starter/generator, hydraulic pump, aircraft accessory drive, vacuum pump and tachometer-generator. Mounting pad on the shaft-turbine reduction gear case for propeller overspeed governor, propeller constant-speed control unit and tachometer generator.

LUBRICATION SYSTEM: One pressure and four scavenge elements in the pump stacks. All are gear type and are driven by the gas generator rotor. Engine has an integral oil tank with a capacity of 8·75 litres (2·3 US gallons). Oil supply pressure is 5·5 bars (80 lb/sq in) on PT6A-11 to -28, 5·85 bars (85 lb/sq in) on -34 to -36, and 7·25 bars (105 lb/sq in) on -38 to -50.

OIL SPECIFICATION: CPW202, PWA522 Type II (7·5 cs vis) (MIL-L-23699, MIL-L-7808 for military engines).

MOUNTING: Up to A-34, three-point ring suspension. A-38 onward, four-point mounting, except -50 has base mounting.

STARTING: Electric starter/generator on accessory case.

DIMENSIONS:
Max diameter	483 mm (19 in)

Length, less accessories:
PT6A-6 to -34	1,575 mm (62 in)
PT6A-38, -41	1,701 mm (67 in)
PT6A-45A	1,829 mm (72 in)
PT6A-50	2,133 mm (84 in)
Frontal area	0·18 m² (1·95 sq ft)

WEIGHT, DRY:
PT6A-10, -11, -21, -27, -28	136 kg (300 lb)
PT6A-110, -112	144·7 kg (319 lb)
PT6A-14AG, -15AG	140·2 kg (309 lb)
PT6A-20	130 kg (286 lb)
PT6A-25	145·6 kg (321 lb)
PT6A-25A, -25C, -135	146·1 kg (322 lb)
PT6A-11AG, -34, -36	141·1 kg (311 lb)
PT6A-38, -41, -42	172 kg (380 lb)
PT6A-45A	192 kg (423 lb)
PT6A-45B	193 kg (425 lb)
PT6A-50	263 kg (580 lb)

PERFORMANCE RATINGS:
T-O rating:
See under model listings

Max continuous rating:
PT6A-10	374 ekW; 354 kW (502 ehp; 475 shp) at 2,200 rpm (to 38°C)
PT6A-110	374 ekW; 354 kW (502 ehp; 475 shp) at 1,900 rpm (to 38°C)
PT6A-11	394 ekW; 373 kW (528 ehp; 500 shp) at 2,200 rpm (to 42°C)
PT6A-11AG	394 ekW; 373 kW (528 ehp; 500 shp) at 2,200 rpm (to 42°C)
PT6A-112	394 ekW; 373 kW (528 ehp; 500 shp) at 1,900 rpm (to 56°C)
PT6A-14AG	433 ekW; 410 kW (580 ehp; 550 shp) at 2,200 rpm (to 54°C)
PT6A-20	432 ekW; 410 kW (579 ehp; 550 shp) at 2,200 rpm (to 21°C)
PT6A-21	432·5 ekW; 410 kW (580 ehp; 550 shp) at 2,200 rpm (to 33°C)
PT6A-25	432·5 ekW; 410 kW (580 ehp; 550 shp) at 2,200 rpm (to 33°C)
PT6A-25C	584 ekW; 559 kW (783 ehp; 750 shp) at 2,200 rpm (to 31°C)
PT6A-15AG, -27, -28	533 ekW; 507 kW (715 ehp; 680 shp) at 2,200 rpm (to 22°C)
PT6A-34	584 ekW; 559 kW (783 ehp; 750 shp) at 2,200 rpm (to 30°C)
PT6A-36	586 ekW; 559 kW (786 ehp; 750 shp) at 2,200 rpm (to 36°C)
PT6A-135	587 ekW; 559 kW (787 ehp; 750 shp) at 1,900 rpm (to 29°C)
PT6A-38	597 ekW; 559 kW (801 ehp; 750 shp) at 2,200 rpm (to 39°C)
PT6A-41	673 ekW; 634 kW (903 ehp; 850 shp) at 2,000 rpm (to 41°C)
PT6A-42	674 ekW; 634 kW (904 ehp; 850 shp) at 2,000 rpm (to 41°C)
PT6A-45A	798 ekW; 761 kW (1,070 ehp; 1,020 shp) at 1,700 rpm (to 27°C)
PT6A-45B	798 ekW; 761 kW (1,070 ehp; 1,020 shp) at 1,700 rpm (to 29°C)
PT6A-50	762 ekW; 725·5 kW (1,022 ehp; 973 shp) at 1,210 rpm (to 32°C)

Max cruise rating:
PT6A-10	374 ekW; 354 kW (502 ehp; 475 shp) at 2,200 rpm (to 19°C)
PT6A-110	374 ekW; 354 kW (502 ehp; 475 shp) at 1,900 rpm (to 19°C)
PT6A-11	394 ekW; 373 kW (528 ehp; 500 shp) at 2,200 rpm (to 37°C)
PT6A-11AG	394 ekW; 373 kW (528 ehp; 500 shp) at 2,200 rpm (to 36°C)
PT6A-112	394 ekW; 373 kW (528 ehp; 500 shp) at 1,900 rpm (to 48°C)
PT6A-14AG	394 ekW; 373 kW (528 ehp; 500 shp) at 2,200 rpm (to 42°C)
PT6A-15AG	as PT6A-27
PT6A-20	389 ekW; 369 kW (522 ehp; 495 shp) at 2,200 rpm
PT6A-21	390 ekW; 309 kW (523 ehp; 495 shp) at 2,200 rpm (to 15°C)
PT6A-25	432·5 ekW; 410 kW (580 ehp; 550 shp) at 2,200 rpm (to 33°C)
PT6A-25C	545 ekW; 522 kW (731 ehp; 700 shp) at 2,200 rpm (to 19°C)
PT6A-27	486 ekW; 462 kW (652 ehp; 620 shp) at 2,200 rpm (to 21°C)
PT6A-28	486 ekW; 462 kW (652 ehp; 620 shp) at 2,200 rpm (to 33°C)
PT6A-34	545 ekW; 522 kW (731 ehp; 700 shp) at 2,200 rpm (to 19°C)
PT6A-135	548 ekW; 522 kW (735 ehp; 700 shp) at 2,200 rpm (to 28°C)
PT6A-36	548 ekW; 522 kW (735 ehp; 700 shp) at 2,200 rpm (to 28°C)
PT6A-38	597 ekW; 559 kW (801 ehp; 750 shp) at 2,000 rpm (to 27°C)
PT6A-41	673 ekW; 634 kW (903 ehp; 850 shp) at 2,000 rpm (to 28°C)
PT6A-42	674 ekW; 634 kW (904 ehp; 850 shp) at 2,000 rpm (to 33°C)
PT6A-45A	749 ekW; 713 kW (1,004 ehp; 956 shp) at 1,425 rpm (to 15°C)
PT6A-45B	749 ekW; 713 kW (1,004 ehp; 956 shp) at 1,425 rpm (to 15°C)
PT6A-50	706 ekW; 671 kW (947 ehp; 900 shp) at 1,020-1,160 rpm (to 23°C)

SPECIFIC FUEL CONSUMPTION:
At T-O rating:
PT6A-10, -110	111·0 μg/J (0·657 lb/h/ehp)
PT6A-11, -11AG	109·4 μg/J (0·647 lb/h/ehp)
PT6A-112	107·6 μg/J (0·637 lb/h/ehp)
PT6A-15AG, -25, 28	101·8 μg/J (0·602 lb/h/ehp)
PT6A-20	109·7 μg/J (0·649 lb/h/ehp)
PT6A-25C, -34, -34B, -34AG	100·6 μg/J (0·595 lb/h/ehp)
PT6A-34, -41	99·7 μg/J (0·590 lb/h/ehp)
PT6A-42	101·5 μg/J (0·601 lb/h/ehp)
PT6A-135	98·9 μg/J (0·585 lb/h/ehp)
PT6A-38	106·3 μg/J (0·629 lb/h/ehp)
PT6A-45A, -45B, -50	94·6 μg/J (0·560 lb/h/ehp)

OIL CONSUMPTION:
Max	0·091 kg (0·20 lb)/h

P&WC T74

T74 is the US designation for military versions of the PT6A turboprop and PT6B turboshaft.

T74-CP-700. US Army counterpart of the PT6A-20. More than 300 T74-CP-700s have been delivered to Beech for 129 U-21A aircraft. Inertial separator system to protect against sand and dust ingestion.

T74-CP-702. Rated at 580 ekW (778 ehp) and retrofitted in Beech U-21.

P&WC PT6B/PT6C

The PT6B is the commercial turboshaft version of the PT6A and has a lower-ratio reduction gear. Principal versions are:

PT6B-9. Rated at 410 kW (550 shp) at 6,230 rpm available to 25°C. Civil certification received in May 1965. Production complete.

PT6B-34. Similar to B-9 except based on PT6A-34. T-O rating 559 kW (750 shp) at 6,188 rpm to 35°C (2½-min contingency 671 kW; 900 shp to 15°C). Certificated July 1976. Installed in experimental Westland Lynx.

PT6B-35F. Based upon PT6A-135 but with single-stage reduction gearbox. T-O rating 485 kW (650 shp) at 6,000 rpm to 43°C. Engine certification expected 1980. Chosen by LearAvia Corporation to power Lear Fan.

PT6C. This series of engines provides direct drive from the power turbine, with no reduction gearing.

DIMENSIONS:
Max diameter: PT6B-34, -35F	572 mm (22·5 in)

Length, less accessories:
PT6B-34	1,499 mm (59·0 in)
Frontal area	0·18 m² (1·95 sq ft)

WEIGHT, DRY:
PT6B-9	116 kg (255 lb)
PT6B-34	135 kg (298 lb)
PT6B-35F	133 kg (294 lb)

PERFORMANCE RATINGS:
T-O:
See under model listings

Max cruise:
PT6B-9	362 kW (485 shp) at 6,230 rpm
PT6B-34	466 kW (625 shp) at 6,188 rpm (to 15°C)
PT6B-35F	485 kW (650 shp) at 6,000 rpm (to 43°C)

SPECIFIC FUEL CONSUMPTION:
At T-O rating:
PT6B-9	112·4 μg/J (0·665 lb/h/shp)
PT6B-34	104·6 μg/J (0·619 lb/h/shp)
PT6B-35F	103·0 μg/J (0·608 lb/h/shp)

OIL CONSUMPTION:
Max	0·091 kg (0·20 lb)/h

P&WC PT6T TWIN-PAC

First run in July 1968, the PT6T Twin-Pac comprises two PT6 turboshaft engines mounted side by side and driving into a combining gearbox to provide a single output drive. The engine was launched as a coupled power unit for a family of twin-engined helicopters based on the Bell Helicopter UH-1 series. First of these, jointly financed by Bell, P&WC and the Canadian government, was the 15-seat Bell Model 212, which first flew with the PT6T-3 in April 1969.

Installation of the 1,342 kW (1,800 shp) PT6T-3 in the Model 212, in addition to offering true engine-out capability, provides an additional 300 shp over the single-engine 205A and gives enhanced hot-day and high altitude performance. Qualified PT6T-3s became available in the third quarter of 1970 coincident with certification of the Model 212, which is also produced under licence by Agusta in Italy.

Another application of the PT6T-3 engine is for conversion from piston engine to turbine power of the Sikorsky S-58. The prototype S-58T flew in August 1970 and certification was received in April 1971.

In these two helicopter applications, total shaft-power output is limited by the helicopter transmission. In the Model 212 the 1,342 kW (1,800 shp) PT6T-3 is restricted to a T-O rating of 962 kW (1,290 shp) and 843 kW (1,130 shp) for continuous power. In the S-58T the limits are 1,122 kW (1,505 shp) at T-O and 935 kW (1,254 shp) for continuous operation. The PT6T-3 is easily adapted to

The 1,342 kW (1,800 shp) P&WC PT6T-3 Twin-Pac coupled free-turbine turboshaft

such power requirements by a simple setting of its torque control. In the event of a power-section failure, torquemeters in the combining gearbox signal the other power section to maximum power. A single-engine 30-minute rating is included for use, at pilot discretion, in such contingencies.

Certificated in late 1979, the PT6T-3B was introduced as an alternative to the PT6T-3 for installation in the Bell 212. The T-3B is basically a PT6T-3 with some T-6 hardware and improved single-engine performance, and has been chosen to power the Bell 412.

An uprated Twin-Pac, the PT6T-6, was certificated in December 1974. The higher power is achieved by material and aerodynamic improvements to the compressor-turbine nozzle guide vanes and rotor blades. Installed in S-58T and Agusta-Bell 212. By the beginning of 1980 a total of 5·2 million equivalent PT6 h had been flown by PT6T engines in 1,430 helicopters in 62 countries.

The following details describe the main features differing from those of the standard PT6:

TYPE: Coupled free-turbine turboshaft.

SHAFT DRIVE: Combining gearbox comprises three separate gear trains, two input and one output, each contained within an individual sealed compartment and all interconnected by drive shafts. Overall reduction ratio 5 : 1. Input gear train comprising three spur gears provides speed reduction between power sections and output gearbox. The two drives into the output gearbox are via Formsprag fully-phased overrunning clutches with input third gear forming outer member of clutch, and interconnect shaft forming inner, overrunning member. Output gear train comprises three helical spur gears, two input pinions meshing with single output gear.

AIR INTAKES: Additional inertial particle separator fitted upstream of engine to reduce sand and dust ingestion. High frequency compressor noise suppressed.

FUEL SYSTEM: As PT6 with manual backup system, and dual manifold for cool starts. Automatic power sharing and torque limiting. Torquemeters provide signals to Bendix fuel system metering valves to maintain power at level set by pilot's selective-collective control. Fuel heaters.

FUEL GRADES: JP-1, JP-4 and JP-5.

JET PIPE: Single upward-facing exhaust port on each gas generator.

ACCESSORIES: Starter/generator and tacho-generator mounted on accessory drive case at front of each power section. Other accessory drives on combining gearbox, including individual power turbine speed governors and tacho-generators, and provision for blowers and aircraft accessories.

LUBRICATION SYSTEM: Independent lubrication system on each power section for maximum safety during single-engine operation. Integral oil tanks. Separate oil system for output section of combining gearbox.

OIL SPECIFICATION: PWA Spec 521. For military engines, MIL-L-7808 and -23699.

STARTING: Electrical, with cold weather starting down to −54°C.

DIMENSIONS:
Height	838 mm (33·0 in)
Width	1,118 mm (44·0 in)
Length	1,702 mm (67·0 in)

WEIGHT, DRY (standard equipment):
PT6T-3	292 kg (645 lb)
PT6T-3B, -6	298 kg (657 lb)

PERFORMANCE RATINGS:
T-O (5 min):
Total output, at 6,600 rpm:
PT6T-3, -3B	1,342 kW (1,800 shp)
PT6T-6	1,398 kW (1,875 shp) (to 21°C)

Single power section only, at 6,600 rpm:
PT6T-3, -3B	671 kW (900 shp)
PT6T-6, -3B (2½ min)	764 kW (1,025 shp)

30 min power (single power section), at 6,600 rpm:
PT6T-3B, -6	723 kW (970 shp)

Max continuous:
Total output, at 6,600 rpm:
PT6T-3, -3B	1,193 kW (1,600 shp)
PT6T-6	1,249 kW (1,675 shp) (to 19°C)

Single power section only, at 6,600 rpm:
PT6T-3, -3B	596 kW (800 shp)
PT6T-6	615 kW (825 shp) (to 19°C)

Cruise A:
Total output, at 6,600 rpm:
PT6T-3, -3B	932 kW (1,250 shp)
PT6T-6	1,014 kW (1,360 shp)

Single power section only, at 6,600 rpm:
PT6T-3, -3B	466 kW (625 shp)
PT6T-6	500 kW (670 shp)

Cruise B:
Total output, at 6,600 rpm:
PT6T-3, -3B	820 kW (1,100 shp)
PT6T-6	891 kW (1,195 shp)

Single power section only, at 6,600 rpm:
PT6T-3, -3B	410 kW (550 shp)
PT6T-6	440 kW (590 shp)

Ground idle, at 2,200 rpm   44·7 kW (60 shp) max

SPECIFIC FUEL CONSUMPTION:
At 2½-min rating (single power section):
PT6T-3B	100·7 μg/J (0·596 lb/h/shp)
PT6T-6	101·6 μg/J (0·602 lb/h/shp)

At 30-min rating (single power section):
PT6T-3	101·9 μg/J (0·603 lb/h/shp)
PT6T-3B	101·0 μg/J (0·598 lb/h/shp)
PT6T-6	101·3 μg/J (0·600 lb/h/shp)

T-O, 5-min rating (total output):
PT6T-3	100·6 μg/J (0·595 lb/h/shp)
PT6T-3B	101·3 μg/J (0·600 lb/h/shp)
PT6T-6	100·0 μg/J (0·592 lb/h/shp)

At max continuous rating (total output):
PT6T-3	101·2 μg/J (0·599 lb/h/shp)
PT6T-3B	103·9 μg/J (0·615 lb/h/shp)
PT6T-6	101·9 μg/J (0·603 lb/h/shp)

OIL CONSUMPTION:
Max (for both gas generators)   0·18 kg (0·4 lb)/h

P&WC T400

Military version of the PT6T Twin-Pac, the T400-CP-400 has castings of aluminium instead of magnesium. For military roles, P&WC describes the T400 as producing a minimum infra-red signature. Military Qualification Tests (MQT) were completed in March 1970, and production deliveries started in the same month.

The T400 is used in the US Air Force and Navy Bell UH-1N (military version of the Model 212), the US Marine Corps Bell AH-1J, and the Canadian Armed Forces Bell CH-135. T400 field operations started in the middle of 1970.

TBO on the T400-CP-400 is 2,000 h on both the power section and reduction gearbox. By the beginning of 1980 deliveries totalled 799 CP-400 engines.

The T400-WV-402 is the military counterpart of the PT6T-6 and is used in the AH-1T. By the beginning of 1980 a total of 494 WV-402s had been delivered.

DIMENSIONS (CP-400 and WV-402):
Height	828 mm (32·6 in)
Width	1,115 mm (43·5 in)
Length	1,659 mm (65·3 in)

WEIGHT, DRY:
T400-CP-400	324 kg (714 lb)
T400-WV-402	338 kg (745 lb)

PERFORMANCE RATINGS:
Intermediate:
T400-CP-400	1,342 kW (1,800 shp) at 6,600 rpm
T400-WV-402	1,469 kW (1,970 shp) at 6,600 rpm

Max continuous:
T400-CP-400	1,141 kW (1,530 shp) at 6,600 rpm
T400-WV-402	1,248 kW (1,673 shp) at 6,600 rpm

SPECIFIC FUEL CONSUMPTION (Intermediate rating):
T400-WV-402	99·9 μg/J (0·591 lb/h/shp)
T400-CP-400	100·4 μg/J (0·594 lb/h/shp)

CHINA
(PEOPLE'S REPUBLIC)

NATIONAL AIRCRAFT ENGINE FACTORY
MAIN LOCATION: Shenyang

As related in the 1977-78 *Jane's,* the first aircraft engine made in numbers in the People's Republic of China was the Soviet M-11 radial.

In 1958 licences were obtained by the 2nd Ministry of Machine Building for two additional Soviet aircooled radial engines, the 194 kW (260 hp) Ivchenko AI-14R and 746 kW (1,000 hp) Shvetsov ASh-62IR (both described under Poland), fitted respectively to the locally-built Chinko No. 1 (Yak-12) and Fong Shou No. 2 (An-2). Both of these aircraft and their engines are believed to have been built in large numbers. By 1959 the Manchurian plants were licence-building the Soviet Mi-4 helicopter and the Czech Super Aero 45 light twin. It is thought that in each case the engine (respectively the 1,268 kW; 1,700 shp Shvetsov ASh-82V 14-cylinder radial and the 104·4 kW; 140 hp M 332 four-in-line, the latter last described in the 1971-72 *Jane's*) was also produced either at Shenyang or at one of the other national factories. One possibility is that the Czech engine was made in the works at Harbin, because it was there that the Chinese version of the Super Aero 45 was produced. Harbin may also have taken over the M-11FR program-

me, because from 1959-60 that factory manufactured the M-11-powered Hai Lun-kiang No. 1, a locally designed liaison aircraft resembling the Yak-12.

GAS TURBINE ENGINES
During the Korean War (1950-53) large numbers of MiG-15 fighters were ferried through Manchuria. Chinese technicians became familiar with the aircraft and its Klimov RD-45 (Rolls-Royce Nene derivative) engine. In 1955 a licence for the manufacture of the MiG-15 fighter and MiG-15UTI trainer was signed in Moscow, and from 1958 several hundred of the latter were produced, powered by the RD-45 of 24·24 kN (5,450 lb st). The MiG-15 fighter was apparently not built in China, but in 1959 the first Chinese F-4, a licence-built MiG-17, began a production run of well over 1,000 aircraft, all probably powered by Chinese-built Klimov VK-1 turbojets rated at 26·47 kN (5,950 lb st).

In February 1959 the Chinese signed a licence agreement for the manufacture of the MiG-19 supersonic fighter, powered by RD-9 turbojets. Soon afterwards the relationship with the Soviet Union was severed; but the Chinese, working alone, managed to fly a locally-built F-6 (MiG-19) in 1961, and have since constructed a number

estimated to reach 1,500. Thus, probably more than 4,000 RD-9 engines have been made at Shenyang. A subsequent production programme concerned the F-7 (MiG-21). As described in the Aircraft section, this fighter and its R-11 axial turbojet were put into production in China without a licence or any Soviet help. Deliveries of the R-11 from Shenyang are thought to have begun in 1965.

Chinese versions or developments of the RD-9 are likely to have been used in locally produced military designs. One of these is the A-5/F-6bis (NATO 'Fantan') twin-engined strike fighter, which has been built in quantity. In 1979 the F-6 and A-5/F-6bis were still in production; but manufacture of the F-7 (MiG-21) was terminated soon after 1970.

In 1975, the Chinese government signed a preliminary contract with Rolls-Royce Ltd for the licensed manufacture of a supersonic afterburning Spey turbofan generally similar to the Spey 202/203 used in F-4 Phantom fighters of the RAF. The value of British contracts on this programme, which includes a new production plant, is tentatively put at £100 million. It is assumed that the engines will power military aircraft, probably of Chinese design, and that the Chinese objective is total self-sufficiency in their production and operation.

CZECHOSLOVAKIA

OMNIPOL
OMNIPOL FOREIGN TRADE CORPORATION
Nekazanka 11, 112 21 Prague 1
Telephone: 268261-8

Omnipol is responsible for exporting products of the Czech aviation industry and for supplying information on those products which are available for export.

AVIA
AVIA NARODNI PODNIK
199 03 Praha 9, Letňany
Telephone: Prague 89 51 21

Originally a member of the Czechoslovak Aviation Industry Group, Avia National Corporation was transferred to the Czechoslovak Automotive Industry (CAZ) Group in 1960. The company is at present engaged in series production of piston engines, as well as propeller and spare parts manufacture.

AVIA M 137

Designed to power light aerobatic, training, and single-engined and multi-engined sports aircraft, the 134 kW (180 hp) M 137A piston engine is a modification of the M 337 with fuel and oil systems for aerobatic operation and without a supercharger. It powers the Zlin 42 M and Z 526 F. The M 137AZ is a modified version, with the air intake port at the rear so that a dust filter can be incorporated. Details are as for M 337, with the following differences:

CRANKSHAFT: No oil holes for propeller control.
FUEL SYSTEM: Type LUN 5150 pump; system designed for sustained aerobatics.
STARTER: LUN 2131 electric.
DIMENSIONS:

Length	1,344 mm (52·9 in)
Width	443 mm (17·44 in)
Height	630 mm (24·80 in)
WEIGHT (including starter):	141·5 kg (312 lb)

PERFORMANCE RATINGS:

T-O	134 kW (180 hp) at 2,750 rpm
Max continuous	119 kW (160 hp) at 2,680 rpm
Max cruising	104·5 kW (140 hp) at 2,580 rpm

SPECIFIC FUEL CONSUMPTION:

At T-O rating	91·26 µg/J (0·540 lb/h/hp)
At max cruise rating	81·96 µg/J (0·485 lb/h/hp)

AVIA M 337

The M 337 six-cylinder aircooled supercharged engine powers several types of light aircraft that were built in Czechoslovakia, including the Morava L-200D, Zlin 43 and Zlin 726K. It can be supplied with hubs for fixed-pitch or controllable-pitch propellers.
TYPE: Six-cylinder inverted in-line aircooled, ungeared, supercharged and with direct fuel injection.
CYLINDERS: Bore 105 mm (4·13 in). Stroke 115 mm (4·53 in). Swept volume 5·97 litres (364·31 cu in). Compression ratio 6·3 : 1. Steel cylinders with cooling fins machined from solid. Cylinder bores nitrided. Detachable cylinder heads are aluminium alloy castings. Cylinder and head assembly attached to crankcase by four studs. Valve seats of special steel. Valve guides and sparking plug bushes of bronze.
PISTONS: Aluminium alloy stampings with graphited surfaces. Two compression rings and two knife-shaped scraper rings in common groove above gudgeon-pin. Gudgeon-pins secured by spring-circlips.

The 134 kW (180 hp) Avia M 137A six-cylinder aircooled piston engine

CONNECTING RODS: H-section aluminium alloy forgings. Two split big-ends bolted together by two bolts. Steel two-piece liner, lead-bronze plated.
CRANKSHAFT: Forged from special chrome-vanadium steel, machined all over. Nitrided crank-pins. Carried in seven steel-backed lead-bronze plated slide bearings which are lightly lead-lined, and in one ball thrust bearing at the front. Terminating in a wedge-shaped cone for the propeller hub mounting.
CRANKCASE: Heat-treated magnesium alloy (Elektron) casting, with top and front covers. Deep-sunk bearing covers forged from aluminium alloy, with double cross webs.
VALVE GEAR: Camshaft on the cylinder heads actuates the valves by means of rocker arms. Camshaft driven by vertical shaft and bevel gears. One inlet valve of heat-treated steel, one sodium-filled exhaust valve of austenitic steel with stellite seat. Nitrided valve stems.
IGNITION: Shielded type. Two vertical PAL-LUN 2221.13 magnetos with automatic sparking advance, driven by bevel gears. Two PAL L 22-62 sparking plugs per cylinder, 12 × 1·25 mm.
LUBRICATION: Dry sump pressure-feed type. The **M 337 AK** has a lubrication system cleared for sustained inverted operation.
SUPERCHARGER: Centrifugal type mounted on engine rear flange. Driven through a damping rubber coupling from crankshaft. Planetary gear, ratio 7·4 : 1, engaged via band friction clutch. Force feed lubrication of supercharger from main engine lubrication system.
FUEL SYSTEM: Low-pressure injection system. LUN 5152 pump driven from camshaft. Fuel injection nozzles located in front of intake valves. Automatic control in relation to engine manifold pressure. Fuel supplied to

injection pump by fuel pressure pump located in common body with injection pump. (The M 337A has a unified fuel injection pump, type LUN 5150, and other minor changes. Specific fuel consumption is slightly higher.)
FUEL GRADE: Minimum 72-78 octane, with maximum TEL 0·06 per cent (volume).
COOLING: Airscoop on port side, designed to provide easy access to sparking plugs and easy removal of scoop and baffles.
STARTING: Electric starter combined with supercharger. Electric motor rotates the starter dog which is engaged by an electromagnet. Gears and clutch of supercharger serve the starter also.
ACCESSORIES: One 600W 28V dynamo. Electric rpm transmitter, drive 1 : 1. Propeller control unit. Mechanical tachometer on oil pump, drive 1 : 2. High-pressure hydraulic pump type P 6121A (to special order).
MOUNTING: Four engine-bearer feet with rubber dampers.
PROPELLER DRIVE: Direct left-hand tractor.
DIMENSIONS:
Overall length, without propeller boss

	1,410 mm (55·51 in)
Width	472 mm (18·58 in)
Height	628 mm (24·72 in)
Frontal area	0·20 m² (2·15 sq ft)
WEIGHT, DRY:	148 kg (326·3 lb)

PERFORMANCE RATINGS:

T-O rating	157 kW (210 hp) at 2,750 rpm
Max continuous power	127 kW (170 hp) at 2,600 rpm

Max cruising power at 1,200 m (3,940 ft)
112 kW (150 hp) at 2,400 rpm
SPECIFIC FUEL CONSUMPTION:

At T-O rating	100·6 µg/J (0·595 lb/h/hp)

At max cruising power at 1,200 m (3,940 ft)
72·7 µg/J (0·430 lb/h/hp)

MOTORLET
MOTORLET NC, ZÁVOD JANA SVERMY
Prague-Jinonice
Telephone: Prague 520714
GENERAL MANAGER: Zdenek Horcík
ASSISTANTS TO GENERAL MANAGER:
TECHNICAL DIRECTOR: Ing Josef Krca
ECONOMIC DIRECTOR: Alois Svoboda
PRODUCTION DIRECTOR: Bohumil Hamerník
HEAD OF DESIGN DEVELOPMENT: Ing Vladimír Pospísil

Motorlet National Corporation operates the main aero-engine establishment in Czechoslovakia, based on the former Walter factory at Jinonice, previously well known for its radial and in-line piston engines. Today, the Walter name continues in use only as a trade-mark for Motorlet piston and turbine engines.

Motorlet started turbine engine manufacture in 1952 with licensed production of the Soviet RD-45 centrifugal turbojet for MiG-15 fighters.

WALTER M 601B

Second of Czechoslovakia's small turbine engines to enter production, the M 601 was designed to power the Czech L-410 twin-engined light transport aircraft. It drives an Avia V 508 constant-speed three-blade propeller with hydraulically variable pitch.

The first version of the M 601, rated at 550 ehp, ran in October 1967. Development of the completely revised M 601B, of increased diameter, started during 1968. The Let L-410M, powered by M 601B engines in place of the Canadian PT6A-34s fitted to the L-410A, was in Aeroflot service in Siberia in early 1979.
TYPE: Free-turbine combined axial-and-centrifugal turboprop.
PROPELLER DRIVE: Reduction gear at front of engine with drive from free-turbine. Reduction ratio 14·9 : 1.
AIR INTAKE: Annular intake at rear of engine, with debris screen, feeds air to compressor plenum chamber.
COMPRESSOR: Two axial stages of stainless steel, plus single centrifugal stage of titanium. Pressure ratio 6·4 : 1 at 36,660 rpm gas generator speed. Air mass flow 3·25 kg (7·17 lb)/s.
COMBUSTION CHAMBER: Annular combustor with rotary fuel injection and low-voltage LUN 2201.01-08 ignition.
COMPRESSOR TURBINE: Single-stage; inlet temperature 952°C.
POWER TURBINE: Single-stage.
FUEL SYSTEM: Low-pressure LUN 6590 regulator, with three-lever control providing gas-generator and power-turbine speed controls.
FUEL GRADE: PL4, PL5 kerosene.
JET PIPE: Collector duct surrounding power turbine shaft. Exhaust through two ports on horizontal centreline.
ACCESSORIES: Mounting pads on accessory case at rear of engine. Propeller controls mounted on reduction gear case at front of engine.
LUBRICATION SYSTEM: Pressure gear-pump circulation. Integral oil tank and cooler.
OIL SPECIFICATION: B3V synthetic oil.
MOUNTING: Three elastically-supported pins on compressor casing.
STARTING: LUN 2132-8 8 kW electric starter/generator.
DIMENSIONS:

Length	1,658 mm (65·27 in)
Width	590 mm (23·23 in)
Height	650 mm (25·59 in)
WEIGHT, DRY:	193 kg (425·5 lb)

PERFORMANCE RATINGS:

T-O rating	515 kW (691 shp)

SPECIFIC FUEL CONSUMPTION:

At T-O rating:	109·55 µg/J (0·648 lb/h/ehp)

The Walter M 601B free-turbine turboprop, rated at 515 kW (691 shp)

FRANCE

G2P
GROUPEMENT POUR LES GROS PROPULSEURS À POUDRE

HEAD OFFICE: 3 avenue du Général de Gaulle, 92800 Puteaux

Telephone: 778 15 15
MAIN ESTABLISHMENT: St Aubin de Médoc 33160
ADMINISTRATOR: Roger Guernon

SEP and SNPE (both listed in this section) formed G2P

to ensure the close co-ordination of their activities and to act as prime contractor in the field of solid-propellant propulsion. Its activities are centred upon the motors of strategic missiles (MSBS, SSBS) and large tactical missiles (Pluton).

MICROTURBO
MICROTURBO SA

HEAD OFFICE AND WORKS: Chemin du Pont de Rupé, 31019 Toulouse Cédex
Telephone: (61) 70 07 77
Telex: 531442
DIRECTORATE:
　G. Bayard
　L. Pech (Commercial Director)
　P. Calmels (Chief Engineer)

Microturbo was established in 1960 for the production of small gas turbines. The initial product was the Noelle 60290 free-turbine starter for the SNECMA Atar turbojet, and from this a wide range of units has been evolved.

Jointly with Soc. Soulé the company formed SA France-Engins (see RPVs and Targets section).

MICROTURBO COUGUAR 022

This single-shaft turbojet was developed as a power plant for small aircraft and RPVs. The 022 version powers the Australian GAF Turana target drone.

The installed engine, which incorporates only the equipment needed for flight, was designed to withstand the high mechanical and thermal stresses imposed by accelerated launch, telemetered shutdown and subsequent immersion in sea-water. Equipment for defuelling, refurbishing, refuelling, starting, ground running and pre-flight checkout is all accommodated in an associated servicing rig connected via an umbilical which is disconnected immediately prior to flight. Starting is accomplished by an air-impingement nozzle integral with the engine impeller shroud, the air supply being controlled from the servicing rig.

DIMENSIONS:
Length (less jet pipe)	628 mm (24·725 in)
Length overall	853 mm (33·58 in)
Width	282 mm (11·1 in)
Height	386 mm (15·2 in)

WEIGHT, DRY:
Basic, less jet pipe	26·5 kg (58·4 lb)
With control box	28·3 kg (62·4 lb)

PERFORMANCE RATINGS (ISA, S/L):
T-O and max continuous	0·79 kN (178 lb st) at 48,500 rpm
Idle	0·138 kN (31 lb st) at 28,000 rpm

SPECIFIC FUEL CONSUMPTION (ISA, S/L, static):
　T-O and max continuous 35·4 mg/Ns (1·25 lb/h/lb st)

MICROTURBO TRS 18-046

This single-shaft turbojet was designed for installation in gliders, to impart a self-launch and climb capability, but has since been adapted for ultra-light aeroplanes such as the Bede BD-5J. It is in production, and an American Type Certificate was issued in May 1976. Applications in 1980 included the twin-jet NASA AD-1 slew-wing research aircraft, Chagnes Microstar version of the Vari-Viggen homebuilt aircraft, Caproni Vizzola A-21SJ and twin-engined Microjet 200.

The TRS 18-046 is of modular construction. The forward module incorporates the air intake, gearbox, electronic governing and protection unit and the start sequencing and indication unit. The 28V 600W starter/generator is located in the nose bullet. The oil tank, with submerged pump, is on the underside, and includes provision for inverted flight. The HP oil filter and pressure transducer are on the top of this module. Adjacent to the compressor are the probes for engine speed and air temperature.

The turbine module comprises: the one-piece centrifugal compressor, with diffuser and straightener vanes; the axial turbine rotor and nozzle diaphragm; and the main frame, carrying the rotor assembly on two ball bearings between the compressor and turbine. The aft module comprises: the turbine casing backplate, carrying the annular folded combustion chamber liner, exhaust cone and nozzle; 10 spill-type burners; two igniter plugs, used only during starting; and the jet pipe with thermocouple.

The fuel pump is driven electrically. The lubrication system is a closed circuit, with pressure supply to the rotor

Microturbo Couguar 022 single-shaft turbojet, rated at 0·79 kN (178 lb st)

Microturbo TRS 18-056 single-shaft turbojet, rated at 0·98 kN (220·5 lb st)

and gearbox bearings. The engine can be shut down and restarted in flight, and incorporates automatic fault and protection systems.

DIMENSIONS:
Length	650 mm (25·59 in)
Width	325 mm (12·797 in)
Height	350 mm (13·78 in)

WEIGHT, DRY:
Basic	32·0 kg (70·5 lb)
With igniter and voltage regulator	33·4 kg (73·63 lb)

PERFORMANCE RATING (ISA, S/L):
T-O and max continuous	0·898 kN (202 lb st) at 44,000 rpm

SPECIFIC FUEL CONSUMPTION:
At above condition	36 mg/Ns (1·27 lb/h/lb st)

MICROTURBO TRS 18-056, -075, -076

These simplified versions of the TRS 18-046 retain only the gas-generator section of earlier versions and were developed to power the France-Engins Mitsoubac and other RPVs. The lubrication system is of the total-loss type. During starting, the engine is cranked either by impingement with air supplied from a bottle or by windmilling, according to the RPV in which it is installed. Ignition for starting is provided by an electrically fired cartridge. At shutdown, two independent systems shut off the fuel supply: one is an instantaneously actuated shut-off valve and the other releases the gas pressure from the fuel tank.

New sub-types in 1980 included the TRS 18-075 for the Flight Refuelling ASAT and TRS 18-076 for the Meteor Mirach 100.

DIMENSIONS (TRS 18-056):
Length	600 mm (23·6 in)
Width	305 mm (12·0 in)
Height	345 mm (13·6 in)

WEIGHT, DRY (TRS 18-056):
Basic, no jet pipe	23·0 kg (50·7 lb)

PERFORMANCE RATING (TRS 18-056, ISA, S/L):
T-O and max continuous	0·98 kN (220·5 lb st) at 45,000 rpm

SPECIFIC FUEL CONSUMPTION (TRS 18-056):
At above condition	36 mg/Ns (1·27 lb/h/lb st)

MICROTURBO TRI 60

Representing a significant French development in the propulsion of cruise-type unmanned vehicles, the TRI 60

Microturbo TRS 18-046 single-shaft turbojet, rated at 0·898 kN (202 lb st)

Microturbo TRI 60 turbojet in configuration used on C.22 RPV (mounted on dummy portion of fuselage, with nozzle to left)

was designed under a contract from the Direction des Recherches et Moyens d'Essais. It is an extremely simple single-shaft turbojet for use in subsonic missiles and RPVs. The design has been biased towards minimal cost and absence of any maintenance or overhaul, though engine design life exceeds 20 hr. In 1976 the TRI 60 was selected to power the Aérospatiale C.22 RPV. In 1978 it was chosen for the British Aerospace Sea Eagle missile. Further applications include the Beech MQM-107A and Saab-Scania RBS 15 missile.

The annular intake contains the accessory gearbox in the central bullet, together with an alternator or starter/generator; the struts house fuel and oil pipes. The simple axial compressor operates at a pressure ratio of about 4 : 1, with airflow of 5·6 kg (12·3 lb)/s, and is carried between front and rear bearings with labyrinth seals. The smokeless combustor is of the axial type, with multiple spray burners fed by a peripheral manifold. The axial turbine is overhung behind the rear bearing on the central diffuser housing.

An air bleed provides up to 1·5 per cent of total airflow. There is an engine-driven fuel pump, but lubrication is by either pre-lubricated bearings or a total-loss system from a pressurised reservoir. Speed control can be mechanical, electronic, fluidic or pneumatic, according to installation. Starting can be by impingement, electrical, cartridge or other means.

DIMENSIONS:
Length overall	882 mm (34·72 in)
Envelope diameter	310 mm (12·20 in)

WEIGHT, DRY: 45 kg (99·2 lb)

PERFORMANCE RATING (ISA, S/L):
Max T-O	3·43 kN (772 lb st) at 28,500 rpm

SPECIFIC FUEL CONSUMPTION (as above):
　　35·4 mg/Ns (1·25 lb/h/lb st)

RECTIMO
RECTIMO AVIATION SA

OFFICES AND WORKS:
　Aérodrome de Chambéry, 73420 Savoie
Telephone: (79) 63 40 06
DIRECTOR: André Rosselot

Rectimo has manufactured over 500 Type 4 AR 1200 single-ignition derivatives of the Volkswagen four-cylinder aircooled car engine, which together with the

larger 4 AR 1600 are used in the Sportavia RF4D powered glider and various ultra-light aircraft. The 30 kW (40 hp) 4 AR 1200 engine has a 1,192 cc cubic capacity, 7 : 1 compression ratio and weighs 61·5 kg (136 lb). Fuel consumption under cruise conditions is 11 litres (2·4 Imp gal)/h. The 4 AR 1600 produces 45·5 kW (61 hp) at T-O and has a cubic capacity of 1,600 cc and an 8 : 1 compression ratio. Weight is 64 kg (141 lb). Both engines have a maximum speed of 3,600 rpm.

Rectimo 4 AR 1200 piston engine of 30 kW (40 hp)

SACMA

Zone Industrielle de Vinon (Var)
Telephone: (92) 78 80 82
PRESIDENT: M Negre

Preliminary details became available in mid-1977 of the family of light piston engines under development by this French company in a new factory inland from the Riviera. Covering a range of take-off power from 74·5 to 179 kW (100-240 hp), they utilise numerous automotive components, notably of Talbot origin, to reduce cost and ensure proven performance. All models have watercooled opposed cylinders, turbocharger or rotary mixture distributor, and 3:1 reduction to the propeller shaft. The adjacent table lists the basic models to be offered. The 112 kW (150 hp) flat-four engine began running in a Socata Rallye in the Spring of 1977.

SEP
SOCIÉTÉ EUROPÉENNE DE PROPULSION

3 avenue du Général de Gaulle, Tour Nobel, 92080 Paris La Défense Cédex 3
Telephone: 772 12 12
Telex: 63906 Putau
CENTRES AND ESTABLISHMENTS: Bordeaux-Le Haillan, Vernon, Melun-Villaroche and Istres
PRESIDENT DIRECTOR GENERAL: P. Soufflet

SEP specialises in the design and development of all categories of propulsion systems and engines for aircraft, missiles, space launchers and satellites, and it possesses the most important rocket facilities in Europe. Two-thirds of its 2,200 personnel are engineers and technicians specialising in research, development and testing.

SEP produces a wide range of solid- and liquid-propellant motors as sustainers and boosters for French and European guided and unguided missiles and space launchers. Some 60 different types of motor have been designed since 1950, including the three stages of the Diamant A and B and B P 4 French space launchers, the second stage and perigee motor of the ELDO Europa II launcher, and motors for the SSBS, MSBS and Pluton nuclear-warhead missiles. The company acquired experience in cryogenic-propellant rockets through developing the HM4 and HM7 engines.

Centre National d'Etudes Spatiales entrusted SEP with the entire propulsion systems of the three stages of the Ariane launch vehicle. A major engine for manned aircraft is the SEP 844 which provides thrust boost for Dassault Mirage III fighters in service with the French Air Force and other air forces.

Other SEP developments include engines using hybrid propellants, fluorine and fluorine compounds, monopropellants, compressed gases, as well as electric 'thrusters'. The company is also applying its missile and space technology to oceanology.

SEP VIKING

The Viking series of turbopump-fed rocket engines was designed for simplicity and low cost. The thrust chamber, fed with unsymmetrical dimethyl hydrazine (UDMH) and nitrogen tetroxide (N_2O_4), has a single wall of HS 25 steel, coated with zirconium oxide, fuel-film cooled. The nozzle throat is of graphite. The light-alloy injector is of the radial type, with alternate doublets.

Mounted directly on the chamber, the turbopump has a two-stage Curtiss turbine, driven by propellant gases cooled by water. The turbine shaft carries impellers for UDMH, N_2O_4 and water. The gas-generator also provides on-board power and pressurises the tanks. Combustion pressure is regulated against a reference by varying turbine speed. Mixture ratio is maintained by controlling the flow of N_2O_4.

In 1972 SEP ran Viking I qualification tests of 150 s duration. The Ariane launch vehicle has a first stage, Lilo, with four Viking II engines. Testing of the cluster began in

SEP P4 solid-propellant propulsion system for Diamant B P 4

Socata Rallye testbed for the 112 kW (150 hp) SACMA engine *(Aviation Magazine International)*

T-O power	Crankshaft	Dry weight	Fuel consumption 75% power	Oil capacity
kW (hp)	rpm	kg (lb)	cc/h (lb/h)	litres (Imp pints)
74·5 (100)	3,600	113 (249)	19 (30)	3 (5·3)
89·5 (120)	3,600	113 (249)	23 (37)	3 (5·3)
112 (150)	5,400	115 (254)	28 (45)	4 (7)
134 (180)	3,600	135 (298)	33·5 (53)	6 (10·5)
179 (240)	5,400	140 (309)	45 (72)	6 (10·5)

1976. The second-stage Ariane engine is Viking IV, a Viking II tuned for vacuum operation, with two-axis thrust vectoring. The nozzle has a bell shape, fabricated by welding rolled and Flo-turned steel sheet.

WEIGHT, DRY:
Viking II	776 kg (1,735 lb)
Viking IV	850 kg (1,876 lb)

PERFORMANCE:
Nominal S/L thrust:
Viking II	588·4 kN (132,275 lb)
Vacuum thrust: Viking II	686·5 kN (154,323 lb)
Viking IV	717·9 kN (161,378 lb)

Chamber pressure:
Viking II	55·5 bars (805 lb/sq in)

Vacuum specific impulse: Viking II   278·6
Viking IV   292·3

SEP P4

The P4 solid-propellant propulsion system was designed as the second stage of the French Navy's MSBS (underwater-to-surface ballistic missile), a weapon now equipped with the Rita II engine.

The P4 has a case of wound glass filament, weighing only 320 kg (705 lb). It is loaded with a grain of Isolane propellant, based on polyurethane binder, of high specific impulse. Ignition is by a solid-propellant microrocket on the front closure, which is also provided with controllable thrust-termination ports. The fixed nozzle is of carbon-fibre laminate with a graphite throat. Pitch and yaw control is effected by freon injection through four electrovalves. Roll is controlled by two separate steerable motors.

P4 replaced Topaze as the second stage of the B P 4 version of the Diamant launch vehicle.

DIMENSIONS:
Length	2,500 mm (98·4 in)
Diameter	1,500 mm (59 in)

SEP hydrazine thruster system for D-5A satellite, shown with conical fairing removed

Propulsion bay of Lilo, first stage of the L 3 S Ariane launch vehicle, showing the four SEP Viking II engines. Total S/L thrust is 2,353·6 kN (529,100 lb)

WEIGHT, LOADED: about 4,000 kg (8,820 lb)
PERFORMANCE:
Vacuum thrust	176·5 kN (39,680 lb)
Constant-thrust burn	55 s

SEP HM7

Under development for upper-stage propulsion, the HM7 is a 70·06 kN (15,750 lb) liquid oxygen/liquid hydrogen engine. It is also referred to in the entry for MBB of the Federal Republic of Germany.
TYPE: Liquid-propellant rocket engine.
PROPELLANTS: Liquid oxygen and liquid hydrogen.
THRUST CHAMBER ASSEMBLY: Single-chamber unit of 48 : 1 nozzle area ratio, regeneratively cooled, and of stainless steel tube construction. Operating sequence initiated by hydrogen pre-cooling and pre-opening of hydrogen injection valve. Concentric-tube propellant injection system with central oxygen flow. Pyrotechnic ignition. Combustion pressure 35 bars (507·5 lb/sq in) and temperature 2,727°C.
THRUST CHAMBER MOUNTING: Gimballed assembly, turbopump integral with chamber.
PROPELLANT PUMPS: Axial-plus-centrifugal pumps, coaxial.
PROPELLANT FLOWS: Liquid hydrogen flow rate 2·76 kg (6·07 lb)/s at 65 bars (942·5 lb/sq in). Liquid oxygen flow rate 14·21 kg (31·26 lb)/s at 52 bars (754 lb/sq in).
TURBINE: Two-stage axial-flow impulse unit in Inconel X 750. Gas inlet temperature 617°C.
GAS GENERATOR: Liquid hydrogen flow rate 0·133 kg (0·29 lb)/s. Liquid oxygen flow rate 0·12 kg (0·26 lb)/s. Pyrotechnic ignition.

LUBRICATION SYSTEM: Uses tributyl phosphate spray into gaseous hydrogen.

STARTING: Solid grain primer.

THRUST CONTROL: Thrust held constant by regulation of turbopump speed via control of gas generator propellant supply.

DIMENSIONS:

Height overall	1,617 mm (63·06 in)
Diameter overall	847 mm (33·03 in)

WEIGHT, DRY: 145 kg (319 lb)

PERFORMANCE:

Max thrust in vacuo	70·06 kN (15,750 lb)
Overall propellant mixture ratio	5·15 : 1
Specific impulse	425

SEP HYDRAZINE THRUSTER

SEP has for a long period been engaged in the development of small monopropellant thrusters for satellite attitude and orbit control. Most of this work has been based on hydrazine, decomposed through a catalyst to serve as a monopropellant. The present SEP hydrazine propulsion system uses CNESRO 1 catalyst, developed jointly by SEP and the Faculté des Sciences of Paris.

SEP delivered to CNES (Space Centre of Toulouse) a flight model of its hydrazine micropropulsion system, comprising: surface-tension tank, engine, European CNESRO catalyst, hydrazine electrovalve, sensor and on-board electronics. This micropropulsion system was assembled on the D-5A satellite, launched by Diamant B P 4. During endurance testing a D-5A thruster operated continuously for 145,000 s, without attention to the catalyst bed.

SEP has since developed a larger thruster for mounting on the GEOS satellite. During qualification testing this thruster operated for 8,600 s (specified time 7,800 s) in 34,000 impulses, and for 3,400 s in continuous operation (specification 3,000 s). In the following data this thruster is referred to as GM, the earlier unit being referred to as D-5A.

WEIGHT, DRY:

D-5A	0·18 kg (0·397 lb)
GM	0·35 kg (0·771 lb)

CHAMBER PRESSURE:

D-5A	15·3-30·5 bars (222-442 lb/sq in)
GM	10-30 bars (145-435 lb/sq in)

ELECTRICAL LOAD:

D-5A	5W
GM	6W

THRUST:

D-5A	0·0028-0·0016 kN (0·629-0·359 lb)
GM	0·014-0·006 kN (3·15-1·35 lb)

SPECIFIC IMPULSE (Vacuum):

D-5A, GM	215-230

SEP HM7 high-energy upper-stage rocket engine (vacuum thrust 70·06 kN; 15,750 lb)

TYPICAL SEP SOLID-PROPELLANT ROCKET ENGINES

Type	Thrust at S/L	Duration of Thrust (s)	Total Weight	Length	Diameter
SEP 163 Sioule	1·4 kN (315 lb)	37	40 kg (88 lb)	1,745 mm (68·7 in)	141 mm (5·5 in)
SEP 6854 Odet	37 kN (8,320 lb)	4	124 kg (273 lb)	2,560 mm (101 in)	226 mm (8·9 in)
SEP 7382 Yonne	94 kN (21,130 lb)	20	1,250 kg (2,756 lb)	4,062 mm (160 in)	584 mm (23 in)
SEP 7392 Rance	162·45 kN (36,520 lb)	17·5	1,565 kg (3,450 lb)	4,605 mm (181·3 in)	578 mm (22·7 in)
SEP 7342 Vienne	293 kN (65,860 lb)	4·6	846 kg (1,870 lb)	3,195 mm (125·8 in)	590 mm (23·2 in)
SEP 299 Arz	43·16 kN (9,702 lb)	1·6	57·5 kg (126·78 lb)	1,076 mm (42·2 in)	250 mm (9·8 in)
SEP 300 Drac	0·96 kN (215·8 lb)	73	52·5 kg (115·76 lb)	1,100 mm (43·3 in)	207 mm (8·1 in)
SEP Dropt	40 kN (9,000 lb)	45	751 kg (1,655·9 lb)	1,500 mm (59 in)	800 mm (31·5 in)
SEP Ball	4·2 kN (944 lb)	4·3	23·1 kg (50·9 lb)	430 mm (16·9 in)	221 mm (8·7 in)
SEP Trap	Start 8·05 kN (1,809 lb) Cruise 1·79 kN (402 lb)	Start 3·8 Cruise 10·2	45·2 kg (99·75 lb)	835 mm (32·87 in)	221 mm (8·7 in)
SEP Arc	Start 90 kN (20,233 lb) Start 53 kN (11,915 lb) Cruise 14·1 kN (3,170 lb)	Start 10·1 Start 20·2 Cruise 3·5	57 kg (125·7 lb)	2,306 mm (90·8 in)	157 mm (6·2 in)
SEP Ciron (GEOS)	16·4 kN (3,687 lb)	45	300 kg (661 lb)	1,070 mm (42·1 in)	684 mm (26·9 in)
SEP Mage	30·4 kN (6,835 lb)	40	345 kg (761 lb)	1,170 mm (46·1 in)	764 mm (30·1 in)

SNECMA
SOCIÉTÉ NATIONALE D'ÉTUDE ET DE CONSTRUCTION DE MOTEURS D'AVIATION

HEAD OFFICE: 2 boulevard Victor, 75724 Paris Cedex 15
Telephone: 554 92 00
Telex: 202 834 Motav
CHAIRMAN AND MANAGING DIRECTOR: René Ravaud
DIRECTOR, PERSONAL ASSISTANT
  TO THE CHAIRMAN: Constantin Davidoff
DEPUTY MANAGING DIRECTOR FOR AERO-ENGINE
  PROGRAMMES AND MARKETING: Jean Péquignot
DIRECTOR, FINANCE AND PLANNING: Jean Sollier

DIRECTOR FOR AERO-ENGINE DEVELOPMENT
  AND PRODUCTION: Jean Calmon
DIRECTOR FOR SUBSIDIARY COMPANIES
  AND DIVISIONS: Gérard Jousseaume
PERSONNEL DIRECTOR: Jean Pascaud
DIRECTOR FOR INTERNATIONAL RELATIONS: Jean Crépin
GENERAL SECRETARY: Henri Forsans
DIRECTOR FOR AERO-ENGINE PRODUCTION: Jean-Marie
  Francillon
TECHNICAL DIRECTOR: Pierre Lachaume
PRESS ADVISOR TO THE CHAIRMAN: Philippe Dreux

Villaroche Centre: 77550 Moissy-Cramayel

Design, development and ground test centre. A subsidiary establishment for flight and noise tests is located at Istres.

Evry-Corbeil:
RN 7, BP 81, 91003 Evry Cedex
Engine production, quality control, service, procurement and laboratories for research and development.

Gennevilliers:
291 avenue d'Argenteuil, BP 30, 92234 Gennevilliers
Forging and casting production, complete machining of mechanical parts.

Suresnes—ELECMA Division:
22 quai Galliéni, 92150 Suresnes
Design, development and production of electronic equipment, especially electronic control systems for the aircraft industry.

SNECMA (Société Nationale d'Etude et de Construction de Moteurs d'Aviation) was born on 29 August 1945 from the merger of several aero-engine companies: Gnome et Rhône, Société Anonyme des Moteurs Renault pour l'Aviation, Société Générale de Mécanique et d'Aviation (former Moteurs Lorraine), and Groupe d'Etudes des Moteurs à Huile Lourde.

These companies already had a long aeronautical tradition and SNECMA has always devoted its main activity to aero-engines. More than 5,130 Atar turbojets have been ordered; they have played a significant part in the worldwide success of Mirage fighters. SNECMA is developing the M53 turbojet for fighters of the 1980s.

SNECMA is also participating in the following international collaborative programmes:

The Olympus 593 for Concorde, developed and produced with Rolls-Royce; the CF6-50 for the Airbus A300B and some 747s (with MTU), and CF6-80 for the A310 under a co-production agreement with General

SNECMA Atar 9K50 turbojet of 70·6 kN (15,870 lb st) with afterburning

Electric; the CF6-32, in co-operation with General Electric; the CFM56, which SNECMA shares equally with General Electric, but with FN associated within SNECMA's share; the Larzac, produced in co-operation with Turboméca and with production also involving the German companies MTU and KHD, and FN in Belgium; and the Tyne, produced by a consortium (SNECMA, MTU, Rolls-Royce, FN).

SNECMA ATAR

The Atar is a single-shaft military turbojet first run in 1946 and since developed and cleared for flight at Mach numbers greater than 2. Major versions are:

Atar 9C. Compared with the earlier 9B this introduced a new compressor, a self-contained starter and an improved overspeed which comes into operation automatically when the aircraft reaches Mach 1·4, giving power equivalent to a sea level thrust of 62·7 kN (14,110 lb). Equips most Mirage III and 5.

Atar 9K50. Derived from the Atar 9C. Designed to offer improved subsonic specific fuel consumption, increased thrust for supersonic acceleration and improved overhaul life. The main improvements are in an entirely redesigned turbine with blades not forged but cast and coated with refractory metal from the vapour phase. Stages 1 and 8 of the compressor have been redesigned, resulting in pressure ratio raised from 6 : 1 to 6·15 : 1, coupled with slightly augmented mass flow. The control and electronic equipment have been revised and extended to improve the security of single-engined aircraft. The 9K50 is the power plant of all production Mirage F1 versions and the Mirage 50.

Atar 8K50. This is essentially the 9K50, the latest variant in production, re-engineered to have a simple unaugmented jet-pipe and fixed nozzle, for the Super Etendard. All parts are protected against sea corrosion. The 8K50 completed its 150 h official type test in May 1975. Production deliveries began in May 1977.

DIMENSIONS:
Diameter	1,020 mm (40·2 in)

Length overall:
Atar 8K50	3,936 mm (155 in)
Atar 9C, 9K50	5,944 mm (234 in)

WEIGHTS:
Dry, complete with all accessories:
Atar 8K50	1,155 kg (2,546 lb)
Atar 9C	1,456 kg (3,209 lb)
Atar 9K50	1,582 kg (3,487 lb)

PERFORMANCE RATINGS:
Max with afterburner:
Atar 9C	58·9 kN (13,230 lb st) at 8,400 rpm
Atar 9K50	70·6 kN (15,870 lb st) at 8,400 rpm

Max without afterburner:
Atar 8K50	49 kN (11,025 lb st) at 8,550 rpm
Atar 9C	42 kN (9,430 lb st) at 8,400 rpm
Atar 9K50	49·2 kN (11,055 lb st)

SPECIFIC FUEL CONSUMPTION:
At max rating with afterburner:
Atar 9C	57·5 mg/Ns (2·03 lb/h/lb st)
Atar 9K50	55·5 mg/Ns (1·96 lb/h/lb st)

At max rating without afterburner:
Atar 8K50	27·5 mg/Ns (0·97 lb/h/lb st)
Atar 9C	28·6 mg/Ns (1·01 lb/h/lb st)
Atar 9K50	27·5 mg/Ns (0·97 lb/h/lb st)

OIL CONSUMPTION: 1·5 litres (2·64 Imp pints)/h

SNECMA M53

The M53 is a single-shaft turbofan—more strictly a continuous-bleed turbojet—capable of propelling fighter aircraft at high altitude at Mach 2·5. The first application is in the Mirage 2000, being developed for the Armée de l' Air. The engine is of modular construction.

The single shaft comprises a three-stage fan and five-stage compressor driven by a two-stage turbine designed for operation at high gas temperature. There are no inlet guide vanes. Max airflow is 86 kg (190 lb)/s. Between the fan and compressor is a mid-frame incorporating accessory drives and front roller bearing and ball thrust bearing. The annular combustion chamber is designed for smoke-free operation. The turbine delivery casing incorporates the third bearing. Fuel to the combustion chamber and reheat system, and the multi-flap nozzle, are controlled by

Longitudinal section through the SNECMA M53 showing LP and HP sections on single shaft (pressure ratio, 9·3 at 10,500 rpm) and bypass duct

SNECMA M53 augmented bypass turbojet of 88·3 kN (19,840 lb st)

a fuel system monitored by an ELECMA electronic computer.

The first prototype engine was tested in February 1970, 18 months after programme go-ahead. The second ran in August, and achieved maximum rpm after 30 minutes of operation. Military rating (51 kN; 11,466 lb) was reached in October, three months ahead of contractual commitment. Testing with afterburner began in November 1970. The first official test took place at 54·92 kN (12,346 lb) in May 1971. In the same month a 50 h test was run at afterburning thrusts up to 81·39 kN (18,298 lb), 98 per cent of the nominal rating. In September thrust exceeded the nominal figure, at 83·4 kN (18,740 lb), and in December simulated altitude trials began at Saclay. By March 1972 three prototype M53 engines were running. Flight trials began on 18 July 1973 in the starboard pod of a Caravelle testbed. The supersonic flight envelope is being explored with the Mirage F1-M 53 flying testbed, which first flew in December 1974. In July 1977 an official 50-h test was completed at 88·5 kN.

The Mirage 2000 first flew in March 1978 and the Mirage 4000 in March 1979. By early 1980, three Mirage 2000s were flying and total running time exceeded 10,700 h.

The initial M53-2 version is rated at 83·4 kN (18,740 lb st). Development is now centred on the M53-5, data for which are given below. This will be the engine of the production Mirage 2000. It passed its 150 h official type test in May 1979 and the first engines for the Armée de l' Air were in production in 1980.

The M53-P2 is an uprated version now under development. It will be rated at 95·2 kN (21,400 lb st).

DIMENSIONS:
Overall length	4,853 mm (191 in)
Max diameter	1,055 mm (42·0 in)

WEIGHT, DRY: 1,450 kg (3,195 lb)

PERFORMANCE RATINGS:
Max thrust, with afterburner	88·3 kN (19,840 lb)
Max thrust, cold	55 kN (12,350 lb)

SPECIFIC FUEL CONSUMPTION:
At max cold rating   24·64 mg/Ns (0·87 lb/h/lb st)

SNECMA M88

A demonstration programme is in progress with the M88, a two-shaft low-bypass-ratio turbofan in the 75-85 kN (16,860-19,100 lb st) class. Compared with the Atar 9K50, the M88 would have 10 per cent lower airflow, much reduced dimensions and 50 per cent higher

thrust/weight ratio. Its advanced design uses concepts developed in a programme called Dextre, in particular research into highly loaded aircooled turbines.

CFM INTERNATIONAL CFM56

SNECMA decided in the Autumn of 1971 to develop the CFM56, a subsonic turbofan in the ten-tonne-thrust (22,000 lb) class, in co-operation with General Electric. The project is covered under CFM in the International section.

GE/SNECMA/MTU CF6-50

To provide engines for the Airbus Industrie A300B and French Boeing 747s, SNECMA and MTU of Federal Germany participate in a co-production programme with General Electric to make the CF6-50 turbofan. SNECMA performs assembly and test, and manufactures parts, with a total share on a cost basis of 27 per cent. MTU's share is 10 per cent, and GE supplies the balance. The agreement is being extended to include the CF6-45, to power initial A310 versions, and the CF6-80.

GE/SNECMA/ALFA ROMEO/VOLVO CF6-32

This engine, described like other CF6 versions in the US section, is designed for a nominal T-O thrust of 162·4 kN (36,520 lb). SNECMA is responsible for the LP turbine, turbine rear frame, and accessory gearbox, and participates in testing of development engines, which began on 1 August 1979.

SNECMA/ROLLS-ROYCE OLYMPUS 593

SNECMA collaborated with Rolls-Royce in development and manufacture of the Olympus 593 turbojet for the Concorde. (See under 'Rolls-Royce/SNECMA' in the International section.)

SNECMA/TURBOMÉCA LARZAC

This 13·2 kN (2,966 lb st) turbofan was designed jointly by SNECMA and Turboméca. A description of the Larzac is given under the entry for Turboméca-SNECMA GRTS, in this section.

SNECMA/MTU/RR/FN TYNE

Under Rolls-Royce licence, the Tyne 22 turboprop for the Transall C-160, was, in October 1977, put back into production by the original four-nation consortium, with the original work-split. SNECMA's share will be made by Hispano-Suiza, and assembly and test will be at Sochata-SNECMA, Châtellerault. First delivery 1980. The similar Tyne 21 is also to be re-ordered, to power the ANG (Atlantic Nouvelle Génération).

SNPE
SOCIÉTÉ NATIONALE DES POUDRES ET EXPLOSIFS

HEADQUARTERS: 12 Quai Henri IV, 75181 Paris Cédex 04
Telephone: 277 15 70

SNPE continues to be the sole supplier of solid-propellant grains to French missile manufacturers. Significant progress has been made in research and development, including smokeless high-impulse propellants, smokeless ramjet solid fuel, and new manufacturing processes for double-base and composite propellants. In the field of strategic missiles, the submarine-launched M4 MSBS has completed development and proved so successful that further developments are being studied. In tactical missiles, active programmes include motors for the MM

38, AM 39 and MM 40 Exocet, the new ASMP and Matra Super 530D, and production deliveries of motors for Shahine. As noted under the G2P heading, SNPE and SEP created a limited joint venture to co-ordinate their activities and act as a unified prime contractor for the propulsion of large missiles such as SSBS, MSBS and Pluton. Available details of important production motors are tabulated:

A selection of small SNPE grains with diameter from 150 to 10 mm (5·9 to 0·4 in)

Missile	Propellant	Grain mass kg (lb)	Total impulse kN-s (lb-s)	Burn time (s)	Status
SSBS, MSBS	Isorgol composite with poly-urethane binder, case-bonded	6,000-16,000 (13,228-35,274)	1,300,000-3,750,000 (292·25-843·02 million)	52-75	Production
Pluton	Isorgol homogeneous dual-composition polyurethane binder, case-bonded	1,215 (2,679)	268,380 (60,333,045)	18	Production
MM 38, MM 40, Otomat	Isorgol composite and homogeneous cast/extruded double-base	41-277 (90·4-611)	21,500-55,000 (4,833,300-12,364,425)	2·5-210	MM 40 development, others production
AM 39	Isolane composite and homo-geneous cast double-base	80 and 165 (176·4 and 364)	17,400, 33,500 (3,911,600, 7,530,950)	2·3, 150	Production
AS 12, Durandal, Martel TV	Butargol/Isorgol/Butalane composite and cast/extruded double-base	7·8-123 (17·2-271)	1,332-25,700 (299,440-5,777,475)	0·4-93	Production
Magic, Super 530	Plastorgol-Butargol composites	21-75 (46·3-165·3)	5,000-17,000 (1,124,020-3,821,680)	1·7-6	Production
Crotale, Hawk, Roland	Homogeneous extruded/cast double-base and Isorgol composite	14·4-143 (31·75-315)	5,500-32,000 (1,236,425-7,193,745)	1·6-23	Production

TURBOMÉCA
SOCIÉTÉ TURBOMÉCA

Bordes, 64320 Bizanos
Telephone: (15-59) 32 84 37
Telex: 560928
OTHER WORKS: Mézières S/Seine (Yvelines) and Tarnos (near Bayonne)
PARIS OFFICE: 1, Rue Beaujon, Paris 8e
PRESIDENT AND DIRECTOR-GENERAL:
   J. R. Szydlowski

The Société Turboméca was formed in 1938 by Messieurs Szydlowski and Planiol to develop blowers, compressors and turbines for aeronautical use. Today, it is the leading European manufacturer of small turbine aero-engines. Since it first started development of gas turbines in 1947, the company has developed about 50 different types of power plant of which some 15 have entered production and ten types have been manufactured under licence in five countries.

By 1 September 1979, a total of 17,839 Turboméca engines for fixed and rotary-wing applications and aircraft auxiliary duties had been delivered to customers in 97 countries, including France. Approximately 14,000 more engines have been built under licence by what are today Rolls-Royce Ltd in the UK, Teledyne CAE in the USA, ENMASA in Spain, Hindustan Aeronautics Ltd in India, Bet-Shemesh in Israel and state factories in Romania and Yugoslavia.

Total covered floor area for Turboméca's three plants at Bordes, Mézières and Tarnos is 136,487 m² (1,469,134 sq ft). At 1 November 1979 the company employed a total of 4,365 people.

Turboméca has 45·6 per cent participation in CGTM, 50 per cent in RRTI, 26 per cent in CGR, 50 per cent in Turboméca SNECMA, 50 per cent in Astadyne (APU development with ABG-Semca), 50 per cent in MTU-Turboméca, 50 per cent in Rolls-Royce Turboméca, 30·22 per cent in Bet-Shemesh Engines, 22·08 per cent in Ormat Turbines and 50 per cent in RR-TM do Brasil.

ROLLS-ROYCE TURBOMÉCA ADOUR

This turbofan was developed jointly by Rolls-Royce and Turboméca for the SEPECAT Jaguar tactical strike fighter and advanced trainer. Other versions were developed subsequently for the BAe Hawk and Mitsubishi T-2 and F-1. A brief description of the Adour is given in the International section.

TURBOMÉCA ASTAFAN

The Astafan is a low-consumption lightweight turbofan of high by-pass ratio, low noise level design which made its first run during the Summer of 1969. Comprising an Astazou turboprop power section, operating at constant speed, driving a single-stage variable-pitch fan via reduction gearing, it is being developed in several versions corresponding to different development stages of the Astazou. All have the high bypass ratio of 7 : 1 and are characterised by very low specific fuel consumption. Variable-pitch blading facilitates constant-speed operation and permits off-loading of the engine during starting.

The following are the first versions under development:
   Astafan IIG. Variant developed for military trainer applications.
   Astafan III. Derived from the Astazou XVIII, with air-cooled turbine.
   Astafan IV. Derived from the Astazou XX, with three-stage axial high-pressure compressor.
   Astafan IVG. Refined engine for Aérospatiale Fouga 90.

Flight development of prototype Astafan engines began in a Hawk Commander on 8 April 1971. Two podded underwing Astafans replaced the original piston engines, conferring a substantial improvement in flight performance and a reduction in noise and vibration.

On 24 January 1976 an Aero Commander 690 flew at Pau for the first time powered by two Astafan IVF6 engines, similar to the basic Astafan IV but rated at 10·49 kN (2,359 lb) take-off thrust and with even lower noise and fuel consumption.

TYPE: Single-shaft turbofan with geared fan.

ENTRY CASING: Annular light alloy entry cowl and fan duct supported on double row of air straightener vanes downstream of fan rotor.
FAN: Single-stage fan with variable-incidence rotor blading overhung at front without entry guide vanes. Drive from gas generator section is via two-stage epicyclic gear train housed in cylindrical casing forming inner wall of fan duct. Astafan IV has fan of increased diameter (700 mm; 27·5 in).
COMPRESSOR, COMBUSTION SYSTEM AND TURBINE: Same as Astazou XVIII. Normal gas-generator operating speed, 43,000 rpm. (Astafan IV has Astazou XX compressor, running at 42,000 rpm.)
JET PIPE: Fixed type with straight frustum inner cone.
ACCESSORIES: Mounted on casing forming rear of secondary air intake.
FUEL SYSTEM: Independent control systems for starting and normal operation. Fuel regulator maintains speed constant with pilot operating single lever controlling fan blade pitch hydraulically to vary thrust output. Turboméca 'thermic' load limiter controls turbine entry temperature.
FUEL GRADES: AIR 3404A, 3405 or 3407A.
LUBRICATION SYSTEM: Pressure lubrication to bearings and reduction gear, with annular engine-mounted oil tank.
STARTING: Automatic electrical starting with compressor blow-off valve and fan in minimum pitch.

Turboméca Astafan IVG geared variable-pitch turbofan

DIMENSIONS:
Length overall:
Astafan IIG	1,980 mm (77·95 in)
Astafan III	2,030 mm (80·0 in)
Astafan IV	2,218 mm (87·5 in)
Astafan IVG	2,088 mm (82·2 in)

Max diameter over fan cowl:
Astafan IIG	693 mm (27·3 in)
Astafan III	665 mm (26·2 in)
Astafan IV	780 mm (30·7 in)
Astafan IVG	700 mm (27·56 in)

WEIGHTS:
Equipped Astafan IIG	285 kg (628 lb)
Astafan III bare engine	210 kg (462 lb)
Equipped Astafan III	approx 230 kg (507 lb)
Astafan IV bare engine	220 kg (485 lb)
Equipped Astafan IVG	305 kg (672 lb)

PERFORMANCE RATINGS:
T-O dry:
Astafan IIG	6·88 kN (1,543 lb st)
Astafan IVG	7·74 kN (1,740 lb st)

T-O, wet:
Astafan III	8·34 kN (1,870 lb st)
Astafan IV	12·06 kN (2,710 lb st)

SPECIFIC FUEL CONSUMPTION:
At T-O rating:
Astafan IIG	10·76 mg/Ns (0·38 lb/h/lb st)
Astafan III	10·34 mg/Ns (0·365 lb/h/lb st)
Astafan IV	8·78 mg/Ns (0·310 lb/h/lb st)
Astafan IVG	11·61 mg/Ns (0·41 lb/h/lb st)

TURBOMÉCA-SNECMA LARZAC

This small turbofan has been developed jointly by Turboméca and SNECMA to power military trainers and other small aircraft. A description of the Larzac is given under Turboméca-SNECMA GRTS.

TURBOMÉCA MARBORÉ

The Marboré turbojet is the most widely used of Turboméca's range of gas turbines. By 1 September 1979, a total of 4,353 Marboré II engines of 3·92 kN (880 lb st) had been delivered by Turboméca and a further 10,000 by Continental Aviation and Teledyne CAE (see US section) as the J69.

This initial version of the engine was joined in production by the 4·71 kN (1,058 lb st) Marboré VI with receipt of type approval in June 1962. By 1 September 1979, a total of 1,194 Marboré VI turbojets had been built. Production by Turboméca is now complete.

The Marboré VI was also built under licence in Spain by ENMASA as the Marboré M21. Details of the engine were given in the 1979-80 *Jane's*.

TURBOMÉCA ARBIZON

Announced in 1970, the Arbizon is a simple single-shaft turbojet, known originally as the TR281 and derived from the Turmo IIIC3 turboshaft. Intended for the propulsion of missiles and RPVs, it has single-stage axial and centrifugal compressors and a single-stage turbine.

Arbizon IIIB. Original version, for Otomat cruise missile. Four-lobed bellmouth inlet ducts surround front face carrying electric starter and other accessories. Mass flow 6 kg (13·2 lb)/s; pressure ratio 5·5. Total of 164 built by 1 September 1979.

Arbizon IV. Smaller version, under development. Design life 30 h. Air-impingement starter.

DIMENSIONS:
Diameter of combustion chamber:
Arbizon IIIB	405 mm (15·95 in)

Max diameter:
Arbizon IV	330 mm (13·00 in)

Length overall, with accessories:
Arbizon IIIB	1,361 mm (53·58 in)
Arbizon IV	1,025 mm (40·35 in)

Turboméca Arbizon IV short-life turbojet (underside shown, with inlet to left)

Turboméca Arbizon IIIB expendable turbojet, rated at 3·73 kN (836 lb st)

WEIGHT, DRY:
Arbizon IIIB	115 kg (253 lb)
Arbizon IV	60 kg (132 lb)

PERFORMANCE RATINGS:
T-O: Arbizon IIIB 3·73 kN (836 lb st) at 33,000 rpm
Arbizon IV	3·60 kN (809 lb st)

Max continuous:
Arbizon IIIB	3·24 kN (727 lb st) at 32,000 rpm
Arbizon IV	3·30 kN (741 lb st)

SPECIFIC FUEL CONSUMPTION:
At max continuous rating:
Arbizon IIIB	31·44 mg/Ns (1·11 lb/h/lb st)
Arbizon IV	29·29 mg/Ns (1·034 lb/h/lb st)

TURBOMÉCA ARRIEL

This turboshaft engine is being used initially in two Aérospatiale helicopters, the single-engined AS 350 Ecureuil and twin-engined SA 365 Dauphin. It could also power a future version of the SA 341 Gazelle.

The Arriel is intended to have low first cost, low maintenance cost and low specific weight. It is characterised by modular construction, and is expected eventually to form the basis for a single-shaft turboprop and a turbofan in the 4·90 kN (1,100 lb st) class. The gas generator ran in 1973. The first complete engine ran on the bench on 7 August 1974. Flight development began on 17 December 1974 in the SA 341-02 Gazelle, which had been converted for Arriel development by Aérospatiale and the CGTM. The twin-engined SA 365 first flew on 24 January 1975, and the AS 350 Ecureuil on 14 February 1975. By 1 September 1979 a total of 203 Arriels had been delivered and the rate of output was increasing.

TYPE: Single-shaft axial-plus-centrifugal free-turbine turboshaft.

AIR INTAKE: Direct pitot entry to axial compressor.

COMPRESSOR: Single-stage axial compressor, machined from titanium forging. Supersonic centrifugal stage also machined from titanium. High rotational speed for maximum attainable pressure ratio (9:1).

COMBUSTION CHAMBER: Annular chamber, with flow radially outwards and then inwards. Centrifugal fuel injection without central tube.

GAS-GENERATOR TURBINE: Two integral cast axial stages with solid blades. Turbine shield capable of disc containment.

POWER TURBINE: Single axial stage with inserted blades.

JET PIPE: Exhaust diffuser fabricated by welding.

REDUCTION GEAR: Light alloy gearbox, containing two stages of helical gears, giving drive at 6,000 rpm to output shaft extending whole length of engine, with drive connections to both front and rear. Hydraulic torquemeter.

ACCESSORY DRIVES: Two bevel gears and radial quill shaft drive accessory gearbox at front end, carried between compressor case and output shaft. Main pad provides for optional 12,000 rpm alternator; other drives for oil pumps, tachometer generator, governor and starter.

LUBRICATION SYSTEM: Independent circuit. Oil from tank passes through gear pump and metallic-cartridge filter. Return from engine via three gear scavenge pumps. Temperature probe and pressure switch to verify operation.

OIL SPECIFICATION: AIR 3512 (mineral) or AIR 3513A (synthetic).

MOUNTING: Multi-point flanges allow easy mounting in single or twin installation.

STARTING: Electric starter or starter/generator.

DIMENSIONS:
Length, excl accessories	1,090 mm (42·91 in)
Height overall	569 mm (22·40 in)
Width	430 mm (16·93 in)

WEIGHT, DRY:
With all engine accessories	109 kg (240 lb)

PERFORMANCE RATINGS:
Max contingency, initial	508 kW (681 shp)
Max contingency, later	544 kW (730 shp)
Take-off and intermediate contingency	478 kW (641 shp)
Max continuous	441 kW (592 shp)

SPECIFIC FUEL CONSUMPTION:
Max contingency	93·1 μg/J (0·551 lb/h/shp)
Intermediate contingency	96·8 μg/J (0·573 lb/h/shp)

TURBOMÉCA ASTAZOU TURBOPROP

The Astazou is the major turboprop in the Turboméca range and is in production in its 636 kW (853 ehp) Astazou XIVC and 760·6 kW (1,020 ehp) Astazou XVI versions. The Astazou XIV was certificated by the French airworthiness authorities in October 1968, followed by ARB/FAA certification of the Astazou XIVC and C1 in March 1969.

Current versions of the Astazou are:

Astazou XII. Powered Shorts Skyvan Srs 2 at 690 shp and Pilatus Turbo-Porter PC-6/A1-H2 at 700 ehp.

Astazou XIV (alias AZ14). Developed from Astazou XII. Powers early Jetstream business aircraft at 853 ehp.

Astazou XVI (alias AZ16). Higher rated version of Astazou XIV and first engine to enter production with new Turboméca aircooled turbine. The XVID, without starter/generator, powers the former production versions of the Jetstream; the XVIZ powers the Nord 260A. The Astazou XVIG, equipped for sustained inverted flight,

Turboméca Arriel 1 free-turbine turboshaft, with initial ratings up to 508 kW (681 shp)

Turboméca Astazou XIVC turboprop engine, rated at 636 ekW (853 ehp)

was certificated by the Services Officiels Français on 30 April 1971; it powers the Argentinian Pucará combat aircraft. By 1 September 1979, a total of 184 Astazou XVI engines had been built.

Astazou XVIII. Higher rated version of Astazou XVI which first ran in early 1969 with T-O rating of 860·5 kW (1,154 ehp).

Astazou XX. Under development. This engine has two transonic axial compressor stages in titanium, in addition to the centrifugal stage machined in steel. Maximum T-O rating is 1,075 ekW (1,442 ehp).

Details of the Astazou series of turboshafts are given separately.

TYPE: Single-shaft axial-plus-centrifugal turboprop.

REDUCTION GEAR: Mounted in tapered cylindrical casing at front of engine, with two-stage epicyclic reduction gear having helical primary gears and straight secondary gears. Reduction ratio 24·115 : 1 (XVIG, 21·8 : 1). (Astazou XX gearbox incorporates torquemeter.)

AIR INTAKE: Annular air intake at rear of reduction gear casing. Hot-air de-icing.

COMPRESSOR: Two-stage axial followed by single-stage centrifugal with single-sided impeller. Two rows of stator blades aft of each axial rotor. Centrifugal stage has radial and axial diffusers. (Astazou XX has a four-stage compressor, comprising three axial followed by one centrifugal.)

COMBUSTION SYSTEM: Reverse-flow annular type with centrifugal fuel injector using rotary atomiser disc. Ignition by two ventilated torch igniters.

TURBINE: Three-stage axial with blades integral with discs. (Air cooling provided for Astazou XVI, XVIII and XX.) Discs attached by curvic couplings and bolts.

JET PIPE: Fixed type with curved inner cone.

ACCESSORIES: Mounted on casing forming rear of air intake. Drive pads provided for starter/generator, oil pump, fuel pump and speed governor, tacho-generator, AC generator and hydraulic pump.

MOUNTING: Trunnion located on each side of turbine casing front flange, plus third trunnion on underside of turbine casing.

FUEL SYSTEM: Automatic constant-speed system with propeller Beta-control and Turboméca 'thermic' load limiter and speed governor.

FUEL GRADES: AIR 3404, 3405, or 3407.

LUBRICATION SYSTEM: Pressure lubrication to bearings and reduction gear, with 8 litre (14 pint) oil tank mounted at front of engine.

OIL SPECIFICATION: AIR 3515 or synthetic AIR 3573.

STARTING: Electric.

DIMENSIONS:
Diameter over intake cowl	546 mm (21·5 in)
Overall length, incl propeller	2,047 mm (80·6 in)

WEIGHTS:
With accessories:
Astazou XIV	approx 206 kg (454 lb)
Astazou XVID	205 kg (452 lb)
Astazou XVIG	228 kg (502 lb)
Astazou XVIZ	213 kg (468 lb)
Astazou XVIII	approx 205 kg (452 lb)
Astazou XX	220 kg (484 lb)

PERFORMANCE RATINGS:
T-O:
Astazou XIV	636 ekW; 596·5 kW
	(853 ehp; 800 shp) at 43,000 rpm
Astazou XVID	723 ekW; 681 kW
	(969 ehp; 913 shp) at 43,000 rpm
Astazou XVIG, XVIZ	761 ekW; 720 kW
	(1,020 ehp; 965 shp) at 43,000 rpm
Astazou XVIII	861 ekW; 813 kW
	(1,154 ehp; 1,090 shp) at 43,000 rpm
Astazou XX	1,075 ekW; 1,030 kW
	(1,442 ehp; 1,381 shp) at 42,000 rpm

Max continuous:
Astazou XIV	574 ekW; 537 kW
	(770 ehp; 720 shp) at 43,000 rpm
Astazou XVID	626 ekW; 586 kW
	(840 ehp; 786 shp) at 43,089 rpm
Astazou XVIG, XVIZ	696 ekW; 654 kW
	(934 ehp; 877 shp) at 43,000 rpm
Astazou XVIII	809 ekW; 768 kW
	(1,085 ehp; 1,030 shp) at 43,000 rpm
Astazou XX	951 ekW; 907 kW
	(1,276 ehp; 1,217 shp) at 42,000 rpm

SPECIFIC FUEL CONSUMPTION:
At T-O rating:
Astazou XIV	92·4 µg/J (0·547 lb/h/shp)
Astazou XVI (all versions)	
	88·7 µg/J (0·525 lb/h/shp)
Astazou XVIII	85·3 µg/J (0·505 lb/h/ehp)
Astazou XX	75·9 µg/J (0·449 lb/h/ehp)

TURBOMÉCA ASTAZOU TURBOSHAFT

This turboshaft series of the Astazou family is derived from the early second-generation Astazou II turboprop fitted to the Mitsubishi MU-2 and Pilatus Turbo-Porter. Variants are as follows:

Astazou IIA. Rated at 390 kW (523 shp) and powers the Aérospatiale SA 318C Alouette II Astazou helicopter. Total of 732 built by 1977.

Astazou III. Definitive turboshaft for Anglo-French helicopter programme for production SA 341 Gazelle. Derived from Astazou IIA but with revised profile of turbine, using higher temperature alloy to match power needs of SA 341. Astazou IIIA, B, C and N for Gazelle versions all certificated in June 1972; uprated IIIA2, B2, C2 and N2 certificated May 1978. Produced jointly by Turboméca and Rolls-Royce Ltd, with 896 delivered by 1 September 1979.

Astazou XIVB and XIVF. In production for the SA 319B Alouette III; XIVB is civil and XIVF military. Flat rated to 441 kW (591 shp) (1 h) up to 4,000 m (13,125 ft) or +55°C.

Astazou XIVH. In production for SA 341 Gazelle, with much increased power. Flat-rated to transmission limit, to remove all altitude and temperature limitations. Certificated October 1974. Total of all XIV versions, 586 by 1 September 1979.

Astazou XVIIIA. Further increase in power gained by improved turbine, allowing higher gas temperature. Powers SA 360 Dauphin.

Astazou XX. Fourth axial compressor stage added. Designed for operation in hot and high countries. Intended to power SA 361 helicopter.

The following description relates to the Astazou IIIN except where indicated:

TYPE: Single-shaft axial-plus-centrifugal turboshaft.

REDUCTION GEAR: Similar to Astazou XIV turboprop. Reduction ratio 7·039 : 1 (Astazou XIVB/F, 7·345; XVIA, XVIIIA, 7·375).

AIR INTAKE: Annular air intake at rear of reduction gear casing.

COMPRESSOR: Single-stage axial (IIA, IIN, IIIN), two-stage axial (XIV, XVIII) or three-stage axial (XX) followed by single-stage centrifugal with single-sided impeller. Air mass flow 2·5 kg/s (5·5 lb/s).

COMBUSTION SYSTEM: Similar to Astazou XIV.

TURBINE: Similar to Astazou XIV.

JET PIPE: Similar to Astazou XIV.

ACCESSORIES: Five drive pads on casing forming rear of air intake.

MOUNTING: At front by flange located at power take-off section, and at rear by two lugs on accessory mounting pad section.

FUEL SYSTEM: Automatic constant speed control with speed governor.

LUBRICATION SYSTEM: Pressure type with gear type pumps. Oil tank of 8 litre (14 Imp pint) capacity mounted at front of engine.

STARTING: Electrical, automatic.

DIMENSIONS:
Height:	Astazou IIA	458 mm (18 in)
	Astazou III, XIVH	460 mm (18·1 in)
	Astazou XVIA, XVIIIA	698 mm (27·48 in)
	Astazou XX	721 mm (28·4 in)
Width:	Astazou IIA	480 mm (18·8 in)
	Astazou III, XIVH	460 mm (18·1 in)
Length overall:	Astazou IIA	1,272 mm (50·0 in)
	Astazou III, XIVB/F	1,433 mm (56·3 in)
	Astazou XVIA, XVIIIA	1,327 mm (52·2 in)
	Astazou XIVH	1,470 mm (57·9 in)
	Astazou XX	1,529 mm (60·22 in)

WEIGHTS:
Equipped:
Astazou III	147 kg (324 lb)
Astazou III (suffix 2)	150 kg (330 lb)
Astazou XIVB/F	166 kg (366 lb)
Astazou XVIA, XVIIIA	155 kg (341 lb)
Astazou XIVH	160 kg (353 lb)
Astazou XX	195 kg (430 lb)

PERFORMANCE RATINGS:
Max power:
Astazou IIA	390 kW (523 shp)
Astazou III	441 kW (592 shp)
Astazou III (suffix 2)	481 kW (645 shp)
Astazou XX	749 kW (1,005 shp)
One hour: Astazou XIVB/F	441 kW (591 shp)
Astazou XVIA	651 kW (873 shp)
	maintained at sea level to 30°C
Astazou XVIIIA	651 kW (873 shp)
	maintained at sea level to 40°C

Max continuous:
Astazou IIA	353 kW (473 shp)
Astazou III	390 kW (523 shp)
Astazou III (suffix 2)	441 kW (592 shp)
Astazou XIVB/F	405 kW (543 shp)
Astazou XVIA, XVIIIA	600 kW (805 shp)
Astazou XIVH flat-rated in SA 341 to 440·7 kW	
	(591 shp) to 55°C or 4,000 m (13,125 ft)
Astazou XX	675 kW (905 shp)

SPECIFIC FUEL CONSUMPTION:
At max power rating:
Astazou IIA	105·3 µg/J (0·623 lb/h/shp)
Astazou III	108·7 µg/J (0·643 lb/h/shp)
Astazou III (suffix 2)	109·9 µg/J (0·65 lb/h/shp)
Astazou XIVB/F	105·5 µg/J (0·624 lb/h/shp)
Astazou XVIA	93·8 µg/J (0·555 lb/h/shp)
Astazou XVIIIA	91·3 µg/J (0·540 lb/h/shp)
Astazou XX	85·9 µg/J (0·508 lb/h/shp)

Turboméca Astazou XX turboshaft, rated at 749 kW (1,005 shp)

TURBOMÉCA BASTAN

The Bastan turboprop is no longer in production. Details were given in the 1979-80 *Jane's*.

TURBOMÉCA ARTOUSTE III

The Artouste IIIB is a single-shaft turboshaft derived from the Artouste II. It is a member of the second generation of Turboméca engines with two-stage axial-centrifugal compressor and three-stage turbine. The Artouste IIIB has a pressure ratio of 5·2 : 1. Air mass flow is 4·3 kg/s (9·5 lb/s) at 33,300 rpm.

Type approval at the rating given below was received on 25 May 1961, following completion of a 150-h official type test. Production at Turboméca continues. In addition, Artouste IIIBs are being built under licence in India by Hindustan Aeronautics Ltd.

The Artouste IIIB, which powers the Aérospatiale SA 316B Alouette III, obtained FAA certification in March 1962 and in August 1968 similar certification of the Artouste IIC1, C2, C5 and C6, powering the SE 3130 and 313B Alouette II Artouste, was also obtained.

An uprated version, the Artouste IIID, was certificated on 30 April 1971. It differs in having a reduction gear giving 5,864 rpm at the driveshaft (instead of 5,773 rpm) and in slightly revised equipment. The IIID powers a late version of the Alouette III. A total of 2,301 Artouste III engines had been built by 1 September 1979.

DIMENSIONS:
Length	1,815 mm (71·46 in)
Height	627 mm (24·68 in)
Width	507 mm (19·96 in)

WEIGHT, DRY:
Fully equipped:
Artouste IIIB	182 kg (400 lb)
Artouste IIID	178 kg (392 lb)

PERFORMANCE RATINGS (maintained up to 55°C at S/L or up to approximately 4,000 m; 13,150 ft):
T-O:
Artouste IIIB	420 kW (563 shp)
Artouste IIID	440 kW (590 shp)
Max continuous (both)	405 kW (543 shp)

SPECIFIC FUEL CONSUMPTION:
T-O:
Artouste IIIB	128·8 μg/J (0·762 lb/h/shp)
Artouste IIID	126·2 μg/J (0·747 lb/h/shp)
Max continuous (both)	130·1 μg/J (0·77 lb/h/shp)

MTU-TURBOMÉCA MTM 380

This new helicopter engine is covered in the International part of this section.

TURBOMÉCA TURMO

The Turmo free-turbine engine is in service in both turboshaft and turboprop versions.

The main variants are as follows:

Turmo IIIC3. This was the original power plant of the triple-engined SA 321 Super Frelon helicopter. Maximum contingency rating is 1,104 kW (1,480 shp).

Turmo IIIC4. Developed from Turmo IIIC3 and with a maximum contingency rating of 1,032 kW (1,384 shp), this all-weather version is manufactured jointly by Turboméca and Rolls-Royce to power SA 330 Puma twin-engined helicopters under the Franco-British helicopter agreement of October 1967. Certificated by the Services Officiels Français on 9 October 1970. Total production of IIIC4 and IV by 1 September 1979 was 1,644 engines.

Turmo IIIC5, IIIC6, IIIC7. Similar to Turmo IIIC3 but with different ratings. The SA 321F and 321J Super Frelons powered by these engines obtained French certification in June 1968. Total production of Super Frelon engines (including E series), 549.

Turmo IIID. Turboprop version, similar in basic construction to Turmo IIIC series but with output speed limited to 6,000 rpm.

Turmo IIIE3. Similar to Turmo IIIC3 but with different ratings. In production for SA 321 Super Frelon.

Turmo IIIE6. Higher turbine temperature.

Turmo IV. The Turmo IVA is a civil engine derived from the IIIC4, with a maximum contingency rating of 1,057 kW (1,417 shp). The IVB is a military version having the same ratings as the IIIC4.

The following description applies generally to the Turmo IIIC3, C4, C5 and E3, except where indicated:

TYPE: Free-turbine axial-plus-centrifugal turboshaft.

REDUCTION GEAR: Turmo IIIC3, C5 and E3 fitted with rear-mounted reduction gear mounted in bifurcated exhaust duct with rear-facing power take-off shaft. Turmo IIIC4 is a direct-drive engine.

AIR INTAKE: Annular forward-facing intake, with de-icing in Turmo IIIC4 and C5.

COMPRESSOR: Single-stage axial followed by single-stage centrifugal with single-sided impeller. Two rows of light alloy stator blades aft of axial stage. Centrifugal stage has steel radial and axial diffusers; impeller located by lugs on turbine shaft. Axial rotor blades, titanium in Turmo IIIC3, C5 and E3 and steel in Turmo IIIC4, pin-mounted in steel disc with integral shaft. Pressure ratio 5·9 : 1 on Turmo IIIC3. Air mass flow 5·9 kg (13 lb)/s.

COMBUSTION SYSTEM: Reverse-flow annular type with centrifugal fuel injector using rotary atomiser disc. Ignition by two ventilated torch igniters.

GAS GENERATOR TURBINE: Two-stage axial unit with integral rotor blades.

POWER TURBINE: Two-stage axial unit in Turmo IIIC3, C5 and E3, and single-stage in Turmo IIIC4. In all advanced production engines of IIIC4 derivation the power turbine speed is 22,840 rpm under all high-power conditions.

JET PIPE: Fixed type with lateral bifurcated exhaust duct in Turmo IIIC3, C5 and E3, and single lateral duct on Turmo IIIC4.

ACCESSORIES: Mounted above and below intake casing with drive pads for oil pump, fuel control unit, electric starter, tacho-generator and, on Turmo IIIC4, oil cooler fan. Control unit remote drive also provided on Turmo IIIC4 from bevel gear drive on power turbine output shaft.

MOUNTING: Two lateral supports fitted to lower part of turbine casing at rear flange output shaft protection tube. On Turmo IIIC4, also on reduction gear case.

FUEL SYSTEM: Fuel control unit for gas generator on Turmo IIIC3, C5 and E3, with speed limiter for power turbine also fitted on E3. Constant-speed system fitted on Turmo IIIC4 power turbine, with speed limiter also fitted on gas generator.

FUEL GRADE: AIR 3405 for Turmo IIIC4.

LUBRICATION SYSTEM: Pressure type with oil cooler and 13 litre (23 Imp pint) tank at front of engine on Turmo IIIC4, with oil tank only around intake casing on Turmo IIIC3, C5 and E3, and by intake accessory drive gear on Turmo IIIC4.

OIL SPECIFICATION: AIR 3155A, or synthetic AIR 3513, for Turmo IIIC4.

STARTING: Automatic system with electric starter motor.

DIMENSIONS:
Height:
Turmo IIIC3, C5 and E3	716·5 mm (28·2 in)
Turmo IIIC4	719 mm (28·3 in)
Turmo IIID3	926 mm (36·5 in)

Width:
Turmo IIIC3, C5 and E3	693 mm (27·3 in)
Turmo IIIC4	637 mm (25·1 in)
Turmo IIID3	934 mm (36·8 in)

Length:
Turmo IIIC3, C5 and E3	1,975·7 mm (78·0 in)
Turmo IIIC4	2,184 mm (85·5 in)
Turmo IIID3	1,868 mm (73·6 in)

WEIGHT, DRY:
Turmo IIIC3 and E3, fully equipped	297 kg (655 lb)
Turmo IIIC5, IIIC6 and IIIC7	325 kg (716 lb)
Turmo IIIC4, equipped engine	225 kg (496 lb)
Turmo IIID3, basic engine	365 kg (805 lb)

PERFORMANCE RATINGS:
T-O: Turmo IIIC3, D3 and E3	1,104 kW (1,480 shp)
Turmo IIIE6	1,181 kW (1,584 shp)

Max contingency:
Turmo IIIC4 at 33,800 gas-generator rpm	1,032 kW (1,384 shp)
Turmo IIIC6 at 33,550 gas-generator rpm	1,156 kW (1,550 shp)
Turmo IIIC7 at 33,800 gas-generator rpm	1,200 kW (1,610 shp)
Turmo IVA at 33,950 gas-generator rpm	1,057 kW (1,417 shp)
Turmo IVC at 33,800 gas-generator rpm	1,163 kW (1,560 shp)

T-O and intermediate contingency:
Turmo IIIC5	1,050 kW (1,408 shp)

SPECIFIC FUEL CONSUMPTION:
At T-O rating:
Turmo IIIC3 and E3	101·9 μg/J (0·603 lb/h/shp)
Turmo IIID3	104·1 μg/J (0·616 lb/h/shp)

At max contingency rating:
Turmo IIIC4, C5, C6, C7 and IV	106·8 μg/J (0·632 lb/h/shp)
Turmo IVA	106·3 μg/J (0·629 lb/h/shp)

The 420 kW (563 shp) Turboméca Artouste IIIB single-shaft helicopter turboshaft

Turboméca Makila free-turbine turboshaft, with initial ratings up to 1,424 kW (1,910 shp)

The 1,032 kW (1,384 shp) Turboméca Turmo IIIC4 turboshaft which powers the SA 330 Puma helicopter

TURBOMÉCA/ROLLS-ROYCE RTM 321
See International section.

TURBOMÉCA MAKILA
This new turboshaft engine, rated at an initial 1,323·5 kW (1,775 shp) for take-off and intermediate contingency, is under development to power the Aérospatiale Super Puma helicopter. Derived partly from the Turmo family, it incorporates all the latest features of the company's advanced engines, including: rapid-strip modular construction; three axial stages of compression plus one centrifugal; later fuel inlet to centrifugal atomiser; two-stage gas-generator turbine (probably with cooled blades); two-stage free power turbine; and lateral exhaust.

During 1974 this engine was confirmed as partner to the Arriel in laying the foundation for the company's marketing in the next 15 years. The world market for this size of engine is put at 10,000 units. The first engine was delivered for bench test in 1976, and the gas generator went on test in November of that year. The first complete Makila engine ran in January 1977 and flew in June of that year.

DIMENSIONS:

Length, intake face to rear face	1,395 mm (54·94 in)
Width	530 mm (20·9 in)
Max diameter	514 mm (20·25 in)

WEIGHT, DRY: Basic 210 kg (463 lb)
    Equipped 242 kg (533 lb)

PERFORMANCE RATINGS (ISA, S/L):
Max contingency
  1,398 kW (1,875 shp) at 36,300 gas-generator rpm
T-O and intermediate
  1,368 kW (1,835 shp) at 35,500 gas-generator rpm
Max continuous
  1,208 kW (1,620 shp) at 34,750 gas-generator rpm

SPECIFIC FUEL CONSUMPTION:
Max contingency 84·0 μg/J (0·497 lb/h/shp)
T-O and intermediate 84·7 μg/J (0·501 lb/h/shp)
Max continuous 85·7 μg/J (0·507 lb/h/shp)

TURBOMÉCA-SNECMA
GROUPEMENT TURBOMÉCA-SNECMA (GRTS)
1 rue Beaujon, BP 37-08, 75362 Paris Cédex 08
Telephone: 924 18 61
ADMINISTRATORS:
  R. Florentini
  E. Delfour
MANAGEMENT CONTROL COMMITTEE:
  R. Martin
  F. Rigaud
FINANCIAL COMMISSARY: C. Hirt

Announced in March 1969, Groupement Turboméca-SNECMA is a company formed jointly by Société Turboméca and SNECMA to be responsible for the design, development, manufacture, sales and service support of the Larzac all-axial small turbofan launched in 1968 as a joint venture by the two companies. Groupement Turboméca-SNECMA has no capital at present and comprises primarily a joint management organisation to produce the engine.

TURBOMÉCA-SNECMA LARZAC
Originally this small turbofan was planned for a wide range of applications, and the first prototype was a 9·8 kN (2,200 lb st) engine aimed at the commercial market. This type of engine ran in May 1969 and began flight development in a pod carried by a Constellation in March 1971. By this time the main immediate market had shifted to military trainers, and GRTS designed the Larzac 04 for this purpose.

In February 1972 the Larzac 04 was selected for a joint Franco-German programme to provide propulsion for the Alpha Jet (see International entry in Aircraft section). In addition to the two French partners in GRTS, two West German companies, MTU and KHD, were added to the programme. Both have played a part in the manufacture of prototype engines and the achievement of endurance tests. All four companies are sharing in production and post-certification development. Complete engines are assembled in both countries for the Alpha Jet programme. The first production engine was delivered in September 1977. The work split is France 56·5 per cent, West Ger-

Turboméca-SNECMA Larzac 04 two-shaft turbofan, rated at 13·2 kN (2,966 lb st)

many 43·5. Engines for Belgium are assembled and tested by FN.

Bench testing of the Larzac 04 began in May 1972. Flight development with the Constellation testbed began in March 1973, and with a Falcon 10 in July 1973. The first Alpha Jet flew on 26 October 1973, and qualification of the Larzac 04 was accomplished on schedule in May 1975. The rating given is at a turbine entry temperature of 1,130°C; growth thrust potential greater than 20 per cent is forecast without dimensional change.

In September 1972 the French Services Officiels approved an agreement between GRTS and Teledyne CAE covering the production, marketing and after-sales support of the Larzac in the USA and Canada.

The Larzac 04 has a two-stage fan, four-stage HP compressor, annular combustion chamber with vaporising burners, single-stage HP turbine with cooled blades and

single-stage LP turbine. Maximum airflow is 27·6 kg (60·8 lb)/s, pressure ratio 10·6 and bypass ratio 1·13. A single fixed-area jet pipe is used. All accessories are driven by the HP spool and grouped under the fan case. The engine is mounted by an isostatic suspension on either side of the centre of gravity. The engine is of modular design and is intended to produce minimum noise and smoke.

DIMENSIONS:
  Overall length of basic engine 1,179 mm (46·4 in)
  Overall diameter 602 mm (23·7 in)
WEIGHT, DRY:
  Larzac 04 290 kg (640 lb)
T-O THRUST (S/L, static):
  Larzac 04 13·2 kN (2,966 lb)
SPECIFIC FUEL CONSUMPTION:
  Larzac 04 20·1 mg/Ns (0·71 lb/h/lb st)

GERMANY
(FEDERAL REPUBLIC)

ERNO
ERNO RAUMFAHRTTECHNIK GmbH
Hünefeldstrasse 1-5, 2800 Bremen
Telephone: 0421 53 91

ERNO, a subsidiary of VFW claims to be Europe's leading producer of hydrazine-based motor systems. Most of its products in this field are small thrusters for space

applications. Thrusts range from 0·05 N to 2·5 kN (0·011-557 lb) for motors operating at about 1,000°C and from 0·001 N to 4·0 N (0·0002-0·899 lb) for cold-gas thrusters. Spacecraft using ERNO thrusters include Intelsat III, Aeros A/B, ECS, OTS, TD-1A, MARECS, Telecom 1 and ISPM. ERNO also produces low-thrust electrothermal hydrazine thrusters and many other devices including complete reaction-control subsystems.

ERNO 2·0 N hydrazine thruster used on OTS, ECS, MARECS, Telecom and ISPM.

KHD
KLÖCKNER-HUMBOLDT-DEUTZ AG
5 Cologne 80, Postfach 80 05 09
Telephone: Cologne (0221) 8221

KHD is a leading manufacturer of diesel engines. In its subsidiary at Oberursel it concentrates its activities in the

gas-turbine field. It designs, manufactures and services gas turbines, power transmissions and complete power systems for aircraft, marine craft and industrial applications. Its most important gas turbine is the T312, the compact lightweight APU (auxiliary power unit) of the Panavia

Tornado. KHD also supplies the complete Tornado secondary power system. It is participating in production of the Larzac 04 turbofan (see Turboméca-SNECMA in French section), and is responsible for assembly and test of these engines for the Luftwaffe.

LIMBACH
LIMBACH MOTORENBAU
HEAD OFFICE AND WORKS: Kotthausener Str 5, D-533
Königswinter 21, Sassenberg
Telephone: (02244) 2322
PRESIDENT: P. Limbach

This company manufactures four-stroke piston engines for ultralight aeroplanes and powered gliders. All are of similar basic design, though two sub-types have a greater cylinder stroke. A two-cylinder two-stroke engine is under development.

LIMBACH SL 1700
Several variants of this engine have been certificated by the Luftfahrt-Bundesamt (Federal Office of Civil Aviation). Apart from the first sub-type listed below all are four-stroke (Otto) engines:

Limbach SL 1700D. Dual-ignition. Not certificated. Fitted to Sportavia-Pützer RF7.

Sportavia-Limbach SL 1700E. Basic engine of the current range. Fitted to Sportavia-Pützer RF5 and RF5B.

Limbach SL 1700EA. Differs in having front-end starter and different induction system. Fitted to Scheibe SF-25C Falke.

Limbach SL 1700EAI. Similar to EA except equipped to drive Hoffmann variable-pitch propeller. Fitted to Scheibe SF-28.

Limbach SL 1700EB. Similar to E except for having increased cylinder stroke and twin carburettors.

Limbach SL 1700EBI. Similar to EB except equipped to drive Hoffmann variable-pitch propeller. Fitted to Schleicher ASK 16.

Limbach SL 1700EC. Similar to E except for having a carburettor intake heating box.

Limbach SL 1700 ECI. Similar to EC except equipped to drive Hoffmann variable-pitch propeller.

Sportavia-Limbach SL 1700EI. Similar to E except equipped to drive Hoffmann variable-pitch propeller. Optional for RF5B.

Unless otherwise stated, the following description refers to the SL 1700E:

TYPE: Four-cylinder horizontally-opposed aircooled piston engine.
CYLINDERS: Bore 88 mm (3·46 in). Stroke 69 mm (2·71 in) (EB, EBI, 74 mm; 2·87 in). Swept volume 1,680 cc (102·51 cu in) (EB, EBI, 1,800 cc; 108·56 cu in). Compression ratio 8 : 1.
INDUCTION: Stromberg-Zenith 150CD carburettor (two in EB, EBI). (EA, EAI, one Zenith 28 RX2).
FUEL GRADE: 90 octane.
IGNITION: Single Slick 4030 magneto feeding one Bosch WB 240 ERT 1 plug in each cylinder.
STARTING: One Fiat 0·37 kW (0·5 hp) starter (EA, EAI, one Bosch 0·3 kW; 0·4 hp).
ACCESSORIES: Ducellier 250W alternator (EA, EAI, 150W Ducati); APG 17.09.001 fuel pump (EA,EAI, 17.09.001 A).
DIMENSIONS:
Length overall:
SL 1700D	649 mm (25·6 in)
SL 1700EA, EAI	558 mm (22·0 in)
SL 1700E, EI, EC, ECI	618 mm (24·33 in)
other variants	580 mm (22·8 in)

Width overall:
SL 1700D	800 mm (31·5 in)
SL 1700EA, EAI	770 mm (30·3 in)
other variants	764 mm (30·1 in)

Height overall:
SL 1700D	451 mm (17·8 in)
SL 1700EA, EAI	392 mm (15·4 in)
other variants	368 mm (14·5 in)

WEIGHT, DRY:
SL 1700E, EI	73 kg (161 lb)
SL 1700EA, EAI	70 kg (154 lb)
SL 1700EB, EBI, EC, ECI	74 kg (164 lb)

PERFORMANCE RATINGS:
T-O:
SL 1700D	48·5 kW (65 hp) at 3,600 rpm
SL 1700E, EI, EC, ECI	51 kW (68 hp) at 3,600 rpm
SL 1700EA, EAI	44·7 kW (60 hp) at 3,550 rpm
SL 1700EB, EBI	53·7 kW (72 hp) at 3,600 rpm

Continuous:
SL 1700E, EI, EC, ECI	45·5 kW (61 hp) at 3,200 rpm
SL 1700EA, EAI	41·7 kW (56 hp) at 3,300 rpm
SL 1700EB, EBI	49·2 kW (66 hp) at 3,200 rpm

LIMBACH L 2000-2600
This family of engines was described in the 1979-80 *Jane's*. At present no plans for production have been announced.

LIMBACH L 275E
This engine is intended for low-cost propulsion of RPVs and ultra-light aircraft.
TYPE: Two-cylinder horizontally-opposed two-stroke aircooled piston engine.
CYLINDERS: Cast aluminium alloy with Nicasil liner. Bore 66 mm (2·6 in). Stroke 40 mm (1·57 in). Swept volume 274 cc (16·72 cu in).
INDUCTION: Two all-attitude diaphragm carburettors.
FUEL GRADE: 90 octane, mixed 25:1 with two-stroke oil.
IGNITION: 12V Bosch transistorised, one Bosch WK 175T6 plug per cylinder.
ACCESSORIES: Leistritz-type turbo silencer (muffler).
DIMENSIONS:
Length overall	226 mm (8·89 in)
Width overall	390 mm (15·35 in)
Height overall	187 mm (7·36 in)

WEIGHT (with silencer): 7·5 kg (16·53 lb)
PERFORMANCE RATING: 18kW (24 hp) at 7,300 rpm

Sportavia-Limbach SL 1700E flat-four four-stroke engine, rated at 51 kW (68 hp)

Limbach SL 1700EA flat-four four-stroke engine, rated at 44·7 kW (60 hp)

Limbach L 275E two-stroke for ultra-light and RPV applications, to be rated at 18 kW (24 hp)

MBB
MESSERSCHMITT-BÖLKOW-BLOHM GmbH
8 München 80, Postfach 801 220
Telephone: (0811) 6 00 01
DEVELOPMENT AND PRODUCTION CENTRES: Ottobrunn bei München; Lampoldhausen; Hamburg; and Bölkow-Apparatebau GmbH at Nabern and Schrobenhausen.

As noted in the Aircraft section, Messerschmitt-Bölkow and Hamburger Flugzeugbau merged in 1969 to form the MBB group. The former Bölkow element of this group is engaged in the design and development of a wide variety of medium- and high-energy rocket engines and motors. Other activities include thrust augmentation by afterburning, engine casing design, propellant insulation and mounting, and preparatory work towards series production and reliability.

Other recent development of liquid-propellant engines by MBB has embraced advanced thermodynamic combustion engines, injection and cooling of engines of low thrust level and engines with high- and medium-energy storable propellants.

MBB MONOPROPELLANT GAS-GENERATORS
MBB has produced 13 different types of gas-generator, with flow rates from 0·00018 kg (0·0004 lb) to 8·2 kg (18·2 lb)/s and using the propellants N_2H_4, $N_2H_4 + H_2O$, and $H_2O_2 + H_2O$. The bigger gas-generators are operating with catalytic and thermic decomposition. The smallest generator supplies a cold-gas satellite attitude-control system, while the bigger types are for propellant-tank pressurisation.

MBB STORABLE ROCKET ENGINES
This engine family includes motors of 0·01/0·03/0·05/0·08/0·3/0·4/0·5/97·9 kN (2·2/6·6/11/18/66/88/110/22,000 lb) thrust. Except for the 0·01 kN (2·2 lb) engine, which uses MMH/N_2O_4, all other engines run on AZ50/N_2O_4. The 0·01 kN (2·2 lb) engine is in use as the attitude-control thruster for the Franco-German Symphonie communications satellite; it is designed for steady-state and pulse-mode operation. The 0·4 kN (88 lb) engine was the vernier for the German third stage of the ELDO-A launcher, and in modified form it was to be used as the apogee motor for ELDO-II. This engine is highly qualified and in several ELDO-A launches operated in space without failure. A total of 135 was produced. In 1973 a new tactical missile engine was developed, operating at thrust levels of 23·5 kN (5,290 lb); 11·77 kN (2,646 lb); 7·85 kN (1,764 lb). The 98 kN (22,000 lb) engine was developed as the prototype power plant for an artillery rocket.

MBB HIGH-ENERGY ROCKET ENGINES
MBB has worked with the cryogenic propellant combination H_2/F_2 since 1962. After the installation of a fluorine liquefaction facility and a technology programme for a 0·3 kN (66 lb) engine, the development of a 4·9 kN (1,100 lb) engine started in 1967-68. It was the aim to use a cluster of two engines of this size as a 'kick stage' for space probes. The programme was discontinued after the first series of tests with regeneratively-cooled chambers had showed high combustion efficiency. The propellant combination H_2/O_2 was used from 1962 in three engine projects at the thrust levels of 0·3/6·67/9·34 kN (66/1,500/2,100 lb). The 66 lb H_2/O_2 engine was presented in 1966 as a flight prototype, the first cryogenic rocket engine in the Federal Republic of Germany. The engine incorporated integral propellant valves and an ignition system. In altitude-simulation tests a specific impulse of 415 s was achieved and multiple restart capability and throttleability were demonstrated. For possible post-Apollo programme participation, the 1,500 lb and 2,100 lb engines were developed in 1970-72. Both are regeneratively cooled, electrically ignited, restartable and pulsable (10Hz). They have high performance and a combustion efficiency of more than 98 per cent. In 1972-73 an LH_2/LO_2 engine rated at 5·0 kN (1,125 lb) in vacuum conditions was developed for multiple-restart use in upper stages. This engine can be throttled over a range of 8 : 1 (possibly 10 : 1).

Since 1973, in partnership with SEP of France, MBB has developed the HM7 engine to power the third stage of the European Ariane space launch vehicle. This LH_2/LO_2 engine has a vacuum thrust of 60 kN (13,500 lb). Its regeneratively cooled thrust chamber of milled copper operates at a pressure of 30 bars (435 lb/sq in), and the specific impulse is 444. Total thrust-chamber weight is 63 kg (138·9 lb). The nozzle extension, with an area-ratio of 61, is dump-cooled with LH_2. By the start of 1977, a total of 220 firings had been completed on MBB's high-pressure test facility under sea-level and simulated altitude conditions. SEP is Ariane propulsion prime contractor. MBB's role is to supply the thrust chamber and main propellant valves.

MBB HIGH-PRESSURE ENGINES
In the course of development of high-pressure liquid-rocket engines MBB developed a turbopump engine utilising staged combustion in 1963. This 49 kN (11,000 lb) lox/kerosene engine was the first to run in the western

MBB 49 kN (11,000 lb) sea-level thrust lox/kerosene rocket engine world, with turbine exhaust completely burned in the main combustor. It was designed for 96·5 bars (1,400 lb/sq in) abs and was throttleable at 14 : 1, and remains the first and most powerful turbopump rocket engine developed in the Federal Republic of Germany since 1945.

For the storable propellants UDMH/N_2O_4 a 9·8 kN (2,200 lb) pressure-fed engine was developed and tested at chamber pressures of more than 193 bars (2,800 lb/sq in) abs to demonstrate high-performance injection systems and electroformed thrust-chamber technology for corrosive propellants.

MBB developed and fabricated some 133·44 kN (30,000 lb) H_2/O_2 engines designed for 207 bars (3,000 lb/sq in) abs. These were tested at Rocketdyne's facilities in California up to chamber pressures of 276 bars (4,000 lb/sq in) abs without failure. The electroforming thrust-chamber technology demonstrated in this programme is now the baseline for the Space Shuttle Main Engine of Rocketdyne (which see).

MBB RAM ROCKETS

Since 1965 MBB has been developing ram rocket engines with liquid and solid propellants, and liquid-fuelled ramjet engines, for the propulsion of missiles with supersonic cruise speed and long range capability.

MBB has studied high-energy boron propellants as well as medium-energy composite grains, UDMH, MMH and kerosene. For missile applications, studies were carried out with semi-integrated and fully integrated engines with many configurations of air inlet. These studies were supported by half-scale burning tests (net thrust 4·0 kN; 899 lb) and aerodynamic tests in wind-tunnels.

Solid-propellant ram rockets are inherently simple in structure and have high reliability because of hypergolic ram combustion.

By 1980 this development was increasing with a view to fields of application in anti-ship, air-to-air and surface-to-air missiles.

A tunnel model of a possible ASSM (Anti-Surface Ship Missile) with MBB ram rocket propulsion

MTU
MOTOREN-UND TURBINEN-UNION MÜNCHEN GmbH

München-Allach, Dachauer Str 655 (postal address, 8 München 50, Postfach 50 06 40)
Telephone: (089) 1489-1
BOARD OF MANAGEMENT MTU GROUP:
Dr Ernst Zimmermann (President)
Dr Hans Dinger (Executive Vice-President)
Dr Peter Beer
Hubert Dunkler
Dr Wolfgang Hansen
Günter Welsch

MTU München is owned half by Maschinenfabrik Augsburg-Nürnberg AG (MAN) and half by Daimler-Benz AG, and manages all aircraft engine programmes formerly managed by MAN Turbo and Daimler-Benz.

MTU handles service support for the J79-MTU-J1K/17A and T64-MTU-7 engines made by MTU under General Electric licence. It also handles service support and parts manufacture of such civil engines as the JT3D, JT8D and CF6, as well as Lycoming piston engines. In November 1979 MTU formed a new subsidiary, MTU Maintenance GmbH, based at Hanover-Langenhagen, to support JT8D, JT9D and CF6 engines.

MTU/GE CF6

Under the terms of a licence agreement signed with the International General Electric Company, MTU has approximately a 10 per cent share in the manufacture of the CF6-50 engine for the Airbus A300, together with SNECMA. The main task of MTU is production of the complete HP turbine.

PRATT & WHITNEY JT10D

MTU is a partner, with Fiat of Italy, in this new turbofan described in the US part of this section.

ROLLS-ROYCE TYNE

MTU has a 28 per cent share in the production of a further batch of about 170 Tyne engines for the re-opened Transall production line. In addition MTU has assumed responsibility for service support of all Tyne 21 engines (Atlantic) and Tyne 22 (Transall), including engines used by civil operators.

TURBO-UNION RB.199

MTU München's largest programme is a 40 per cent share in this engine, more than 2,000 of which are now in production as described under Turbo-Union in the International part of this section.

SNECMA/TURBOMÉCA LARZAC

MTU has approximately a 25 per cent share in production of this French engine used in the Alpha Jet. MTU also supports the hot-end components for the Luftwaffe.

ALLISON 250-C20B

MTU is licence-producing 687 of these turboshaft engines, designated 250-MTU-C20B, for the PAH-1 and VBH helicopter programmes (see MBB in Aircraft section). MTU also supports C20 and C20B engines used by civil operators.

MTU/TURBOMÉCA MTM 380

This is a proposed new turboshaft engine for helicopters, especially the proposed PAH-2 anti-tank helicopter. Final drive from the power turbine would be via a coaxial shaft. For further details see International part of this section.

The MTU J79-MTU-J1K turbojet with afterburner

PARODI
ROLAND PARODI

Klettgau-Erzingen

This engineer has developed a four-cylinder four-stroke aircooled piston engine for ultralight aircraft and motor gliders. With various designations in the HP 45 series, these are derived from a Honda design, with a new crankcase and lubrication system. Crankshaft speed of 8,000 rpm is reduced by belt to about 2,800 at the propeller. Maximum ratings are 33·5 or 37·3 kW (45 or 50 hp).

PIEPER
PIEPER MOTORENBAU GmbH

495 Minden/Westf, Postfach 1229
Telephone: (0571) 34088

STAMO MS 1500

Pieper manufactures the 33·5 kW (45 hp) Stamo MS 1500-1 modified Volkswagen four-cylinder aircooled piston engine, applications for which have included the Scheibe SF-25B Falke two-seat motor glider. The capacity of this is 1,500 cc, compression ratio 7·2 : 1, length 640 mm (25 in), width 745 mm (29·3 in), height 395 mm (15·5 in) and dry weight 52 kg (115 lb). The MS 1500-1 operates on either 80/86 or 90 octane fuel, and is started by a pull-cord. A variant is the MS 1500-2, with electric starter and generator. This increases overall height to 450 mm (17·7 in) and dry weight to 60 kg (132 lb). By 1979 well over 600 engines had been delivered, and the period between complete overhauls had been extended to 1,000 h.

Pieper-built Stamo MS 1500-1 four-cylinder four-stroke engine, rated at 33·5 kW (45 hp)

PULCH
OTTO PULCH

Hölderlinstrasse 21, 7513 Spöck-Stutensee
Telephone: 07249 8509

PULCH 003

As a private venture Otto Pulch (OUV, EAA-Chapter 308) has developed a four-stroke radial piston engine for light aircraft. Using BMW motorcycle cylinders and pistons, he designed a new crankcase and connecting-rod assembly, reduction gear and dual ignition system. The first prototype Pulch 003A ran in Autumn 1976. In summer 1977 it was awarded the Wolf-Hirth-Preis by *Flug Revue* magazine as the most outstanding achievement in light aircraft technology in West Germany in 1977. The second prototype Pulch 003B, incorporating substantial improvements, ran in 1978, and has a demonstrated noise level of only 96 dBA at full power at a distance of 10 m (33 ft). The 003B is described as "an ideal engine for homebuilt aircraft," and will be available in kit form.
TYPE: Six-cylinder radial aircooled piston engine.
CYLINDERS: Pulch 003A (BMW R 90/6) Bore, 90 mm (3·55 in). Stroke, 70 mm (2·76 in). Swept volume, 2,700 cc (165 cu in). Pulch 003B (BMW R 100S) Bore, 94 mm

(3·71 in). Stroke, 70 mm (2·76 in). Swept volume, 2,900 cc (177 cu in).
INDUCTION: Pulch 003A, two SUM carburettors. Pulch 003B, fuel-injection system, Bosch K-Jetronic.
IGNITION: Both versions, electronic system.
PROPELLER DRIVE: Geared, ratio (003A) 2·29:1, (003B) 2·56:1.
DIMENSIONS:
Length overall:
Pulch 003A, 003B   800 mm (31·5 in)
Width overall:
Pulch 003A, 003B   750 mm (29·55 in)
WEIGHT, DRY:
Pulch 003A   110 kg (242·5 lb)
Pulch 003B   120 kg (264·5 lb)
PERFORMANCE RATING (T-O):
Pulch 003A   110 kW (150 hp) at 5,000 rpm
Pulch 003B   132 kW (180 hp) at 5,500 rpm

PULCH THREE-CYLINDER

This new engine for motorised gliders ran in 1979. It has three four-stroke BMW cylinders driving a vertical crankshaft and with 1:3 angle box to the propeller shaft. Swept volume is 1,500 cc (91·7 cu in) and rating 55 kW (75 hp).

Pulch 003A six-cylinder radial, to be rated at 110 kW (150 hp)

RFB
RHEIN-FLUGZEUGBAU GmbH
(Subsidiary of VFW GmbH)

HEAD OFFICE AND MAIN WORKS: D-4050 Mönchengladbach 1, Flugplatz, Postfach 408
Telephone: (0 21 61) 662031
OFFICERS: See Aircraft section

Though not a constructor of aircraft engines, Rhein-Flugzeugbau is marketing a Fan Pod as a complete unit for fitment to power-assisted sailplanes and ultra-light aircraft, as well as to surface vehicles.

RFB FAN POD SG 85

This is a fixed-geometry pod marketed as a complete unit for installation by the purchaser. It was run on the bench in 1974, with Fichtel & Sachs Wankel engines, and was subsequently flight tested in a Blanik sailplane. In certain types of motor-glider with side-by-side seating it should be possible to make the installation retractable.
ENGINE: Dual rotating-combustion (Wankel-type) engines mounted in tandem. Fichtel & Sachs KM 914/2 V-85 engines are regarded as standard, with a combined rating of 50 hp. Engines are equipped with 12V starter and generator, and with silenced exhaust system.
FAN ROTOR: Three-blade fan moulded in Friedel-Krafts reinforced plastics material, with hard erosion-resistant strip along each leading-edge. Direct drive from engines without separate bearings. Rotating spinner.
FAN DUCT: Single shell in FK sandwich reinforced plastics with PUR foam filling.
PYLON: Light alloy construction, with downward projecting spigot attachment 200 mm (8 in) long mating with airframe.
FUEL GRADE: Automotive gasoline and oil mixture in ratio 30 : 1.
DIMENSIONS:
Length   1,200 mm (47·24 in)
Fan duct external diameter   750 mm (29·53 in)
Height, incl aircraft spigot   1,000 mm (39·37 in)

WEIGHT, DRY: 56 kg (123·5 lb)
PERFORMANCE RATING:
Full throttle, S/L   0·932 kN (209·5 lb st)
FUEL CONSUMPTION:
At full throttle (5,500 rpm), S/L   15 l (3·3 Imp gal)/h
At cruise at 5,000 rpm, S/L   11·5 l (2·5 Imp gal)/h
NOISE (full throttle, from 305 m; 1,000 ft)   57 dBA

Prototype installation of RFB fan pod SG 85, as mounted for flight testing on Blanik motor-glider (0·932 kN, 209·5 lb st at S/L)

L-13 Blanik motor-glider in sustained flight with RFB SG 85 fan pod

---

INDIA

HAL
HINDUSTAN AERONAUTICS LTD

Indian Express Building, Vidhana Veedhi, PO Box 5150, Bangalore 560 001
Telephone: 76091

OFFICERS: See Aircraft section

The Bangalore and Koraput Engine Divisions of HAL comprise the main aero-engine design, development and manufacturing elements of the Indian aircraft industry.

BANGALORE COMPLEX (Engine Division)

This Division is engaged in the manufacture of gas-turbine engines. Adour 811 engines for all except the initial batch of Jaguars for the Indian Air Force will be manufactured by HAL under Rolls-Royce Turboméca licence. The Orpheus 701 to power the Ajeet and Kiran II, the Orpheus 703 to power the Marut and the Dart 531 to power the BAe 748 are made under licence from Rolls-Royce. The Artouste IIIB to power the Alouette III and SA 315 is made under licence from Turboméca. The division also overhauls Dart, Avon, Orpheus, Artouste,

Gnome and J34 engines for the Indian Air Force and other customers.

KORAPUT DIVISION

This Division of HAL is located at Koraput in Orissa. It was established to manufacture under Soviet government licence the Tumansky R-11 afterburning turbojet for HAL-built MiG21 fighters. With help from the Soviet Union, the first engine was run on the bench (which it was used to calibrate) in early 1969.

INDONESIA

LAPAN
LEMBAGA PENERBANGAN DAN ANTARIKSA NASIONAL (The National Institute of Aeronautics and Space)

HEAD OFFICE: Jalan Pemuda Persil No 1, Jakarta Timur
MAILING ADDRESS: PO Box 3048, Jakarta
Telephone: (021) 48 28 02
CHAIRMAN: Air Vice-Marshal J. Salatun
VICE-CHAIRMAN: Prof Wiranto Arismunandar

PUSAT TEKNOLOGI DIRGANTARA (Aerospace Technology Centre)

Rumpin Airfield, Bogor, West Java
HEAD, AEROSPACE TECHNOLOGY CENTRE: Dr Haryono Djojodihardjo
MANAGER, ROCKET DEVELOPMENT PROJECT: Ir Kisman Subandhi

LAPAN was established in 1963, to exploit indigenous capabilities in aeronautics and space in support of the

National Five Year Plan. At the beginning of 1978 LAPAN had 527 personnel, of whom 195 were university graduates, divided among the Space Applications Centre (Jakarta), the Aerospace Technology Centre (Rumpin Airfield, near Bogor), the Atmospheric and Space Research Centre (Bandung) and the Aerospace Study Centre (Jakarta).
In 1974 LAPAN began the design of the RC-741 liquid propellant rocket engine, the first prototype of which was completed in February 1978. The RC-741 is the first

liquid-propellant rocket engine made in Indonesia. Component and static tests at LAPAN's Aerospace Technology Centre are planned for 1980-81.

LAPAN RC-741

The RC-741 is designed for use in a boosted single-stage sounding rocket.

TYPE: Single-chamber liquid-propellant rocket engine.

PROPELLANTS: RFNA and xylidine, mixture ratio 3:1.

THRUST CHAMBER: Single chamber of 7:1 nozzle area ratio, using regenerative and radiative cooling, and with double-wall machined casing. Wall material nickel-chrome steel. Coaxial propellant injection, with hypergolic ignition. Combustion pressure 55·7 bars (808·28 lb/sq in) and temperature 2,700°C.

MOUNTING: Chamber bolted on four mountings concentric with engine axis.

PROPELLANT PUMPS: Centrifugal.

PROPELLANT FLOW: Fuel flow 2·45 kg (5·4 lb)/s; oxidiser flow rate 8·12 kg (17·9 lb)/s

TURBINE: Single-stage axial impulse type.

THRUST CONTROL: Thrust held constant by regulation of turbopump speed via control of gas-generator propellant supply.

DIMENSIONS: Length overall	605 mm (23·819 in)
Diameter overall	210 mm (8·268 in)
WEIGHT, DRY:	41 kg (90·38 lb)
PERFORMANCE (S/L): Max thrust	20·6 kN (4,630 lb)
Specific impulse	240 s

The LAPAN RC-741 liquid rocket engine (20·6 kN; 4,630 lb thrust)

INTERNATIONAL PROGRAMMES

CFM INTERNATIONAL
CFM INTERNATIONAL SA

160 avenue de Versailles, 75016 Paris, France
Telephone: 524 43 62
CHAIRMAN AND CHIEF EXECUTIVE: J. C. Malroux
EXECUTIVE OFFICERS:
N. Epstein (Marketing and Product Support)
P. Alesi (Project)
A. O. Kohn (Technical)
C. E. Adams (Finance)
T. G. Homburg (Logistic and Product Support Services)

CFM International, a joint company, was formed by General Electric and SNECMA in early 1974 to provide overall programme management for the CFM56 engine and a single customer interface for sales and service. Owned and managed on a 50/50 share basis, the company has been staffed with experienced people from the two parent companies.

In addition to the CFM International management team which directs the overall programme, the parent companies have their own CFM56 programme managers. For SNECMA, this position is held by J. Rossignol. His GE counterpart is R. B. Smith.

The SNECMA/GE agreement is not a profit-sharing arrangement. Responsibilities for hardware design, development and production are assigned through CFM International on an equal basis to the parent companies. Each company then assumes responsibility and funding for its assigned task throughout the life of the programme. This is a unique concept among international co-operative ventures in the aerospace field. SNECMA has from the outset been agreeable to participation of other European engine companies within its 50 per cent share. FN of Belgium has joined SNECMA for certain low-pressure system components.

GE is responsible for design integration, the core engine and the main engine control. The core engine is that of the F101 turbofan developed for the B-1 bomber. SNECMA is responsible for the low-pressure system, reverser, gearbox and accessory integration and engine installation.

Each company is responsible for its assigned hardware from design through development, production and product improvement. CFM International will provide the planning and integration of the product support programme.

CFM INTERNATIONAL CFM56

In the late 1960s General Electric and SNECMA made independent studies of the market requirement for the next generation of high bypass ratio engines. The GE studies were centered around an engine designated GE13, the core of which is now being used in the F101. SNECMA's studies were based on an engine designated M56. Each company concluded that a large market existed for a high bypass ratio engine in the ten tonne class (97·9-106·8 kN; 22,000-24,000 lb st), with low noise low emissions and low fuel consumption, coupled with ease of maintenance and low operating costs.

In April 1971 SNECMA began a search for possible partners to undertake development of a commercial engine in this class. By December 1971 SNECMA had chosen GE as its partner and, after obtaining French government approval, detailed design activity began. Work was stopped, however, in September 1972 when the export licence restriction applied by the US State Department Office of Munitions Control made the programme untenable for the two companies. It was resumed a year later when negotiations led to a workable licensing agreement which also protected US technology. Since that time, a working agreement and management structure have been defined and the development programme led to engine certification on 8 November 1979. This marked the first time that an engine had been certificated simultaneously to both US and European standards by the French and US certification authorities. As part of its certification, the CFM56 had to comply with FAR Pt 33 for the USA and JAR-E (Joint Airworthiness Requirements-Engine) for France and most of Europe. In addition, its demonstrated noise reduction is sufficient to enable the aircraft in which it is installed to comply with the latest, more stringent noise regulations.

The first CFM56 demonstrator engine ran at the GE Evendale plant on 20 June 1974. The engine reached its full rated thrust within 10 h of running, with fuel consumption lower than specification. Since then, 10 more engines have entered the test programme. The engine first flew in a US Air Force YC-15 transport prototype. Engine-development flight testing began in March 1977 when an engine installed with a full-length fan duct flew in a Caravelle at the SNECMA flight test centre.

CFM56 engine 011 (106·8 kN; 24,000 lb st) prepared for certification testing

A post-certification programme of endurance testing is being followed, to complete more than 22,000 extra-severe cycles, simulating short-haul operations, before entry into service.

The certified engine, designated **CFM56-2** and rated at 106·8 kN (24,000 lb st) is described below. CFM International has plans for other versions of the CFM56, including a growth engine, the **CFM56-4**, with ratings up to 120 kN (27,000 lb st) within the existing fan diameter, and a reduced-thrust derivative, the **CFM56-3**, rated at 89 kN (20,000 lb st), using the same basic core engine but with a reduced-diameter fan.

CFM56 production was launched in early 1979 when United, Delta and Flying Tiger announced their decision to re-engine their DC-8 Series 60 aircraft. The DC-8 re-engining programme is managed by CAMMA Corporation. Modification work on the re-engined aircraft, designated DC-8 Series 70, is carried out by Douglas Aircraft at Tulsa, Oklahoma. By the end of 1979 six airlines had firm contracts with CFM International and CAMMA Corporation to re-engine 64 DC-8s, plus a number of options. The first DC-8 Series 70 is scheduled to fly in May 1981; deliveries to airlines will begin in late 1981.

Flight evaluation of a Boeing 707 equipped with four CFM56 engines is underway at Boeing Commercial Airplane Company. First flight of the 707-CFM56 test aircraft was on 27 November 1979.

The CFM56 was selected by the US Air Force for its KC-135A tanker re-engining programme on 22 January 1980. The US Air Force has awarded an R & D contract to the Boeing Military Airplane Company. Installation of CFM56 engines on a KC-135 will begin in 1982,

followed by one year of flight and operational testing.

Other potential commercial and military applications are the Airbus Industrie SA1, SA2 and TA11, DC-9, Fokker F29, 707 Tanker and Patrol, new Boeing commercial transport and CX programmes.

TYPE: Two-shaft turbofan for subsonic applications.

AIR INTAKE: Direct entry, without inlet guide vanes.

FAN: Single-stage axial. Forged titanium disc holding 44 inserted titanium blades, each with a tip shroud to form a continuous peripheral ring. Fan and the attached LP compressor (booster) run in front roller bearing and rear ball bearing. Pointed conical spinner rotates with fan. Alloy steel fan frame of continuous ring construction, carried by 12 radial struts of low thickness/chord ratio well downstream of fan. Max airflow 376 kg (830 lb)/sec. Bypass ratio 6 : 1.

LP COMPRESSOR: Three axial stages on titanium drum bolted to fan disc serve as booster to supercharge core. Downstream flow curves inwards to match diameter of HP compressor. In this section are main fan frame and sumps and bearings for front end of both shafts. Ring of bleed doors allows core airflow to escape into fan duct at low power settings. Bleed doors are closed at all normal flight power settings.

HP COMPRESSOR: Nine-stage axial with tapering tip diameter. Rotor of high-strength corrosion-resistant alloy, with blades of titanium (to stage 3) or steel. Stators steel, with first four stators variable. Split titanium front casing with steel liners. Based upon HP compressor of F101, with minor modifications. Overall pressure ratio in 25 : 1 class.

COMBUSTION CHAMBER: Fully annular with advanced film cooling. Based upon F101 combustor but modified for reduced emissions. Level of pollution from the core is claimed to be below that of any engine at present in airline service.

HP TURBINE: Single-stage axial with aircooled stator and rotor blades. Entry gas temperature in 1,260°C class. High stage loading. HP system carried in only two bearings.

LP TURBINE: Four-stage axial.

EXHAUST UNIT (FAN): Constant-diameter duct of sound-absorbent construction. Outer cowl and engine cowl form convergent plug nozzle, with airframe-mounted reverser.

EXHAUST UNIT (CORE): Fixed-area type with convergent plug nozzle. Sound-absorbent construction.

ACCESSORY DRIVE: Gearbox in front sump transmits drive from front of HP spool, via radial shaft in fan frame, to transfer gearbox mounted on underside of fan case. Drive faces on both front and rear sides. Air starter at transfer gearbox.

FUEL SYSTEM: Hydromechanical with electronic trim.

LUBRICATION: Non-pressure-regulated system.

DIMENSIONS:
Front flange diameter	1,828 mm (72·0 in)
Length, excl spinner	2,430 mm (95·7 in)

WEIGHT, DRY: 2,091 kg (4,610 lb)

PERFORMANCE RATINGS:
Max T-O 106·8 kN (24,000 lb st) flat rated to 30°C
Cruise at 9,144 m (30,000 ft) at Mach 0·80
28·26 kN (6,350 lb st)

SPECIFIC FUEL CONSUMPTION:
Cruise rating, as above 18·4 mg/Ns (0·65 lb/h/lb st)

GARRETT/VOLVO FLYGMOTOR
THE GARRETT CORPORATION
HEAD OFFICE: 9851 Sepulveda Boulevard, Los Angeles, California 90009, USA
Telephone: (213) 670 0131

VOLVO FLYGMOTOR AB
HEAD OFFICE: 461 81 Trollhättan, Sweden
Telephone: 0520 30100

Agreement on co-operative development of a low bypass ratio derivative of the TFE731 turbofan engine (described under Garrett in the US section) was signed on 2 March 1978 in Trollhättan. The agreement was approved later by the US and Swedish authorities.

GARRETT/VOLVO FLYGMOTOR TFE1042
With this new engine the two parent companies are aiming at the market for the next generation of training, ground support, lightweight strike and fighter aircraft.

The TFE1042 will be offered at two ratings, one **(1042-5)** with a thrust of 16·15 kN (3,630 lb) at S/L ISA, and another **(1042-6)** with 18·95 kN (4,260 lb). This latter version will also be offered with an afterburner, giving 30·23 kN (6,800 lb) as the **1042-7**.

The engine will be developed around the core of the commercial TFE731 turbofan and will utilise the same accessory drive system. Garrett will provide the manufacturing facilities for all parts common to the two engine models, and will be responsible for the overall design. Volvo Flygmotor will be responsible for the detail design and manufacture of the non-common parts, such as the new two-stage fan, fan gearbox and afterburner.

The first phase of the development programme culminated in the start of testing a prototype unaugmented engine (1042-4) in August 1979. Flight prototype engines can be made available in two years from the start, Saab-Scania having agreed to provide a flight-test aircraft.

TYPE: Two-shaft military turbofan, with geared front fan. Optional fully modulated afterburner.

AIR INTAKE: Direct entry, fixed, without inlet guide vanes.

FAN: Two-stage axial, with titanium inserted blades. Total airflows and bypass ratios at max rating, S/L ISA, are: (1042-5) 33·6 kg (74·1 lb)/s, 0·84:1; (1042-6, -7) 35·6 kg (78·4 lb)/s, 0·70:1.

COMPRESSORS, COMBUSTION CHAMBER, FUEL SYSTEM and ACCESSORY DRIVES: As TFE731

TURBINES: Single axial-HP stage with aircooled inserted blades and cooled nozzle guide vanes (basically as TFE731-33). Turbine inlet temperature for TFE1042-5 is similar to that of TFE731-3. For 1042-6 and -7, turbine temperature is increased, requiring cooling also of guide vanes and blades of first stage of three-stage LP turbine.

EXHAUST SYSTEM: Mixed fan and turbine exhaust discharged to atmosphere through common convergent nozzle. For augmented version, mixed streams pass through afterburner with outer casing of titanium and inner wall of special alloys. One high-energy spark igniter. Fuel-actuated fully-variable iris-type con-di nozzle. Aircraft-mounted digital system containing torque-motor valves for afterburner fuel metering and nozzle actuation.

MOUNTINGS: Main mount transmitting thrust, weight and moment is at front frame. Engine can be mounted from either side. Single mount on turbine casing for vertical loads only.

SHAFTING: HP spool consists of HP turbine and HP compressor, on shaft supported by one roller bearing and one ball bearing. This drives accessory gearbox through tower-shaft transfer box. LP spool consists of LP turbine and LP compressor, interconnected by curvic couplings and supported on one ball bearing at compressor and one roller bearing at turbine. Drives through reduction gear with ratio of 1·416:1. Fan shaft supported by roller bearing under first-stage fan disc and ball thrust bearing under second-stage disc.

First photograph of a TFE1042 in the Volvo Flygmotor factory; this is a basic engine without afterburner

DIMENSIONS:
Length:
1042-5, -6	1,620 mm (63·75 in)
1042-7	3,545 mm (140 in)
Max diameter	676 mm (26·6 in)

WEIGHT, DRY:
1042-5	363 kg (800 lb)
1042-6	370 kg (815 lb)
1042-7	544 kg (1,200 lb)

PERFORMANCE RATINGS (SL, ISA):
Max T-O:
1042-5	16·15 kN (3,630 lb st)
1042-6	18·95 kN (4,260 lb st)
1042-7 (dry)	18·37 kN (4,130 lb st)
1042-7 (augmented)	30·23 kN (6,800 lb st)

SPECIFIC FUEL CONSUMPTION (ratings as above):
1042-5	19·6 mg/Ns (0·692 lb/h/lb st)
1042-6	20·6 mg/Ns (0·728 lb/h/lb st)
1042-7 (dry)	21·2 mg/Ns (0·749 lb/h/lb st)
1042-7 (augmented)	63·5 mg/Ns (2·24 lb/h/lb st)

MTU/TURBOMÉCA SARL
MOTOREN-UND TURBINEN-UNION MÜNCHEN GmbH
München-Allach, Dachauer Str 655, Postfach 50 06 40, Federal Republic of Germany

SOCIÉTÉ TURBOMÉCA
Bordes, 64320 Bizanos, France

MTU/TURBOMÉCA MTM 380
This turboshaft engine will be developed by MTU/Turboméca SARL, a joint company owned equally by both partners. The reason for developing the engine, with a specification almost identical to that of the Rolls-Royce Gem, is said to be to power the proposed PAH-2 Franco-German anti-tank helicopter. MTU is responsible for the combustion chamber, gas generator and power turbine, the French partner being assigned the rest, representing a 50/50 work-split by cost. The first gas generator ran before the end of 1979.

The MTM 380 is of modular design and is intended for minimum emissions.

COMPRESSOR: Single-shaft, with four axial stages (with variable stators on at least the first two) and one centrifugal stage. Mass flow over 3 kg (6·6 lb)/s. Pressure ratio about 13.

MTU/Turboméca MTM 380 turboshaft engine
(Brian M. Service)

COMBUSTION CHAMBER: Reverse-flow annular with vaporising burners.
TURBINES: Two-stage aircooled gas-generator turbine. Two-stage power turbine.

CONTROL SYSTEM: Digital.
DIMENSIONS:
Length 990 mm (38·98 in)
Max diameter 475 mm (18·7 in)

WEIGHT, DRY: about 145 kg (320 lb)
RATINGS:
Max T-O 772 kW (1,035 shp)
Contingency 1,000 kW (1,341 shp)

ROLLS-ROYCE/ALLISON
ROLLS-ROYCE LIMITED

HEAD OFFICE: 65 Buckingham Gate, London SW1E 6AT, England

THE DETROIT DIESEL ALLISON DIVISION, GENERAL MOTORS CORPORATION

HEAD OFFICE: Detroit, Michigan, USA

Co-operation between Rolls-Royce and Allison started in November 1958, when the two companies began work on the design and development of high-performance jet engines for commercial and military applications.

ALLISON/ROLLS-ROYCE TF41

Manufacturers' designations: Rolls-Royce Spey RB. 168-62 and -66, Allison Model 912-B3 and -B14

In August 1966 Allison and Rolls-Royce were awarded a joint contract by US Air Force Systems Command for the development and production of an advanced version of the RB.168-25 Spey turbofan, to power Vought A-7D Corsair II fighter-bomber aircraft for the US Air Force.

Development and production were undertaken jointly by Rolls-Royce and Allison, with Rolls-Royce supplying parts common to existing Spey variants and Allison, which is manufacturing under licence, being responsible for items peculiar to the TF41. This provided an approximately 50/50 division of manufacturing effort, but with Allison also undertaking assembly, test and delivery.

Design of the RB.168-62 started in June 1966 and, following the award of the US Air Force contract, the engine was given the US Air Force designation TF41-A-1. Major change compared with the RB.168-25 is the move forward of the bypass flow split into the LP compressor, to give a larger three-stage fan followed by a two-stage IP compressor, all five stages being driven by the two-stage LP turbine. The number of HP compressor stages is reduced from 12 to 11, the HP turbine remaining at two stages. These modifications raise the mass flow and the bypass ratio (from 0·7 : 1 to 0·76 : 1). No afterburner is fitted.

Other design changes compared with the RB.168-25 include omission of the fan inlet guide vanes, the first rotor stage being overhung on a bearing supported by the first-stage stator vanes. The fan and IP compressor are of more modern aerodynamic design, and the HP and LP turbine nozzle throat areas have been increased to pass the additional flow. The HP turbine is of modified aerodynamic design, and an annular exhaust mixer replaces the RB.168-25's chuted design.

First run of the TF41-A-1/RB.168-62 was at Rolls-Royce, Derby, in October 1967, the first Allison engine following at Indianapolis in March 1968.

A second version of the TF41 is the A-2, developed for the US Navy and ordered in 1968 to power the Vought A-7E Corsair. Differences are slight, although the thrust rating is appreciably increased by raising the engine speed.

Cutaway drawing of the Allison/Rolls-Royce TF41-A-1 (Spey RB.168-62) turbofan (64·5 kN; 14,500 lb st)

This required restressing the disc of the LP turbine and HP compressor. Mass flow is slightly increased, the by-pass ratio being 0·74 : 1. The engine has additional protection against corrosion.

By 1977 more than 1,300 engines had been delivered, and production of the TF41 for the A-7 was expected to continue into the 1980s. In combat service both versions of the TF41 have shown outstanding reliability. The exceptional overhaul life (for a combat engine) of 1,500 h has been reached.

TYPE: Military turbofan.
AIR INTAKE: Direct entry, fixed, without intake guide vanes.
COMPRESSOR: Two-shaft axial. 3 fan stages, 2 intermediate stages on same shaft and 11 high-pressure stages. All rotor blades carried on separate discs. Fan and LP rotor blades of titanium, held by dovetail roots in slots broached in discs which are bolted together through curvic couplings and similarly attached to the stubshafts. HP rotor blades also of titanium, except stages 9, 10 and 11 of stainless steel, the first HP stage being pinned and the remainder being dovetailed into broached slots; discs similarly bolted together but driven through splined shaft coupling. Overall pressure ratio 20 : 1 (A-2, 21·4 : 1); mass flow 117 kg/s (258 lb/s) (A-2, 119 kg/s; 263 lb/s). HP compressor pressure ratio, 6·2 : 1; mass flow, 67 kg/s (148 lb/s).
COMBUSTION CHAMBER: Tubo-annular, with 10 interconnected Ni-Co alloy flame tubes in steel outer casing. Duple spray atomising burner at head of each chamber. High-energy 12-joule igniter plug in chambers 4 and 8.
FUEL SYSTEM: Hydromechanical HP system with automatic acceleration and speed control and emergency manual override. Variable-stroke dual fuel pump.
FUEL GRADE: JP-4 (A-2, JP-5).

NOZZLE GUIDE VANES: Two HP stages with air cooling; two LP stages uncooled.
TURBINE: Impulse-reaction axial type, two HP stages and two LP. All blades forged in Ni-Co alloy; first HP stage blades cooled internally by HP compressor air.
JET PIPE: Fixed, heat-resistant steel.
ACCESSORY DRIVES: External gearbox driven by radial shaft from HP system; provision for starter, fuel boost pump, two hydraulic pumps, HP fuel pump, fuel control, HP tachometer, CSD and alternator, permanent-magnet generator, LP fuel pump and oil pumps. Additional low-speed (LS) gearbox, driven from LP shaft, serving LP rotor governor and tachometer.
LUBRICATION SYSTEM: Self-contained, with engine-mounted tank, fuel/oil heat exchanger and gear type pump; pressure 3·45 bars (50 lb/sq in). Tank capacity: A-1, 4·5 litres (1·0 Imp gal); A-2, 10·3 litres (2·27 Imp gal).
MOUNTING: Main ball-type trunnions on compressor intermediate casing; rear tangential steady-type at rear of bypass duct.
STARTING: Integral gas turbine (air turbine).
DIMENSIONS:
Length overall 2,610 mm (102·6 in)
Intake diameter 953 mm (37·5 in)
Height overall 1,026 mm (40 in)
WEIGHT, DRY:
A-1 1,353 kg (2,980 lb)
A-2 1,370 kg (3,018 lb)
PERFORMANCE RATING (Max T-O):
A-1 64·5 kN (14,500 lb st) to ISA +8°C
A-2 66·7 kN (15,000 lb st) to ISA
SPECIFIC FUEL CONSUMPTION (Max T-O):
A-1 17·93 mg/Ns (0·633 lb/h/lb st)
A-2 18·33 mg/Ns (0·647 lb/h/lb st)

ROLLS-ROYCE/JAPAN
ROLLS-ROYCE & JAPANESE AERO ENGINES LTD

Moor Lane, Derby DE2 8BJ, England
CHAIRMAN: Ashley Raeburn

This international company has been formed by Rolls-Royce Ltd (UK) and a consortium of Japanese companies to develop and produce a new turbofan engine in the ten-tonne (22,000 lb) st class, derived from the RB.432 which was designed originally at Rolls-Royce, Bristol. A design office staffed by engineers from all participants is completing the RJ.500 design at Bristol.

The Japanese companies are:
Ishikawajima-Harima Heavy Industries (IHI), Kawasaki Heavy Industries (KHI) and Mitsubishi Heavy Industries (MHI).

RJ.500

The engine is the result of a decade of study of the requirements of the short/medium-haul airliner market. It incorporates thermodynamic cycle and design features aimed at improving fuel efficiency, durability and maintainability relative to existing turbofan engines in this thrust class. To meet these aims, with environmental acceptability and minimum manufacturing and maintenance costs, the RJ.500 is broadly based on the existing

RB.401 engine, and incorporates experience gained on the high-technology RB.211 series of turbofans.
Maximum airflow is 288 kg (635 lb)/s. Cruise pressure ratio and bypass ratio are respectively 20·1 and 4·9.
DIMENSIONS:
Fan diameter 1,499 mm (59·0 in)
Length (flange-to-flange) 2,694 mm (106·1 in)
WEIGHT, DRY:
Basic engine 1,851 kg (4,081 lb)
RATINGS:
Max T-O (S/L, static)
89·0 kN (20,000 lb st) to ISA + 15°C
Cruise, Mach 0·8 at 9,145 m (30,000 ft)
22·1 kN (4,965 lb st) to ISA + 10°C

ROLLS-ROYCE/SNECMA
ROLLS-ROYCE LTD

HEAD OFFICE: 65 Buckingham Gate, London SW1E 6AT, England
Telephone: 01-222 9020

SOCIÉTÉ NATIONALE D'ÉTUDE ET DE CONSTRUCTION DE MOTEURS D'AVIATION

HEAD OFFICE: 2 Boulevard Victor, 75724 Paris Cédex 15, France
Telephone: 554 92 00

Rolls-Royce Ltd and SNECMA were jointly responsible for the Olympus 593 turbojet of the Anglo-French Concorde supersonic transport.

ROLLS-ROYCE/SNECMA OLYMPUS 593

The Olympus 593 was developed by Rolls-Royce Ltd in Britain and SNECMA in France as the power plant for the Concorde supersonic airliner. The work was shared on a 60/40 per cent basis, respectively. Rolls-Royce produced the gas generator and SNECMA the convergent/divergent exhaust nozzle, thrust reverser and afterburner system.

Full certification of the Olympus 593 Mk 610 was achieved in September 1975, when total running time exceeded 50,000 h. In January 1976, at the start of scheduled services by British Airways and Air France, more than 54,000 h had been run. This far exceeded the time logged by any other engine at the start of service (and does not include the much greater time logged by earlier Olympus engines). By the end of 1979 a further 143,500 h had been flown in scheduled service.

Details of the Olympus 593 were given in the 1978-79 *Jane's.*

ROLLS-ROYCE TURBOMÉCA
ROLLS-ROYCE TURBOMÉCA LIMITED
4/5 Grosvenor Place, London SW1, England
Telephone: 01-235 3641

This company was formed jointly by Rolls-Royce and Turboméca in June 1966 to control the design, development and production programmes for the Adour two-shaft turbofan. The main function of the company is to receive contracts from the British Ministry of Defence on the Adour for both the British and French governments. The company can also enter into commercial contracts for the sale of the Adour to customers other than the British and French governments and grant licences for its manufacture.

ROLLS-ROYCE TURBOMÉCA ADOUR

The Adour was designed originally for the SEPECAT Jaguar strike/trainer aircraft to meet requirements laid down by the British and French joint air and naval staffs. It is a two-shaft turbofan engine fitted with an integral, modulated afterburner of advanced design. The whole engine is simple and robust and contains features permitting modular exchange, major engine sections being replaceable in the field, avoiding the need for return to an overhaul base.

The complete propulsion unit has been designed for an overhaul life of 1,000 h. The engine temperatures and rotational speeds are moderate and a thrust growth of the order of 40 per cent within the confines of existing installations is envisaged.

Bench testing began at Derby on 9 May 1967. Engines are assembled at Derby (R-R) and Tarnos (Turboméca) from parts made at single sources in Britain and France. Turboméca makes the compressors, casings and external pipework (to preserve Anglo-French parity the afterburner is subcontracted to SNECMA); Rolls-Royce makes the remainder. By January 1980 total flight time exceeded 750,000 h on over 1,600 engines.

The Adour has been selected for the Japanese Mitsubishi T-2 trainer and F-1 fighter/support aircraft, and since 1970 Ishikawajima-Harima Heavy Industries has been producing the Adour under a licence agreement. In 1972 a non-afterburning Adour was selected to power the British Aerospace Hawk advanced trainer. Further applications of the Adour are under consideration.

Current versions of the engine are as follows:

Mk 102. Original production engine for Jaguars in service with RAF and Armée de l'Air. Qualified in 1972.

Mk 104. Uprated RT.172-26 version similar to Mk 804; RAF Mk 102 engines are being converted to this standard.

Mk 151. Non-afterburning version for Hawk. Internal components and certification temperatures identical to Mk 102 and Mk 801A. Qualified in 1975.

Mk 801A. Japanese designation TF40-IHI-801A. Standard production engine for Mitsubishi T-2 and F-1. Qualified in 1972. (See Ishikawajima-Harima in Japanese section.)

Mk 804. Uprated engine for Jaguar International. Installationally interchangeable with Mk 102. General increase in thrust of some 10 per cent, with greater increase at high forward speeds (rating with full afterburner at Mach 0·9 at S/L, ISA, increased by 27 per cent) giving improved aircraft performance throughout flight envelope. Qualified in 1976.

Mk 811. Augmented version of Mk 861, with increased fuel flow to afterburner. Rated at 37·4 kN (8,400 lb st) at S/L. For delivery in 1980. Powers Indian Jaguar; engines supplied initially from Europe but later to be assembled by Hindustan Aeronautics with increasing Indian-manufactured content.

Mk 851. Non-afterburning version of Mk 804 for export Hawk; ordered by Finland, Kenya and Indonesia.

Mk 861. Further uprated non-afterburning version for increased thrust and greatly reduced specific fuel consumption, with changed LP compressor blading and HP and LP turbines. Rated at 25·4 kN (5,700 lb st) at S/L. Has achieved guaranteed performance. Installationally interchangeable with earlier versions. For delivery in 1981.

Further versions of the Adour, giving substantial increases in thrust, are projected.

The following description refers to the afterburning versions:

TYPE: Two-shaft turbofan for subsonic and, with augmentation, supersonic aircraft.

INTAKE: Formed by forward extension of fan casing. No radial struts or inlet guide vanes.

FAN: Two-stage. Rotating spinner, anti-iced by turbine-bearing cooling air, on front of first-stage disc. Individually replaceable blades with no part-span or tip shrouds. Fixed stators and exit vanes. Unit overhung on spring-loaded ball bearing of squeeze-film type. Full-length bypass duct leading to afterburner. Bypass ratio, 0·75-0·80.

COMPRESSOR: Five-stage compressor on HP shaft. Large-diameter double-conical shaft for rigidity with bolted curvic couplings. Wide-chord blades of titanium. Steel stator blades. Overall pressure ratio 11 : 1.

COMBUSTION CHAMBER: Annular, with straight-through flow. Fitted with 18 air-spray fuel nozzles and two igniter plugs. Engine fuel system by Lucas GTE.

Cutaway drawing of the Rolls-Royce Turboméca Adour Mk 102 augmented turbofan (32·5 kN; 7,305 lb st)

Rolls-Royce Turboméca Adour Mk 151 for British Aerospace Hawk T.1, rated at 23·1 kN; 5,200 lb st

HP TURBINE: Single-stage, aircooled.
LP TURBINE: Single-stage. Both turbine bearings of squeeze-film type.
JET PIPE: Fully modulated afterburner of compact, short-length design incorporating four concentric but staggered spray rings and vapour gutters. Catalytic igniters between inner gutters. Variable nozzle has eight master and eight slave petals positioned by eight-sided frame moved axially by four fuel-operated nozzle rams. Afterburner fuel flow and nozzle system by Dowty Fuel Systems, with vapour-core pump.

DIMENSIONS:

Inlet diameter (all)	559 mm (22 in)
Max width (all)	762 mm (30 in)
Max height (all)	1,041 mm (41 in)
Length:	
Mks 102, 801A, 804, 811	2,970 mm (117 in)
Mks 151, 851, 861	1,956 mm (77 in)

WEIGHT, DRY: See table
PERFORMANCE RATINGS: See table
SPECIFIC FUEL CONSUMPTION (Mk 102):

S/L static, dry	21 mg/Ns (0·74 lb/h/lb st)
Mach 0·8, 11,890 m (39,000 ft)	27 mg/Ns (0·955 lb/h/lb st)

ROLLS-ROYCE TURBOMÉCA RTM 321

At the 1979 Paris Salon Rolls-Royce and Turboméca both exhibited full-scale display examples of this new turboshaft engine which they are to develop jointly, subject to government approval. No mention was made of Alfa-Romeo of Italy, which had been the first company to mention the project. Though Westland has ordered 11 General Electric T700 engines for the WG 34 helicopter programme, the two engine companies hope that the RTM 321 will be adopted as the standard production engine on this helicopter. It offers an alternative to the T700 in other new helicopters in the 7/11-tonne class. The RTM 321 incorporates all the experience gained with such modern engines as the Gem and Makila to achieve extreme simplicity, good sfc and low costs. It comprises four modules and can be configured for any desired installation, with front or rear drive. Features will include an inlet particle-separator and anti-IR protective measures.

COMPRESSOR: Three-stage axial, single-stage centrifugal.
COMBUSTION CHAMBER: Annular reverse-flow.
TURBINES: Two-stage (presumably aircooled, but not yet announced) gas-generator turbine. Two-stage power turbine with drive to front or rear.

Rolls-Royce Turboméca RTM 321 turboshaft engine
(Brian M. Service)

DIMENSIONS:
Length overall	1,050 mm (41·34 in)
Diameter	515 mm (20·28 in)

WEIGHT: approx 180 kg (396 lb)

RATINGS:
Max contingency
initially in 1,430 kW (1,917 shp) range,
rising later to 1,865 kW (2,500 shp)
Intermediate   initially in 783 kW (1,050 shp) range
Long-range   initially in 582 kW (780 shp) range

SPECIFIC FUEL CONSUMPTION:
Intermediate	86·0 μg/J (0·509 lb/h/shp)
Cruise, as above	86·2 μg/J (0·51 lb/h/shp)

ROLLS-ROYCE TURBOMÉCA ADOUR ENGINES

Version	Application	Basic wt dry kg (lb)	Max S/L thrust kN (lb st)
* Mk 102/801A	Jaguar, T-2, F-1	704 (1,552)	32·5 (7,305)
Mk 104	Jaguar	713 (1,571)	35·1 (7,900)
Mk 151	Hawk	553 (1,220)	23·1 (5,200)
Mk 851	Hawk	568 (1,252)	23·1 (5,200)
* Mk 804	Jaguar	715 (1,576)	35·6 (8,000)
Mk 861		577 (1,273)	25·4 (5,700)
* Mk 811		738 (1,627)	37·4 (8,400)

* afterburning versions

TURBO-UNION
TURBO-UNION LTD

PO Box 3, Filton, Bristol BS12 7QE, England
Telephone: 0272 693871
Munich Office: 8 München 81, Arabellastrasse 4/7, Federal Republic of Germany
CHAIRMAN: Dr G. C. Boffetta

Formed in October 1969, this international company was established to manage the entire programme for the RB.199 engine for the Panavia Tornado multi-role combat aircraft. Shares are held in the ratio Fiat Aviazione SpA, 20 per cent; MTU München GmbH, 40 per cent; Rolls-Royce Ltd, 40 per cent. The stated intention is that the overall work-share shall be in proportion to the numbers of aircraft bought by the three partner countries.

TURBO-UNION RB.199

A three-shaft augmented turbofan of extremely advanced design, the RB.199 has a lightweight fan based on that of the Pegasus on a reduced scale, an advanced afterburner designed for an extremely wide operating envelope, and an integral thrust-reverser. The RB.199 offers low fuel consumption for long-range dry cruise, even at sea level, and approximately 100 per cent thrust augmentation with full afterburner for combat manoeuvre and supersonic acceleration. Further design goals included minimal weight and frontal area, moderate first cost and economic maintenance and overhaul. Strip, inspection and rebuild are facilitated by modular construction, and by the use of advanced manufacturing techniques to reduce the number of separate components.

The first RB.199 ran in September 1971. Flight testing began in April 1973 with an engine installed in a dummy portion of the Tornado, complete with inlet and duct system and 27 mm Mauser gun, carried beneath a Vulcan flying testbed. The engine first flew in Tornado P.01 on 14 August 1974. The flight-development designations RB.199-01 to -04 were described in the 1979-80 *Jane's*.

The 150-h FQT (Formal Qualification Test) was completed in November 1978, and over half the first production batch had been delivered by March 1980. Some of these engines are available for flight testing the production standard in development and pre-series Tornadoes. Firm production orders (three batches) at March 1980 stood at 823. The fourth batch of 425 engines is covered by contracts for long lead-time items.

The basic designation RB.199-34R defined the original rating for Tornado. The two production designations so far announced are the RB.199 Mk 101, which applies to the first production standard currently being delivered, and the RB.199 Improved Mk 101. This is the second production standard being developed under the three-year Post FQT Programme, which started at the beginning of 1979, and is aimed at modest performance increases and a significant extension of life.

Versions are being considered for air-superiority fighters, especially the British, West German and French requirement for a Euro-fighter. The proposals under consideration include various upratings which, if proceeded with, could be available for Tornado applications.

TYPE: Three-shaft turbofan with afterburner and integral thrust reverser.

INTAKE: Annular, without inlet guide vanes.

LP COMPRESSOR: Three-stage axial LP compressor of titanium alloy. Casing of three bolted sections, comprising a ring of stator vanes welded at their outer ends to form the casing and at their inner ends to form the interstage seal. Rotor of three discs welded together. Rotor blades secured by dovetail roots, all with snubbers to control vibration and provide greater resistance to foreign-object damage. Blade containment by local increase of casing thickness. Mass flow approx 70 kg (154 lb)/s. Bypass ratio more than 1:1.

IP COMPRESSOR: Three-stage of titanium alloy. Rotor has welded discs in which blades are secured by dovetail roots. Stator rings bolted together, with rear pair of flanges forming attachment to intermediate casing, holding blades in dovetail grooves.

HP COMPRESSOR: Six-stage; material changes from titanium at front to heat-resisting alloy at rear, except stator blades are heat-resisting steel throughout. Casing of six rings bolted together. Each ring forms track of corresponding rotor and each pair of rings forms groove in which stators are located by dovetail roots. Rotor

The first detailed longitudinal section of the RB.199 Mk 101

Cutaway drawing of Turbo-Union RB.199-34R three-shaft augmented turbofan

discs secured by ten through-bolts, carrying blades by dovetail roots. Provides bleed air for aircraft services, turbine cooling and air motors for reverser and nozzle. Bevel gear provides radial drive to gearbox. Overall pressure ratio greater than 23:1.

INTERMEDIATE CASING: Fabricated titanium inner and outer casings, with main thrust spigot and front side-mounting links. Inner casing houses IP and HP compressor bearings, supported on eight hollow vanes across bypass and core flows.

BYPASS DUCT: Fabricated in titanium, forms outer shell between intermediate casing and jetpipe.

COMBUSTION CHAMBER: Annular flame tube fabricated from nickel-based alloy, bolted at rear end between outer casing, forged and chemically milled in nickel-iron alloy, and inner casing, fabricated in nickel alloy. Carries 13 double-headed fuel vaporisers which give combustion without visible smoke. Two igniter plugs combined with primary fuel injectors. Hot-streak injector for afterburner ignition.

TURBINES: Rotor blades and stator vanes machined from precision castings in heat-resisting nickel-based alloy. All rotor blades shrouded and secured by fir-tree fixings. Stator vanes of all four stages carried in single casing machined from nickel forging.

HP TURBINE: Entry temperature over 1,327°C. Rotor blades and stator vanes aircooled. Stator cooling provided by HP air which passes through root and tip of each hollow vane into a perforated sheet-metal insert. This cooling air passes through holes in the insert before exhausting into through-holes in the vane leading and trailing edges. Remainder of cooling air is ducted to HP rotor-blade roots via pre-swirl nozzles and a turbine cover plate which increases cooling-air pressure. Air leaves blades through holes in leading edge, at tip and in trailing edge.

IP TURBINE: Aircooled stator vanes and rotor blades. Cooling air from third HP compressor stage passes into perforated central insert in stator vanes. Approximately half air cools vane and exhausts through holes in trailing edge; rest feeds via pre-swirl nozzles into rotor-blade roots and via machined holes to exit at tips.

LP TURBINE: Two-stage with hollow uncooled rotor blades. First-stage stator vanes cooled by third-stage HP compressor air, and contain support struts for IP/LP bearing.

LP SPOOL: LP compressor rotates clockwise (from rear), overhung on two widely spaced roller bearings, on bearing support welded to inner wall of third-stage stator ring. LP turbine shaft runs in ball thrust bearing in combined IP/LP bearing housing.

IP SPOOL: Front end of shaft, which also has clockwise rotation, runs in ball thrust bearing carried by intermediate casing. Rear end runs in roller bearing supported by IP/LP bearing housing.

HP SPOOL: Rotates anticlockwise in two roller bearings. Front bearing is carried in intermediate casing; rear is a contra-rotating intershaft bearing carried on IP shaft sleeve. Compensating shaft is located at front by ball thrust bearing in intermediate casing and at rear is attached to HP turbine, locating whole spool axially. This shaft of low-expansion steel matches thermal expansion of casings to maintain axial seal clearances.

AFTERBURNER: Front end of titanium fabricated jetpipe carries afterburner in which bypass air and core gas burn concurrently, without a mixing section. For core flow, two gutter flameholders fed by upstream atomisers. For bypass flow, reverse colander with radial extensions, each containing vaporising primary burner, between which multiple jets inject remainder of afterburner fuel. Provides fully-modulated augmentation. Aircooled heat shield protects jetpipe from afterburner temperature greater than 1,627°C.

NOZZLE: Variable-area, short-petal, convergent nozzle operated by shroud actuated by four screwjacks, driven by fourth-stage HP air motor via flexible shafting. Each of 14 master and 14 secondary petals is precision casting in cobalt alloy which minimises friction.

REVERSER: External two-bucket type driven via flexible shafts by motor using HP air. In stowed position outer skins form aircraft profile. Deployment takes 1 s at any thrust setting from idle to max dry.

ACCESSORY DRIVES: Accessory gearbox on underside of intermediate casing (quick attach/detach coupling) carries hydromechanical portions of main and afterburner fuel systems, oil tank and pump, and output shaft to aircraft gearbox carrying KHD gas-turbine starter/APU.

FUEL SYSTEM: The electronic Main Engine Control Unit (MECU), which is aircraft-mounted, uses signals from pilot's lever and power plant sensors to control hydromechanical engine and afterburner fuel systems and nozzle. Duplicated electronics provide integrity, with

automatic switching. Flow through main gear pump determined by metering orifice commanded by MECU, with recirculation for cooling aircraft and engine systems. Afterburner fuel from engine-driven vapour-core pump controlled by main and distribution actuators, both under MECU command.

LUBRICATION SYSTEM: Main bearings, with squeeze-film damping, in three chambers; each is supplied with pressure oil and scavenged through return pipes which have

filters and magnetic detector plugs. Oil samples drawn from tank for spectrographic analysis.

DIMENSIONS:
Max diameter	approx 870 mm (34·25 in)
Overall length	approx 3,200 mm (126 in)

WEIGHT, DRY:
Excluding reverser	approx 900 kg (1,980 lb)

PERFORMANCE RATINGS (S/L, ISA, static):
Max dry	35·5 kN (8,000 lb) class
Max afterburning	71 kN (16,000 lb) class

ISRAEL

BET-SHEMESH
BET-SHEMESH ENGINES LTD
Mobile Post Haela, Bet-Shemesh
Telephone: 02 911661-2

The first section of a 12,077 m² (130,000 sq ft) Israeli aero-engine factory, Bet-Shemesh Engines Ltd, was inaugurated officially on 15 January 1969. The company is owned by the Israeli government (majority holding), Turboméca SA and M J. R. Szydlowski. The manufac-

turing plant was based on the Turboméca factory at Tarnos. On 1 January 1977 Israel Aircraft Industries (IAI) took over the Israeli shareholding and assumed responsibility for management. Over the subsequent year the number of employees increased from 550 to about 1,200.

At first Bet-Shemesh manufactured turboprop components on behalf of Turboméca. By 1973 complete Marboré VI turbojets for CM 170 Super Magister trainers were being produced. The company also manufactures

parts of the Marboré II, Artouse II and III, Turmo II and Astazou II. Today the plant is the centralised source for all aircraft gas-turbine manufacture in Israel. It makes most portions of the General Electric J79 and will shortly produce the complete engine. It also makes parts of the Pratt & Whitney F100 and Teledyne CAE J69 and provides support for the Allison 250-C20.

Other operations include a precision foundry, and gas-turbine programmes for surface applications.

ITALY

ALFA ROMEO
SOCIETÀ PER AZIONI ALFA ROMEO
Via Gattamelata 45, 20149 Milan
Telephone: Milan 3977
AVIATION WORKS: 80038 Pomigliano D'Arco, Naples
Telephone: 8841 344

Alfa Romeo participated in the European production programme for General Electric J79-GE-11A turbojets to power Lockheed F-104G Starfighters. It is collaborating with Rolls-Royce in the manufacture and overhaul of Gnome H.1000, H.1200 and H.1400 turboshafts. A licence agreement has also been signed for the manufacture of General Electric T58 and T700 turboshafts.

Alfa Romeo was prime contractor for the manufacture, under General Electric licence, of the J85-GE-13A turbojet to power the G91Y aircraft. It is manufacturing the hot section of the J79-GE-19 turbojet for the F-104S, as well

as many parts for the J79-11B, -17 and -1K. Alfa Romeo manufactures CF6 combustors under subcontract to General Electric; assembles the kits and overhauls P&WC PT6T engines for the AB 212 helicopter; under GE licence, it is responsible for the hot section of the T64-P4D turboprop co-produced with Fiat; and participates in development and hot-section component manufacture for the Turbo-Union RB.199 for the Panavia Tornado. The company would probably be a major partner in Italian development and licence production of the Rolls-Royce Spey 807 for the AMX aircraft. It has taken over a small turboprop that was originally a collaborative project with Rolls-Royce.

The company overhauls many engines of Rolls-Royce, General Electric and Pratt & Whitney manufacture.

Alfa Romeo is a member of the Finmeccanica-IRI group of companies.

ALFA ROMEO RB.318
In the mid-1970s Alfa Romeo's Aero Engine Division began collaboration with Rolls-Royce on a small gas turbine for general-aviation applications, known as the RB.318. This was never formally announced by either partner. By 1979 a successful study, design and development programme had led to component and engine testing, including flight testing of a turboprop in a Beech King Air A90, which met or exceeded all performance targets.

By 1980 the programme was being transferred entirely to Alfa Romeo in accordance with an agreed time schedule. The definitive engine, a turboprop covering a range of powers from 298 to 596 kW (400-800 shp), will probably have a different designation. The programme is matched to the company's resources, and will draw upon Rolls-Royce under a contract for technical support. Certification is expected in 1982.

CSTM
CENTRO STUDI TRASPORTI MISSILISTICI
(Missile Transport Research Centre)

HEAD OFFICE: Via Squarcialupo 19-A, 00162 Rome
Telephone: 423.833
PRESIDENT: Glauco A. Partel

CSTM has begun work on the P-77 self-pressurised monopropellant rocket engine. Starting and reaction is by a special heating system. This project has in turn led to a powder/powder hypergolic bipropellant motor.

FIAT
FIAT AVIAZIONE SpA
Via Nizza 312, 10127 Torino, Italy
Telephone: (011) 6399
Telex: 23320 Fiatavio
CHAIRMAN: C. E. Rossi
MANAGING DIRECTOR: G. C. Boffetta
PRODUCTION DIRECTOR: S. Innocenti Torrini
DESIGN AND ENGINEERING DIRECTOR: L. La Rocca

Fiat Aviazione SpA was incorporated in 1976 as a wholly Fiat-owned company. It took over all the aero-engine activities carried out formerly by the Fiat Aviation Division, and the participation in Turbo-Union Ltd and Turbomotori Internazionale, as well as control of Motoravio Sud at Brindisi where overhaul of jet and piston engines and construction of jet engine parts are carried out.

Fiat's main aircraft engine programmes now concern the Turbo-Union RB.199, Rolls-Royce Viper 600, Pratt & Whitney JT10D and General Electric J79, J85, CF6 and T64, all of which are referred to below. In addition the company overhauls many types of engine, including the J79 and Orpheus, and the R-2800 piston engine. It is engaged in the design, development and production of the LM 2500 marine gas turbine, in collaboration with Gen-

eral Electric, and the design and production of main gearboxes for Aérospatiale helicopters.

TURBO-UNION RB.199
Fiat holds 20 per cent of the shares of Turbo-Union Ltd, the joint company set up to produce the RB.199-34R engine for the Panavia Tornado. Fiat's responsibility is the LP turbine and shaft, exhaust diffuser, jetpipe and nozzle. The programme is described under Turbo-Union in the International part of this section.

PRATT & WHITNEY JT10D
Since 1974 Fiat has been responsible for design and development of the accessory drive gearbox for the Pratt & Whitney JT10D civil turbofan engine. The programme is described under Pratt & Whitney in the US part of this section.

GENERAL ELECTRIC CF6
Fiat is engaged in the manufacture of components for the CF6 civil turbofan for both General Electric and SNECMA. For GE the company supplies complete accessory gearboxes, transfer gearboxes, inlet gearboxes and shafts. SNECMA is supplied with various gearbox components and shafts for CF6-50 engines for the Airbus A300.

GENERAL ELECTRIC T64-P4D
This free-turbine turboprop powers most versions of

the Aeritalia G 222 military transport aircraft. Under a licence agreement between the General Electric Company and the Italian government, the engine is being manufactured in Italy under the leadership of Fiat as prime contractor.

GENERAL ELECTRIC J79-19
This afterburning turbojet powers Lockheed F-104S fighters of the Italian Air Force. Fiat, as prime contractor for Italy, produced the engine under a licence agreement between the General Electric Company and the Italian government.

GENERAL ELECTRIC J85-13
With Alfa-Romeo as prime contractor, Fiat participated in production under licence of the J85-13A, power plant of the Aeritalia G91Y aircraft.

ROLLS-ROYCE VIPER 600
Development of this turbojet for business aircraft and military trainers was undertaken in collaboration with Rolls-Royce. For most versions, components rearward of the compressor housing (except turbine discs and blades) are Fiat's responsibility. However, the Mk 632-43 engine for the Aermacchi MB.339 is licensed to Piaggio. The Viper 600 is described in the Rolls-Royce entry in this section.

PIAGGIO
INDUSTRIE AERONAUTICHE E MECCANICHE RINALDO PIAGGIO SpA
HEAD OFFICE: Viale Brigata Bisagno 14, 16129 Genoa (426)
Telephone: 540 521
WORKS AND OFFICERS: See Aircraft section

The Aero-Engine Division of Piaggio is currently manufacturing the following engines under various licence agreements: Rolls-Royce Viper 11, 526, 540 and 632-43 turbojets to power the Aermacchi M.B. 326 and 339 and Piaggio PD-808 (a sublicence for the manufacture of the Viper 11 and 540 was issued to Atlas Aircraft to power

South African-built M.B. 326 aircraft); Avco Lycoming T53-L-13A/B and T55-L-11A/D turboshaft engines ordered by the Italian government for installation in Agusta-Bell 204B/205 and Agusta-Boeing Vertol CH-47C Chinook helicopters, respectively; and Avco Lycoming VO-435 and GSO-480 piston engines.

SNIA VISCOSA
DEFENCE AND SPACE DIVISION

Via Sicilia 162, 00187 Rome
Telephone: (06) 4680
Telex: 610114 SNIA
FACTORIES: Colleferro (Rome) and Ceccano (Frosinone)
DIVISION MANAGER: Ing E. Svizzeretto
CHIEF OF ROCKET, MISSILES AND SPACE R & D DEPARTMENT: Ing P. Laurienzo

The SNIA Viscosa Defence and Space Division is engaged in the production of conventional ammunition and the research, design and production of solid propellants, solid-propellant rocket motors, complete rockets and missiles, as well as air-to-surface and surface-to-surface unguided weapons. It possesses all necessary installations for the production of double-base solid propellants. Composite solid-propellant grains and motors incorporating polyurethane or polybutadiene polymers as binder are also produced in all sizes.

Complete propulsion units of up to 1,500 mm (59 in) diameter, with combustion times ranging from a fraction of a second to about 1 minute, are manufactured by SNIA Viscosa's Defence and Space Division for use in military rockets and missiles.

SNIA's Defence and Space Division produced the motors for the Italian Sparrow air-to-air missile programme, and developed an advanced motor for the Aspide air-to-air missile, now coming into the production phase. The Division is also involved in the development of many weapon systems in co-operation with such companies as MBB, OTO Melara, Breda Meccanica Bresciana and Sistel.

In the space field, a new amagnetic high-performance apogee motor, with a titanium-alloy case and improved polybutadiene propellant, was developed and qualified for the Italian Siro experimental satellite successfully launched in August 1977. The solid-propellant apogee motor for the GEOS satellite, developed and qualified in co-operation with SEP of France, has operated twice successfully, in April 1977 and July 1978. For OTS and Meteosat, a high-performance apogee motor with carbon-fibre case was qualified by a consortium formed by SNIA, SEP and MAN. The same consortium has since begun development of a larger apogee motor for Ariane payloads. SNIA has also completed, on behalf of CNES, the development and qualification of retro and ullage motors for the separation of all three stages of the Ariane vehicle. In 1980, it signed an agreement with Aeritalia for development of the IRIS (Italian Research Interim Stage) propulsion stage for transferring payloads from low orbit (mainly ex-Shuttle) to geosynchronous or transfer orbits.

JAPAN

IHI
ISHIKAWAJIMA-HARIMA JUKOGYO KABU-SHIKI KAISHA (Ishikawajima-Harima Heavy Industries Co Ltd)

HEAD OFFICE: No 2-1, 2 chome, Ohte-Machi, Chiyoda-ku, Tokyo
AERO ENGINE AND SPACE DEVELOPMENT GROUP: 3-5-1, Mukodai-cho, Tanashi-shi, Tokyo 188
Telephone: (0424) 66 1225
PRESIDENT: Dr Hisashi Shinto
EXECUTIVE VICE-PRESIDENT: Dr Osamu Nagano
MANAGING DIRECTOR AND GENERAL MANAGER, AESD GROUP: Dr Kaneichiro Imai

In February 1960 IHI began the licence production of General Electric J79-IHI-11A turbojet engines for Japanese-built Lockheed F-104J Starfighters.

Under further licensing agreements with General Electric, IHI is producing the J79-IHI-17 turbojet for the McDonnell Douglas F-4EJ, the T58 turboshaft for helicopters and other applications, including the propulsion of air cushion vehicles and hydrofoil boats, and the T64-IHI-10 turboprop engine to power the JMSDF's PS-1 anti-submarine flying-boat and US-1 search and rescue amphibian, and the Kawasaki P-2J maritime patrol aircraft. By January 1980 deliveries totalled 723 T58s, 395 T64s and 593 J79s.

In 1979 IHI linked with other Japanese companies in the 50/50 development with Rolls-Royce of the RJ.500, described under Rolls-Royce/Japan in the International part of this section.

The manufacture of the Rolls-Royce Turboméca Adour augmented turbofan in Japan under licence agreement received government approval in September 1970. Its production began in early 1973, under the Japanese designation TF40-IHI-801A, to power the supersonic T-2 trainer and F-1 fighter. By 1980 IHI had delivered 275 TF40s.

IHI was nominated in 1978 as prime contractor of Pratt & Whitney F100 engines for the Japanese-built F-15 fighter and Allison T56 engines for the Japanese-built Lockheed P-3C. Kawasaki and Mitsubishi will be subcontractors. Production of 32 F100 and 12 T56 engines was ordered in Fiscal Year 1979, followed by 60 F100 and 40 T56 engines in FY 1980.

IHI undertakes overhaul and repair of Pratt & Whitney JT8D and Rolls-Royce RB.211 commercial turbofans, and General Electric J79, T58 and T64, and R-R Turboméca TF40 military engines, and Turboméca Artouste and Astazou turboshafts.

Prior to the start of licence production, in April 1959, IHI had been responsible for the J3 turbojet engine which had been under development by the Nippon Jet-Engine Company since 1956. The J3-IHI-7 version is installed in Fuji T-1B intermediate jet trainer and Kawasaki P-2J aircraft.

IHI participated in developing the XJ11 liftjet, as well as the JR100 and JR200 built under supervision of the NAL. In addition, in collaboration with Mitsubishi and Kawasaki, IHI made the prototypes of the FJR710 turbofan. The JR100, JR200 and FJR710 are described in the NAL entry.

IHI is co-operating with JDA in studies of small turbofans in the 11·8 kN (2,645 lb) thrust class.

IHI XF3

This new military turbofan was unveiled at the International Gas Turbine Conference in England in April 1978. Development had begun just two years earlier, with funding by the JDA's Technical Research & Development Institute. The initial Phase I (XF3) form has a single-stage fan with bypass ratio of 1·9, five-stage transonic compressor, 12-burner combustion chamber and single-stage HP and LP turbines. Rating in this form is to be 11·79 kN (2,650 lb st). The more powerful Phase II engine (XF3-20) has a two-stage fan, two-stage LP turbine and higher turbine temperature. The second engine reached 16·28 kN (3,660 lb st) in 1979. Five more engines were to be built in 1980. The eventual version is intended for the MT-X twin-engined trainer, at a rating of 15·68 kN (3,530 lb st).

IHI J3

The J3-IHI-7C is a derivative of the J3-1, of which a description appeared in the 1959-60 *Jane's*, under the entry for Nippon Jet-Engine Company. It is installed in the Kawasaki P-2J aircraft currently in service with the JMSDF, and is in production. By 1980 deliveries totalled 246.

An experimental version with augmentation reached a thrust of 20·2 kN (4,542 lb) during bench tests in December 1972. The J3-IHI-7D is an uprated version (15·2 kN, 3,415 lb st), which is replacing the -7C in P-2J aircraft.

The following data apply to the J3-IHI-7C:
TYPE: Axial-flow turbojet.
AIR INTAKE: Annular nose air intake. Anti-icing system for front support struts.
COMPRESSOR: Eight-stage axial-flow type, built of Ni-Cr-Mo steel. Rotor consists of a series of discs and spacers bolted on to shaft. Rotor and stator blades of AISI 403 steel. Stator blades brazed on to fabricated base which is fixed in casing with circumferential T-groove. Rotor blades dovetailed to discs. Light alloy casing in upper and lower sections, flange-jointed together. Pressure ratio 4·5 : 1. Air mass flow 25·4 kg (56 lb)/s.
COMBUSTION CHAMBER: Annular type. AISI 321 steel outer casing. L 605 steel flame tube. Thirty fuel supply pipes located in combustion chamber outer casing and 30 vaporiser tubes located at front of flame tube. Ignition by low-voltage high-energy spark plug in each side of combustion chamber.

Ishikawajima-Harima J3-IHI-7C turbojet engine (13·7 kN; 3,090 lb st)

FUEL SYSTEM: Hydromechanical, with IHI FC-2 fuel control.
FUEL GRADE: JP-4.
NOZZLE GUIDE VANES: Single row of aircooled fabricated vanes.
TURBINE: Single-stage axial-flow type. Disc bolted to shaft. Precision-forged blades.
BEARINGS: Rotating assembly carried in front (double ball) and rear (roller) compressor rotor bearings and rear (roller) turbine shaft bearing.
JET PIPE: Fixed-area type.
ACCESSORY DRIVES: On gearbox under compressor front casing.
LUBRICATION SYSTEM: Forced-feed system for main bearings and gear case. Dry sump. Vane-type positive displacement supply and scavenge pump.
OIL SPECIFICATION: MIL-L-7808.
MOUNTING: Three-point suspension, with one pickup by a pin on starboard side of compressor front casing and a trunnion on each side of the compressor rear casing.
STARTING: Electrical starter in intake bullet fairing.
DIMENSIONS:

Length, less tailpipe	1,661 mm (65·4 in)
Length overall with rear cone	1,994 mm (78·5 in)
Diameter overall	627 mm (24·7 in)
Frontal area	0·28 m² (3·01 sq ft)

WEIGHT, DRY:

Bare	380 kg (838 lb)
With accessories	430 kg (948 lb)

PERFORMANCE RATING:

T-O	13·7 kN (3,090 lb st)

SPECIFIC FUEL CONSUMPTION:

At T-O rating	29·74 mg/Ns (1·05 lb/h/lb st)

OIL CONSUMPTION:

At normal rating (max)	
	0·60 litres (1·06 Imp pints)/h

IHI TF40-IHI-801A

This is the Rolls-Royce Turboméca Adour augmented turbofan engine, as built under licence by IHI. For details see Rolls-Royce Turboméca entry in International section.

KAWASAKI
KAWASAKI JUKOGYO KABUSHIKI KAISHA
(Kawasaki Heavy Industries Ltd)

2-16-1 Nakamachi-Dori, Ikuta-ku, Kobe
Telephone: Kobe (078) 341 7731
WORKS: Akashi, Hyogoken
OFFICERS: See Aircraft section

Kawasaki's factory at Akashi started repair, overhaul and component manufacturing for aircraft engines, on behalf of the US armed forces and the Japan Defence Agency, in 1953. Since then, it has overhauled more than 11,900 engines, mainly of the Allison J33, General Electric J47, Rolls-Royce Orpheus, Westinghouse J34, and Kawasaki KT5311A and KT5313B series. Since 1968 the company has also been making spare parts for the J33, and since 1973 for the Orpheus.

In 1967, under a licence agreement with Avco Lycoming, Kawasaki started manufacturing T53 turboshaft engines. Deliveries of the resulting KT5311A, KT5313B and T53-K-13B engines totalled 238 units by early 1980.

In 1977, under a licence agreement with Rolls-Royce, Kawasaki began making Industrial/Marine Olympus TM-3B and Tyne RM-1C engines, with deliveries starting in September 1980.

Kawasaki shares in parts manufacturing for the Rolls-Royce Turboméca Adour, the Pratt & Whitney F100 and JT8D (for Kawasaki C-1 transport, with Kawasaki noise suppressor) and the IHI-assembled Allison T56. In 1979 Kawasaki became a member of the Japanese consortium responsible for a 50 per cent share in the development and manufacture of the Rolls-Royce RJ.500.

MITSUBISHI
MITSUBISHI JUKOGYO KABUSHIKI KAISHA
(Mitsubishi Heavy Industries Ltd)

HEAD OFFICE: 5-1, Marunouchi 2 chome, Chiyoda-ku, Tokyo 100
ENGINE WORKS: Daiko Plant, Nagoya Aircraft Works, 1-1, Daiko-cho, Higashi-ku, Nagoya 455
Telephone: (052) 721 3111
Komaki North Plant, Nagoya Aircraft Works, 1200, Higashi-Tanaka, Komaki-Shi, Aichi 485

Telephone: (0568) 79 2111
OFFICERS: See Aircraft section

Since 1952 Mitsubishi has been responsible for the repair and overhaul of engines of the Japan Defence Agency and domestic and foreign airlines.

In 1967 Mitsubishi resumed its activity in the aviation gas-turbine field by undertaking manufacture of the CT63 turboshaft engine to power Hughes 369HM helicopters of the JGSDF under a licence agreement with Allison. A total of 217 engines were delivered to the Japan Defence Agency by March 1978. In 1972, under licence agreement with Pratt & Whitney Aircraft, Mitsubishi began the manufacture of the JT8D-M-9 turbofan. The first was delivered in January 1973. By 1981 a total of 72 engines are to be delivered to the Japan Defence Agency for use in the Kawasaki C-1 military transport. Deliveries by September 1979 had reached 69.

In collaboration with IHI and Kawasaki, Mitsubishi participates in the FJR710 turbofan programme (see NAL entry).

NAL
NATIONAL AEROSPACE LABORATORY

1880 Jindaiji-machi, Chofu City, Tokyo
Telephone: 0422 47 5911
DIRECTOR: Toshio Kawasaki
HEAD OF AERO-ENGINE DIVISION: Masakatsu Matsuki

The National Aerospace Laboratory (NAL) is a government establishment responsible for research and development in the field of aeronautical and space science. Since 1962 it has extended its activity to include V/STOL techniques. The decision was made in that year to initiate development of an engine to fulfil the requirement for a lightweight lift-jet power plant for VTOL aircraft.

The more advanced NAL/IHI JR200 was developed in 1966, the NAL/IHI JR220 was completed in 1971.

In 1971 the Agency of Industrial Science and Technology, Ministry of International Trade and Industry (MITI), funded a high by-pass ratio turbofan engine (FJR710) development programme. NAL has completed the basic design of this engine, and many component tests are being made at NAL. The FJR710 is being developed by an industry consortium comprising IHI, Kawasaki and Mitsubishi, in co-operation with NAL and MITI.

MITI/NAL FJR710

In the late 1960s the Japanese government and industry, seeking an engine programme that might remain competitive for many years, decided to embark on the design of a subsonic turbofan of high by-pass ratio. After a preliminary study by the NAL, funding was provided by the Ministry of International Trade and Industry in 1971 for a prototype demonstrator and test programme.

NAL has managed the design of the resulting FJR710. Manufacture of the prototype and development engines was subcontracted to IHI, Kawasaki and Mitsubishi. The first engine made its first run in May 1973. By the end of 1978 six engines (three FJR710/10 and three FJR710/20 with small changes) had run a total of 1,300 h. Tests completed included 150-h endurance and low-cycle fatigue. In November 1977 high-altitude performance testing was completed successfully at the NGTE in the UK.

In the 1978-9 *Jane's* brief details were given in the Addenda of the more powerful FJR710-600; but NAL has deleted all mention of this, saying only "the first engine of the second phase ran in December 1978". NAL makes no mention of the proposed C-1 testbed, rebuilt with upper-surface blowing from four FJR710-20s. The current test programme is hoped to lead to a production engine in the 44·5-66·8 kN (10,000-15,000 lb st) class.

The following description applies to the prototype engine, and is provisional:
TYPE: Two-shaft high bypass ratio turbofan for subsonic commercial or military aircraft.
AIR INTAKE: Direct annular entry around fan spinner.
FAN: Single-stage fan, with rotating spinner and inserted titanium blades with part-span shrouds. Metal fan duct held by eight aerofoil struts, preceded by ring of flow-straightening vanes. Bypass ratio 6·5 : 1.
COMPRESSOR: Mechanically independent HP compressor. Multi-stage axial assembly with inserted blades of titanium and, at delivery end, high-nickel alloy. Several rows of variable stator blades held in upper and lower half-casings and operated by peripheral rings scheduled by hydraulic ram.
COMBUSTION CHAMBER: Smokeless annular type.
TURBINE: Two-stage HP gas-generator turbine with cooled blades. Multi-stage LP fan turbine.
JET PIPE: Fixed area.
DIMENSIONS (approx):
Length	3,300 mm (130 in)
Diameter	1,520 mm (60 in)
WEIGHT, DRY: 980 kg (2,160 lb)
PERFORMANCE RATINGS (ISA):
T-O	49 kN (11,025 lb st)
Cruise at 6,100 m (20,000 ft) at Mach 0·7	16·7 kN (3,748 lb st)
SPECIFIC FUEL CONSUMPTION:
T-O	9·83 mg/Ns (0·347 lb/h/lb st)
Cruise, as above	17·7 mg/Ns (0·623 lb/h/lb st)

NAL/IHI JR200 and JR220

Following work on the NAL/IHI JR100, NAL designed and developed the higher-thrust NAL/IHI JR200 of improved thrust/weight ratio, and this was manufactured by IHI.

An improved version, the NAL/IHI JR220 with higher pressure ratio and higher turbine entry temperature, is under initial development.

The following details relate to the JR200:
TYPE: Single-shaft axial lift-jet.
AIR INTAKE: Forward-facing annular type.
COMPRESSOR: Five-stage axial unit of 4 : 1 pressure ratio and 37·2 kg (82 lb)/s air mass flow at 12,450 rpm. Air bleed 3 kg (6·6 lb)/s.
COMBUSTION CHAMBER: Annular type.
TURBINE: Single-stage axial unit with 850°C entry temperature.
JET PIPE: Fixed area.
WEIGHT, DRY: 127 kg (280 lb)
PERFORMANCE RATINGS:
Max without air bleed	20·4 kN (4,585 lb st)
Max with air bleed	17·8 kN (4,012 lb st)
SPECIFIC FUEL CONSUMPTION:
At max rating, without air bleed	32·0 mg/Ns (1·13 lb/h/lb st)
At max rating, with air bleed	33·2 mg/Ns (1·17 lb/h/lb st)

MITI/NAL FJR710 two-shaft turbofan (49 kN; 11,025 lb st)

ZENOAH
KOMATSU ZENOAH COMPANY

HEAD OFFICE: 2-142-1 Sakuragaoka, Higashiyamato, Tokyo 189
PRESIDENT: Shiro Sakuma

This company was established in 1910 as Tokyo Gasu Denki (Tokyo Gas & Electric) and has made aircraft engines for 65 years, during the second World War as Hitachi Aircraft Co. Since 1950 it has become famous as Xenoah Co, but changed its name on 1 October 1979 to Komatsu Zenoah, a subsidiary of Komatsu Ltd.

ZENOAH G72C-C

This engine has been type-tested by the JCAB and FAA (Pacific-Asia) and was certificated by the JCAB on 24 July 1978; FAA certification followed on 28 April 1979.

TYPE: Three-cylinder aircooled two-stroke piston engine.

CYLINDERS: Bore 72·0 mm (2·835 in). Stroke 59·5 mm (2·342 in). Swept volume 726·7 cc (44·34 cu in). Compression ratio 7·0.
INDUCTION: Three Mikuni VM34SS float-type carburettors with mixture control. Two Mikuni DF52-501 fuel pumps. One Mikuni 4M-501 oil injection pump.
FUEL GRADE: 100/130 octane gasoline and Shell Super two-stroke oil injected separately into induction system.
IGNITION: Dual capacitor-discharge.
EXHAUST SYSTEM: 3:1 manifold and tuned silencer.
STARTING: Hitachi SI 08-62 electric starter, 12V, 1kW.
ACCESSORIES: Optional Mitsubishi 14V 35A alternator and mounting bracket for instrument vacuum pump.
DIMENSIONS:
Length with exhaust manifold   564 mm (22·2 in)

Width including carburettors   443 mm (17·44 in)
Height overall (incl plugs)   390 mm (15·35 in)
WEIGHT, DRY:
Bare   59·4 kg (131 lb)
With exhaust system, silencer, starter, alternator and vacuum pump   71·2 kg (157 lb)
PERFORMANCE RATING:
Max T-O   44·7 kW (60 hp) at 6,080 rpm
Max continuous   40·25 kW (54 hp) at 6,080 rpm
SPECIFIC FUEL CONSUMPTION:
Max at 75% power (33·6 kW; 45 hp)
                                      135 μg/J (0·8 lb/h/hp)
FUEL CONSUMPTION:
Max at 75% power
22·5 litres (4·95 Imp gallons; 5·95 US gallons)/h

The Zenoah G72C-C three-cylinder engine

POLAND

PZL
POLSKIE ZAKLADY LOTNICZE
HEADQUARTERS: ul. Miodowa 5, 00251 Warsaw

SALES REPRESENTATIVE: Pezetel, ul. Przemyslowa 26, 00450 Warsaw

Telephone: Warsaw 285071

The entire Polish aircraft industry is subordinate to the Zjednoczenie Przemyslu Lotniczego i Silnikowego PZL (Aircraft and Engine Industry Union). Pezetel handles all export sales of Polish aeronautical material.

BORZECKI
JOZEF BORZECKI
Wroclaw, ul. Sernicka 20/4

BORZECKI 2RB
The 2RB is a small piston engine designed and built by J. Borzecki for use in motor gliders. The prototype was built in 1970 and in the same year underwent bench tests. A flat-four, it may be used with tractor or pusher propeller. The engine began flight testing in early 1972 in the Borzecki Alto-Stratus motor glider. Development is continuing. The engine is based on the Riedel engine used to start German turbojets in the second World War.
TYPE: Four-cylinder two-stroke horizontally-opposed air-cooled piston engine.
CYLINDERS: Bore 70 mm (2·76 in). Stroke 35 mm (1·38 in). Swept volume 540 cc (33 cu in). Compression ratio 7·2 : 1. Aluminium alloy cylinders and heads attached to crankcase by four studs. Steel liners.

PISTONS: Aluminium alloy, with two compression rings.
CONNECTING RODS: Milled from steel.
CRANKSHAFT: Steel shaft, supported in four ball bearings and one ball-thrust bearing at the front.
CRANKCASE: Aluminium alloy case, divided at the vertical longitudinal and transverse centrelines with aft cover.
INDUCTION: Jawa 250 motor-cycle carburettor.
FUEL: Mixture of 76 octane petrol and oil.
IGNITION: Battery ignition. One M14-250 14 mm (0·55 in) sparking plug per cylinder.
MOUNTING: Four rubber dampers at rear of crankcase or four studs at cylinder heads.
PROPELLER DRIVE: Direct tractor or pusher.
DIMENSIONS:
Length overall, with propeller boss 450 mm (17·7 in)
Width   250 mm (9·8 in)
Height, with carburettor   260 mm (10·2 in)
WEIGHT, DRY: 15 kg (33 lb)
PERFORMANCE RATINGS:
T-O   17·9 kW (24 hp) at 6,000 rpm
Continuous   12 kW (16 hp) at 4,500 rpm

The Borzecki 2RB light piston engine

SPECIFIC FUEL CONSUMPTION:
At max T-O rating   145·3 μg/J (0·86 lb/h/shp)
At continuous rating   126·75 μg/J (0·75 lb/h/shp)

IL
INSTYTUT LOTNICTWA (Aeronautical Institute)
HEADQUARTERS: Al. Krakowska 110/114, 02-256 Warsaw-Okecie
Telephone: Warsaw 460993
MANAGING DIRECTOR: Dr Ing Andrzej Wierzba
CHIEF CONSULTANT FOR SCIENTIFIC AND TECHNICAL CO-OPERATION: Dipl Ing Jerzy Grzegorzewski
CHIEF OF TECHNICAL INFORMATION DIVISION: Dipl Ing Andrzej Glass

The Aeronautical Institute is an establishment concerned with aeronautical research, aerodynamic tests, strength tests, test flights of aeroplanes, helicopters and gliders, aviation equipment, materials, technical information and standardisation. The Institute has a special manufacturing plant responsible for constructing prototypes to its own design.

IL SO-1
The Aeronautical Institute designed the SO-1 turbojet to power the Polish TS-11 Iskra (Spark) jet basic trainer. It was designed to permit the full range of aerobatics, including inverted flight. Guaranteed overhaul life is 200 h. Production was handled by the WSK-Rzeszów, as noted in that organisation's entry.
TYPE: Single-shaft axial-flow turbojet.
AIR INTAKE: Annular intake casing manufactured as a cast shell. Fixed inlet guide vanes.
COMPRESSOR CASING: Manufactured as a cast shell in two parts, split along horizontal centreline, in aluminium alloy.
COMPRESSOR: Seven-stage axial-flow compressor. Drum-type rotor built up of disc assemblies, with constant diameter over tips of rotor blades. Carried in ball bearing at front and roller bearing at rear. Steel stator blades bonded with resinous compound into slots in carrier rings. Rotor of steel and duralumin, with first three blade rows of steel and remainder of aluminium alloy. Pressure ratio 4·8.
COMBUSTION CHAMBER: Annular type with 24 integral vaporisers. Outer casing made of welded steel.
FUEL SYSTEM: Two independent systems supplied by one pump. Starting system consists of six injectors, with direct injection. Main system consists of twelve twin injectors with outlets towards the vaporisers.

IL SO-1 turbojet (9·8 kN; 2,205 lb st), initial power plant of the TS-11 Iskra (Spark) trainer *(BIIL)*

FUEL SPECIFICATION: Kerosene P-2 or TS-1.
TURBINE: Single-stage axial-flow type. Blades attached to disc by fir-tree roots. Supported in roller bearing at rear.
JET PIPE: Outer tapered casing and central cone connected by streamlined struts. Nozzle area adjusted by exchangeable inserts.
LUBRICATION SYSTEM: Open type for rear compressor and turbine bearings, supplied by separate pumps. Closed type for all other lubrication points, fed by separate pumps.
OIL SPECIFICATION: Type AP-26 (synthetic).
ACCESSORY DRIVES: Gearbox mounted at bottom of air intake casing and driven by bevel gear shaft from front of compressor.
STARTING: 27V starter/generator and bevel gear shaft, driven by aircraft battery or ground power unit, mounted on air intake casing.
DIMENSIONS:
Length overall   2,151 mm (84·7 in)
Width   707 mm (27·8 in)
Height   764 mm (30·1 in)
WEIGHT, DRY: 303 kg (668 lb)

PERFORMANCE RATINGS:
T-O   9·8 kN (2,205 lb st) at 15,600 rpm
Max cont   8·7 kN (1,958 lb st) at 15,100 rpm
SPECIFIC FUEL CONSUMPTION:
At T-O rating   29·6 mg/Ns (1·045 lb/h/lb st)
OIL CONSUMPTION:
0·8 litres (1·4 Imp pints)/h

IL SO-3
This improved version of the SO-1 replaced the earlier type in production at the WSK-Rzeszów. The SO-3 is intended for tropical use and incorporates minor changes in compressor, combustion chamber and turbine, data remaining the same as for the SO-1. It is fitted to all current versions of the TS-11. TBO has been doubled, to 400 h. In 1978 testing began on the SO-3B, with all-steel compressor rotor, modified vaporisers and new flame tube. By 1979 this was in production alongside the SO-3, with the following changed particulars:
WEIGHT, DRY: 325 kg (715 lb)
PERFORMANCE RATINGS:
T-O   10·8 kN (2,426 lb st) at 15,600 rpm
Max cont   9·8 kN (1,958 lb st) at 15,100 rpm

JANOWSKI
JAROSLAW JANOWSKI
Lodz 11, ul. Nowomiejska 2/29

JANOWSKI SATURN 500
The Saturn 500 was designed by Mr Jaroslaw Janowski and built by Mr S. Polawski for the Janowski J-1 ultra-light amateur-built aircraft (see 1979-80 *Jane's*). The prototype Saturn 500 was built in 1969. This two-cylinder two-stroke engine may be used with tractor or pusher propeller, and is intended for ultra-light aircraft built by amateurs.

In 1972 work began on a new version of the Saturn 500, with new cylinder heads, improved crankshaft and dual ignition. Its rating (max T-O) is increased to 22·5 kW (30 hp); dry weight is believed to be about 25 kg (55 lb).

The following description applies to the initial 25 hp version:

TYPE: Two-cylinder two-stroke horizontally-opposed air-cooled piston engine.
CYLINDERS: Bore 70 mm (2·76 in). Stroke 65 mm (2·56 in). Swept volume 500 cc (30·5 cu in). Compression ratio 8·5 : 1. Steel barrels with aluminium alloy cylinder heads. Cylinder and head assembly attached to crankcase by four studs.
PISTONS: Of aluminium alloy. Two compression rings and one oil scraper ring.
CONNECTING RODS: Steel forgings.
CRANKSHAFT: Steel counterbalanced shaft, supported in two lead-bronze plain bearings and one ball-thrust bearing at the front.
CRANKCASE: Aluminium alloy case, split in the vertical plane, with front and aft covers.
INDUCTION: Two BVF 28N1 carburettors.
FUEL: Petrol/oil mixture using aviation 90 octane.
IGNITION: Two magnetos. One M14-250 14 mm (0·55 in) sparking plug per cylinder.
MOUNTING: Four rubber dampers at rear of crankcase.
PROPELLER DRIVE: Direct tractor or pusher.

DIMENSIONS:
Length overall, with propeller boss   430 mm (16·93 in)
Width, without sparking plugs   515 mm (20·27 in)

WEIGHT, DRY: 27 kg (59·5 lb)

PERFORMANCE RATING:
T-O   18·65 kW (25 hp) at 4,000 rpm

SPECIFIC FUEL CONSUMPTION:
Max T-O rating   118·23 μg/J (0·70 lb/h/hp)
Normal cruising power   111·48 μg/J (0·66 lb/h/hp)

Saturn 500 two-cylinder two-stroke engine designed by Jaroslaw Janowski

WSK-PZL-KALISZ
WYTWÓRNIA SPRZETU KOMUNIKACYJNEGO-PZL-KALISZ
HEAD OFFICE AND WORKS: ul. Czestochowska 140, 62800 Kalisz
Telephone: 77351
GENERAL MANAGER: Dipl Ing Henryk Jaruzel
In 1952 the Soviet Union transferred responsibility for manufacture and service support of Soviet aircooled radial piston engines to the WSK (transport equipment manufacturing centre) at Kalisz.

Current production is centred on: the 1,000 hp ASh-62IR (Polish designation ASz-62IR) for all versions of the An-2; and the 260 hp AI-14RA for the PZL-104 Wilga (see Aircraft section). Production of the ASz-62IR exceeds 15,000 engines. WSK-Kalisz has developed a version of the AI-14 with electric starter, the AI-14RC.

PZL (IVCHENKO) AI-14R
The original 260 hp AI-14R version of this nine-cylinder aircooled radial engine has been produced in very large quantities, in both the Soviet Union and Poland. Since 1960 several later versions have gone into production in the Soviet Union for fixed-wing aircraft and helicopters. Both of the following were developed at Kalisz.

AI-14RA. Basic production engine, rated at 194 kW (260 hp); fitted to Yak-12, Yak-18, PZL-101A Gawron and PZL-104 Wilga 35.
AI-14RC. Version fitted with electric starter.
The following description refers to the AI-14RA:
TYPE: Nine-cylinder single-row aircooled radial, geared with blower.
CYLINDERS: Bore 105 mm (4·125 in). Stroke 130 mm (5·125 in). Displacement 10·16 litres (620 cu in). Nitrided steel barrel; cast light alloy head incorporating air starting valve. Two spark plugs and single inlet and exhaust valves. Compression ratio 5·9.
PISTONS: Aluminium forgings, each with two chromium-plated compression rings and two scraper rings.
CONNECTING RODS: One master rod, with lead-bronze big-end bearing; eight link rods articulated by steel cemented knuckle pins fixed in the master-rod cheeks against rotation and secured laterally by retaining plates.
CRANKSHAFT: Heat-treated steel in two parts, the front portion being gripped in the split cheek of the rear portion and held by a pinch bolt. Both portions carry a counterweight, the rear counterweight being pendulum type which balances inertia forces and also serves as vibration damper. Shaft held in two main roller bearings and ball thrust bearing.
CRANKCASE: Comprises gearcase, thrust-bearing cover, mid-case, mixture chamber and rear casing.

PZL ASz-62IR piston engine

VALVE GEAR: Each valve is opened by push/pull rod, from a cam plate geared to rotate in opposition to the crankshaft.
INDUCTION SYSTEM: Carburettor type K-14A, fed by fuel pump type 702M.
FUEL GRADE: 91 to 100 octane.
BLOWER: Aluminium forged impeller. Magnesium cast diffuser
LUBRICATION: Gear-type pressure and scavenge pumps.
IGNITION: Two M-9 magnetos; automatic timing and fully screened.
PROPELLER DRIVE: Planetary gears, ratio 0·787.
STARTING: By compressed air from airborne or ground bottle to cylinder-head valves.

DIMENSIONS:
Diameter   985 mm (38·78 in)
Length   956 mm (37·63 in)
WEIGHT, DRY   197 kg (434 lb)
PERFORMANCE RATINGS:
T-O   194 kW (260 hp) at 2,350 rpm
Rated   164 kW (220 hp) at 2,050 rpm
Cruise   98·4 kW (132 hp) at 1,730 rpm
SPECIFIC FUEL CONSUMPTION:
T-O   95-104·3 μg/J (0·562-0·617 lb/h/shp)
Cruise   76·4-83·8 μg/J (0·452-0·496 lb/h/shp)

PZL AI-14RA piston engine

PZL (SHVETSOV) ASz-62R
Power plant of the An-2 transport biplane, the ASz-62R is a 1,000 hp nine-cylinder aircooled radial engine. It was developed from the Wright Cyclone R-1820 by Arkadiya Shvetsov's bureau in the Soviet Union, as the ASh-62. Several variants have been built in the Soviet Union, including the ASh-62IR/TK driving a turbo-compressor to maintain 850 hp up to a height of 9,500 m (31,000 ft).

ASz-62IR. Standard power plant of the Li-2 (Soviet DC-3) and all versions of the An-2 except for the An-2M. Transferred to WSK-PZL-Kalisz in 1959.
All versions have a cylinder bore of 155·5 mm (6⅛ in), swept volume of 29·87 litres (1,823 cu in) and compression ratio of 6·4 : 1.
The planetary reduction gear has a ratio of 0·637 : 1.
DIMENSIONS:
Length overall   1,130 mm (44·50 in)
Diameter   1,375 mm (54·13 in)
WEIGHT, DRY:
Without power take-off   579 kg (1,276 lb)
PERFORMANCE RATINGS:
T-O   746 kW (1,000 hp) at 2,200 rpm
Rated power   611 kW (820 hp) at 2,100 rpm
Cruise (50% power)   306 kW (410 hp) at 1,670 rpm
SPECIFIC FUEL CONSUMPTION:
T-O   112 μg/J (0·661 lb/h/hp)
Cruise   80 μg/J (0·474 lb/h/hp)

WSK-PZL-RZESZÓW
WYTWÓRNIA SPRZETU KOMUNIKACYJNEGO-PZL-RZESZÓW
HEAD OFFICE AND WORKS: ul. Obrońców Stalingradu 120, 35078 Rzeszów, Postbox 340
Telex: 83411
GENERAL MANAGER: Dipl Ing Jozef Rokoszak

WSK-Rzeszów, founded in 1938 as PZL-Rzeszów, at first produced Bristol Pegasus and Walter Junior and Minor engines under licence. After World War 2 the works expanded considerably. The first product was the Soviet M-11D, followed by series production of the ASz-62IR and LiT-3 piston engines and HO-10 and SO-1 turbojets.

Current production is centred on: the Soviet-designed GTD-350 turboshaft, together with WR-2 reduction gear for Mi-2 helicopters; the tropicalised SO-3 turbojet for the TS-11 Iskra trainer; and the PZL-3S piston engine for agricultural aircraft. The SO-3 is described (with the SO-1) on an earlier page, under the heading IL.

PZL GTD-350
The GTD-350 is a free-turbine helicopter power plant. In the version used in the twin-engined Mi-2, the drive is taken from the rear, with the twin jet pipes of each engine exhausting to port (port engine) and starboard (starboard engine). The GTD-350 can be supplied with downward-facing jet pipe and with drive from the front, if required. Though developed and initially produced by the Isotov

bureau in the Soviet Union, it is now in production only in Poland. WSK-Rzeszów has developed a new version rated at 331 kW (444 shp) and designated GTD-350P. TBO of the GTD-350 is 3,000 h, and work is in hand to extend this.
TYPE: Axial/centrifugal-flow free-turbine turboshaft engine.
AIR INTAKE: Annular intake casing and inlet guide vanes of stainless steel. Automatic de-icing of inlet guide vanes and central bullet by air bleed from compressor.
COMPRESSOR: Seven axial stages and one centrifugal stage, all of steel, connected together with a tie-bolt. Discs shrunk-fitted to shaft. Blades of axial stages have dovetail roots. Shaft carried in front roller bearing and rear ball bearing. Pressure ratio 6·05 : 1. Air mass flow 2·19 kg (4·83 lb)/s at 45,000 rpm.

COMPRESSOR CASING: Horizontally-split aluminium alloy casing, with stator blades brazed to semi-rings. No diffuser blades.

COMBUSTION CHAMBER: Reverse-flow type with air supply through two tubes. Centrifugal duplex single-nozzle burner. Ignition system comprises burner and semiconductor spark-plug. Eight thermocouples at gas outlet.

FUEL SYSTEM: Includes NR-40TA pump governor with shut-off cock, which feeds fuel to burner, controls gas-generator rpm and limits max output; RO-40TA power turbine rpm governor, DS-40 signal transmitter controlling bleed valves; and electromagnetic valve to provide fuel for starting. Provision against power-turbine overspeed and (GTD-350P only) helicopter transmission overload.

FUEL GRADE: TS-1 or TS-2.

COMPRESSOR TURBINE: Single-stage turbine with aircooled disc. Shrouded blades with fir-tree roots. Precision-cast fixed guide vanes. Turbine casing has metal-graphite insert in plane of blades. Shaft supported in ball bearing at rear. Temperature before turbine 970°C (GTD-350P, 985°C).

POWER TURBINE: Two-stage constant-speed type (24,000 rpm). Shrouded blades with fir-tree roots. Discs bolted together. Stator blades welded to rings. Airflow is again reversed aft of power turbine.

JET PIPES: Two fixed-area jet pipes.

REDUCTION GEARING: Two sets of gears, with ratio of 0·246 : 1, in cast magnesium alloy casing. Output shaft speed, 5,900 rpm.

LUBRICATION SYSTEM: Closed type. Gear-type pump with one pressure and four scavenge units. Nominal oil pressure 2·94±0·5 bars (43 lb/sq in). Oil cooler and oil tank, capacity 12·5 litres (2·75 Imp gallons), fitted to airframe.

OIL GRADE: B3-W (synthetic).

ACCESSORIES: STG3 3kW starter/generator, NR-40T governor pump, D1 tachometer generator and oil pumps mounted on reduction gear casing and driven by gasgenerator. RO-40T rotating speed governor, D1 tachometer generator and centrifugal breather, also mounted on reduction gear casing, driven by power turbine.

STARTING: STG3 starter/generator suitable for operation at up to 4,000 m (13,125 ft) altitude.

DIMENSIONS:

Length overall	1,385 mm (54·53 in)
Max width	520 mm (20·47 in)
Width (with jet pipes)	626 mm (24·65 in)
Max height	630 mm (24·80 in)
Height (with jet pipes)	760 mm (29·9 in)

WEIGHT, DRY:

Less jet pipes and accessories	135 kg (298 lb)

PERFORMANCE RATINGS:

Max contingency at 97% max gas-generator rpm:
GTD-350	322 kW (431 shp)
GTD-350P	331 kW (444 shp)

T-O rating (6 min) at 94% max gas-generator rpm:
GTD-350	295 kW (395 shp)
GTD-350P	331 kW (444 shp)

Nominal rating (1 hr) at 89% gas-generator rpm:
GTD-350	235 kW (315 shp)
GTD-350P	257 kW (345 shp)

Cruising rating (II)
210 kW (281 shp) at 86·5% gas-generator rpm
Cruising rating (I)
173 kW (232 shp) at 83·5% gas-generator rpm

SPECIFIC FUEL CONSUMPTION:

T-O	136 µg/J (0·805 lb/h/shp)
Nominal	146 µg/J (0·861 lb/h/shp)
Cruising (II)	154 µg/J (0·913 lb/h/shp)
Cruising (I)	165 µg/J (0·978 lb/h/shp)

OIL CONSUMPTION:

Max	0·3 litres (0·53 Imp pints)/h

PZL-3S

With ancestry going back via the LiT-3 to the AI-26W, this radial was the only type in its class to be developed in the 1970s. It has an FAA Type Certificate and Polish CACA certificate to BCAR. Applications include the PZL-106A Kruk, and conversions of the Grumman Ag-Cat and IAR-827A, Thrush Commander.

TYPE: Seven-cylinder aircooled radial.

CYLINDERS: Bore 155·5 mm (6·12 in). Stroke 155 mm (6·1 in). Swept volume 20·6 litres (1,265 cu in). Compression ratio 6·4 : 1.

PISTONS: Forged aluminium.

INDUCTION SYSTEM: Float-type carburettor. Mechanically driven supercharger.

FUEL GRADE: Aviation gasoline, minimum 91 octane.

LUBRICATION: Gear-type oil pump. Oil grade Aero Shell 100 or other to MIL-L-6082.

PZL (Isotov) GTD-350 turboshaft engine (322 kW; 431 shp)

PZL-Franklin 6AS-350A with turbocharger

PROPELLER DRIVE: Direct. Provision for constant-speed propeller Type US-132000 or Dowty Rotol R303/3-110-F.

ACCESSORIES: ANG 6423 Prestolite alternator and two output shafts, one 27 hp (35 max) for spraying pump and the other 5 hp.

STARTING: Electrical.

DIMENSIONS:

Diameter	1,267 mm (49·88 in)
Length	1,110 mm (43·72 in)

WEIGHT, DRY:
411 kg (906 lb)

PERFORMANCE RATINGS:

Max T-O	448 kW (600 hp) at 2,200 rpm
Max continuous	410 kW (550 hp) at 2,050 rpm
Cruise (75 per cent)	310 kW (415 hp) at 2,000 rpm

SPECIFIC FUEL CONSUMPTION:

T-O, max cont	105 µg/J (0·61 lb/h/hp)
Cruise	86 µg/J (0·51 lb/h/hp)

PZL-3R

This is the geared version of the PZL-3S. The following are the main differences:

PROPELLER DRIVE: Planetary gear of 0·7 ratio. Provision for constant-speed propeller, Type US-133000.

DIMENSION: Length 1,271 mm (50·06 in)

WEIGHT, DRY: 446 kg (983 lb)

PZL-FRANKLIN ENGINES

In 1975 Pezetel acquired rights to manufacture and market the entire range of aircooled piston engines formerly produced by the Franklin Engine Company (Aircooled Motors) of the USA. These engines are being produced in Poland for light aircraft of all kinds, including helicopters and motor-gliders.

An SZD-45-2 Ogar F motor glider was flown for the first time on 13 March 1979 with the 2A-120C (later 120CP). The 4A-235B3 and 6A-350C have Polish CACA certificate. The 6AS-350 is on test.

PZL-3S seven-cylinder radial

All these engines are of the horizontally-opposed type, with cylinders of 117·48 mm (4·625 in) bore and 88·9 mm (3·5 in) stroke. All have direct drive and operate on 100/130 grade fuel. Accessories normally include electric starter, alternator and fuel pump. Other details are tabulated:

PZL-FRANKLIN ENGINES

Engine model	Cylinder arrangement	Capacity cc (cu in)	Compression ratio	Max T-O rating at S/L (kW, hp at rpm)	Overall dimensions mm (in)			Weight dry kg (lb)	Remarks
					length	width	height		
2A-120C	2 horiz	1,916 (117)	8·5	45 (60) at 3,200	581 (22·9)	795 (31·3)	515 (20·3)	75·8 (167)	
4A-235B	4 horiz	3,850 (235)	8·5	93(125) at 2,800	774 (30·5)	795 (31·3)	637 (25·1)	117·6 (259)	
6A-350C	6 horiz	5,735 (350)	10·5	164 (220) at 2,800	952 (37·5)	795 (31·3)	641 (25·25)	167 (367)	
6AS-350A	6 horiz	5,735 (350)	7·4	186 (250) at 2,800*	1,097 (43·2)	868 (34·2)	983 (38·7)	189 (417)	turbocharged
6A-350D	6 horiz	5,735 (350)	10·5	175 (235) at 3,200	825 (32·5)	795 (31·3)	642 (25·3)	145 (320)	helicopter engine
6V-350B	6 vert	5,735 (350)	10·5	175 (235) at 3,200	968 (38·0)	795 (31·3)	779 (30·6)	144 (320)	helicopter engine

*Rated at 175 kW (235 hp) at 2,800 rpm at 5,000 m (16,400 ft).

SOUTH AFRICA

ATLAS
ATLAS AIRCRAFT CORPORATION OF SOUTH AFRICA (PTY) LTD

ADDRESS AND OFFICERS: See Aircraft section

Atlas is manufacturing the Rolls-Royce Viper 540 turbojet under sublicence from Piaggio of Italy, for use in Atlas Impala attack trainers.

SWEDEN

FLYGMOTOR
VOLVO FLYGMOTOR AB

HEAD OFFICE AND WORKS: S-461 01 Trollhättan
Telephone: 0520 301 00

This company was founded in 1930 and began by building under licence the Bristol Pegasus I aero-engine, under the designation My VI. Since 1970 Volvo Flygmotor has been a wholly owned subsidiary of AB Volvo.

Volvo Flygmotor AB holds a licence to build Rolls-Royce Avon engines and is also engaged in research and development work on turbojet engines, ramjet engines and rocket engines. Its major current programme involves the production of two versions of the RM8 supersonic turbofan developed from the Pratt & Whitney JT8D to power different sub-types of the Saab 37 Viggen combat aircraft.

It is also engaged in the development of experimental hybrid and liquid-fuel rocket engines. The company has a technical collaboration agreement on ramjet development with Rolls-Royce Ltd.

Volvo Flygmotor is the manufacturer of the combustion (thrust) chambers for the first and second stages of the Ariane European space launcher. The engines concerned, Viking II and Viking IV, are described in the SEP entry of the French section.

Volvo Flygmotor RM8B augmented turbofan for JA 37 fighter version of Viggen, rated at 125 kN (28,110 lb st) with maximum augmentation

FLYGMOTOR RM8

The RM8 is a Swedish military version of the Pratt & Whitney JT8D civil subsonic turbofan which Flygmotor developed to power the Saab 37 Viggen supersonic multi-purpose combat aircraft.

Until 1970 the main effort was devoted to development and manufacture of the RM8A version for the AJ 37, SF 37, SH 37 and SK 37 versions of the Viggen. Production of this was almost complete by the beginning of 1979. The substantially modified **RM8B** was conceived to meet the propulsion requirements of the fighter Viggen, the JA 37. Research at Pratt & Whitney and Flygmotor showed that a changed design could improve the reliability of operations at high altitudes and in severe manoeuvres, as well as increase thrust in all regimes. In collaboration with Pratt & Whitney the design of the RM8B was completed in late 1971. The major change to improve functional reliability at high altitude involved taking the first stage off the LP compressor and adding it to the fan, giving a three-stage fan and three-stage LP spool, both having a revised aerodynamic configuration according to the latest P&W research. To increase thrust the RM8B has a four-nozzle burner combustion system and a new HP turbine. Delivery of production RM8B engines began in 1978.

The following description refers to the RM8A:

TYPE: Axial-flow two-spool turbofan with modulated afterburner.
AIR INTAKE: Annular, with 19 fixed inlet guide vanes.
FAN: Two-stage front fan. Titanium blades.
LP COMPRESSOR: Four-stage axial-flow, integral with fan stages, on inner of two concentric shafts. Blades of titanium. Steel casing.
HP COMPRESSOR: Seven-stage axial-flow on outer hollow shaft. Blades made of special high-temperature alloys. Overall pressure ratio 16·5 : 1. By-pass ratio approximately 1 : 1. Total air mass flow 145 kg (320 lb)/s.
COMBUSTION CHAMBER: Cannular type with nine cylindrical flame tubes, each downstream of a single Duplex fuel nozzle. Two high-energy spark plugs, each with its own igniter box.
HP TURBINE: Single-stage axial-flow, with cast aircooled blades.
LP TURBINE: Three-stage axial-flow, with cast blades. Exit guide vanes after turbine.

VR35 longitudinal cross-section

AFTERBURNER: Double-skinned to provide duct for cooling air. Outer skin of titanium. Inner skin of special alloys. One hot-streak igniter. Hydraulically-actuated fully-variable nozzle, using fuel as the operating fluid.
BEARINGS: Main shafts run in total of six bearings.
CONTROL SYSTEMS: There are two systems. The main system for the gas-generator comprises a Bendix hydromechanical control of advanced design. A further Bendix unit controls the fuel flow to the afterburner and the nozzle area. A single power lever controls thrust from maximum afterburner down to idle; further movement below idle actuates the fuel cut-off valve.
MOUNTING: Three-point. Main mountings on each side of compressor casing; one under turbine casing.
ACCESSORY DRIVE: Via gearbox, under engine, driven from HP turbine shaft.
DIMENSIONS:
Length overall:
  RM8A   6,160 mm (242·5 in)
  RM8B   6,230 mm (245·25 in)
Max diameter (both versions)   1,397 mm (55 in)
Inlet diameter (both)   1,030 mm (40·55 in)
WEIGHT, DRY:
  RM8A   2,100 kg (4,630 lb)
  RM8B   2,350 kg (5,181 lb)
PERFORMANCE RATINGS (ISA, S/L):
Max T-O, augmented:
  RM8A   115·6 kN (25,990 lb st)

Volvo Flygmotor VR35 prepackaged liquid rocket on static test at dive angle

  RM8B   125 kN (28,110 lb st)
Max T-O, dry:
  RM8A   65·6 kN (14,750 lb st)
  RM8B   72 kN (16,200 lb st)

SPECIFIC FUEL CONSUMPTION:
Max augmented:
  RM8A   70·0 mg/Ns (2·47 lb/h/lb st)
  RM8B   71·4 mg/Ns (2·52 lb/h/lb st)
Max dry:
  RM8A   17·8 mg/Ns (0·63 lb/h/lb st)
  RM8B   18·1 mg/Ns (0·64 lb/h/lb st)
Max continuous (both)   17·3 mg/Ns (0·61 lb/h/lb st)

GARRETT/FLYGMOTOR TFE 1042

This collaborative family of turbofans is covered in the International part of this section.

FLYGMOTOR VR35

The VR35 is a prepackaged liquid-propellant rocket engine with positive expulsion of the storable inhibited red fuming nitric acid (IRFNA) and Hydyne propellants. A solid-propellant gas generator delivers the expelling gas and programmes the thrust into a boost phase followed by a sustain blow-down period.

The positive expulsion is accomplished by a gas-pressurised piston for the fuel, contained in a central tank, and an inward-collapsible aluminium bladder for the oxidiser in its concentric tank. This expulsion system enables the engine to be fired under any acceleration direction, a capability which is essential for a missile engine with a thrust programme that includes the sustain phase.

Another advantage with this type of engine is the completely smoke-free exhaust, leaving no signature at launch or during flight.

The VR35 is used in the Saab-Scania RB05 air-to-surface missile, which is one of the main weapons for the AJ 37 Viggen (see Air-Launched Missiles section).

DIMENSIONS:
Length overall	1,770 mm (69·7 in)
Max diameter	300 mm (11·8 in)

WEIGHT: 127 kg (280 lb)
PROPELLANT MASS FRACTION: 0·59
OPERATING TEMPERATURE RANGE: −50°C to +65°C
PERFORMANCE:
Boost	20-25 kN (4,496-5,620 lb) depending on temperature
Sustain	5 kN (1,124 lb)
Total impulse	160 kN-s (35,970 lb-s)

FLYGMOTOR RAMJETS

Ramjet engine research and development have been under way at Volvo Flygmotor since 1952, when the company's underground high-pressure air magazine was completed. The stored air drives the combustion test rigs and wind tunnels necessary for this kind of work.

The engine research culminated in several flight tests with the RR2, designed for a Mach number of 2·85 and intended for pod-mounting on a ground-to-air missile. The RR2 engine has a diameter of 260 mm (10·25 in) and an empty weight 42·0 kg (92·5 lb). The kerosene-type fuel is stored in the missile main body and is delivered to the ramjet combustion chamber by means of an air-driven turbopump integrated into the engine forebody.

The main research effort is now directed towards an integral rocket-ramjet engine. This new concept is a ramjet engine containing a solid-propellant grain in its combustion chamber. The rocket is fired to launch and accelerate the vehicle. After completion of the boost phase the chamber is used for ramjet combustion. The transition between the boost and the ramjet-sustain phase is accomplished by suddenly increasing the nozzle area, opening the air inlet and injecting the liquid fuel.

Two basic types of rocket-ramjet have been investigated and tested. The RRX1 has a circumferential nose air intake and is designed for a Mach number of 5·0. The body diameter is 190 mm (7·5 in). The RRX5 has four side-mounted air intakes to free the nose for a missile warhead and guidance. It is intended for a Mach-number range of 1·8-3·5, with a diameter varying between 300-450 mm (11·8 and 17·7 in).

Research is in hand on solid ducted rockets or simpler form using fuel-rich gases from underoxidised solid propellant.

UNION OF SOVIET SOCIALIST REPUBLICS

GDL

The Gas Dynamics Laboratory was founded in Leningrad in 1929. Since that time it has completed a very large number of rocket-engine programmes, mainly using liquid propellants. The laboratory has occupied many facilities, but is still headquartered in Leningrad. Four of its best-known engines are described below.

GDL RD-107

This four-chamber liquid-propellant rocket engine was developed during 1954 to 1957. The RD-107 and its derivatives have been in use for many years as first-stage engines for the launch vehicles for Vostock, Voskhod and derived programmes. Each complete RD-107 comprises four main chambers and two small vernier chambers.
TYPE: Four-chamber liquid-propellant rocket engine.
PROPELLANTS: Liquid oxygen and kerosene.
THRUST CHAMBERS: Four primary thrust chambers of double-wall construction, with fabricated corrugations between walls and inner walls of copper or copper-rich alloy. Conical nozzles. All-welded heads. Flat-plate injectors, with concentric rings of tubes in which propellants are pre-mixed before injection. Estimated diameters: throat 150-165 mm (6-6·5 in), nozzle 685 mm (27 in). Combustion pressure 60·8 bars (882 lb/sq in).
VERNIER CHAMBERS: Two chambers of double-wall construction, with finning between walls. Estimated diameters: throat 75 mm (3 in), nozzle 305 mm (12 in).
TURBOPUMP: One single-shaft turbopump mounted in tubular thrust frame and feeding all chambers. Assembly comprises turbine exhaust hood containing coiled heat exchanger, single-sided shrouded centrifugal kerosene pump, double-sided shrouded centrifugal liquid oxygen pump, gearbox, and two auxiliary centrifugal pumps, one of which supplies the monopropellant gas generator. Fuel lines to main chambers pass through common valve.
PERFORMANCE (in vacuum):
Rated thrust	1,000 kN (224,870 lb)
Specific impulse	314 s

GDL RD-119

This more modern single-chamber liquid-propellant engine, which has been in use since 1962, forms the second-stage engine of a launch vehicle for Cosmos research satellites. More than 1,000 of these satellites have been launched, using two-, three- and four-stage launch vehicles of various types and having lifting capacities ranging from hundreds of pounds to 7·6 tonnes (7·5 tons).
TYPE: Single-chamber liquid-propellant rocket engine.
PROPELLANTS: Liquid oxygen and dimethyl-hydrazine.
THRUST CHAMBER: Single fixed chamber, possibly of tubular-wall construction, with fuel entry above base of nozzle. Estimated diameters: throat 100 mm (4 in), nozzle 940 mm (37 in). Combustion pressure 81·1 bars (1,176 lb/sq in).
TURBOPUMP: One single-shaft turbopump, driven by monopropellant (hydrazine) gas generator. Exhaust from gas generator taken to multiple auxiliary nozzles for control in roll, pitch and yaw.
PERFORMANCE (in vacuum):
Rated thrust	108 kN (24,250 lb)
Specific impulse	352 s

GDL RD-214

This neat liquid-propellant rocket engine, developed at GDL in 1952-57, has been adopted as the standard first-stage propulsion for launching the Cosmos series of Soviet satellites. It has four thrust chambers, burning nitric acid and kerosene, each chamber being rated at 176·6 kN (39,700 lb thrust) at sea level. Vacuum rating of the engine is 725·7 kN (163,142 lb). The propellants are fed by a single large turbopump group mounted above the chamber group, the fuel being supplied straight to a bolted connection on the welded chamber heads and the nitric acid passing through part-flexible pipes to the regeneratively cooled chamber nozzle and throat. Chamber pressure is given by GDL as 3·1 bars (45 lb/sq in) and specific impulse as 246. The four chambers are rigidly fixed to the Cosmos launcher first stage, vehicle control being accomplished by four refractory deflector vanes, one per chamber, mounted on the vehicle skirt control packages and projecting into the rocket exhaust. More than 1,000 RD-214 engines have been flown from Kapustin Yar on non-recoverable Cosmos missions.

GDL RD-219

Since the mid-1950s the emphasis in Soviet development of large liquid-propellant rockets has swung from lox/kerosene to storable mixtures, particularly RFNA/UDMH. This combination offers good specific impulse, can be left in the vehicle tanks indefinitely and is hypergolic. The first large GDL engine of this type to be disclosed was the RD-219, a twin-chamber unit developed in 1958-61 and used for second-stage propulsion of large vehicles (possibly the SS-9 ICBM, or the Type G or Proton/Zond launcher). The chambers have a vacuum expansion ratio, and are fed by a single turbopump. They are fixed rigidly to a welded tubular thrust frame extending down to the vehicle skirt.

PERFORMANCE (in vacuum):
Rated thrust	883 kN (198,441 lb)
Specific impulse	293 s

The RD-219 powers the second stage of launchers; a nitric acid/UDMH engine, its twin chambers have vacuum thrust of 883 kN (198,441 lb)

Exhibition model of the RD-107 rocket engine, with two-chamber vernier engine in front (*TAM Air et Cosmos*)

The 706·4 kN (158,800 lb) thrust GDL RD-214 rocket engine used to power the first stage of the Cosmos launcher. Vacuum rating 725·7 kN (163,142 lb)

GLUSHENKOV

This design bureau became known in 1969 when it was revealed as that responsible for the TVD-10 engines fitted in the Beriev Be-30 STOL transport. The TVD-10 is a small turboprop in the 950 shp class, supplied to Beriev as a complete cowled unit with a reversing propeller produced specially for this application. The engine air intake is positioned below the propeller axis, but no details of the TVD-10 have yet been made available. It has been reported that it was mainly due to difficulties with the TVD-10 that the Be-30 programme was terminated in 1973.

In 1978 the improved TVD-10B, rated at 723 kW (970 shp) went into production for the An-28 twin-engined STOL aircraft. It is also reported that the TVD-10B powers the An-3 agricultural aircraft. In 1979 photographs were released of one of these engines mounted in a Yak-18PM fully aerobatic trainer.

Glushenkov is also responsible for the 671 kW (900 shp) GTD-3 turboshaft engine, two of which power the Kamov Ka-25 helicopter. This engine and the TVD-10 appear to have a generally similar layout, with a free power turbine, and it is possible that they use a common gas generator.

ISOTOV

GENERAL DESIGNER IN CHARGE OF BUREAU: Sergei Pietrovich Isotov

This bureau was responsible for the GTD-350 and TV2-117A turboshaft engines which power the Mil Mi-2 and Mi-8 helicopters respectively. The former is in production in Poland, and is described under the WSK-PZL-Rzeszów entry in this edition. Isotov was also responsible for the TVD-850 turboprop engines which powered early Antonov An-28 transport aircraft (see Polish Aircraft section).

ISOTOV TV2-117A

The power plant of the Mi-8 comprises two TV2-117A engines coupled through a VR-8A gearbox. As is common with modern Soviet helicopters, the engines and gearbox are delivered and thereafter treated as a single unit. The complete package incorporates a control system (separate from the control system of each gas generator) which maintains desired rotor speed, synchronises the power of both engines, and increases the power of the remaining engine if the other should fail.

The TV2 engine is of conservative design, being biased in favour of long and trouble-free life rather than attempting to rival the small size and weight of some Western engines in the same power class.

A version of the TV2-117A also powers the Mil Mi-24 military assault and gunship helicopter.

TYPE: Free-turbine helicopter turboshaft engine.

AIR INTAKE: Direct pitot, with main front casing providing vertical upper and lower drive-shafts to accessory packages. Main accessory group above the engine projects ahead of intake face. Casing incorporates variable-incidence inlet vanes.

COMPRESSOR: Ten-stage axial. Construction principally in titanium to reduce weight in comparison with the steel that would otherwise be used. Inlet guide vanes and stators of stages 1, 2 and 3 are of variable incidence to facilitate starting and increase compressor efficiency over a wide speed range; for the same reasons the casing incorporates automatic blow-off valves. Pressure ratio 6·6 : 1 at 21,200 rpm.

COMBUSTION CHAMBER: Annular, with eight burner cones. Fabricated from inner and outer diffuser casings, flame tube, casing, burners, and anti-icing bleed air pipe.

FUEL GRADE: T-1 or TS-1 to GOST 10227-62 specification (Western equivalents, DERD.2494, MIL-F-5616).

TURBINE: Two-stage axial compressor turbine bolted to rear of splined shaft with front extension to drive accessories. Solid rotor blades, held by fir-tree roots in discs cooled by bleed air (first disc 10th-stage air, all other discs 8th-stage). First- and second-stage stators have 51 and 47 inserted blades respectively. Free power turbine of similar two-stage design; its rotors have 43 and 37 blades respectively.

EXHAUST UNIT: Large fixed-area duct which deflects the gas out at 60°. It comprises a pipe, pipe shroud and tie-band, shroud connector links and exhaust pipe attachments. The exhaust pipe and shroud together form a double-wall assembly which minimises heat transfer into the power plant nacelle, the pipe being cooled by air circulating in the double wall.

OUTPUT SHAFT: The main drive-shaft is an extension of the power turbine rotor shaft. It conveys torque from the free turbine to the overrunning clutch of the helicopter main gearbox (VR-8A) and is also coupled to the speed governor of the free-turbine rotor. Max output speed 12,000 rpm; main rotor speed 192 rpm.

ACCESSORIES: Mounted on the main drive box above the intake casing, in which a train of bevel and spur gears provides drives for airframe and engine accessories. The engine automatic control system includes a fuel system, hydraulic system, anti-icing system, gas temperature restriction system, engine electric supply and starting system, and monitoring instruments. The hydraulic system positions the variable stators according to a preset programme, depending on compressor speed and air temperature at the inlet; it also sends electrical signals to control the starter/generator system, close the starting bleed air valves and restrict peak gas temperature to 600°C. Air up to 1·8 per cent of the total mass flow can be used to heat the intake and other parts liable to icing. Fire extinguishant can be released manually by the pilot, upon receipt of a fire warning, through a series of spray rings and pipes.

LUBRICATION: Pressure circulation type. Oil is supplied by the upper pump and scavenged from the five main bearings by the lower pump, returned through the helicopter-mounted air/oil heat exchanger and thence to the helicopter tank. The oil seals and air/oil labyrinth seals are connected to a centrifugal breathing system.

OIL GRADE: Synthetic, permitting operation at oil temperatures above 200°C, combined with easy starting at minus 40°C without heating the oil. Grade B-3V to MRTU 38-1-157-65 (nearest foreign substitute Castrol 98 to DERD.2487). Consumption, not over 0·5 litre per hour per engine.

STARTING: Electrical, fuel, and ignition systems are integrated. The SP3-15 system comprises DC starter/generator, six storage batteries, control panel, ground supply receptacle, and control switches and relays; of these all are airframe mounted except for the GS-18TP starter/generator which cranks the compressor during the starting cycle. The ignition unit comprises a control box, two semiconductor plugs, solenoid valve, and switch. The starting fuel system comprises an automatic starting unit on the NR-40V fuel regulating pump, constant-pressure valve, and two igniters.

DIMENSIONS:

Length, with accessories and exhaust pipe
2,835 mm (111·5 in)
Length, intake face to rotor gearbox connection
2,391 mm (94·25 in)
Width   547 mm (21·5 in)
Height   745 mm (29·25 in)

WEIGHT, DRY:

Engine, without generator, transducers, etc
330 kg (727 lb)
VR-8A gearbox, less entrapped oil 745 kg (1,642 lb)

PERFORMANCE RATINGS:

Max	
T-O (S/L, static)	1,118 kW (1,500 shp)
Max cont	895 kW (1,200 shp)
Cruise (122 knots; 225 km/h; 140 mph at 500 m; 1,640 ft)	746 kW (1,000 shp)

Max   1,267 kW (1,700 shp)

SPECIFIC FUEL CONSUMPTION:

T-O, as above   102·4 μg/J (0·606 lb/h/shp)
Cruise, as above   115·4 μg/J (0·683 lb/h/shp)

ISOTOV TV3-117

The A-10 (Mi-24) helicopter in which Gourguen Karapetyan set the current speed record for helicopters over a 15/25 km course, on 21 September 1978, was said to be powered by two TV3-117 turboshaft engines, each rated at 1,640 kW (2,200 shp). The designation and application suggest that the TV3-117 is an uprated version of the TV2-117, but no other details are available.

ISOTOV TVD-850

Power plant of early Antonov An-28 STOL transports, the TVD-850 turboprop has a rating of 810 shp. The cowled engine looks almost identical to the Turboméca Astazou, and the reduction gearbox must be housed in the centre of an annular air intake section. This engine appears to have lost in competition with the Glushenkov TVD-10B.

Isotov TV2-117A turboshaft engine (1,118 kW; 1,500 shp)

IVCHENKO

The collective headed by general designer Alexander G. Ivchenko until his death in June 1968 was based in a factory at Zaparozhye in the Ukraine. The bureau is now headed by General Designer Lotarev, who has his own entry on a later page.

The first engine with which Ivchenko was associated officially was the 41 kW (55 hp) AI-4G piston engine used in the Kamov Ka-10 ultra-light helicopter. He progressed ultimately, via the widely used AI-14 and AI-26 piston engines, to become one of the Soviet Union's leading producers of gas turbine engines. Since 1952 all Soviet piston engines have been assigned to Poland (see under WSK-PZL-Kalisz in Polish section).

IVCHENKO AI-20

This engine was developed as the NK-4 at the Kuznetsov bureau in 1947-52, with the assistance of German engineers. Eventually preferred to the VK-2, it was ordered into production, and the Zaporozhye collective was charged with the final refinement and production.

Redesignated AI-20, it was produced from 1955 in several versions for aircraft that included the An-10, An-12, An-32, Be-12, Il-18 and Il-38.

AI-20K. Rated at 2,942 kW (3,945 ehp). Used in Il-18V, An-10A and An-12.

AI-20M. Initial T-O rating of 3,124 kW (4,190 ehp). Used in Il-18D/E, An-10A and An-12. Probably fitted to Il-38 and Beriev M-12. Capable of operation on a wide range of fuels and lubricating oils. Power increased to 3,169 kW (4,250 ehp) for later engines as in detailed description below. Uprated again for An-32.

The AI-20 was designed to operate reliably in all temperatures from −60°C to +55°C at heights up to 10,000 m (33,000 ft). It is a constant-speed engine, the rotor speed being maintained at 12,300 rpm by automatic variation of propeller pitch. Gas temperature after turbine is 560°C in both current versions. TBO of the AI-20K was 4,000 h in the Spring of 1966; the same life was reached by the -20M in 1968.

In the Il-18 installation, the AI-20 turboprop is supplied as a complete power plant with cowling, mounting and automatically-feathering reversible-pitch four-blade propeller.

TYPE: Single-shaft turboprop.

AIR INTAKE: Inner and outer cones connected by six radial struts. Outer casing carries accessories and front mountings. Centre casing carries reduction gear.

Ivchenko AI-20M turboprop of 3,169 ekW (4,250 ehp) *(courtesy of Aviation Magazine International, Paris)*

COMPRESSOR: Ten-stage assembly of discs running in roller bearing in front casing, joined to first disc by tubular extension shaft, and ball-thrust bearing in combustion chamber casing on through-bolted rear shaft. Magnesium alloy stator casing in upper and lower halves, bolted together. Pressure ratio 9·2 under altitude cruise conditions. Air mass flow 20·7 kg (45·6 lb)/s.

COMBUSTION CHAMBER: Annular chamber with ten burner cones welded to front ring, and separate inner and outer shrouds. Burners anchored by flanges on chamber casing. Pilot burners and ignition plugs at top of casing.

FUEL GRADE: T-1 or TS-1 to GOST-10227-62 (DERD.2492, JP-1 to MIL-F-5616).

TURBINE: Three stages overhung on cantilevered shaft running in roller bearing in tapered cone of combustion chamber casing and splined to compressor drive-shaft. Rotor blades shrouded at inner and outer ends and installed in pairs in slots in aircooled discs. Stator blades secured in grooves in casing, first stage being aircooled and second stage being hollow to ensure uniform heating.

JET PIPE: Fixed-area type with five radial struts. Nozzle area 0·225 m² (2·42 sq ft).

REDUCTION GEAR: Planetary type, incorporating six-cylinder torquemeter and negative-thrust transmitter (type IKM), with self-checking device, for autofeathering AV-681 propeller. Ratio 0·08732 (input speed 12,300 rpm except ground-idle 10,400 rpm).

LUBRICATION: Pressure-feed type with full re-circulation; hourly consumption not over 0·8 litres (0·175 Imp gal).

OIL GRADE: Mixture 75% transformer oil GOST 982-56 or MK-8 to GOST 6457-66 (equivalent to DERD.2490 or MIL-O-6081B) and 25% MS-20 or MK-22 to GOST 1013-49 (DERD.2472 or MIL-O-6082B).

ACCESSORIES: Engine and airframe accessories driven off compressor front extension shaft, via radial shafts at 6 and 12 o'clock. Full ice-protection and fire-extinguishing systems.

STARTING: Two electric starter/generators, Type STG-12 TMO-1000, supplied from ground source or from APU Type TG-16.

DIMENSIONS:
Length	3,096 mm (121·89 in)
Width	842 mm (33·15 in)
Height	1,180 mm (46·46 in)

WEIGHT, DRY: 1,040 kg (2,292 lb)

PERFORMANCE RATINGS:
T-O	3,169 kW (4,250 ehp)
Cruise (350 knots; 650 km/h; 404 mph at 8,000 m; 26,000 ft)	2,013 kW (2,700 ehp)

SPECIFIC FUEL CONSUMPTION:
T-O	104·3 μg/J (0·617 lb/h/shp)
Cruise, as above	73·3 μg/J (0·434 lb/h/shp)

IVCHENKO AI-24

This turboprop powers the An-24 and its derivatives. Production began in 1960 and the following data refer to engines of the second series, which were in production by the Spring of 1966.

The AI-24 of 1,875 kW (2,515 ehp) powered the An-24V Series I, and was followed by the AI-24A with provision for water injection, in the main production version of that aircraft.

The more powerful AI-24T of 2,103 kW (2,820 ehp) with water injection is used in the An-26. This engine has in-flight vibration monitoring, automatic relief of power overloads and gas temperature behind the turbine, and auto-shutdown and feathering.

The AI-24 is a constant-speed engine, maintained at 15,100 rpm by automatic variation of propeller pitch. The engine is flat-rated to maintain its nominal output to 3,500 m (11,500 ft). TBO was 3,000 h in the Spring of 1966; by 1968 the later AI-24T had reached 4,000 h.

TYPE: Single-shaft turboprop.

The 1,875 ekW (2,515 ehp) Ivchenko AI-24 turboprop *(courtesy of Aviation Magazine International, Paris)*

AIR INTAKE: Large magnesium alloy casting, comprising inner and outer cones joined by four radial struts. Carries accessories, reduction gear, front mountings and compressor inlet guide vanes.

COMPRESSOR: Ten-stage axial. Stainless steel rotor, comprising rigidly-connected discs carrying dovetailed blades. Front shaft runs in roller bearing and is bolted to propeller drive-shaft of reduction gear; rear shaft runs in ball-thrust bearing and is splined to turbine shaft. Welded steel casing in bolted left and right halves, with welded front and rear connecting flanges. Pressure ratio (max continuous, 6,000 m; 18,300 ft; 272 knots; 505 km/h; 314 mph) 7·85 : 1. Air mass flow 14·4 kg (31·7 lb)/s.

COMBUSTION CHAMBER: Annular, of spot-welded heat-resistant steel, with eight simplex burners inserted into swirl-vane heads. Contains two starting units, each comprising a body, pilot burner and igniter plug.

FUEL GRADE: T-1, TS-1 to GOST 10227-62 (DERD.2494 or MIL-F-5616).

TURBINE: Three-stage axial. Three discs carry solid blades in fir-tree roots, and are automatically centred on each other when connected by stay-bolts to the extended flange at the rear of the turbine shaft. Shaft splined to compressor rear shaft and held by tie-rod; runs in roller bearing ahead of first turbine disc. Three stator diaphragms through-bolted together and to combustion-chamber casing. First nozzle diaphragm cooled by secondary air from combustion chamber. Rotor/stator sealing effected by soft inserts mounted in grooves in nozzle assemblies. Peak exhaust temperature during starting 750°C.

JET PIPE: Fixed-area type. Inner and outer rings connected by three hollow struts carrying 12 thermocouples.

REDUCTION GEAR: Planetary type, incorporating hydraulic torquemeter and electromagnetic negative-thrust transmitter for propeller auto-feathering. Magnesium alloy casing. Front flange of propeller shaft has end splines and 12 stud holes for type AV-72 propeller (AI-24T drives AV-72T propeller). Ratio 0·08255.

LUBRICATION: Pressure circulation system; hourly consumption not over 850 g (1·87 lb).

OIL GRADE: Mixture of 75% transformer oil GOST 982-56 or MK-8 (DERD.2490 or MIL-O-6081B) and 25% MS-20 or MK-22 (DERD.2472 or MIL-O-6082B).

ACCESSORIES: Mounted on front casing are starter/generator, alternator, propeller speed governor and centrifugal breather. Below casing are oil unit, air separator and removable box containing LP and HP fuel pumps and drives to hydraulic pump and tachometer

generators. Also on front casing are an aerodynamic probe, ice detector, and negative-thrust feathering valve, torque transmitter and oil filter.

STARTING: Electric STG-18TMO starter/generator supplied from ground power or from TG-16 APU.

DIMENSIONS:
Length overall	2,346 mm (92·36 in)
Width	677 mm (26·65 in)
Height	1,075 mm (42·32 in)

WEIGHT, DRY: 600 kg (1,323 lb)

PERFORMANCE RATINGS:
T-O:	
AI-24A	1,875 kW (2,515 ehp)
AI-24T	2,103 kW (2,820 ehp)
Cruise rating at 243 knots (450 km/h; 280 mph) at 6,000 m (18,300 ft):	
AI-24A	1,156 kW (1,550 ehp)
AI-24T	1,178 kW (1,580 ehp)

SPECIFIC FUEL CONSUMPTION:
At cruise rating:
AI-24A	91·3 μg/J (0·540 lb/h/shp)
AI-24T	90·1 μg/J (0·533 lb/h/shp)

OIL CONSUMPTION: 0·85 kg (1·87 lb)/h

IVCHENKO AI-25

This turbofan powers the three-engined Yakovlev Yak-40 STOL transport. The Aeroflot Yak-40 has the basic AI-25 engine, but the Yak-40B of the Soviet Air Force has an AI-25 with an aircooled HP turbine and rating of 17·13 kN (3,850 lb st). The AI-25 also powers the Czech L-39 trainer, and it was to be manufactured by Motorlet, Czechoslovakia, as the Walter Titan. The emergence of the Polish WSK-PZL-Mielec M-15 agricultural aircraft led to transfer of AI-25 activity to Poland, and mass production is now likely to take place in that country to provide engines for an M-15 programme estimated at 3,000 aircraft for the Soviet Union alone.

The Ivchenko bureau planned the engine for small transports, trainers and business jet aircraft. It is claimed to have an exceptional margin of flow stability and to be unusually robust and simple.

TYPE: Two-shaft turbofan.

AIR INTAKE: Fabricated from titanium sheet. Central bullet and intake leading-edges anti-iced by hot bleed air.

FAN: Three-stage axial. Drum/disc construction with pin-jointed blades. Casing and fan duct of magnesium alloy. Peak pressure ratio, 1·695 at 10,750 rpm. Bypass ratio 2.

COMPRESSOR: Eight-stage axial. Drum/disc construction of titanium, with aluminium and magnesium casing. Dovetailed blades. Peak pressure ratio, 4·68 at 16,640 rpm. Overall pressure ratio, 8.

COMBUSTION CHAMBER: Annular. Inner and outer casings joined upstream to 12 burner heads with stabilisers.

FUEL GRADE: T-1, TS-1 to GOST 10227-62 (DERD.2494, MIL-F-5616).

TURBINE: Single-stage HP turbine; two-stage LP turbine. Shrouded solid rotor blades held by fir-tree roots in cooled discs.

JET PIPE: Plain fixed convergent nozzles for core and bypass airflow. No mixer.

LUBRICATION: Self-contained, pressure circulating.

OIL GRADE: MK-8 to GOST 6457-66 or MK-6 to GOST 10328-63 (Western equivalents, DERD.2490 or MIL-O-6081B). Consumption 0·3 litres (0·53 Imp pints)/h.

ACCESSORIES: All shaft-driven accessories mounted on gearbox on underside of engine and driven off HP spool. Equipment includes automatic fire extinguishing (agent can be supplied into oil-contacted labyrinth cavities), ice protection, automatic starting and control system, oil-system chip detector and casing vibration monitor.

STARTING: Pneumatic. Air starter type SV-25 is supplied from ground hose coupling or from APU type AI-9 or an operating engine bleed. System claimed to develop high torque for rapid start in any climatic condition, and

Ivchenko AI-25 turbofan (14·68 kN; 3,300 lb st)

to be cleared for exceptional number of starts in given overhaul life.

DIMENSIONS:
Length overall	1,993 mm (78·46 in)
Width overall	820 mm (32·28 in)
Height overall	895 mm (35·24 in)

WEIGHT, DRY:
Without accessories	290 kg (639 lb)

PERFORMANCE RATINGS:
T-O	14·68 kN (3,300 lb st)
Long-range cruise rating, 6,000 m (20,000 ft) and 296 knots (550 km/h; 342 mph)	3·49 kN (785 lb st)

SPECIFIC FUEL CONSUMPTION:
T-O	15·86 mg/Ns (0·56 lb/h/lb st)
Cruise, as above	23·71 mg/Ns (0·837 lb/h/lb st)

KOLIESOV

During an official tour of the Soviet aircraft industry in mid-1973, a representative of *Air Force Magazine* was told of the existence of the hitherto-unreported Koliesov engine design bureau. It was then developing an alternative engine to the Kuznetsov NK-144, the power plant used in the Tu-144 and, probably, in the Tupolev Tu-22M/Tu-26 bomber, known to NATO as 'Backfire'.

The Koliesov engine was described as a variable-geometry, variable by-pass ratio engine which functions as a turbojet in supersonic flight and as a turbofan in the subsonic regime. No such advanced design exists in the West. This engine could power a reported new Soviet strategic bomber (unofficially said to be the Tu-160).

Soviet engine designers are reported to be experimenting also with hypersonic vehicles powered by scramjet propulsion systems and capable of operating in the Mach 5 to Mach 7 range.

KUZNETSOV

GENERAL DESIGNER IN CHARGE OF BUREAU: Nikolai Dmitrievich Kuznetsov

Kuznetsov was deputy to General V. Ya. Klimov during the second World War. In the late 1940s his own bureau at Kuibyshev developed a series of large turboprop and turbofan engines. One of the first, the NK-4, was transferred to Ivchenko, and is described under that collective's heading, as the AI-20. The much larger NK-12 turboprop was used in the Tu-95 and Tu-126 military aircraft and in the Tu-114 civil transport, and was produced subsequently in small numbers for the An-22. The NK-8 and NK-144 may no longer be produced in their original forms.

KUZNETSOV NK-8

One of the first Soviet civil turbofans, the NK-8 has been developed through a number of variants, the most powerful of which is the NK-144 supersonic augmented engine for the Tupolev Tu-144 supersonic transport. Basic versions are the 99·1 kN (22,273 lb st) **NK-8-4** which originally powered the Ilyushin Il-62 four-engined transport, and the further-developed 93·2 kN (20,950 lb) **NK-8-2** which was the original engine of the Tupolev Tu-154. At one time it was planned to replace the NK-8-2 by the Soloviev D-30K, which replaced the NK-8-4 in the Il-62M. It is believed that all current Tu-154A/B aircraft are powered by the **NK-8-2U** of greater thrust (details unknown in the West). The NK-8-4 remains in service with several Il-62 (not Il-62M) operators, including LOT. It led to the NK-86 described later.

TYPE: Two-shaft turbofan.

AIR INTAKE: Fabricated from outer ring, inner splitter and welded stator blades (15 in core airflow, 30 ahead of fan). Hot-air ice-protection.

FAN: Two-stage axial, with anti-flutter sweptback blades on first rotor stage. Pressure ratio 2·15 at 5,350 rpm. Bypass ratio 1·02 (NK-8-2, 1·00).

COMPRESSOR: Two IP stages on fan shaft. Six-stage HP compressor. Construction of both rotors and stators, including blading, almost wholly of titanium alloy. Core pressure ratio, 10·8 at 6,950 HP rpm (NK-8-2, 10 at 6,835 rpm).

COMBUSTION CHAMBER: Annular, with 139 burners. Claimed to produce no visible smoke.

FUEL GRADE: T-1 and TS-1 to GOST 10227-62 or T-7 to GOST 12308-66 (equivalent to Avtur 50 to DERD.2494 or MIL-F-5616).

TURBINE: Single-stage HP turbine, two-stage LP turbine, all with shrouded rotor blades, aircooled discs and hollow nozzle blades (stators). All shafting carried between shock-absorbing bearings at each end, with labyrinth and contact (rubbing) graphite seals to prevent gas leakage. Gas temperature, not over 870°C (1,143°K) ahead of turbine, not over 670°C (NK-8-2, 650°C) downstream, both values sea level, static.

JET PIPE: Mixer leads bypass flow into common jet pipe which may be fitted with blocker/cascade-type reverser giving up to 48% (NK-8-2, 45%) reverse thrust, and noise suppressor.

LUBRICATION: Continuous pressure feed and recirculation. Oil consumption not over 1·3 kg (2·87 lb)/h. Pressure not less than 2·28 bars (33 lb/sq in).

OIL GRADE: Mineral oil MK-8 or MK-8P to GOST 6457-66 (DERD.2490 or MIL-O-6081B). External tank on left side of front casing.

ACCESSORIES: These include automatic flight-deck warning of vibration exceeding permissible limit, ice and fire. All accessories grouped beneath fan duct casing. Engine claimed to need no attention for long periods, other than inspection of fuel and oil filters. RTA-26-9-1 turbine gas temperature controller by Smiths Industries.

STARTING: HP spool driven by constant-speed drive type PPO-62M, or started pneumatically by air from APU type TA-6, from ground hose or by air from another engine (NK-8-2, pneumatic starter only). Time to idling speed not over 80 s. Engine can be windmill-started in the air under all conditions, up to altitudes of 11,000 m (36,000 ft).

DIMENSIONS:
NK-8-4:
Length, no reverser	5,100 mm (201 in)

NK-8-2:
Length, with reverser	5,288 mm (208·19 in)
Length, without reverser	4,762 mm (187·48 in)
Diameter	1,442 mm (56·8 in)

WEIGHT, DRY:
NK-8-4:
No reverser	2,100 kg (4,629 lb)
With reverser	2,400 kg (5,291 lb)

NK-8-2:
No reverser	2,100 kg (4,629 lb) max
With reverser	2,350 kg (5,180 lb) max

PERFORMANCE RATINGS:
NK-8-4:
T-O rating	99·1 kN (22,273 lb st)
Cruise rating at 11,000 m (36,000 ft) and 458 knots (850 km/h; 530 mph)	27 kN (6,063 lb st)

NK-8-2:
T-O rating	93·2 kN (20,950 lb st)
Cruise (as above)	17·65 kN (3,968 lb st)

SPECIFIC FUEL CONSUMPTION:
At cruise rating at 11,000 m (36,000 ft) and 458 knots (850 km/h; 530 mph):
NK-8-4	22·1 mg/Ns (0·78 lb/h/lb st)
NK-8-2	21·53 mg/Ns (0·76 lb/h/lb st)

Kuznetsov NK-8-2 turbofan with thrust reverser (93·2 kN; 20,950 lb st)

KUZNETSOV NK-86

Though described by the Ilyushin aircraft bureau as a new engine, this turbofan of 127·5 kN (28,660 lb st) appears to be closely related to the lower-thrust NK-8 series used in the Il-62 and Tu-154. The thrust is the same as the unaugmented rating of the NK-144 (see below) and the NK-86 may bear an even closer resemblance to the supersonic engine, which was itself derived from the NK-8. Four NK-86s power the Il-86 wide-body transport.

KUZNETSOV NK-144

This is the two-spool augmented turbofan developed for the Soviet Union's first supersonic transport aircraft, the Tu-144. It is a development of the NK-8 and the first five pre-production NK-144s completed some 1,500 h of bench-testing by October 1965. The engine flew in at least one testbed aircraft before the start of the Tu-144 flight programme in 1968.

Since 1972 the afterburner augmentation has been increased, raising maximum rating from 171·6 kN (38,580 lb) to the figure given below. A version of the NK-144 is believed to be the engine of at least the first sub-type of the Tupolev Tu-22M/Tu 26 supersonic bomber known to NATO as 'Backfire'.

The NK-144 is reported to have a two-stage titanium fan, three-stage IP compressor, eleven-stage HP compressor, annular combustion chamber, single-stage HP turbine and two-stage LP turbine. Aircooled blades are used in the HP turbine, and titanium is used extensively in construc-

Kuznetsov NK-12MV single-shaft turboprop of 11,033 ekW (14,795 ehp)
(courtesy of Aviation Magazine International, Paris)

tion of the engine. Bypass ratio is reported to be 1 : 1, maximum mass flow 250 kg (551 lb)/s, and pressure ratio 15 : 1. The jet pipe incorporates an afterburner, with hydraulically-actuated variable-area nozzle. Gas temperature at turbine entry is 1,050°C.

DIMENSIONS:

Length overall	5,200 mm (204·7 in)
Diameter	1,500 mm (59 in)

WEIGHT:

Without jet pipe, but with afterburner	2,850 kg (6,283 lb)

PERFORMANCE RATINGS:

Max, without afterburning	127·5 kN (28,660 lb st)
Max, with afterburning	196·1 kN (44,090 lb st)

KUZNETSOV NK-12M

Designed at Kuibishev under the leadership of N. D. Kuznetsov and former German engineers, the NK-12M is the most powerful turboprop engine in the world. In its original form as the NK-12M it developed 8,948 kW (12,000 ehp). The later NK-12MV is rated at 11,033 kW (14,795 ehp) and powers the Tupolev Tu-114 transport, driving four-blade contra-rotating propellers of 5·6 m (18 ft 4 in) diameter. As the NK-12MA, rated at 11,185 kW (15,000 shp), it powers the Antonov An-22 military transport, with propellers of 6·2 m (20 ft 4 in) diameter. A third application is in the Tupolev Tu-95 bomber and its derivatives, and Tu-126 'AWACS'.

The NK-12M has a single 14-stage axial-flow compressor. Compression ratio varies from 9 : 1 to 13 : 1 according to altitude, and variable inlet guide vanes and blow-off valves are necessary. A cannular-type combustion system is used: each flame tube is mounted centrally on a downstream injector, but all tubes merge at their maximum diameter to form an annular secondary region. The single turbine is a five-stage axial. Mass flow is 65 kg (143 lb)/s.

The casing is made in four portions, from sheet steel, precision welded. An electric control for variation of propeller pitch is incorporated, to maintain constant engine speed.

DIMENSIONS:

Length	6,000 mm (236·2 in)
Diameter	1,150 mm (45·3 in)

WEIGHT, DRY: 2,350 kg (5,181 lb)

PERFORMANCE RATINGS:

T-O	11,033 kW (14,795 ehp)
Nominal power	8,826 kW (11,836 ehp) at 8,300 rpm
Idling speed	6,600 rpm

LOTAREV

GENERAL DESIGNER IN CHARGE OF BUREAU: Vladimir Lotarev

LOTAREV D-36

As successor to Alexander Ivchenko at Zaparozhye, Vladimir Lotarev has developed the three-shaft turbofan engine that powers the An-72 and Yak-42. With a bypass ratio of 5·34 : 1 the D-36 is the first avowed turbofan—as distinct from a bypass turbojet—to emerge in the Soviet Union. Bench testing was in progress in September 1973, and flights in a pod carried beneath a Tu-16 testbed aircraft preceded the Yak-42 first flight by several years.

No details had been disclosed as this edition went to press, though Western engineers visiting the Soviet Union report that the D-36 is a more advanced and modern engine than other Soviet commercial gas turbines in current production.

WEIGHT, DRY: 1,080 kg (2,480 lb)

PERFORMANCE RATINGS:

T-O rating	63·74 kN (14,330 lb st)
Max cont	49·0 kN (11,025 lb st)
Max cruise rating at 8,000 m (26,200 ft) at Mach 0·75	15·7 kN (3,525 lb st)

SPECIFIC FUEL CONSUMPTION:

At T-O rating	10·62 mg/Ns (0·375 lb/h/lb st)
At max cont rating	9·83 mg/Ns (0·347 lb/h/lb st)
At max cruise rating as above	18·4 mg/Ns (0·65 lb/h/lb st)

LYULKA

GENERAL DESIGNER IN CHARGE OF BUREAU: Arkhip Mikhailovich Lyulka

During the late 1930s Arkhip Lyulka worked on the design of an axial turbojet that became an early war casualty. In 1942 he planned a more advanced engine that finally materialised as the TR-1, of 12·75 kN (2,866 lb st), run on the bench in 1944 and used in the Ilyushin Il-22 four-jet bomber and Sukhoi Su-11 twin-jet fighter prototypes, both of 1947. Ultimately, in 1948, this pioneer Soviet-designed turbojet was developed to give 14·71 kN (3,307 lb st).

In 1946 Lyulka began the design of a very ambitious axial engine to give a thrust of 44·13 kN (9,920 lb), and in 1950 this began bench trials under the designation AL-5. Although of basically simple, single-shaft configuration, with a seven-stage compressor and single-stage turbine, the AL-5 was more powerful than any Western engine apart from the prototype Olympus and J57. By 1951 it was rated at 45·1 kN (10,140 lb st) and flew in the prototype Ilyushin Il-30 twin-jet bomber; later in 1951-52 uprated AL-5 engines, giving a static thrust of 49·1 kN (11,032 lb), powered the Il-46 twin-jet bomber and the transonic Lavochkin La-190 and Yakovlev Yak-1000 fighters. An advanced civil version of the same engine, the AL-5 rated at 53·93 kN (12,125 lb st) powered the Tu-110 four-engined derivative of the Tu-104 airliner that did not go into production (at the time, in 1959, this engine was reported in the West as the 'Lu-4').

By the time the AL-5 was running, Lyulka had conducted extensive research with axial compressors having supersonic airflow through some or all of the stages. It was clear that, if problems of flow breakdown and inefficiency could be resolved, such a compressor would enable turbojets to be made much smaller and lighter for a given thrust and with greater thrust per unit frontal area, and thus much better suited to the propulsion of supersonic fighters. By 1952 a supersonic-compressor engine had been designed and built. This, the AL-7, became Lyulka's first major success.

LYULKA AL-7

The first AL-7 ran on the bench in late 1952 and the first production version was cleared for use in 1954 at a design rating of 63·74 kN (14,330 lb st). Its initial application was on the Il-54, yet another Ilyushin twin-jet bomber that failed to see production, despite the fact that its speed at low altitude of 620 knots (1,150 km/h; 714 mph) was probably unrivalled by any other bomber in 1955. In the same year the Sukhoi Su-7 single-seat ground-attack fighter was designed around the AL-7F afterburning version of this engine, with thrust increased by about 40 per cent (see data below). By 1956 the Su-7 was flying, and the AL-7F had also been chosen for the basically similar Su-9 all-weather fighter. Subsequently the -7F was also produced for the Su-11 and -11U.

By 1958 a further developed version of the basic unaugmented engine, the AL-7PB, had been chosen by Beriev for the Be-10 reconnaissance flying-boat, which—apart from being the only pure-jet flying-boat ever to go into service anywhere—set up a number of world records for speed, load-carrying and altitude. Other versions of the AL-7, in both cases of the -7F afterburning family, powered the unsuccessful Tu-98 bomber and La-250 strike fighter of 1956.

The AL-7F, or a development of it, has been persistently reported to be the power plant of the Tu-28P twin-engined interceptor. This is not confirmed. The Tu-28P is considered to need greater thrust, greater even than provided by the AL-21 which was not available when the Tu-28 entered service in the early 1960s.

TYPE: Single-shaft axial-flow turbojet, available with or without afterburner.

AIR INTAKE: Central bullet fairing and 14 fixed aerofoil struts anti-iced by compressor bleed air.

COMPRESSOR: Nine-stage axial (probably eight stages in original AL-7 design). First two stages widely separated axially, with variable stators ahead of second stage. Each stage has blades inserted in centreless disc held by peripheral spacers at correct distance from adjacent discs, the whole being coupled together finally by the central drive-shaft in tension. Pressure ratio probably about 8 : 1.

COMBUSTION CHAMBER: Annular type with perforated inner flame tube. Multiple downstream fuel injectors inserted through cups in forward face of liner. Liner outer casing provided with multiple inward secondary-air injection ducts.

TURBINE: Two-stage axial-flow type. Both wheels overhung behind rear bearing; front disc bolted to flange on hollow tubular driveshaft which, in turn, is splined to rear of compressor shaft running in main centre bearing which locates compressor axially against end loads.

AFTERBURNER (AL-7F): Comprises upstream diffuser and downstream combustion section. Pilot combustor on turbine exit cone includes single nozzle ring and flame-holder; main spray ring and gutter flame-holder assembly located further downstream at greater radius. Refractory liner in combustion section. Variable-area nozzle, with multiple hinged flaps which govern nozzle size and profile according to signals from reheat control system based on turbine exit temperature and throttle lever position.

ACCESSORIES: Fuel pump and control unit, oil pumps, hydraulic pump, electric generator, tachometer and other items grouped into quickly replaceable packages beneath compressor casing.

PERFORMANCE RATINGS:

Max rating:

AL-7F, unaugmented	68·64 kN (15,432 lb st)
AL-7F, afterburning	98·1 kN (22,046 lb st)
AL-7PB	63·74 kN (14,330 lb st)

LYULKA AL-21

When continued development of the Su-7 family by the Sukhoi bureau was matched with increased thrust it was logical to suppose that the engine would be a derivative of the AL-7. This is reported to have happened, and the designation AL-21 has been given. The AL-21 resembles the AL-7 closely, and may be installationally interchangeable, but has significant improvements to the compressor and other components. The first production version was the AL-21F-3, for the Su-17 variable-geometry tactical aircraft. The very important twin-engined Su-24 has engines in the same thrust class and possibly from the Lyulka bureau.

PERFORMANCE RATINGS:

Max S/L, unaugmented	80·1 kN (18,000 lb st)
Max S/L, afterburning	109 kN (24,500 lb st)

MIKULIN

GENERAL DESIGNER IN CHARGE OF BUREAU: Alexander Alexandrovich Mikulin

Eighty years old on 16 February 1975, Mikulin has been engaged in aircraft engine design since 1916. Notable Vee-12 water-cooled engines from his designs were the AM-13, AM-34, AM-38 (used in the Il-2 and Il-10 Stormovik) and AM-42.

Very large numbers of M-11 five-cylinder radial engines have been built in the Soviet Union and (from 1949) Poland to power a variety of light aircraft and helicopters. Best-known variants are the 93 kW (125 hp) M-11D and the 119 kW (160 hp) M-11FR which powers the Yak-18 primary trainer. Brief descriptions appeared in the 1975-76 *Jane's*.

The large turbojet described below was designed immediately after the second World War. Though a version was fitted to M-4 four-engined prototypes, it is not known if Mikulin's bureau was involved with the Soloviev D-15 fitted to later M-4 aircraft.

MIKULIN RD-3M-500

The basic RD-3M (or AM-3M) single-spool axial-flow turbojet was developed under the design leadership of P. F. Zubets from the original Mikulin M-209 (civil RD-3 or AM-3) engine which powers the Tu-16 and early M-4 bombers and was adapted for the USSR's first jet transport, the Tu-104.

The RD-3M-500 was evolved, in turn, from the RD-3M and powers the Tu-104A and Tu-104B commercial transports. It has a simple basic configuration, with an eight-stage axial-flow compressor, annular-type combustion system with 14 flame tubes, and a two-stage turbine. The compressor casing is made in front, centre and rear portions, the front casing housing a row of inlet guide vanes. A bullet fairing mounted centrally in the annular ram-air intake houses a type S-300M gas-turbine starter, developing 90-100 hp at 31,000-35,000 rpm. The jet pipe consists of a central cone and fixed nozzle with an orifice diameter of approximately 840 mm (33 in). Pressure ratio is 6·4 : 1; temperature after turbine 720°C.

DIMENSIONS:

Length overall	5,340 mm (210·23 in)
Diameter	1,400 mm (55·12 in)

PERFORMANCE RATING:

T-O	93·15 kN (20,940 lb st)

SHVETSOV

FOUNDER OF BUREAU: Arkadiya Dmitrievich Shvetsov

Arkadiya Shvetsov had meteoric rise to fame with his aircooled radial engines based on original US designs, which transformed Soviet fighters, bombers and transport aircraft during and after the second World War. The most important, and most powerful, of these engines was the ASh-82 series, derived from the Pratt & Whitney Twin Wasp, which at ratings up to 1,491 kW (2,000 hp) powered Lavochkin fighters, the Tu-2 and Tu-4 bombers, Il-12 and -14 transports and Mi-4 and Yak-24 helicopters (see 1975-76 *Jane's*). The ASh-62, originally based on the Wright Cyclone, was made in large numbers at ratings in the 750 kW (1,000 hp) class for the Li-2 and An-2. The ASh-62M agricultural version, developed by Vedeneev, and all An-2 engines after 1952, were transferred with all other Soviet aircooled radials to Poland (see WSK-PZL-Kalisz and WSK-PZL-Rzeszów in Polish part of this section). Another important Shvetsov piston engine was the 545 kW (730 hp) ASh-21, fitted to the Yak-11. All these engines have been described in earlier editions.

SOLOVIEV

GENERAL DESIGNER IN CHARGE OF BUREAU: P. A. Soloviev

Engines for which Soloviev's design team is responsible include the turbofans fitted in the Ilyushin Il-62M and Il-76 and Tupolev Tu-124 and Tu-134 transport aircraft, and the turboshafts which power the Mi-6, Mi-10 and V-12 helicopters.

SOLOVIEV D-15

This engine was first reported, in 1959, as that fitted to the four-engined Type 201-M aircraft which gained a number of world records for speed and altitude. Over the years it has become apparent that the aircraft was a special Myasishchev M-4, and that the engine was standard in the later service versions of this aircraft. Details of the D-15 are still unknown in the West, but it is probably safe to deduce that it is a two-shaft bypass turbojet (low bypass ratio turbofan). It is likely that it laid the foundation upon which Soloviev's bureau produced the civil D-20 and D-30, both of which are considerably smaller engines.

PERFORMANCE RATING:
T-O   128·6 kN (28,660 lb st)

SOLOVIEV D-20P

The D-20P is a two-spool turbofan fitted to the Tupolev Tu-124 twin-engined passenger transport. Of conservative design, it underwent prolonged testing before entering service. It was designed for maximum economy and reliability over the range of ambient temperatures between −40°C and 40°C.

TYPE: Two-shaft turbofan (bypass turbojet).
AIR INTAKE: Eight radial struts and central bullet fairing, de-iced by hot bleed air from fourth HP stage (from final stage at low rpm).
FAN: Three-stage axial, with supersonic blading in first stage. Mass flow 113 kg (249 lb)/s at 8,550 rpm. Pressure ratio (S/L, static at max cont 7,900 rpm) 2·4 : 1. Bypass ratio 1 : 1.
COMPRESSOR: Eight-stage axial. Automatically-controlled flap valves downstream of the third and fourth stages bleed air into the fan duct to stabilise behaviour. Pressure ratio (at max continuous, 11,170 rpm) 5 : 1; overall pressure ratio 13 : 1.
COMBUSTION CHAMBER: Can-annular, with 12 flame tubes each fitted with duplex burner.
FUEL GRADE: T-1, TS-1 to GOST 10227-62 (Avtur-50 to DERD.2494, MIL-F-5616).
TURBINE: Single-stage HP turbine with cast blades; stator blades and both sides of disc cooled by bleed air. Two-stage LP turbine with forged blades. Max gas temperature downstream of turbine 650°C.
JET PIPE: Concentric pipes for fan airflow and core gas, terminating in supersonic nozzles of fixed-area type.
LUBRICATION: Open type, with oil returned to tank. Consumption in flight, not over 1 kg (2·2 lb)/h. Typical pressure 3·4-4·5 kg/cm² (50-64 lb/sq in).
OIL GRADE: Mineral oil MK-8 or MK-8P to GOST 6457-66 (DERD.2490 or MIL-O-6081B).
ACCESSORIES: Two gearboxes provide drives for starter/generator, tachometer, air compressors, hydraulic pump, oil pump and other controls and instruments. For restarting in flight, an altitude sensing device meters fuel flow appropriate to height. An automatic fire extinguishing system is fitted. De-icing of the air intake and inlet guide vanes is controlled automatically. The engine also has oil chip detectors, vibration monitors and turbine gas temperature limiters.
STARTING: Electric (DC) system, incorporating STG-18TM starter/generator.
DIMENSIONS:
Length overall   3,304 mm (130 in)
Diameter, bare   976 mm (38·3 in)
WEIGHT, DRY: 1,468 kg (3,236 lb)

Soloviev D-20P turbofan (52·96 kN; 11,905 lb st)

PERFORMANCE RATINGS:
Max T-O rating   52·96 kN (11,905 lb st)
Long-range cruise, Mach 0·75, 11,000 m (36,000 ft)
                        10·79 kN (2,425 lb st)
SPECIFIC FUEL CONSUMPTION:
Max T-O   20·4 mg/Ns (0·72 lb/h/lb st)
Long-range cruise, as above
                        25·5 mg/Ns (0·90 lb/h/lb st)

SOLOVIEV D-25V

D-25V is the Soloviev bureau designation for the free-turbine turboshaft which powers the Mil Mi-6, Mi-10 and V-12 helicopters and was also fitted to the Kamov Ka-22 experimental convertiplane. It is usually referred to by its official designation of **TV-2BM**.

The complete helicopter power plant comprises two D-25V engines, identical except for handed jet pipes, and an R-7 gearbox. The latter has four stages of large gearwheels providing an overall ratio of 69·2 : 1. The R-7 is 2,795 mm (110·04 in) high, 1,551 mm (61·06 in) wide and 1,852 mm (72·91 in) long. Its dry weight is 3,200 kg (7,054 lb), more than that of the pair of engines.

The D-25V is flat rated to maintain rated power to 3,000 m (10,000 ft) or to temperatures up to 40°C at sea level.

The D-25VF turboshafts fitted to the Mil V-12 helicopter are uprated to 6,500 shp. These engines are believed to incorporate a zero stage on the compressor and to operate at higher turbine gas temperatures. The following details apply to the basic D-25V:

TYPE: Single-shaft turboshaft with free power turbine.
AIR INTAKE: Six hollow radial struts, the two vertical struts housing splined shafts driving upper and lower accessory drive boxes. Vertical struts de-iced by oil drained from upper drive box; four inclined struts and bullet fairing de-iced by hot oil returned from engine to tank.
COMPRESSOR: Nine-stage axial. Comprises fixed inlet guide vane assembly, first-stage stator ring, upper and lower casings with dovetailed stator blades, ninth-stage stator ring and exit vanes, rotor, and air blow-off valves. Pressure ratio 5·6 at T-O power, 10,530 rpm.
COMBUSTION CHAMBER: Can-annular. Assembled from diffuser (the structural basis of the engine), inner shroud, 12 flame tubes with transition liners, diaphragm and compressor-shaft shroud.
FUEL GRADE: T-1, TS-1 to GOST 10227-62 (DERD.2494, MIL-F-5616).

TURBINE: Single-stage compressor turbine, overhung behind rear roller bearing. Two-stage power turbine, overhung on end of rear output shaft. Both turbines rotate counter-clockwise, seen from the rear. Normal power turbine rpm, 7,800-8,300; maximum 9,000. Transmission shaft in three universally-jointed sections, allowing for 10 mm (4 in) misalignment between engine and gearbox.
JET PIPE: Large fabricated assembly in heat-resistant steel, curved out to side to allow rotor transmission to pass through duct wall in aircooled protecting pipe.
LUBRICATION: Pressure circulation at 3·45-4·41 bars (50-64 lb/sq in). Separate systems for gas-generator and for power turbine, transmission and gearbox.
OIL GRADE: Gas-generator, MK-8 to GOST 6457-66 or transformer oil to GOST 982-56. Power turbine and gearbox, mixture (75-25 Summer, 50-50 Winter) of MK-22 or MS-20 to GOST 1013-49 and MK-8 or transformer oil. Hourly oil consumption, gas-generator not over 1 kg (2·2 lb), power turbine and transmission not over 2 kg (4·4 lb).
ACCESSORIES: SP3-12TV electric supply and starting system; fuel supply to separate LP and HP systems; airframe accessories driven off upper and lower gearboxes on inlet casing.
STARTING: The SP3-12TV system starts both engines and also generates electric current. It comprises an STG-12TM starter/generator on each engine, igniter unit, two spark plugs with cooling shrouds, two switch-over contactors, solenoid air valve, pressure warning, PSG-12V control panel and electro-hydraulic cutout switch of the TsP-23A centrifugal governor. In the starter mode the system draws current from a ground supply receptacle or from batteries.
DIMENSIONS:
Length overall, bare   2,737 mm (107·75 in)
Length overall with transmission shaft
                              5,537 mm (218·0 in)
Width   1,086 mm (42·76 in)
Height   1,158 mm (45·59 in)
WEIGHT, DRY:
With engine-mounted accessories 1,325 kg (2,921 lb)
PERFORMANCE RATINGS:
T-O   4,101 kW (5,500 shp)
Rated power   3,504 kW (4,700 shp)
Cruise (1,000 m; 3,280 ft, 135 knots; 250 km/h; 155 mph)
                              2,983 kW (4,000 shp)
SPECIFIC FUEL CONSUMPTION:
T-O, as above   108 μg/J (0·639 lb/h/shp)
Cruise, as above   118·1 μg/J (0·699 lb/h/shp)

SOLOVIEV D-30

This two-spool turbofan powers the Tu-134 twin-engined airliner and is derived from the D-20. Major portions of the core and carcase are similar, but the complete power plant is larger than the D-20, and more powerful and efficient.

In turn the D-30 has been developed into the considerably larger D-30K, described separately. They showed a continuing allegiance to the form of power plant pioneered by Rolls-Royce as the 'bypass turbojet', a term still used in the Soviet Union to describe these engines, in which the LP system comprises several stages and the bypass ratio is not greater than unity (in the West most turbofans have single-stage fans with a bypass ratio of from 3 to 8).

The 4,101 kW (5,500 shp) Soloviev D-25V turboshaft

TYPE: Two-shaft turbofan (bypass turbojet).
AIR INTAKE: Titanium alloy assembly, incorporating air bleed anti-icing of centre bullet and radial struts.
FAN: Four-stage axial (LP compressor). First stage has shrouded titanium blades held in disc by pinned joints. Pressure ratio (T-O rating, 7,700 rpm, S/L, static), 2·65 : 1. Mass flow 125 kg (265 lb)/s. Bypass ratio 1 : 1.
COMPRESSOR: Ten-stage axial (HP compressor). Drum and disc construction, largely of titanium. Pressure ratio (T-O rating, 11,600 rpm, S/L, static), 7·1 : 1. Overall pressure ratio, 17·4 : 1.
COMBUSTION CHAMBER: Can-annular, with 12 flame tubes fitted with duplex burners.
FUEL GRADE: T-1 and TS-1 to GOST 10227-62 (equival-, ent to DERD.2494 or MIL-F-5616).
TURBINE: Two-stage HP turbine. First stage has cooled blades in both stator and rotor. LP turbine also has two stages. All discs aircooled on both sides, and all blades shrouded to improve efficiency and reduce vibration. All shaft bearings shock-mounted.
JET PIPE: Subsonic fixed-area type, incorporating main and bypass flow mixer with curvilinear ducts of optimum shape. D-30-2 engine of Tu-134A fitted with twin-clamshell reverser.
LUBRICATION: Open type, with oil returned to tank.
OIL GRADE: Mineral oil MK-8 or MK-8P to GOST 6457-66 (equivalent to DERD.2490 or MIL-O-6081B). Consumption in flight not over 1·0 kg (2·2 lb)/h.
ACCESSORIES: Automatic ice-protection system, fire extinguishing for core and bypass flows, vibration detectors on casings, oil chip detectors and automatic limitation of exhaust gas temperature to 620°C at take-off or when starting and to 630°C in flight (5 min limit). Shaft-driven accessories driven via radial bevel-gear shafts in centre casing, mainly off HP spool, accessory gearboxes being provided above and below centre casing and fan duct. D-30-2 carries constant-speed drives for alternators.
STARTING: Electric DC starting system incorporating STG-12TVMO starter/generators.
DIMENSIONS:
Overall length	3,983 mm (156·8 in)
Base diameter of inlet casing	1,050 mm (41·3 in)
WEIGHT, DRY:	1,550 kg (3,417 lb)

PERFORMANCE RATINGS:
T-O	66·68 kN (14,990 lb st)
Long-range cruise rating, 11,000 m (36,000 ft) and Mach 0·75	12·75 kN (2,866 lb st)

SPECIFIC FUEL CONSUMPTION:
T-O	17·56 mg/Ns (0·62 lb/h/lb st)
Cruise, as above	21·81 mg/Ns (0·77 lb/h/lb st)

SOLOVIEV D-30K

Despite its designation, this turbofan is very different from the D-30 described previously. It is larger, and has a much higher rating, a bypass ratio considerably higher, and very few parts (in the core) common to the D-30.

The basic **D-30KU** version, to which the specification details below apply, replaced the Kuznetsov NK-8 as power plant of the Ilyushin Il-62M long-range transport. The more powerful **D-30KP**, rated at 117·7 kN (26,455 lb st), powers the Ilyushin Il-76 freight transport. Clamshell-type thrust reversers are fitted to all four engines of this aircraft, and to the outer engines of the Il-62M. These reversers are not an integral part of the engine but are airframe assemblies incorporated in the nacelle.
TYPE: Two-shaft turbofan, with integral flow mixer and reverser.
AIR INTAKE: Fabricated from titanium alloy. Fixed spinner and 26 cambered inlet guide vanes anti-iced by air bled from sixth or eleventh stage of HP compressor (depending on rpm). Integral front roller bearing for LP shaft.
FAN (LP compressor): Three stages, mainly of titanium alloy. First-stage rotor blades held in dovetail slots, with

part-span anti-vibration snubbers. Other two stages have pinned rotor blades. Spool rotates between front roller bearing and rear ball bearing, with additional roller bearing behind LP turbine. Drum/disc construction, coupled with tie-bolt and driven by splined shaft connection. Mass flow at take-off, 269 kg (593 lb)/s at 4,730 rpm (87·9 per cent), with bypass ratio of 2·42.
DIVISION CASING: Linking the LP and HP compressors, this is the main structural attachment band to the aircraft. Magnesium-alloy casting, held by front and rear rows of peripheral bolts. Carries LP mid bearing and HP front bearing and incorporates vertical radial drive to front drive box for accessories on underside.
HP COMPRESSOR: Eleven stages. Drum/disc rotor, with discs centred on shaft by rectangular splines. Rotor blades held in dovetail slots, first two stages having part-span snubbers. Construction of titanium alloys, except for shafts, rear casing, and rotor blades and discs of stages 9-11, and stator vanes of stages 10-11, which are steel. To reduce blade vibration inlet guide vanes are turned through up to 30° according to preset programme over speed range of 7,900-9,600 rpm, while air is bled from fifth and sixth stages under transient conditions; in addition a closed peripheral chamber with perforated walls surrounds the first-stage rotor blades. HP shaft supported in front roller bearing in division casing, ball thrust bearing at rear of compressor spool and roller bearing ahead of turbine. Casing split horizontally. Overall pressure ratio (S/L, static) 20 at HP speed of 10,460 rpm (96 per cent).
COMBUSTION CHAMBER: Cannular type with 12 flame tubes in annular chamber. Each tube comprises hemispherical head and eight short sections welded with gaps for dilution air. Single swirl-type main/pilot burner centred in each tube. Igniter plugs in two tubes. Outer casing and duct shroud provided with longitudinal joints for access to flame tubes and HP turbine nozzle ring.
FUEL GRADE: T-1, TS-1, GOST-10227-62, A-1 (D1655/63t), DERD.2494 or 2498, Air 3405/B or 3-GP-23e.

TURBINES: Two-stage HP turbine with first-stage nozzles, part of second-stage nozzles and both sets of discs and rotor blades cooled by HP bleed air. Second-stage rotor blades tip-shrouded. Both discs interchangeable. Take-off inlet gas temperature 1,122°C. Four-stage LP turbine with uncooled shrouded rotor blades carried in four identical discs cooled by bypass air.
JET PIPE: Downstream of LP turbine a rear support frame serves as the rear structural band attaching the engine to the aircraft. This frame incorporates the rear LP shaft roller bearing and 12 thermocouples, and also includes the 16-chute mixer for the core and bypass flows.
LUBRICATION: Closed type, with oil returned to tank. Incorporates fuel/oil heat exchanger and centrifugal air separator with metal-particle warning unit.
OIL GRADE: MK-8 or MK-8P to GOST 6467-66 (mineral) or BNII NP-50-1-4F to GOST 13076-67 (synthetic) or Western equivalents.
ACCESSORIES: Front and rear drive boxes underneath engine carry all shaft-driven accessories. Differential constant-speed drive to alternator and air-turbine starter.
STARTING: Pneumatic air-turbine starter fed by ground supply, APU or cross-bleed from running engine. Start cycle time to idling rpm, 40-80 s depending on ambient temperature (limits, −60° to +50°C). In-flight starting up to 9,000 m (27,430 ft) by windmilling.
DIMENSIONS:
Length with reverser	5,700 mm (224 in)
Inlet diameter	1,464 mm (57·6 in)
Maximum diameter of casing	1,560 mm (61·4 in)

WEIGHT, DRY:
With reverser	2,650 kg (5,842 lb)
Without reverser	2,300 kg (5,071 lb)

PERFORMANCE RATINGS (ISA):
T-O	108 kN (24,250 lb st) to 21°C
Cruise at 11,000 m (36,000 ft) and Mach 0·8	27 kN (6,063 lb st)

SPECIFIC FUEL CONSUMPTION:
At T-O rating	13·88 mg/Ns (0·49 lb/h/lb st)
Cruise, as above	19·83 mg/Ns (0·70 lb/h/lb st)

Soloviev D-30 turbofan (66·68 kN; 14,990 lb st) with thrust reverser

Soloviev D-30KU turbofan (108 kN; 24,250 lb st)

TUMANSKY

Academician Sergei K. Tumansky, who died in 1973, left a legacy of turbojet and bypass jet engines which were the propulsion basis on which the MiG bureau created the MiG-21, in world-wide service, and the extremely high-performance MiG-25. Tumansky is believed also to have designed the engine of the MiG-23/27 and Su-15.

TUMANSKY R-11 and R-13

Designated TRD Mk R37F (turbojet R37F) by the Soviet armed forces, the R-11/R-13 family have been built in very large numbers, and two versions have been licence-built by HAL in India. At least one version is produced, without a licence, in China.

A single-shaft turbojet with afterburner, the R-11 entered production in 1956 with dry and afterburning ratings of 38·25 kN (8,600 lb) and 50 kN (11,240 lb) respectively. In 1959 a world speed record was set by the E-66, powered by an R-11-F2-300, with the same dry rating but a new afterburner giving a maximum thrust of 58·36 kN (13,120 lb). This engine also powered the production variant of the E-66, the MiG-21F, as well as MiG-21PF, FM, FL and possibly other versions.

A very similar engine is the R-11-F2S-300, which powers the Indian-built MiG-21M. It is believed that versions of the R-11 power all known versions of the twin-engined Yak-28.

The R-13-300 incorporates major changes to handle an increased airflow, and has dry and afterburning ratings of 50 kN (11,240 lb) and 64·72 kN (14,550 lb) respectively. It powers the latest known MiG-21 versions, including the MF. It is believed not to be installationally interchangeable with the R-11 series.

TUMANSKY R-266

In about 1961 the Tumansky bureau began the design of a jet engine with afterburner considerably more powerful than the R-11 and intended for flight at speeds higher than Mach 3. This engine was adopted by the MiG bureau for the MiG-25 twin-engined fighter. Existence of this Mach 3·2 aircraft was disclosed in April 1965 when its first world record was announced. At that time the aircraft was referred to as the E-266, and its engine as the TRD Mk 31. Thrust rating was given as 98·1 kN (22,046 lb).

Most production versions of the MiG-25 have a pair of R-266 engines. These are extremely simple afterburning turbojets similar in concept to the earlier de Havilland

Gyron. The single-shaft compressor has five stages and works at a peak pressure-ratio of about 7 : 1. The single-stage turbine is reported to be uncooled, an extraordinary feature for a Mach 3 engine. Construction is mainly of steel, with a little titanium. Turbine entry temperature is estimated at only 847°C (again a scarcely credible low figure). At supersonic speeds almost all the thrust is provided by the variable inlets, three-ring afterburner and variable nozzle. Special T-6 fuel is used with freezing point of −62·2°C and flash point of 54·4°C. Dry and augmented ratings are (S/L, static) 9,300 kg (20,500 lb) and 12,250 kg (27,010 lb).

A more powerful (R-266F ?) engine powers the latest 'Foxbat' interceptor (said to be the MiG-25MP), and possibly other variants. This engine is rated at 14,000 kg (30,865 lb st), and is almost certainly the same as the RD-F engines of the same rating which power the E-266M aircraft which set time-to-height records in 1975.

TUMANSKY MiG-23 ENGINE

Despite its importance, the engine of the MiG-23 is unknown in the West, though generally attributed to the Tumansky bureau. Basic design of the single-engined variable-geometry MiG-23 dates from 1962-63. Prototypes were flying by 1967, and the MiG-27 tactical attack version was in service by 1970. This has an engine, unofficially said to be designated R-29B, designed for STOL and low-level operation, with large LP compressor (fan) and simple afterburner. Dry and augmented ratings are estimated at 66·72 kN (15,000 lb) and 88·96 kN (20,000 lb) respectively. The engine is installed with simple fixed inlets and has a short two-position nozzle. The MiG-23S all-weather fighter has an engine sharing a common core but having a smaller LP compressor and large afterburner. This engine is designed for supersonic operation at Mach 1·8-2·1, and is fed by fully-variable supersonic inlets and discharges through a large fully modulated primary and secondary nozzle of variable profile. Dry and augmented ratings are estimated at 62·28 kN (14,000 lb) and 107 kN (24,000 lb) respectively. As far as can be judged, the same engine is fitted to the MiG-23U two-seat trainer, though it has been suggested that the lower-thrust R-27 is fitted to most aircraft (of all versions) for export.

By early 1979 Western observers seemed to be agreed that a smaller, but possibly related, engine is used in the Su-15 interceptor; the designation is said to be R-25, and the dry and augmented thrusts are given as 40 kN (9,000 lb st) and 73·4 kN (16,500 lb st) respectively.

Tumansky R-11 built under licence by HAL in India

VEDENEEV

GENERAL DESIGNER IN CHARGE OF BUREAU: Ivan M. Vedeneev

This designer was responsible for the improvement and development of certain models of the AI-14 piston engine designed by the Ivchenko bureau. He also developed the ASh-62M, produced in Poland as the ASz-62M, from Shvetsov's ASh-62IR nine-cylinder radial. He now heads his own bureau.

M-14V-26

Derived from the Ivchenko AI-14 family of engines for fixed-wing aircraft, the M-14V-26 powers the Kamov Ka-26 helicopter. In this installation the stub-wing carries an engine on each tip. Beneath the rotor an R-26 gearbox combines the power of the engines and distributes it equally between the two coaxial main rotors turning in opposite directions.

It is said to incorporate all the experience gained in many years of developing engines in this class, and shows numerous areas of refinement compared with the AI-14 series. The engine has forced cooling by an axial fan driven via a friction clutch and extension shaft ahead of the main output bevel box at 1·452 times crankshaft speed. The engine planetary gearbox has a ratio of 0·309 and incorporates friction and ratchet clutches. The central R-26 gearbox has a ratio of 0·34; it also drives the generator, hydraulic pump, oil pump and tachometer generator.

DIMENSIONS:
Diameter	985 mm (38·78 in)
Length	1,145 mm (45·08 in)

WEIGHT, DRY: 245 kg (540 lb)

PERFORMANCE RATINGS:
T-O	242 kW; 325 hp at 2,800 rpm
Max continuous I	205 kW; 275 hp at 2,450 rpm
Max continuous II	142 kW; 190 hp at 2,350 rpm
Cruise I	142 kW; 190 hp at 2,350 rpm
Cruise II	108 kW; 145 hp at 2,350 rpm

SPECIFIC FUEL CONSUMPTION:
At cruise ratings 77·7 μg/J (0·46 lb/h/hp)

VEDENEEV M-14P

With this engine Vedeneev reverted to the original fixed-wing application, apparently independently of the Ivchenko bureau. The M-14P is used with direct drive to a fixed-pitch two-blade propeller in the Moscow Aviation Institute OSKB-1-3PM and the Yak-18T.

In the former aircraft the T-O rating is given as 242 kW (325 hp), and in the Yak-18T as 269 kW (360 hp).

Vedeneev M-14V-26 radial piston engine, with cooling fan, for Kamov Ka-26 helicopter

ENGINES OF UNKNOWN DESIGN

1. RU 19-300. Auxiliary turbojet of 8·83 kN (1,985 lb st) for which the initial application was in the Antonov An-24/26/30 transports. Mounted in the rear of the starboard nacelle in place of the TG-16 APU, the RU 19-300 provides additional take-off thrust and also drives an integrally-mounted generator to relieve the aircraft's AI-24T turboprops of supplying electrical power during take-off. This arrangement increases the An-24RV's take-off performance under hot and high conditions, and improves single-engine handling and stability. After take-off, the auxiliary turbojet is shut down and the AI-24Ts are coupled mechanically to the engine-mounted generators. In this dual role the RU 19-300 provides 2·16 kN (485 lb st) for take-off. During flight the auxiliary turbojet is available for use as an APU. The version installed in the An-30 is designated RU 19A-300.

In 1976 it became known in the West that the RU 19 is used to power the La-17 target (see RPVs and Targets section in 1977-78 *Jane's*).

2. Lift-Jet. Soviet design bureaux conducted extensive research into jet lift from the late 1950s, and purpose-designed lift-jets were probably flying by 1962 (possibly much earlier). At the 1967 air show at Domodedovo three lift-jet V/STOL research aircraft were displayed. A MiG aircraft based on the MiG-21 had two lift-jets in the mid-fuselage, with a single large inlet door above. A larger MiG, with fuselage and tail closely similar to the eventual MiG-23 but with a small delta wing, had a similar arrangement, differing in detail design of the dorsal door. A Sukhoi aircraft, similar to the twin-engined Su-15, had three lift engines fed by two upper doors. All these installations had large open slots in the dorsal doors (which were hinged at the rear) and transverse louvres filling the ventral jet aperture (probably hinged and under pilot control to give variable forward thrust). Photographs of these aircraft last appeared in the 1971-72 *Jane's*. The two lift-jets used in the Yak-36MP VTOL aircraft carried on board the carriers *Kiev* and *Minsk* are probably developments of the same engines, though details are not yet known. They could be turbojets or turbofans. The inlet door has open louvres, and it is safe to assume pilot-controlled exit cascades. Thrust estimates for these engines are agreed at around 25 kN (5,600 lb) each.

3. Lift/Cruise Engine. The Yakovlev V/STOL research aircraft (NATO 'Freehand') demonstrated at the 1967 Domodedovo air show was powered by a twin-nozzle vectored-thrust propulsion system. The use of a large bifurcated nose intake and only two exhaust nozzles suggests that the installation may have used two standard turbojets or turbofans, each fitted with a single swivelling nozzle. On balance, however, it is likely that the 'Freehand' research aircraft used the same large single engine as the Yak-36MP combat aircraft carried on board the *Kiev* and *Minsk*. This is probably a turbofan, similar in essentials to the British Pegasus and Anglo-German RB.193 (used in the VAK 191B), but with the entire efflux discharged through left and right rear nozzles. The HP spool must be bled to provide air for the reaction control jets at the tail and wingtips. There is no afterburning in this engine, and estimates put its T-O thrust in the 78 kN (17,500 lb st) class.

UNITED KINGDOM

BAJ VICKERS
BAJ VICKERS LIMITED

HEAD OFFICE AND WORKS: Banwell, Weston super Mare, Avon BS24 8PD
Telephone: Banwell (0934) 82 2251
DIRECTORS:
C. N. Davies (Chairman)
R. M. Howarth (Managing Director)
J. M. Harper (Managing Director Designate)
M. A. Bowen
R. Enticott
A. C. Johnson
Dr F. Llewellyn Smith, CBE

In 1952 a team was formed to meet the rocket-motor requirements of early British guided missile projects. This team constituted the nucleus of a company named Bristol Aerojet, formed in 1958 by the Bristol Aeroplane Company and the Aerojet-General Corporation of California. In March 1979 Bristol Aerojet became a wholly-owned subsidiary of Vickers Ltd, and was subsequently renamed as above.

BAJ Vickers has supplied production motors for the Bloodhound, Seaslug, Seacat, Tigercat, Rapier, Seawolf, Sea Skua, USD-501, Skylark, Skua, Petrel, Fulmar and INTA Flamenco, and for other flight and ground applications.

The company's rocket-motor manufacturing processes have been licenced to Breda Meccanica Bresciana in Italy

and to Instituto Nacional de Tecnica Aeroespatial (INTA) in Spain, and are used under different arrangements in Canada and Australia. Under an agreement with the British government the company is supplying British 'plastic' propellant manufacturing and filling technology and equipment for a rocket-motor filling facility set up by INTA, and is able to supply a similar service to other approved organisations.

BAJ Vickers produces rocket motors to customer requirements, undertakes launcher design, and provides a technical service for assembly and firing of experimental rockets at British and overseas ranges. The company also produces research rockets and ballistic targets.

BAJ VICKERS LIQUID MOTORS

Pre-filled, fully sealed motors have been developed in collaboration with the MoD Propellants, Explosives and Rocket Motor Establishment. Flight-proven motors give complex thrust/time programmes on command, and have a shut-down and restart capability. The simple propellants are smoke-free and offer instant readiness after long storage.

BAJ VICKERS SOLID MOTORS

The following details may be published of the principal types of solid rocket motor manufactured for non-military purposes:

Motor Name	Diam mm (in)	Length mm (in)	Burn Time (s)	Total impulse (kN-s)	Application
Bantam	125 (4·92)	1,473 (58)	33·6	52·0	Skua
Chick	68 (2·68)	554 (21·8)	0·18	4·45	Skua and Petrel boost
Cuckoo	431·8 (17)	1,312 (51·65)	4·1	360·0	Skylark boost
Goldfinch	431·8 (17)	2,224 (87·56)	3·6	701·0	Skylark boost
Lapwing	176·8 (6·96)	1,826 (71·9)	25·0	153·0	Petrel
Raven	431·8 (17)	5,232 (206)	30·0	1,510·0	Skylark
Siskin	141·2 (5·56)	600·0 (23·62)	3·58	16·5	
Waxwing	712 (28)	(spherical)	55·0	845·5	
Heron	257·3 (10·13)	3,364 (132·45)	3·1	418	Flamenco/Fulmar
Snipe	259·8 (10·23)	2,212 (87·1)	15·5	237	Flamenco/Fulmar

BONNER
AERO BONNER LTD

Shoreham Airport, East Sussex BN4 5FJ
Telephone: 079 17 5764

This company has developed a watercooled V-6 piston engine for general aviation. In 1976 the first flight prototype was installed in a Chipmunk, flight testing of which began on 2 July 1979.

BONNER SUPER SAPPHIRE

This engine is expected to set a new level of lightweight, compact, quiet and smooth power for aircraft requiring engines in the 149 kW (200 hp) class. After exhaustive development, production began in 1979, about four-fifths of the engine being made at Shoreham.
TYPE: Six-cylinder four-stroke piston engine, turbocharged with geared drive.
CYLINDERS: V-6 configuration. Watercooled. Swept volume 3,000 cc (183 cu in).
INDUCTION: Garrett-AiResearch turbocharger. Direct fuel injection.
IGNITION: Dual, with one magneto and electronic system.
LUBRICATION: Dry sump.
PROPELLER DRIVE: Reduction gear with quill shaft, 0·5 ratio.

Looking down on a Bonner Super Sapphire, with turbocharger on the right

DIMENSIONS:
Length overall   991 mm (39·0 in)
Width overall   559 mm (22·0 in)
Height overall   609 mm (24·0 in)
WEIGHT, DRY: 149 kg (328 lb)

PERFORMANCE RATING:
Max T-O   149 kW (200 hp) at 5,500 rpm
FUEL CONSUMPTION:
At cruise (74·5 kW; 100 hp) 29·5 litres (6·5 Imp gal)/h

DOWTY ROTOL
DOWTY ROTOL LTD

Cheltenham Road East, Gloucester GL2 9QH
Telephone: 0452 712424

Known primarily as a producer of propellers and related rotary devices, Dowty Rotol has developed the propulsion system described below. Though *Jane's* does not include propellers as such, this new development—in the form of an integrated propulsion unit—is exceptional.

DOWTY DUCTED PROPULSOR

Starting with the premise that propeller-driven aircraft are too noisy to meet future noise legislation, and in many cases even existing limits (80 dBA flyover), Dowty began in 1972 to seek an answer. One is the propeller of increased diameter, turning at lower rpm and driven through a large gearbox. This was soon discarded as too costly, heavy and limited in noise reduction, and as generally inapplicable to existing general-aviation aircraft because of propeller-blade clearance and landing gear height. A much better answer was found to be the multiblade ducted fan, looking superficially like a high bypass ratio turbofan, which can produce not only dramatic reduction in noise but also markedly increased aircraft performance.

In the Spring of 1976 a static test rig was run, driven by a 224 kW (300 hp) Continental IO-520. The fan had seven blades and a diameter of 1,219 mm (48·0 in). The target static thrust was 5·38 kN (1,200 lb st) and the achieved figure at first build was 5·56 kN (1,250 lb st). The target noise at 305 m (1,000 ft) was 65 dB; the achieved figure was 62 dB. Further development showed how to obtain substantial net thrust from the engine cooling air and exhaust, ducted to a propulsive nozzle at the rear of the nacelle. Very good engine cooling was achieved, despite the extra-tight cowling, and vibration was reduced well below that with a propeller.

In the Autumn of 1976 the Islander was selected as a suitable research and demonstrator aircraft, and Miles-Dufon at Shoreham handled the conversion of both engines (224 kW/300 hp Avco Lycoming IO-540), each being lowered on a pylon below the wing and coupled directly to a fan with large spinner and seven aluminium variable-pitch blades running inside a specially profiled duct carried on six downstream flow-straightener vanes. At full power the 1,219 mm (48 in) fan has a tip speed of only 172 m (565 ft)/s, compared with 287 m (942 ft)/s for the original 2,032 mm (80·0 in) propeller. The reduction in noise is exceptional, and there is a gain in thrust. The Ducted Propulsor Islander flew for the first time on 10

Close-up of Dowty Ducted Propulsor on the Islander

June 1977, and has given remarkable demonstrations of quietness and improved performance in the hands of the test pilot, Neville Duke. Noise in the cabin and on the ground has been reduced from about 85 to 65 dB, far below any future environmentalist goal. There are many side benefits, such as reduced pollution from leaner mixture.

LEONIDES
HARKER & ASSOCIATES

40 Pont Street, London SW1X 0AD
Telephone: 01-584 6720, 01-584 4725

Formerly of Rolls-Royce, Mr Harker is trying to get the Alvis Leonides nine-cylinder geared aircooled radial into agricultural aviation. Over 3,000 h have been flown with the Leonides 125/7 of 418 kW (560 hp) in an Ag-Cat and a

Rockwell Thrush Commander R in California, and two Ag-Cat B aircraft are certificated and in use. Approximately 300 used engines are available for use. The intention is to start new production, and negotiations to this end are in progress with companies, in the USA and the UK.

Harker & Associates can offer overhauls, and hopes to offer new engines of the Leonides 531 (long-stroke 485 kW, 650 hp) type in 1983. Alvis is supplying technical assistance and spares. Plans are in hand to convert a Stearman and Air Tractor to Leonides power. Riddell Flying Services, of West Helena, Arkansas, has been appointed US distributor.

LUCAS
LUCAS AEROSPACE LTD

HEAD OFFICE: Shirley, Solihull, West Midlands B90 2JJ
Telephone: 021-744 8522
DIRECTOR AND GENERAL MANAGER: J. Blyth

Lucas Aerospace was formed in 1971 to bring together Lucas Gas Turbine Equipment Ltd and Rotax Ltd. The Electrical Division at Hemel Hempstead is producing the CT 3201, originally designed by Rover as the TJ.125.

LUCAS CT 3201

This small turbojet was developed as a power plant for surveillance RPVs. Delivery of production engines to MBLE is continuing, for the Belgian company's Epervier surveillance RPV. Discussions are in progress with other drone manufacturers.

TYPE: Single-shaft turbojet.
AIR INTAKE: Aluminium alloy bifurcated.
COMPRESSOR: Single-stage centrifugal. Cast aluminium with steel rotating guide vanes. Rotor hydraulically pressed to shaft. Mass flow 0·93 kg (2·05 lb)/s.
COMBUSTION CHAMBER: Annular reverse-flow. Six spray burners. High-energy 2 Joule igniter.
FUEL SYSTEM: Double-datum piston type.
FUEL GRADE: JP-4, JP-5 and equivalents.
TURBINE: Single, radial-flow, 12 blades integral with steel disc. Retained by sleeve/bolt on shaft, hung behind needle and roller bearings. Inlet gas temperature 917°C.
ACCESSORY DRIVES: Fuel pump and alternator between intakes driven by toothed belts.
LUBRICATION SYSTEM: Self-contained, 100 cc. SAE.5 below 25°C, SAE.10 above.

Installation of Leonides 125/7 in Ag-Cat (popularly called Leo-Cat)

DIMENSIONS:
Length overall	584 mm (23·0 in)
Max width	269 mm (10·6 in)
Max depth	311 mm (12·25 in)
WEIGHT, DRY:	18·6 kg (41·0 lb)
PERFORMANCE RATINGS:	
Max thrust at ISA	0·51 kN (114 lb)
Reduced thrust	0·32 kN (73 lb)
SPECIFIC FUEL CONSUMPTION:	
At max rating	37·1 mg/Ns (1·31 lb/h/lb st)

Lucas CT 3201 turbojet of 0·51 kN (114 lb st) as fitted to the MBLE Épervier RPV

NPT
NOEL PENNY TURBINES LTD

Siskin Drive, Toll Bar End, Coventry CV3 4FE
Telephone: 0203 301528
DIRECTORS:
E. R. Ponsford (Chairman)
R. N. Penny (Managing Director)
The Earl of Minto
S. Penny (Secretary)

Noel Penny Turbines was incorporated in 1972. It continues to derive much of its turnover from packaged research and engineering programmes for worldwide clients across the entire spectrum of small gas turbines. It also manufactures its own products.

With modular design philosophy, basic gasifier units can be built up to cover a wide variety of duties. The NPT 101 and 401 turbojets are also available as NPT 109 and 409 blower modules, providing large volumes of low-pressure uncontaminated air for hovercraft and airfield servicing use.

NPT is developing engines of high power/weight and power/bulk ratios which will combine low first cost with economy of operation. Again, the modular design concept will enable these to be offered as single- or two-shaft units, in turbojet, turboprop or ground-power form.

The current aerospace programme is concentrated on small turbojets for unmanned vehicles. Several projects are subject to security classification, but the NPT 401A and simple low-cost NPT 151 and 251 can be described.

NPT 401A, 251

The following description refers to the NPT 401A, except where indicated otherwise.
TYPE: Single-shaft turbojet.
AIR INTAKE: Forward-facing annular.
COMPRESSOR: Axial stage followed by centrifugal. Maximum airflow 2·27 kg (5·0 lb)/s. Pressure ratio 4·5.
COMBUSTION CHAMBER: Reverse-flow annular with vaporising burners. Single 3kV spark igniter.

FUEL SYSTEM: LP, pressurised-inlet electric pump, electronic control.
FUEL GRADES: Kerosene, Jet A-1, JP-5.
TURBINE: Single-stage axial, integral blades, cast nickel alloy. Max inlet gas temperature 955°C (977°C in NPT 251).
ACCESSORY DRIVES: Alternator on compressor shaft.
LUBRICATION: Total-loss oil mist.
MOUNTING: Pads at compressor-housing flange.
STARTING: External air source on compressor.
DIMENSIONS:
Diameter	343 mm (13·5 in)
Length: NPT 401A	597 mm (23·5 in)
NPT 251	577 mm (22·72 in)
WEIGHT, DRY:	
NPT 401A	43 kg (95 lb)
NPT 251	34 kg (75 lb)
PERFORMANCE RATING (Max S/L):	
NPT 401A	1·468 kN (330 lb st)
NPT 251	1·334 kN (300 lb st)
SPECIFIC FUEL CONSUMPTION (Max rating):	
NPT 401A	28·8 mg/Ns (1·016 lb/h/lb st)
NPT 251	33·4 mg/Ns (1·18 lb/h/lb st)

NPT 151

This recently developed small turbojet is a low-cost engine for single-mission vehicles. It may be adapted later to longer-life applications.
TYPE: Single-shaft turbojet.
AIR INTAKE: Forward-facing annular.
COMPRESSOR: Centrifugal, aluminium alloy. Maximum airflow 1·25 kg (2·75 lb)/s.
COMBUSTION CHAMBER: Straight-through annular with vaporising burners. Ignition by electrically fired pyrotechnic cartridge.
FUEL SYSTEM: LP single-speed, pump mounted on compressor shaft. Control by pump mechanical governor and acceleration unit.

Noel Penny NPT 401A turbojet

FUEL GRADES: Jet A-1, JP-5.
TURBINE: Inward-radial flow, cast nickel alloy. Max inlet temperature 897°C.
ACCESSORY DRIVES: None.
LUBRICATION: Total-loss oil.
MOUNTING: Three brackets on front casing.
STARTING: Windmilling, or by external air source on compressor.
DIMENSIONS:
Diameter	275 mm (10·83 in)
Length	310 mm (12·2 in)
WEIGHT, DRY	15·0 kg (33·0 lb)
PERFORMANCE RATING (Max S/L):	
	0·672 kN (151 lb st)
SPECIFIC FUEL CONSUMPTION (Max rating):	
	34 mg/Ns (1·20 lb/h/lb st)

ROLLASON
ROLLASON AIRCRAFT AND ENGINES LTD

Brighton, Hove and Worthing Joint Municipal Airport, Shoreham-by-Sea, Sussex BN4 5FJ
Telephone: 079 17 62680

In support of its manufacture (now ended) of the Druine Turbulent light aeroplane, Rollason Aircraft and Engines Ltd undertook the conversion of Ardem 4CO2 power plants for this aircraft, from motor car engines.

Rollason has developed versions of the Ardem engine with capacities of 1,500 or 1,600 cc. Any of these engines can be installed in Nipper aircraft. The Mk X is also used in the Australian Corby Starlet and other homebuilts. A version with single ignition and electric starter powers the Slingsby-built Motor-Falke.

ARDEM Mk X (1,500 cc)

The standard model has a compression ratio of 7·8 : 1 and gives 33·6 kW (45 hp) at 3,300 rpm for take-off, with a fuel consumption of 17 litres (3·75 Imp gallons)/h at max rating. In addition, a high-compression version is available, as follows:

CYLINDERS: Bore 83 mm (3·27 in). Stroke 69 mm (2·72 in). Cast steel barrels, light alloy heads. Compression ratio 8·5 : 1.
PISTONS: Aluminium alloy high-compression pistons, each with two compression rings and one scraper ring. Floating gudgeon pins.

CONNECTING RODS: White metal bearings in big-end. Bronze bearings in little-end.

CRANKSHAFT: Runs in four white metal bearings.

CRANKCASE: Magnesium case.

VALVE GEAR: Two valves per cylinder. Camshaft geared to crankshaft.

INDUCTION: Zenith 32 KL P10 carburettor.

FUEL GRADE: 80 octane.

IGNITION: Lucas SR4 magneto mounted below engine, with chain drive. Two Lodge LH spark plugs per cylinder.

LUBRICATION: Wet sump type, with single gear-type pump.

OIL SPECIFICATION: Shell W80.

PROPELLER DRIVE: Direct drive.

ACCESSORIES: SEV 46C fuel pump.

DIMENSIONS:
Length	426 mm (16·75 in)
Width	750 mm (29·50 in)
Height	559 mm (22·00 in)

PERFORMANCE RATING:
Max	39·5 kW (53 hp) at 3,600 rpm

FUEL CONSUMPTION:
At max rating	18·2 litres (4·0 Imp gallons)/h

ARDEM Mk XI (1,600 cc)

After extensive testing this engine was approved and is produced as the Ardem Mk XI. It differs from the Mk X in having cylinders of 85·5 mm (3·365 in) bore and dual ignition.

WEIGHT:
With accessories	71·6 kg (158 lb)

PERFORMANCE RATINGS:
Max	41 kW (55 hp) at 3,300 rpm
Cruise	26·5 kW (35·5 hp) at 2,500 rpm

FUEL CONSUMPTION:
At cruise rating	12·5 litres (2·75 Imp gallons)/h

ROLLS-ROYCE
ROLLS-ROYCE LIMITED

HEAD OFFICE: 65 Buckingham Gate, London SW1E 6AT
Telephone: 01-222 9020
MAIN LOCATIONS:
PO Box 31, Moor Lane, Derby DE2 8BJ
Telephone: 0332 42424
PO Box 3, Filton, Bristol BS12 7QE
Telephone: 0272 693871
PO Box 72, Ansty, Coventry CV7 9JR
Telephone: 0203 613211
Leavesden, Watford WD2 7BZ
Telephone: 09273 74000
Scottish group of factories to the south of Glasgow
CHAIRMAN AND CHIEF EXECUTIVE: Sir Frank McFadzean
VICE CHAIRMEN:
D. J. Pepper
A. R. G. Raeburn
MANAGING DIRECTOR, AERO DIVISION: D. A. Head
BOARD MEMBERS:
Sir George Burton
Sir St John Elstub
S. L. Higginbottom
P. J. Molony
Sir Denis Spotswood
Sir Peter Thornton
Sir Neil Wheeler
R. T. Whitfield
COMPANY SECRETARY: J. R. L. Southam

Rolls-Royce Ltd, which produces a range of gas turbines and ramjets, retains the experience in aircraft engines built up over more than 60 years by the predecessor companies that it incorporated. The company also represents British experience in lightweight high-power gas turbines for industrial and marine purposes, since such engines were first derived from aircraft gas turbines.

More than 230 million hours of operating experience have been accumulated with Rolls-Royce civil and military gas turbines, which are used by 241 airlines and 105 armed forces.

In addition to the products designed, developed and manufactured solely in Britain, the company works with partners abroad on a number of joint civil and military aircraft engine programmes. Licences for the manufacture of Rolls-Royce engines or components are also held by many countries throughout the world.

The main activities are at Derby, Glasgow, Bristol, Coventry and Leavesden, where aircraft gas turbines are produced, and at Ansty, where aircraft gas turbine techniques are applied to industrial and marine uses. A total of 59,400 people are employed.

Rolls-Royce engines in commercial service include the RB.211, Spey, M45H and Conway turbofans, Avon, Viper and RB.162 turbojets, and Dart and Tyne turboprops. New civil engines include the RB.211-535, RB.401 and proposed RJ.500. Military engines include the Pegasus vectored-thrust turbofan and Odin ramjet, as well as versions of the Spey, Conway, Avon, Viper, Dart and Tyne. Helicopter engines include the Gem, Gnome and (with Turboméca) Turmo and Astazou. Under the International heading in this section are described the RB.199 (Turbo-Union), Adour (with Turboméca) and TF41 (with Detroit Diesel Allison).

Versions of several Rolls-Royce aircraft gas turbines are used as power units for large and small ships, hydrofoils, air cushion vehicles, electricity-generating sets, gas and oil pumping equipment and for other industrial uses.

ROLLS-ROYCE TURBOMÉCA ADOUR

This turbofan was designed by Rolls-Royce and Turboméca. It is described in the International part of this section.

ROLLS-ROYCE RB.199

This advanced augmented turbofan is the power unit for the Panavia Tornado. The RB.199 programme is managed by Turbo-Union (see International part of this section).

ROLLS-ROYCE RB.211

The RB.211 is a family of advanced technology three-shaft turbofans of high bypass ratio and high pressure ratio, with thrusts so far announced from 163 kN (36,720 lb) to 244·65 kN (55,000 lb). The engine was selected by Lockheed in March 1968 to power the L-1011 TriStar, and later by Boeing as an alternative option on the 747. In

Rolls-Royce RB.211-524B three-shaft turbofan (222·4 kN; 50,000 lb st)

August 1978 the lowest-thrust version was selected as launch engine for the Boeing 757. In June 1979 Rolls-Royce and Airbus Industrie agreed to initiate a programme to develop versions of the A300 and A310 powered by RB.211 engines.

Rolls-Royce initiated design studies of three-shaft turbofans in 1961 and a twin-spool engine, the RB.178, was tested in 1967 to provide relevant component and gas generator experience. Among the advantages afforded by a three-shaft layout are its ready use of a high pressure ratio with fewer compressor and turbine stages while maintaining excellent handling. The need for compressor variable stator mechanisms can also be minimised and the rotating assemblies can be made relatively short and rigid while preserving light construction. As a result the RB.211 has demonstrated outstandingly low seal and aerofoil wear, thus maintaining a high level of performance throughout engine life.

For the Lockheed TriStar, Rolls-Royce developed and has responsibility for the complete propulsion system, comprising the engine, fan airflow reverser, pod cowlings and related systems, and noise attenuation for the intake, fan cowl and turbine exhaust duct.

The engine is divided into seven modules. This permits rapid change of engine parts, and enables service life to be set up individually for each module. It also facilitates rapid repair, as a damaged or time-expired module can be replaced with the engine installed in the aircraft. Maximum provision is made for in-service monitoring of engine condition and visual inspection on the ground of all engine sections.

The RB.211 combustion chamber is of annular design, giving significant advantages over tubo-annular systems in terms of reduced cost, weight and length, and improved efficiency. The reduced length makes a two-bearing HP system possible, with both bearings located away from the high temperatures of the combustion area. Detailed design has been aimed at reducing exhaust contaminants to a minimum. To reduce fan noise the RB.211 has no inlet guide vanes. Throughout the compressors and turbines the blade spacing, and the numerical ratios of rotor and stator blades in each stage, have been carefully chosen for minimum noise generation consistent with optimum performance. Additional noise attenuation is achieved by the use of acoustic lining material in the intake, fan and turbine exhaust ducts.

The RB.211-22B, the standard engine of the L-1011-1 and -100 TriStar, is flat rated at 187 kN (42,000 lb st) to 28·9°C. This engine was certificated in February 1973 by the CAA and in April 1973 by the FAA. By the end of 1979 more than 580 engines had been delivered, and engine flight hours in service were in excess of 6 million.

The RB.211-524 represents the initial step in the RB.211's programme of growth. It preserves maximum commonality with the -22B but has increased core airflow, slightly higher turbine gas temperature and improved component efficiency. The -524 entered airline service in 1977 with the L-1011 and 747. By the end of 1979 more than 160 RB.211-524 engines had been delivered and 500,000 h flown.

The RB.211-524B, currently fitted to both the extended-range L-1011-500 TriStar and the 747, has been certificated at 222·4 kN (50,000 lb st) to 28·9°C for both aircraft. A further development at the same thrust rating but offering a 4·8 per cent reduction in specific fuel consumption, designated RB.211-524B4, was scheduled for certification during 1980.

The RB.211-524D is an improved engine for heavier versions of the Boeing 747 and other aircraft. It is rated at 235·75 kN (53,000 lb st) and was scheduled for certification in 1980.

The RB.211-524G is an improved engine due to be certificated in 1984-85 at 244·65 kN (55,000 lb st).

The RB.211-535C is rated at 166 kN (37,400 lb st) for the Boeing 757. In this application a policy of flexible thrust rating means that the -535C will normally operate with significant derate. It has the HP module of the RB.211-22B, a six-stage IP compressor and a scaled-down version of the RB.211-524B fan. Fan airflow is 25 per cent lower than that of the -22B, and core airflow 16 per cent lower. The engine runs at lower temperatures, pressures and velocities than the -22B, resulting in exceptionally low noise and high propulsive efficiency.

The RB.211-535D is offered for future applications at a rating of 175 kN (39,410 lb st).

The following description relates to the RB.211-22B:

TYPE: Three-shaft axial turbofan.

AIR INTAKE: Forward-facing pitot.

LP FAN: Single-stage overhung fan driven by LP turbine, the whole rotor assembly being supported on three bearings. Front bearing is large roller, squeeze-film supported behind fan. Axial location of rotor is by inter-shaft ball bearing in rear end of IP compressor drum. LP turbine supported on roller bearing, squeeze-film mounted in exhaust cone panel. Rotating spinner supported from fan rotor disc and hot-air anti-iced via central feed-tube within shaft. Titanium alloy used for 33 fan rotor blades, and steel for 70 fan outlet guide vanes. Titanium fan disc bolted with curvic coupling to LP shaft. Aluminium fan casing. Total fan airflow (T-O rating), 626 kg (1,380 lb)/s (-524, 657·7 kg; 1,450 lb). Bypass ratio 5 : 1 (-524, 4·4 : 1.)

IP COMPRESSOR: Seven-stage compressor rotor driven by IP turbine and supported on three bearings located directly in support panels. Front squeeze-film bearing is roller. Mid bearing at rear of IP compressor is ball bearing providing axial location for IP rotor. Rear bearing is roller, squeeze-film supported in panel between HP and IP turbines. Two drums, one of titanium discs welded together and the other of welded steel discs, are bolted to form one rotor, carrying titanium rotor blades. Aluminium and steel casings carry aluminium and stator steel blades. Single-stage titanium variable inlet guide vanes.

HP COMPRESSOR: Six-stage compressor rotor driven by HP turbine connected by large-diameter shaft and carried on ball location bearing at front and roller bearing mounted at the rear in panel behind HP turbine disc. Welded titanium discs, a single steel disc and welded nickel alloy discs are bolted together to form the rotor, carrying titanium, steel and nickel alloy blades. Steel casing carries steel and Nimonic stator blades. Overall pressure ratio 25 : 1.

COMBUSTION CHAMBER: Fully annular, with steel outer casings and Nimonic combustor. Downstream fuel injection by 18 airspray burners with annular atomisers. Ignition by high-energy igniter plugs in Nos 8 and 12 burners.

HP TURBINE: Single-stage axial unit with nozzle guide vanes and nickel-alloy rotor blades, both convection- and film-cooled. Blades mounted in Nimonic disc by fir-tree roots.

IP TURBINE: Single-stage axial unit with Nimonic nozzle guide vanes and Nimonic rotor blades. NGVs aircooled. Rotor blades fir-tree mounted in Nimonic disc.

LP TURBINE: Three-stage axial unit with Nimonic rotor blades fir-tree mounted in steel discs.

JET PIPE: Steel jet pipe without spoiler.

ACCESSORY DRIVES: Radial drive from HP shaft to gearbox on fan casing. Accessories driven include integrated-drive generator and aircraft hydraulic pumps.

LUBRICATION SYSTEM: Continuous circulation 'dry sump' system with single gear-type pressure pump and multiple gear-type scavenge pumps. Oil tank 21 litres (37 Imp pints) capacity integral with gearbox.

MOUNTING: Two-point mounting system. Front mount on fan casing takes thrust, vertical and side-loads. Rear link mount on exhaust casing takes torsional, side and vertical loads. Both mounts are fail-safe and allow for carcase expansion.

DIMENSIONS:
Length overall	3,033 mm (119·4 in)
Intake diameter	2,182 mm (85·9 in)

WEIGHT, DRY:
RB.211-22B	4,171 kg (9,195 lb)
RB.211-524B4	4,452 kg (9,814 lb)

PERFORMANCE RATINGS:
T-O, flat rated to 28·9°C:
RB.211-535C	166 kN (37,400 lb st)
RB.211-22B	187 kN (42,000 lb st)
RB.211-524	213·5 kN (48,000 lb st)
RB.211-524B4	222·4 kN (50,000 lb st)
RB.211-524D	235·75 kN (53,000 lb st)
RB.211-524G	244·65 kN (55,000 lb st)

T-O flat-rated to 34·2°C:
RB.211-535D	175 kN (39,410 lb st)

Cruise at 10,670 m (35,000 ft) and Mach 0·85:
RB.211-22B	43·9 kN (9,875 lb st)
RB.211-524B4	48·9 kN (11,000 lb st)

SPECIFIC FUEL CONSUMPTION:
At cruise rating, as above:
RB.211-22B	17·7 mg/Ns (0·625 lb/h/lb st)
RB.211-524B4	17·6 mg/Ns (0·620 lb/h/lb st)

ROLLS-ROYCE RJ.500

This new turbofan in the 'ten-tonne' class is described under Rolls-Royce/Japan in the International section.

ROLLS-ROYCE RB.163 CIVIL SPEY

Design of the Spey RB.163 began in September 1959, and the first engine ran at the end of December 1960. Civil Speys are in service in the Trident, BAe One-Eleven, Grumman Gulfstream II and F28 Fellowship, and in the C-8A augmentor-wing research aircraft of NASA. In 1978 the Spey was selected for the Gulfstream III, which like current One-Elevens has noise-suppressing features; it was also subject of a major collaborative production programme between Rolls-Royce and the government of Romania.

The following versions of the civil Spey are in service:

Mk 505-5F. T-O rating of 44·6 kN (10,050 lb st) at 12,150 rpm, for Trident 1C.

Mk 506-14. T-O rating of 46·3 kN (10,410 lb st) at 12,530 rpm, for One-Eleven.

Mk 506-14A. As 506-14 with smaller capacity turbine.

Mk 511-8 and 511-14. T-O rating of 50·7 kN (11,400 lb st) at 12,390 rpm. Mk 511-5 for Trident, Mk 511-8 for Gulfstream II and Mk 511-14 for One-Eleven.

Mk 511-5W and 511-14W. As 511-5 and 511-14 but with water injection to maintain rating to 35°C.

Mk 512-5 and 512-14. T-O rating 53·0 kN (11,930 lb st) in Mk 512-5/50 for Trident 3B, Mk 512-5W and 5W/50 at same rating for Trident 2E, Mk 512-14E at 55·26 kN (12,420 lb st) for One-Eleven, and Mk 512DW at 55·8 kN (12,550 lb st), all at 12,640 rpm.

Comparative cross-sections of Rolls-Royce RB.211-22B and RB.211-535 turbofans

Rolls-Royce Spey 555 simplified turbofan rated at 44·0 kN (9,900 lb st)

Mk 555-15. Lightened and simplified version for F28 Fellowship. Has changed company project number of **RB.183.** Current production version is the 555-15H, flat rated at 44·0 kN (9,900 lb) to 29·7°C; on a 40°C day it gives 6 per cent higher T-O thrust than the original 555-15.

The military versions are described separately.

The following details refer specifically to the Spey Mk 512-14DW, as fitted to the BAe One-Eleven Series 500, except where indicated:

TYPE: Two-spool axial-flow turbofan engine.

AIR INTAKE: Annular, with bleed air thermal anti-icing.

COMPRESSOR: Two spools. Five-stage (four-stage on Mks 505, 506 and 555) low-pressure (LP) and 12-stage high-pressure (HP). First-stage HP stator vanes variable-incidence. LP compressor steel drum type, pinned to shaft. HP compressor is of the steel disc type, first stage bolted to shaft, remaining stages splined. HP stator blades steel; LP stators aluminium. LP rotor blades aluminium (Mk 512 titanium 1st stage); HP blades titanium. Stators slotted into casing; rotor blades pinned or dovetailed. LP casing two-piece magnesium. HP casing steel. Pressure ratio 21·2 : 1 (15·0 on Mk 505 and 555, 17·2 on Mk 506, 18·9 on Mk 510 and 511). Air mass flow 94·4 kg (208 lb)/s (90·27 kg; 200 lb on Mk 505 and 555, 92 kg; 203 lb on Mk 506, 92·5 kg; 204 lb on Mk 510 and 511). Bypass ratio 0·64 : 1 (1·0 on Mk 505, 555 and 506).

COMBUSTION CHAMBER: Tubo-annular with 10 Nimonic sheet liners. Duplex downstream burners, one per chamber. High energy igniters in chambers 4 and 8.

FUEL SYSTEM: Plessey LP pump feeding through fuel-cooled oil cooler and Marston Excelsior fuel heater to LP filter at inlet to Lucas GD pump. HP metered by Lucas regulator, embodying combined speed and acceleration control and fed through Lucas LP governor and shut-off valve to Duplex spray nozzles. Maximum pressure 124 bars (1,800 lb/sq in).

FUEL GRADE: DERD.2482 or 2486.

WATER INJECTION SYSTEM: (engines bearing 'W' suffix): Water supplied by Lucas air turbopump through engine-mounted automatic shut-off valve to injector passages in fuel spray nozzles (water sprays into primary airflow through flame tube swirlers).

NOZZLE GUIDE VANES: Hollow cast in nickel-based alloy. HP aircooled.

TURBINES: Two two-stage. First HP aircooled. HP discs nickel-based alloy, bolted to shaft (HP discs steel on Mks 505, 506 and 555). LP discs creep-resisting ferritic steel. Nickel-based alloy blades attached by fir-tree roots.

BEARINGS: LP compressor supported in roller bearings, plus ball thrust bearing. HP compressor has front roller bearing and ball thrust bearing. Turbine bearings all roller type flexibly mounted.

JET PIPE: Fixed-area stainless steel sheet.

REVERSER AND SUPPRESSOR: Normally internal clamshell (Gulfstream II target type, not Rolls-Royce supplied, and F28 has no reverser). Five- or six-chute silencing nozzles available.

ACCESSORY DRIVES: Port gearbox, driven from LP rotor, carries LP governor and LP tacho. Starboard gearbox, driven from HP rotor, carries LP and HP fuel pumps, fuel regulator, main oil pumps, airflow control rpm signal transmitter, starter and HP tacho. Provision in starboard gearbox for aircraft ancillaries.

LUBRICATION SYSTEM: Self-contained continuous circulation. Single pressure pump feeds oil from tank through fuel-cooled cooler and HP filter to gearboxes and shaft bearings. Five main scavenge pumps. Tank capacity 6·8 litres (12 Imp pints). Usable oil 5·1 litres (9 Imp pints). Normal pressure 2·41-3·45 bars (35-50 lb/sq in).

OIL SPECIFICATION: DERD.2487.

MOUNTING: Two trunnions, two saddle mountings and one rear mounting.

STARTING: Plessey 220 air-turbine starter. Rotax alternative on Mks 505, 511 and 512; AiResearch on Mk 555.

DIMENSIONS:
Length, less tailpipe:
Mk 505, 506, 555	2,795 mm (110·0 in)
Mk 510, 511	2,911 mm (114·6 in)

Diameter:
Mk 505, 506, 555	940 mm (37·0 in)
Mk 510, 511	942 mm (37·1 in)

Weight, Dry:

Mk 505-5	998 kg (2,200 lb)
Mk 506-14	1,024 kg (2,257 lb)
Mk 506-14AW	1,038 kg (2,288 lb)
Mk 510-5, 511-5	1,049 kg (2,312 lb)
Mk 510-14, 511-14	1,058 kg (2,332 lb)
Mk 510-14W, 511-14W	1,188 kg (2,621 lb)
Mk 511-5W	1,050 kg (2,317 lb)
Mk 512	1,168 kg (2,574 lb)
Mk 555-15	1,008 kg (2,222 lb)

Performance Ratings:
Max T-O: See under series descriptions
Max continuous:

Mk 505	42 kN (9,450 lb st) at 12,260 rpm
Mk 506	44·4 kN (9,990 lb st) at 12,385 rpm
Mk 511	48·7 kN (10,940 lb st) at 12,240 rpm
Mk 512, Mk 512DW	
	51·5 kN (11,580 lb st) at 12,450 rpm
Mk 555-15	42·1 kN (9,470 lb st) at 11,900 rpm

Typical cruise rating at 450 knots (834 km/h; 518 mph)
at 9,750 m (32,000 ft):
All versions   13·7 kN (3,070 lb st)

Specific Fuel Consumption:
At T-O rating:

Mk 505	15·9 mg/Ns (0·560 lb/h/lb st)
Mk 506	15·95 mg/Ns (0·563 lb/h/lb st)
Mk 511	17·3 mg/Ns (0·612 lb/h/lb st)
Mk 555-15	15·9 mg/Ns (0·560 lb/h/lb st)

At typical cruise rating:

Mks 505, 506	21·5 mg/Ns (0·760 lb/h/lb st)
Mk 510, 511	22·3 mg/Ns (0·790 lb/h/lb st)
Mks 512, 555	22·7 mg/Ns (0·800 lb/h/lb st)

Oil Consumption:
Max (all Marks)   0·42 litres (0·75 Imp pints)/h

ROLLS-ROYCE RB.168 MILITARY SPEY

The military Spey RB.168 incorporates modifications to meet higher-duty conditions.

Design of the RB.168-1, **Mk 101,** started in November 1960; this mark powers the Hawker Siddeley Buccaneer strike aircraft.

The RB.168-25R (**Mks 202/3**) supersonic engine with afterburner has a dry rating of 54·5 kN (12,250 lb) plus a 67 per cent static augmentation and powers the McDonnell Douglas Phantom FG.1 and FGR.2. Major change is the introduction of a robust shaft-and-disc LP compressor. As with Mk 101, use is made of HP compressor bleed air for aircraft BLC purposes. A Plessey gas-turbine starter is fitted. Augmentation is thrust-modulating from an initial boost, at sea level static, of ten per cent.

In December 1975 the chairman of Rolls-Royce signed contracts with the Chinese government for an initial supply of supersonic augmented Spey engines and for licence-production of such engines in China. The initial agreement is valued at over £80 million, and the eventual total, including plant and equipment, is expected to exceed £100 million.

In 1978 the Spey was selected by Aeritalia for the proposed AMX (G91 replacement) aircraft; if this materialises, engines will be produced at least partly under licence by Italian companies. The engine selected is the unaugmented **Mk 807**, rated at 49·0 kN (11,030 lb st), derived from the Mk 101 and the civil Spey 555. The development and production of the Mk 807 is expected to be a two-nation programme lasting into the next century.

The Spey RB.168-20 **Mk 250,** closely based on the commercial Spey, powers the British Aerospace (HS) Nimrod. Embodying extensive anti-corrosion treatment, this variant provides a higher thrust than its civil counterpart, through operation at higher rpm and higher turbine entry temperature. Provision is made for driving a large alternator.

Dimensions:

Diameter	825 mm (32·5 in)
Length:	
Mks 101, 250	2,985 mm (117·5 in)
Mks 202, 203	5,204 mm (204·9 in)

Weight, Dry:

Mk 101	1,181 kg (2,603 lb)
Mk 250	1,227 kg (2,704 lb)
Mks 202, 203	1,857 kg (4,093 lb)

The 1,700 ekW (2,280 ehp) Rolls-Royce Dart 535 single-shaft turboprop, typical of the versions in production

Performance Rating:
Max T-O:

Mks 101, 807	49·0 kN (11,030 lb st)
Mks 202, 203	91·25 kN (20,515 lb st)
Mk 250	53·4 kN (11,995 lb st)

ROLLS-ROYCE/ALLISON SPEY TF41

Versions of the Spey produced jointly by Rolls-Royce and the Detroit Diesel Allison Division of General Motors are described in the International section.

ROLLS-ROYCE TYNE

The 4,570 ekW (6,100 ehp) Tyne 22 two-shaft turboprop has been put back into production for the additional Transall C-160 aircraft to be built by Aérospatiale. Like engines for previous Transall aircraft they are made by a consortium comprising Rolls-Royce, SNECMA, MTU and FN. Brief details are given under SNECMA.

Limited production is also being undertaken of the Tyne 20 Mk 801, derated to 4,090 ekW (5,480 ehp) for an export version of the Aeritalia G222.

ROLLS-ROYCE DART

Beginning life in 1945 at 738 kW (990 hp), this classic turboprop was developed to give 2,420 ekW (3,245 ehp) in military and 2,256 ekW (3,025 ehp) in civil versions. Current production of new engines is centred on the less powerful models listed in the accompanying table. About 7,000 Dart engines have been delivered, and demand remains strong.

Type: Single-shaft centrifugal-flow turboprop engine.
Reduction Gear: Double helical high-speed train and final helical drive. Ratio in current engines: 0·093.
Air Intake: Circular intake with annular duct leading to impeller eye of first-stage compressor. Oil tank cast integral with casing. Secondary air intake supplies air to oil cooler.
Compressor: Two-stage centrifugal. Each impeller has nineteen vanes and steel rotating guide vanes. Mass air flow at maximum rpm typically 10·66 kg (23·5 lb)/s at 5·62 : 1 pressure ratio.
Combustion Chambers: Seven inclined flame tubes with atomisers for downstream injection. High-energy igniter plugs in Nos. 3 and 7 chambers.
Fuel System: Variable-stroke pump delivers fuel to burners through flow control unit, which incorporates a filter, throttle valve, shut-off cock and barometric pressure control. Automatically-progressive injection of water/methanol to maintain take-off power under high ambient temperature. System linked with throttle lever to prohibit use except at take-off rpm. Fuel filter de-icing by hot air from compressor.
Turbine: Three-stage axial.
Exhaust Unit: Inclined to suit installation.

Accessory Drives: Gearbox drive from main-shaft centre-coupling immediately behind compressor.
Lubrication: Integral oil tank (14 litres; 25 Imp pints) feeds via standpipe and feathering pump through tank base, to ensure feathering possible even after prolonged system oil leak. Gear pump supplies oil to all bearings and reduction-gear jets.
Controls: Throttle interconnected with propeller controller and high-pressure cock linked with feathering controls. Propeller feathered by moving shut-off cock past closed position.
Mounting: Four feet at 90° on compressor casing, although only three need be used.
Dimensions, Weights and Performance:
See table.

ROLLS-ROYCE ALFA ROMEO RB.318

This engine in the 448 kW (600 shp) class for general aviation is briefly described in the International part of this section.

ROLLS-ROYCE VIPER

This turbojet remains in production for civil and military customers. More than 5,000 Vipers have been ordered by 41 countries, 29 of which have chosen the engine for trainer and light attack aircraft.

Current versions are as follows:
Viper 11 (Mk 200 Series). Single-shaft seven-stage axial-flow compressor driven by single-stage turbine. Air mass flow 20 kg/s (44 lb/s). Type-tested at 11·12 kN (2,500 lb st) and powers Jindivik Mk 3 drone, BAC Jet Provost T.4 and 5, Yugoslav Soko Galeb and Hindustan HJT-16 Kiran trainers.

A Viper 11 version, the 22-1, was built under licence in Italy by Piaggio for the Aermacchi M.B.326 trainer and by Atlas of South Africa and Commonwealth Aircraft of Australia for similar aircraft.

Viper 500 Series. Development with increased airflow, achieved by zero stage on compressor. Major applications early HS.125 (Mks 521, 522) and PD-808 executive aircraft (Mk 526) and BAC 167 Strikemaster (Mk 535), Aermacchi M.B.326GB (Mk 540) and Soko Jastreb (Mk 531) training and light combat aircraft. Mk 540 built under licence by Piaggio and Atlas.

Viper 600 Series. Eight-stage axial-flow compressor driven by two-stage turbine; annular vaporising combustion chamber. Take-off rating 16·7 kN (3,750 lb st) civil and 17·8 kN (4,000 lb st) military. Agreement signed with Fiat (Italy) in July 1969 for technical collaboration in design, development and production (see Fiat entry).

The civil Viper 601 powers the HS.125-600, and the military Viper 632 is fitted to the Aermacchi M.B.326K

ROLLS-ROYCE DART TURBOPROP ENGINES (current production)

Mark Number	Take-off Guaranteed Maximum Power	Maximum Cruise Rating and Specific Fuel Consumption (250 knots; 463 km/h; 288 mph at 6,100 m; 20,000 ft)	Maximum Basic Dry Weight	Length (without jet pipe)	Diameter	Application
535-2	1,700 ekW; 1,551 kW (2,280 ehp; 2,080 shp) at 15,000 rpm	957 kW (1,284 shp); 104 µg/J; at 14,200 rpm	639 kg (1,409 lb)	2,496 mm (98·27 in)	963 mm (37·9 in)	BAe.748
536-7R	1,730 ekW; 1,580 kW (2,320 ehp; 2,120 shp) at 15,000 rpm	957 kW (1,284 shp); 104 µg/J; at 14,200 rpm	639 kg (1,409 lb)	2,496 mm (98·27 in)	963 mm (37·9 in)	F27 Fokker

and M.B.339. An engine similar to the 632 powers the SOKO/CNIAR Orao/IAR-93. The Viper 632 is now built under licence in Italy, Romania and Yugoslavia. The Viper 633 has an afterburner of the three-gutter type, with hot-streak ignition and a two-position nozzle. Thrust with maximum augmentation is 22·3 kN (5,000 lb st).

The following details apply to the Viper 600 series:

TYPE: Single-shaft axial turbojet.

AIR INTAKE: Direct pitot. Anti-icing by hot compressor air. No inlet guide vanes.

COMPRESSOR: Eight-stage. Steel drum-type rotor with disc assemblies. Magnesium alloy casing with blow-off valve. Stator blades mounted in carrier rings slotted into casing. All stator blades and 1st, 2nd and 8th stage rotor blades of steel; remainder aluminium alloy. Zero-stage and first-stage rotor blades attached by fir-tree roots; stages 3-8 riveted. Pressure ratio 5·8 : 1. Air mass flow 26·5 kg (58·4 lb)/s.

COMBUSTION CHAMBER: Short annular type with 24 vaporising burners and six starting atomisers. Electric ignition.

FUEL SYSTEM: Hydromechanical, consisting primarily of fuel pump, barometric fuel control and air/fuel ratio control.

FUEL GRADE: JP-1 or JP-4.

TURBINE: Two-stage axial. Shrouded blades attached to discs by fir-tree roots and locking strips. Discs attached by Hirth couplings.

BEARINGS: Ball-thrust type at forward end of compressor, roller bearings at centre section and at rear end of combustion chamber inner casing.

JET PIPE: Cone of heat-resisting steel rings butt-welded together. (Viper 601: eight-lobe convoluted nozzle to meet FAR Pt 36 noise requirements).

ACCESSORY DRIVES: Gearbox driven from front of compressor by bevel gear.

LUBRICATION SYSTEM: Self-contained. Recirculatory system supplying front bearing and gearbox, metered feed supplied to centre and rear bearings by micro-pumps. Military version fully aerobatic.

OIL SPECIFICATION: Mobil Jet 2, Shell ASTO 500 and Castrol 580.

MOUNTING: Civil: cantilevered, side mounted, single spherical bearing in centre-section casing, with top and bottom links and attachment at intake casing. Military: trunnion mounted at centre-section with additional support at intake casing.

STARTING: 24V starter/generator.

DIMENSIONS:

Max casing diameter:
All versions 624 mm (24·55 in)
Length (flange to flange):
Viper 11 1,626 mm (64·0 in)
Viper 531, 535, 540, 632 1,806 mm (71·1 in)
Viper 601 (plus jet pipe) 2,270 mm (89·4 in)

WEIGHTS, DRY:
Viper 11 284 kg (625 lb)
Viper 531 345 kg (760 lb)
Viper 535 331 kg (730 lb)
Viper 540 342 kg (755 lb)
Viper 601, 632 358 kg (790 lb)

PERFORMANCE RATINGS:
T-O:
Viper 11 11·12 kN (2,500 lb st)
Viper 531 13·9 kN (3,120 lb st)
Viper 535, 540 14·9 kN (3,360 lb st)
Viper 601 16·7 kN (3,750 lb st)
Viper 632 17·8 kN (4,000 lb st)

SPECIFIC FUEL CONSUMPTION:
Viper 11 30·3 mg/Ns (1·07 lb/h/lb st)
Viper 500 series 28·3 mg/Ns (1·00 lb/h/lb st)
Viper 601 26·6 mg/Ns (0·94 lb/h/lb st)
Viper 632 27·5 mg/Ns (0·97 lb/h/lb st)

OIL CONSUMPTION:
All versions 0·57 litres (1 Imp pint)/h

ROLLS-ROYCE RB.401

The RB.401 is a two-shaft, medium bypass ratio turbofan. The 24·5 kN (5,500 lb) thrust class was chosen to meet the requirements of the next generation of business jets and military trainer/light attack aircraft. Increased pressure ratio, reduced bypass ratio and turboshaft versions have also been studied for specific applications.

A demonstrator engine, the RB.401-06, ran on the testbed on 21 December 1975. The engine now under development for the business-aviation market is the RB.401-07. This engine first ran in November 1977, exceeding its T-O rating after six hours of testing, with fuel flow within 2·0 per cent of brochure specification.

The RB.401 incorporates components already proven in company research programmes, with technology which reads across from the RB.211 and other advanced commercial engines. It has been designed to meet all foreseeable requirements regarding noise and exhaust pollution, in addition to having an extremely low specific fuel consumption.

The following data apply to the RB.401-07:

TYPE: Two-shaft turbofan.

FAN: Single-stage axial, based on latest RB.211 technology. Low aspect ratio titanium blades without snubbers. Maximum airflow 82·5 kg (182 lb)/s. Bypass ratio 4·2 : 1.

Cutaway drawing of the Rolls-Royce Viper 632 single-shaft turbojet (take-off rating 17·8 kN; 4,000 lb st)

BY-PASS DUCT: Full-length, giving installational simplicity with optimum overall nacelle performance.

INTERMEDIATE CASING: One-piece magnesium casting incorporating accessory-gearbox drive.

HP COMPRESSOR: Eight-stage axial. Titanium rotor blades and nickel-alloy stator blades. Inlet guide vanes and first-stage stators have variable stagger. Pressure ratio of HP spool alone, 11·5 : 1.

COMBUSTION SYSTEM: Annular, with vaporising burners.

FUEL SYSTEM: Hydromechanical, with provision for electronic supervision of engine parameters.

TURBINES: Single-stage HP turbine, with aircooled rotor and stator blades. Two-stage LP turbine, with uncooled fully-shrouded blades.

LUBRICATION SYSTEM: Self-contained, including tank, pumps, filter, scavenge strainer, tubes, fittings, and cooler.

DIMENSIONS:
Length, flange to flange 1,544 mm (60·8 in)
Diameter, fan casing 823 mm (32·4 in)
WEIGHT, DRY: 447 kg (985 lb)
PERFORMANCE RATINGS:
T-O (flat-rated to 15°C):
S/L, ISA 24·7 kN (5,540 lb st)
Cruise:
Mach 0·7 and 12,000 m (40,000 ft) ISA
5·0 kN (1,130 lb)
SPECIFIC FUEL CONSUMPTION:
T-O 12·72 mg/Ns (0·449 lb/h/lb st)
Cruise (as above) 20·0 mg/Ns (0·707 lb/h/lb)

ROLLS-ROYCE ORPHEUS

This single-spool turbojet was initiated in December 1953 as a private venture. The Orpheus 701 was type-tested in November 1956 at 20·1 kN (4,520 lb st) and is used in the Gnat fighter; a modified version powers the Indian HAL Ajeet. The Mk 703, rated at 21·6 kN (4,850 lb st), powers the HF-24 Marut. For all Indian applications the engine is built under licence at Bangalore by Hindustan Aeronautics Limited (HAL). A description appeared in the 1967-68 *Jane's*.

ROLLS-ROYCE PEGASUS

The Pegasus is a turbofan for V/STOL applications. It has two main rotating systems which are mechanically independent and rotate in opposite directions, thus minimising gyroscopic effects. It has a three-stage axial-flow fan of transonic design and an eight-stage high-pressure compressor, each driven by a two-stage turbine.

Thrust vectoring is achieved by four rotatable nozzles simultaneously operated and symmetrically positioned on each side of the engine. The front nozzles discharge by-pass air, whilst the rear nozzles discharge the turbine efflux. The total thrust is divided between the four nozzles, and the resultant thrust passes through a fixed point irrespective of nozzle angle, thus minimising aircraft control problems. HP bleed air is used for aircraft stabilisation. The Pegasus was the first engine designed with an overhung fan, without inlet guide vanes, requiring no anti-icing.

By varying the angle of the nozzles, an aircraft powered by the Pegasus can take off vertically or with a short run or with a conventional long run. The reserve of power in the normal runway take-off allows for an appreciable increase in payload. The engine is stressed for operation up to Mach 2, ISA tropopause, at maximum thrust.

The Pegasus ran in August 1959, and flight trials in the Hawker Siddeley P.1127 prototypes began in October 1960. The **Pegasus 3**, which powered prototype P.1127 aircraft, was rated at 60 kN (13,500 lb st). The engine entered service in the Harrier with the RAF in 1969 and later with the AV-8A of the USMC and Matador of the Spanish Navy. These aircraft have the Pegasus 11 Mk 103, rated at 95·6 kN (21,500 lb st).

A maritime version of the Pegasus 11 is designated **Mk 104**. Developed for the Sea Harrier, it embodies material changes to the LP and intermediate casings, sacrificial protective coatings on ferrous components, and an increased-capacity gearbox. The Sea Harrier entered service with the Royal Navy in September 1979 and has been ordered by the Indian Navy for service from 1982.

A version of the Pegasus also powers the AV-8B, being developed by McDonnell Douglas and BAe. The first full-scale development aircraft, due to fly in October 1981, is powered by the standard **Mk 103 (F402-RR-402)**, but production aircraft will have the **F402-RR-404**, with improved maintainability features and a TBO of 1,000 h. The YAV-8B prototypes completed their flight demonstration programme during 1979 and met or exceeded all performance targets.

Work has restarted on a thrust augmentation system, known as Plenum Chamber Burning (PCB), for possible future supersonic V/STOL applications.

The following data apply specifically to the Pegasus 11:

TYPE: Two-shaft vectored-thrust turbofan.

AIR INTAKE CASING: One-piece casting in ZRE magnesium-zirconium alloy (Mk 104, aluminium).

Cutaway drawing of the Rolls-Royce RB.401-07 turbofan (24·7 kN; 5,540 lb st)

FAN: Three-stage axial, overhung ahead of front bearing. Titanium blades with part-span snubbers. Maximum airflow 196 kg (432 lb)/s. Pressure ratio 2·3 : 1. Bypass ratio 1·4 : 1.

INTERMEDIATE CASING: Houses front fan bearing, accessory drives and HP compressor front bearing. All engine-driven accessories mounted above this casing.

HP COMPRESSOR: Eight-stage with titanium rotor blades. Overall pressure ratio 14 : 1.

COMBUSTION SYSTEM: Annular, with low-pressure vaporising burner system.

FUEL SYSTEM: Hydromechanical, comprising centrifugal backing pump, gear-type pressure pump, HP shut-off cock and overspeed governors and emergency manual control.

TURBINES: Two-stage HP turbine and two-stage LP turbine. First-stage HP blades precision cast. Remaining three rotor stages have forged blades. Both HP stages aircooled.

THRUST NOZZLES: Two steel cold front-thrust nozzles and two Nimonic hot thrust nozzles, actuated by duplicated air motors through shafts and chains. Vectored-thrust control by pilot command lever.

LUBRICATION SYSTEM: Self-contained, comprising pressure pump and three scavenge pumps, with fuel-cooled oil cooler.

MOUNTING: Four-point suspension, with main trunnions on each side of delivery casing and tie link at rear of turbines.

STARTING: Gas-turbine starter/APU on intermediate casing.

DIMENSIONS:

Length, without nozzles	2,510 mm (98·84 in)
Diameter, fan casing	1,220 mm (48·05 in)
Length, with nozzles	3,480 mm (137 in)

WEIGHT, DRY (without nozzles):

Mk 103	1,404 kg (3,096 lb)
Mk 104	1,429 kg (3,148 lb)

PERFORMANCE RATINGS:
See under sub-type descriptions.

ROLLS-ROYCE ODIN

The Odin ramjet powers the British Aerospace Sea Dart medium-range surface-to-air and surface-to-surface missile. Sea Dart is in service on HMS *Bristol* and Type 42 destroyers of the Royal Navy, and with the Armada Republica Argentina. It will also be standard equipment on the anti-submarine carriers being supplied to the Royal Navy.

A lightweight Sea Dart installation is being developed by BAe for ships down to 300 tonnes.

The Odin ramjet is mounted integrally with the Sea Dart body and gives longer range and better performance than a rocket-powered missile. Details of the Odin are classified.

ROLLS-ROYCE TURBOMÉCA RTM.321

This turboshaft engine is described in the International section.

ROLLS-ROYCE GEM

The Gem was designed and developed at Leavesden, for the Lynx helicopter. Although this is an element of the Anglo-French helicopter programme, the Gem development programme has been funded entirely by the British government. Production engine deliveries, with a proportion of parts supplied by Turboméca of France, began in 1975. In 1978 the Arab British Engine Company was

Cutaway drawing of the Rolls-Royce Pegasus 103 turbofan (95·6 kN; 21,500 lb st)

formed to build an expected 750 Gems and spares under licence in Egypt.

Choice of a two-spool gas generator gives fast response to power demand without the need for a complex control system. Conservative stressing and thermo-dynamic loading, and use of proven design and manufacturing techniques, are features which experience has shown to contribute to engine reliability.

The design concept of the engine is based upon seven major modules, each capable of being assembled, tested and released as an interchangeable unit for service use in the interest of reducing the operator's product support commitments.

The nine main bearings each have labyrinth seals pressurised by LP compressor air which also cools the bearings and minimises heat transfer to the oil, and oil cooler and fan requirements.

Provision is made for in-flight and on-ground condition monitoring systems. Features include access ports for intrascope inspection of each LP compressor stage, HP compressor, combustor, LP turbine and power turbine, and mountings for vibration pickups.

Three versions have been announced:

Gem Mk 10001. Engine-change unit for Lynx, rated at 671 kW (900 shp). In quantity production, shared with Turboméca. Entered service in 1976.

Gem 2. Export military engine, rated at 900 shp. In service with foreign governments.

Gem 4. First stage of uprating programme; rated at 1,050 shp. Based on Gem 2 with modified LP compressor to increase mass flow by approximately 10 per cent, together with small increase in turbine entry temperature. In production for 4,762 kg (10,500 lb) Lynx.

Gem 41. Based on Gem 2 with modified LP compressor to increase mass flow by about 10 per cent, plus small

increase in turbine entry temperature. In production for 4,762 kg (10,500 lb) Lynx and fitted to Westland WG.30.

The following description relates to the Gem Mk 10001; other versions are generally similar:

TYPE: Free-turbine turboshaft, with two-spool gas generator.

AIR INTAKE: Annular forward facing.

SHAFT DRIVE: Compact single-stage double-helical reduction gear with rotating planet cage carried by ball bearing at front and roller bearing at rear. Reduction gear mounted within intake casing and driven by power turbine shaft. Gearbox comprises No. 1 module, and power turbine shaft No. 2 module. Gearbox provides governed output speed of 6,000 rpm. No. 2 module provides for signal to phase-displacement torquemeter (customer option).

LP COMPRESSOR: Four-stage axial. LP compressor and intake case comprise No. 3 module.

HP COMPRESSOR: Single-stage centrifugal impeller having alternate inducer and radial vanes. Combined radial-and-axial diffuser feeds compressor delivery air to annular combustor. Overall pressure ratio 12·0 : 1.

COMBUSTION CHAMBER: Fully annular reverse-flow with air-atomiser fuel sprays supplied by external fuel manifold. High-energy ignition box mounted on power turbine/jet pipe case.

HP TURBINE: Single-stage axial close-coupled to HP impeller. Rotor blades and aircooled nozzle guide vanes based on R-R Dart technology. HP spool with compressor intermediate casing and combustor comprise No. 4 module.

LP TURBINE: Single-stage axial with shrouded rotor blades, drives LP compressor. LP turbine and main shaft comprise No. 6 module.

POWER TURBINE: Two-stage axial with shrouded rotor blades. Rear of power drive shaft drives output speed governor and overspeed fuel cut-off trip mechanism via spur and bevel gear train in exhaust cone. Power turbine and jet pipe form No. 7 module.

JET PIPE: Short-length duct with casing extending forward to combustor rear casing. Four cruciform struts integral with exhaust cone.

ACCESSORY DRIVES: Bevel gear on front of HP compressor shaft drives accessory shaft extending through compressor intermediate casing to spiral bevel gear drive to accessory wheelcase mounted atop intermediate casing. Drives provided for starter/generator, fuel pump, oil cooler fan and other accessories. Wheelcase forms No. 5 module.

FUEL SYSTEM: Plessey fuel system with fluidics circuit providing fully automatic control, and power matching for multi-engine installation. Also automatic restoration of power from 'good' engine in event of single engine failure. Incorporates fuel filter.

LUBRICATION SYSTEM: Engine-mounted oil tank and cooler to provide self-contained system. Magnetic chip detectors fitted in each scavenge line. Oil filter incorporated in accessory wheelcase.

DIMENSIONS:

Height overall	596 mm (23·5 in)
Width overall	575 mm (22·6 in)
Length overall	1,095 mm (43·1 in)

WEIGHT, DRY:

Gem 10001, 2	150 kg (330 lb)
Gem 4	156 kg (343 lb)

Cutaway drawing of the Rolls-Royce Gem free-turbine turboshaft, with initial service rating of 671 kW (900 shp)

PERFORMANCE RATINGS:
  Max contingency (2½ min):
    Gem 10001, 2   671 kW (900 shp)
    Gem 41-1   835 kW (1,120 shp)
  Intermediate contingency (1 h)/max T-O (5 min):
    Gem 10001, 2   619 kW (830 shp)
    Gem 41-1   746 kW (1,000 shp)
  Max continuous:
    Gem 10001, 2   559 kW (750 shp)
    Gem 41-1   664 kW (890 shp)
SPECIFIC FUEL CONSUMPTION:
  Max T-O:
    Gem 10001, 2   89·57 μg/J (0·53 lb/h/shp)
    Gem 41-1   82·47 μg/J (0·488 lb/h/shp)
  50 per cent max T-O:
    All versions   111·5 μg/J (0·66 lb/h/shp)

ROLLS-ROYCE GNOME

Gnome is the name given to the versions of the General Electric T58 turboshaft which Rolls-Royce manufactures in the UK. The first ran on 5 June 1959.

The major difference between the Gnome and T58 lies in the replacement of the Hamilton Standard fuel control system by a Lucas system controlled by an electrical computer.

More than 1,800 Gnome engines have been delivered. Four versions have been announced:

H.1000. Initial version, rated at 783 kW (1,050 shp). Power plant for military Whirlwind HAR.Mk 9, HAR.Mk 10 and HCC.Mk 12, civil S-55 Series 3 and Agusta-Bell 204B.

H.1200. Rated at 932 kW (1,250 shp). Used in Agusta-Bell 204B, Boeing Vertol 107 and some Kawasaki KV-107/II-5s. Coupled version for Wessex Mks 2, 5, 50 and 60 series comprises two H.1200s driving through a coupling gearbox designed and manufactured by Rolls-Royce.

H.1400. Rated at 1,044 kW (1,400 shp). Based on the H.1200, with modified compressor to increase airflow. Turbine diaphragm cooling redesigned to increase temperature capacity and life. Dimensions unchanged.

H.1400-1. Rated at 1,145 kW (1,535 shp). Uprated from H.1400, without change in size or weight, by increasing gas-generator speed and using improved gas-generator turbine-blade material allowing increased temperature. In production for Westland Sea King and Commando.

The following description refers specifically to the H.1400-1:

TYPE: Axial-flow free-turbine turboshaft engine.

AIR INTAKE: Annular forward-facing. Centre housing carrying front main bearing supported by four radial struts. Struts and inlet guide vanes anti-iced with hot compressor bleed air and oil drainage.

COMPRESSOR: Ten-stage axial. Controlled variable incidence for inlet guide vanes and first three rows of stator blades. Air mass flow 6·26 kg (13·8 lb)/s.

Cutaway drawing of the Rolls-Royce Gnome H.1400-1 free-turbine turboshaft

COMBUSTION SYSTEM: Straight-through annular chamber with outer casing split along horizontal centreline. Sixteen Simplex-type fuel injectors, eight on each of two sets of manifolds. One Lodge capacitor-discharge high-energy igniter plug.

FUEL SYSTEM: Lucas hydromechanical units, comprising variable-stroke multi-plunger pump, flow control unit and throttle controlled by HSDE electrical control computer and throttle actuator.

FUEL GRADE: DERD.2452, 2453, 2454, 2486, 2494 and 2498 (NATO F44, F34, F40, F35 and F43).

GAS-PRODUCER TURBINE: Two-stage, coupled to compressor shaft by conical shaft. Extended-root blading with fir-tree attachments.

POWER TURBINE: Single-stage free turbine. Extended-root blading with fir-tree attachments.

EXHAUST SYSTEM: Curved exhaust ducting arranged to suit individual applications.

REDUCTION GEAR: Optional double-helical gear providing reduction from nominal 19,500 rpm power turbine speed to 6,600 rpm at output shaft. Provision for power take-off to left or right.

ACCESSORY DRIVES: Quill shaft drive through lower intake strut. Fuel and lubrication systems mounted beneath compressor casing. Power take-off shaft up to 100 shp on primary reduction gear casing for separate accessories gearbox.

LUBRICATION: Fully scavenged gear pumps. Serck oil cooler.

MOUNTING: Three forward mounting faces on intake casing. Two rear mounting faces on upper portion of primary gear casing. When no reduction gear fitted, rear mounting face on engine centreline at power-turbine output shaft housing.

STARTING: Rotax electric starter in nose bullet.

DIMENSIONS:
  Length:
    H.1000, H.1200, H.1400-1 (all ungeared)
                               1,392 mm (54·8 in)
    Coupled H.1200 (Wessex)   1,747 mm (68·8 in)
  Max height:
    H.1000, H.1200, H.1400-1 (all ungeared)
                               549 mm (21·6 in)
    Coupled H.1200 (Wessex)   1,031 mm (40·6 in)
  Max width:
    H.1000, H.1200 (ungeared) 462 mm (18·2 in)
    H.1400-1 (ungeared)   577 mm (22·7 in)
    Coupled H.1200 (Wessex)   1,059 mm (41·7 in)
WEIGHT, DRY:
  H.1000 (ungeared)   134 kg (296 lb)
  H.1200 (ungeared)   142 kg (314 lb)
  H.1400-1 (ungeared)   148 kg (326 lb)
  Reduction gearbox   52·6 kg (116 lb)
  Coupled H.1200 with coupling gearbox:
    for Wessex   422 kg (930 lb)
PERFORMANCE RATINGS (at power-turbine shaft):
  Max contingency (2½ min; multi-engine aircraft only):
    H.1200   1,007 kW (1,350 shp)
    H.1400-1   1,238 kW (1,660 shp)
  Max one-hour (single engine):
    H.1000   783 kW (1,050 shp)
    H.1200   932 kW (1,250 shp)
    H.1400-1   1,145 kW (1,535 shp)
  Max continuous:
    H.1000   671 kW (900 shp)
    H.1200   783 kW (1,050 shp)
    H.1400-1   932 kW (1,250 shp)
SPECIFIC FUEL CONSUMPTION:
  At max contingency rating:
    H.1200   104·4 μg/J (0·618 lb/h/shp)
    H.1400-1   102·75 μg/J (0·608 lb/h/shp)

ROLLS-ROYCE MOTORS
ROLLS-ROYCE MOTORS LTD

HEAD OFFICE: Crewe, Cheshire CW1 3PL
Telephone: 0270 55155
MAIN LOCATIONS:
  Crewe (Car Division, Specialist and Light Aircraft Engine Division, Precision Components Division)
  Shrewsbury, Shropshire SY1 4DP (Diesel Division, Military Engine Division)
  London NW (Mulliner Park Ward Division)

DIRECTORS:
  I. J. Fraser (Chairman)
  D. A. S. Plastow (Managing Director)
  C. S. Aston
  G. R. Fenn
  H. P. N. Benson
  L. W. Harris (Commercial Director)
  T. Neville (Financial Director)
  H. Wuttke
  P. J. Vinson
  G. Lewis

DIRECTOR OF GROUP PUBLIC RELATIONS: W. D. J. Roscoe

Rolls-Royce Motors, which began operations on 24 April 1971, comprises the businesses formerly carried on by the Motor Car and Oil Engine Divisions of the former Rolls-Royce Ltd. The company has four factories employing 10,000 people; annual turnover is more than £120 million. It is unconnected with today's Rolls-Royce Ltd.

Under the terms of a licence agreement signed in 1960 with Teledyne Continental Motors of the USA, Rolls-Royce Motors markets Continental light-aircraft engines and spare parts throughout the world, with the exception

Rolls-Royce Continental piston engines; left, O-200, rated at 74·5 kW (100 hp); right, O-240, rated at 97 kW (130 hp)

of North and South America and certain Far Eastern countries. Five models from the Continental range, and one developed from the start by Rolls-Royce Motors, are manufactured by the company's Specialist and Light Aircraft Engine Division at Crewe, and these are described hereafter.

ROLLS-ROYCE CONTINENTAL C90

This is the 70·8 kW (95 hp) Continental C90 four-cylinder engine built under licence.

ROLLS-ROYCE CONTINENTAL O-200-A

This is the 74·5 kW (100 hp) Continental O-200-A four-cylinder engine, built under licence.

ROLLS-ROYCE CONTINENTAL O-240-A

The O-240-A is the first light-aircraft engine to be developed by Rolls-Royce Motors in conjunction with Teledyne Continental. Rolls-Royce took over the programme in 1968 with a view to developing the engine specifically for the European market. Certification was completed in January 1970 and FAA Type Validation was awarded in February 1971. Production deliveries began in mid-1970, initially for the Reims Aviation Aerobat and Rollason Condor. The O-240 is being marketed in the USA by Teledyne Continental Motors.

TYPE: Four-cylinder, horizontally-opposed, aircooled, carburetted, unsupercharged.

CYLINDERS: Bore 112·5 mm (4·438 in). Stroke 98·4 mm (3·875 in). Capacity 3,933 cc (240 cu in). Compression ratio 8·5 : 1. Cast aluminium alloy finned heads are screwed and shrunk on to forged steel barrels.

PISTONS: Heat-treated aluminium alloy. Two compression rings and one oil control ring above the gudgeon pin, one scraper below. Fully floating, ground steel tube gudgeon pins with pressed-in aluminium end plugs.

CONNECTING RODS: Forged steel I-section. Big-end bearings are thin steel backed overlay plated copper lead. Little-end bearings are roller bronze bushings.

CRANKSHAFT: Alloy steel forgings, nitrided all over for greater fatigue strength, having three journals running in thin steel backed overlay plated copper lead bearings.

CRANKCASE: Cast aluminium alloy, split along the vertical centreline.

VALVE GEAR: Two valves per cylinder. Steel inlet valves with hardened tips. Steel exhaust valves with hardened tips faced with Stellite F. Valve seats shrunk into position. Camshaft, in centre of crankcase beneath the crankshaft, driven by gear from the crankshaft.

INDUCTION: Float-type carburettor with a manual mixture control.

FUEL GRADE: 100/130 octane minimum.

IGNITION: Two Slick type 4001 or two Bendix Scintilla S4LN-21 magnetos on rear of crankcase driven by gears from camshaft. Two Champion REM 38EC, REM 38W or Lodge RSE 23/3R 18 mm spark plugs per cylinder.

LUBRICATION SYSTEM: Wet sump. Magnesium crankcase cover houses the engine-driven gear type oil pump. An oil pressure relief valve is mounted in the cover. Provision is made for an airframe-mounted oil cooler and optional full-flow filter.

PROPELLER DRIVE: Direct drive, clockwise when viewed from rear. ARP 502 Type 1 flange.

ACCESSORIES: Ford 15V 60A alternator. Mechanical tachometer drive from oil pump at rear of engine. Fuel pump is operated from an eccentric on the camshaft at front of engine. An AND 20,000 accessory drive pad is provided at the front of the crankcase.

STARTING: Prestolite EO 19508 12V starter.

MOUNTING: Four rear-mounted ring type mounting brackets to which vibration isolators can be attached.

DIMENSIONS:

Length	826 mm (32·5 in)
Width	798 mm (31·4 in)
Height	633 mm (24·9 in)
WEIGHT, DRY: incl accessories	112 kg (246 lb)

PERFORMANCE RATINGS:

Take-off	97 kW (130 hp) at 2,800 rpm
Maximum recommended cruise	72·7 kW (97·5 hp) at 2,540 rpm

SPECIFIC FUEL CONSUMPTION:

Max rich	81·1μg/J (0·48 lb/h/hp)
Max lean	71·0μg/J (0·42 lb/h/hp)

Rolls-Royce Continental IO-360 piston engine, rated at 156·6 kW (210 hp)

Rolls-Royce Continental IO-368 piston engine, rated at 134 kW (180 hp)

OIL CONSUMPTION:

Maximum	2·53μg/J (0·015 lb/h/hp)

ROLLS-ROYCE CONTINENTAL O-300

This is the 108 kW (145 hp) Continental O-300 six-cylinder engine, built under licence.

ROLLS-ROYCE CONTINENTAL IO-360

This is the 156·6 kW (210 hp) Continental IO-360 six-cylinder horizontally-opposed aircooled engine built under licence. The turbocharged TSIO-360 of 156·6 or 168 kW (210 or 225 hp) is also produced by Rolls-Royce Motors.

ROLLS-ROYCE CONTINENTAL IO-368

At the 1979 Paris Air Show this new engine was announced jointly by Rolls-Royce Motors and Teledyne Continental. Unlike previous light-aircraft engines from Rolls-Royce Motors, the IO-368 was a Crewe project from its early design stage.

TYPE: Four-cylinder, horizontally-opposed, aircooled, unsupercharged.

CYLINDERS: Bore 133·35 mm (5·25 in). Stroke 107·95 mm (4·25 in). Capacity 6,022 cc (367·9 cu in). Compression ratio 8·2.

INDUCTION: Direct fuel injection.

FUEL GRADE: 100 LL.

IGNITION: Two Slick magnetos facing forward on rear gearcase. Two Champion RHM 38E plugs per cylinder.

ACCESSORIES: Integral accessory gearcase. Prestolite electric starter and provision for refrigeration compressor. Belt-driven alternator.

MOUNTING: Choice of dynafocal or bed-type.

DIMENSIONS:

Length	752·4 mm (29·62 in)
Width	850·9 mm (33·5 in)
Height	590·6 mm (23·25 in)

WEIGHT, DRY: incl accessories	approx 136 kg (300 lb)

PERFORMANCE RATINGS (S/L):

T-O and rated	134 kW (180 hp)
Cruise	108 kW (145 hp)

SPECIFIC FUEL CONSUMPTION:

T-O and rated	77·7μg/J (0·46 lb/h/hp)
Cruise	74·4μg/J (0·44 lb/h/hp)

WESLAKE
WESLAKE AEROMARINE ENGINES LTD

Yeovil, Somerset BA20 2YB
Telephone: Yeovil (0935) 5181
OFFICERS:
 B. D. Blackwell, MA, BSc(Eng)
 W. T. C. Miller, OBE, MA, CEng, MIMechE, MInstM
SECRETARY: K. Stansfield
DIVISIONAL MANAGER: D. P. Short, MA, CEng, MIMechE

On 1 May 1979 Weslake Aeromarine Engines Ltd was acquired by Westland Aircraft Ltd, whose subsidiary company, Normalair-Garrett Ltd, from that date undertook management control. In 1980 the company was relocated at Yeovil, to take advantage of the high-quality manufacturing facility available there for quantity production.

WESLAKE TYPE 116

Two-cylinder two-stroke with bore and stroke of 46 mm (1·81 in) and 35 mm (1·38 m) respectively. Weight including ignition, carburettor and stub exhausts about 4·5 kg (10 lb). Rated output 6 kW (8 hp) at 6,500 rpm.

WESLAKE TYPE 200

Two-cylinder, simultaneous-firing two-stroke for RPV applications. Bore and stroke 55 mm (2·17 in) and 42 mm (1·65 in) respectively. Weight with ignition, carburettor, stub exhausts and alternator drive, about 8·2 kg (18 lb). Rating 9 kW (12 hp) at 6,500 rpm.

WESLAKE TYPE 274

The Type 274 is the first production engine available. It is being produced in two basic versions for RPVs, ACVs (Hovercraft) and powered hang gliders. The 274-6 is used

in the Westland Wideye, Shorts Skeet, Cranfield A2 and other aircraft.

TYPE: Two-cylinder aircooled two-stroke, simultaneous-firing (274-6 loop scavenged).

CYLINDERS: Die-cast aluminium with plated bore (274-6, treated bore). Bore 66 mm (2·60 in). Stroke 40 mm (1·575 in). Capacity 274 cc (42·50 cu in).

CONNECTING RODS: Forged steel, caged needle bearing at both ends (274-3, single-piece; 274-4, -6, split type).

CRANKSHAFT: Forged steel. 274-3, three-piece, vertical, running in caged needle and thrust bearings at both ends, with drive at both ends. 274-4 and -6, single-piece with large-diameter propeller mounting at one end.

CRANKCASE: 274-3, two-piece cast in LM25 aluminium with mounts for vertical operation. 274-4, similar but rear radial mounts. 274-6, single-piece with radial anti-vibration mounts.

INDUCTION: 274-3 and -4, twin Tillotson carburettors incorporating fuel pump. 274-6, single carburettor at rear feeding through rotary disc valve.

FUEL GRADE: 274-3, regular road-vehicle gasoline plus branded two-cycle oil in ratio 50:1. 274-4, same in ratio 25:1. 274-6, three-star gasoline plus oil in ratio 25:1 reducing to 50:1.

IGNITION: 274-3 and -4, specially developed SEM electronic flywheel magneto, type AM3/90; fully shielded, no external power. 274-6, modified AM3/90.

DIMENSIONS:
Length: 274-3, -4	228·5 mm (9·0 in)	
274-6	355·5 mm (14·0 in)	
Width	355·5 mm (14·0 in)	
Height	228·5 mm (9·0 in)	

WEIGHT, DRY (complete to run):
274-3, -4	7·7 kg (17·0 lb)
274-6	7·26 kg (16·0 lb)

PERFORMANCE RATING:
274-3, -4, -6	13·43 kW (18 hp) at 6,500 rpm

SPECIFIC FUEL CONSUMPTION:
274-3, -4, -6	below 186 μg/J (1·1 lb/h/hp)

WESLAKE TYPE 342

Two-cylinder simultaneous-firing two-stroke for RPV applications. Bore and stroke 66 mm (2·60 in) and 50 mm (1·97 in) respectively. Weight with ignition, carburettor, stub exhausts and alternator control system, about 12·7 kg (28 lb). Rating 19·4/22·4 kW (26/30 hp) at 6,000/8,000 rpm.

WESLAKE TYPE 430

This is a larger two-cylinder two-stroke engine, generally following the principles of the 274. Single-piece connecting rods drive a three-piece crankshaft driving at both ends. A twin-plug version is available.

Weslake Type 274-6 fitted in Shorts Skeet target

DIMENSIONS:
Length	305 mm (12·0 in)
Width	432 mm (17·0 in)
Height	254 mm (10·0 in)
WEIGHT, DRY (complete):	11·3 kg (25·0 lb)
PERFORMANCE RATING:	up to 30 kW (40 hp)
SPECIFIC FUEL CONSUMPTION:	149 μ/J (0·8 lb/h/hp)

WESLAKE TYPE 548

This is basically a four-cylinder version of the 274-6, with an aluminium or magnesium alloy crankcase incorporating ports for reed-valve induction.
WEIGHT, DRY:	16·3 kg (36·0 lb)
PERFORMANCE RATING:	26·9 kW (36 hp)

WESLAKE TYPE 860

A four-cylinder two-stroke; details restricted.

WESLAKE TYPE 1527

Based on well-proven production components, this is a flat-four four-stroke aircooled RPV engine.

Weslake Type 200 RPV engine rated at 9 kW (12 hp)

CYLINDERS: Die-cast aluminium barrels and heads. Aluminium liner with internal coating. Bore 90·0 mm (3·54 in). Stroke 60 mm (2·36 in). Capacity 1,527 cc (93·2 cu in).

CRANKSHAFT: Single-piece, four-throw, three-bearing.

INDUCTION: Twin Stromberg or Weber carburettors.

FUEL GRADE: Pump four-star or Avgas 100R.

IGNITION: Lucas Rita breakerless system.

DIMENSIONS:
Length	355·5 mm (14·0 in)
Width	647·4 mm (25·5 in)
Height (dry-pump version)	228·5 mm (9·0 in)
WEIGHT, DRY (inc starter):	under 45·4 kg (100·0 lb)

PERFORMANCE RATING (ISA):
	74·6 kW (100 hp) at 5,500 rpm

SPECIFIC FUEL CONSUMPTION (at rating):
	under 84·5 μg/J (0·5 lb/h/hp)

UNITED STATES OF AMERICA

AEROJET
AEROJET-GENERAL CORPORATION (Subsidiary of The General Tire & Rubber Company)

10300 N Torrey Pines Road, La Jolla, California 92037
Telephone: (714) 455 8500
CHAIRMAN OF THE BOARD: M. G. O'Neil
PRESIDENT: J. H. Vollbrecht
GROUP VICE-PRESIDENT: J. L. Heckel
Aerojet Liquid Rocket Company
PRESIDENT: Roger I. Ramseier
Aerojet Services Company
PRESIDENT: R. W. Warden
Aerojet Strategic Propulsion Company
PRESIDENT: K. R. Collins
Aerojet Solid Propulsion Company
TACTICAL SYSTEMS GROUP
VICE-PRESIDENT AND GENERAL MANAGER: W. M. Necoechea

Aerojet-General Corporation has activities in four major areas of business: chemicals, electronics, engineering and construction, and mechanical systems and metal products.

In the chemical area, two organisations produce solid-propellant rocket motors for the Department of Defense. The Aerojet Strategic Propulsion Company designs, develops and produces solid-propulsion strategic ballistic-missile rocket motors; Aerojet Tactical Systems produces a variety of tactical missile motors.

In the mechanical systems area, the Aerojet Liquid Rocket Company is active in research, development, testing and production of liquid-propellant rocket engines, waterjet propulsors and lift fan systems for surface-effect ships. The Aerojet Services Company, formed in 1977, provides technical services and products for defence and space programmes including rocket launch support, engine repair and overhaul, systems engineering and related management activities.

Aerojet Liquid Rocket Company (ALRC), Sacramento, California. Development and manufacture of all liquid-fuel engines for the US Air Force's Titan family of vehicles, including the improved Transtage; second-stage propulsion for the uprated Delta 3920 and Japanese Space Agency (NASDA) N-2 launch vehicles; Orbital Manoeuvring System (OMS) engines for the Space Shuttle; and application of Titan engines to the Liquid Boost Module (LBM), to provide Space Shuttle thrust augmentation for significant increases in payload capability.

ALRC Space Shuttle OMS engine

AEROJET TITAN III ENGINES

The production of Titan III first, second and Transtage engines for use as booster propulsion on the Titan family of vehicles has been under way continuously since 1962 by Aerojet Liquid Rocket Company and its predecessor Aerojet organisations. These engines, utilising storable propellants, develop 2,353 kN (529,000 lb), 445 kN (100,000 lb) and 71·2 kN (16,000 lb) thrust respectively. Their flight reliability is in the 90-99 per cent class. The nominal weights of these engines are 1,977, 564 and 196 kg (4,360, 1,245 and 432 lb) respectively.

In January 1978 ALRC was awarded a $38·5 million contract by the US Air Force Space and Missile Organisation for nine additional Titan propulsion systems. This will extend production until June 1981.

AEROJET SPACE SHUTTLE OMS ENGINE

The Space Shuttle Orbiter has two Orbiter Manoeuvring System (OMS) engines, in pods on each side of the vertical stabiliser (fin). The OMS engine, produced by ALRC, provides thrust for orbit insertion, circularisation and plane change, rendezvous and de-orbit manoeuvres.

ASPC Minuteman III second-stage motor

AEROJET SOLID PROPULSION COMPANY MOTORS

Name	Designation	Fuel	Oxidiser	Average thrust kN (lb)	Max length m (in)	Max dia m (in)	Total weight kg (lb)	Remarks/Primary Application
Strategic Motors								
Minuteman 2nd stage	SR19-AJ-1	Polybutadiene	NH₄ClO₄	269·5 (60,000)	4·01 (162)	1·32 (52)	7,076 (15,600)	Minuteman LGM-30G second stage, titanium case, single submerged nozzle, liquid injection TVC.
Polaris 1st stage	A3P	Polyurethane	NH₄ClO₄	—	4·62 (182)	1·37 (54)	10,886 (24,000)	Polaris A3, glass case, four rotatable nozzles; nitroplasticiser additive.
Tactical Motors								
Phoenix	Mk 60 Mod 0	Polybutadiene	NH₄ClO₄	—	1·78 (70)	0·38 (15)	199 (439)	Propulsion for Navy's fleet-defence air-to-air missile.
Sparrow III, AIM-7E	Mk 52 Mod 2	Polybutadiene	NH₄ClO₄	—	1·32 (52)	0·2 (8)	68·5 (151)	Propulsion for Navy's Sparrow air-to-air missile and UK BAe Sky Flash.
Shrike	Mk 53 Mod 2	Polybutadiene	NH₄ClO₄	—	1·32 (52)	0·2 (8)	71 (157)	Propulsion for Navy's AGM-45 anti-radiation air-to-surface missile.
Shrike, Improved	Mk 78 Mod 0	Polyurethane	NH₄ClO₄	—	1·30 (51)	0·2 (8)	78 (172)	Dual-thrust propulsion for anti-radiation air-to-surface missile.
Tartar	Mk 1 Mod 0	Polyurethane	NH₄ClO₄	—	2·62 (103)	0·34 (13·5)	345 (760)	Dual-thrust propulsion for Navy ship-to-air missile.
Tartar, Improved	Mk 27 Mod 2, 3	Polyurethane	NH₄ClO₄	—	2·62 (103)	0·34 (13·5)	354 (780)	Dual-thrust propulsion for Navy ship-to-air missile.
Standard Missile	Mk 56 Mod 2	Polybutadiene Polyurethane	NH₄ClO₄	—	2·62 (103)	0·34 (13·5)	411·5 (907)	Dual-thrust propulsion for Navy ship-to-air Missile Type 1, MR.
Harpoon	MX-(TBD)B446-2	Polyurethane	NH₄ClO₄	—	0·61 (24)	0·34 (13·5)	119 (262)	Booster for Navy Harpoon anti-ship missile.
2·75 in FFAR, Improved	SR105-AJ-1	Polybutadiene	NH₄ClO₄	—	0·34 (33)	0·07 (2·75)	5·9 (13)	Air-launched forward firing.
Hawk	XM22E8	Polyurethane	NH₄ClO₄	—	2·77 (109)	0·36 (14)	388 (856)	Dual-thrust motor for Army's surface-to-air Hawk missile.
Hawk, Improved	XM112	Polyurethane	NH₄ClO₄	—	2·77 (109)	0·36 (14)	395 (870)	Dual-thrust motor for Army's surface-to-air Hawk missile.
Sidewinder	Mk 17	HTPB	NH₄ClO₄	Classified	1·91 (75)	0·127 (5)	40·4 (89)	Propulsion for AIM-9J/9P Sidewinder air-to-air missiles.
Maverick		HTPB	NH₄ClO₄	*	1·00 (39·5)	0·28 (11)	48·4 (107)	Propulsion for AGM-65 Maverick missile.
Launch Vehicle Boosters and Space Motors								
Alcor 1B		Polybutadiene	NH₄ClO₄	44·5 (10,000)	1·43 (76)	0·51 (20)	455·5 (1,004)	Third stage of Athena test vehicle and 2nd stage for Astrobee 1500 launch vehicle.
Astrobee F		HTPB	NH₄ClO₄	169/37 (38,000/ 8,300)	7·11 (280)	0·43 (15)	1,255 (2,768)	Dual-thrust sounding rocket (200 lb to 235 miles altitude).
SVM-4A	SVM-4A	Polybutadiene	NH₄ClO₄	—	1·52 (60)	0·94 (37)	706 (1,557)	Apogee-boost motor for Intelsat IV synchronous communications satellite.
SVM-5	SVM-5	Polybutadiene	NH₄ClO₄	21·8 (4,900)	0·91 (36)	0·76 (30)	318·5 (702)	Apogee-boost motor for NASA Synchronous Meteorological Satellite.
SVM-7	SVM-7	Polybutadiene	NH₄ClO₄	43·2 (9,520)	1·45 (57)	0·76 (30)	440 (970)	Apogee-boost motor for RCA Comsat.
Gas Generators and JATOs								
Turbine Start Cartridge		Butyl Rubber	NH₄NO₃	n.a.	0·41 (16)	0·18 (7)	11 (24)	For Titan II first stage.
Turbine Start Cartridge		Butyl Rubber	NH₄NO₃	n.a.	0·48 (19)	0·10 (4)	5·5 (12)	For Titan II second stage.
Gas Gen Mk 46		Butyl Rubber	NH₄NO₃	n.a.	1·09 (43)	0·305 (12)	—	Prime power source for the Navy's Mk 46 Mod 0 torpedo.
Controllable Motors								
SCCSRM		Polyurethane	NH₄ClO₄	—	0·38 (15)	0·51 (20)	415 (915)	Single-chamber controllable solid-rocket motor.
Air Launched (VTM)		Polybutadiene	NH₄ClO₄	—	1·37 (54)	0·43 (17)	185 (407)	Variable-thrust motor; has both thrust-magnitude and vector control.
Air-to-Air Controllable (ATAC)		Polybutadiene	NH₄ClO₄	—	1·70 (67)	0·20 (8)	95 (210)	Throttling over wide temperature range.
Stop-Start Motor (SSM)		Polyurethane	NH₄ClO₄	—	2·21 (87)	0·51 (20)	396·5 (874)	Stop/start operation on command.

*Boost 44·5 kN (10,000 lb), sustainer 8·0 kN (1,800 lb)

The propellants are monomethylhydrazine (MMH) and nitrogen tetroxide. At launch the basic system carries 4,087 kg (9,010 lb) of usable MMH and 6,743 kg (14,866 lb) of usable oxidiser. The following are chief characteristics:

THRUST (in vacuo)	26·7 kN (6,000 lb)
CHAMBER PRESSURE (in vacuo)	8·62 bars (125 lb/sq in)
SPECIFIC IMPULSE	313·2 s
MIXTURE RATIO	1·65 : 1
NOZZLE AREA RATIO (flight)	55 : 1
DRY WEIGHT	118 kg (260 lb)
THRUST VECTOR LIMITS	±7°
STORAGE LIFE	10 years
FIRING LIFE (100 missions)	15 h
NUMBER OF STARTS	1,000
LONGEST SINGLE FIRING	1,250 s

AEROJET MINUTEMAN MOTORS

Aerojet Strategic Propulsion Company is currently remanufacturing the second stage of the LGM-30G Minuteman III ICBM. This motor has polybutadiene/ammonium perchlorate propellant packaged in a titanium case, and the single submerged nozzle has liquid injection thrust-vector control. Loaded weight is 7,076 kg (15,600 lb) and average thrust 269·5 kN (60,000 lb).

Aerojet Solid Propulsion Company (ASPC), Tactical Systems Group, Sacramento, California. Development and manufacture of the motors for Hawk, Sparrow and Standard ARM, and the booster for Harpoon. Production starting on advanced Sidewinder and Maverick motors.

AEROJET MAVERICK MOTOR

The Aerojet Maverick rocket motor, Type SR115-AJ-1, utilises a reduced-smoke HTPB propellant system and is completely interchangeable in all Maverick missile systems. The primary use will be in improved systems following the AGM-65B configuration. Aerojet has completed qualification of this boost/sustain rocket motor, and was anticipating a production programme beginning in 1980.

AEROJET SIDEWINDER MOTOR

Aerojet qualified a rocket motor in 1979 for use on the AIM-9B/E/J/N/P air-to-air missile systems. The motor utilises a reduced-smoke HTPB propellant. Production was scheduled to begin in 1980.

AEROJET HAWK MOTOR

The single-chamber solid-propellant rocket motor of the Hawk surface-to-air missile was the first dual-thrust dual-grain motor to be mass-produced.

Within its single propellant mass, the motor has an inner core of propellant constituting a short-duration booster grain which launches and accelerates the missile to super-sonic speed. When this inner core is consumed, a slower-burning outer core, forming the sustainer portion of the propellant, takes over and keeps the missile at the required velocity.

An Improved Hawk propulsion system, using an upgraded and higher-impulse polyurethane propellant, passed its qualification testing at the US Army Test and Evaluation Command, White Sands Missile Range. Several hundred Improved Hawk motors have been test fired and flight tested without failure, demonstrating the same high degree of reliability and long life as the Basic Hawk motor. The Improved Hawk motor is now in production at Sacramento. Aerojet Solid Propulsion Company has signed agreements with several foreign firms for its production.

AEROJET STANDARD MISSILE MOTOR

This motor is a dual-thrust design for the boost and sustain phases of the Standard I medium-range missile trajectory. This motor fits the same envelope as the test motors that were used in an earlier version of Standard Missile. The chamber has been lengthened, and the extension or blast tube eliminated, to accommodate more propellant and increase performance. These motors have been in production for the US Navy since 1970. Improvement is expected in the future to enhance missile performance.

Cross-section of Aerojet Maverick motor   Cross-section of Aerojet motor used in advanced models of Sidewinder

ASPC motor for Standard I MR surface-to-air missile   ASPC Mk 78 motor for Improved Shrike   ASPC boost motor for RGM-84 Harpoon missile

AEROJET SPARROW / SHRIKE MOTORS

The Mark 52 and Mark 53 motors are the sustainer or 'all boost' thrust units for the Sparrow AIM-7E and Shrike AGM-45A missiles. They are similar in construction and dimensions. The principal difference lies in the performance characteristics, which are tailored to match the air-to-air and air-to-ground missions. These motors have been in production since the mid-1960s and several thousand have been produced to meet US Navy and Air Force requirements. In 1969 an improvement programme was initiated to develop the Mark 78 motor. This is a dual-thrust (boost and sustain) motor which greatly enhances the performance of the AGM-45B Improved Shrike. Production of this motor started in 1972, with several thousand produced to date.

AEROJET HARPOON BOOSTER MOTOR

The Harpoon booster motor is used to launch the RGM-84 surface-launched version of the US Navy's Harpoon missile. It is mounted in tandem and provides thrust

during the boost phase before the cruise engine starts. The motor has completed all research and development and is now in production. The design incorporates many advanced features such as a submerged nozzle, developed over many years by Aerojet Solid Propulsion Company. Use of this missile/motor combination is planned for many fleet units of the US Navy and other navies.

AEROJET ALCOR 1B

The Alcor 1B is a high-performance Aerojet Solid Propulsion Company motor featuring a high specific-impulse polybutadiene propellant and extremely light-weight inert components. The nozzle is a unique combination of laminated reinforced-plastics materials, and the chamber is a very thin, welded, high-strength titanium 6Al-4V alloy structure. This highly efficient chamber has demonstrated excellent resistance to external flight loads in structural tests.

The Alcor 1B is used as third stage on the Athena test vehicle and is the second-stage propulsion system on the

Astrobee 1500 launch vehicle. It can be applied as an upper-stage sounding rocket motor, a small component test vehicle, a synchronous orbit injection motor, or an upper-stage booster for low and medium orbits. The motor can be spin-stabilised and is fabricated to a very small thrust-misalignment tolerance (0·0004 radians angular and 0·51 mm; 0·020 in linear). This motor has been used on more than 100 flights without a failure.

AEROJET ASTROBEE F

The Astrobee F is a dual-thrust sounding-rocket motor incorporating many of the design features, including HTPB propellant, of the successful Astrobee D. The boost thrust averages 169 kN (38,000 lb) for 3 s followed by a sustain thrust of 36·9 kN (8,300 lb) for 53 s. The 381 mm (15 in) diameter motor is designed to be compatible with the Aerobee payload systems and vehicle facilities. The initial Astrobee F test design is capable of delivering 90·7 kg (200 lb) payloads up to altitudes of 378 km (235 miles). By 1979 over 20 successful flights had been made.

ALLISON
DETROIT DIESEL ALLISON DIVISION, GENERAL MOTORS CORPORATION

Detroit, Michigan
Telephone: (313) 531 7100
INDIANAPOLIS OPERATIONS: PO Box 894, Indianapolis, Indiana 46206
Telephone: (317) 244 1511
GENERAL MANAGER: Donald J. Atwood
GENERAL SALES MANAGER: Chester B. Clum
MANAGER, INDIANAPOLIS OPERATIONS: Robert M. Clark

Detroit Diesel Allison's Gas Turbine Operations continue to produce T56 turboprop engines for the Lockheed C-130 Hercules, Lockheed P-3 Orion and Grumman E-2 Hawkeye. The commercial counterpart of the T56, the Model 501, powers the Lockheed Electra, commercial Hercules and Convair 580 airliners.

The Allison T63 small gas turbine, and its commercial counterpart, the Model 250, have been developed through many versions with numerous applications, as listed under each model heading. A turboprop version of the Model 250 was certificated in March 1969 for light fixed-wing aircraft applications.

It was announced in January 1976 that Allison and Rolls-Royce of England would develop and produce jointly a version of the Rolls-Royce Spey turbofan engine, under the designation TF41, to power advanced versions of the LTV A-7 Corsair II aircraft. The TF41 remains in production for the US Navy's A-7E carrier-based attack aircraft. Further details can be found in the International section.

ALLISON MODEL 250
US military designation: T63

The Model 250 is a small turboshaft engine in which

power is derived from a free power turbine and is delivered through an offset gearbox which includes all accessory drive pads.

A development contract for the T63 military version was received by Allison in June 1958 and the engine was first run in the Spring of 1959. Details of early versions last appeared in the 1978-9 *Jane's*; the following are current models:

T63-A-720. Hot-end improvements, increasing T-O rating to 313 kW (420 shp). Corresponds to commercial C20B. In production for the Bell OH-58C.

250-B17. Announced in 1972, the B17 is an uprated version of the earlier B15 turboprop, corresponding to the C20 turboshaft. Current model is the **B17B**, operating at 17°C higher turbine gas temperature and with hot-end improvements similar to those of the C20B, which maintain full power at high ambient temperatures. The B17B entered production in September 1974. In production for Turbostar 402 conversions, Turbostar 414, GAF Nomad N22 and 24, Ahrens AR-404, SIAI-Marchetti SM.1019E and a growing variety of agricultural aircraft modifications.

250-C20B. Introduced in 1974, and rated at 313 kW (420 shp). In production for Bell 206B JetRanger III and 206L LongRanger, MBB BO 105D, Agusta A 109A, Hughes 500D, and Soloy UH-12E and Bell 47G conversions.

250-C28. Representing Series III of the Model 250 evolutionary process, the 373 kW (500 shp) C28 is a near-total redesign. The axial multi-stage compressor, one of the primary features of the original design, has been eliminated. Instead a single-stage front-entry centrifugal impeller is used, handling a considerably increased airflow. The philosophy behind Series III was to reduce noise and emissions, and despite the increase in power the

sound pressure level of the bare engine has been reduced. The compressor-acceleration bleed is eliminated, and the exhaust leaves through a single low-velocity stack which also has a minimal infra-red signature. The main gearbox has new gears with increased helix and decreased pressure angles. Flight-cleared prototype engines were first available in September 1975 in two forms: C28B, with particle separator; C28C with plain inlet. Certificated December 1977.

250-C28B. Improved model with 2½-min rating of 410 kW (550 shp).

250-C28C. Improved model with 2½-min rating of 410 kW (550 shp).

250-C30. Representing Series IV of the Model 250 growth programme, the C30 has a more advanced single-stage compressor, handling a higher mass flow at an increased pressure ratio. The engine has numerous new features, one of which is dual ignition to comply with FAR Pt 29. The C30 will have an initial rating of 485 kW (650 shp). Prototype engines were delivered in 1976. Certification was completed in March 1978.

The following description applies to Model 250 engines currently in production or development:
TYPE: Light turboshaft or turboprop.
COMPRESSOR: The C20, C20B, and B17B incorporate an axial/centrifugal compressor with six axial stages and one centrifugal. The C28B and C and the C30 have a single-stage centrifugal compressor only. Pressure ratio: C20, 7·0:1; C20B, B17B, 7·2:1: C28B/C, C30, 8·5:1. Air mass flow: C20, 1·5 kg (3·4 lb)/s; C20B, B17B, 1·56 kg (3·45 lb)/s; C28B/C, 2·02 kg (4·45 lb)/s; C30, 2·54 kg (5·6 lb)/s.
COMBUSTION CHAMBER: Single can-type chamber at rear of engine. Single duplex fuel nozzle in rear face of chamber. One igniter on C20, C20B, B17B, C28B/C. Dual igniters on C30, optional on C28B/C.

The 313 kW (420 shp) Allison Model 250-C20B turboshaft engine

The 485 kW (650 shp) Allison Model 250-C30 turboshaft engine

TURBINES: Two-stage gas-producer turbine and two-stage free power turbine. Integrally-cast rotor blades and wheels. Gas-producer turbine outlet temperature: C20B, B17B, 810°C; C28B/C, 730°C; C30, 740°C.

GEARCASE: Magnesium casting which forms primary structure of engine and contains all power and accessory gear trains, torque sensor and oil pumps. Compressor and turbine assemblies bolted to front and rear faces respectively. Rated shp available at either front or rear output-shaft spline or any combination totalling both. Turboshaft output speed, 6,016 rpm. Turboprop output speed, 2,030 rpm.

CONTROL SYSTEM: Pneumatic-mechanical system consisting essentially of fuel pump and filter assembly, gas producer fuel control and power turbine governor (B17B, hydromechanical; C20B, C28, C30, pneumatic-mechanical).

FUEL: Primary fuels are ASTM-A or A-1 (Model 250-C20, ASTM D-1655) and MIL-T-5624, JP-4, JP-5 and diesel fuel.

LUBRICATION: Dry sump.

OIL SPECIFICATION: MIL-L-7808 and MIL-L-23699.

DIMENSIONS:

Length:	
B17B	1,143 mm (45·0 in)
C20B	1,046 mm (40·8 in)
C28B	1,239 mm (48·78 in)
C28C	1,032 mm (40·63 in)
C30	1,097 mm (43·2 in)
Width:	
B17B, C20B	483 mm (19·0 in)
C28, C30	557 mm (21·94 in)
Height:	
B17B	572 mm (22·5 in)
C20B	589 mm (23·2 in)
C28, C30	638 mm (25·13 in)

WEIGHT, DRY:

B17B	88·4 kg (195 lb)
C20B	71·5 kg (158 lb)
C28	99·3 kg (219 lb)
C28B	104 kg (230 lb)
C28C	102·5 kg (226 lb)
C30	106·6 kg (235 lb)

PERFORMANCE RATINGS (S/L, ISA):

T-O:	
C20B (5 min)	313 kW (420 shp)
C28, 28B, 28C (30 min)	373 kW (500 shp)
C30 (2½ min)	522 kW (700 shp) to 32·2°C
Max continuous:	
B17B	287 kW (385 shp)
C20B	298 kW (400 shp)
C28	373 kW (500 shp)
C30	485 kW (650 shp)
Cruise B (75 per cent):	
B17B	205 kW (275 shp)
C20B	207 kW (278 shp)
C28	274 kW (367 shp)
C30	312 kW (418 shp)

SPECIFIC FUEL CONSUMPTION:

At T-O rating:	
B17B	110·7µg/J (0·655 lb/h/shp)
C20B	110µg/J (0·650 lb/h/shp)
C28	102·5µg/J (0·606 lb/h/shp)
C30	100µg/J (0·592 lb/h/shp)
At cruise B rating:	
B17B	121µg/J (0·716 lb/h/shp)
C20B	120µg/J (0·709 lb/h/shp)
C28	112µg/J (0·664 lb/h/shp)
C30	111µg/J (0·657 lb/h/shp)

ALLISON GMA 300

This is the latest core engine developed under the USAF/USN Ategg (Advanced Turbine Engine Gas Generator) programme. Projected applications include a wide range of turbofans, some with variable-pitch blades, and turboshaft engines for air and surface applications.

ALLISON GMA 500

Advanced 600 kW (800 shp) class demonstrator engine under development for US Army.

ALLISON T56

Current versions of the T56 are as follows:

T56-A-14. Rated at 3,661 ekW (4,910 ehp). Generally similar to T56-A-15, but seven-point suspension like T56-A-10W and detail changes. Powers the P-3B and C Orion.

T56-A-15. Rated at 3,661 ekW (4,910 ehp). Introduced aircooled turbine blades. Powers C-130H (all versions), C-130K, HC-130N, HC-130P and some AC-130s.

T56-A-422. Rated at 3,661 ekW (4,910 ehp). Powers Grumman E-2C Hawkeye and C-2A Greyhound.

T56-A-423. Rated at 3,661 ekW (4,910 ehp). Powers US Navy versions of the C-130.

Including the Model 501 commercial engines, production of these engines reached 11,000 by February 1976. Production is continuing.

Model 501-D22D. This civil engine was proposed in 1977 to power the Lockheed L-400 Twin Hercules. It incorporates water/alcohol augmentation and autofeathering.

Model 501-M71. The latest version of T56/501 offered for C-130 and P-3 aircraft would have 24 per cent greater power and 10 per cent lower sfc.

The following details apply to the T56-A-15:

TYPE: Axial-flow turboprop engine.

PROPELLER DRIVE: Combination spur/planetary gear type, primary step-down by spur, secondary by planetary. Overall gear ratio 13·54 : 1. Power section rpm 13,820. Cast magnesium reduction-gear housing. Gearbox assembly supported from power section by main drive shaft casing 711 mm (28 in) long and two inclined struts. Weight of gearbox assembly approximately 249 kg (550 lb) with pads on rear face for accessory mounting.

AIR INTAKE: Circular duct on engine face. Thermal de-icing.

COMPRESSOR: Fourteen-stage axial-flow. Series of fourteen discs with rotor blades dovetailed in peripheries and locked by adjacent discs. Rotor assembly tie-bolted to shaft which runs on one ball and one roller type bearing. Fifteen rows of stator blades, welded in rings. Disc, rotor and stator blades and four-piece cast casing of stainless steel. Compressor inlet area 1,004 cm² (155·65 sq in). Pressure ratio 9·5 : 1. Air mass flow 14·70 kg (32·4 lb)/s.

COMBUSTION CHAMBER: Six stainless steel cannular-type perforated combustion liners within one-piece stainless steel outer casing. Fuel nozzles in forward end of each combustor liner. Primary ignition by two igniters in diametrically-opposite combustors.

The 3,661 ekW (4,910 ehp) Allison T56-A-15 turboprop engine which powers late versions of the Lockheed C-130 Hercules transport

FUEL SYSTEM: High-pressure type. Bendix control system. Water/alcohol augmentation system available.

FUEL GRADE: MIL-J-5624, JP-4 or JP-5.

NOZZLE GUIDE VANES: Hollow aircooled blades of special high-temperature alloy.

TURBINE: Four-stage. Rotor assembly consists of four stainless steel discs, with first stage having hollow air-cooled blades of special high-temperature alloy, secured in peripheries of discs by fir-tree roots. Discs splined to rotor shaft which runs on front and rear roller bearings. Steel outer turbine casing. Gas temperature before turbine 1,076°C.

JET PIPE: Fixed. Stainless steel.

ACCESSORY DRIVES: Accessory pads on rear face of reduction-gear housing at front end of engine.

LUBRICATION SYSTEM: Low-pressure. Dry sump. Pesco dual-element oil pump. Normal oil supply pressure 3·8 bars (55 lb/sq in).

OIL SPECIFICATION: MIL-L-7808.

MOUNTING: Three-point suspension.

STARTING: Air turbine, gearbox-mounted.

DIMENSIONS:
Length (all current versions)	3,708 mm (146 in)
Width (all current versions)	686 mm (27 in)

Height:
A-15, A-422, A-423	991 mm (39 in)
A-14	1,118 mm (44 in)

WEIGHT, DRY:
A-14	855 kg (1,885 lb)
A-15	828 kg (1,825 lb)
A-422	859 kg (1,984 lb)
A-423	836 kg (1,844 lb)
D22D	840 kg (1,851 lb)

PERFORMANCE RATINGS (S/L, ISA, static):
T-O:
  D22D augmented
          3,728 kW (5,000 shp) at 13,820 rpm
  A-14, A-15, A-422, A-423, D22D
          3,661 ekW; 3,424 kW (4,910 ehp; 4,591 shp)
          at 13,820 rpm
Normal:
  A-14, A-15, A-422, A-423, D22D
          3,255 ekW; 3,028 kW (4,365 ehp; 4,061 shp)
          at 13,820 rpm

SPECIFIC FUEL CONSUMPTION:
At max rating:
  A-14, A-15   84·67µg/J (0·501 lb/h/ehp)
At normal rating:
  A-14, A-15, A-422, A-423
                      87·4µg/J (0·517 lb/h/ehp)

OIL CONSUMPTION:
  A-14, A-15   1·3 litres (0·35 US gallons)/h

ALTURDYNE
ALTURDYNE
8050 Armour Street, San Diego, California 92111
Telephone: (714) 565 2131
PRESIDENT: Frank Verbeke

This company, "dedicated to bringing the advantages of the small gas turbine to new areas of industry and commerce", has developed small engines for RPVs and ultra-light aircraft. It was formed in 1970 and employs 90. At present it purchases the basic gas generator and incorporates this into a complete engine for various purposes. The two main products are of 112 kW (150 hp) and 187 kW (250 hp).

The larger units are based upon the Solar T62 Titan single-shaft gas turbine (last described in *Jane's* for 1975-76). Alturdyne is marketing turboshaft, air compressor, turboprop and turbojet versions of this engine in the 187-260 kW (250-350 shp) class. The turbojet weighs 32 kg (70 lb) and has a take-off rating of 1·1 kN (250 lb st). The data below are for the turboprop, with normal propeller speed of 2,600 rpm.

DIMENSIONS:
Length (without propeller shaft)	667 mm (26·25 in)
Width	286 mm (11·25 in)
Height (without optional sump)	460 mm (18·12 in)

WEIGHT, DRY: 56·7 kg (125 lb)
PERFORMANCE RATING:
  T-O, S/L   187 kW (250 shp)

ALTURDYNE SP-440
This RC (Wankel-type) engine is offered from 1980. Although intended chiefly for surface applications, its aviation appeal is self-evident.

TYPE: Rotary-combustion engine, with oil-cooled rotor and overall air cooling.
DISPLACEMENT: 440 cc (26·9 cu in).
COMPRESSION RATIO: 7·6.
DIMENSIONS:
Length (typical mainshaft)	428 mm (16·85 in)
Width	471 mm (18·56 in)
Height	368 mm (14·49 in)

WEIGHT, DRY: 30 kg (66·0 lb)
MAX RATING: 22·4 kW (30 hp) at 5,500 rpm

Rated at 187 kW (250 shp) the shaft-drive Alturdyne engine based on the T62 can be used as a turboshaft or, as shown here, a turboprop (*Howard Levy*)

ATLANTIC RESEARCH
ATLANTIC RESEARCH CORPORATION
5390 Cherokee Avenue, Alexandria, Virginia 22314
Telephone: (703) 354 3400

This is a privately held company of some 920 employees, organised into four operating divisions: Propulsion, Research and Technology, Teleproducts, and Advanced Programs. The Propulsion Division is a leading designer and manufacturer of small solid-propellant rockets and gas generators; it also produces industrial mixers and air-purification systems (for example, for all US Navy nuclear submarines). R & T includes in its work many areas relevant to aerospace propulsion. Teleproducts is concerned mainly with communications. APD's work is very diverse.

ARC SOLID ROCKET MOTORS
Atlantic Research claims to make solid propellants that "propel missiles, spin satellites, provide thrust-vector control, inflate air cushions, produce non-toxic exhaust, burn fast, burn slow, separate nose shrouds, gobble up electrons, produce smoke, produce no smoke, radiate IR or lase". The company supplies sustainer motors for Terrier and Standard ship/air missiles, the launch and sustainer motors for Redeye and Stinger infantry/air missiles, the complete Arcas, Super Arcas and Boosted Arcas meteorological and atmosphere-research rockets, motors for later Minuteman ICBMs that eject shrouds and perform other functions, the gas generator for UpSTAGE (unaffected by extreme launch acceleration), the gas generators and auxiliary rockets for the Polaris and Poseidon programmes, and the very-long-burning dual-pressure gas generator for C-4 Trident. ARC Propulsion Division is under contract to General Dynamics Convair Division to design and manufacture the boost motor for the BGM-109 sea-launched Tomahawk cruise missile, and to Vought to supply the solid propulsion system for GSRS (General Support Rocket System). R & T Division is involved in external-burning rockets.

AVCO LYCOMING
AVCO LYCOMING STRATFORD DIVISION OF AVCO CORPORATION
HEAD OFFICE: 550 South Main Street, Stratford, Connecticut 06497
Telephone: (203) 378 8211
PRESIDENT OF AVCO CORPORATION: Ross M. Hett
VICE PRESIDENTS (STRATFORD):
  J. S. Bartos (General Manager)
  D. D. Weidhuner (Senior VP-Programmes)
  M. T. Anderson (Quality)
  A. J. Burrows (Washington Operation)
  D. H. Carpenter (Industrial Resources)
  P. J. Foley (LT 101/T53 Programmes)
  H. J. Frederick (Finance)
  T. Ivanko (Special Projects/AGT 1500 Facilitisations)
  C. Kuintzle (Engineering)
  M. J. Leff (Marketing/Product Support)
  J. Laborde (AGT 1500 Programme)
  B. A. Rose (Manufacturing Engineering)
  M. S. Saboe (T55/ALF 502/Marine Programmes)
  J. F. Shanley (Administration)
  W. I. Tierney (Personnel)
  J. W. Treat (Manufacturing)

Avco Lycoming Stratford is the gas-turbine manufacturing division of Avco Corporation. Together with the Williamsport division, it forms the Avco Lycoming Engine Group.

Stratford division is producing several families of engines, including the T53, T55, LTS 101 and LTP 101, with turboshaft, turboprop, turbofan, vehicular and marine variants. More than 21,600 T53 and T55 engines have been produced, with production ensured well into the 1980s. Several versions of the LTS 101 have been certificated. The LTS 101 turboshaft powers the Bell 222, the Aérospatiale AS 350, the MBB/Kawasaki BK 117, and the Agusta A 129. The LTP 101 turboprop was selected to power the Piaggio PD 166, Snow Air Tractor,

Avco Lycoming ALF 502L geared turbofan rated at 33·4 kN (7,500 lb st)

Riley Aircraft turbo conversions, the Page Aircraft Turbo Thrush and Ag-Cat conversions and Aerospace Fletcher Cresco. The ALF 502 turbofan has been selected for the Canadair Challenger and the British Aerospace 146.

Avco Lycoming is working upon two significant development contracts. For NASA, Stratford will build and demonstrate a high bypass ratio turbofan of 7·1 kN (1,600 lb st), with low fuel consumption aimed at general aviation but also suitable for use in training aircraft. The US Army selected Avco Lycoming to develop an advanced technology engine in the 600 kW (800 shp) range.

AVCO LYCOMING ALF 502

The ALF 502 turbofan is being developed primarily for applications in the commercial and executive market. It is FAA type certificated at 29·8 kN (6,700 lb st). The core gas-generator is the T55.

The ALF 502 was launched as a commercially directed, company-sponsored effort in 1969. Its first application was in the Northrop A-9A, with the military engine designation F102. Nonetheless, the engine design remained aimed at the commercial requirement for low cost of operation and high reliability. Construction was made totally modular, and the basic design was refined to satisfy commercial needs of long life and low cost of operation, with on-condition maintenance instead of a fixed TBO. Thus, a TBO of 4,000 h has been granted, with on-condition authorisation.

The ALF 502 has flown in several aircraft, demonstrating low noise signature, and at simulated altitudes up to 22,900 m (75,000 ft).

It has been selected for the Canadair Challenger in 502L form at 33·4 kN (7,500 lb st), and for the British Aerospace 146 in 502R-3 standard at 29·8 kN (6,700 lb st). Initial Challenger flying was done on the 502R-3, but the more powerful model was installed in early 1979. Should a military BAe 146 be ordered it would probably be powered by the F102 at 502L rating. It also powers the four-engined NASA Quiet Short-haul Research Aircraft (QSRA).

Engine deliveries off production tooling were made in December 1977, with quantity production starting in 1979. The 502L was certificated in February 1980.

TYPE: High bypass ratio, two-shaft geared turbofan.

FAN MODULE: Cast fan frame includes four engine mounts 90° apart, and may be used for mounting thrust reverser. Fan rotor blades are base and part-span shrouded and individually replaceable. Containment ring surrounds rotor. Mounted directly behind rotor, (6,700 lb st engines) is single or (7,500 lb st engines) two stages of compression. Individually replaceable fan exit stators are located to minimise noise. Inlet spinner bolted to fan rotor is anti-iced by oil flow. Anti-icing of compressor stators by bleed air. Accessory gearbox on fan frame takes HP shaft power. Additional services such as fuel, oil, pneumatic and electrical lines, are routed through other hollow struts. Reduction gear within centre of fan frame couples LP turbine to fan. Bypass ratio: 502R-3, 5·89; 502L, 5·0.

COMPRESSOR: Core supercharged by one or two LP stages, as described above. HP compressor has seven axial stages and single radial stage, driven by two-stage HP turbine. Supported by roller bearing and aft ball bearing. Acceleration bleed control between stages 6 and 7 operated by main fuel control. Upper and lower casings contain stator half-rings, removable for maintenance, and borescope ports. Overall pressure ratio 13·7.

TURBINE: HP has two air-cooled stages. LP has two stages, splined to fan reduction gear. All rotor blades base shrouded: LP additionally tip shrouded.

COMBUSTION CHAMBER: One-piece annular combustor wraps around turbine. Atomising nozzles inserted through outer chamber at rear. Four customer bleed ports around exterior. Combustion liner and housing bolted to compressor diffuser. Disconnecting permits removal of cumbustor/turbine module, providing access to HP turbine. Borescope ports permit inspection of combustor and turbine without removal.

ACCESSORY DRIVES: Accessory gearbox carries main fuel control, oil pump and filter, tachometer (if required) and provisions for customer accessories.

EXHAUST UNIT: Fan and core exhaust include flanges for bolted ducts and nozzles.

DIMENSIONS:
Diameter	1,067 mm (42·0 in)
Length overall	1,443 mm (56·8 in)

WEIGHT, DRY:
ALF 502H, 502R	565 kg (1,245 lb)
ALF 502L	578 kg (1,275 lb)

PERFORMANCE RATINGS (T-O, S/L, static):
ALF 502H, 502R	29·8 kN (6,700 lb)
ALF 502L	33·4 kN (7,500 lb)

SPECIFIC FUEL CONSUMPTION (T-O):
All versions	11·9 mg/Ns (0·42 lb/h/lb st)

AVCO LYCOMING ALF 101

Supported by NASA through the QCGAT (Quiet Clean General-Aviation Turbofan) programme, the ALF 101 is a high-bypass ratio turbofan based on the same gas generator as the LTP 101 turboprop and LTS 101 turboshaft. The total engine airflow passing through the front fan is split into two paths. The larger portion bypasses the core engine and exhausts directly to atmosphere through the mixed flow or annular exhaust nozzles. The smaller portion is ducted into the core engine through the core inlet stator. The core air is further compressed by a two-stage axial compressor in tandem with a single-stage centrifugal compressor prior to entering the reverse-flow annular combustor.

A single-stage axial gas-producer turbine, coupled to the compressor shaft, drives the high-pressure compressor. A single-stage low-pressure power turbine, with a shaft extending forward concentrically through the hollow compressor shaft to a fixed-planetary reduction gear, provides the drive for the fan. The front frame includes main engine mounting provisions and ducting for the fan and core airflows. Hollow struts provide fairings for services across the fan and core streams. Accessory power from the

compressor rotor is transmitted through a bevel drive in the front frame to the accessory gearbox, which is mounted externally to optimise accessibility.

The NASA QCGAT commitments were completed during 1979, with the delivery of an engine to NASA's Lewis Research Center for further testing. Available data appear in the table.

AVCO LYCOMING LTS 101
US military designation: YT702-LD-700

This series of small turboshaft engines includes seven models with maximum power ratings between 459 and 548 kW (615 and 735 shp) and output speeds of 6,000 or 9,265 rpm. All commercial models are certificated by the FAA, and the military YT702 has completed a 60-h PFRT. This simple modular engine was designed to provide low life cycle costs. It has a single axial compressor stage followed by a single centrifugal stage, a reverse-flow annular combustor, and single-stage axial gas-generator and power turbines. The front-mounted gearbox provides forward or aft drives, or a combination. The radial-flow inlet provides for an optional particle separator. Mass flow is 2·03 kg (4·8 lb)/s, and pressure ratio 8·5 : 1.

The LTS 101 first flew in a Bell JetRanger testbed in 1973. Since then it has been selected to power the Bell 222, Aérospatiale AS 350D, Aérospatiale SA 366, MBB/Kawasaki BK 117, Agusta A 129 and Aérospatiale HH-65A Dolphin for the US Coast Guard. Lycoming has also received US Government contracts which will provide a turbofan and an airborne APU both based on the LTS 101 core.

DIMENSIONS:
Length	785 mm (30·9 in)
Width	406 mm (16·0 in)
Height:	
LTS 101-600A/600B/650A	568 mm (22·38 in)
LTS 101-650C	483 mm (19·0 in)

WEIGHT, DRY:
LTS 101-600A/600B/650A	110 kg (241 lb)
LTS 101-650	105 kg (232 lb)

PERFORMANCE RATINGS:
2·5 min contingency:
LTS 101-650A, 650C	504 kW (675 shp)

T-O:
LTS 101-600A, -600B, -650A,-650C	459 kW (615 shp)
LTS 101-700	507 kW (680 shp)

Maximum continuous:
LTS 101-600A, -600B, -650A, -650C	440 kW (590 shp)

SPECIFIC FUEL CONSUMPTION (T-O rating):
LTS 101-600A, -600B, -650A	95·8 μg/J (0·567 lb/h/shp)
LTS 101-650C	95·6 μg/J (0·566 lb/h/shp)

AVCO LYCOMING LTP 101

The LTP 101 is a modular turboprop derived from the LTS 101. It incorporates a free power turbine, provisions for tractor or pusher installation, hydraulic propeller governor, radial screened inlet and anti-icing protection. The output shaft speed lies in the range 1,700-1,950 rpm,

AVCO LYCOMING GAS TURBINE ENGINES

Manufacturer's and civil designation	Military designation	Type*	T-O Rating kN (lb st) or max kW (hp)	SFC μg/J; ‡ mg/Ns (lb/hr/hp; ‡lb/hr/lb st)	Weight dry less tailpipe kg (lb)	Max dia mm (in)	Length overall mm (in)	Remarks
T5313B	—	ACFS	1,044 kW (1,400 shp)	98 (0·58)	245 (540)	584 (23)	1,209 (47·6)	Powers Bell 205A
T5317A	—	ACFS	1,119 kW (1,500 shp)	99·7 (0·59)	256 (564)	584 (23)	1,209 (47·6)	Based on T5319A
T5319A	—	ACFS	1,342 kW (1,800 shp)	96·3 (0·57)	256 (564)	584 (23)	1,209 (47·6)	Awaiting FAA certification
T5311A	—	ACFS	820 kW (1,100 shp)	115 (0·68)	225 (496)	584 (23)	1,209 (47·6)	Bell 204B
—	T53-L-13B	ACFS	1,044 kW (1,400 shp)	98 (0·58)	245 (540)	584 (23)	1,209 (47·6)	Advanced UH-1H and AH-1G
—	T53-L-702	ACFS	1,417 kW (1,900 shp)	94·6 (0·56)	254 (561)	584 (23)	1,209 (47·6)	Military T5319A
—	T53-L-703	ACFS	1,155 kW (1,549 shp)	101·4 (0·60)	247 (545)	584 (23)	1,209 (47·6)	Bell AH-1Q, AH-1S TOW/Cobra
LTC1K-4C	—	ACFS	1,119 kW (1,500 shp)	98 (0·58)	247 (545)	584 (23)	1,209 (47·6)	Canadair CL-84
T5321A	—	ACFP	1,393 ekW (1,868 ehp)	96·3 (0·57)	306 (675)	584 (23)	1,656 (65·2)	Turboprop T5319A
—	T53-L-15	ACFP	897 ekW (1,203 ehp)	101·4 (0·60)	274 (605)	584 (23)	1,483 (58·4)	Grumman OV-1D
LTC4R-1	—	ACFP	2,837 ekW (3,804 ehp†)	87·9 (0·52)	422 (930)	615 (24·2)	1,580 (62·2)	Turboprop T55-L-11A
—	T55-L-7B	ACFS	1,976 kW (2,650 shp)	104·8 (0·62)	263 (580)	615 (24·2)	1,118 (44)	Boeing CH-47A, Bell HueyTug
—	T55-L-7C	ACFS	2,125 kW (2,850 shp)	101·4 (0·60)	267 (590)	615 (24·2)	1,118 (44)	Boeing CH-47B and Bell 214A
T5508D (LTC4B-8D)	—	ACFS	1,750 kW (2,347 shp) (flat-rated)	106·5 (0·63)	274 (605)	610 (24)	1,118 (44)	Bell 214A, 214B
—	T55-L-11A§	ACFS	2,796 kW (3,750 shp)	89·6 (0·53)	322 (710)	615 (24·2)	1,181 (46·5)	Boeing CH-47
LTC4B-12	—	ACFS	3,430 kW (4,600 shp)	86·2 (0·51)	329 (725)	615 (24·2)	1,118 (44)	Improved T55-L-11A
LTS 101-600	YT702-LD-700	ACFS	459 kW (615 shp)	98 (0·58)	110 (241)	584 (23)	785 (30·9)	Bell 222, AS 350D, BK-117, A 129, HH-65A
LTS 101-700	—	ACFS	507 kW (680 shp)	94 (0·56)	110 (241)	584 (23)	785 (30·9)	
LTP 101-600	—	ACFP	462 ekW (620 ehp)	93 (0·55)	148 (325)	533 (21)	914 (36)	Piaggio P.166-DL3, Air Tractor AT-302
LTP 101-700	—	ACFP	522 ekW (700 ehp)	93 (0·55)	148 (325)	533 (21)	914 (36)	
ALF 101	—	ACFF	7·2 kN (1,620 lb)	‡10·19 (‡0·36)	156 (343)	584 (23)	890 (35)	NASA QCGAT
ALF 502H, R-3	—	ACFF	29·8 kN (6,700 lb)	‡11·89 (‡0·42)	565 (1,245)	1,067 (42)	1,443 (56·8)	BAe 146 (R-3)
—	F102-LD-100	ACFF	35 kN (7,860 lb)	‡11·89 (‡0·42)	500 (1,100)	1,041 (41)	1,422 (56)	NASA QSRA
ALF 502L	—	ACFF	33·4 kN (7,500 lb)	‡11·89 (‡0·42)	579 (1,275)	1,067 (42)	1,443 (56·8)	Canadair Challenger

*ACFS = axial plus centrifugal, free-turbine shaft; ACFP = axial plus centrifugal, free-turbine propeller; AFS = axial, free-turbine shaft; ACFF = axial plus centrifugal, free-turbine fan

†2,752 kW (3,690 shp); also has military rating of 2,574 ekW/2,494 kW (3,452 ehp/3,344 shp).

§Applies to T55-L-11A, C**, D, E** and 712**, those designated ** having 2½ min contingency rating of 3,357 kW (4,500 shp).

Avco Lycoming turbine engines in the 600 shp class (from left to right): LTS 101-600B/650A (459 kW; 615 shp), LTS 101-650C (504 kW; 675 shp) and LTP 101-600 (462 ekW; 620 ehp)

consistent with available three-blade reversible-pitch propellers.

FAA certification was received in 1976. The LTP 101 has since been selected for the Piaggio P.166-DL3, Air Tractor Turbo Tractor and New Zealand Aerospace Industries Fletcher agricultural aircraft, Riley conversion of Cessna 421, Page Aircraft Turbo Thrush and Ag-Cat conversions and OMAC I. It is also flying in Turbo-Islander and Turbo-Skyservant prototypes.

DIMENSIONS:

Length overall	938 mm (36·94 in)
Height overall	521 mm (20·53 in)

WEIGHT, DRY: 147 kg (325 lb)

PERFORMANCE RATINGS (S/L, ISA):

T-O:

LTP 101-600	462 ekW (620 ehp)
LTP 101-700	522 ekW (700 ehp)

Max continuous:

LTP 101-600	410 ekW (585 ehp)

SPECIFIC FUEL CONSUMPTION:
All above ratings   92·9 µg/J (0·55 lb/h/ehp)

AVCO LYCOMING LTC1
US military designation: T53

The T53 is a turboshaft with a free power turbine, which was developed under a joint US Air Force/US Army contract. A total of 18,000 units had logged over 26·2 million hours of operation, with every US armed service and in 29 other countries, by January 1979.

Licences for manufacture of the T53 are held by Klöckner-Humboldt-Deutz in Federal Republic of Germany, Piaggio in Italy, Kawasaki in Japan, and in Taiwan.

Versions currently in production or under development are as follows:

T53-L-13. Uprated version of L-11, which it superseded in production in August 1966. Redesigned 'hot end' and initial stages of compressor section to provide substantially increased power for hot-day and high-altitude performance. Four turbine stages, compared with two in earlier models, and variable-incidence inlet guide vanes combined with redesigned first two compressor stages, permit greater airflow and lower turbine temperatures. This version has atomising combustor to facilitate operation on a wider range of fuels. Powers Bell UH-1C and UH-1D and AH-1G HueyCobra. The **T5313A** commercial version of the T53-L-13 received FAA type cetification in Spring 1968 and powers Bell 205A.

T53-L-701. Turboprop version of the L-13 incorporating the Lycoming 'split-power' propeller reduction gear. Produced for Grumman OV-1D previously powered by T53-L-15, and specified for stretched version of Air-Metal AM-C111. In production for T-CH-1 (Taiwan).

T53-L-703. Turboshaft engine similar to L-13. Flat rated for AH-1Q and AH-1S HueyCobra.

LTC1K-4C. Generally similar to the T53-L-13, but incorporating special seals to allow operation in the attitude range from 105° nose up to 90° nose down. Has 10-minute rating of 1,500 shp and powered Canadair CL-84-1 VTOL aircraft; powers Bell XV-15 tilt-rotor VTOL aircraft.

T5319A. Latest growth version of T53 turboshaft family. Improvements over L-13 include new, gearing, improved cooling of first gas producer turbine nozzle plus aircooled blades in first turbine rotor. Also incorporates new materials in other turbine stages. Rated at 1,800 shp at take-off.

T5317A. Flat rated version of -19A with take-off rating limited to 1,500 shp by use of standard L-13 reduction gear.

T5321A. Turboprop version of -19A with 'split-power' gear. Uses standard SBAC No. 4 propeller shaft with through-the-shaft oil provisions.

The following details apply to the T53-L-13 and L-701:

TYPE: Free-turbine turboshaft engine.

AIR INTAKE: Annular casing of magnesium alloy, with 6 struts supporting reduction gearbox and front main bearings. Anti-icing by hot air tapped from engine.

COMPRESSOR: Five axial stages followed by a single centrifugal stage. Four-piece magnesium alloy casing with one row of variable-incidence inlet guide vanes and five rows of steel stator blades, bolted to one-piece steel

alloy diffuser casing with tangential outlet to combustion chamber. Rotor comprises one stainless steel and four aluminium alloy discs with stainless steel blades and one titanium impeller mounted on shaft supported in forward ball thrust and rear roller bearings. Compression ratio 7·4 : 1. Air mass flow 4·85 kg/s (10·7 lb/s) at 25,240 gas producer rpm.

COMBUSTION CHAMBER: Annular reverse-flow type, with one-piece sheet steel outer shell and annular liner. Twenty-two atomising fuel injectors.

FUEL CONTROL SYSTEM: Hydromechanical controls for gas generator and for power sections. Chandler Evans TA-2S system with one dual fuel pump. Pump pressure 41·4 bars (600 lb/sq in). Main and emergency flow controls. Separate interstage air bleed control.

FUEL GRADE: ASTM A-1, MIL-J-5624, MIL-F-26005A, JP-1, JP-4, JP-5, CITE.

TURBINE: Four axial-flow turbine stages. Casing fabricated from sheet steel. First two stages, driving compressor, use hollow aircooled stator vanes and cored-out cast steel rotor blades and are mounted on outer coaxial shaft to gas producer. Second two stages, driving reduction gearing, have solid steel blades, and are spline-mounted to shaft.

EXHAUST UNIT: Fixed-area nozzle. Steel outer casing and inner cone, supported by four radial struts.

ACCESSORIES: Electric starter or starter/generator (not furnished). Bendix-Scintilla TGLN high-energy ignition unit. Two igniter plugs.

LUBRICATION: Recirculating system, with gear pump with one pressure and one scavenge unit. Filter. Pump pressure 4·83 bars (70 lb/sq in).

OIL GRADE: MIL-L-7808, MIL-L-23699.

DIMENSIONS:

Length overall:

L-13	1,209 mm (47·6 in)
L-701	1,483 mm (58·4 in)
T5321A	1,656 mm (65·2 in)

Diameter:

All versions   584 mm (23·0 in)

WEIGHT, DRY:

Less tailpipe:

L-13	249 kg (549 lb)
T5317A, T5319A	256 kg (564 lb)
T5321A	306 kg (657 lb)
LTC1K-4C, L-703	247 kg (545 lb)
L-701	312 kg (688 lb)

PERFORMANCE RATINGS:

Max at S/L:

L-13	1,044 kW (1,400 shp)
L-701	1,082 ekW; 1,044 kW (1,451 ehp; 1,400 shp plus 0·57 kN (128 lb) at 20,430 rpm
LTC1K-4C, T5317A	1,119 kW (1,500 shp)
T5319A	1,342 kW (1,800 shp)
T5321A	1,393 ekW; 1,342 kW (1,868 ehp; 1,800 shp)
L-703	1,107 kW (1,485 shp) to 28°C

SPECIFIC FUEL CONSUMPTION:

At max rating:

L-13, LTC1K-4C	98 µg/J (0·58 lb/h/shp)
L-701, T5319A, T5321A	96·3 µg/J (0·57 lb/h/shp)
T5317A	99·7 µg/J (0·59 lb/h/shp)
L-703	101·4 µg/J (0·60 lb/h/shp)

OIL CONSUMPTION:
All versions   450 gr (1·0 lb)/h

AVCO LYCOMING LTC4
US military designation: T55

This engine is based on the T53 design concept but with higher mass flow. It was developed under a joint US Air Force/US Army contract. Total operating time by early 1978 was 3·4 million hours. Most of this time was logged by L-7 versions fitted to the CH-47A and CH-47B Chinook.

Current production and development versions are as follows:

LTC4B-8D. Modified version of the T55-L-7C. Powers Bell 214A and 214C utility helicopters for Iran, flat rated to transmission limit of 1,678 kW (2,250 shp).

T5508D. Commercial version of LTC4B-8D. Powers Bell 214B.

T55-L-11 (LTC4B-11B) series. Uprated and redesigned version of L-7, with a second stage added to the compressor turbine, and variable-incidence inlet guide vanes ahead of the compressor. First two compressor stages transonic. New atomising fuel nozzles. Powers CH-47C Chinook, first deliveries having been made in August 1968.

T55-L-712. Supersedes the T55-L-11D and specified for the US Army's modernised Boeing Vertol YCH-47D. The basic engine is the T55-L-11D, with wide-chord compressor blades and one-piece rotor. Improvements in

Cutaway drawing of the 1,044 kW (1,400 shp) Avco Lycoming T53-L-13 turboshaft engine

Avco Lycoming T55-L-712 turboshaft rated at 2,796 kW (3,750 shp)

FUEL GRADE: MIL-J-5624 grade JP-4, JP-5, MIL-F-46005A or CITE.

TURBINE: Two mechanically independent axial turbines. Gas-generator turbine has single stage (two stages on T55-L-11 series) with cored-out cast steel blades having inner cooling airflow. Disc flange-bolted to drive shaft. Hollow stator vanes. Two-stage power turbine has solid steel blades.

EXHAUST UNIT: Fixed-area nozzle, with inner cone, supported by six radial struts.

ACCESSORIES: Electric starter or starter/generator, or air or hydraulic starter. Bendix-Scintilla TGLN high-energy ignition unit. Four igniter plugs.

LUBRICATION: Recirculating type. Integral oil tank and cooler on L-11, external tank for 4R-1.

OIL GRADE: MIL-L-7808, MIL-L-23699.

DIMENSIONS:

Diameter (all versions)	616 mm (24·25 in)
Length overall:	
L-7, LTC4B-8D, T5508D, LTC4B-12	1,119 mm (44·03 in)
L-9, LTC4R-1	1,580 mm (62·2 in)
L-11A	1,181 mm (46·5 in)
L-712	1,196 mm (47·1 in)

WEIGHT, DRY:

L-7B	263 kg (580 lb)
L-9, LTC4R-1	422 kg (930 lb)
L-11A	322 kg (710 lb)
LTC4B-8D, T5508D	274 kg (605 lb)
LTC4B-12	329 kg (725 lb)
L-712	341 kg (750 lb)

PERFORMANCE RATINGS (T-O, S/L):

L-7B	1,976 kW (2,650 shp)
L-9, LTC4R-1	2,837 kW; 2,752 kW (3,804 ehp; 3,690 shp plus 1·27 kN; 285 lb st)
L-11A	2,796 kW (3,750 shp)
LTC4B-8D, T5508D	2,200 kW (2,950 shp) flat rated to 1,678 kW (2,250 shp)
LTC4B-12	3,430 kW (4,600 shp)
L-712	2,796 kW (3,750 shp)

SPECIFIC FUEL CONSUMPTION (T-O, S/L):

L-7B	104·8 µg/J (0·62 lb/h/shp)
L-9, LTC4R-1, L-11A, C, D, E, 712	89·6 µg/J (0·53 lb/h/shp)
LTC4B-8D, T5508D (flat rated)	106·5 µg/J (0·63 lb/h/shp)
LTC4B-12	86·2 µg/J (0·51 lb/h/shp)

design and materials are aimed at achieving a time between overhauls of 2,500 h.

LTC4B-12. Proposed growth version with 3,430 kW (4,600 shp) maximum power rating, 3,258 kW (4,370 shp) on hot day. Higher turbine entry temperature and increased turbine cooling.

LTC4R-1. Proposed turboprop version of L-11 with Lycoming split-power reduction gear.

The following description applies to the T55-L-11 and LTC4R-1:

TYPE: Free-turbine turboshaft engine.

AIR INTAKE: Annular type casing of magnesium alloy with four struts supporting reduction gearbox and front main bearings. Anti-icing by hot air tapped from engine. Provision for intake screens.

COMPRESSOR: Seven axial stages followed by a single centrifugal stage. Two-piece magnesium alloy stator casing with one row of variable inlet guide vanes and seven rows of steel stator blades, bolted to steel alloy diffuser casing to which combustion chamber casing is attached. Rotor comprises seven stainless steel discs and one titanium impeller mounted on shaft supported in forward ball-thrust bearing and rear roller bearing. Pressure ratio 8·2 : 1. Air mass flow 12·25 kg (27 lb)/s.

COMBUSTION CHAMBER: Annular reverse-flow type. Steel outer shell and inner liner. Twenty-eight fuel burners with downstream injection.

FUEL SYSTEM: Hamilton Standard JFC 31 fuel control system. Gear-type fuel pump, with gas producer and power shaft governors, flow control with altitude compensation and shut-off valve.

AVCO LYCOMING WILLIAMSPORT DIVISION

Williamsport, Pennsylvania 17701
Telephone: (717) 323 6181
VICE-PRESIDENTS:
Peter J. Goodwin (General Manager)
A. E. Light (Engineering)
S. T. Jedrziewski (Product Planning)
W. R. Bower (Operations)
H. A. Schuck (Controller)
F. W. Riddell (Advanced Planning)

Williamsport Division is engaged primarily in the production of well-known Lycoming series of horizontally-opposed aircooled reciprocating engines ranging from 110 to 450 hp. Turbocharging is being offered on additional models and the horsepower, in some cases, has been increased. Development efforts are being directed to improvements resulting in lower cost of manufacturing and longer time between overhauls, to help offset increasing labour and material costs. During recent years FAA approval has been received for several new engine models. Turbocharged versions of four- and six-cylinder engines have been certificated, along with several versions of new high-compression, simplified-design engines.

The 231 kW (310 hp) Avco Lycoming TIO-540 six-cylinder engine fitted to the Piper Navajo C

Avco Lycoming O-235-L rated at 86 kW (115 hp)

The 175 kW (235 hp) Avco Lycoming O-540-J six-cylinder engine

AVCO LYCOMING O-235 SERIES

Smallest and basic engine of the Lycoming range. Four cylinders of 111 mm (4⅜ in) bore and 98·4 mm (3⅞ in) stroke. The high-compression O-235-L2C is the most recent production version of the O-235, used in several primary trainers. It requires 100-octane (minimum) aviation fuel.

AVCO LYCOMING O-320 and IO-320 SERIES

Cylinder bore increased to 130 mm (5⅛ in). The O-320 is an engine in the 112-119 kW (150-160 hp) class. Both carburetted and fuel-injected versions are produced in low- and high-compression models for use with 80/87 or 100-octane minimum grade fuels, respectively. Fully aerobatic models are available.

AVCO LYCOMING O-360 and IO-360 SERIES

The O-360 series is basically the same as the O-320 except for an increase in stroke to 111 mm (4⅝ in). Like the O-320, this engine is manufactured with low or high compression, with carburettor or fuel injection. The various models include aerobatic capability, a specific design for helicopters and a turbocharged version. The IO-360 is built in several versions; the IO-360-A series has fuel injection, tuned induction and high-output cylinders, while the IO-360-B series has continuous-flow port injection and standard cylinders.

Latest addition to this family is the TO-360-C series rated at 157 kW (210 hp). These engines have a simple turbocharger, controlled mechanically by the pilot's throttle.

AVCO LYCOMING O-540 and IO-540 SERIES

The O-540 is basically a direct-drive, six-cylinder version of the four-cylinder O-360. It is available in low- and high-compression versions, and the VO-540 is in production as a helicopter powerplant with crankshaft vertical. Fuel-injected IO-540 models are manufactured in a variety of configurations, with rating of 186-224 kW (250-300 hp). An aerobatic version is available. Many of these engines, particularly in the higher horsepower range, have a tuned induction system. Continuous monitoring and computer analysis of engine service records has made it possible to increase the recommended time between overhaul (TBO) for these engines; most models have a TBO of 2,000 h. The most recent members of this family are the -J series of direct-drive engines.

AVCO LYCOMING TIO-540 SERIES

This is a turbocharged version of the fuel-injected IO-540, with tuned induction. It is manufactured in a wide range of horsepowers and is used in the Piper Turbocharged Aztec, the Rockwell Commander 700 and all unpressurised models of the Piper Navajo. The latest addition to the TIO-540 series is the -S model with simple turbocharger interconnected with the pilot's throttle.

AVCO LYCOMING TIO-541 SERIES

Although the displacement of this turbocharged, six-cylinder series is the same as the TIO-540, the TIO-541

AVCO LYCOMING HORIZONTALLY-OPPOSED PISTON ENGINES

Engine Model*	No. of Cylinders	Rated output at Sea Level kW (hp) at rpm	Capacity litres (cu in)	Compression Ratio	Fuel grade Minimum	Weight Dry kg (lb)	Length Overall mm (in)	Width Overall mm (in)	Height Overall mm (in)	Gear Ratio†
O-235-C	4	86 (115) at 2,800	3·85 (233)	6·75	80/87	97·5 (215)	751 (29·56)	812 (32·00)	569 (22·53)	D
O-235-H	4	81 (115) at 2,600	3·85 (233)	6·75	80/87	96 (213)	738 (29·05)	812 (32·00)	569 (22·40)	D
O-235-L	4	86 (115) at 2,700 78 (105) at 2,400	3·85 (233)	8·5	100	98 (218)	738 (29·05)	812 (32·00)	569 (22·40)	D
O-320-A	4	112 (150) at 2,700	5·2 (319·8)	7·0	80/87	110 (243)	751 (29·56)	819 (32·24)	584 (22·99)	D
O-320-D	4	119 (160) at 2,700	5·2 (319·8)	8·5	91/96	114 (253)	808 (31·82)	819 (32·24)	488 (19·22)	D
O-320-E	4	112 (150) at 2,700	5·2 (319·8)	7·0	80/87	113 (249)	738 (29·05)	819 (32·24)	584 (22·99)	D
O-320-H	4	119 (160) at 2,700	5·2 (319·8)	9·0	100	115 (253)	819 (32·26)	830 (32·68)	621 (24·46)	D
AEIO-320-E	4	112 (150) at 2,700	5·2 (319·8)	7·0	80/87	117 (258)	738 (29·05)	819 (32·24)	589 (23·18)	D
O-360-A	4	134 (180) at 2,700	5·92 (361)	8·5	91/96	118 (260)	808 (31·82)	848 (33·37)	488 (19·22)	D
LO-360-A	4	134 (180) at 2,700	5·92 (361)	8·5	91/96	120 (266)	808 (31·82)	848 (33·37)	488 (19·22)	D
O-360-C	4	134 (180) at 2,700	5·92 (361)	8·5	91/96	116 (258)	757 (29·81)	848 (33·37)	625 (24·59)	D
O-360-E	4	134 (180) at 2,700	5·92 (361)	9·0	100	122 (269)	819 (32·26)	859 (33·81)	535 (21·08)	D
LO-360-E	4	134 (180) at 2,700	5·92 (361)	9·0	100	122 (269)	819 (32·26)	859 (33·81)	535 (21·08)	D
O-360-F	4	134 (180) at 2,700	5·92 (361)	8·5	100	122 (269)	808 (31·81)	859 (33·38)	507 (19·96)	D
IVO-360-A	4	134 (180) at 2,900	5·92 (361)	8·5	100	124 (274)	762 (30·00)	848 (33·37)	583 (22·95)	DV
TO-360-C	4	157 (210) at 2,575 to 3,050 m (10,000 ft)	5·92 (361)	7·3	100	154 (343)	876 (34·50)	921 (36·25)	534 (21·02)	D
IO-360-A	4	149 (200) at 2,700	5·92 (361)	8·7	100	133 (293)	757 (29·81)	870 (34·25)	491 (19·35)	D
IO-360-B	4	134 (180) at 2,700	5·92 (361)	8·5	100	122 (268)	757 (29·81)	848 (33·37)	631 (24·84)	D
IO-360-C	4	149 (200) at 2,700	5·92 (361)	8·7	100	134 (298)	855 (33·65)	870 (34·25)	495 (19·48)	D
HIO-360-C	4	153 (205) at 2,900	5·92 (361)	8·7	100	132 (291)	791 (31·14)	870 (34·25)	495 (19·48)	D
HIO-360-D	4	142 (190) at 3,200 to 1,280 m (4,200 ft)	5·92 (361)	10·0	100	132 (290)	894 (35·23)	904 (35·62)	495 (19·48)	D
HIO-360-E	4	142 (190) at 2,900	5·92 (361)	8·0	100	132 (290)	797 (31·36)	870 (34·25)	507 (19·97)	D
AEIO-360-A	4	149 (200) at 2,700	5·92 (361)	8·7	100	139 (307)	780 (30·70)	870 (34·25)	492 (19·35)	D
AEIO-360-B	4	134 (180) at 2,700	5·92 (361)	8·5	91/96	125 (277)	738 (29·05)	848 (33·37)	631 (24·84)	D
AEIO-360-H	4	134 (180) at 2,700	5·92 (361)	8·5	91/96	122 (270)	738 (29·05)	848 (33·37)	631 (24·84)	D
O-540-B	6	175 (235) at 2,575	8·86 (541·5)	7·2	80/87	166 (366)	945 (37·22)	848 (33·37)	624 (24·56)	D
O-540-E	6	194 (260) at 2,700	8·86 (541·5)	8·5	91/96	167 (368)	976 (38·42)	848 (33·37)	624 (24·56)	D
O-540-G	6	194 (260) at 2,700	8·86 (541·5)	8·5	91/96	174 (386)	999 (39·34)	848 (33·37)	624 (24·56)	D
O-540-J	6	175 (235) at 2,400	8·86 (541·5)	8·5	100	162 (357)	989 (38·93)	848 (33·37)	519 (20·43)	D
VO-540-B	6	227 (305) at 3,200	8·86 (541·5)	7·3	80/87	202 (446)	882 (34·73)	880 (34·70)	617 (24·29)	D V
VO-540-C	6	227 (305) at 3,200 to 915 m (3,000 ft)	8·86 (541·5)	8·7	100	200 (441)	882 (34·73)	880 (34·70)	649 (25·57)	D V
IO-540-C	6	186 (250) at 2,575	8·86 (541·5)	8·5	91/96	170 (375)	976 (38·42)	848 (33·37)	622 (24·46)	D
IO-540-E	6	216 (290) at 2,575	8·86 (541·5)	8·7	100	187 (416)	999 (39·34)	870 (34·25)	498 (19·60)	D
IO-540-K	6	224 (300) at 2,700	8·86 (541·5)	8·7	100	201 (443)	999 (39·34)	870 (34·25)	498 (19·60)	D
IO-540-S	6	224 (300) at 2,700	8·86 (541·5)	8·7	100	201 (444)	997 (39·24)	870 (34·25)	498 (19·60)	D
IO-540-T	6	194 (260) at 2,700	8·86 (541·5)	8·5	91/96	171 (381)	989 (38·93)	848 (33·37)	546 (21·50)	D
AEIO-540-D	6	194 (260) at 2,700	8·86 (541·5)	8·5	91/96	174 (386)	999 (39·34)	848 (33·37)	621 (24·46)	D
TIO-540-A	6	231 (310) at 2,575 to 4,575 m (15,000 ft)	8·86 (541·5)	7·3	100	232 (511)	1,304 (51·34)	870 (34·25)	577 (22·71)	D
TIO-540-C	6	186 (250) at 2,575 to 4,575 m (15,000 ft)	8·86 (541·5)	7·2	100	205 (456)	1,026 (40·38)	848 (33·37)	770 (30·33)	D
TIO-540-F	6	242 (325) at 2,575 to 4,575 m (15,000 ft)	8·86 (541·5)	7·3	100	233 (514)	1,304 (51·34)	870 (34·25)	570 (22·42)	D
LTIO-540-F	6	242 (325) at 2,575 to 4,575 m (15,000 ft)	8·86 (541·5)	7·3	100	233 (514)	1,304 (51·34)	870 (34·25)	570 (22·42)	D
TIO-540-J	6	261 (350) at 2,575 to 4,575 m (15,000 ft)	8·86 (541·5)	7·3	100	235 (518)	1,308 (51·50)	870 (34·25)	573 (22·56)	D
LTIO-540-J	6	261 (350) at 2,575 to 4,575 m (15,000 ft)	8·86 (541·5)	7·3	100	235 (518)	1,308 (51·50)	870 (34·25)	573 (22·56)	D
TIO-540-R	6	261 (350) at 2,500 254 (340) to 4,575 m (15,000 ft)	8·86 (541·5)	7·3	100	238 (524)	1,309 (51·52)	870 (34·25)	574 (22·60)	D
TIO-540-S	6	224 (300) at 2,700 to 3,660 m (12,000 ft)	8·86 (541·5)	7·3	100	228 (502)	1,004 (39·56)	915 (36·02)	667 (26·28)	D
TIO-541-E	6	283 (380) at 2,900 to 4,575 m (15,000 ft)	8·86 (541·5)	7·3	100	270 (596)	1,282 (50·70)	905 (35·66)	640 (25·17)	D
TIGO-541-D	6	336 (450) at 3,200 314 (420) at 4,575 m (15,000 ft)	8·86 (541·5)	7·3	100	311 (685)	1,470 (57·90)	885 (34·86)	611 (24·05)	0·667
TIGO-541-E	6	317 (425) at 3,200 to 4,575 m (15,000 ft)	8·86 (541·5)	7·3	100	319 (704)	1,462 (57·57)	885 (34·86)	575 (22·65)	0·667
IO-720-A	8	298 (400) at 2,650	11·84 (722)	8·7	100	257 (567)	1,179 (46·41)	870 (34·25)	573 (22·53)	D
IO-720-B	8	298 (400) at 2,650	11·84 (722)	8·7	100	252 (556)	1,218 (47·97)	870 (34·25)	530 (20·88)	D

*Model designation code: A, Aerobatic; AE, Aerobatic engine; G, Geared; H, Helicopter; I, Fuel injected; L, Left-hand rotation crankshaft; O, Opposed-cylinders; S, Supercharged; T, Turbocharged; V, Vertical crankshaft; †D, Direct drive; V, Vertical mounting

The 317 kW (425 hp) Avco Lycoming TIGO-541-E six-cylinder engine

The 298 kW (400 hp) eight-cylinder Avco Lycoming IO-720-A1A engine

and geared TIGO-541 are totally redesigned. The accessory housing is an integral part of the crankcase, and the new design features allow these engines to operate at the high end of the Lycoming power spectrum. The TIO-541-E is rated at 283 kW (380 hp) and the geared TIGO-541-E at 317 kW (425 hp). Times between overhauls are recommended at 1,600 and 1,200 h, respectively. A double-scroll blower is available to provide cabin pressurisation.

AVCO LYCOMING IO-720 SERIES

This eight-cylinder version of the IO-540 is used in a variety of aircraft at ratings from 280 to 298 kW (375 to 400 hp). Time between overhauls is 1,800 h (1,200 in agricultural applications).

AVCO LYCOMING NEW RANGE

Avco Lycoming, Williamsport, is continuing the development of a new series of high-performance, normally-aspirated and turbocharged flat opposed piston engines. In addition, extensive study and testing are being devoted to finding ways of reducing noise and improving overall efficiency.

BELL
BELL AEROSPACE TEXTRON

HEAD OFFICE AND WORKS: PO Box 1, Buffalo, New York 14240
Telephone: (716) 297 1000
OFFICERS: See Aircraft section

Bell has been engaged in the design, development and production of liquid-propellant rocket engines since 1946.

A single-chamber engine which Bell developed originally to power a nuclear weapon pod to be carried by the B-58 Hustler bomber is now being used in modified form in the Agena space vehicle and provides upper-stage propulsion for numerous spacecraft. The latest version is able to offer multiple re-start capability and was used for the Gemini rendezvous programme. The Agena vehicles used in this programme were also fitted with a Bell-produced secondary propulsion system of 0·071 kN (16 lb) and 0·88 kN (200 lb) S/L thrust radiation-cooled rocket motors for fine adjustment of their velocity prior to the docking manoeuvre.

On 20 February 1979, Bell completed 20 years of space use of the Agena series of engines. In that time the Models 8096, described hereunder, and 8247 had been used in almost 340 missions by the US Air Force and NASA.

BELL MODEL 8096 AGENA ENGINE

This engine was first developed as the power plant for one of the weapon pods that was to be carried by the B-58 Hustler supersonic bomber. It is used in modified form, with gimballed chamber, as the power unit of the Lockheed-built Agena vehicle, forming the second stage of the Thor-Agena, Atlas-Agena and other space vehicles.

During its development the engine has undergone five major modifications, each resulting in an improvement in specific impulse. The present version, designated Model 8096, has a specific impulse of nearly 300 s, which is more than 10 per cent better than the original version of 1959, an increase equivalent to 225 kg (500 lb) in payload for Earth orbital missions.

The Model 8096 engine is a single-chamber pump-fed engine, running on red fuming nitric acid and unsymmetrical dimethyl-hydrazine (UDMH) hypergolic propellants.

Bell Agena single-chamber liquid-propellant rocket engine

It gives 71 kN (16,000 lb) S/L thrust, and has re-start capability in space. This feature can be used, for example, to change from a circular to an elliptical orbit.

The Model 8096 engine has the ability to be re-started twice in space. It powers the Agena vehicles used in many US Air Force and NASA programmes.

Bell has qualified the Agena engine to run on high-density acid (HDA), which burns at increased temperature to give increased thrust and efficiency; it requires a silicone additive to protect the thrust chamber. A higher-performance baffled injector has been developed and qualified for the current production engine.

DIMENSIONS:
Length overall	approx 2,134 mm (84 in)
Nozzle diameter	825·5 mm (32·5 in)

WEIGHT: approx 132 kg (290 lb)

PERFORMANCE:
Thrust	75·62 kN (17,000 lb)
Chamber pressure approx	34·5 bars (500 lb/sq in)
Specific impulse	approx 300 s

CHOTIA
WEEDHOPPER OF UTAH INC

1148 Century Drive, PO Box 2253, Ogden, Utah 84404
Telephone: (801) 621 3941

This company has produced a 'clean sheet of paper' two-stroke specifically for ultra-light aircraft, in the belief that a large market exists. Unlike most such engines, originally designed for other applications, the Chotia 460 gives large torque at low rpm. It is designed for long life, reliability and ease of tuning.

CHOTIA 460

TYPE: Single-cylinder, aircooled, direct-drive, two-stroke.
CYLINDER: Bore 88·0 mm (3·47 in). Stroke 75·0 mm (2·95 in). Swept volume 456 cc (27·85 cu in). Schnurle-port design. Four-bolt exhaust flange.
CONNECTING ROD: Machined bar stock. Needle bearings at both ends.
CRANKSHAFT: Three ball bearings. Reversible rotation. Direct drive.
INDUCTION: Impulse fuel pump. Bowl-type carburettor. Fuel/oil ratio 50:1.

IGNITION: Four D-size flashlight batteries giving 25 h operation before full-power misfire (then still 4 h cruise available); standard 14 mm plug.
DIMENSIONS:
Length	305 mm (12·0 in)
Width	178 mm (7·0 in)
Height	406 mm (16·0 in)

WEIGHT, DRY: 14·3 kg (31·5 lb)

PERFORMANCE RATINGS (S/L):
T-O	18·6 kW (25 hp) at 4,700 rpm
Continuous	14·9 kW (20 hp) at 3,500 rpm

CSD
CHEMICAL SYSTEMS DIVISION
(A division of United Technologies Corporation)

HEADQUARTERS: Sunnyvale, California 94086
Telephone: (408) 739 4880
DIVISION PRESIDENT: Barnet R. Adelman

DIVISION SENIOR VICE-PRESIDENTS:
Dr David Altman
Eugene Roberts
CSD is currently engaged in research, development and production of rockets, rocket propellants and advanced propulsion systems, as well as a range of 'spin-off' by-products. Since its founding in the late 1950s it has conducted a continuous programme of rocket technology and is now producing a variety of advanced space propulsion systems for both the Department of Defense and the National Aeronautics and Space Administration.

CSD's largest programme is the production of 3,048 mm (120 in) diameter, segmented solid-propellant booster rockets. Other programmes described hereafter include the Algol III and FW-5 rocket motors, which are fully operational, and development of IUS.

In 1976 a specially formed subsidiary, United Space Boosters Inc (USBI), was selected by NASA as boost assembly contractor for the Space Shuttle. USBI will be responsible, under a $122 million contract, for assembly, checkout, launch, post-launch disassembly and refurbishment of the motors for re-use. The present contract covers six development flights, with an option for 21 operational flights.

CSD 3,048 mm (120 in) SEGMENTED MOTOR

Mass-produced at CSD's Coyote, California, rocket production facility, this 3,048 mm (120 in) diameter solid-propellant rocket motor centre segment is interchangeable with any other centre segment. Its cylindrical metal case is manufactured from high-strength steel (D6AC) and heat treated to an ultimate strength of 13,790 bars (200,000 lb/sq in). Less than 12·7 mm (0·5 in) thick, each case is equipped with clevis-type end joints with holes for cylindrical fastening pins. Loaded with propellant, a synthetic rubber (polybutadiene acrylonitrile) with aluminium additives as fuel and ammonium perchlorate as oxidiser, a segment has an overall length of 3,276 mm (10 ft 9 in) and weighs 36,400 kg (80,300 lb). Designed as the basic building block for large solid-propellant booster rockets, the segmented motor can be assembled in from one- to seven-segment configurations with thrusts ranging from 1,112-6,673 kN (250,000 to 1·5 million lb). A fully configured motor contains a destruct system, a forward-end ignition system, a liquid-injection thrust-vector control system for steering and has its own staging sequence capability.

CSD has made progress in the development of more efficient and economical means of fabricating the steel motor cases used in the 120 in programme, through production processes known as internal roll extrusion and shear forming. Both techniques reduce production time and result in a more reliable and economical product.

A five-segment configuration of this motor is used in pairs as the zero (launch) stage of the US Air Force Titan IIIC and D space launch vehicles. Operating together, the 26·12 m (86 ft) tall motors produce a thrust of 10,675 kN (2,400,000 lb). Launched for the first time on 18 June 1965, the boosters have flown 57 successful missions in as many launches, using 114 motors.

Production continued in 1975, following a $59 million US Air Force contract for 16 five-segment motors for delivery in 1976 and 1977. This raised total purchase by the USAF Space and Missile Systems Organisation to 116. An additional $50 million contract called for 20 more motors for delivery in the 13 months from June 1979.

In 1979 CSD completed production of five-segment motors and started production of its six-segment boosters for the Titan 34D, the advanced version of the USAF's Titan standard space launch vehicle. Two of these boosters will launch the Titan 34D on its maiden flight from Cape Canaveral in 1981. The ten-tonne additional segment (actually six-tenths the length of a full segment) is located just below the rocket's forward closure and provides increased thrust (11,565 kN; 2,600,000 lb for the pair) for payloads of the 1980s. In 1978 CSD received contract awards for $89 m for eight pairs of the six-segment systems. Delivery of the first pair was made in December 1979. In August and October 1979 CSD successfully conducted static test firings of the six-segment motor at its Coyote research and test centre.

Essentially a lengthened version of the five-segment motor, a seven-segment motor has been statically test-fired four times. Producing a record 6,227 kN (1·4 million lb) of thrust, the motors operated perfectly while testing an advanced steering system, called an ullage blow-down,

Full-scale mockup of Boeing IUS, showing the forward and aft CSD motors

which is now used on all flights of Titan IIIC and IIID vehicles.

CSD IUS

In October 1976 the US Air Force awarded the Boeing/CSD team a contract to develop the Inertial Upper Stage (IUS) for the Space Shuttle and the Titan 34D space launch vehicle. CSD's all-solid IUS proposal won the award over five competitors' liquid-propellant submissions. The Air Force cited highest reliability and safety at lowest cost in its choice. The Boeing/CSD IUS completed its validation phase on 19 December 1977, after a successful test firing of the 2,310 mm (91 in) diameter rocket motor at the Arnold Engineering Development Center (AEDC). During the firing, the 9,979 kg (22,000 lb) motor encountered no difficulties during an unusually long (154 s) burn. Key components, including the advanced flight-weight nozzle, proved their survivability. Average thrust was 173·6 kN (39,000 lb) and maximum 249·2 kN (56,000 lb) at a simulated height of 33,800 m (111,000 ft). Full-scale development of the IUS propulsion system began on 1 March 1978 under a $32 million contract award from Boeing Aerospace. The propulsion system for the two-stage IUS consists of two solid rocket motors designed by CSD: a 2·31 m (91 in) aft motor containing 9,707 kg (21,400 lb) of propellant and a 1·6 m (63 in) forward stage motor with 2,722 kg (6,000 lb) of propellant. In May 1978 CSD received a $3 million award from Boeing to develop the thrust vector control (TVC) servo-actuator system to control the movable nozzle. The basic TVC system consists of two controllers and four actuators powered by 28V batteries. In December 1978 CSD received a $2 million award to produce a servo-actuator system to raise the IUS to deployment position inside the Shuttle Orbiter's cargo bay.

The first full-scale development large motor for the IUS was test-fired on 19 December 1979 at AEDC, for approx 150 s in near-vacuum conditions. The motor's nozzle was vectored ±4° during the firing.

The first firing in the full-scale development phase of the small motor was conducted successfully on 26 June 1979. The motor fired for approx 95 s at a simulated altitude of 30,480 m (100,000 ft) and generated over 111·2 kN (25,000 lb) thrust. Its carbon/carbon nozzle was vectored to full deflection of 7° during the firing.

The first firing of the small solid spin motor was conducted on 5 December 1979 at AEDC. The motor was spun at 70 rpm for 100 s. Maximum thrust was 106·8 kN (24,000 lb). The second spin test firing was planned for mid-1980. This unit will feature an extendible exit cone, designed and produced by CSD, which increases the expansion ratio from 47·3 to 173·6.

There were no failures in test firings of the first nine motors of the IUS propulsion system. Three more development tests were scheduled for the large motor at AEDC in 1980. Six qualification test firings were also planned, the last in June 1981.

CSD ALGOL III

CSD is in full production of Algol III, a more powerful solid-propellant first stage for NASA's Scout space launch vehicle. 9·14 m (30 ft) tall and 1·14 m (45 in) in diameter, the improved solid booster permits an increase of 40-54 per cent in the Scout's payload/weight capability. When loaded with its propellant (PBAN with aluminium additives and ammonium perchlorate oxidiser) Algol III weighs 13,605 kg (30,000 lb). Its nozzle is fabricated from steel with a graphite cloth-phenolic and silica cloth-phenolic cone liner. Ignition is by a small nose-mounted solid rocket. Producing 623 kN (140,000 lb) of lift-off thrust, Algol III burns for 75 s to boost the Scout to an altitude of 48 km (30 miles) before burnout. The motor flew for the first time in August 1972 and by the end of 1979 had completed 19 missions. About three launches per year are planned for the 1980s.

CSD FW-5

The FW-5 is designed to be interchangeable with existing upper-stage motors. While its primary application is that of an apogee motor, it can be used for orbital, probe or re-entry missions, as well as retro-rocket propulsion for space vehicles.

The FW-5 is 691 mm (27·2 in) in diameter with an overall length of 1,123 mm (44·2 in). Its case is fabricated from glassfibre and epoxy resin, with a cylindrical wall thickness of 3·3 mm (0·13 in) and end domes with solar isotensoid contours with a nominal wall thickness of 15·2 mm (0·60 in). The igniter and nozzle attachment fittings are fabricated from aluminium, and the aluminium interstage flange is bonded and riveted to the integrally-wound glassfibre skirt of the motor case.

The standard FW-5 has an inert weight of 29·7 kg (65·6 lb) and a propellant weight of 260 kg (575 lb), resulting in a motor mass fraction of 0·89. The average motor thrust is 25·04 kN (5,630 lb) with a burn time of 42·1 s.

FW-5 operated perfectly on its first mission in November 1972 when it placed Telesat Canada's Anik communications satellite into final orbit. The second Anik was put on station by an FW-5 in April 1973, followed by a third in May 1975.

By 1980 the FW-5 had completed 12 additional consecutive successful flights on the Delta 2914 launch vehicle. The FW-5 was used to put on station communications satellites such as the Anik, Westar, Marisat, and Palpa. CSD has also developed a version of the FW-5 with a 178 mm (7·0 in) extension to the nozzle exit cone. The flight unit was used to launch the Martin Marietta/Denver Scatha satellite in early 1979.

CSD BOOSTER SEPARATION MOTOR

In late 1975 NASA selected CSD to develop and produce solid-propellant booster separation motors (BSM) to be used on the first six development flights of the Space Shuttle programme beginning in 1980.

The BSMs will be used to separate the two reusable solid rocket boosters (SRB) approximately 110 s after

Three of CSD's advanced rocket nozzle systems: left, cutaway model showing operation of Techroll; centre, a test EEC during firing; right, a hot ball and socket

launch of the Space Shuttle. Each SRB will require eight BSMs, four forward and four aft, which will fire for less than 1 s to achieve safe separation. In September 1978 the motor passed acceptance by NASA. The last of the 104 motors ordered was shipped in early 1980.

Each BSM has a length of 838 mm (33·0 in) and a diameter of 327 mm (12·88 in), with a weight of 73·0 kg (161 lb). It uses CSD UTP-19048 (HTPB) propellant, and will have 62·5 kN-s (14,000 lb-s) minimum total impulse WEB action time, and 67·0 kN-s (15,000 lb-s) minimum action time. Burn-time (WEB) performance time limit is 0·8 s. Maximum thrust called for is 129·5 kN (29,000 lb), with a WEB action time average thrust of 82·6 kN (18,500 lb) minimum.

Each motor consists of solid propellant, motor case with attachments, nozzle, igniter and pyrotechnic initiators. Aft motors are provided with cork insulation for protection from the Shuttle's main engine plumes and solid rocket booster exhaust. Forward separation motors are equipped with an aerodynamic heat-shield which opens instantly on motor ignition but does not discharge any debris that could damage the Orbiter.

CSD HAHST HYBRID PROPULSION

CSD's hybrid rocket for the Department of Defense High Altitude High-Speed Target (HAHST) drone is 330 mm (13 in) in diameter, has an overall length of 3,556 mm (140 in) and weighs 390 kg (860 lb). It uses a polybutadiene and methyl methacrylate fuel grain, and nitric acid as its liquid oxidiser. Ablative-cooled, its thrust ranges from 0·88-5·34 kN (200 to 1,200 lb) at altitudes between 10,670 and 30,480 m (35,000 and 100,000 ft). The HAHST successfully completed all its initial flight-readiness test-firings in 1973. In 1978 the HAHST was flown successfully three times by the US Navy at the Pacific Missile Test Center.

CSD LIQUID ROCKET ENGINES

The company's liquid rockets range in size from 1,321 mm (52 in) long and 660 mm (26 in) in diameter and weighing 32·6 kg (72 lb) to 1,918 mm (75·5 in) long, 1,219 mm (48 in) in diameter and weighing 83·9 kg (185 lb). Their propellant is 50/50 hydrazine and unsymmetrical dimethyl hydrazine and nitrogen tetroxide. The engine nozzles are a composite structure with a glassfibre shell and silica-phenolic liner. Ignition is hypergolic.

CSD AIR-BREATHING PROPULSION

In early 1973, CSD was selected to spearhead the efforts of its parent, United Technologies Corporation, in the research and development of ramjet propulsion systems, with the support of UTC's Hamilton Standard Division and United Technologies Research Center. In mid-1973 CSD was awarded a contract by the US Navy to research, design and develop a Modern Ramjet Engine (MRE). Called an integral rocket/ramjet, the propulsion device involves both solid rocket and liquid fuel ramjet technology. It operates as a solid rocket booster until it reaches supersonic speeds. At that point, through a series of mechanical changes that take place in flight, it becomes a ramjet. These changes involve the opening of air inlets, an increase in the nozzle diameter and a switch to the burning of liquid fuel and air in the combustion chamber within a common system. The propulsion technology acquired in carrying out this project will be applied to the development of an advanced air-to-air missile system.

In mid-1974 CSD was awarded another ramjet programme by the US Air Force, to design and ground test an advanced integral rocket/ramjet propulsion system which would satisfy the requirements of an advanced strategic air-launched missile (ASALM).

In the ASALM programme, CSD had by 1978 embarked on a project to demonstrate the feasibility of two design approaches, one by McDonnell Douglas, the other by Martin Marietta. CSD was carrying out extensive ground testing, including numerous hot firings at its ramjet test facility near San Jose. This testing also involved simulated flight-test missions, in preparation for the next phase of development. In late 1979 the ASALM combustor underwent a successful test firing at Coyote which simulated a supersonic mission lasting nearly ten minutes. Post-fire analysis revealed that the combustor, its quartz phenolic thermal-protection system and its moulded silica phenolic nozzle were in excellent condition. A free-jet test firing of the system was scheduled at AEDC for mid-1980.

In mid-1977, the division received a subcontract from

Simplified section of HAHST showing CSD hybrid propulsion

Vought, funded by the Navy, to refine the earlier Advanced Low Volume Ramjet (ALVRJ) for the Supersonic Tactical Missile (STM).

On 21 April 1979 the STM, powered by a liquid rocket/ramjet system produced by CSD, successfully completed a test flight at the Naval Pacific Missile Test Center. The missile was launched from an A-7 and achieved speeds as high as 3,220 km/h (2,000 mph) during its 132 km (82 mile) flight over the Pacific before executing a programmed terminal dive.

In 1979 CSD was chosen by Hughes Aircraft to supply the propulsion subsystem for the ducted rocket missile that Hughes is developing for the US Air Force. CSD is responsible for design, development, integration and ground testing of the gas generator and air induction system. Flight testing of 12 of these missiles is scheduled to begin early in 1982. The division completed a ducted rocket engine development programme in 1979 which was the precursor of its current work for Hughes.

In the ducted rocket a solid rocket fuel produces a fuel-rich gas. This is injected into a combustion (ramburner) chamber, mixed with ram air and further burned to provide sustained thrust at supersonic speeds. The ram air is introduced through inlet ducts alongside the vehicle. Compared to a conventional rocket, the ducted rocket is claimed to offer many times the thrust duration, permitting powered flight all the way to a target and a greater range with less weight.

In early 1979 CSD announced that it had demonstrated the feasibility of a side-dump combustor for solid-fuel ramjet systems that may allow an increase in missile range without increasing combustor size. By late 1979 CSD had completed a series of semi-free-jet tests of its solid-fuel ramjet. The three-year programme of development of a solid-fuel ramjet for future air-to-air missiles was scheduled to culminate in wind tunnel tests at NASA's Lewis Center in early 1980.

Also in 1979 CSD was awarded a two-year contract to develop and test advanced integral rocket/ramjet combustors which utilise the technology of swirl combustion. CSD engineers expect to realise a significant improvement in combustor performance while reducing combustor length by as much as 50 per cent.

Work also proceeded on a programme to develop a ramjet capable of cruising at Mach 6.

CSD/SEP ADVANCED APOGEE MOTOR

In November 1979, the Advanced Apogee Motor and Nozzle, produced jointly by CSD and the Société Européenne de Propulsion (SEP) of France, was test-fired successfully at AFRPL.

The 762 mm (30 in) diameter motor was test-fired for 60 s at a simulated altitude of 30,500 m (100,000 ft). Maximum thrust was 22·25 kN (5,000 lb) and maximum pressure 41·5 bars (600 lb/sq in). Specific impulse of 302·9

s was the highest ever recorded for composite aluminised propellant.

The experimental motor embodies important technological advances, including 'head end' web solid-propellant grain design, free-standing carbon/carbon ITE, and an extensible exit cone which employs reinforced rubber tube actuators.

ADVANCED PROPULSION TECHNOLOGY

Testing of CSD's patented Techroll joint continues. This is a fluid-filled, constant-volume bearing which allows easy pivoting of the nozzle by the steering system. It is considered to be the first major improvement in rocket steering in almost a decade. Both IUS motors use the Techroll seal. Other uses being researched include a main rotor bearing for helicopters and a joint in high-pressure and transmission lines.

The extensible exit cone (EEC) is a device which enlarges mechanically as a rocket motor fires in space, improving performance by over five per cent. The first test at operational pressures and temperatures of an EEC system for ICBM nozzle applications was successfully carried out in June 1977. This CSD system uses nested cones of an advanced composite material, which lock into place by a latching mechanism. An EEC is fitted to the IUS small motor, as described earlier.

CSD is continuing developmental work on its Bolt Extrusion Thrust Termination (BETT) system, considered to be the only new thrust-termination system for solid rocket motors developed in the last 20 years. BETT replaces nozzle flange bolts with a combination of

CSD/SEP Advanced Apogee Motor and Nozzle

Artist's impression of future vehicles with CSD propulsion: left, Hughes Aircraft ducted rocket; right, Mach 6 cruise ramjet

explosive-released and extrudable bolts. Upon command, explosive bolts are actuated and the nozzle moves aft, dropping the motor's internal pressure drastically. This halts propellant burning and neutralises motor thrust. A 1978 test of the system used a 2·34 m (92 in) Kevlar case. Upon command all explosive bolts operated within 0·001 s and the nozzle moved 146 mm (5·76 in) rearward in 0·016 s. Two tests of BETT on third-stage Minuteman motors took place in 1979. In both, thrust-termination was initiated 5 s into the firing, resulting in motor depressurisation in 180 ms.

CSD's "hot ball and socket" rocket steering system employs an integral carbon/carbon nozzle and thrust vector control system without the use of any seals, insulators or metallic structures. The materials are self-lubricating, and loads are transmitted between the surfaces even while white hot. This allows ball diameter to be reduced to a minimum, sharply reducing vectoring torque. The hot ball and socket completed its first test firing in 1978 under contract to the US Naval Sea Systems Command.

In early 1979 CSD tested a nozzle employing a one-piece freestanding integral throat and entrance which

needs no insulation or structural support. The FSITE replaces the entire submerged area of a solid-propellant motor nozzle, consisting typically of numerous phenolic and steel parts.

In 1979 CSD was awarded a contract by the US Army Missile Command to develop solid motor cases made of chemically treated layers of papers. The motors will be fabricated at CSD and delivered to Redstone Arsenal for test firing.

CURTISS-WRIGHT
CURTISS-WRIGHT CORPORATION, WOOD-RIDGE FACILITY

HEAD OFFICE AND WORKS: One Passaic St, Wood-Ridge, New Jersey 07075
Telephone: (201) 777 2900
CHAIRMAN OF THE BOARD AND PRESIDENT: T. Roland Berner
EXECUTIVE VICE-PRESIDENTS:
Charles E. Ehringer
Richard P. Sprigle
VICE-PRESIDENT, ENGINEERING: A. F. Kossar
VICE-PRESIDENTS:
D. Lasky
W. Figart

The Wood-Ridge facility of Curtiss-Wright Corporation is engaged in the research, development and licensing of Wankel-type rotary engines, manufacture of engine parts, aircraft and industrial engine overhaul, electric power generation systems and advanced marine and turbine technology.

CURTISS-WRIGHT SETE

In competition with Garrett-AiResearch and Pratt & Whitney, Curtiss-Wright is participating in the SETE (Supersonic Expendable Turbine Engine) programme of the US Navy. The objective is the cheapest possible jet engine capable of unfailingly-reliable instant starting and flight propulsion, under severe conditions of manoeuvre, over a wide band of speeds and heights, on a single flight of a missile. Details are restricted, but several sources give thrust class as 10·23 kN (2,300 lb st).

CURTISS-WRIGHT RC ENGINES

In 1958 Curtiss-Wright Corporation obtained a licence for the NSU-Wankel type of rotating-combustion (RC) engine and embarked on a major programme of independent development of a range of such engines aimed at a wide spectrum of applications. At first the company concentrated on large engines in the power range around 500 hp for aircraft use, but during the past decade much smaller engines have dominated the hardware test and development programme, some of which has been funded by US military agencies, including the Naval Air Systems Command, and NASA.

Curtiss-Wright RC2-75, rated at 254 kW (340 hp), on bench with three-blade propeller

Most research has been carried out on versions of the **RC2-60** (twin rotors each of about 0·983 litre; 60 cu in capacity), rated at up to 149 kW (200 hp) at 5,500 rpm.

In 1965 the 310 hp **RC2-90** was run, with helicopter applications in mind, and the 1·47 litre (90 cu in) rotor has since been used in extensive development of stratified charge engines capable of operating on a range of fuels including JP-4 and JP-5 gas turbine kerosenes.

The **RC2-75-Y3** is one of a very important family of engines, regarded as optimally sized for a wide range of general aviation aircraft. As the designation indicates, it is based on two rotors each of nominal 1·23 litres (75 cu in) capacity, and has liquid cooling and a geared drive. Current work is centred on reducing fuel consumption and pollution.

DREHER
DREHER ENGINEERING COMPANY

708 Lincoln Boulevard, Santa Monica, California 90402
Telephone: (213) 395 6510

Mr Max Dreher, an aeronautical engineer, has built a series of small turbojet engines over a period of 24 years. One of them, known as the TJD-76 Baby Mamba, was mounted on his Prue 215A all-metal 12·0 m sailplane.

Development of the TJD-76C has been virtually completed, apart from the recent addition of an automatic fuel control device which is operating well and will later be applied to the larger engines. It has become evident that the main market favours the TJD-76E, and a production manufacturer is being sought.

DREHER TJD-76C BABY MAMBA

TYPE: Single-shaft turbojet.
AIR INTAKE: At front. Air flow 0·50 kg (1·1 lb)/s.
COMPRESSOR: Single-stage mixed-flow. Stainless steel impeller with sixteen vanes. Pressure ratio 2·8 : 1.
COMPRESSOR CASING: Of 2024 alloy and 347 stainless steel.
COMBUSTION CHAMBER: Annular type vaporising system with fuel/air pre-mix. One spark plug in flame tube.
FUEL SYSTEM: Manual with pressurised fuel supply, or electrically-driven fuel pump. Fuel pressure 5·52 bars (80 lb/sq in). Automatic system for drone applications.
FUEL GRADE: Kerosene or petrol.
NOZZLE GUIDE VANES: Single axial stage, with sixteen investment-cast vanes in Stellite 31.
TURBINE: Single-stage axial-flow, with nineteen integrally-cast blades, of Inconel 713 LC. Gas temperature 770°C before turbine, 675°C after turbine, at continuous cruising power.

Two views of the Dreher Baby Mamba single-shaft turbojet: *(left)* TJD-76C on mount; *(right)* TJD-76C Jet Pack installed on sailplane. Thrust rating is 0·245 kN (55 lb st)

LUBRICATION: Air/oil mist system with total loss, using bleed air equivalent to 2·5 per cent of total mass flow.

OIL GRADE: MIL-L-7808E (Turbo 15).

STARTING: Compressed air 10·34 bars (150 lb/sq in), via three nozzles driving turbine wheel.

DIMENSIONS:
Length overall	416 mm (16·38 in)	
Diameter	151 mm (5·94 in)	

WEIGHTS:
Dry	6·4 kg (14·1 lb)	
Complete with fuel tank	10·0 kg (22 lb)	

PERFORMANCE RATINGS:
Max	0·245 kN (55 lb st)
Continuous	0·20 kN (45 lb st)

SPECIFIC FUEL CONSUMPTION:
at max rating 42·5 mg/Ns (1·5 lb/h/lb st)

DREHER TJD-76D and E

These versions were derived from the TJD-76C in 1972 to meet a need for a very low-cost short-life unit for the propulsion of mini-RPVs and other expendable vehicles. Both have similar performance to the TJD-76C but weigh approximately 6·5 kg (14·33 lb), complete with 2 kW alternator. Envelope diameter is 165 mm (6·5 in) and length 400 mm (15·75 in).

DSI
DEVELOPMENTAL SCIENCES INC

15747 East Valley Boulevard, City of Industry, California 91749

Telephone: (213) 330 6865
PRESIDENT: Dr Gerald R. Seemann

DSI RESONATING RAMJET

This programme, described in the 1979-80 *Jane's*, is no longer active.

GARRETT-AIRESEARCH

AIRESEARCH MANUFACTURING COMPANY of Arizona (a division of The Garrett Corporation)

Sky Harbor Airport, 111 S 34th St, PO Box 5217, Phoenix, Arizona 85010
Telephone: (602) 267 3011
VICE-PRESIDENT AND MANAGER: Jack Marinick
SALES MANAGER: Larry D. Huppert

The Garrett Corporation's AiResearch Manufacturing Company of Arizona, at Phoenix, has been called the world's largest producer of small gas turbines. Development of the first Garrett small turbines began in 1946 and the division claims to have produced over 70 per cent of the total of gas-turbine units with power ratings from 60 to 2,500 hp built in the USA and Europe.

Since 1970 Garrett, one of The Signal Companies, has extensively penetrated the market for small turboprop and turbofan engines. It is now developing a mainly military series of derivative low-bypass-ratio engines in partnership with Volvo Flygmotor of Sweden, and in 1980 signed agreements with Volvo for development and production of uprated models of turbofan and turboprop engines.

GARRETT-AIRESEARCH ATF3

US military designation: F104-GA-100

Considered to be the first three-spool engine to run in the USA, the Garrett-AiResearch ATF3 is the first engine in the world to combine the three-spool features with a reverse-flow combustion system and turbines, and mixed-flow exhaust.

The arrangement of components allows the fan design to be determined largely independently of the gas-generator compressor requirements, and permits operation at optimum fan speed. Omission of fan inlet guide

Cutaway of the Garrett-AiResearch ATF3-6 three-shaft turbofan with double flow-reversal (22·46 kN; 5,050 lb st)

vanes, mixing of the gas-generator exhaust with the fan airflow, and double reversal of the internal airflow enable the ATF3 to offer significant reductions in overall noise generation.

Other design considerations include reliability, maintainability and elimination of visible smoke. The accessories are revealed by removing the tailcone fairing, and their positioning at the rear of the engine is claimed to reduce installed drag.

All design and early development of the ATF3 took place at the AiResearch Torrance (Los Angeles) facility. The conceptual design was completed in early 1966, and testing of demonstrator engines was initiated in May 1968. Under US Air Force contract, the ATF3 successfully completed preliminary flight rating tests in 1972 at 18 kN (4,050 lb) thrust. Both the aerodynamic and mechanical design criteria were established around sea-level, ISA +15°C take-off rating of 22·47 kN (5,050 lb).

In May 1976 it was announced that the **ATF3-6** had been selected by Dassault-Breguet to power the Falcon 20G business jet, with US coast-to-coast range. Commercial certification was achieved in early 1980 after 15,000 h of testing, and production shipments began in that year. The ATF3-6 is offered under a retrofit programme for existing Falcon 20 aircraft. It powers the HU-25A Falcon Guardian that is in production for the US Coast Guard and is specified for the Falcon 20H.

TYPE: Three-shaft axial-flow turbofan.

INTAKE: Direct pitot, fixed type. No inlet vanes or struts. Total airflow 73·5 kg/s (162 lb/s).

LOW-PRESSURE (FAN) SYSTEM: Single-stage titanium fan, driven by three-stage IP turbine. Bypass ratio 2·8 at take-off.

INTERMEDIATE-PRESSURE SYSTEM: Five-stage titanium axial IP compressor, each stage having a separate disc, driven by two-stage LP turbine. Airflow is then delivered to rearward-facing HP compressor via eight tubes feeding into an annular duct concentric with the bypass duct. Core airflow 18·15 kg (40 lb)/s.

HIGH-PRESSURE SYSTEM: Single-stage titanium centrifugal compressor, driven by single-stage HP turbine. IP airflow enters the single-sided impeller from the rear. Overall pressure ratio (T-O) 21, (high-altitude cruise) 25.

COMBUSTION SYSTEM: Reverse-flow annular type.

TURBINES: Single-stage HP, three-stage IP and two-stage LP turbines drive, respectively, the HP, fan (LP) and IP compressors. IP and LP turbines have fully shrouded blades. Aircooled first-stage nozzle vanes and HP rotor blades. Exhaust gases turned 180° through eight sets of cascades to mix with fan bypass flow.

FUEL SYSTEM: Electromechanical, incorporating solid-state computer. Manual emergency backup system.

ACCESSORY DRIVES: Three drive pads on rear-mounted gearbox driven by HP shaft, providing for hydraulic pump, starter/generator and one spare. Accessory cooling by fan discharge air which is exhausted through a nozzle at the tip of the fairing.

EXHAUST SYSTEM: Mixed fan and turbine exhaust discharged to atmosphere through annular nozzle surrounding combustion section.

LUBRICATION SYSTEM: Self-contained hot-tank type; tank integral with gearbox.

MOUNTING: Two-plane pickup system.

STARTING: Electrical or pneumatic.

DIMENSIONS:
ATF3-6:	
Length	2,316 mm (91·2 in)
Max diameter	853 mm (33·6 in)

WEIGHT, DRY:
ATF3-6	431 kg (950 lb)

Cross-section (top) and external view (above) of the 15·57 kN (3,500 lb st) Garrett-AiResearch TFE731-2 geared front-fan engine

PERFORMANCE RATINGS (uninstalled):
T-O (S/L, static):
ATF3-6   22·46 kN (5,050 lb), ISA+15°C
Cruise (12,200 m; 40,000 ft at Mach 0·8):
ATF3-6   4·5 kN (1,012 lb)
SPECIFIC FUEL CONSUMPTION:
At T-O rating (S/L, ISA static)
13·6 mg/Ns (0·48 lb/h/lb st)
At cruise (as above)   22·38 mg/Ns (0·79 lb/h/lb st)

GARRETT-AIRESEARCH TFE731

Announced in April 1969, the TFE731 is a two-spool geared turbofan designed to confer US coast-to-coast range upon business jet aircraft. Use of a geared fan confers flexibility in operation and yields optimum performance both at low altitudes and at up to 15,250 m (50,000 ft).

Component testing began in March 1969. The first engine ran in September 1970, and was tested at Phoenix in a Learjet 25. FAA certification and first production deliveries to Dassault for the Falcon 10 took place in August 1972.

In October 1972 it was stated that the Lockheed JetStar would be re-engined with the TFE731-3, flat rated at 16·46 kN (3,700 lb st) by a modest increase in turbine inlet temperature. The TFE731-3 was certificated in 1974. The modified aircraft is designated JetStar II, and first flew in July 1974. AiResearch Aviation converted a number of JetStar I aircraft to have TFE731-3 power.

Since 1973 the TFE731, in various sub-types, has been selected for the Gates Learjet 35/36, Cessna Citation III, Dassault-Breguet Falcon 50, HS 125-700, IAI 1124 Westwind, Rockwell International's Sabreliner 65A, CASA C-101 trainer and light attack aircraft, Learjet 54/44/56 Longhorn, and ICX X-Avia, and proposals have been made for RPV and other short-life programmes.

By early 1980 deliveries of TFE731-2 and -3 engines had reached 2,000. Output had risen to 40 per month, with expansion planned to rise to 50 per month.

In 1980 the 731-5 was announced, to offer higher thrust and reduced noise, while maintaining low smoke characteristics. The -5 is installationally similar to earlier models but has a higher-bypass-ratio fan driven by a new LP turbine, the design of which was demonstrated in a NASA programme. Development and production are in partnership with Volvo Flygmotor of Sweden which, on a risk-sharing basis, will produce the outer structure. Certification is due in the second half of 1982.

TYPE: Turbofan with two shafts and geared front fan.
AIR INTAKE: Direct pitot, fixed, without guide vanes.
FAN: Single-stage axial titanium fan, with inserted blades. The fan shaft is connected directly to the planetary gearbox ring gear. Max fan airflow, sea level static, 51·25 kg (113 lb)/s (-3, 53·7 kg; 118·3 lb/s; -4, 54·6 kg; 120·4 lb/s). Bypass ratio 2·66 (-3, 2·80; -4, 2·28).
COMPRESSOR: Low-pressure compressor has four stages (TFE731-4, five stages), each with a separate disc. Rotors and stators have inserted blades and vanes. High-pressure compressor, carried on a separate shaft running at higher speeds, is centrifugal. Overall pressure ratio (S/L, static): -2, 14·0; -3, 14·6; -4, 17·5.
COMBUSTION CHAMBER: Annular combustion chamber of reverse-flow type, with 12 fuel nozzles inserted radially and injecting fuel tangentially.
FUEL SYSTEM: Hydro-electronic, with single-lever control to mechanical and electronic elements.
TURBINES: High-pressure turbine has a single axial stage with inserted blades. Low-pressure turbine has three axial stages, all with inserted blades. Average inlet gas temperature to HP turbine, S/L, max T-O thrust, 1,010°C (-3 and -4, higher).

JET PIPE: Short fan duct facilitating installation of fan reverser. Fixed core nozzle.
ACCESSORY DRIVES: Accessories driven from HP spool are grouped around underside of the forward section of the fan duct. Pads are provided on the front side of the accessory gearbox for the airframe-type accessories: hydraulic pump, starter/generator or starter motor and alternators. Pads on the back side of the gearbox drive the engine accessories: fuel control unit and oil pump.
DIMENSIONS:
Intake diameter   716 mm (28·2 in)
Length overall (-2, -3)   1,263 mm (49·73 in)
Width   869 mm (34·20 in)
Height overall   992 mm (39·07 in)
WEIGHT, DRY:
TFE731-2, -3   329 kg (725 lb)
PERFORMANCE RATINGS:
Max T-O (S/L, 24·4°C):
TFE731-2   15·57 kN (3,500 lb st)
TFE731-3   16·46 kN (3,700 lb st)
TFE731-5   17·79 kN (4,000 lb st)
Cruise (12,200 m; 40,000 ft at Mach 0·8):
TFE731-2   3·36 kN (755 lb)
TFE731-3   3·64 kN (817 lb)
SPECIFIC FUEL CONSUMPTION:
Max T-O (as above):
TFE731-2   13·88 mg/Ns (0·49 lb/h/lb st)
TFE731-3   14·33 mg/Ns (0·506 lb/h/lb st)
Cruise (as above):
TFE731-2   23·08 mg/Ns (0·815 lb/h/lb)
TFE731-3   23·65 mg/Ns (0·835 lb/h/lb)

GARRETT-AIRESEARCH/FLYGMOTOR TFE1042

This low-bypass derivative of the TFE731 is a joint project with Volvo Flygmotor of Sweden and is described in the International part of this section.

GARRETT-AIRESEARCH ETJ131

Evolving from Garrett's long turbocharger experience, the ETJ131 turbojet is designed for military applications such as low-cost decoys and target vehicles. Although details are not available, it is generally known that the design uses turbocharger components mated to a single-can combustor. In the 0·445 kN (100 lb) thrust class, the engine is described as "low-cost, with very simplified controls". Unofficial sources report the engine has been tested at 0·89 kN (200 lb) with an afterburner. The company designation is Model 1030, and it is based on the T18A turbocharger.

GARRETT-AIRESEARCH TJE341

In the 4·45 kN (1,000 lb) thrust class, the TJE341 turbojet is derived from earlier Garrett low-cost expendable engine technology and demonstration programmes. Intended initial application is in medium-range RPVs now under study. The TJE341 has a re-usable rating for recoverable RPVs, yet is expected to retain the overall simplicity and potentially low production cost that were design goals for earlier Garrett turbojets.

GARRETT-AIRESEARCH TPE331
US military designation: T76

Originally based upon extensive experience with APUs, this was the first AiResearch engine for aircraft propulsion; it has since been the main product which has helped to provide funding for later engines. The military T76 has achieved only modest sales, but the civil TPE331 has been most successful and developed in a series of versions. Deliveries in mid-1980 were at the rate of more than 55 engines per month, and total deliveries then exceeded 7,000. Flight time exceeded 17,000,000 h.

The following are major versions:
TPE331 series I, II. Initial production version, FAA certificated in February 1965. Rated at 451 ekW; 429 kW plus 0·33 kN (605 ehp; 575 shp plus 75 lb st). Redesignated TPE331-25/61 and -25/71 and produced until 1970. Powers Mitsubishi MU-2 (A to E models), Fairchild Industries/Pilatus Porter, Carstedt Jet Liner, Volpar Super Turbo 18, Aerospace FU-24, Rockwell International Hawk Commander and 680 and DHC-2 Turbo Beaver.
TPE331-1 series. Certificated December 1967 at 526 ekW; 496 kW plus 0·44 kN (705 ehp; 665 shp plus 100 lb st). Powers Mitsubishi MU-2 (F and G), Pilatus Turbo-Porter and Fairchild Industries AU-23A Peacemaker, Mid West CJ600, Volpar Turboliner, Interceptor 400, Rockwell International Turbo Commander and (customer option) Thrush Commander, Swearingen Merlin IIB, Aerospace Fletcher 1284, Marsh Turbo Thrush and Marsh Turbo Ag-Cat.
TPE331-2 series. The -201 was certificated in December 1967 at 563 ekW; 533 kW plus 0·45 kN (755 ehp; 715 shp plus 102 lb st). Powers Shorts Skyvan, CASA 212 pre-series and Volpar Turbo Goose and Turbo Beaver.
TPE331-3 series. Certificated in March 1970 at 674 ekW; 626 kW plus 0·71 kN (904 ehp; 840 shp plus 159 lb st). Uprated gas generator with increased airflow and pressure ratio, but same turbine temperature as in original TPE 331. Powers Swearingen Merlin III, IV and Metro, and Century Jetstream III.
TPE331-5/6 series. The -251 was certificated in March 1970; this matches the gas generator of the -3 series with the 715 shp gearbox, and is flat-rated to 2,134 m (7,000 ft). Powers Shorts Skyvan 3 (-201), Beech King Air B100 (-252), CASA 212 Aviocar (-251) and Rockwell International Turbo Commander 690A (-251). The -5 designation indicates output speed of 1,591 rpm; the -6 has an output speed of 2,000 rpm.
TPE331-8. Matches compressor and gearbox of -251 with new turbine section. Thermodynamic power of 676 ekW; 645 kW (865 shp plus 47·7 kg, 105 lb st), but flat rated at 533 kW (715 shp) to 36°C. Certification was received in September 1976. Powers Cessna Conquest.
TPE331-9. Rated at 645 kW (865 shp).
TPE331-10. Rated at 746 kW (1,000 shp). Certificated February 1978 and for use in new MU-2 models, Merlin IIIB, Jetstream and CASA 212.
TPE331-14. Since 1979 Garrett-AiResearch has analysed the market and launched an uprated TPE331 to meet future needs. It is essentially a scaled-up model, with thermodynamic power in the 1,118 kW (1,500 shp) class, and will be available either with an existing gearbox as a flat-rated engine or with a new gearbox matched to the uprated gas-generator. Development and production are in partnership with Volvo Flygmotor of Sweden which, on a risk-sharing basis, will produce the compressor structure and combustor module. Certification and initial production are scheduled for the third quarter of 1982.
T76. Military engine, with gas generator similar to TPE331-1 series but with front end inverted, to give inlet above instead of below spinner. Two versions, originally designated T76-G-10 and G-12 and restyled G-410 and G-411, respectively giving clockwise and anticlockwise propeller rotation (seen from rear). Development near completion of revised T76-G-420/421 rated at 776 kW (1,040 shp), with certification in September 1976. All models power Rockwell International OV-10 Bronco.

Except for the TPE331-14 all versions of the TPE331 and T76 are of similar frame size, and the following data apply generally to both models:
TYPE: Single-shaft turboprop.

Garrett-AiResearch ETJ131 low-cost turbojet for short-life applications (0·445 kN; 100 lb st class). The air inlet is on the left, and the combustor at upper right

Garrett-AiResearch TPE331 series commercial turboprop engine. This has the air intake below the spinner, unlike the T76 military engines

PROPELLER DRIVE: Two-stage reduction gear, one helical spur and one planetary, with overall ratio of 20·865 : 1 or 26·3 : 1. Rotation clockwise or anticlockwise.

AIR INTAKE: Single scoop intake duct at top (T76) or bottom of engine, at front. Provision for bleed air de-icing.

COMPRESSOR: Tandem two-stage centrifugal type. Each impeller is single-sided, and is made from titanium. First-stage casing of magnesium, with aluminium diffuser. Second-stage casing and diffuser of stainless steel. Mass flow, 2·61 kg (5·78 lb)/s for 25/61, 25/71, 2·81 kg (6·2 lb)/s for -1, 2·80 kg (6·17 lb)/s for -2 and T76, 3·52 kg (7·75 lb)/s for -251 and 3·54 kg (7·8 lb)/s for -3. Pressure ratio 8·0 for 25/61, 25/71, 8·34 for -1, 8·54 for 2 and T76, 10·37 for -251 and -3.

COMBUSTION CHAMBER: Annular type of high-temperature alloy. High-energy capacitor discharge ignition. Igniter plug on turbine plenum.

FUEL SYSTEM: Woodward or Bendix control system for use with Beta propeller governing control system. Five radial primary nozzles in continuous operation. Ten axial simplex nozzles. Max fuel pressure 41·4 bars (600 lb/sq in).

FUEL GRADE (TPE331): Aviation turbine fuels ASTM designation D1655-64T types Jet A, Jet B and Jet A-1; MIL-F-5616-1, Grade JP-1.

FUEL GRADE (T76): MIL-L-5624F(2), Grades JP-4 and JP-5; MIL-G-5572, Grade 115/145.

NOZZLE GUIDE VANES: Axial vanes made from Inco 713C castings.

TURBINE: Three-stage axial-flow type. Discs of first two stages of Inco 100, third stage of Inco 713C, attached to shaft by curvic couplings. Blades cast integrally with

disc. Turbine inlet gas temperature, 987°C for 25/61, 25/71, 993°C for T76, 1,005°C for all other models.

JET PIPE: Fixed type, stainless steel.

ACCESSORIES: AND 20005 Type XV-B tachometer generator, AND 20002 Type XII-D starter/generator, AND 20010 Type XX-A propeller governor and AND 20001 Type XI-B hydraulic pump, all mounted on aft face of accessories case.

LUBRICATION SYSTEM: Medium-pressure dry sump system. Gerotor internal gear-type pressure and scavenge pumps. Normal oil supply pressure 6·90 bars (100 lb/sq in). Provision for automatic fuel filter anti-icing.

OIL SPECIFICATION: MIL-L-23699-(1) or MIL-L-7808.

MOUNTING: Five-point suspension. Three pads on aft face of accessory case, two pads at aft end of turbine plenum.

STARTING: Pad for 399A starter/generator on aft face of accessory case.

DIMENSIONS (approx):

Length overall:

TPE331	1,092 to 1,168 mm (43-46 in)
T76	1,118 mm (44 in)

Width:

TPE331	533 mm (21 in)
T76	483 mm (19 in)

Height:

TPE331	660 mm (26 in)
T76	686 mm (27 in)

WEIGHTS, DRY:

TPE331-25/61, 71	152 kg (335 lb)
TPE331-1, -2	152·5 kg (336 lb)
T76	155 kg (341 lb)
TPE331-251	163 kg (360 lb)
TPE331-3	161 kg (355 lb)

PERFORMANCE RATINGS:

T-O	see under model listings

Military (30 min):

T76-G-410/411	533 kW; 563 ekW (715 shp; 755 ehp)

Normal:

T76-G-410/411	485 kW; 514·5 ekW (650 shp; 690 ehp)

Max cruise (ISA, 3,050 m; 10,000 ft and 250 kt; 463 km/h; 288 mph):

TPE331-25/61, 71	332 kW (445 shp)
TPE331-1	404 kW (542 shp)
TPE331-2, T76	430 kW (577 shp)
TPE331-251, -3	530 kW (710 shp)

SPECIFIC FUEL CONSUMPTION:

At T-O rating:

TPE331-25/61, 71	111·5 μg/J (0·66 lb/h/shp)
TPE331-1	107·0 μg/J (0·633 lb/h/shp)
TPE331-2	99·4 μg/J (0·588 lb/h/shp)
TPE331-251	105·8 μg/J (0·626 lb/h/shp)
TPE331-3	99·7 μg/J (0·59 lb/h/shp)
T76-G-410/411	101·4 μg/J (0·60 lb/h/shp)

OIL CONSUMPTION:

Max	0·009 kg (0·02 lb)/h

GARRETT-AIRESEARCH TSE331-3U

This turboshaft, derived from the TPE331-3 turboprop, was certificated in April 1970. It powers the Sikorsky S-55T helicopter conversion certificated by Aviation Specialties Inc of Mesa, Arizona, flat rated at 522 kW (700 shp). Details were given in the 1979-80 *Jane's*.

GENERAL ELECTRIC
GENERAL ELECTRIC COMPANY AIRCRAFT ENGINE GROUP

Cincinnati, Ohio 45215

Telephone: (513) 243 2000

GROUP LOCATIONS: Lynn and Everett, Massachusetts; Cincinnati, Ohio; Rutland and Ludlow, Vermont; Hooksett, New Hampshire; Albuquerque, New Mexico and Madisonville, Kentucky. Also test facilities at Edwards Air Force Base, California, and Peebles, Ohio. Further facilities at Seattle, Washington; Arkansas City, Kansas; Ontario, California.

SENIOR VICE-PRESIDENT AND GROUP EXECUTIVE: B. H. Rowe

Military Engine Operations:
VICE-PRESIDENT AND GENERAL MANAGER: J. N. Krebs

Commercial Engine Operations:
VICE-PRESIDENT AND GENERAL MANAGER: J. E. Worsham

Engineering Division:
VICE-PRESIDENT AND GENERAL MANAGER: F. E. Pickering

Manufacturing Division:
VICE-PRESIDENT AND GENERAL MANAGER: R. F. Letts

Marine and Industrial Division:
GENERAL MANAGER: O. R. Bonner

Strategic Planning & Development Operation:
MANAGER: J. J. Kramer

Current products of the GE Aircraft Engine Group include the F101, F103, F404, J79, J85, T58, T64, T700 and TF34 for military use, and the CF6, CF34, CF700, CJ610, CT58, CT7 and CT64 for the commercial and general aviation market. In partnership with SNECMA of France a company was formed to develop and market the CFM56 turbofan, as described in the International part of this section under CFM International.

GENERAL ELECTRIC J79

Development of the J79, America's first high-compression variable-stator turbojet, began in 1952. In addition to US manufacture, it was produced by Orenda of Canada to power the Canadair CF-104/F-104G (MAP), by Ishikawajima-Harima in Japan for the licence-built F-104DJ, and by MTU of West Germany, Fiat of Italy and FN of Belgium for the European-built F-104G. The Italian production team, including Alfa Romeo, also produced the J79-GE-19, an improved engine similar to the J79-GE-17 but configured for the F-104S Starfighter. More than 17,000 J79s were built by GE and licensees by January 1980.

Derivatives of the J79 have been the CJ805-3 turbojet and CJ805-23 turbofan, powering the Convair 880 and 990 Coronado airliners, respectively, as well as the LM1500 industrial and marine gas turbine.

Versions of the J79 in service are as follows:

J79-GE-7A. Built under licence by Orenda (as J79-OEL-7) for Canadair CF-104.

J79-GE-8. McDonnell Douglas F-4B and RF-4B. Air mass flow 76·5 kg (169 lb)/s. Pressure ratio 12·9 : 1.

J79-GE-10. RA-5C and F-4J. Pressure ratio 13·5 : 1. Improved -10A has smoke-free combustor for F-4S.

J79-GE-11A. Lockheed F-104G. Built under licence in Japan (as J79-IHI-11A), West Germany, Italy, Belgium and Canada.

J79-GE-15. Powers F-4C, F-4D and RF-4C for USAF. Similar to J79-GE-8 except for self-contained starting.

General Electric J79-GE-17 turbojet (79·24 kN; 17,820 lb st with afterburning)

J79-GE-17. Similar to J79-GE-10, but for F-4E, F-4G, RF-4E, F-4EJ and F-4F.

J79-GE-19. F-104S and F-104A. Differs from J79-GE-10/17 only in external characteristics. Guided expansion jet nozzle. Afterburner provides continuous fuel-flow modulation from 1,225 kg (2,700 lb)/h to 15,420 kg (34,000 lb)/h; similar engine used in IAI Kfir.

Full details of the J79 can be found in the 1977-78 and 1978-79 editions of *Jane's*.

TYPE: Variable-stator single-shaft axial-flow turbojet.

AIR INTAKE: Annular type.

COMPRESSOR: Seventeen-stage axial-flow.

COMBUSTION CHAMBER: Cannular type consisting of 10 combustion cans.

FUEL SYSTEM: Hydromechanical.

FUEL GRADE: JP-4 or JP-5.

TURBINE: Three-stage.

DIMENSIONS:

Length overall:

J79-GE-7A, 11A	5,283 mm (207·96 in)
J79-GE-8	5,295 mm (208·45 in)
J79-GE-10, 17, 19	5,301 mm (208·69 in)

Diameter at compressor:

J79-GE 7A, 8, 11A, 15	973 mm (38·3 in)
J79-GE-10, 17, 19	992 mm (39·06 in)

WEIGHT, DRY:

J79-GE-7A	1,644 kg (3,625 lb)
J79-GE-8	1,676 kg (3,695 lb)
J79-GE-10	1,749 kg (3,855 lb)
J79-GE-11A	1,658 kg (3,655 lb)
J79-GE-15	1,678 kg (3,699 lb)
J79-GE-17, 19	1,745 kg (3,846 lb)

PERFORMANCE RATINGS:

T-O, with afterburning:

J79-GE-7A, 11A	70·3 kN (15,800 lb st)
J79-GE-8, 15	75·6 kN (17,000 lb st)
J79-GE-10, 17, 19	79·24 kN (17,820 lb st)

Military:

J79-GE-7A, 11A	44·5 kN (10,000 lb st)
J79-GE-8, 15	48·5 kN (10,900 lb st)
J79-GE-10, 17, 19	52·5 kN (11,810 lb st)

Cruise:

J79-GE-7A, 11A	11·8 kN (2,650 lb st)
J79-GE-8, 10, 15, 17, 19	11·6 kN (2,600 lb st)

SPECIFIC FUEL CONSUMPTION:

At T-O rating:

J79-GE-7A, 11A	55·8 mg/Ns (1·97 lb/h/lb st)
J79-GE-8	54·67 mg/Ns (1·93 lb/h/lb st)
J79-GE-15	55·1 mg/Ns (1·945 lb/h/lb st)
J79-GE-10, 17, 19	55·66 mg/Ns (1·965 lb/h/lb st)

At military rating:

J79-GE-8, 15	24·36 mg/Ns (0·86 lb/h/lb st)
J79-GE-7A, 10, 11A, 17, 19	23·79 mg/Ns (0·84 lb/h/lb st)

At cruise rating:

J79-GE-7A, 8, 11A, 15	29·74 mg/Ns (1·05 lb/h/lb st)
J79-GE-10, 17, 19	26·91 mg/Ns (0·95 lb/h/lb st)

GENERAL ELECTRIC J85

The following are major versions of the J85 small military turbojet, the -21 being the main production version. By 1979 more than 12,000 J85 engines had been delivered to air forces in 26 nations.

General Electric J85-21 turbojet (22·2 kN; 5,000 lb st with afterburning)

J85-4A. Powers the Rockwell International T-2C Buckeye trainer.

J85-5. Afterburning version with 6·6 : 1 thrust-to-weight ratio; powers Northrop T-38 Talon supersonic trainer.

J85-13. Developed from J85-5, with increased turbine inlet temperature for Northrop F-5A/B supersonic fighter. As the J85-13A, licence-built by Alfa Romeo, also powers Aeritalia G91Y.

J85-15. Version of J85-13 with improved turbine and hydraulically actuated exhaust nozzle to power CF-5 and NF-5. Manufactured under licence in Canada by Orenda.

J85-17A/B. Powers Saab 105G attack/reconnaissance aircraft and Cessna A-37B attack aircraft. Also used as take-off and climb booster for Fairchild C-123K and AC-119K.

J85-21. Higher airflow version with zero stage to give total of nine compressor stages. Equipped with afterburner for supersonic aircraft. Powers Northrop F-5E/F Tiger II.

J85/J1. Non-afterburning derivative with nine-stage compressor.

Civil version of the J85 is the CJ610 turbojet, to which the aft-fan CF700 turbofan is closely related. Both are described separately.

The following data refer specifically to the J85-21:

TYPE: Single-shaft turbojet.

AIR INTAKE: Annular type, surrounding central bullet fairing. Variable-incidence inlet guide vanes, with hot-air anti-icing.

COMPRESSOR: Nine-stage axial-flow type, with variable inlet guide vanes and first three stator stages. Titanium rotor blades, first two stages having part-span shrouds. Discs joined at periphery. Casing in upper and lower halves. Pressure ratio approximately 8·3 : 1. Air mass flow 24·0 kg (53·0 lb)/s.

COMBUSTION CHAMBER: Annular type with perforated liner. Twelve duplex fuel injectors. Ports in outer casing facilitate inspection of liner.

TURBINE: Two-stage axial-flow type. Casing is in halves, split horizontally. Turbine inlet temperature 977°C.

AFTERBURNER: Consists of a diffuser and a combustor. A pilot burner with four spraybars and a main burner of 12 spraybars are located in the diffuser section. Combustion is initiated by a single igniter plug and is then self-sustained. Nozzle position governs exit area and is regulated automatically by the afterburner control system as a function of turbine exit temperature and throttle lever position.

LUBRICATION: Positive displacement, pressurised recirculating type.

STARTING: Air impingement starter on afterburning engines. Provision for starter/generator on non-afterburning engines.

DIMENSIONS:
Length overall   2,858 mm (112·5 in)
Max diameter   533 mm (21·0 in)
WEIGHT, DRY:
J85-21   310 kg (684 lb)
PERFORMANCE RATINGS:
Max rating, with afterburner   22·2 kN (5,000 lb st)
Military rating, without afterburner:
                          15·6 kN (3,500 lb st)
SPECIFIC FUEL CONSUMPTION:
At max rating, with afterburner:
                          60·3 mg/Ns (2·13 lb/h/lb st)
At military rating, without afterburner:
                          28·3 mg/Ns (1·00 lb/h/lb st)

GENERAL ELECTRIC CJ610

Announced in May 1960, the CJ610 is a power plant tailored for commercial and executive aircraft of 5,700-7,500 kg (12,500-16,500 lb) gross weight. It is essentially similar to the basic J85 turbojet, without afterburner.

By January 1979, a total of 1,850 CJ610s had accumulated more than 5,000,000 h. TBO reached 4,000 h in 1977.

There are seven versions:

CJ610-1, CJ610-4. Initial production versions, differing only in accessory gearbox location.

CJ610-5, CJ610-6. Developed versions of -1 and -4 respectively, providing increased T-O thrust. Power Gates

Learjet 24D, 25B and 25C, Hansa and IAI Westwind 1121.

CJ610-8, CJ610-9. Developed for production deliveries beginning in 1969. Power Hansa, IAI Westwind 1123 and NAL (Japan) experimental VTOL.

CJ610-8A. FAA certificated in April 1977 for operation at up to 15,500 m (51,000 ft), to give better economy and over-weather capability to Learjet Century III 24E, 24F, 25D and 25F. Main differences are longer-life turbine and turbine-nozzle area change.

DIMENSIONS:
Length overall:
CJ610-1, -5, -9   1,298 mm (51·1 in)
CJ610-4, -6, -8, -8A   1,153 mm (45·4 in)
Max flange diameter   449 mm (17·7 in)
WEIGHT, DRY:
CJ610-1   181 kg (399 lb)
CJ610-4   176 kg (389 lb)
CJ610-5   183 kg (402 lb)
CJ610-6   180 kg (396 lb)
CJ610-8, -8A   185 kg (407 lb)
CJ610-9   191 kg (421 lb)
PERFORMANCE RATINGS (guaranteed):
T-O:
CJ610-1, -4   12·7 kN (2,850 lb st)
CJ610-5, -6, -8A   13·1 kN (2,950 lb st)
CJ610-8, -9   13·8 kN (3,100 lb st)
Max continuous:
CJ610-1, -4   12 kN (2,700 lb st)
CJ610-5, -6   12·4 kN (2,780 lb st)
CJ610-8, -9   13 kN (2,925 lb st)
CJ610-8A   12·7 kN (2,850 lb st)
SPECIFIC FUEL CONSUMPTION:
At T-O rating:
CJ610-1, -4   28·05 mg/Ns (0·99 lb/h/lb st)
CJ610-5, -6, -8, -9   27·75 mg/Ns (0·98 lb/h/lb st)
CJ610-8A   27·5 mg/Ns (0·97 lb/h/lb st)
At max continuous rating:
CJ610-1, -4, -8A   27·5 mg/Ns (0·97 lb/h/lb st)
CJ610-5, -6   27·2 mg/Ns (0·96 lb/h/lb st)
CJ610-8, -9   27·2 mg/Ns (0·96 lb/h/lb st)

GENERAL ELECTRIC CF700

Like the CJ610 turbojet, the CF700 is also derived from the J85 engine. Utilising the same gas generator, it is an aft-fan turbofan suitable for military and commercial aircraft. Since it can be tilted while in steady-state operation and operate vertically, it affords lift/cruise capability in VTOL aircraft.

FAA certification of the original version was received on 1 July 1964. The uprated CF700-2D was certificated in early 1968. The CF700-2D has an improved compressor turbine with higher thermodynamic efficiency. The CF700-2D2 incorporates a new design of tailpipe.

General Electric CF700-2D turbofan (18·9 kN; 4,250 lb st)

General Electric CJ610-4 (12·7 kN; 2,850 lb st) and (right) CJ610-5 (13·1 kN; 2,950 lb st) turbojet engines

CF700 engines power the Dassault-Breguet Falcon 20 and Rockwell Sabre 75A executive transports. By 1974 the TBO had reached 3,000 h. By January 1979 more than 1,100 CF700s had flown 3,000,000 h.

The general description of the J85 turbojet applies also to the CF700, with the following additional assembly:

AFT FAN: Single-stage free-floating fan. Bypass ratio 1·6 : 1. Mass air flow through fan 39·9 kg (88·0 lb)/s.

DIMENSIONS:

Overall length, compressor nose to tailcone tip	1,912 mm (75·57 in)
Length, flange to flange	1,361 mm (53·6 in)
Max diameter	840·4 mm (33·1 in)
Max diameter less fan	447 mm (17·6 in)

WEIGHT, DRY:

CF700-2C	330 kg (725 lb)
CF700-2D, -2D2	334 kg (737 lb)

PERFORMANCE RATINGS:

Max T-O (flat-rated to 30°C):

CF700-2C	18·35 kN (4,125 lb st)
CF700-2D	18·90 kN (4,250 lb st)
CF700-2D2	20·02 kN (4,500 lb st)

Max continuous:

CF700-2C	17·8 kN (4,000 lb st)
CF700-2D, 2D2	18·3 kN (4,120 lb st)

SPECIFIC FUEL CONSUMPTION:

Max T-O:

CF700-2C, -2D, -2D2	18·4 mg/Ns (0·65 lb/h/lb st)

Max continuous:

CF700-2C, -2D	18·4 mg/Ns (0·65 lb/h/lb st)
CF700-2D2	18·1 mg/Ns (0·64 lb/h/lb st)

GENERAL ELECTRIC F404

The F404 is an advanced technology augmented turbofan described as being "in the 16,000 lb thrust class". It is the US Navy derivative of the YJ101 engine flown in the US Air Force's YF-17 aircraft (see 1975-76 Jane's). The changed designation from J to F (turbofan) reflects a higher bypass ratio, and the number in the 400-series indicates funding by the US Navy.

In contrast, the YJ101 was funded by the US Air Force, in April 1972, to power the twin-engined Northrop YF-17 Air Combat Fighter. Seven engines in two YF-17 prototypes logged 719 h in 302 flights. These test flights explored a large part of the flight envelope, and a maximum of Mach 2·05 was reached at 12,500 m (41,000 ft). All engine commitments were achieved during the seven-month YF-17 flight programme.

In May 1975 the US Navy selected the McDonnell Douglas/Northrop team to develop its Navy Air Combat Fighter (NACF), designated F-18 Hornet. The F-18 is a derivative of the YF-17, powered by two F404 engines. The F404 has been selected also for the single-engined F-5G export fighter, currently under development by Northrop.

Compared with that of the J101, the F404 fan diameter is increased less than 25·4 mm (1·0 in) while increasing the bypass ratio from 0·20 to 0·34. The fan is driven by a slightly larger LP turbine. The technology, and the core, comprising the HP compressor, combustion chamber and HP turbine, remain the same.

First F404 engine test took place one month ahead of schedule in January 1977 and soon demonstrated sea-level production performance. Preliminary flight rating test took place in May 1978 and first F-18 flight took place

General Electric F404 augmented turbofan (71·2 kN; 16,000 lb st class)

in November 1978. Nine engines were delivered in 1978 and 24 in 1979, and MQT (Model Qualification Test) was completed in July 1979. The first production delivery took place in January 1980.

TYPE: Two-shaft augmented low-ratio turbofan (turbojet with continuous bypass bleed).

AIR INTAKE: Plain annular. Fixed central bullet, fixed and variable inlet vanes.

FAN: Three-stage axial. Outer flow diverted to bypass duct. Bypass ratio 0·34. Airflow 63·5 kg (140 lb)/s.

HP COMPRESSOR: Seven-stage axial. Overall pressure ratio, 25 : 1 class.

COMBUSTION CHAMBER: Single-piece annular.

HP TURBINE: Single-stage axial. Highly loaded aircooled blades.

LP TURBINE: Single-stage axial.

EXHAUST SYSTEM: Close-coupled high-augmentation afterburner with combustion in both core and bypass flows. Convergent-divergent exhaust nozzle with hydraulic actuation.

CONTROL SYSTEM: Electrical-hydromechanical.

DIMENSIONS:

Length overall	4,030 mm (158·8 in)
Max diameter	880 mm (34·8 in)

WEIGHT, DRY: approx 908 kg (2,000 lb)

PERFORMANCE RATING:

Max T-O	71·2 kN (16,000 lb st) class

GENERAL ELECTRIC TF34

It was announced in April 1968 that the US Naval Air Systems Command had awarded General Electric a contract for development of the TF34. This high bypass ratio turbofan had won a 1965 US Navy competition aimed at providing a tailor-made engine in the 40 kN (9,000 lb st) category for the VS(X) aircraft by 1972 within a budget of $96 million. In August 1972 the TF34-GE-2, the initial variant for the VS(X) application (the Lockheed S-3A Viking), completed its Model Qualification Test (MQT)

and subsequently entered production. The S-3A entered fleet service in February 1974, and GE and the US Navy have defined a 4,000 h TBO extension programme.

In January 1975 GE began shipment of the TF34-GE-400A, which replaced the GE-2 as S-3A engine. The later model incorporates various improvements, with changed external piping, an adaptive control system for optimising accessory power extraction, and a simplified rocket gas ingestion system.

In 1970 the TF34 was selected to power the twin-engined Fairchild Republic A-10A Thunderbolt II attack aircraft to compete in the AX competition. The A-10A application led in July 1972 to an Air Force contract for development of the TF34-GE-100. This was re-engineered to minimise unit price. It has a long fan duct and side mountings. The GE-100 flew in the first A-10A in May 1972. The A-10A won the AX competition, and the TF34-GE-100 was formally qualified for production in October 1974.

In 1974 a third version of the TF34, most nearly resembling the GE-2, was selected to provide auxiliary (thrust) power for the Sikorsky S-72 RSRA (Rotor Systems Research Aircraft) for NASA and the US Army.

TYPE: Two-shaft high bypass ratio turbofan.

AIR INTAKE: Plain annular intake. No fixed inlet struts or guide vanes. Small spinner rotates with fan.

FAN: Single-stage fan has blades forged in titanium, without part-span shrouds. Blades replaceable with engine installed. Performance at max S/L rating, mass flow 153 kg (338 lb)/s at 7,365 rpm with pressure ratio 1·5. Bypass ratio 6·2.

COMPRESSOR: 14-stage axial on HP shaft. Inlet guide vanes and first five stators variable. First nine rotor stages titanium, remainder high-nickel alloy. Performance at max S/L rating, core airflow 21·3 kg (47 lb)/s at 17,900 rpm with pressure ratio 14 : 1, overall engine pressure ratio 21.

COMBUSTION CHAMBER: Annular Hastelloy chamberliner and front dome, providing ports for primer nozzles, igniters and 18 carburetting burners.

TURBINE: Two-stage HP gas generator turbine with convection-cooled rotor blades and stator vanes, the first-stage nozzle vanes having film and impingement cooling. Four-stage LP fan turbine with tip-shrouded blades. Turbine entry gas temperature 1,225°C maximum.

FUEL SYSTEM: Contamination-resistant, carburetting type. Integrated hydromechanical control unit with electronic amplifier. Fuel grade JP-4 or JP-5.

ACCESSORY DRIVES: Engine and customer accessories mounted around horseshoe-shaped gearbox, fitting closely around lower half of compressor casing. Radial shaft drive from front of HP shaft.

LUBRICATION: Enclosed, pressurised, dual system with vent along centre shaft.

DIMENSIONS:

Max diameter:

TF34-GE-400A	1,326 mm (52·2 in)
TF34-GE-100	1,259 mm (48·6 in)
Basic length (both)	2,540 mm (100·0 in)

WEIGHT, DRY:

TF34-GE-400A	661 kg (1,458 lb)
TF34-GE-100	647 kg (1,427 lb)

PERFORMANCE RATINGS:

Max T-O (S/L, static):

TF34-GE-400A	41·3 kN (9,275 lb st)
TF34-GE-100	40·3 kN (9,065 lb st)

SPECIFIC FUEL CONSUMPTION:

Max T-O, S/L static:

TF34-GE-400A	10·3 mg/Ns (0·363 lb/h/lb st)
TF34-GE-100	10·5 mg/Ns (0·370 lb/h/lb st)

GENERAL ELECTRIC CF34

In April 1976 General Electric's General Aviation Engine Department, at Lynn, announced the CF34 as a new turbofan in the 31-36 kN (7,000-8,000 lb st) class for

General Electric TF34-GE-400A turbofan of 41·3 kN; 9,275 lb st

business and commercial aircraft. A natural derivative of the military TF34 at Cincinnati, the CF34 is closely similar to the TF34-100, but with external configuration tailored to FAA and customer requirements.

Total fan airflow is 139 kg (307 lb)/s, with pressure ratio 1·4. Core pressure ratio is 12·5, giving overall pressure ratio of 17·5. Bypass ratio is 6·3.

In January 1980 the CF34 was selected by Canadair to power the Challenger E. It is also available for other Challengers.

DIMENSIONS: As TF34-100
WEIGHT, DRY: 692 kg (1,525 lb)
PERFORMANCE RATINGS:
  T-O (S/L static)
        35·5 kN (7,990 lb st) flat-rated to 22·8°C
  Cruise (11,000 m; 36,000 ft at Mach 0·8)
                                            7·83 kN (1,760 lb)
SPECIFIC FUEL CONSUMPTION:
  T-O, as above   10·18 mg/Ns (0·359 lb/h/lb st)
  Cruise, as above   19·48 mg/Ns (0·687 lb/h/lb)

GENERAL ELECTRIC CF6
US military designation (CF6-50E): F103-GE-100

On 11 September 1967 General Electric announced the commitment of corporate funding for development of the CF6 turbofan for the then-forthcoming generation of wide-body transports. From the initial family of 142 to 160 kN (32,000 lb to 36,000 lb st) CF6 two-shaft engines announced in September 1967 to cover the anticipated thrust requirements of the Lockheed and McDonnell Douglas airbus projects, the CF6 evolved through a series of variants to the CF6-6D, flat rated at 178 kN (40,000 lb) to 31°C and tailored to the McDonnell Douglas DC-10 Series 10 intermediate-range transport. Announcement that this engine had been selected by United Air Lines and American Airlines was made on 25 April 1968. Further orders have since been placed by many airlines for the CF6-6, 45, 50 and 80 series.

Basic configuration of the CF6-6 comprises a '1¼-stage' fan driven by a five-stage LP turbine energised by a slightly modified TF39 core engine, consisting of a 16-stage HP compressor, annular combustor and two-stage turbine. Modifications have been introduced to enable the accessory systems to suit airline installation requirements, while other changes are aimed at enhancing reliability, durability and maintainability.

A typical General Electric CF6-50 series turbofan, rated at up to 233·5 kN (52,500 lb st)

CF6-6D. Initial 178 kN (40,000 lb st) version of engine in production for intermediate-range DC-10 Series 10. First ran on 21 October 1968 and 18 days later attained 203·5 kN (45,750 lb st). Following a series of successful factory and outdoor tests, engine was released for production in February 1969. The second CF6-6D, built to the production configuration, first ran in May 1969. By December 1970 a total of 30 engines had been shipped and flight testing with a single engine hung on the starboard inner pylon of a B-52 had extended to 15,250 m

Features of the General Electric CF6-80A

Features of the General Electric CF6-32

(50,000 ft), Mach 0·896 and 420 knots (779 km/h; 484 mph) indicated airspeed. Delivery of flight test engines to McDonnell Douglas started in late 1969, with aircraft first flight following in September 1970. Certification of the CF6-6D for commercial service was granted by the FAA in September 1970, and the engine entered airline service in the DC-10 Series 10 in August 1971.

CF6-6D1. In August 1971 this growth version was FAA certificated and offered to take advantage of the demonstrated margin of the -6D. The D1 rating is increased by 1,000 lb to 182·4 kN (41,000 lb st) at 28·9°C. By 1979 more than 400 -6D and -6D1 engines had been delivered.

CF6-6K. This new version of the -6D1, rated at 184·6 kN (41,500 lb st) at 31·1°C, is planned for certification in June 1981. It features improved sfc, improved performance retention and further improved reliability, and is planned for applications currently using CF6-6D1 engines. Mechanical changes include improved-performance fan, -50 type HP turbine and external-case LP turbine case cooling.

CF6-32. This simplified, reduced-thrust engine, rated at 162 kN (36,500 lb st), is a joint programme with SNECMA (France), Volvo (Sweden) and Alfa Romeo (Italy) and is intended primarily to power the Boeing 757. It is covered here because it is a GE-controlled programme, the foreign partners having only manufacturing responsibility. Volvo is responsible for HP compressor and HP turbine components. SNECMA is responsible for the LP turbine, turbine rear frame and accessory gearbox, and Alfa Romeo is manufacturing components.

The core is that of the CF6-6K, mated with a smaller fan with 36 blades. The LP booster is removed, together with the turbine mid-frame. HP turbine blades and vanes are of CF6-50 type but operated at -6K speed and temperature. The LP turbine has only four stages and a casing with no horizontal split line. The new 757-tailored gearbox is under the fan case.

FAN: Diameter 1,938 mm (76·3 in); mass flow 501 kg (1,104 lb)/s; bypass ratio 4·9. Overall engine pressure ratio 24·4.

CF6-45A and -45B. Economical derated CF6-50E (described later) giving flat rating of 206·8 kN (46,500 lb st) to 36·1°C (-45A for 747SR) or 43·3°C (-45B for 747SP).

CF6-50A. Announced by GE in January 1969, the 218 kN (49,000 lb st) CF6-50A is a growth version of the CF6-6. The increased thrust is achieved by increased flow through the core engine (reducing the bypass ratio from 5·9 to 4·4) at slightly decreased turbine entry temperature. A major change is the introduction of two additional stages behind the single-stage LP compressor of the CF6-6, with no change in the turbofan's external dimensions. To provide for flow matching between the two rotors, variable bypass doors are incorporated between the LP and HP compressors. A 41 per cent scale model fan with three-stage compressor and variable bypass doors started testing in January 1969. In October 1970 a CF6-50A attained a thrust of 258 kN (58,000 lb) in a test cell at 5·6°C. FAA certification testing was completed in March 1972. The CF6-50A entered airline service in December 1972 in the DC-10 Series 30. The CF6-50 series also powers the Airbus Industrie A300 and some versions of the Boeing 747.

Labels for CF6-80A diagram:
- Higher Flow Fan Blade
- Shorter Low Pressure Shaft
- Active Clearance Control
- New Low Pressure Turbine
- Improved Booster
- Improved High Pressure Compressor
- Shorter Diffuser
- Shorter Combustor
- No Turbine Mid-Frame

Labels for CF6-32 diagram:
- Scaled CF6 Fan
- CF6-50 Type High Pressure Turbine
- New 4 Stage Low Pressure Turbine
- No Booster
- New Gearbox
- Common CF6-6D2C/-32 Core
- No Turbine Mid-frame

CF6-50C. The CF6-50C is rated at 226·8 kN (51,000 lb st) up to 30°C. Higher thrust is provided by an increase in turbine temperature, with improved cooling of hot-section components. Certificated November 1973.

CF6-50C1/E1. Rated 233·5 kN (52,500 lb st) to 30°C.

CF6-50C2/E2. Similar to C1 and E1 but improved SFC and EGT margins and new fan case and blades with improved bird-strike resistance. Certification 1978.

CF6-50E. (Military designation **F103-GE-100**). This engine is rated to give 233·5 kN (52,500 lb st) up to 26°C. Certificated November 1973. Powers some versions of Boeing 747-200 and E-4A.

CF6-80. New family of engines, with significant sfc improvement, derived from the CF6-50. Thrust ratings from 196 kN (44,000 lb st) (-80AR) to 240 kN (54,000 lb st) (-80B) and 249 kN (56,100 lb st) (-80C) are possible with the current fan size and engine configuration. These engines are shorter because of elimination of the turbine mid-frame, a new combustor and compressor rear frame, and a totally new LP turbine with only four stages of increasing diameter. Fan blades are improved, the all-steel compressor has long-life variable-stator bushings and the booster is improved. The -80B has increased airflow and reduced bypass ratio, and the -80C has a larger fan driven by a five-stage turbine. Launched November 1977 as choice of American and Delta for 767-200 at 213 kN (48,000 lb st) (-80A) and adopted for Airbus A310. Engines for the 767 have accessories mounted on the core, while A310 engines have accessories on the fan case. First engine was run 21 October 1979, and achieved a thrust of 246 kN (55,500 lb st). Certification is due in 1981.

By December 1979 CF6-6 engines had accumulated over 6,265,000 h. Engine-attributable three-month in-flight shut-down rate was 0·04 per 1,000 h. During the same time period CF6-50 engines had accumulated over 8,207,500 h with the same engine-attributable in-flight shutdown rate.

The following data relate to the CF6-6D, with the differing features of the CF6-50 series also detailed.

TYPE: Two-shaft high bypass ratio commercial turbofan.

AIR INTAKE: Single forward-facing annular configuration.

FAN: Single-stage fan with integrally-mounted single-stage LP compressor (described together as a 1¼-stage fan), both driven by LP turbine. Fan has rotating spinner and omits inlet guide vanes. Blade-containment shroud provided against possible blade failure. The 38 fan rotor blades are individually removable from the thick-section disc bolted to forward conical extension of LP shaft system. Blade aerofoil has anti-vibration shrouds at two-thirds span. Fan exit airflow split between LP compressor and fan slipstream. Fan frame has 12 radial struts across fan slipstream exit. Fan frame provides support for LP and HP rotor front bearings, fan being overhung ahead of large-diameter ball-thrust bearing with rear roller bearing ahead of core engine. Blades, discs, spool of titanium; exit guide vanes of aluminium; fan frame and shaft of steel; spinner and fan case of aluminium alloy. Total airflow 591 kg/s (1,303 lb/s), bypass ratio 5·7. Configuration of CF6-50 is similar but with two added LP stages and bypass doors (described below). Total airflow 658 kg (1,450 lb)/s; bypass ratio 4·3. CF6-80B, 680 kg (1,500 lb)/s; -80C, 737 kg (1,624 lb)/s. Bypass ratio, -80B, 4·28; -80C, 4·69.

LP COMPRESSOR: Single-stage compressor acting as booster to airflow into core engine. Rotor blades carried on rear rim of tapered drum bolted to rear of fan disc. Stators cantilevered off short-chord shroud ring, supported by radial outer struts and radial/tangential inner struts located on fan front frame. Compressor exit flow free to balance between core engine and fan slipstream exit. Configuration of CF6-50 modified to three compressor booster stages carried on flanged rotor drum. Continuous shroud extends to fan front frame with 12 integral bypass doors located between canted radial struts in fan exit inner casing. These doors maintain proper flow matching between the fan/LP system and core by opening at low power settings to permit LP supercharged flow to bleed into the fan airstream. The doors are closed during take-off and cruise.

HP COMPRESSOR: Sixteen-stage compressor of near-constant tip diameter, with inlet guide vanes and first six stator rows having variable incidence. Provision for interstage air bleed for airframe use and engine cooling. Rotor is of combined drum-and-disc construction with front stage and rear three stages overhung on conical shaft providing location on HP front bearing and HP main shaft. All rotor blades held in rabbeted discs and individually replaceable without rotor disassembly. Stages 1-7 blades forged titanium, 8-16 steel. Stages 1-10 disc titanium, 11-16 and aft casing Inconel 718. Casing split on horizontal centreline: stator vanes held in dovetail slots and replaceable individually. All blading now steel. Double-skin inner casing shrouds the LP main shaft. Outlet frame contains compressor diffuser and incorporates support structure for HP rotor mid-bearings. Overall pressure ratio (T-O), 24·3 (6D), 24·9 (6D1). Core airflow (-6D) 88 kg (194 lb)/s. CF6-50A has 15th and 16th stages removed to pass greater core airflow of 125 kg (276 lb)/s and reduce pressure and

temperature of air entering combustion chamber. Titanium blades in stages 1-5, steel 6-14. Overall pressure ratio (T-O), 27·1 (45B), 28·4 (50A), 29·13 (50C), 30·1 (50E).

COMBUSTOR: Fully annular with comprehensive film-cooling. Separate snout, dome and inner/outer skirts, with nozzles, igniter, leads and manifold externally removable. Dome contains ports for two igniters and axial swirler cups for 30 fuel nozzles. Igniters of high-voltage surface-gap type with energy level of 2·0 joules, each igniter operated independently. Forged steel nozzles with liner of Hastelloy X. Nozzle and dome designed to minimise smoke, and entrance diffuser has gradual profile to assure low temperature gradient to turbine under all flight conditions. CF6-50 combustor is shorter, of improved material (HS 18-8), and can be removed with fuel nozzles in place.

HP TURBINE: Two-stage aircooled turbine with 1,330°C entry temperature. Rotor blades are film and convection cooled. Rotor blades cast from René 80; discs and forward and rear shafts of Inconel 718. First-stage nozzle guide vanes supported at inner and outer ends, second-stage cantilevered from outer ends, with inner ends carrying interstage labyrinth seals. First-stage vanes cast from X40 and film cooled by compressor discharge pressure. Second-stage vanes are cast from René 80 material and are convection cooled. Vanes are welded into pairs to decrease number of gas leakage paths. Thin-section discs with heavy-section centreless hubs are bolted to front and rear conical shafts, including conical and arched inter-disc diaphragms. Configuration for CF6-50 is similar but introduces improved materials and cooling, and blades are not Siamesed but individual.

LP TURBINE: Five-stage constant tip-diameter turbine with nominal 871°C inlet temperature. Rotor blades tip-shrouded and cast in René 77, not aircooled. Forward and rear shafts, case and discs of Inconel 718. First-stage nozzle guide vanes supported at inner and outer ends, remaining stages are cantilevered from outer ends, with inner ends carrying inter-stage labyrinth seals. Stages 1-3 guide vanes cast in six-vane segments in René 77, stages 4 and 5 cast in pairs in René 41. Vanes held in slots machined in the two half-stator casing. Drum and centreless disc construction, located on LP rotor by front and rear conical shafts attached to third- and fourth-stage discs. Drive to rotor by means of long fan midshaft. On CF6-50 a four-stage LP turbine is used, all stages being modified in geometry and cooled by 7th HP-stage compressor air instead of 9th. CF6-80, new four-stage turbine.

EXHAUST UNIT (FAN): Fixed-area annular duct with outer cowl and engine cowl forming convergent plug nozzle for fan slipstream.

EXHAUST UNIT (TURBINE): Short-length fixed-area exhaust duct with convergent plug nozzle. Provision for exhaust thrust reverser.

THRUST REVERSER (FAN): Annular cascade reverser with blocker doors across fan duct. For reverse thrust, rear portion of fan outer cowl translates aft on rotating ballscrews to uncover cascade vanes. Blocker doors (16) flush-mounted in cowl on link arms hinged in inner cowl, rotate inwards to expose cascade vanes and block fan duct. Reverser hinged at top to open in L/R halves for access to HP casing and combustor.

THRUST REVERSER (TURBINE): Post nozzle exit, cascade type. Two cascade screens are mounted in vertical plane on fixed pivot aft of turbine exhaust and are enclosed in fairing forming aerofoil-shaped plug. Aft translation of fairing uncovers cascades which open across nozzle exit and divert turbine exhaust radially outward and slightly forward in horizontal plane. Configuration for CF6-50 similar to fan thrust reverser with nine blocker doors, but not split. CF6-50 available with long fixed core nozzle; short nozzle also designed, for performance

General Electric F101-DFE engines are being built at Evendale for flight-test programmes in the F-14 and F-16

improvement. Acoustic treatment is provided in the nozzle flow path.

ROTOR SUPPORT SYSTEM: Eight bearings (four for each rotor) at seven locations. Fan and LP compressor carried on ball thrust bearing (1) behind fan disc and roller bearing (2) at front of LP main shaft; both bearings mounted in fan front frame structure, which also supports HP compressor front roller bearing (3). LP turbine carried on roller bearings at front and rear of turbine rotor assembly—rear bearing (7) being mounted in spider structure across turbine exit, and front bearing (6) on major spider structure between HP and LP turbines. HP compressor carried at rear on adjacent roller bearing (4R) and ball-thrust bearing (4B) at interconnection with HP turbine front conical shaft, both bearings being mounted on support structure integral with compressor outlet diffuser. A roller bearing (5), mounted in the inter-turbine structure, carries the aft HP conical shaft.

ACCESSORY DRIVE: This consists of the inlet gearbox, radial gearbox, radial driveshaft, transfer gearbox, horizontal driveshaft and accessory gearbox. The inlet gearbox is located in the forward sump of the engine. The gearbox transfers energy from the core-engine (HP) rotor to the radial driveshaft located in a housing aft of the bottom vertical strut of the fan frame. The transfer gearbox is mounted on the bottom of the fan frame. Accessory mounting pads are provided on both the forward and aft faces of the gearbox. The engine accessories mounted on the gearbox are starter, fuel pump, main engine control, lubrication pump and tachometer. Pads are also provided for mounting the aircraft hydraulic pumps, constant-speed drive and alternator.

FUEL SYSTEM: Hydromechanical fuel control system regulates steady-state fuel flow and schedules acceleration and deceleration fuel flow. It also schedules and powers variable-stator vane position. A governor in the Woodward control provides core-engine speed stability during steady-state operation. During transient operation, core-engine fuel flow is scheduled on the basis of throttle position, compressor inlet temperature, compressor discharge pressure and core-engine speed. The fuel control and fuel pump are mounted in the accessory package as an integrated unit which avoids interconnecting high-pressure fuel lines and potential leakage points (they are separable for change or maintenance). This configuration provides a single drive mounting flange. The filter, fuel/oil heat exchanger and control pressurising valve may be removed individually without removing the entire assembly. The fuel manifold is double-wall constructed for safety and mounted on the exterior of the engine. For CF6-50, fuel control is modified to provide scheduling function for LP compressor variable bypass doors.

FUEL GRADES: Fuels conforming to ASTM-1655-65T, Jet A, Jet A1 and Jet B, and MIL-T-5624G2 grades JP-4 or JP-5 are authorised, but Jet A is primary specification.

LUBRICATION SYSTEM: Dry-sump centre-vented system in which oil is pressure-fed to each engine component requiring lubrication. Oil is removed from the sump areas by scavenge pumps, passed through a fuel/oil heat exchanger and filter to the engine tank. Nominal lubrication system pressure is 2·07-6·21 bars (30-90 lb/sq in) above sump reference pressure. All pressure and scavenge pumps and filters are located in the lubrication centre on the forward side of the gearbox.

OIL SPECIFICATION: Conforming to General Electric specification D50TFI classes A & B, equivalent to MIL-L-7808 or MIL-L-23699A.

MOUNTING: Main thrust mount located on the inner fan frame; aft mount located on the turbine mid-frame.

STARTING: Air-turbine starter mounted on the front of the accessory gearbox at the through shaft.

NOISE SUPPRESSION EQUIPMENT: Acoustic panels integrated with fan casing, fan front frame and thrust reverser.

DIMENSIONS:

Fan tip diameter	2,195 mm (86·4 in)
Max width (cold)	2,390 mm (94·1 in)
Max height (over gearbox)	2,675 mm (105·3 in)
Length overall (cold):	
CF6-6D	4,775 mm (188·0 in)
CF6-32	3,734 mm (147·0 in)
CF6-50 series	4,648 mm (183·0 in)
CF6-80A	3,988 mm (157·0 in)
CF6-80C	4,115 mm (162·0 in)

WEIGHT, DRY (basic engine):

CF6-6D, -6D1	3,679 kg (8,111 lb)
CF6-32	3,239 kg (7,140 lb)
CF6-45A/B, -50E, -50E1	3,851 kg (8,490 lb)
CF6-50A, -50C, -50C1	3,956 kg (8,721 lb)
CF6-80A	3,826 kg (8,435 lb)
CF6-80A1, -80B	3,769 kg (8,310 lb)
CF6-80C	3,951 kg (8,710 lb)
Fan and turbine reverser:	
CF6-6D, -6D1	932 kg (2,054 lb)
CF6-50A, -50C	968 kg (2,135 lb)
CF6-50E	962 kg (2,121 lb)

PERFORMANCE RATINGS:
Max T-O, uninstalled, ideal nozzle:
See under model listings
Max altitude and Mach No:
CF6-6 and -50: 13,700 m (45,000 ft) at Mach 1·0
Max cruise thrust at 10,670 m (35,000 ft) and Mach 0·85, flat rated to ISA, + 10°C, uninstalled, real nozzle:

CF6-6D	40·6 kN (9,120 lb)
CF6-6D1	41·1 kN (9,250 lb)
CF6-32	36·9 kN (8,290 lb)
CF6-45A	48·9 kN (11,000 lb)
CF6-50A, -50C	48·0 kN (10,800 lb)
CF6-50E, -45B	50·3 kN (11,300 lb)
CF6-80A, -80A1	45·9 kN (10,320 lb)
CF6-80B	52·7 kN (11,850 lb)
CF6-80C	52·9 kN (11,900 lb)

SPECIFIC FUEL CONSUMPTION:
At T-O thrust, as above:

CF6-6D	9·86 mg/Ns (0·348 lb/h/lb st)
CF6-6D1	9·91 mg/Ns (0·350 lb/h/lb st)
CF6-45A, -45B	10·28 mg/Ns (0·363 lb/h/lb st)
CF6-50A	10·90 mg/Ns (0·385 lb/h/lb st)
CF6-50C	11·05 mg/Ns (0·390 lb/h/lb st)
CF6-50E	10·65 mg/Ns (0·376 lb/h/lb st)

OIL CONSUMPTION: 0·9 kg (2·0 lb)/h

GENERAL ELECTRIC F101-DFE

The F101-GE-100 was designed by General Electric for the Rockwell International B-1 strategic bomber. It was qualified for production in November 1976. By early 1980 the F101 had logged over 25,000 h, including over 6,000 h in flight. It was described in the 1979-80 *Jane's*.

From it has been derived the F101-DFE advanced augmented turbofan for supersonic fighters, in particular as a candidate engine for re-engining the F-14 Tomcat and F-16. Based largely on components from the F101, YJ101 and F404, the F101-DFE was announced in June 1979. At that time development was being accelerated under a $79·7 million US Air Force contract, leading to flight test in both the F-14 and F-16 in 1981. The first of four prototypes ran at Evendale in late 1979, and achieved full speed and maximum power on the first run.

FAN: Inlet guide vanes with variable trailing flaps. Three axial stages scaled up from F404, with solid titanium blades. Split case. Blades and vanes individually replaceable. Pressure ratio greater than 3. Mass flow approx 122 kg (270 lb)/s. Bypass ratio 0·87.

COMPRESSOR: Similar to F101, with nine stages on one-piece inertia-welded rotor. Inlet guide vanes and first three stators variable. Split casing is titanium at front and steel at rear. Blades and vanes individually replaceable. Pressure ratio over 10.

COMBUSTION CHAMBER: Similar to F101, with very short annular design fed by dual cone nozzles injecting into 20 small scroll cups.

HP TURBINE: Identical to F101. Advanced single stage with hollow blades and vanes both impingement and film-cooled. Blades individually replaceable without rotor disassembly. Segmented shroud providing tip clearance control.

LP TURBINE: Based on F101, with two stages, tip-shrouded but uncooled. Blades individually replaceable; second-stage vanes replaceable in groups.

AFTERBURNER: Scaled from F101. Mixed-flow with convoluted mixer of fan and core streams in plane of flameholder, where ignition begins on inner ring. Core oxygen is 90 per cent consumed upstream of fuel injection into bypass air.

NOZZLE: Scaled from F404 with primary, divergent and outer flaps and seals. Translating hydraulically powered ring drives triple flaps with hinged connections running on cams and rollers.

DIMENSIONS:

Diameter	1,270 mm (50·0 in)
Length (F-16)	5,156 mm (203·0 in)

WEIGHT, DRY: not disclosed

RATING:
T-O   116-129 kN (26,000-29,000 lb st) class

GENERAL ELECTRIC T58

The T58 is a small free-turbine turboshaft engine which was developed for helicopter propulsion for the US Navy Bureau of Weapons. A civil version, the CT58, was awarded a Type Certificate by the FAA on 1 July 1959 and is described separately.

Hydromechanical constant-speed control system featured in the T58 maintains essentially constant rotor speed by regulating the engine power automatically, so eliminating the need for speed adjustment by the pilot during normal operation.

Rolls-Royce Ltd produces modified versions of the T58 under licence in the United Kingdom as the Gnome. The T58 is also licensed for manufacture in Italy and Japan. Industrial and marine version of the T58 is the LM100. By January 1978 more than 7,000 T58 engines had been manufactured.

Versions currently in service or in production are as follows:

T58-GE-3. Five-minute rating of 988 kW (1,325 shp). Powers Bell UH-1F.

T58-GE-5. Five-minute rating of 1,119 kW (1,500 shp). Powers Sikorsky CH-3E, HH-3E/F and NASA RSRA (Sikorsky S-72).

T58-GE-8E, F. Rated at 1,007 kW (1,350 shp). Powers Boeing Vertol CH-46A, Kaman SH-2, Sikorsky SH-3A/G and HH-52A.

T58-GE-10. Rated at 1,044 kW (1,400 shp). Powers Sikorsky SH-3D/H, and Boeing Vertol CH-46D/F.

T58-GE-16. Rated at 1,394 kW (1,870 shp). US military qualified. Aircooled gas-generator turbine and two-stage power turbine. Powers Boeing Vertol CH-46E.

T58-GE-100. Uprated T58-GE-5. Ten-minute rating 1,119 kW (1,500 shp) to 15°C or 1,100 kW (1,475 shp) to 26°C. Powers selected CH/HH-3E. Qualified 1976.

TYPE: Free-turbine turboshaft.

AIR INTAKE: Annular intake casing with four hollow radial struts supporting central housing for starter drive clutch and front main roller bearing. Casing and struts anti-iced by air bled from compressor.

COMPRESSOR: Ten-stage axial-flow. Variable-incidence inlet guide vanes. First three of the eleven rows of stator blades also have variable incidence. One-piece steel construction for last eight stages of rotor hub. Casing divided into upper and lower halves. Pressure ratio 8·4 : 1. Air mass flow 5·62 kg (12·4 lb)/s in T58-GE-3 and 8E 6·21 kg (13·7 lb)/s in T58-GE-5, -10 and -100, 6·30 kg (13·9 lb)/s in T58-GE-16.

COMBUSTION CHAMBER: Annular type. Sixteen fuel nozzles (eight on each of two manifolds) mounted on front of inner liner. Dual capacitor discharge ignition unit. Outer casing in two halves to facilitate inspection.

GAS GENERATOR TURBINE: Two-stage short-chord axial-flow type, coupled directly to compressor by hollow conical shaft. Centre ball thrust bearing, rear roller bearing. Cooling by air bled from compressor. T58-GE-16 has aircooled first-stage turbine nozzle and blades and second-stage nozzle.

POWER TURBINE: Single-stage (two-stage in T58-GE-16) axial-flow type, mechanically independent of gas generator turbine. Operated nominally at 19,500 rpm. Engines with single-stage power turbine can have reduction gear giving output at 6,000 rpm. Power turbine accessory drive unit and flexible feed-back cable provide a speed signal to the control.

TORQUE SENSOR SPEED DECREASER GEARBOX (optional): Gearbox with integral lubrication system. Reduces power speed to 6,000 rpm. Assembly includes an integral torque sensing system.

JET EXHAUST: Two positions (90° left or right) on all versions. T58-GE-16 can also be supplied with downward-ejecting or multiple-position exhaust.

CONTROLS (except T58-GE-10 and -16): Free turbine constant-speed control. Hydromechanical controls.

CONTROLS (T58-GE-10, -16): Integrated hydro-mechanical/electrical power control system for isochronous speed governing and twin-engine load sharing.

ACCESSORY DRIVES: Engine accessories driven from compressor shaft. Airframe accessories mounted on free-turbine reduction gearbox or rotor hub.

DIMENSIONS:
Max width:

except T58-GE-16	526 mm (20·7 in)
T58-GE-16	607 mm (23·9 in)

Length overall:

except T58-GE-16	1,499 mm (59·0 in)
T58-GE-16	1,626 mm (64·0 in)

WEIGHT, DRY:

T58-GE-3	140 kg (309 lb)
T58-GE-5, -100	152 kg (335 lb)
T58-GE-8E, F	138 kg (305 lb)
T58-GE-10	159 kg (350 lb)
T58-GE-16	201 kg (443 lb)

PERFORMANCE RATINGS:
Five-minute:
See under model listings
Military:

T58-GE-3	988 kW (1,325 shp) at 20,960 rpm
T58-GE-5, 10	1,044 kW (1,400 shp) at 19,500 rpm
T58-GE-8E, F	1,007 kW (1,350 shp) at 19,500 rpm
T58-GE-16	1,394 kW (1,870 shp) at 19,500 rpm
T58-GE-100	1,119 kW (1,500 shp) at 19,500 rpm

Cruise:

T58-GE-3	798 kW (1,070 shp)
T58-GE-5, 10	932 kW (1,250 shp)
T58-GE-8E, F	857·5 kW (1,150 shp)
T58-GE-16	1,320 kW (1,770 shp)
T58-GE-100	1,015 kW (1,360 shp) at 19,500 rpm

SPECIFIC FUEL CONSUMPTION:
At military rating:

T58-GE-3	103 µg/J (0·61 lb/h/shp)
T58-GE-5, 8E/F, 10, 100	101 µg/J (0·60 lb/h/shp)
T58-GE-16	89·5 µg/J (0·53 lb/h/shp)

At cruise rating:

T58-GE-3	106·5 µg/J (0·63 lb/h/shp)
T58-GE-5, 100	103 µg/J (0·61 lb/h/shp)
T58-GE-8E, F	105 µg/J (0·62 lb/h/shp)
T58-GE-10	105 µg/J (0·62 lb/h/shp)
T58-GE-16	91 µg/J (0·54 lb/h/shp)

GENERAL ELECTRIC CT58

The commercial version of the T58 is designated CT58 and was the first US helicopter turbine to receive FAA certification.

Current versions are as follows:

CT58-110. Rated at 932 kW; 1,250 shp (1,007 kW; 1,350 shp for 2½ min) at 19,500 rpm. Air mass flow 5·67 kg (12·7 lb)/s. Pressure ratio 8·2 : 1.

CT58-140. Rated at 1,044 kW; 1,400 shp (1,119 kW; 1,500 shp for 2½ min) at 19,500 rpm. Air mass flow 6·21 kg (13·7 lb)/s. Pressure ratio 8·4 : 1.

The CT58 powers the Sikorsky S-61 and S-62 and Boeing Vertol 107 Model II.

DIMENSIONS:

Max width	406 mm (16·0 in)
Length overall	1,500 mm (59·0 in)

The 1,394 kW (1,870 shp) General Electric T58-GE-16 turboshaft

WEIGHT, DRY:
CT58-110	143 kg (315 lb)
CT58-140	154 kg (340 lb)

PERFORMANCE RATINGS:
2½ min and normal T-O:
  See under model listings
Cruise:
CT58-110	783 kW (1,050 shp)
CT58-140	932 kW (1,250 shp)

SPECIFIC FUEL CONSUMPTION:
At normal T-O rating   103 μg/J (0·61 lb/h/shp)
At cruise rating:
CT58-110	108 μg/J (0·64 lb/h/shp)
CT58-140	105 μg/J (0·62 lb/h/shp)

GENERAL ELECTRIC T64

The T64 is a versatile aircraft gas turbine engine which was developed initially for the US Navy. The basic T64 turboshaft engine becomes a turboprop with the addition of a two-part speed-reduction gearbox.

Current versions include:

T64-GE-7. Direct-drive turboshaft rated at 2,928 kW (3,925 shp). Powers US Air Force CH-53B, CH-53C and HH-53C. Also powers VFW-built CH-53D/G. Produced under licence by MTU (see entry under Germany, Federal Republic).

T64-GE-7A. Direct-drive turboshaft flat-rated at 2,935 kW (3,936 shp) to 28°C. Powers Sikorsky S-65.

T64-GE-10. Turboprop engine with propeller gearbox above centreline. Rated at 2,215 kW (2,970 shp). Produced under licence by Ishikawajima Harima Heavy Industries in Japan for Shin Meiwa PS-1 flying-boat (four engines) and Kawasaki P-2J patrol aircraft (two engines).

T64-GE-413A. Direct-drive turboshaft rated at 2,935 kW (3,936 shp). Two engines power the US Navy CH-53D and RH-53D.

T64-GE-415. Growth version with improved combustion liner and turbine cooling. Max rating 3,266 kW (4,380 shp). Powers Sikorsky RH-53D and three-engined CH-53E helicopters.

CT64-GE-820. CT64-820-1, -2 and -3 turboprops based on early turboshaft versions power DHC-5C Buffalo and prototype Aeritalia G222. FAA certificated CT64-820-4 has improved components of T64-415 and is flat-rated at 2,336 kW (3,133 shp) to 38°C, in production for DHC-5D Buffalo.

T64-P4D. Turboprop version flat rated at 2,535 kW (3,400 shp) to 45°C. Two P4D engines power most Aeritalia G222 transports. Production by Fiat, supported by Alfa Romeo, with deliveries beginning in 1975.

All T64s are qualified to operate from 100° nose-up to 45° nose-down. The T64 was designed for extensive growth: current production engines rated at 3,266 kW (4,380 shp) are a result of growth made possibly largely by aircooling of the first-stage gas generator turbine rotor and stator. The addition of aircooling to the second turbine stage provides further horsepower growth beyond 3,729 kW (5,000 shp) without significant change in external dimensions.

By January 1980 a total of over 2,000 T64 engines of all kinds had been delivered by GE to customers in 13 countries. In addition licences to produce the T64 are held by MTU in West Germany, Fiat in Italy, Rolls-Royce in the UK and IHI in Japan.

TYPE: Free-turbine turboshaft/turboprop engine.

COMPRESSOR: Fourteen-stage axial-flow. Single-spool steel rotor for -10 and -820-1/2/3. Titanium and steel compressor for -7A, -413A, -415, -P4D and CT64-820-4. Inlet guide vanes and first four stages of stator blades variable. Compressor blades can be removed individually without rotor disassembly. Casing flanged along centreline. Stator blades removable. Air mass flow per second: -10, 11·6 kg (25·5 lb); -7A, -413A, 12·8 kg (28·3 lb); -415, 13·3 kg (29·4 lb); -820-4, 11·9 kg (26·2 lb); P4D, 12·2 kg (27·0 lb). Pressure ratio: -10, 820-4, 12·5; -7A, -413A, 14·1; -415, 14·8; P4D, 13·0.

COMBUSTION CHAMBER: Annular type. Double fuel manifold feeds twelve duplex-type fuel nozzles with external flow divider. Nozzles mounted on outer diffuser wall of compressor rear frame.

GAS GENERATOR TURBINE: Two-stage axial-flow type, coupled directly to compressor rotor by spline connection.

POWER TURBINE: Two-stage axial-flow type, mechanically independent of gas generator turbine.

REDUCTION GEAR: Remotely-mounted basic reduction gear for turboprop versions is offset and accessible for inspection and replacement. Gear-driven by power turbine, using co-axial shafting through the compressor. Propeller gear ratio 13·44 : 1.

STARTING: Mechanical, airframe supplied.

DIMENSIONS:
Length:
T64-GE-7A, 413A, -415	2,006 mm (79 in)
T64-GE-10, P4D	2,793 mm (110 in)
CT64-820	2,870 mm (113 in)

Width:
T64-GE-7A, -413A, -415	60 mm (26·0 in)
T64-GE-10, -P4D, -820	683 mm (26·9 in)

Height:
T64-GE-7A, 413A, -415	825 mm (32·5 in)

The 2,935 kW (3,936 shp) General Electric T64-GE-413A turboshaft

General Electric T700-GE-700 turboshaft engine, showing (light coloured duct rising at mid-section) the extractor for solid particles removed by the inlet separator. Intermediate (T-O) rating, 1,151 kW (1,543 shp)

T64-GE-10, -P4D	1,168 mm (46 in)
CT64-820	1,026 mm (40·4 in)

WEIGHT, DRY:
T64-GE-413A	325 kg (716 lb)
T64-GE-7A, -415	327 kg (720 lb)
T64-GE-10	529 kg (1,167 lb)
CT64-820-1	513 kg (1,130 lb)
CT64-820-2, -4	520 kg (1,145 lb)
CT64-820-3	518 kg (1,140 lb)
T64-P4D	538 kg (1,188 lb)

PERFORMANCE RATINGS:
Max rating (sea level):
T64-GE-10
  2,215 kW (2,970 shp) at 1,160 output rpm
T64-GE-7A, -413A	2,935 kW (3,936 shp)
CT64-820-4	2,336 kW (3,133 shp)
T64-P4D	2,535 kW (3,400 shp)
T64-415	3,266 kW (4,380 shp)

SPECIFIC FUEL CONSUMPTION (S/L):
At max rating:
T64-GE-7A, -415	79·4 μg/J (0·47 lb/h/shp)
T64-GE-10	84·5 μg/J (0·50 lb/h/shp)
T64-GE-413A, P4D	81 μg/J (0·48 lb/h/shp)
CT64-820-4	83 μg/J (0·49 lb/h/shp)

GENERAL ELECTRIC T700

Under a contract awarded by the US Army Aviation Materiel Laboratories Propulsion Division, General Electric initiated a two-year demonstration programme in August 1967 to design, build and test a new 1,118·5 kW (1,500 shp) advanced technology turboshaft. Designated GE12, the engine was developed by the Aircraft Engine Group's Military Engine Division. During the latter part of 1968 the basic contracts for the GE12 and competing Pratt & Whitney ST9 demonstrator turboshaft were extended to the end of 1969 and additional work was also funded to carry the GE12 programme through to 30 September 1971. The GE12 demonstrator was illustrated in the 1971-72 Jane's.

A new competition was conducted in 1971 to provide the power plant for the Army's projected utility tactical transport system (UTTAS) proposed as a replacement for the present Bell UH-1 family of Army helicopters. In late 1971 it was announced that the winner was the GE engine, and that a contract for a production version, the T700-GE-700, was being negotiated with the US Army Aviation Systems Command.

The first T700 engine was tested in February 1973. Shipment of ground test engines was accomplished on schedule in February 1974, and flight qualification testing was completed ahead of schedule in August 1974. Shipments for UTTAS flight aircraft began immediately, with first flights of the Boeing YUH-61A and Sikorsky YUH-60A following during the autumn of 1974. Identical T700 engines powered the two advanced attack helicopter (AAH) contenders, the Bell YAH-63A and Hughes YAH-64A.

In December 1976 the first contract for production engines was received to power the winning Sikorsky UH-60A Black Hawk. Engines have been delivered from early 1978. The Hughes AH-64 was also selected over its rival, with a production decision due in 1980. By 1979 more than 40,000 h had been logged, including 20,000 flying in the four competing helicopters. A Navy T700, with 95-97 per cent commonality, has been selected for the Sikorsky SH-60B (LAMPS Mk III) helicopter (Light Airborne Multi-Purpose System).

The T700 has been designed to be compatible with the Army's special operating and environmental conditions, and embodies high reliability, simplicity of maintenance, low vulnerability to combat damage, and high performance combined with compact dimensions. Use is made of higher pressure ratios and turbine entry temperatures than with existing small turboshafts to assist in reducing size and weight.

To reduce vulnerability, all external lines and leads are short in length and are grouped compactly for minimum exposure. Self-contained electrical and lubrication systems are fitted. Multiple mounting points allow for ease of installation and the necessary airframe connections have been minimised and are located close to the engine centreline. The whole engine is of modular construction for swift field maintenance or section replacement without special tools.

GE has announced studies for derivatives, including a family of turbojets for RPVs and other fixed-wing aircraft. Other possibilities include turboprops and high bypass ratio turbofans, while front and rear drive modifications make surface applications possible.

A programme of growth has been started to meet the widening spectrum of applications. As envisaged, 10 per cent greater power will be available from the existing basic engine. Addition of an LP booster (zero stage) will then provide 20-30 per cent growth, depending on the increase in turbine temperature chosen. These growth versions are planned to be interchangeable with the present T700-GE-700 aircraft installation.

TYPE: Ungeared free-turbine turboshaft engine.

INTAKE: Annular type, with anti-iced integral inlet particle separator containing no moving parts yet designed to remove 95 per cent of sand, dust and foreign-object ingestion. Extracted matter discharged by separator blower driven from accessory gearbox.

COMPRESSOR: Combined axial/centrifugal. Five axial stages and single centrifugal stage mounted on same shaft. Each axial stage is one-piece 'blisk' (blades plus disc) in AM355 steel highly resistant to erosion. Inlet guide vanes and first two stator stages are variable. Pressure ratio, about 15 : 1. Airflow about 4·5 kg (10 lb)/s at 44,720 rpm.

COMBUSTION CHAMBER: Fully annular. Compact short-length configuration, designed for maximum reliability and long life. Central fuel injection to maximise acceptance of contaminated fuel and give minimal smoke generation and uniform temperature profile into the turbine. Flame tube is machined ring in Hastelloy X. Ignition system obtains power from separate winding on engine-mounted alternator and serves dual plugs.

TURBINE: Two-stage gas-generator (HP) turbine operates at gas temperatures exceeding 1,100°C. First-stage nozzle investment-cast in X40. Second-stage nozzle investment-cast in two-vane segments in R80. Discs, cooling plates, and blades of both stages clamped by five short tiebolts; five larger bolts then tighten turbine to shaft, driving via curvic joint. Rated shaft speed (S/L, ISA, max T-O power), 44,720 rpm. Two-stage free power turbine, designed for high efficiency at part-power levels (especially 30 and 60% of military power), with tip-shrouded blades and segmented nozzles. Power turbine inlet temperature at intermediate power, 827°C. Nozzle guide vanes René 77, rotor discs Inco 718, rotor blades René 80 uncooled. Output speed, 17,000-21,000 rpm. Power output shaft for front drive.

CONTROLS: Hydromechanical control can be replaced in less than 12 minutes and requires no adjustment or lockwire. Electrical control, coupled with hydromechanical control, provides twin-engine speed and torque matching.

ACCESSORIES: Grouped at top of engine, together with engine control system, for maximum simplicity, accessibility and combat survivability. Integral lubrication supply tank, plus an emergency supply of mist lubrication following total loss of main supply. Torque sensor provides signal to electrical control system.

DIMENSIONS:
Length overall	1,181 mm (46·5 in)
Width	635 mm (25 in)
Height overall	584 mm (23 in)

WEIGHT, DRY (with particle separator):
188 kg (415 lb)

PERFORMANCE RATINGS:
Intermediate (30 min)	1,151 kW (1,543 shp)
Max continuous	933 kW (1,251 shp)
75% max continuous	699 kW (937 shp)

SPECIFIC FUEL CONSUMPTION:
Intermediate	79·25 μg/J (0·469 lb/h/shp)
Max continuous	80·6 μg/J (0·477 lb/h/shp)
75%	87 μg/J (0·514 lb/h/shp)

GENERAL ELECTRIC CT7

In September 1976 General Electric announced the introduction of a new commercial helicopter engine based on the T700 military engine developed for the US Army. Certification testing to Federal Aviation Administration standards was completed in April 1977.

DIMENSIONS:
Length	1,194 mm (47·0 in)
Width	635 mm (25·0 in)
Height	584 mm (23·0 in)

WEIGHT, DRY:
195 kg (430 lb)

PERFORMANCE RATINGS (S/L, static, 15°C):
Contingency (2½ min)	1,209 kW (1,620 shp)
T-O (5 min) and en route contingency (30 min)	1,164 kW (1,560 shp)
Max cruise	940 kW (1,260 shp)

GESCHWENDER
GESCHWENDER AEROMOTIVE INC

4131 NW 36 Street, Lincoln, Nebraska 68524
Telephone: (402) 470 3333

Geschwender Aeromotive is developing a line of liquid-cooled V-8 engines for aircraft application. Based upon engines of 351 and 460 cu in displacement, the Geschwender engines range from 330 to 430 hp naturally aspirated, and to 600 hp when turbocharged.

The engines incorporate a reduction unit which uses a high-velocity chain to transmit crankshaft power to the propeller. Reduction ratios currently available are 2·423, 2·307 and 1·923:1. These ratios meet a wide variety of propeller applications.

The primary objective of Geschwender Aeromotive is to provide engines for agricultural aircraft. FAA type certification of the V460 engine was anticipated during 1980.

DIMENSIONS:
Length overall	1,422 mm (56·5 in)
Width	584 mm (23·0 in)
Height	635 mm (25·0 in)

WEIGHT, DRY:
351 CID	272 kg (600 lb)
460 CID	318 kg (700 lb)

MAX POWER (S/L):
351 CID	246 kW (330 hp) at 5,500 rpm
460 CID normally aspirated	321 kW (430 hp) at 5,250 rpm
460 CID turbocharged	447 kW (600 hp) at 5,250 rpm

Geschwender V460 liquid-cooled engine of 321 kW (430 hp)

GLUHAREFF
EMG ENGINEERING COMPANY

18518J South Broadway Avenue, Gardena, California 90248
Telephone: (213) 321 8699

Eugene M. Gluhareff, a pioneer of ultra-light rotorcraft, has been developing a unique type of air-breathing jet engine which he considers to offer notable advantages over all other systems for rotor tip-drive. The first model is the G8-2, which was designed in 1955 and fully developed over the next ten years for tip-drive or sailplane auxiliary propulsion. It has also been used for surface application in a go-kart, and in numerous static rigs sold to universities and other organisations. Production has been hard pressed to keep up with demand, a fast-growing market being

radio-controlled flight vehicles. Manned platforms and small helicopters are also proving to be a large market for various sizes of the family of engines described below.

GLUHAREFF G8-2

Although extremely simple, the G8 series corresponds to no prior jet system. The design is based on propane, a readily-available volatile fuel. The pressure of the liquid propane in the tank delivers the fuel, via a needle valve serving as the throttle, to the burner unit. The fuel enters the burner duct and is immediately vaporised in a hot heat-exchanger. Vapour then passes back down an insulated pipe to the injector where its residual pressure is converted to kinetic energy. The high-velocity gas jet induces air through three 'supercharger' intakes, each synchronised to the internal flow, which gives the correct final

fuel/air ratio to the mixture entering the combustion chamber. Here the mixture is initially ignited by a spark plug and thereafter burns continuously. The intake ducts are tuned to each other to create one-way flow. Resonance in the tailpipe is undesirable and is prevented by making the propelling nozzle of fishtail shape.

By 1979 three more models were available, the G8-2-20, -80 and -130 (20, 80 and 130 lb st), and a G8-2-250 (1·1 kN, 250 lb st) was on bench test. The best specific fuel consumption had been dramatically reduced from 170 mg/Ns (6 lb/h/lb st) to only 21·8 mg/Ns (0·77 lb/h/lb st).

The units are manufactured by Gluhareff's subsidiary EMG Engineering Co. Customers have the option of buying plans only, a construction package, partly prefabricated or an assembly kit or finished engine.

JACOBS
PAGE INDUSTRIES INC

HEAD OFFICE: C.E. Page Airport, PO Box 191, Yukon, Oklahoma 73099
Telephone: (405) 354 5385
PRESIDENT: O. J. Butts
VICE-PRESIDENT AND TREASURER: Currie Smith
VICE PRESIDENT, ENGINEERING: Merrill H. Bumbaugh

Page Industries is the successor to the Jacobs Aircraft Engine Co, which had manufactured aircooled radial piston engines since 1929. Current production is centred upon the various versions of the R-755 described below.

JACOBS R-755

This long-established seven-cylinder radial is being manufactured in several versions. The basic engine is the **R-755A** which is the subject of the detailed description. The current engines in this series are the R-755A2, and the A2M with dual ignition. The **R-755B** has a lower power rating, and is available as the R-755B1, driving a fixed-pitch propeller, and the B2 which can have a control

valve for a two-position propeller or provision for a hydraulically-operated constant-speed propeller. The **R-755S** is a turbocharged version, available with dual ignition as the R-755SM.

The Piper Pawnee Brave PA-36-285 conversion uses the R-755S engine driving a Hamilton Standard 2B20-AG-CF 6135A-11S propeller as modified by Pacific Propeller Inc of Kent, Washington. Approval for the conversion is held by STC Engineering, of Oklahoma City.

TYPE: Seven-cylinder aircooled radial piston engine.

CYLINDERS: Bore 133 mm (5·25 in). Stroke 127 mm (5 in). Swept volume 12·3 litres (757 cu in). Barrels machined from steel forgings with close-spaced fins. Aluminium alloy heads screwed and shrunk on. Aluminium-bronze valve-seats shrunk into heads.

PISTONS: Forged aluminium alloy. Three compression rings and one scraper ring above gudgeon-pin (piston-pin) and two scraper rings below. Fully-floating nitrided gudgeon-pins.

CONNECTING RODS: One-piece steel master rod. Forged aluminium alloy link rods bearing directly upon nitrided-steel pins.

CRANKSHAFT: Two-piece clamp type, machined from forgings in chrome-nickel-molybdenum steel.

CRANKCASE: Assembled from five parts. Aluminium alloy.

VALVE GEAR: Cam ring, drive gears, tappets and pushrods all in nose section, with all moving parts enclosed. Tulip-type inlet valves and sodium-cooled exhaust valves, each with two springs.

INDUCTION: Single updraught Stromberg NA-R7A carburettor. R-755S and SM have this carburettor fed at up to 35 in Hg by AiResearch exhaust-gas turbocharger between Nos. 2 and 3 cylinders. System set to maintain power to 5,945 m (19,500 ft), with aneroid relief valve to prevent overboosting beyond 36 in Hg.

FUEL: 80 octane (755S, SM, 80/87 octane).

IGNITION: One Scintilla magneto and battery distributor, incorporating automatic advance (engines with "M" suffix, two magnetos).

LUBRICATION: Single unit comprising gear pressure pump and two scavenge pumps feeds all plain bearings. Dry sump. Automatic valve lubrication. Optional provision for adjustable-pitch or constant-speed propeller.

PROPELLER DRIVE: Direct, RH tractor, SAE 20 spline.

MOUNTING: Choice of eight crankcase locations.

DIMENSIONS:
Diameter	1,118 mm (44 in)
Length overall	1,020 m (40⁷/₃₂ in)

WEIGHT, DRY:
R-755A, B1	229 kg (505 lb)
R-755B2	232 kg (511 lb)
R-755S	261 kg (576 lb)

R-755SM	264 kg (583 lb)

PERFORMANCE RATINGS:
Rated power:
R-755A	224 kW (300 hp) at 2,200 rpm
R-755B	205 kW (275 hp) at 2,200 rpm

R-755S, SM:
rated power 205 kW (275 hp) at 2,030 rpm maintained to 5,945 m (19,500 ft); take-off (1 min limit) 261 kW (350 hp) at 2,200 rpm

Jacobs R-755A seven-cylinder radial piston engine, rated at 224 kW (300 hp)

MARQUARDT
THE MARQUARDT COMPANY (a division of CCI Corporation)
HEAD OFFICE: 16555 Saticoy Street, Van Nuys, California 91409
Telephone: (213) 781 2121
PRESIDENT: G. H. Hanauer
VICE-PRESIDENTS:
K. E. Woodgrift (Engineering)
A. L. Sorensen (Operations)
B. E. Huston (Finance)
C. Long (Advanced Programs)

The Marquardt company was formed in November 1944 to undertake research and development of ramjet engines, and it produced the first American subsonic ramjet in 1945. Its main engineering business continues to be advanced aerospace propulsion and the supply of ram-air turbine power systems. A major portion of sales is currently associated with manufacture of sophisticated structures and components for the aerospace industry, and the production of clustered munitions.

Marquardt is currently developing security-classified types of composite rocket/air-breathing propulsion systems for the US Air Force and Navy. These are regarded by the company as likely to lead to a new generation of power plants for supersonic strategic missiles and expendable tactical vehicles.

Marquardt also has been developing precision rockets for spacecraft since 1959. The company developed and qualified attitude-control rockets for the service module and lunar module of the Apollo and for the Orbiter vehicle of the Space Transportation System. Marquardt has been prominent in the development of monopropellant rocket engines and systems, and an engine for a fluorine/hydrazine space-propulsion system. Advanced development activities include resistojet thrusters, a water-electrolysis system and oxy/hydrogen thrusters for long-life spacecraft reaction-control systems. Marquardt is currently producing propulsion subsystems and bipropellant rocket engines for the India satellite and the System Applications Laboratories satellite, and monopropellant engines for the US Air Force's Defense Meteorological System satellite.

Marquardt maintains extensive test facilities at Van Nuys for research and testing of air-breathing rocket engines, and controls and accessories. Total land area occupied exceeds 56 acres, and covered buildings exceed 46,400 m² (500,000 sq ft); employment exceeds 900.

MARQUARDT DUCTED ROCKET
In October 1977 Marquardt announced a new $2 million contract from the US Air Force Aero Propulsion Laboratory for further work on the ducted-rocket propulsion system. According to the company president: "It is designed to combine the best features of the ramjet engine and the solid rocket into a simple low-cost high-efficiency propulsion system. It employs a fuel-rich solid-rocket gas-generator and, like the basic ramjet, utilises the atmosphere as its primary source for oxidiser. The specific impulse is significantly higher than that of conventional solid rockets, yet it maintains the inherent simplicity desired for tactical applications".

The programme's objective was to demonstrate system performance in flight-weight hardware, culminating in an integrated engine demonstration in September 1979. Supporting Marquardt are Hughes (integration of aircraft, missile and engine), and Rocketdyne McGregor Division (solid-rocket gas-generator). Applications centre on both tactical and strategic missiles.

MARQUARDT FIREBRAND RAMJET
In May 1977 Marquardt began work on a Teledyne Ryan contract, expected to be valued at about $6 million, for design and development of ramjet engines for the Teledyne Ryan Firebrand (see RPVs and Targets section). Each Firebrand will be powered by two of the new engines. At completion of the present programme in February 1982 six R & D targets and two special test vehicles will have flown; a production quantity is expected to follow. Firebrand will be highly supersonic, simulating advanced anti-ship missiles, and is designed to be reusable.

MARQUARDT R-40A
This precision control rocket has been developed and qualified for the Space Shuttle Orbiter vehicle.
TYPE: Liquid-propellant reaction control rocket.
PROPELLANTS: Nitrogen tetroxide and monomethyl hydrazine.
THRUST CHAMBER ASSEMBLY: Single chamber. Area ratio 20. Made of welded coated columbium, with welded-on orthogonal and scarfed nozzle extension in same material. Internal film cooling. Exterior insulated for buried installation. Started by electrical signal to on/off solenoid valve. Multiple doublet injector with hypergolic ignition.
THRUST CHAMBER MOUNTING: Flange bolt circle on injector head.
PROPELLANT FEED SYSTEM: Pressurised tanks, with feed of 0·526 kg (1·16 lb)/s fuel and 0·838 kg (1·85 lb)/s oxidant at 16·4 bars (238 lb/sq in abs).
DIMENSIONS:
Length overall	472 mm (18·6 in)
Nozzle exit diameter	267 mm (10·5 in)

WEIGHT, DRY: 9·5 kg (21·0 lb)
PERFORMANCE RATINGS:
Max thrust (vacuum)	3·87 kN (870 lb)
Chamber pressure	10·5 bars (152 lb/sq in)
Specific impulse	281

MARQUARDT R-30
This precision control rocket has been qualified for use on the kick stage of the US Air Force's Defense Meteorological Satellite and NASA Tiros-No.
TYPE: Liquid monopropellant precision control rocket.
PROPELLANT: Hydrazine.
THRUST CHAMBER: Single chamber. Area ratio 22. Fabricated in L605 stainless steel. Shell 405 catalyst bed in combustion chamber. Multiple element injection.
THRUST CHAMBER MOUNTING: Fixed, by flange bolt circle on injector head.

PROPELLANT FEED SYSTEM: Pressurised tank. Flow rate 0·297 kg (0·657 lb)/s at 31 bars (450 lb/sq in abs).
DIMENSIONS:
Length overall	273 mm (10·75 in)
Diameter	103 mm (4·0 in)

WEIGHT, DRY: 1·36 kg (3·0 lb)
PERFORMANCE RATINGS:
Max thrust (vacuum)	0·69 kN (155 lb)
Chamber pressure	15·5 bars (225 lb/sq in)
Specific impulse	236

MARQUARDT R-1E
This small high-performance rocket was qualified for use on the reaction control subsystem of the subsequently-abandoned US Air Force Manned Orbital Laboratory, and is now qualified as the vernier engine for the Space Shuttle Orbiter.
TYPE: Liquid bipropellant rocket for use in space.
PROPELLANTS: Nitrogen tetroxide and monomethyl hydrazine.
THRUST CHAMBER: Single chamber. Minimum area ratio 26 with orthogonal and scarfed nozzles. Made of metal-coated columbium. Insulated for buried installation. Started by electrical signal to on/off solenoid valve. Single doublet injector with hypergolic ignition.
THRUST CHAMBER MOUNTING: Fixed, by flange bolt circle on injector head.
PROPELLANT FEED SYSTEM: Pressurised tank. Flow rate 0·016 kg (0·0354 lb)/s fuel and 0·0256 kg (0·565 lb)/s oxidant.

Marquardt R-1E vernier long-scarf thruster   **Marquardt R-40A reaction control rocket**

Marquardt R-6C (0·022 kN; 5·0 lb st)

Marquardt MA212-XAA conical-inlet supersonic ramjet (net thrust 6·05 kN; 1,360 lb at Mach 2·5 at 12,200 m; 40,000 ft)

DIMENSIONS:
Length overall	279 mm (11·0 in)
Width	147 mm (5·8 in)
Height (depth)	145 mm (5·7 in)

WEIGHT, DRY: 3·7 kg (8·2 lb)

PERFORMANCE RATINGS:
Max thrust (vacuum)	0·11 kN (25·0 lb)
Chamber pressure	7·45 bars (108 lb/sq in)
Specific impulse (area ratio 40)	272

MARQUARDT R-4D-11 AND R-4D-12

These small attitude-control and manoeuvre rockets are the latest derivatives of the R-4D engine, first developed and qualified for the Apollo programme. Both were qualified in early 1980 and the R-4D-11 is to be used on the INSAT-1 communications satellite being developed by Ford Aerospace & Communications. The R-4D-12 is intended for application on the Hughes Aircraft spin-stabilised System Applications Laboratories satellite.

TYPE: Liquid-propellant reaction control rocket.

PROPELLANTS: Nitrogen tetroxide and monomethyl hydrazine.

THRUST CHAMBER ASSEMBLY: Single chamber. Area ratio of 164. Made of welded coated columbium. Started by electrical signal to on/off solenoid valve. Multiple doublet injector with hypergolic ignition.

THRUST CHAMBER MOUNTING: Flanged bolt circle on injector head.

PROPELLANT FEED SYSTEM: Pressurised tanks with feed of 0·056 kg (0·122 lb)/s fuel and 0·091 kg (0·201 lb)/s oxidant at 15·17 bars (220 lb/sq in).

DIMENSIONS:
Overall length	554·1 mm (21·8 in)
Nozzle exit diameter	279·4 mm (11·00 in)

WEIGHT, DRY: 3·36 kg (7·4 lb)

PERFORMANCE RATINGS:
Max thrust (vacuum)	0·445 kN (100 lb)
Chamber pressure	6·84 bars (100 lb/sq in)
Specific impulse	310

MARQUARDT R-6C

This engine is designed to provide attitude-control and station-keeping forces for satellites. It is a derivative of the engine designed by Marquardt for the Advent satellite in the early 1960s. Present applications are on the INSAT-1 and Hughes Aircraft spin-stabilised System Applications Laboratory satellites. The engine was to be qualified for these applications in early 1980. It has been tested extensively at both NASA laboratories and by Marquardt.

TYPE: Liquid-propellant reaction control rocket.

PROPELLANTS: Nitrogen tetroxide and monomethyl hydrazine.

THRUST CHAMBER ASSEMBLY: Single chamber. Area ratio of 100. Made of welded coated columbium. Started by electrical signal to on/off solenoid valve; multiple doublet injector with hypergolic ignition.

THRUST CHAMBER MOUNTING: Flanged bolt circle on injector head.

PROPELLANT FEED SYSTEM: Pressurised tanks with feed of 0·003 kg (0·006 lb)/s fuel and 0·005 kg (0·011 lb)/s oxidant at 15·17 bars (220 lb/sq in).

DIMENSIONS:
Overall length	251·6 mm (9·88 in)
Nozzle exit diameter	55·9 mm (2·20 in)

WEIGHT, DRY: 0·544 kg (1·2 lb)

PERFORMANCE RATINGS:
Max thrust (vacuum)	0·022 kN (5 lb)
Chamber pressure	6·84 bars (100 lb/sq in)
Specific impulse	290

MARQUARDT MA210/212

Two versions of this low-cost ramjet engine have been developed. The pitot-inlet MA210-XAA is designed primarily for the high-subsonic speed regime of Mach 0·7 to 0·9, although it has been tested at Mach 2·0. The conical-inlet version, MA212-XAA, provides higher thrust and better cruise fuel consumption in supersonic flight conditions. The engines use the same combustor system with an interchangeable inlet-diffuser assembly selected for either subsonic or supersonic flight operation. Both versions are of single-wall all-steel construction with two-point mounting to the vehicle pylon. Ignition is by pyrotechnic flare.

DIMENSIONS:
Length overall:	
MA210-XAA	2,070 mm (79 in)
MA212-XAA	2,134 mm (84 in)
Diameter	381 mm (15 in)

WEIGHT, DRY:
MA210-XAA	31·75 kg (70 lb)
MA212-XAA	35·2 kg (77·5 lb)

PERFORMANCE:
Operating envelope:	
MA210-XAA	S/L to 9,145 m (30,000 ft), Mach 0·7-1·5
MA212-XAA	S/L to 18,300 m (60,000 ft), Mach 1·0-2·5
Design thrust (net):	
MA210-XAA	2·94 kN (660 lb), S/L, Mach 0·9
MA212-XAA	6·05 kN (1,360 lb), 12,200 m (40,000 ft), Mach 2·5

NELSON

NELSON AIRCRAFT CORPORATION

HEAD OFFICE: PO Box 454, Irwin, Pennsylvania 15642
Telephone: (412) 863 5900
PRESIDENT: Charles R. Rhoades
VICE-PRESIDENT: Lawrence J. Rhoades

Nelson Aircraft Corporation, among its many industrial activities, produces to order the Nelson H-63 four-cylinder two-cycle aircooled engine, which has been certificated by the FAA as a power unit for single-seat helicopters, and is now available also as a power plant for propeller-driven aircraft. All these engines are capable of sustained inverted flight. Recommended overhaul period is 800 h.

NELSON FOUR-STROKE RANGE

Nelson Aircraft is developing a new range of lightweight four-stroke engines. They will be compact, and will have liquid cooling. The three sizes have outputs of 44·7 kW (60 hp), 89·5 kW (120 hp) and 112 kW (150 hp). Dry weights are, respectively, 39·95 kg (88 lb), 57·2 kg (126 lb) and 70·37 kg (155 lb).

By 1978 the 112 kW (150 hp) engine and a range of 89·5 kW (120 hp) engines had been run. Emphasis is on the latter. Future engines will include a Roots-type blower running at the 6,000 rpm of the engine, propeller speed being 2,000 rpm.

NELSON H-63

US military designation: YO-65

Developed originally as a power unit for single-seat helicopters, the H-63 is now available in two versions, as follows:

H-63C. Basic helicopter power unit for vertical installation. Battery ignition and direct drive. Certificated by FAA. Supplied as complete power package, including clutch, cooling fan and shroud.

H-63CP. Basically as H-63C, but without clutch, fan and shroud. Intended primarily for installation in horizontal position, with direct drive to propeller. FAA certificated.

H-63CPM. Magneto ignition (see 'Ignition' in detail description).

H-63CPMR, CPR. Versions with speed-reducing propeller drive (see 'Power Take-off' in detail description).

Nelson has developed a 1·07 m (42 in) wooden propeller with glassfibre covering for use with the H-63. It is suitable for either tractor or pusher installation.

TYPE: Four-cylinder horizontally-opposed aircooled, two-stroke.

CYLINDERS: Bore 68·3 mm (2¹¹/₁₆ in). Stroke 70 mm (2¾ in). Total capacity 1·03 litres (63 cu in). Compression ratio 8 : 1. Each complete cylinder is machined from an aluminium alloy casting, the bore being porous-chrome plated for wear resistance. Cylinders bolted to and detachable from crankcase.

PISTONS: Aluminium alloy casting. Two piston rings. Two needle roller bearings pressed in boss. Piston (gudgeon) pin pressed into small end of connecting rod.

CONNECTING RODS: Alloy steel forging. Caged roller bearing at big-end.

CRANKSHAFT: Four-throw. Nitralloy shaft on ball and roller bearings.

CRANKCASE: Two-piece case divided on horizontal centreline. Each half is a magnesium alloy casting.

Nelson four-stroke prototype engine in 89·5 kW (120 hp) size

First photograph of the Nelson H-63CPR with speed-reducing chain drive. Maximum rating will be 35·4 kW (47·5 hp)

INDUCTION: Nelson diaphragm-type all-angle fuel control carburettor. Hot-air anti-icing. Fuel/oil mixture valves from crankcase through specially-designed rotary valve driven by crankshaft. Intake to and exhaust from cylinders through ports. Exhaust stacks are of aluminium alloy.

FUEL: 80/87 octane gasoline and SAE 30 ash-free-base oil in 16 : 1 mixture for fuel and lubrication.

IGNITION: (except M models): Battery-type dual-ignition with automatic retard for starting. (M models): Two Slick magnetos. Two Champion D-9 or 5 COM spark plugs.

LUBRICATION: See under 'Fuel'.

POWER TAKE-OFF: (H-63C): Hollow shaft extension from Salisbury centrifugal clutch output drive. (R models): Hy-Vo high-speed chain drive with ratio of 8 : 5 (0·0625).

STARTING: 12V DC Autolite electric motor and Bendix drive.

COOLING: (H-63C): Centrifugal aluminium fan and two-piece glassfibre shrouding designed to maintain all temperatures within acceptable limits on an FAA hot day of 37·8°C, S/L. (Other versions): by propeller slipstream.

The 35·8 kW (48 hp) Nelson H-63CP for fixed-wing aircraft

The 32 kW (43 hp) Nelson H-63C four-cylinder two-stroke engine

MOUNTING: Four Lord-type mounts, two on each half of crankcase.

DIMENSIONS (H-63C):
Length	508 mm (20·0 in)
Height	376 mm (14·8 in)
Width	605 mm (23·8 in)

WEIGHT, DRY:
H-63C, with accessories	34·5 kg (76 lb)
H-63CP, with accessories	30·8 kg (68 lb)
H-63CPM	30·8 kg (68 lb)
H-63CPR, H-63CPMR	38·6 kg (85 lb)

POWER RATINGS:
T-O:
H-63C	32 kW (43 hp) at 4,000 rpm
H-63CP, H-63CPM	
	35·8 kW (48 hp) at 4,400 rpm
H-63CPR, H-63CPMR	
	35·4 kW (47·5 hp) at 2,750 output rpm

Max continuous:
H-63C	32 kW (43 hp) at 4,000 rpm
H-63CP, H-63CPM	33·6 kW (45 hp) at 4,000 rpm
H-63CPR, H-63CPMR	
	33·25 kW (44·6 hp) at 2,500 output rpm

FUEL CONSUMPTION:
R models
16 litres (4·2 US gal; 3·47 Imp gal)/h at 2,500 output rpm

NORTHROP
NORTHROP CORPORATION, VENTURA DIVISION

1515 Rancho Conejo Boulevard, Newbury Park, California 91320
Telephone: (805) 498 3131

In 1972 Northrop Corporation acquired the rights to this engine from McCulloch Corporation. The 4318 series continues in production at Ventura Division, to power the KD2R-5 target (see RPVs and Targets section).

NORTHROP MODEL 4318F
US military designation: O-100-3

TYPE: Four-cylinder opposed aircooled two-stroke.
CYLINDERS: Bore 80·8 mm (3³/₁₆ in). Stroke 79·4 mm (3⅛ in). Displacement 1·6 litres (100 cu in). Compression ratio 7·8 : 1. Die-cast aluminium with integral head and hard chrome plated walls.
PISTONS: Cast aluminium. Two rings above pins. Piston (gudgeon) pins of case-hardened steel.
CONNECTING RODS: Forged steel. 'Free-roll' silver-plated bearings at big-end. Small-end carries needle bearing.
CRANKSHAFT: Four-throw one-piece steel forging on four anti-friction bearings, two ball and two needle, one with split race for centre main bearing.
CRANKCASE: One-piece heat-treated permanent-mould aluminium casting, closed at rear end with cast aluminium cover which provides mounting for magneto.
VALVE GEAR: Fuel mixture for scavenging and power stroke introduced to cylinders through crankshaft-driven rotary valves and ported cylinders.
INDUCTION: Crankcase pumping type. Diaphragm-type carburettor with adjustable jet.
FUEL SPECIFICATION: Grade 100/130 aviation fuel (20 parts), two-cycle oil (1 part).
IGNITION: Single magneto and distributor. Directly connected to crankshaft through impulse coupling for easy starting. Radio noise suppressor included. BG type RB 916S, AC type 83P or Champion REM-38R spark plugs. Complete radio shielding.
PROPELLER DRIVE: RH tractor. Keyed taper shaft.
STARTING: By separate portable hydraulic starter.
MOUNTING: Three mounting lugs with rubber bushings.
DIMENSIONS:
Length	686 mm (27·0 in)
Width	711 mm (28·0 in)
Height	381 mm (15·0 in)

WEIGHT, DRY:
Less propeller hub	34·9 kg (77 lb)

POWER RATING:
Rated output 62·6-71·6 kW (84-96 hp) at 4,100 rpm
SPECIFIC CONSUMPTION (fuel/oil mixture at S/L at rated power): 127 μJ (0·75 lb/h/hp)

Northrop Ventura targets powered by O-100-3 piston engines rated at 62·6-71·6 kW (84-96 hp)

PRATT & WHITNEY
THE PRATT & WHITNEY AIRCRAFT GROUP OF UNITED TECHNOLOGIES CORPORATION

GROUP HEADQUARTERS: East Hartford, Connecticut 06108
Telephone: (203) 565 4321
GROUP PRESIDENT: Robert J. Carlson
GROUP EXECUTIVE VICE-PRESIDENT, TECHNOLOGY AND STRATEGIC PLANNING: Richard J. Coar
GROUP PUBLIC RELATIONS DIRECTOR: Edward R. Cowles
Commercial Products Division
East Hartford, Connecticut
DIVISION PRESIDENT: David J. Hines
Government Products Division
West Palm Beach, Florida
DIVISION PRESIDENT: Frank W. McAbee Jr
Manufacturing Division
East Hartford, Connecticut
DIVISION PRESIDENT: Donald Nigro
Pratt & Whitney Aircraft of Canada
See separate entry under Canada.

Pratt & Whitney Aircraft was formed in 1925 and rapidly became a world leader in aircraft piston engines. It is now the world's largest producer of gas-turbine engines.

On 23 April 1976 Pratt & Whitney was restructured as the Pratt & Whitney Aircraft Group, composed of four divisions listed above.

Commercial Products Division is responsible for commercial aircraft engines. Government Products Division is responsible for military engines. Manufacturing Division provides plant and facilities for making the products of the

Pratt & Whitney J52-P-408 two-shaft turbojet rated at 50 kN (11,200 lb st)

CPD and GPD. Pratt & Whitney Aircraft of Canada (P&WC), which has its own entry under that country on an earlier page, is responsible for engines for general aviation.

The Pratt & Whitney Aircraft Group has approximately 36,000 employees at locations in Connecticut, and about another 14,000 in Florida and Canada.

Excluding P&WC, the divisions of the Group had by 1980 manufactured more than 62,000 gas-turbine engines, most of them for aircraft. These engines had accumulated over 503 million flight hours in military and commercial service. Most of this time has been logged by the JT3D, JT8D and JT9D turbofans on which the major part of the world's air transport is based.

In August 1975 Pratt & Whitney and Rolls-Royce signed an agreement for joint further development of the Pegasus vectored-thrust turbofan, which includes an option to take up a manufacturing licence for the British engine.

PRATT & WHITNEY JT8
US military designation: J52

The J52 is a medium-sized turbojet which was designed under the auspices of the US Navy Bureau of Weapons. It powers all versions of the Grumman A-6 Intruder/Prowler attack and ECM aircraft and current versions of the McDonnell Douglas A-4 Skyhawk.

J52-P-6A, 6B, 8A, 8B. Rated at 37·8 kN (8,500 lb) (6A, 6B) or 41·4 kN (9,300 lb) (8A, 8B). Powers A-4E, A-4F, TA-4F, TA-4J, A-6A, A-6B, A-6C, A-6E.

J52-P-408. Rated at 50 kN (11,200 lb). Powers A-4F, A-4M, some export A-4 versions, EA-6B.

The J52 is a two-spool turbojet, with total of 12 compressor stages, a 'cannular' type combustion system fed by 36 dual-orifice injectors and independent high-pressure and low-pressure single-stage turbines. Pressure ratio ranges from 12·4 to 14·6 : 1. Several advanced design features are incorporated to achieve the rating increases

Pratt & Whitney TF33-P-7 turbofan rated at 93·4 kN (21,000 lb st)

with a minimum change in engine envelope and weight compared to previous JT8 (J52) models. These include two-position inlet guide vanes and aircooled first-stage turbine vanes and blades. In addition, the burner cans include features for reduced smoke. Data are for P-408:

DIMENSIONS:
Diameter	814·3 mm (32·06 in)
Length	3,020 mm (118·9 in)

WEIGHT, DRY: 1,052 kg (2,318 lb)

PRATT & WHITNEY JT4
US military designation: J75

Last described in the 1970-71 *Jane's*, about 50 of these large two-shaft turbojets, of J75-P-13 type, are being rebuilt by Pratt & Whitney Aircraft to power Lockheed TR-1 reconnaissance aircraft. Afterburners will be removed and other changes made.

PRATT & WHITNEY JT3D
US military designation: TF33

The JT3D is a turbofan version of the J57 turbojet, handling almost 2·5 times more air than the J57 and with pressure ratio ranging from 13 : 1 on the JT3D-1 to 14·3 : 1 on the JT3D-8A (TF33-P-7).

Flight trials in a B-52 Stratofortress bomber and Boeing 707 and DC-8 transports began in 1960. The JT3D powers all late versions of these aircraft. The Lockheed C-141A StarLifter military transport uses the TF33-P-7 version, with an additional stage of compression. In January 1973 the -7 engine, modified to incorporate additional accessory drives, was selected to power the Boeing E-3A (AWACS) aircraft. Designation of the E-3A engine is TF33-PW-100A (JT3D-8B).

More than 8,480 JT3D turbofans, including converted JT3C engines, had been delivered by the end of 1979. Additional engines remain to be delivered.

DIMENSIONS:
Diameter:
JT3D-3B	1,350 mm (53·14 in)
TF33-PW-100A	1,373 mm (54·06 in)

Length:
JT3D-3B	3,479 mm (137 in)
TF33-PW-100A	3,607 mm (142 in)

WEIGHT, DRY:
JT3D-3B	1,969 kg (4,340 lb)
TF33-PW-100A	2,173 kg (4,790 lb)

PERFORMANCE RATINGS (T-O, S/L, static):
JT3D-3B	80 kN (18,000 lb st)
TF33-PW-100A	93·4 kN (21,000 lb st)

SPECIFIC FUEL CONSUMPTION (T-O rating):
JT3D-3B	15·5 mg/Ns (0·535 lb/h/lb st)
TF33-PW-100A	15·86 mg/Ns (0·560 lb/h/lb st)

PRATT & WHITNEY JT8D

This turbofan engine was developed as a company-sponsored project to power the Boeing 727. It was later selected for other types of aircraft, and supersonic military versions of the JT8D have been developed in Sweden by Volvo Flygmotor (see RM8 in that company's entry).

Construction of the JT8D is largely of steel and titanium. An annular by-pass duct runs the full length of the engine, with balanced mixing of the hot and cold air streams in the tailpipe.

The JT8D entered commercial service on 1 February 1964. It has since become the most widely used commercial jet engine, over 9,700 having logged more than 160 million flight hours.

The following are the basic versions:

JT8D-1, -1A, -1B. Initial version rated at 62·3 kN (14,000 lb st). Powers Boeing 727-100 and -100C, McDonnell Douglas DC-9-10 and -10F, and Aérospatiale Caravelle 10B and 10R.

Pratt & Whitney JT8D-209 two-shaft turbofan rated at 85·6 kN (19,250 lb st) to 28·9°C

JT8D-7, -7A, -7B. Develops 62·3 kN (14,000 lb st) to 28·9 °C at S/L. Specified for Boeing 727-100, -100C and -200, Boeing 737-100 and -200, McDonnell Douglas DC-9-10, -30 and -30F, Aérospatiale Caravelle 10R and 11R.

JT8D-9, -9A. Develops 64·5 kN (14,500 lb st) to 28·9°C at S/L. Specified for Boeing 727-100, -100C and -200, 737-200, -200C and T-43A, McDonnell Douglas DC-9-20, -30, -40, C-9A, C-9B and VC-9C, Aérospatiale Caravelle 12 and Kawasaki C-1. Deliveries began in July 1967. Produced under licence in Japan (see entry under Mitsubishi).

JT8D-11. Develops 66·7 kN (15,000 lb st) to 28·9°C at S/L. Specified for McDonnell Douglas DC-9-20, -30 and 40 series aircraft and Boeing 727-200. Deliveries began in November 1968.

JT8D-15. Develops 69 kN (15,500 lb st) to 28·9°C. FAA certification was received and deliveries began in April 1971. Powers Dassault Mercure, Boeing Advanced 727 and 737, and DC-9. Entered service 1972.

JT8D-17. Develops 71·2 kN (16,000 lb st) to 28·9°C. Certificated on 1 February 1974. Entered service July 1974. Powers advanced versions of Boeing 727 and 737, and DC-9.

JT8D-17R. Alternative T-O rating 72·95 kN (16,400 lb) but has capability of providing 4·448 kN (1,000 lb) additional thrust in the event of significant thrust loss on any other engine. Certificated at 77·40 kN (17,400 lb st) T-O rating in April 1976. Delivery of Advanced 727-200 August 1976 and certification with reserve-thrust feature November 1976.

JT8D-200 Series. Described separately.

Since February 1970 all new JT8D engines have incorporated smoke-reduction hardware, and conversion kits are available for in-service engines. Low-emission burners using aerating nozzles are being developed for the JT8D. Two noise-reduction options are also available for all

JT8D models. Maximum TBO for the JT8D is 16,800 h.

TYPE: Axial-flow two-spool turbofan.

AIR INTAKE: Annular with 19 fixed inlet guide vanes.

FAN: Two-stage front fan. First stage has 27 titanium blades (30 in -1 and -7) dovetailed into discs. First-stage blades have integral shroud at about 61 per cent span. Airflow: -1, -1A, -7, -7A, 143 kg (315 lb)/s; -9, -9A, 145 kg (319 lb)/s; -11, -15, 146 kg (322 lb)/s; -17, 147 kg (324 lb)/s; -17R, 148 kg (326 lb)/s. Bypass ratio: -1, 1A, -7, -7A, 1·10; -9, -9A, 1·04; -11, 1·05; -15, 1·03; 17, 1·02; -17R, 1·00.

LP COMPRESSOR: Six-stage axial, integral with fan stages, on inner of two concentric shafts. Blades made of titanium. Shaft carried in double ball bearings, either half of each bearing being able to handle the complete loading.

HP COMPRESSOR: Seven-stage axial-flow on outer hollow shaft which, like the inner shaft, is carried in double ball bearings. One-piece casing. Blades made of steel or titanium. Overall pressure ratio: -1, -1A, -7, -7A, 15·8; 9, -9A, 15·9; -11, 16·2; -15, 16·5; -17, 16·9; -17R, 17·3.

COMBUSTION CHAMBER: Cannular type with nine cylindrical flame-tubes, each downstream of a single Duplex burner and discharging into a single annular nozzle.

HP TURBINE: Single-stage axial-flow. Solid blades in -1 to 9, aircooled in -11 and later; guide vanes hollow and aircooled in all models.

LP TURBINE: Three-stage axial-flow. Solid blades and guide vanes.

DIMENSIONS (-1 to -17R):
Diameter	1,080 mm (42·5 in)
Length	3,048 mm (120·0 in)

WEIGHT, DRY:
JT8D-1, -1A, -1B	1,431 kg (3,155 lb)
JT8D-7, -7A, -7B	1,454 kg (3,205 lb)
JT8D-9	1,475 kg (3,252 lb)
JT8D-9A	1,520 kg (3,352 lb)
JT8D-11, -15	1,537 kg (3,389 lb)
JT8D-17	1,546 kg (3,410 lb)
JT8D-17R	1,585 kg (3,495 lb)

PERFORMANCE RATINGS:
T-O thrust (S/L, static): see model descriptions
Max cruise thrust (10,665 m; 35,000 ft at Mach 0·8):
JT8D-1, -1A	15·7 kN (3,520 lb)
JT8D-7, -7A	16·1 kN (3,630 lb)
JT8D-9, -9A	18·2 kN (4,100 lb)
JT8D-11	17·6 kN (3,950 lb)
JT8D-15	18·3 kN (4,100 lb)
JT8D-17, -17R	18·9 kN (4,240 lb)
	(at 9,145 m; 30,000 ft at Mach 0·8)

SPECIFIC FUEL CONSUMPTION:
T-O rating:
JT8D-1, -1A, -7, -7A	16·57 mg/Ns (0·585 lb/h/lb st)
JT8D-9, 9A	16·85 mg/Ns (0·595 lb/h/lb st)
JT8D-11	17·56 mg/Ns (0·620 lb/h/lb st)
JT8D-15	17·84 mg/Ns (0·630 lb/h/lb st)
JT8D-17	18·27 mg/Ns (0·645 lb/h/lb st)
JT8D-17R (alt T-O)	18·55 mg/Ns (0·655 lb/h/lb st)

Max cruise rating, as above:
JT8D-1, -1A	22·24 mg/Ns (0·785 lb/h/lb st)
JT8D-7, -7A	22·38 mg/Ns (0·790 lb/h/lb st)
JT8D-9, -9A	22·86 mg/Ns (0·807 lb/h/lb st)
JT8D-11	23·14 mg/Ns (0·817 lb/h/lb st)
JT8D-15	22·97 mg/Ns (0·811 lb/h/lb st)
JT8D-17, -17R	23·37 mg/Ns (0·825 lb/h/lb st)

Pratt & Whitney JT8D-17R two-shaft turbofan rated at 77·40 kN (17,400 lb st) to 25°C

PRATT & WHITNEY JT8D-200 SERIES

The first member of this series is the JT8D-209, rated at 82·2 kN (18,500 lb st) to 25°C, for normal use and 85·6 kN (19,250 lb st) to 28·9°C following loss of thrust on any other engine. This reduced-noise derivative of the JT8D family is substantially redesigned. The JT8D-209 combines the HP compressor, HP turbine spool and combustion section of the JT8D-9 with advanced LP technology derived from the NASA JT8D Refan Programme and other recently developed P&WA engines. The 200 Series offers substantially increased thrust with reduced noise and specific fuel consumption, together with the established reliability and low maintenance cost of the JT8D HP spool. The new single-stage fan has increased diameter. The new six-stage LP compressor, integral with the fan, offers increased pressure ratio. The LP turbine has 20 per cent greater annular area and achieves a higher efficiency. Surrounding the engine is a new bypass duct. The exhaust system includes a 12-lobe internal mixer to provide forced mixing of the fan and primary streams. A JT8D-209 prototype engine began flight development in a McDonnell Douglas YC-15 AMST prototype transport aircraft on 4 March 1977. Later that month Pratt & Whitney launched the -209 as a commercial product, the first application being the McDonnell Douglas DC-9 Super 80, first flown in June 1979. FAA certification of the JT8D-209 was awarded in the same month, with first production engine delivery in July 1979.

Studies of growth beyond the JT8D-209, by further application of the same derivative engine concept, or by proven turbine section changes, are in progress. The first growth engine, the JT8D-217, is rated at 88·96 kN (20,000 lb st) for normal use and 92·75 kN (20,850 lb st) following loss of thrust on any other engine. Engine certification and production availability were scheduled for October 1980. McDonnell Douglas will begin delivery of DC-9-80 aircraft powered by the JT8D-217 in 1981.
TYPE: Axial-flow two-spool turbofan.
AIR INTAKE: Annular, with 23 fixed inlet guide vanes.
FAN: Single-stage front fan has 34 titanium blades, with part-span shrouds, dovetailed into discs. Airflow: -209, 213 kg (469 lb)/s; -217, 217 kg (483 lb)/s. Bypass ratio: -209, 1·78; -217, 1·70.
LP COMPRESSOR: Six-stage axial, integral with fan; blades of titanium.
HP COMPRESSOR: Seven-stage axial on outer hollow shaft. One-piece casing. Blades of steel or titanium. Overall pressure ratio: -209, 17·1; -217, 18·6.
COMBUSTION CHAMBER: Nine cannular low-emissions burners with aerating fuel nozzles.
HP TURBINE: Single-stage axial. Aircooled guide vanes; solid rotor blades in -209, aircooled in -217.
LP TURBINE: Three-stage axial. Solid blades and guide vanes.
DIMENSIONS:
  Diameter   1,250 mm (49.2 in)
  Length   3,911 mm (154 in)
WEIGHT, DRY:
  JT8D-209   2,001 kg (4,410 lb)
  JT8D-217   2,025 kg (4,465 lb)
PERFORMANCE RATINGS:
  T-O (S/L static): see model descriptions
  Max cruise thrust (10,665 m; 35,000 ft at Mach 0·8):
  JT8D-209   21·9 kN (4,950 lb)
  JT8D-217   23·75 kN (5,350 lb)
SPECIFIC FUEL CONSUMPTION:
  Max cruise rating, as above:
  JT8D-209   20.50 mg/Ns (0.724 lb/h/lb st)
  JT8D-217   21.32 mg/Ns (0.753 lb/h/lb st)

PRATT & WHITNEY JT9D
US military designation (JT9D-7): F105-PW-100

Based on technology stemming from the US Air Force heavy freighter propulsion of 1961-63, the JT9D was the first of the new era of very large, high bypass ratio turbofans on which the design of the present generation of wide-body commercial transports rests.

In its basic design the JT9D is compact, being shorter than the JT3D, and has two shafts, each supported in two bearings. In cruising flight the installed sfc is 22-23 per cent lower than for the JT3D or JT8D. Careful attention has been paid to maintenance.

First run of the JT9D was in December 1966, and first engine flight test, with the engine mounted on the starboard inboard pylon of a Boeing B-52E, was in June 1968. The first flight of the Boeing 747 occurred on 9 February 1969. The DC-10-40 flew on 28 February 1972, and a JT9D-powered A300B4 in 1978.
Versions of the JT9D include:
JT9D-3. The initial production model, rated at 193·5 kN (43,500 lb) to 26·7°C. Fitted to first production Boeing 747. Engines delivered from April 1969 and certificated the following month.
JT9D-3A. Incorporates water injection for wet rating of 200 kN (45,000 lb) to 26·7°C. Powers Boeing 747-100 and -200B. Engines delivered from December 1969 and certificated on 9 January 1970.
JT9D-7. This engine incorporates improvements resulting from -3A service experience. The LP compressor has blades and vanes sloped back perpendicular to the inclined

Cutaway drawing of Pratt & Whitney JT8D-200 series turbofan, showing noise-reducing mixing nozzle

Comparative cross-sections of the Pratt & Whitney JT9D-7A *(upper half)* and JT9D-7R4 turbofans

Cutaway drawing of Pratt & Whitney JT9D-7Q turbofan, rated at 236 kN (53,000 lb st)

core airflow for increased stability and life; pylon-matched fan exit vanes reduce sfc; HP compressor discs have a longer life, and the stators are driven through a low-friction mechanism; a short-cone hooded burner increases durability and reduces smoke emission far below the visible level; changes to HP and LP turbines increase life, and improved HP disc sealing improves performance. The -7 was certificated in June 1971. It powers the 747-200B, C, F and SR, raising the certificated take-off weight from 322,050 to 351,530 kg (710,000 to 775,000 lb). On 30 November 1971 the 747-200 was certificated at full weight and thrust, and with a fixed-inlet cowl, quieter than the original type with blow-in doors (104 EPNdB 'traded' compared with 112).

JT9D-7A. This incorporates a number of aerodynamic improvements which provide higher component efficiencies. The result is an increased thrust capability at the same turbine temperature. This has been reflected in rating increases over the JT9D-7. A version of the -7A, with improved component efficiencies to reduce specific fuel consumption, powers the 747SP.

JT9D-7F. Aerodynamically identical to the JT9D-7A, the -7F has first- and second-stage turbine rotor blades and second-stage stator vanes of directionally solidified material, allowing a rise in turbine gas temperature. This is reflected in further increase in thrust. The -7F permits operation at the Boeing 747 basic structural limit of

362,870 kg (800,000 lb). The -7F was certificated in September 1974; first deliveries were made in March 1975.

JT9D-7J. Aerodynamically identical to -7F this has improved cooling and HP turbine to achieve -7F wet T-O rating without water injection.

JT9D-7Q, 7R. Described later.

JT9D-20. In this engine the T-O rating with water injection has been increased to 220 kN; 49,400 lb to 30°C. With this engine, the DC-10-20 was redesignated DC-10-40 and certificated at a gross weight of 530,000 lb for dry operation. At the wet rating (**JT9D-20W**) it is certificated at 251,745 kg (555,000 lb). The D-20 is similar to the D-7, except for external configuration changes such as accessory-gearbox location, thrust-transmitting points and plumbing hardware locations. The gearbox is under the fan exit casing, and the new mounting has enabled the thrust-frame yoke (added to earlier engines to prevent ovalising of the casing) to be eliminated. The D-20 was certificated in October 1972.

JT9D-59A. This engine is the first member of the family of growth versions selected to power the DC-10 and A300B. It evolved from an intensive component development programme begun in 1970, which led to the running of a complete experimental engine at 276 kN (62,000 lb st). The Dash 59A differs from earlier JT9D engines mainly in the following respects: the fan has a diameter approximately 25·4 mm (one inch) larger and reprofiled blades of higher efficiency; the low-pressure compressor has a zero (fourth) stage and is completely redesigned and the whole hot end is entirely redesigned. The burners are recontoured, an HP turbine carbon seal is added, the HP turbine rotor blades are of directionally solidified PWA 1422 superalloy, the HP turbine annulus is of greater area, and the LP turbine is mechanically and aerodynamically redesigned. The carcase of the engine is stressed for 249 kN (56,000 lb st). With a dry rating of 236 kN (53,000 lb) the JT9D-59A was certificated on 12 December 1974; production deliveries began in January 1975. These engines are configured for installation in a common nacelle, developed jointly by P&WA and Rohr Industries, for the 747, DC-10 and A300B. The growth potential of this size of engine is predicted at 267 kN (60,000 lb).

JT9D-70A. This is the corresponding growth version of the JT9D for the Boeing 747. The engine was certificated on 12 December 1974, and first deliveries were made in January 1975 at a rating of 236 kN (53,000 lb). First application is the 747F certificated at 371,946 kg (820,000 lb).

JT9D-7Q Series. These have the same gas path as the -59A and -70A but an exterior configured like the -7 for installation in the Boeing 747-200 nacelle. The combination of improved performance, reduced drag and reduced propulsion-system weight significantly improve 747-200 performance. The -7Q was certificated in October 1978. This series spans a thrust range of 236-249·1 kN (53,000-56,000 lb).

JT9D-7R4 Series. This family comprises eight models (7R4A to 7R4H), with common fan, LP and HP compressor and gearbox modules, incorporating the latest technology and materials. Compared with the 1977 D-7A the 7R4 series has a larger fan with wide-chord blades, a zero-stage on the LP compressor, improved combustor, single-crystal HP turbine blades and many smaller changes. The new engines offer a TSFC reduction of 4·0-6·2 per cent, and weight reduction of 25 kg (55 lb). Compared with the D-59A and D-70A the 7R4F to H offer weight reductions up to 184 kg (405 lb). In 1979 the 7R4A to D were released to manufacturing, for certification in 1980. Selected for A310 (7R4C) and Boeing 767 (7R4D).

Since entry to service on 21 January 1970 the JT9D has gained experience in the 747 more rapidly than any previous engine. Within one year 653 engines had been delivered, and early in 1973 the total exceeded 1,132. Rate of delivery has since slowed but the total now exceeds 2,000 and flight time in early 1980 was in excess of 30 million h.

The following description applies to early versions of the JT9D, with data for later models given in parentheses:

TYPE: Two-shaft turbofan of high bypass ratio.

INTAKE: Direct pitot, annular fixed geometry (except that airframe inlet on early 747 aircraft has blow-in side doors around periphery). No inlet guide vanes ahead of fan. Airflow improved by rotating spinner.

FAN: Single stage, with 46 titanium blades of 4·6 aspect ratio and two part-span shrouds held by dovetails in steel LP rotor. Downstream are 108 aluminium alloy exit guide vanes (96 on the -59A, -70A and -7Q), followed by nine discharge-case radial struts. Fan case of stainless steel and aluminium alloy, designed to contain fan blades. Discharge case lined with perforated acoustic material. Nominal airflow 684 kg (1,509 lb)/s at 3,650 rpm (-7, 698 kg; 1,540 lb/s at 3,750 rpm; -59A, 70A, 734 kg; 1,619 lb/s). Pressure ratio: typically 1·6 : 1. Bypass ratio: -3A, 5·17 : 1; -7, 5·15 : 1; -59A, -70A, 4·9 : 1.

LP COMPRESSOR: Three stages (JT9D-59A, -70A, 7Q/Q1, four different stages), rotating with fan. Rotor made up of rings, spacers and conical disc splined to steel LP shaft and held by lock-nut ahead of fan and overhung ahead of main LP ball thrust bearing. Hyd-

raulically opened bleed ring at LP exit to increase flight-idle stall margin and excess air during deceleration. Rotor stages have 124, 132 and 130 dovetailed blades of titanium alloy. First stator stage anti-iced by 9th stage bleed air. Stator stages have 88, 128 and 126 titanium vanes and 120 (4th stage) nickel alloy vanes, all riveted to outer rings. Casing of aluminium alloy. Core airflow typically 118 kg (260 lb)/s (all versions).

HP COMPRESSOR: Eleven stages. All stages have rings or centreless discs with integral spacers carried on conical discs at 3rd and 11th stages on HP shaft of titanium alloy (front) and high-nickel alloy (rear), bolted at rear hub. Rotor stages have 60, 84, 102, 100, 110, 108, 104, 94 and 100 dovetailed titanium blades and 102 and 90 nickel alloy blades. Stator has 76, 70, 80, 106, 100 and 112 titanium alloy vanes and 126, 146, 154, 158 and 92 vanes of nickel alloy, all brazed to inner and outer rings. First four stator stages are variable, positioned by hydraulic actuator to provide adequate stall margin for starting, acceleration and part-power operation. Casing of titanium alloys (last two stages, nickel alloy) has bleed ports supplying 8th-stage air for airframe requirements. Max HP speed: -3A, 7,580 rpm; -7, 8,000 rpm. Overall engine pressure ratio: -3A, 21·5 : 1; -7, 22·3 : 1; -59A, -70A, 24 : 1.

COMBUSTION CHAMBER: The diffuser case, which extends from the HP compressor to the midpoint of the combustion section, incorporates two sets of bleed ports for 15th-stage air for airframe requirements. The forward set takes air from the outside case via an integral manifold and the rear set bleeds air from the inner diameter via four of the ten radial struts. The combustor itself is fabricated in nickel alloy and is annular, with the forward end of the liner extended in 20 conical primary zones held in 20 burners fed from external fuel manifolds. In early models (-3A, -7 and -20), the outer casing can be slid forward over the diffuser for access to the HP turbine. Ignition by dual AC 4-joule capacitor system serving two plugs just above chamber centreline on each side.

FUEL SYSTEM: Pressure type with hydraulic control system operating at up to 76 bars (1,100 lb/sq in). Main components are fuel control, pump, fuel/air heater and fuel/oil heat exchanger. Provision for water injection, as customer option, with regulator, piping and spray nozzles, adds 18·1 kg (40 lb) to engine weight.

FUEL GRADE: P&W specification PWA 522.

HP TURBINE: Two stages. Both have high-nickel discs splined to HP shaft, secured by lock-nut, carrying high-nickel blades in fir-tree roots; first stage has 116 aircooled blades and second has 138 solid blades. Stators have 66 and 90 high-nickel alloy vanes, both rows aircooled. Turbine inlet temperature (-3A, max T-O), typically 1,243°C (-59A, -70A, 1,350-1,370°C).

LP TURBINE: Four stages. Stages have 108, 126, 122 and 116 solid nickel alloy blades held in fir-tree roots in discs of nickel alloy (last disc, iron alloy). Stators have 122, 120, 110 and 102 solid nickel alloy vanes. Exhaust gas temperature after turbine, typically 452°C (-3A) or 482°C (-7, -20).

JET PIPE: Fixed Inconel assembly, with large central plug cone.

REVERSER: Fan duct reverser comprises a translating sleeve (the rearmost portion of fan duct) which moves aft, causing long links to close the blocker doors and simultaneously pulling aft the cascade vanes. Primary (core) reverser, largely of Inconel 625, uses fixed cascades which are uncovered by aft movement of translating sleeves to which are hinged blocker doors pulled by links against the central nozzle plug. No primary reverser is used on -59A, -70A or -7Q.

ACCESSORY DRIVES: Main accessory gearbox driven by tower bevel shaft from front of HP spool and mounted under central diffuser case (-20, -59A, -70A, under fan discharge case). Main driven accessories include CSD, fuel pump and control, starter, hydraulic pump, alternator and N₂ tachometer; Boeing 747 includes primary reverser motor and the DC-10-40 a second hydraulic pump and a fuel boost pump. The box also includes numerous lubrication system items, and provides for hand-turning the HP spool during borescope inspection.

LUBRICATION SYSTEM: Pressure feed through fuel/oil cooler to four main bearings and return through scavenge pumps (-20 also centrifugal scavenge) to 18·8-37·6 litre (5-10 US gal; 4·16-8·32 Imp gal) tank.

OIL GRADE: PWA 521 (blend of synthetic and/or mineral oils).

MOUNTING: From above, in two planes. Front mount (-3A, -7) is double flange at top of fan discharge case, absorbing vertical and side loads. On -20, -59A, -70A the mount is rectangular block above intermediate case, taking vertical and side loads, and thrust brackets at 40° each side of vertical on intermediate-case outer flange. Rear mount (-3A, -7) in double flange above casing in plane of turbine LP bearing, to which engine thrust is transmitted via Y-shaped thrust frame from intermediate case in arrangement that prevents thrust loads reaching (and distorting) the turbine exhaust case. On -20, -59A, -70A, the frame is eliminated and rear mount takes only vertical, side and torsional loads.

STARTING: Pneumatic, by HamStan PS 700 or AiResearch ATS100-384 (DC-10, PS 700 only). Supplied at 2·76-3·10 bars (40-45 lb/sq in) from APU, ground cart or cross-bleed.

DIMENSIONS:
JT9D-3A, -7, -7A, -7F, -7J, -20:
Diameter	2,428 mm (95·6 in)
Length (flange to flange)	3,256 mm (128·2 in)

JT9D-59A, -70A, -7Q:
Diameter	2,482 mm (97·7 in)
Length	3,358 mm (132·2 in)

JT9D-7R4A to H:
Diameter	2,464 mm (97·0 in)
Length	3,371 mm (132·7 in)

WEIGHT, DRY:
Guaranteed, including standard equipment:
JT9D-3A	3,905 kg (8,608 lb)
JT9D-7, -7A	3,982 kg (8,780 lb)
JT9D-7F, -7J	4,014 kg (8,850 lb)
JT9D-20	3,833 kg (8,450 lb)
JT9D-59A	4,146 kg (9,140 lb)
JT9D-70A	4,153 kg (9,155 lb)
JT9D-7Q, -7Q1	4,262 kg (9,395 lb)
JT9D-7R4A to E	3,934 kg (8,675 lb)
JT9D-7R4F	3,968 kg (8,750 lb)
JT9D-7R4G, H	4,014 kg (8,850 lb)

PERFORMANCE RATINGS:*
T-O thrust, dry:
JT9D-3A	196·9 kN (44,250 lb) to 26·7°C
JT9D-7	206 kN (46,300 lb) to 26·7°C
JT9D-7A	208·29 kN (46,950 lb) to 26·7°C
JT9D-7F	213·5 kN (48,000 lb) to 26·7°C
JT9D-7J	222·5 kN (50,000 lb st) to 30°C
JT9D-20	206 kN (46,300 lb) to 28·9°C
JT9D-59A, -70A, -7Q	236 kN (53,000 lb) to 30°C
JT9D-7Q1	242 kN (54,500 lb st) to 30°C
JT9D-7R4A	197·1 kN (44,300 lb) to 30°C
JT9D-7R4B	205·1 kN (46,100 lb) to 30°C
JT9D-7R4C	208·6 kN (46,900 lb) to 30°C
JT9D-7R4D	213·5 kN (48,000 lb) to 30°C
JT9D-7R4E	222·4 kN (50,000 lb) to 30°C
JT9D-7R4F	231·3 kN (52,000 lb) to 30°C
JT9D-7R4G	240·2 kN (54,000 lb) to 30°C
JT9D-7R4H	249·1 kN (56,300 lb) to 30°C

T-O thrust, wet:
JT9D-3A	203·8 kN (45,800 lb) to 26·7°C
JT9D-7	213·1 kN (47,900 lb) to 30°C
JT9D-7A	215·8 kN (48,500 lb) to 30°C
JT9D-7F*	222·5 kN (50,000 lb) to 30°C
JT9D-20*	220 kN (49,400 lb) to 30°C

Max cruise thrust, 10,665 m (35,000 ft) at Mach 0·85:
JT9D-3A, -7	45·4 kN (10,200 lb)
JT9D-7A	47·5 kN (10,680 lb)
JT9D-7F, -7J	49·2 kN (11,050 lb)
JT9D-20	47·5 kN (10,680 lb)
JT9D-59A*, -70A*, -7Q*	53·2 kN (11,950 lb)
JT9D-7Q1	54·3 kN (12,200 lb)
JT9D-7R4A	47·8 kN (10,750 lb)
JT9D-7R4B-E	49·8 kN (11,200 lb)
JT9D-7R4G	52·5 kN (11,800 lb)
JT9D-7R4H	54·5 kN (12,250 lb)

SPECIFIC FUEL CONSUMPTION:
Cruise, Mach 0·85 at 10,665 m (35,000 ft):
JT9D-3A	17·84 mg/Ns (0·630 lb/h/lb)
JT9D-7	18·01 mg/Ns (0·636 lb/h/lb)
JT9D-7A	18·16 mg/Ns (0·641 lb/h/lb)
JT9D-7F*	18·55 mg/Ns (0·655 lb/h/lb)
JT9D-20*	17·67 mg/Ns (0·624 lb/h/lb)
JT9D-59A*, -70A*	17·67 mg/Ns (0·624 lb/h/lb)
JT9D-7Q*	18·66 mg/Ns (0·659 lb/h/lb)
JT9D-7Q1	18·75 mg/Ns (0·662 lb/h/lb)
JT9D-7R4A	17·84 mg/Ns (0·630 lb/h/lb)
JT9D-7R4B, C	17·99 mg/Ns (0·635 lb/h/lb)
JT9D-7R4D, E	18·01 mg/Ns (0·636 lb/h/lb)
JT9D-7R4G	18·47 mg/Ns (0·652 lb/h/lb)
JT9D-7R4H	18·61 mg/Ns (0·657 lb/h/lb)

*Ideal nozzles

PRATT & WHITNEY JT10D

The JT10D is a second-generation high bypass ratio turbofan, intended for medium-sized transport aircraft. Work on the engine began in 1972, and the first JT10D flightweight demonstrator engine ran in August 1974, at a thrust level of 102·3 kN (23,000 lb). Major changes to the engine have been made since that time, to keep abreast of increased thrust requirements and to incorporate advanced-technology features.

The development programme on the **JT10D-232** began in January 1980. This engine is rated at 142·3 kN (32,000 lb st). It incorporates technology advancements such as single-crystal turbine blades, higher-strength disc material, aerodynamically superior aerofoils and an electronic control system. It therefore represents a substantial improvement over the JT10D engines which were proposed earlier.

Specific fuel consumption is reduced 30 per cent compared with first-generation turbofans. Configuration changes have lightened the engine, resulting in a thrust:weight ratio higher than 5·5. The JT10D-232 incorporates the low-noise features of the JT9D, including the use of a single-stage fan without inlet guide vanes, wide axial separation between the blade and vane rows, and a moderate fan tip speed.

The engine is designed to be compatible with acoustically treated nacelles, to achieve noise levels below FAR Pt 36 requirements. The engine is also configured with a low-emissions burner. The first engine test run is scheduled for early 1982. FAA certification is scheduled for mid-1984.

Companies participating in development of the JT10D are Motoren-und Turbinen Union GmbH (MTU) of Federal Germany and Fiat SpA of Italy. P&WA is expected to bear 83·2 per cent of the programme, MTU 12·8 per cent and Fiat 4 per cent. A collaboration agreement between these companies was signed in July 1977.

P&WA is also proceeding with design studies for a smaller version of the JT10D, to be rated at 115·6 kN (26,000 lb st), for application on both new and derivative aircraft. The new JT10D engine family is expected to consist ultimately of a series of models which will span a take-off thrust range of 111·2 to 155·7 kN (25,000 to 35,000 lb), filling the gap between the JT8D and JT9D.

TYPE: Two-shaft turbofan of high bypass ratio.

AIR INTAKE: Direct front entry. No inlet guide vanes or anti-icing.

FAN: Single-stage. Titanium forged hub, with 36 inserted titanium alloy blades with part-span shrouds. Downstream are a single row of exit guide vanes and radial struts supporting the fan case. Rotating fan spinner. Bypass ratio 5 to 6.

LP COMPRESSOR: Three or four stages.

HP COMPRESSOR: Twelve stages. Overall engine pressure ratio 27 to 33.

COMBUSTION CHAMBER: Annular, with flame-tube fabricated in nickel alloy.

HP TURBINE: Two-stage axial with aircooled blades.

LP TURBINE: Four- or five-stage axial.

WEIGHT, DRY: 2,359-2,676 kg (5,200-5,900 lb)

PERFORMANCE RATING (T-O, S/L, Static): See text

PRATT & WHITNEY JTF10A
US military designation: TF30

Development of this high-compression two-spool turbofan was begun in 1958 as a private venture, and resulted in testing of the first turbofan with afterburning. It was chosen subsequently as the power plant for the General Dynamics F-111.

The version used initially in the F-111 was designated TF30-P-1 (JTF10A-20) which provides 82·3 kN (18,500 lb st) with afterburning. It was superseded in the F-111A by the TF30-P-3 (JTF10A-21) which provides the same thrust with reduced sea level supersonic specific fuel consumption. The F-111D is powered by the TF30-P-9 (JTF10A-36) engine with afterburning, rated at 92·7 kN (20,840 lb st). The FB-111 bomber is equipped with the TF30-P-7 (JTF10A-27D) engine, which is in the 89 kN (20,000 lb) thrust class with afterburning. The F-111F is equipped with the TF30-P-100 (JTF10A-32C) engine, an advanced version with higher thrust. The Vought A-7A and A-7B Corsair II tactical attack aircraft are powered by the TF30-P-6 (JTF10A-8) and TF30-P-408 (JTF10A-16A), these being simplified versions without afterburning and rated at 50·5 kN (11,350 lb) and 59·6 kN (13,400 lb st) respectively.

Most recent application of the TF30 is the US Navy's Grumman F-14A Tomcat fighter, powered by the **TF30-P-412A**, a modified TF30-P-12, with a revised form of afterburning nozzle. The P-412A has an afterburning rating of 93 kN (20,900 lb st). In 1977 the P-412A was modified to **TF30-P-414** standard with new first-stage compressor rotor blades and strengthened fan case to ensure containment. The US Navy is converting F-14A engines to P-414 standard.

The most advanced TF30 production version was the USAF **TF30-P-100**, qualified in January 1971, in which weight is held below 1,815 kg (4,000 lb) while increasing thrust to the 111 kN (25,000 lb) class, with reduced fuel consumption.

Time between overhauls of the various TF30 models varies from 850 h (P-100) to 1,500 h.

Pratt & Whitney JT10D demonstrator, run at 102·3 kN (23,000 lb st)

TYPE: Two-shaft axial-flow turbofan.

INTAKE: Direct pitot annular type with 23 fixed inlet guide vanes (19 on P-8 and P-408). Hollow vanes pass anti-icing air.

FAN: Three stages (two on P-8 and P-408). Rotor and stator and casings all of titanium, except for steel containment case on P-412A. Three rotor stages have 28 (with part-span shrouds), 36 and 36 blades, all dovetailed; stator stages have 44, 44 and 48 vanes, all rivet-retained. Pressure ratio 2·14 to 2·4. Mass flow typically 112 kg (247 lb)/s (P-100 118 kg; 260 lb/s).

LP COMPRESSOR: Six stages (seven on P-8 and P-408), constructed integrally with fan to form nine-stage spool. Wholly of titanium construction, except stator blades of steel.

HP COMPRESSOR: Seven stages, constructed mainly of nickel-based alloy.

COMBUSTION CHAMBER: Can-annular, with steel casing and eight Hastelloy X flame cans each held at the front by four dual-orifice burners. Spark igniters in chambers 4 and 5.

FUEL SYSTEM: HP system (above 69 bars; 1,000 lb/sq in), with conventional hydromechanical control. Main elements comprise fuel pump, filter, fuel control, P & D valve and nozzles. Separate afterburner system for A/B engines. No water injection.

FUEL GRADE: JP-4, JP-5, JP-8.

HP TURBINE: Single stage, with aircooled nozzle guide vanes (stators) of cobalt alloy and aircooled rotor blades of nickel-based alloy (P-100 vanes and blades of directionally solidified alloy). Max gas temperature, early models 1,137°C, P-100 1,240°C.

LP TURBINE: Three stages of nickel-based alloys. Rotor stages have 94, 96 and 80 (P-100, 72) fir-tree root blades. Gas temperature after turbine, typically 587°C.

JET PIPE (non-A/B engine): Simple steel pipe where fan airflow and core gas mix before passing through fixed nozzle.

AFTERBURNER: Diffuser leads to combustion section comprising double-wall outer duct and inner liner carrying five-zone combustion system. Ignition by auxiliary squirt in A/B diffuser, coupled with main squirt in No. 4 burner can which produces hot-streak of fuel through the turbine (P-100 engine, fully modulated light-up by 4-joule electrical ignition system). Max gas temperature 1,677°C.

NOZZLE (A/B engines): Primary nozzle has variable area, with six hinged segments actuated by engine-fuel rams (P-100, 18 iris segments translated along curved profile by six long-stroke rams). Ejector nozzle has six blow-in doors with free tail-feathers (P-414, 18 iris segments and no blow-in doors).

Pratt & Whitney TF30-P-412A afterburning turbofan, rated at 93 kN (20,900 lb st)

Longitudinal cross-section through Pratt & Whitney JT10D-232, to be rated at 142·3 kN (32,000 lb st)

Cutaway drawing of Pratt & Whitney TF30-P-100 afterburning turbofan, rated at 111·7 kN (25,100 lb st)

ACCESSORY DRIVES: Main gearbox under compressor, driven by bevel shaft from HP spool. Contains major elements of lubrication and breather systems. Drive pads at front and rear for main and A/B fuel pumps, main oil pump, N_2 tachometer, starter, fluid power pumps and power take-off.

LUBRICATION SYSTEM: Self-contained dry-sump hot-tank system. Accessory gearbox housing forms 15 litre (4 US gal; 3·3 Imp gal) tank. Oil circulated at 3·10 bars (45 lb/sq in) through pump, filter, coolers (air/oil on airframe, fuel/oil on engine and A/B fuel/oil cooler) and three main bearing components; returned by scavenge pumps and de-aerator.

OIL GRADE: MIL-L-7808, MIL-L-23699.

MOUNTING: Two-planar. Front peripheral pair of flanges absorb vertical, side and thrust loads; rear pair of peripheral flanges (in line with No. 6 bearing behind LP turbine) absorb vertical and side loads.

STARTING: Air-turbine starter on left forward drive pad of accessory gearbox.

DIMENSIONS:
Max diameter:
TF30-P-414   1,293 mm (50·9 in)
TF30-P-100   1,242 mm (48·88 in)
Length overall:
TF30-P-414   5,987 mm (235·7 in)
TF30-P-100   6,139 mm (241·7 in)
WEIGHT, DRY:
TF30-P-414   1,905 kg (4,201 lb)
TF30-P-100   1,813 kg (3,999 lb)

PERFORMANCE RATINGS (T-O, S/L):
TF30-P-414   93 kN (20,900 lb st)
TF30-P-100   111·7 kN (25,100 lb st)
SPECIFIC FUEL CONSUMPTION (T-O):
TF30-P-414   78·75 mg/Ns (2·78 lb/h/lb st)
TF30-P-100   69·40 mg/Ns (2·450 lb/h/lb st)

PRATT & WHITNEY JTF22
US military designation: F100

Stemming partly from the JTF16 demonstrator engine designed in 1965-66, the JTF22 is an advanced-technology military turbofan with afterburner for supersonic applications. Basic development was funded as a demonstrator programme for the US Air Force. In February 1970 the decision was taken to use the JTF22 core engine as the basis for the **F100-PW-100** (JTF22A-25A) to power the twin-engined McDonnell Douglas F-15 Eagle fighter for the US Air Force. Subsequently, the F100 was adopted for the single-engined General Dynamics F-16, production versions of which are powered by a slightly modified engine designated **F100-PW-200**, with a backup fuel control system, revised control-system cooling and a forward extension of the compressor inlet.

Some 3,000 h of development testing were accomplished between 1968 and the 60 h PFRT (preliminary flight rating test) in February 1972. The 150 h QT (qualification test) was completed in October 1973. In January 1980 running time exceeded 660,000 h, of which more than 420,000 h had been in the F-15 and 5,800 in the F-16. More than 1,200 engines had been delivered, and

shipments were at the rate of 25 per month. The F100 has a current maximum operating time interval of 1,250 h.

TYPE: Two-shaft turbofan with high-augmentation afterburner.

INTAKE: Direct pitot type. Fabricated titanium, with fixed nose bullet. Single row of 21 inlet guide vanes, with hot-air anti-iced leading-edges and variable-camber trailing-edge flaps.

FAN: Three stages. Fan blades have part-span shrouds. Discs of titanium 6-2-4-6, blades titanium 8-1-1. Entry diameter 928 mm (36·5 in). Bypass ratio 0·7.

COMPRESSOR: Ten-stage axial, on HP shaft. First three stages have variable stators. Discs 1-2, forged Ti 6-2-4-6; 3, forged Ti 8-1-1; 4, forged PWA 1016; 5, 7 and 9, PWA 1027; 6, 8 and 10, Gatorised (isothermal squeeze forging) IN-100. Blades 1-3, Ti 8-1-1; 4, Ti 6-2-4-6; 5-9 Incoloy 901; 10, PWA 1005. Pressure ratio 8 : 1. Overall engine pressure ratio 25 : 1.

COMBUSTION CHAMBER: Annular. Fabricated in nickel alloy with film cooling throughout. Large-diameter air-blast fuel nozzles. Capacitor-discharge ignition.

HP TURBINE: Two stages. Discs forged IN-100. Blades and vanes PWA 1422 directionally solidified alloy with PWA 73 coating; first rotor impingement cooled, second with convective (HP bleed air) only. Maximum gas temperature 1,399°C. Maximum speed 13,450 rpm.

LP TURBINE: Two stages. Discs forged IN-100. Blades, uncooled, cast in IN-100 with PWA 73 coating. Maximum speed 10,400 rpm.

Pratt & Whitney F100-PW-100 augmented turbofan; shown also below in longitudinal cross-section

AFTERBURNER: Five concentric spray rings in flow from core engine; two slightly farther downstream in bypass airflow. Flameholder assembly downstream of spray nozzles, with high-energy electrical ignition to give modulated light-up. Outer bypass duct and other major portions fabricated in sheet and stringer titanium. Interior liner of coated refractory material.

NOZZLE: Multi-flap balanced-beam articulated nozzle giving very wide range in area and profile.

CONTROL SYSTEM: Unified hydromechanical fuel and nozzle-area control, with electronic supervisory control. The F100-PW-200 also has a hydromechanical backup control.

DIMENSIONS:

Overall diameter	1,180 mm (46·5 in)
Length, excl bullet	4,851 mm (191·0 in)

WEIGHT, DRY:

F100-PW-100	1,371 kg (3,020 lb)
F100-PW-200	1,390 kg (3,066 lb)

PERFORMANCE RATINGS (S/L, ISA):

Max T-O, dry	66·7 kN (15,000 lb st) class
Max T-O, augmented	111·2 kN (25,000 lb st) class

PRATT & WHITNEY RL10

The RL10 rocket engine, for the propulsion of space vehicle upper stages, is a regeneratively cooled, turbopump-fed engine with a single chamber. The current RL10A-3-3 production version is rated at 66·7 kN (15,000 lb st) at an altitude of 61,000 m (200,000 ft), and has a nominal specific impulse of 444 s. Propellants are liquid oxygen and liquid hydrogen, injected at a nominal oxidizer-to-fuel mixture ratio of 5·0 : 1. Rated engine thrust is achieved at a nominal design chamber pressure of 27·6 bars (400 lb/sq in) absolute, with a nominal nozzle area ratio of 57 : 1. The engine can be used for multi-engine installation on an interchangeable basis and is capable of multiple starts after extended coast periods.

First deliveries were made in August 1960 for use in NASA's Centaur stage of the Atlas-Centaur rocket, which is powered by two RL10 engines. A six-engine cluster of RL10A-3 engines powered the S-IV stage of the Saturn I, achieving a perfect performance record for the entire launch programme. Over 9,700 RL10 firings have been accomplished, and 146 engines have flown on operational Saturn and Centaur vehicles, accomplishing 226 successful in-flight starts. In the Titan-Centaur 5 mission two RL10 engines accomplished a record seven in-flight starts, five of them after spacecraft separation. Between two starts there was a 5·25 h coast at zero-g.

Experimental versions of the RL10 have been tested at the Pratt & Whitney Aircraft Group's Government Products Division. These tests include variable-thrust operation, low idle operation, pumped idle operation, operation with a 205 : 1 ratio nozzle extension, operation on fluorine/hydrogen, lox/propane and flox/methane propellants. NASA ordered additional RL10 engines to power Centaur missions during the late 1970s.

Pratt & Whitney RL10A-3-3 rocket engine

ROCKETDYNE
ROCKETDYNE DIVISION OF ROCKWELL INTERNATIONAL

HEADQUARTERS: 6633 Canoga Ave, Canoga Park, California 91304
Telephone: (213) 884 4000
OTHER FACILITIES: Santa Susana, California
PRESIDENT: N. J. Ryker
EXECUTIVE VICE-PRESIDENT: N. C. Reuel (Advanced Programmes)
VICE-PRESIDENTS:
  D. J. Sanchini (SSME Programme Manager)
  S. J. Domokos (Laser Programmes)
  E. B. Monteath (MX Programme)
  C. G. Fargo (Engineering and Test)
  A. T. Fiore (Finance and Administration)

Rocketdyne is a division of Rockwell International, devoted primarily to the design and manufacture of rocket engines for the US Air Force and Army and the National Aeronautics and Space Administration. It was established as a separate division on 8 November 1955.

Rocketdyne liquid-propellant engines power more than three-quarters of all large US space vehicle stages.

ROCKETDYNE SSME

On 13 July 1971, the Rocketdyne Division of Rockwell International was selected by the US National Aeronautics and Space Administration to design and develop the main engine for the Orbiter stage of the US Space Shuttle. Three of these engines provide a total of 6,833 kN (1,536,000 lb) vacuum thrust.

Two large solid-propellant boosters are strapped on the sides of the Orbiter's expendable propellant tank which will carry the liquid oxygen and liquid hydrogen for the three main engines in the Orbiter. The Orbiter rides piggyback on the propellant tank in a parallel configuration. The solid motors and the three Space Shuttle Main Engines (SSME) produce 29,037 kN (6,527,000 lb st) to lift the vehicle from the pad in a conventional vertical flight path. The solid motors will burn out at about 40 km (25 miles) altitude, separate from the Orbiter stage, and be lowered by parachutes into the ocean for recovery. The three main engines will continue to power the vehicle to near orbit; the external tank will then separate and be de-orbited and disposed of in a safe area of the ocean. After mission completion the Orbiter will re-enter the Earth's atmosphere and manoeuvre to a landing site for an unpowered horizontal landing similar to that of a conventional jet aircraft.

In overall configuration, the SSME is slightly smaller in size than the F-1 engine used in the Saturn V vehicle first stage. It burns liquid oxygen and liquid hydrogen propellants and has been designed for high reliability, reusability, multiple re-start capability and low cost. It is capable of 7½ h of burn time, accrued during 55 flights. Modified airline maintenance procedures are used to service the engine between flights without removing it from the vehicle.

The design combines the merits of high-chamber-pressure operation, an optimum-performance contoured bell-shaped nozzle, and a regeneratively-cooled thrust chamber, capable of 11° gimballing, for maximum performance and long life. The chamber wall is cooled so efficiently that it is at 567°C, although the combustion temperature is about 3,300°C. No propellants are wasted in the cooling process. The combustion chamber wall is made of slotted metal, rather than tubes, using

Rocketdyne assemblers installing the third SSME on to its handler prior to delivery in December 1977

Rocketdyne-developed NARloy-Z, a copper alloy that is easily machined, has higher strength than pure copper, and has very high thermal conductivity. Tubes are incorporated in the lower nozzle section.

The SSME is controlled by a unique system incorporating dual-redundant digital computers. This system monitors engine parameters such as pressure and temperature and the engine is automatically adjusted to operate at the required thrust and mixture ratio. The system also develops a record of engine operating history for maintenance purposes to improve serviceability and extend total engine life.

The emphasis of the SSME development programme is currently on preparation for the first manned orbital flight (FMOF). Nineteen engines have been tested, including those which are to be used on the first flight. Approximately 500 single-engine tests have been conducted, with a total duration of over 55,000 s. A minimum of 65,000 s is planned prior to FMOF. A major milestone preceding FMOF, the first engine certification cycle, has been completed. Three additional cycles are planned, and two of the three were in progress in early 1980. In addition, component design verification, a form of component qualification, was progressing toward completion prior to FMOF.

Each certification cycle consists of a minimum of 13 tests and 5,000 s, including simulation of nominal and abort mission profiles. The first certification cycle was completed in June 1979 and demonstrated excellent engine operation. After an extensive inspection of component parts, to assess potential wear, the engine was reassembled and was then subjected to a second cycle. A second engine will demonstrate two cycles of similar cer-

Rated at 911·8 kN (205,000 lb) at sea level, the RS2701A is the main engine of the Rocketdyne RS-27 propulsion system

The Rocketdyne MA-5 propulsion system comprises a central sustainer and two booster engines, and (not shown) two small vernier engines for fine control of vehicle velocity and trajectory

tification test requirements. Both engines were in test in early 1980, and the second and third certification cycles were progressing well. All four cycles were scheduled to be completed before the end of June 1980.

The three engines for Orbiter 102 were acceptance tested in early 1979, and delivered to Kennedy Space Center, where they were installed in the vehicle. In addition to a successful acceptance test, the engine specific-impulse performance was demonstrated to be 2 s greater than the specified minimum.

COMBUSTION CHAMBER: Channel-wall construction with regenerative cooling by the hydrogen fuel. Concentric-element injector.

TURBOPUMPS: Two low-pressure pumps boost the inlet pressures for two high-pressure pumps. Dual pre-burners provide turbine-drive gases to power the high-pressure pumps. Hydrogen-pump discharge pressure is 478·3 bars (6,937 lb/sq in) at 37,250 rpm; it develops 56,554 kW (75,840 hp).

CONTROLLER: Honeywell digital computer controller provides closed-loop engine control, in addition to data processing and signal conditioning for control, check-out, monitoring engine status, and maintenance data acquisition.

CONTROLS: A hydraulic-actuation control system is used. The dual-redundant self-monitoring servo-actuators respond to signals from the controller to position the ball valves. A pneumatic system provides backup for the hydraulic system for engine cut-off. Main subcontractors: Honeywell Inc (controller); Hydraulic Research and Manufacturing Co (actuators).

MAINTENANCE: Engine to be maintained using airline-type maintenance procedure for on-the-vehicle servicing. Time between overhauls is 55 flights or 7·5 h of cumulative operation.

DIMENSIONS:
Length	4,242 mm (13 ft 11 in)
Diameter at nozzle exit	2,388 mm (7 ft 10 in)

PERFORMANCE:
S/L thrust (one engine)	1,819 kN (409,000 lb)
Vacuum thrust	2,277 kN (512,000 lb)
Specific impulse	455 s
Chamber pressure	207 bars (3,000 lb/sq in)
Throttling ratio	2 : 1
Expansion ratio:	
Test	35 : 1
Flight	77·5 : 1

ROCKETDYNE RS-27

The RS-27 power plant consists of an RS2701A main engine and two LR101-NA-11 vernier engines. The ver-

niers provide vehicle control during flight and vehicle stabilisation prior to stage separation. The RS-27 is used as the booster propulsion system for the Delta launch vehicle, replacing the Rocketdyne MB-3 (US Air Force designation LR79) propulsion system.

The RS2701A is a single-chamber bipropellant fixed-thrust gimballed engine. It utilises liquid oxygen and RP-1 propellants at a nominal mixture ratio of 2·245 : 1. Its rated thrust is 911·8 kN (205,000 lb) at sea level, with a maximum duration of 242 s. The thrust and mixture ratio are controlled by fixed orifices. The engine is a hybrid design which utilises the turbopump, turbine, gas generator, valves and thrust chamber of the H-1 engine, and the control system, start system and component-packaging arrangement of the MB-3 engine.

DIMENSIONS:
Overall length	3,607 mm (11 ft 10 in)
Envelope max diameter	1,900 mm (6 ft 4 in)

WEIGHT, DRY (approx): 1,025 kg (2,261 lb)

ROCKETDYNE MA-5
USAF designations: YLR89-NA-7 booster, YLR105-NA-7 sustainer and YLR101-NA-15 vernier

The MA-5 propulsion system consists of a dual-chamber liquid-propellant booster engine, a single-chamber liquid-propellant sustainer engine, and two vernier engines to control vehicle roll and to trim final velocity and directional control after burnout of the sustainer. This propulsion system powers the Atlas-Agena and Atlas-Centaur launch vehicles.

The design consists of two gimballed tubular-wall booster chambers, with twin-turbopump feed for the liquid oxygen and RP-1 propellants, and a single gimballed tubular-wall sustainer chamber, with similar feed. Ignition of both boosters and the sustainer engine takes place shortly before the vehicle is launched. Each YLR89-NA-7 booster is rated at 1,646 kN (370,000 lb) but can be derated to 1,495 kN (336,000 lb). The YLR105-NA-7 is rated at 267 kN (60,000 lb) but can be derated to 254 kN (57,000 lb). The YLR101 verniers are rated at 3 kN (669 lb) each.

Production is continuing, and the MA-5 will be used to boost launches until at least 1981.

DIMENSIONS:
Length	2,490 mm (98·0 in)
Diameter, nozzle exit	1,242 mm (48·88 in)

WEIGHT, DRY:
Booster	1,424 kg (3,140 lb)
Sustainer	471 kg (1,037 lb)

Rocketdyne P8E-9 packaged liquid rocket engine for Lance, rated at 222·4-22·24 kN (50,000/5,000 lb)

ROCKETDYNE MA-3
USAF designations: LR89-NA-5 booster, LR105-NA-5 sustainer, and LR101-NA-7 vernier

The MA-3 propulsion system consists of two independent liquid-propellant booster engines, a single-chamber liquid-propellant sustainer engine, and two vernier engines to control vehicle roll and to trim final velocity and directional control after burnout of the sustainer. This propulsion system is used to power Atlas E/F launch vehicles.

The booster and sustainer engines consist of gimballed tubular-wall thrust chambers, and independent bipropellant turbopumps for liquid oxygen and RP-1. The vernier has a gimballed solid-wall regeneratively cooled thrust chamber which receives propellants from the sustainer and propellant tanks after sustainer shutdown. Both the booster engines and sustainer engines are ignited prior to vehicle lift-off, whereas the vernier engines are ignited approximately 3·5 s after the sustainer is started. Each LR89-NA-5 booster engine is rated at 734 kN (165,000 lb) and the LR105-NA-5 sustainer is rated at 254 kN (57,000 lb). The LR101-NA-7 vernier engines are rated at 4·45 kN (1,000 lb) each.

Although not currently in production, the MA-3 will be used to boost launch vehicles until 1983.

DIMENSIONS:
Length	3,371 mm (132·7 in)
Diameter, nozzle exit	1,242 mm (48·88 in)

WEIGHT, DRY:
Booster (each)	626 kg (1,380 lb)
Sustainer	412 kg (909 lb)

ROCKETDYNE P8E-9

Rocketdyne has been under contract to the US Army since August 1971 to deliver production quantities of the P8E-9 rocket engine to power the Lance surface-to-surface missile; previous Lance propulsion had been procured through Vought, the prime contractor. The P8E-9 operates on storable bipropellants (IRFNA, inhibited red fuming nitric acid, and UDMH, unsymmetrical dimethyl hydrazine). The engine uses dual concentric thrust chambers for booster and sustainer operation, with propellants fed from pressurised tanks. Ignition is hypergolic, and chamber and nozzle cooling of both chambers is ablative.

Start of the system is initiated by ignition of the solid-propellant gas generator, which pressurises the propellant tanks, provides engine start, and provides a gas flow through side-mounted spin nozzles for missile rotation. Booster duration is 6 s, with both booster and sustainer engines operating; sustainer operation continues for 120 s with variable thrust. Booster thrust is in the 222·4 kN (50,000 lb) class and sustainer thrust range is from 22·24 kN (5,000 lb) to zero. Area ratio values are 5·7 (booster) and 4·0 (sustainer). Mixture ratio is 3·4, chamber pressure is 65·5 bars (950 lb/sq in), and the motor measures 492·8 mm (19·4 in) long by 538·5 mm (21·2 in) diameter.

ROTORWAY
ROTORWAY INC

14805 S. Interstate 10, Tempe, Arizona 85284
Telephone: (602) 961 1001

RotorWay Inc is a builder of small helicopters (see entry in Aircraft section). For a considerable period it has been developing its own power plant, for these and for other light aircraft. The following is preliminary information:

ROTORWAY RW-100

This is the fixed-wing version of the RotorWay horizontally opposed four-cylinder engine. Like the growing number of builders or converters of water-cooled general-aviation engines, the company expects the RW-100 to be competitive with established aircooled units. It is demonstrating the ability to cruise at 90-95 per cent of maximum power, and thus offers slightly greater cruise power than larger aircooled engines, for fractionally less installed weight, smaller bulk, similar consumption, but using 92-octane automotive fuel, with extended air-

RotorWay RW-100 horizontally-opposed fixed-wing aircraft engine (74·5 kW; 100 hp)

RotorWay RW-133 vertical-crankshaft turbocharged helicopter engine (flat-rated at 119 kW; 160 hp) craft range and much-reduced noise. The RW-100 is offered normally aspirated as a tractor or pusher engine.

DIMENSIONS:
Length, excl exhaust	610 mm (24·0 in)
Width overall	781 mm (30·75 in)
Height overall	457 mm (18·0 in)

WEIGHT, DRY: 74·8 kg (165 lb)
PERFORMANCE RATING: 74·5 kW (100 hp) at 3,000 rpm
SPECIFIC FUEL CONSUMPTION: 64·2 µg/J (0·38 lb/h/shp)

ROTORWAY RW-133
This engine was designed to power the Scorpion Too

light helicopter, but is expected to find a wide market. It was designed with the following objectives in mind: high power/weight ratio; improved fuel economy; reduced noise and emissions; smooth operation; and long, reliable life. It has been developed with and without turbocharger.
TYPE: Horizontally-opposed, vertical-crankshaft, water-cooled four-stroke piston-engine.
CYLINDERS: Offset left and right for plain connecting rods side-by-side. Swept volume 2·19 litres (133 cu in). Compression ratio 9·6 : 1.
INDUCTION: Through circular air cleaner to single downdraught carburettor with fixed main jet and adjustable idle jet.

IGNITION: Aircraft-type magnetos, dual ignition.
LUBRICATION: Oil temperature 82°-99°C. Oil pressure 2·72-4·1 bars (40-60 lb/sq in).
COOLING: Closed water system, operating temperature 82°C.
WEIGHT, DRY (with starter):
Without turbocharger	77·1 kg (170 lb)
With turbocharger	83·9 kg (185 lb)

PERFORMANCE:
Without turbocharger 99·1 kW (133 hp) at 4,500 rpm
With turbocharger (flat-rated) 119 kW (160 hp) at 4,500 rpm

TELEDYNE CAE
TELEDYNE CAE DIVISION OF TELEDYNE INC
HEAD OFFICE: 1330 Laskey Road, Toledo, Ohio 43697
Telephone: (419) 470 3000
PRESIDENT: James L. Murray
EXECUTIVE VICE-PRESIDENT: Raymond Ortiz
VICE-PRESIDENTS:
Dennis E. Barbeau (Engineering)
Eugene R. Sullivan (Finance)
Robert P. Schiller (Marketing, Plans, Contracts)
Frank X. Marsh (Programmes)

The headquarters for management, marketing, finance, engineering and production is the Toledo, Ohio, facility of over 32,500 m² (350,000 sq ft).

From 1951 until 1960 almost all development was based on Turboméca designs. By far the most important of these was the Marboré, from which stemmed the J69 series of turbojets on which the manufacturing programme has depended. Since 1960 Teledyne CAE has embarked on an in-house development programme on a large scale with engine designs for RPVs, targets, cruise missiles and trainer aircraft.

In September 1978 Teledyne CAE was selected by Williams Research as the latter's licensee to be second-source manufacturer of the F107-WR-101 and -400 cruise-missile engines. Full production is planned for 1982.

TELEDYNE CAE 352 and 356
US military designation: J69
The J69 was originally the Turboméca Marboré, which has been developed to meet American requirements. Four versions are currently available as follows:
J69-T-25 (Teledyne CAE Model 352-5A). Long-life version, which powers the Cessna T-37B trainer and is FAA certificated as the Model CJ69-1025. Its air mass flow is 9 kg (19·8 lb)/s. Operational ceiling is 13,720 m (45,000 ft). In production.
J69-T-29 (Teledyne CAE Model 356-7A). Powers the Teledyne Ryan BQM-34A subsonic target drone. Operational ceiling is 18,300 m (60,000 ft). This is a Marboré II with a single-stage transonic axial compressor supercharging the centrifugal stage. In production.
J69-T-41A (Teledyne CAE Model 356-29A). Transonic axial compressor and revised centrifugal stage handling airflow of 13·5 kg (29·8 lb)/s with pressure ratio of 5·45 : 1. Operational ceiling in excess of 21,030 m (69,000 ft). Production is now spares only.
YJ69-T-406 (Teledyne CAE Model 356-34A). Produced for the US Navy's BQM-34E and the US Air Force's BQM-34F supersonic target drones. Initial qualification testing was completed during 1967 and deliveries of production engines began in 1970. The T-406 engine can propel the BQM-34E to Mach 1·5 at 18,300 m (60,000 ft) altitude. Production is now spares only.

The J69-T-29, YJ69-T-406 and J69-T-41A have a single-stage axial compressor ahead of the standard centrifugal compressor. Combustion system and turbine arrangements are basically the same as on the J69-T-25.
DIMENSIONS (nominal):
Length overall:
J69-T-25	899 mm (35·39 in)
YJ69-T-406, J69-T-41A and J69-T-29	1,138 mm (44·8 in)

Width:
J69-T-25	566 mm (22·30 in)
J69-T-41A, J69-T-29	568 mm (22·36 in)
YJ69-T-406	572 mm (22·52 in)

WEIGHT, DRY:
J69-T-25	165 kg (364 lb)
J69-T-29	154 kg (341 lb)
J69-T-41A	159 kg (350 lb)
YJ69-T-406	163 kg (360 lb)

PERFORMANCE RATINGS:
Max rating:
J69-T-25	4·56 kN (1,025 lb) at 21,730 rpm
J69-T-29	7·56 kN (1,700 lb) at 22,000 rpm
J69-T-41A	8·54 kN (1,920 lb) at 22,000 rpm
YJ69-T-406	8·54 kN (1,920 lb) at 22,150 rpm

Normal rating:
J69-T-25	3·91 kN (880 lb) at 20,700 rpm
J69-T-29	6·12 kN (1,375 lb) at 20,790 rpm
J69-T-41A	7·34 kN (1,650 lb) at 20,900 rpm
YJ69-T-406	7·65 kN (1,719 lb) at 21,450 rpm

Teledyne CAE J69-T-29 turbojet of 7·56 kN (1,700 lb st)

Teledyne CAE YJ69-T-406 turbojet of 8·54 kN (1,920 lb st)

Teledyne CAE J100-CA-100 turbojet of 12·01 kN (2,700 lb st)

SPECIFIC FUEL CONSUMPTION:
At max rating:
J69-T-25	32·30 mg/Ns (1·14 lb/h/lb st)
J69-T-41A, J69-T-29	31·16 mg/Ns (1·10 lb/h/lb st)
YJ69-T-406	31·44 mg/Ns (1·11 lb/h/lb st)

TELEDYNE CAE 356-28A
US military designation: J100-CA-100

The Model 356-28A was developed by Teledyne CAE as a power plant for RPVs and other unmanned aircraft. The engine is derived from the J69 family but has no parts in common with the J69 family. It has a two-stage trans-onic axial compressor ahead of the centrifugal stage, handling a mass flow of 20·4 kg (44·9 lb)/s with a pressure ratio of 6·3 : 1. The combustion chamber is annular with centrifugal fuel injection. The turbine has two axial stages, each fitted with replaceable blades. Fixed geometry is used throughout, although the engine is at present operating at altitudes in excess of 22,860 m (75,000 ft).

The J100-CA-100 completed a 108 h qualification test in June 1969. Applications included the Teledyne Ryan 147TE and 147TF medium-altitude intelligence-collection RPVs.

DIMENSIONS:
Length, intake flange to jet pipe flange
	1,225 mm (48·21 in)
Max width	629 mm (24·75 in)
Max height	663 mm (26·10 in)
WEIGHT, DRY:	195 kg (430 lb)

PERFORMANCE RATINGS:
Max	12·01 kN (2,700 lb st) at 20,700 rpm
Normal	10·81 kN (2,430 lb st) at 20,120 rpm

SPECIFIC FUEL CONSUMPTION:
At max rating	31·16 mg/Ns (1·10 lb/h/lb st)

TELEDYNE CAE 356-28F
US military designation: J100-CA-101

This version of the J100 has been optimised for low-altitude performance with minimal cost. Changes include a slight increase in shaft speed, revised radial-diffuser vane angle and reduced turbine inlet nozzle area. Application has not been disclosed.

DIMENSIONS:
Length overall	1,234 mm (48·6 in)
Max width	627 mm (24·7 in)
Max height	643 mm (25·3 in)
WEIGHT, DRY:	195 kg (430 lb)

PERFORMANCE RATINGS:
Military S/L static	13·6 kN (3,050 lb)

SPECIFIC FUEL CONSUMPTION:
Military S/L static	31·16 mg/Ns (1·10 lb/h/lb st)

TELEDYNE CAE 365
US military designation: LJ95

This family of engines had its inception in a lift-jet, the Model 365-7, developed for the US Air Force as the XLJ95-T-1. Details remain classified, except that the engine is in the 22·24 kN (5,000 lb st) class, has an above-average turbine gas temperature and offers a ratio of thrust to weight exceeding 20 : 1, yet is intended for propulsion of manned aircraft.

TELEDYNE CAE 370
US military designation: J402-CA-400

This low-cost expendable engine was designed for the propulsion of cruise-type missiles and is in production for the US Navy AGM-84A and RGM-84A Harpoon missiles. The J402 is noteworthy for its compact component and accessory disposition, giving minimum frontal area. Though the entire design minimises production time and cost, high reliability was a prime requirement. Flight limits are 12,200 m (40,000 ft) and Mach 0·9 continuous or

Mach 1·1 for limited periods. Engine life is reported unofficially to be 1 h.

In 1974 the J402-CA-400 was selected as cruise power plant for the tactical versions of the US Navy Tomahawk Sea Launched Cruise Missile. In partnership with the competing SLCM contractors, Vought Systems Division and GD Convair, Teledyne CAE supported extensive testing, leading to selection of the GD tactical SLCM in mid-1976. Subsequently there were changes in the Tomahawk programme, and though the J402 has been flown in Tomahawk test flights the missile now has a turbofan engine of different manufacture.

TYPE: Single-shaft turbojet.

INTAKE: Direct pitot inlet with four struts.

COMPRESSOR: Single transonic axial compressor with precision cast construction. Single centrifugal compressor with precision cast construction. Max airflow 4·35 kg (9·6 lb)/s. Pressure ratio 5·8.

COMBUSTION CHAMBER: Annular type.

FUEL SYSTEM: Low-pressure supply to centrifugal injection nozzles in compressor shaft. Electronic control system with automatic sequencing and regulation to meet demands of missile flight profile.

TURBINE: Single-stage axial.

JET PIPE: Fixed-area.

ACCESSORIES: Pyrotechnic starting and ignition systems. Optional integral alternator and alternator regulator to give 6 kW of DC power.

MOUNTING: Four main mountings disposed radially around main (compressor diffuser) frame.

DIMENSIONS:
Length (excl bullet)	748 mm (29·44 in)
Overall diameter	318 mm (12·52 in)
WEIGHT, DRY:	45·36 kg (100 lb)

PERFORMANCE RATING:
Max S/L static	2·94 kN (660 lb) at 41,200 rpm

SPECIFIC FUEL CONSUMPTION (S/L, static):
	34·0 mg/Ns (1·20 lb/h/lb st)

TELEDYNE CAE 372-2
US military designation: J402-CA-700

This turbojet is in production for the Beech MQM-107 variable-speed training target. It is based on the Model 370 (J402) but differs in detail engineering and equipment, reflecting the need for repeated missions of extended duration. The electronic fuel control governs engine operation throughout the starting cycle and over the whole operating range. A shaft-mounted high-speed alternator provides 1·2 kW of DC power. Engine life is unofficially reported to be 15 h.

DIMENSIONS:
Length (excl bullet)	753 mm (29·65 in)
Overall diameter	317 mm (12·50 in)
WEIGHT, DRY:	52 kg (115 lb)

PERFORMANCE RATING:
Max S/L static	2·85 kN (640 lb) at 40,400 rpm

SPECIFIC FUEL CONSUMPTION (S/L, static):
	33·71 mg/Ns (1·19 lb/h/lb st)

TELEDYNE CAE 373

A growth version of the basic J402 described above, the CAE 373 is a new turbojet in the 4·00-4·45 kN (900-1,000 lb st) class. Addition of a second axial compressor stage increases pressure ratio to 8·7 : 1 and airflow to 6·2 kg (13·7) lb/s. The engine retains low-cost features but is designed for both expendable and long-life applications. It will be available with various starting options and either high-speed alternator or a centreline reduction gear and starter/generator. The CAE 373 is a company-funded development, and a demonstrator engine ran in 1976. It is intended for missile and RPV applications.

TELEDYNE CAE 440/555

A possible basis for a wide family of advanced small engines for the period after 1975, the 440 and 555 core engines developed as a result of the company's participation in the US Air Force Advanced Turbine Engine Gas Generator programme. Like ATEGG studies by other companies, the Models 440 and 555 have design parameters (pressure ratio, turbine entry temperature and specific fuel consumption) similar to those of the most advanced large engines. Most likely applications of these engine cores would be in turbofans in the 13·3-22·24 kN (3,000-5,000 lb) thrust class for piloted aircraft or high-performance RPVs. A photograph appeared in the 1978-79 *Jane's*.

TELEDYNE CAE 455

In 1979 preliminary details were disclosed of the Model 455H-2, first of the three rival JTDE (Joint Technology Demonstrator Engine) types to complete initial objectives for the US Air Force and Navy APSI (Aircraft Propulsion Subsystem Integration) programme. The 455H-2 uses a USAF-sponsored LP (fan) turbine, Navy-sponsored single-stage fan and HP spool based on the Model 555 described previously. It is intended to lead to a new family of durable, low-cost engines in the 31 kN (7,000 lb st) class for cruise missiles, trainers and liaison aircraft until the end of the century.

Teledyne CAE J402-CA-700 turbojet of 2·85 kN (640 lb st) for MQM-107 variable-speed training target

T-8422-1

Teledyne CAE J402-CA-400 expendable low-cost turbojet of 2·94 kN (660 lb st)

This slightly retouched photograph remains the only illustration of the Teledyne CAE 455H-2 turbofan demonstrator cleared for publication

TELEDYNE CAE 490

This is the French-designed Turboméca-SNECMA Larzac (see Turboméca-SNECMA GRTS in French section), an 'exclusive agreement' for which was announced by Teledyne CAE in January 1973. The American company will "market, manufacture and service" the European turbofan for the USA and Canada.

The president of Teledyne CAE said that the Larzac, the initial US version of which is designated Model 490-4, "provides a valuable new source of flight-ready jet engines for strike and trainer aircraft, missiles and remotely piloted vehicles". A Model 490-4 demonstrator engine began running at Toledo in March 1973, and it is planned eventually to market a commercial Model 490-6. The CAE 490 is also being evaluated as a candidate engine for a future US Navy and/or US Air Force undergraduate pilot trainer.

TELEDYNE CONTINENTAL
TELEDYNE CONTINENTAL MOTORS
Aircraft Products Division
PO Box 90, Mobile, Alabama 36601
Telephone: (205) 438 3411
PRESIDENT: D. G. Bigler
EXECUTIVE VICE-PRESIDENT: J. H. Engler
SENIOR VICE-PRESIDENT: Ralph Hillard
VICE-PRESIDENTS:
  S. A. Riggs (Marketing)
  N. DeLaunay (Operations)
  E. Wallace, Jr (Quality)
  L. Waters (Engineering)
  J. Ishee (Finance)
  K. Oehler (Industrial Relations)
  A. Barkley (Procurement)
DIRECTOR OF MARKETING SUPPORT: Larry Jensen
DIRECTOR OF SERVICE: Larry Anderson
DIRECTOR OF FIELD INVESTIGATION: Robert Moore
DIRECTOR OF COMMUNICATIONS: Don Fairchilds

In 1927, the former Continental Motors Corporation, one of the largest automobile engine manufacturers in the world, produced its first aero-engine, a sleeve-valve aircooled radial incorporating the Argyll (Burt-McCollum) patents, which had been purchased by the Corporation from the British Argyll Company in 1925.

In 1931 the 38 hp A40 flat-four was put on the market. This was followed by the A50, A65, A75, A80 and C90 engines.

In October 1960 it was announced that Rolls-Royce Ltd of England had acquired the licence to manufacture and sell certain engines from the complete range of Continental piston engines throughout the world, apart from the Americas and certain countries in the Far East. (See Rolls-Royce Motors Ltd in UK section.)

CONTINENTAL O-200 SERIES
The O-200-A engine is a four-cylinder horizontally-opposed aircooled engine. It is fitted with a single updraught carburettor, dual magnetos and starter and generator.

The O-200-B is similar to the O-200-A, but is designed for pusher installation.

For other details see table.

CONTINENTAL IO-360 SERIES
The IO-360 is a six-cylinder horizontally-opposed aircooled engine with fuel injection. Design and materials are generally similar to those of IO-346-A (1970-71 *Jane's*), except for number and size of cylinders. Accessories include oil cooler, two magnetos, propeller governor drive, vacuum pump and 24V alternator. The IO-360 has a sandcast crankcase, with the accessory case mounted at the rear. The cylinders are shell-moulded.

The IO-360-C has dual accessory drive. The TSIO-360-A, B and C have a turbocharger pressurised induction system, revised fuel system, starter and accessory drive, scavenge pump and full-flow oil cooler. These engines power the Cessna T337 Skymaster. The TSIO-360-E, F and G are equipped with a complete exhaust system, and the turbocharger is engine mounted. The LTSIO-360-E is identical except that the crankshaft rotates in the opposite direction; they power the Piper Seneca II, Arrow III and Mooney 231.

For further details see table.

CONTINENTAL O-470 SERIES
Engines in the O-470 series (including the E-185 and E-225) are all basically similar. Engines prefixed 'IO' have direct fuel-injection.

The 168 kW and 172 kW (225 hp and 230 hp) models have a compression ratio of 7 : 1, the 186 kW (250 hp) models a ratio of 8 : 1, and the 194 kW (260 hp) models a ratio of 8·6 : 1. The exception is the O-470-U, which has a ratio of 8·6 : 1 and runs on 100LL grade fuel.

The following description refers specifically to the O-470-R, but is generally applicable to all versions:
TYPE: Six-cylinder horizontally-opposed aircooled.
CYLINDERS: Bore 127 mm (5 in). Stroke 101·6 mm (4 in). Swept volume 7·7 litres (471 cu in). Compression ratio 7 : 1. Forged steel barrels with integral cooling fins. Heat-treated cast aluminium alloy heads screwed and shrunk on to barrels.
PISTONS: Aluminium. Four rings, two compression and one oil control above pin and scraper ring below. Steel gudgeon pins with permanently forged-in aluminium end plugs.
CONNECTING RODS: Forged steel. Trimetal bronze replaceable type big-end bearings, bronze bushing little-ends.
CRANKSHAFT: One-piece six-throw chrome-nickel-molybdenum steel forging. Outer surfaces nitrided. One 5th and one 6th order counterweights attached to shaft. Five bearings of replaceable shell type.
CRANKCASE: Two-piece heat-treated aluminium casting divided at vertical lengthwise plane through crankshaft, with integral cast accessory section. The O-470-S and IO-470-VO have squirt nozzles installed in the crankcase to provide oil cooling to the piston inner dome.
VALVE GEAR: Two poppet-type valves per cylinder: one steel inlet and one steel exhaust with Stellite seat. Camshaft gear-driven from crankshaft in lower part of crankcase.
INDUCTION: Updraught gravity-feed carburettor.
FUEL: 80/87 octane (most models use 100LL/100).
IGNITION: Two magnetos on top of accessory section. Two spark plugs per cylinder. Shielded ignition harness.

REPRESENTATIVE TELEDYNE CONTINENTAL HORIZONTALLY-OPPOSED ENGINES

Engine Model	No. of Cylinders	Bore and Stroke mm (in)	Capacity litres (cu in)	Power Ratings kW (hp) at rpm Take-off	M.E.T.O.	Comp. Ratio	Dry Weight* kg (lb)	Dimensions Length mm (in)	Width mm (in)	Height mm (in)	Octane Rating
O-200-A	4	103·2×98·4 (4¹/₁₆×3⅞)	3·28 (201)	74·5 (100) at 2,750	74·5 (100) at 2,750	7·0	99·8 (220)	725 (28·53)	802 (31·56)	589 (23·18)	80/87
IO-360-D	6	112·5×98·4 (4⁷/₁₆×3⅞)	5·9 (360)	157 (210) at 2,800	157 (210) at 2,800	8·5	148·3 (327)	877 (34·53)	798 (31·40)	618 (24·33)	100/130
TSIO-360-C, D	6	112·5×98·4 (4⁷/₁₆×3⅞)	5·9 (360)	168 (225) at 2,800	168 (225) at 2,800	7·5	136 (300)	910† (35·84)	838 (33·03)	603 (23·75)	100/130
TSIO-360-E, F	6	112·5×98·4 (4⁷/₁₆×3⅞)	5·9 (360)	149 (200) at 2,575	149 (200) at 2,575	7·5	175 (385)	1,437§ (56·58)	795 (31·30)	671 (26·44)	100/130
IO-470-H	6	127×101·6 (5×4)	7·7 (471)	194 (260) at 2,625	194 (260) at 2,625	8·6	202·5 (446·5)	1,100 (43·31)	852 (33·56)	502 (19·75)	100/130
O-470-R, S	6	127×101·6 (5×4)	7·7 (471)	172 (230) at 2,600	172 (230) at 2,600	7·0	193·2 (426)	915 (36·03)	852 (33·56)	723 (28·42)	80/87
TSIO-470-D	6	127×101·6 (5×4)	7·7 (471)	194 (260) at 2,600	194 (260) at 2,600	7·5	231·8 (511)	1,465 (58·07)	852 (33·56)	514 (20·25)	100/130
IO-520-A	6	133×101·6 (5¼×4)	8·5 (520)	213 (285) at 2,700	213 (285) at 2,700	8·5	215·9 (476)	1,053 (41·41)	852 (33·56)	502 (19·75)	100/130
IO-520-BA	6	133×101·6 (5¼×4)	8·5 (520)	213 (285) at 2,700	213 (285) at 2,700	8·5	207·3 (457)	1,009 (39·71)	853 (33·58)	678 (26·71)	100/130
IO-520-D	6	133×101·6 (5¼×4)	8·5 (520)	224 (300) at 2,850	213 (285) at 2,700	8·5	208·2 (459)	949 (37·36)	901 (35·46)	604 (23·79)	100/130
IO-520-M	6	133×101·6 (5¼×4)	8·5 (520)	213 (285) at 2,700	213 (285) at 2,700	8·5	188 (415)	1,189 (46·80)	852 (33·56)	518 (20·41)	100/130
TSIO-520-B	6	133×101·6 (5¼×4)	8·5 (520)	213 (285) at 2,700	213 (285) at 2,700	8·5	219 (483)	1,490 (58·67)	852 (33·56)	516 (20·32)	100/130
TSIO-520-C	6	133×101·6 (5¼×4)	8·5 (520)	213 (285) at 2,700	213 (285) at 2,700	7·5	208 (458)	1,040† (40·91)	852 (33·56)	509 (20·04)	100/130
TSIO-520-E	6	133×101·6 (5¼×4)	8·5 (520)	224 (300) at 2,700	224 (300) at 2,700	7·5	219 (483)	1,010† (39·75)	852 (33·56)	527 (20·74)	100/130
TSIO-520-J, N	6	133×101·6 (5¼×4)	8·5 (520)	231 (310) at 2,700	231 (310) at 2,700	7·5	221·3 (487·8)	997 (39·25)	852 (33·56)	516 (20·32)	100/130
TSIO-520-L	6	133×101·6 (5¼×4)	8·5 (520)	231 (310) at 2,700	231 (310) at 2,700	7·5	244·5 (539)	1,286 (50·62)	852 (33·56)	508 (20·02)	100/130
TSIO-520-M, R	6	133×101·6 (5¼×4)	8·5 (520)	231 (310) at 2,700	213 (285) at 2,600	7·5	198 (436)	1,040† (40·91)	852 (33·56)	598 (23·54)	100/130
GTSIO-520-C	6	133×101·6 (5¼×4)	8·5 (520)	254 (340) at 3,200	254 (340) at 3,200	7·5	252·7 (557)	1,081 (42·56)	880 (34·04)	587 (23·1)	100/130
GTSIO-520-F, K	6	133×101·6 (5¼×4)	8·5 (520)	324 (435) at 3,400	324 (435) at 3,400	7·5	290·3 (640)	1,426 (56·12)	880 (34·04)	664 (26·15)	100/130
GTSIO-520-H, L‡, M‡	6	133×101·6 (5¼×4)	8·5 (520)	280 (375) at 3,400	280 (375) at 3,400	7·5	250 (550·37)	1,081 (42·56)	880 (34·04)	680 (26·78)	100/130

*With accessories; †Not including turbocharger;
‡Similar to -H except length 1,114 mm (43·87 in) and weight 248 kg (547 lb) (-M, height 662 mm; 26·08 in)

The 149 kW (200 hp) Teledyne Continental TSIO-360-E

The 280 kW (375 hp) Teledyne Continental GTSIO-520-L

LUBRICATION: Pressure type. Oil cooler on front of crankcase. Oil filter in crankcase. One impeller type pump. Oil pressure 2·07-4·14 bars (30-60 lb/sq in).

PROPELLER DRIVE: RH drive. Direct. Flanged propeller shaft. Provision for constant-speed propeller.

ACCESSORIES: Generator on accessory section. Drives for vacuum pump and tachometer.

STARTING: Electric starter.

MOUNTING: Four mounting points, one at each lower corner of crankcase.

DIMENSIONS, WEIGHTS AND PERFORMANCE:
See table.

CONTINENTAL IO-520 SERIES

These engines are basically similar to the IO-470, but with cylinders of larger bore. They are fitted with an alternator driven either by a belt or by a face gear on the crankshaft. All IO-520 series engines are rated at 213 kW (285 hp) except for the IO-520-D, -E and -F which have a take-off rating of 224 kW (300 hp). IO-520 engines power the Beechcraft Baron and Bonanza, Navion and Cessna 210. New in 1970 were the generally similar IO-520-J, -K and -L, also rated at 213 kW (285 hp) (-K and -L are cleared to 224 kW; 300 hp at 2,850 rpm at take-off). The IO-520-M was developed in 1975 for use in the Cessna 310, replacing the IO-470-V.

The TSIO-520 series are turbocharged. Take-off rating is 213 kW (285 hp) except for the -E and -G, rated at 224 kW (300 hp), and the TSIO-520-J rated at 231 kW (310 hp) and equipped with an intercooler and provision for an overboost valve. These engines power the Cessna 320D, T210 and 210F, and turbocharged Bonanza. The TSIO-520-L was developed for use in the Beech Pressurised Baron. It develops 231 kW (310 hp) at 2,700 rpm, has a complete exhaust system and an engine mounted turbocharger. The TSIO-520-N is used in the Cessna 340A and 414.

For other details see table.

CONTINENTAL GTSIO-520

This is similar to the TSIO-520 range but is geared and uprated. The -C model, rated at 254 kW (340 hp) at 3,200 rpm, powers the Cessna 411. The GTSIO-520-D, rated at 280 kW (375 hp) at 3,400 rpm, powers the Cessna 421. The -K has an integral turbocharger and complete exhaust system; the most powerful Continental engine in production, used in the Rockwell Commander 685. The -G is used in a military application, the -H powers the Cessna 421A Golden Eagle. The -L is used in the Cessna 421C and the -M in the Cessna Titan.

THERMO-JET
THERMO-JET STANDARD INC

PO Box 55976, Houston, Texas 77055
Telephone: (713) 465 5735
MANAGER: John A. Melenric

This company specialises in the design and manufacture of valveless pulse-jet units for remotely piloted vehicles and the homebuilt aircraft markets. These engines are devoid of moving parts and are characterised by multiple reverse-flow air inlets to a combustion chamber in which is burned propane, butane or compressed natural gas, obviating the need for a fuel pump. Intermittent combustion and expulsion takes place at a cycle frequency deter-

Thermo-Jet J13-202 valveless pulse-jet (0·40 kN; 90 lb st)

mined by the chamber size and geometry and combustion pressure.

At present Thermo-Jet is offering four sizes of unit, the J7-300 (0·09 kN, 21 lb st at S/L), J8-200 (0·044 kN, 10 lb st at S/L), J10-200 (0·244 kN, 55 lb st at S/L), and J13-202 (0·4 kN, 90 lb st at S/L). Full details were given in the 1979-80 *Jane's*.

From the top: Thermo-Jet J7-300, J8-200 and J10-200

THIOKOL
THIOKOL CORPORATION

CORPORATE OFFICE: PO Box 1000, Newtown, Pennsylvania 18940
Telephone: (215) 968 5911

GOVERNMENT SYSTEMS GROUP: PO Box 9258, Ogden, Utah 84409
Telephone: (801) 399 1191

SOLID PROPELLANT ROCKET MOTOR PLANTS: Elkton, Maryland; Huntsville, Alabama; Marshall, Texas; Brigham City and Ogden, Utah

PYROTECHNIC AND ORDNANCE PLANTS: Shreveport, Louisiana; Marshall, Texas

CHAIRMAN OF THE BOARD, PRESIDENT AND CHIEF EXECUTIVE: R. E. Davis

VICE-PRESIDENT AND TREASURER: A. P. Roeper

GROUP VICE-PRESIDENTS:
R. N. Thompson (Chemical)
James M. Stone (Government Systems)
E. R. Kearney (General Products)

Organised in 1929, Thiokol Chemical Corporation produced and marketed the first synthetic rubber manufactured in the USA. In 1943, the discovery by Thiokol of liquid polymer, a new type of synthetic rubber, paved the way for the practical development of the 'case-bonded' principle of rocket power plant design. The company's polysulphide liquid polymer proved to be the catalyst for the first mass production of efficient solid-propellant rocket motors, as well as for the development of large solid-propellant motors. The firm's operations have now been organised into separate groups to serve widening areas of related products. Reflecting this diversity, the name was changed to Thiokol Corporation.

Details of some of the more important solid-propellant rocket motors used in missiles, sounding rockets, spacecraft and space launch vehicles are given below. Important current rocket motor activity, of which details cannot be reported, includes: production of gas generators for the Poseidon missile; recent completion of production of the TX-481 Maverick motor, and engineering development of the TX-486 motor for the Patriot air-defence missile.

In 1974 Thiokol Corporation was awarded a contract to develop the solid rocket motors for the NASA Space Shuttle.

THIOKOL SPACE SHUTTLE SRM

The Space Shuttle Solid Rocket Motor is a segmented design which is 3·708 m (146 in) in diameter, 38·1 m (125 ft) long, weighs 569,268 kg (1,255,000 lb), and contains 503,000 kg (1,109,000 lb) of propellant. The SRM is cast in four segments, which are rail-shipped to launch sites at Kennedy Space Center and Vandenberg Air Force Base. At the sites the motors are stacked vertically in pairs as part of the Solid Rocket Booster for the Space Shuttle.

At lift-off, the SRMs are burning in parallel with the three Space Shuttle liquid main engines mounted in the Orbiter. The two SRMs develop 10,535 kN (2,368,000 lb) average thrust each (vacuum conditions) and burn for about two minutes. Thrust-vector control for each SRM is provided by a flexible-bearing movable nozzle, driven by two hydraulic actuators.

After burnout, the two boosters are separated from the vehicle, which continues under the power of the three main engines. The boosters fall into the Earth's atmosphere, where parachutes are deployed to control impact velocity into the ocean. The boosters are then towed back to the launch site, disassembled, preserved, and returned to the factory for propellant reloading (see under CSD in this section).

The motor case consists of 11 weld-free ring-rolled forgings fabricated from Ladish D6AC steel. The ends of

Thiokol Space Shuttle SRM being prepared for static firing

the forged case sections are machined to form tang-and-clevis joints by means of which the sections are assembled into 'casting segments'. Four casting segments (consisting of a forward segment, two centre segments and one aft segment) make up the basic manufacturing and shipping configuration of a single SRM.

The propellant is a PBAN terpolymer composite, bonded to the asbestos-silica filled nitrile-butadiene rubber internal insulation by means of a compatible liner. The propellant grain in the forward end is configured to an 11-point star which transitions into a tapered centre-perforated (CP) cross-section for the centre and aft sections of the motor. The nozzle is a 20·4 per cent submerged, omni-directionally movable, flexible-bearing nozzle with a throat diameter of 1·38 m (54·5 in) and an exit-plane diameter of 3·76 m (148 in). The nozzle consists of insulated aluminium and steel components. The flexible bearing which provides thrust vector control (TVC) consists of a series of 10 semi-spherical steel shims laminated between flexible elastomer pads.

The ignition system is mounted internally at the forward end of the forward segment. The system consists of an electro-mechanical safe/arm device, an initiator which is a small, multi-nozzled rocket motor containing about 0·7 kg (1·5 lb) of fast-burning propellant, and the main igniter which is an insulated steel-case rocket motor containing about 59 kg (130 lb) of fast-burning propellant. A moulded-silica throat insert in the main igniter directs the flame pattern to the SRM's main propellant grain. Ignition time for the SRMM is approximately 0·2 s.

THIOKOL SSUS-A MOTOR

The Thiokol TU-844 motor provides propulsion for the McDonnell Douglas Spinning Solid Upper Stage (SSUS-A) which launches Atlas-Centaur-class payloads from the Space Shuttle. The motor is a slightly modified third-stage Minuteman III with TVC and roll-control systems removed. Lengths of the nozzle and case are optimized to minimise Space Shuttle user changes. The motor uses an S-901 glassfibre case and is loaded with CTPB propellant. It is 2·12 m (83·4 in) long and 1·32 m (52 in) in diameter, and weighs 3,662 kg (8,074 lb).

TRIDENT MOTORS

The three propulsion stages for the Trident C-4 fleet ballistic missile are being developed and manufactured jointly by Thiokol and Hercules Inc. The motors are loaded with high-energy cross-linked double-base propellant. High-performance subsystems, including Kevlar cases, flex-seal TVC and low-erosion nozzles, have been developed and are being manufactured by the joint venture. Technical data are classified.

POSEIDON FIRST-STAGE MOTORS

The motors for the Poseidon C-3 fleet ballistic missile were manufactured jointly by Thiokol and Hercules Inc. Dimensions and performance of the propulsion stages are not available, due to the classified nature of the programme. Production has been completed, and the motors are currently deployed in the Navy's Poseidon fleet ballistic missile.

THIOKOL LONG-LIFE SRAM MOTOR

Thiokol is under contract to Boeing to improve the ageing and life of the motor for the US Air Force's AGM-69 SRAM missile. A motor with a projected service life of over 10 years has been developed and is currently being qualified. The SRAM motor is 2·54 m (100 in) long, 0·44 m (17·5 in) in diameter, and is loaded with 449 kg (990 lb) of HTPB propellant. The grain configuration consists of an aft-end boost grain and a forward sustain grain. They are separated by a barrier and have separate igniters. The motor has a fixed nozzle and a steel case.

THIOKOL TX-690 (FIREBRAND BOOSTER)

The Thiokol TX-690 is being used to provide initial launch impulse for the US Navy's Firebrand aerial target. The target simulates a family of supersonic anti-ship missiles and provides threat simulation for test and evaluation of anti-ship missile defence systems of the 1980s. The booster motor, designed and built by Thiokol's Huntsville Division, accelerates the drone to supersonic speeds, at which the main ramjet engines take over. The motor is a modification of the Patriot propulsion system. The primary modifications are a canted nozzle and attachment fittings. Thirty motors were ordered for test and evaluation flights.

THIOKOL TE-M-707 (HARPOON)

The TE-M-707 is Thiokol's version of the US Navy's 642AS7000 solid-propellant rocket motor. It provides boost propulsion for the ship- and submarine-launched versions of the Harpoon anti-ship missile. The booster has an outside diameter of 0·34 m (13·5 in) and a length of 0·74 m (29 in); it contains approximately 65 kg (143 lb) of C-1 polyurethane composite propellant. The motor case and nozzle shell are of heat-treated 4130 steel. Glass phenolic insulation material is employed as nozzle insulation, and high-density graphite acts as a throat. The ignition system consists of a basket igniter in line with an electromechanical arm/fire device. The booster provides a nominal total impulse of 160 kN-s (36,000 lb-s). Qualification was to be completed during 1980.

Thiokol SSUS-A motor shown as cutaway drawing

THIOKOL TX-174

The TX-174 is the first stage of the Pershing tactical weapon system. The motor case is a thin-wall flight design fabricated from modified AISI H-11 or type D6AC steel. The contoured nozzle has an expansion ratio for sea-level operation.

The TX-174 has an overall length of 2·61 m (102·61 in) and an outside diameter of 1·02 m (40 in). The nominal propellant weight is 2,019 kg (4,451 lb). The nominal total weight of the TX-174 is 2,270 kg (5,004 lb). It provides an average thrust of 117 kN (26,290 lb) and a total impulse of 1,017,200 lb-s. The web burning time is 38·30 s. The TX-174 utilises a cylindrical-core propellant configuration.

THIOKOL TX-175

The TX-175 is the sustainer stage for the Pershing. The motor case is a thin-wall flight design fabricated from modified AISI H-11 or type D6AC steel. The forward dome of the case has three ports for impulse control. The contoured nozzle is sized for altitude operation.

The TX-175 has an overall length of 2·46 m (96·72 in) and an outside diameter of 1·02 m (40·0 in). The nominal propellant weight is 1,263 kg (2,785 lb). The nominal total weight of the TX-175 is 1,471 kg (3,244 lb). At vacuum conditions, it provides an average thrust of 85·5 kN (19,220 lb) and a total impulse of 757,200 lb-s. The web burning time is 39·0 s. The TX-175 utilises a cylindrical-core propellant configuration.

THIOKOL TE-260G

The TE-260G rocket motor for the Subroc missile incorporates both directional control and thrust reversal. It consists of a cylindrical case containing the Thiokol propellant charge, a dual forward bulkhead design incorporating a thrust-reversal system, and an aft bulkhead containing four nozzles, each of which is equipped with a jetevator thrust vector control system. Six cable-carrying conduits run the full length of the case on the inside wall to allow guidance signals to be transmitted to the aft vector control system.

The TE-260G employs a composite solid propellant which is bonded to the case wall. Its principal constituents are polyurethane fuel binder and ammonium perchlorate oxidiser in a propellant system designed to provide a high specific impulse and a low burning rate. Thiokol developed the polyurethane system specifically to meet the Subroc requirements.

THIOKOL TU-289
US military designation: SR49-TC-1

The TU-289 solid-propellant rocket motor powers the AIR-2A Genie unguided air-to-air missile. It replaced an earlier motor, and has an improved propellant which increases the storage life and permits the missile to be deployed in a wide range of environmental temperatures.

THIOKOL TX-354 CASTOR II

TX-354 motors are used in a variety of applications such as first and second stages, and as strap-on boosters for launch vehicles. The TX-354-3 has a high-altitude nozzle and is used as the second stage of the Scout vehicle. TX-354-4 has a sea-level straight nozzle for first-stage application. TX-354-5 is the strap-on booster for the Delta vehicle. It has an 11° canted sea-level nozzle and is used in groups of three, six, or nine. TX-354 weighs 4,320 to 4,410 kg (9,525 to 9,743 lb). The case without nozzle is 5,130 mm (202 in) long and has a diameter of 787 mm (31

Thiokol Long-life SRAM motor

in). Sea-level thrust is 232 kN (52,150 lb) over a total burning time of 39 s for a total impulse of 886,043 kg-s (1,953,400 lb-s).

THIOKOL TX-481 (MAVERICK)

TX-481 motors are used in the AGM-65A and AGM-65B Maverick missiles. The motor has an overall length of 1,020 mm (40·16 in), is 272 mm (10·7 in) in diameter, and has a total weight of 47·2 kg (104 lb). The case and blast-tube are aluminium. The composite propellant employs a Thiokol polysulphide polymer binder with ammonium perchlorate oxidiser. The motor operates in a boost/sustain mode with thrust levels of 44·5 kN (10,017 lb) in boost for 0·575 s and 9·68 kN (2,175 lb) in sustain phase for 3·495 s. The overall impulse is 6,169 kg-s (13,600 lb-s). The operational temperature range for the motor is −54°C to 71·1°C. Excellent shelf life has been demonstrated.

Production of motors for the A and B models of Maverick began in 1972 and was continuous until 1978 at delivery rates varying from approximately 250 to 1,000 motors per month. The total quantity of motors delivered is 26,213; batch acceptance static firings totalled 1,299.

THIOKOL TX-486 (PATRIOT)

The TX-486 motor is the propulsion system for the Patriot missile which provides defence against high-performance aircraft. The overall length of the motor is 3,302 mm (130 in) and its outside diameter is 406 mm (16·0 in). It weighs approximately 590 kg (1,300 lb). Ballistic parameters for the motor are classified. The motor case is D6AC steel, and the nozzle adapter is 4130 steel. Silica phenolic materials are employed in the nozzle throat and exit cone. The propellant and liner use a hydroxyl-terminated polybutadiene polymer binder; ammonium perchlorate is the propellant oxidiser. The Engineering Development programme for the motor was successfully completed in 1978. Initial production is scheduled for early 1981.

THIOKOL TX-581

The TX-581 (Castor II-X) is an extended-length version of the TX-354 (Castor II) motor and was developed as a strap-on booster with an 11° canted nozzle. It can also be used in first- or second-stage applications with a straight nozzle. The motor is 787·4 mm (31 in) in diameter, 8,000 mm (315 in) long and weighs about 5,806 kg (12,800 lb). Sea-level performance provides an average thrust of approximately 339·4 kN (76,300 lb) over a total burning time of 35·8 s, giving a total impulse of 11,720 kN-s (2,634,900 lb-s), a 35 per cent increase over Castor II.

THIOKOL TX-526 CASTOR IV

TX-526 motors are used in a variety of booster/strap-on applications. The TX-526-0 motor, combined with four Recruit strap-on motors, is the booster for the Athena H vehicle. The TX-526-1 with 7° canted nozzle is qualified for strap-on booster applications. The TX-526-2 with 11° canted nozzle is used as a strap-on booster for the Delta 3914 vehicle, with each vehicle having nine motors. The 9,093 mm (358 in) long, 1,016 mm (40 in) diameter solid-propellant motor weighs 10,550 kg (23,250 lb). It provides an average thrust of 379·3 kN (85,270 lb), with a total burning time of approximately 58 s for a total impulse of 2,159,544 kg-s (4,760,900 lb-s) at sea-level.

THIOKOL TX-633 (MAVERICK)
US military designation: SR-114-TC-1

The TX-633 was developed as a reduced-smoke version of the Maverick rocket motor (see TX-481). Qualification testing was completed in 1977.

Compared with the original Maverick motor, the reduced-smoke model produces equal performance within the same envelope, varying only in the propellant and liner system, ignition system and protective closure. Motor case, blast-tube, nozzle, grain configuration and insulation are identical to the original model. The propellant and liner for this motor employ a hydroxyl-terminated polybutadiene polymer binder; the oxidiser is ammonium perchlorate. The reduced-smoke version of the motor could phase in with the next element of production.

THIOKOL (HARM)
US military designation: XAGM-88A

The HARM motor is a reduced-smoke, dual-thrust rocket that powers the Navy's High-speed Anti-Radiation Missile. The motor is approximately 254 mm (10 in) in diameter and 2,120 mm (83·5 in) long. It utilises a D6AC steel case loaded with 127 kg (280 lb) of reduced-smoke, non-aluminized HTPB propellant, and has a single fixed nozzle. The propellant grain provides a boost/sustain thrust profile.

THIOKOL TE-M-416 TOMAHAWK

The Tomahawk is a high-performance motor designed specifically for use in sounding rocket systems. It is used in the Tomahawk vehicle as a single stage and in several other vehicles, such as Nike-Tomahawk and Terrier-Tomahawk, as the second stage. The motor is 3,607 mm (142 in) long and has a diameter of 229 mm (9 in). It weighs 220 kg (486 lb) and produces 48·9 kN (11,000 lb) thrust at sea level. This motor has been used by NASA in scale studies of the Shuttle SRM acoustic effects on an operational launch.

THIOKOL TX-683 (AIM-9L)

This is a reduced-smoke replacement for the Mk 36 Mod 5, used in the AIM-9L Sidewinder. It uses the same case and has the same performance. Propellant is HTPB/AP; diameter is 127 mm (5 in), length 1,803 mm (71 in) and weight about 45·4 kg (100 lb). Qualification 1980; production 1981.

THIOKOL TX-732 (AMRAAM)

This motor is tailored to the Advanced Medium-Range AAM. It has an operating temperature from −54° to 62·8°C and nozzle/blast tube with composite insulation in a metal shell. The Validation Phase was to be completed in July 1980, with engineering development to start in 1981.

THIOKOL TE-M-29-8

Super Recruit, TE-M-29-8, is an improved version of previous Recruit motor configurations. The burn-time motor total impulse is increased from 55,000 to 62,000 lb-s, while keeping burn time unchanged. Weight is increased by about 6 per cent.

THIOKOL TE-M-307 (APACHE)

The TE-M-307-3 rocket motor was designed for second-stage applications, and therefore includes a 20 second delay igniter. It is 2,741 mm (107·91 in) long, 174·2 mm (6·86 in) in diameter and is used both as a sounding rocket and as a target missile. The TE-M-307-4 version was designed for single-stage applications. It uses the same loaded case and headcap assembly as the TE-M-307-3, with a 3·32 : 1 expansion ratio nozzle and an instantaneous TE-P-415 pyrogen. It is also used as a sounding rocket and as a target missile.

THIOKOL TE-M-364 (STAR-37)

The TE-M-364-2 (STAR-37B) is a 939·8 mm (37 in) diameter spherical main retro-rocket designed for the Surveyor and modified for use on the Burner II stage.

Thiokol TE-M-364-19 (STAR-37F) motor

Modifications consisted of increasing propellant loading to 653 kg (1,440 lb) and strengthening the attachment structure to accommodate higher inertial loads.

The TE-M-364-3 (STAR-37D) is a Surveyor main retro-rocket modified for use as third stage propulsion on the Improved Delta vehicle. Modifications consisted of again increasing propellant load, to 1,440 lb, redesigning the attachment structure to mate with the Delta launch vehicle and changing the diameter to 952·3 mm (37·49 in).

The TE-M-364-4 (STAR-37E) is an elongated version of the Delta motor, the AP/hydrocarbon/Al propellant grain being increased in mass from 653 kg (1,440 lb) to 1,040 kg (2,290 lb) by adding a 355 mm (14 in) cylinder to the case. Average thrust is 68·8 kN (15,472 lb) for a burn time of 41·96 s. This motor provides third-stage propulsion on Improved Delta.

The TE-M-364-19 (STAR-37F) is a shorter (1,518 mm), version of the Delta motor, accommodating 865·5 kg (1,908 lb) of propellant. The nozzle is of composite asbestos, glass and graphite phenolic structure. The titanium case has a 178 mm (7 in) cylindrical section. Average thrust is 59·8 kN (13,440 lb) for a burn time of 40 s. It provides the impulse to circularise the orbit of the FltSatCom satellite at the apogee of the launch orbit. This motor has been selected as the AKM (apogee-kick motor) for Intelsat V.

The TE-M-364-11 (STAR-37G) is a very similar extended Delta motor, likewise used for Improved Delta third-stage propulsion. Average thrust is 62·9 kN (14,145 lb) for a burn time of 45·48 s.

The TE-M-364-14 (STAR-37N) is a version having a propellant loading of 557·9 kg (1,230 lb). Average thrust is 38·4 kN (8,634 lb) for a burn time of 37·7 s. This motor provides third-stage propulsion on the Japanese N vehicle.

The TE-M-364-15 (STAR-37S) is a titanium (6Al-4V) spherical-cased version with modified attachment and propellant loading of 657·7 kg (1,450 lb). Average thrust is 43·5 kN (9,790 lb) for a burn time of 42·2 s. It provides the third-stage propulsion for weather satellites flown on the US Air Force's Thor vehicle.

THIOKOL TE-M-442-1 (STAR-26B)

This motor is spherical, 663 mm (26·1 in) in diameter and 839 mm (33·05 in) long; propellant weight is 238 kg (525 lb) and total motor weight is 261 kg (576 lb). The TE-M-442-1 was developed from the TE-M-442 of 1965 and features a case of titanium instead of steel. It flies as an additional stage to the standard Burner II launch vehicle, atop the TE-M-364-2 second stage.

THIOKOL TE-M-479 (STAR-17)

The TE-M-479 is a 442 mm (17·4 in) spherical rocket motor developed for NASA's Radio Astronomy Explorer satellite programme. The motor is 687 mm (27·06 in) long and serves as the apogee kick stage which makes the orbit of the spacecraft truly circular. Total motor weight is 78·8 kg (173·8 lb); propellant weight is 69·4 kg (153 lb). High mass-fraction and excellent performance reproducibility characterise this motor for space systems application. The TE-M-479 was first flown in July 1968.

THIOKOL TE-M-521 (STAR-17A)

This 444 mm (17·5 in) diameter and 980 mm (38·6 in) long motor was developed by adding a 175 mm (6·9 in) straight section to the spherical TE-M-479 (RAE) motor. The TE-M-521 has a propellant weight of 112 kg (247 lb) and a total weight of 123·9 kg (273·2 lb). It served to 'circularise' the orbit of the Skynet I, NATO I and IMP-H and -J satellites. The motor has a titanium case and flight-proven propellant.

THIOKOL TE-M-541/542 (STAR-6)

This small glassfibre motor measures 157 mm (6·2 in) in diameter and 356 mm (14 in) long and serves in a classified space application. Using the same hardware, with minor insulation changes, the motor is loaded to either of two

Thiokol TE-M-541 (STAR-6) motor

configurations: 4·85 kg (10·7 lb), 1,395 kg-s (3,075 lb-s) total impulse, 5·99 kg (13·2 lb) total weight (TE-M-541); and 3·27 kg (7·2 lb), 930 kg-s (2,050 lb-s) total impulse, 4·8 kg (10·6 lb) total weight (TE-M-542). These motors have an extensive flight history.

THIOKOL TE-M-473 (SANDHAWK)

The Sandhawk TE-M-473 is a high-performance 330 mm (13 in) diameter, 5,105 mm (201 in) long rocket motor designed for sounding rocket use. It features a regressive thrust-time trace, which results in near-constant vehicle acceleration during its 15 s burn time and provides an extremely smooth flight environment. This motor is suited for use in single-stage, two-stage and three-stage vehicle configurations.

THIOKOL TE-M-236 (SARV RETRO)

This is a retrograde motor for an unmanned satellite. It uses an internal-burning case-bonded grain weighing 18·3 kg (40·34 lb) in a case of 4130 steel, with a re-entrant conical rear closure to keep overall length to only 324 mm (12·76 in). Burn-time (7·5 s) average thrust is 5·6 kN (1,250 lb).

THIOKOL TE-M-640 ALTAIR III (STAR-20)

This 0·5 m (19·67 in)-diameter, 1·49 m (58·45 in)-long motor is the fourth stage of the Scout launch vehicle. The 273·3 kg (602·5 lb) AP/CTPB/Al propellant grain is cast in a filament-wound glassfibre case. The external nozzle is a composite of graphite, plastics and steel. Motor thrust is 26·9 kN (6,050 lb) for a burn time of 27·8 s.

THIOKOL TE-M-458 (STAR-13)

This is a deceleration motor used in the Anchored Interplanetary Monitoring Platform (AIMP) programme. The 31 kg (68·3 lb) charge of AP/Al urethane is contained in a spherical case of 6Al-4V titanium, with graphite/vitreous silica phenolic nozzle. Loaded weight is 35·65 kg (78·6 lb) and average thrust 3·8 kN (850 lb) for a burn time of 21·8 s.

THIOKOL TE-M-516 (STAR-13A)

This apogee-boost motor is made by mating the propellant and nozzle of the TE-M-444 with the case and igniter of the TE-M-458. Average thrust is 5·8 kN (1,309 lb) for a burn time of 15·3 s. The motor was used as an injection stage of the Thor Burner II carrying two satellites: Secor and Aurora.

THIOKOL TE-M-604 (STAR-24)

This apogee-boost motor has a 199·5 kg (439·8 lb) charge of AP/hydrocarbon/Al propellant contained in a spherical case of 6Al-4V titanium with graphite/carbon phenolic nozzle. Average thrust is about 20 kN (4,500 lb) for a burn time of 30·21 s. The motor was used as the apogee kick stage on the UK Skynet II and US Air Force Space Test Platform, and successfully placed the Lageos spacecraft in orbit. It is being modified for use on the NASA IUE, and was the orbit-insertion motor for the Pioneer-Venus spacecraft which reached Venus in 1978.

THIOKOL TE-M-616 (STAR-27)

This 694 mm (27·3 in) diameter, 1,303 mm (51·3 in) long apogee boost motor has a 334 kg (736 lb) charge of AP/CTPB/Al propellant in a case of 6 Al-4V titanium and a graphite/carbon-phenolic nozzle. It has a Model 2130 remotely located electromechanical safe/arm device. Motor weight is 363 kg (800 lb); mass fraction is 0·920. Propellant weight can be reduced up to 25 per cent. Average thrust in vacuum is 27 kN (6,080 lb) for a burn time of 34·2 s. This motor was used to place in orbit the Canadian Communications Technology, Japanese Geometeorological, Japanese Broadcast and several US Air Force Navstar satellites. It will also be used for the US Air Force P78-1 and NASA GOES satellites.

THIOKOL TE-M-696/TE-M-697

These qualified 35 mm (1·38 in) diameter motors were developed to provide total impulse reproducibility of 0·77 per cent. The propellant provides exhaust with low radar signature through a canted nozzle. The titanium alloy case minimises weight, and the TAM molybdenum nozzle controls thrust vector. The spin motor is 142 mm (5·6 in) long, weighs 0·28 kg (0·62 lb), and delivers 377·5 N (84·9 lb) thrust in vacuum for 0·30 s. The de-spin motor is 92 mm (3·6 in) long, weighs 0·23 kg (0·51 lb), and delivers 219·2 N (49·3 lb) thrust in vacuum for 0·29 s.

THIOKOL TE-M-700 (STAR-30)

This 762 mm (30 in) diameter, 1,508 mm (59·37 in) long apogee-boost motor has a 472·7 kg (1,042 lb) charge of AP/HTPB/Al propellant in a case of 6Al-4V titanium and with a graphite/carbon-carbon nozzle. The aft-end igniter is initiated by a Model 2130 remotely located safe/arm device. Motor weight is 505·3 kg (1,114 lb); propellant mass fraction is 0·935. The propellant weight can be increased 6 per cent and decreased 10 per cent.

Average thrust in vacuum is 26·6 kN (5,980 lb) over a 51·5 s burn time.

THIOKOL TE-M-711 (STAR-48)

This 1,247 mm (49·1 in) diameter, 1,829 mm (72 in) long perigee kick motor has 1,996 kg (4,400 lb) of AP/HTPB/Al propellant in a case of 6Al-4V titanium and has a deeply submerged nozzle with a graphite throat insert and carbon/carbon exit cone. The aft-end igniter is initiated from a remotely located Model 2130 safe/arm device. Motor weight is 2,109 kg (4,650 lb); propellant mass fraction is 0·946. Average thrust in vacuum is 66 kN (14,900 lb) over an 85 s burn time. The motor is being developed for the Payload Assist Module for spacecraft launches from the Delta launch vehicle and Space Shuttle.

THIOKOL TE-M-762 ANTARES III (STAR-31)

This 762 mm (30 in) diameter, 2,873 mm (113 in) long motor has 1,228 kg (2,840 lb) of AP/HTPB/Al propellant in a filament-wound Kevlar case and a carbon/phenolic nozzle with a carbon/carbon throat insert. Motor weight is 1,393 kg (3,070 lb), including external insulation. Aver-

age thrust is 80 kN (18,000 lb) over a 46 s burn time. The motor is being qualified as an improved third stage for the Scout launch vehicle and was scheduled for initial flight in late 1979.

THIOKOL TE-M-714 (STAR-37X)

This is a high-performance, high-technology motor, series complementing the basic TE-M-364 (STAR-37) series.

The TE-M-714-4 (STAR-37XE) is a 939·8 mm (37 in) diameter, 1,890 mm (74·4 in) elongated spherical rocket motor. Propellant weight is 1,324 kg (2,918 lb), propellant mass fraction is 0·945. The average thrust is 62·3 kN (14,000 lb) for a burn time of 60 s. It will provide upper-stage propulsion for weather satellites flown on the US Air Force Thor vehicle.

The TE-M-714-6 (STAR-37XF) is a shorter, 1,514 mm (59·6 in) long version of the STAR-37XE. The propellant weight is 875 kg (1,929 lb). Average thrust is 40·0 kN (9,000 lb) for a burn time of 62 s. It provides apogee boost propulsion for Intelsat V spacecraft flown on Atlas Centaur, Shuttle and Ariane vehicles.

TRW
TRW DEFENSE AND SPACE SYSTEMS GROUP

HEAD OFFICE: One Space Park, Redondo Beach, California 90278

Telephone: (213) 535 4321

TRW developed, built and launched the first mono-propellant hydrazine propulsion system to enter and be started in space.

TRW produces a wide variety of chemical propulsion engines. One of these, the man-rated Lunar Module Descent Engine, landed Astronauts on the Moon. Another engine was built to provide midcourse trajectory corrections for the Mariner '69 missions to Mars and the Mariner 10 (Venus-Mercury) missions. TRW provided the monopropellant hydrazine orbit-adjust propulsion system for three NASA Atmospheric Explorer Satellites launched in 1973, 1974 and 1975.

TRW's propulsion research programmes include low-thrust monopropellant, bipropellant, colloid, ion, radio-isotope and electro-thermal engines. In addition, an active research programme in low-cost propulsion technology is being continued. Tests of TRW rocket engines are conducted at the company's test site at San Juan Capistrano, California.

TRW TR-201 (DELTA)

A bipropellant engine designed for vacuum operation, the TR-201 serves as propulsion of the second stage of the

NASA/McDonnell Douglas Delta launch vehicle. This is one of NASA's standard production launch vehicles.

TYPE: Liquid bipropellant rocket engine.

PROPELLANTS: Nitrogen tetroxide and 50/50 mix of hydrazine and UDMH.

THRUST CHAMBER: Single chamber. Area ratio 43. Chamber of quartz phenolic construction with ablative cooling. Nozzle of columbium, with radiation cooling. Coaxial injector with hypergolic ignition. Starting by 28V electrical signal to on/off solenoid valves.

THRUST CHAMBER MOUNTING: Gimbal attachment above injector.

PROPELLANT FEED SYSTEM: Pressure feed system by McDonnell Douglas Astronautics. Gas pressure 15·51 bars (225 lb/sq in). Flow rate 5·62 kg (12·4 lb)/s fuel and 8·92 kg (19·7 lb)/s oxidant.

DIMENSIONS:

Length overall	2,156 mm (84·9 in)
Nozzle diameter	922 mm (36·3 in)

WEIGHT, DRY: 113 kg (250 lb)

PERFORMANCE RATING:

Max thrust (vacuum)	43·6 kN (9,800 lb)
Combustion pressure	7·03 bars (102 lb/sq in)
Combustion temperature	2,700°C
Specific impulse	302

TRW TR-201 Delta engine, with vacuum thrust of 43·6 kN (9,800 lb)

VOUGHT
VOUGHT CORPORATION

HEAD OFFICE: PO Box 225907, Dallas, Texas 75265

Telephone: (214) 266 2011

OFFICERS: See Aircraft section

VOUGHT STM

This integral rocket/ramjet vehicle, the first produced under the US Navy's Supersonic Tactical Missile programme, made its initial flight on 21 April 1979, continuing an unbroken string of successes accomplished under the previous Low-Volume Ram Jet (LVRJ) programme. In the STM programme the ramjet vehicles incorporate new low-cost propulsion features and guidance elements in the continuing development of an advanced high-performance long-range missile powered all the way to its target. In the predecessor LVRJ programme, five successful flights were made with range exceeding 87 nm (161 km; 100 miles) and sustained speeds of approx 1,735 knots (3,220 km/h; 2,000 mph).

Vought STM carried by A-7E Corsair

WILLIAMS
WILLIAMS RESEARCH CORPORATION

2280 W Maple Road, Walled Lake, Michigan 48088

Telephone: (313) 624 5200

PRESIDENT: Sam Williams

VICE-PRESIDENTS:
- E. L. Klein (Executive V-P and Chief Operating Officer)
- John Jones (Technical)
- Robert Haas (Engineering)
- Robert Katz (Finance)
- Myron Goers (Operations)
- David C. Jolivette (Public Relations)

Sam Williams believed in 1955 that gas-turbine technology could be extended down to very small sizes, and that if a small turbojet were made available it would find a market. The WR2 first ran at a thrust of 0·31 kN (70 lb) in 1962 and has since been developed into the WR2-6 and WR24-6. The more advanced WR19 uses an aerodynamically similar core and Williams Research is also building a range of shaft-drive engines.

All versions of the US Air Force and Navy cruise missiles, ALCM and Tomahawk, are propelled by the F107 turbofan. New engine production facilities for the F107 have been established in Ogden, Utah, and in September 1978 Teledyne CAE was named as second-source producer, with mass production due in early 1982.

WILLIAMS WR2 and WR24
US military designation (WR24): J400

Air enters at the eye of a single-sided light alloy centrifugal compressor which handles an air mass flow of 1 kg (2·2 lb)/s at a pressure ratio of 4·1 : 1. After passing through the diffuser which provides the structural basis for the engine the air divides, part of it flowing radially inwards as primary combustion airflow and the main bulk entering the short outward-radial annular combustor, through dilution apertures around the outer and rear face of the flame tube.

Fuel is sprayed centrifugally through a group of fine holes in the main compressor drive shaft. Surrounding the fuel pipe along the centreline of the main drive shaft is a cool airflow bled from the diffuser, which escapes through

holes in the drive shaft to cool the combustion flames and reduce metal shaft and bearing temperatures, the main bearing being behind the compressor. A single igniter is mounted in the chamber at 12 o'clock. The hot gas, at about 955°C, then turns inwards and exits rearwards through the single-stage axial turbine and simple jet pipe.

The first production versions of the WR2 are the WR2-6, fitted to the Canadair AN/USD-501 high-performance battlefield reconnaissance vehicle; and the WR24-6 and -7 (YJ400-WR-400 and J400-WR-401) which power, respectively, the Northrop Chukar I and II target drones. The WR2-6 has a variable-area exhaust nozzle with translating central bullet, and drives a DC generator. The WR24 family have a minimal fixed-area jet pipe and drive a 4,000 Hz alternator. The WR24-7 runs at higher temperature than the WR24-6 and incorporates detail modifications which increase mass flow to 1·36 kg (3 lb)/s and pressure ratio to 5·3. The WR24-17, not yet in production, is further uprated though similar externally. More than 4,000 WR2 and WR24 turbojets had been delivered by 1979.

Left: Williams Research WR2-6 turbojet, for the Canadair CL-89 (AN/USD-501) reconnaissance drone (0·56 kN; 125 lb st). Right: Williams Research WR24-7 turbojet (0·76 kN; 170 lb st); the 0·89 kN (200 lb st) WR24-17 is visually identical

DIMENSIONS:
Overall length:
WR2-6	566 mm (22·3 in)
WR24-6	490 mm (19·3 in)
WR24-7, WR24-17	about 635 mm (25 in)

Max diameter:
WR2-6, WR24-6	274 mm (10·8 in)
WR24-7, WR24-17	about 305 mm (12 in)

WEIGHT, DRY:
WR2-6, WR24-6	about 13·6 kg (30 lb)
WR24-7	20 kg (44·0 lb)

MAXIMUM RATINGS (S/L, static):
WR2-6	0·56 kN (125 lb) at 60,000 rpm
WR24-6	0·54 kN (121 lb) at 60,000 rpm
WR24-7	0·76 kN (170 lb)
WR24-17	0·89 kN (200 lb)

SPECIFIC FUEL CONSUMPTION:
WR2-6, WR24-6	35·41 mg/Ns (1·25 lb/h/lb st)

WILLIAMS WR19

To produce this two-shaft turbofan Williams Research used the WR2 as core and added an additional fan, axial compressor and drive turbine on a separate shaft, together with a by-pass duct. The LP turbine is related to those developed for the company's shaft-drive engines.

The WR19 was the power plant used in the Bell Aerosystems Flying Belt. It has also been used in the Williams Aerial Systems Platform (WASP) and Kaman Stowable Aircrew VEhicle Rotoseat (SAVER). From it has been derived the US Air Force/Navy F107, and the WR44 for general aviation, described separately.

In early 1970 the company received a $1,400,000 contract from the US Air Force for further development of a turbofan for future decoys. The company is making great efforts to increase the maximum gas temperature, particularly in the WR19 and derived engines. At present the temperature actually used is about 955°C, with potential of the present materials (Haynes 31 cobalt-base alloy for inlet guide vanes, Inco 100 for first-stage turbine blades and Inco 713 for other hot parts) limited to about 1,010°C.

Despite the mechanical difficulty of working on such small components, with turbine rotor discs and blades cast as single units, Williams is experimenting with aircooled turbine rotor blades and expects soon to be able to operate at gas temperatures higher than 1,100°C. The WR19 would be the first engine offered with cooled blades, and it also continues the company philosophy of using specially developed alternators, governors and other accessories capable of running at the full 60,000 rpm of the main shaft.

AIR INTAKE: Direct pitot type with four struts but no fixed inlet guide vanes. Unlike most WR2 engines the WR19 has a plain annular entry instead of a side intake downstream of an alternator or generator on the nose of the main shaft.

COMPRESSOR: Two-stage metal fan and two-stage axial IP compressor on common shaft leading to HP centrifugal compressor, handed to rotate in opposite direction to minimise gyroscopic couple. Total air mass flow, about 2 kg (4·4 lb)/s; overall pressure ratio, 8·1; by-pass ratio, approximately 1 : 1.

COMBUSTION CHAMBER: Folded annular type, with fuel sprayed from revolving slinger on HP shaft. Dilution airflow admitted through perforated liner; cooling air injected through two sets of holes in HP shaft. Single igniter mounted diagonally on engine upper centreline.

FUEL SYSTEM: Fuel fed at low pressure through transfer seal into pipe in HP shaft and ejected at high centrifugally-induced pressure, through calibrated fine orifices drilled radially through HP shaft in line with combustion chamber.

TURBINE: Single-stage axial-flow HP turbine, with Haynes 31 nozzle guide vanes and rotor wheel cast as single unit in Inco IN 100. Two-stage LP turbine, again with both wheels cast as single units, in Inco 713. Provision to be made for aircooling to raise entry gas temperature from 955°C to above 1,100°C.

JET PIPE: Mixer unit immediately downstream of LP turbine allows by-pass flow to merge with core gas flow to pass through plain propelling nozzle.

ACCESSORIES: Fuel and control system, filters, oil pump, tacho-generator and optional other accessories grouped into flat packages around upper part of fan/IP compressor casing. Starting system, depending on application, drives HP spool.

MOUNTING: Depending on application, main mounting above centrifugal diffuser casing with two double-lug pickups on horizontal centreline at LP turbine casing.

DIMENSIONS:
Length overall	787 mm (31·0 in)
Width	338 mm (13·31 in)
Height	407 mm (16·20 in)

WEIGHT, DRY:
With starter/generator	64·0 kg (141·0 lb)

PERFORMANCE RATING (S/L, static):
Standby/T-O (wet)	3·19 kN (718 lb st)
Maximum continuous	2·22 kN (500 lb st)

WILLIAMS WR19-A7
US military designation: F107

The F107 two-shaft turbofan is an advanced and uprated WR19 originally designed to propel the US Air Force/Boeing ALCM (Air-Launched Cruise Missile). Rated in the 2·67 kN (600 lb st) class, the F107 also powers the General Dynamics Convair Tomahawk Sea-Launched Cruise Missile, and General Dynamics ALCM. Williams has emerged clear winner in the competition to propel US cruise missiles, simplifying the attempt to maximise commonality exerted since 1977 by the JCMPO (Joint Cruise Missiles Project Office). All F107 versions are basically similar, but differ in mission and equipment, as follows:

F107-WR-100. Also designated WR19-A7, this was the engine selected for the Boeing AGM-86A ALCM, making the first ALCM flight at White Sands on 5 March 1976. Prototype engines only.

F107-WR-101. Selected to power the Boeing AGM-86B (ALCM-B). Improved configuration and performance. Qualification testing began in October 1978.

F107-WR-102. Selected to power the General Dynamics AGM-109 Tomahawk ALCM (Air-Launched Cruise Missile).

F107-WR-400. Selected to power the General Dynamics BGM-109 SLCM (Sub/Ship-Launched Cruise Missile) and the GLCM (Ground-Launched Cruise Missile) for the US Air Force, all versions of Tomahawk. An early -400 engine powered the first Tomahawk to fly (air-launched by A-6A) on 5 June 1976.

TYPE: Two-shaft turbofan.

AIR INTAKE: Direct pitot type.

LP COMPRESSOR: Two-stage fan coupled to two-stage IP compressor.

HP COMPRESSOR: Single-stage centrifugal.

COMBUSTION CHAMBER: Folded annular with rotary fuel injection.

TURBINE: Single-stage HP, two-stage LP.

ACCESSORIES: Grouping varies with sub-type. Self-contained lubrication system. Solid-propellant gas-impingement starter.

DIMENSIONS:
Length overall:
F107-WR-100	800 mm (31·5 in)
F107-WR-101	1,232 mm (48·5 in)
F107-WR-102, -400	937 mm (36·9 in)
Envelope diameter	305 mm (12 in)

WEIGHT, DRY:
F107-WR-100	58·7 kg (130 lb)
F107-WR-101	64·0 kg (141 lb)
F107-WR-102	65·8 kg (145 lb)
F107-WR-400	64·4 kg (142 lb)

PERFORMANCE RATING: 2·67 kN (600 lb st) class

WILLIAMS WR 44

In February 1978 Foxjet International signed a contract for exclusive supply for three years of the WR44-800

Williams Research WR19-3-1 two-shaft turbofan. Rating is 3·19 kN (718 lb st)

Williams Research F107-WR-100 two-shaft turbofan, developed for the Air-Launched Cruise Missile. Rating is "in the 2·67 kN/600 lb st class"

Williams Research F107-WR-400 two-shaft turbofan for BGM-109 Tomahawk SLCM and GLCM

Williams Research F107-WR-101 two-shaft turbofan for AGM-86B Air-Launched Cruise Missile

turbofan to power the twin-engined Foxjet. A single WR44 is also planned as a rear engine/APU in one version of the Gulfstream American Hustler.

Development of the WR44 began in 1971, using the WR19 as a basis. By-pass ratio was increased to 3, and overall pressure ratio increased. Claimed to be outstandingly quiet and suitable for general-aviation applications, the WR44 is expected to power the Foxjet on its first flight.

DIMENSIONS:
Length (with tailpipe)	1,143 mm (45·0 in)
Max diameter	419 mm (16·5 in)

WEIGHT, DRY:	87·5 kg (193 lb)
PERFORMANCE RATING (S/L):	
T-O	3·78 kN (850 lb st)

WILLIAMS WR34

This family of simple turboshaft engines is aimed at a wide spectrum of applications, including aviation. Based on a centrifugal compressor and radial inflow turbine, it is robust and reliable, and has unchanged configuration over power outputs from 11-26 kW (15-35 hp) at output speeds of 3,600, 6,000, or 12,000 rpm. Equipped weight is 29·5 kg (65 lb).

Williams Research WR34 turboshaft

ADDENDA
AIRCRAFT

ARGENTINA

AMC (FMA) (page 2)

FMA IA 63

Design of this tandem two-seat jet trainer was reported to be in the final definition phase in mid-1980, with a first flight planned for late 1982 or early 1983.

General appearance of the IA 63 can be seen in the accompanying three-view drawing. The shoulder-mounted wings are of supercritical section, with thickness/chord ratios of 15% at root and 12% at tip, and have two-segment large-area flaps inboard of the ailerons. There is a door-type airbrake on each side of the rear fuselage. The wide-track retractable tricycle landing gear has emergency free-fall extension. Power plant will, it is understood, consist of a single TFE731-3 or JT15D-5 turbofan engine. Pupil and instructor sit on ejection seats beneath individual cockpit canopies, the rear (instructor's) seat being elevated in the now-customary fashion. Accommodation for both occupants is pressurised and air-conditioned. Underwing attachments for drop-tanks and/or armament are intended to be optional, and the aircraft will be capable of up to 20 s of inverted flight. Dual controls are standard.

DIMENSIONS, EXTERNAL:
Wing span	9·68 m (31 ft 9 in)
Wing area, gross	15·11 m² (162·6 sq ft)
Length overall	10·63 m (34 ft 10½ in)
Height overall	3·73 m (12 ft 3 in)

WEIGHT AND LOADING:
T-O weight, 'clean'	3,430 kg (7,560 lb)
Wing loading, 'clean'	227 kg/m² (46·5 lb/sq ft)

PERFORMANCE (estimated, at 'clean' T-O weight):
Never-exceed speed	Mach 0·8
Max level speed at 4,000 m (13,125 ft)	Mach 0·73
Stalling speed, flaps and landing gear down	83 knots (154 km/h; 96 mph)
Ferry range, with auxiliary fuel, at 4,000 m (13,125 ft)	810 nm (1,500 km; 932 miles)

FMA IA 63 tandem two-seat trainer *(Pilot Press, provisional)*

AUSTRALIA

GAF (page 5)

GAF NOMAD

GAF now identifies eight different versions of the Nomad, as follows:

Cargomaster. Cargo transport, with quick-change passenger-carrying capability; available in both N22B and N24A versions (see main entry).

Commuter Liner. Passenger transport, available in 12-passenger N22B and 'stretched' 16-passenger N24A versions.

Floatmaster. Twin-float version of N22B; available in both floatplane and amphibian versions.

Medicmaster. 'Flying doctor' version; available in both N22B and N24A forms.

Missionmaster. Military battlefield support transport, based on N22B.

Searchmaster B. Low-cost surveillance aircraft, based on N22B.

Searchmaster L. More advanced version of B, as described in main entry.

Surveymaster. Photographic or geophysical survey version of N22B.

FRANCE

AÉROSPATIALE (page 56)

AÉROSPATIALE AS 366G DAUPHIN 2

The first HH-65A Dolphin (AS 366G) for the US Coast Guard flew for the first time at Marignane on 23 July 1980.

SOCATA (page 76)

In its production form, the Aérospatiale Epsilon trainer (page 76) will have a new rear fuselage, revised tail surfaces and modified wingtips, as shown in this redrawn three-view *(Pilot Press)*

The first Aérospatiale HH-65A Dolphin for the US Coast Guard

DASSAULT-BREGUET (page 59)

The two-seat Dassault Mirage 2000 B, first flown on 11 October 1980

GERMANY (FEDERAL REPUBLIC)

MBB (page 82)

The CCV (control configured vehicle) technology research programme undertaken by MBB for the Federal German Ministry of Defence had entered its final test stage in the Autumn of 1980. Under this programme, MBB modified a Luftwaffe F-104G Starfighter (see accompanying illustration) by fitting it with a pylon-mounted canard surface just aft of the cockpit, a trimming ballast system, and a digital fly-by-wire redundant flight control system. Flight testing of the modified F-104G began in 1976; following successful component tests, and progressive destabilisation, flight testing in full CCV configuration began in February 1980. A total of 75 full-scale CCV flights was due to be made by the time that the programme ended.

Lockheed F-104G modified by MBB as part of its five-year CCV research programme

INTERNATIONAL

AÉROSPATIALE/AERITALIA

REGIONAL TRANSPORT AIRCRAFT

On 15 July 1980, Aérospatiale of France and Aeritalia of Italy announced that the two companies had concluded a preliminary agreement to study the possibility of joint development of a 44/50-seat regional transport aircraft. Studies are based on the earlier Aérospatiale AS.35 and Aeritalia AIT.230 projects for aircraft in this category. Dependent on the outcome of discussions with potential airline customers, and upon approval by their respective governments, the two manufacturers believe that a jointly-developed aircraft could enter service in 1985.

ITALY

AERITALIA (page 115)

Prototype of the Tyne-engined Aeritalia G222T

AERMACCHI (page 120)

AERMACCHI M.B. 339K VELTRO 2 (GREYHOUND)

The Veltro 2, which perpetuates the name of the Macchi M.C. 205V fighter of the second World War, is a single-seat development of the M.B. 339A, optimised for the roles of light close air support and operational training. It is based on experience gained in the production and operation of the M.B. 326K. The M.B. 339K prototype (I-BITE) flew for the first time on 30 May 1980 and made its first public appearance at the Farnborough International air show in the United Kingdom in August/September 1980.

The airframe and power plant of the M.B. 339A are retained, except for a new forward fuselage with re-designed single-seat cockpit, and a small change in fin and rudder areas; the other major changes concern the avionics and equipment relevant to the different roles performed by the Veltro 2. The following description applies to the basic M.B. 339K; operational capability can, at customer's option, be extended by adopting such additional features as a head-up display, cockpit TV display, ECM, and other improved avionics.

TYPE: Single-seat ground attack aircraft and operational trainer.

AIRFRAME: Structural design criteria based on MIL-A-8860 series of specifications; +8/−4g limit load factor in 'clean' configuration. In the ground attack role, service life requirement is 5,000 flying hours with 10,000 landings. Entire structure is specially treated to prevent corrosion.

WINGS: Servo-powered ailerons, with manual backup, embody aerodynamic balance provisions, and are statically balanced along their entire span. Electrically-actuated trim, operated via artificial feel system. Otherwise as M.B.339A.

FUSELAGE: As M.B.339A, except for modified nose.

TAIL UNIT: As M.B.339A, except for slight changes in fin and rudder areas.

LANDING GEAR: Similar to M.B.339A, but suitable for operation under extremely adverse conditions and having low-pressure main-wheel tubeless tyres, size 545 × 175-10 (14-ply rating).

POWER PLANT: As M.B.339A. Fuel in one fuselage tank, consisting of three rubber cells with a total capacity of 1,030 litres (226·5 Imp gallons), and two integral wing-tip tanks. Standard tip-tanks have a combined capacity of 630 litres (138·5 Imp gallons); this can be increased to 1,000 litres (220 Imp gallons) by the use of tip-tanks with a constant circular section. Total usable internal fuel capacity 1,660 litres (365 Imp gallons) standard, 2,030 litres (446·5 Imp gallons) with circular-section tip-tanks. Single-point pressure refuelling receptacle in port side of fuselage, aft of wing trailing-edge. Gravity refuelling points on top of fuselage and each tip-tank. Provision for two drop-tanks, each of 325 litres (71·5 Imp gallons), on centre underwing stations. Anti-icing system, for engine air intake lips and ducts, is optional.

ACCOMMODATION: Pilot only, on Martin-Baker IT10F zero-zero ejection seat in pressurised cockpit. Rearview mirror standard. One-piece moulded transparent jettisonable canopy, opening sideways to starboard.

SYSTEMS: As M.B.339A.

AVIONICS AND EQUIPMENT: Typical avionics installation includes Collins AN/ARC-159(V) UHF (or Perkin-Elmer SRT-194B VHF) primary com transceiver; Collins 618M-3A or equivalent ARINC 566A VHF/AM (or Collins AN/ARC-186(V) VHF/AM and FM) secondary com transceiver; Collins 1A-210 interphone; Collins AN/ARN-118(V)1 Tacan (or Collins 860E-5 or equivalent ARINC 568 DME) nav system; Fiar/Bendix AN/AP-100(V) IFF; Collins 51RV-4B or equivalent ARINC 547A-4 VOR/ILS, including localiser and glideslope receivers; Collins MKI-3 marker beacon receiver; Collins DF-206 or equivalent ARINC 570 ADF; Marconi Avionics AD-620C computerised radio and dead reckoning area navigation system. Standard instrumentation includes Astronautics ARU-2B/A attitude director indicator; AQU-6/A horizontal situation indicator and flight director system; Sperry P-140 attitude and heading reference system; and Microtecnica AG-5 standby attitude indicator. Retractable landing light beneath port wing; taxying light on nose-wheel leg.

ARMAMENT AND OPERATIONAL EQUIPMENT: Two 30 mm DEFA cannon, with 125 rds/gun, mounted internally in lower forward fuselage, with external fairings. Firing rate 1,200 rds/min. Loads on six underwing hardpoints as for M.B.339A. Saab-Scania RGS 2 gunsight, with gyro lead computer; gunsight can be equipped with a fully-automatic Teledyne TSC 116-2 gun camera. Provision for towing type A-6B (1·83 × 9·14 m; 6 × 30 ft) aerial banner target.

DIMENSIONS, EXTERNAL: As for M.B.339A except:
Wing span over tip-tanks:
standard tanks	10·858 m (35 ft 7½ in)
circular-section tanks	11·045 m (36 ft 2¾ in)
Height overall	3·90 m (12 ft 9½ in)

AREAS: As for M.B.339A except:
Fin	2·21 m² (23·79 sq ft)
Rudder, incl tab	0·68 m² (7·32 sq ft)

WEIGHTS:
Weight empty, equipped	3,174 kg (6,997 lb)
Unusable fuel and oil	14 kg (31 lb)
Fuel load (internal, usable, with circular-section tip-tanks)	1,582 kg (3,487 lb)
T-O weight 'clean', incl ammunition for internal guns	4,978 kg (10,974 lb)
Max T-O weight with external stores	6,150 kg (13,558 lb)
Landing weight with 10% fuel reserves	3,554 kg (7,835 lb)

PERFORMANCE:
Max level speed at S/L	480 knots (889 km/h; 553 mph)
Landing speed	89 knots (165 km/h; 102 mph) IAS
Time to 9,150 m (30,000 ft) from brake release	9 min 9 s
Service ceiling	13,565 m (44,500 ft)
T-O run	575 m (1,886 ft)
Landing run	410 m (1,345 ft)

Prototype Aermacchi M.B.339K light close air support aircraft, developed from the two-seat M.B.339A

Combat radius with two 30 mm cannon (125 rds/gun) and four 500 lb Mk 82 bombs (total military load 1,088 kg; 2,400 lb):

lo-lo-lo, incl 2½ min over target
                                        203 nm (376 km; 234 miles)
hi-lo-hi, out at 9,150 m (30,000 ft), back at 12,190 m (40,000 ft), 2½ min over target
                                        350 nm (648 km; 403 miles)

Mission radius with two 30 mm cannon (125 rds/gun), two Matra 550 air-to-air missiles, four-camera photo-reconnaissance pod and two 325 litre (71·5 Imp gallon) drop-tanks:

hi-lo-hi, out at 9,150 m (30,000 ft), back at 10,670 m (35,000 ft), 5 min photographic run at 61 m (200 ft)
                                        455 nm (843 km; 524 miles)

PARTENAVIA (page 126)

PARTENAVIA P.78

Design details of this enlarged development of the P.68 Victor have now been finalised. Of high-wing configuration, with non-retractable landing gear, it has an unpressurised fuselage and is powered by two Alfa Romeo/Rolls-Royce RB.318 turboprop engines, each flat rated to 333·5 kW (450 shp) and driving a Dowty Rotol propeller. Fuel capacity (usable) is 1,140 litres (251 Imp gallons).

The cabin, wider than that of the P.68, accommodates up to 12 passengers, in three-abreast and two-abreast seating, and there is a flight crew of two. Two flight-deck doors and a large double door at the rear make possible the optimum use of the cabin for alternative loads such as light cargo and stretchers.

DIMENSIONS, EXTERNAL AND INTERNAL:
Wing span   14·00 m (45 ft 11¼ in)
Wing area, gross   23·80 m² (256·2 sq ft)
Wing aspect ratio   8·24

GENERAL AVIA (page 125)

First production example of the General Avia F.20 Pegaso six-seat light business twin

Length overall	11·05 m (36 ft 3 in)	Stalling speed, flaps down	68 knots (126 km/h; 79 mph)
Height overall	3·60 m (11 ft 9¾ in)	Max rate of climb at S/L	533 m (1,750 ft)/min
Cabin: Max width	1·40 m (4 ft 7 in)	Rate of climb at S/L, one engine out	122 m (400 ft)/min
WEIGHTS:		Service ceiling	9,145 m (30,000 ft)
Basic weight empty	2,430 kg (5,357 lb)	Service ceiling, one engine out	4,875 m (16,000 ft)
Max T-O weight	4,000 kg (8,818 lb)	T-O run	448 m (1,470 ft)
Max landing weight	3,800 kg (8,377 lb)	T-O to 15 m (50 ft)	747 m (2,450 ft)
PERFORMANCE (estimated, at max T-O weight, ISA):		Landing from 15 m (50 ft)	640 m (2,100 ft)
Max level speed	223 knots (413 km/h; 257 mph)	Landing run	381 m (1,250 ft)
Max cruising speed	207 knots (383 km/h; 238 mph)	Accelerate/stop distance	700 m (2,300 ft)
Econ cruising speed	189 knots (350 km/h; 217 mph)	Range with max fuel, econ cruising speed at 3,050 m	
Best climbing speed	120 knots (222 km/h; 138 mph)	(10,000 ft)	830 nm (1,538 km; 955 miles)

NETHERLANDS

FOKKER (page 147)

Fokker F27 Maritime coastal patrol aircraft, built for the air force of Angola

NEW ZEALAND

AEROSPACE (page 151)

In the three-view drawing at the top of this page, it is the *upper* side view which depicts the Fletcher FU-24-954.

SPAIN

CASA (page 168)

In the dimensions (external) for the CASA C-212 Series 200 Aviocar, the length overall should be corrected to 15·16 m (49 ft 9 in).

SWEDEN

JAS

In June 1980 the Swedish government approved the allocation of SKr 200 million to finance project definition and initial development during 1980-82 of a Viggen replacement to enter service from about 1990. Tentatively known as JAS (Jakt/Attack/Spaning: fighter/attack/reconnaissance), the new multi-role combat aircraft would replace, successively, the AJ/SH/SF/JA 37 versions of the Viggen. A similar financial commitment is being made by a Swedish aerospace industry group formed by Saab-Scania, Volvo Flygmotor, L. M. Ericsson and SRA Communications, which is to submit its JAS proposals by 1 June 1981. These will be presented to the government by the Supreme Commander of the Armed Forces by 1 October that year, and a final decision to go ahead, or not, will be taken in 1982, when a new five-year defence plan is due to be considered by the Swedish Parliament.

The JAS is intended to have a performance at least as good as that of the Viggen, and to weigh only half as much. During the lifetime of the programme, the air defence fighter role is expected to assume increasing importance. The aircraft is expected to have a distinct Swedish profile, but some subsystems may be developed in collaboration with foreign industry: for example, the power plant (the RB.199 and F404 have been mentioned as possible choices) and a fly-by-wire control system.

SWITZERLAND

ALR

ARBEITSGRUPPE FÜR LUFT- UND RAUMFAHRT (Aerospace Task Group)
Postfach 63, CH-8050 Zürich
Telephone: Zürich (01) 311 58 14
Telex: 56970 FEYER
PROGRAMME DIRECTOR: Dr G. Bridel

ALR PIRANHA

This group of Swiss scientists started work on the design of the Piranha in September 1977, in an attempt to develop a new-generation lightweight supersonic combat aircraft at a cost that could be afforded by the world's less affluent air forces, so enabling them to embody both quality and quantity of new aircraft in their re-equipment programmes.

Primary missions of the Piranha are seen as: clear-weather, low/medium-altitude air defence; low-level FEBA strike, mainly under VFR conditions; reconnaissance; electronic warfare; and operational training. A limited amount of active ECM and reconnaissance equipment is carried as standard, but all-weather interception and strike systems are not. This avoids the weight and performance penalties that such systems would inevitably attract, and keeps the pilot's workload to a minimum. STOL capability was considered essential, to permit operation from dispersed airfields with runways no more than 1,000 m (3,280 ft) long.

Principal design features include a short-coupled canard configuration, with all-moving foreplanes; shoulder-mounted wings, to provide an optimum stores attachment layout; fly-by-wire flight control; and a centrally-located high-performance gun. Other inherent advantages claimed for the Piranha are low procurement and operating costs, small radar and infra-red signatures, and transonic speed capability.

Details have been released of four basic proposed single-seat versions:

Piranha 2C. Transonic ground attack version, with single Rolls-Royce Turboméca Adour Mk 811 turbofan engine, rated at 24·6 kN (5,520 lb st) dry and 37·4 kN (8,400 lb st) with afterburning. No radar.

Piranha 2D. Combined ground attack/air superiority version of 2C, with more powerful RT.172-63 Adour turbofan rated at 29·2 kN (6,570 lb st) dry and 44·9 kN (10,100 lb st) with afterburning. General appearance shown in accompanying side-view drawing.

Piranha 4. Twin-engined ground attack/air superiority version, with two 15·5 kN (3,485 lb st) Turboméca-SNECMA Larzac 05 turbofan engines (each 25·0 kN; 5,620 lb st with afterburning) in shorter and wider fuselage. General appearance shown in accompanying three-view drawing.

Piranha 5. Similar to Piranha 4, but powered by two Garrett/Volvo Flygmotor TFE1042-7 turbofans (each 18·4 kN; 4,135 lb st dry, 30·2 kN; 6,800 lb st with afterburning).

Each of the above models could be produced in tandem two-seat form for ECM and training purposes. Preliminary design, and selection of the major systems, has been completed for the Piranha 2D and Piranha 4, and negotiations with several possible customers were under way in mid-1980. At that time, the Piranha 4 was considered to be the principal version.

The following description applies to all currently-projected versions, except where specifically indicated otherwise:

TYPE: Proposed multi-purpose lightweight combat aircraft.

WINGS: Tandem arrangement of shoulder-mounted, all-moving canard foreplanes, each with powered elevator on trailing-edge for pitch control. Immediately aft of foreplanes, mounted slightly lower on fuselage, are low aspect ratio sweptback main wings, each with single flap/aileron ('flaperon') on trailing-edge. Main wings have compound sweep on leading-edges, which have extended chord outboard on outer panels. Thickness/chord ratio of main wings decreases from 5·5% at root to 4% at tip. Main wings have 4° of anhedral from roots, and are set at incidence of 1° 24'. Sweepback at quarter-chord 45° on outer panels, 31° on inner panels. Multi-spar main wings, which form torsion box passing through fuselage, are of light alloy construction with machined skins. Flaperons are of honeycomb sandwich construction. Fly-by-wire control of foreplanes, elevators and flaperons. No tabs or slats.

FUSELAGE: Conventional metal semi-monocoque structure. Door-type airbrake in upper surface of rear fuselage on each side of fin.

TAIL UNIT: Vertical surfaces only, comprising sweptback fin (with small dorsal fin) and fly-by-wire powered rudder.

LANDING GEAR: Retractable type, of Dowty (Piranha 2) or Messier-Hispano-Bugatti design (Piranha 4 and 5), with single wheel on each unit; all units retract forward into fuselage. Nose unit offset from centreline to provide clear field of fire for centrally-mounted gun. Oleo-pneumatic shock-absorbers. Dowty gear for Piranha 2 has size 350 × 157 mm nosewheel tyre and 560 × 215 mm main-wheel tyres, all at nominal pressure of 8·6 bars (125 lb/sq in). Anti-skid units for all versions. Irvin braking parachute (9·5 m²; 102·3 sq ft or 13·0 m²; 140·0 sq ft) in bullet fairing on top of rear fuselage.

POWER PLANT: One or two turbofan engines (for details see under model listings), installed in rear fuselage. Lateral intake on each side of fuselage, with auxiliary inlet doors, spring-loaded for low-speed and high-angle-of-attack manoeuvres. Fuel in one main fuselage tank and two integral wing tanks. Provision for one external auxiliary tank on underfuselage station and one on each inboard underwing station. No in-flight refuelling capability.

ACCOMMODATION: Single Martin-Baker Mk 10L ejection seat under rearward-sliding canopy; or, on ECM and operational training versions, tandem seats under sideways-opening canopy.

SYSTEMS: BAe Dynamics cockpit pressurisation system, with pre-cooler and two-wheel bootstrap cold-air unit. Triplex hydraulic system (pressure 207 bars; 3,000 lb/sq in), comprising two main systems and a pump-driven auxiliary system. Two generators, each of 12kVA minimum rating, for AC electrical power. Electrical fly-by-wire system, with four actuators powering all control surfaces. No pneumatic, oxygen or de-icing systems.

AVIONICS AND EQUIPMENT (Piranha 2D, 4 and 5): Ferranti LINAS nav/attack system with lightweight inertial platform; laser rangefinder; Smiths head-up display; Ferranti Comed multi-purpose head-down display; Thomson-CSF Agave lightweight search/track/designation/telemetry/navigation radar; internally-mounted passive ECM, chaff and flares.

ARMAMENT: One high-performance cannon (27 mm Mauser BK 27 or 30 mm Oerlikon KCA), mounted in underside of fuselage, on aircraft centreline, beneath cockpit. One underfuselage, four underwing and two wingtip attachment points for air-to-surface weapons such as Maverick, Beluga and Durandal; or air-to-air missiles such as AIM-9L Sidewinder and Matra Magic. Provision for active ECM and reconnaissance equipment to be carried in underfuselage pod.

DIMENSIONS, EXTERNAL (Piranha 4):
Wing span (excl missile rails)	6·49 m (21 ft 3½ in)
Wing aspect ratio	2·63
Foreplane span	3·14 m (10 ft 3½ in)
Length overall	10·50 m (34 ft 5½ in)
Height overall	4·12 m (13 ft 6¼ in)

AREAS:
Wings, gross (reference area)	16·00 m² (172·22 sq ft)
Flaperons (total)	1·28 m² (13·78 sq ft)
Foreplanes, gross (reference area)	4·57 m² (49·19 sq ft)
Elevators (total)	0·73 m² (7·86 sq ft)
Fin	3·33 m² (35·84 sq ft)
Rudder	0·56 m² (6·03 sq ft)

WEIGHTS AND LOADINGS (Piranha 4*):
Max external weapons/fuel load
approx 2,000 kg (4,410 lb)
Max T-O weight (air superiority configuration, with gun ammunition and two air-to-air missiles)
6,200 kg (13,668 lb)
Wing loading at T-O (air superiority configuration)
388 kg/m² (79·5 lb/sq ft)
Thrust/weight ratio (50% internal fuel)
greater than 1·0
*2D slightly lighter, 5 heavier

PERFORMANCE (Piranha 4, estimated, at max T-O weight; other versions not significantly different):
Never-exceed speed   Mach 1·9
Max level speed at 11,000 m (36,100 ft)
Mach 1·8 (1,033 knots; 1,915 km/h; 1,190 mph)
Max rate of climb at S/L
more than 13,800 m (45,275 ft)/min
Service ceiling   16,000 m (52,500 ft)
T-O run at S/L, ISA (air superiority configuration)
less than 500 m (1,640 ft)
Landing run at S/L, ISA (minimum fuel, using brake 'chute)   less than 500 m (1,640 ft)
Range with typical combat load, incl 5 min combat (lo-lo-lo)   more than 189 nm (350 km; 217 miles)

ALR Piranha 4, with additional side elevation of Piranha 2D (bottom right) and scrap view of two-seat nose
(Michael A. Badrocke)

UNION OF SOVIET SOCIALIST REPUBLICS

ILYUSHIN (page 184)

Never before illustrated in *Jane's*, this veteran Ilyushin Il-14 (NATO reporting name 'Crate') is equipped for ECM/elint duties with the Soviet Air Forces

MIL (page 202)

The four-barrel gun, sensor pack and other details of the Mil Mi-24 ('Hind-D') gunship are shown in new detail in this photograph of a Czechoslovak Air Force aircraft

SUKHOI (page 206)

First photograph seen in the West of the new and improved single-seat development of the Sukhoi Su-17 which may have the NATO reporting name 'Fitter-H'

UNITED KINGDOM

ADA
AERONAUTICAL DEVELOPMENT
ASSOCIATES LTD

14 Bishops Avenue, Elstree, Borehamwood, Hertfordshire WD6 3LZ
Telephone: 01 953 1250
DIRECTORS:
  P. L. Cronbach, BSc (Eng), CEng, FRAeS
  J. W. Allam, OBE, FRAeS

ADA APOLLO JETSTREAM

ADA is undertaking, on behalf of Apollo Airways Inc of Goleta, California, the modification of a number of Handley Page Jetstream Mk 1 light transport aircraft. Designed to meet the October 1979 requirements of SFAR 41, the purpose of the Apollo Jetstream is to exploit fully the potential of the basic Jetstream airframe in commuter operations under FAR Pt 135 in the western USA. Airframe alterations, which are minimal, are chiefly of a detail nature to meet requirements which differ slightly from those envisaged during the initial design. The major changes concern the power plant and air-conditioning system. The Turboméca Astazou XVI F3 turboprop engines installed by ADA are identical to the Astazou XVI F1s installed previously, but are flat rated to 626 kW (840 shp)

each at 31°C at S/L. An improved air-conditioning distribution system, with Garrett-AiResearch cooling turbines, is also installed.

ADA's Apollo Jetstream modifications are cleared by the British CAA to US requirements under a bilateral agreement with the FAA. Flight testing, by ADA, is certificated by the CAA, this also qualifying as FAA type approval for US operation by Apollo Airways.

WEIGHTS AND LOADINGS:
Basic weight empty, equipped (18-seat commuter)
    3,952 kg (8,714 lb)
Max fuel   1,370 kg (3,020 lb)
Max payload   1,717 kg (3,786 lb)
Max T-O weight   6,236 kg (13,750 lb)
Weight/altitude/temperature T-O limitations, ISA + 24°C:
  airfield at 305 m (1,000 ft) 6,236 kg (13,750 lb)
  airfield at 915 m (3,000 ft) 6,087 kg (13,420 lb)
  airfield at 1,375 m (4,500 ft) 5,969 kg (13,160 lb)
  airfield at 1,830 m (6,000 ft) 5,670 kg (12,500 lb)
Max Landing weight   6,123 kg (13,500 lb)
Max zero-fuel weight (limited by SFAR 41)
    5,670 kg (12,500 lb)
Max wing loading 248·4 kg/m² (50·9 lb/sq ft)
Max power loading 4·99 kg/kW (8·2 lb/shp)

PERFORMANCE (at max T-O weight, ISA, except where indicated):
Never-exceed speed 300 knots (556 km/h; 345 mph)
Max level and cruising speed at 3,050 m (10,000 ft)
    244 knots (452 km/h; 281 mph)
Cruising speed for max range, mean cruise weight, at 6,700 m (22,000 ft)
    211 knots (391 km/h; 243 mph)
Stalling speed, flaps and landing gear down
    80 knots (149 km/h; 93 mph) EAS
Max rate of climb at S/L, ISA + 15°C
    610 m (2,000 ft)/min
Rate of climb at S/L, one engine out, ISA + 15°C
    122 m (400 ft)/min
Service ceiling (certificated) 7,625 m (25,000 ft)
Service ceiling, one engine out 3,050 m (10,000 ft)
T-O run at S/L, ISA + 15°C 762 m (2,500 ft)
T-O to 15 m (50 ft) at S/L, ISA + 15°C
    1,046 m (3,430 ft)
Landing from 15 m (50 ft) at S/L 959 m (3,144 ft)
Range, reserves for 45 min hold and 5% total fuel:
with max payload (18 passengers)
    323 nm (598 km; 372 miles)
with max fuel and 8 passengers
    1,193 nm (2,210 km; 1,373 miles)

NASH AIRCRAFT LTD (a subsidiary of Kinetrol Ltd)

REGISTERED OFFICE: Trading Estate, Farnham, Surrey GU9 9NU
Telephone: 0252 723688
Telex: 858567
DIRECTORS:
A. R. B. Nash (Managing)
Roy G. Procter
R. C. Nash

NASH PETREL

As indicated briefly on page 498 of the Homebuilt Aircraft section, a controlling interest in Procter Aircraft Associates Ltd was acquired by Mr. Alan Nash. As a result, the company was renamed Nash Aircraft Ltd in 1980.

It continues to be responsible for the Petrel two-seat light aircraft, for which it was pursuing certification in the late Summer of 1980. After certification, subject to the interest generated, it was planned to begin small-scale production of the Petrel. By 14 August 1980 the company's prototype Petrel (G-AXSF) had been completed,

Company-owned prototype of the Nash Petrel two-seat light aircraft

but had not flown. This aircraft has a 119 kW (160 hp) Avco Lycoming O-320-D2A flat-four engine; production Petrels will be offered with a choice of power plants in the 88-134 kW (118-180 hp) range.

NDN (page 242)

NDN 6 FIELDMASTER

NDN Aircraft has under development an agricultural aircraft known as the NDN 6 Fieldmaster, which is being financed jointly by the company and the UK National Research Development Corporation. Representing an entirely new approach to the design of agricultural aircraft, it has a titanium chemical hopper which is an integral part of the fuselage structure, its outer surface being contoured to serve as the skin of that fuselage section. The power plant is mounted on the front of this hopper, the aft fuselage to its rear, and the wings are built directly on to each side of the hopper's base. The cockpit, in the rear fuselage, is protected by a strong rollover structure, and is large enough to accommodate a second seat in tandem. Removable dual controls are standard, to simplify flight training and check-out procedures. The wing is fitted with full-span auxiliary aerofoil trailing-edge flaps, embodying a liquid spray dispersal system that discharges directly into the downwash of the flaps, and so ensures that the spray droplets achieve the best possible crop penetration.

The first flight of the Fieldmaster is planned for mid-1981.

TYPE: Two-seat large-capacity agricultural aircraft.

WINGS: Low-wing monoplane, with an overwing streamline-section bracing strut each side. Conventional all-metal structure with full corrosion proofing. Electrically-actuated full-span auxiliary aerofoil trailing-edge flaps, which incorporate plumbing for 20 standard spray nozzles on each wing. Two narrow-chord ailerons on each wing, adjacent to wingtip and forward of trailing-edge flaps.

FUSELAGE: Forward fuselage comprises structural titanium hopper with capacity of 1,996 kg (4,400 lb) dry, or 2,642 litres (581 Imp gallons) of liquid chemicals, and incorporating large access door, vent system, inspection windows, and light. Rear fuselage, attached to the rear of this hopper, is of semi-monocoque light alloy construction, fully corrosion proofed, and with easy access for cleaning and maintenance.

TAIL UNIT: Braced conventional structure of light alloy. Trim tab in rudder and port elevator.

LANDING GEAR: Non-retractable tricycle type, with single wheel on each unit. Nosewheel has alternative steerable or castoring facility. Main units of levered-suspension type. Nosewheel tyre size 7·00-8; main wheels have tubed tyres, diameter 736 mm (29 in). Hydraulic disc brakes. Landing gear incorporates wire cutters.

POWER PLANT: One 559 kW (750 shp) Pratt & Whitney Aircraft of Canada PT6A-34AG turboprop engine, driving a Hartzell three-blade fully-feathering reversible-pitch metal propeller with spinner. Two integral fuel tanks in each wing, with combined capacity of 946 litres (208 Imp gallons). Engine air intake has a Centrisep filtration system.

ACCOMMODATION: Standard accommodation for pilot and trainee/passenger on fully-adjustable tandem seats in an enclosed cockpit, with roll-over protective structure. Dual controls standard, those for pupil easily removable. Crew safety helmets with headsets optional. Baggage space in fuselage. Birdproof windscreen standard; two-speed windscreen wiper and windscreen washer installation optional. Accommodation ventilated; heating system optional. Wirecutters forward of windscreen, and cable deflecting wire from top of windscreen to tip of fin.

SYSTEMS: Electrical system includes 24V 300A starter/generator. Hydraulic system for brakes only. Central warning system standard, including engine fire warning.

AVIONICS AND EQUIPMENT: Intercom standard. Avionics available to customer requirements. Standard equipment includes an external power socket. Optional equipment includes blind-flying instrumentation and vacuum system; airframe and engine hour meter; instrument lighting, navigation lights, fin and wingtip

NDN 6 Fieldmaster agricultural aircraft. The landing gear is now intended to have a single wheel on each unit *(Pilot Press)*

strobe lights; two forward-looking and/or two retractable sideways-looking work lights, each 600,000 candlepower; automatic flagman installation; fire bombing dump door; adapters to convert standard 40-nozzle to 80-nozzle spray system; Transland gatebox, high-volume spreader, quick-disconnect flange kit, and side loading system; and Micronair 8-unit installation, with flowmeter and rpm indicator.

DIMENSIONS, EXTERNAL:

Wing span	15·32 m (50 ft 3 in)
Length overall	11·02 m (36 ft 2 in)
Height overall	3·48 m (11 ft 5 in)
Wheel track	5·08 m (16 ft 8 in)
Wheelbase	3·35 m (11 ft 0 in)
Propeller diameter	2·69 m (8 ft 10 in)

AREA:

Wings, gross	31·40 m² (338 sq ft)

WEIGHTS (estimated):

Weight empty, equipped	1,588 kg (3,500 lb)
Max T-O weight	3,856 kg (8,500 lb)

PERFORMANCE (estimated, at max T-O weight, except as indicated):

Never-exceed speed	191 knots (354 km/h; 220 mph)
Max level speed, clean	163 knots (303 km/h; 188 mph)
Cruising speed, 75% power	149 knots (275 km/h; 171 mph)
Design manoeuvring speed	135 knots (249 km/h; 155 mph)
Stalling speed, flaps down	59 knots (109 km/h; 68 mph)
Stalling speed, flaps down, at 2,268 kg (5,000 lb) AUW	45 knots (84 km/h; 52 mph)
Max rate of climb at S/L	366 m (1,200 ft)/min
T-O run	177 m (580 ft)
Landing run with propeller reversal, at normal operating weight	85 m (280 ft)
Range with max fuel, no reserves	1,020 nm (1,889 km; 1,174 miles)

WESTLAND (page 252)

WESTLAND SEA KING

The first two **Sea King HAS. Mk 5** helicopters were officially handed over to the Royal Navy on 2 October 1980. Fifteen more are currently on order. In addition, the Navy's existing fleet of Sea King HAS. Mk 2 helicopters will be updated to the new standard.

The Sea King HAS. Mk 5 has a Decca 71 radar and

One of the first two Westland Sea King HAS.Mk 5 helicopters delivered to the Royal Navy on 2 October 1980

tactical air navigation system, sonobuoy dropping equipment, and associated Marconi LAPADS data processing equipment, with provision for all-digital longer-range MEL Sea Searcher radar to be fitted later. The increased size of the rotating antenna has necessitated the Mk 5's larger dorsal radome.

Using this new equipment, the Sea King can pinpoint the position of an enemy submarine at far greater range than has been possible in the past, and to attack it with torpedoes. In addition to monitoring signals from its own sonobuoys, the Sea King can handle information from buoys dropped by RAF Nimrod aircraft in a joint search. It can remain on station, up to 87 nm (160 km; 100 miles) from its parent ship, for long periods.

The Sea King HAS. Mk 5 carries a crew of four, with the dunking sonar operator also monitoring the LAPADS

equipment at an additional crew station. To make room for the extra equipment, the cabin has been enlarged by moving the rear bulkhead nearly 1·83 m (6 ft 0 in) further into the tail. Improvements envisaged for the future include the carriage of more powerful torpedoes and further anti-submarine sensors.

Max T-O weight of the Sea King HAS. Mk 5 is 9,525 kg (21,000 lb), the same as that of the Mk 2.

UNITED STATES OF AMERICA

BELL (page 278)

BELL MODEL 206L-1 TEXASRANGER

Bell has built and flown a demonstration prototype of this multi-purpose light military helicopter which is based on the LongRanger. The basic airframe, two-blade main rotor and power plant are unchanged. Equipment added for the primary anti-tank role includes four TOW missiles, carried in pairs on outriggers on each side of the cabin; a roof-mounted sight, pilot's steering indicator, and armoured seats, side by side, for the weapons operator and pilot. The TOW missile launchers can be replaced quickly by two seven-round packs of 2·75 in rockets or two 7·62

mm machine-guns, each with 250 rounds of ammunition. Alternative mission roles include troop transport (pilot and six passengers), armed reconnaissance and surveillance, search and rescue, medical evacuation, command control and battlefield re-supply.

WEIGHTS:
Weight empty, standard configuration
                                        1,003 kg (2,211 lb)
Max T-O weight   1,882 kg (4,150 lb)

PERFORMANCE (at max T-O weight):
Max cruising speed   114 knots (211 km/h; 131 mph)
Range with max fuel   299 nm (554 km; 344 miles)
Endurance with max fuel   3 h 54 min

BELL HUEYCOBRA

The YAH-1S (16019) that has been fitted with a four-blade main rotor (see page 282) is designated **Model 249** by Bell. The rotor is similar to that of the Bell Model 412, but its diameter is reduced by 0·61 m (2 ft).

Bell has also built and flown an experimental version of the twin-engined AH-1T with the usual Turbo Twin Pac power plant replaced by two General Electric CT7-2 turboshaft engines, driving the transmission and advanced-technology glassfibre main rotor of a Model 214ST. Known unofficially as the AH-1T Plus, the modified aircraft can fly at weights up to 40 per cent greater than those of the standard AH-1T, with much improved high-altitude and single-engined performance.

CESSNA (page 306)

CESSNA OA-37B DRAGONFLY

During 1981, Nos 45 and 47 Squadrons of the US Air Force Reserve will re-equip from Cessna A-37B Dragonflies on to Fairchild A-10A Thunderbolt IIs. The Dragonflies will then be converted into **OA-37Bs** for forward air control duty with Nos 103 and 172 Squadrons of the Air National Guard, replacing O-2As.

FAIRCHILD (page 335)

FAIRCHILD REPUBLIC THUNDERBOLT II

The House-Senate conference on the FY 1981 Defense Authorization Bill provided $24 million, unrequested by the Department of Defense, for conversion of A-10A Thunderbolt II attack aircraft into two-seat combat-ready trainers. The modified aircraft would not be fitted with the sophisticated avionics of the private-venture two-seat Night and Adverse Weather A-10.

GENERAL DYNAMICS (page 344)

GENERAL DYNAMICS FB-111A

Using technology and hardware supplied by General Dynamics' Fort Worth Division, the US Air Force's Air Logistics Center at Sacramento, California, is upgrading 65 FB-111A strategic bombers under a $300 million modification programme. Installation of avionics compatible with the Air Force Satellite Communications System will enhance the aircraft's combat readiness, by enabling their crews to send and receive teletype messages while airborne anywhere in the world. Other new equipment will include a stall inhibitor system that will interface with the FB-111A's flight control system; AN/ALE-62 radar warning receivers; and AN/ALQ-137 countermeasures systems with greater frequency range than earlier systems.

MCDONNELL DOUGLAS (page 380)
MCDONNELL DOUGLAS F-15 STRIKE EAGLE

McDonnell Douglas has developed as a company-funded project an all-weather interdiction version of the F-15, identified as the F-15 Strike Eagle. Demonstrated publicly each day at the 1980 Farnborough International Air Show, it is structurally generally similar to the F-15 Eagle, but has a synthetic aperture radar (SAR) configuration of the lightweight APG-63 pulse-Doppler radar which was developed by Hughes Aircraft Company for the standard F-15. SAR represents an advance in digital electronics which uses programmable signal processors with high-density storage elements in the radar. The SAR modification of the APG-63 provides a significant breakthrough in ground target resolution, making it possible for small targets to be 'seen' in any weather, or by night, from ranges of approximately 17 nm (32 km; 20 miles). It was intended to install the Hughes SAR in the Strike Eagle airframe in October 1980, and it was anticipated that by December it would be possible for the radar to demonstrate a resolution of 3·05 m (10 ft) from a range of 8·5 nm (16 km; 10 miles).

When fully developed, Strike Eagle will be capable of making night and all-weather attacks against ground targets from stand-off ranges. It is planned to demonstrate this capability by May 1981, at which time blind weapon-delivery techniques will be simulated. It is hoped that within two months of that demonstration it will be possible to integrate SAR imagery with the FLIR (forward-looking infra-red) system of the Pave Tack targeting pod, leading to the first launching trials of live weapons, and the completion of all company-funded testing in late 1981. In the two-seat F-15 Strike Eagle, the aft seating position is

equipped for a specialist officer to handle both the SAR and the Pave Tack systems. He is provided with four displays, two of which will be used for navigation to the target area. Of the others, one is dedicated to weapon selection, while the second monitors enemy tracking systems. Approach to the target area would be made at low level, followed by a brief 'look-see' at a height of approximately 760 m (2,500 ft) to enable the radar officer to locate a specific target. After some 10 to 20 seconds the low-level track would be resumed, with the onboard computer programmed with details of azimuth and range, and the FLIR system being used for pinpoint designation of the target.

The F-15 Strike Eagle retains the air superiority capability of the basic F-15, but will be equally suitable for deployment in close air support and interdiction roles. Three 30 mm gun pods can be carried on underfuselage and underwing racks, or up to 10,885 kg (24,000 lb) of other stores. These can include air-to-ground weapons such as HARM (High-speed Anti-Radiation Missile), Harpoon anti-ship missile, Mk 20 Rockeye bombs in an MER-200 dispenser which allows their delivery at supersonic speed, Mk 82 (500 lb) and Mk 84 (2,000 lb) bombs, Maverick television-guided missiles, and Pave Tack infra-red tracking and laser-spot designation pods. Strike Eagle is able to carry the two low-drag conformal fuel tanks, known as FAST (Fuel and Sensor Tactical) Packs, to provide increased range. These can themselves be used to mount two AIM-7F Advanced Sparrow missiles, or 1,995 kg (4,400 lb) of air-to-ground weapons on each tank, or Pave Tack pods, or similar more advanced systems now under consideration.

GULFSTREAM AMERICAN (page 353)

Gulfstream American announced on 9 October 1980 that it had signed a letter of intent to purchase Rockwell International's General Aviation Division, located in Bethany, Oklahoma. The sale was expected to be concluded in November, after which Gulfstream American intended to continue the Division's current production of Jetprop Commander business aircraft, product development programme and product support.

MCDONNELL DOUGLAS F-15 EAGLE
(ADVANCED WILD WEASEL)

As a continuation of Advanced Wild Weasel studies which led to production of the F-4G version of the Phantom II, McDonnell Douglas has now proposed to the US government a defence suppression version of the F-15 Eagle. In the accompanying illustration, an F-15 is shown with a HARM high-speed anti-radiation missile on its outboard underwing pylon, in addition to Snakeye bombs and Sidewinder missiles on the inner pylon and Sparrow missiles on the fuselage mountings. Its more sensitive ECM sensors and higher performance would make it capable of suppressing or destroying an increasing number of surface-to-air threats by comparison with the F-4G.

McDonnell Douglas F-15 Strike Eagle, carrying 4,535 kg (10,000 lb) of additional fuel in FAST Pack conformal fuel tanks, plus 22 Mk 82 500 lb bombs

Proposed Advanced Wild Weasel configuration for the McDonnell Douglas F-15 Eagle

BAe AV-8A Harrier converted to AV-8C configuration by McDonnell Douglas. Details of this conversion programme are given on page 234

MCDONNELL DOUGLAS DC-XX

To compete against the Boeing 757, McDonnell Douglas began studies for an advanced-technology medium-range (ATMR) transport aircraft. This has now been allocated the provisional designation DC-XX, and in its current form is envisaged as a twin-aisle six-abreast 180-seat mixed-class airliner. With a fuselage width of 4·39 m (14 ft 5 in), it would be possible for the cabin to accommodate 214 passengers in a seven-abreast high-density layout at 76 cm (30 in) pitch.

Changes which have been made since the original ATMR study include the introduction of a new lower aspect ratio wing, and more powerful engines. The proposed power plant consists of two 155·2 kN (34,900 lb st) Pratt & Whitney JT10D-234 turbofans, mounted in underwing pods, with 162·4 kN (36,500 lb st) General Electric CF6-32C1 or 165·9 kN (37,300 lb st) Rolls-Royce RB.211-535D turbofans available optionally. A range of 2,600 nm (4,800 km; 2,990 miles) is contemplated.

The design is intended to take full advantage of advanced-technology materials and aerodynamic features. McDonnell Douglas claims that these, together with fuel-efficient turbofans and the latest propulsion and flight management systems, will enable the DC-XX to demonstrate fuel consumption figures some 8-10% below those of its competitors. No decision to proceed with production of this aircraft had been made by October 1980.

McDonnell Douglas DC-XX advanced-technology medium-range transport proposal *(Pilot Press)*

NORTHROP (page 397)

ROCKWELL INTERNATIONAL (page 433)
ROCKWELL JETPROP COMMANDER 1000

This increased-capacity development of the Jetprop Commander 980 was introduced at the 33rd US National Business Aircraft Association convention, in September 1980. Overall dimensions are unchanged, as are the TPE331-10 turboprop engines, but a 96 cm (38 in) rearward shift of the aft pressure bulkhead has increased the cabin volume by 21 per cent. Additional cabin side windows are installed. Standard accommodation is for two pilots and seven passengers. Max T-O weight is increased to 5,103 kg (11,250 lb).

This Northrop F-5E, delivered to Thailand, is fitted with the new 'shark' nose, modified wing leading-edge extensions and automated manoeuvring flaps that were developed as part of the improved flight handling package of the new F-5G (page 399). All future F-5Es and F-5Fs will embody these design changes

HOMEBUILTS

BRAZIL

MOURA
MAURICIO IMPELIZIERI P. MOURA
Belo Horizonte, Minas Gerais State

MOURA ESQUALO

Sr Moura has designed and built, with some technical assistance from the CEA Universidade Federal de Minas Gerais, a two-seat sporting aircraft which he has named Esqualo. Its structure is stressed to +6*g* and −3*g*. The first flight of this aircraft was expected in early 1980. All available details follow:

TYPE: Two-seat homebuilt sporting aircraft.
WINGS: Cantilever low-wing monoplane of all-metal construction. Plain ailerons and trailing-edge flaps of similar construction. No trim tabs.
FUSELAGE: Conventional semi-monocoque structure of light alloy.
TAIL UNIT: Cantilever structure of light alloy. Horn-balanced control surfaces. Dorsal fin. No trim tab in rudder or elevators.
LANDING GEAR: It is known only that this is of retractable type.
POWER PLANT: One 134 kW (180 hp) Avco Lycoming flat-four engine of the O-360 series, driving a two-blade variable-pitch propeller with spinner. Fuel capacity 140 litres (30·8 Imp gallons).
ACCOMMODATION: Two seats side by side beneath rearward-sliding transparent cockpit canopy.

Moura Esqualo two-seat sporting aircraft *(Michael A. Badrocke)*

DIMENSIONS, EXTERNAL:		Height overall	2·22 m (7 ft 3½ in)
Wing span	7·98 m (26 ft 2¼ in)	WEIGHTS (estimated):	
Wing area, gross	8·86 m² (93·43 sq ft)	Weight empty	450 kg (992 lb)
Length overall	6·68 m (21 ft 11 in)	Max T-O weight	804 kg (1,773 lb)

PERFORMANCE (estimated, at max T-O weight):

Max level speed	243 knots (450 km/h; 280 mph)
Cruising speed	183 knots (340 km/h; 211 mph)
Stalling speed, flaps and gear up	
	68 knots (125 km/h; 78 mph)
Stalling speed, flaps and gear down	
	49 knots (90 km/h; 56 mph)
Range with max fuel	755 nm (1,400 km; 870 miles)
Endurance at cruising speed	4 h 24 min

FRANCE

NICOLLIER
HENRI NICOLLIER
69 rue des Cras, 25000 Besançon

M Nicollier was responsible for design and construction of the HN 433 Menestrel single-seat homebuilt light aircraft, first flown in November 1962 and last described in the 1972-73 *Jane's*. Several examples of the Menestrel were built by enthusiasts. In 1969 M Nicollier began construction of a two-seat easy-to-build all-wood lightplane which he named Pacific, but no further news of its progress was received. However, it was reported in January 1980 that construction of a very similar aircraft was well advanced as the HN 500 Bengali. It was anticipated that this would be completed in time for exhibition at the RSA annual fly-in in 1980.

NICOLLIER HN 500 BENGALI
TYPE: Two-seat homebuilt light aircraft.
WINGS: Cantilever low-wing monoplane. Wing section of NACA 23000 series, tapering in thickness from root to wingtip. Tapered leading- and trailing-edges, with dihedral from roots. All-wood one-piece structure, plywood covered forward of front spar, and incorporating the wing centre-section. Ribs and ailerons of Warren girder construction. No trim tabs. Manually-operated three-position trailing-edge flaps. Wings and control surfaces Dacron-covered overall.

PIK (page 471)
PIK-23 SUHINO
Latest known design by the students of Helsinki University Flying Club, the PIK-23 is a side-by-side two-seat sporting, training and glider-towing aircraft, powered by a 134 kW (180 hp) Avco Lycoming O-360 flat-four engine. Construction is partly of glassfibre, and the wings have a carbonfibre main spar.

DIMENSIONS, EXTERNAL:

Wing span	10·00 m (32 ft 9¾ in)
Wing area, gross	14·00 m² (150·7 sq ft)
Wing aspect ratio	7·14
Length overall	7·10 m (23 ft 3½ in)

FUSELAGE: Conventional all-wood structure of basic rectangular section, with curved top-decking.
TAIL UNIT: Cantilever wooden structure. Very small inset fixed horizontal surface, and large 'semi-monobloc' mass-balanced control surface with two tabs. Rudder of Warren girder construction, fabric-covered. Trim tab in rudder.
LANDING GEAR: Non-retractable tricycle type, with single wheel on each unit. Spring steel cantilever main legs of Wittman type. Self-centering nosewheel, with helicoidal spring shock-absorption. Fairings of plastics material over all three wheels. Toe-actuated hydraulic brakes and parking brake.
POWER PLANT: One 74·5 kW (100 hp) Rolls-Royce Continental O-200-A flat-four engine, driving an EVRA Type D11-28·8C two-blade fixed-pitch wooden propeller. Glassfibre engine cowling. Fuel in two tanks in wing-root leading-edges, each with capacity of 27 litres (5·9 Imp gallons), and main fuselage tank aft of firewall holding 67 litres (14·7 Imp gallons) Total fuel capacity 121 litres (26·5 Imp gallons). Refuelling point on upper surface of fuselage, forward of cockpit canopy.
ACCOMMODATION: Two seats, side by side, beneath a tinted two-piece canopy, each side hinged to open upward.

FINLAND

Height overall	2·65 m (8 ft 8¼ in)

WEIGHTS AND LOADING:

Weight empty	560 kg (1,234 lb)
Max T-O weight	870 kg (1,918 lb)
Max wing loading	62 kg/m² (12·7 lb/sq ft)

PERFORMANCE (at max T-O weight):

Max cruising speed (75% power)	
	113 knots (210 km/h; 130 mph)
Stalling speed, flaps down	
	43 knots (79 km/h; 49·5 mph)
Max rate of climb at S/L	408 m (1,338 ft)/min
T-O to 15 m (50 ft)	320 m (1,050 ft)
Landing from 15 m (50 ft)	280 m (917 ft)
Range	431 nm (800 km; 497 miles)

Baggage space aft of seats, capacity 30 kg (66 lb). Accommodation is ventilated and soundproofed.
SYSTEM: Hydraulic system for brakes only.

DIMENSIONS, EXTERNAL:

Wing span	8·39 m (27 ft 6¼ in)
Wing area, gross	11·25 m² (121·10 sq ft)
Length overall	6·20 m (20 ft 4 in)
Wheel track	2·52 m (8 ft 3¼ in)
Wheelbase	1·51 m (4 ft 11½ in)
Propeller diameter	1·76 m (5 ft 9¼ in)

WEIGHTS (estimated):

Weight empty	395 kg (871 lb)
Max T-O weight	650 kg (1,433 lb)

PERFORMANCE (estimated, at max T-O weight):

Never-exceed speed	183 knots (340 km/h; 211 mph)
Max cruising speed	113 knots (210 km/h; 130 mph)
Approach speed	59 knots (110 km/h; 68 mph)
Stalling speed, flaps down	
	46 knots (85 km/h; 53 mph)
Max rate of climb at S/L	240 m (787 ft)/min
Range with max fuel	540 nm (1,000 km; 621 miles)
Endurance with reserves	5 h

GERMANY (FEDERAL REPUBLIC)

PFLUMM
MANFRED PFLUMM
Vahingerstrasse 60, D-7000 Stuttgart 80

Herr Manfred Pflumm, a member of the Oskar-Ursinus-Vereinigung (OUV), the West German Chapter of the EAA, has designed and constructed a simple single-seat unpowered rotor-kite. This needs to be towed to remain airborne, but can continue in limited autorotational flight after release of the towing cable.

As can be seen in the accompanying illustration, it is largely of tubular construction, with the fuselage structure welded together and the landing gear and rotor pylon attached by bolts. The two-blade rotor is of the simple teetering type; the strut-braced tail unit includes fin, fixed tailplane, and rudder. The landing gear comprises a steerable nosewheel, main units with spring-in-tension shock-absorption, plus a small bumper wheel beneath the tail. The towing coupling is incorporated in the triangular frame at the nose.

SCHÖNENBERG
HEINRICH SCHÖNENBERG
Kranachweg 2, D-5880 Lüdenscheid
SCHÖNENBERG HS 9 BIPLANE

Herr Heinrich Schönenberg, a member of the Oskar-Ursinus-Vereinigung (OUV), has built an aircraft similar to the EAA Biplane which he has designated HS 9. It differs primarily in being of smaller dimensions and lighter weight; but the main landing gear units with rubber cord shock-absorption, as detailed in the EAA plans, have been replaced by cantilever metal struts. Power plant of the HS 9 consists of a 74·5 kW (100 hp) Continental O-200 flat-four engine, driving a three-blade wooden propeller with spinner.

No further details or dimensions are available.

Unpowered rotor-kite built by Manfred Pflumm (*Wolfgang Wagner*)

Heinrich Schönenberg's HS 9 homebuilt biplane (*Wolfgang Wagner*)

POLAND

JARZAB
KAZIMIERZ JARZAB
38-400 Krosno, ul. Staszica 11/22
JARZAB KLOS (EAR)
Mr Kazimierz Jarzab, with assistance from Mr S. Kustron and Mr S. Wojton, has designed and built an ultralight single-seat aircraft which has been named Klos. Design and construction began in 1974, and the aircraft was flown by Mr Jarzab for the first time in July 1977. All available details follow:
TYPE: Single-seat ultralight sporting aircraft.
WINGS: Braced high-wing monoplane, with single bracing strut each side. Wing section Clark Y. Constant-chord single-spar structure of wood, with plywood skins, and light alloy wingtips. Ailerons of wooden construction. No flaps or trim tabs.

FUSELAGE: Structure of pod and boom type. Forward fuselage has basic frame of welded steel tube, covered with light alloy. Tailboom consists of a light alloy tube.
TAIL UNIT: All-moving V tail, which has a light alloy tubular leading-edge spar, and is covered with fabric. Fixed triangular endplate fin at each tip of V tail. No trim tabs.
LANDING GEAR: Non-retractable tailwheel type with single

wheel on each unit. Cantilever main legs of light alloy. Main-wheel tyres size 225 × 110 mm. Tailwheel diameter 90 mm (3½ in).
POWER PLANT: One 12 kW (16 hp) modified MZ-250 motorcycle engine, driving via V-belt reduction gear a two-blade metal pusher propeller with spinner. Fuel capacity 20 litres (4·4 Imp gallons).
ACCOMMODATION: Pilot only, in open cockpit.
DIMENSIONS, EXTERNAL:

Wing span	7·00 m (22 ft 11½ in)
Wing chord, constant	0·90 m (2 ft 11½ in)
Wing area, gross	6·00 m² (64·59 sq ft)
Length overall	4·20 m (13 ft 9¼ in)
Height overall	1·10 m (3 ft 7¼ in)
Tailplane span	1·76 m (5 ft 9¼ in)
Wheel track	0·90 m (2 ft 11½ in)

WEIGHTS:

Weight empty	95 kg (209 lb)
Normal T-O weight	190 kg (419 lb)

Mr Jarzab's Klos ultralight monoplane

PERFORMANCE (at normal T-O weight):

Cruising speed	59 knots (110 km/h; 68 mph)
Max rate of climb at S/L	120 m (394 ft)/min

T-O run from grass	200 m (656 ft)
Range with max fuel	540 nm (1,000 km; 621 miles)
Endurance with reserves	5 h

UNION OF SOVIET SOCIALIST REPUBLICS

Photographs of two Soviet homebuilt aircraft were received as this edition was closing for press. They are reproduced on this page. Full descriptions of the aircraft will appear in the 1981-82 *Jane's*. Brief details follow:

STREKOZA

Built by students of Kuibyshev Polytechnic, this simple 'bathtub' single-seater is powered by an 18·4 kW (25 hp) Wichr-25 aircooled engine. Control surfaces comprise conventional rudder and elevators, and almost full-span auxiliary-aerofoil ailerons. Wing section is R-P-14.
DIMENSIONS, EXTERNAL:

Wing span	7·20 m (23 ft 7½ in)
Wing chord (constant)	1·1 m (3 ft 7¼ in)
Wing area, gross	9·8 m² (105·5 sq ft)
Length overall	6·07 m (19 ft 10¾ in)
Height overall	2·0 m (6 ft 6¾ in)
Propeller diameter	1·1 m (3 ft 7¼ in)

WEIGHTS:

Weight empty	150 kg (330 lb)
Max T-O weight	230 kg (507 lb)

PERFORMANCE:

Max level speed	54 knots (100 km/h; 62 mph)
T-O speed	27 knots (50 km/h; 31 mph)
Landing speed	25 knots (45 km/h; 28 mph)
T-O run	200 m (656 ft)
Landing run	180 m (590 ft)

SZMIEL (BUMBLE BEE)

Also built by students at Kuibyshev, the Szmiel is a single-seat strut-braced high-wing monoplane of conventional layout, except for its almost-full-span auxiliary-aerofoil ailerons. Wing section is again specified as R-P-14. The M-63 motorcycle engine is rated at 28 kW (38 hp).

DIMENSIONS, EXTERNAL:

Wing span	7·60 m (24 ft 11¼ in)
Wing chord (constant)	1·10 m (3 ft 7¼ in)
Wing area, gross	10·24 m² (110·2 sq ft)
Length overall	5·42 m (17 ft 9½ in)
Height overall	1·88 m (6 ft 2 in)
Propeller diameter	1·5 m (4 ft 11 in)

WEIGHTS:

Weight empty	220 kg (485 lb)
Max T-O weight	310 kg (683 lb)

PERFORMANCE:

Max level speed	65 knots (120 km/h; 74 mph)
T-O speed	30 knots (55 km/h; 34 mph)
Landing speed	27 knots (50 km/h; 31 mph)
T-O run	400 m (1,312 ft)
Landing run	300 m (985 ft)

The Strekoza (left) and Szmiel homebuilt aircraft, made by students of the Kuibyshev Polytechnic

UNITED KINGDOM
PLUMB
BARRY PLUMB
11 Copperbeech Way, Leighton Buzzard, Bedfordshire LU7 8BD

PLUMB BGP1 BIPLANE

In the Summer of 1980 Mr Barry Plumb was well advanced with the construction of a single-seat biplane of original design, with design load factors of +6·5g and −3·5g. It is to be powered by a Volkswagen motorcar engine, the modification of which has been carried out by Mr D. Burden. All available details follow:
TYPE: Single-seat sporting biplane.
WINGS: Single-bay biplane, with N-type interplane struts, centre-section support struts, and a streamline-section bracing strut each side. Wing section N-71, of approx 12% thickness/chord ratio. Unequal-span staggered constant-chord wings of conventional two-spar construction. Spruce spars, ribs of marine plywood, and fabric covering. Plain fabric-covered ailerons on upper wings only.
FUSELAGE: All-wood rectangular-section structure, with spruce longerons, frames and bracing, plywood-covered. Turtle-back aft of cockpit faired into fin.
TAIL UNIT: Wire-braced all-wood structure with fixed-incidence tailplane. Rudder and elevators fabric-covered.
LANDING GEAR: Non-retractable tailwheel type, with single wheel on each unit. Cantilever main units of light alloy.
POWER PLANT: One 1,834 cc modified Volkswagen motorcar engine, driving a two-blade fixed-pitch wooden propeller with spinner. Fuel tank in forward fuselage, immediately aft of firewall, capacity 36·4 litres (8 Imp gallons). Refuelling point on upper surface of fuselage, forward of windscreen.

ACCOMMODATION: Single seat in open cockpit.
DIMENSIONS, EXTERNAL:

Wing span, upper	4·88 m (16 ft 0 in)
Wing span, lower	4·27 m (14 ft 0 in)
Wing chord, constant (both)	1·07 m (3 ft 6 in)
Wing area, gross	8·83 m² (95 sq ft)
Length overall	4·57 m (15 ft 0 in)
Height overall	1·75 m (5 ft 9 in)
Tailplane span	1·98 m (6 ft 6 in)

Wheel track	1·12 m (3 ft 8 in)
Wheelbase	2·95 m (9 ft 8 in)
Propeller diameter	1·37 m (4 ft 6 in)

WEIGHT:

Max T-O weight	329 kg (725 lb)

PERFORMANCE (estimated, at max T-O weight):

Max level speed	90 knots (167 km/h; 104 mph)
Stalling speed	43 knots (79 km/h; 49 mph)

UNITED STATES OF AMERICA

CARMICHAEL
BOB CARMICHAEL
Roanoke, Texas

CARMICHAEL LASER 200

Mr Bob Carmichael, a member of the US Aerobatic Team, has built a single-seat sporting monoplane named the Laser 200 (N26SS), which is derived from the Stephens Akro (which see). It is basically similar to Leo Loudenslager's Laser 200, and to the Super Star built by Henry Haigh, US National Aerobatics Champion in 1979. It incorporates the original wing of the Super Star, which became surplus when Mr Haigh decided to rebuild this aircraft; is stressed to design load factors of ±10g and to

Carmichael Laser 200 aerobatic aircraft (*Don Berliner*)

±13·5g ultimate; and is powered by a 149 kW (200 hp) Avco Lycoming IO-360-A1A flat-four engine, driving a two-blade constant-speed metal propeller with spinner. Mr Carmichael first used this aircraft in competition during the 1979 US National Championships held at Sherman, Texas.

Brief specification and performance details of the Laser 200 are as follows:

DIMENSIONS, EXTERNAL:
Wing span	7·47 m (24 ft 6 in)
Wing area, gross	8·70 m² (93·6 sq ft)
Length overall	6·10 m (20 ft 0 in)
Propeller diameter	1·93 m (6 ft 4 in)

WEIGHTS:
Weight empty	386 kg (850 lb)
Max T-O weight	499 kg (1,100 lb)

PERFORMANCE (at max T-O weight):
Max level speed	174 knots (322 km/h; 200 mph)
Cruising speed	148 knots (274 km/h; 170 mph)
Landing speed	56 knots (105 km/h; 65 mph)
Max rate of climb at S/L	915 m (3,000 ft)/min

DR PAUL MacCREADY

AeroVironment Inc, 145 Vista Avenue, Pasadena, California 91107

MacCREADY SOLAR CHALLENGER

Under the leadership of Dr Paul MacCready, two world-beating manpowered aircraft have been designed and built. The first, Gossamer Condor, won on 23 August 1977 the £50,000 Kremer Prize for the first manpowered aircraft to complete a figure-of-eight flight around two pylons half a mile apart. The second, Gossamer Albatross, completed on 12 June 1979 the first crossing of the English Channel by a manpowered aircraft, winning a Kremer Prize of £100,000 for this achievement. Both of these aircraft have been described in *Jane's*, in the 1978-79 and 1979-80 editions respectively.

As a result of the above successes, Dr MacCready and his team had gained an appreciation of the possibilities for improving the efficiency and energy conservation potential of lightweight vehicles, leading to the conclusion that it should be possible to build a practical solar-powered aircraft. To gain an appreciation of the problems involved, battery-powered flights were made with two existing aircraft: Gossamer Albatross II (a backup that had been prepared for the cross-Channel flight) and the Gossamer Penguin, a three-quarter scale version of the Albatross, which had been almost completed as a second backup vehicle for the cross-Channel attempt. Dr MacCready's 13 year old son Marshall, weighing only 36·3 kg (80 lb), served as test pilot during approximately 50 battery-powered flights of the Penguin, his light weight being of considerable help in keeping the airspeed as low as possible.

This latter aircraft has since been used as a testbed for the initial exploration of manned solar-power flight, provided with a tilting solar cell panel that makes it possible to obtain maximum power from each cell with the sun at low angles. This applies at the only times when flight was possible, in calm early morning conditions, for this early solar panel had a limited number of cells, and the Penguin itself is of delicate construction with only limited control, demanding calm conditions for successful flight. With this aircraft, on 18 May 1980, a short climbing flight was recorded on solar power alone, following an assisted take-off, the Penguin again being piloted by Marshall MacCready. A straight flight of about 1·7 nm (3 km; 2 miles) was made by this aircraft on 7 August 1980, piloted by Janice Brown, a 43 kg (95 lb) school teacher and glider pilot. In theory it should be possible for the aircraft to be flown over an out-and-return course, but the mid-turn would require it to exceed the 3 m (10 ft) height limit which, for safety reasons, is mandatory at the present time.

As a result of intensive studies, plus the initial success recorded by the Penguin, a decision was made to proceed with the construction and development of a purpose-designed solar-powered aircraft under the sponsorship of the Du Pont Company. Named appropriately Solar Challenger, it was required that this aircraft should be strong enough to cope with turbulence and permit safe flight at all heights; therefore, its configuration differs considerably from the Gossamer family which preceded it. This has been imposed by the need to eliminate drag-inducing bracing wires and the use of a kingpost which, at times, would shade the solar cells on the wing upper surface. This was

Gossamer Penguin, with tilting solar panel

MacCready solar-powered Solar Challenger *(Michael A. Badrocke)*

important, because a slight shadow on one cell of a chain of cells can destroy the power output of the entire chain. A flight of this aircraft over a range of approximately 87 nm (161 km; 100 miles) was planned for the late Summer of 1980. The design load factors of the Solar Challenger are +6g and −4g; all available details follow:

TYPE: Solar-powered research aircraft.

WINGS: Cantilever high-wing monoplane of constant chord. Dihedral 5° on outer wing panels. Wing spar of Kevlar and Nomex construction. Rib doublers, leading- and trailing-edge stiffeners, internal bracing cables and control cables of Kevlar. Plain ailerons of similar construction. Mylar covering on wings and ailerons. Solar panels on upper surface of wings.

FUSELAGE: Pod fuselage beneath wing. Kevlar structure, with Mylar covering and acrylic windscreen.

TAIL UNIT: Tailboom of Kevlar carries on its upper surface, forward of the fin/rudder assembly, a fixed-incidence tailplane and an elevator of similar construction to that of the wing, and with solar panels incorporated in the upper surface of the tailplane. Fin and rudder, of similar construction, mounted at aft end of tailboom, at approximate midpoint of the fin. All surfaces Mylar covered.

LANDING GEAR: Support structure of Kevlar beneath the fuselage, with nylon nosewheel and a Nomex monowheel in tandem.

POWER PLANT: One Astro 2500 electric motor with gear drive. Two-blade fixed-pitch Kevlar tractor propeller mounted at the nose of a forward extension of the tailboom, and driven through Kevlar motor drive belts and Delrin belt reduction gears. Approximately 15,000 Spectrolab photovoltaic cells provide maximum power of 2·5 kW (3·35 hp). No batteries.

ACCOMMODATION: Pilot only, with seat harness and parachute of nylon. Conventional flight controls and basic flight instruments.

DIMENSIONS, EXTERNAL:
Wing span	13·72 m (45 ft 0 in)
Wing chord, constant	1·78 m (5 ft 10 in)
Length overall	8·59 m (28 ft 2 in)
Tailplane span	3·28 m (10 ft 9 in)
Propeller diameter	2·97 m (9 ft 9 in)
Propeller ground clearance	0·17 m (6½ in)

WEIGHTS (estimated):
Weight empty, without solar cells	35 kg (77 lb)
Weight of solar cells	21 kg (47 lb)
Design T-O weight	107 kg (235 lb)

PERFORMANCE (estimated, at max T-O weight):
Never-exceed speed	35 knots (64 km/h; 40 mph)
Max cruising speed	30 knots (56 km/h; 35 mph)
Stalling speed	14·8 knots (27·4 km/h; 17 mph)
Max rate of climb, S/L at 19 knots (35·5 km/h; 22 mph)	55 m (180 ft)/min
Range	over 182 nm (338 km; 210 miles)

RED BARON
RED BARON FLYING SERVICE

PO Box 497, Idaho Falls, Idaho 83401
Telephone: (208) 523 1812
PRESIDENT: J. E. Browning

Red Baron Flying Service, a company which provides flying instruction, maintenance, sales, and charter services, sponsored Darryl Greenamyer's modified Lockheed F-104 Starfighter (see 1978-79 *Jane's*) and a modified version of the North American P-51D Mustang last flown by Steve Hinton.

RED BARON RB-51 MUSTANG

This ex-USAAF P-51D (N7715C) was first raced in standard form in 1966, flown by its owner, Chuck Hall. Modifications completed in 1969 included a reduction of wing span to 10·06 m (33 ft 0 in), and the introduction of computer-designed Hoerner wingtips, a low-profile canopy faired into the built-up turtle-deck, and an Aero-

products propeller from a P-51H, with pointed spinner. In addition, the wing skins were filled with glassfibre and smoothed. In this form, flown by new owner Gunther Balz, it won the Unlimited Class race at Reno, Nevada, in 1972 at a new US national record speed of 361·63 knots (669·74 km/h; 416·16 mph).

In 1975 the aircraft was given additional power by the installation of an extensively modified Rolls-Royce Griffon 57 engine, driving two de Havilland three-blade constant-speed propellers on co-axial contra-rotating shafts, and necessitating vertical tail surfaces of greater area. Flown at Reno in 1975 by Roy McClain, it gained second place at 371·32 knots (687·69 km/h; 427·31 mph). Under Red Baron sponsorship, it was flown as the RB-51 by Darryl Greenamyer at Reno in 1977, and won at a record 374·270 knots (693·148 km/h; 430·702 mph). Still sponsored by Red Baron, it was first flown by Steve Hinton

in 1978. On 14 August 1979, at Tonopah, Nevada, this pilot established a new world record in Class C, Group I (aeroplanes with piston engines), for speed in a straight line. With the Griffon engine rated at 2,834 kW (3,800 hp) for this attempt, the RB-51 was flown over a 3 km course at a speed of 433·660 knots (803·138 km/h; 499·047 mph), which was ratified subsequently by the FAI. In capturing this record, Steve Hinton beat the record estab-

lished by Darryl Greenamyer in a Grumman F8F-2 Bearcat almost exactly ten years earlier.

Later in 1979 the RB-51 was destroyed in an accident, Steve Hinton receiving serious injuries from which he has since recovered. The aircraft is illustrated on the World Records page at the front of this edition of *Jane's*.

MILLER

Miller Lil' Rascal two-seat sporting aircraft, described on page 503 of the 1979-80 *Jane's (J. M. G. Gradidge)*

MONNETT (page 532)

Monnett Monex high-performance single-seat homebuilt *(J. M. G. Gradidge)*

WEEKS
KERMIT WEEKS
Miami, Florida

WEEKS SPECIAL

Mr Kermit Weeks developed his Weeks Special from the standard production Pitts Special S-1S single-seat sports biplane. It differs primarily in the wing structure, which has lower panels with the same 6° 40′ sweepback at quarter-chord as the standard upper wings. The span of the upper and lower wings is reduced by 0·41 m (1 ft 4 in), and symmetrical ailerons are fitted on all four wings. Power plant changes include the installation of a 149 kW (200 hp) Avco Lycoming AEIO-360-A1D flat-four engine, driving a Hoffmann two-blade constant-speed propeller with spinner, plus the introduction of a crossover exhaust system and moulded glassfibre engine pressure cowlings. In addition, the usual main landing gear with rubber-cord shock-absorption is replaced by cantilever light alloy legs, and the normally-open cockpit is enclosed by a one-piece blown bubble canopy. Design load factors of the Weeks Special are ±9g.

Mr Weeks flew this aircraft to second place in the 1978 World Aerobatic Championships. He was winner of the International Aerobatic Club Championships of 1979, and second in the 1979 US National Championships. Brief

ROTORWAY (page 541)

The new RotorWay Exec homebuilt helicopter *(J. M. G. Gradidge)*

specification and performance details follow:

DIMENSIONS, EXTERNAL:
Wing span, upper	4·76 m (15 ft 7½ in)
Wing span, lower	4·60 m (15 ft 1 in)
Wing area, gross	8·36 m² (90 sq ft)
Length overall	4·90 m (16 ft 0¾ in)
Propeller diameter	1·93 m (6 ft 4 in)

WEIGHTS:
Weight empty	345 kg (760 lb)
Competition T-O weight	454 kg (1,000 lb)

PERFORMANCE (at competition T-O weight):
Max level speed	174 knots (322 km/h; 200 mph)
Cruising speed	139 knots (257 km/h; 160 mph)
Max rate of climb at S/L	915 m (3,000 ft)/min

Weeks Special aerobatic biplane *(Bob Morrison)*

The aerobatic Young Sunbird, derived from the Pitts Special S-1S *(Don Berliner)*

YOUNG
DR JIM YOUNG

YOUNG SUNBIRD

The late Dr Jim Young of Anaheim, California, developed the single-seat aerobatic Sunbird (N7YJ) from the standard Pitts Special S-1S. Intended to be the pro-

totype of a series of Unlimited aerobatic aircraft, it differed from the basic S-1S in having a 194 kW (260 hp) Avco Lycoming O-540 flat-six engine, driving a two-blade propeller with spinner. Modifications to improve aerodynamic efficiency included the use of a moulded

glassfibre engine cowling, cantilever main landing gear, close fitting wheel fairings of glassfibre, and a moulded one-piece bubble canopy.

This aircraft was destroyed when it crashed in bad weather on 3 March 1980.

SAILPLANES
FINLAND

EIRI (page 564)

EIRI PIK-20F

This latest version is available in a 15 metre Class (with 140 kg; 308 lb water ballast) and a Club Class version (with non-retractable monowheel). Features include car-

bonfibre spars, carbon-reinforced cockpit area, forward-opening carbon-reinforced canopy, double-thickness cockpit floor, modified wing profile, lower-drag fuselage, Schempp-Hirth airbrakes, and new wing/fuselage epoxy finish.

DIMENSIONS, EXTERNAL:
Wing span	15·00 m (49 ft 2½ in)
Wing area, gross	10·00 m² (107·64 sq ft)
Wing aspect ratio	22·5
Length overall	6·65 m (21 ft 9¾ in)

WEIGHTS AND LOADINGS:
Weight empty 220 kg (485 lb)
Max T-O weight 450 kg (992 lb)
Max wing loading:
without water ballast 29 kg/m² (5·9 lb/sq ft)
with water ballast 45 kg/m² (9·2 lb/sq ft)
PERFORMANCE (at max T-O weight):
Best glide ratio at 63 knots (117 km/h; 73 mph) 40·5
Min sinking speed at 49·5 knots (92 km/h; 57 mph)
0·69 m (2·26 ft)/s
Max speed (smooth air) 157 knots (292 km/h; 181 mph)

GERMANY (FEDERAL REPUBLIC)

AKADEMISCHE FLIEGERGRUPPE HANNOVER eV
Welfengarten 1a, 3000 Hanover

AKAFLIEG HANNOVER AFH 22
The AFH 22, under development in 1980, is a tandem two-seat sailplane with a mid-mounted sweptforward wing, T tail and retractable monowheel.
SPECIFICATION:
Wing span 17·50 m (57 ft 5 in)
Length overall 8·50 m (27 ft 10¾ in)
Weight empty 390 kg (860 lb)
Max T-O weight 600 kg (1,322 lb)

DOKTOR FIBERGLAS, GfK-FLUGZEUG-SERVICE
Postfach 74, 6147 Lautertal 1

This company is now responsible for the H 101 Salto single-seat V-tailed sailplane produced formerly by Start + Flug. A description of the Salto can be found under the latter company's entry in the 1978-79 *Jane's*.

FRANÇOIS GROSS
Bertrichamps-Le Clairupt, 54120 Baccarat

GROSS (FAUVEL) AV.451
This modified version of a Fauvel AV.45 self-launching sailplane (F-CRRM) was designed and built by M Gross, with the help of his son, in less than a year. Principal changes include an increase in wing span from 13·60 m (44 ft 7½ in) to 15·00 m (49 ft 2½ in), giving an aspect ratio of 13·5; adoption of a new Wortmann aerofoil section; a longer fuselage, modified in the cockpit area to accept the canopy from an Astir sailplane; and the installation of a 28·3 kW (38 hp) Rotax 642 two-cylinder two-stroke engine aft of the cockpit, driving a two-blade Hoffmann pusher propeller.

AKADEMISCHE FLIEGERGRUPPE STUTTGART eV
Pfaffenwaldring 35, 7000 Stuttgart 80
Telephone: (0711) 784 2442/3
PRESIDENT: Harald Joos

Details of Akaflieg Stuttgart's FS-29 can be found in the 1976-77 *Jane's*. Its latest known design is the FS-31.

AKAFLIEG STUTTGART FS-31
This tandem two-seat sailplane has mid-mounted wings

FVA AACHEN
Templergraben 55 (c/o U. Solies), 5100 Aachen

FVA-20
The FVA-20 single-seat Standard Class sailplane was designed to explore experimental methods of glassfibre construction. The prototype (D-6020) flew for the first time on 28 November 1979; production is not intended.
AIRFRAME: Cantilever shoulder-wing monoplane; wing sections Wortmann FX-61-168 at root, FX-60-126 at tip. Schempp-Hirth airbrakes. Cantilever T tail. Retractable monowheel; tail bumper.
DIMENSIONS, EXTERNAL:
Wing span 15·00 m (49 ft 2½ in)

FRANCE

The wood-and-fabric construction of the standard AV.45 is retained, as are the regular control surfaces.

BERNARD PONSOT
5 rue Bicquilley, 54200 Toul

A French press report in September 1979 referred briefly to a Fauvel AV.45 built by M Ponsot, which had recently made its first flight powered by a Microturbo Eclair turbojet in place of the Nelson piston engine previously fitted. No further details were known at the time of closing for press.

of Eppler E 603 section, a T tail and a retractable monowheel. Carbonfibre and Kevlar 49 are used in its construction, to save weight.
SPECIFICATION:
Wing span 17·50 m (57 ft 5 in)
Length overall 8·70 m (28 ft 6½ in)
Weight empty 340 kg (750 lb)
Max T-O weight 560 kg (1,234 lb)

Wing area, gross 12·80 m² (137·8 sq ft)
Wing aspect ratio 17·6
Length overall 7·00 m (22 ft 11½ in)
Height over fuselage 0·90 m (2 ft 11½ in)
WEIGHTS AND LOADING:
Weight empty 260 kg (573 lb)
Max T-O weight 360 kg (793 lb)
Max wing loading 26·8 kg/m² (5·5 lb/sq ft)
PERFORMANCE:
Best glide ratio at 49 knots (90 km/h; 56 mph) 37
Min sinking speed at 37 knots (68 km/h; 42 mph)
0·60 m (1·97 ft)/s
Stalling speed 34 knots (62 km/h; 39 mph)
Max speed (smooth air) 135 knots (250 km/h; 155 mph)

H 101 Salto single-seat sailplane *(Peter F. Selinger)*

FVA Aachen FVA-20 Standard Class sailplane *(Peter F. Selinger)*

GLASER-DIRKS (page 568)
GLASER-DIRKS DG-202
First flown on 30 April 1980, the DG-202 is a development of the DG-200 series, with improved cockpit and controls, and other detail changes. Deliveries were expected to begin in December 1980, with three versions available: an all-glassfibre 15 m Class model, a similarly-built Open Class model with 17 m (55 ft 9¼ in) span, and a 17 m version with carbonfibre main spar.

Glasflügel 304
single-seat 15 metre
Class sailplane
(Peter F. Selinger)

GLASFLÜGEL (page 568)
GLASFLÜGEL 304
Design of the Glasflügel 304 began in 1979 under the direction of Herr Martin Hansen, and the prototype (D-9304) flew for the first time on 10 May 1980. Deliveries of production aircraft were expected to begin in August 1980.

In configuration and construction the 304 is very similar to its predecessor, the Glasflügel 303 Mosquito (see main section), the principal structural differences being in the

wings, which have trailing-edge flaps of a new HQ 014-1642 aerofoil section; the nose, which is slimmer and more pointed; and the instrument panel, which is integral with the front-hinged, upward-opening canopy.
TYPE: Single-seat 15 metre Class sailplane.
DIMENSIONS, EXTERNAL:
Wing span 15·00 m (49 ft 2½ in)
Wing area, gross 9·88 m² (106·35 sq ft)
Wing aspect ratio 22·78
Length overall 6·45 m (21 ft 2 in)
Height over tail 1·36 m (4 ft 5½ in)

WEIGHTS AND LOADING:
Weight empty 235 kg (518 lb)
Max water ballast 115 kg (253 lb)
Max T-O weight 450 kg (992 lb)
Max wing loading 44·5 kg/m² (9·12 lb/sq ft)
PERFORMANCE (at max T-O weight):
Best glide ratio at 63 knots (116 km/h; 72 mph) 43
Min sinking speed at 50 knots (93 km/h; 58 mph)
0·69 m (2·26 ft)/s
Stalling speed 40 knots (73 km/h; 46 mph)
Max speed (smooth air) 135 knots (250 km/h; 156 mph)

WOLF HOFFMANN FLUGZEUGBAU KG
DIRECTOR: Dipl-Ing Wolf D. Hoffmann
HOFFMANN H-36 DIMONA
Details of this side-by-side two-seat motor glider became available in the Spring of 1980. Constructed

mainly of GfK, it has Wortmann wing (FX-63-137) and tail (FX-71-L150/25 and FX-71-L150/40) sections, a non-retractable tailwheel-type landing gear (with main leg and wheel fairings), and a 59·5 kW (80 hp) Limbach SL 2000 EBI engine driving a two-blade propeller. It is

intended that series production should be undertaken in Israel, by IDI Aviation Production Ltd.
DIMENSIONS, EXTERNAL:
Wing span 16·00 m (52 ft 6 in)
Wing area, gross 15·20 m² (163·6 sq ft)

Wing aspect ratio	16·8	Max power loading	10·89 kg/kW (17·90 lb/hp)
Length overall	6·85 m (22 ft 5¾ in)	PERFORMANCE (power off):	
Height over tail	1·60 m (5 ft 3 in)	Best glide ratio at 56·5 knots (105 km/h; 65 mph) 27	
WEIGHTS AND LOADINGS:		Min sinking speed at 43 knots (80 km/h; 50 mph)	
Weight empty	400 kg (882 lb)		0·90 m (2·95 ft)/s
Max T-O weight	650 kg (1,433 lb)	Stalling speed	38 knots (70 km/h; 44 mph)
Max wing loading	42·7 kg/m² (8·75 lb/sq ft)	Max speed (smooth air)	156 knots (290 km/h; 180 mph)

Max speed (rough air)	92 knots (170 km/h; 106 mph)
PERFORMANCE (power on):	
Max level speed	113 knots (210 km/h; 130 mph)
Econ cruising speed	97 knots (180 km/h; 112 mph)
Max rate of climb at S/L	210 m (689 ft)/min
Max range	540 nm (1,000 km; 621 miles)

BERNHARD HUFNAGEL
Bernhardswiesen 53, 8800 Ansbach

HUFNAGEL ZAMBERLE

This single-seat, open-cockpit primary glider, designed and built by Herr Hufnagel, made its first flight on 23 March 1979. It is of mid-wing configuration (see accompanying illustration), and fabric-covered plywood construction.

SPECIFICATION:

Wing span	8·00 m (26 ft 3 in)
Wing area, gross	12·00 m² (129·2 sq ft)

Length overall	5·00 m (16 ft 4¾ in)
Weight empty	48·6 kg (107 lb)
Max T-O weight	130 kg (286·5 lb)
Max speed (approx)	19·5 knots (36 km/h; 22 mph)
Best glide ratio	15-17

Hufnagel Zamberle single-seat homebuilt glider (*Peter F. Selinger*)

Rhönlerche IIM motorised glider built by Ing Wilhelm Knechtel (*Peter F. Selinger*)

ING WILHELM-J. KNECHTEL
Raulinenstrasse 24, 6301 Rodheim

KNECHTEL RHÖNLERCHE IIM

Herr Knechtel has converted a Rhönlerche (Rhône Lark) glider into a motor glider by installing a 32 kW (43 hp) Volkswagen 1500 motorcar engine above the wings, driving two small two-blade propellers mounted on outriggers. This aircraft (D-KABQ) is shown in an accompanying illustration.

Herr Knechtel also has under construction a two-seat motor glider, powered by a Volkswagen omnibus engine and utilising a fuselage of his own design in combination with the wings of a Grob Twin Astir sailplane.

SPECIFICATION (Rhönlerche IIM):

Wing span	13·00 m (42 ft 7¾ in)
Length overall	7·00 m (22 ft 11½ in)
Weight empty, equipped	405 kg (893 lb)
Max T-O weight	535 kg (1,179 lb)
Max level speed	86 knots (160 km/h; 99 mph)
Service ceiling	4,500 m (14,765 ft)
Range	135 nm (250 km; 155 miles)

LINDNER (FIBERGLAS-TECHNIK RUDOLF LINDNER GmbH & Co KG)
Ortsstrasse 70, 7959 Walpertshofen

LINDNER PHOEBUS B 3

Features of the Phoebus B 3 are 'elastic' flaps and automatically-actuated plain flaps, developed jointly by Lindner and Prof Eppler and first flight tested in 1978. The aircraft is illustrated in an accompanying photograph.

Prototype of the Rolladen-Schneider LS4 Standard Class sailplane (*Peter F. Selinger*)

Lindner Phoebus B 3 sailplane, with experimental flap system (*via Peter F. Selinger*)

ROLLADEN-SCHNEIDER (page 570)

ROLLADEN-SCHNEIDER LS4

The LS4 utilises a modified LS3-a fuselage combined with a new, thin-section wing having a thickness/chord ratio of 16% at the root and 13% at the tip, and mid-mounted on the fuselage. The aircraft has a cantilever T tail, and fully-retractable monowheel landing gear. Series production was expected to begin in September 1980. Initial flight testing indicated a best glide ratio at 54 knots (100 km/h; 62 mph) of better than 40, and a min sinking speed at 40 knots (74 km/h; 46 mph) of 0·60 m (1·97 ft)/s.

ROLLADEN-SCHNEIDER LS5

The LS5 is a 22 m (72 ft 2¼ in) span Open Class sailplane of GRP construction, with a new carbonfibre wing of thin Wortmann section, fitted with four flaps/airbrakes, of which the inner segments can be deflected 60°. The aircraft will have a fuselage similar to that of the LS3-a, with a larger tail unit and modified landing gear. Performance is expected to be at least as good as that of the LS3-17.

Schempp-Hirth Ventus b single-seat 15 metre Class sailplane (*Peter F. Selinger*)

SCHEIBE (page 570)

SCHEIBE SF-36

A prototype of this new two-seat motor glider was under construction in the Spring of 1980. It is powered by a 59·5 kW (80 hp) Limbach SL 2000 engine, and is of GfK construction, utilising the wings and tail unit of the SF-H34 sailplane. The two-wheel main landing gear is similar to that of the C-Falke '80.

SCHEMPP-HIRTH (page 572)

SCHEMPP-HIRTH VENTUS

First flown on 3 May 1980, the Ventus (Latin for wind) is a 15 metre Class sailplane with a thin-section carbonfibre wing. It is available with a choice of two fuselages, the Ventus b having a slightly larger cockpit for pilots more than 1·75 m (5 ft 9 in) tall.

DIMENSIONS, EXTERNAL:

Wing span	15·00 m (49 ft 2½ in)

Wing area, gross	9·51 m² (102·4 sq ft)
Wing aspect ratio	23·7
Length overall	6·35 m (20 ft 10 in)

WEIGHTS AND LOADING:

Weight empty: Ventus a	215 kg (474 lb)
Ventus b	220 kg (485 lb)
Max T-O weight, incl 150 kg (330 lb) water ballast (both versions)	430 kg (948 lb)
Max wing loading	45 kg /m² (9·22 lb/sq ft)

PERFORMANCE:

Best glide ratio at 51 knots (95 km/h; 59 mph)	44
Min sinking speed	0·57 m (1·87 ft)/s
Stalling speed	44 knots (81 km/h; 51 mph)
Max speed (smooth air)	135 knots (250 km/h; 155 mph)

ICA (page 577)

SCHLEICHER (page 572)

SCHLEICHER ASW 22

Extensive use is made of glassfibre, carbon-based and aramid fibres in the construction of this new Open Class sailplane, which has a standard wing span of 22 m, extendable to 24 m by the addition of detachable tip extensions. A 21 m span version, with higher max T-O weight, is also to be made available for competition and record attempts in rough weather conditions. Combined flaps/airbrakes on the wing trailing-edge are similar to those fitted to the ASW 20. Main landing gear is a twin-wheel retractable unit, with oleo-pneumatic shock-absorption and disc brakes; the tailwheel is also retractable.

DIMENSIONS, EXTERNAL:

Wing span: standard	22·00 m (72 ft 2¼ in)
extended	24·00 m (78 ft 9 in)
Wing area, gross: 22 m	22·68 m² (244·1 sq ft)
24 m	23·32 m² (251·0 sq ft)

Prototype of the IS-30 motor glider, exhibited at the 1980 Hanover Air Show (Brian M. Service)

Wing aspect ratio: 22 m		21·3
24 m		24·7
Length overall	8·20 m (26 ft 10¾ in)	
Height over tail	1·75 m (5 ft 9 in)	

WEIGHTS:

Weight empty: 22 m	400 kg (882 lb)
24 m	408 kg (899 lb)

Max T-O weight:

22 m with 200 litres (44 Imp gallons) water ballast	700 kg (1,543 lb)
24 m with 100 kg (220 lb) water ballast	608 kg (1,340 lb)
Max wing loading: 22 m	30·8 kg/m² (6·3 lb/sq ft)
24 m	26·1 kg/m² (5·3 lb/sq ft)

PERFORMANCE (estimated):

Best glide ratio	55
Min sinking speed	0·50 m (1·64 ft)/s

UNION OF SOVIET SOCIALIST REPUBLICS

LAK (page 580)

Articles in the Soviet magazine *Krilya Rodiny* during 1980 contained references to designs designated LAK-5 Nyamunas (a motor glider), LAK-10, and LAK-12. The LAK-5 is powered by a 56 kW (75 hp) engine, has maximum level and stalling speeds of 135 knots (250 km/h; 155 mph) and 40·5 knots (75 km/h; 47 mph) respectively, and a best glide ratio of 42-43. The following details were given for the LAK-12, which is externally similar to the LAK-9 and apparently also has the name Lietuva:

SPECIFICATION (LAK-12):

Wing span	20·42 m (67 ft 0 in)
Wing area, gross	14·63 m² (157·5 sq ft)
Length overall	7·25 m (23 ft 9½ in)
Weight empty	320 kg (705 lb)
Max T-O weight	430-650 kg (948-1,433 lb)
Best glide ratio	48
Stalling speed	37 knots (68 km/h; 42·5 mph)
Max speed (smooth air)	135 knots (250 km/h; 155 mph)

UNITED KINGDOM

PETER W. WRIGHT
3 The Close, Burton Lazars, near Melton Mowbray, Leicestershire
Telephone: Melton Mowbray 4361

WRIGHT FALCON 15 m

Mr Wright began the design and construction of this single-seat 15 metre Class homebuilt sailplane in 1975. It flew for the first time on 16 September 1979, and in March 1980 was certificated for semi-aerobatic and cloud flying. Kits for amateur constructors may be made available at a later date.

TYPE: Single-seat homebuilt 15 metre Class sailplane; *g* limits +12/−8 (design), +6/−4 (operating).

AIRFRAME: Cantilever mid-wing monoplane. Wings have a 16% laminar-flow section, with low Reynolds number, and a constant thickness/chord ratio of 16% from root to tip. Dihedral 3°. Incidence 3°. No sweepback. Wings are formed from a foam/glasscloth spar web, pultruded stringers and GRP spar caps, and a glasscloth skin. Wide-chord, 1·22 m (4 ft) span flap/airbrake on each trailing-edge. Mass-balanced ailerons, of glasscloth on foam ribs, have electrically-operated spring trim. Fuselage is a five-ply glasscloth shell, moulded in top and bottom halves, with foam bulkhead stiffeners and GRP/foam longitudinal top-hat stiffeners. Cantilever V tail surfaces (included angle 80°), fins being built integrally with fuselage. Mass-balanced 'ruddervators', with horn aerodynamic balance. Non-retractable unsprung monowheel, size 12 × 4½ in, semi-recessed in under-fuselage fairing; 3 in diameter tailwheel, with leaf spring, in similar but smaller fairing under rear fuselage. Stainless steel band brake on main wheel. Semi-reclining seat under detachable framed canopy.

Wright Falcon 15 m single-seat homebuilt sailplane (R. G. Moulton)

DIMENSIONS, EXTERNAL:

Wing span	15·00 m (49 ft 2½ in)
Wing area, gross	8·76 m² (94·3 sq ft)
Wing aspect ratio	25·7
Length overall	5·94 m (19 ft 6 in)
Height over tail	1·02 m (3 ft 4 in)

WEIGHTS AND LOADING:

Weight empty, equipped	238 kg (525 lb)
Max T-O weight	363 kg (800 lb)
Max wing loading	41·38 kg/m² (8·48 lb/sq ft)

PERFORMANCE:

Best glide ratio at 55 knots (102 km/h; 63 mph)	39
Min sinking speed at 46 knots (85 km/h; 53 mph)	0·61 m (2·0 ft)/s
Stalling speed	40 knots (74·5 km/h; 46·5 mph)
Max speed (smooth air)	135 knots (250 km/h; 155 mph)
Max speed (rough air)	100 knots (185 km/h; 115 mph)
Max aero-tow speed	100 knots (185 km/h; 115 mph)
Max winch-launching speed	70 knots (130 km/h; 81 mph)

UNITED STATES OF AMERICA

GLA INC
841 Winslow Court, Muskegon, Michigan 49441

GLA MINIBAT

TYPE: Single-seat homebuilt ultralight powered glider; building time 40-60 h.

AIRFRAME: Cantilever high-wing monoplane, with single fin and rudder; no horizontal tail surfaces. Fuselage is of elliptical shape. Non-retractable semi-recessed mono-wheel and tailwheel. Entire airframe, built mainly of Kevlar and foam plastics, comprises only 18 major components; it can be dismantled for transportation and stowage, and reassembled in 5 min.

POWER PLANT: One 2·2 kW (3 hp) piston engine, driving a 'pusher' propeller. Engine is for boosting flying speed only, and does not develop enough power for self-launched take-off (aircraft is launched by aero-tow or winch).

WEIGHTS:

Weight empty	36·3 kg (80 lb)
Max T-O weight	136 kg (300 lb)

HOLLMANN AIRCRAFT
11082 Bel Aire Court, Cupertino, California 95014
DIRECTOR: Martin Hollmann

KLEPEIS-HOLLMANN CONDOR

Designed jointly by Mr Eddie Klepeis and Mr Martin Hollmann, the Condor is a two-seat motor glider, of composite construction, powered by a Volkswagen motorcar engine fitted with a turbocharger. One prototype was under construction by each co-designer, in New York and California respectively, in early 1980, with first flights anticipated in 1982.

The Condor is of sweptback mid-wing configuration, with turned-down wingtips, a central fuselage nacelle containing the tandem two-seat cockpit and rear-mounted engine, and two short tailbooms which support twin, sweptback, inward-canted endplate fins and rudders bridged at the top by a fixed tailplane and elevator. Landing gear comprises a retractable nosewheel and non-retractable semi-recessed main wheel. The power plant drives a pusher propeller. Cockpit canopy identical to that of NASA/Ames AD-1.

DIMENSIONS, EXTERNAL:
Wing span　　　　　　　12·19 m (40 ft 0 in)

Length overall	5·33 m (17 ft 6 in)
Length of fuselage (excl propeller spinner)	3·40 m (11 ft 2 in)
Height overall	1·93 m (6 ft 4 in)
Propeller diameter	1·52 m (5 ft 0 in)

PERFORMANCE (estimated):
Cruising speed for max range
　　　　　　　82·5 knots (153 km/h; 95 mph)

Stalling speed, flaps down	31·5 knots (58 km/h; 36 mph)
Ceiling	12,200 m (40,000 ft)
Max range (single-seat)	1,172 nm (2,173 km; 1,350 miles)

JIM MAUPIN
PO Box 5127, San Pedro, California 90733

MAUPIN WOODSTOCK ONE
Notwithstanding the report on page 582 that DSK had acquired the production and marketing rights in this single-seat homebuilt sailplane, the sale of plans from the above address was still being advertised in mid-1980.

Of Douglas fir and birch construction, with some fabric covering, the Woodstock is a single-seat homebuilt sailplane of shoulder-wing configuration, with a non-retractable monowheel. The wings are fitted with upper-surface spoilers. It was reported in mid-1980 that only a prototype was then flying, but that more than 100 were being built by amateur constructors. Plans depict both

open and enclosed cockpits, and a powered version with a pylon-mounted power plant aft of the cockpit.

SPECIFICATION:
Wing span	11·89 m (39 ft 0 in)
Wing area, gross	9·75 m² (105 sq ft)
Wing aspect ratio	14·5
Weight empty	106·5 kg (235 lb)
Max T-O weight	204 kg (450 lb)
Max wing loading	20·9 kg/m² (4·29 lb/sq ft)

HANG GLIDERS

GERMANY (FEDERAL REPUBLIC)

PFLUMM
MANFRED PFLUMM
Vahingerstrasse 60, D-7000 Stuttgart 80

Herr Manfred Pflumm, a member of the Oskar-Ursinus-Vereinigung (OUV), has designed and built an unusual powered hang glider. Believing that many potential enthusiasts were deterred by the exposed position of the pilot, he has attached a miniature aircraft fuselage beneath a Rogallo-type wing. This fuselage is of metal tube construction, fabric-covered, has a tail unit comprising fin and rudder only, and non-retractable tailwheel-type landing gear. A small piston engine, mounted conventionally in the nose of the fuselage, drives a two-blade fixed-pitch propeller, permitting powered take-off and flight.

No further details or dimensions are available.

Powered hang glider built by Herr Manfred Pflumm (*Wolfgang Wagner*)

POLAND

AKL (AKADEMICKI KLUB LOTNIARSKI)
AKL MOTOLOTNIA
The students' aero club of Warsaw Polytechnic has designed, built and flown the Motolotnia, a hang glider powered by a 3·3 kW (4·5 hp) 75 cc engine driving a two-blade ducted propulsion unit. General appearance of the Motolotnia is shown in an accompanying illustration; data include the following:

Wing span	9·60 m (31 ft 6 in)
Wing area	18·00 m² (193·75 sq ft)
Nose angle	110°
Weight of glider	20 kg (44 lb)
Weight of power plant	12 kg (26·5 lb)

AKL Motolotnia powered hang glider built by students of Warsaw Polytechnic
(*Skrzydlata Polska*)

SWITZERLAND

NEUKOM (page 580)
This well-known designer of sailplanes has designed two ultralight powered gliders, the AN-20M and AN-21.

Neukom AN-20M one-man ultralight powered glider

PAWEL WIERZBOWSKI (page 599)
Details were received after the main hang glider pages closed for press of two new models, the Vega SST-A and Vega SST-B. By the Spring of 1980 six SST-As had been sold (of ten built), plus 30 sets of plans; corresponding figures for the SST-B were three sold (of five built), plus 25 sets of plans.

Both models are FAI Class 1 gliders, suitable for competition flying. The SST-A is also suitable for private flying. They can be flown prone (both) or seated (A only), and are stressed to +5/−3g. Airframes are of duralumin, with a single-thickness nylon (A) or Dacron (A and B) sail and vinyl-coated stainless steel cables. Kingpost, pre-formed battens and a floating keel pocket are standard on both types.

SPECIFICATION:
Wing span: A	9·60 m (31 ft 6 in)
B	10·10 m (33 ft 1¾ in)
Leading-edge: A	5·70 m (18 ft 8½ in)
B	6·00 m (19 ft 8¼ in)
Keel: A	3·50 m (11 ft 5¾ in)
B	3·13 m (10 ft 3¼ in)
Nose/billow angle: A	116/0·8°
B	116/0·5°
Wing area: A	18·60 m² (200·2 sq ft)
B	18·90 m² (203·4 sq ft)
Wing aspect ratio: A	4·9
B	5·4

Wierzbowski Vega SST

Weight: A	20·5 kg (45·2 lb)
B	22·0 kg (48·5 lb)
Glide ratio: A	9
B	9+
Min sink rate: A, B	60 m (197 ft)/min
Pilot weight: A	65-90 kg (143-198 lb)
B	68-97 kg (150-214 lb)
Stalling speed: A, B	10 knots (18 km/h; 11·5 mph)

NEUKOM AN-20M
Shown in an accompanying photograph, the AN-20M powered hang glider has an open-frame 'fuselage' beneath the wing, fin and rudder extending above and below the slender tailboom, a T tailplane, and a three-wheel (nose, main and tail) landing gear. Power plant, mounted aft of the pilot's seat and driving a two-blade pusher propeller, is a 9·7 kW (13 hp) Solo motorcar engine.

SPECIFICATION:
Wing span	12·60 m (41 ft 4 in)
Wing area, gross	10·08 m² (108·5 sq ft)

Length overall	5·00 m (16 ft 4¾ in)
Height overall	1·10 m (3 ft 7¼ in)
Weight empty	100 kg (220 lb)
Max T-O weight	200 kg (440 lb)
Max wing loading	19·84 kg/m² (4·06 lb/sq ft)
Best glide ratio, power off	15-20
Min sinking speed, power off	1·0 m (3·28 ft)/s
Max level speed	81 knots (150 km/h; 93 mph)
Cruising speed	54 knots (100 km/h; 62 mph)
Range	135 nm (250 km; 155 miles)

NEUKOM AN-21

Of canard configuration, the AN-21 was designed by Mr Albert Neukom, and the first completed example was constructed by Herr Klaus-Jurgen Richter at his factory at Ulm-Lehr in West Germany. It is powered by a 22·5 kW (30 hp) King engine, driving a pusher propeller, mounted aft of the pilot's seat.

The braced wings of the AN-21 have 20° of sweepback, and are fitted with upper-surface spoilers, ailerons, and endplate fins and rudders at their tips. The non-swept, constant-chord foreplane is fitted with an elevator. The aircraft is of mixed construction, and has a non-retractable tricycle landing gear. The cockpit/fuselage can be an openwork frame, or covered.

DIMENSIONS, EXTERNAL:

Wing span	12·60 m (41 ft 4 in)
Foreplane span	3·00 m (9 ft 10 in)
Length overall	4·90 m (16 ft 1 in)
Height overall	2·40 m (7 ft 10½ in)

WEIGHTS AND PERFORMANCE: No details known

Neukom AN-21 ultralight glider, in unpowered form (Peter F. Selinger)

UNITED KINGDOM

THE ULTRALIGHT AVIATION CENTRE LTD

Wellesbourne Airfield, Wellesbourne, Warwick CV35 9EU
Telephone: 0789 841114
DIRECTORS: Paul Baker and David Garrison

The High School of Hang Gliding (see page 600) is a part of The Ultralight Aviation Centre, from which in the late Summer of 1980 further details were received of the Pterodactyl Fledgling powered hang glider described under Pterodactyl Ltd in the main US section.

The aircraft in its powered form is based upon the Manta Fledge 2B FAI Class 2 hang glider wing, modified by Mr Jack McCornack of Pterodactyl Ltd, and has been in production in the USA since 1978. The Ultralight Aviation Centre began to import and assemble the Pterodactyl in September 1979. In its current (Summer 1980) form, it is powered by a 430 cc two-cylinder two-stroke engine, driving a 0·91 m (3 ft) diameter pusher propeller, which gives it a max rate of climb at S/L of 168-183 m (550-600 ft)/min and a max cruising speed of 48 knots (88 km/h; 55 mph). A joystick is now standard, replacing the two twist-grips formerly used to actuate the overwing drag rudders. These produce yaw-induced roll; pitch control is by a combination of weight shift and drag rudders.

In 1980, Mr David Garrison and Mr John Leigh-Pemberton became the first pilots to fly ultralight aircraft from Land's End to John O'Groats, completing the distance, in stages, in a total flying time of 17 h 5 min. In the United States, four Pterodactyls made a west-to-east coast-to-coast crossing in 1979, a total distance of approx 2,605 nm (4,830 km; 3,000 miles), during the course of which they overflew the 4,570 m (15,000 ft) Grand Teton Mountains. The greatest known height yet reached by a Pterodactyl is 5,485 m (18,000 ft).

UNITED STATES OF AMERICA

STRIPLIN AIRCRAFT CORPORATION (page 552)

The FLAC prototype was fitted with a non-retractable landing gear; the retractable nosewheel was introduced later, but one result of this was to reduce legroom for the pilot. Striplin has now introduced the Super FLAC, with a roomier cockpit and a twin-engine power plant. A recovery parachute is available for both powered models, as are snow skis for all three wheels.

STRIPLIN SUPER FLAC

Announced in the Spring of 1980, the Super FLAC retains the overall dimensions of the standard FLAC, but has an enlarged pilot pod which not only provides greater legroom but also has a compartment for up to 2·25 kg (5 lb) of baggage. The aircraft can also be flown by pilots heavier than those for whom the standard FLAC is suitable.

Striplin Super FLAC twin-engined powered hang glider

Power plant of the Super FLAC is a pair of Soarmaster two-cylinder engines, for which there are two glassfibre fuel tanks in the wings, combined capacity 19 litres (5 US gallons).

WEIGHTS AND LOADINGS:

Weight empty	91 kg (200 lb)
Max T-O weight	197 kg (435 lb)
Max wing loading: FLAC	12·2 kg/m² (2·50 lb/sq ft)
Super FLAC	13·7 kg/m² (2·80 lb/sq ft)

PERFORMANCE:

Never-exceed speed	69 knots (129 km/h; 80 mph)
Max level speed	52 knots (96·5 km/h; 60 mph)
Cruising speed	48 knots (88·5 km/h; 55 mph)
Stalling speed	21 knots (39 km/h; 24 mph)
Best glide ratio at 33 knots (61 km/h; 38 mph), power off	20
Min sinking speed at 31 knots (58 km/h; 36 mph), power off	55 m (180 ft)/min

STRIPLIN AIR CYCLE II

Details of this new two-seat ultralight aircraft were released in the Spring of 1980, at which time major components for the prototype had been completed by Striplin. Flight testing was expected to begin in May 1980.

The Air Cycle II has a pod-and-boom fuselage, with a cantilever high wing and cantilever T tail. Power plant consists of two wing-mounted 7·5 kW (10 hp) Chrysler West Bend engines, each driving a two-blade propeller.

There is a 9·5 litre (2·5 US gallon) fuel tank in each wing, and the wings fold outboard of the engine nacelles to facilitate transportation and stowage. The aircraft is foot-launchable, but has a non-retractable tricycle gear for landing. The enclosed cockpit seats two persons side by side.

DIMENSIONS, EXTERNAL:

Wing span	11·28 m (37 ft 0 in)
Wing chord, constant	1·52 m (5 ft 0 in)
Wing area, gross: flaps in	17·19 m² (185 sq ft)
flaps out	19·42 m² (209 sq ft)
Wing aspect ratio (flaps in)	7·4
Width, wings folded	5·64 m (18 ft 6 in)
Length overall	2·39 m (7 ft 10 in)
Height overall	1·83 m (6 ft 0 in)
Propeller diameter	1·22 m (4 ft 0 in)

WEIGHTS AND LOADINGS:

Weight empty	113 kg (250 lb)
Max T-O weight	249 kg (550 lb)
Max wing loading: flaps in	14·49 kg/m² (2·97 lb/sq ft)
flaps out	12·83 kg/m² (2·63 lb/sq ft)

PERFORMANCE (estimated):

Never-exceed speed	87 knots (161 km/h; 100 mph)
Max level speed	69 knots (129 km/h; 80 mph)
Cruising speed	56 knots (105 km/h; 65 mph)
Stalling speed, flaps up	26·5 knots (48·5 km/h; 30 mph)
Stalling speed, flaps down	20 knots (37 km/h; 23 mph)

RPVs & TARGETS

GERMANY (FEDERAL REPUBLIC)

MBB (page 621)

MBB KDAR-LOCUST

First launch of this anti-radiation mini-RPV (see main section) was made in the Spring of 1980. The booster motor is now known to have a solid (powder) propellant; the following data have also been published:

DIMENSIONS, EXTERNAL:

Wing span (deployed)	2·60 m (8 ft 6½ in)
Length	2·20 m (7 ft 2½ in)
Body diameter	0·183 m (7¼ in)

VFW (page 622)

VFW KDAR-LOCUST

VFW's contender for the US/West German Locust anti-radiation mini-RPV programme, developed in association with General Dynamics, was launched for the first time on 1 April 1980 at Meppen. A progressive development of the RT 910 Tucan described in the main section, it has cruciform wings, fitted with control surfaces, and is powered by a small piston engine driving a two-blade pusher propeller. The VFW vehicle is container-launched, and has a launching weight of 60 kg (132 lb).

JAPAN

FUJI (page 625)

The Japan Defence Agency has authorised the design, development and construction of the first all-Japanese RPV. Intended for use by all three Self-Defence forces, its missions will include reconnaissance, surveillance and target designation.

Fuji Heavy Industries has been selected as prime contractor, with Nippon Avionics providing the guidance system, Hitachi the onboard TV camera, and Nippon Electric the ground control equipment. Other Japanese participants are Nippon Aviation Electronics and Daicel; the power plant will probably be of US origin.

UNITED KINGDOM

INTERGARD ELECTRONICS LTD

No. 5, 34 Frognal, Hampstead, London NW3
Telephone: 01 435 1622
Telex: 8951859 Basil G

This company has in production the Shrike small aerial target, or target tug, and the Sky-Eye real-time TV surveillance mini-RPV; it has also developed a third miniature target drone aircraft known as the Pipit.

INTERGARD IETS 7501 SHRIKE

This in-sight vehicle, for gunnery practice with small arms and anti-aircraft guns, has been ordered by two Middle Eastern countries; a few were expected to be ordered by the Royal Aircraft Establishment in the Summer of 1980. Shrike can be flown in a low-flying attack mode, to simulate an attack directly upon the operator's gun position; as a target towing system for live weapon practice; and as a target training system for ground-to-air

Intergard Shrike aerial gunnery target

Intergard Sky-Eye RPV on four-wheeled launch dolly

missiles. The complete system includes the air vehicle, self-contained transporter and optional launcher, ground control and support equipment, operator spares pack, drogue assembly, and spare drogue.

TYPE: Miniature aerial gunnery target or target-towing vehicle.

AIRFRAME: Cantilever shoulder-wing monoplane, with dihedral wings, built of balsa wood, plywood, expanded plastics foam and glassfibre. Twin-skid metal landing gear.

POWER PLANT: One 32-56 cc spark ignition or glow ignition two-stroke piston engine, driving a small-diameter two-blade propeller. Petrol/oil or methanol/oil mixture fuel, depending upon engine chosen.

LAUNCH AND RECOVERY: Aircraft can be launched from a four-wheeled drop dolly or bungee launcher, or can take off conventionally with skid landing gear. Recovered by conventional landing on skids.

GUIDANCE AND CONTROL: Radio command guidance system, operating on one of 12 spot frequencies in 27MHz band with a bandwidth of approx 25kHz. Different frequency required for each system if more than one target is flown at the same time within radio control range of each other (approx 2·2 nm; 4 km; 2·5 miles). Aerodynamic control by rudder and elevators.

EQUIPMENT: Electronic fail-safe device automatically closes engine throttle if aircraft is accidentally flown beyond visual range or suffers a radio link malfunction.

DIMENSIONS, EXTERNAL:
Wing span	3·05 m (10 ft 0 in)
Wing chord (average)	0·425 m (1 ft 4¾ in)
Length overall	2·31 m (7 ft 7 in)

WEIGHT:
Launching weight	14 kg (31 lb)

PERFORMANCE:
Max speed (depending on engine fitted)
80-120 knots (148-222 km/h; 92-138 mph)
Cruising speed 60 knots (111 km/h; 69 mph)

Operating altitude, and range
limited only by operator's visual range
Flight duration up to 50 min

INTERGARD GTS 7901 SKY-EYE

Sky-Eye, also in production for customers in two countries in the Middle East, was developed as a close-support information relay vehicle for use by forward and front-line troops. It is designed to provide, directly to a command headquarters or forward artillery control centre, information about the deployment and movement of hostile troops or armour. Alternatively, by removing the TV camera and transmitter, a chaff dispenser or radar jammer can be installed for use against enemy ground radar sites; or, for use in conjunction with close-support aircraft, a laser designator can be fitted for accurate target identification.

Other applications include TV surveillance of urban riot areas, border surveillance, and forest fire location and assessment.

TYPE: Multi-purpose surveillance/ECM mini-RPV.

AIRFRAME: Cantilever high-wing monoplane, with pod-and-boom fuselage and sweptback fin and rudder; non-swept dihedral wings and non-swept tailplane. Construction of balsa wood, plywood, expanded plastics foam, glassfibre and aluminium alloy. Rudder and full-span elevator standard; ailerons optional.

POWER PLANT: As for Shrike, but installed at rear of fuselage pod to drive a pusher propeller.

LAUNCH AND RECOVERY: As for Shrike.

GUIDANCE AND CONTROL: Similar to that for Shrike. For flight programmes in areas of high air turbulence an electrostatic stabilisation system, using a slightly radioactive polonium element at each wingtip, can be installed for improved pitch and roll control. Ailerons are required if this system is fitted, since for it to be effective the RPV must initially be unstable in flight.

EQUIPMENT: TV camera and transmitter standard; these can be replaced, according to mission, by a multi-frame

35 mm still camera, 8 mm movie camera, chaff dispenser, radar jammer, laser designator or other sensor. Electronic fail-safe throttle closure/engine stop, as in Shrike.

DIMENSIONS, EXTERNAL:
Wing span	2·44 m (8 ft 0 in)
Wing chord (constant)	0·38 m (1 ft 3 in)
Length overall	2·03 m (6 ft 8 in)

WEIGHT:
Launching weight	12 kg (26·5 lb)

PERFORMANCE:
Max speed (depending on engine fitted)
60-80 knots (111-148 km/h; 69-92 mph)
Cruising speed 30 knots (56 km/h; 35 mph)
Operating altitude
limited only by operator's visual range
Range
limited only by operator's visual range, but guidance system range is up to 5·4 nm (10 km; 6·2 miles) with high-power transmitter
Flight duration up to 45 min

INTERGARD IETS 7502 PIPIT

Pipit, designed to train radio control operators to use the larger Shrike, is of generally similar configuration, construction and operation to the latter vehicle. Being smaller, it has a less powerful engine (1·1 kW; 1·5 hp 10 cc glow plug ignition type), and has twin landing skids attached directly to the underside of the fuselage.

DIMENSIONS, EXTERNAL:
Wing span	2·01 m (6 ft 7 in)
Length overall	1·22 m (4 ft 0 in)

WEIGHT:
Launching weight	3 kg (6·6 lb)

PERFORMANCE:
Max speed 60 knots (111 km/h; 69 mph)
Cruising speed 25 knots (46 km/h; 29 mph)
Operating altitude, and range
limited only by operator's visual range
Flight duration up to 30 min

UNITED STATES OF AMERICA

BEECHCRAFT (page 630)

BEECHCRAFT MODEL 1089

According to a statement issued in March 1980 by the French aerospace industry society GIFAS, a version of the Model 1089 (reportedly designated MQM-107-1) has been test-flown successfully with a 3·7 kN (827 lb st) Microturbo TRI 60-2 turbojet engine. Computed performance was achieved and, in some cases, exceeded: the mission duration time was bettered by 10 per cent, and a speed of 507 knots (940 km/h; 584 mph) was attained.

E-SYSTEMS (page 634)

E-SYSTEMS E-55S

During 1979, three examples of the E-55 (see main section) were modified for the US Army's Superfly demonstration programme. The major significant airframe change was the addition of side-force generators ('vertical wings'), to enable the aircraft to turn without banking during a terminal dive.

AIRFRAME: Shoulder-wing twin-tailboom monoplane, with central fuselage nacelle for engine and avionics. No dihedral on outer wing panels. Twin fins and rudders. Side-force generator panel above and below each wing, outboard of tailboom/wing joint. Lower side-force panels are frangible.

POWER PLANT: As for E-55. Fuel capacity 3·8 litres (1 US gallon).

LAUNCH AND RECOVERY: Pneumatic catapult launch; recovery by radio-controlled conventional landing.

GUIDANCE AND CONTROL: Either by autonomous, programmed autopilot; or by intermittently updated autopilot; or by continuous, real-time autopilot com-

mand. Manual control available for recovery. Addition of side-force generators provides increased guidance accuracy and permits a simplified electronic control system.

DIMENSIONS, EXTERNAL: As E-55 except:
Wing span	2·44 m (8 ft 0 in)
Wing area, gross	0·69 m² (7·40 sq ft)
Height overall	0·61 m (2 ft 0 in)
Side-force generator span	0·61 m (2 ft 0 in)
Side-force generator area (each)	0·31 m² (3·33 sq ft)

WEIGHTS AND PERFORMANCE: As E-55 except:
Rate of climb at S/L	137 m (450 ft)/min
Service ceiling	2,745 m (9,000 ft)

E-Systems E-55S RPV, evaluated in the US Army Superfly programme

E-Systems E-130, with underwing side-force generator panels

E-SYSTEMS E-130

The E-130 is essentially a scaled-up version of the E-90 (see main section), utilising the proven very-low-cost constructional features and materials of the E-75/E-90 series but able to carry significantly more payload. A wind tunnel model (83·3% of full size) was tested at the University of Washington during 1979, and in early 1980 a batch of ten full-size E-130s was under construction. A distinctive feature is the provision of side-force generator panels below each wing.

AIRFRAME: Cantilever shoulder-wing monoplane with pod-and-boom fuselage. Foam plastics wings; moulded polyethylene fuselage, with pneumatic resin-coated cardboard tailboom stiffener. Side-force generator panel beneath each wing, at approx half-span.

POWER PLANT: One 13·4 kW (18 hp) Herbrandson DH 220 flat-twin two-stroke engine, driving a two-blade pusher propeller.

EQUIPMENT: Pre-programmed autonomous autopilot/navigation system, using an onboard microprocessor.

DIMENSIONS, EXTERNAL:

Wing span	3·05 m (10 ft 0 in)
Wing area, gross	1·29 m² (13·89 sq ft)
Length overall	2·36 m (7 ft 9 in)
Height overall	0·61 m (2 ft 0 in)

Fuselage: Max width	0·305 m (1 ft 0 in)
WEIGHTS:	
Weight empty, equipped	27 kg (60 lb)
Payload	20 kg (45 lb)
Fuel	7 kg (15 lb)
T-O weight	59 kg (130 lb)
PERFORMANCE:	
Max level speed	116 knots (216 km/h; 134 mph)
Cruising speed	87 knots (161 km/h; 100 mph)
Stalling speed	52 knots (97 km/h; 60 mph)
Rate of climb at S/L	610 m (2,000 ft)/min
Service ceiling	3,660 m (12,000 ft)
Endurance	4 h

MISSILES

UNITED KINGDOM

BRITISH AEROSPACE (page 652)

A new fully-guided short-range air-to-air missile developed by British Aerospace Dynamics Group has undergone a series of successful test firings, in which it has demonstrated outstanding manoeuvrability. Shown in an accompanying illustration, the missile is wingless, uses an infra-red seeker, is steered by swivel-nozzle thrust vector control, and has motor bleed roll control. Motor and actuation systems were developed by Imperial Metal Industries and Sperry Gyroscope.

HUGHES (page 656)

Hughes Aircraft Company's Wasp anti-armour missile with wings and fins folded (top) and spread

UNITED STATES OF AMERICA

British Aerospace's new wingless infra-red homing air-to-air development missile *(Brian M. Service)*

Fired from a Hunter aircraft, the missile intercepted an airborne target over the Aberporth range on 18 August 1980. The trial was set up to provide severe interception conditions, using a missile that is the result of a substantial development programme. The technologies used and experience gained will make a valuable contribution to the European Advanced Short Range Air-to-Air Missile (ASRAAM) programme in which British Aerospace is UK lead contractor.

In 1980, an ASRAAM pre-feasibility study was being conducted jointly by British Aerospace Dynamics Group in the UK and Bodenseewerk Gerätetechnik, the lead contractor in West Germany.

SPACEFLIGHT

INDIA

ISRO (page 666)

On 18 July 1980 the Indian Space Research Organisation successfully launched its 40 kg (88 lb) Rohini RSI test satellite from Sriharikota Island, north of Madras, using a four-stage, solid-propellant SLV-3 booster. In orbit the satellite is working well, with its Indian-built solar arrays developing 3W of electrical power. India is the seventh country, and the first third-world nation, to build and launch its own satellite.

UNION OF SOVIET SOCIALIST REPUBLICS

PROGRESS (page 672)

Progress 8, launched on 27 March 1980, carried equipment and consumables to Salyut 6 (which see). While docked it was used to raise the orbit of the space station. The spacecraft undocked on 25 March, for disposal over the central Pacific the following day.

Progress 9, launched on 27 April 1980, carried equipment and consumables to Salyut 6 (which see). It was disposed of on 3 June.

Progress 10, launched on 29 June 1980, carried fuel and other consumables to Salyut 6 (which see), with which it docked on 1 July. After completion of the orbital refuelling, the spacecraft undocked on 19 July for disposal during re-entry.

SOYUZ (page 673)

Soyuz T-2. Launched on 5 June 1980, the first manned Soyuz T was commanded by Yuri Malyshev with Vladimir Aksenov as flight engineer. The spacecraft docked with Salyut 6 (which see) which had been occupied by Popov and Ryumin since 10 April. After a relatively short period, the Soyuz undocked and made a successful re-entry on 9 June, landing 200 km (124 miles) south-east of Dzhezkazgan.

Soyuz 36. Launched on 26 May 1980, Soyuz 36 was commanded by Valery Kubasov with Bertalan Farkash, the first Hungarian cosmonaut, as flight engineer. The spacecraft docked with Salyut 6 (which see) on 27 May for a week of experiments. Kubasov and Farkash returned to Earth in Soyuz 35, leaving a fresh spacecraft at Salyut 6 for the long-duration cosmonauts Leonid Popov and Valery Ryumin.

Soyuz 37. Launched on 23 July 1980, Soyuz 37 was commanded by Col. Viktor Gorbatko with Col. Pham Tuan, the first Vietnamese cosmonaut, as flight engineer. The spacecraft docked with Salyut 6 (which see), using the aft port, on 24 July for a period of experiments. The cosmonauts returned safely to Earth on 31 July in Soyuz 36. This manoeuvre left the Soyuz 37 as a fresh spacecraft for the two long-serving cosmonauts aboard Salyut 6. Popov and Ryumin returned safely to Earth in Soyuz 37 on 11 October, after a record 185 days in space.

ENGINES

CANADA

PRATT & WHITNEY AIRCRAFT OF CANADA
(page 687)   **P&WC PT7A**

The version of this new turboprop selected by de Havilland Aircraft of Canada for the Dash-8 STOL transport is the PT7A-2R. T-O rating will be 1,268 kW (1,700 shp), with specific fuel consumption "approximately 15 per cent better than other turboprops". Propeller speed will be 1,200 rpm. Full-scale development of the PT7 began in June 1979, and the first engine was scheduled to run in December 1980. Production deliveries are due in 1984, the Dash-8 being scheduled to enter commercial service in the same year.

FRANCE

GRTM

In April 1980 the presidents of Microturbo and Turboméca signed an agreement launching GRTM, a joint enterprise for the study, design, development and production of a turbojet tailored to the propulsion of supersonic cruise missiles.

ITALY

SNIA VISCOSA

In May 1980 it was announced that this company, a specialist in solid-propellant rockets, has been awarded a contract by the European Space Agency for preliminary research into plasma (electromagnetic) propulsion. The objective is to complete three development phases, in collaboration with FIAR (the Italian factory for radioelectrical equipment) and the University of Rome, culminating in an operating plasma motor prototype. This technology should not be confused with ion (electrostatic) propulsion.

SNECMA (page 696)

Artist's impression of the SNECMA M88 turbojet, under development for future fighter aircraft

POLAND

PZL (page 713)

PZL-10

An accompanying photograph is the first to show the Soviet designed Glushenkov TVD-10 turboshaft engine, rated at 715 kW (960 shp), which is now made under licence in Poland. It is worth noting that in the Soviet Union the TVD-10 designation is reserved for the turboprop version, used in the An-28 STOL light transport which is soon to enter production in Poland at WSK-PZL Mielec. The turboprop is designated TVD-10B.

The turboshaft version is almost certainly the same engine as the GTD-3, which powers the twin-engined Kamov Ka-25 family of co-axial helicopters. The Polish designation for this engine is PZL-10W, and it is the power plant of the PZL Swidnik Sokól twin-engined helicopter. The engines are handed, with left- and right-facing jet-pipes. There are probably two or three axial compressor stages followed by a centrifugal stage. The free power turbine drives to the rear.

PZL-10W free-turbine turboshaft (rated at 715 kW; 960 shp) designed by Glushenkov and licensed for production in Poland

UNITED KINGDOM

ROLLS-ROYCE (page 727)

In May 1980 Rolls-Royce Ltd and the Pratt & Whitney division of UTC announced jointly their agreement to collaborate in production of F402 (Pegasus) engines for any AV-8B production programme. Should Congress allow procurement of the AV-8B, at least 450 F402 engines would be needed, costing, with spares, an estimated $1,500 million. Pratt & Whitney would receive 25 per cent of the work, and would also participate in supersonic developments of the Pegasus, on which Rolls-Royce has maintained a study programme.

ROLLS-ROYCE MOTORS (page 732)

In June 1980 it was announced that Rolls-Royce Motors had been acquired by Vickers Ltd. The name of the company is being changed to Rolls-Royce Vickers Ltd.

BONNER (page 725)

Chipmunk testbed powered by the Bonner Super Sapphire V6 piston engine *(Brian M. Service)*

Comparative cross-sections of Rolls-Royce RB.211-22B and RB.211-535 turbofans

WALLIS/ROLLS-ROYCE VICKERS

Reymerston Hall, Norfolk NR9 4QY (see Aircraft section)
Telephone: 036 285 418

With the agreement of Rolls-Royce Motors (now Rolls-Royce Vickers), Wg Cdr K. H. Wallis has constructed a flat-twin engine for his autogyros based on components of the Rolls-Royce Continental O-240. Known as the Wallis/RR O-120, it first ran in December 1978. Ground testing confirmed thrust more than half that of the O-240 engine, probably owing to greater propeller efficiency. It is hoped to fly the O-120 in a WA-116, but development is on low priority in view of the comparable engine now under development by Weslake & Company.

RB211-535

RB211-22B

WESLAKE & COMPANY

Harbour Road, Rye Harbour, Sussex TN31 7TH
Telephone: 07973-2755

Last appearing in the 1977-78 *Jane's*, this company is no longer connected with its former associate, Weslake Aeromarine Engines (see main section). Weslake & Co has spent many years refining the design of a cylinder head for high-performance piston engines with central spark plug and four valves. The work has now led to the design of a flat-twin tailored for outstanding fuel economy, adequate performance for a light two-seat aircraft (fixed- or rotary-wing) and acceptably low noise and vibration. Pent-roof heads were running in 1980 with both central and top plug locations, with rear-facing inlets and forward-facing exhausts. A conventional impulse magneto is used for starting and standby, and an electronic system with speed and manifold-pressure controlled ignition advance to assist leanest operation at all times.

The engine measures 711 mm (28·0 in) across the rocker-box covers; target weight with ignition system is 57 kg (125 lb). Rating is 56 kW (75 hp) at 3,500 rpm, with normal running at 48·5 kW (65 hp) at 2,800 rpm.

UNITED STATES OF AMERICA

GENERAL ELECTRIC (page 749)

GENERAL ELECTRIC CF6-32

This reduced-thrust derivative of the CF6, tailored to the propulsion requirements of the Boeing 757, achieved its first sale in May 1980 to Aloha Airlines of Hawaii. This established the CF6-32 as an alternative 757 engine to the RB.211-535C. It is a joint programme with SNECMA of France, Volvo Flygmotor of Sweden and Alfa Romeo of Italy, though managed by GE.

GENERAL ELECTRIC CT7

Essentially a turboprop derivative of the T700 helicopter turboshaft engine, the CT7 achieved its first sale in June 1980 when it was selected to power the new 34-passenger STOL airliner being developed jointly by Saab-Scania of Sweden and Fairchild Republic of the USA. Described as a "new-technology fuel-efficient 1,500-plus shaft horsepower turboprop", the CT7 was selected (according to Saab-Scania) because it gave the lightest and most economic aircraft, with the lowest fuel consumption per passenger-kilometre and the best customer warranty. Fuel consumption is described as "5 to 15 per cent lower than that of competing new engines". The Saab-Fairchild 340 airliner is due to fly in 1982 and to enter service in early 1984.

GENERAL ELECTRIC T700

The engine of the Sikorsky SH-60B Seahawk (LAMPS III) helicopter of the US Navy is the T700-GE-401, a growth derivative of the T700-GE-700 used in the UH-60A Black Hawk and using 95 per cent common parts. It has greater power, additional corrosion protection (exhaustively proved in severe corrosion and subsequent stall testing at the Navy Air Propulsion Center) and emergency power provisions. Some of the material specifications are tailored to a salt-water environment, anti-corrosive coatings are used, and the stage-1 turbine blades have corrosion-resistant tips welded on. Production deliveries are due in July 1983. The following specification figures differ from those of the GE-700:

DIMENSIONS:

Length overall	1,194 mm (47·0 in)
Width	635 mm (25·0 in)

General Electric CT7-5 turboprop, power plant of the Saab-Fairchild 340 commuter transport

WEIGHT, DRY: 194 kg (427 lb)

PERFORMANCE RATINGS:
  Contingency (one engine inoperative)
                1,268 kW (1,701 shp) to 32°C
  Intermediate 1,260 kW (1,690 shp) to 15°C

SPECIFIC FUEL CONSUMPTION:
  Contingency   79·76 µg/J (0·472 lb/h/shp)
  Intermediate   78·40 µg/J (0·464 lb/h/shp)

INDEXES

(Items in italics refer to the ten previous editions)

AIRCRAFT (including Homebuilt Aircraft)

SAILPLANES AND HANG GLIDERS

LIGHTER-THAN-AIR

RPVs AND TARGETS

AIR-LAUNCHED MISSILES, SPACEFLIGHT

AERO-ENGINES

Printed in England by Netherwood Dalton & Co. Ltd., Huddersfield

EXPORTER
OMNIPOL
Foreign Trade Corporation
Nekázanka 11, 112 21 Praha 1
Czechoslovakia

Quality Safety Economy

Successful jet trainer L 39

MODERN L 39 TRAINING SYSTEM

— mobile automatic testing station KL 39
— flight simulator TL 39
— ground-borne ejection trainer NKTL 29/39